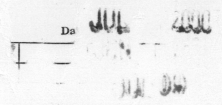

PHYSIOLOGY
AND
BIOPHYSICS

AN AMERICAN TEXT-BOOK OF PHYSIOLOGY
edited by William H. Howell, Ph.D., M.D.
W. B. SAUNDERS AND COMPANY   1896

A TEXT-BOOK OF PHYSIOLOGY FOR MEDICAL
STUDENTS AND PHYSICIANS
written by William H. Howell, Ph.D., M.D., LL.D.
W. B. SAUNDERS AND COMPANY   1905

HOWELL'S TEXTBOOK OF PHYSIOLOGY
15th edition
edited by John F. Fulton, M.D.
W. B. SAUNDERS COMPANY   1946

A TEXTBOOK OF PHYSIOLOGY
16th and 17th editions
edited by John F. Fulton, M.D.
W. B. SAUNDERS COMPANY   1949 and 1955

MEDICAL PHYSIOLOGY AND BIOPHYSICS
18th edition
edited by Theodore C. Ruch, Ph.D., and John F. Fulton, M.D.
W. B. SAUNDERS COMPANY   1960

nineteenth edition

HOWELL — FULTON

PHYSIOLOGY
AND
BIOPHYSICS

edited by

THEODORE C. RUCH, Ph.D.

Professor of Physiology and Biophysics
University of Washington School of Medicine

and

HARRY D. PATTON, Ph.D., M.D.

Professor of Physiology and Biophysics
University of Washington School of Medicine

W. B. SAUNDERS COMPANY, Philadelphia and London

Reprinted March, 1966
Physiology and Biophysics

CONTRIBUTORS

GEORGE BRENGELMANN, B.S.

Department of Physiology and Biophysics, University of Washington School of Medicine

JOHN R. BROBECK, Ph.D., M.D.

Professor of Physiology, University of Pennsylvania School of Medicine

ARTHUR C. BROWN, Ph.D.

Assistant Professor of Physiology and Biophysics, University of Washington School of Medicine

ALAN C. BURTON, Ph.D.

Professor of Biophysics, University of Western Ontario Faculty of Medicine

HUBERT R. CATCHPOLE, Ph.D.

Research Professor, Department of Pathology, University of Illinois College of Medicine

JOHN T. CONRAD, Ph.D.

Assistant Professor, Department of Physiology and Biophysics, University of Washington School of Medicine

D. HAROLD COPP, Ph.D.

Head, Department of Physiology, University of British Columbia

THOMAS R. FORBES, Ph.D.

Professor of Anatomy and Associate Dean, Yale University School of Medicine

MITCHELL GLICKSTEIN, Ph.D.

Associate Professor of Physiology and Biophysics and of Psychology, University of Washington School of Medicine, and the Regional Primate Research Center, Seattle, Washington

CHARLES J. GOODNER, M.D.

Assistant Professor of Medicine, University of Washington School of Medicine, and Director, Diabetes Clinic, King County Hospital, Seattle, Washington

ALBERT M. GORDON, Ph.D.

Assistant Professor of Physiology and Biophysics, University of Washington School of Medicine

JACOB HILDEBRANDT, M.Sc.

Department of Physiology and Biophysics, University of Washington School of Medicine

CHARLES W. HOOKER, Ph.D.

Professor of Anatomy, University of North Carolina

THOMAS F. HORNBEIN, M.D.

Assistant Professor of Anesthesiology and of Physiology and Biophysics, University of Washington School of Medicine

SEYMOUR J. KLEBANOFF, M.D., Ph.D.

Associate Professor of Medicine, University of Washington School of Medicine, and Chief, Division of Metabolism and Radioisotopes, United States Public Health Service Hospital, Seattle, Washingon

ALAN KOCH, Ph.D.

Research Assistant Professor of Physiology and Biophysics, University of Washington School of Medicine

ROBERT B. LIVINGSTON, M.D.

Professor of Neurology, University of California at San Diego School of Medicine

DONAL F. MAGEE, B.M., B.Ch., Ph.D.

Professor of Physiology and Pharmacology, The Creighton University School of Medicine

EDWARD J. MASORO, Ph.D.

Professor and Chairman, Department of Pysiology, Woman's Medical College of Pennsylvania

JOHN L. PATTERSON, Jr., M.D.

Research Professor of Medicine, Medical College of Virginia

HARRY D. PATTON, Ph.D., M.D.

Professor of Physiology and Biophysics, University of Washington School of Medicine

RICHARD L. RILEY, M.D.

Professor of Environmental Medicine, The Johns Hopkins School of Hygiene and Public Health

THEODORE C. RUCH, Ph.D.

Professor of Physiology and Biophysics, University of Washington School of Medicine; and Director, Regional Primate Research Center, Seattle, Washington

ROBERT F. RUSHMER, M.D.

Professor of Physiology and Biophysics, University of Washington School of Medicine; Senior Consultant, Madigan General Hospital, Fort Lewis, Washington

JANE A. RUSSELL, Ph.D.

Professor of Biochemistry, Emory University

ALLEN M. SCHER, Ph.D.

Professor of Physiology and Biophysics, University of Washington School of Medicine

ORVILLE A. SMITH, Jr., Ph.D.

Associate Professor of Physiology and Biophysics, University of Washington School of Medicine; Assistant Director, Regional Primate Research Center, Seattle, Washington

ARNOLD L. TOWE, Ph.D.

Professor of Physiology and Biophysics, University of Washington School of Medicine

ROBERT L. VAN CITTERS, M.D.

Associate Professor of Physiology and Biophysics, Robert L. King Chair of Cardiovascular Research, Department of Physiology and Biophysics, University of Washington School of Medicine, and Regional Primate Research Center, Seattle, Washington

FRANK W. WEYMOUTH, Ph.D.*

Professor of Physiology, Emeritus, Stanford University; Professor of Physiological Optics, Los Angeles College of Optometry

DIXON M. WOODBURY, M.S., Ph.D.

Professor of Pharmacology, University of Utah College of Medicine

J. WALTER WOODBURY, Ph.D.

Professor of Physiology and Biophysics, University of Washington School of Medicine

ALLAN C. YOUNG, Ph.D.

Professor of Physiology and Biophysics, University of Washington School of Medicine

* Deceased

PREFACE

This, the nineteenth edition of Howell's *Textbook of Physiology,* has advanced farther along the pathways pursued in the previous edition.

The amount of clinical or pathologic physiology, especially emphasized in the treatment of the nervous system, has been extended, particularly in the discussions of the circulation and the endocrines. Nevertheless, the word "medical" has been deleted from the title because it is not clear that all systems can be treated in their pathophysiologic aspects within the confines of one volume while doing justice to fundamental biophysical and cellular phenomena.

In a world where splinter disciplines stake claims on words as though they were gold mines (which they are), perhaps our meaning of the word "biophysics" is not evident to all. What we meant to express by "biophysics" in the title and what we have increasingly emphasized in this new edition has many synonyms and definitions. Perhaps the simplest is "the physics and physical chemistry of the organism" at all levels from the subcellular through the cell and organs to the study of the organism from the standpoint of control systems. (Confining systems analysis to the control of organ function is only temporary; it is predicted that function at the molecular level will require systems analysis.) A synonym for "biophysics" is "physical or quantitative biology" since the study of function calls heavily upon mathematical expression, analysis and models. Although many sciences are quantitative in the sense that things are measured and arithmetic is used, they are not mathematical. Physiology is rapidly becoming the most mathematical of the biological sciences, both in depth and breadth of the mathematical processes involved. If some of this creeps into the textbook, it is the harbinger of what is to come. We have attempted to cover the broad outlines of subject matter in regular type and put much of the mathematical treatment in fine print.

In respect to biophysics, many chapters have been totally rewritten and emphasis has been placed on the quantitative (mathematical) physical or physical chemical approach. In addition to those in the biophysical category added in the eighteenth edition are the following: active transport (Brown), anatomy and physics of respiration (Hildebrandt and Young), gas exchange and transport (Riley), regulation of pH (J. W. Woodbury), energy metabolism (Brown), temperature regulation (Brengelmann and Brown).

The discipline of physiology has grown along another dimension. Behavior is proving both a tool for and an object of physiologic investigation. The understanding of the brain rests upon four legs: electrophysiology, behavioral studies, neurochemistry and, not least, biologic structure, fine and gross. Sciences flourish along their edges and this is true along the boundary between physiology and psychology, where the edge is becoming less sharp. In recognition of the mutual infiltration, several new chapters have been added, e.g., chapters on learning and memory (Glickstein), motivation (O. Smith) and separate chapters are devoted to emotion and the "association areas." Several of the chapters on the afferent systems emphasize the neurophysiology of sensation and perception.

Other newly written chapters are: the receptor (Patton), nerve impulse (J. W. Woodbury), muscle (J. W. Woodbury, Gordon and Conrad), and the chemical control of respiration (Hornbein), and eight new chapters on the cardiovascular system (Rushmer, Catchpole, Scher, O. Smith and Van Citters).

The entire section on the gastrointestinal tract has been newly written and organized according to function: motility, secretion, digestion and absorption, rather than as an anatomic sequence (Magee, Masoro and Brown). Body fluids, including those in the brain, have been given a rigorous treatment (D. M. Woodbury). With the exception of two chapters, the entire section on the endocrines is new (Goodner, Klebanoff, Copp). Altogether, there are twenty-six new chapters, nearly half the book. The other chapters have been considerably revised, with the exception of a few chapters on relatively static subjects and a few that were extensively revised for the last edition.

This book departs from the tradition that a textbook presents only the contemporary concensus of knowledge. It is written by scholars and when they have seen a way to anticipate developments in the field, they have done so. Thus, Riley presents a new tricompartment view of the lung; Woodbury has contributed a new point of view on pH; Scher has treated the circulation as a control system in the engineering sense; Masoro has approached intermediary metabolism from a physiologic viewpoint rather than a chemical one.

This is not an easy textbook for students, nor is physiology an easy subject lending itself to memorization. Students accustomed to descriptive and detailed phenomena of metabolic cycles, determinative bacteriology and classical anatomy may find it initially difficult, but with application, the know-how comes and with it the pleasures of following the quantitative pathway which the cognate sciences will soon have to follow.

I want to thank my co-editor, Dr. Harry D. Patton, for undertaking some of the more difficult parts of the editing, and to express appreciation to Drs. Koch, Young, Luft and Brown, who have assisted us in the editorial work. Finally, we owe much to Mr. Walter Eva for his manuscript editing and Mrs. Helen Halsey for her art work.

T. C. RUCH

Seattle, Washington

CONTENTS

Chapter 26

NEUROPHYSIOLOGY OF EMOTION 508
By Theodore C. Ruch

SECTION VI.   BIOPHYSICAL PRINCIPLES OF THE CIRCULATION

Chapter 27

HEMODYNAMICS AND THE PHYSICS OF THE CIRCULATION 523
By Alan C. Burton

SECTION VII.   CIRCULATION OF BLOOD AND LYMPH

Chapter 28

GENERAL CHARACTERISTICS OF THE CARDIOVASCULAR SYSTEM 543
By Robert F. Rushmer

Chapter 29

MECHANICAL EVENTS OF THE CARDIAC CYCLE 550
By Allen M. Scher

Chapter 30

ELECTRICAL CORRELATES OF THE CARDIAC CYCLE 565
By Allen M. Scher

SECTION VIII.   RESPIRATION

NEURAL CONTROL OF RESPIRATION 788
    By Allan C. Young

    Peripheral Neural Mechanisms 788
    Central Neural Mechanisms 791
    Genesis of the Respiratory Rhythm 796

Chapter 42

THE CHEMICAL REGULATION OF VENTILATION 803
    By Thomas F. Hornbein

    The Peripheral Chemoreceptors 805
    The Central Chemosensitive Area 807
    Ventilatory Responses 808

SECTION IX.   BIOPHYSICS OF TRANSPORT ACROSS
              MEMBRANES

    Chapter 43

PASSIVE AND ACTIVE TRANSPORT 820
    By Arthur C. Brown

    Introduction 820
    Passive Mechanisms 824
    Active Transport 832
    Quantitative Aspects of Membrane Transport 837
    Annotated Bibliography 841

SECTION X.   KIDNEY FUNCTION AND BODY FLUIDS

    Chapter 44

THE KIDNEY 843
    By Alan Koch

    Fluid Dynamics 847
    Tubular Transport 852
    Integration of Tubular Functions 866
    Regulation of Plasma Composition 867
    Diuresis 868
    Endocrine Control of Renal Function 868

    Chapter 45

PHYSIOLOGY OF BODY FLUIDS 871
    By Dixon M. Woodbury

    Volume and Composition of Body Fluids 872
    Exchanges of Water and Electrolytes between Body Compartments 889
    Exchanges of Water and Electrolytes between Body and External
        Environment 892
    Regulation of Volume and Osmolarity of Extracellular Fluid 894

SECTION XII.   METABOLISM

SECTION XIV. REPRODUCTION

PHYSIOLOGY
AND
BIOPHYSICS

SECTION I

BIOPHYSICS OF THE CELL MEMBRANE

CHAPTER 1

The Cell Membrane: Ionic and Potential Gradients and Active Transport

By J. WALTER WOODBURY

1

ANY animal tissue such as muscle or brain is composed of closely packed cells and the solution surrounding and bathing them, the *interstitial* fluid. The cell plasm or *intracellular* fluid and the interstitial fluid are similar; both consist largely of water and both fluids have roughly equal numbers of particles per unit volume dissolved in them. The functional boundary between the intracellular and interstitial fluids is a thin (75 Ångstroms, 7.5 nanometers), highly organized, bimolecular lipoprotein layer which severely restricts the interchange of materials. The differences between the intracellular and interstitial fluids are more striking than their similarities. This chapter deals with two of these differences. (i) The concentrations of ions are markedly different. The concentrations of sodium (Na+) and chloride (Cl−) are much higher in the interstitial fluid than in the intracellular fluid. The situation is just reversed for potassium (K+); its concentration is much higher in intracellular than in interstitial fluid (see Table 1). (ii) There is an electric potential difference between the intracellular and interstitial fluids. In skeletal muscle cells, the cell plasm is about 90 mV. (.09 V.) negative to the interstitial fluid. It must be kept in mind that the cell interior is highly organized, containing the nucleus, nucleolus, mitochondria, endoplasmic reticulum, etc. Nevertheless, it is convenient and meaningful to regard the cell fluid as a single aqueous phase when discussing ion exchange across cell membranes.

Since these large differences in concentration and potential appear across the thin functional membrane of the cell, it is reasonable to suppose that this membrane plays an important role in the maintenance of these differences. Two aspects of the cell membrane are largely responsible for the observed concentration and potential differences. (i) Ions diffuse through the membrane at a minute fraction of the rate at which they diffuse through water. This barrier to diffusion is a result of the nonpolar nature of the lipid portion of the membrane. In most cell membranes, the rate of diffusion of Na+ is much slower than is the diffusion rate of K+ and Cl−. (ii) Energy derived from metabolism is used by cells to transport Na+ out of the cell and K+ into the cell. These ionic movements just balance, on the average, the diffusion of Na+ into and K+ out of the cell. This *active transport* of Na+ and K+ maintains the intracellular Na+ concentration at low values and the intracellular K+ at

high values. The voltage arises because potassium permeates the membrane much more readily than does sodium.

More generally, the role of the membrane in cellular function is to regulate the interchange of materials between a cell and its environment. The nature of the membrane is such that nutrients enter and waste products leave the cell relatively easily, while those substances necessary to cellular function, whether inside or outside the cell, cross only with difficulty. Because of the crucial functions of the cell membrane in regulating interchange of ions and other substances, a description of its properties is a useful starting point for a study of physiology. The transfer of nonionized* substances is not treated here. The permeation and active transport of ions through the membrane and the consequences of these ion movements are the subject matter of this chapter. These concepts are necessary for an understanding of a wide range of physiologic phenomena: (i) the electrical activity of nerve and muscle cells and the processes of synaptic transmission (Chaps. 2, 3, 5 and 6); (ii) the distribution of ions and water between the various body fluid compartments (Chap. 45) and the regulation of interstitial and intracellular *p*H (Chap. 46); (iii) the role of active ion transport in the secretive and absorptive processes of the gastrointestinal tract and in the formation of urine by the kidney (Chap. 44).

In this chapter the main ideas concerning the origins of transmembrane concentration and potential differences will first be sketched. Then the step-by-step development of present concepts of the origins of these potential and concentration differences will be described, and, where necessary, the underlying physical and chemical principles will be briefly reviewed in the text or in more detail in the appendix to Chapter 2. Lastly, the problems of regulation of cell volume and of intracellular *p*H are discussed briefly. Most of the concepts presented in this and the next chapter were developed during the past 20 years, largely through the efforts of A. L. Hodgkin, A. F. Huxley and their co-workers at Cambridge.[8,9,10] Hodgkin and Huxley received the 1963 Nobel Prize in physiology for their pioneering efforts in this field. There are numerous reviews[1,3,6,23,24,29] and symposia[5,22,25,26,27] on various aspects of this subject.

* Substances lacking an electric charge are more appropriately termed "un-ionized"—a word which becomes ambiguous in the unhyphenated form.

ELECTRIC POTENTIALS AND ION CONCENTRATIONS IN MUSCLE

As stated above, there are two striking characteristics of cells to be considered in this chapter: the large difference in ion concentrations and the large difference in electric potential between the inside of the cell and the interstitial fluid.

Although these facts have been known for several decades, refinements in old techniques and introduction of new techniques were required to establish them with sufficient accuracy to make possible crucial tests of the various possible interpretations. The advent of radioactive isotopes made it possible to show, contrary to previous belief, that sodium can penetrate the membrane; the development of intracellular potential recording techniques made possible accurate estimates of transmembrane voltages. In order to give a concrete picture of the existence and size of a transmembrane potential difference in muscle cells one method for making such measurements is described here. Radioactive tracer methods are described later.

Intracellular Recording. Figure 1 is a schematic diagram showing how the difference in electric potential between the inside and the outside of a cell can be measured directly and accurately. The technique for this was perfected by Ling and Gerard.[20] An ultramicroelectrode* is made by drawing a piece of glass tubing down to a small tip and then filling the tubing with a concentrated solution of KCl. If the electrode tip is no larger than about 1 μ, it can be inserted transversely through the cell membrane of a muscle fiber without detectable damage to the membrane. Any electrode larger than this at the tip appreciably damages the membrane and lowers the measured potential. The potential of the microelectrode tip when it is in the solution bathing the muscle is taken as zero. When the microelectrode is advanced toward the surface of the muscle, the potential of the electrode does not change until the tip penetrates a cell membrane. At this time (*arrow* in Fig. 1), the potential drops abruptly to -90 mV. (inside negative) and remains at this value as long as the electrode is in the cell. This transmembrane potential is commonly called the *resting potential*

---

* This designation is in conformity with the histologists' conventions—the tip size being just below visibility by light microscopy.

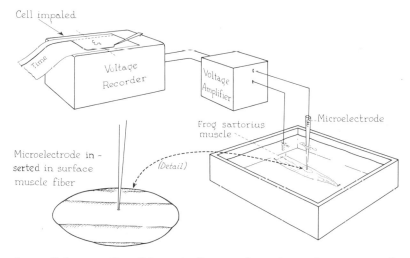

Fig. 1. Intracellular recording. Schematic diagram of experimental arrangement for measuring transmembrane electric potential differences. A frog sartorius muscle is dissected free and pinned to a wax-bottomed chamber (right) filled with a physiologic (Ringer's) solution. A capillary ultramicroelectrode is held in position over the muscle with a micromanipulator (not shown). Electrical connection is made to microelectrode and chamber by means of spirals of chlorided silver wires. Potential difference between tip of microelectrode and bathing medium is amplified and displayed as a function of time by recorder. When electrode penetrates the cell membrane (arrow on record at left), pen is suddenly deflected, thus indicating the existence of a steady transmembrane potential ($\mathcal{E}_s$). Drawing at lower left is enlarged view of electrode inserted through membrane of a single cell to show that tip of electrode (0.5 μ) is much smaller than diameter of muscle fiber (100 μ).

TABLE 1. *Approximate Steady State Ion Concentrations and Potentials in Mammalian Muscle Cells and Interstitial Fluid**

INTERSTITIAL FLUID		INTRACELLULAR FLUID		$\dfrac{[\text{Ion}]_o}{[\text{Ion}]_i}$	$\mathcal{E}\text{ion} = \dfrac{61}{Z} \log \dfrac{[\text{Ion}]_o}{[\text{Ion}]_i}$ (mV.)
[Ion] μM. per cm.^{3}		[Ion] μM. per cm.^{3}			
Cations		Cations			
Na$^+$	145	Na$^+$	12	12.1	66
K$^+$	4	K$^+$	155	1/39	-97
H$^+$	3.8×10^{-5}	H$^+$	13×10^{-5}	1/3.4	-32
pH	7.43	pH	6.9		
others	5				
Anions		Anions			
Cl$^-$	120	Cl$^-$	.4†	30	-90
HCO$_3^-$	27	HCO$_3^-$	8	3.4	-32
others	7	A$^-$	155		
Potential	0	-90 mV.		1/30†	-90

*Vertical double line represents membrane

†Calculated from membrane potential using the Nernst equation for a univalent anion, i.e.,
$$Z = -1$$

but also will be referred to here as the *steady** potential ($\mathcal{E}_s$), the $\mathcal{E}$ being derived from electromotive force. Measured transmembrane steady potentials in different tissues vary from about -20 mV. to -100 mV., but their generation by active Na$^+$ transport is probably the same in all tissues.

Ion Concentrations in Muscle. The term "extracellular fluid" refers to all fluids not inside cells. Blood, lymph, cerebrospinal fluid, etc., are in this category. "Interstitial fluid" is the fluid in direct contact with the tissue cells, and, therefore, knowledge of the concentrations of ions in this fluid is necessary in the study of membrane phenomena. The concentrations of ions in the interstitial fluid are slightly different from those in blood plasma, because plasma contains an appreciable concentration of ionized protein, i.e., there is a Gibbs-Donnan equilibrium (Chap. 45) between plasma and interstitial fluid, maintained across the capillary wall. However, ion concentrations in interstitial fluid can be calculated from measured concentrations in the blood if the concentrations of plasma proteins and their charges are known.

The left hand columns in Table 1 give the approximate concentrations of the more important ions in the interstitial fluid of mammals. Intracellular concentrations are estimated from chemical analysis of a known weight of tissue and a measurement of the fraction of the tissue water which is in the interstitial space. The total amount of any ion in the interstitial fluid is then obtained by the product of the interstitial concentration and the fractional volume. This amount is subtracted from the total amount of ion in the tissue sample to give the amount of ion in the intracellular water. Intracellular concentration is the ratio of the amount of ion to the amount of water in the cells. The middle columns in Table 1 show the concentrations of the more important ions in the intracellular water of mammalian skeletal muscle. Although intracellular concentrations vary considerably from tissue to tissue, the electrolyte pattern of muscle is fairly representative. To summarize Table 1, interstitial fluid has high concentrations of Na$^+$ and Cl$^-$; the intracellular fluid has high concentrations of K$^+$ and the largely unknown organic anions (A$^-$). The right hand columns are explained later.

Factors Affecting Ion Diffusion Through Membranes. *Passive factors.* Because of their random thermal motion, the individual molecules of a dissolved substance are continually intermixing (diffusing). If the concentration of the dissolved substance is higher in one region

*The term *steady* emphasizes that this unvarying voltage is one aspect of a steady-state of cellular function maintained by metabolism. On the other hand, *resting* contrasts with *active* in describing impulse conduction in excitable tissues.

than in an adjacent one, molecules will move both ways, but more will move from the region of higher to the region of lower concentration. Thus Na^+ and Cl^- tend to diffuse into cells and K^+ and A^- tend to diffuse out of cells. The rate of diffusion of these substances through the membrane depends not only on the concentration difference but also on the ease with which they pass through the membrane. In fact, the cell membrane so severely limits the rate at which substances diffuse through it that the rate of movement is determined solely by the membrane. That is, diffusion of ions through water is so much faster than through the membrane that the ion concentrations near the membrane differ negligibly from those in the surrounding bulk medium.

If the substance is ionized, the transmembrane potential also affects the rate of diffusion of the substance through the membrane. This effect is exerted because a transmembrane potential difference means that electric charges are separated by the cell membrane. This follows from the definition of potential difference between two points as the work done against electrical forces in carrying a unit positive charge from one point to the other. No electrical work is done in carrying a charge through the membrane unless charges are separated by the membrane. These separated charges (inside negative) exert a force on any ions in the membrane. This force tends to drive cations (+) into the cell and anions (−) out of the cell; i.e., any cations which enter the membrane are attracted by the negative charges on the inside and are repelled by the plus charges on the outside of the membrane.

K^+ tends to diffuse out of the cell because of its high internal concentration, but it tends to diffuse into the cell because of the electric charges separated by the membrane. These two tendencies nearly, but not quite, cancel each other, so that there is a slight tendency for K^+ to diffuse out of the cell. A similar argument holds for Cl^-, but in this instance the tendency for Cl^- to diffuse into the cell because of its high interstitial concentration is exactly balanced by the tendency of the electric forces to keep the negatively charged Cl^- from entering the cell. Since there is no net tendency for Cl^- to diffuse through the membrane, the inside and outside concentrations of Cl^- are in electrochemical equilibrium.

Active transport. The situation is quite different for Na^+ and A^-; both the concentration and potential difference act in the same direction. There is a strong tendency for A^- to diffuse out of the cell and for Na^+ to diffuse into it. However, the membrane is believed to be impermeable to A^- and is much less permeable to Na^+ than to K^+. Nevertheless, there is an appreciable steady leakage of Na^+ into cells. Despite this leakage, the internal concentration of Na^+ remains at low values in living cells. Therefore, some mechanism present in the cell must carry Na^+ out of the cell as fast as it enters, on the average. Since work must be done to carry Na^+ from a region of lower to a region of higher concentration and from a lower to a higher electric potential, it must be concluded that energy derived from cellular metabolism is used to carry Na^+ out of the cell.

Little is known of how metabolic energy is used to extrude Na^+ from the cell. It is known that the extrusion of a Na^+ is usually accompanied by the uptake of a K^+. This process is often referred to as active Na^+ transport, as the *Na^+–K^+ pump*, or more simply as the *Na^+ pump*. The word "pump" denotes that metabolic energy is required by the process. *Active transport* is a generic term referring to the process whereby metabolic energy is continuously expended to maintain transport of a substance in a direction opposite to that in which it tends to diffuse because of differences in concentration, potential, pressure, etc. The linkage of K^+ uptake to Na^+ extrusion accounts for the slight unbalance in the distribution of K^+; the net outward diffusion of K^+ is balanced by the inward pumping of K^+. The transmembrane potential arises because the membrane is much more permeable to K^+ than it is to Na^+ and because the Na^+–K^+ pump maintains the internal Na^+ concentration at a low value. K^+ would diffuse out of the cell faster than Na^+ would diffuse into it if there were no membrane potential; K^+ diffusing out must leave the nonpermeating A^- behind and thus the membrane is charged.

Summary. The factors that determine the rates at which ions move through the membrane can be expressed quantitatively, either as forces per mol or as potential energy per mol of ions. Thus it is easy to see that the charges separated by the membrane exert a force on charged particles within the membrane. The size of this force is expressed as the electric field intensity (force per unit charge) or, since the thickness of the membrane is constant, as the transmembrane potential (work done to carry a unit positive charge across the membrane against the electric field). Similarly, but not nearly so obviously, an ion concentration difference existing between the two solutions which bathe the membrane can be thought of as exerting a force on these ions, tending to make them move from regions of higher to regions of lower concentration.

Four factors which together determine the rate of flow of ions through the membrane have been mentioned: (i) transmembrane concentration differences, (ii) transmembrane potential differences, (iii) active Na^+-K^+ transport, and (iv) the mechanical barrier to ion movement imposed by the structure of the cell membrane, which can be thought of as a frictional force. The remainder of this chapter describes these forces, their interrelationships, and their role in the functioning of the cell.

PASSIVE FACTORS AFFECTING ION MOVEMENTS

Concentration Gradient. *Diffusion.* All the molecules in a solution, both solute and solvent, move in random directions between collisions with other molecules. The average kinetic energy of the molecules attributable to random motion is directly proportional to the absolute temperature. The random motion of the molecules is such that the rate at which molecules diffuse out of a small volume is proportional to the concentration [mols (M.) per liter or millimols (mM.) per cm.^{3}] of the substance in the small volume. Even in a solution in which the concentration of a substance is everywhere constant, a molecule found in one region at one time may be found in any region at a later time. This process of intermixing of solute (and solvent) particles is called *diffusion*.

Gradient and flux. In a solution where the concentration of a substance varies from one region to another, there will be a net movement of solute particles from regions of higher to regions of lower concentration, because more molecules per second leave than enter the region of higher concentration. This net diffusion is most conveniently expressed quantitatively in terms of the *flux* (**M**), defined as the number of mols per second passing through an area of 1 cm.^{2} oriented perpendicularly to the direction of flow of the substance (mols per cm.^{2}-sec.). The net diffusion of a substance from regions of higher to lower concentrations is analogous to the flow of water in a river. The rate of flow is proportional to the steepness of the stream bed:

the steeper the grade, the faster the flow. Water flows directly downhill, i.e., in the direction of steepest slope; a substance diffuses "downhill" in the direction of "steepest slope." The magnitude of the steepest slope or rate of change of concentration and the direction of this steepest slope constitute a vector. This vector is called the *concentration gradient*, abbreviated "**grad** [S]." Square brackets are used to denote concentration of the substance included in them; thus, [S] denotes the concentration of the substance S (usually given as μM. per cm.^{3}). Similarly flux (**M**) is a vector whose direction is opposite to that of the concentration gradient.

Any quantity that varies with distance has a gradient which can be calculated at any point. If concentration increases with increasing distance, then **grad** [S] is positive. However, net flux is in the opposite direction, so the net flux of S (M_S) is proportional to $-$**grad** [S] (Fig. 2*a*). For a given concentration gradient, M_S depends on the ease with which the molecules of S move through the solvent; the greater the ease of movement (the less the frictional resistance to flow), the greater the flux. The measure of the ease of motion is called the *diffusion constant* (D). Therefore, $M_S = -D_S$ **grad** [S] (for nonionized substances or for ions in regions *with no* electric field). In words, the net flux of S (M. per cm.^{2}-sec.) is given by the product of the diffusion constant of that substance (D_S; in cm.^{2} per sec.) and the concentration gradients of S (in M. per cm.^{3}-cm. or M. per cm.^{4}).

The presence of a cell membrane in a system greatly simplifies the description of the diffusion of a substance because most dissolved substances diffuse through the membrane so much more slowly than they diffuse through water that the diffusion time in water usually can be neglected (Fig. 2*b*). More precisely, the rate of diffusion of a substance through the membrane is so slow that a negligibly small concentration gradient in the aqueous media suffices to bring the substance up to the membrane as rapidly as it diffuses through the membrane. Thus, appreciable changes in concentration occur only in and near the membrane. Therefore, the rate of penetration of a substance depends on the properties of the membrane and on the concentration gradient of the substance in the membrane. Since the membrane is a thin, fixed structure and the concentration gradient in the solution is negligible, the average concentration gradient through the membrane is obtained, to a good approximation, by dividing the difference in concentration between the interstitial and intracellular fluids by the thickness of the membrane (δ). Thus, in the membrane, **grad** $[S]_m = ([S]_o - [S]_i)/\delta$. (Distance increases in the direction from inside to outside.) The subscript "m" is used to denote the value of a quantity in the *m*embrane; the subscript "o" (for *o*utside the cell), the value in the interstitial fluid; and the subscript "i" (for *i*nside the cell), the value in the intracellular fluid. Thus, $[S]_o$ means the concentration of S in the interstitial fluid.

Cell Membrane. The concentration gradient of a substance can be thought of as a force tending to move the substance. However, the rate of movement of S is determined not only by **grad** [S] but also by the frictional resistance to flow. Resistance is one of the forces listed above as affecting the movement of a substance. In a tissue, most resistance to flow of materials is in the cell membrane and its immediate vicinity. Therefore, the membrane structure and the various mechanisms whereby a substance may cross the membrane are important for understanding transport of materials into and out of cells. Also the high frictional resistance of the membrane ensures that the directions of the concentration and voltage gradients are perpendicular to the membrane.

Permeability. The net efflux (M_S) of a non-ionized substance through the membrane is simply calculated from the following equation (see Fig. 2*b*):

$$M_S = -D_S \text{ grad} [S]_m = -(D_S/\delta)([S]_o - [S]_i)$$
$$= P_S([S]_i - [S]_o) \tag{1}$$

The ratio D_S/δ is called the *permeability* of the membrane to the substance S (P_S). D_S is the diffusion constant of S in the membrane. P_S depends only on the properties of the membrane and of the substance. Permeability is thus a measure of the ease with which a substance can penetrate the membrane; i.e., the greater the permeability, the less the frictional drag force exerted by the membrane on the substance. In words, equation 1 states that the net flux of a substance (number of mols leaving the cell each second through 1 cm.^{2} of membrane minus the number of mols per cm.^{2}-sec. entering the cell) is equal to the permeability constant times the difference between the internal and external concentrations of the substance. In amphibian skeletal muscle the permeability of the cell membrane to K+ (P_K) is about 10^{-6} cm. per second, whereas P_{Na} is about 10^{-8} cm. per second. The permeability to K+ of a layer of water of the same thickness as the membrane (75 Ångstroms) is about 10 cm. per second, or ten million times greater than the P_K of the cell membrane. This

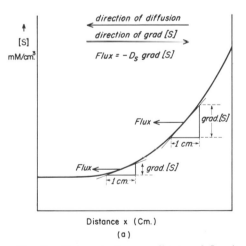

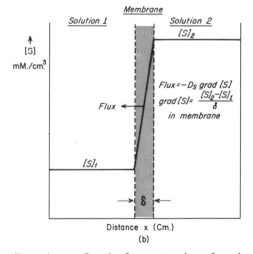

Fig. 2. Concentration gradient and flux in one dimension. *a*, Graph of concentration of a substance ([S]) against distance in a one compartment aqueous system. [S] increases from left to right; consequently, net diffusion of S is from right to left. Rate of diffusion is proportional to concentration gradient, **grad** [S], i.e., flux = $-D_S$ **grad** [S], where D_S is the diffusion constant. **Grad** [S] is defined, in one dimension, as the slope of the [S]-x curve as shown. *b*, A thin membrane divides the system into two compartments. S is assumed to diffuse much more slowly through the membrane than through the aqueous media on both sides. Therefore, **grad** [S] in the water is nearly zero, and **grad** [S] across the membrane is large. The average gradient of S in the membrane is difference in [S] across the membrane ($[S]_2 - [S]_1$), divided by the membrane thickness, δ. **Grad** [S] is large if δ is thin, but flux is small because D_S is so small in the membrane.

ratio indicates the extreme effectiveness of the cell membrane in limiting the flow of ions.

One way fluxes. It is natural to regard the net flux of a substance through a membrane as consisting of the difference between outward and inward one way fluxes: net flux = efflux − influx. Thus, efflux is the number of mols of a substance which diffuses from the internal medium to the external medium in one second through one cm.[2] of membrane and similarly for influx. On this basis, efflux can be calculated from equation (1) by setting the external concentration to zero so that net efflux consists solely of one way efflux: $M_S = P_S [S]_i$. However, this calculation is based on the assumption that each particle moves through the membrane independently of any other particle (the independence principle), a situation that does not always exist in the membrane, as will be seen below.

Experimentally it is usually not feasible to reduce the concentration of a particular substance to zero in one or the other of the solutions bathing the membrane since this change at the very least would likely alter the permeability characteristics of the membrane. However, the same effect can be obtained without producing appreciable changes in the media by adding a small amount of a radioactive isotope of the substance under study to the bathing medium. The concentration of radioactive material is zero inside the cell initially; the total concentration of the substance is normal. Measurements of the uptake rate of the isotope is a measure of the influx. Similarly, reducing the external isotope concentration to zero and measuring the rate of loss of isotope from the "loaded" tissue gives a measure of efflux. The measurement of one way fluxes under various conditions gives important information concerning the means by which substances penetrate the membrane, even—or especially—in those cases in which the independence principle does not hold, e.g., carrier mediated transport (see next section).

Membrane structure.[4, 5, 10, 23, 24] The cell membrane probably consists of outer and inner monomolecular layers of protein separated by a bimolecular lipid layer. In the lipid layer, the long, thin lipid molecules are closely packed, with their long axes parallel and oriented perpendicular to the membrane. The nonpolar ends of the lipid molecules are opposed. The protein layers are bonded to the lipids at their polar ends. Lipids are hydrophobic, and it seems unlikely that water and water-soluble substances can penetrate the membrane in a region where the lipid layer is closely packed.

In view of this probable membrane structure, the problem becomes not one of accounting for the low permeability of the membrane to water-soluble substances but of explaining the occurrence of any penetration at all. Lipid-soluble substances presumably penetrate by dissolving in the membrane substance. The available data suggest that ions and some other substances traverse the membrane by one or both of the following means:

(i) The membrane is perforate, containing small-diameter (about 7 Ångstroms), water-filled pores.[24,26] Ions could diffuse through these pores rapidly. The limitation of fluxes is attributed to the comparatively small number of pores per unit area of membrane and to restrictive effects of the pores. The membrane is normally about 100 times more permeable to K[+] than it is to Na[+]. This difference is apparently due to the greater hydrated radius of the Na[+] ion; the smaller positively charged Na atom attracts and holds more dipolar water molecules than does K. Na[+] ions are about 5 Ångstroms and K[+] ions are about 4 Ångstroms in diameter[26] and it is reasonable to suppose that the movements of Na[+] through a 7 Ångstrom pore are appreciably hindered with respect to those of K[+]. Most ions appear to move through the membrane independently of each other but the "in file" behavior of K[+] in *Sepia* giant axon membranes[14] is an exception.

(ii) There is a special lipid-soluble *carrier* molecule (possibly a phosphatide), limited to the membrane, which combines highly preferentially with particular ions. An ion from the interstitial fluid could combine with this carrier molecule at the outer surface of the membrane; the ion-carrier complex might then diffuse through the membrane to the inner surface. The ion might there dissociate from the carrier and enter the intracellular fluid. It has become increasingly necessary to postulate carriers to explain some aspects of both passive (diffusion) and active transport of ions and other substances. The exact manner in which ions cross the membrane is not known, but for passive movements it does not matter. When transport is passive, the net flux is approximately proportional to the concentration gradient of the ion across the cell membrane; the concept of permeability still applies.

Membrane Charge and Voltage Gradient. *Ion diffusion and charge separation.* Electric forces also affect the rate at which ions move through a membrane or solution. For an uncharged (nonionized) substance in a nonflowing solution, the only passive force tending to cause a net movement of the solute is the concentration gradient. However, if particles in solution are electrically charged, their movements may also be influenced by electric forces; and, conversely, their diffusion may generate a voltage. More precisely, voltage gradients as well as concentration gradients exert forces on charged particles in solution. The mechanism whereby voltage gradients can affect the diffusion of ions is most easily understood in terms of the forces acting on an ion moving through a membrane permeable only to small diameter ions.

Figure 3 is a diagram of a portion of a simplified membrane bathed by interstitial and intracellular fluid. This hypothetical membrane has been drawn with holes or pores piercing it at intervals. The diagram should be used only as an aid to thinking, not as a portrayal of a real membrane, for the scheme is far too simple. Nevertheless, the concept is useful in describing the generation of voltage gradients by the diffusion of ions.

The pores in the membrane are assumed to be just large enough to permit easy passage of K^+ and Cl^- but small enough that the slightly larger Na^+ can penetrate only with difficulty, i.e., P_K and P_{Cl} are much greater than P_{Na}. The large A^- are presumed too large to penetrate; i.e., $P_A = 0$. The concentration of each ionic species in the interstitial and intracellular fluid is shown qualitatively in Figure 3 by the size of its symbol at the left and right edges. Even if it

is supposed that there is no potential difference (no charges are separated) across the membrane at some instant, a voltage will be generated immediately thereafter by the diffusion of K^+ and Cl^- along their concentration gradients. This potential arises because K^+, which permeate the membrane easily, diffuse out of the cell through the pores and Cl^- diffuse inward. Hereafter, the behavior of K^+ only will be described, but it must be kept in mind that Cl^- give rise to the same effects. Wherever the outward diffusion of K^+ is mentioned, the inward diffusion of Cl^- would produce the same electrical effects.

Consider the sequence of events as each K^+ diffuses out of the cell. Although K^+ are charged particles, their outward movement cannot be accompanied by a corresponding movement of A^-, nor can an equal number of Na^+ move inward in exchange for outflowing K^+. Thus, K^+ ions reach the outside of the membrane alone and are not replaced within the cell by Na^+. Consequently, the outside acquires a net positive charge and the inside a net negative charge. Since electric charges of opposite sign attract each other, the excess K^+ ions on the outside are

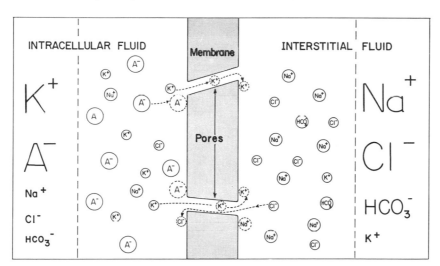

Fig. 3. Development of transmembrane voltage by an ion concentration gradient. Diagram of an intracellular fluid–membrane–interstitial fluid system. Membrane shown has some, but not all, properties of a real cell membrane. Hypothetical membrane is pierced by pores of such size that K^+ and Cl^- can move through them easily, Na^+ with difficulty, and A^- not at all. Sizes of symbols in left- and right-hand columns indicate relative concentrations of ions in fluids bathing the membrane. Dashed arrows and circles show paths taken by K^+, A^-, Na^+ and Cl^- as a K^+ or Cl^- travels through a pore. Penetration of the pore by a K^+ or Cl^- follows a collision between the K^+ or Cl^- and water molecules (not shown), giving the K^+ or Cl^- the necessary kinetic energy and proper direction. An A^- or Na^+ unable to cross the membrane is left behind when a K^+ or Cl^-, respectively, diffuses through a pore. Because K^+ is more concentrated on left than on right, more K^+ diffuses from left to right than from right to left, and conversely for Cl^-. Therefore, right-hand border of membrane becomes positively charged (K^+, Na^+) and left-hand negatively charged (Cl^-, A^-). Fluids away from the membrane are electrically neutral because of attraction between $+$ and $-$ charges. Charges separated by membrane stay near it because of their attraction.

attracted to the excess A^- left inside the cell. Therefore, the excess charges stay in the immediate vicinity of the membrane, as shown in Figure 3. Note that, despite the electrical attraction between the K^+ and A^-, movement of the K^+ back toward the inside of the cell is counteracted by the concentration gradient of K^+, which exerts an outward force on them. The outward diffusion of K^+ due to the concentration gradient separates positive and negative charges and thus generates a *voltage gradient* or an *electric field. Electric field intensity,* E, at a point is a vector defined as the force that would be exerted on a unit positive exploring charge placed at that point. This electric field retards further outward diffusion of K^+ (or any cation) and speeds their inward diffusion. Any positively charged ion in the membrane (Fig. 3) is acted upon by the charges the membrane separates. The positive charges on its outer surface exert an *inward* repulsive force on a positive ion in the membrane; the negative charges on the inner surface exert an additive inward attractive force.

In the hypothetical situation in which the membrane is permeable only to one ion species, the diffusion of that ion species through the membrane is self-limiting because the charges separated create an electric field which must build up until the influx and efflux are equal (net flux is zero). In this equilibrium condition, the tendency for K^+ to diffuse out, resulting from the high value of $[K^+]_i$, is exactly balanced by the tendency for them to diffuse inward that results from the electric field in the membrane. Because K^+ inside the cell are more concentrated, they will enter pores in the membrane as a result of their random motion much more frequently than will the K^+ outside. However, a cation entering a pore from the inside must have much kinetic energy to move through the membrane against the retarding electric field. Conversely, because of the low $[K^+]_o$ few K^+ enter the pores from the outside, but nearly all those that do will continue on through the membrane, aided by the electric field. Since much of present knowledge of cell membrane function has come from measurements of the electrical characteristics of the membrane, knowledge of some principles of electricity is necessary for an understanding of membrane function. Thus, a brief review of the pertinent principles of electricity is included as an appendix at the end of Chapter 2 for use by readers whose physics is "rusty." Some problems related to the material presented in this and in Chapters 2 and 3 are in the appendix.

Cell membrane capacity and charge. An animal cell and its surrounding fluids form a capacitor: two conductors, the interstitial and intracellular fluids, are separated by an insulator, the cell membrane. Since ions can penetrate the membrane to a limited extent, the cell is not a perfect capacitor. Charges separated by the membrane will eventually leak through unless there are some means of restoring the charge as fast as it leaks through. Membrane capacity is relatively high because the membrane is extremely thin. The cell may be regarded as a parallel plate capacitor, because the distance between the conductors is small compared to the diameter of a cell. It is convenient to give membrane capacities in terms of capacity per unit area, because the capacity of a parallel plate capacitor is proportional to its surface area and cells vary considerably in size. The nerve fibers of the squid, which have been studied extensively because they are large, have membrane capacities of about 1 μf. per cm.^{2}. The capacities of frog skeletal muscle fibers are nearly 10 μf. per cm.^{2}. The amount of charge (q) separated by 1 cm.^{2} of muscle cell membrane is the product of the steady potential difference ($\mathcal{E}_s$) across the cell membrane and the capacity (C_m) q = $C_m \mathcal{E}_s$ (see appendix, Chap. 2). $\mathcal{E}_s$ for a frog muscle fiber is -90 mV., so q = 10×10^{-6} f. per cm.$^2 \times 0.09$ V. = 9×10^{-7} coulombs per cm.^{2}.

Since the charges separated by the membrane are ions, the amount of charge can be given more meaning by expressing it in mols per cm.^{2} rather than in coulombs per cm.^{2}. There are 6.023×10^{23} molecules in 1 M. of any substance, and a monovalent ion has a charge of ± 1 electronic charge; therefore, since one electron has a charge of 1.6×10^{-19} coulombs, the charge of 1 M. of monovalent ions is (6.023×10^{23} monovalent ions per M.) $\times$ (1.6×10^{-19} coulombs per monovalent ion) = 96,500 coulombs per M. of monovalent ions. It follows that a charge of 9×10^{-7} coulombs per cm.^{2} on a muscle fiber membrane means that there are only 9.5×10^{-12} M. of ions separated by 1 cm.^{2} of cell membrane. By comparison, 1 cm.^{3} of interstitial or intracellular fluid contains 155×10^{-6} M. of cations (or anions). In other words, a layer of interstitial fluid only 6×10^{-8} cm. (6 Ångstroms) thick is sufficient to supply the ions necessary to charge the cell membrane capacity to 90 mV.

Charge neutrality. The charging of the membrane by the outward movement of K^+ produces a readily measurable voltage across the membrane. However, the change in $[K^+]_i$ necessary to charge the membrane is not detectable by chemical measurements. Despite the extremely small changes in ion concentration required to charge the membrane capacity, it is worth emphasizing that the law of macroscopic electroneutrality does not apply to macroscopic parts of the intracellular fluid–membrane–interstitial fluid system. The whole system is electrically neutral, but the intracellular fluid contains a slight excess of anions and the interstitial fluid an equal excess of cations. These excess charges are, of course, attracted to each other, and thus distribute themselves with uniform density over the surfaces of the membrane.

Charging membrane capacity. The process whereby the diffusion of an ionic species down its concentration gradient can generate a counteracting voltage gradient, briefly discussed above, can now be summarized in terms of the charging of the membrane capacitor and the consequent generation of an electric field in it (Fig. 3). When a K^+ traverses a pore (dashed lines, Fig. 3) and leaves the cell, this cation leaves behind a nonpermeating Λ^-. The outside fluid thus acquires a positive charge and the inside a negative charge. In other words, the membrane capacity is slightly charged, and a voltage difference is built up between the conductors. More simply, the separation of charge means that there is an electric field in the membrane and that work must be done on a unit $+$ charge to carry it out of the cell. The electric field in the membrane is uniform because the separated charges must distribute themselves uniformly over its surfaces in order to make the electric field zero everywhere in the inside and outside conducting fluids (see appendix, Chap. 2). This is true even in the case of penetration of the membrane by a single ion; the excess cation on one side and the excess anion on the other move the charges in the conducting media. This movement has the effect of distributing the single charge over the cell membrane surface. The electric field in the membrane is approximately constant, so the voltage across the membrane is simply the product of the electric field ($\mathbf{E}$) and the membrane thickness (δ), $\mathscr{E}_s = -\mathbf{E}(-\delta) = \mathbf{E}\delta$.

IONIC EQUILIBRIUM

As pointed out above, if a membrane's permeability to one ion is greater than to another and if ion concentration differences exist across the membrane, then a transmembrane voltage will develop. For example, if a membrane is permeable only to K^+, the diffusion of K^+ through the membrane down its concentration gradient is self-limiting. The first K^+ to penetrate the membrane generate an electric field which retards the diffusion of other K^+ ions. As long as there is a net efflux of K^+, $+$ and $-$ charges are being separated and the electric field is increasing, so that eventually $\mathbf{E}$ must attain a strength to permit influx to equal efflux. Outflowing K^+ are driven by the high $[K^+]_i$ and retarded by $\mathbf{E}$; inflowing ions are accelerated by $\mathbf{E}$, but the low $[K^+]_o$ means that K^+ enter the membrane at a slower rate. *If no work is needed to carry a small amount of a substance across the membrane, that substance is said to be distributed at equilibrium.* An alternative statement of the equilibrium condition is that influx and efflux are equal. This statement is true because there can be no net flux of the substance unless there is a force acting on it, and the existence of a force acting on ions means that a potential energy difference must also exist.

The equilibrium condition for uncharged molecules is simply that the internal and external concentrations are equal, for this is the condition at zero net flux (equation 1). The equilibrium condition for ions is more complicated: both the concentration and the voltage difference across the membrane must be known in order to calculate the potential energy difference between the inside and outside and thus the equilibrium condition. Any inside concentration of an ionic species may be brought into equilibrium with any outside concentration by applying the appropriate transmembrane voltage. Experimentally, this situation may be achieved by separating the two ionic solutions with a membrane permeable only to the ionic species for which the equilibrium is desired. The charging process illustrated in Figure 3 then generates a potential difference which equalizes influx and efflux. *The transmembrane potential which equalizes fluxes for a particular ion is called the equilibrium potential for that ion.* Its value depends on the ratio of the internal and external concentrations of the ion.

Electrochemical Potential. The relationship between the external and internal concentrations of an ion and the transmembrane potential at equilibrium is obtained by setting to zero the expression for the total transmembrane potential energy difference for that ion. This total potential difference per mol of ion is called the *electrochemical potential difference* ($\Delta\mu$) and is the sum of the electrical and concentration energy differences across the membrane for that ion. An expression for the electrochemical difference for K^+ will be developed here, but the same considerations hold for any ion present in a tissue.

The *electric potential energy difference* of 1 mol of K^+ is the work that must be done solely against electric forces to carry 1 mol of K^+ across the membrane, from outside to inside, with the transmembrane potential held at its original value. This work (W_E) is simply the product of $\mathcal{E}_m$, the transmembrane voltage (joules per coulomb), F, the Faraday (number of coulombs per mole of charge) and Z_K, the valence of the K^+ ion: $W_E = Z_K F \mathcal{E}_m$. The *concentration potential energy difference* W_C is the work required to carry 1 mol of K^+ from outside to inside solely against the concentration gradient, with the external and internal K^+ concentrations held at their original values. W_C is not easily calculable, but it can be shown that W_C is proportional to the difference between the logarithms of the internal and external concentrations* rather than directly proportional to their difference. Thus $W_C = RT(\log_e[K^+]_i - \log_e[K^+]_o)$, where R is the universal gas constant, T is the absolute temperature, and e is 2.718 (the base of natural logarithms); RT has the unit of energy per mol. The electrochemical potential difference for K^+ is, then, $\Delta\mu_K = W_E + W_C$, so

$$\Delta\mu_K = Z_K F \mathcal{E}_m + RT \log_e \frac{[K^+]_i}{[K^+]_o} \qquad (2)$$

If $\mathcal{E}_m$, $[K^+]_o$ and $[K^+]_i$ are such that $\Delta\mu_K = 0$, then K^+ are equilibrated across the membrane. If $\Delta\mu_K$ is not zero, it is a measure of the net tendency of K^+ to diffuse through the membrane. The larger $\Delta\mu_K$, the greater the net efflux of K^+.

Nernst Equation. The condition for ionic equilibrium is that the electrochemical potential of an ion is zero. Setting $\Delta\mu_K = 0$ in equation 2, replacing $\mathcal{E}_m$ by $\mathcal{E}_K$, and solving for $\mathcal{E}_K$ gives

$$\mathcal{E}_K = \frac{RT}{FZ_K} \log_e \frac{[K^+]_o}{[K^+]_i} \qquad (3)$$

---

* Strictly speaking, activities rather than concentrations should be used. However, the activities appear only as ratios and these ratios are close to the equivalent concentration ratios in value. Thus, the error is not large and does not affect the conclusions reached here.

This is the Nernst equation. The term $\mathcal{E}_K$ indicates that this equation determines the value that $\mathcal{E}_m$ must have if K^+ are to be in equilibrium. $\mathcal{E}_K$ is called the *potassium equilibrium potential*. By substituting the values R = 8.31 joules per mol-degree abs., T = 310 degrees abs. (37° C.), F = 96,500 coulombs per mol, and $Z_K = +1$, converting to logarithms to the base 10 and expressing $\mathcal{E}_K$ in millivolts, a useful form of the Nernst equation is obtained:

$$\mathcal{E}_K = 61 \log_{10} \frac{[K^+]_o}{[K^+]_i} \text{ mV.} \qquad (4)$$

Note that if $\mathcal{E}_K = 0$, the equilibrium condition for ions reduces to that for neutral substances, i.e., $[K^+]_o = [K^+]_i$. The Nernst equation can be written for every ion present in the system.

An ion whose equilibrium potential is equal to the steady membrane potential, that is, equilibrated, is said to be distributed *passively*. This term means that there are no active forces on the ion. With the equilibrium conditions for ion concentrations quantitatively stated by the Nernst equation, it is possible to determine which ions in a cell's environment are distributed passively. The requisite numbers for the most important ions in mammalian skeletal muscle are given in Table 1. The external and internal concentrations, their ratio, and the equilibrium potentials are given in the main body of the table. The steady transmembrane potential $\mathcal{E}_s$, as measured with an intracellular microelectrode, is given at the bottom of the table to facilitate comparison with calculated ionic equilibrium potentials. $\mathcal{E}_s$ is defined as the potential of the inside solution minus the potential of the outside solution. Since the cell interior is negatively charged, $\mathcal{E}_s$ is a negative number. K^+, Cl^- and Na^+ will be discussed here and H^+ and HCO_3^- in Chapter 46.

Potassium ions. From Table 1, $[K^+]_o = 4$ μM. per cm.^{3} and $[K^+]_i = 155$ μM. per cm.^{3}; therefore, $\mathcal{E}_K = 61 \log_{10} (4/155) = -97$ mV. This value is close to the measured $\mathcal{E}_s$, -90 mV. This calculation accords with qualitative arguments given above that the concentration gradient for K^+ is largely counteracted by the membrane voltage gradient; i.e., little energy is needed to carry 1 mol of K^+ across the membrane. Experimental errors make it uncertain whether or not $\mathcal{E}_K$ and $\mathcal{E}_s$ are different in this case, but there is good evidence, nevertheless, that K^+ are not quite at equilibrium in tissues.

Chloride ions. The extracellular concentration of chloride is high, and its intracellular concentration is low. Because of the negative valence of Cl⁻, the electrical and concentration forces affecting Cl⁻ act in opposite directions. However, the value of ε_{Cl} is uncertain because $[Cl^-]_i$ is difficult to estimate from analyses of the chloride content of the tissues, since these determinations include both extracellular and intracellular fluids, and most of the tissue Cl⁻ is in the interstitial fluid. Hence, less direct means must be used to determine cell chloride concentration in tissues. There is good indirect evidence that chloride is equilibrated in frog skeletal muscle. Hodgkin and Horowicz[12] found that sudden changes in $[Cl^-]_o$ can produce large but always transient changes in transmembrane potential. This means that P_{Cl} is comparable to P_K and that the net fluxes of Cl⁻ resulting from sudden changes in its concentration affect the potential until such times as Cl⁻ redistribution is completed and net flux of Cl⁻ returns to zero. Also, there is little doubt that Cl⁻ is equilibrated in red blood cells. However, Cl⁻ is not passively distributed in all tissues. Keynes[16] has direct evidence that the giant axon of the squid (see Chapter 2) actively accumulates Cl⁻. Nevertheless Cl⁻ distribution in tissues is assumed to be passive hereafter unless a specific statement is made to the contrary. The value of $[Cl^-]_i = 4 \mu M.$ per cm.³ given in Table 1 was calculated on this assumption, i.e., ε_{Cl} is set equal to the $\varepsilon_s = -90$ mV. and Nernst's equation solved for $[Cl^-]_i$.

Sodium ions. To a first approximation, K⁺ and Cl⁻ are distributed across the membrane in equilibrium with the membrane voltage ($\varepsilon_{Cl} = \varepsilon_s \simeq \varepsilon_K$). Two interpretations of this finding are possible: (i) the membrane voltage is generated by the existing concentration gradients of K⁺ and Cl⁻ ions in the manner described above, the mechanism whereby these concentration gradients are maintained not being specified, or (ii) the membrane voltage is maintained by unspecified means and the K⁺ and Cl⁻ distribute themselves in equilibrium with the voltage. Even though the evidence presented thus far does not permit differentiation between these two possibilities, they highlight the question of how the resting potential and the concentration gradients are generated and maintained by the cell. The key to this question lies in the behavior of Na⁺. Sodium is distributed far out of equilibrium with the membrane voltage; both the concentration gradient and the voltage gradient act

to drive Na⁺ into the cell. The Na⁺ equilibrium potential, ε_{Na}, is given by Nernst's equation: $\varepsilon_{Na} = (61/1) \log (145/12) = +66$ mV. This means that the membrane potential would have to be +66 mV. (inside positive) in order to counteract the inward concentration force on Na⁺, whereas ε_s is actually −90 mV. (inside negative) in the steady state.

Membrane Ionic Flux, Current and Conductance. As mentioned in connection with equation 2, the transmembrane electrochemical potential difference of an ion species is a measure of the tendency for that ion to move through the membrane. The rate at which an ion moves through the membrane depends not only on the electrochemical potential but also on the ease with which the ion can penetrate the membrane, i.e., its permeability. Thus it is reasonable to write transmembrane flux of an ion as the product of a potential energy difference term and a permeability term. Such a relationship is actually a generalization of Ohm's law (see appendix, Chap. 2) relating current flow (I) and potential difference (ε): $I = (1/R)\varepsilon = g\varepsilon$, where R is resistance and $g = 1/R$ is called the conductance (unit: mho, ohm spelled backwards). Thus, by making use of Nernst's equation for the equilibrium potential (equation 3), and by using K⁺ as an example, the description of the electrochemical potential (equation 2) can be greatly simplified by expressing it as an electric potential difference:

$$\Delta\mu_K = Z_K F \left(\varepsilon_m - \frac{RT}{ZF} \log_e \frac{[K^+]_o}{[K^+]_i} \right)$$
$$= Z_K F(\varepsilon_m - \varepsilon_K) \qquad (5)$$

where ε_K is the K⁺ equilibrium potential.

Ohm's law for ion fluxes. Current is defined as the number of coulombs passing a point in a second (units: coulombs/sec. = amperes). Current density is directly related to flux; current density is defined as coulombs per second and per cm.² of area perpendicular to direction of flow and flux is mols per sec.-cm.². The proportionality factor is the Faraday (F, units: coulombs per mol of monovalent ions) times the valence (Z): $I = ZFM$. The direction of current flow is defined as the direction of movement of positive charge; hence current and flux are in the same direction for positive ions and in opposite directions for negative ions as indicated by the valence, Z. The current density of K⁺ (I_K)

through the membrane is proportional to the electrochemical potential difference:

$$I_K = M_K Z_K F = g_K(\mathcal{E}_m - \mathcal{E}_K) \qquad (6)$$

where the proportionality factor, g_K, is called the specific membrane conductance to potassium or simply potassium conductance (units: mho per cm.²). I_K is actually current density but is usually referred to simply as potassium current.

Equation 6 expresses the rate of movement of an ion species through the membrane in terms of its ease of penetration and the divergence of the actual membrane potential from the equilibrium potential for that ion. Ion current is zero when $\mathcal{E}_m = \mathcal{E}_K$, which is, of course, the equilibrium condition. Similarly, the greater the difference between the two potentials, the greater the ion movement through the membrane.

Membrane ionic conductance. Membrane ionic conductance is a measure of the ease with which an ion penetrates the membrane; i.e., the measurement is made when the ions are driven by an electrical force. On the other hand, permeability is a measure of the ease with which a substance penetrates the membrane when driven by a concentration force. Thus ion conductance and ion permeability must be closely related quantities. However, the relationship between them is not simple, depending, among other things, on the transmembrane voltage itself. For example, in frog skeletal muscle, it has been found experimentally that g_{Cl} varies considerably with voltage but in the manner expected if P_{Cl} is constant. Despite the complicated nature of conductance, the Ohm's law approach is most frequently used in describing ion fluxes through membranes because conductances are usually easier to measure experimentally than permeabilities, because the relationship is easy to visualize and simple to use and because the relationship between flux, permeability and concentration and potential differences is complicated and difficult to use. Hence, Ohm's law for ion fluxes (equation 6) is used throughout the remainder of this chapter and in Chapters 2, 4 and 5 where appropriate. Thus it is extremely important at this juncture to understand the concepts of the ion equilibrium potential as defined by Nernst's equation (3) and Ohm's law (appendix, Chap. 2); e.g., Figure 6 (page 20), based on these concepts, shows the important factors in maintenance of steady transmembrane concentration and potential differences by active Na⁺–K⁺ transport.

ACTIVE SODIUM TRANSPORT

Sodium Influx. Na⁺ is distributed so far from equilibrium—i.e., $\Delta\mu_{Na}$ is so high—as to pose forcefully the question of how this disequilibrium is maintained in living cells. There are at least two possibilities. If Na⁺ ions are unable to penetrate the membrane, the disequilibrium would persist indefinitely. If Na⁺ can penetrate the membrane, some other energy term must be included in the calculation of the expected Na⁺ distribution. The first possibility is simple and, therefore, attractive. However, it must be rejected, since studies with radioactive Na⁺ have shown that these ions penetrate the membrane, although not so readily as K⁺ and Cl⁻. Therefore, the second possibility must be explored.

Sodium tracer experiments.[11, 13] The penetration of Na⁺ through the membrane is demonstrated experimentally by placing a small muscle or a single large nerve cell into a solution with an ionic composition the same as that of the interstitial fluid, a radioactive isotope of Na⁺ constituting part of the Na⁺. If Na⁺ can penetrate the membrane, part of the nonradioactive Na⁺ in the intracellular fluid will, in time, exchange positions with radioactive Na⁺ in the bathing medium. The amount of radiosodium taken up by the muscle after a period of soaking is measured by counting the number of disintegrations per minute occurring in the tissue. The total Na⁺ entry during soaking can be ascertained by comparing the number of counts per minute from the muscle with the number of counts per minute from a known volume of the radioactive bathing medium and its known Na⁺ concentration. The result must, of course, be corrected for the amount of radiosodium in the interstitial fluid in the muscle and for the interstitial concentration of sodium. If the total surface area of all fibers in the muscle is known, the influx of Na⁺ (mols per cm.²-sec.) can be calculated.

Measured Na⁺ influx in frog sartorius muscle is of the order of 5×10^{-12} M. per cm.²-second.[11] If this influx were not matched by an equal efflux,* the internal Na⁺ concentration in a muscle fiber 100 μ in diameter would increase at the rate of about 14 μM. per cm.³-hour. Since [Na⁺] is about 12 μM. per cm.³, [Na⁺]$_i$ would about double in the first hour.

Sodium Efflux. To return to the second possibility mentioned above, namely, that another term is needed to balance influx and efflux of Na⁺, there are three apparently contradictory facts about the behavior of Na⁺ in tissues which must be considered. (i) The distribution of Na⁺ in tissues is far from equilibrium. (ii)

---

* The expected passive efflux is negligible, less than 0.1 per cent of influx.

Na$^+$ can penetrate the cell membrane. (iii) This disequilibrium is maintained by living cells; [Na$^+$]$_i$ remains low and $\Delta\mu_{Na}$ remains high despite an appreciable influx of Na$^+$. Therefore, for some reason, Na$^+$ efflux must equal Na$^+$ influx; i.e., it is necessary to postulate that some force other than voltage and concentration gradients is expelling Na$^+$ from the cell at an average rate equal to the rate of passive entry.

Since Na$^+$ enters cells spontaneously, work must be done to carry Na$^+$ out of the cell. Further, Na$^+$ is entering all the time, so work must be continuously expended to eject the entering Na$^+$ and maintain a low [Na$^+$]$_i$. The power (time rate of supplying energy or of doing work) to eject Na$^+$ continually comes ultimately from the oxidation of glucose or other metabolites by the cell. *The process whereby the cell continuously uses metabolic energy to maintain an efflux of Na$^+$ is called active Na$^+$ transport* or, colloquially, *the Na$^+$ pump.*

The term "active transport" implies that the transport process requires a continuous supply of energy. By contrast, the diffusion of a substance down its electrochemical gradient is called "passive transport." The detailed mechanism involved in active Na$^+$ transport is not known. Nevertheless, in addition to the reasons given above for supposing there must be an active Na$^+$ transport, there is considerable direct experimental evidence that such a mechanism exists in many types of cells, e.g., giant nerve fibers of the squid,[13] human red blood cells[6, 7, 27] and frog skin (from outside to inside).[19, 22, 28, 29] In addition, active Na$^+$ transport almost certainly occurs in all nervous tissue and all skeletal,[1, 11, 17, 18] cardiac and smooth muscle. Active Na$^+$ reabsorption is probably the major energy-consuming process in the kidney. Na$^+$ pumping is also importantly involved in the formation of saliva and other ion-containing gastrointestinal secretions. Many substances besides Na$^+$ are actively transported by cells. The kidney is specialized for the active secretion or reabsorption of many inorganic and organic substances.

Energy requirements for active sodium transport. The postulate that the disequilibrium of Na$^+$ between cells and bathing medium is maintained through the expenditure of metabolic energy is subject to a stringent yet simple experimental test. The minimum power required to transport Na$^+$ out of a cell at the observed rate must be less than the rate of energy production of the cell. The rate of energy production can be calculated from the oxygen consumption of the cell. The minimum transport power is the product of the transport work per mol of Na$^+$ and the number of mols of Na$^+$ transported per second, i.e., the product of the negative of the electrochemical potential of Na$^+$ and the Na$^+$ active efflux ($\mathbf{M}_{Na}^{out}$). Thus, the Na$^+$ transport power ($\dot{W}_{Na}$)* is $\dot{W}_{Na} = -\Delta\mu_{Na}\mathbf{M}_{Na}^{out}$. The negative sign is used in front of $\Delta\mu_{Na}$ because it is defined as the electrical and concentration work to carry 1 M. of Na$^+$ into the cell through the membrane; this work is, of course, the negative of the work to carry the Na$^+$ out. $\Delta\mu_{Na}$ is of the same form as $\Delta\mu_{K}$, given in equation 2, so

$$\dot{W}_{Na} = -\left(Z_{Na}F\mathcal{E}_m + RT\log_e\frac{[Na^+]_i}{[Na^+]_o}\right)\mathbf{M}_{Na}^{out}(7)$$

Keynes and Maisel[17] have made the necessary measurements on frog skeletal muscle to test whether the Na$^+$ transport power requirement is less than the energy production rate of a cell. In one experiment, they obtained the following data:

$\mathcal{E}_s = -88$ mV., [Na$^+$]$_o = 115$ μM. per cm.^{3}, [Na$^+$]$_i = 20$ μM. per cm.^{3}, $\mathbf{M}_{Na}^{out} = 8.7$ μM.

per hour and per gram of muscle.† Energy production, calculated from oxygen consumption, was 0.17 calorie per hour and per gram of muscle. Substituting these values in equation 5 gives the value $\dot{W}_{Na} = 0.027$ calorie per hour and per gram of muscle as the power requirement for Na$^+$ transport, assuming 100 per cent efficiency for the process. In other words, a minimum of 15 per cent of the oxygen consumption of a noncontracting muscle is used to pump Na$^+$. Keynes and Maisel obtained values of about 10 per cent in most of their experiments. It should be borne in mind that the pumping efficiency is unlikely to be greater than about 50 per cent, so that at least 20 per cent of resting oxygen consumption, probably more, goes for Na$^+$ transportation. In any event, the energy demands of the Na$^+$ pump are not excessive, and the postulate of active Na$^+$ transport is possible energetically. More recently, Keynes and Swan[18] have shown

---

*A dot over a symbol for a quantity means the time rate of change of the quantity; orally, such a symbol is referred to as "W-dot." Thus W$_{Na}$ is work done on or energy of 1 M. of Na$^+$; $\dot{W}_{Na}$ is the time rate of doing work, or power.

†Strictly speaking this is not efflux, but it is the desired figure, since oxygen consumption is given in cubic millimeters per hour and per gram of tissue.

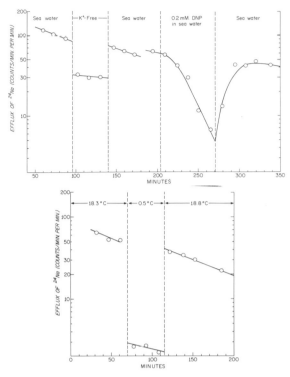

Fig. 4. Na+ efflux in giant axon of *Sepia* (cuttlefish). Ordinates are efflux of radioactive Na+ from cell; total (radioactive + normal) Na+ of efflux is proportional to radioactive efflux except for gradual dilution of radioactive Na+ by normal Na+ as these ions exchange (the gradual fall shown under sea water).

Upper, Effects of various bathing media. Second column from left shows that reducing $[K^+]_o$ from 10 μM. per cm.[3] to zero immediately reduces Na+ efflux to about one-third that in artificial sea water; this effect is immediately reversed when the axon is returned to artificial sea water (middle column). Next, adding the metabolic inhibitor DNP reduces Na+ efflux to values near zero within one to two hours; this effect is slowly reversible (right column).

Lower, The effects of temperature on another axon. Reduction of temperature from 18° to 0.5° C. immediately reduces Na+ efflux to near zero; raising the temperature immediately restores efflux. (From Hodgkin and Keynes. *J. Physiol.,* 1955, *128:*28–60.)

that about one-half of Na+ efflux is a one-for-one forced exchange for external Na+; i.e., Na+ efflux is reduced to one-half when $[Na^+]_o$ is reduced to zero. This *exchange diffusion,* first postulated by Ussing,[28] does not require the expenditure of energy. Thus the calculated minimum power requirement for Na+ pumping in resting muscle is about twice too large.

Active Sodium–Potassium Exchange. Although the detailed mechanism for utilization of metabolic energy to carry Na+ out of the cell

is not yet known, the process has been intensively studied in many tissues and some of the broad characteristics of Na+ pumping have been defined. These characteristics seem to be much the same in all the tissues studied. Hodgkin and Keynes[13] carefully investigated Na+ and K+ movements in giant axons (150 to 300 μ in diameter) of *Sepia* (cuttlefish). These findings form a compact summary of the present state of knowledge. (i) Na+ efflux is a direct function of $[Na^+]_i$. (ii) Na+ efflux is decreased to values near zero by the addition, at appropriate concentrations, of a metabolic inhibitor to the bathing medium (Fig. 4). Metabolic inhibitors are substances which block the metabolic cycle at some point. Such an inhibitor would be expected to stop Na+ extrusion by depriving the pump of its source of energy. (iii) K+ influx is greatly reduced by metabolic inhibitors. These inhibitors produce about equal decreases in K+ efflux and Na+ influx. (iv) Na+ influx and K+ efflux are not greatly affected by metabolic inhibitors. (v) Na+ efflux is greatly reduced, but not abolished, by removal of K+ from the external bathing medium (Fig. 4) and increases when $[K^+]_o$ is increased. (vi) Na+ efflux (Fig. 4) and K+ influx are highly temperature-dependent; a reduction in temperature markedly decreases the fluxes (Q_{10} of 3 to 4, i.e., a temperature reduction of 10° C. reduces these fluxes to $\frac{1}{3}$ to $\frac{1}{4}$ of their original values). On the other hand, Na+ influx and K+ efflux are relatively insensitive to temperature changes (Q_{10} from 1.1 to 1.4).

Figure 4 shows the effects of a K+-free solution, of the metabolic inhibitor 2,4 dinitrophenol (DNP), and of low temperature on the Na+ efflux of a *Sepia* axon. The ordinate, which indicates the number of disintegrations of radiosodium atoms per minute that occur among radiosodium ions that have left the cell in one minute, is nearly proportional to Na+ efflux.* It can be seen that removal of K+ from the bathing medium immediately reduces the Na+ efflux to

---

*The number of radioactive sodium ions in a sample is proportional to the number of counts per minute. After correction is made for the gradual dilution of the radioactive ions by inactive ones, the total number of Na+ present is proportional to the number of radioactive Na+ present. Counts per minute appearing in the external medium in one minute are thus of the form of mols per minute. Dividing by the surface area of the axon involved gives the flux in mols per cm.[2]-minute.

about 0.3 of its previous value. In contrast, the addition of DNP (0.2 μM. per cm.[3]) leads to a slow decline in efflux requiring one to two hours for completion. The slow onset of the effect of DNP is attributed to the time required for the axon to consume the energy stores on hand when metabolism is inhibited.

These findings are strong evidence for the existence of an active Na+ transport process in cells. Further, the findings suggest that there is also an active uptake of K+ and that this uptake is coupled with Na+ extrusion. A reduction in the amount of available energy, either by metabolic inhibitors or by temperature reduction, has parallel effects in reducing Na+ efflux and K+ influx. A coupled Na+–K+ exchange mechanism is also suggested by the reduction in Na+ efflux when all the K+ is removed from the bathing medium and the increase in Na+ exit when $[K^+]_o$ is increased. However, since Na+ efflux is 30 per cent of normal when $[K^+]_o = 0$, the linkage between Na+ and K+ is not rigid. The dependence of Na+ extrusion on $[K^+]_o$ has been observed in a number of other tissues and the existence of such a relationship is presumptive evidence of a one-for-one Na+–K+ exchange. It will be assumed hereafter that Na+ pumping is coupled with an equal uptake of K+. This assumption, although not strictly true, simplifies, without invalidating, deductions on the consequences of active Na+ for K+ transport. The effects of active inward K+ transport on the distribution of K+ will be discussed later.

Since the existence of active Na+ K+ transport is well established, it is reasonable to ask how the cell does use metabolic energy to extrude Na+ and take up K+. Although no detailed answer can be given to this question, it is worthwhile, for the sake of concreteness, to describe a specific model of Na+–K+ transport (Fig. 5) and to describe a recently established correlation between Na+ efflux and an adenosine triphosphatase activity which is found in red blood cell membranes and which is activated by Na+ and K+.

Model of active sodium–potassium exchange.[6] The hypothetical scheme of active cation transport illustrated in Figure 5 accounts for all the known phenomena but there are numerous other possible mechanisms. There are insufficient experimental data at present to distinguish between the various possibilities. The most probable method of pumping Na+ is to "disguise" or "smuggle" it, i.e., to let Na+ diffuse through the membrane down a concentration gradient of an organo-Na+ compound that is continuously produced inside the cell and destroyed outside the cell. Another way of saying this is that the "force other than the concentration and potential gradients" that was invoked earlier to explain the efflux of Na+ is simply a concentration gradient, maintained by metabolism, of an organo-Na+ compound.

Figure 5 is a scheme of a hypothetical Na+–K+ exchange mechanism. Na+ is carried out of the cell combined with a substance (Y) which has a high affinity for Na+; that is, the reaction Na+ + Y = Na+Y is far to the right. Y may or may not have a negative charge. Once outside the cell, or at the outer surface of the cell membrane, some of the Na+Y dissociates into Na+ + Y. Y is immediately converted into a K+-specific carrier substance (X), the rate of the spontaneous reaction being increased by an enzyme on the outer surface of the cell membrane. X combines with K+ and the K+X diffuses into the cell under its own concentration gradient.

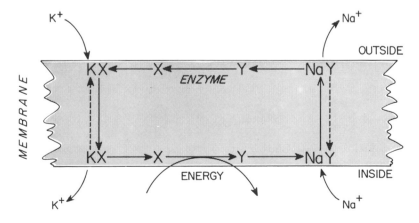

Fig. 5. Hypothetical scheme of a Na+–K+ exchange pump. The substances X and Y are assumed to be confined to the membrane. X has a high affinity for K+; Y has a high affinity for Na+. X and Y move through the membrane only when in combination with an ion. (Modified from Shaw by Glynn. *Progr. Biophys.*, 1957, *8*:241–307.)

The X formed when K+X dissociates inside the cell is converted to Y by an energy-requiring reaction, thus completing the transport cycle.

This scheme does not require a rigid Na+–K+ coupling. Thus, the maintenance of some Na+ efflux when external [K+] is zero can be explained by assuming either that Na+ has some affinity for the K+ carrier, X, or that Na+Y is shuttling back and forth across the membrane and that the Na+ bound to Y may exchange with Na+ in the interstitial fluid as well as in the intracellular fluid. This latter process does not require an energy supply and thus is a model of exchange diffusion.[18]

Sodium–potassium transport and membrane ATPase activity.[27]   Recent discoveries have given an inkling of the molecular basis of Na+–K+ transport: (i) Adenosine triphosphate (ATP) is an energy source sufficient to maintain pumping in squid nerve and in human red cell ghosts. (ii) There is present in human red cell membranes, in crab nerves and brain microsomes ("membrane" fraction of centrifuged cell fragments) an adenosine triphosphatase activity which requires Mg^{++} and whose activity, i.e., rate of ATP hydrolysis, is increased by the presence of Na+ and K+ in the medium. (iii) This ATP-ase activity is inhibited by cardiac glycosides (digitalis-like substances). These glycosides are also potent inhibitors of Na+–K+ active transport; indeed glycoside inhibition of a measured flux is presumptive evidence of active transport. (iv) Tosteson's[27] experiments have established a striking correlation between the amount of Na+–K+ activated ATP-ase present in red cell membranes and an index of intact red cell pumping activity. He did this by taking advantage of marked differences in the Na+ and K+ contents of red blood cells from genetically different sheep. The red cells of most sheep have high Na+ and low K+ concentrations, while the red cells of a few of the sheep in the same herd have low Na+ and high K+ concentrations. The low $[K^+]_i$ condition is a simple dominant. Tosteson found that the ratio of the pumped K+ influxes between red cells having high $[K^+]_i$ and those having low $[K^+]_i$ was 4.1. Similarly, the ratio of Na+–K+ stimulated ATP-ase activities between the high and low $[K^+]_i$ red cells had the identical value, 4.1. This is strong evidence that some membrane ATP-ase activity is closely related to the active Na+–K+ transport process and that the pumping mechanism is located in the membrane.

GENERATION AND MAINTENANCE OF ION AND POTENTIAL DIFFERENCES

If all the important factors affecting the movements of ions have been analyzed in the previous section, then it should be possible to explain the observed transmembrane concentration and voltage differences of cells solely in terms of these factors. In this section it will be shown (i) that the Na+–K+ exchange pump is sufficient to maintain voltages and concentrations at their observed values (steady state) and (ii) how, starting with interstitial fluid on both sides of the membrane, a neutral Na+–K+ pump can establish the observed voltage and intracellular ion concentrations (transient state). Although the picture presented here accounts in a satisfactory way for a large amount of our knowledge of these matters, it should be remembered that it is simplified and thus inaccurate; all membrane phenomena are not taken into account.

Maintenance of Ionic Distributions by a Sodium–Potassium Pump.   *Steady state.*   In this discussion of a cell system, the term *steady state* indicates that the concentrations and voltages are unvarying in time but that the system is not in equilibrium. Energy must be continuously expended to maintain the steady state. There is a steady flow of oxygen and glucose into the cell and a steady flow of carbon dioxide and H_2O out of the cell. Substance Y is constantly made from X and flows out of the cell; X is made from Y and flows into the cell (Fig. 5). "Unchanging ionic concentrations" means that the net flux of each ion is zero. Thus the steady state condition occurs when the influx and efflux of a substance are equal if the substance is neither manufactured nor destroyed in the cell; otherwise net efflux is equal to the rate of production of the substance in the cell, or the net influx equals the rate of destruction in the cell. If a chemical species is distributed at equilibrium, its influx and efflux are equal and passive; in the steady state the influx equals the efflux, although the fluxes may have both active and passive components if the species is neither produced nor destroyed.

Potassium ion distribution.   The one-way flux of an ion equals the sum of the passive and active fluxes. The influx of K+ consists of a passive component, K+ driven inward by the voltage gradient, and an active component, the inward leg of the Na+–K+ exchange pump. K+ efflux is passive. If the steady state membrane potential ($\mathcal{E}_s$) were just equal to the K+ equilibrium potential ($\mathcal{E}_K$), the passive fluxes would be equal; the active influx would thus be unbalanced, and $[K^+]_i$ would be increasing at a rate determined by the pumping rate and cell volume. Therefore, in the steady state, $\mathcal{E}_s$ cannot be as large a number as $\mathcal{E}_K$. In other words, $[K^+]_i$ must be larger than predicted from the Nernst equation in order to make the passive efflux equal to the summed passive and active influxes. The steady state values given in Table 1 show that $\mathcal{E}_K$ (-97 mV.) has a slightly larger negative value than $\mathcal{E}_s$ (-90 mV.). The difference need be no greater than this in the steady state, because of the relatively high permeability of the membrane to K^+. A small increase in $[K^+]_i$ suffices to increase K^+ efflux enough to match the active influx. In view of the possible errors in the measurement of $[K^+]_i$ and $\mathcal{E}_s$, the difference between $\mathcal{E}_K$ and $\mathcal{E}_s$ is not significant. However, significant differences have been consistently found in other tissues; e.g., in frog muscle the difference is about 20 mV., which means that $[K^+]_i$ in these cells is about twice what it would be if $\mathcal{E}_K = \mathcal{E}_s$ (however, see Mullins and Noda[21]). In human red blood cells $\mathcal{E}_K$ is about -90 mV., whereas $\mathcal{E}_s$ is about -10 mV.

Sodium ion distribution. Qualitatively, Na^+ distribution across the membrane is a mirror image of K^+ distribution: Na^+ low inside, K^+ low outside; Na^+ pumped out, K^+ pumped in; Na^+ high outside, K^+ high inside. The arguments concerning K^+ fluxes given in the preceding paragraph apply equally well to Na^+ fluxes simply by interchanging the words "influx" and "efflux" wherever they occur. Here, however, the symmetry ends. The membrane is more than 50 times more permeable to K^+ than to Na^+. $[K^+]_i$ need be only slightly higher than at equilibrium for net passive efflux to balance the active influx. However, because P_{Na} is low, $[Na^+]_i{}^*$ will fall to values much lower than the equilibrium value before the net inward driving force is large enough to make the passive influx equal active efflux. These arguments indicate that the steady state transmembrane potential is near $\mathcal{E}_K$, because P_K is much greater than P_{Na}, but they do not reveal what processes lead to the separation of charge across the membrane that generates $\mathcal{E}_s$.

Figure 6 is a schematic diagram which com-

*The arguments given here are based on the assumption that the composition of the extracellular fluid is constant in the face of changes in intracellular concentrations. This is a good approximation in view of the effectiveness of the regulatory mechanisms (see Section IX).

pactly summarizes the fluxes of Na^+ and K^+ in the steady state. Although the diagram is explained in detail in the legend, it should be emphasized that the ordinate is the difference between the transmembrane potential and the equilibrium potential for either Na^+ or K^+, i.e., an indication of the driving force on the ion. Cl^- and A^- are not discussed here nor included in the diagram, because Cl^- are probably distributed in equilibrium with $\mathcal{E}_s$ and because the membrane is assumed to be impermeable to A^-.

Generation of Transmembrane Potential by a Sodium–Potassium Pump. *Transient state.* If a system is not in a steady state—if some quantities are changing in time—then the system is in a *transient* or *changing state*. The transient state in a cell with respect to changes in ionic concentrations and membrane potential can be classified according to the rate at which these quantities change. For example, if in a steady state system, $[K^+]_o$ is suddenly increased and $[Na^+]_o$ is decreased the same amount by changing the bathing medium, the transient state preceding the establishment of a new steady state is characterized by two distinct transients: (i) a fast transient lasting a few milliseconds during which there is a net penetration of charge; i.e., some of the added K^+ cross the membrane and reduce the potential. This net charge influx continues until $\mathcal{E}_m$ is reduced to the value where increasing K^+ efflux and Cl^- influx just balance the increased K^+ influx; i.e., net membrane charge flow is zero. (ii) However, this is not a steady state; the cell is gaining K^+ and Cl^- and losing Na^+. This slow transient lasts minutes or hours. During this time, the internal concentrations are changing toward their new steady state values. Some aspects of the slow transient are described here. Other aspects of it and the fast transient are discussed in Chapter 2.

Slow transient in cells. The existence of a steady potential difference across a membrane always means that electric charges are separated by the membrane. If the extrusion of a Na^+ is always accompanied by the uptake of a K^+, how does this electrically neutral pump give rise to the transmembrane potential? This question can be conveniently answered by considering the sequence of changes that occurs when a Na^+–K^+ pump is started up in a hypothetical cell whose membrane potential is zero and whose intracellular fluid has nearly the same composition as the interstitial fluid. In this way, the processes which lead to the separation of

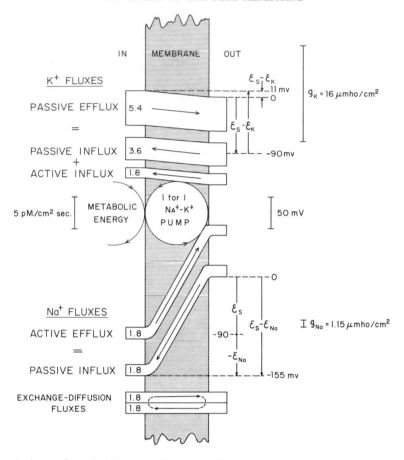

Fig. 6. Active and passive Na+ and K+ fluxes of a frog skeletal muscle fiber in the steady state. Intracellular fluid is represented at left, membrane in middle and interstitial fluid at right. Circle represents a 1 for 1 Na+–K+ pump driven by metabolic energy. Each band represents a one-way flux whose magnitude is proportional to the width of the band and whose direction is given by the arrow. Numbers within the bands just to left of membrane give the one-way flux in picamols per cm.²-sec. (1 picamol [pM.] $= 10^{-12}$ mols). Driving force on ion is given by slope of band within the membrane and also by total height difference as shown to the right and is equal to the difference between the steady membrane voltage, ε_s, and the ion equilibrium potential, ε_{Na} or ε_K. Net passive flux of an ion is proportional to product of driving force and ionic conductance, g_{Na}, or, g_K (equation 6). In steady state, net fluxes are zero. For Na+, passive efflux is negligible, so passive influx = active efflux = 1.8 pM. per cm.²- sec. This flux results from a large driving force (-155 mV.) and a small conductance (0.07 g_K) as shown by the steepness of the band and the small bar representing g_{Na}. Active efflux of Na+ must be accomplished against this electrochemical gradient. For K+, net passive efflux = passive efflux − passive influx = 5.4 − 3.6 = 1.8 pM. per cm.²-sec. In contrast to Na+, the passive flux of K+ is the product of a small driving force (11 mV.) and a large conductance. Since active fluxes of Na+ and K+ are equal and opposite, net passive efflux of K+ must also equal net passive influx of Na+ = 1.8 pM. per cm.²-sec. The equal and opposite exchange diffusion fluxes of Na+ are shown at the bottom. (After Eccles. The Physiology of Nerve Cells. Baltimore, Johns Hopkins Press, 1957. Flux data are from Hodgkin and Horowicz, *J. Physiol.*, 1959, *145*:405–432, and Keynes and Swan, *J. Physiol.*, 1959, *147*:591–625.)

charges across the membrane and to the establishment of ionic concentration differences will become evident.

It is not possible to build up the observed steady state from an intracellular fluid having a composition identical to the interstitial fluid, because the cell finally has a high concentration of anions (A−), absent from the bathing medium,

which are unable to penetrate the membrane. This difficulty can be avoided by supposing that the hypothetical cell has an initial volume large compared to its final volume and that the cell fluid consists of interstitial fluid containing K+A− at a low concentration. The membrane is assumed to be perfectly elastic, to contain a Na+–K+ pump, and to have the same ion permeabilities as a real cell membrane. As will be shown below, operation of the pump gradually reduces cell volume until in the steady state the A⁻ ions have been concentrated to their observed high value (Table 1).

Figure 7 illustrates the changes that occur initially when the Na⁺–K⁺ pump is suddenly started at a fixed rate at some instant, t = 0. Suppose that in a jiffy* 400,000 Na⁺ are extruded and that simultaneously 400,000 K⁺ are

* A "jiffy" is a short length of time—in this case about 20 thousandths of a second.

taken into the cell. This exchange slightly reduces [Na⁺]$_i$ and increases [K⁺]$_i$. As mentioned above, extracellular volume is assumed to be infinite, so the external concentrations are not altered by the exchange. Although the concentration gradients set up by this exchange are small, some of the pumped Na⁺ will diffuse back into the cell and some of the K⁺ will diffuse out of it. P$_K$ is about 50 times as large as P$_{Na}$, so that, since the concentration gradients of Na⁺ and K⁺ are equal, the net flux of K⁺ initially is 50 times as great as the net flux of Na⁺. Thus 4

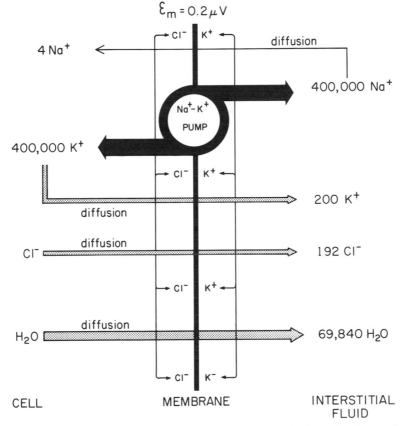

Fig. 7. Simplified scheme of ion and water movements during the first jiffy of operation of a Na⁺-K⁺ pump in a hypothetical cell. Cell membrane is assumed to contain a one-for-one Na⁺–K⁺ exchange pump and to be 50 times more permeable to K⁺ and Cl⁻ than to Na⁺. Cell is assumed to have a large initial volume, and ionic compositions of interstitial and intracellular fluid are assumed to be the same except that the latter also contains K+A⁻ at a low concentration. Width of arrow indicates size of flux. As shown, exchange of 400,000 Na⁺ for 400,000 K⁺ by the pump in a jiffy results in net movement of 399,800 K⁺ into the cell and 399,996 Na⁺ and 192 Cl⁻ out of the cell. The net efflux of 200 + 192 − 4 = 388 ions requires a net efflux of 69,840 H₂O molecules to maintain osmotic balance. Four K⁺ and Cl⁻ have separated, charging the membrane capacity (fine line branches from K⁺ and Cl⁻ efflux lines and generated a transmembrane potential of 0.2 microvolts which maintains the Cl⁻ concentration difference, a 192 Cl⁻ deficit inside the cell. Operation of pump gradually reduces cell volume and increases ε$_m$; [Cl⁻]$_i$ decreases and [A⁻]$_i$ increases. In steady state, all net fluxes are zero and cell volume has decreased until [A⁻]$_i$ is approximately equal to [Cl⁻]$_o$. Na⁺–K⁺ pumping rate and membrane permeabilities in real cells are such that hours would be required to achieve steady state condition. Final cell diameter = 10 μ; P$_K$ = P$_{Cl}$ = 4.5 × 10⁻⁶ cm. per second; P$_{Na}$/P$_K$ = 1/50 active flux = 10 pMol per cm.²-sec.; 1 jiffy = 20 milliseconds; C = 10⁻⁶ F. per cm.². Fluxes calculated on basis of steady state membrane area.

Na$^+$ will diffuse into and 200 K$^+$ out of the cell in a jiffy (Fig. 7). This net efflux of + ions attracts Cl$^-$ so that the net charge efflux is only 4 cations in the first jiffy. The resultant membrane voltage (0.2 μV.) is just sufficient to maintain the Cl$^-$ concentration difference resulting from the net exit of 192 Cl$^-$.

In other words, the Cl$^-$ will not completely neutralize the excess K$^+$, because the only force acting to move Cl$^-$ out of the cell is the voltage gradient; therefore, the outside must be slightly positive to maintain the now slightly lower [Cl$^-$]$_i$. The concentration gradients of K$^+$ and Cl$^-$ both act to maintain a transmembrane potential which is inside negative.

Since the pump is neutral, the transmembrane voltage results from the fact that K$^+$ penetrates the membrane more readily than does Na$^+$, so that the back diffusion of K$^+$ (out of the cell) generates an outside positive potential difference.

In addition to the ion movements, water will also move out of the cell during the first jiffy. The cell has lost a net of $200 - 4 = 196$ cations and 192 Cl$^-$. Thus 388 particles dissolved in water have left the cell. This exit increases the concentration of water in the cell, so that a slight gradient develops across the membrane. Since the membrane is highly permeable to water, this gradient forces water out of the cell. Each liter (55.5 M.) of water in extracellular fluid contains 0.31 M. of solute particles. For every particle that leaves the cell, $55.5/0.31 = 180$ molecules of water must also leave. Therefore, $180 \times 388 = 69,840$ water molecules leave the cell in the first jiffy. One jiffy's operation of the Na$^+$ — K$^+$ pump results, then, in a net loss of Na$^+$, Cl$^-$ and water and a net gain of K$^+$ by the cell and an increase in [A$^-$]$_i$ due to water loss.

In the second and each succeeding jiffy following the start of the Na$^+$–K$^+$ pump, 400,000 more Na$^+$ and 400,000 more K$^+$ are pumped across the membrane. There is now a small potential difference across the membrane which hinders the back diffusion of K$^+$ and helps the back diffusion of Na$^+$. Nevertheless, [K$^+$]$_i$ increases and [Na$^+$]$_i$ decreases. The resulting concentration gradients are larger and so, therefore, is back diffusion. The voltage increases slightly during each jiffy, causing more Cl$^-$ to move out, and water accompanies the Na$^+$ and Cl$^-$. The changes in concentration, voltage and volume are smaller in each succeeding jiffy. The net extrusion of Na$^+$, Cl$^-$ and water reduces the cell volume and, therefore, increases [A$^-$]$_i$. In other

words, as [Cl$^-$]$_i$ decreases, [A$^-$]$_i$ increases equally. Eventually, a steady state is reached in which the net fluxes of Na$^+$, K$^+$, Cl$^-$ and water are zero, the membrane potential is constant, and [A$^-$]$_i$ is about equal to [Cl$^-$]$_o$, as illustrated in Figure 6 for Na$^+$ and K$^+$.

The steady state value of the transmembrane potential depends on the ratio of P_{Na} to P_K and the Na$^+$ pumping rate. For example, an increase in P_{Na} would increase the net influx of Na$^+$ and thus reduce the charge separation and $\mathcal{E}_s$. Similarly, $\mathcal{E}_s$ is near zero if there is no Na$^+$ pumping; the steady-state condition is that illustrated in Figure 7 for t = 0, i.e., before the pump is started.

Factors determining cell volume. The volume of a cell depends directly on the number of particles dissolved in the cell water. Since the membrane is highly permeable to water, there can be no appreciable concentration gradient of water across the membrane in the steady state. As a result, the concentration of water in the cell equals the concentration in the bathing fluid. The greater the number of dissolved particles per unit volume of solution, the lower the concentration of water; so an equivalent statement of the equality of water concentrations is that total solute concentrations are equal.

A large fraction of the substances dissolved in interstitial and intracellular water is ionized. In the cell, A$^-$ constitute about half of the dissolved particles. Because A$^-$ cannot penetrate the membrane, and because they do not exist in appreciable quantities outside the cell, cell volume would be very large in the absence of Na$^+$ pumping. Operation of the Na$^+$ pump reduces [Na$^+$]$_i$, and the consequent development of a membrane potential reduces [Cl$^-$]$_i$. A net exit of NaCl reduces the cell volume correspondingly. Since the total amount of A$^-$ in a cell is relatively fixed, cell volume changes reflect changes in [Cl$^-$]$_i$, which in turn depends on $\mathcal{E}_s$. However, if $\mathcal{E}_s$ is 60 mV. or greater, [Cl$^-$]$_i \leq$ 0.1 [Cl$^-$]$_o$. A rather large reduction in $\mathcal{E}_s$ is therefore required to increase cell volume appreciably; e.g., at $\mathcal{E}_s$ = 18 mV. cell volume would be increased about 50 per cent. On the basis of the simple picture of ion transport developed here, it is seen that the Na$^+$–K$^+$ pump not only maintains the transmembrane differences in ion concentration and potential, but also prevents swelling and bursting of the cells. Cell volume also depends on intracellular H$^+$ concentration since the A$^-$ are weak acids and also exist in the form HA (Chap. 46).

Control of sodium pumping rate. As pointed out above, an adequate rate of active sodium extrusion is necessary for cellular integrity. Excitable cells, in particular, must maintain a low internal [Na^+] because the upstroke of the action potential is generated by the net inflow of sodium resulting from a transient increase in P_{Na} (Chap. 2). Thus it would be expected that an increase in internal Na^+ concentration would act through some (unknown) regulatory mechanism to increase the rate of active Na^+ extrusion. In frog muscle the relationship between extrusion rate and [Na^+]$_i$ is S-shaped. Keynes and Swan[18] found that Na^+ efflux varies roughly with the third power of [Na^+]$_i$ over the range of concentrations normally found. The curve is less steep at both higher and lower than normal internal sodium concentrations. Clearly the curve must level off when the [Na^+]$_i$ is high because the maximum extrusion rate is limited by the cell's ability to supply energy to the pump. The flattening of the curve at low Na^+ concentrations is probably due to lack of saturation of the reaction $Na^+ + Y = Na^+Y$; i.e., there is an appreciable amount of Y in the uncombined form. Further, the third power relationship suggests that the reaction with Y is of the form $3 Na^+ + Y = Na_3^+ Y$ and that Y can penetrate the membrane only in the form $Na_3^+ Y$. A calculation of steady state potential made on the assumption that pumping rate is proportional to [Na^+]$_i$ is given in the appendix, Chapter 2. The effects of increasing Na^+ influx by increasing the rate of stimulation of frog skeletal muscle on the steady-state voltage and internal Na^+ and K^+ concentrations for first, second and third power relationships between Na^+ pumping rate and [Na^+]$_i$ have been calculated by Woodbury.[30] The results show that a third power relationship is necessary to prevent inordinately large changes in these quantities even at quite modest stimulus rates.

Human red blood cells.[6, 7, 27] Human red cells have an interesting pattern of intracellular electrolyte concentrations: [Na^+]$_i$ = 20 μM. per cm.^{3} [K^+]$_i$ = 140 μM. per cm.^{3} and [Cl^-]$_i$ = 80 μM. per ml. The intracellular concentrations of Na^+ and K^+ are about the same as those in muscle, but [Cl^-]$_i$ is much higher than it is in muscle. Also, the red cell membrane is several thousand times more permeable to Cl^- and HCO_3^- than it is to K^+ or Na^+. The high anion permeability is important for the carrying of carbon dioxide by the blood (Chap. 40). The ionic distribution of red cells is easily explained by supposing that the cell membrane has a Na^+–K^+ exchange pump and that the membrane is nearly as permeable to Na^+ as to K^+. If it is assumed that Cl^- and HCO_3^- are passively distributed, then the transmembrane potential is: $\mathcal{E}_s = \mathcal{E}_{Cl} = -61 \log_{10} 120/80 = -10$ mV. As pointed out above, $\mathcal{E}_s$ depends on the ratio of P_{Na} to P_K; the higher P_{Na}/P_K, the lower $\mathcal{E}_s$.

There is considerable evidence for the existence of a Na^+–K^+ exchange pump in red cells.[27] Indeed, some of the earliest evidence of this type of pumping process was found in red cells.[7] Flux measurements indicate that ion movements are more complex than expected from this simple explanation, but there seems little doubt that it is generally correct. Because of the high [Cl^-]$_i$ and high P_{Cl}, the cell is quite liable to rather large, rapid changes in volume. However, these cells can swell considerably without bursting, owing to their shape, biconcave discs.

Cellular Hydrogen and Bicarbonate Ion Concentrations.[2, 3] The concentrations of hydrogen (H^+) and bicarbonate (HCO_3^-) ions in the interior of the cell are not those that would be expected from the external concentrations and the membrane potential; i.e., these ions are not at equilibrium with $\mathcal{E}_s$. With glass electrodes, Caldwell[2] measured directly the intracellular pH in crab muscle fibers. The intracellular pH (pH_i) is normally about 7.0, as compared with the pH_o = 7.4 of the blood plasma. (By definition, $pH = -\log_{10}[H^+]$, so [H^+]$_i$ = 10^{-7} M. per liter or mM. per cm.^{3}) This value agrees well with indirect measurements in other tissues. If H^+ were distributed in accordance with membrane voltage, [H^+]$_i$ would be about 30 times [H^+]$_o$, or pH_i would be $-\log(30 H_o) = pH_o - \log 30 = 5.9$ and, since [H^+] · [HCO_3^-] = $K[H_2CO_3]$ (Chap. 46), [HCO_3^-]$_i$ would be [HCO_3^-]$_o$/30.

If, as seems likely, either or both H^+ and HCO_3^- can penetrate the membrane, then the existence of a disequilibrium between the external and internal concentrations of H^+ and HCO_3^- forces the conclusion that one or both ions must be actively transported—H^+ out of the cell or HCO_3^- into the cell. Nothing is known of the mechanism of this active transport process but it does seem more probable that H^+ is extruded than that HCO_3^- is taken up Further, it is natural to hypothesize that H^+ has some affinity for the Na^+ carrier substance Y (Fig. 5): $H^+ + Y = H^+Y$. This hypothesis has been given some experimental basis by the findings of Keynes[15] that raising [H^+]$_i$ by means of increasing pCO_2 from 0 to about 40 mm. Hg at constant [H^+]$_o$ changes the relationship between Na^+ extrusion rate and [Na^+]$_i$ from a direct dependence on the cube of [Na^+]$_i$ to a direct dependence on the square of [Na^+]$_i$. This suggests that H^+ can be one of the three ions which must be attached to the Y carrier before it can penetrate the membrane, the other two being Na$^+$. Regulation of [H$^+$]$_o$ and [H$^+$]$_i$ will be discussed in Chapter 46.

SUMMARY

A brief review of the physics and physical chemistry pertinent to the material in this chapter is given in the appendix of Chapter 2.

Cell Membrane. The interchange of materials between a cell and its environment is greatly limited by the cell membrane; substances dissolved in the interstitial and inter cellular fluids penetrate the membrane at rates only a small fraction of the rates at which they penetrate through an equal thickness of water. The structure which limits diffusion, the membrane, consists of outer monomolecular layers of protein facing the aqueous solutions and an inner bimolecular layer of closely packed lipid molecules. It is the closely packed hydrophobic lipid layer which acts as a barrier to movements of dissolved particles and water. Ionized substances probably cross the membrane via water-filled pores or in combination with carrier molecules which are limited to the membrane (Figs. 3 and 5).

Transmembrane Concentration and Potential Differences. The interstitial fluid contains high concentrations of Na$^+$ and Cl$^-$ and low concentrations of K$^+$. In contrast, intracellular fluid contains K$^+$ in high and Cl$^-$ and Na$^+$ in low concentrations. In addition, there is a potential difference across the cell membrane which is about -90 mV. (inside negative) in mammalian skeletal muscle (Table 1). The existence of a potential difference means that there are charges separated by the membrane in an amount proportional to the voltage. The cell is a capacitor; the interstitial and intracellular fluids are electrolyte solutions and hence ionic conductors and the membrane separating them is an insulator. Ions can penetrate the membrane to a limited extent so the maintenance of charge separation and a potential difference implies that there are nonelectrical, nonmechanical forces present which act to keep charges separated.

Ion Penetration Through Membrane. The passive rate of penetration of the membrane by an ionized substance (net flux, mol per cm.^{2}-sec.) is determined by three quantities: (i) The concentration gradient of the substance across the membrane is a measure of the force which tends to drive a substance from a region of higher to a region of lower concentration (diffu-

sion). The average concentration gradient is outside concentration minus inside concentration divided by membrane thickness. (ii) The voltage gradient across the membrane (from outside to inside) tends to drive cations into the cell and anions out of the cell. (iii) The permeability of the membrane, i.e., the ease with which a substance penetrates the membrane, determines how many particles per second cross the membrane for a given driving force (the sum of the concentration and voltage gradient driving forces). If ions penetrate the membrane through water-filled pores, then permeability is proportional to the number of pores per square centimeter of membrane. Diffusion through the membrane is so much slower than through the surrounding aqueous solutions that the concentration gradients in the solutions necessary to supply substances which are diffusing through the membrane are negligibly small, i.e., concentrations near the membrane are equal to those in the bulk medium in most cases.

Ionic Equilibrium. A nonionized substance is distributed at equilibrium across the membrane when the concentrations on the two sides are equal. Ionic equilibrium concentrations depend on the transmembrane potential difference. Alternatively, if concentrations are specified, then these can be brought into equilibrium by setting the transmembrane potential difference to a value given by the Nernst equation; e.g., for K$^+$, $\mathcal{E}_K = (RT/Z_KF) \log_e [K^+]_o/[K^+]_i$. The equilibrium potential of a substance can also be thought of as the potential that would be developed across a membrane permeable only to that substance. Thus, a membrane permeable only to potassium ions would become positively charged on the side of lowest concentration because of diffusion down the concentration gradient of the positive ions. The Nernst equation furnishes a simple test to determine if an ionized substance is distributed at equilibrium across an actual membrane; if the equilibrium potential of the substance is equal to the actual transmembrane potential then the substance is equilibrated. Nonequilibrium indicates either that the substance cannot penetrate the membrane or that other forces than those exerted by concentration and voltage gradients are acting on the substance.

Ion Distribution in Muscle. Comparison of the various ion equilibrium potentials with the actual transmembrane potential shows that Cl$^-$ is distributed at equilibrium, i.e., $\mathcal{E}_{Cl} = \mathcal{E}_s$, that [K$^+$]$_i$ is about twice as great as expected, i.e.,

$\mathcal{E}_K$ is more negative than $\mathcal{E}_s$, and that the Na^+ equilibrium potential is opposite in sign from the actual potential (Table 1). In other words, both the concentration gradient (outside high, inside low) and voltage gradient (inside negative) tend to force Na^+ into the cell. Radioactive tracer studies show that all these ions can penetrate the membrane. K^+ and Cl^- penetrate with about equal ease and about 50 times more easily than Na^+. The organic anion, A^-, is assumed to be nonpermeating.

Active Na^+–K^+ Transport. Since internal Na^+ concentration remains at its low levels in the living animal, it follows that some force besides concentration and voltage gradients is acting to carry Na^+ out of the cells. Further since Na^+ flows spontaneously from outside to inside, work must be done continuously by the cell to expel Na^+. This expenditure of the cell's metabolic energy is termed active transport. Available experimental evidence indicates that the transport process is mediated by carriers limited to the membrane and that the extrusion of Na^+ is accompanied by a coupled uptake of K^+ (Fig. 5).

Origin of Transmembrane Potential. A coupled one-for-one Na^+-for-K^+ exchange pump is capable of maintaining observed ion concentrations and the membrane potential (Fig. 6). A neutral pump extruding Na^+ and taking up K^+ generates concentration gradients of these ions across the membrane but in itself does not separate charges. Charges are separated, however, by the back diffusion of these ions; K^+ can penetrate 50 times more easily than Na^+ so, for the equal concentration gradients which are generated by the neutral pump, 50 times as many K^+ will diffuse out of the cell as Na^+ will diffuse in if the transmembrane potential is zero. This imbalance in back diffusion does separate charge; the excess K^+ diffusing outward charges the outside of the membrane positively and thus generates the transmembrane voltage. This voltage in turn draws Cl^- out of the cell, almost but not quite neutralizing the membrane charge, since some potential is required to hold out the Cl^-. The net result is an outward movement of Na^+, Cl^- and water and an accumulation of K^+ (Fig. 7). Thus the movements of Na^+ and K^+ down their gradients is balanced by the exchange pump. The size of the steady-state membrane voltage depends on the pumping rate and the ratio, P_{Na}/P_K. $[Cl^-]_i$ and cell volume thus depend on the potential.

Cell Volume. The cell membrane is permeable to water and has little mechanical strength; hence the volume of the cell depends on the number of solute particles within it. The internal anions are nonpermeating and thus the minimum volume is determined by the number of these anions and their counter ions. In addition, there is a small amount of internal Na^+, determined by the sodium pumping rate and a small amount of Cl^-, determined by the transmembrane potential. Hence any reduction in pumping rate or increase in P_{Na} increases the number of internal particles and hence the volume of the cell. Cell volume also depends on internal H^+ concentration because A^- can exist in the undissociated form HA in appreciable amounts.

REFERENCES

1. ADRIAN, R. H. *Circulation*, 1962, *26*:1214–1223.
2. CALDWELL, P. C. *J. Physiol.*, 1954, *126*:169–180.
3. CALDWELL, P. C. *Int. Rev. Cytol.*, 1956, *5*:229–277.
4. FINEAN, J. B. *Exp. Cell Res.*, 1958, Suppl. *5*:18–32.
5. FISHMAN, A. P., ed. *Symposium on the plasma membrane.* New York, New York Heart Association, Inc., 1962.
6. GLYNN, I. M. *Progr. Biophys.*, 1957, *8*:241–307.
7. HARRIS, E. J. and MAIZELS, M. *J. Physiol.*, 1951, *113*:506–524.
8. HODGKIN, A. L. *Biol. Rev.*, 1951, *26*:339–409.
9. HODGKIN, A. L. *Proc. roy. Soc.*, 1957, *B148*:1–37, pl. 1.
10. HODGKIN, A. L. *The conduction of the nervous impulse,* Springfield, Ill., Charles C Thomas, 1964.
11. HODGKIN, A. L. and HOROWICZ, P. *J. Physiol.*, 1959, *145*: 405–432.
12. HODGKIN, A. L. and HOROWICZ, P. *J. Physiol.*, 1959, *148*: 127–160.
13. HODGKIN, A. L. and KEYNES, R. D. *J. Physiol.*, 1955, *128*: 28–60.
14. HODGKIN, A. L. and KEYNES, R. D. *J. Physiol.*, 1955, *128*: 61–88.
15. KEYNES, R. D. *J. Physiol.*, 1963, *166*:16P–17P.
16. KEYNES, R. D. *J. Physiol.*, 1963, *169*:690–705.
17. KEYNES, R. D. and MAISEL, G. W. *Proc. roy. Soc.*, 1954, *B142*:383–392.
18. KEYNES, R. D. and SWAN, R. C. *J. Physiol.*, 1959, *147*: 591–625.
19. KOEFOED-JOHNSEN, V. and USSING, H. H. *Acta physiol. scand.*, 1958, *42*:298–308.
20. LING, G. and GERARD, R. W. *J. cell. comp. Physiol.*, 1949, *34*:383–396.
21. MULLINS, L. J. and NODA, K. *J. gen. Physiol.*, 1963, *47*: 117–132.
22. MURPHY, Q. R., ed. *Metabolic aspects of transport across cell membranes.* Madison, University of Wisconsin Press, 1957.
23. ROBERTSON, J. D. *Progr. Biophys.*, 1960, *10*:343–418.
24. SHANES, A. M. *Pharmacol. Rev.*, 1958, *10*:59–164.
25. SHANES, A. M., ed. *Biophysics of physiological and pharmacological actions.* Washington, D.C., American Association for the Advancement of Science, 1961.
26. SOLOMON, A. K. *J. gen. Physiol.*, 1960, *43*:1–15.
27. TOSTESON, D. C. *Fed. Proc.*, 1963, *22*:19–26.
28. USSING, H. H. *J. gen. Physiol.*, 1960, *43*:135–147.
29. USSING, H. H., KRUHØFFER, P., HESS THASEN, J. and THORN, N. A. *The alkali metal ions in biology.* Berlin, Springer-Verlag, 1960.
30. WOODBURY, J. W. *Fed. Proc.*, 1963, *22*:31–35.

SECTION II
NERVE AND MUSCLE

CHAPTER 2

Action Potential: Properties of Excitable Membranes

By J. WALTER WOODBURY

INTRODUCTION

PROPERTIES OF ELONGATED, EXCIT-
ABLE CELLS
  The resting or steady potential
  The action potential
    Overshoot, duration and propagation
    Threshold, all-or-nothing properties

SUBTHRESHOLD CURRENTS IN ELON-
GATED CELLS; CABLE PROPERTIES
  Stimulation
  Current flow in conductors; Ohm's law
  Measurement of cable properties
  Explanation of cable properties
    Capacitative current
    Early current distribution pattern
    Transition to the steady state
      Time constant
    Steady state current distribution
      Space constant
    Summary

THRESHOLD PHENOMENA IN ELON-
GATED CELLS
  Events near threshold voltage
  Threshold and the all-or-nothing law
  General features of threshold and recovery
  Strength–duration relation
  Effect of subthreshold currents on excitability
  Refractory period; recovery following excita-
tion

IMPULSE GENERATION AND PROPAGA-
TION
  Sequence of events during the action potential
  Effects of external sodium and potassium con-
centrations on membrane potentials
    Resting potential and changes in external
potassium concentration

IMPULSE GENERATION AND PROPAGATION—continued
    Effects of external sodium concentration on
the action potential
      Role of acetylcholine

PROPAGATION
  Measurement of conduction speed
    Impulse as a wave
  Local circuit propagation
  Myelinated nerves: saltatory conduction
  Determinants of conduction speed
    Physical factors
    Fiber geometry and conduction speed

INTRINSIC PROPERTIES OF EXCITABLE
MEMBRANES
  Voltage clamping
  Sodium ion current
  Potassium ion current
  Sodium and potassium ion conductances
  Voltage dependence of sodium and potassium
ion conductances
  Activation and inactivation of sodium ion con-
ductance
    Hypothetical model of sodium conductance
activation–inactivation
  Kinetics of potassium conductance changes

PREDICTION OF EVENTS OF ACTION
POTENTIAL FROM VOLTAGE CLAMP
DATA
  Depolarization
  Repolarization
  Threshold
  Refractory period
  Accommodation and block
  Ion exchange during activity

APPENDIX

THE initiation and propagation of the nerve impulse is a subject which has been greatly illuminated in recent years by the invention of ingenious experimental techniques and by the application of physical and mathematical principles. These advances have resulted largely from studies begun twenty years ago at Cambridge University by Hodgkin and Huxley, who were awarded the 1963 Nobel Prize in Physiology. The main advances resulted from the development of the technique of "voltage clamping" by K. S. Cole in the late 1940's. The explanations of impulse conduction worked out by Hodgkin and Huxley make considerable use of the principles of physics and physical chemistry and hence are not easily comprehended by those not well trained in these fields and in biology. For this reason, the material in this chapter is mostly descriptive of the process of impulse generation and conduction; qualitative explanations are given for the various basic factors: stimulating and recording techniques; effects of current flow on long, thin cells (cable properties); threshold, all-or-nothing behavior; and propagation by local circuit currents. This is followed by a somewhat more quantitative explanation of the voltage clamping experiments which furnished the information for the mechanism of impulse conduction given in the earlier sections. Necessary physical concepts, notably Ohm's law, are described briefly in the text and more quantitatively in the appendix at the end of the chapter. Ohm's law and cable properties are described in some detail and illustrative problems are included.

The reader desiring more detailed and comprehensive presentation of this material is referred to Hodgkin's lucid writings, particularly his recent book,[9] his reviews,[5, 7, 8] the original Hodgkin and Huxley papers,[10,11,12,13,14,15] and Huxley's summary.[19] Another review[26] may also be consulted.

In Chapter 1 was shown how a cell develops and maintains a steady transmembrane potential. In addition, the membranes of some cells possess the highly distinctive property of being *excitable*. In excitable cells, an environmental change (called a *stimulus*) brings about a transient depolarization usually by increasing the permeability of the membrane to Na^+ or to Na^+ and K^+. Influx of Na^+ depolarizes the membrane, thereby in turn increasing Na^+ permeability, which leads to further depolarization, and so on in a regenerative manner.

Depolarization is followed shortly by a spontaneous recovery or repolarization process which restores the original state. This sequence of changes is called an impulse and the accompanying voltage change is called an *action potential*. The definitive property of an excitable membrane is a regenerative interaction between depolarization and permeability to Na^+.

Most excitable cells are long and thin, e.g., nerve and muscle cells. In elongated cells, an impulse once initiated by a stimulus is propagated rapidly from the stimulus site to adjacent regions of the membrane and thus spreads as a wave over the membrane of the entire cell. This property is known as *conductivity* or *self-propagation*. The properties of excitability and conductivity adapt nerve cells for the function of transmitting information from one part of the body to another. The ability of nerve cells to generate and conduct impulses and of synapses to modify the impulse discharge patterns are the basis of an animal's adaptive behavior to environmental changes or stimuli.

A simple, concrete example may serve to illustrate how the nervous system detects changes in the environment and transmits messages to the muscles which, by contraction, make the appropriate response. If the hand touches a hot object, the muscles of the arm contract so that the hand is withdrawn and tissue damage is either avoided or limited. Although this protective response occupies only a fraction of a second, it can be shown that the following sequence of events, illustrated diagrammatically in Figure 1, takes place. The stimulus (heat and tissue damage) initiates impulses in nerve endings in the skin (*A*). Once initiated, these impulses are propagated over the *afferent nerve fibers* (*B*) which traverse the dorsal root to reach the spinal cord, where they make connections (*C*) with a second nerve cell, an *interneuron*. The impulses in the intraspinal afferent endings constitute stimuli to the interneurons; the resulting impulses in turn initiate impulses in the *motor* or *efferent* neurons. The latter impulses are propagated over the ventral root to the muscle, where they constitute stimuli (*D*) giving rise to muscle impulses which then spread rapidly over the membranes of the muscle cells. The spread of impulses over the muscle membranes activates the contractile elements within the cells (*E*) and movement occurs. The entire system including the afferent neurons, the interneurons, the motor neurons and the muscle is a

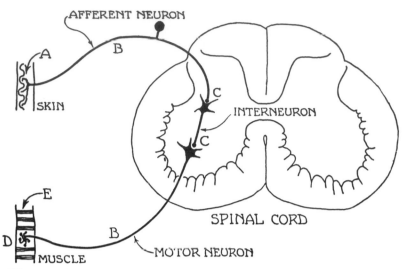

Fig. 1. Diagram of simple reflex arc. Excitation of afferent neurons occurs at point *A*. Conduction of impulses takes place in nerve fibers, *B*. Impulses are conducted toward central nervous system in the afferent fibers and away from central nervous system in motoneurons. Synaptic transmission between neurons occurs at *C*. Neuromuscular transmission occurs at *D*. Contraction occurs in muscle fiber, *E*.

simple *reflex arc*. In more complex reflex systems more interneurons may be interposed. The afferent neuron may arise in tissues other than skin, e.g., viscera, special sense organs, muscle itself. The final effector organ need not be skeletal muscle (*somatic reflex arc*), but may be smooth muscle, heart muscle or gland tissue (autonomic reflex arc).

The somatic reflex arc is the physiologic mechanism by which the organism reacts to its external environment. Autonomic reflex arcs are responsible for automatic regulation or adjustment of the functional level of visceral structures (e.g., the heart and blood vessels)—adjustments which adapt the organism not only to external environmental changes (e.g., temperature) but also to internal environmental changes occasioned by somatic behavior (e.g., exercise). *The principle of the reflex arc is that regulation of an organ's function is based in large part on sensory information from the organ being regulated. This is the most important single concept in physiology.* The description of reflex regulation of function culminates description of function. Analysis of reflexes thus permeates all phases of physiology and is, therefore, treated in some detail in the initial chapters of this book.

For this purpose it is convenient to break the reflex arc up into its component parts. In this and the next two chapters the nature of the message—i.e., the impulse and the way in which it is initiated—is considered. Chapter 4 de-

scribes the receptor mechanisms whereby a stimulus is translated (transduced) into a train of impulses (*A* in Fig. 1). In Chapter 5 the transfer of the message from nerve to muscle, the muscle membrane, and the contractile mechanism of muscle are described (*D* and *E* in Fig. 1). Chapter 6 deals with the mechanism of excitation of nerve cell by nerve cell (*C* in Fig. 1) and Chapters 7, 10 and 11 describe synthetically the functional organization of somatic and autonomic reflex regulatory systems.

Moreover, the description of a system's function is usually followed by a description of its regulation. Frequently, a system's level of functioning is under both endocrine and nervous control.

PROPERTIES OF ELONGATED, EXCITABLE CELLS[5, 7, 8, 9, 19, 24]

It has been recognized for more than a century that the nerve impulse is an electrical phenomenon. A clear picture of the mechanism of the action potential was not developed, however, until critical experiments were made possible by intracellular recording techniques, which were introduced independently in 1939–1940 by Cole and Curtis in the United States and by Hodgkin and Huxley in England.

Direct measurement of transmembrane potentials was delayed until this late date because most mammalian nerve and muscle fibers are exceedingly small (usually less than 100 μ in diameter) and hence difficult to penetrate with a recording electrode. In 1936, J. Z. Young discovered in the squid and cuttlefish giant nerve fibers or axons as large as 1 mm. in diameter. With such large nerve fibers it is relatively easy to introduce an internal electrode longitudinally down the axon and measure its potential with respect to an externally located electrode. Also, sufficient quantities of axoplasm can be extruded from the giant axon to permit chemical analysis. The first studies of transmembrane potentials of resting and excited nerve fibers were made on such giant fibers. Subsequently, with the development of ultramicroelectrodes (see Chap. 1), it became possible to confirm in mammalian nerve and muscle fibers many of the observations made on giant axons.

The Resting or Steady Potential. ·Like other cells, nerve and muscle fibers maintain a steady potential (inside negative) across their membranes. This steady potential is usually referred to as the *resting potential* to distinguish it from the action potential. In Chapter 1 it was shown that the size of the resting potential generated by the sodium–potassium pump depends largely on the relative permeability of the membrane to sodium and potassium ions; the greater the ratio of the permeability to potassium to the permeability to sodium, the greater the potential. In nerve and muscle this ratio is quite high, more than 50 to 1, and the resting potential is -70 to -90 mV. In the steady state, chloride anions are equilibrated with the resting potential in most excitable tissues, with the notable exception of the squid giant axon (see reference 16, Chap. 1). Internal sodium concentration is much lower and the internal potassium concentration higher than expected from the membrane potential. The resting potential creates the conditions necessary for regenerative interaction between depolarization and Na^+ permeability increase.

The Action Potential. When a sufficiently strong, brief electric current* is passed outward through the membrane of an axon or a muscle cell, the membrane potential undergoes a unique stereotyped sequence of changes which is peculiar to excitable cells. This sequence constitutes the *action potential.*

---

*Excitable tissues may also be stimulated by mechanical or chemical means; but in experimental work electrical stimuli are used almost exclusively, because the intensity and duration can be easily and quantitatively varied and because mild electrical stimuli, even when repeated many times, do not damage the tissue.

Overshoot, duration and propagation. Figure 2*A* shows diagrammatically the experimental arrangement for eliciting and recording an action potential in a nerve fiber and introduces the symbols for a stimulator with its electrodes and the recording device with its leads. The fiber is supplied with two pairs of stimulating electrodes (S_1 and S_2) placed at different distances from the recording site (R). When the microelectrode penetrates the axon, the steady or resting potential is registered. When a sufficiently large, brief electric shock (signaled by the shock artifact, a deflection in the recorded signal at the time of and due to the stimulus) is applied to the nerve through S_1, the membrane potential decreases rapidly toward zero but *overshoots, so that for a brief period the membrane potential is reversed*, i.e., the inside becomes positive to the outside. Thereafter the potential reverts somewhat more slowly to the resting level. The action potential of a cat dorsal root fiber is shown in Figure 2*C*. For such large myelinated fibers the duration of the action potential is 0.5 to 0.6 millisecond, and the total amplitude is 120 mV., the overshoot accounting for 30 mV. When the shock is applied at the more distant electrode S_2 rather than at S_1, the sequence of events is exactly the same, except that the *latency* (time interval between shock artifact and the beginning of the action potential) is longer. Systematic investigation reveals that this latency is directly proportional to the distance between the stimulating and recording electrodes. The action potential is thus revealed as a brief potential reversal of the membrane, beginning at the stimulating electrodes and sweeping at a constant speed as a wave along the axon. Large mammalian myelinated nerve fibers conduct at speeds of up to 120 meters per second.

Threshold, all-or-nothing properties. The action potential of a single fiber has two other unique characteristics: (i) There is a minimal strength of stimulus, the *threshold*, required to evoke a propagating action potential; an insufficient (subthreshold) stimulus has no effect at a distant recording electrode, while a sufficient (suprathreshold) stimulus, no matter how strong, evokes a stereotyped response like that of Figure 2*C*. (ii) This response is fixed in size, shape, duration and conduction speed no matter where recorded from a fiber. This is termed *all-or-none* or *all-or-nothing* behavior. Threshold and all-or-nothing behavior are different

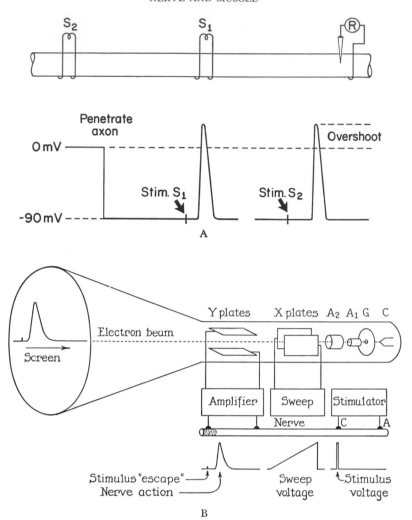

A

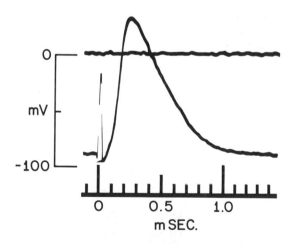

CAT DORSAL ROOT NERVE
FIBER

C

Figure 2. (See opposite page for legend.)

aspects of the same regenerative mechanism, as will be shown. Threshold (all-or-nothing) behavior is obscured when a whole nerve is studied with external electrodes as explained in Chapter 3.

SUBTHRESHOLD CURRENTS IN ELONGATED CELLS; CABLE PROPERTIES

A weak current flowing through a nerve fiber may not initiate an action potential; nevertheless, there are always local changes in transmembrane potential. These subthreshold changes will be described first, since an explanation of them is necessary for understanding impulse generation and propagation. The effects of electric currents are particularly prominent in nerve and muscle fibers because these fibers are approximately cylindrical and have lengths many thousands of times their diameters. With this geometry, the cell plasm is highly resistant to current flow, and different potentials exist at different distances from the current source during current flow. The combination of cell plasm resistance and membrane resistance and capacitance found in nerve fibers acts in a typical manner to attenuate in distance and slow in time the effects of current flow on membrane potentials. This behavior of a nerve cell is denoted by the term "cable properties." This term is used because an undersea telephone cable may have very similar electrical characteristics.* The general nature of cable properties can be usefully introduced by describing how a current applied to a nerve by means of two external electrodes can excite the

*The words "electrotonus," "electrotonic potential" and "polarization potential" have frequently been used in the physiologic literature to denote the cable properties of nerve. For reasons given by Hodgkin and Rushton[17] these terms are misleading and hence undesirable.

Fig. 2. *A, upper,* A method for studying electrical activity of nerve fibers. Two pairs of stimulating electrodes, S_1 and S_2, are applied to a dissected nerve trunk at different distances from recording microelectrode (far right). Microelectrode may be inserted into any fiber in trunk. *Lower,* Sequence of potential changes recorded by microelectrode inserted into a fiber when nerve trunk is stimulated by short shocks applied first at S_1 and then at S_2. *Abscissa,* time, a few milliseconds; *ordinate,* transmembrane potential in millivolts. When microelectrode is inserted into a nerve fiber, recorded potential changes abruptly from 0 to about -70 to -90 mV. Following stimulation at S_1 (indicated in recording by stimulus "escape" or "artifact"), an action potential (AP) is recorded after a short but definite delay. An AP rises rapidly to a peak (depolarization) and then recovers somewhat more slowly to the steady value (repolarization). At peak of AP, transmembrane potential has reversed in sign, the inside being positive to the outside. Depolarization and repolarization processes occupy about 0.5 millisecond. After a pause, indicated by break in line, nerve is stimulated at S_2. An identical AP is recorded but delay following stimulus is longer.

B, Apparatus for stimulating nervous tissue and for obtaining records of its response. Recording instrument is a cathode ray oscilloscope. Records are obtained by photographing screen while spot formed by electron beam striking fluorescent material of screen traces electrical changes impressed upon X and Y deflecting plates. Within tube itself, hot cathode (C) serves as source of electrons, grid (G) controls intensity of electron beam and so brightness of spot, first anode (A_1) compresses flow of electrons into narrow beam (in effect "focuses" the beam) and second anode (A_2) or "gun," being highly positive, accelerates beam of electrons. Stimulator applies a brief (or any chosen) voltage pulse to nerve via stimulating electrodes, one of which is cathode (C), the other anode (A). Potential changes in nerve, nerve action potential, are led to amplifier by means of recording electrodes and thence to Y plates of cathode ray oscillograph to cause vertical displacement of spot. The left recording lead is placed on a crushed region of the nerve. The crushing destroys the membranes and thus the lead is analogous to a connection to the insides of the fibers. The right lead is placed on an intact region and is thus the external electrode (see Chap. 3). At instant of stimulation a stimulus "escape" causes deflection in amplifier. Time between this and beginning of action potential is the latency, which in this example would be due to conduction time. Sweep generates a "saw-tooth" sweep voltage that moves beam from left to right at a constant speed. Sweep is repeated many times each second. Stimulus is given at a fixed time after beginning of each sweep so that nerve activity is repeatedly traced as a function of time, as indicated on screen in diagram. (After Erlanger and Gasser, *Electrical signs of nervous activity.* Philadelphia, University of Pennsylvania Press, 1937.)

C, Tracing of action potential recorded from cat dorsal root fiber. Conduction distance about 1 cm. Photograph is a double exposure, consisting of one sweep when microelectrode was in fiber and one sweep immediately after electrode was withdrawn from fiber.

nerve. This account, in turn, necessitates a brief description of the factors determining current flow in conductors (Ohm's Law).

Stimulation. Experimentally, a stimulus is usually electrical and applied by means of two platinum or silver wire electrodes placed in direct contact with the nerve or muscle to be stimulated. Excitation, the initiation of an impulse, occurs in membrane regions which have been depolarized to threshold.* A current flowing between two electrodes in contact with a nerve (Fig. 2B) has two effects, hyperpolarization of membranes in the region of the stimulating anode (positive terminal) and depolarization in the region of the cathode. Current is defined as the number of charges passing through a cross-section of the conductor in a unit time (see appendix) and its direction is that of the movement of positive charges. Thus, some of the positive charges leaving the anode tend to pile up on the outside of the membrane, forcing positive charges inside the cell away from this region and toward the cathode. At the cathode, positive charges tend to pile up inside the membrane and free positive charges outside the membrane to move to the cathode, thus completing the circuit. The same arguments apply to negative charges flowing in the opposite direction; no distinction can be made in this case since the current flow in an electrolytic solution is carried by both positive and negative ions. The result of current flow then is that regions of membrane near the anode have increased amounts of charge on them, i.e., are hyperpolarized, and regions near the cathode are depolarized. A current which depolarizes to threshold the region of membrane under the cathode will initiate an impulse.

Current Flow in Conductors; Ohm's Law. The physical factors determining current flow in a conductor will be briefly reviewed here; a more extensive development and discussion of Ohm's law is given in the appendix. Three concepts or definitions are involved: (i) There are

---

*The process of charge separation is often called *polarization*. A cell is said to be *polarized* when the transmembrane charge and voltage are at their steady-state values. Any increase in the amount of charge separated by the membrane and hence in the size of the transmembrane potential is called *hyperpolarization;* any decrease is called *depolarization*. Although *hypopolarization* is a more accurate term than depolarization, it is difficult to distinguish between *hyper*polarization and *hypo*polarization both when written and when spoken.

devices capable of maintaining a constant potential difference between two conducting terminals, e.g., a battery; these devices supply power by doing electrical work on charges continuously. (ii) Current consists of a flow of electric charges. (iii) Charges flowing in a conductor give up energy to its molecules by colliding with them and increasing their random kinetic energy.

A battery is a device that transforms chemical potential energy into electrical potential energy, i.e., does work on charges. The most obvious example here is the transmembrane potential of living cells. Even without active ion transport, the potential across the membrane is maintained relatively constant for long periods because of the large amount of chemical potential energy stored in the potassium concentration differences even though there is a constant current drain in the form of the inward leakage of sodium. Flashlight batteries function because the zinc ions in metallic zinc tend to go into solution more readily than do the carbon atoms in the graphite anode; when the zinc goes into solution, two electrons are left behind.

A conductor is defined as a material in which a substantial number of charges are free to move. An electric field is generated in a conductor when it is connected to the terminals of a battery. This field exerts a force on *every* charge in the material; those free to move are accelerated simultaneously by the electric field. However, each charge travels only a short distance before colliding with some molecule of the conductor and giving up some kinetic energy to it. Thus the random kinetic energy of all the molecules (temperature) is increased and the potential energy of each free charge is decreased. The potential energy given to charges by the battery is changed into kinetic energy of accelerating charges and this in turn is converted into heat in the conductor. On the average, a fixed amount of energy is given up per collision. If the conductor is uniform, the loss of energy per charge (and hence the voltage fall) per unit distance is constant. The acceleration–collision process goes on continuously for all free charges (ions in electrolytic solutions) and the net result is that the charges move through the medium at an unvarying, rather slow average speed. It must be emphasized that although the average speed of charge movement is slow, all free charges start to move simultaneously upon application of an electric field and that therefore current flow begins immediately because charges immediately move through every cross-section in the circuit. One battery terminal supplies charges of that sign to the conductor; the other accepts them from the conductor. The battery, at the expense of chemical energy, does work on the charges and supplies them to the first terminal. Thus current flow involves the circulation of charges in a closed path.

Ohm's law describes current flow in a conductor if the average speed of charge movement is directly proportional to the electric field and hence to the applied voltage, i.e., friction is proportional to speed. The situation is somewhat akin to a steel ball falling through molasses; the ball is accelerated by gravity but this kinetic energy is converted to heat due to friction and the ball falls with constant speed; if its speed of fall is proportional to the applied force, the fall is "ohmic." Ohm's law states that the current flowing through a conductor is proportional to the applied voltage. This relationship follows because the force on the charges is proportional to voltage, the speed of the ions is proportional to the force on them, and the current is proportional to their speed; the faster the charges move, the greater the number of charges passing a given cross-section per second.

Ohm's law can be written in the form $I = \mathcal{E}/R = G\mathcal{E}$ where G is called the conductance and is equal to the reciprocal of the resistance, R. The resistance of a particular block of material depends on its physical properties and dimensions. For a fixed applied force, the average speed of charge movement depends on the properties of the material, such as the frictional resistance to charge movement and the number of free charges per unit volume. In a solution of univalent strong electrolyte (e.g., NaCl) the number of free charges per unit volume is proportional to the sum of the individual ion concentrations. A large frictional resistance to charge movement means there is a large electrical resistance; large ion concentrations mean low electrical resistance. Dimensionally, resistance is proportional to length and inversely proportional to cross-sectional area: The resistance of a block of material 2 cm. long is twice that of a 1 cm. block because for the same applied voltage, the force exerted on a charge is only one-half as great in the 2 cm. sample. Similarly, for a fixed length, doubling the cross-sectional area of a block halves its resistance

because the force on each charge is the same but the number of free charges affected by the applied field has been doubled; for the same applied voltage, the current is twice as great and hence the resistance is halved.

Measurement of Cable Properties. In Figure 3*A* and *B* is shown an experimental arrangement for measuring the effects of current flow on the transmembrane potentials of a giant axon or a skeletal muscle fiber. Two microelectrodes are inserted into a cell (Fig. 3*B*); an abruptly applied current (Fig. 3*A*) is passed out through one electrode, and the other is used to record the resulting changes in the transmembrane potential ($\Delta\mathcal{E}_m$).* Current flows out of the electrode into the axoplasm and then out through the membrane by the lowest resistance path available. $\Delta\mathcal{E}_m$ as a function of time is recorded at one position of the recording electrode. This electrode is then removed from the cell and reinserted at another distance from the current-applying electrode (Fig. 3*B*). In this way, $\Delta\mathcal{E}_m$'s at several distances are recorded. The results of such an experiment, conducted on frog sartorius muscle fibers, are shown in Figure 3*C*. These results are typical of those obtained for all long, thin cells—myelinated and unmyelinated nerve and skeletal, cardiac and smooth muscle cells. In response to an abruptly applied constant current (internal electrode positive), $\Delta\mathcal{E}_m$, recorded near the current electrode, increases rapidly at first and then gradually levels off to a fixed value (Fig. 3*C*, x = 0). $\Delta\mathcal{E}_m$ rises progressively more slowly and reaches a smaller final value as the recording electrode is moved farther from the current electrode in either direction (Fig. 3*B*, x = 2.5 or x = 5.0 mm.).

Figure 3*C* (t = ∞) shows the way the final, maximum voltage change across the membrane varies with distance from the current-applying electrode. The curve for t = 8 milliseconds shows that the voltage changes are much more closely confined to the region of the current electrode shortly after the current is turned on than at longer times.

Explanation of Cable Properties. Cable properties are inherent in the structure of long

*A capital delta (Δ) is placed before a symbol to indicate a change in the value of the quantity represented by the symbol. Here $\Delta\mathcal{E}_m$ refers to a change in $\mathcal{E}_m$ from its steady value; $\Delta\mathcal{E}_m = \mathcal{E}_m - \mathcal{E}_s$. $\mathcal{E}_m$ symbolizes the transmembrane voltage at any time and place.

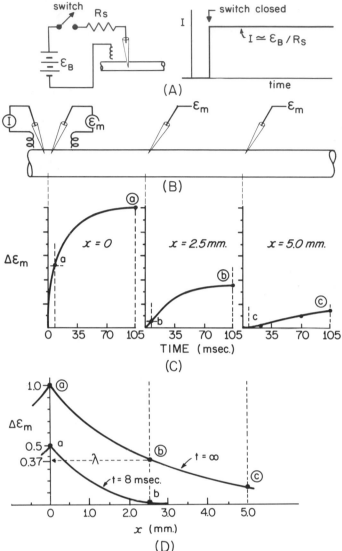

Fig. 3. Experimental measurement of cable properties in a skeletal muscle fiber. *A, Left,* Generation of a constant current and its application to a fiber via an intracellular electrode. A battery whose voltage ($\mathcal{E}_B$) is hundreds of times larger than transmembrane potential is connected to fiber through the high resistance (R_S), microelectrode resistance (R_e) and return electrode in bathing medium of negligible resistance. Current flows when switch is closed and is $I = \mathcal{E}_B/(R_S + R_e + R_f)$ where R_f is the resistance of fiber. R_S is made much larger than R_e and R_f so $I = \mathcal{E}_B/R_S$ approximately and is independent of R_e and R_f. *Right,* Applied current as a function of time, zero with switch open and constant with switch closed.

B, Constant current is suddenly applied to fiber at extreme left ($x = 0$) via the intracellular electrode labeled with circled I. Changes in transmembrane potential, $\Delta\mathcal{E}_m$, at several points along the fiber are measured with another intracellular electrode system, $\mathcal{E}_m$.

C, Transmembrane potential changes as a function of time after switch closure are recorded at the distances indicated by the dashed upward extensions of ordinate lines. Note that as distance increases, potential rises progressively more slowly and reaches lower final value.

D, Replot of data shown in C. Voltage change is plotted as function of distance along fiber on same scale as in *B* and for two different times, t = 8 milliseconds (lower curve) and t greater than 150 milliseconds (labeled t = ∞, upper curve). Lettered points in *D* correspond to the same lettered points in *C*. Note that spatial spread at early times is much less than at later times.

---

thin cells: (i) Although a relatively good conductor, the cell plasm is so long with respect to its diameter that its resistance plays an important role in determining the pattern of current flow. (ii) The cell plasm is separated from the interstitial fluid by the thin insulating membrane, forming the membrane capacitor. (iii) Ions can penetrate the membrane; hence it is an imperfect insulator and has a high electrical resistance. The slowing of the time rate of change in transmembrane potential at a distance from the current electrode (Fig. 3C) is a consequence of membrane capacitance; it takes time for an applied current to change the amount of charge on the membrane. The dim-

inution of the final $\Delta\mathcal{E}_m$ with distance (Fig. 3D) is a consequence of both protoplasmic and membrane resistance.

Precise understanding of cable properties requires an analysis of the complicated network of resistors and capacitors which is equivalent to a fiber (appendix). However, the general nature of cable properties can be comprehended from a study of Figure 4. The two ways that current can go through the membrane are shown in part *A*. The arrow indicating a K+ penetrating the membrane via a pore represents an ionic current flow, an actual physical transfer of the same charge from the inside to the outside. Similarly a Cl− moving into the

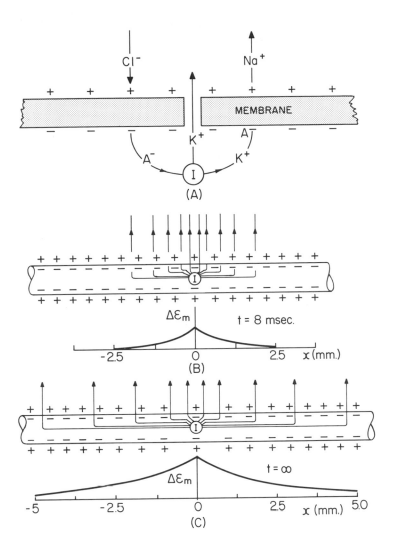

Fig. 4.   Current flow patterns in elongated cells. *A,* Diagram showing the two types of membrane current flow, ohmic and capacitative. Circled I represents tip of current-supplying intracellular micro-electrode. Arrows indicate some of the paths of charge movement (current flow). Arrow showing passage of K^+ through pore represents ionic current flow through membrane resistance (ohmic flow). Current can also be carried out by inflow of Cl^- (not shown). Arrows originating and terminating on membrane at left and right represent ion flow neutralizing membrane charge. Arrow at right shows a K^+ migrating from plasm to inside of cell membrane and neutralizing A^- and releasing a plus charge (Na^+) from outside of membrane which moves into the bathing medium. Thus, current can, in effect, flow through the membrane without actual penetration of charge (capacitative current).

B, Diagram illustrating current distribution in fiber 8 milliseconds after beginning of current (upper) and transmembrane potential as a function of distance (lower). Distance scale applies to both parts. Compare with Figure 3*D.* Upper, applied current flows out of cell in all directions perpendicular to axon axis but only the current flowing upward is represented. Most current lines are interrupted at membrane to indicate that current is mostly capacitative at this early time and confined to the region immediately around the electrode. The greater the spacing between + signs the greater the reduction in ε_m. Diameter of the fiber is greatly exaggerated (about ten times) with respect to length to show current pattern more clearly.

C, Current distribution for longer periods; otherwise same as *B.* All current flow through membrane is resistive. Current has spread much farther along axon. See text for further explanation.

cell through a pore constitutes an outward ionic current. Such ion flows are calculable from Ohm's law; the change in transmembrane voltage is equal to applied current times membrane resistance, $\Delta \mathcal{E}_m = IR_m$.

CAPACITIVE CURRENT.   Current can, in effect, also flow through the membrane capacitor without actual ion penetration of the membrane. This is shown in Figure 4A; right and left hand arrows show ions, forced by the electric field, moving up to the membrane and neutralizing charges stored thereon; e.g., a K^+ moves up to the inside of the membrane and neutralizes one of the negative charges shown on the right as an A^-. The neutralized internal negative charge now has no attraction for the corresponding external plus charge, and this plus charge is now free to migrate in the outside fluid under the influence of the electric field. In this case also, there are charges moving through the internal and external media (i.e., current), but the charges which carry the current change at the membrane; there is no actual penetration of the membrane by charges. It does not matter which particular ion carries the current; the chemical identities of charges are indistinguishable electrically. Capacitive current is defined as the rate of accumulation of charge on the conductors of a capacitor; this is a slightly different physical meaning for current flow than previously given but the units are the same and there is actual current flow in the conductors, carrying charges to and from a capacitor. A current flowing into a capacitor changes the amount of charge on the conductors and thus changes the voltage, which is proportional to charge. A constant current supplies charge at a fixed rate, so the voltage increases linearly with time. When a current is first applied to a fiber, all of it must go to charging or discharging the membrane capacitor, since it is not possible for ionic current to flow through the membrane until the transmembrane voltage is altered from its steady-state value and a net driving force is built up across the membrane.

EARLY CURRENT DISTRIBUTION PATTERN.   The path followed by the charges flowing through a conductor is determined at any point by the direction of the electric field at that point. In the complicated geometry of a nerve or muscle fiber, the direction of flow is not easily calculated. However, a general idea can be obtained by application of the rule that the pattern of current flow adjusts itself so that the total resistance of the circuit is a minimum; i.e., for a given applied current the developed voltage is minimum, the charges taking the paths of least resistance. Many charges follow the most direct electrical paths; fewer follow more circuitous paths.

Figure 4B represents the pattern of current flow shortly (8 milliseconds) after the current is turned on. Most of the arrows which represent paths of current flow are interrupted at the membrane to indicate that the flow is capacitive. The electric field generated by the current supplying battery (Fig. 3A) acts simultaneously on all ions and they start migrating. Some leave the electrode (circled I) and enter the plasm; those in the plasm move through the plasm; some leave the plasm and neutralize charges on the membrane. On the outside, some charges stored on the membrane are freed to move into the interstitial fluid and on toward the external electrode (not shown in Fig. 4). At first the path of least resistance for charge flow is straight from the electrode and out through the immediately adjacent membrane (x = 0). The charge neutralizing process does not impede flow, for the current does not go through the membrane. At the somewhat later time represented in Figure 4B, the current flow has appreciably altered the transmembrane charge (and voltage) in the immediate vicinity of the electrode. This means that some of the current is now traversing the membrane via pores and thus encountering resistance as shown by the two lines drawn through the membrane (Fig. 4B). In this situation, the path of least resistance is for the current to spread through the plasm to adjacent regions of membrane where the current flow is capacitive. However, this spreading process is limited by the resistance of the cell plasm; the farther the current spreads, the greater the plasm resistance and the less the current taking this particular path. This is shown in the figure by the decreasing number of current flow lines with increasing distances from the current electrode (Fig. 4B, C).

The slower changes in voltage at greater distances from the current electrode are explained by the foregoing argument; the changes near the electrode are rapid from the start because initially *all* of the current is used to charge the small area of membrane in the immediate vicinity. Later the same amount of current has to charge larger areas of membrane at greater distances, so the rate of charging and hence rate of voltage change is less. Furthermore, current does not even start to flow at the more distant regions until the closer regions have been partially charged (or, in this case, discharged). The farther the recording electrode is from the current electrode, the longer it is before any appreciable current is diverted to that region by the progression of charging at nearer regions. This accounts qualitatively for curves of voltage versus time of the type shown in Figure 3C.

TRANSITION TO THE STEADY-STATE. As the current flow proceeds, charging the membrane capacity and altering the membrane voltage, progressively more of the current is carried through the membrane by ion flow; as the voltage departs from its normal steady-state value, an increasingly large electrochemical gradient acts to drive ions through the membrane. Thus for an outward current, the membrane is discharged and depolarized and the concentration gradient of K^+ acts increasingly to drive K^+ out of the cell as the counteracting voltage gradient diminishes. Similarly, the concentration gradient of Cl^- is greater than the opposing voltage gradient and a net influx (outward current) of Cl^- results. Eventually, the depolarization *must* reach a value where all of the current supplied by the intracellular electrode is carried out of the cell by ions, and none goes to charge the membrane, i.e., the voltage stops changing. As long as any of the current charges the membrane, the voltage is changing and the driving forces on ions are increasing; the voltage cannot continue to change indefinitely.

Time constant. The time required for the attainment of the steady state depends on both the membrane capacitance and resistance: a longer time is required to charge a larger capacity up to the final value. For a larger membrane resistance, the membrane voltage must be altered more to make ionic current equal applied current; hence a longer time is required to reach the steady-state. Thus, the time scale depends on the product of membrane resistance and capacitance. This product is called the *time constant* of the membrane, $\tau_m = R_m C_m$. In the examples of Figure 3 the time constant is 35 milliseconds. This is a typical value for skeletal muscle fibers. The time constant of a squid giant axon is about 1 millisecond.

STEADY-STATE CURRENT DISTRIBUTION. After the applied current has flowed for a sufficiently long time (about 150 milliseconds in the example of Fig. 3) all the membrane has charged to its final value (Fig. 4C), and the voltage is unchanging in time. In the steady-state, the current spreads far down the plasm in both directions so as to pass out through a large membrane area; the larger the area of high resistance membrane perpendicular to the direction of current flow, the lower the total resistance offered by the membrane. However, the current will not spread indefinitely in the plasm, seeking a greater membrane area to exit through because such longitudinal current flow also encounters the plasm resistance. Some balance must be struck between the spreading out to achieve low membrane resistance and a lack of spread to achieve low plasm resistance.

Space constant. Quantitatively, the measure of the extent of current spread in the steady-state is the *space constant*, λ, defined as the distance at which the change in transmembrane voltage has fallen to 0.37 ($= 1/e$, $e = 2.718$ is the base of natural logarithms) of the maximum value as shown in Figure 3D. The relative values of plasm resistance and surface membrane resistance determine how far a current will spread; the space constant is the fiber length where the resistance of the membrane covering that fiber segment is equal to the longitudinal plasm resistance of the segment. Clearly such a distance exists because, as the segment's length increases, the plasm resistance increases in proportion while the transverse resistance of the membrane decreases because the membrane area increases. In large fibers, the space constant is of the order of a few millimeters; in the example illustrated in Figures 3 and 4, λ is 2.5 mm. The space constant is proportional to the square root of fiber diameter if the electrical properties of the plasm and membrane are held constant.

Summary. When a constant current is suddenly applied to an axon at x = 0 (Figs. 3, 4), at first all the current flows directly through the membrane because $\mathcal{E}_m$ cannot change until the charge on the membrane at that point is changed. Since $I = \mathcal{E}/R$, no current will flow laterally through the plasm or directly through the membrane until $\mathcal{E}_m$ is altered. Immediately after the current is applied, it is confined to the immediate region of application. As time passes $\Delta\mathcal{E}_m$ gradually changes and some current is diverted to adjacent regions of membrane. As the charge and $\mathcal{E}_m$ rise in immediately adjacent regions, the current spreads to still greater distances. Finally, after a long time, the membrane is fully charged and all the current is carried through the membrane by ions.

The transition between initial and final states is shown in the curves giving potential as a function of time at different distances (Fig. 3C). Hodgkin and Rushton[17] have analyzed mathematically the passive cable properties of an unmyelinated nerve and have developed methods for measuring membrane resistance and capacitance and plasm resistance.

A different, possibly helpful way to think of resistors and capacitors representing a fiber is as reservoirs and partially clogged or small-bore pipes, respectively. Voltage is analogous to pressure (height of water in a reservoir), charge to amount of water and current to flow of water. The applied current is analogous to the constant flow from a high pressure source through a very small pipe. At first all the flow goes to filling the reservoir at the point of entry. Later some of the water flows slowly through the clogged or small pipes and starts to fill adjacent reservoirs or to drain out through leaks in the reservoirs (membrane resistance).

THRESHOLD PHENOMENA IN ELONGATED CELLS

Events Near Threshold Voltage.   The cable properties of a fiber are such that a signal in the form of membrane hyperpolarization or depolarization at one point is undetectable more than a few millimeters (a few space constants) away. Since signals are transmitted for distances of up to two meters in man, some method of boosting the signal at least every few millimeters is needed. The energy for boosting the signal is supplied by the sodium concentration difference across the membrane. The signal is kept to a fixed height by means of the threshold, all-or-nothing regenerative mechanism. The boost occurs at all points in unmyelinated nerve fibers and in muscles and at nodes of Ranvier in myelinated nerve fibers.

Experimentally, an action potential may be initiated in a nerve or muscle fiber by sufficiently depolarizing the membrane with an outward current applied through an intracellular microelectrode. Another microelectrode, for measuring membrane potential, may be inserted near the stimulating electrode (Fig. 5A). The changes in $\mathcal{E}_m$ associated with the initiation

of an impulse are shown diagrammatically in Figure 5B. Hyperpolarizing currents (curve 1) of any size and small depolarizing currents (curve 2) change $\mathcal{E}_m$ in the manner expected from the cable properties of the fiber (compare with x = 0, Fig. 3C). When the depolarizing current applied to skeletal muscle fibers is just strong enough to reduce $\mathcal{E}_m$ from resting values (-90 mV.) to threshold voltage (about -55 mV.) (curve 3, Fig. 5B), there are two possible responses. The response to about half of the stimuli is a propagating action potential (curve 3b). If an action potential is not initiated, there is a *local response* (curve 3a); i.e., the voltage falls back toward the resting level, but initially more

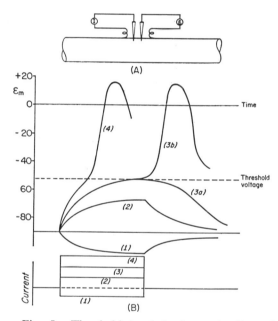

Fig. 5.   Threshold in skeletal muscle fiber. *A,* Schematic diagram of experimental arrangement showing intracellular stimulating (*I*) and recording (*$\mathcal{E}$*) electrodes. *B,* Changes in $\mathcal{E}_m$ (*upper records*) produced by suddenly applied and terminated constant currents (*lower records*). Curve *1* in current records produced voltage changes shown by Curve *1* in $\mathcal{E}$ records, and so forth for Curves *2* to *4*. Hyperpolarizing and subthreshold depolarizing currents of any strength produce the $\mathcal{E}_m$ changes expected from cable properties (Curves *1* and *2*). Current of just threshold strength will produce one of two responses: Either membrane potential returns to steady value after a delay (*3a*), or an action potential is generated with its typical rapid rise and fall (*3b*). Any stronger stimulus (*4*) also generates an action potential, but progressively shorter times are required to depolarize membrane to threshold. Duration of action potentials is greatly exaggerated to show time course of action potential more clearly. Every action potential has the same time course.

slowly than expected from the cable properties. As the name implies, a local response is non-propagated, i.e., local membrane activity. If the recording electrode impales the fiber farther from the stimulating electrode, a potential quite similar to curve *3b* is recorded but delayed in time when an action potential is initiated; otherwise, only the cable response is seen which is negligible a few space constants away. The value of ε_m at which an action potential is just initiated by a depolarizing current is called the *threshold voltage*. A lesser depolarization does not produce a propagated response, but a greater depolarization does. A current that barely depolarizes the membrane to threshold is called a *threshold stimulus*.

Threshold and the All-or-Nothing Law. Once the membrane has been depolarized to threshold, the action potential develops explosively and is thereafter independent of the stimulus. *The energy for the action potential is contained in the axon; the stimulus, by lowering the membrane potential, serves merely to trigger the axon into activity.* Thus, once the stimulus reaches threshold intensity, any additional increase in stimulus intensity has no effect on the amplitude of the action potential. For a given stimulus the axon either responds with a full-sized action potential or it does not; its behavior is thus "all-or-nothing." It should not be inferred that the action potentials of an axon always have the same amplitude; many factors can alter the energy stores of the axon and hence alter the amplitude of the action potential. For any given state, however, the axon always responds maximally to a threshold stimulus.

General Features of Threshold and Recovery. Threshold, all-or-nothing properties are not unique to excitable cells or to living systems; many objects encountered in everyday life have these properties. Possibly the simplest example is that of a brick standing on its end. A small sideways push on the top edge of the brick may tip it slightly; releasing the brick allows it to fall back to its original stable equilibrium position, perhaps with a little rocking back and forth. Such a push is a subthreshold stimulus. A stronger push may tip the brick so that it balances on its edge, a position of unstable equilibrium. A slight further displacement tips the brick over and it falls rapidly to the flat position, an even more stable (lower potential energy) equilibrium position. This is

clearly threshold, all-or-nothing behavior; when displaced to or past threshold, the brick always goes to the same final position regardless of the strength of the stimulus.

Many useful devices have thresholds, e.g., light switches, thermostats, mouse traps, matches. However, excitable tissues differ from these devices in having an additional property: spontaneous recovery to the original threshold state. This means that the cell must be supplied further energy to restore the original state, i.e., to recover excitability. In contrast, a brick has to be stood on end again to restore its threshold to tipping. The most common device having a threshold and spontaneous recovery is the flushing mechanism of a water closet. A slight rotation of the handle is the required threshold stimulus; this lifts the float valve in the bottom of the tank sufficiently that it floats upward, releasing a torrent of water. The flow continues until the tank is empty, the float valve reseats and the tank begins to refill from a water source at higher pressure through another valve whose orifice depends on the level of another float such that, as the water rises, the inflow rate is reduced. The cycle is completed and the system is back to its original low threshold state when the tank is filled to that level which shuts off the inflow valve. The system will not respond to a rotation of the handle when the tank is emptying and for a short part of the refilling period. In the language of neurophysiology and speaking of a nerve, this would be called the *absolutely refractory period*. At some time during the refilling cycle a small flush can be initiated by a larger rotation of the handle. As the tank fills, the needed initiating stimulus becomes smaller and the response grows; this period of subnormal responsiveness corresponds to the *relatively refractory period* in nerves. These phenomena in nerves, then, are examples of the behavior of threshold systems having spontaneous recovery.

Strength–Duration Relation. The strength of an abruptly applied and terminated current (square wave) required to initiate an impulse in an axon or muscle fiber depends on the length of the time during which the current flows. For an impulse to be initiated, the membrane must be depolarized to threshold over a small region. If a current applied at a point on an axon flows for a long time, the membrane capacitors will become fully charged, and the change in membrane potential will be maximal

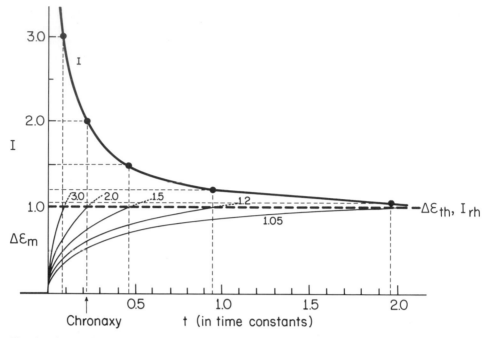

Fig. 6. Strength–duration relation (solid, heavy curve) of an excitable cell or tissue. Both the cause, square pulses of current (dashed, fine lines) applied to a fiber or tissue, and the effect, the resulting changes in transmembrane potential at the stimulus site (solid, fine lines), are plotted as functions of time. Horizontal, dashed, heavy line at 1.0 represents both threshold current strength at long times (I_{rh}) and difference ($\Delta\mathcal{E}_{th}$) between threshold membrane voltage ($\mathcal{E}_{th}$) and resting voltage ($\mathcal{E}_{S}$). Ordinates, strength of applied current, (I) turned on at t = 0, measured in units of I_{rh}, the strength a long lasting current pulse must have to depolarize the membrane to threshold; and the change in transmembrane potential measured in units of $\Delta\mathcal{E}_{th}$. Abscissa, time since start of current pulse measured in units of the membrane time constant (τ), i.e., if the time constant is 30 milliseconds, t = 1 time constant means t = 30 milliseconds. I_{rh} (as defined above) is termed the *rheobasic current* or *rheobase*. Individual points on the strength–duration curve are obtained in the following way: A current of strength I = 1.05 (actually, I = 1.05 I_{rh}) causes the voltage changes at the site of the stimulating electrode shown by the lowermost light, solid line (labeled 1.05). This curve is identical in shape to that in Figure 3C (x = 0). The transmembrane voltage crosses threshold ($\Delta\mathcal{E}_{th}$) at t = 1.96 time constants. An action potential (not shown) would be initiated at this time and hence the current could be turned off as shown without affecting action potential generation; leaving the current on would also have no effect. This exactly threshold stimulus is represented by the pulse jumping from zero to 1.05 at t = 0, continuing at this value until t = 1.96 and then dropping back to zero; the heavy dot at the pulse's termination is a point on the strength–duration curve. Other points are obtained in the same way by selecting a stimulus current value, letting it flow until the membrane potential crosses threshold and then terminating the current. The stronger the stimulating current, the shorter the time it must flow to carry the membrane potential to threshold; doubling the current doubles the change in voltage at any particular time (dashed curve labeled 2.0). The time required for a stimulus of twice rheobasic strength to carry the membrane potential to threshold is called the *chronaxy*. In this example the chronaxy is 0.21 time constants. The number by each voltage curve refers to the current strength which produces that voltage change. Current strength is read directly off the ordinate scale.

for that current. Therefore, the threshold current strength for a prolonged stimulus is less than that for a shorter stimulus. A curve relating the strength of a threshold stimulus to its duration is called a *strength–duration* curve. Clearly, the shape of such a curve is directly related to the cable properties of the fiber. The relation is derived graphically in Figure 6. The shape of the strength–duration curve is very nearly the same for all tissues, although the time and current scales vary. One way of calculating its shape is derived in the appendix to this chapter. *Chronaxy* is one point on the strength–duration curve, i.e., the length of time a current twice rheobase strength (see legend, Fig. 6) must flow in order to excite a cell. Chronaxy is directly proportional to the membrane time constant and hence is greater in muscle than in nerve. With external electrodes chronaxy can be measured easily in a whole nerve or muscle; hence an estimate of membrane time constant can be made without recourse to technically difficult intracellular stimulating and recording techniques.

Effect of Subthreshold Currents on Excitability. *Excitability* is defined as the reciprocal of threshold. If an applied current is slightly subthreshold, the depolarization persists for some time after the termination of the current; the size of a threshold stimulus is reduced during this period, and the excitability is increased. To measure the change in excitability produced by a subthreshold shock it is necessary to probe or test the excitability at varying time intervals by using a second shock of an intensity which can be varied. The time course of an excitability change caused by the first shock can be determined. This procedure, known as the *conditioning–testing technique,* is widely used in neurophysiology; the shock used to induce the change is called the "conditioning" shock, and that used to measure or test the change is called the "test" shock.

The heightened excitability persisting after a subthreshold conditioning shock is a consequence of the cable properties of the cells. The slowly waning voltage change induced by the conditioning shock persists after the shock and can sum with the voltage changes induced by the test shock. Moreover, as expected from cable properties, the heightened excitability is not spatially confined to the stimulus site but extends on either side; the threshold increases more and more gradually with distance, finally reaching the resting threshold level.

The same procedure can be used to test the effect of prolonged rather than brief subthreshold conditioning shocks. In this instance excitability increases at the stimulating cathode with the onset of current flow, but, even though current flow continues at a constant level, excitability then drops to a steady intermediate value. This decline from peak excitability during constant current flow is called *accommodation.* Following cessation of current flow, excitability at the cathode declines below the resting level and recovers only slowly. This is known as *postcathodal depression.* The mechanisms of accommodation and postcathodal depression will be discussed later.

Refractory Period; Recovery Following Excitation. The conditioning–testing procedure can be used to study the changes in excitability which follow the generation of an action potential. In this instance the conditioning shock is suprathreshold, and the intensity of test shock required to elicit a second action potential at varying conditioning–testing intervals is determined. For a brief period following the action potential it is impossible to elicit a second action potential, no matter how intense the test shock. As mentioned above, this interval is known as the *absolutely refractory period.* Thereafter a second action potential (usually of less than normal amplitude) can be elicited, but only if the test shock is considerably above the resting threshold value. Excitability then returns to the resting threshold along an approximately exponential time course. The interval between absolute refractoriness and complete recovery to resting excitability is known as the *relatively refractory period.* Refractoriness limits the frequency of impulse discharge in nerve fibers; for example, an axon with an absolutely refractory period of 0.5 millisecond can be driven continuously at rates not exceeding 1000 impulses per second—and then only if the stimulus is considerably more intense than that required to initiate a single action potential in the axon at rest. With continous high frequency stimulation, the minimum interval between spikes is about double the absolutely refractory period.

IMPULSE GENERATION AND PROPAGATION[9]

Active Na+–K+ transport and cable properties are attributes of all animal cell membranes. The membrane of an excitable cell has certain unique properties in addition. These properties were precisely described by Hodgkin and Huxley in their classic studies on the behavior of the squid giant axon when its membrane potential was held constant by artificial means (voltage clamping). The defining property of excitable cells is that rapid depolarization (reduction of transmembrane voltage) increases the membrane permeability to Na+ (P_{Na}). Within limits, the greater the depolarization, the greater the increase in P_{Na}. An ancillary property is that the increase in P_{Na} induced by depolarization is transient; even if the membrane voltage is maintained near ε_{Na} by other means (e.g., external current), P_{Na} falls to its resting value in a matter of a few milliseconds. The properties of the excitable membrane are described in terms of changes in membrane permeability or conductance, because no information is yet available regarding the molecular mechanisms which give rise to the large and specific changes in membrane ionic permeability.

There are three principal methods of studying the changes in ionic permeability during activity: (i) observing the effects of changes in external ion concentrations on the action potential, (ii) studying by means of radioisotopes the net and one-way ionic fluxes during activity, and (iii) voltage-clamping, measuring membrane current as a function of time while ε_m is fixed. The first two methods yield only a rough estimate of peak or mean ion permeabilities during activity. Voltage clamping,[15] however, made possible a detailed quantitative analysis of the time and voltage dependencies of Na^+ and K^+ conductances.

Sequence of Events during the Action Potential.   In 1902, Bernstein formulated the membrane theory in a form which has endured to this day in its essential aspects. He proposed that the surface membrane is permeable only to potassium in the resting state, giving rise to the resting potential. He attributed the action potential to a transient loss of the membrane's selectivity for potassium, the membrane becoming permeable to all ions and the potential falling to near zero. This hypothesis was sufficient until the introduction of intracellular recording techniques in about 1940 showed that there is an overshoot of the action potential, the inside becoming positive with respect to the outside. This finding necessitated modification of Bernstein's hypothesis. Reference to Table 1 in Chapter 1 reveals that the only biologically occurring ion which has a positive equilibrium potential and can penetrate the membrane is sodium. In 1949, Hodgkin and Katz[16] proposed and tested the hypothesis that the upstroke or depolarization phase of the action potential is brought about by a brief and highly specific increase in the membrane's permeability to Na^+. This increase would permit Na^+ to enter the cell at a greatly increased rate, driven both by the concentration and voltage gradients and thus charge the membrane toward the sodium equilibrium potential. Repolarization to the resting state would occur as the increased Na^+ permeability died out and the efflux of K^+ exceeded influx of Na^+. A simplified version of this hypothesis is that the action potential can be represented as a sudden switch from the resting state with the membrane potential near the potassium equilibrium potential, a "potassium membrane," to the active state with the potential changing rapidly toward the sodium equilibrium potential, a "sodium membrane," followed by a somewhat slower reversion to the potassium membrane condition. Of course, the membrane is not permeable solely to K^+ in the resting state nor to Na^+ in the active state. Hodgkin and Katz supported their hypothesis by showing that the overshoot and the rate of rise of the action potential vary with changes in external Na^+ concentration in approximately the manner expected from the Nernst equation. Before presenting this evidence it is pertinent to answer briefly two questions raised by this hypothesis: (i) How does a threshold depolarization act to produce the dramatic increase in Na^+ permeability? (ii) What processes bring about the rapid repolarization to the original resting condition?

(i) The large (500-fold) increase in permeability to sodium is brought about by depolarization; sodium permeability varies rapidly with voltage in the region of threshold. This change is an intrinsic property of the excitable membrane; the molecular basis is unknown. Thus there is a regenerative or vicious circle relationship between depolarization and sodium permeability; depolarization increases sodium permeability, increasing Na^+ entry and further depolarizing the membrane. This regenerative, circular sequence of events was compactly summarized by Hodgkin[5] in the following diagram, which might, therefore, be aptly termed the "Hodgkin cycle":

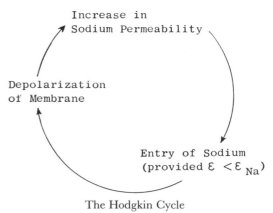

The Hodgkin Cycle

(ii) The recovery from the rapid depolarization produced by the Hodgkin cycle is due to two factors: (a) The increased permeability to Na+ during activity is transient; the permeability falls to near resting values in a millisecond or so. This spontaneous fall in Na+ permeability is called *inactivation*. (b) When the membrane is depolarized, the permeability to K+ commences to increase comparatively slowly (after a delay of about a millisecond). This property is also intrinsic to the membrane. Both the increase in permeability to K+ and the decrease in permeability to Na+ make the potential fall rapidly toward the resting level. Following the return of the membrane potential to the resting level, permeability to K+ falls slowly to its normal value. Both these events limit the duration of the action potential and lead to repolarization.

Effects of External Sodium and Potassium Concentration on Membrane Potentials. The flux of an ion depends on the membrane permeability to that ion, on the transmembrane voltage and on the external and internal concentrations of the ion. Thus, a change in concentration should alter membrane voltage to an extent which depends on the membrane's relative permeability to the ion. If the membrane is solely permeable to the ion (S) being studied, the change in voltage with external or internal concentration is given by the Nernst equation $\mathcal{E}_m = \mathcal{E}_S = 61 \log [S]_o/[S]_i$. A lesser change is expected if other ions permeate the membrane. In most experiments, only external ion concentrations can be varied. However, it has been recently discovered that, in some circumstances, the axoplasm can be squeezed out of squid giant fibers without destroying the membrane and the inside can be perfused with an artificial solution.[9] The excitability of an axon bathed in sea-water is restored by perfusing the interior with a solution having a high potassium concentration, regardless of the accompanying anion. External potassium concentration is ordinarily increased by replacing some of the sodium with potassium, leaving chloride unchanged. Sodium can be reduced either by replacing Na+ with some presumably inert cation such as choline+ or by replacing NaCl with an inert, nonionized substance such as dextrose or sucrose.

RESTING POTENTIAL AND CHANGES IN EXTERNAL POTASSIUM CONCENTRATION. Since the resting membrane is relatively highly permeable to potassium, an increase in external potassium concentration should have substantial effects on the resting potential. Such an increase momentarily increases the K+ influx until membrane charge and voltage are reduced to such a level that the efflux is increased to equal the increased influx. If the only permeable ion were potassium, the change in potential would be predictable by the Nernst equation; the extent to which this is found experimentally to be not true gives an estimate of the contributions of other ions under the particular circumstances. The effects of external potassium concentration on the resting potential of excised frog skeletal muscle are shown in Figure 7. Since $\mathcal{E}_K = 58 \log_{10} [K^+]_o/[K^+]_i$ at room temperature, a plot of the resting potential against the logarithm of the external potassium concentration will give a straight line with a slope of 58 mV. per tenfold change in external potassium concentration if the transmembrane potential is a potassium equilibrium potential.

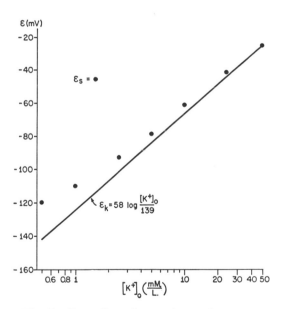

Fig. 7. Immediate changes in steady transmembrane potential ($\mathcal{E}_S$) of frog sartorius muscle fibers produced by alterations in external potassium concentration, $[K^+]_o$. *Abscissa*, $[K^+]_o$ on a logarithmic scale; *ordinate*, $\mathcal{E}_S$ potential of intracellular fluid minus potential of extracellular fluid. Points are experimental results. Straight line is plot of equilibrium potential for potassium, $\mathcal{E}_K$ at room temperature. Note that at high values of $[K^+]_o$, $\mathcal{E}_S$ changes with $\mathcal{E}_K$ and that at K+ concentrations in normal range, $\mathcal{E}_S$ changes much less rapidly than $\mathcal{E}_K$. (After Adrian, *J. Physiol.*, 1956, *133*: 631–658.)

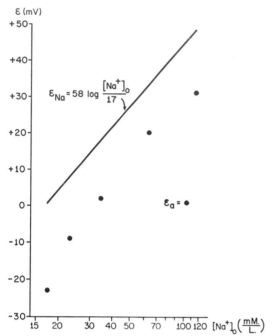

Fig. 8. Changes in peak value of the action potential of frog sartorius muscle fibers produced by changes in external Na+ concentration. NaCl in bathing solution was replaced by choline chloride. *Abscissa*, [Na+]o on logarithmic scale; *ordinate*, potential of intracellular fluid minus potential of extracellular fluid at peak of action potential. Points $\mathcal{E}_a$ are experimental results; straight line is plot of equilibrium potential for Na+ ($\mathcal{E}_{Na}$). Note that peak of action potential is considerably lower than $\mathcal{E}_{Na}$, but that both change at about same rate with changes in [Na+]o. (After Nastuk and Hodgkin, *J. cell. comp. Physiol.*, 1950, *35*:39–74.)

The solid points show the measured membrane potential for different values of [K+]o, the latter being plotted on a logarithmic scale; the solid line shows the relation between $\mathcal{E}_K$ and [K+]o calculated from the Nernst equation. The membrane potential changes toward zero as [K+]o increases, and when [K+]o = [K+]i the membrane potential is zero. Through a considerable range, the membrane potential varies linearly with log [K+]o, as would be expected from the Nernst equation. However, at low values of [K+]o (near the normal values for extracellular fluid) the curve deviates markedly from linearity, and increments of [K+]o cause less than the expected change in the potential. This deviation of observed from calculated values reflects the action of the Na+–K+ pump. With normal and near normal values of [K+]o, a significant part of the K+ influx is propelled by the pump. At higher values of [K+]o the passive K+ influx increases, so the *proportion* of the total K+ influx due to the steady action of the pump is diminished, and the membrane potential approaches $\mathcal{E}_K$, as predicted from the Nernst equation. It should be kept in mind that the potential reached immediately after the change in [K+]o is not steady; internal concentrations are slowly changing; e.g., [K+]i and [Cl−]i increase. However, these concentrations change so slowly (order of hours) that they can be considered constant during an experiment.

EFFECTS OF EXTERNAL SODIUM CONCENTRATION ON THE ACTION POTENTIAL. Hodgkin and Katz[16] supported their explanation of overshoot by studying the effects of changes in [Na+]o on the amplitude of the action potential in the squid giant axon. They found that replacing some of the NaCl in the bathing medium with dextrose reduced the amplitude of the action potential by about the amount that would be expected from the Nernst equation for Na+: $\mathcal{E}_{Na} = 58 \log_{10} [Na^+]_o/[Na^+]_i$. For example, there should be no overshoot unless the concentration of Na+ is greater outside than inside the fiber. If the two concentrations are equal, the equilibrium potential is zero.

A dependence of the action potential on [Na+]o is found in nearly all types of excitable tissues and is strong evidence of the validity of the Na+ hypothesis. Figure 8 shows the changes in peak value of the action potential of excised frog skeletal muscle as [Na+]o is varied. For comparison, the value of the sodium equilibrium potential as calculated from the Nernst equation for [Na+]i = 17 μM. per cm.³ is also shown. It can be seen that the membrane reversal during activity is rather less than the Na+ equilibrium potential but varies with [Na+]o about as rapidly as does this potential. Hodgkin and Katz interpreted the failure of the action potential to reach the Na+ equilibrium potential as evidence that the contributions of other ions are not negligible, i.e., that the permeability to K+ and Cl− ions is an appreciable but not large fraction (about one-tenth) of the permeability to Na+ at the peak of the action potential.

Role of acetylcholine. Nachmansohn[23] has forcefully advanced the hypothesis that the liberation and destruction of acetylcholine (ACh) are essential steps in the generation of the action potential in nerve as well as at the neuromuscular junction (Chap. 5). The postulated role of ACh in nerve conduction is as follows: (i) Depolarization liberates ACh from a bound, inactive form already present in the membrane. (ii)

The ACh acts to increase membrane permeability to Na+ by combining with a "receptor" protein. (iii) The ACh is in equilibrium with the receptor protein, so that some of the ACh is unbound and thus susceptible to rapid hydrolysis (inactivation) by the high concentration of AChE present in the membrane. (iv) Destruction of the acetylcholine reduces Na+ permeability and repolarization occurs. The wide distribution and high concentration of AChE in nervous tissue leave little doubt that ACh has an important role in nervous function. However, the evidence that this hypothesis describes ACh's function is no more than suggestive. Furthermore, it is difficult to acount for some experimental findings with this hypothesis; e.g., if ACh causes the specific increase in permeability to Na+ during activity, inhibition of the AChE would allow ACh to accumulate in the membrane and repolarization and recovery of excitability should be greatly prolonged or prevented. Anticholinesterase drugs in high concentrations do block conduction, but the slight elongation of the action potential that occurs just before block is far less than expected on the basis of this hypothesis and about the same as occurs when conduction is blocked by local anesthetics. Thus, Nachmansohn's hypothesis is attractive but not convincing.

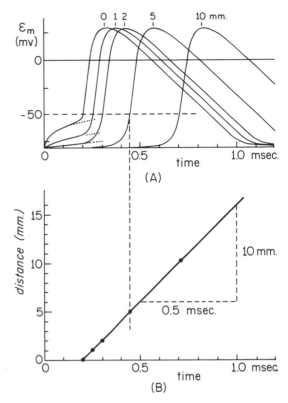

PROPAGATION

Measurement of Conduction Speed. The propagation of an action potential along an excitable fiber can be measured with the technique used for measuring cable properties (Fig. 3). If a threshold, depolarizing current is applied to a fiber at x = 0 (Fig. 3*B*), an action potential will be generated at that point after the length of time necessary for the membrane potential to reach threshold (curve 0, Fig. 9*A*). The action potential propagates in each direction at constant speed and amplitude. Thus, if the experiment is repeated with the recording electrode implanted 1 millimeter away, the potential changes due to cable properties are much smaller and slower; the action potential appears with full amplitude but is delayed by about 0.05 millisecond (curve 1, Fig. 9*A*). Repetition of the experiment at recording distances of 2, 5 and 10 millimeters gives the corresponding curves in Figure 9*A*. At distances greater than about 2 millimeters, the cable effects are negligibly small and the shape of the action potential becomes constant and concave upward at subthreshold values. Except for the cable effects near the stimulating electrode, the action potential is fixed in shape but occurs in-

Fig. 9. Measurement of conduction speed. *A*, Action potentials initiated and recorded by the technique illustrated in Figure 3*A* and *B*. Ordinate, transmembrane potential ($\mathcal{E}_m$); abscissa, time since beginning of stimulating current pulse. Number attached to each action potential is the distance in millimeters of the intracellular recording electrode from the stimulating electrode. Note that records at 0, 1 and 2 mm. show, at subthreshold levels, the decrementing potential changes characteristic of cables (compare with Fig. 3*C*).

B, Distance–latency relation of action potentials shown in *A*. Ordinate, distance between stimulating and recording electrodes in millimeters; abscissa, latency of the action potential measured from time of start of stimulating current to the time the action potential reached the fixed level of −50 millivolts. Scale is same as in *A*. Dashed horizontal line in *A* is at this level; its intersection with the action potential recorded at 5 millimeters is shown by the vertical line which extends down to the 5 mm. distance on the ordinate in *B*. Other points, obtained in the same way, fall on a straight line whose slope, 10 mm. per 0.5 milliseconds = 20 meters per second, is the conduction speed of the impulse. This is typical for a 10 μ diameter frog myelinated nerve fiber. The intercept of the line on the abscissa is the time for the stimulus to bring the fiber to threshold and for the spontaneous depolarization process to carry the voltage to −50 mV. and thus has no great significance.

creasingly later at increasingly greater recording distances from the stimulus site. If the time from the beginning of the stimulus to the time some particular voltage is reached (− 50 mV. in Fig. 9A) by the action potential is plotted against the distance of the recording electrode from the stimulating electrode, a curve like that in Figure 9B is obtained. It is seen that the time delay or latency increases linearly with distance; i.e., the action potential is propagated with a constant speed along the fiber. The speed is given by the slope of the distance–time curve and is 10 millimeters per 0.5 millisecond = 20 meters per second. This is about the conduction speed of squid giant axons and of a 10 μ frog myelinated nerve fiber. A mammalian myelinated nerve fiber of the same diameter would have a conduction speed of about 60 meters per second.

IMPULSE AS A WAVE. In the physical sense, a wave is any disturbance that moves with constant velocity and unchanging shape. Thus, the nerve impulse is a wave. Common examples of true waves are ocean waves, radio and light waves and sound waves. The most characteristic property of a wave is that its shape is the same as a function of time and as a function of distance, e.g., a disturbance of fixed shape moving at constant speed. A person standing in the ocean can see a wave approaching; he sees the shape of the wave in space. As the wave passes him, he can feel the water level rise and recede around him as the wave passes; he can feel it in time. The nerve impulse cannot be seen but the time course can be measured at many different points, and hence the space distribution can be found at any particular time. In both cases, the space course is the same as the time course; the conversion factor from time to distance is simply the conduction speed. The spatial extent (L) of an impulse can be calculated from the duration of the action potential (t_{AP}) and the conduction speed (v): $L = vt_{AP}$. In the example of Figure 9, the duration is about 0.8 millisecond and the conduction speed is 20 millimeters per millisecond; the spatial extent is thus 0.8 millisecond × 20 millimeters per millisecond = 16 millimeters (Fig. 10A). In the fastest mammalian nerve fibers, the wave length is about 60 millimeters or 4 inches, a distance of 3,000 times the diameter of the fiber (20 μ).

Local Circuit Propagation.[4, 9] Once an action potential has been initiated, the Na+ per-

meability is high in a local region and the membrane potential is near the Na+ equilibrium potential. The potential of the adjacent inactive membrane is near the K+ equilibrium potential. There is a potential difference between these regions; consequently, current flows from the active region through the intracellular fluid to the inactive region (arrows directed to left in Fig. 10B, C), and discharges the membrane capacitor. The return current flows through the interstitial fluid back to the active region (arrows directed to right in Fig. 10B, C) and through the membrane as inward Na+ current, driven by $\mathcal{E}_{Na}$. This *local circuit* current

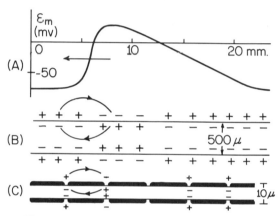

Fig. 10. Propagation by local circuit stimulation. *A,* Spatial variation of an action potential at a fixed time. Ordinate, transmembrane potential, $\mathcal{E}_m$; abscissa, distance along fibers shown in *B* and *C*. Action potential is the same as shown in Figure 9 and is propagated at a speed of 20 meters per second to the left, as shown by the arrow crossing its upstroke. Note that the upstroke is much steeper than the downstroke.

B, Unmyelinated nerve fiber. Plus and minus signs represent approximately the transmembrane voltage given accurately in *A*. Distance scale of *A* applies. Diameter of cell is grossly exaggerated with respect to length as shown. Arrows represent current flow in a local circuit or loop due to the differences in transmembrane potential caused by the different properties of the membrane: highly permeable to K+ on left and right, even more highly permeable to Na+ in central regions. Local circuit flow acts to reduce charge in inactive regions but has much less effect on charge in active regions because of high Na+ permeability. Propagation is achieved by depolarizing action of local current flow.

C, Same as *B* except myelinated. For clarity, distance between nodes is shown as 4 mm. or twice actual distance. Because of low capacity of sheath, charge is shown only at nodes (amount of charge in whole internodal region is about one half that at the node). Local circuit flow is thus largely from node to node as shown by arrows.

flow acts to reduce membrane charge and voltage in the inactive region. When threshold is reached, permeability to Na$^+$ increases rapidly, the inactive region becomes active and the membrane potential approaches the Na$^+$ equilibrium potential here also. Thus, by local circuit current flow an active region stimulates the adjacent inactive regions to threshold and an impulse is conducted away from a stimulating cathode in both directions at a constant speed. The stimulation of an inactive region by an active region is analogous to the sudden connection of a battery, of voltage $\mathcal{E}_{Na}$, through a comparatively low axoplasmic resistance (because the distance is short) to a capacitor, charged to $\mathcal{E}_K$. The high permeability to Na$^+$ of the active membrane means that the battery can supply a large current and thus quickly discharge the inactive region to threshold and makes it active. Figure 10 illustrates the principle of local circuit stimulation. Local current loops flow around the point of fastest voltage change. There are many such loops, but for clarity only one is shown in Figure 10*B* and *C*.

As mentioned above, recovery to the resting state is brought about by a spontaneous fall in Na$^+$ permeability and a delayed rise in K$^+$ permeability. In a matter of a few tenths of a millisecond, outward movement of K$^+$ exceeds inward movement of Na$^+$ and repolarization begins. This process follows depolarization automatically, so that the propagated wave has the typical humplike shape shown in Figures 2, 9 and 10. There is also local circuit flow behind the impulse as a consequence of the repolarization process (not shown in Fig. 10).

Myelinated Nerves: Saltatory Conduction.[18, 20, 24] The myelinated or medullated nerve fiber is one of the functional developments which make large size possible among the cold-blooded vertebrates and the elevated body position among mammals. Myelination greatly increases nerve fiber conduction speed without greatly increasing diameter and thus decreases reaction time. Invertebrates have achieved high conduction speed by developing giant axons. The sheer physical size of these axons prevents an animal from having large numbers of them.

The myelin sheath of medullated nerve fibers is formed by Schwann cells. A Schwann cell covers about 2 millimeters of axon in the largest diameter fibers (20 μ). The Schwann cell surrounds the fiber and then wraps itself around the fiber many times to form the sheath. In the wrapping process, all the Schwann cell plasm is squeezed out, leaving the membranes closely opposed and forming a layer 170 Ångstroms thick. Since the myelin sheath is 2 μ thick in large fibers, there are at least 100 wrappings. There is a gap of approximately 1 μ between adjacent Schwann cell wrappings where the axon membrane is in free communication with the interstitial fluid. This interruption in the myelin sheath is called a *node of Ranvier* and the sheathed portion is called the *internode*.

Since the myelin sheath is composed of many layers of closely packed membranes, it is a good insulator. If there are 100 double membrane layers in the sheath, then the resistance of a 1 cm.^{2} patch of sheath will be 200 times the resistance of 1 cm.^{2} of membrane, since current flow is perpendicular to the membrane surface. Similarly, the capacity of 1 cm.^{2} of sheath is 200 times smaller than that of 1 layer of membrane and thus, *the amount of charge stored across the sheath for a given potential difference is also 200 times less.* Because of the thick sheath, the amount of charge stored on the whole internodal region (2 mm.) is only about one-half of the charge on the nodal region (1 μ). This is the reason that membrane charges are shown only at the nodes in Figure 10. There are, of course, some charges separated by the myelin sheath.

Resting and action potentials are generated only at the nodes in myelinated nerves. The voltages generated at the node by ion diffusion down concentration gradients charge up the internodal capacity. When a fiber is depolarized only the nodes become active. If one node is active and an adjacent node is inactive (Fig. 10*C*), there is a local circuit flow between the nodes, depolarizing the inactive node. The length of time taken for an active region to depolarize an adjacent inactive one to threshold is determined by the amount of charge that must be removed and the resistance of the axoplasm between the regions. Since the membrane charge is greatly reduced by the myelin sheath, the conduction speed of a myelinated nerve fiber is many times greater than that of an unmyelinated fiber of the same diameter and membrane properties. Impulse propagation in myelinated nerve fibers can be summarized as the hopping of excitation from node to node; internodal regions have a low charge, are well insulated and unexcitable. Propagation by this means is called *saltatory conduction* (from the Latin *saltare,* to dance).

Determinants of Conduction Speed. Two classes of factors determine the speed of impulse conduction in excitable fibers: physical properties of the cell and geometry of the cell.

PHYSICAL FACTORS. (i) The most important physical property of an excitable cell is the extent of the depolarization-induced increase in sodium permeability. The greater the peak permeability, the greater the sodium current and hence the greater the rate of rise of the action potential. In turn, a faster rising action potential means a larger spatial voltage gradient along the fiber and hence greater local circuit currents, faster excitation of adjacent regions and greater conduction speed. (ii) A reduction in the amount of depolarization to reach threshold would increase conduction speed, other things being equal, because the local current would not have to flow for as long to excite an inactive region. (iii) The size of the membrane capacitor per unit area determines the amount of charge stored on the membrane per unit area for a given voltage and hence the length of time a current must flow to depolarize to threshold. A larger capacity means a smaller speed. (iv) Similarly, the size of local current flow is determined by the resistivity of the cell plasm. Other things being equal, the greater the concentration of highly mobile ions, the greater the current flow for a given voltage. (v) Temperature has large effects on the rate of increase of sodium conductance;[15] conduction speed increases with temperature.

FIBER GEOMETRY AND CONDUCTION SPEED.[6, 9] The foregoing arguments indicate that conduction speed depends on membrane capacity and plasm resistance and thus on fiber diameter. In myelinated fibers speed also depends on the thickness of the myelin sheath relative to axon diameter and on the distance between nodes. Sheath thickness and internodal distance have values which maximize conduction speed. The resistance of the axoplasm is inversely proportional to the cross-sectional area and hence to the square of the diameter; conduction speed therefore increases rapidly with fiber diameter. On the other hand, the capacity of the fiber membrane per unit length is directly proportional to diameter, tending to decrease speed. The net result is that speed increases with fiber diameter. In unmyelinated fibers, the speed is proportional to the square root of the diameter,[6] whereas in myelinated fibers it is directly proportional to diameter (Chap. 3). Thus it is not possible to generalize about how much myelination increases conduction speed. A squid giant axon has a conduction speed of about 20 meters per second and a diameter of about 500 μ. On the basis of the square root rule, a squid axon 20 μ in diameter would have a speed of about 4 meters per second. A frog myelinated fiber this size has a speed of 40 meters per second, 10 times greater than that of the unmyelinated fiber. Perhaps a better comparison is that a 10 μ frog fiber has the same conduction speed as a 500 μ squid axon and that nearly 2500 10 μ fibers can be packed into the same volume as the giant axon. It is this characteristic—fast conduction in small axons—that makes possible the fast, precise control of muscle contraction necessary in warm-blooded vertebrates for maintaining an elevated posture. A mammalian muscle nerve typically contains about 1000 large fibers (10 to 20 μ in diameter) and is about 1 millimeter in diameter. If a similar nerve were composed of unmyelinated nerve fibers having the same conduction speeds, it would be about an inch and a half in diameter.

INTRINSIC PROPERTIES OF EXCITABLE MEMBRANES

Voltage Clamping.[1-3, 10-13, 15] It is difficult to learn the detailed kinetics of an explosive process by studying the explosions as such. A better way to study them is by controlling a variable so that threshold, all-or-nothing characteristics are eliminated. In the example of the brick given previously, the threshold behavior can be eliminated by applying sufficient external force (e.g., by holding it) so that the brick's position is determined by the experimenter rather than by the force of gravity. The kinetics of the threshold process can then be obtained in detail simply by measuring the force required to hold the brick in a particular position as a function of that position. For slight displacements of the brick, the force exerted by the brick is small and opposed to the applied force. At the threshold, unstable equilibrium point the applied force has decreased to zero and for larger displacements it becomes negative, i.e., a pull rather than a push must be exerted on the brick. The curve of force against displacement is smooth and shows no threshold behavior in this kind of experiment.

In nerve, the equivalent of the position of the brick is voltage and the equivalent of the applied force is applied current. Thus threshold behavior can be eliminated by "clamping" the voltage at values set by the experimenter. The relation between membrane voltage and membrane ionic current is measured by supplying to the nerve, from an external source, whatever current is required to maintain the membrane voltage constant—i.e., connecting it to a battery—for different values of the voltage. For small depolarizations, an outward current must be applied to carry K^+ outward. The supplied current must be decreased to zero at threshold voltage and directed inward to carry sodium ions at larger depolarizations where increasing sodium permeability makes sodium current exceed potassium current. In other words, the dependence of Na^+ current, and hence sodium permeability (P_{Na}), on $\mathcal{E}_m$ and on time can be measured directly by the voltage clamp technique. Regenerative interactions between $\mathcal{E}_m$ and P_{Na} are prevented by artificially maintaining $\mathcal{E}_m$ constant. This procedure is equivalent to connecting a battery between the inside and the outside of the cell so that $\mathcal{E}_m$ must equal the battery voltage. If $\mathcal{E}_m$ is not changing in time, all the membrane current must be carried by ions, since none would go to charge the membrane capacity. If voltage is clamped at only one point on a nerve fiber, part of the current supplied by the external source will spread away from that point because of the fiber's cable properties. Therefore, voltage clamping requires that $\mathcal{E}_m$ must be held constant over the length of the fiber. If $\mathcal{E}_m$ does not change with distance, no current will flow from one region to another, and all applied current must flow with uniform density through the membrane. Figure 11A is a highly simplified schematic diagram of a voltage clamp experiment on squid giant axon. Figures 11B and C show the results obtained.

When the potential of the battery is set equal to $\mathcal{E}_S$, no current will flow through the membrane (switch is in position 1, Fig. 11A) because $\mathcal{E}_S$ is the voltage at which the net flow of charge is zero. When the switch is moved to position 2, current will flow through the external circuit and bring $\mathcal{E}_m$ to the new voltage ($\mathcal{E}$) if the resistance between the long internal and external electrodes is mostly in the membrane, i.e., if the resist-

ance of the axoplasm and the external bathing fluid and the resistance between the electrodes and the solution are negligible compared to the membrane resistance. In practice, the resistance between the internal electrode and the axoplasm is an important factor, and rather elaborate measures are necessary to circumvent this and other difficulties.[15, 22]

When the switch is thrown to position 2, the membrane potential is abruptly changed to a new value. In order to change $\mathcal{E}_m$ it is necessary to change the charge on the membrane capacity. This process, however, is brief, because the low radial resistance of the axoplasm allows a high current flow from the battery to the membrane capacitance. The membrane conductance does not change immediately after a sudden change in $\mathcal{E}_m$; therefore, there is an immediate membrane current proportional to $\Delta\mathcal{E}_m$; i.e., K^+ flows outward and Cl^- inward. This change is reflected in a sudden small initial jump in outward current (visible in middle record, Fig. 11C). Shortly after a sudden depolarization and the consequent outward current, the total membrane ionic current (I_i) begins to decrease, passes through zero, reaches a negative peak in about 1 millisecond, and then slowly changes back to a large maintained positive value. The contributions of Na^+ and K^+ to the total current at various times can be deduced from varying the amount of depolarization and the external Na^+ concentration. Cl^- current is nearly negligible and is neglected here.

Sodium Ion Current. The curves of membrane current versus time for different depolarizations differ in detail, but the sequence of events in each curve is nearly the same until $\Delta\mathcal{E}_m$ exceeds about 100 mV. (curves 4 and 5, Fig. 11B). The early inward current disappears at a particular $\Delta\mathcal{E}_m$ (about 95 mV.), and an early outward current hump appears at larger depolarizations (curve 5). From measurements of $[Na^+]_i$ and $[Na^+]_o$, $\mathcal{E}_{Na}$ can be calculated. Such analysis demonstrates that the early current hump changes sign when $\mathcal{E}_m = \mathcal{E}_{Na}$, or $\Delta\mathcal{E}_m = \mathcal{E}_{Na} - \mathcal{E}_S$. This finding, together with the finding that changes in the early current reversal voltage vary exactly with changes in $\mathcal{E}_{Na}$ (varied by altering $[Na^+]_o$), leads to the conclusion that early membrane current is carried by Na^+. *The crucial evidence is that this current reverses sign at exactly the $\mathcal{E}_m$ at which the driving force on Na^+ changes sign.*

Potassium Ion Current. The late, maintained outward current appears to be largely an outflow of K^+. Direct evidence for this conclusion has been obtained only recently because $[K^+]_i$ could not be changed rapidly until the development of a technique for internal perfusion. The membrane must be depolarized to

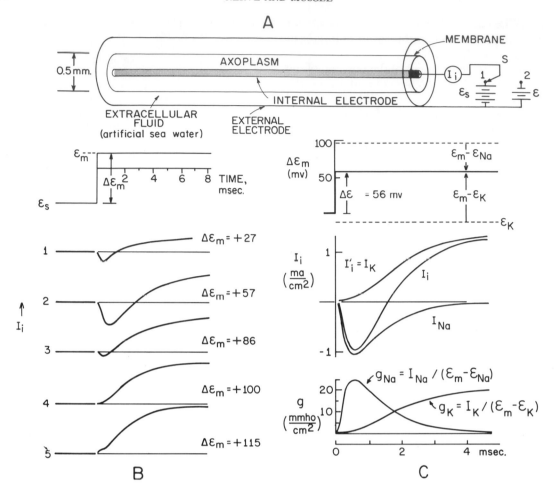

Fig. 11. Voltage clamping in squid giant axon.   *A,* Transmembrane voltage (ε_m) is held constant over a considerable length of membrane by connecting internal and external media to battery through long electrodes. ε_m can be changed suddenly from ε_s ($I_i = 0$) to any other value by flipping switch, S, to position 2. Total current (I_i) through membrane is measured as function of time by ammeter (cathode ray oscilloscope).

B, Transmembrane current flow as function of time after a sudden change in ε_m. Uppermost curve is ε_m as function of time. Curves 1 to 5 show membrane current which flows after membrane is depolarized, increasing amounts (in millivolts) shown at right. In curve 4, depolarization was near ε_{Na} and, in curve 5, ε_m was greater than ε_{Na}. Thus, for all but largest depolarizations, early component of current flows in direction opposite to that expected from change in ε_m and late current flows in the same direction. Time scale at top applies to all records in *B.*

C, Components of total membrane current and conductance. Top curve, ε_m as function of time; ε_{Na} and ε_K are indicated by dashed lines. Middle curve, total membrane ionic current (I_i) broken up into its two components, I_{Na} and I_K. (I_{Cl} is constant, small and neglected here.) Separation was made by reducing $[Na^+]_o$ to a value at which a depolarization of 56 mV. equaled ε_{Na}. Since $I_{Na} = 0$ under these conditions, total ion current (I_i') is equal to I_K as labeled. Bottom curve, g_{Na} and g_K as functions of time for the step change in ε_m shown in top curve. Conductances are same shape as current curves because they are calculated, as shown, by dividing ionic current by effective voltage driving ion (indicated in top curves). Time scale at bottom applies to all records in *C.* The g_{Na} versus ε_m curve of Figure 12 was obtained by measuring peak height of g_{Na} for different depolarizations. (Part *B* after Hodgkin and Huxley, *J. Physiol.*, 1952, *116*:449–472; part *C* after Hodgkin, *Proc. roy. Soc.*, 1958, *B148*:1–37.)

produce the delayed, prolonged outward current, and such depolarization tends to drive K^+ out of the cell. Tracer studies with radioactive K^+ have shown that membrane depolarization increases K^+ efflux sufficiently so that it could carry the late outward current.[14] As mentioned above, a high $[K^+]_i$ with almost any anion restores excitability in perfused axons; the repolarization phase of the action potential is, however, somewhat slower than in normal axons.[9]

Sodium and Potassium Ion Conductances.[10, 11] The total membrane current can be separated into Na^+ and K^+ currents by analyzing the manner in which changes in $[Na^+]_o$ affect the shapes of curves relating current to time. It has been found that changes in $[Na^+]_o$ change I_{Na} but not I_K. Thus, the change in I_i due to a change in $[Na^+]_o$ is carried by Na^+. Figure 11C shows the partition of I_i into Na^+ and K^+ currents for a depolarization of 56 mV. I_{Na} rises rapidly along an S-curve, reaches a peak in about 0.5 millisecond and then declines to near zero in another 2 milliseconds. I_K also rises along an S-curve, but much more slowly, and then levels off at a high maintained value in about 4 milliseconds. If Na^+ and K^+ components are correctly identified, the conductance of Na^+ (g_{Na}) and that of K^+ (g_K) as functions of time can be determined by dividing the ionic current by the driving force on that ion. The term g_K was explained and defined in Chapter 1 [see equation (6)]. Thus, $g_K = I_K/(\mathcal{E}_m - \mathcal{E}_K)$ and $g_{Na} = I_{Na}/(\mathcal{E}_m - \mathcal{E}_{Na})$. In voltage clamp, $\mathcal{E}_m$ is held constant, so g_{Na} and g_K have the same shape as I_{Na} and I_K, respectively (Fig. 11C).

Since the voltage clamp technique has made possible precise measurements of the changes in membrane conductance that accompany changes in membrane potential, the properties of the membrane which give rise to the action potential can be defined more clearly. The time course of the action potential, the recovery of excitability, the conduction speed, and the ion exchanges and resistance changes during activity of a squid giant axon can be accurately predicted. However, there is still no definite knowledge of the physiochemical and structural bases for the active changes in membrane conductance.

Voltage Dependence of Sodium and Potassium Ion Conductances. The upstroke of the action potential results from a depolarization-induced increase in P_{Na}. The dependence of g_{Na} (equivalent to P_{Na}) on voltage can be measured quantitatively from voltage clamp experiments by making a series of measurements of g_{Na} as a function of time for different clamping voltages and plotting the peak g_{Na} against these voltages. Figure 12 shows peak g_{Na} as a function of clamping voltage; e.g., the peak g_{Na} in Figure 11C is 25 mmho. per cm.[2] for a depolarization of 56 mV. The curve is S-shaped. Small depolarizations have little effect on g_{Na}, moderate depolarizations cause large increases in g_{Na}, and large depolarizations have little further effect. The final value of g_K depends on $\mathcal{E}_m$ in much the manner that peak g_{Na} does.

Activation and Inactivation of Sodium Ion Conductance. A suddenly applied, fixed depolarization produces a large increase in Na^+ conductance. However, despite the continuance of the depolarization, the conductance falls rapidly. This drop is called *inactivation* of Na^+ conductance. Inactivation begins as soon as the membrane is depolarized; the greater

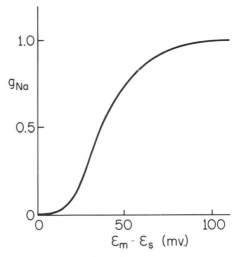

Fig. 12. Effects of sudden changes in membrane voltage on peak membrane sodium conductance (g_{Na}). Ordinate, ratio of peak g_{Na} for a given depolarization to the peak g_{Na} for a large (120 mV.) depolarization. Maximum value of curve is thus 1.0. The g_{Na} vs. time curve in Figure 11C has a peak value of 25 mmho. per cm.[2] for a depolarization of 56 mV., corresponding to a value of 0.8 on this curve. Resting g_{Na} is about 0.04 mmho. per cm.[2], not discernible on the scale used here. Abscissa, displacement, $\mathcal{E}_m - \mathcal{E}_S$, of membrane potential from its resting value. Threshold depolarization is at about 12 mV.—about the voltage where the curve is first noticeably different from zero. (After Hodgkin and Huxley, *J. Physiol.*, 1952, *116*:449–472).

the depolarization, the faster the rate of inactivation. Fast depolarization of the membrane has two effects which relate to Na^+ conductance: g_{Na} increases rapidly, and the *rate* at which inactivation of g_{Na} proceeds also increases immediately. Repolarization of the membrane has the reverse effects; any Na^+ conductance not already inactivated will decrease rapidly. Simultaneously the rate of inactivation decreases and the rate of activation increases. There is an important difference between the decrease in Na^+ conductance due to inactivation and that due to polarization of the membrane. Time is required to reactivate inactivated g_{Na}, whereas a decrease in g_{Na} brought about by polarization is immediately available; i.e., a depolarization following shortly after a repolarization will cause an increase in g_{Na}. Inactivation is the main cause of the refractory period (see below).

HYPOTHETICAL MODEL OF ACTIVATION–INACTIVATION OF SODIUM CONDUCTANCE. The activation–inactivation process is undoubtedly the most difficult and also the most crucial concept in understanding action potential generation and the refractory period. Hodgkin and Huxley[13] developed a hypothetical model which accurately describes the variations of g_{Na} with time and voltage in terms of two separate but interacting rate processes. They supposed that a membrane channel or pathway through which Na^+ can pass relatively easily is formed when three M molecules and one H molecule are situated at specific sites in the membrane (Fig. 13). Sodium conductance is assumed to be proportional to the number of these channels per cm.^{2} of membrane. The probability that an M or H molecule is at the proper site for channel formation depends on the transmembrane voltage. Such variation in probability can be explained by supposing that M and H molecules are charged or dipolar, so that the molecules' position or orientation is affected by membrane voltage.

At the resting potential, the kinetics of the M substance are such that most of these molecules are not at the proper site for channel formation. If M designates molecules at effective sites and M′ those at ineffective sites, then the reaction between the two, M = M′, is equilibrated far to the right. However, a large depolarization greatly increases the rate of movement of M′ molecules to the M position and greatly decreases the opposite reaction, the equilibrium

of the M = M′ now being far to the left. The time required for equilibration is well under 1 millisecond but depends on the final voltage. Three M molecules must be in place to form a channel; only one need be absent to close the channel. Thus on sudden depolarization, the number of channels having three M molecules in place increases slowly at first and then more rapidly (third order kinetics); the rise in g_{Na} is S-shaped (Fig. 11C, rising phase of g_{Na} curve). Repolarization closes the channels rapidly because only one M need move out of place.

The kinetics of the H substance are the same as those of the M substance except that the variation of the forward and backward rate constants with voltage is reversed; the reaction H = H′ is equilibrated far to the left at the resting potential; most of the H are in position. The equilibration rate of the H reaction is about 10 times slower than for M, several milliseconds being required (Fig. 11C, falling phase of g_{Na} curve). The fraction of H molecules at effective sites is called the *activation* of g_{Na}. Under the circumstances of the voltage clamp experiments, the resting potential was somewhat depressed and the resting activation was about 0.6. Maintained hyperpolarization increases activation to 1.0 (all H form) and it is decreased to zero (all H′ form) by maintained depolarization.

A sudden depolarization thus has two effects on sodium conductance: M molecules move rapidly into effective sites and establish Na^+ channels at sites where H molecules are in position; hence g_{Na} rises rapidly. Even as M molecules are moving into position, H molecules are moving out but at a much slower rate. Thus g_{Na} rises to a peak as M molecules align with H molecules to form channels and then falls over a period of several milliseconds as the H molecules move away from the effective sites (Fig. 11C, g_{Na} curve). If the membrane is repolarized after inactivation is completed, there would be little change in the already low g_{Na} but M molecules would move out of place rapidly and H molecules would move into place slowly. Thereafter, another depolarization would produce an increase in g_{Na} proportional to the fraction of H molecules that had moved into place during the polarized state. This consideration suggests the experimental method actually used by Hodgkin and Huxley[12] to measure the kinetics of the activation–inactivation process—a two-step or pulse experiment

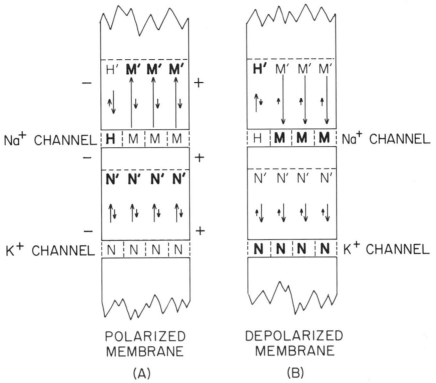

Fig. 13. Hypothetical scheme of Na+ and K+ conductance kinetics. A channel or pathway through which sodium ions can pass easily is formed if and only if 3 M molecules and 1 H molecule are in proper positions or sites (Na+ channel). Similarly, a K+ channel is formed when 4 N molecules are in position. For all these substances, there is an equilibrium distribution of molecules between effective and ineffective sites or positions. Ineffective sites (primed letters) are shown diagrammatically vertically above effective sites. The arrows between effective and ineffective sites represent the rates of the two one-way reactions; heavy letters represent equilibrium positions of most molecules.

A, Polarized membrane. Transmembrane potential near resting value. Kinetics of M are such that, in reaction M = M', equilibrium is far to right (above in figure, heavy letters) and, in II — H' reaction, equilibrium is far to left (below, heavy H); Na+ channels are closed because most M's are out of position. Shorter arrows indicate that H reactions are about ten times slower than M reactions. M reactions are completed in a few tenths of a millisecond; H reactions require several milliseconds. At rest, K+ channels are closed because equilibrium of N = N' is far right (above, heavy letters). Reaction rates are about the same as for H but equilibrium is far in opposite direction.

B, Depolarized membrane. Depolarization greatly changes the rate constants of all the reactions; all equilibria are shifted to the opposite side as shown by arrows. The result is that immediately after a depolarization, M molecules move rapidly to M positions and open Na+ channels until H molecules have moved out of position (inactivation). At about the same time, N's move into position and open K+ channels which remain open for duration of depolarization.

analogous to the conditioning–testing stimulus technique previously described.

Kinetics of Potassium Conductance Changes. The kinetics of g_K are much the same as those for M, only about ten times slower. A potassium channel is formed when four N molecules are at four effective sites simultaneously (Fig. 13). At rest the reaction M = M' is equilibrated far right (top in Fig. 13*A*); depolarization shifts the equilibrium point far to the left (bottom). Thus depolariza-

tion produces an S-shaped increase in g_K Fig. 11*C*) but much slower than that of g_{Na}. Repolarization produces an uninflected, rapid fall to low levels.

PREDICTION OF EVENTS OF ACTION POTENTIAL FROM VOLTAGE CLAMP DATA[2, 3, 13, 19]

Hodgkin and Huxley[13] expressed their volt-

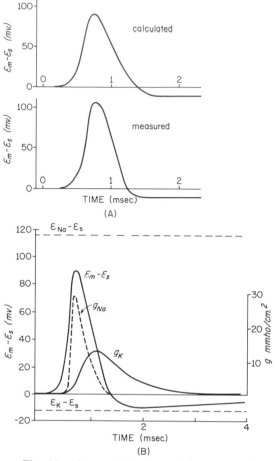

Fig. 14. *A, top,* Action potential calculated from measurements on voltage clamped axon. Calculated conduction speed, 18.8 meters per second. *Bottom,* Propagated action potential in an axon. Measured conduction speed 21.2 meters per second. Calculated and measured action potentials differ somewhat, but both show same general features. (After Hodgkin and Huxley, *J. Physiol.*, 1952, *117*:500–544.) *B,* Calculated time courses of membrane voltage ($\varepsilon_m - \varepsilon_s$), sodium conductance ($g_{Na}$) and potassium conductance (g_K) in squid giant axon. Note time relationships between upstroke of action potential and g_{Na} and between g_K and downstroke and after hyperpolarization. (After Hodgkin, *Proc. roy. Soc.*, 1958, *B148*:1–37.)

age clamp data from squid giant axons in mathematical form. The model described above was used in formulating their equations. The solutions of these equations were found to predict accurately the size and shape of the action potential, the refractory period, the existence and size of threshold, conduction speed and other properties of the nerve impulse. The analysis permitted calculation of the time course of the changes in Na+ and K+ conductances during the action potential and the

degree of inactivation of g_{Na}, factors which are not directly measurable but are the "essence" of the impulse. These calculations are also the basis of the statements made above concerning the sequence of events during the action potential. Recently, Frankenhaeuser and Huxley[3] have shown that the same type of analysis accurately predicts the excitable properties of frog myelinated nerve fibers. This finding greatly extends the generality of the Hodgkin–Huxley analysis.

Depolarization. Calculated conductance and voltage changes during the impulse are shown in Figure 14. The experimentally measured action potential (Fig. 14*A*, bottom) is noticeably but not significantly different from the calculated one (top). The differences are mainly in the falling phase. The regenerative sequence of changes in Na+ conductance and membrane voltage which generate the rising phase of the action potential has already been adequately described (Hodgkin cycle) and will not be further considered. Note, however, that g_{Na} does not start to rise rapidly until the membrane has been considerably depolarized. This initial depolarization is due to local current flow to the active region; g_{Na} rises rapidly at threshold depolarization. It can be seen from Figure 14*B* that g_{Na} reaches its peak slightly before the voltage does. Also note that g_{Na} has fallen to about one-sixth of its peak value at a time when repolarization is only half completed. This indicates, and direct calculation confirms, that the major factor acting to decrease Na+ conductance at this time is inactivation, not repolarization.

The calculated conduction speed of the top action potential in Figure 14*A* is 18.8 meters per second; the measured value of a representative axon is 21.2 meters per second. This is remarkably good agreement considering the uncertainties in the measurements and calculations. This accurate prediction of a propagating response is strong evidence for the general validity of the Hodgkin–Huxley analysis.

Repolarization. The regenerative nature of the depolarization process insures that it proceeds at the fastest possible rate; i.e., the greater the depolarization, the faster the rate of depolarization until the saturation point is reached. Repolarization, on the other hand, is a *de*generative process; the greater the degree of repolarization, the more slowly it proceeds. The delayed increase in K+ conductance (Fig. 14*B*) is the membrane change responsible for rapid repolarization. If g_K did not increase during activity, nearly complete repolarization would still occur because of the inactivation of Na^+ conductance. However, in such a case the rate of depolarization would be much slower, little faster than the changes in a passive membrane due to its cable properties.

The sequence of events in repolarization is as follows. At the peak of depolarization g_{Na} is falling because of inactivation, and g_K is beginning to increase (Fig. 14B). The resulting increase in K^+ efflux and decrease in Na^+ influx bring about repolarization. This voltage change in turn hastens the decrease in g_{Na} and, after a delay, g_K. As a consequence, g_K is still above normal when repolarization is complete, and the membrane hyperpolarizes, i.e., the potential goes nearer to $\mathcal{E}_K$ than the resting potential is. Thereafter, g_K and $\mathcal{E}_m$ fall slowly back to their resting values.

The conductance changes which occur during propagation can be compactly summarized on the basis of the hypothetical scheme described above (Table 1). This scheme also aids in understanding the basis of the refractory period.

Threshold. Threshold is one of three values of $\mathcal{E}_m$ at which the inward Na^+ current just equals the outward K^+ and Cl^- currents (Cl^- influx). The other two values of $\mathcal{E}_m$ are the resting potential and the peak of the action potential. Thus, as the membrane is depolarized by current outflow, P_{Na} (or g_{Na}) increases (Fig. 12) and the inflow of Na^+ ions increases. This increase more than compensates for the slightly decreased electrochemical gradient of Na^+. The net K^+ and Cl^- fluxes increase because the reduction of $\mathcal{E}_m$ has increased the electrochemical gradients driving these ions. If the net movement of ionic charges through the membrane is zero (i.e., if net Na^+ influx equals net

K^+ efflux plus net Cl^- influx), the membrane voltage is steady. The potential will stay constant only until inactivation of P_{Na} reduces Na^+ influx. The potential will then begin to fall, and the fall in potential will in turn further reduce P_{Na}. The potential in this case follows a path similar to curve $3a$, Figure 5B. On the other hand, if the applied depolarizing current is made slightly larger or the threshold of the fiber has fallen slightly owing to random fluctuations, the net Na^+ influx through the membrane slightly exceeds the sum of the net K^+ efflux and the net Cl^- influx, so that there is a net movement of positive ions into the fiber and the action potential upstroke ensues via the Hodgkin cycle: A decrease in membrane voltage acts to increase P_{Na}; this increase, in turn, causes additional depolarization.

Refractory Period. Since inactivation of g_{Na} is almost complete at the end of the action potential, a depolarizing current applied at this time will not cause much increase in g_{Na}. Therefore, the fiber is refractory (inexcitable); a stimulating current, no matter how strong, cannot initiate a regenerative response. A little later, after some activation has occurred, a depolarizing current will cause a larger increase in g_{Na}, and an action potential smaller than normal may be generated. The threshold current will be above normal because the available g_{Na} is low and also because g_K is still above normal. Inactivated Na^+ conductance means that excitability is low (threshold high), because greater depolarization is needed to increase g_{Na} enough to make net Na^+ inflow exceed net K^+ outflow. A raised g_K means that more current is required to produce a given depolarization; hence this factor decreases excitability also. Taken together, these two effects, which disappear in a few milliseconds, account for both the absolute and the relatively refractory periods.

TABLE 1. *Sodium and Potassium Conductance Channel Patterns During the Action Potential*

RESTING MEMBRANE		RISING PHASE		REPOLARIZATION		AFTER HYPERPOLARIZATION	
Na^+ Channels	K^+ Channels	Na^+ Channels	K^+ Channels	Na^+ Channels	K^+ Channels	Na^+ Channels	K^+ Channels
—	—	M	—	M	N	—	N
—	—	M	—	M	N	—	N
—	—	M	—	M	N	—	N
H	—	H	—	—	N	—	N

Ion channels are open if a column is filled with letters. See legend to Figure 13 for meanings of terms.

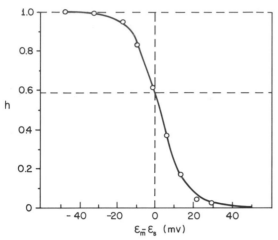

Fig. 15. Steady-state activation of sodium conductance as a function of transmembrane potential. Ordinate, fraction (h) of H molecules at effective sites (see Fig. 13); abscissa, difference between transmembrane potential ($\mathcal{E}_m$) and the resting potential ($\mathcal{E}_s$). A sudden depolarization causes a transient increase in g_{Na} but h steadily declines to a lower steady-state value. Similarly, hyperpolarization increases steady-state value of h. Note that small changes in $\mathcal{E}_s$ would have a large effect on h: A hyperpolarization of 20 millivolts increases h to nearly 1.0 (the reaction rates of H = H' are changed so that equilibrium is far to the left). Similarly, a depolarization of 20 millivolts reduces h to nearly 0 and the reaction H = H' equilibrates far to the right. Actual g_{Na} at any time is determined by both the H and M systems; the fraction of H's in position determines the size of the increase in g_{Na} following a sudden depolarization.

Accommodation and Block. A brief subthreshold stimulus applied to a nerve fiber increases excitability (lowers threshold) in the region of application which can be detected by the response to a second stimulus delivered to the same or a nearby point. In contrast, a prolonged subthreshold stimulus may either increase or decrease excitability. The change in excitability depends on the relative effect of the depolarizing current on $\mathcal{E}_m$, and on the effect of the changes in $\mathcal{E}_m$ on the steady state inactivation of g_{Na}. The curve relating activation to $\mathcal{E}_m$ is a very steep S-shaped curve as shown in Figure 15; a depolarization reduces the g_{Na} available. If, as in the squid giant axon, the resting potential is such that an appreciable amount of g_{Na} is always inactivated (dashed lines, Fig. 15), the depolarization produced by a prolonged subthreshold stimulus may reduce g_{Na} to such low levels that the stimulus required to initiate an impulse must be

stronger than normal; i.e., the reduction in g_{Na} has increased the threshold voltage (toward zero) more than the current has reduced actual membrane voltage. This is quite possible in view of the steepness of the curve in Figure 15. An additional factor may be the depolarization-induced increase in g_K, which makes an applied current less effective in changing $\mathcal{E}_m$. If a prolonged subthreshold depolarization reduces the excitability of a nerve, or increases it less than expected, the nerve is said to have *accommodated* to the stimulus. The process of *accommodation* is evidently closely related to the g_{Na} activation–inactivation process.[2]

Conduction can be blocked at a point on a nerve fiber by a strong, slowly rising, depolarizing current. If the depolarizing current increases slowly enough, inactivation occurs concomitantly. As a result, g_{Na} will not increase sufficiently to reverse the membrane current. Similarly, a suddenly applied suprathreshold current may block conduction after first initiating one or more impulses; the block occurs when inactivation has proceeded far enough. The blockage of impulse generation by depolarizing current occurs only in the region of the stimulating cathode. Impulses will propagate on either side of the blocked region, but not through it. This method of blocking impulse conduction is often called *cathodal block*. Better terms are *depolarization block* or *inactivation block*.

Depolarization block can be produced in many ways other than by applying current. Since a sufficient increase in $[K^+]_o$, anoxia and injury all depolarize the membrane, they all block impulse conduction. An expected characteristic of depolarization block is that stimuli not strong enough to cause block increase the excitability. Anoxia probably blocks indirectly by reducing the activity of the Na^+–K^+ pump, so that K^+ ions lost from cells accumulate in the extracellular fluid. An injury such as crushing blocks by destroying the structure of the membrane; its selective permeability properties are lost and depolarization occurs. At the moment of the crush, a number of impulses are discharged before inactivation is completed in adjacent undamaged, depolarized regions. Local anesthetics block conduction in nerve by increasing inactivation without altering membrane voltage.[25] Depolarization block, no matter how induced, is relieved by a hyperpolarizing current simply because it increases the absolute value of $\mathcal{E}_m$ and activates g_{Na}.

A sufficient hyperpolarization of the membrane can also block conduction in a nerve. Block occurs if ε_m is made so large that local circuit flow from the hyperpolarized region into an approaching active region is insufficient to depolarize the hyperpolarized region to threshold. This phenomenon is called *anodal* or, better, *hyperpolarization block*.

Ion Exchange During Activity.[13, 21] It has been stressed that the rising phase of the action potential is brought about by a sudden, large influx of Na^+ ions and repolarization by an efflux of K^+ ions. It might be supposed that these "large" fluxes involve the movement of enough ions to change greatly the internal concentrations of Na^+ and K^+. Actually, the concentration changes are very small, the reason being that, although the fluxes are high, they flow only for a short time, and, chemically speaking, the amount of ions necessary to charge the membrane is small. The minimum net influx of Na^+ required during activity is simply the amount of charge necessary to change the voltage across the membrane capacitor roughly from ε_K to ε_{Na}. A similar net efflux of K^+ suffices to recharge the membrane.

The amount of charge on a capacitor is the product of its capacity and the voltage across it. Such a calculation for squid giant axon shows that the minimum Na^+ entry (or K^+ exit) during one impulse is 1.6 picamols per cm.[2] (pM. $= 10^{-12}$ M.) of membrane. A crucial test of the $Na^+–K^+$ theory of the action potential is to measure net fluxes of Na^+ and K^+ during an impulse by means of radioactive Na^+ and K^+. These measured net fluxes must be greater than the minimum required because, as can be seen from Figure 14*B*, there must be considerable simultaneous inflow of Na^+ and outflow of K^+ during the action potential; such an ion exchange does not affect the charge on the membrane. The measured net Na^+ influx in the squid giant axon is about 4.0 pM. and the net K^+ efflux about 3.0 pM per cm.[2]-impulse.[21] These values are greater than the minimum and about what is predicted by the equations.[13]

The change in internal concentrations during an impulse depends not only on the net entry or loss of the ion but also on the volume of axoplasm in which the extra ions distribute themselves. The bigger the fiber, the smaller the concentration change per impulse. For example, in a squid axon 500 μ in diameter, a net Na^+ entry of 3 pM. per cm.[2]-impulse raises the internal concentration by only 1.5 $\times$ 10^{-10} M. per cm.[3] The internal concentration of Na^+ in the squid is about 50 μM. per cm.[3], some 300,000 times greater. However, under the same conditions, the increase in internal Na^+ concentration for a 50 μ fiber would be ten times as great. Nevertheless, the conduction of 30,000 impulses in such a fiber would only double internal Na^+ concentration, even if the Na^+ pump were inoperative. Thus in ordinary sized axons, the increase in $[Na^+]_i$ and decrease in $[K^+]_i$ during one impulse is very small. Some mammalian unmedullated axons are only 0.1 μ in diameter and rough calculation shows that one impulse will increase internal Na^+ concentration by 10 per cent. Hence, the Na^+ pumping rate must be quickly responsive to activity. The large post-spike hyperpolarization in these fibers is probably associated with increased active Na^+ extrusion (see Chap. 3).

Nerve fibers conduct impulses up to 100 times per second in normal bodily function. At rest, the amount of Na^+ extruded by the Na^+ pump in one second is about the same as the net entry of Na^+ during one impulse. Therefore, during impulse conduction at 100 per second Na^+ entry is 100 times greater than the resting entry. Since, in order to maintain excitability, $[Na^+]_i$ must be kept at a low and $[K^+]_i$ at a high value, the rate of Na^+ pumping must increase as much as 100 times during maintained activity. The function of nerve fibers is to conduct impulses, so the main energy production of nerve likely is used to transport sodium.

REFERENCES

1. Cole, K. S. and Moore, J. W. *Biophys. J.*, 1960, *1*:1–14.
2. Frankenhaeuser, B. and Vallbo, A. B. *Acta physiol. scand.* 1965, *63*:1–20.
3. Frankenhaeuser, B. and Huxley, A. F. *J. Physiol.*, 1964, *171*:302–315.
4. Hodgkin, A. L. *J. Physiol.*, 1937, *90*:183–210.
5. Hodgkin, A. L. *Biol. Rev.*, 1951, *26*:339–409.
6. Hodgkin, A. L. *J. Physiol.*, 1954, *125*:221–224.
7. Hodgkin, A. L. *Proc. roy. Soc.*, 1958, *B148*:1–37.
8. Hodgkin, A. L. *Science*, 1964, *145*:1148–1154.
9. Hodgkin, A. L. *The conduction of the nervous impulse.* Springfield, Ill., Charles C Thomas, 1964.
10. Hodgkin, A. L. and Huxley, A. F. *J. Physiol.*, 1952, *116*: 449–472.
11. Hodgkin, A. L. and Huxley, A. F. *J. Physiol.*, 1952, *116*: 473–496.
12. Hodgkin, A. L. and Huxley, A. F. *J. Physiol.*, 1952, *116*: 497–506.

13. HODGKIN, A. L. and HUXLEY, A. F. *J. Physiol.*, 1952, *117*: 500–544.
14. HODGKIN, A. L. and HUXLEY, A. F. *J. Physiol.*, 1953, *121*: 403–414.
15. HODGKIN, A. L., HUXLEY, A. F. and KATZ, B. *J. Physiol.*, 1952, *116*:424–448.
16. HODGKIN, A. L. and KATZ, B. *J. Physiol.*, 1949, *108*:37–77.
17. HODGKIN, A. L. and RUSHTON, W. A. H. *Proc. roy. Soc.*, 1946, *B133*:444–479.
18. HODLER, J., STAMPFLI, R. and TASAKI, I. *Amer. J. Physiol.*, 1952, *170*:375–389.
19. HUXLEY, A. F. *Science*, 1964, *145*:1154–1159.
20. HUXLEY, A. F. and STAMPFLI, R. J. *Arch. Sci. Physiol.*, 1949, *3*:435–448

21. KEYNES, R. D. *J. Physiol.*, 1951, *114*:119–150.
22. MOORE, J. W. and COLE, K. S. In: *Physical techniques in biological research*, Volume 6: *Electrophysiological methods*, part B, W. L. Nastuk, ed. New York, Academic Press, 1964.
23. NACHMANSOHN, D. *Chemical and molecular basis of nerve activity*. New York, Academic Press, 1959.
24. TASAKI, I. Chap. 3 in *Handbook of physiology. Section 1: Neurophysiology*, vol. 1, J. Field, ed. Washington, D.C., American Physiological Society, 1959.
25. TAYLOR, R. E. *Amer. J. Physiol.*, 1959, *196*:1071–1078.
26. WOODBURY, J. W. Chap. 11 in *Handbook of physiology. Section 2: Circulation*, vol. 1, W. F. Hamilton and P. Dow, eds. Washington, D.C., American Physiological Society, 1962.

CHAPTER 2 APPENDIX

By ALBERT M. GORDON and J. WALTER WOODBURY

ELECTROSTATICS

Charge. Electric charge, like mass, is a fundamental property of matter. There are two kinds of charge, arbitrarily designated as positive ($+$) (protons) and negative ($-$) (electrons). Like electric charges repel and unlike charges attract each other. Since each atom contains one or more electrons and an equal number of protons, the total number of charges in a macroscopic object is extremely large, but there is little or no net charge. The strong mutual attraction of unlike charges is sufficient to insure electroneutrality in any object unless other forces (e.g., mechanical or chemical) act to separate the charges and keep them separated. The common unit of electric charge is the *coulomb*. A coulomb is the charge of 6.25×10^{18} electrons. The charge on an electron is thus 1.6×10^{-19} coulombs. The force between charges is most easily considered in a system in which all the charges are held in a fixed position in vacuum (electrostatics). Nonelectrical forces are required to keep the charges separated and static.

Electric Field Intensity. The magnitude of the force (F) of attraction or repulsion between two point charges (q_1 and q_2) in a vacuum is given by Coulomb's law:

$$F = K(q_1 q_2 / r^2)$$

where K is a constant determined by the units chosen and r is the distance between the two point charges. If q is in coulombs, r is in meters, and F in newtons (1 kg.-m. per second^2), $K = 9 \times 10^9$ joule-meter per coulomb^2. The force is a vector* and is in the direction of the line joining the two charges. Repulsion is defined as a positive force, attraction as a negative force.

The *electric field intensity* (**E**) at a point is defined as the electric force that would be exerted on a unit positive charge placed at that point (Fig. 16). In other words, the electric field is the electric force per unit charge (**E** = **F**/q). **E**, like **F**, is a vector. The existence of an unchanging electric field at any point in space means that electric charges of opposite sign have been separated. These separated charges attract each other and also either attract or repel any other charge brought into the neighborhood. The electric field at any point is a convenient way of specifying the electric forces acting in a region. A more convenient way to describe the field is to calculate the electric potential, a scalar quantity.

Electric Potential, Voltage. Because of the force of attraction between + and − charges, work must be done to separate them. Work is done when a force acts through a distance and is defined as the product of force and distance in the direction of the force. Since the work done depends only on the size of the force and the distance moved, work is a scalar.

The *potential* or *voltage difference* between two points is defined as the amount of work, done against electrical forces, required to carry a unit positive charge (1 coulomb) between the two points. Since in electrostatics the charge is fixed and the exploring charge is halted at the two end points, A and B, the potential difference is the difference in potential energy per unit charge between the two points. The electrical *potential* or *voltage* ($\mathcal{E}_p$) at a point (P) is defined as the work done in bringing a unit positive charge to that point from a large distance away, i.e., the potential difference between that point and one at a large distance.

The work done in moving an exploring charge (q_e) a distance, ds, (path P_2, Fig. 16) in the electric field is dW = − Eq_e (cos θds). To obtain the potential difference between two points ($\mathcal{E}_{AB}$, Fig. 16), the work, dW, must be summed for all ds distances along any path between A and B with q = +1. It is important to note that since the electric field is directed out radially from the charge +q and work is done only when a charge is moved in the direction of the field, work is done only when motion is in a radial direction; i.e., cos θds = dr. Since any small motion (see path P_1) can be broken up into a radial component (cos θ = −1 or 1, depending on whether ds is toward or away from +q) and a circumferential component (cos θ = 0), along the arc of a circle centered at +q,

the total work along any path is the work in moving the unit + charge radially from r_B to r_A. Thus, the work done in moving along path P_1 is the same as that along path P_2 or P_3. Therefore, because work done on a charge is independent of path, the concept of potential is useful. If r_A (Fig. 16) is less than r_B, work must be done to move a positive charge from B to A; the potential difference is positive. If work is done by the charge (this would happen if +q were replaced by a negative charge), the potential difference is negative.

In the example of Figure 16, the potential between A and B ($\mathcal{E}_{AB}$) is most easily calculated along BA'A. The force (E) on a unit + charge at any distance (r) from q is E = K(q/r^2). The work done (d$\mathcal{E}$) to move the unit + charge a radial distance (−dr) is d$\mathcal{E}$ = − Edr. The negative sign is used because r is measured outward from q and because potential is defined as increasing when a + charge is moved toward another + charge. The electric field is directed radially in this case. The total work done on the charge as it moves from B to A is shown in the following equation:

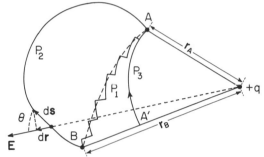

Fig. 16. Voltage and voltage difference in the neighborhood of a fixed charge of +q coulombs. E is the force, due to charge +q, on a charge of +1 coulomb at any point. E is directed radially outward, and F = K(q/r^2); distance from +q to any point is r; dr is a small movement in a radial direction away from +q. Distance traveled by exploratory +1 charge along any path between B and A (P_1, P_2, P_3) is s; ds is a small movement along any path. Arrows on path P_2 illustrate the relationship between force, displacement and work. Work done in displacing a charge, q, a distance, ds, in the electric field, E, is by definition dW = − qE cos θ ds, where qE is the size of the force on the charge and θ is the angle between the direction of **ds** and **E**. Cos θ ds gives the projection of ds along the direction of E. Since cos θ ds = dr, all the work is done in moving in a radial direction. Voltage at point B ($\mathcal{E}_B$) is work required to bring +1 charge from a large distance up to point B; $\mathcal{E}_B$ = Kq/r_B. Voltage difference ($\mathcal{E}_{AB}$) between A and B is work required to carry +1 charge from B to A; $\mathcal{E}_{AB}$ = $\mathcal{E}_A$ − $\mathcal{E}_B$. Since work is done only when the +1 moves in a radial direction, the work to go from B to A is the same no matter what path (P_1, P_2, P_3, etc.) is taken. Along path P_2 (BA'A) all the work is done along BA' (radial); no work is done along A'A. So $\mathcal{E}_{AB}$ depends only on r_A and r_B; $\mathcal{E}_{AB}$ = Kq(1/r_A − 1/r_B).

---

* A vector has both magnitude and direction, e.g., force, velocity and displacement (distance and direction). A scalar has magnitude only (i.e., charge, concentration, volume, time, speed). Bold-faced type will be used to represent vectors. Regular type will be used to represent scalars and magnitudes of vectors. The magnitude of a force is designated F, vector force **F**. The velocity of an object is represented by **v**, its speed (magnitude of the velocity) by v.

$$\mathcal{E}_{AB} = \int_{r_B}^{r_A} - E dr = \int_{r_B}^{r_A} - K\frac{q}{r^2}dr = Kq\left(\frac{1}{r_A} - \frac{1}{r_B}\right)$$

The potential at point A is obtained by taking $r_B = \infty$. Since $1/\infty = 0$, $\mathcal{E}_A = Kq/r_A$. Similarly, $\mathcal{E}_B = Kq/r_B$;

thus, $\mathcal{E}_{AB} = Kq\left(\dfrac{1}{r_A} - \dfrac{1}{r_B}\right) = \mathcal{E}_A - \mathcal{E}_B$, the same as

that computed above from the work done in moving a unit + charge from A to B along path P_3. This additive property of the potential, a scalar quantity, is the source of its usefulness; if $\mathcal{E}_A$ and $\mathcal{E}_B$ are known, $\mathcal{E}_{AB}$ may be computed directly without having to integrate as has been done above. For example, $K = 9 \times 10^9$ joule-meter per coulomb^2, and if $q = 10^{-12}$ coulombs (1 picocoulomb), $r_A = 0.1$ m., and $r_B = 1$ m., then $\mathcal{E}_A = (9 \times 10^9 \times 10^{-12})/0.1 = 0.09$ joules per coulomb $= 0.09$ V. and $\mathcal{E}_{AB} = 9 \times 10^9 \times 10^{-12} [(1/0.1) - (1/1)] = 9 \times 10^{-3} (10 - 1) = 0.081$ V. In words, 0.09 joules of work must be done on a +1 coulomb charge to carry it from a large distance to 0.1 m. away from a charge of 10^{-12} coulombs.

Voltage gradient. The electric field is often referred to as the (negative) voltage gradient (**grad** $\mathcal{E}$)—the rate at which voltage changes with distance in the direction in which the voltage is changing most rapidly. This reverse definition of electric field in terms of voltage follows from the definition of voltage as the potential energy per unit charge and the definition of a gradient. This potential energy is derived from the work done on the charge in order to move it against the electric field. Thus, the rate of change of work (energy) with distance is the force, and the rate of change of voltage with distance is the electric field.

By definition $d\mathcal{E} = -E \cos\theta ds$ where, as before, θ is the angle between the direction of **ds** and **E.** If the electric field is due to a point charge as in Figure 16, $d\mathcal{E} = -Edr$; therefore, $E = -(d\mathcal{E}/dr) = -$**grad** $\mathcal{E}$, the components in other directions being zero. In general, $E = -$**grad** $\mathcal{E}$, where **grad** has the direction of the maximum rate of voltage change.

Because of this relation, the electric field is referred to as the negative of the voltage gradient and is the electric force on a unit positive charge, just as $-$**grad** [S] is the diffusional force per unit volume.

Capacitors. *Conductors.* A *conductor* is a substance in which charges are free to move. Metals are good conductors because their outer shell electrons are loosely bound to the nuclei. Salt solutions are also good conductors because their solute particles are charged (ionized) and can move freely in the solvent. Because charges can move freely in a conductor, no electric field can exist inside it when charges are not moving. If the conductor contained a field, it would exert forces on the free charges, and some of them would move into positions on the surface of the conductor such that the field would be reduced to zero. Since the field must be zero in a conductor, all points in and on it must be at the same potential, for no electric work is required to move a charge through a region where **E** is zero.

The potential of an isolated conductor is not necessarily zero. For example, if some excess charges, all positive or all negative, are put on an isolated conductor, they will exert a force on any charge outside the conductor, and work will be required to bring a +1 charge from infinity. The excess charges must be on the surface of the conductor in order to cancel **E** everywhere in the interior. More simply, the excess charges repel each other and so distribute themselves as widely as possible on the surface.

Insulators. An *insulator* is any region in which there are no free charges, e.g., a vacuum. In an insulating material called a *dielectric,* all electrons are tightly bound to their nuclei and cannot migrate under the influence of an external electric field. The charges in a dielectric are not rigidly fixed, so they separate slightly in an external field. This charge separation in the dielectric is usually proportional to **E** and is such as to reduce **E**. However, the force on an exploring charge in a dielectric varies in the same way as the force on a charge *in vacuo*, but the forces in a dielectric are reduced by a factor $1/\kappa$. The denominator κ is the *dielectric constant*. Its value depends on the nature of the material; for example, κ is 5 to 10 for most oils. The cell membrane is a dielectric. Its dielectric constant is unknown, but since the membrane contains a high proportion of lipids κ is likely 5 to 10. This figure is also obtained from electrical measurements of membrane capacity and electron-microscopic estimates of membrane thickness (see problem 5 below).

Capacity. In a static situation, the existence of a potential difference between two points (A and B) means that + and − charges have been separated. This condition follows from the definition of $\mathcal{E}_{AB}$ as the work done against *electric* forces in carrying a +1 charge from B to A and because there are no electric forces in a region unless charges are separated there. The greater the amount of charge separated, the greater the electric field and the greater is $\mathcal{E}_{AB}$. In particular, if + charges are put on an insulated fixed conductor (A) and an equal number of − charges are put on a second fixed conductor (B), the potential difference between the two conductors is directly proportional to the amount of charge on either conductor. Any arrangement of two conductors, A and B, separated by an insulator is called a *capacitor* or *condenser.* The proportionality constant relating charge to voltage is called the *capacity* or *capacitance* (C) of a capacitor and is given by the equation $C = q/\mathcal{E}_{AB}$, where q is the total amount of charge on either conductor.

The capacity of a capacitor depends on the geometry of the conductors (i.e., on their spatial extent and separation) and on the dielectric constant of the insulating material. These dependencies arise because the force between two charged conductors is determined by the distance separating them and because the relative distribution of the charges on the surface of an insulated conductor is the same no matter how much charge there is on the conductor. The less the work per unit charge required to place a fixed amount of charge on a capacitor, the higher its capacity. Hence, the closer two conductors are together, the higher the capacity between them, for less work is required to move a unit charge through the shorter distance. In addition, the higher the dielectric constant of the insulating material, the larger the capacity. This is reasonable since both the electric field in the insulator and therefore the work done in moving a charge between the conductors decrease with increasing dielectric constant. It follows, then, that the capacity between two closely spaced parallel sheets or plates of metal separated by an insulator is high. Since the electric field in the region between the plates depends only on the number of charges per unit area (charge density), increasing the area of the plates permits the addition of charges to the plates without an increase in the electric field between them. Therefore, the greater the surface area of the plates, the greater the capacity between them. The opposite charges on the plates of a capacitor attract each other, and so they must be on the inner surfaces of the conductors. The charges are prevented from recombining by the insulator separating the conductors. However, if the insulation is not perfect—if some charge can move through the insulator—charges placed on the conductors will slowly leak off.

The unit of capacity is the farad (f.). A capacitor has a capacity of 1 f. if 1 coulomb of charge taken from one plate and placed on the other produces a potential difference of 1 V. between the plates. In terms of physical size, a 1 f. capacitor is large;* the capacitors commonly encountered have capacities of about 1 microfarad (1 μf. = 10^{-6} f.).

Problems. The following problems deal with the electrical membrane of the squid giant axon. Assume that the membrane thickness is 75 Å. = 7.5×10^{-9} meters, capacity is 1 μf. per cm.^{2} = 10^{-2} f. per meter^2 and transmembrane potential difference is 75 mV. = 7.5×10^{-2} V. (inside negative).

1. Assuming that the electric field is uniform and constant inside the membrane, what is the magnitude and direction of the field in the membrane?

Ans. $\mathbf{E} = -\mathbf{grad}\ \mathcal{E}$. Since the membrane is very thin, it is equivalent to a parallel plate condenser with the plates separated by 7.5×10^{-9} meters. In the space between the plates, $\mathbf{E}$ is constant and perpendicular to them. The potential varies linearly with distance between the plates; thus $-\mathbf{grad}\ \mathcal{E} = -d\mathcal{E}/dx = \mathcal{E}/\delta$, where δ = membrane thickness. Thus, $\mathbf{E} = 7.5 \times 10^{-2}$ V./7.5×10^{-9} meters = 10^7 V. per meter (10 million V. per meter). The direction of $\mathbf{E}$ is inward through the membrane, perpendicular to the two boundaries.

2. What is the force on a sodium ion in the membrane due to the electric field computed above? e = 1.6×10^{-19} coulombs (electronic charge).

Ans. 1.6×10^{-12} newtons.

3. How much charge per unit area separated by the membrane is due to the resting potential? Calculate answer in coulombs per meter^2 and mols of univalent ion per cm.^{2}

Ans. 7.5×10^{-4} coulombs per meter^2, 7.8×10^{-13} mols per cm.^{2}

4. An axon is 100 μ in diameter and 10 cm. long. Sodium ions are actively transported out of this axon at the rate of 3×10^{-11} mols per cm.^{2} per second. How much work must be done per hour by the active transport mechanism against the electrical forces only tending to hold the sodium ions in the cell? (The resting potential is 75 mV.)

Ans. 2.45×10^{-4} joules per hour.

5. The formula for the capacity of a parallel plate capacitor is C = $\kappa \mathcal{E}_o A/\delta$ where κ is the dielectric constant of the insulating material, $\varepsilon_o = 8.85 \times 10^{-12}$ coulomb^2 per joule-meter (K = $1/4\pi\varepsilon_o$), A is the area of the plates, and δ is the separation of the plates. What is the dielectric constant of the membrane material, if the membrane, considered to be the insulator in a parallel plate capacitor, is 75 Å. = 7.5×10^{-9} meters thick and has a capacity of 1 μf. per cm.^{2}?

Ans. 8.5.

ELECTRIC CURRENT, OHM'S LAW

Current, Current Density. As mentioned above, when an electric field is applied to a conductor, whether metallic or an ionic solution, charges flow in a manner which tends to neutralize the field applied. Unless energy is supplied to keep + and − charges separated, the field in the conductor rapidly decreases to zero. In order to keep charges separated, positive charges must be taken continuously from the negative region, given energy and supplied to the positive region by an appropriate energy source, e.g., a battery or generator. Thus, charges move continuously; i.e., a current flows in a conductor under the influence of an electric field.

Electric current is a vector; it has direction and magnitude. The current strength or magnitude is defined as the amount of charge passing per unit time through a cross section of the conductor perpendicular to the direction of flow of charge or, more simply, as the time rate of flow of charge, I = dq/dt. Direction of flow traditionally is defined as that of positive charges. The unit of current (I) is the ampere (1 coulomb per second). The net passage of 6.25×10^{18} unitary charges (electrons, sodium ions) per second is an ampere. For convenience, charge flow frequently is expressed as current per unit area (current density, J, amperes per cm.^{2}), rather than as current. Current density is directly proportional to ionic flux (M); flux is mols per cm.^{2}-sec.; current density is coulombs per cm.^{2}-sec. The relationship is thus J = FZM, where F is the Faraday.

Ohm's Law. It is found that for many conductors $\mathbf{J} = \sigma\mathbf{E}$, where σ is called the *conductivity* of the conductor. This form of Ohm's law states that the current density is proportional to the electric field and in the same direction. This is equivalent to the statement

*To attain a capacity of 1 farad, two parallel metal plates separated by an air gap of 0.1 mm. would each have to have an area of about 4 square miles!

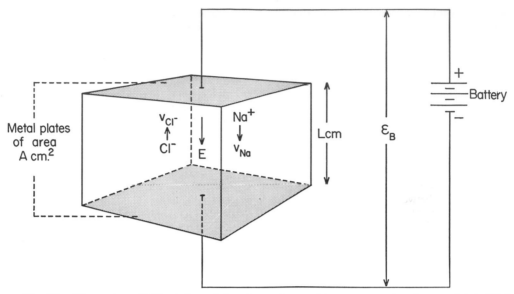

Fig. 17. Illustration of Ohm's law. A box L cm. long with a cross-sectional area of A is filled with solution of NaCl in water. A battery of voltage $\mathcal{E}_B$ is connected to metal plates at each end of box. E is electric field set up in medium by applied voltage; v_{Na} and v_{Cl} are average drift velocities of Na^+ and Cl^- ions, respectively, and are proportional to E.

that the average velocity of the charges in the conductor is proportional to the electric field (see below). This relationship between current density and field is known as Ohm's law; its more usual form is that current is proportional to voltage.

A more detailed description and derivation of Ohm's law is as follows. Figure 17 is a diagrammatic representation of an electrolytic conductor and some of the factors governing the flow of the ions in the solution. The metal plates at the opposite ends of the box are charged by the battery to $\mathcal{E}_B$, and these charges exert a downward force ($E = \mathcal{E}_B/L$) on a $+$ charge anywhere in the box, where L is the length of the box. The Na^+ ions in the solution are acted upon by a downward electric force (Ee) and the Cl^- ions by an upward force ($-Ee$), e being the charge of a cation in coulombs. Gravitational forces are negligible. The direction of the force is determined by the valence (Z), so force equals EeZ.

In the absence of opposing forces, the ions would accelerate in the electric field. However, an ion moving through a solution encounters frictional resistance to flow. The ion frequently collides with H_2O molecules; between collisions the ion accelerates under the influence of the applied force, but some kinetic energy is lost in each collision. The ion soon reaches a velocity at which, on the average, the energy lost in each collision just equals the kinetic energy gained from acceleration between collisions; i.e., there is a net movement of the ion at a constant velocity in the direction of the applied force superimposed on its random motion. The greater the applied force, the greater the average velocity $(\bar{v})^*$ of the ions; under most circumstances, v is proportional to E; $\bar{v} = \eta EeZ$,

$\bar{v}_{Na} = \eta_{Na}Ee$, $\bar{v}_{Cl} = -\eta_{Cl}Ee$. The constant η is a measure of the *mobility* of the ion, the ease with which it can move through the solution. The mobility constant and the diffusion constant are closely related properties of an ion in solution.

The current I (in amperes) flowing through the box in Figure 17 is defined as the total amount of charge (in coulombs) flowing through any cross section in 1 second. By definition, current flows in the direction in which the positive charges move, which is the direction of E. In an electrolyte, the total current is the sum of the currents carried by each ionic species; anions flowing upward and cations flowing downward both constitute a downward current. The current flowing through the box can be calculated from the average velocity of the ions. For example, suppose that the Na^+ are moving downward with an average velocity of 0.3 cm. per second, that the concentration of Na^+ is 10 μM. per cm.^{3}, and that the cross sectional area (A) is 10 cm.^{2}; then the Na^+ current passing through 1 cm.^{2} (current density) is 10 μM. per cm.^{3} $\times$ 0.3 cm. per second $=$ 3 μM. per cm.^{2}-second, and the total Na^+ current (I_{Na}) is 30 μM. per second. To convert this current to amperes, multiply by F $=$ 0.0965 coulombs per μM.; $I_{Na} = 2.9$ coulombs per second $=$ 2.9 amperes. In algebraic form,

$$I_{Na} = Z_{Na}\bar{v}_{Na}[Na^+]FA, \text{ and } I_{Cl} = Z_{Cl}\bar{v}_{Cl}[Cl^-]FA$$

For Cl^- both Z and $\bar{v}_{Cl}$ are negative, so the current is positive.

* A line above a symbol is a common convention for indicating an average or mean quantity.

In words, current density is proportional to the velocity and the concentration of the ions. Ion velocity is proportional to the electric field, and the field is proportional to the applied voltage. Thus current flow is proportional to the applied voltage. This is *Ohm's law*.

The proportionality between I and $\mathcal{E}$ can be obtained by combining the equations relating $\mathcal{E}_B$ and E, v and E, and I and v. The relationship obtained is:

$$I = \frac{AFe}{L}(Z^2_{Na}[Na^+]\eta_{Na} + Z^2_{Cl}[Cl^-]\eta_{Cl})\mathcal{E}_B = \frac{A}{L\rho}\mathcal{E}_B$$

$$R = \frac{L\rho}{A},$$

where R is the resistance of the box. All terms in the middle portion except T, L and $\mathcal{E}_B$ have been combined into the constant ρ, called the *specific resistivity* of the substance. From the equation it can be seen that resistivity depends inversely on ionic concentrations and mobility. Concentrated solutions containing ions of high mobility and valence have a low resistance. The numerical value of ρ (in ohm-cm.) is the resistance between the faces of a 1 cm. cube. In mammalian extracellular fluid ρ approximately equals ($\simeq$) 60 ohm-cm.

The resistance of a block of conductor depends on the properties of the material (e.g., number of free charges, energy loss per collision) and on the dimensions of the block. Consider the box containing a solution of NaCl illustrated in Figure 17. The greater the cross-sectional area of the box (perpendicular to the direction of current flow), the lower the resistance, because more ions are available to carry current; the greater the length of the block (parallel to flow), the higher the resistance. In longer blocks, ions move at a slower velocity because the force on each ion is reduced. Thus, the resistance of a block of conducting material (a resistor) depends on the properties of the material (*specific resistivity*), is directly proportional to the length of the block, and is inversely proportional to its cross-sectional area.

Current Flow in Capacitors. In principle any amount of charge can be put on a capacitor, but the greater the charge, the greater the work per unit charge (voltage) that must be done to add charge to the capacitor. In a capacitor, current is the time rate of flow of charge onto the capacitor's conductors or the time rate of accumulation of charge on them. Since, for a capacitor, q = C$\mathcal{E}$, capacitative current is proportional to the rate of change of voltage across the capacitor: I = dq/dt = C d$\mathcal{E}$/dt. A constant current flowing through a resistor produces an unchanging voltage across it: $\mathcal{E}$ = IR. A constant current (charge flow) to a capacitor produces a constant voltage change rate. In practice, a constant or unidirectional current cannot flow into a capacitor indefinitely because this would require a battery of infinite voltage.

Time constant. The simplest case of transient capacitative current flow occurs in the circuit (Fig. 18*D*, left) in which a battery is suddenly connected to a resistor (r) and a capacitor (c) in series. The voltage

on the capacitor ($\mathcal{E}_c$), initially zero, must increase eventually to the battery voltage ($\mathcal{E}_S$) but this takes time since the charge must be delivered through the resistor, which limits current flow to a maximum value of $\mathcal{E}_S$/R (when $\mathcal{E}_c$ = 0). However, after a long time the current declines to zero because the capacitor is fully charged; $\mathcal{E}_c$ = $\mathcal{E}_S$ and, hence, the potential difference across the resistor is zero. Since current flow in the circuit is everywhere the same, the current through the resistor, ($\mathcal{E}_S$ − $\mathcal{E}_c$)/r, is equal to the current through the capacitor, I = dq/dt = cd$\mathcal{E}_c$/dt. This relationship can be solved to get an equation describing the time course of the voltage across c and of the current through r; e.g., $\mathcal{E}_c$ = $\mathcal{E}_S$ (1 − $e^{-t/rc}$). The graph of this function has the same shape as the curve in Figure 19*A*, right. The product (rc), having the units of time, is called the time constant (τ) of the circuit: rc = ($\mathcal{E}$/I) (q/$\mathcal{E}$) = q/I = q/(q/t) = t where the symbols refer to the units of these quantities rather than to the quantities themselves. The time constant is a measure of how long it takes the capacitor to charge to a fixed fraction (0.63) of its final value.

The membrane has resistance and capacitance in parallel and hence can show the transient behavior just described. However, in this case, the time constant of the membrane is measured by applying a constant current to the membrane with an intracellular electrode; part of the current flows through the resistor and part through the capacitor (Fig. 19*A*, left). In this case, the voltage ($\Delta\mathcal{E}_m$) across the membrane rises slowly in response to the abruptly applied current (Fig. 19*A*, right). The reason is that time is required for the flow of charges (current) to alter the amount of charge on the capacitor and thus the voltage across it. At the instant the switch is closed all the charge supplied by the current source goes to charging the capacitor; there is no current through the resistor because the potential across it and the capacitor is zero. As time passes, the charge on the capacitor increases; $\Delta\mathcal{E}_m$ increases, and some current is diverted to the resistor, the rate of charging the capacitor being correspondingly decreased. This process continues—more and more current flowing through the resistor and less and less through the capacitor—until, finally, all the current is flowing through the resistor.

The time course of these potential changes is shown in Figure 19*A*, right. Also shown is $\Delta\mathcal{E}_m$ as a function of time after the switch is opened. In this case, the charge on c_m leaks off through r_m, rapidly at first and then progressively more slowly. The time constant (τ) of this circuit is defined as the product of the resistance (r_m) and the capacitance (c_m): τ = $r_m c_m$. If r_m is in ohms and c_m is in farads, τ is in seconds. A means of measuring the time constant is also shown in Figure 19*A*, right. The shape and time course of $\Delta\mathcal{E}_m$ are the same no matter what values r_m and c_m have individually, as long as their product is a constant.

Equivalent Circuit of an Axon. The membrane has capacity because of its insulating, charge-separating properties and has high resistance because ions are able to penetrate it at a limited rate. The axo-

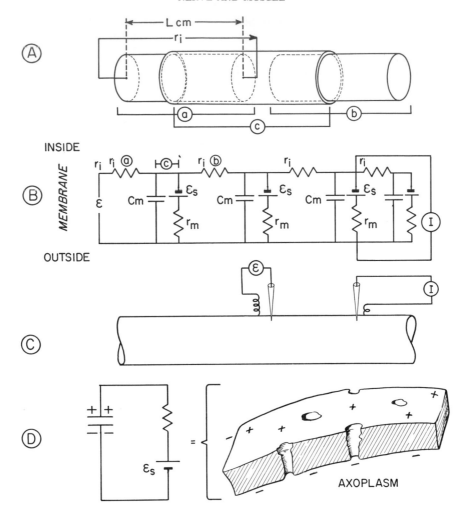

Fig. 18.   Derivation of approximate equivalent electrical circuit of a long, thin, cylindrical axon. In an electrical circuit diagram, a straight line (———) represents an ideal conductor (zero resistance), a zigzag line (〜〜〜) represents an ideal resistance (no capacitance between its terminals), and ——|⊢—— represents an ideal capacitor (infinite resistance between its terminals). In A, the axoplasm and membrane are each marked off into halfway overlapping segments L cm. long (accurate representation of the nerve requires that L be no more than about 0.05 cm.). Any segment of axoplasm has a resistance (r_i) which is in series with the adjoining segments. Thus the upper line in B consists of a series of resistors, each of which is the electrical equivalent of the correspondingly labeled segment of axoplasm in A. Extracellular fluid is large and is assumed to have no resistance; this is represented by lower horizontal line in B. Equivalent circuit of a segment of membrane (c) must be connected between intracellular and extracellular fluid equivalents at the junction of two r_i's. For example, segment c is connected between the axoplasmic segments a and b.

C, Experimental arrangement for measuring cable properties. Compare with B, where a current source is shown applied across the membrane at one point; the "transmembrane potential" of the equivalent circuit can be measured at any other point. If B is an accurate electrical representation of the nerve fiber, then curves of the type shown in Figure 15 should be obtained in the equivalent experiment.

D, Derivation of equivalent circuit of a membrane segment. Equivalent consists of a capacitor (c_m) representing the insulating, ion-impermeable regions of membrane in parallel with a resistor (r_m) representing the ion-permeable regions of membrane. (For convenience, ion-permeable region is indicated by pores penetrating the membrane.) A battery of potential $\mathcal{E}_s$ is connected in series with r_m to signify the existence of a steady transmembrane potential.

plasm and interstitial fluids, being solutions of ions, are resistors. If an axon is marked off into short segments, an approximately equivalent circuit consisting of resistors and capacitors can be drawn for each segment. When connected, the circuit equivalents of adjacent segments will constitute an equivalent circuit for the whole axon. This equivalent circuit has the same response to an applied current as has the nerve fiber it represents.

Figure 18 illustrates how the equivalent circuit is obtained. The electrical equivalent of a segment of axoplasm is simply a resistor (r_i) whose resistance is that of the segment (segments a and b in Figure 18A and the correspondingly marked resistors in Figure 18B).

Since the axoplasm is a rather dilute (0.3 M. per liter) solution of ionized substances, it has a comparatively high specific resistivity ($\rho \simeq 200$ ohm-cm.). The

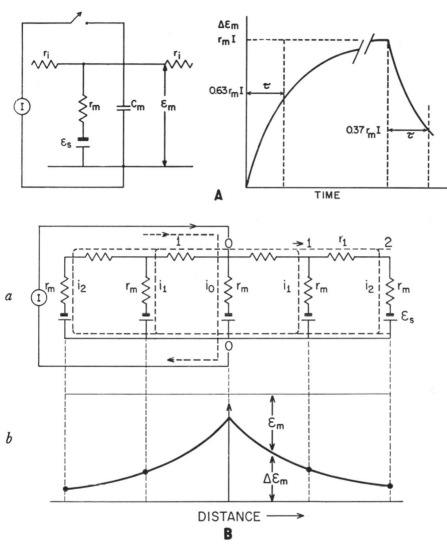

Fig. 19. *A,* Time constant; properties of a resistance–capacitance (RC) circuit. *Left,* Equivalent circuit of a segment of membrane and means for switching on or off an external current source (I). *Right,* Time course of voltage changes ($\Delta\mathcal{E}_m = \mathcal{E}_m - \mathcal{E}_s$) across the capacity when the switch is closed and then, after a long time, opened. A method for measuring the time constant ($\tau = r_m c_m$) of the membrane is shown.

B, Space constant. *a,* Approximate equivalent circuit of an axon with the membrane capacity removed. Current flow in a circuit with capacitors is the same, after a long time, as the current flow in this circuit at any time. Arrows show various paths of flow of applied current, I. The longer the current flow path, the greater the resistance and hence the smaller the proportion of current flowing in that branch. *b,* Graph of membrane voltage as a function of distance from point of current application.

resistance to axial current flow in the axoplasm of a nerve fiber is high because of the high specific resistivity and the small cross-sectional area. For instance, in a myelinated nerve fiber 14 μ in diameter, the axoplasm is only 10 μ in diameter, and the *longitudinal resistance* (r_i) of a segment 1 cm. long is 260 million ohms ($r_i = \rho_i L/A = 200$ ohm-cm. $\cdot$ 1 cm./$\pi \cdot (5 \times 10^{-4}$ cm.$)^2 = 2.6 \times 10^8$ ohm). The larger the diameter, the less r_i is; in a muscle fiber 100 μ in diameter, $r_i = 2.6$ million ohms per cm. Current inside the cell must flow within the volume surrounded by the cell membrane. The interstitial medium, on the other hand, is large; hence current can spread widely as it flows. Therefore, although the specific resistivity of the extracellular fluid is half as large as for intercellular fluid, the total resistance (r_o) of the interstitial fluid is negligible in comparison with r_i. Thus, r_o is not included in the equivalent circuit of Figure 18B. If r_o were appreciable, it would be put in the bottom horizontal line opposite the r_i's (Fig. 18B).

The equivalent circuit of a segment of membrane is more complicated, consisting of three components derived as shown in Figure 18D: (i) a capacity (c_m) representing the insulating charge-storing aspect of the membrane, (ii) a resistance (r_m) representing the limited ability of ions to penetrate the membrane, and (iii) a battery of voltage $\mathcal{E}_S$, the steady potential. The battery and the resistance are drawn in series because the membrane capacity is charged by ions (principally K^+ and Cl^-) driven through the membrane resistance by concentration gradients. In Figure 18A, the segment of membrane (c) is placed halfway between the two segments of axoplasm (a and b) to illustrate how the circuits representing the axoplasmic and membrane segments must be connected: the r_i's in series and the membrane portions connected between the junction of two r_i's and the line (representing a zero resistance conductor) that is equivalent to r_o, the extracellular resistance (Fig. 18B). An axon has cable properties because it has the particular electrical circuit properties shown in Figure 18B. In turn, these circuit properties are a consequence of the axon's structure.

Figure 18C is a duplicate of Figure 3B, which illustrates how cable properties are observed experimentally. Current is applied through an intracellularly placed electrode (I electrode), and the changes in membrane potential some distance away are recorded with the other ($\mathcal{E}$) electrode. The same type of experiment on the equivalent circuit is shown in Figure 18B, right; current is applied across a segment of membrane and the potential is recorded across a membrane segment one r_i away.

The advantage of drawing an equivalent circuit for an axon is that the behavior of this type of circuit is amenable to mathematical analysis. Such an analysis shows that the circuit always behaves in the manner described above and that the cable properties are completely characterized by two numbers: (i) the *time constant* (τ), which is a measure of the slowness of voltage changes in time, and (ii) the *space constant* (λ), a measure of the rate at which the voltage falls off with distance.

Membrane Time Constant. Since a segment of membrane can be represented electrically by a resistor and a capacitor in parallel (the battery does not affect the properties under discussion), the segment has a time constant associated with it. The time constant of the membrane segment shown in Figure 19A is $\tau_m = r_m c_m$. The time constant of any other segment of membrane of the same properties but different area is exactly the same although the resistance and capacitance are each different. Thus, this time constant characterizes the time behavior of the voltage changes across the membrane. It should be borne in mind, however, that the membrane voltage changes in a whole fiber are much more complex than those in a single resistance-capacitance circuit, although both are determined by τ. The differences arise because current applied at one point is not restricted to one segment of membrane but spreads out through the axoplasm to other segments of membrane. The result is that the voltage rises more quickly at the point of current application than in a simple RC circuit and more slowly at distant points. The equality of the time constants of any two segments of different length can be seen by calculating τ for segments 1 and 2 mm. long. Membrane resistance of the 2 mm. segment is half that of the 1 mm. segment, because, with respect to current flow from the interior to the exterior of the cell, two adjacent 1 mm. segments are in parallel. Alternatively, doubling the membrane area doubles the number of ions in a position to penetrate the membrane under a particular driving force. Thus the membrane conductance is doubled and the resistance halved. The double segment has twice the capacity because capacity is proportional to membrane area. The time constant of the double segment is 2 $c_m \times r_m/2 = r_m c_m$. Since the same arguments apply to segments of any length, the number $\tau = r_m c_m$ depends only on the properties of the membrane. In *Carcinus* (crab) axons specific membrane resistance is about 7500 ohms-cm.^{2}, and specific capacity is about 1 μf. per cm.^{2}; hence $\tau = 7.5$ milliseconds. τ is about 1 millisecond in squid giant axons and about 35 milliseconds in frog sartorius muscle fibers. This large value results from the high membrane capacity of muscle, about 10 μf. per cm.^{2}

Membrane Space Constant. The other factor necessary to specify completely the cable properties of a nerve fiber is the space constant, a measure of the spatial decay of $\Delta\mathcal{E}_m$. The diminution of membrane voltage changes with increasing distance from the current-applying electrode results from the series-parallel relationship between the resistance of a segment of membrane (r_m) and the longitudinal resistance of a segment of axoplasm (r_i). Each successive segment reduces the voltage.

Figure 19B shows the equivalent circuit of a nerve fiber with the membrane capacitors removed so that the spatial features of cable properties are emphasized. The current flow in the resistors is the same as would occur in a nerve fiber a long time after the application of the current when all the capacitors are fully charged. If a constant current is applied to the resistor network (Fig. 19B, top) at O, some of the current spreads into adjoining regions. Most of the current will flow directly through branch O. Because the axoplasm has a high resistance, successively lesser amounts will flow through other branches of the circuit (1, 2, 3, etc.). The longer the current flow path, the greater is its resistance and hence the less the current, because the voltage drop around any current flow path must be the same as that across branch O; $\Delta\mathcal{E}_o = r_m i_o$.

Experimentally, the quantity measured is the transmembrane potential at any point. Internal longitudinal current flow causes a voltage drop in the axoplasm, but changes in $\mathcal{E}_m$ result *only* from current flow through the membrane. However, to reach the point where it penetrates the membrane, this current must flow in the axoplasm as well and is thus attenuated. If the internal resistance were zero, the axoplasm would be isopotential, and all membrane elements would be in parallel. The cable properties would then consist merely of simple resistance–capacitance charge and discharge curves; i.e., there would be no spatial component. This situation obtains, approximately, in nearly spherical cells such as the nerve cell body. In such a case, the applied current produces nearly equal $\Delta\mathcal{E}_m$'s at every point.

The decay of potential with distance has the same shape as the decay of potential with time in a resistance–capacitance circuit, i.e., exponential. Figure 19*B*, bottom, shows a plot of $\Delta\mathcal{E}_m$ as a function of distance from the point of application of the current. The size of the space constant (λ) depends directly on membrane resistance and inversely on axoplasmic resistance. More precisely $\lambda = \sqrt{r_m/r_i}$, where r_m is the membrane resistance and r_i is the axoplasmic resistance of a 1 cm. length of fiber. Since both r_m and r_i depend on fiber diameter as well as on fiber properties, λ also depends on diameter: the larger the diameter, the larger the space constant. In frog skeletal muscle fibers 100 μ in diameter, λ is about 2.5 mm. Similar or smaller values are found in nerve fibers. Thus if a fiber were depolarized to zero at one end by a current, changes in membrane potential would be undetectable 1 cm. away. This fact shows how rapidly a fiber attenuates an applied "signal." It also shows that some method is needed to boost the signal at suitable intervals if information is to be transmitted over the distances found in the body.

Strength–Duration Relation. The equivalent circuit for an axon which was derived above can be used to derive an equation for the strength–duration curve shown in Figure 6. Assume that the area of membrane affected by the stimulating current is small enough to be represented by a single resistance–capacitance circuit (Fig. 19) and that the requirement for a threshold stimulus is that $\mathcal{E}_m$ be depolarized a fixed amount. The change in $\mathcal{E}_m$ ($\Delta\mathcal{E}_m = \mathcal{E}_m - \mathcal{E}_t$) is described by the equation

$$\Delta\mathcal{E}_m = I_s r_m(1 - e^{-t/\tau})$$

where I_s is the portion of the stimulating current flowing through the membrane resistance (r_m) at the site of the stimulating electrode, and $\tau = r_m c_m$ (the membrane time constant). The fiber will fire if $\Delta\mathcal{E}_m$ reaches

some critical value ($\Delta\mathcal{E}_{th}$). Setting $\Delta\mathcal{E}_m = \Delta\mathcal{E}_{th}$ in the above equation and solving for I_s as a function of t gives

$$I_s = \frac{\Delta\mathcal{E}_{th}}{r_m(1 - e^{-t/\tau})}$$

This is a relation between the length of time (t) that a stimulating current flows and the strength of the current. If t is large, the strength of the stimulating current (I_m) is minimum; $I_m = \Delta\mathcal{E}_{th}/r_m$. If t is small, larger currents are required. If $I_m = \Delta\mathcal{E}_{th}/r_m$ is substituted into this equation, it becomes, for a time, much less than τ; $I_s = I_m\tau_m/t$, or $I_s t = I_m\tau_m$. In other words, for short shocks, a constant amount of charge ($I_m\tau_m$) will stimulate the fiber; i.e., all the applied current enters the membrane capacity. Chronaxy, defined in Figure 6, is directly proportional to the membrane time constant. Chronaxy = $\tau_m \log_e 2$. Actually, the time course of the voltage change at the stimulating electrode is faster than given above. A somewhat more accurate version of the strength duration curve is obtained if this difference is taken into account, as has been done in plotting the curve in Figure 6.

Problems

1. The resistance of 1 cm.^{2} of squid axon membrane is 1000 ohm·cm.^{2}. If the membrane is uniform and 75 Å thick, what is the specific resistivity of the membrane?

Ans.

$R = \rho\delta/A$ ρ = specific resistivity
                δ = thickness
                A — area (= 1 cm.^{2} in this problem)
                R = resistance

Therefore, $\rho = (RA)/\delta$. In this problem RA = 1000 ohm-cm.^{2} = 10^{-1} ohm-cm.^{2} $\rho = 10^{-1}/7.5 \times 10^{-9}$ = 1.33×10^7 ohm-meter.

2. Suppose the resistance of the squid axon membrane of problem 1 is due to the presence of cylindrical holes or pores 0.7×10^{-9} meters in diameter and 75 Å long (membrane thickness), in a perfect insulating membrane material and filled with fluid of specific resistivity 0.15 ohm-meter (sea water). If Ohm's law holds for the fluid in the pores, how many pores must exist in 1 cm.^{2} of membrane to account for an R_m of 1000 ohms-cm.^{2}? How far apart are these pores if they are arranged in a square pattern?

Ans. 2.9 × 10^6 pores per cm.^{2}, 5.9 × 10^{-4} cm. (5.9 μ) between pores.

3. Calculate the specific resistivity in ohm-meters of a 0.15 M. NaCl solution when the mobility of (η_{Na}) of Na ions is 3.2 × 10^{11} (meters per sec.-newton) and of Cl ions is 4.9 × 10^{11} (meters per sec.-newton.).

Ans. 0.53 ohm-meter.

4. The resistance of the membrane covering a unit length of a long, thin cell is 1.25 × 10^5 ohm-cm. and the capacity per unit length is 0.008 μf. per cm. The resistance per unit length of the cytoplasm is 4.1 × 10^7 ohm per cm. Calculate the space constant and time constant of this cell.

Ans. $\lambda = 5.5 \times 10^{-2}$ cm. $= 0.5$ mm.; $\tau = 1 \times 10^{-3}$ seconds $= 1$ millisecond.

5. A long, thin cylindrical cell 100 μ in diameter is covered by a membrane with a specific resistance of 100 ohms-cm.^{2} and with a time constant of 10^{-3} seconds. If the cytoplasm of this cell has a specific resistivity of 1 ohm-meter, what is the space constant and membrane capacity per square meter of this cell?

Ans. $\lambda = 1.6 \times 10^{-3}$ meters, $c_m = 10^{-2}$ f. per meter.^{2}

6. The rheobase of a muscle to external stimulating electrodes is 2 milliamperes and the average membrane time constant is 30 milliseconds. Calculate and plot several points on the strength–duration curve. Measure the chronaxy from the plotted curve and compare with the calculated value of chronaxy $= \tau_m \log_e 2$. Note that $\log_e 2 = 0.69$ and $e^{-x} = 1/e^x = 1/10^{x/2.3}$.

PHYSICAL CHEMISTRY

Electrochemical Potential. The electrochemical potential is a useful concept in discussing the physical chemistry of the system composed of two solutions separated by a membrane which are at or near equilibrium. Electrochemical potential is defined as the rate of change of free (or available) energy of a system with respect to the number of mols of the particular substance considered (units: joules per mol), the number of mols of other substances, the temperature and pressure being held constant. The formula for the electrochemical potential used in Chapter 1 can be derived rather simply, but not rigorously, in the following way. The electrochemical potential, μ_s, of species of substance, S, is $\mu_s = Z_s F \mathcal{E} + RT \log_e[S]$. The contribution of the electrical potential to the energy of 1 mol of S is simply $Z_s F \mathcal{E}$, the work done per mol in bringing the substance to a region where the potential is $\mathcal{E}$; $Z_s F$ converts from joules per coulomb to joules per mol. The calculation of concentration potential energy is more difficult. The RT $\log_e$-[S] term is obtained by using the approximation that the species, S, acts like a perfect gas in the solution, i.e., there is no interaction between the S molecules. For a perfect gas $PV = nRT$ where P is the pressure, V the volume, n the number of mols, R the universal gas constant, and T the absolute temperature. Work is done on a gas by compressing it; hence $dW = -Fds = -PAds = -PdV$ where A = cross-sectional area. The concentration potential energy is thus the work to compress a mol of S from infinite volume to its actual concentration in the solution. By definition, $[S] = n_s/V$, so $V = n_s/[S]$ and $dV = -n_s\, d[S]/[S]^2$. Writing the gas law in the form $P = RTn_s/V = RT[S]$, substituting into $dW = -PdV$ and dividing through by n_s gives $\dfrac{dW}{n_s} = RT\,\dfrac{d[S]}{[S]}$, the work per mol of S done in changing the concentration of S by $d[S]$. Integrating gives the work done in changing the concentration from $[S]_o$ to $[S]_i$.

$$\frac{W}{n_s} = \int_{[S]=[S]_o}^{[S]=[S]_i} \frac{dW}{n_s} = RT\int_{[S]=[S]_o}^{[S]=[S]_i} \frac{d[S]}{[S]} = RT\,(\log_e[S]_i - \log_e[S]_o)$$

$$= RT\,\log_e \frac{[S]_i}{[S]_o} \quad (1)$$

If all electrochemical potentials are referred to the value for $[S] = [S]_o$ (only electrochemical potential differences are considered), then

$$\mu_s = Z_s F \mathcal{E} + RT \log_e[S] \quad (2)$$

Activity coefficient. There are, however, interactions between ions and so [S] must be multiplied by a factor γ to describe the observed behavior, $\gamma[S]$ being called the activity. The factor, γ, depends on concentration, approaching one for very dilute solutions, e.g., for a 0.15M NaCl solution it is 0.75. Tables and approximate formulae for γ are available if more exact values of the electrochemical potential are needed. The frequently made assumption that $\gamma = 1$ is not as inaccurate as a γ of 0.75 indicates since nearly all calculations involve concentration (or activity) ratios in which γ is usually canceled; i.e., the concentration ratio is an accurate approximation to the activity ratio in most circumstances.

Ionic Fluxes. *The flux equation.* Most animal systems are in osmotic equilibrium, because osmotic pressures are very large for relatively small concentration differences (see below). As pointed out in Chapter 1, biologic membranes separate solutions in which the concentrations of various species differ, although the total number of particles is nearly the same. Since most membranes are somewhat permeable to many of the ions, it is important to derive an expression for the flow of these ions through membranes as an aid in interpreting experimental data. Several assumptions are made to simplify this derivation: (i) The only force acting on the ions are concentration and voltage gradients. (ii) The individual ions move through the membrane independently of each other. (iii) The system is in osmotic equilibrium. (iv) Concentration gradients and electric fields exist only in and very near the membrane; concentrations are the same everywhere in each solution (but may differ between solutions), and the electric field is zero everywhere in each solution.

The passive forces acting on ions are concentration gradients and electric fields. The ionic flux of the species, S, due to the concentration gradient (M_s^D) is $M_s^D = -D_s \,\mathbf{grad}\,[S]$ (see Chap. 1) where D_s is the diffusion coefficient for S in the membrane and $[S]$ is its concentration at any point in the membrane. $D_s = 0$ if the membrane is impermeable to S.

The ionic flux of S through the membrane due to an electric field (M_s^E) can be computed from the formula for ionic current in the section above on Ohm's law. Thus, $M_s^E = J_s/Z_s F = I_s/AFZ_s = \dfrac{\mathcal{E}_m}{L} Z_s e[S]\eta_s$. $\mathcal{E}_m/L$ is a simple form of the potential gradient in the membrane, **grad** $\mathcal{E}$. The mobility, η_s, of S in the membrane, the average velocity per unit force on the ion, and D_s are related since both represent the ease with which an ion moves through the membrane. Einstein first showed that $\eta_s = \dfrac{FD_s}{eRT}$. The total flux is the sum of the concentration and voltage gradient fluxes:

$$-\mathbf{M}_s = -(\mathbf{M}_s^D + \mathbf{M}_s^E) = D_s \ \mathbf{grad} \ [S] +$$
$$Z_s \frac{FD_s}{RT} [S] \ \mathbf{grad} \ \mathcal{E} \qquad (3)$$

This equation specifies the flux of an ion but the difficulty arises that both [S] and $\mathcal{E}$ must be specified at each point in the membrane; if one is known the other may be calculated. The calculation of both [S] and $\mathcal{E}$ from first principles is difficult and requires a specific membrane model. However, the equilibrium potential can be calculated without further assumptions.

Equation 3 can be put in a simpler form by multiplying both sides by $e^{FZ_s\mathcal{E}/RT}$ to obtain

$$-\mathbf{M}_s e^{FZ_s\mathcal{E}/RT} = D_s e^{FZ_s\mathcal{E}/RT} \ \mathbf{grad} \ [S] +$$
$$\frac{D_s Z_s F \ [S] e^{FZ_s\mathcal{E}/RT}}{RT} \ \mathbf{grad} \ \mathcal{E} = D_s \ \mathbf{grad} \ ([S] e^{FZ_s\mathcal{E}/RT}) \ (4)$$

since **grad** $AB = A$ **grad** $B + B$ **grad** A. This is the ordinary diffusion equation with [S] replaced by $[S]e^{FZ_s\mathcal{E}/RT}$. Thus, with respect to transmembrane fluxes, voltage affects concentrations exponentially.

Equilibrium potential.   The equilibrium potential ($\mathcal{E}_s$) of an ion is the $\mathcal{E}_m$ at which $\mathbf{M}_s = 0$. It is the potential across a membrane that is permeable only to this ion species.

$$-\mathbf{M}_s e^{FZ_s\mathcal{E}/RT} = D_s \ \mathbf{grad} \ ([S] e^{FZ_s\mathcal{E}/RT}) = 0 \qquad (5)$$

If the membrane is considered as a plane of thickness δ oriented perpendicular to the x direction, the boundary conditions are $[S] = [S]_o$ and $\mathcal{E} = 0$ on the outside of the membrane and $[S] = [S]_i$ and $\mathcal{E} = \mathcal{E}_s$ on the inside. Equation (5) can be integrated directly to give: $[S]_o e^o - [S]_i e^{FZ_s\mathcal{E}/RT} = 0$.

$$\mathcal{E}_s = \frac{RT}{FZ_s} \log_e \frac{[S]_o}{[S]_i} \qquad (6)$$

the Nernst equation for the equilibrium potential of an ion. This is the electric potential necessary to balance out diffusional forces on the ion species, S. In Chapter 1 the Nernst equation was derived from the electrochemical potential difference $\Delta\mu_s$, across the membrane. $\Delta\mu_s = FZ_s\mathcal{E}_m + RT \log_e [S]_i/[S]_o$. If $\Delta\mu_s = 0$, $\mathcal{E}_m = \mathcal{E}_s$ and $\mathcal{E}_s = \dfrac{RT}{FZ_s} \log_e [S]_o/[S]_i$. Hence the equilibrium potential can be calculated from equating electrical and diffusional forces or potential energies.

Membrane Potential.   *Non-steady state: Goldman equation.*   In cells, most ions are not equilibrated and the net passive fluxes of permeating ion species are not zero. This is true in the steady state maintained by active transport and generally in transient states produced by changes in the external solution, in membrane potential (e.g., voltage clamping), or in membrane permeability (e.g., action potential). The relationship between ion fluxes and transmembrane potential is complicated and depends on the specific membrane model used. However, in conditions in which the voltage is changing so slowly that capacitative current is negligible (seconds or greater), the assumption made by Goldman (see reference 16) that the electric field inside the membrane is everywhere constant yields an accurate relationship. For a constant field, the potential at any distance (x) through the membrane is $\mathcal{E} = \mathcal{E}_m(1 - x/\delta)$. (The positive x direction is outward.) Inserting this into equation 4 and integrating, when I_S is in a steady state (charges would pile up in the membrane if I_S varied with x) gives

$$I_S = P_s \frac{F^2 Z_s^2 \mathcal{E}_m}{RT} \left[\frac{[S]_i e^{FZ_s\mathcal{E}_m/RT} - [S]_o}{e^{FZ_s\mathcal{E}_m/RT} - 1^1} \right] \qquad (7)$$

where $P_s = D_s/\delta$. I_S is positive if the net current due to S is outward.

If $\mathcal{E}_m$ is changing slowly, capacitative current is zero and the total ionic flow through the membrane must be zero. In most animal cells, the only ions carrying appreciable currents through the membrane are Na^+, K^+ and Cl^-. Hence $I_{Na} + I_K + I_{Cl} = 0$ or $M_{Na} + M_K - M_{Cl} = 0$. Writing separate equations like 7 for each of these ions, adding the equations and setting the sum to zero give a relationship which can be solved for $\mathcal{E}_m$:

$$\mathcal{E}_m = \frac{RT}{F} \log_e \left[\frac{P_K[K]_o + P_{Na}[Na]_o + P_{Cl}[Cl]_i}{P_K[K]_i + P_{Na}[Na]_i + P_{Cl}[Cl]_o} \right] \qquad (8)$$

Curves of $\mathcal{E}_m$ versus $[K^+]_o$ like the one in Figure 7 are accurately predicted by this equation with a proper choice of the ratios P_{Na}/P_K and P_{Cl}/P_K.

Steady state in cells.   The preceding discussions deal only with passive fluxes through membranes, no account being taken of active transport. However, active transport is required to maintain a nonequilibrium steady state in which concentrations and voltage are not changing in time and net ion fluxes (passive plus active) are zero.

It is of importance to know whether a one-for-one sodium–potassium exchange pump can develop and maintain a steady state resembling the one actually found in cells. Since the pump is neutral and chloride is equilibrated ($I_{Cl} = 0$), the transmembrane potential is given by equation 8 with the chloride terms omitted:

$$\mathcal{E}_s = \frac{RT}{F} \log_e \left[\frac{[K]_o + \dfrac{P_{Na}}{P_K}[Na]_o}{[K]_i + \dfrac{P_{Na}}{P_K}[Na]_i} \right] \qquad (9)$$

$\mathcal{E}_s$ instead of $\mathcal{E}_m$ is used to denote steady state. This expression shows that the membrane potential is closest to the equilibrium potential of the most readily permeating ion; $\mathcal{E}_s$ is close to $\mathcal{E}_K$ if the ratio P_{Na}/P_K is much less than one ([Na] terms small compared to [K] terms).

Equation 9 is adequate for calculating steady state membrane potentials if the internal concentrations are known. However, these depend on the active transport rate, so an adequate test of whether a one-for-one pump can produce a steady state comparable to the actual one is to calculate $\mathcal{E}_s$ as a function of external concentrations, passive permeabilities and active transport rates only.

The dependence of $\mathcal{E}_s$ and cell volume (V_c) on P_{Na}/P_K and the Na$^+$ pumping rate can be calculated approximately by making certain assumptions: (i) Total cellular A$^-$ content is known. (ii) P_{Na} and P_K are known. (iii) All Na$^+$ extrusion is by means of a one-to-one Na$^+$–K$^+$ exchange. (iv) The rate of active Na$^+$ extrusion (M_{Na}^{out}) is directly proportional to [Na$^+$]$_i$; $M_{Na}^{out} = j_{Na}$[Na$^+$]$_i$, where j_{Na} is the specific active transport rate of Na$^+$ and has the units of permeability. Active Na$^+$ extrusion is probably proportional to [Na$^+$]$_i^3$ in this range (Chap. 1). However, this assumption simplifies the mathematics without changing the final result for high pumping rates. (v) The cell is in osmotic equilibrium. (vi) Only Na$^+$, K$^+$, Cl$^-$ and A$^-$ ions are considered. (vii) The constant field flux equation describes passive fluxes. Equations based on these assumptions give $\mathcal{E}_s$ and V_c in terms of external ion concentrations, the total amount of intracellular A$^-$ and its valence (Z_A), and the ratios j_{Na}/P_{Na} and P_{Na}/P_K. However, in most cells (but not in red cells) Z_A is about 1 and j_{Na}/P_{Na} is so large that $\mathcal{E}_s$ and V_c do not depend on the exact value of j_{Na}/P_{Na}. The large value of j_{Na}/P_{Na} reduces [Na]$_i$ to a very low value. In this case, the steady state transmembrane potential and the cell volume are given by the following equations:

$$\mathcal{E}_s = -\frac{RT}{F} \log_e \frac{[Na^+]_o + [K^+]_o}{[K^+]_o + [Na^+]_o \frac{P_{Na}}{P_K}} \quad (10)$$

$$V_c = \frac{A^-}{[Na^+]_o \left(1 - \frac{P_{Na}}{P_K}\right)} \quad (11)$$

These equations are somewhat more complicated if Z_A is not equal to 1, or if j_{Na}/P_{Na} is less than about 100. The term $(P_{Na}/P_K)[Na^+]_o$ can be considered an effective external Na$^+$ concentration. From the values in Table 1, $P_{Na}/P_K = 1/650$ for mammalian skeletal muscle. The equation for cell volume shows that V_c is constant for values of P_{Na}/P_K much less than 1. If $P_{Na}/P_K = 1$, cell volume is infinite, as expected. These equations are only approximately correct, but they clearly indicate the important factors in the determination of $\mathcal{E}_s$ and V_c; both are sensitively dependent on P_{Na}/P_K.

Osmotic Pressure and Balance. If two aqueous solutions are separated by a membrane which is permeable only to water, water tends to flow through the membrane equalizing its concentration and thus the total dissolved particles per unit volume in both solu-

tions. A hydrostatic pressure must be applied to the more concentrated solution to prevent this movement. The hydrostatic pressure difference necessary to maintain the unequal concentration of total dissolved particles in the two solutions is equal and opposite to the *osmotic* pressure. Water (only aqueous solutions will be dealt with here) tends to flow down its concentration gradient and hence from the solution with the lower concentration of dissolved particles to that with the higher concentration.

The pressure needed to stop the net flow of water is approximated by the formula, $\pi = RT(\Delta C)$, where R is the universal gas constant (8.21×10^{-2} liter-atmospheres/deg. K mol), T is the absolute temperature (degrees Kelvin), ΔC is the difference in concentration of the dissolved particles between the two solutions (mol per liter) and π is the osmotic pressure in atmospheres. The concentration of dissolved particles in a solution is usually expressed in osmols per liter. An *osmol* is 6.023×10^{23} particles (Avogadro's number—the number of particles in a gram molecular weight of a substance) without regard to the species of the particle (as long as it is not water). In calculating the number of particles, it should be noted that ionized substances contribute one particle for every ion formed in the dissociation of a molecule (i.e., NaCl gives 2 particles per molecule, Na$_2$SO$_4$ gives 3, etc.). The osmotic strength of a solution can be found by summing the molar concentrations of all the ions and undissociated molecules.

The term "tonicity" is used to describe the osmolarity of one solution in comparison to another. A solution is said to be *hypertonic, isotonic* or *hypotonic* with respect to another solution, depending upon whether it contains more, the same number of, or fewer dissolved particles per liter. Although these terms are relative, they are frequently used in an absolute sense. When used in this manner, the reference solution is the interstitial fluid or plasma. Mammalian serum contains approximately 310 milliosmols per liter. Thus a 155 millimolar solution of NaCl is isotonic to mammalian serum.

In living systems the effective osmotic pressure of a solution is less than the total osmotic pressure because cell membranes are permeable to many substances besides water. The osmotic pressures of intracellular and interstitial fluids are equal. However, the blood plasma contains about one millimol of protein molecules which are too large to penetrate the capillary wall and which are not as concentrated in interstitial fluid. Smaller molecules penetrate the capillary, so the osmotic pressure difference between the two fluids is due only to the plasma protein. Since one osmol has an osmotic pressure of about 25 atmospheres at body temperature (22.4 at 0° C.), one milliosmol has a pressure of $0.025 \times 760 = 19$ mm. Hg. A capillary hydrostatic pressure of more than 19 mm. Hg is necessary to overcome the osmotic pressure of the plasma protein alone. Additional pressure will be needed because of a second condition in the ionic distributions, the Gibbs–Donnan equilibrium.

Gibbs–Donnan Equilibrium and Osmotic Pressure. It was shown above that the net osmotic pressure across a membrane is $[S]RT$, where $[S]$ represents the total concentration of all nonpermeating substances. However, if one of the nonpermeating substances is ionized, the net osmotic pressure is modified and a transmembrane potential is developed. Consider the case of a membrane permeable to Na^+, Cl^- and water, and impermeable to A^- separating two solutions. On side 1 are $[Na^+]_1$, $[Cl^-]_1$ and $[A^{Z-}]_1$, with valence size Z, and on side 2, $[Na^+]_2$ and $[Cl^-]_2$ as shown by the table:

1	2
$[Na^+]_1$	$[Na^+]_2$
$[Cl^-]_1$	$[Cl^-]_2$
$Z[A^{Z-}]_1$	

If the osmotic pressure is balanced by an external pressure, $[Na^+]$ and $[Cl^-]$ will equilibrate across the membrane (active transport is assumed to be absent).

The Gibbs–Donnan equilibrium condition can be determined from the $[Na^+]$ and $[Cl^-]$ concentrations on the two sides by equating their electrochemical potentials:

$$RT \log_e [Na^+]_1 + RT \log_e [Cl^-]_1 = $$
$$RT \log_e [Na^+]_2 + RT \log_e [Cl^-]_2$$

$$[Na^+]_1[Cl^-]_1 = [Na^+]_2[Cl^-]_2 \qquad (12)$$

The nonpermeating anions do not contribute to the electrochemical potential difference across the membrane, and the voltage terms cancel. However, there is a transmembrane potential; since $[Na^+]_1/[Na^+]_2$ does not equal unity, a voltage is necessary to balance the concentration gradient so that net flux of this permeating ion is zero. Charge neutrality requires that $[Na^+]_1 = [Cl^-]_1 + Z[A^{Z-}]_1$ and $[Na^+]_2 = [Cl^-]_2$, where Z is the size of the valence of the nonpermeating anion, A^-. Substitution in the Gibbs–Donnan relation (equation 12) gives

$$([Cl^-]_1 + Z[A^{Z-}]_1)[Cl^-]_1 = ([Cl^-]_2)^2 \qquad (13)$$

Dividing through by $[Cl^-]_2$ and $([Cl^-]_1 + Z[A^{Z-}]_1)$ gives a more understandable form:

$$\frac{[Cl^-]_1}{[Cl^-]_2} = \frac{[Cl^-]_2}{[Cl^-]_1 + Z[A^{Z-}]_1} = \frac{[Na^+]_2}{[Na^+]_1} \qquad (14)$$

It can be seen from this relationship that $[Cl^-]_2$ is greater than $[Cl^-]_1$ and less than $([Cl^-]_1 + Z[A^-]_1)$. Since $[Cl^-]_2 > [Cl^-]_1$, the contributions of the diffusible ions to the osmotic pressure must be investigated. This will be done in the example below. The concentration ratio (ρ) for any diffusible univalent ion is the same as that for Na^+ and Cl^- in this equation. The potential is given by the Nernst equation, $RT/ZF \log_e \rho$.

The chloride concentration ratio between blood plasma and interstitial fluid is about 0.95. This ratio arises from the plasma protein, which has a concentration of about 1 millimol per liter and a valence of about -18. Also, $[Na^+]_2 = [Cl^-]_2 = 155$ millimols

per liter in interstitial fluid. Substituting in equation 13 gives

$$([Cl^-]_1 + 18 \times 1)[Cl^-]_1 = 155^2$$

Solving the quadratic equation gives $[Cl^-]_1 = 146.25$ millimols per liter for the plasma chloride concentration. Charge neutrality requires $[Na^+]_1 = [Cl^-]_1 + Z[A^-]_1 = 146.25 + 18 = 164.25$ millimols per liter. The Donnan concentration ratio for Na^+ is thus $155/164.25 = 0.944$ and the voltage across the capillary wall is $61 \log_{10} 0.944 = -1.5$ millivolts (plasma negative to interstitial fluid).

The total osmotic pressure is proportional to the difference between the total particle concentrations on the two sides of the membrane. On the plasma side this is $[Na^+]_1 + [Cl^-]_1 + [A^-]_1 = 164.25 + 146.25 + 1 = 311.5$ millimols per liter and on the interstitial side the sum of sodium and chloride concentrations is simply $2 \times 155 = 310$ millimols per liter. The difference is 1.5 millimols per liter, 50 per cent more than that due to the nondiffusible anion. The remainder is composed of diffusible ions held by the nondiffusible anions. The osmotic pressure is thus 50 per cent greater than the value of 19 mm. Hg due to 1 millimol of plasma protein. The total osmotic pressure, which is balanced by the hydrostatic pressure of the blood in the capillaries is thus about 29 mm. Hg, a value in agreement with measured capillary hydrostatic pressures (Chap. 32).

Problems

1. (a) If the membrane of the unicellular plant *Chara* has a permeability coefficient to glycerol of 2×10^6 cm. per second, what is the net movement of glycerol in mols per second across an area of 10^{-2} cm.^{2} if a concentration difference of 10^{-1} mols per liter exists across the membrane?

(b) Calculate the net movement of glycerol through a "membrane" made of water of the same area (10^{-2} cm.^{2}) and thickness (assumed to be 7.5×10^{-9} meters) as the *Chara* membrane for the same concentration gradient if the diffusion constant of glycerol (D_G) in water is 7.2×10^{-6} cm.^{2} per second.

Ans. (a) 2×10^{-12} mols per second. (b) 9.6×10^{-6} mols per second.

2. Calculate the hydrogen ion equilibrium potential across a muscle cell membrane if the *p*H of the intracellular fluid is 7.0 and the *p*H of the extracellular fluid is 7.4. If the transmembrane potential is -90 mV. (inside negative), is the hydrogen ion equilibrated? RT/F has the value 26.7 mV.

Ans. 24 mV. (inside negative). Not in equilibrium.

3. In a voltage clamping experiment, the peak sodium conductance (g_{Na}) following a sudden change in membrane potential from the resting level to a value of -20 mV. (inside negative) is found to be 5×10^{-2} mhos per cm.^{2} What is the peak sodium current density at this membrane potential if the sodium equilibrium potential is $+35$ mV.? What is the direction of the current?

Ans. 2.8×10^{-3} amps. per cm.^{2}; inward.

4. Using equation 7 for ion current as a function of $\mathcal{E}_m$ and P_K, compute the net potassium flux. Assume that $[K]_i = 155$ mM per liter, $[K]_o = 4$ mM. per liter, $\mathcal{E}_m = -90$ V. (inside negative), $P_K = 10^{-6}$ cm. per second.

Ans. With the constant field approximation the equation for passive current and net passive flux is

$$M_K = \frac{I_K}{F} = P_K \frac{F\mathcal{E}_m}{RT} \left[\frac{[K]_i e^{\dot{F}\mathcal{E}_m/RT} - [K]_o}{e^{F\mathcal{E}_m/RT} - 1} \right]$$

Inserting the given values for F/RT, P_K, $\mathcal{E}_m$, and $[K]$ and converting the concentrations to mols per meter^3 gives

$$M_K = 10^{-8} \times 37.5 \,(-9 \times 10^{-2}) \left[\frac{155 \, e^{-(37.5)(0.09)} - 4}{e^{-(37.5)(0.09)} - 1} \right]$$

$$= 10^{-8} \times 3.4 \times \frac{1.32}{.966}$$

$$= 4.6 \times 10^{-8} \text{ mol per meter}^2\text{-sec. outward flux.}$$

5. Using equation 9, compute the membrane potential for a muscle cell in which $[K]_i = 155$ mM. per liter, $[Na^+] = 12$ mM. per liter, $[K^+]_o = 4$ mM. per liter, $[Na^+]_o = 145$ mM. per liter, and $P_K/P_{Na} = 100$.

Ans. -89 mV.

CHAPTER 3

Special Properties of Nerve Trunks and Tracts

By HARRY D. PATTON

METHODS OF COMPARING SPECIAL PROPERTIES

IN the preceding chapters attention was focused on the general electrical properties common to the membranes of all excitable elements. For that purpose it was desirable to concentrate on data obtained from single nerve and muscle cells with the aid of intracellularly placed ultramicroelectrodes because such methods provide the most direct measure of membrane properties. Also, in initial consideration of the general properties of excitable membranes, quantitative variances arising from differences in cell species could profitably be overlooked.

Even though all axons are qualitatively alike, close scrutiny reveals that individual specimens display considerable quantitative variance in such parameters as, for example, conduction speed and threshold to externally applied electrical currents. It is the purpose of this chapter, then, to describe these special properties of the individual constituents of nerve trunks and tracts and to relate these properties to structural differences such as fiber diameters.

Data for comparison of the special properties of individual nerve fibers may be obtained in two ways. First, intracellular recordings from a great many individual fibers may be made in an attempt to sample the entire population of a trunk. This method has been employed on a limited basis,[17] but is tedious and time consuming. In addition, it suffers from the defect that sampling is distributed in time, so that the conditions may alter from sample to sample or from preparation to preparation. Also, intracellular sampling is biased, because small fibers are less tolerant of penetration than are larger axons. A more satisfactory method is to record the activity of a bundle of nerve fibers excited in concert. Such activity in a nerve trunk is called the *compound action potential,* a term which implies that the recorded potential is compounded from the individual action potentials of the constituent axons.

To record compound potentials the recording electrodes must, of course, be placed extracellularly, for an intracellular electrode is little influenced by activity in fibers adjacent to the one penetrated. Usually, one electrode is placed on the nerve trunk; the other is placed either on some other part of the same trunk or on some inactive structure such as bone or skin. With this arrangement, a difference of potential is re-

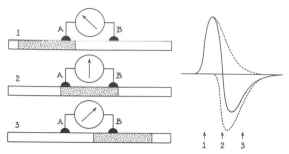

Fig. 1. Diphasic recording of action potential of nerve.

Left, Stippled area represents action potential progressing from left to right in 1, 2, and 3. In 1, electrode *A* is negative to electrode *B;* on 2, *A* and *B* are equipotential; in 3, *B* is negative with respect to *A*.

Right, Solid line trace is recorded diphasic action potential; numbered arrows below indicate instantaneous potential differences corresponding to three stages of conduction shown at left. Broken lines indicate true electrical changes at each electrode; recorded potential is their algebraic sum.

corded between the "active" electrode as it is passed by conducted action potentials and the "reference" electrode on some structure which is inactive at that time.

An important feature of extracellular recording is that the potential sources, i.e., the nerve fibers, are invariably surrounded by an aqueous conducting medium, either the interstitial fluid or some artificially constructed electrolytic medium applied to the trunk to prevent desiccation. Such a system, in which the potential source is immersed in a conducting medium is called a *volume conductor,* and interpretation of differences of potential between two points in the conducting medium requires special knowledge of the properties of volume conductors.

The influence of the external conducting medium is appreciable only when its volume is very large with respect to the volume of the structure generating the potential. Such is the case when potentials are recorded through electrodes placed on the surface of the brain or the spinal cord, or when the electrical activity of the contracting heart is recorded through electrodes placed on the surface of the body (electrocardiogram). In these instances, the entire body acts as a uniform conducting medium surrounding the relatively small structures generating the potentials. Happily, the volume of the external conducting medium surrounding peripheral nerve trunks can be limited simply by lifting the nerve onto electrodes in air or, better still, by suspending the nerve in an insulating medium

such as mineral oil so that only a thin film of external conductor surrounds the fibers and the trunk. The relatively simple compound action potential of peripheral nerve trunks will therefore be considered first, the discussion of potential configurations recorded in volume being postponed.

Diphasic and Monophasic Recording. Figure 1 shows diagrammatically an electrode arrangement suitable for recording the compound action potential of a nerve trunk. The nerve is equipped with a pair of recording electrodes, *A* and *B;* to minimize contact with the surrounding tissues, it is either lifted into the air or immersed in a pool of mineral oil. In the resting state the fibers under both recording leads are externally electropositive, and no difference of potential between them is recorded. When a volley of impulses* (stippled area) approaching *A* from the left reaches the position indicated in *1,* a difference of potential is recorded between *A* and *B,* because the active fibers at *A* are externally electronegative to the as yet quiescent portion of the same fibers at *B*. This difference in potential is registered as an upward deflection of the recording beam, as shown in the accompanying trace (heavy line).† In diagram *2,* the conducted volley has progressed so that both electrodes are in contact with equally depolarized fibers; consequently, the recording beam has returned to the zero potential. In diagram *3,* the wave of depolarization has progressed beyond *A* (i.e., the fibers under *A* have repolarized), so that *B* is now relatively negative to *A* and the recording beam is accordingly deflected downward. As the depolarization passes beyond *B,* the beam returns to zero. The potential configuration recorded in this way, shown diagrammatically by the heavy line tracing in Figure 1, is known as a *diphasic compound action potential.*

Diphasic recording is useful if one wishes to determine whether an electrical change is propagated, but for other purposes the method has certain undesirable features. First, if, as in Fig-

*A *volley of impulses* means a discharge set up in a multifibered nerve trunk or tract by a single brief stimulus, so that, although many constituent fibers are excited, none discharges more than once. The term should not be confused with a *train* or *burst of impulses,* terms which imply repetitive discharge of the constituent fibers, as, for example, when the trunk is *tetanically* or repetitively stimulated.

†The direction of the deflection is, of course, arbitrary and can be reversed by reversing the connections to the recording system.

ure 1, the distance between the recording electrodes is less than the wave length of the action potential (i.e., the length of fiber occupied by an action potential at any time), both the time course and the amplitude of the electrical events at each electrode are distorted, because activity reaches the distal electrode before repolarization occurs at the proximal electrode. The extent of this distortion may be seen in Figure 1 by comparing the traces depicted by the dotted lines (which are extrapolations of the electrical changes at each electrode) with the actually recorded algebraic summation of these changes (heavy line). This kind of cancellation is difficult to avoid, since the wave length of an action potential in a large nerve fiber is as much as 6 cm.

An even more serious defect arises from the fact, shortly to be developed, that the speed of conduction differs in different fibers in the trunk. Consequently, activity in rapidly conducting nerve fibers can reach the distal electrode at a time when the action potentials in more slowly conducting fibers have proceeded only as far as the proximal electrode. Hence, the contributions of rapidly and slowly conducting fibers may tend to cancel one another, for the recording arrangement detects only differences of potential.

Fortunately, the defects inherent in diphasic recording are easily circumvented by changing the experimental conditions to those shown in Figure 2. To block conduction, the fibers underlying electrode B are permanently depolarized by crushing, burning, cutting, or topically applying potassium salts. As a result, a steady difference of potential, the *injury* or *demarcation potential,** develops between electrodes A and B. Now, when a volley of impulses approaches and passes A, the full course of the activity at A is recorded as a negative-going variation of the steady demarcation potential, as illustrated in Figure 2. Activity recorded in this manner is called a *monophasic compound action potential.* For the reasons mentioned above, monophasic recording is used almost exclusively in studies of the compound action potential of nerve trunks.

In physiology the convention is to arrange the recording leads so that external negativity (i.e., activity under the "active" electrode) yields an upward deflection. This deviation from the convention in physics of displaying potentials "positive-up, negative-down" originally resulted from esthetic considerations. The first bioelectric transient observed was the negative-going monophasic action potential, or negative variation, and since rising deflections are generally more pleasing psychologically and esthetically than descending ones, the arbitrary convention of "negative-up, positive-down" was adopted. On a sheer priority basis, therefore, physiologists who record positive-going deflections (e.g., cortical surface potentials) have the choice of heretical nonconformism or submission to the fate of purveying depressing descending deflections.

Components of the Compound Action Potential of Peripheral Nerves. The compound action potential recorded monophasically from

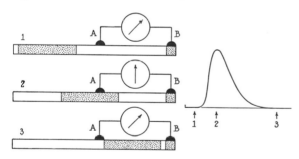

Fig. 2. Monophasic recording of nerve action potential.

Left, Small stippled area under B indicates nerve has been injured at this point. Consequently a steady injury potential is recorded in 1, B being negative to A. As action potential (long stippled area) progresses to A in 2, A and B become equipotential. In 3, action potential progresses beyond A and B is once more negative to A.

Right, Recorded monophasic action potential; numbered arrows indicate instantaneous potentials recorded at three stages of conduction shown at left.

*The demarcation potential might be expected to approximate the membrane potential of the injured fiber, since electrode B is connected to a region in which the steady membrane potential has been reduced to zero by destruction of the membrane. However, current will flow in the external medium from adjacent uninjured regions into the injured region and return through the axoplasm in each fiber. Consequently, the potential drop between the electrodes depends on the relative external and internal resistances of each fiber. Since internal resistance in fibers of the size considered here is quite high, the demarcation potential is only about one-fourth to one-third of the steady transmembrane potential. The shunting can be minimized by increasing the resistance of the external medium, e.g., by bathing the nerve at one recording site with isotonic sucrose. In such instances the demarcation potential approaches closely the true membrane potential. This method has proved useful in measuring action and membrane potentials of fibers too small to tolerate direct measurements with intracellular electrodes.

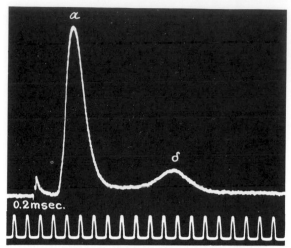

Fig. 3. Compound action potential of cat's saphenous nerve recorded 3.4 cm. from locus of stimulation. Temperature 37.5° C. (Courtesy of Dr. H. S. Gasser.)

a nerve trunk excited by a maximal* shock is usually irregular in contour, displaying two or more elevations displaced in time. Figure 3 shows a representative tracing, on a fast time base, of the first portion of the compound action potential in the cat saphenous nerve, recorded 3.4 cm. from the locus of stimulation; the successive components are labeled with Greek letters. Two hypotheses may be formulated to explain the polymodal contour of the compound potential: (i) some fibers may discharge repetitively to the stimulus, or (ii) the constituent fibers may conduct impulses at different speeds so that arrival time at the recording electrode is different for impulses in different fibers.

The second hypothesis can be put to a simple experimental test; if different fibers conduct impulses at different speeds, the temporal separation of the elevations should increase as the conduction distance increases. Figure 4 shows an experiment in which the first two components (labeled α and β) of the compound action potential in a frog sciatic nerve were tested for compliance with this requirement. Monophasic recording leads were attached to the nerve at four sites to sample the configuration of the compound action potential at four distances from

*Generally, a maximal stimulus or shock is one which produces a maximal response of the stimulated structure; i.e., stronger stimuli do not produce greater responses. For a nerve trunk a maximal stimulus is one which is adequate to excite all of the constituent fibers of the trunk and therefore produces a maximal compound action potential.

the stimulating electrode (S). At the farthest recording site (distance: 143 mm.), the α and β components were clearly separated. At the successively shorter conduction distances, the two elevations merged progressively until, at the most proximal electrode site (distance: 21 mm.), the overlap was so nearly complete that the individual components were scarcely distinguishable. Diagonal lines were then drawn between zero distance and the respective beginnings of α and β in the lowermost record, where the two components are clearly separated. The line so constructed for α intercepts with satisfactory precision the beginning of the α deflection in all

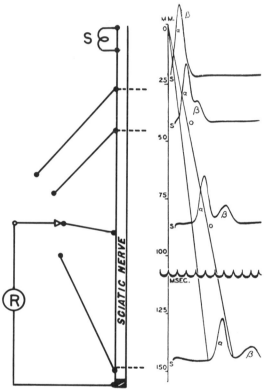

Fig. 4. Compound action potential of frog sciatic nerve recorded at different distances from site of stimulation.

Left, Diagram of recording apparatus: *S,* stimulus; *R,* recorder.

Right, Only the first two elevations, α and β, are shown. As conduction increases, α and β become clearly separated in time (temporal dispersion) because they reflect activity of fibers' conduction at different rates. Diagonal straight lines are drawn through onsets of α and β deflections; slopes of these lines give conduction rates of most rapidly conducting α and β fibers. (After Erlanger and Gasser, *Electrical signs of nervous activity.* Philadelphia, University of Pennsylvania Press, 1937.)

traces. Similarly, the line for the β deflection falls close to the computed onset of the β component indicated by small circles in the two intermediate traces. These results are best explained if it is assumed that impulses beginning together at S become temporally dispersed as the conduction distance increases because they traverse fibers with different uniform conduction speeds.

Closer scrutiny of the traces in which the components are clearly separated reveals that at increasing distances each deflection becomes broader in base and lower in amplitude. Nevertheless, planimetric measurements indicate that the area lying under each deflection remains constant, irrespective of the conduction distance. This finding suggests that within a group, as well as from group to group, there is a continuous spectrum of conduction speeds. This conclusion is borne out by determinations of conduction velocity in single axons. Among mammalian myelinated somatic fibers, representatives can be found for all speeds between about 5 m. per second and 120 m. per second. It will be pointed out later that the separation of peaks in the compound action potential results not from absolute discontinuities in the velocity spectrum but rather from unequal numerical distribution of fibers representing restricted bands of the spectrum.

Another readily demonstrable difference between fibers contributing to the various components (α, β, γ, etc.) of the compound action potential lies in the *thresholds to externally applied electrical stimuli*. As the shock to a nerve trunk is increased progressively from its threshold to maximal intensities, the successive components appear in the recording in the order α, β, γ, etc. In other words, conduction velocity and electrical threshold are inversely related, the rapidly conducting axons being more easily excited than the slower ones. It can be justifiably argued that axon thresholds to externally applied electrical stimuli have little intrinsic physiologic significance, but the relationship just described provides a valuable experimental maneuver, for it permits selective excitation of rapidly conducting fibers to the exclusion of slowly conducting fibers.

This maneuver is used repeatedly in neurophysiologic experimentation. An example pertinent to the present discussion is shown in Figure 5, which illustrates an experiment demonstrating conclusively that the α and β components of frog nerve arise independently from activity in different nerve fibers. The compound action potential was recorded from a site on the nerve trunk at a distance from the stimulating electrodes sufficient to separate clearly the α and β deflections. Two shocks of different intensities

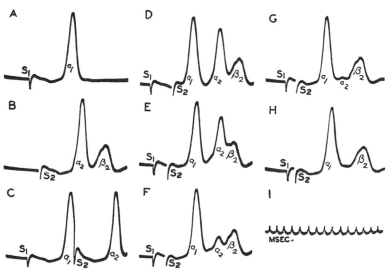

Fig. 5. Demonstration of independent conduction of α and β elevations of frog sciatic nerve. *A*, Stimulation by single shock (S_1) at strength just sufficient to produce maximal alpha elevation (α_1). *B*, Stimulation by stronger shock (S_2) produces an alpha elevation (α_2) and a beta (β_2) elevation. In records *C-H*, S_2 follows S_1 at progressively shorter intervals, so that deflection α_2 falls increasingly into refractory period of deflection α_1 until, in *H*, α_2 is completely obliterated. β_2 deflection is unaltered by refractory obliteration of α_2. *I*, Time scale. (From Erlanger and Gasser, *Electrical signs of nervous activity*. Philadelphia, University of Pennsylvania Press, 1937.)

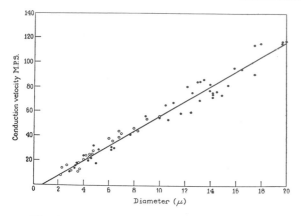

Fig. 6. Linear relation between conduction rate and diameter of mammalian myelinated nerve fibers. Slope of line is approximately 6 m. per second per μ of diameter. (After Hursh, from Gasser, *Ohio J. Sci.*, 1941, *41*:145–159.)

were used. The first stimulus was relatively weak and elicited only an α deflection, seen in *A*. The second shock was more intense and produced both α and β deflections (labeled α_2 and β_2 in *B*). In traces *C-H*, both shocks were applied to the nerve at gradually decreasing intershock intervals. At short intervals (traces *E-H*) α_2, coming in the refractory period of α, was progressively delayed and attenuated until, in trace *H*, α_2 was completely obliterated. At all intervals β_2 remained constant in amplitude and latency. The failure of α activity to induce refractoriness in elements responsible for β activity is an elegant and compelling proof that α and β components of the compound action potential are independently conducted by different fibers. Similar observations on later components indicate that these, too, are mediated by separate groups of axons.

RELATION BETWEEN CONDUCTION SPEED AND FIBER DIAMETER. The finding that nerve trunks are composed of elements having different properties (conduction speed and electrical threshold) leads naturally to the question: Can these differences in properties be correlated with morphologic differences between axons? There are numerous structural differences between axons, such as diameter and the presence or absence of a myelin sheath. At present, attention is focused on variations in diameter. For this purpose it is instructive to examine the myelinated somatic axons, or A fibers, as they are called, because they constitute a set in which diameter is the only prominent morphologic variable. It is the A fibers that are responsible

for the elevations labeled α and δ in Figure 3. When cross sections of various somatic nerve trunks treated with the myelin stain osmic acid are examined, the largest stained fibers are about 22 μ in diameter, the smallest about 1 μ. Between these two extremes there is a continuous spectrum of diameters, but the number of fibers in each portion of the diameter spectrum varies; indeed, in some nerve trunks certain bands of the spectrum may lack representation altogether.

The A fibers taken as a whole constitute a similar spectrum with respect to conduction rates. On purely theoretical grounds one would expect the largest fibers to conduct most rapidly, since their internal longitudinal resistance (the local circuit through which, according to theory, current must flow to excite adjacent nodes) is relatively low. In fact, it can be shown that the conduction rate and the fiber diameter of A fibers are linearly related. Hursh[11] plotted maximal conduction rates of various nerve trunks against the sizes of the largest myelinated fibers he found when he examined the trunks histologically, the trunks having been selected so that they provided a wide range of maximal fiber diameters. As shown in Figure 6, his results indicate that a straight line with a slope of 6 m. per second per μ of over-all diameter fits the observed points with reasonable accuracy.

Gasser and Grundfest[9] found an even closer approximation to exact linearity when they measured the diameter of the axon within the myelin sheath, rather than the over-all diameter; in their study, the ratio between conduction rate (in meters per second) and axon diameter (in microns) was 8.7. The relationship between conduction speed and fiber diameter is exceedingly useful because it permits reasonably accurate computation of one variable if the other is known. It must be emphasized, however, that the specific quantitative relationships just described apply only to the A fibers and not to other fiber types.

Once the relationship between fiber diameter and conduction velocity is recognized, it is easy to understand why large, rapidly conducting axons have lower thresholds to externally applied electrical shocks than do smaller, slowly conducting axons. When a shock is delivered through two electrodes placed in external contact with a nerve trunk, current flows between the two electrodes. Much of this current flows through the low-resistance interstitial fluid be-

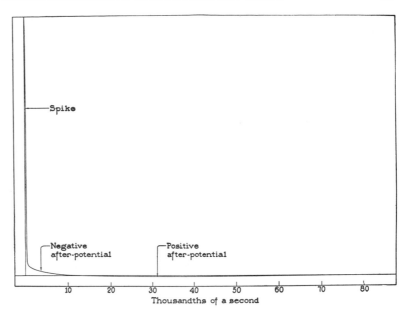

Fig. 7. Scale diagram of complete action potential of large myelinated nerve fibers in the cat, drawn so that spike potential and afterpotentials appear in their correct relative sizes and time relations. (From Gasser, *J. appli. Physiol.*, 1938, 9:88–96.)

tween the fibers and is ineffective in excitation. If the shock is sufficiently strong, however, some current flows in through the membrane at the anode, longitudinally through the axoplasm and out through the membrane at the cathode. Outward transmembrane current flow depolarizes the membrane underlying the cathode and, if of threshold magnitude, triggers the Hodgkin cycle as described in Chapter 2. This condition is easy to obtain with large axons because the longitudinal resistance is relatively low; with small axons the longitudinal resistance is higher and larger currents must be passed before adequate amounts traverse the effective path in through the membrane, longitudinally through the axoplasm and out through the membrane at the cathode. Thus the relationships of conduction velocity and of threshold to fiber diameter are both relatively simple and predictable consequences of the relationship between internal longitudinal resistance to fiber diameter.

Afterpotentials.   The compound action potential recorded at short conduction distances to minimize dispersion of components does not always terminate with the negative variation or spike potential. Often, a negative deflection, the *negative afterpotential,* is grafted onto the tail of the declining spike. Following the decline of the negative afterpotential to the baseline, a prolonged positive deflection, the *positive afterpotential,* occurs.

Negative and positive afterpotentials have certain features in common. (i) Both are consequences of, and hence dependent upon, ante-

cedent spike activity. (ii) Both are of very low amplitude and (iii) of long duration relative to the spike (see Fig. 7). (iv) Both are highly labile and heavily dependent upon the metabolic state and previous history of the fiber.

Since the afterpotentials reflect post-spike changes in the degree of polarization of the fibers, it is not surprising that they are accompanied by changes of excitability. During the negative afterpotential, the axons are slightly

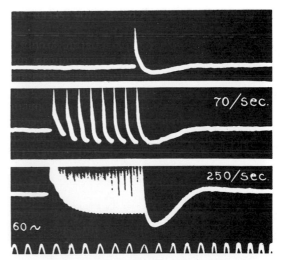

Fig. 8.   Afterpotentials of phrenic nerve following single (*upper* trace) and repetitive (*middle* and *lower* traces) stimulation. Amplification is so high that spike crest is far off this page. Records shown begin with negative afterpotential and continue below baseline into positive afterpotential. Time scale, 16.7 milliseconds. (From Gasser, *J. appl. Physiol.*, 1938, 9:88–96.)

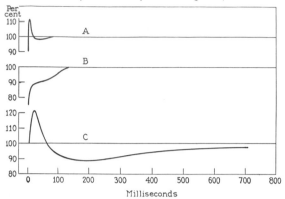

Fig. 9. Recovery cycles of A, B and C fibers. *Ordinates,* Excitability in terms of resting threshold set at 100. *Abscissae,* Time interval between conditioning and test shocks. (From Gasser, *Ohio J. Sci.,* 1941, *41:*145–159.)

depolarized and their excitability is elevated; during the positive afterpotential the fibers are slightly hyperpolarized and their excitability is depressed (Fig. 9). These post-spike alterations of excitability are called the *supernormal* and *subnormal periods,* respectively.

The origin of the afterpotentials is not entirely clear. Their timing suggests that they reflect metabolic processes associated with recovery. It is significant that 95 to 98 per cent of the increase in heat production of tetanized nerve occurs during the recovery period and runs a time course roughly corresponding to that of the afterpotentials. It is also significant that afterpotentials (especially the positive afterpotential)

are markedly accentuated in magnitude and duration by repetitive activity, which imposes a recovery "debt" on the fibers. Moreover, afterpotentials are most prominent in small fibers; for example, the positive afterpotential of C fibers may be as much as 10 to 30 per cent of the amplitude of the spike. Other things being equal, the influx of Na^+ during the passage of a spike along a segment of axon depends on the surface area of membrane, which is proportional to the radius. The change in intracellular concentration of Na^+, however, is inversely related to the volume of the segment, which varies with the *square of the radius.* It might therefore be expected that spike activity would produce a greater change in axoplasmic composition in a small fiber than in a larger fiber.

It has been suggested that the negative afterpotential results from extracellular accumulation of K^+ following the spike.[10] Calculations of the ion exchange during the spike indicate that this explanation is valid only if there is some barrier outside the axon which prevents ready diffusion of extruded K^+ throughout the extracellular space and thereby keeps the K^+ concentration high in the space immediately surrounding the axon membrane. As described in more detail below, C fibers lie in invaginations of Schwann cells (Fig. 10) so that the immediate extracellular space is peculiarly restricted in such a way that extracellular accumulation of K^+ during activity may well produce appreciable increases in external concentration of this ion.

Two mechanisms appear to be responsible for

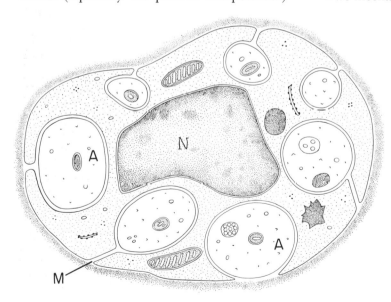

Fig. 10. Diagram of relation of C fibers to Schwann cells. Drawing represents cross section through single Schwann cell surrounding seven C fibers. *N,* Nucleus of Schwann cell; *A,* axon; *M,* mesaxon. Note that Schwann cell membrane is everywhere intact but is invaginated by nerve fibers. (After Elfvin, *J. Ultrastructure Res.,* 1958, *1:*428–454.)

TABLE 1. *Properties of Mammalian Nerve Fibers*

	A	B	s.C	d.r.C
Fiber diameter, μ	1–22	≤ 3	0.3–1.3	0.4–1.2
Conduction speed, m. per sec.	5–120	3–15	0.7–2.3	0.6–2.0
Spike duration, msec.	0.4–0.5	1.2	2.0	2.0
Absolutely refractory period, msec.	0.4–1.0	1.2	2.0	2.0
Negative afterpotential amplitude,				
per cent of spike	3–5	none	3–5	none
Duration, msec.	12–20	. . . .	50–80	. . . .
Positive afterpotential amplitude,				
per cent of spike	0.2	1.5–4.0	1.5	*
Duration, msec.	40–60	100–300	300–1000	*
Order of susceptibility to asphyxia	2	1	3	3
Velocity/diameter ratio	6	?	?	1.73 average

*A post-spike positivity 10 to 30 per cent of spike amplitude and decaying to half size in 50 msec. is recorded from d.r.C fibers. This afterpositivity differs from the positive afterpotential of other fibers (see text).

positive afterpotentials. (i) It has already been pointed out that the downstroke of the spike is due to a waning of Na^+ permeability and a rather prolonged increase in K^+ permeability. Since in the resting state K^+ is actively pumped into the axon, the resting membrane potential is slightly less than the K^+ equilibrium potential. During the post-spike period of elevated K^+ permeability, the membrane seeks a potential level closer to the K^+ equilibrium potential, i.e., becomes hyperpolarized. In accord with this theory, the positive afterpotential of C fibers is diminished by artificially increasing the external K^+ concentration.[10] (ii) The rate of the Na^+–K^+ pump increases with increased internal Na^+ concentration. Increased active extrusion of Na^+ drives the membrane potential farther from the Na^+ equilibrium potential, i.e., in a hyperpolarizing direction. Acceleration of the Na^+–K^+ pump appears to be principally responsible for the large positive afterpotentials following repetitive activity (Fig. 8), for replacing extracellular Na^+ with lithium or blocking the Na^+–K^+ pump with metabolic poisons abolishes post-tetanic positive afterpotentials.[15]

Types of Nerve Fibers.[6, 7] Systematic examination of the compound action potentials of various nerves of different composition reveals that axons can be classified into four distinctive types known as A, B, s.C and d.r.C fibers. The A fibers have already been described as myelinated, somatic, afferent and efferent fibers. The B fibers are myelinated, efferent, preganglionic

axons found in autonomic nerves. The C fibers are unmyelinated, the s.C group being the efferent postganglionic sympathetic axons, and the d.r.C group the small unmyelinated afferent axons found in peripheral nerves and dorsal roots. The distinctive properties of these fiber types are summarized in Table 1 and Figure 9.

It should be noted that the A fibers, although comprising a wide range of fiber diameters, constitute a homogeneous group except in respect to conduction speed, which varies predictably with diameter in the manner already described.

The B fibers are histologically indistinguishable from small A fibers and, as can be seen in Table 1, have conduction rates within the range exhibited by the A group, the smallest of which conduct impulses at speeds as low as 5 m. per second. B fibers are principally distinguished from A fibers by the absence of a negative afterpotential. Correspondingly, the recovery cycle of B fibers lacks a supernormal period, the relatively refractory period merging directly with the subnormal period (Fig. 9B). B fibers also differ from A fibers in spike duration, which for B is more than twice as great as for A fibers. Although a sizable range of conduction rates is represented, the compound action potential of B fibers, even at long conduction distances, is relatively smooth and does not break up into discrete elevations. This configuration is seen because all parts of the velocity spectrum have relatively equal numerical representation.

Unlike both A and B fibers, C fibers lack a

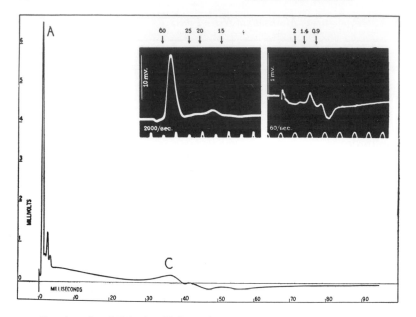

Fig. 11. Scale drawing of complete compound action potential of mammalian saphenous nerve. *Left inset,* Recording of A fiber components. *Right inset,* Recording of C fiber components. Numbers above arrows give maximal conduction rates (m. per sec.) of each component. (Combined from Gasser, *J. appl. physiol.,* 1938, *9*:88–96 and *Ohio J. Sci.,* 1941, *41*:145–159.)

myelin sheath visible by light microscopy and exhibit a unique relation between the Schwann sheath and the axon.[5, 8] A single Schwann cell forms the sheath of several C fibers, which lie in grooves formed by the invagination of the outer surface of the Schwann cells (Fig. 10). When the fibers are deeply embedded, the edges of the invaginated Schwann membrane lie in close approximation, forming narrow channels (*mesaxons*) to the outside. The space between the Schwann membrane and the axon membrane and that between the bounding membranes of the mesaxon appears to be of the order of 100 Ångstroms. It is this narrow communication with the outside which presumably forms the external diffusion barrier mentioned above.

Functionally, C fibers are distinguished from A fibers by slow conduction rates, long spike durations, high electrical thresholds and relatively great resistance to asphyxia. The various parts of the velocity and diameter spectra are unequally represented in the nerve trunks, and the conducted compound action potential displays a number of discrete elevations of surpassing complexity.

C fibers are divided into two groups, s.C and d.r.C, largely on the basis of differences in their afterpotentials.[7] The s.C group, postganglionic sympathetic axons, has pronounced negative and positive afterpotentials. The d.r.C group, comprised of the unmyelinated afferent fibers of peripheral nerves and dorsal roots, has no negative afterpotential but typically displays a large afterpositivity, which differs from the conventional positive afterpotential in that it is converted by repetitive activity into a negative deflection.

Composition of Peripheral Nerves. A typical peripheral nerve such as the sciatic nerve contains both afferent and efferent A fibers, afferent d.r.C fibers and s.C fibers supplying smooth muscle and glandular structures. Because the discrepancy in conduction rate and amplitude between the A and C groups is so great, it is not feasible to record the entire compound action potential of a mixed peripheral nerve on a single sweep of the oscilloscope, but the picture may be resynthesized graphically from several records taken with appropriate amplifications and time bases. Figure 11 shows such a resynthesized action potential, drawn to scale, for the saphenous nerve (a purely afferent cutaneous nerve), along with the recordings which provided the requisite data.

To prepare for discussions in subsequent chapters it is important to know the respective diameter spectra of the afferent and efferent A fibers in the various nerves. For cutaneous nerves, in which all the A fibers are afferent, the spectrum is determined simply by inspection of sections of the whole nerve stained with osmic acid. To ascertain the spectra for mixed nerves, it is necessary to cut the contributory ventral or dorsal roots (distal to the ganglion) and allow the efferent or afferent fibers, respectively, to degenerate. The remaining fibers may then be counted. Figure 12 shows the diameter distributions of the afferent fibers in a cutaneous nerve

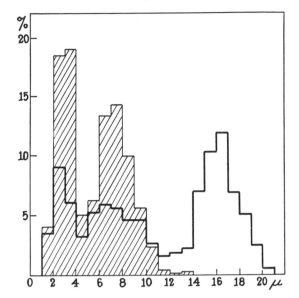

Fig. 12. Comparison of afferent fiber diameter distribution in a muscle nerve (heavy line) and a cutaneous nerve (hatched area). *Ordinates,* Number of fibers expressed as percentage of total. *Abscissae,* Fiber diameter in μ.

(thin line, crosshatched area) and in a "demotored," deep or muscle nerve (heavy line). The cutaneous afferent fibers have a bimodal distribution, one peak lying between 1 μ and 5 μ and the other between about 6 μ and 12 μ. The histogram for the muscle nerve, however, shows three peaks, two of which are approximately coextensive with the two peaks in the cutaneous nerve distribution. The third peak is comprised of large fibers, 12 to 21 μ in diameter, which are almost completely lacking in the cutaneous nerve. Systematic examination of the afferent fiber composition of different nerves shows that the relationships indicated in Figure 12 can be generalized: *the large (12 to 21 μ) afferent fibers are confined to muscle nerves, whereas the other two groups (1 to 5 μ and 6 to 12 μ), although varying somewhat in proportions, are represented in all somatic nerve trunks.*

It should be remembered that both cutaneous and "demotored" muscle nerves contain a great many unmedullated d.r.C fibers as well as the medullated A fibers. In fact, in some cutaneous nerve trunks unmedullated fibers may be three or four times as prevalent as A fibers.

The diameter spectra of efferent fibers is illustrated in Figure 13, which shows the diameter distributions in a ventral root and in a typical muscle nerve deafferented by degenerative dorsal root section. In both the root and the nerve the distribution is distinctly bimodal,

the two prominent clusters, from 12 to 20 μ and from 2 to 8 μ, being separated by a definite nadir in the range from 8 to 12 μ. Corresponding to the two distinctly separated clusters in the histogram are two distinct elevations in the conducted compound action potential (see Fig. 17, Chap. 7). As will be discussed in a subsequent chapter, these two groups of motor fibers differ functionally.

Deafferented nerve trunks (but not ventral roots) contain, in addition to the A fibers, unmedullated postganglionic autonomic axons (s.C) which supply smooth muscle and glandular structures.

The diameter distribution shown in Figure 13 is, in general, typical of all ventral roots, but there are minor individual differences. The most marked difference is between those roots (thoracic and upper lumbar) which contribute white rami to the sympathetic chain and those which do not. In the former, but not in the latter, there is a sizable peak below 3 μ in the range of distribution; this peak is composed of B fibers.

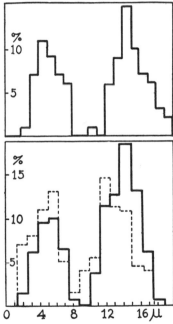

Fig. 13. Diameter distributions of efferent fibers. Coordinates as in Figure 12. *Upper,* Data from ventral root. *Lower,* Data from gastrocnemius nerve, from which afferent fibers were removed by degenerative section of dorsal roots. *Solid line,* Data from sample taken 50 mm. from muscle. *Broken line,* Data from sample 8 mm. from muscle. Since daughter fibers are of lesser diameter than parent fibers, spectrum shifts slightly to left at the closer distance. (After Eccles and Sherrington, *Proc. roy. Soc.,* 1930, *B106:*326–357.)

Terminology. It has already been mentioned that the Greek letters α, β, γ, δ (and sometimes ϵ) are often used to designate the successive elevations of the compound action potential of the A fibers in a nerve trunk. Since these elevations result from activity in fibers conducting at different velocities, proportional to fiber diameter, the Greek-letter designation may also be used as a categorization of fiber diameters. A difficulty arises, however, because an elevation in the compound action potential reflects not only the diameter but also the number of fibers involved. In nerves with similar function and origins, e.g., cutaneous sensory nerves, the diameter spectra are surprisingly constant. However, when nerves with different origins and functions are compared, striking discrepancies are evident; for example, the first major deflection of the compound action potential of a "demotored" muscle nerve occupies fibers of a diameter range which is sparsely represented in cutaneous nerves. For the afferent fibers of deep nerve trunks, it is current practice to use Lloyd's[12] Roman-numeral designations, which are based on fiber diameter rather than on electrogram elevations. According to this classification, the A fibers of muscle nerves are divided into three groups: I, 12 to 21 μ; II, 6 to 12 μ; and III, 1 to 6 μ. The C fibers (both the d.r. and the s. subgroups) are sometimes referred to as Group IV.

For cutaneous afferent fibers the Greek-letter designations are preferable: *alpha* (6 to 17 μ) and *delta* (1 to 6 μ). Cutaneous unmyelinated afferent fibers are called simply C fibers.

Unfortunately, Greek-letter and Roman-numeral designations are often used interchangeably. The following relations approximately equate the two designations: (i) A-alpha corresponds to Groups I and II. (ii) A-delta corresponds to Group III. (iii) The C group corresponds to Group IV. In cat nerve the deflections originally labeled beta and gamma are apparently largely or wholly artifacts and have no equivalents in the Roman-numerical classification.

Conduction in Regenerating Axons.

When an axon is severed, the portion disconnected from the cell body undergoes a sequence of morphologic changes known as *Wallerian* or *secondary degeneration.** These changes consist of

---

*Changes occurring in the cell body after its axon has been amputated are called *retrograde degeneration*. These changes include disappearance of Nissl granules (chromatolysis), swelling of the perikaryon, and displacement of the nucleus from its typical central position to the periphery. In some neurons (e.g., spinal motoneurons) retrograde degeneration is reversible, and the cell body eventually regains its normal morphologic features and functional properties. In others (e.g., thalamic neurons) retrograde degeneration is irreversible, and the dead perikaryon is removed by phagocytes. Rarely, morphologic changes similar to those of irreversible retrograde degeneration occur in a cell body

---

chemical alteration of the myelin, leading ultimately to its complete dissolution, along with fragmentation and eventual dissolution of the axis cylinder. The degeneration products of both the myelin and the axis cylinder are removed by macrophages.

This process would leave a hollow tube of Schwann sheath if an exuberant proliferation of the Schwann cells did not fill the lumen with a solid column of Schwann cells. At the level of transection, the Schwann cells also grow out of the end of the stumps and, if the gap is not excessive, bridge the space between them, reestablishing continuity. From the end of the axon in the proximal stump, a multitude of sprouts develop and grow between the Schwann cells of the bridge into the column beyond. Although many such sprouts cross the bridge, usually only one survives and continues to advance distally at a rate which may be as great as 3.5 to 4.5 mm. per day. The advancing tip of the regenerating fiber is unmyelinated, and its diameter is small compared to that of the Schwann column in which it grows. Maturation of the fiber, i.e., increase in diameter and acquisition of a myelin sheath, eventually restores the morphological picture typical of mature nerves. Maturation is much slower than longitudinal advance. There is evidence that maturation is progressive along a regenerating stretch of nerve; i.e., at any time the proximal segments are more mature than are the distal segments.

The conduction speed in a regenerating nerve increases as regeneration progresses and constitutes a reliable measure of the time course of maturation. It may be that normal conduction rates are never regained after nerves are cut and resutured. For example, Berry *et al.*[1] found that the maximum conduction rate in a sciatic nerve more than a year (450 days) after section and suture was about 85 m. per second, whereas a normal sciatic nerve contains fibers conducting at rates up to 120 m. per second. Histologic examination revealed that the largest fiber in the regenerated nerve measured 16 μ, compared with 20 μ in the normal nerve. Failure to mature completely appears to be re-

---

after section of the axons making synaptic connections with it; this phenomenon is known as *transneuronal degeneration*. An example is degeneration of neurons in the lateral geniculate body following section of the optic nerve.

lated to extensive branching (which results in daughter fibers smaller than the parent axon) at the suture line. When the nerve is crushed rather than sectioned, complete maturation occurs, apparently because the continuity of the sheaths is not broken, and the axons grow into their own sheaths without branching.

In the clinical treatment of injuries to peripheral nerves, the major consideration is to establish continuity of the stumps, for, if the gap is large, the probability of sprouts successfully traversing the bridge and reaching the distal stump is reduced. Sprouts meeting an obstruction may form a painful tumor called a *neuroma*. When the nerve has merely been crushed, the prognosis is good. If the trunk is interrupted, the ends of the stumps are approximated by suturing through the epineurium or by gluing the ends together with fibrinogen. When the gap is too large to permit approximation of the severed ends, *cable grafts* are sometimes employed; i.e., segments of expendable nerves (for example, cutaneous nerves) are removed and sutured between the stumps to provide the framework for a bridge.

POTENTIALS IN A VOLUME CONDUCTOR* [14]

A nerve fiber is surrounded by interstitial fluid and by other fibers. Although the other fibers, especially if they are myelinated, are good insulators,† the interstitial fluid is a volume conductor which extends throughout the body. Unless current is flowing in a volume conductor, it is isopotential. In the body, current flows in the interstitial fluid only during impulse conduction in excitable cells; no current flows in quiescent cells. The existence of a current flow in a volume conductor means that there must be a voltage source present. This

*This section written by J. W. Woodbury.

†In tissues other than myelinated nerve, membrane resistance is much lower and capacitance much higher than in nerve, and an appreciable part of the local current may flow through adjacent inactive cells. Part of this current flows through the membrane resistor and, during rapid changes in potential in the interstitial fluid, part flows through the membrane capacitor. Thus, to a limited extent, inactive cells are a portion of the volume conductor surrounding an active cell.

source, in an impulse, is the voltage difference between the active region and the inactive region.

In comparison with the potentials recorded from an isolated nerve trunk, the potential at a point in a volume conductor (recorded with respect to an electrode so distant that its potential is negligible) is difficult to interpret. (i) It is difficult to determine the location of the active fibers because their currents spread throughout the body. (ii) The size and time course of the volley are uncertain because, as the distance between the recording electrode and the active tissue is increased, the recorded potential becomes smaller and slower. (iii) The relationship between the changes in transmembrane potential and the resulting current flow in the volume conductor is quite complicated.

However, the estimation of potentials occurring in a volume conductor as a result of nerve activity is made fairly simple if the action potential is approximated by a square wave, i.e., if depolarization and repolarization are treated as if they were instantaneous (see Fig. 19b). The potential set up at a point in a volume conductor by a square action potential is proportional to the product of the height of the transmembrane action potential and the solid angle of the wave boundaries as measured at the recording electrode. The solid angle is a measure of the apparent size of an object as viewed from a particular point. The square wave approximation to the action potential is quantitatively inaccurate, but this approximation does give an accurate estimate of the sequence of potential changes. The use of this approximation is justified by the great conceptual and computational simplification that results.

Since the variation of recorded potential with distance from the active tissue depends solely on the solid angle of the wave boundaries, and since the concept of a solid angle is unfamiliar to most students, the first parts of this section present a definition of the solid angle. It is then shown that the potential due to a dipole layer is proportional to the solid angle subtended by the potential at the recording electrode. The section concludes with a description of how this principle is applied to the interpretation of the potentials set up in a volume conductor by nerve activity.

Solid Angle. A solid angle is measured in a manner analogous to measurement of a plane angle, and therefore, the manner of measur-

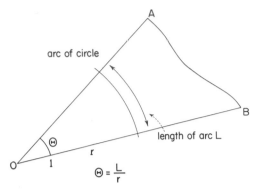

a. PLANE ANGLE

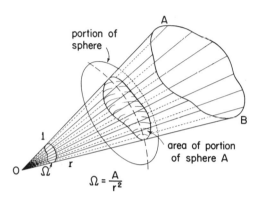

b. SOLID ANGLE

Fig. 14. Calculation of plane and solid angles. *a*, Measurement of plane angle Θ, subtended by a curving line AB from point O. Arc of a circle of radius r with center at O is inscribed. Length of arc, L, between lines OA and OB is measured. Θ is defined as equal to L/r. *b*, Measurement of solid angle, Ω, subtended by surface AB from O. Radii are drawn from O to all points on periphery of AB. This irregular cone is a solid angle. Ω is measured by inscribing a sphere of radius r with center at O and measuring the area, A, on the surface of sphere cut out by the irregular cone. Ω is defined as A/r².

ing a plane angle will be reviewed here. The angle Θ, subtended at O by a curved line AB (Fig. 14*a*), may be measured in degrees; but a more general and natural way to measure the angle is as follows. A circle of any radius (r) with a center at O is drawn. The angle Θ, in radians, is defined as the ratio of the length of an arc (L) between lines OA and OB to the radius; $\Theta = L/r$. This definition conforms with experience; when the angle is fixed, L increases proportionately with r, so L/r remains constant. An angle of 1 radian is such that the arc length is equal to the radius. The circumference of a circle is $2\pi r$, so a full circle is an

angle of $2\pi r/r = 2\pi$ radians. Therefore, 1 radian $= 360°/2\pi = 57.4°$. Angular measure in radians is dimensionless.

A solid angle is the three-dimensional equivalent of a plane angle. The solid angle subtended at a point by any object is proportional to the apparent size of the object when the object is viewed from the point. For this reason, the potential at a point in a volume conductor is often referred to as being "seen" by the electrode. An object looms larger as it is brought nearer to the eye, even though the dimensions of the object do not change. The solid angle subtended at point O (Fig. 14*b*) by the object AB may be outlined by drawing lines from O to every point on the perimeter of AB. The size of a solid angle Ω (omega) is calculated by drawing a sphere of radius r about O as the center; the area (A) cut out by the solid angle on the surface of the sphere is then measured, just as the length of the arc was measured to determine the size of a plane angle. Since the surface area of a sphere is $4\pi r^2$, A depends on the square of the radius. Therefore, just as $\Theta = L/r$, $\Omega = A/r^2$. The dimensionless unit of solid angle measure is the *steradian*. One steradian is the solid angle subtended by an area of 1 cm.² (of any shape) on the surface of a sphere with a radius of 1 cm. The solid angle of an object that completely surrounds O is $4\pi r^2/r^2 = 4\pi$ steradians.

Potential Due to Dipole Layer. Two equal and opposite charges (q) held a short distance (δ) apart constitute a *dipole* of moment (m); $m = q\delta$ (Fig. 15*a*). The electric field of a dipole

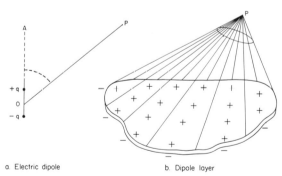

a. Electric dipole   b. Dipole layer

Fig. 15. Dipole and dipole layer. *a*, In dipole charges +q and −q are the distance δ apart. Potential at P is calculated in terms of angle Θ, between lines OA and OP, and r, the length of OP. *b*, Potential at P is proportional to Ω, the solid angle subtended at P by the dipole layer. q_A is surface charge per unit area and δ is thickness of dipole layer.

falls off rapidly with distance, because the + and − charges exert nearly equal and opposite forces on an exploring charge. At distances large compared with δ, the electric field is inversely proportional to the cube of the distance r; and the potential is inversely proportional to r^2 rather than to r, as it is with a single charge. A *dipole layer* or surface is formed by separating + and − charges across a layer of thickness δ (Fig. 15*b*). Each region of the layer contains equal numbers of + and − charges; i.e., the + and − charges have been separated from each other. However, the number of + or − charges per unit area of the surface may vary from one region to the next. The dipole moment per unit area (m_A) of a dipole layer is the product of the charge per unit area (q_A) and the thickness of the layer; $m_A = q_A\delta$. A charged cell membrane is a closed dipole layer since + and − charges are separated across the membrane. In a quiescent cell m_A is a constant. During activity m_A at a fixed point varies rapidly in time, or, at a fixed time, m_A varies rapidly with distance.

Since the membrane is a capacitor, the amount of charge per unit area is directly pro-

portional to the transmembrane potential at any point. The calculation of the potential arising from cell membrane charge is the same as the computation of the potential of a dipole layer. The potential (ℰ) of a point in a volume conductor is defined as the difference in potential between that point and a point a large distance from the dipole layer. The potential due to a dipole layer is inversely proportional to the square of the distance to it, and so the potential at a sufficiently distant second or indifferent recording electrode can be made arbitrarily small. *At any point, the potential due to a dipole layer of constant moment is proportional to the solid angle subtended by the surface at the point;* $ℰ = (ℰ_m/4\pi)\Omega$, where $ℰ_m$ is the transmembrane potential (Fig. 15*b*). The sign of the potential is the same as the sign of the charge on the face of the dipole layer nearest to P. This rule reduces the problem of computing the potentials in a volume conductor to a problem in solid geometry.

Derivation of potential due to dipole layer. Figure 16*a* shows the geometry involved in computing the potential at P due to the dipole AB. Since the membrane is only about 100 Ångstroms thick, any recording elec-

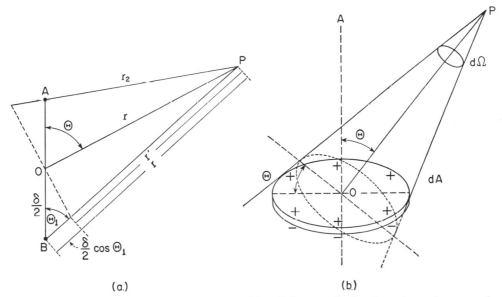

(a.)   (b.)

Fig. 16. *a*, Diagram used to calculate potential at P due to a dipole when r is much greater than δ (r is disproportionately short in this drawing). When r is much greater than δ, lines AP, OP, and BP are considered to be parallel and $\Theta_1 = \Theta_2$.

b, Solid angle, $d\Omega$, subtended at point P by a small circular segment, of area dA, of dipole layer. (Both δ and dA are actually much smaller than r, but dA is shown disproportionately large here for clarity.) Sphere of radius r is drawn around P. Area cut out on surface of sphere by dA is dA cos Θ, where Θ is the angle between OA and OP. OA is drawn from center of dA, perpendicular to dA and toward its positively charged surface. If Θ is greater than $\pi/2$ (90°), $d\Omega$ is negative. Therefore, $d\Omega = $ dA cos Θ/r^2.

trode is a large distance away from the membrane compared to its thickness. Although, for the sake of clarity, Figure 16a is drawn with δ nearly as large as r, in the real situation r is much larger than δ; so lines AP, OP and BP are nearly parallel, and $\Theta = \Theta_1$. The potential at P is the sum of the potentials due to the charge $+q$ at A and $-q$ at B:

$$\mathcal{E} = K \left(\frac{q}{r_2} - \frac{q}{r_1} \right) \tag{1}$$

To a good approximation, r_1 and r_2 are given by

$$r_1 = r + \frac{\delta}{2} \cos \Theta$$
$$r_2 = r - \frac{\delta}{2} \cos \Theta$$

Substitution of these into Equation 1 gives

$$\mathcal{E} = Kq \left(\frac{1}{r - \frac{\delta}{2} \cos \Theta} - \frac{1}{r + \frac{\delta}{2} \cos \Theta} \right) = \frac{Kq\delta \cos \Theta}{r^2 - \frac{\delta^2}{4} \cos^2 \Theta}$$

or

$$\mathcal{E} = K \frac{m \cos \Theta}{r^2} \tag{2}$$

The last step follows from the definition of m and the approximation that $\delta^2/4$ is negligible compared with r^2. Equation 2 shows that the potential at a point depends inversely on r^2, as stated above, and also on the angle between the dipole and the point. This dependence is expected because the potential along a line through O and perpendicular to AB must be zero, since the component of the electric field along this line is always zero.

Exactly the same arguments apply to any small area (dA) of a dipole layer (Fig. 16b), since each element of area has charges, $+q_A dA$ and $-q_A dA$, at points separated by the distance δ. Therefore, the contribution of dA to the potential at P is

$$d\mathcal{E} = K \frac{q_A dA \delta \cos \Theta}{r^2} = K \frac{m_A dA \cos \Theta}{r^2} \tag{3}$$

Part of Equation 3, dA/r^2, is in the form of an element of solid angle, $d\Omega$. This fact suggests that the solid angle of dA at P should be calculated (Fig. 16b). To calculate $d\Omega$, a sphere of radius r and center P is drawn through dA; dA is then projected onto the surface of this sphere. The area of this projection is dA $\cos \Theta$, so the solid angle is, by definition:

$$d\Omega = \frac{dA \cos \Theta}{r^2} \tag{4}$$

Substitution of Equation 4 in Equation 3 gives

$$d\mathcal{E} = K m_A \frac{dA \cos \Theta}{r^2} = K m_A d\Omega \tag{5}$$

Integration of Equation 5 over the whole of the dipole surface (S) gives

$$\mathcal{E} = K \int_S m_A d\Omega \tag{6}$$

If m_A is constant, Equation 5 is a perfect differential and Equation 6 becomes simply

$$\mathcal{E} = K m_A \Omega \tag{7}$$

where Ω is the solid angle of the surface as seen from P. The simplicity of Equation 7 compared to Equation 6 is the reason for approximating the action potential by a square wave. The integration indicated by Equation 6 is accurate* but is difficult and tedious for the action potential. Equation 7 is comparatively easy to evaluate. The quantity Km_A can be evaluated in terms of $\mathcal{E}_m$, the transmembrane potential. As will be shown below, the potential outside a quiescent cell is everywhere zero because the effective solid angle of the cell is zero. Moving the recording electrode inside the cell changes the potential from zero to $\mathcal{E}_m$ and the effective solid angle from 0 to 4π. Therefore, inside the cell Equation 7 becomes

$$\mathcal{E}_m = K m_A \cdot 4\pi \text{ or } K m_A = \frac{\mathcal{E}_m}{4\pi} \tag{8}$$

The relation then becomes

$$\mathcal{E} = \frac{\mathcal{E}_m}{4\pi} \Omega \tag{9}$$

POTENTIAL OF QUIESCENT CELL. The proportionality between potential and the solid angle of the dipole layer means that the potential depends only on the apparent size of the layer and is independent of its detailed shape. Figure 17 shows that the transmembrane potential of a quiescent cell does not influence the potential at an external point, because any point outside the cell is faced by two equally but oppositely charged surfaces of the same solid angle. Since the transmembrane potential is everywhere constant in a quiescent cell, the potential due to the part of the surface of the cell facing P (Fig. 17b) is $+(\mathcal{E}_m/4\pi)\Omega$, and that due to the portion facing away from P (Fig. 17c) is $-(\mathcal{E}_m/4\pi)\Omega$ because the negatively charged surface faces P. The total potential at P is the sum of the potentials due to all portions of the dipole layer, so

$$\mathcal{E} = +(\mathcal{E}_m/4\pi)\Omega - (\mathcal{E}_m/4\pi)\Omega = 0.$$

* Equation 6 is correct for a nerve fiber only if the specific resistivity of the intracellular fluid is equal to that of the interstitial fluid. The specific resistivity of the axoplasm is about twice that of the interstitial fluid.

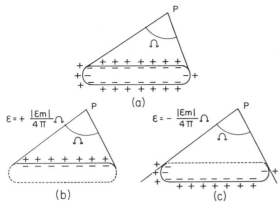

Fig. 17. Axial section of a closed cylindrical cell, drawn to illustrate that the potential outside a quiescent cell is zero. *a*, From point P, the electrode "sees" two equally and oppositely polarized cell membranes subtending the solid angle Ω. *b*, Calculation of potential at P due to the near membrane; potential is $+(|\mathcal{E}_m|/4\pi)\Omega$ because positive side of membrane faces P. *c*, Potential of the far membrane is $-(|\mathcal{E}_m|/4\pi)\Omega$ because negative side of membrane faces P. Total potential is sum of the individual potentials: $\mathcal{E} = (|\mathcal{E}_m|/4\pi)\Omega - (|\mathcal{E}_m|/4\pi)\Omega = 0$, where $|\mathcal{E}_m|$ indicates absolute value of E_m.

This rather formal method of calculation conforms with earlier statements that the external potential due to a quiescent cell is zero because there is no external current flow. It should be emphasized that potential changes in a volume conductor arise from current flow. The current flow due to a dipole layer is such that the potential is proportional to the solid angle.

POTENTIAL OF ACTIVE CELL. As mentioned above, the calculation of the potential generated in a volume conductor by an active cell is simplified by approximating the smoothly rising and falling action potential wave with an abruptly rising and falling square wave. A nerve fiber carrying an impulse can be divided into two regions, quiescent and active. In the square wave approximation it is assumed that the quiescent region has a constant potential $(\mathcal{E}_s)$, that the active region has a constant potential equal to the overshoot of the action potential $(\mathcal{E}_a)$, and that the transition between the two regions occurs at a point.* Figure 18 shows

* The action potential of a large myelinated nerve fiber rises in about 0.1 millisecond and has a velocity of 100 m. per second. Therefore, the wavefront occupies 100 mm. per millisecond × 0.1 millisecond = 10 mm. This is 500 times the fiber diameter. Because of this slow rise, potentials recorded in volume from an active nerve are longer and lower than those expected from square-wave solid-angle analysis.

how the potential due to a wavefront of depolarization can be calculated. Figure 18*a* is a diagram of an axial section of an excitable cell with a wave of depolarization near the center. The solid angles Ω_1 and Ω_3 contribute no potential to P, because the proximal and distal portions of the membrane contribute equal and opposite potentials. However, in Ω_2 the proximal membrane is active and contributes a negative potential to P; the distal membrane is inactive and also contributes a negative potential to P. The potential at P is $-(\mathcal{E}_a/4\pi)\Omega_2$, where $\mathcal{E}_a$ is about 130 mV. As Ω_2 is the solid angle of the wavefront, it is seen that the potential at an external point depends only on the solid angle subtended by the boundaries between the ac-

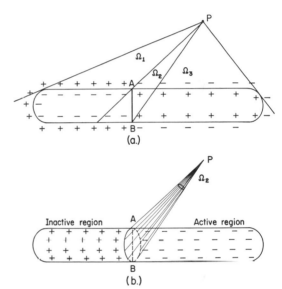

Fig. 18. Potential at an external point P due to the rising phase of action potential in a cell at some instant. Line AB indicates where the transmembrane potential reverses; for simplicity the reversal is assumed to occur abruptly.

a, Axial section through a cylindrical cell showing cell membrane; diameter has been exaggerated. Total solid angle of cell is divided into three portions, Ω_1, Ω_2 and Ω_3 by lines PA and PB. Potential at P due to solid angles Ω_1 and Ω_3 is zero, since the nearer and farther membranes contribute equal but opposite potentials (see Fig. 17). However, in Ω_2 the nearer membrane is active (outside negative) and contributes a potential at P of the same sign as the more distant, inactive membrane.

b, Diagram to show that under conditions in *a*, the potential at P is the same as would be obtained if the membrane charges were placed on the cross section AB. The size of the potential at P at any instant is proportional to the apparent size of the cross section of the nerve at the wavefront.

tive and inactive regions. Figure 18*b* is a perspective sketch of the solid angle of a wave boundary in a nerve fiber.

A nerve impulse is a wave traveling at constant speed, so Figure 18 represents the situation at one instant in time. As this wavefront moves from right to left, the solid angle first increases and then gradually decreases to zero. Figure 19 shows the method of estimating the sequence of potential changes as a single wave-

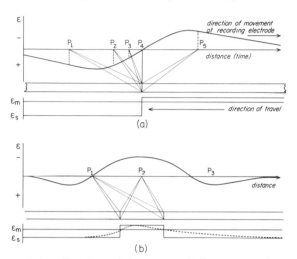

Fig. 19. Potential generated by propagating wavefronts.

a, Diphasic potential due to a wavefront traveling from right to left at constant velocity. Time sequence of potential changes at a fixed point is shown along line parallel to nerve fiber. Sequence is constructed by supposing that wavefront is stationary and that a recording electrode is moved from left to right along a line parallel to nerve. When the recording electrode is at points P_1, P_2, P_3, it "sees" positive side of wavefront. Dashed line at P_1 has a height proportional to the solid angle of the wavefront from P_1 and thus proportional to the voltage recorded at P_1. As the recording electrode moves toward the right, solid angle of wavefront at first increases slowly owing to closer approach and then decreases rapidly as the electrode sees the wavefront more and more on edge. At P_4 the potential is zero and immediately thereafter becomes negative. The plot is both of $\mathcal{E}$ as a function of distance at a fixed time and of $\mathcal{E}$ as a function of time at a fixed point.

b, Triphasic potential due to an idealized impulse. Solid angles of waves of both depolarization and repolarization must be added to obtain $\mathcal{E}$. Construction method same as in *a*. P_1 is point of zero potential; note that it is to left of wavefront. Triphasic $(+,-,+)$ potential is typical of a propagated nerve impulse. Note that the maximum external potential is much smaller than the internal potential. An internal electrode at P_2 would see positive changes over 4π; while outside, even on the surface of the fiber, the solid angle is of the order of $4\pi/100$.

front (*a*) or a nerve impulse (*b*) travels from right to left at a constant velocity. A recording electrode put anywhere on the line P_1P_5 (Fig. 19*a*) would record the positive-negative sequence of potential changes as the wavefront approaches, passes and leaves the point nearest the electrode. The curve may be constructed by supposing that the wave is fixed and that the recording electrode is moving in the opposite direction (left to right) at the same constant velocity. The solid angle at each point P_1, P_2, etc. is measured and an ordinate proportional to the solid angle is drawn at that point. In this way the diphasic positive-negative potential sequence is constructed. The graph can be a plot of potential as a function of distance at a fixed time, or as a function of time with the recording electrode fixed. This diphasic volume-conductor potential is frequently seen in recordings from heart tissue during depolarization, because about 0.5 second elapses between depolarization and repolarization in a heart cell.

Figure 19*b* shows the sequence of potential changes expected from a nerve impulse. The triphasic wave $(+, -, +)$ arises because the waves of depolarization and repolarization are sufficiently close together that both contribute significantly to the potential. To the left of P_1 the wavefront dominates and the potential is positive. At P_1 the two solid angles are equal and opposite in sign, and $\mathcal{E}$ is zero; at P_2 both boundaries contribute a negative potential; and at P_3 the departing wave of repolarization dominates, and the potential is again positive. Triphasic waves are recorded from active nerve fibers in volume, but the last positive phase is much smaller and longer than the first, because repolarization is slower than depolarization (Fig. 20*b*).

Consider the situation in which an impulse originates at a distance from a recording electrode and travels away from it. Such a situation is encountered when an electrode is inserted in the vicinity of a cell body: an impulse initiated in the cell body by synaptic activity travels along the axon away from the cell body. When the cell body becomes active, the electrode sees negativity. $\mathcal{E}$ remains negative but gradually diminishes as the wave of depolarization recedes. Repolarization in the cell body rapidly changes the potential to a large positive value, which falls off as the repolarization recedes.

Figure 20*a* shows the potential recorded from a bullfrog sciatic nerve at a region near its entry

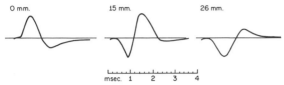

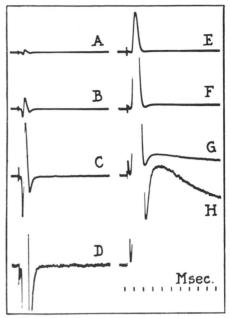

Fig. 20. Nerve action potentials in a volume conductor. An excised bullfrog nerve is arranged so that it enters a volume conductor at x = 0 and exits from it at x = 26 mm. *Ordinate,* Potential of a close electrode with respect to a distant one (negative upward). *Abscissa,* Time.

a, Potential set up by a nerve volley when recording electrode is at level of nerve entry (x = 0) and distant electrode is 3 mm. away from nerve (y = 3). *b,* Potential recorded at x = 15 mm., y = 3 mm. *c,* Potential at x = 26 mm., y = 3 mm. (After Lorente de Nó, *Stud. Rockefeller Inst. Med. Res.,* 1947, *132*(2): 384–482.)

Fig. 21. Responses of frog sciatic nerve recorded in volume (*left*) and in an insulating medium (*right*). Each pair of traces (*A–E, B–F,* etc.) recorded at same gain, but between each pair from above downward gain was progressively increased approximately five-fold. Note in volume recorded responses relatively small amplitudes and absence of any sign of negative afterpotential, which is clearly seen in *G* and *H.* (From Lloyd in *Biology of mental health and disease.* New York, Hoeber, 1952.)

into a volume conductor.[14] The geometry is the same as that just described for a cell body and an axon. The negative-positive diphasic sequence is as expected. The same type of argument shows that an impulse that approaches but does not reach a recording electrode sets up a positive-negative diphasic sequence of potential changes (Fig. 20*c*). A recording situation of this sort is found where a fiber terminates before reaching the recording electrode or, more commonly, where the recording electrode has penetrated, injured and blocked the active fibers so that activity cannot reach the electrode.

PROPERTIES OF SPINAL TRACTS

Activity in spinal structures must of necessity be recorded in volume, for it is usually impossible to reduce the extracellular conducting medium to negligible proportions. As already mentioned, this circumstance creates some special problems. The first relates to identification of the structures that originate potentials recorded from the spinal cord. This problem arises because potentials in a volume conductor may be recorded at points distant from the site of activity. One method of localizing activity is to thrust an electrode into the suspected tract. The injury thus inflicted blocks activity in the conducting fibers, and the recorded response then consists of a monophasically positive deflection typical of approaching activity ("killed end" recording).* Conversion of a triphasic (positive-

---

* The response is +, − diphasic, but the negative part is usually negligibly small.

negative-positive) response to a monophasic positive response by penetration indicates that the electrode has damaged active fibers. When the potential sequence remains triphasic, inactive tracts have been penetrated.

A related problem is the computation of conduction times from volume recordings. In insulated nerve trunks conduction times are estimated by measuring the time interval between the shock artifact and the onset of the action potential. In volume, however, positive potentials are recorded before the activity reaches the electrode. The arrival of the conducted wave of depolarization at the level of the recording electrode is approximately signaled by the reversal from positivity to negativity.†

A final peculiarity of volume recording is that the recording electrode records a potential only when the conducting structures are un-

---

†A somewhat better measure is to a point midway between the first reversal and peak negativity. For synchronous volleys when the negative component rises rapidly, little error is incurred by using the reversal point.

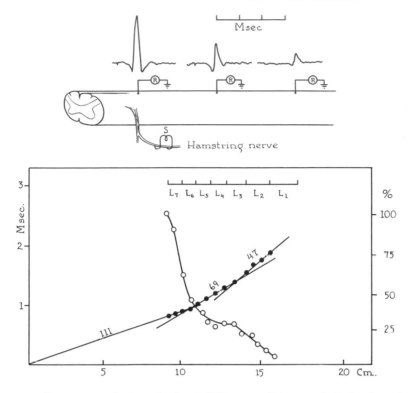

Fig. 22. Conduction in intramedullary projections of Group I afferent fibers. *Upper diagram,* Recordings from surface of dorsal column following a Group I afferent volley originating in hamstring nerve. *Graph* shows conduction time (filled circles, ordinate on left) and relative amplitude (open circle, ordinate on right) of response as a function of conduction distance. Conduction speed indicated by numbers above lines. Scale above locates spinal segments. (After Lloyd and McIntyre, *J. Neurophysiol.,* 1950, *13:*39–54.)

equally or oppositely polarized. When a cell is completely polarized or completely depolarized, no potential is recorded, because every solid angle is matched by an equal and electrically opposite solid angle. It follows that prolonged changes in polarization with decay constants which are long in relation to conduction time do not appear in volume recordings. The afterpotentials have these characteristics and are not observed in volume recordings (Fig. 21).

Fiber Constitution of Spinal Tracts. The white matter of the spinal cord consists chiefly of fibers extending longitudinally for varying distances. All sizes of myelinated and unmyelinated fibers are represented. As yet, histologic and oscillographic studies have yielded only scattered information on the fiber constitution and conduction properties of spinal tracts, but several important generalizations can be made.

PROPRIOSPINAL FIBERS. The spinal cord contains vast numbers of fibers that arise and terminate wholly within the spinal cord. These are known by several names, the most usual being "propriospinal" fibers or "intrinsic" spinal fibers. Tower *et al.*[16] studied the propriospinal fibers after all other fibers (the "extrinsic" fibers) were removed by section of the cord above and below a selected region and division

of all the dorsal roots to that region. When sufficient time elapses for degeneration of the extrinsic fibers after such an operation, only propriospinal fibers remain. Upon examination of histologic preparations after this procedure, there are still so many fibers in the cord that it is difficult to appreciate the loss of fibers. The propriospinal fibers exist everywhere throughout the white matter, although they are not evenly distributed. In the dorsal columns most of the propriospinal fibers are small (about 1 μ), but there is a scattering of larger fibers. In contrast, the ventrolateral columns contain fibers of all sizes, many being as large as any found in the normal spinal cord. These large propriospinal fibers are the only ones that have been studied oscillographically; they are known to conduct impulses at rates up to 120 m. per second.

EXTRINSIC FIBERS. The *ascending fibers* in the spinal cord arise from neurons within the cord itself or, in the case of the dorsal columns, from neurons in the dorsal root ganglia. In the dorsal columns the largest fibers are ascending branches of Group I afferent fibers arising from muscle nerves.[13] After a Group I afferent volley, a surface electrode on the ipsilateral dorsal column at the level of the activated dorsal roots records a large triphasic deflection, which has a latency compatible with a maximal conduction rate of 110 to 120 m. per second (Fig. 22). As the electrode is moved rostrally along the dorsal column, two changes occur in the recorded response: (i) its amplitude diminishes and eventually reaches zero, and (ii) its conduction rate progressively decreases.

For example, a Group I afferent volley initiated in the quadriceps nerve is traveling at a rate of 117 m. per second at the time of entry at L_5, has decelerated to a rate of 24 m. per second when L_1 is reached, and cannot be traced much beyond the T_{12} segment. The explanation is that the conducting fibers branch along their ascending course, giving off collaterals to the cells of Clarke's column. With each branching the parent fiber becomes smaller and hence conducts more slowly. Eventually all the activity of the Group I fibers is relayed into Clarke's column and thence upward in the dorsal spinocerebellar tract. The Group I fibers are thus temporary occupants of the dorsal columns. The most rapidly conducting permanent occupants of these columns (i.e., the fibers which remain in the dorsal columns throughout the length of the cord) have conduction rates which usually do not exceed 70 m. per second. This tract also contains many smaller fibers (Fig. 23).

The dorsal spinocerebellar tract, which originates from cells in Clarke's columns, occupies the dorsolateral white matter. This tract is characterized by a significant number of large fibers (Fig. 23), some of which conduct at velocities exceeding 120 m. per second. Mixed in with these fibers are others originating in unidentified cell groups in the lumbar gray matter. These are destined to pass, via a relay in the cervical cord, to the contralateral olive and are called spino-olivary fibers. They conduct impulses at rates up to about 60 m. per second.[4]

The fibers comprising the spinothalamic tract in the anterolateral white matter are small (Fig. 23), and their conduction rates are not known. Some of the larger fibers (greater than 5 μ) in the anterolateral white matter of the lumbar segments are said to constitute the ventral spinocerebellar tract and have conduction rates ranging from 30 to 80 m. per second.[3]

The *descending tracts* include the pyramidal or corticospinal tract, the vestibulospinal tract and the reticulospinal tract. The latter two tracts are of fairly uniform size and conduct at rates comparable to those of the large A fibers. The pyramidal tract contains fibers ranging through a wide band of fiber sizes, the largest conducting at rates of about 65 m. per second. The compound action potential of the bulbar and upper cervical portions of this tract includes two elevations, one conducting at 35 to 40 m. per second and the other at 12 to 16 m. per second.[2] This finding is surprising because the fiber spectrum of the tract at the bulbar level is not bimodal.

Despite the lack of systematic observations such as we have on peripheral fibers, it may be said in general conclusion that nerve fibers in the central nervous system have the same properties of conduction as do peripheral nerve fibers. Scattered data on the refractory period, the diameter-velocity relation, the velocity-threshold relation and the velocity-spike relation of fibers in the central nervous system indicate that their properties do not vary greatly from those of peripheral fibers.

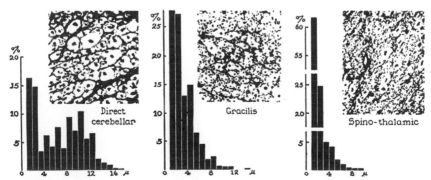

Fig. 23. Fiber distribution plots and typical sections of areas of white matter containing dorsal spinocerebellar tract, fasciculus gracilis and spinothalamic tract. Selected areas contain, in addition to tracts named, numerous propriospinal fibers. Note striking representation of large-diameter fibers in spinocerebellar tract as contrasted with small fibers which make up spinothalamic tract. Fasciculus gracilis is intermediate in fiber constitution. (After Häggqvist, *Z. micr.-anat. Forsch.*, 1936, *39*:1–34.)

REFERENCES

1. BERRY, C. M., GRUNDFEST, H. and HINSEY, J. C. *J. Neurophysiol.,* 1944, *7:*103–115.
2. BISHOP, P. O., JEREMY, D. and LANCE, J. W. *J. Neurophysiol.,* 1953, *16:*537–550.
3. CARREA, R. M. E. and GRUNDFEST, H. *J. Neurophysiol.,* 1954, *17:*203–238.
4. DIBIAGIO, F. and GRUNDFEST, H. *J. Neurophysiol.,* 1955, *18:*299–304.
5. ELFVIN, L. G. *J. Ultrastructure Res.,* 1958, *1:*428–454.
6. GASSER, H. S. *Ohio J. Sci.,* 1941, *41:*145–159.
7. GASSER, H. S. *J. gen. Physiol.,* 1950, *33:*651–690.
8. GASSER, H. S. *Exp. Cell Res.,* 1958, Suppl. *5:*3–17.
9. GASSER, H. S. and GRUNDFEST, H. *Amer. J. Physiol.,* 1939, *127:*393–414.
10. GREENGARD, P. and STRAUB, R. W. *J. Physiol.,* 1958, *144:*442–462.
11. HURSH, J. B. *Amer. J. Physiol.,* 1939, *127:*131–139.
12. LLOYD, D. P. C. *J. Neurophysiol.,* 1943, *6:*293–315.
13. LLOYD, D. P. C. and MCINTYRE, A. K. *J. Neurophysiol.,* 1950, *13:*39–54.
14. LORENTE DE NÓ, R. *Stud. Rockefeller Inst. med. Res.,* 1947, *132*(2):384–482.
15. RITCHIE, J. M. and STRAUB, R. W. *J. Physiol.,* 1957, *136:*80–97.
16. TOWER, S., BODIAN, D. and HOWE, H. *J. Neurophysiol.,* 1941, *4:*388–397.
17. WOODBURY, J. W. *J. cell. comp. Physiol.,* 1952, *39:*323–339.

CHAPTER 4

Receptor Mechanism

By HARRY D. PATTON

In Chapter 2 it was emphasized that the distinctive and unique property of axon and muscle fiber membranes is the ability to undergo transient permeability changes when the *transmembrane voltage is decreased.* Specifically, depolarization increases sodium permeability of excitable membranes. Depolarization to a critical threshold value so increases sodium permeability that the resulting Na^+ influx in itself causes further transmembrane voltage drop which, in turn, by further increasing Na^+ permeability, leads to greater Na^+ influx and to greater depolarization. These explosive self-perpetuating events, known as the Hodgkin cycle (see p. 42), underlie the rapid reversal of membrane potential which constitutes the upstroke of the action potential. A region of membrane thus reversed in electrical polarity provides a sink for outward current flow through adjacent regions of membrane which are, in turn, depolarized to threshold and driven toward the Na^+ equilibrium potential. Depolarization begets depolarization and so the action potential progresses from point to point or, more precisely, from node to node.

Thus the critical initial event in impulse initiation is membrane depolarization. Experimentally, depolarization is simply but artificially accomplished by passing outward through the membrane a current from a battery or other suitable device. In nature, however, apart from chance accidents to amateur electricians, nerve impulses are rarely so initiated; indeed, the physical stimuli which normally initiate neural action include a variety of energy forms, none of which is electrical—light, heat, mechanical distortion of nerve endings, chemicals, etc. Such nonelectrical stimuli are effective because, applied to appropriate specialized afferent fiber terminals, they produce depolarization of the ending. The magnitude of the resultant depolarization is directly related to the intensity of the physical stimulus; if the latter is sufficiently intense, depolarization may reach threshold value and initiate impulse discharge by the mechanisms already described. The terminal afferent endings which undergo depolarization in response to specific kinds of physical stimuli are called *receptors,* and the membrane potential decrease thus produced in the terminals is called the *generator* or *receptor potential.*[6]

It is important to recognize clearly the difference between the generator potential and the

95

action potential. The stationary, nonpropagated generator potential is confined to the terminals and diminishes rapidly with distance along the fiber. In contrast, the action potential is a self-propagating process and is conducted without decrement along the fiber. The generator potential is graded; i.e., through a large range, amplitude is a direct function of stimulus intensity. The action potential is "all or nothing"; provided the stimulus exceeds threshold, response amplitude is fixed and independent of stimulus intensity. The generator potential is *graded* and *stationary;* the action potential, *all-or-nothing* and *conducted.*

RECEPTORS AS TRANSDUCERS

The receptor performs as a transducer, i.e., as a structure which transforms one kind of energy into another. Irrespective of the kind of physical stimulus which excites it, the immediate response of any receptor is an electrical change—a depolarization which is an approximate analog of the physical stimulus in time and magnitude. Depolarization, in turn, leads to repetitive discharge of all-or-nothing conducted action potentials, the frequency of discharge being directly related to the amplitude of the depolarizing generator potential. In a single receptor, then, the spike discharge frequency is the coded indicator of stimulus intensity. The sequence may be summarized as follows: Physical stimulus of intensity I $\rightarrow$ Generator potential of amplitude A $=$ f(I) $\rightarrow$ Spike discharge of frequency F $=$ f(A). Stated in engineering terminology, the receptor transduces one form of energy (e.g., pressure or heat) to an electrical change, the intensity being coded by amplitude modulation; in the transformation from local, graded to conducted, all-or-nothing signals, intensity is coded by frequency modulation.

Although the principles described above apply generally to all receptors, the transducer process sometimes includes other intermediate events. This is particularly true of the organs of special sense. For example, the initiation of visual signals involves an intermediate chemical event, photic breakdown of a visual pigment being an essential step in the development of the generator potential. In some receptive systems, e.g., the ear, the initial graded response probably arises in accessory elements closely related to the nerve terminals rather than in the neural membrane itself.*

In the present chapter, attention is confined to some simple representative receptors chosen to illustrate general receptor properties and their range of variation. Detailed descriptions of more complex receptors are found in subsequent chapters.

DIFFERENTIAL SENSITIVITY OF RECEPTORS

A basic postulate concerning receptor function is that each receptor is adapted for detecting a particular kind of energy. Thus, we speak of photoreceptors, thermoreceptors, chemoreceptors and mechanoreceptors. Among the mechanoreceptors are numerous types which preferentially respond to various kinds of mechanical stimuli, e.g., stretch of muscles or tendons, rotation of joints, light deformation of the skin, bending of hairs, distension of hollow structures such as blood vessels or abdominal viscera. Selective sensitivity of receptors and the range of their sensitivities determine what kinds of external energy are signaled to the central nervous system. Some forms of energy (e.g., very long or very short electromagnetic wave lengths, very high and very low frequency vibrations of air) neither arouse sensations nor evoke reflex response because man lacks receptors capable of detecting and signaling such environmental stimuli. Receptors behave as "pass filters" admitting to the central nervous system some kinds of information about the external world and rejecting other kinds.

The concept of differential or selective sensitivity is subject to certain qualifications. Even the most specialized receptors may be excited by more than one kind of stimulus provided that the stimulus intensity is sufficiently high. Receptor selectivity is thus relative and takes

---

* Davis[2] has proposed that the term "generator potential" be reserved for graded depolarizations arising in neural membranes and directly triggering the conducted spikes and that the term "receptor potential" be used to describe electrical responses of specialized accessory receptor cells which are incapable of conducting all-or-nothing responses. Unfortunately, for most receptors detailed knowledge of basic mechanisms is inadequate to permit clear distinction and most authors use the two terms interchangeably.

the form of a relatively low threshold to one kind of energy without excluding responsiveness to intense stimuli of other kinds. The energy form to which the receptor responds most readily is called the *adequate stimulus* of that receptor. Thus, as Sherrington put it, the receptor serves to lower the threshold of excitability of reflex arcs to the adequate stimulus and to heighten it to others.

Some receptors respond only to stimuli which are sufficiently intense to cause tissue damage, and the energy form (crushing, strong pressure, cutting, burning) employed to produce damage is unimportant. In other words, the adequate stimulus for these receptors is not a particular kind of energy but rather the immediate consequence of strong stimulation, viz., tissue damage. Such high-threshold receptors are called *nociceptors;* their excitation gives rise to sensations of pain and elicits stereotyped protective reflex patterns which are described in Chapter 7.

An exception to the principle of differential sensitivity is found in one kind of cutaneous receptor which responds both to light mechanical distortion of the skin and to thermal changes.[14, 18, 19, 34] At temperatures above 42° C. or below 22° C., discharge of these receptors ceases and even mechanical deformation of the skin fails to excite them. Such receptors thus appear to have dual roles as mechanoreceptors and thermoreceptors. Other cutaneous receptors are selectively responsive to thermal changes and insensitive to mechanical distortion, while still others respond readily to mechanical stimuli but not to thermal changes even through the broad range of 12 to 43° C.[14, 34]

Differential Sensitivity and Morphological Differentiation. Although the peripheral terminations of most afferent nerve fibers consist fundamentally of thin unmyelinated prolongations of the parent axon, the morphological configuration and shape of the terminals and their relations with non-neural structures are highly variable. Some fibers branch repeatedly to form a fine but extensive terminal arborization; in others the terminal branches may anastamose to form a network. Still other fibers terminate in complicated whorls or helices or in flattened plates, knobs or beaded terminals. Many endings are surrounded by elaborate connective tissue capsules; others terminate in baskets around specialized non-neural cells.

The organs of special sense show an even greater range of morphological specialization.

Morphological differentiation of receptor types suggests a correlated functional differentiation and consequently much effort has been directed toward assigning to the various morphological species of receptors specific functional properties. To some extent these efforts have been successful; for example, there is little doubt that the fine nerve endings surrounding the base of the hair follicle are selectively sensitive to mechanical distortion occasioned by displacement of the hair. Similarly, the elaborately encapsulated pacinian corpuscle found in the cat's mesentery, in subcutaneous tissue and in the interosseus membrane is selectively sensitive to distortion produced by rapid compression of the laminated capsule.[8, 9, 27] However, correlation between gross morphological structure and functional specificity of receptors is not always possible. For example, hairy skin is sensitive to mechanical distortion (touch), to thermal stimuli (warmth and cold) and to noxious stimuli (pain) but contains only two morphologically identifiable receptors: hair follicle endings and free unencapsulated nerve endings.[12] The cornea contains only free nerve endings but is sensitive to each of the modalities listed above.[25] It is therefore obvious that receptor function is not necessarily morphologically labeled. Differential sensitivity of receptors probably depends on more subtle structural differences than are revealed by light microscopy, viz., molecular structure of the receptor membrane.

Lack of correlation between gross morphological and functional properties is not in itself a contradiction of the principle of differential sensitivity of receptors. Discovery that the multisentient cornea contains only one structurally identifiable species of ending does not mean that each of the structurally similar endings is promiscuously sensitive to all energy forms but rather that the "tuning" of a receptor to specific kinds of energy cannot be determined by simple histological inspection. Differential sensitivity can be tested only by functional studies in which the responsiveness of single receptors to various kinds of stimuli is tested. Such studies have, with the exceptions mentioned in the preceding section, confirmed the principle of differential sensitivity.[9]

MEASUREMENT OF GENERATOR POTENTIALS

The receptor terminal's initial response to an

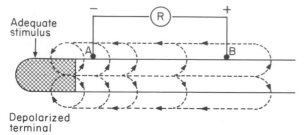

Fig. 1. Diagram illustrating method of recording with externally placed electrodes the generator potential of a receptor. Hatched area at left represents terminal depolarized by adequate stimulus. Direction of current indicated by dotted lines and arrows. Dense outward current flow at A drops transmembrane potential to a level below that at B. Recorder R registers voltage (IR) drop due to external current flow from B to A.

applied adequate stimulus is a graded non-propagated depolarization—the generator potential. To measure this local response in isolation and uncomplicated by propagated spikes it is necessary either to employ only stimuli so weak that the resultant generator potential does not exceed threshold or to block selectively the spike-generating mechanism by drugs such as procaine or tetrodotoxin, a toxin obtained from the puffer fish, which in low concentrations appear to have no influence on the generator mechanism. The latter procedure, while carrying with it the hazard that the drug may not be entirely selective in its action and may thus cause some unsuspected aberration of the generator process, has the advantage that it permits quantitative investigation of stimulus–response relations through a large range of stimulus strengths.

Since the stimulus-induced depolarization is normally restricted to the unmyelinated terminal, the ideal recording would measure with an intracellular electrode the transmembrane potential of the terminal. Unfortunately, this ideal arrangement is not possible because the fineness of the terminals precludes successful impalement and also because, in many instances, the terminals are surrounded by tough, impenetrable connective tissue elements. Therefore indirect methods employing external electrodes are usually employed to detect generator potentials. In Chapter 2 it was pointed out that a stationary depolarization confined to a segment of membrane causes in adjacent segments outward current flow which diminishes exponentially with distance from the site of the

stationary depolarization as in Figure 1. Since outward current flow is greater at A than at B, the membrane is depolarized more at A than at B and current flows in the external circuit from B to A. An external recording circuit thus registers a voltage drop due to the current flowing between B and A through the resistance of the external medium. Since the current is small, it is desirable to make the external resistance between A and B as high as possible to increase the voltage (or IR) drop. This is accomplished by immersing the segment between A and B in a high-resistance medium such as mineral oil, isotonic sucrose or air. It should be emphasized that such indirect measurements do not provide absolute values of the generator potential but, instead, smaller voltages which are proportional to the depolarization of the terminal.*

In some receptors it is possible to record the transmembrane potential near, but not within, the region of the generator terminal. In such instances, the recorded potentials again only approximate the magnitude of the generator potential because transmembrane potential changes due to a stationary depolarization attenuate rapidly with distance along the fiber.

PROPERTIES OF GENERATOR POTENTIALS IN DIFFERENT RECEPTORS

Generator potentials have been clearly demonstrated in several receptors which have been studied intensively because their structures favor detection of such potentials. One such receptor is the pacinian corpuscle, an encapsulated ending found in the mesentery of the cat (Fig. 2A). The organ consists of a single myelinated nerve fiber which penetrates the central core of a macroscopic (about 1.2 mm. by 0.8 mm.) multilaminated connective tissue capsule. Within the capsule, the fiber loses its myelin coat and runs as a nearly straight, naked fiber to end blindly near the distal end of the core. The receptor is exquisitely and selectively sensitive to mechanical compression of the capsule; a displacement of 0.2 to 0.5 μ causes a detectable generator potential.[8, 27] Figure 3 shows generator potentials recorded from a pacinian

---

* Because of the cable properties of the nerve fiber, this method of recording also produces some distortion of the time course of generator potentials, especially if the rates of potential change are rapid.

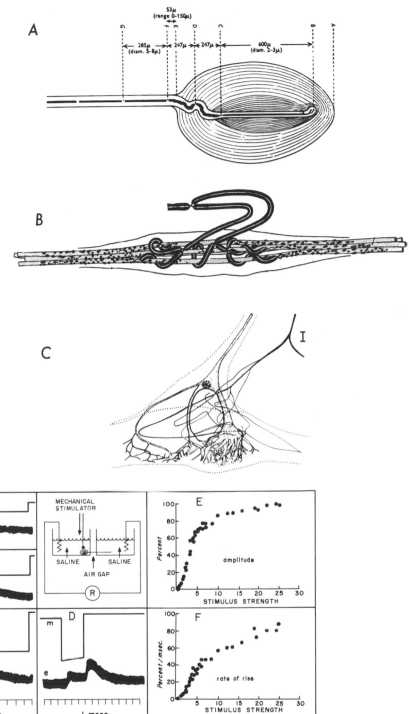

Fig. 2. Some receptors from which generator potentials have been recorded. *A,* Pacinian corpuscle. (From Quilliam and Sato, *J. Physiol.,* 1955, *129*:167–176.) *B,* Muscle spindle of frog. (After Gray, *Proc. roy. Soc. (Lond.),* 1957, *B146*:416–430.) *C,* Crayfish stretch receptor. Dotted lines indicate sheath and muscle bundle which is omitted to show clearly the dendritic endings. (After Florey and Florey, *J. gen. Physiol.,* 1955, *39*:69–85.)

Fig. 3. Generator potentials of pacinian corpuscle. Insert shows stimulating and recording arrangement. *A, B* and *C,* Generator potentials (e) elicited by mechanical compressions of different magnitudes shown by m. Upward deflections of e indicate relative negativity of terminal. *D,* Short mechanical pulse elicits both "on" and "off" responses which sum. *E,* Relation between amplitude of generator potential and stimulus strength; ordinate, amplitude of generator potential expressed as percentage of maximum; abscissa, stimulus strength in arbitrary units. *F,* Relation between rate of rise of generator potential and stimulus strength. Ordinate, percentage of maximum amplitude attained in 1 msec.; abscissa, stimulus strength in arbitrary units. (After Gray and Sato, *J. Physiol.,* 1953, *122*:610–636.)

corpuscle treated with a weak solution of procaine to block spike generation. The recording arrangement is shown in the inset. The stimulus was a minute mechanical compression of the capsule with a fine glass rod moved by a piezoelectric crystal; in each frame the displacement is indicated by the upper trace (m) and the receptor response is shown in the lower trace (e), an upward deflection signaling negativity of the receptor ending. In A, B and C rectangular mechanical pulses of increasing magnitudes were applied to the corpuscle for about 9 milliseconds. Several important characteristics of the recorded generator potentials are evident. First, both the peak amplitude and the rate of rise of the generator potential increase as stimulus intensity increases. The graphs in Figure 3E and F show the relationships between those variables plotted over a wide range of stimulus intensities. As stimulus intensity increases, generator potential amplitude increases approximately exponentially to a steady value beyond which further increments of stimulus intensity cause little further increase. In the intermediate range of stimulus strengths, potential amplitude signals stimulus intensity although not in simple linear proportionality. The rate of rise of the potential (Fig. 3F), on the other hand, continues to increase with increasing stimulus intensity even through the range at which potential amplitude has become relatively stable; within the latter range the relationship between stimulus intensity and rate of change of potential is approximately linear.

In addition, it should be mentioned that the pacinian corpuscle is rate-sensitive. If the magnitude of the mechanical stimulus is held constant, the amplitude of the generator potential varies with velocity of displacement.

Another peculiarity of the generator potential of the pacinian corpuscle is illustrated in Figure 3A, B and C: when a long mechanical pulse is applied to the corpuscle, the generator potential rises to peak value and then declines to zero although the mechanical stimulus persists. Figure 3D further shows that when the mechanical compression is released, a second generator potential (the "off-response") is generated. The receptor thus behaves in an "on-off" fashion signaling the onset and cessation of the stimulus. When, as in Figure 3D, the stimulus is discontinued before the "on" response is dissipated, "on" and "off" responses sum. This peculiarity is discussed in more detail later; for the present it should be noted that, because of this property, the generator potential of the pacinian corpuscle is an imperfect analog of the mechanical stimulus.

A second receptor in which generator potentials can be readily recorded is the stretch receptor of frog muscle.[7] This structure, similar to the somewhat more complex stretch receptor of mammalian muscle (see Chap. 7), consists of three to twelve slender specialized muscle fibers (called intrafusal fibers) which are segregated from the surrounding muscle fibers (extrafusal fibers) by a spindle-shaped connective tissue capsule (Fig. 2B). At several points the capsule is penetrated by the branches (usually two) of individual afferent axons which, after traversing the lymph-filled capsular space, intertwine around the intrafusal fibers, eventually losing their myelin sheaths and terminating in fine naked varicosities. The adequate stimulus for the spindle is stretch that mechanically distorts the endings. Figure 4 shows the generator potential recorded from a procaine-treated spindle during a 1.3 mm. stretch. During the stretch

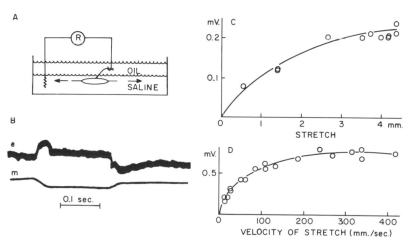

Fig. 4. Generator potential of frog muscle spindle. A, Diagram of recording arrangement. B, Generator potential (e) elicited by 1.3 mm stretch of muscle indicated by m. Upward deflection in e signifies relative negativity of terminal. C, Relation between amplitude of the static component (ordinate) and magnitude of stretch (abscissa). D, Relation between amplitude of the dynamic component (ordinate) and velocity of stretch (abscissa). (After Katz, J. Physiol., 1950, 111:261–282.)

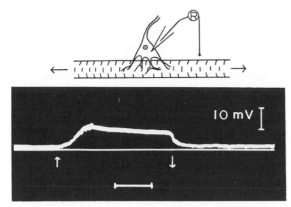

Fig. 5. Generator potential of crayfish stretch receptor. Diagram shows recording arrangement. Muscle bundle stretched at first arrow and released at second arrow. Upward deflection signifies reduction of transmembrane potential. Horizontal bar below, 1 sec. (From Eyzaguirre and Kuffler, *J. gen. Physiol.*, 1955, *39*:87–119.)

the ending becomes depolarized to a maximal value, which declines, when the lengthening is complete, to a lower steady value that persists throughout the stretch. Finally, when the stretch is discontinued, the generator potential transiently reverses ("off-effect") and then slowly climbs to the baseline value. The generator potential of the stretch receptor is thus divisible into three components: (i) a dynamic phase, which coincides with the period of active lengthening of the muscle, (ii) a static phase during sustained but invariant stretch, and (iii) the off-response at the termination of stretch. The amplitude of the dynamic phase is related to the velocity of stretch of the muscle as in Figure 4*D*, which shows the amplitude of the dynamic component when the muscle was stretched by a constant amount but at variant rates. The static component, on the other hand, varies with the magnitude of the stretch, as shown in Figure 4*C*, and is little influenced by velocity of stretch. The off-response is highly variable but when present is, unlike the depolarizing off-response of the pacinian corpuscle, always in the hyperpolarizing direction.

A third receptor in which generator potentials are readily measured is the muscle stretch receptor of the crayfish (Fig. 2*C*). It consists of a large (100 μ diameter), peripherally located neuron with a complex system of dendrites that terminate among the muscle fibers bridging the abdominal segments. As shown in Figure 2*C*, the dendrites also receive an innervation via an efferent axon I, the function of which will be

discussed later. The receptor cell has a single axon directed toward the central nervous system. Stretch of the muscle fibers mechanically distorts and depolarizes the dendrites. The large receptor cell body can be easily impaled with a microelectrode to measure the transmembrane potential shifts induced by depolarization in the dendrites. Figure 5 shows the intracellular recorded potential induced by brief stretch of the muscle bundle of such a receptor. The potential declines slightly during the stretch and decays to the baseline at the termination of the stimulus. In some instances a hyperpolarizing off-response, similar to that seen in the frog muscle spindle, may occur.

ADAPTATION

In neither the pacinian corpuscle nor in the two stretch receptors described is the generator potential a perfect analog of the applied stimulus, for if the stimulus is prolonged, the amplitude of the potential declines. This decrease of the magnitude of the generator potential during sustained stimulation is called *adaptation*.* In the case of the pacinian corpuscle the departure from analog is extreme, for the depolarization declines to zero during a sustained stimulus; in the stretch receptor the generator potential during a prolonged stretch drops only from the high value of the dynamic phase to the steady lower value of the static phase. Receptors like the pacinian corpuscle in which adaptation reduces the membrane potential below the firing level are sometimes called rapidly adapting receptors, whereas those (e.g., the stretch receptor) in which the generator potential shows only a limited decrease with time are called slowly adapting receptors. Since the important distinction is between magnitudes rather than between rates of adaptation, the two types are more appropriately called *phasic*

* More commonly the term "adaptation" is used to describe the decrease in spike frequency during a sustained stimulus. Since frequency of firing is largely determined by the amplitude of the generator potential, there is usually no confusion in using the same term to describe both phenomena. However, it should be remembered that adaptation of spike discharge may be influenced by properties (e.g., inactivation of sodium conductance) which are peculiar to the all-or-nothing spike mechanism and which are not necessarily applicable to the adaptation of the generator potential.

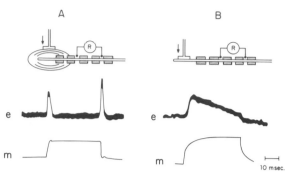

Fig. 6. Generator potential in pacinian corpuscle before (*A*) and after (*B*) removal of connective tissue capsule; e, generator potential; m, mechanical stimulus. (After Mendelson and Lowenstein, *Science*, 1964, *144*:554–555.)

and *tonic* receptors. Examples of phasic receptors, other than the pacinian corpuscle, are the mechanoreceptors ending around hair follicles; tonic receptors include, among others, the mammalian muscle stretch receptor and the tendon stretch receptor, the pressoreceptors in the carotid sinus and certain cutaneous touch and thermal receptors. Phasic receptors signal only the onset and cessation of stimulation, whereas tonic receptors continuously signal a persistent stimulus.

The mechanism of adaptation is not known and may be different for different receptors. One might suspect that the physical properties of the structures surrounding mechanoreceptor terminals might account in part or wholly for adaptation, because mechanical stimuli must be transmitted through these structures to reach the nerve endings. Hubbard,[16] using an ingenious technique of flash microphotography, measured the displacement of capsular lamellae in the pacinian corpuscle during compression. During a prolonged pulse the deeper lamellae nearest the nerve terminal moved inward transiently and then gradually resumed their location with a time course comparable to the decay of the generator potential. Since displacements of the inner laminae are those which are directly transmitted to the sensitive neural membrane, he suggested that adaptation results wholly, or in large part, from the viscoelastic properties of the capsule. Displacements during release of compression were not studied.

Recently Mendelson and Lowenstein[31] have investigated directly the role of the lamellated capsule in adaptation. By careful microdissection the capsule can be removed almost completely, and the response of such denuded receptors to mechanical stimuli can be compared with that of intact receptors. Figure 6*A* shows the generator potentials recorded from an intact receptor subjected to a prolonged mechanical pulse. Depolarization occurs at the onset of compression but decays to the baseline in about 6 milliseconds. At the end of the stimulus an "off-response" of similar duration occurs. Figure 6*B* shows the response of a "stripped" receptor to a long mechanical pulse. Depolarization, although declining slowly from the initial peak value, persists throughout the period of mechanical compression. The slow decay of the generator potential in the denuded receptor must be ascribed to some property of the receptor membrane perhaps akin to accommodation. The rapid and complete adaptation of the intact corpuscle signifies the contribution of the lamellated capsule. Evidently the capsule is a poor transmitter of elastic force; only velocity-dependent viscous force is significantly transmitted to the center of the capsule, where the receptor ending is located. A puzzling and as yet unexplained finding is the absence of a depolarizing off-response in the denuded preparation.

To what extent non-neural structures contribute to adaptation in other receptors is not certain. Matthews[29] suggested that the dynamic phase of the stretch receptor might result from the viscous properties of the intrafusal fibers so that sudden extending forces cause momentarily high tensions which diminish as the intrafusal fibers belatedly adjust to a new length. Katz[22] suggested that the dynamic component and the off-effect result from changes of capacitance of the endings. If stretching a polarized membrane decreases the thickness of the barrier between the charges and increases its surface area, the capacitance would be expected to increase and the voltage to diminish momentarily, returning along a time course determined by the newly established time constant. But these are merely speculations and the precise mechanism of adaptation is obscure.

IONIC MECHANISM OF THE GENERATOR POTENTIAL

In all three receptors described, the adequate stimulus decreases the transmembrane potential of the terminals. This transducer action is most highly developed in the unmyelinated terminals. For example, the terminal 700 μ of the pacinian receptor stripped of its capsule responds to minute local compressions of only 0.4 to 0.8 μ, whereas at the adjacent first node of Ranvier compressions sufficient to reduce axon diameter by 60 to 80 per cent (displacements up to 10 μ) are ineffective (Fig. 7).

Although highly developed in some receptor terminals, mechanotransduction is not a unique property of axon terminals. Sufficient (10 to 15 μ) mechanical distortions applied to regions of axons far removed from the terminals cause depolarization and may induce discharge.[21] It may be that the high mechanical sensitivity of terminals as compared to that of other regions of the axon is a simple consequence of size difference; a given displacement should increase surface area relatively more (and thus stretch the membrane more) in small than in large fibers.

Because transducer action occurs in the minute terminals, investigation of the intimate details of the process is difficult. Nevertheless, several indirect lines of evidence suggest that the stimulus produces depolarization of the terminal by *nonselectively increasing membrane permeability to ions.*

In Chapters 1 and 2 it was pointed out that the value of the axon transmembrane potential depends immediately upon the transmembrane concentration gradients of charged ions and upon the *permeability of the membrane* to these ions. In the resting axon Cl⁻ is at equilibrium and is distributed in the extra- and intracellular compartments in accordance with the Nernst equation. Both K⁺ and Na⁺, however, are actively pumped across the membrane against their concentration gradients. In the resting cell, Na⁺ and K⁺ are in a steady state (i.e., influx equals efflux) but not in true equilibrium as defined by the Nernst equation. For such actively transported ions the discrepancy between the true equilibrium potential and the steady-state transmembrane potential is a function of the membrane permeability to the ion. The resting membrane is about 50 times more permeable to K⁺ than to Na⁺; accordingly, the steady-state membrane potential deviates from the K⁺ equilibrium potential by only a few millivolts but is some 155 mV. removed from the equilibrium potential for Na⁺ (cf. Table 1, Chap. 1). It follows that an increase of membrane permeability to an actively transported ion will establish a new steady-state po-

tential value closer to the equilibrium potential of that ion. Thus, it has already been emphasized that the upstroke of the action potential results from transient selective increase of P_{Na^+}, a change which drives the transmembrane potential in the direction of the Na⁺ equilibrium potential.

A nonselective increase of membrane permeability to Na⁺, K⁺ and Cl⁻ might be expected to drive the membrane potential toward a value near zero. A simple way to visualize the process is to think of a polarized membrane in which holes have been punched permitting ions to flow freely along their concentration gradients and thus to dissipate the transmembrane charge. If the number of such leaks is large, the membrane potential will in time reach zero; fewer leaks would cause the membrane potential to reach a value intermediate between the resting level and zero. In other words, the degree of depolarization might be expected to vary with the number of shunting holes in the membrane. Conversely, the amount of depolarization occasioned by perforating the membrane with a given number of shunting holes should vary as a direct function of the initial transmembrane potential.

It follows from the foregoing considerations that the steady state potential toward which the transducer process drives the membrane of the crayfish stretch receptor can be determined by measuring the amplitudes of generator potentials produced by standard equal stretches when the resting membrane potential is artificially adjusted to different levels. Such meas-

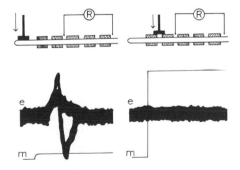

Fig. 7. Localization of mechanosensitive portion of pacinian corpuscle. Decapsulated preparation. On left, small mechanical stimulus (m) to denuded terminal produced generator potential and sometimes a diphasic spike. Record e contains many superimposed traces. On right, much larger mechanical compression to first node of Ranvier consistently failed to excite. (After Lowenstein, *J. Neurophysiol.,* 1961, *24:*150–158.)

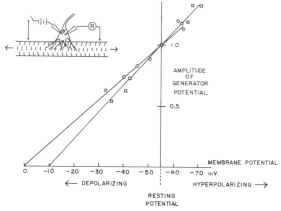

Fig. 8. Estimation of equilibrium level of generator potential in crayfish stretch receptor. Inset shows receptor impaled with two microelectrodes. Circuit on left was used to pass current through the membrane and thus to adjust the membrane potential to any desired level. Standard stretch of muscle bundle produced generator potential the amplitude of which is plotted on the ordinate against the membrane potential on the abscissa. Data from two experiments showing by extrapolation that generator potential amplitude is zero when initial membrane potential is near zero. (After Terzuolo and Washizu, *J. Neurophysiol.,* 1962, 25:56–66.)

urements require impaling the receptor with two microelectrodes (Fig. 8). One electrode is connected with a battery which can be used to drive current through the membrane and thus to adjust the membrane potential to any desired level. The other electrode records the generator potential produced by a standard stretch of the muscle bundle.

Figure 8 shows the results of such an experiment and indicates that, as predicted, the amplitude of the generator potential diminishes linearly as the resting membrane potential is decreased. Extrapolation indicates that the amplitude of the generator potential would be zero when the resting potential is about zero and that zero is therefore the steady state potential toward which the generator mechanism drives the membrane potential. These data are thus consistent with the hypothesis that stretch depolarizes the dendritic endings by inducing in them a nonselective increase in ionic permeability. An ancillary bit of information is that membrane resistance can be reduced to about one half by stretching the muscle bundle,[33] a finding consistent with the hypothesis of altered ionic permeability.

Such measurements are not possible on the minute terminals of pacinian corpuscles, but less direct clues suggest that in this receptor also the generator potential results from nonselective increase in membrane permeability. Permeability increase to Na^+ would be expected to contribute most to depolarization for, as has been mentioned, Na^+ is the ion most removed from equilibrium. It might therefore be expected that reducing the external Na^+ concentration would markedly reduce, but not abolish, the generator potential. Simply immersing the corpuscle in a Na^+-free bathing solution abolishes the spike but does not alter the generator potential. This disappointing negative result is, on reflection, not surprising, for the critical extracellular space of the receptor terminal is segregated from the Na^+-deficient medium by the thick impervious capsule, which is an efficient barrier to diffusion.* To change periterminal extracellular ion concentrations it is necessary to perfuse solutions through the tiny capillary which penetrates the capsule along with the axons.[3] When Na^+-deficient solutions are thus perfused, the generator potential undergoes the anticipated diminution, the reduction varying directly with Na^+ reduction. However, perfusion with Na^+-free solutions (made isotonic with choline chloride or sucrose) does not abolish the generator potential but only reduces it to about 10 per cent of the control value. This residue probably represents the contribution to the membrane current by ions other than Na^+ (K^+ and/or Cl^-). It thus seems likely that the generator potential of the pacinian corpuscle derives from increased permeability to Na^+ and probably to other ions as well.

The proposed model for the transducer process explains the changes in the generator potential with increasing intensities of stimulus.[8] Imagine that mechanical distortion opens pores in the membrane through which ions can pass readily. The membrane potential then shifts toward the steady state value of zero. If the number of holes is progressively increased (by increased compression) the potential will approach and eventually reach zero, after which further perforation will produce no additional depolarization (Fig. 3E). The rate of rise of the potential suffers no such limitation, however, for this variable depends on the rate of discharge of the membrane capacity, which continues to increase with further reduction of membrane resistance (Fig. 3F).

* Probably for a similar reason, the generator potential of the frog muscle spindle bathed in Na^+-free solutions also persists unaltered.[22]

DISCHARGE OF TONIC RECEPTORS

In the procaine-treated receptor impulse generation is blocked and stimulation elicits only the steady depolarization of the generator region. In the unblocked preparation this depolarization in turn triggers repetitive discharge of all-or-nothing spikes, which are then propagated along the fiber by the local circuit mechanism described in Chapter 2. The spike discharges are the ultimate product of the generator process and compose the message that reaches the central nervous system.

If spikes are recorded close to the terminal by the methods described, they ride superimposed on the generator potential; conventional recordings from the fiber more than a few millimeters central to the terminal register conducted spikes but give no evidence of the generator potential, which, being stationary, attenuates rapidly with distance. Only in selected re-

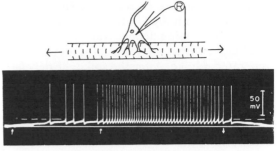

Fig. 9. Generator potential and spike discharge in crayfish stretch receptor. Slight stretch applied at first arrow. At second arrow stretch increased. Stretch released at third arrow. Dotted line indicates firing level. (From Eyzaguirre and Kuffler, *J. gen. Physiol.,* 1955, *39:* 87–119.)

ceptors are recordings close to the terminal possible, but recordings of axon spikes have been made on a wide variety of receptors.

Figure 9 shows an intracellular recording

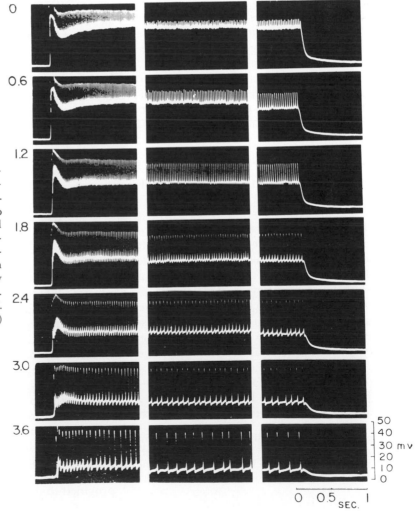

Fig. 10. Generator potential and spike discharge recorded intracellularly from photoreceptor of horse-shoe crab eye. Responses to 20-second light stimuli. Gaps between records are 8.4 seconds each. Figures at left indicate attenuation of light intensity (i.e., intensity diminishes from top to bottom). (From Fuortes and Poggio, *J. gen. Physiol.,* 1963, *46:*435–452.)

from a crayfish stretch receptor. Slight stretch of the muscle initiated at the first arrow elicited a slowly developing depolarization which, upon reaching a threshold value of about 12 mV., generated a spike. After the spike the depolarization again built up slowly to discharge at the same threshold value a second, third, fourth and fifth spike. At the second arrow the stretch was increased and held constant until the third arrow, when the stretch was discontinued. The increased stretch was accompanied by an accelerated discharge rate. The threshold firing level (marked by the dotted line) remained the same as before* but the rate of depolarization following each spike was much greater than during the period of mild stretch. Finally, it is clear that during the stretch the frequency declined from an initial high value to a stable lower value (adaptation). When at the third arrow the stretch was relaxed, the receptor discharged one impulse and the potential declined slowly to the resting level.

The discharge properties illustrated in Figure 9 have been duplicated in a wide variety of tonic receptors, including the frog stretch receptor, mammalian stretch receptors, carotid sinus pressoreceptors, photoreceptors (Fig. 10) and many others. Particular attention is directed to adaptation and the relationship between intensity of stimulus and frequency of discharge.

ADAPTATION OF SPIKE DISCHARGE AND OFF-EFFECTS

Adaptation of spike discharge is as mysterious as adaptation of the generator potential. It has already been mentioned that the amplitude of the dynamic, but not of the static, component of the stretch receptor potential is directly related to the *velocity* of muscle stretch. The same relations hold for discharge rates; if the displacement amplitude is held constant but the velocity is varied, the final adapted discharge rate is invariant but the discharge frequency during and immediately following stretch is directly related to velocity (Fig. 11).

The hyperpolarizing off-effect of the stretch

* At higher intensities, the firing level increases, for with increasing discharge rate, the interspike interval is so reduced that each spike falls within the relatively refractory period created by its predecessor.

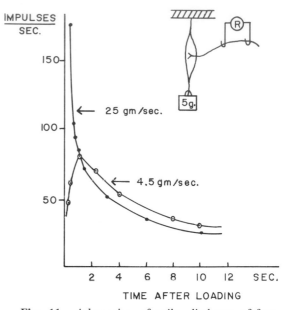

Fig. 11. Adaptation of spike discharge of frog muscle spindle subjected to different rates of stretch. With higher velocity loading initial discharge rate is greater but steady state discharge rate is little affected by rate of loading. (After Matthews, *J. Physiol.*, 1931, *71*:64–110.)

receptor potential also has its correlate in discharge properties. If in an adapted stretch receptor an imposed stretch is suddenly reduced to a lower value, discharge rate decelerates or ceases briefly only to build up once again to a value appropriate to the newly established milder stretch.[29]

INTENSITY-FREQUENCY RELATIONSHIPS AND INFORMATION CODING

All tonic receptors studied display graded increases of discharge rates when the stimulus intensity is increased. In many, the relationship is such that the steady adapted discharge frequency is a linear function of the log of the stimulus intensity. Much has been made of the logarithmic relationship, principally because of its presumed relationship to Fechner's famous generalization that sensation is proportional to the log of stimulus intensity, a "law" which is currently disputed. For receptors the logarithmic intensity–frequency relationship is a fair approximation provided that the range of stimulus intensities is appropriately chosen and provided that the appropriate parameter of the stimulus is measured as "intensity." For example, in the crayfish stretch receptor, discharge frequency is, over a considerable range, directly related to the log of the load or force producing the stretch, but is directly proportional to the length of the muscle.[33] Lacking intimate details of the mechanical distortion sustained by the dendrites when the muscle bundle in which they are imbedded is stretched and put under tension, we have no way to decide which parameter they signal.

However, apart from these semiphilosophical considerations, the fact remains that, within limits, the frequency–log load relationship is descriptively accurate and it is of interest to enquire at which stage of the transducer process the logarithmic function enters. For the crayfish receptor[33] and photoreceptors of the horseshoe crab eye,[5] the answer is: at the transducer stage. In these receptors amplitude of the generator potential (static component) is directly related to the log of stimulus intensity, whereas firing rate is linearly related to amplitude of generator potential. These transformations are diagrammatically illustrated in Figure 12. Similar relationships may be deduced for the frog stretch receptor, since frequency of firing is directly related to amplitude of the generator potential[22] and to the log of the load.[29]

Because of the rate–intensity relationship, the individual tonic receptor is able to provide continuously graded, frequency-coded information

concerning stimulus intensity within the range between threshold and the intensity at which the generator potential is maximal. At higher intensity levels the transducer mechanism is saturated, limiting further information transmission. In a population of receptors, however, intensity of stimulation is signaled not only by the firing rate of individual receptors but also by the number of receptors active. In such a population, thresholds are distributed in accordance with a normal frequency curve so that, with increasing intensity of stimulation, more and more receptors of progressively higher thresholds are recruited, each firing at a rate determined by its threshold and the instantaneous magnitude of the intensity. The phenomenon of progressive recruitment of receptors expands the range of stimulus intensities that can be signaled to the central nervous system beyond that which can be signaled by any one receptor.

Variance of receptor thresholds is probably determined more by geometry and location than by variance of transmembrane voltage thresholds for discharge. In a population of muscle stretch receptors, for example, location within the muscle makes some bear more of the brunt of the stretch than others.

MECHANISM OF REPETITIVE FIRING IN TONIC RECEPTORS

Repetitive firing of sense organs was ingen-

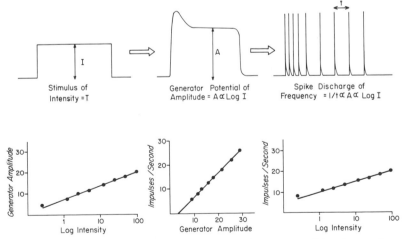

Fig. 12. Diagram of steps in intensity coding in a tonic receptor. Stimulus produces generator potential shown here as it might be recorded in a procainized receptor. The amplitude of the static phase is directly proportional to the logarithm of stimulus intensity. Generator potential elicits repetitive discharge of spikes. In the adapted state frequency of discharge is directly proportional to generator potential amplitude and thus proportional to the log of stimulus intensity. Graphs below show data obtained from photoreceptor of crab eye. (After Fuortes, *Amer. J. Ophthalmol.*, 1958, *46*:210–223.)

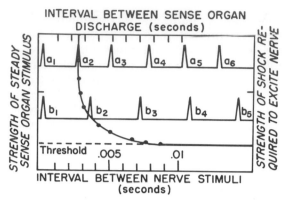

Fig. 13. Diagram illustrating refractory period hypothesis of sense organ rhythmicity. Curve is conventional recovery curve (absolutely and relatively refractory periods) for frog nerve and represents actual experimental data. Schematized action potential records (*a, b*) are hypothetical. They show how a strong, continuous sensory stimulus might excite earlier in the refractory period and fire the sensory axon at a higher rate. (Redrawn from Adrian, *The basis of sensation*, London, Christophers, 1928.)

iously explained by Adrian,[1] who proposed that the frequency–intensity relationship was determined by the recovery cycle of the fiber. In Chapter 2 it was pointed out that after a nerve fiber has generated a spike, the threshold to a second stimulus is increased. For a short period of time (the absolutely refractory period) the threshold is infinite and a second stimulus, no matter how strong, is ineffective. Thereafter, for a period (relatively refractory period) a second shock will excite, but only if it is of greater than resting threshold intensity. Figure 13 shows graphically the time course of the threshold changes in a frog nerve after it has conducted an impulse. Adrian suggested that the physical stimulus induces in a receptor a steady, maintained change to which the neural element can respond only periodically because of its characteristic recovery cycle. (Adrian's steady change would, in modern parlance, be the generator potential, then undiscovered.) An intense steady stimulus would fire the fiber in Figure 13 at a_1 and again after the threshold has dropped to the level of the steady stimulus, at a_2. Recovery from the a_2 spike would lead to a_3, etc. A weaker steady stimulus (b) would yield a longer interspike interval because after each spike a longer recovery time is required for the threshold to fall to the level of the weaker steady stimulus.

A difficulty with this explanation is that receptors, except under abnormal conditions, do not fire as rapidly as measured refractory periods would predict, the upper limit being 100 to 200 impulses per second rather than 800 to 1000, as calculated from refractory periods. Also, weakly excited receptors fire rhythmically and regularly at frequencies far below those anticipated from mere refractoriness. The discrepancy may mean, as Adrian suggested, only that the fine unmyelinated receptor terminal has a slower recovery cycle than its parent axon.

Another factor determining discharge frequency is the rate of depolarization following each spike in the train.[15] Figure 14 shows superimposed traces of spikes in a crayfish stretch receptor adapted to three magnitudes of stretch, the oscilloscope sweep being triggered in each instance by the first spike on the left. The straight horizontal line marks the firing level (spike threshold) for the conditions in *A*. The firing level is unchanged in *B*, but in *C* the spikes do not arise until the depolarization has proceeded about 7 mV. farther because the interspike interval encroaches on the relatively refractory period. Refractoriness thus appears to limit discharge rate significantly only at higher frequencies. The striking difference between records *A* and *B* is in the rate of depolarization during the interspike interval. Following each spike the membrane repolarizes beyond the threshold level and then depolarizes slowly in *A*, more rapidly in *B*, and still more rapidly in *C*. The traces in *D* show the time course of depolarization over an even greater range of frequencies. Although the complex mechanisms governing transmembrane potential during the interspike interval are not known, it may be postulated that Na^+ inactivation and elevated K^+ conductance act to promote repolarization, while the steadily maintained nonselective conductance increase associated with the transducer process tends to drive the membrane in a depolarizing direction. It has already been mentioned that the rate of rise of the generator potential in a blocked receptor is directly related to stimulus intensity (see Fig. 3*F*). The graded slopes of depolarization in Figure 14 are a manifestation of the same phenomenon superimposed upon post-spike repolarization.

In summary, the intensity–frequency relationship of receptors through the range of slight to moderate intensities appears to depend almost exclusively on the rate of depolarization.

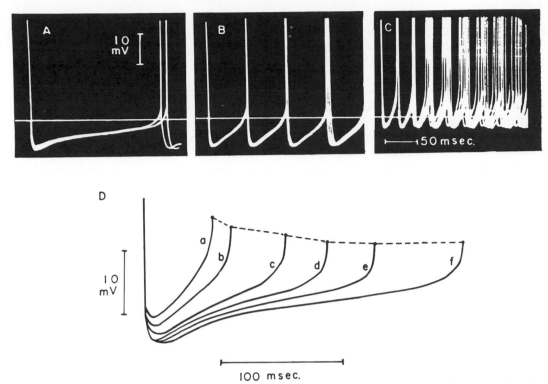

Fig. 14. Interspike events in repetitively discharging crayfish stretch receptor. Traces A, B and C are superimposed traces, each sweep being triggered by the first spike of the left. Gain very high so that peak of spike is off record. Horizontal line marks firing level for near-threshold stretch in A. Note firing level is same in B for greater stretch, but is about 7 mV. higher in C where stretch was still greater. D shows interspike events at six levels of stretch; dotted line shows firing levels. (From Eyzaguirre and Kuffler, *J. gen. Physiol.*, 1955, *39*:87–119.)

At higher intensities interspike interval encroaches on relative refractoriness, and elevated threshold becomes a controlling factor.

DISCHARGE OF PHASIC RECEPTORS

In phasic receptors the intensity–frequency relationship does not hold because prompt adaptation limits the discharge. Even with displacements up to 30 times threshold, a pacinian corpuscle rarely responds to a square wave compression with more than one spike.[10] Subjected to vibratory stimuli, however, these receptors respond repetitively,[17, 31] discharging one spike per cycle (Fig. 15). Maximum sensitivity is to frequencies of about 300 cycles per second; on either side of this frequency thresholds become higher. Intensity of stimulus thus determines the range of frequencies to which the corpuscle responds. At high intensities oscillation between 40 and 1000 cycles per sec-

ond are faithfully signaled. With weaker stimuli the effective frequency range shrinks.

SITE OF IMPULSE ORIGIN IN RECEPTORS

In this chapter the fundamental difference between the *graded* generator potential and the

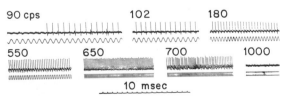

Fig. 15. Responses of pacinian corpuscle to sinusoidal vibratory stimuli. Upper trace shows spikes recorded from axon; lower trace shows sinusoidal stimulus. Numbers above traces give stimulus frequencies. Time trace 10 milliseconds. (From Hunt, *J. Physiol.*, 1961, *155*:175–186.)

all-or-nothing spike has been emphasized repeatedly. The all-or-nothing behavior of the action potential is a consequence of the voltage sensitivity of sodium permeability. Depolarization increases sodium permeability, which in turn leads to sodium entry and further depolarization; the response, once triggered, is self-sustaining and explosively independent of the stimulus. In the graded receptor response to a physical stimulus, the underlying process is not voltage-sensitive and hence not regenerative; within wide limits each increment of stimulus produces an increment of depolarization. Impressed by these fundamental differences, some neurophysiologists have argued that the two processes cannot be supported by the same membrane.[11] Thus, it has been widely believed that the unmyelinated terminal is incapable of all-or-nothing behavior and responds to mechanical distortion with only a graded depolarization; impulse generation was postulated to result from outward current flow through the voltage-sensitive membrane of the first node of Ranvier.[8, 9, 26, 28]

Although some neural membranes may be capable of only graded, nonpropagated responses to stimulation, there is no outrageous inconsistency in the simple hypothesis that a macroscopic area of membrane may display both graded and all-or-nothing processes. Indeed, in the denuded pacinian corpuscle it has been shown conclusively that the unmyelinated portion which undergoes graded depolarization

in response to mechanical deformation can conduct all-or-nothing spikes throughout its full extent.[20]

INHIBITION IN RECEPTORS

Some receptors are impinged upon by efferent axons. Excitation of these axons reduces the sensitivity of the receptor to its adequate stimulus. The process by which discharge of a nerve fiber depresses the excitability of the structure it supplies is called *inhibition*. Excitation is a mechanism for "turning on" a cell, inhibition for "turning off." In receptors receiving an inhibitory innervation, sensitivity to adequate stimulation is continuously biased by impulse traffic in the inhibitory fibers, and discharge behavior is determined by the balance between the influences of inhibitory action and of excitatory depolarization.

A simple example of a receptor supplied with inhibitory fibers is the crayfish stretch receptor.[24] The inhibitory axon derives from a centrally located cell body and terminates in the muscle bundle in close apposition to the stretch-sensitive dendrite of the receptor (Fig. 2C). Figure 16A shows the effect of low-frequency stimulation of the inhibitory axon supplying a receptor discharging repetitively in response to constant stretch. During the inhibitory action firing ceases. At higher gain (Fig. 16B) it can be seen that each inhibitory impulse drives the

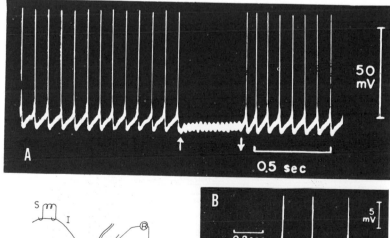

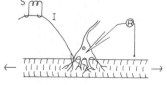

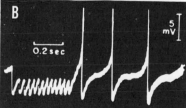

Fig. 16. Inhibition of crayfish stretch receptor. *A,* Discharge in receptor subjected to stretch is inhibited by stimulating inhibitory axon during period between arrows. *B,* Amplifier gain much higher to show that each inhibitory volley (first part of record) causes hyperpolarization of cell. (After Kuffler and Eyzaguirre, *J. gen. Physiol.*, 1955, *39*:155–184.)

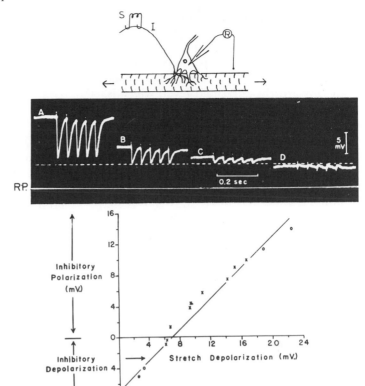

Fig. 17. Equilibrium potential of inhibitory process in crayfish stretch receptor. Cell depolarized to varying degrees by stretch was subjected to five inhibitory volleys. Solid line RP marks resting potential; dotted line marks potential at which sign of inhibitory potential reverses. Figure below shows graphically that inhibitory potential reverses when the cell is depolarized by about 6.5 mV. (After Kuffler and Eyzaguirre, *J. gen. Physiol.*, 1955, *39*:155–184.)

membrane in the direction of repolarization, thus preventing the stretch-induced depolarization from reaching threshold.

Some idea of the mechanism of inhibition can be obtained by determining the steady state potential toward which inhibitory impulses drive the membrane.[13, 24] The analysis is similar to that employed to study the intimate mechanism of the generator potential. Figure 17*A* shows the consequences of stimulating repetitively the inhibitory nerve fiber of a stretch receptor depolarized about 16.5 mV. by stretch. Each inhibitory impulse caused a peak repolarization of 9.7 mV. In *B* and *C,* when the receptor was held under less stretch and was therefore less depolarized, the inhibitory repolarization became progressively smaller. In *D* still further relaxation decreased the depolarization to only 6 mV. (dotted line) beyond the resting level, and each inhibitory impulse then produced a small *depolarization.* The reversal level for the inhibitory potential thus lies between the potential levels of *C* and *D.* The lower part of Figure 17 shows graphically results from another experiment in which the straight line connecting the points intersects the abscissa at a membrane potential 7 mV. less than the resting level. Studies in which

membrane potentials were shifted by passing currents through the membrane rather than by stretching the receptor also indicate that the inhibitory process invariably seeks a stable value within a few millivolts of the resting level.[13]

The implication of such results is that the inhibitory process results from selectively increased permeability of the membrane to one or more ions which are close to true electrochemical equilibrium in the resting cell. This consideration eliminates Na^+, which is far removed from equilibrium. K^+ and Cl^- are equally likely candidates, for both are near equilibrium in the resting cell. Experiments in which inhibitory potentials were recorded in cells bathed in solutions deficient in these ions suggest that both are involved. In K^+-deficient solutions resting membrane potentials of receptors increase and the inhibitory potential becomes more strongly hyperpolarizing.[4] Depletion of extracellular Cl^-, on the other hand, shifts the reversal level of the inhibitory potential toward zero; i.e., in the same direction as the anticipated change of Cl^- equilibrium potential.[13] Inhibitory impulses thus appear to exercise their influence on the stretch receptor membrane by increasing selectively the permeability to K^+ and Cl^- ions. This change tends to stabilize the membrane at a voltage near the resting level, and as long as this condition persists it is more difficult to depolarize the membrane toward the threshold level, which is, of course, a necessary condition for discharge. The cell is inhibited and discharge ceases.

A final question relates to the mechanism by which nerve impulses in the inhibitory axon alter dendritic membrane permeability. The answer is that nerve impulses liberate from the inhibitory axon terminals a chemical agent which diffuses across the minute gap between axon and dendrite and selectively alters the ionic permeability of the dendritic membrane. There is much, although not conclusive, evidence that in crayfish inhibitory fibers the transmitter is *gamma aminobutyric acid.* This substance can be extracted from neural tissue and, when topically applied to the isolated receptor, mimics in many ways the permeability and excitability changes induced by stimulating the inhibitory axon.[13, 23, 30]

REFERENCES

1. ADRIAN, E. D. *The basis of sensation.* London, Christophers, 1928.
2. DAVIS, H. *Physiol Rev.,* 1961, *41:*391–416.
3. DIAMOND, J., GRAY, J. A. B. and IMMAN, D. R. *J. Physiol.,* 1958, *142:*383–394.
4. EDWARDS, C. and HAGIWARA, S. *J. gen. Physiol.,* 1959, *43:* 315–321.
5. FUORTES, M. G. F. *Amer. J. Ophthal.,* 1958, *46:*210–223.
6. GRANIT, R. *Receptors and sensory perception.* New Haven, Yale University Press, 1955.
7. GRAY, E. G. *Proc. roy. Soc.,* 1957, *B146:*416–430.
8. GRAY, J. A. B. *Prog. Biophys. biophys. Chem.,* 1959, *9:*286–324.
9. GRAY, J. A. B. Chap. 4 in *Handbook of Physiology, Section 1: Neurophysiology,* vol. 1, J. Field, ed. Washington, D. C., American Physiological Society, 1959.
10. GRAY, J. A. B. and MALCOLM, J. L. *Proc. roy. Soc.,* 1950, *B137:*96–114.
11. GRUNDFEST, H. Chap. 5 in *Handbook of physiology, Section 1: Neurophysiology,* vol. 1, J. Field, ed. Washington, D. C., American Physiological Society, 1959.
12. HAGEN, E., KNOCHE, H., SINCLAIR, D. C. and WEDDELL, G. *Proc. roy. Soc.,* 1953, *B141:*279–286.
13. HAGIWARA, S., KUSANO, K. and SAITO, S. *J. Neurophysiol.,* 1960, *23:*505–515.
14. HENSEL, H. and BOMAN, K. K. A. *J. Neurophysiol.,* 1960, *23:*564–578.
15. HODGKIN, A. L. *J. Physiol.,* 1948, *107:*165–181.
16. HUBBARD, S. J. *J. Physiol.,* 1958, *141:*198–218.
17. HUNT, C. C. *J. Physiol.,* 1961, *155:*175–186.
18. HUNT, C. C. and McINTYRE, A. K. *J. Physiol.,* 1960, *153:* 99–112.
19. HUNT, C. C. and McINTYRE, A. K. *J. Physiol.,* 1960, *153:* 88–98.
20. HUNT, C. C. and TAKEUCHI, A. *J. Physiol.,* 1962, *160:*1–21.
21. JULIAN, F. J. and GOLDMAN, D. E. *J. gen. Physiol.,* 1962, *46:*297–313.
22. KATZ, B. *J. Physiol.,* 1950, *111:*261–282.
23. KUFFLER, S. W. and EDWARDS, C. *J. Neurophysiol.,* 1958, *21:*589–610.
24. KUFFLER, S. W. and EYZAGUIRRE, C. *J. gen. Physiol.,* 1955, *39:*155–184.
25. LILE, P. P. and WEDDELL, G. *Brain,* 1956, *79:*119–154.
26. LOWENSTEIN, W. R. *Ann. N.Y. Acad. Sci.,* 1959, *81:*367–387.
27. LOWENSTEIN, W. R. *J. Neurophysiol.,* 1961, *24:*150–158.
28. LOWENSTEIN, W. R. and RATHKAMP, R. *J. gen. Physiol.,* 1958, *41:*1245–1265.
29. MATTHEWS, B. H. C. *J. Physiol.,* 1931, *71:*64–110.
30. McLENNAN, H. *Synaptic transmission.* Philadelphia, W. B. Saunders Co., 1963.
31. MENDELSON, M. and LOWENSTEIN, W. R. *Science,* 1964, *144:*554–555.
32. SATO, M. *J. Physiol.,* 1961, *159:*391–409.
33. TERZUOLO, C. A. and WASHIZU, Y. *J. Neurophysiol.,* 1962, *25:*56–66.
34. WITT, I. and HENSEL, H. *Pflüg. Arch. ges. Physiol.,* 1959, *268:*582–596.

CHAPTER 5

Muscle

By J. WALTER WOODBURY, ALBERT M. GORDON,
and JOHN T. CONRAD

THE function of a muscle is to contract. Skeletal muscles are attached to bones by tendons and act to move these bones with respect to each other. Cardiac muscle and visceral smooth muscle occur in the walls of hollow viscera and act by exerting pressure on the fluid visceral contents. The contraction of skeletal muscle is wholly and directly controlled by reflex and voluntary activity of the central nervous system. Cardiac and smooth muscle contractions, although regulated by nervous activity, are intrinsically rhythmic; these muscles, notably the heart, contract at regular intervals even when denervated. This automaticity of cardiac and smooth muscle is in accord with their functions in maintaining the internal environment of the body, the pumping of blood and the movements of the digestive tract. However, motor nerves do regulate the contractile activity of arteriolar smooth muscle and thus control the blood flow through the arterioles. Muscular contraction is the most impressive example of "living machinery."

Skeletal muscle has been more intensively studied and is better understood than cardiac or smooth muscle. Hence, in this chapter the current concepts of skeletal muscle contractile activity and its control are presented first to give a more comprehensive framework for understanding the physiology of muscle. This is followed by shorter sections in which the properties of cardiac muscle and the various types of smooth muscle are compared and contrasted with those of skeletal muscle. Finally diseases of the motor unit are presented, showing how pathologic conditions can be illuminated and organized from physiologic study.

SKELETAL MUSCLE

Skeletal muscle is the means by which an organism reacts to its external environment. "All the endless diversity of the external manifestations of the activity of the brain can be finally regarded as one phenomenon—that of muscular movement" (Sechenov, 1863). The preoccupation of the brain with skeletal muscle was also stressed by Sherrington, who pointed out that any path traced in the brain leads directly or indirectly to muscle. The performance of a smooth, efficient and coordinated bodily movement is the outward sign of complex and extensive activity in the central nervous system.

A bodily movement involves three more or less distinct types of activity: (i) central nervous system activity, reflex and voluntary; (ii) events intervening between the impulse in a motor nerve and the beginning of contraction; and (iii) the contractile process itself. Reflex control of movement is discussed in Chapter 7; this section covers the remaining types of activity. The following brief description may help to keep the details of the processes in their proper perspective.

Events Leading to Contraction. A number of distinct events intervene between the synaptic initiation of an impulse in a spinal motoneuron and the contractions of the muscle fibers it innervates. (i) The impulse is conducted along the motoneuron axon to its termination on the muscle's motor end-plate. (ii) The impulse causes the liberation of a chemical transmitter substance, acetylcholine, from the axon terminals. (iii) By inducing a greater than threshold depolarization of the muscle fiber membrane, acetylcholine initiates a self-propagating impulse in it. (iv) The depolarization of the muscle membrane by the conducted impulse is followed by a brief phasic contraction of the muscle fiber—a *twitch*. The phrase *neuromuscular transmission* refers to the events between the arrival of the nerve impulse at the nerve endings and the initiation of an impulse in the muscle; the events between the muscle fiber impulse and contraction are referred to as *excitation–contraction coupling* to distinguish them from the contraction process itself.

These events are more conveniently studied with experiments of the type illustrated in Figure 1. A single supramaximal shock applied to the motor nerve initiates a volley of impulses in the nerve, which in turn initiates a volley in all of the muscle's fibers, these latter impulses arising at the motor end-plate. In Figure 1B is shown the diphasic action potential generated by the passage of the volley across the recording electrodes, R. After a delay of a few milliseconds, the muscle action potentials initiate a twitch—a synchronous, phasic contraction of all fibers. The contractile tension rises to a peak in about 50 milliseconds and then declines more slowly to the initial or resting tension. The contractile response of a single muscle fiber to a conducted action potential is the

A.

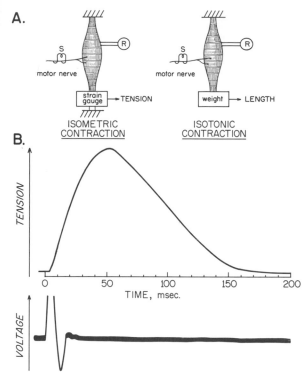

ISOMETRIC CONTRACTION | ISOTONIC CONTRACTION

B.

Fig. 1. Twitch contraction of whole muscle. *A,* Arrangement for recording contractile responses of whole muscle. Left, isometric recording arrangement; length is held constant, and developed force (tension) is measured with a strain gauge and recorded as a function of time. Contraction is initiated by a supramaximal stimulus delivered to motor nerve via a pair of electrodes, S. Muscle action potential recorded by surface electrodes, R. Right, isotonic recording arrangement; tension is held constant by hanging a weight on muscle and changes in length are measured as a function of time. Stimulating and recording as at left. *B,* Action potential (below) and isometric tension (above) recorded in tibialis muscle of cat. Abscissae represent time; upper ordinate, tension in arbitrary units; and lower ordinate, voltage in arbitrary units (upward deflection incomplete). Note that electrical activity starts several milliseconds before contraction but contraction far outlasts electrical activity. Action potential is diphasic because both electrodes are on active tissue. (After Creed *et al., Reflex activity of the spinal cord.* Oxford, Clarendon Press, 1932.)

same as for the whole muscle; the whole muscle's twitch is the summated tensions of the twitches of its individual fibers.

GRADATION OF CONTRACTION. The number of motor axons innervating a muscle is a small fraction of the number of fibers in the muscle. Counts have shown that a motor axon innervates from 3 to 150 muscle fibers, the number depending on the function of the muscle. The

motoneuron and the muscle fibers it innervates are termed a *motor unit.* The contractile response to one impulse in one motoneuron is a twitch contraction in all the fibers it innervates. Thus the smallest unit of muscular activity that occurs normally is the contraction of a single motor unit. The twitch response typical of a motor unit contrasts sharply with the smooth maintained contraction of muscle during normal movements. This observation raises a further question: How is the contraction of a muscle smoothly *graded* in strength?

Functional Structure of Muscle: the Sliding Filament Theory. RESTING MUSCLE. Understanding of muscular contraction requires a detailed knowledge of muscle's fine structure. Although the structure of cross-striated skeletal muscle is described here, many of the same features are found in cardiac muscle. The main features of muscle structure are shown in Figure 2. A muscle is composed of many fibers, each bounded by a cell membrane. Each fiber (top, Fig. 2) consists of many bundles of closely packed fibrils. (A fibril is the smallest natural

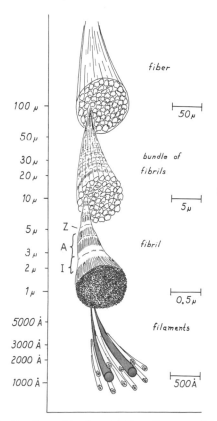

Fig. 2. Logarithmic extension diagram of skeletal muscle and filament structure. (After Buchthal and Kaiser, *Dan. Biol. Medd.,* 1951, *21:*1–318.)

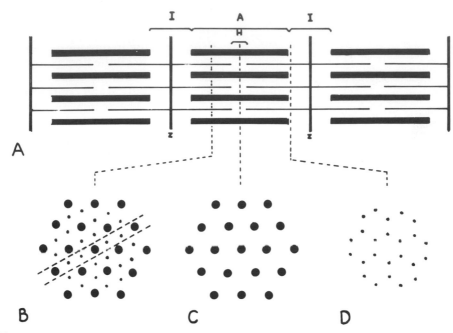

Fig. 3. Arrangement of filaments within the bands of a myofibril. Sarcomere length corresponds to slightly extended length in the body. Transverse distances grossly exaggerated. *A,* Longitudinal view showing overlap of thick and thin filaments and their relationship to striation bands. *B,* Cross section of region of overlap showing double hexagonal array. Dotted lines indicate direction and width of electron micrograph sections shown in Figure 4. *C,* Cross section through H band showing hexagonal array of thick filaments only. *D,* Cross section through I band showing thin filaments only. (After H. E. Huxley, Chap. 7 in *The cell,* vol. IV, Brachet and Mirsky, eds. New York, Academic Press, Inc., 1962.)

muscle unit from which a contraction has been obtained.) Fibrils in turn are made up of two types of myofilaments—thick and thin—which so interact that they slide past each other during shortening. These filaments are closely packed in a parallel array with both ends of like filaments in register (Figs. 3 and 4). This organization gives the characteristic cross-striated or banded appearance of whole muscle, as seen with the light microscope, and of fibrils, as seen with the electron microscope.

Striation bands. These bands were named by light microscopists but can be seen much more clearly with the electron microscope (Fig. 4, top). The darker regions indicating greater absorption of electrons (electron-dense) are called the A bands; these are the more highly refractive, *a*nisotropic regions seen with the light microscope. The lighter bands bisected by the dark lines are I bands or *i*sotropic regions. The lighter region in the center of the A band is called the H band and is less refractive than its surroundings. The region between two adjacent Z lines traditionally is termed the sarcomere,

which is the basic repetitive unit of muscle structure. However, the functional sarcomere is centered on, rather than between, Z lines. In resting vertebrate skeletal muscle the sarcomere is about 2.5 μ long and decreases in length as the muscle shortens.

Filaments.[46, 57] The A band, as shown by Figure 4 (middle), is composed of thick parallel filaments (100 to 120 Å in diameter and 1.6 μ long), which give rise to the band's anisotropy and high electron density. The I band consists of thinner filaments (60 to 70 Å in diameter) and thus is less electron-dense. The I band filaments are attached at their center point to Z line structures and extend about 1 μ on each side. The two sets of filaments overlap in the A band. The A band's central region, which has no filament overlap, is the H band. These characteristics are summarized in Figure 3. A transverse section through the H band shows that the thick filaments are spaced about 450 Å apart in a hexagonal pattern. Where the thick and thin filaments overlap, the thick filament hexagonal pattern remains intact while

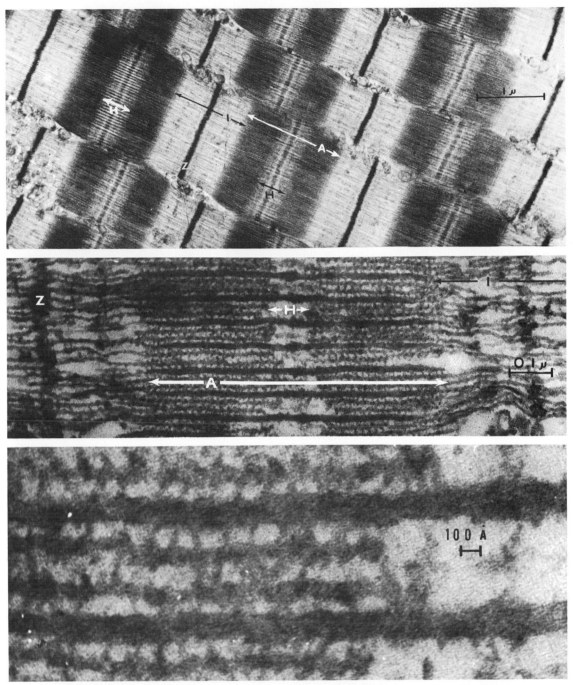

Fig. 4. Electron micrographs of longitudinal sections of rabbit psoas muscle. *Top,* Low-power view of several sarcomeres, showing A, H, and I bands and Z line. *Middle,* One sarcomere. Direction and width of section shown in Figure 3B. Thick filaments run from one end of the A band to the other. Pairs of thin filaments are attached at the Z line, interdigitate with the thick filaments, and terminate at the edge of the H band. *Bottom,* High magnification of A band showing bridges between thick and thin filaments. Direction and width of section shown in Figure 3B. (From H. E. Huxley, Chap. 7 in *The cell,* vol. IV, Brachet and Mirsky, eds. New York, Academic Press, Inc., 1962.)

each thin filament is surrounded by three thick filaments. In the I band, only thin filaments are seen.

The thick and thin filaments apparently are connected by "bridges" (Fig. 4, bottom). Bridges to each neighboring thin filament occur approximately every 400 Å; these project out from the thick filament along its entire length, except in the central 0.15 μ section.[46]

CONTRACTING MUSCLE. When a muscle is stimulated, it contracts and exerts a force on its tendons. If the force is sufficient, shortening occurs and the two sets of interdigitating filaments slide past each other. Light microscope observations in isolated muscle fibers and fibrils have shown that, during active shortening, I and H bands narrow equally while the A band, if such shortening is not too great, is unchanged.[42] "Contraction bands" form at sarcomere lengths of less than 2 μ in active shortening. Electron micrographs of muscles in various stages of contraction show that over wide ranges the lengths of the thick and thin filaments are nearly constant. Hence, all changes in sarcomere length are due to a relative motion of the two sets of filaments.[42, 44] This and other evidence[45] have firmly established that the sliding filament model provides an accurate description of the contractile process.

The relative motion implies that, during contraction, the interaction of the two filaments generates a force, tending to pull the thin filament toward the center of the A band. The interaction may take place at many sites along the filaments, possibly at the bridges. As the filaments slide past one another, connections are made and broken in such a way that a net shortening force is developed even if the muscle does not change length.[41] Furthermore, shortening usually occurs without any change of length in the filaments; e.g., a collapsible telescope can be shortened without changing the length of its tubular elements.

SARCOPLASMIC RETICULUM. An extensive membranous cytoplasmic component, the *sarcoplasmic reticulum*, plays an important role in the excitation–contraction coupling process. This structure is a continuous, membrane-limited system of tubules which form a close network around each fibril (Fig. 5, top). The sarcoplasmic reticulum differs from the endoplasmic reticulum of most other cells in that it lacks ribosomes and thus is agranular and in that certain characteristic features reoccur at fixed positions in every sarcomere. Longitudinal sections show a characteristic triad structure consisting of a central or transverse tubule with terminal cisternae on both sides (Fig. 5, bottom). The dilated, circumferential terminal cisternae are formed by anastomoses of the longitudinally oriented, finger-like tubules which surround the fibril. The central tubules run transversely through most of the fiber, weaving among the fibrils. These tubules appear to be separate from, but in close contact with, the longitudinal tubular system. The transverse tubules extend toward and may coalesce with the surface membrane so that they open to the extracellular space. Such openings have been observed in the muscles of some species[29] but not as yet in mammalian skeletal muscle. However, large (110 Å in diameter), electron-dense, nonpermeating ferritin molecules do enter the transverse tubules from the extracellular space but not the terminal cisternae.[47] The reticular triad is always fixed in position with respect to striation pattern, but the position varies according to species. In most mammals the triad is centered near the A-I junction; in frogs, it coincides with the Z line (Fig. 5, bottom).

Molecular Basis of Contraction.* CONTRACTILE PROTEINS. There are at least three sarcoplasmic proteins—actin, myosin and tropomyosin—which probably play a role in contraction. Neither the localization of tropomyosin nor its role in muscular contraction has been established. However, the localization of actin and myosin with respect to the striation pattern has been determined from selective extraction[45] and labeling with fluorescent antibodies.[68] With appropriate solvents, myosin can be extracted quantitatively from the A bands of glycerol-extracted muscle preparations (see p. 120). The I band and Z line are little affected. However, the I band can then be dissolved with solutions known to extract actin. This, along with other evidence,[45] indicates that the thin I band filaments are composed almost exclusively of actin and the thick A band filaments largely of myosin and possibly of other protein components.

*Since this chapter was written, a discussion on the subject "The Physical and Chemical Basis of Muscular Contraction" has appeared in *Proc. roy. Soc.*, 1964, *B460*:433–542. In that discussion, organized by A. F. Huxley and H. E. Huxley, much of the material presented in this section is reviewed in greater detail.

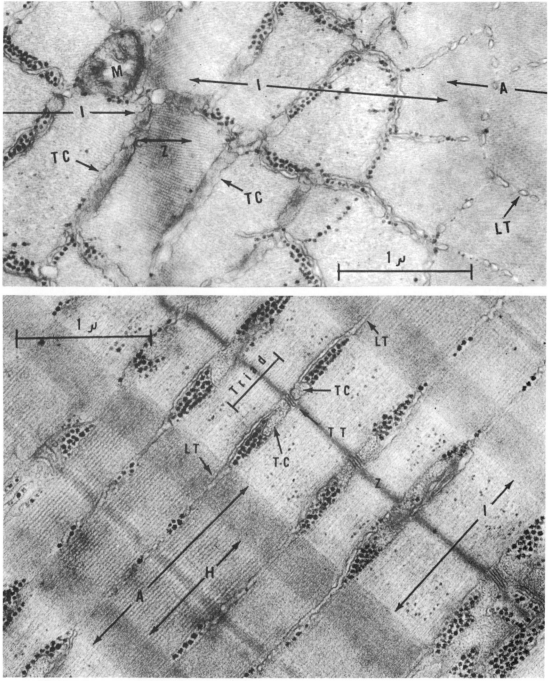

Fig. 5. Electron micrographs of frog sartorius muscle showing the sarcoplasmic reticulum and its relationship to the contractile structures. Sections were cut in different orientations. *Top,* Slightly oblique transverse section through a fiber. The Z line, A and I bands are indicated. Note that the reticulum completely surrounds most of the fibrils. Larger spaces in the I band near the Z line are terminal cisternae (TC). M is a mitochondrion. Dark spots are clusters of glycogen granules. *Bottom,* Longitudinal section of a fiber. Note A band, I band, Z line, components of the triad structure of the sarcoplasmic reticulum [transverse tubule (TT) and terminal cisternae (TC)] and the longitudinal tubules (LT). In this muscle, the triad is centered on the Z line. (*Top,* courtesy of Dr. Lee D. Peachey. *Bottom,* from Peachey, *J. cell. Biol.,* in press.)

Actin molecules (M.W. about 70,000) can unite to form long filaments which probably have the same structure as the thin filaments of the I band. In dried preparations, these filaments consist of two chains wound in a double helix. Myosin (M.W. about 428,000) can be fragmented by trypsin into two components, one consisting of two molecules of light meromyosin (M.W. 96,000) and the other of one molecule of heavy meromyosin (M.W. 236,000).[45] In solution, the myosin molecule is in the form of a rod with a ball at one end.[46] When solutions of actin and myosin are mixed, they combine to form *actomyosin*, a compound normally having a high association constant.

Myosin, but not actin, is an enzyme (an ATP-ase) which catalyzes the hydrolysis of adenosine triphosphate (ATP) to adenosine diphosphate (ADP) and phosphate. Actomyosin, also an ATP-ase, has somewhat different properties. For example, myosin ATP-ase is activated by Ca^{++} and inhibited by Mg^{++}, whereas actomyosin ATP-ase is activated by both Ca^{++} and Mg^{++}. The ATP-ase activities of myosin and actomyosin reside in the heavy meromyosin fraction. Through this enzymatic action, part of the free energy of the ATP terminal phosphate bond can be made available to actomyosin for contractile activity.

ROLES OF ATP AND CALCIUM IN CONTRACTILE ACTIVITY. *Contraction and relaxation in model systems.* Much has been learned about the contractile mechanism of muscle by studying the contractile-like properties of a "model system" derived from muscle subjected to various analytic procedures. Such procedures primarily are designed to remove the large diffusion barrier presented by the surface membrane so that the effects of various substances—e.g., Ca^{++} and ATP—on the contractile mechanism can be studied directly. Investigation of these model systems has revealed that ATP plays a dual role in the contraction–relaxation process, that ATP is the energy source for contraction and that Ca^{++} is mainly concerned with the control of contraction. Two model systems are discussed here—the glycerol-extracted preparation[64] and the actomyosin solution. Of course, the relevance to the intact system of any conclusions drawn from either model system must be determined.

GLYCEROL-EXTRACTED MUSCLE.[45, 72] Storage of a muscle in a strong glycerol solution at low temperature for several days destroys the membranes and extracts most of the soluble proteins and crystalloids. The contraction machinery seems intact. This glycerol-extracted muscle cannot be made to contract by electrical stimulation, but chemical stimulation can produce contraction–relaxation cycles in which the tension and degree of shortening are quantitatively comparable to responses of whole muscle to electrical stimulation. If extracted muscle is suspended in a medium resembling the intracellular medium—e.g., isotonic KCl—the extracted muscle is quite stiff or unextensible, a condition resembling the rigor of poisoned or dead muscle. Raising the ATP concentration to about 3 mM. causes shortening and development of tension. Since the actomyosin hydrolyzes ATP, the stiff state slowly returns and the extracted muscle "sets" at its new length. If an extracted muscle is undergoing an ATP-induced contraction, addition of actomyosin ATP-ase inhibitors causes relaxation; the preparation remains in an extensible or *plasticized* state as long as the ATP is present. Substances such as inorganic pyrophosphate and ADP also plasticize muscle but, unlike ATP, do not cause contraction. Thus, ATP has two actions: It causes development of tension, accompanied by hydrolysis of ATP, and it also plasticizes the muscle.

ACTOMYOSIN SOLUTION.[45, 55] Actin and myosin bind strongly together in isotonic KCl to form soluble actomyosin. Adding Ca^{++}, Mg^{++} and ATP initiates a dramatic "superprecipitation" of actomyosin, accompanied by hydrolysis of ATP. But the reaction is not controlled by Ca^{++} (see below) if the solution is formed from pure actin and myosin. Solutions obtained by less precise methods apparently contain impurities required for Ca^{++} control—possibly tropomyosin. The superprecipitation reaction, since it is produced by similar conditions, is believed analogous to contraction in whole muscle. It is partly reversed by chelating Ca^{++}. Measuring viscosity, sedimentation and light-scattering in appropriate solution shows that ATP separates actin and myosin. This effect, unaccompanied by ATP hydrolysis, is also produced by ADP and inorganic pyrophosphate. This dissociation reaction is believed analogous to relaxation in extracted muscle.

Role of calcium.[27] Calcium and magnesium are intimately involved in the mechanism which gives rise to the dual role of ATP: Ca^{++} stimulates the ATP-ase of both actomyosin and myosin, but Mg^{++} stimulates the ATP-ase of actomyosin only. Of the two ions, calcium seems to play the more important physiologic role. Injection of Ca^{++} into an intact muscle fiber causes local contraction,[33] as does the more quantitative procedure of dropping Ca^{++} solutions onto fibers whose membranes have been partially dissolved away or stripped off.[59] Reducing the Ca^{++} concentration to below 10^{-6} mols. per liter in actomyosin solutions brings about the relaxation-like effects of ATP; higher concentrations are required for the contraction-like effects of ATP.[71] These findings suggest that contractile activity is controlled by variations in sarcoplasmic calcium concentration. If this is so, the excitation–contraction coupling mechanism must release calcium to induce contraction and some mechanism must take up or sequester* it to induce relaxation of the muscle. There is considerable evidence for the existence of the latter mechanism, less for the former. This relaxing factor has been discussed in a recent symposium.[27]

A muscle fraction consisting mainly of sarcoplasmic reticulum has been found capable, if ATP is present in physiologic concentrations, of picking up enough Ca^{++} that its concentration in the medium surrounding the muscle is lowered to about 10^{-7} mols. per liter. This sequestering of Ca^{++} requires energy obtained from ATP hydrolysis. Thus, muscle apparently has a mechanism whereby its Ca^{++} concentration can be reduced to the value required for relaxation.[71] Whether this is the primary sequestering mechanism in the intact system is not known.

Although the exact site is unknown, experiments on frog muscle indicate that Ca^{++} is released near the transverse tubule of the sarcoplasmic reticulum. This observation also coincides with the present knowledge of the excitation–contraction coupling mechanism (see discussion of excitation–contraction coupling, p. 124). Further, the turnover rate of Ca^{++} in muscle is directly dependent on the muscle's contractile activity.[5]

Thus, the experiments on model systems clearly indicate that ATP plays a dual role in the contraction–relaxation process. When the actomyosin ATP-ase is active, addition of ATP causes a contraction-like event; when the ATP-

*Sequestering of Ca^{++} refers to its removal from the contractile elements and the medium surrounding them and its storage in a separate compartment.

ase is inhibited, addition of ATP causes a relaxation-like event.

ENERGY SOURCES FOR CONTRACTION.[12, 55] Experiments on model systems have established that the energy source for their contraction-like events is the hydrolysis of the ATP terminal phosphate group. However, work on the disappearance of ATP failed for many years to establish ATP as the energy source for contraction in intact muscle. All sources of ATP synthesis must be blocked, of course, if a decrease in ATP concentration is to be a measure of ATP consumption. Addition of iodoacetic acid (IAA) to and removal of O_2 from the bathing medium has long been known to block the major ATP synthesizing pathways. The ATP concentration in anoxic, IAA-treated contracting muscles does not decrease as long as the contractile activity is normal. However, if the muscle "fatigues" or goes into "rigor" (a stiff, relatively inextensible state, akin to or duplicating dead muscle) ATP concentration does decrease.[12, 55] On the other hand, contraction in anoxic, IAA-treated muscles is accompanied by a decrease in creatine phosphate (CP) concentration[13] (CP is a high energy phosphate compound). Indeed, CP decreases proportionately to both the work done by the muscle and to the total heat produced during a twitch.[13] Total heat and work are also proportional to each other for each normal muscle twitch. Nevertheless, CP is not considered the immediate energy source for contraction. Rather, it is believed that ATP concentration is maintained at the expense of CP by means of the Lohmann reaction, $CP + ADP = ATP + C$. This idea has long been held but only recently has it been given experimental support. Davies found that, when the Lohmann reaction is inhibited with fluorodinitrobenzene and when other ATP-synthesizing pathways are sufficiently slowed, ATP decreases concomitantly with contraction.[48] Muscles poisoned with fluorodinitrobenzene give normal contractile responses until the ATP supplies are depleted.

MOLECULAR INTEPRETATION OF THE SLIDING FILAMENT THEORY. Electron microscopic and physiologic evidence for the sliding filament theory in intact muscle and the chemical data obtained from model systems and other studies form two somewhat separate bodies of information concerning muscle function. The objective is, of course, to fit all the facts together into a coherent, reasonable picture of the kinetics of

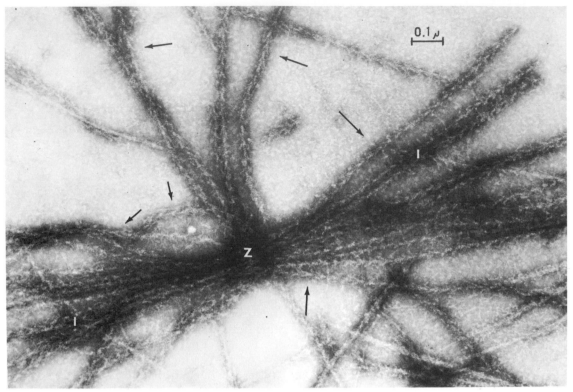

Fig. 6. An isolated I segment has been treated with heavy meromyosin, which attaches to the thin filaments, producing arrowhead-like structures (note places indicated by arrows). These are polarized and point outward from either side of the Z line. Segment prepared by blending glycerol extracted muscle in a medium which separates thick and thin filaments. (From H. E. Huxley, *J. molec. Biol.*, 1963, 7:281–308.)

the contraction process. Although a satisfactory picture is not presently available, certain speculations can be made which are helpful in understanding the types of processes occurring during contraction. This picture has emerged rapidly during the past half-dozen years.

Asymmetry of filament interactions. The mechanism using the energy in the ATP bond to produce contractile tension must be asymmetrical in the sense that the bonding between ATP, actin and myosin must form in a preferential direction to generate a net translational force. If the bonds at two successive sites exert their forces in opposite directions, no net force is developed. More specifically, the interaction of the two filaments is probably via ATP and must tend to pull the thin filaments toward the center of the A band. In other words, the thick filaments on each side of a Z line are pulled toward that Z line. H. E. Huxley[46] has direct electron micrographic evidence which gives a structural basis for this functional asymmetry. By reacting heavy meromyosin with thin fila-

ments, he formed filaments which, as shown in electron micrographs (Fig. 6), consisted of arrowhead-like structures (heavy meromyosin) with the heads always pointing away from the center. Note that the filaments join at their central points, presumably in a Z line-like combination.

Sliding filaments and dual action of ATP. The ideas of Davies,[17] A. F. Huxley[41] and H. E. Huxley[45] form the basis of a reasonable, but speculative, picture of how muscle might work. This picture, which serves mainly to integrate the known facts, should not be taken too literally. The data from muscle models indicate that ATP is directly involved in the formation of bridges between the thick and thin filaments. Thus, it might be supposed that in the relaxed state ATP is normally attached at only one side of a bridge site—i.e., on the heavy meromyosin —near the ATP-ase, preventing combination of actin and myosin and thus permitting the filaments to slide freely past each other. Tension could develop with the release of divalent calcium ions if they connected the two filaments by combining with ATP on one side and with special sites on the thin filament on the other. Shortening could result if the Ca^{++} were to bond to a flexible portion of a bridge projecting from the thick filament and extending by mutual repulsion between the quadrivalent ATP anions and some fixed negative charges on the thick filament. The Ca^{++} would neutralize some of the net negative charge on ATP, causing the extended bridge to shorten.[17] Shortening of the bridges would exert a force parallel to the filaments if the bridges were formed and broken at acute angles with respect to the filaments. This shortening of the bridge could in turn bring the ATP into the immediate vicinity of the ATP-ase and thus cause hydrolysis of ATP and breakage of the bond. In this way Ca^{++} may activate the ATP-ase. Creatine phosphate could then regenerate ATP and, if the muscle had shortened, another bond would form with the next site on the thin filament. This process would be happening more or less simultaneously at many sites along the filaments so that the contraction would be smooth and sustained. Thus, in normal shortening, many ATP molecules could be hydrolyzed by a single thick filament site interacting with a number of thin filament sites as they moved by. If there were no shortening, the force would be produced by the repetitive interaction and consequent turnover of ATP at fixed sites. In this case no external work is done but energy is consumed in maintaining tension. Relaxation would occur as the calcium was removed by the sequestering mechanism, thereby resulting in removal of the bridging link and inactivation of ATP-ase activity. Quite possibly, removal and inactivation are closely related, both being an intimate part of the contractile process. Although the foregoing is speculative, it can be seen how the data from muscle models can form a basis for a coherent picture of muscular contraction.

Rigor. The stiff, unextensible state of muscle, called rigor, results from conditions which reduce organic pyrophosphate activity—i.e., death and stimulation of IAA-poisoned muscle. Thus, it seems reasonable to suppose that rigor is caused by an *in vivo* formation of actomyosin —i.e., tight cross-bridges between thin and thick filaments—which is normally blocked by various pyrophosphates. The stiffness would arise from the cross-binding of the filaments and their consequent inability to slide past each other.

Membrane Properties of Skeletal Muscle. The electrical properties of skeletal muscle are similar to those of the squid giant axon. The differences in most cases are clearly related to the role of the muscle membrane in conducting impulses and initiating contraction.

CONDUCTION OF THE IMPULSE. The action potentials of skeletal muscle normally have an overshoot of about 20 mV. which can be varied by changing the external sodium concentration. Thus, the upstroke of the action potential is much like that of the squid giant axon. The action potential lasts a few milliseconds, excluding the long-lasting negative afterpotential (see Figs. 20, 21*A*). In mammalian muscle, the action potential spreads from its point of initiation, normally at the neuromuscular junction, by means of the local circuit mechanism at a speed of about 5 meters per second. An impulse initiated at the center of a fiber 10 cm. long would require 10 milliseconds to reach the ends, an appreciable fraction of the contraction time of about 30 milliseconds.

MEMBRANE CAPACITY. Another indication that the transverse tubular system of the sarcoplasmic reticulum may be electrically connected to the surface membrane is the finding that the electrical capacity per unit area of fiber surface is about 10 times as large in skeletal muscle as it is in squid axon.[26] Since, for constant membrane thickness, capacity is directly proportional to the total surface area of membrane, this finding suggests that membrane area is much greater than surface area and thus that the reticulum is electrically continuous with the surface membrane. A more detailed analysis[23] has shown that the capacity can be divided into two components, one about the same value as for squid axon and another much larger one which is in series with a small resistance that possibly represents the transverse tubular resistance.

POTASSIUM PERMEABILITY. The upstroke of the action potential results from a regenerative interaction between membrane permeability to Na^+ and transmembrane voltage. Although this interaction is much like that found in squid axons, the recovery process is quite different: (i) Following depolarization, the increase in potassium permeability is delayed, as in squid axons. Unlike squid, however, the increase is not appreciable for depolarizations of less than about 20 mV. Therefore, the rapid repolarization phase of the action potential terminates while the fiber is incompletely polarized. Thereafter, the potential returns to the resting level over a period determined by the resting time constant of the membrane (about 30 milliseconds) (see Fig. 21A). (ii) In squid axons, a maintained depolarization maintains an increased potassium permeability, whereas, in muscle, a depolarization greater than 20 mV. produces only a transient rise in P_K. This indicates that potassium permeability is inactivated by a process similar to, but slower than, that for sodium permeability.

In the resting state, potassium permeability exhibits "anomalous" behavior in that it is much higher when the K^+ electrochemical gradient is inward than when it is outward.[38] This is just the reverse of the behavior which occurs on depolarization, i.e., the delayed increase in potassium permeability. This anomalous behavior appears to be associated with a special region of the muscle which also accumulates potassium during activity.[30, 38] The special region seems to consist of the sarcoplasmic reticular membranes and contents or, at least, the transverse tubular portions of them. In this interpretation, the surface membrane seems to have more normal properties with respect to its potassium permeability; the significance of the peculiar permeability properties of the reticular membrane is not known.

Excitation–Contraction Coupling. Skeletal muscle contraction begins when the membrane is depolarized at least 40 mV. from the resting value. This is normally accomplished by an action potential. Membrane depolarization itself, rather than accompanying longitudinal currents, brings about contraction. This implies that depolarization of the surface membrane can initiate contraction in the interior of the cell within a few milliseconds in the faster muscles (Fig. 1). Since Ca^{++} is directly involved in the activation of the contractile mechanism, the question arises: If Ca^{++} is released at the surface by depolarization, can it diffuse into the interior fast enough to cause contraction in the experimentally observed time? A. V. Hill[35] has calculated that diffusion is too slow to account for the contraction times of larger or faster fibers. This discrepancy can be eliminated by supposing that a portion of the sarcoplasmic reticulum is directly connected to the surface membrane and hence is depolarized with it and by further supposing that calcium is released from the reticulum, where the diffusion distance to the contractile material is much shorter.

A. F. Huxley and Taylor[43] found that there are specific sites on the muscle fiber's surface where it can be stimulated to contract by local depolarization, whereas most regions are insensitive to the local depolarization (see Fig. 7). In those muscle fibers where the center of the triad of the sarcoplasmic reticular system is at the Z line, local depolarization at a Z line often produces local contraction. The shortening is symmetrical in the two halves of the I band on either side of the Z line below the electrode. On the other hand, local depolarization between neighboring Z lines produces no contractions at the same current strengths. When the triad is centered near the junction of the A and I bands, local stimulation near the A–I junction often produces local contraction of the neighboring half of the I band. No contraction is produced at the same current strengths if the electrode tip is between neighboring triads. Thus, depolarization of the surface membrane probably also depolarizes the transverse tubules of the sarcoplasmic reticulum by direct electrotonic spread. These tubules are large enough (about 400 Å in diameter)[47] to permit this spread with little delay. This transverse activation greatly decreases the diffusion path from depolarizable membrane to contractile material—e.g., in a 100 μ fiber, the diffusion distance is reduced from 50 μ to 1 μ. Various mechanical, thermal and optical changes, collectively termed activation, precede the actual mechanical response of a pull on the tendon.

The events leading to contraction include the following: (i) Depolarization of the surface membrane by the action potential causes passive depolarization of the transverse tubules and possibly of the remainder of the sarcoplasmic reticulum. (ii) This depolarization causes some part of the reticulum to release Ca^{++}, which diffuses to the region of thick and thin filament overlap. (iii) The Ca^{++} completes the conditions necessary for tension-generating reactions between thick and thin filaments; thus, these reactions continue as long as Ca^{++} is present. (iv) Relaxation seems to result from the sequestering of Ca^{++} into special regions, possibly into the remainder of the reticular system. On this basis calcium is released on depolarization of the reticulum and sequestered on repolarization.

Mechanical Properties of Muscle. CLASSES OF CONTRACTION.

The term "contraction" as used here refers to the muscle's internal events which are manifested externally by either shortening or tension development or both. Indeed, the tension a muscle can develop between its points of attachment is the fundamental functional property of muscle.* This tension is utilized mechanically in several ways. The contracting muscles may shorten and produce movement. Since a force acts through a distance during this movement, whether it is walking, running or lifting, work is performed by the muscle. This type of contraction—shortening under constant load—has been called *isotonic* (equal tension) since Fick introduced the term in the last century. He applied the term *isometric* (equal length) to contractions in which the whole system does not change length. Such contractions produce tension rather than short-

---

* The force exerted by a muscle on its attachment is surprisingly high. At a very moderate rate of walking, the triceps surae exerts a tension almost four times the person's weight, and during running the gastrocnemius may exert a tension some six times the runner's weight. According to Fick's estimate, the human gluteus may exert a force of 1450 pounds. If all our muscles, containing an estimated 2.7×10^8 individual fibers, exerted their tensions in the same direction, they could develop a force of at least 25 tons.

ening and work. The tension or force developed in contracting muscles that do not shorten is utilized to oppose other forces (usually gravity), in holding an object and in posture. In this type of contraction no external work is done; the tension developed is used to prevent motion. This classification of contractions is useful but not realistic; although isometric contraction is common in postural muscles, isotonic contraction seldom occurs in normal bodily movements because the load ordinarily varies considerably during shortening. Nevertheless, the gross contractile properties of muscle can be understood from study of the two types of contraction.

If the opposing force or load is greater than the maximum isometric contraction tension, the muscle is stretched or lengthened while actively contracting. Such lengthening occurs, for example, when the extensor muscles of the hip check the velocity of the leg as it approaches the forward limit of its swing during walking or running. Thus physical work is done on the muscle by its antagonist in stretching it. The extensor muscle cannot store all this energy while actively contracting and some appears as heat. However, less energy is degraded to heat in the extensor muscle than that resulting from the sum of the work done on the extensor and the energy necessary to maintain the extensor in the contracted state.[37] After checking the forward velocity, the stretched muscle will

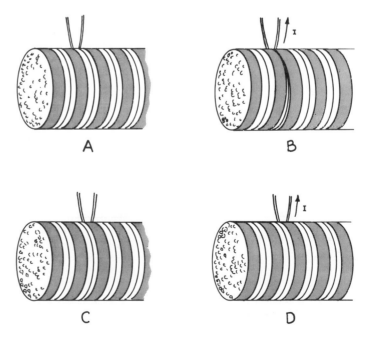

Fig. 7. Diagrammatic representation of local stimulation experiments of A. F. Huxley and Taylor.[43] The sarcoplasmic reticular triads are centered on the Z lines. *A*, Electrode applied to muscle surface at sensitive spot near Z line. *B*, Current passed while electrode is in same position as in *A*. Adjacent half sarcomeres contract locally. *C*, Electrode applied to surface over an A band. *D*, Current flow produces no local contraction. (After Fawcett, in *The myocardium, its biochemistry and biophysics*, Fishman, ed. New York, New York Heart Association, 1961.)

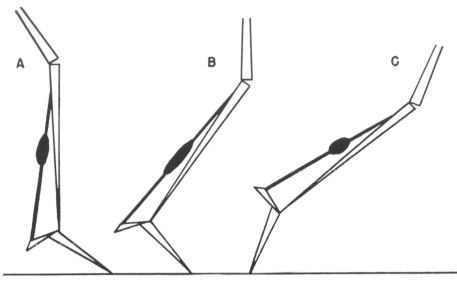

Fig. 8. Length changes of a contracting leg muscle bundle during running. Tension developed during contraction which has begun in position *A* is not sufficient to check forward movement of body, thus causing contracting muscle bundle to be stretched to length shown in position *B*. After this phase in running cycle, muscle is in position to shorten, propelling leg forward to position *C*. (Prepared and kindly furnished by Dr. H. Elftman.)

shorten as it accelerates the limb in the opposite direction. We thus have an example of both lengthening and shortening in a contracting muscle, as is schematically illustrated in Figure 8. This type of contraction normally occurs in muscles operating in antagonistic pairs. Note that in isometric, shortening and lengthening contractions the muscles perform no work or positive external work or negative external work. This classification, shown in Table 1, was proposed by Fenn.[28]

RECORDING MUSCLE CONTRACTION. Methods for recording isometric and isotonic contractions are illustrated in Figure 1. In isotonic recording, one end (usually the bony origin) of the muscle is held fixed, and the tendon on the other end is attached to a freely movable weight or weighted lever (to set tension). Shortening of the muscle is measured by recording the position of the weight or weighted lever mechanically, optically or electronically. If the recording system responds rapidly enough, the time course of muscle shortening can be accurately measured. For isometric recording, one end (usually the bony origin) is held fixed and the tendon of the other end is attached to a rigidly mounted tension-measuring device (strain gauge) that is moved only negligibly by the contraction of the muscle but develops a signal proportional to the tension which the muscle exerts on it. The signal from the strain gauge (or mechano-electric transducer, a device for transforming a mechanical signal into a more easily amplified and recorded electrical signal) is amplified and recorded on film or paper as a function of time.

TWITCH. The brief contractile response of skeletal muscle to a single maximal volley of

TABLE 1. *Classes of Muscular Contraction*

TYPE OF CONTRACTION	FUNCTION	EXTERNAL FORCE ON MUSCLE	EXTERNAL WORK BY MUSCLE
Shortening	Acceleration	Less	Positive
Isometric	Fixation	Same	None
Lengthening	Deceleration	More	Negative

impulses in the motor neurons supplying it is called a *twitch*.* The mechanical response in Figure 1 is a record showing the isometric twitch of the cat tibialis anterior muscle elicited by a single maximal stimulus to its motor nerve. The interval between the beginning of the electrical response and the peak of the tension record is the *contraction time*. By definition, the whole system (i.e., the muscles, the tendon and the isometric lever) does not shorten during isometric contraction. There is, however, *internal* shortening. The activation induced by stimulation results not only in sudden development of internal tension but also in a capacity to shorten. Under isometric conditions, the contractile elements shorten and pull on the tendon and on the series-elastic components within the fiber, thereby transmitting the tension to the recording lever or, in the body, to the bony lever. The twitch curve, recorded isotonically and isometrically, is the external manifestation of the activated contractile machine. The actual curves differ markedly in shape from those expected from the contractile machine. In an isometric twitch elastic components of the fibers and tendon in series with the contractile parts must be stretched before the muscle pulls on its tendons. Thus, tendon tension rises much more slowly than does contractile element tension. The rise is slowed so much that the contractile elements are starting to relax before tendon tension reaches its maximum.

The twitch response to a single stimulus is as

---

*Not all striated muscle fibers respond with a twitch to an impulse in their motor nerve fibers. A *slow* or *tonus* fiber differs from an ordinary twitch fiber in that it (i) has a great many motor end-plates instead of one or two; (ii) is usually incapable of propagating an action potential; and (iii) has a small diameter (15 to 20 μ) and a poorly developed sarcoplasmic reticulum. Tonus fibers are found widely in nonmammalian vertebrates but have been identified recently in the extraocular muscles of the cat.[34] As explained below, the effect of a motor nerve impulse on a muscle end-plate is a local depolarization of the muscle membrane. Since local depolarization causes local contraction, a maintained contraction can be produced in these fibers by a continuous barrage of impulses to the multiple end-plates. The rate of contraction of these muscles is much slower than twitch fibers (about one second). Thus, they are adapted for maintaining a steady tension. Only twitch fibers will be considered further in this chapter; reference to "slow" fibers means slowly contracting twitch fibers.

typical of a single isolated muscle fiber as it is of a whole muscle. As can be seen from Figure 1 the action potential is almost over before the contraction begins. In terms of the hypothesis of the contractile mechanisms given above, this delay would be made up of the time necessary for the transverse tubules to depolarize, plus the time needed for the release and diffusion of Ca^{++} to the sites on the filaments plus the time needed for Ca^{++} to react with these sites and activate the contractile process. Since a fixed amount of Ca^{++} is released, relaxation occurs when the Ca^{++} sequestering system reduces the Ca^{++} concentration below the critical value.

The form of the twitch contraction curve, when recorded under the same conditions, is similar for all striated twitch muscles, but the contraction time and the total twitch duration vary a great deal in different types of muscle and in different animals. There are "fast" and "slow" twitch muscles. The most rapidly contracting mammalian muscle studied is the internal rectus of the eye, which has a contraction time of 7.5 milliseconds. The limb muscles of the cat fall into two ranges. Physiologic flexors (e.g., tibialis anterior) and superficial extensor muscles bridging two joints (e.g., gastrocnemius) tend to be fast muscles, having contraction times between 25 and 40 milliseconds. Usually a deep extensor muscle acting at a single joint (e.g., soleus) is a slow muscle with a contraction time in the range of 94 to 120 milliseconds.[14] In the cat, slow muscles are red (owing to greater concentration of myoglobin) and fast muscles are pale or "white"; however, it is better to speak of "slow" and "fast" muscles, since not all fibers in the soleus are red but all are slow. Furthermore, in many vertebrate muscles red and pale fibers are completely intermixed. In the cat, fast muscles are those called upon for rapid phasic movement; slow muscles are concerned with posture. Thus, relative to the maximal tension each muscle can produce, the myotatic stretch reflex (Chap. 7) is larger in the soleus than in the gastrocnemius.

SUMMATION AND TETANUS. When a single maximal stimulus is delivered to a motor nerve or directly to a muscle, all the fibers of the muscle are activated and the maximum twitch tension is developed. Even if the electrical stimulus to the motor nerve is increased to a supramaximal intensity, the response will not be greater than that to a maximal stimulus. If, however, two maximal stimuli are delivered rapidly

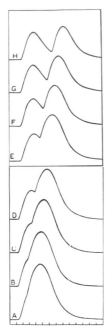

Fig. 9. Summation of muscular contraction by double stimulation. Isometric records of median head of gastrocnemius responding to two supramaximal stimuli to the motor nerve in succession. Ordinate, tension, arbitrary units; abscissa, time, 20 millisecond time marks below A. Intervals in milliseconds between stimuli in different records are: *A,* 24; *B,* 32; *C,* 40; *D,* 48; *E,* 57; *F,* 69; *G,* 77; *H,* 88. (After Cooper and Eccles, *J. Physiol.,* 1930, *69*:377–385.)

a twitch, because of the series elastic elements, the contractile elements have partially relaxed before the external tension reaches a peak. This indicates that a larger external response can be obtained by reactivating the contractile elements during the twitch. This is possible because the mechanical response far outlasts the electrical response (Fig. 1). A second action potential causes the release of more Ca^{++} while the first mechanical response is still present, thus reactivating the partially relaxed contractile elements and giving a larger external response. There is thus a mechanical fusion or summation of contractions. The degree of fusion is greater when the stimulus interval is shortest, and the tension of such a summated contraction may be more than twice the tension of a single twitch. The degree of summation decreases as the interval between the stimuli approaches the duration of a single twitch response (Fig. 9).

If a series of several stimuli is delivered at a rapid rate, the third summates with the first two, each subsequent volley adding a diminishing increment of tension until further volleys add no more tension but do maintain the contraction. This response is called a *tetanus.** It occurs when all contractile elements are maximally activated and elastic elements have attained a fixed length. The tension developed in a tetanus is usually about four times that of a single twitch. With rates of repetitive stimulation too slow to cause complete mechanical fusion, an undulatory jerky response termed an incomplete tetanus is obtained. As the rate of stimulation is increased, the responses to individual volleys become less distinct, and the mechanical fusion becomes progressively greater until complete tetanus occurs (Fig. 10). Similarly, the tension produced increases progressively as the tetanus becomes more fused. Any

* The physiologic term "tetanus" has been used in naming two neuromuscular disorders: (i) tetany, caused by hypocalcemia, and (ii) tetanus, caused by the toxin of a bacillus. Tetanic contractions of muscles occur in both diseases.

enough in succession that the second stimulus arrives before the contraction cycle is over, the response will be greater than that elicited by a single maximal stimulus. This is true for a single fiber or the whole muscle. The extent of increase in isometric tension or total shortening depends upon the interval between the two stimuli (Fig. 9). The stimulus interval, however, must be greater than the refractory period of the muscle to allow for two propagated responses. It must be emphasized that, in contrast to the action potential, the activation of the contractile material is not all-or-none. Since the state of activation depends on Ca^{++} concentration, there is a continuum of states of activation between fully activated and relaxed. In

Fig. 10. Isometric tension of single muscle fiber (ordinate) as a function of time (abscissa) during continuously increasing and decreasing stimulation frequency (2 to 50 per sec.). Time intervals at top of record, 0.2 second. (From Buchthal, *Dan. Biol. Medd.,* 1942, *17*(2):1–140.)

Fig. 11. Recordings of electrical (e) and mechanical (m) activities of the cat extensor digitorum longus, showing the development of tetanus. Ordinates, tension (m) or voltage (e), arbitrary units; abscissa, time, 15 milliseconds between successive action potentials in (e). Rate of stimulation, 67 per second; onset and termination of stimulation shown by electrical record. Note that action potentials are discrete whereas contractions are fused. (From Creed *et al., Reflex activity of the spinal cord.* Oxford, Clarendon Press, 1932.)

additional increase in frequency of stimulation beyond this critical rate increases tension only slightly.

This rate is, as might be expected, higher for fast muscles with their relatively brief contraction times and lower for slow muscles with their longer contraction times. A rate of 350 stimuli per second, for example, is necessary to produce a complete tetanus in the internal rectus of the eye, whereas a rate of 30 per second is adequate for the slower soleus (i.e., the "slowlyest") muscle. About 100 stimuli per second are required for complete tetanus in a fast limb muscle. In contrast to the mechanical fusion of responses to repetitive stimuli, the spike potentials accompanying such contractions always remain discrete and discontinuous (Fig. 11). This finding emphasizes the fundamental difference between membrane and contractile mechanisms.

LENGTH–TENSION RELATION. Skeletal, cardiac and smooth muscles are elastically extensible. Unstimulated skeletal muscle in the body is normally under slight tension, since it shortens (about 20 per cent) if the tendons are cut. The muscle length at which maximal contractile tension is developed is called the *resting length* because this is also near the length the muscle normally has in the body. The elastic tension of unstimulated muscle is negligible for lengths somewhat shorter than the resting length, but increases exponentially for greater lengths (Fig. 12). Stretch is reversible up to 1.5 times resting length. Cardiac muscle has this same general type of passive length–tension relation.

Since muscles change length during contraction, it is essential to know how such changes influence the contractile tension developed. The maximum force developed by a contracting muscle when all its fibers are stimulated at

optimal frequencies is specifically related to the initial length at the time of stimulation. Figure 12 shows the relation between tension developed during maximal voluntary effort and the change in length of the triceps muscle in man. The net or active, voluntary tension curve is obtained by first determining the passive tension produced by stretching the muscle fibers and connective tissue to any given length and then subtracting the value obtained from the total tension exerted by the contracting muscle at the same length. As can be seen the net ac-

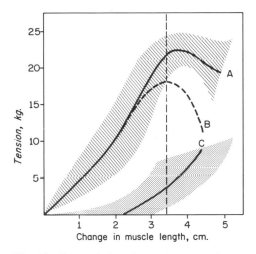

Fig. 12. Isometric length–tension curve for human triceps muscle. Muscle length changes taken from length at which total muscle tension is zero. The curves are a summary of many results. A, Most probable total-tension curve. Shaded area around this curve indicates range of results. C, Most probable passive tension curve with range indicated. B, Net voluntary tension curve obtained by subtracting C from A. (After University of California, *Fundamental studies of human locomotion and other information relating to design of artificial limbs,* vol. 2, 1947.)

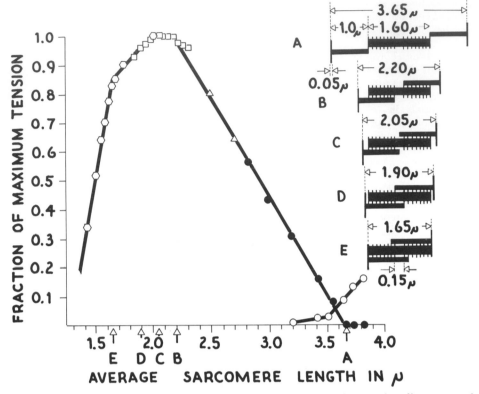

Fig. 13. "Sarcomere" isometric length–tension curve from single frog semitendinosus muscle fibers which were so controlled that length of a short central section is held constant (see text for details of technique). Ordinate, maximum active isometric tetanic tension and passive tension in fractions of maximum tension. The curve is the result of experiments on many single fibers. The accuracy of the curve requires that, in each region of sarcomere length, different fibers be used for obtaining the data. When stimulation is continued and tension is high, nonuniformities in sarcomere length may develop in the fiber's central region. The data from a few fibers (different types of points) are plotted on the curve to show agreement between data from individual fibers and data from all fibers used. The open circles indicate passive tension in the fiber giving the closed circle points. On the right are shown filament positions for the five sarcomere lengths. A, No overlap. B, Maximum overlap of thin filaments with bridges on one-half of thick filaments. C, Thin filaments meet in center of A band. D, Double overlap of thin filaments. E, Thick filaments meet Z lines. The figures are drawn with the following dimensions: thick filaments, 1.60 μ, thin filaments (including Z line), 2.05 μ,[57] Z line, 0.05 μ, region in center of thick filaments without bridges, 0.15 μ.[46] (Data from Gordon, A. F. Huxley, and Julian, *J. Physiol.*, 1964, *171*:28P–30P.)

tive tension increases more or less linearly with increasing initial length until a maximum is reached. If the initial length is greater than this maximum, less tension is developed. The optimal initial length corresponds roughly to the "natural" or resting length of the muscle in the body. This same general shape of the length–tension relationship for contracting muscle has been observed in many types of striated whole muscle and single fibers for both maximum tetanic tension and maximum twitch tension. The contractile tension developed by cardiac muscle depends on ventricular volume in much the same way. Thus the length–tension rela-

tionship is a fundamental property of contracting muscle and reflects the nature of contractility.

Length–tension relation of sarcomere.[31] The most crucial requirement for any theory of muscular contraction is that it explain the length–active tension curve. The sliding filament hypothesis can easily explain the general features of the curve, but whether it can explain the curve in greater detail depends on knowledge of the length–tension relation for a single sarcomere. The length–tension curve for a single sarcomere would be the same as that for a whole muscle or muscle fiber if all sarcomeres in the muscle were equal in length for all total muscle lengths during contraction. If this were the case, the length of each sarcomere would be directly proportional to the total muscle length. However, the lengths of individual sarcomeres along a fiber vary considerably during contraction. They are much shorter near the ends of the fiber than in the middle, where the lengths are reasonably constant. A. F. Huxley[31] has gotten a good estimate of sarcomere length–tension relation by holding constant the length of a short segment in the central region of a single fiber and measuring the tension developed during tetanic stimulation; this "length clamping" technique is similar in principle to "voltage clamping" (Chap. 2). This "sarcomere" length–tension diagram consists of a series of straight lines of different slopes, the transition between linear regions being sharply curved (Fig. 13). The striking correlation between relative overlap of thick and thin filaments at various sarcomere lengths and the length–tension diagram can be seen by comparing the lettered points on the abscissa with the corresponding inset drawings. As is shown by the negative slope on the right, the tension falls off linearly as the overlap of thick and thin filaments decreases (sarcomere length changing from 2.2 μ to 3.65 μ). At 3.65 μ there is no overlap and little active tension. The horizontal plateau from 2.2 μ to 2.0 μ occurs when filament overlap is increasing but in a region with no bridges on the thick filament. This is strong evidence that maximum isometric tetanic tension is directly proportional to the number of such bridges and further that the bridges are the sites of interaction and force generation between the two sets of filaments. The break in the curve at about 2.0 μ occurs where the thin filaments meet in the center of the A band (2.05 μ) or where they start to interact with the oppositely-directed bridge sites past the midline gap of the thick filaments (1.9 μ). Thus, tension drops off rapidly with length in this region because of the collision of opposing thin filaments with each other or the interaction of the thin filaments with the bridges on the opposite side of the thick filaments, or both. The break in the curve at 1.65 μ occurs where the thick filaments come into contact with the Z lines. The "corners" on the length–tension curve occur precisely at points predicted by the sliding filament hypothesis, thus giving it strong support.

The total amount of tension that a muscle can exert under optimal conditions is a function of the total number of fibers and the number of myofilaments per fiber. This tension, when expressed as kilograms per square centimeter of area perpendicular to the fiber direction, represents the absolute muscle force. This force is about 4 kg. per sq. cm. in man. To do external work a muscle must shorten; thus, the realizable work depends upon the fiber's length as well as on its cross section. In man this length varies from 5 mm. for the shortest bundles of the multifidus to more than 400 mm. for the sartorius muscle. Parallel-fibered muscles in the human body can shorten during contraction to about 60 per cent of their maximal extended lengths. In pennate muscles the excursions are less.

Load–speed of shortening relation. Both the rate and the degree of muscle shortening during contraction depend upon the load. With a greater load, the muscle shortens less and more slowly. It is a common experience that lighter objects can be lifted more rapidly than heavier ones. The relation between speed of shortening and load in the human pectoralis is given by the load–speed curve in Figure 14. To measure this relation, the muscle is kept slightly stretched and then is stimulated to contract maximally. The muscle lifts a load (weight or weighted lever) which has been supported by a block, and the muscle's length is then recorded as a function of time. The rate or speed of shortening starts at a high value and slowly decreases to zero as shortening approaches the maximum. The initial high speed is defined as the shortening velocity or speed. The rate of shortening must be measured at a fixed length for each load lifted since the maximum isometric tension varies with length. When the short-

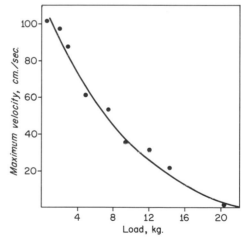

Fig. 14. Load–maximum shortening velocity (magnitude of velocity or speed) curve for human right pectoralis major muscle. Muscle initially was stretched by a load of 0.32 kg. to a length slightly beyond resting. Greater loads were supported by a block at this same length before excitation. (Based on data of Ralston, Inman, Strait, and Shaffrath, *Amer. J. Physiol.,* 1928, *86*:312–319.)

ening is maximal, the speed is zero and isometric tension develops for that length. At this point, the length is the shortest at which the muscle can lift the load. The general form of the load–shortening velocity curve follows directly from the sliding filament hypothesis (although it is not unique in this respect): When a muscle shortens rapidly, the filaments slide past one another rapidly, leaving little time for interaction of thick and thin filaments and consequent generation of tension. Thus there are fewer interacting sites and less tension development than if the muscle shortens slowly. In any case, the muscle never exerts as much force while shortening as it does when contracting isometrically. In the body, muscle speed is also limited by the mechanical inertia of the moving parts. Since the absolute amount of shortening depends on the length of the muscle, the intrinsic speed of the muscle is given by its maximum velocity divided by its length. The intrinsic speed, as mentioned in the discussion of the twitch, varies a good deal among muscles of the same animal and between different animals.

For further analysis of the relation between mechanical power, developed efficiency, total power used and speed of shortening, the student may refer to the paper of A. V. Hill.[36] A. F. Huxley[41] and H. E. Huxley[45] discuss more completely the mechanical properties of whole muscle. For an analysis of the dynamics of motion, the effective utilization of forces of muscle contraction, and the interrelationship of the geometric arrangement of the bony levers and the dynamics of muscle contraction, refer to Elftman[22] and to the University of California studies.[69]

The Motor Unit and Gradation of Muscular Activity. MOTOR UNIT. The functional unit of the motor system is neither the entire muscle nor the individual muscle fiber but the *motor unit*. Just before and just after entering the muscle, the axon from each ventral horn cell (motoneuron) branches many times and innervates a number of muscle fibers. Therefore, *the motor unit consists of a single motoneuron, its axon and the group of muscle fibers innervated by this single axon.* The motor unit, not the single muscle fiber, represents the unitary, minimum or quantum basis of normal muscular activity; normal skeletal muscle responses are quantitatively graded in terms of motor units and, in Sherrington's words, "a muscle with its motor nerve may be thought of as an additive assemblage of motor units."

The average size of the motor unit—the number of muscle fibers in a motor unit—is learned from the innervation ratio. The innervation ratio is determined by dividing the number of motor axons in the nerve serving the muscle by the number of fibers in a muscle. For example, innervation ratios in cat muscles vary from 1:3 in extrinsic eye muscles to 1:150 in some leg muscles; the ratio depends on the function of the muscle. Fine gradation of eye muscle contraction is necessary for object fixation, but only coarse gradation is needed for postural muscles; smaller ratios (fewer muscle fibers per nerve fiber) permit greater delicacy in gradation of movement.

Average motor unit tension. The tension yielded by a whole muscle under maximal stimulation of its nerve divided by the number of motor fibers in the nerve gives the average tension of the individual motor units. Following this reasoning, Eccles and Sherrington[21] determined the total tension developed by representative muscles during motor twitches and tetani after the dorsal root ganglia had been removed and the afferent fibers in the muscle nerves allowed to degenerate. Subsequently, the motor fibers passing to the tested muscle were enumerated and the average motor unit tension was calculated. In cat leg muscles, these values ranged from 8 to 25 grams for tetanic stimulation and from 2 to 6 grams for twitches. The number of motor units ranged from 250 to 550. It has since been learned that many of the nerve fibers which would be counted in such preparations are γ efferents innervating intrafusal fibers of the muscle spindles. These fibers, which constitute about 30 per cent of the motor fibers, do not add to the tension of muscle contraction. Eccles and Sherrington's values for motor unit tension should therefore be increased by 40 per cent ($100/0.7 - 100$). If, as Hunt and Kuffler claim,[40] a single muscle fiber may be innervated by more than one nerve fiber, the average tension value of a unit would be still greater.

MECHANISMS OF GRADATION. Since motor units are the smallest functional units of muscle, the weakest possible *natural* movement due to twitch fibers is the twitch of a single motor unit. As more force is required, three things happen in an overlapping sequence: (i) more motor units are activated (recruitment); (ii) the active motor units discharge more frequently but not rapidly enough for muscular summation (i.e., the response is subtetanic); and (iii) with further increase of frequency, the motor unit twitches summate to form a tetanus. In both stage ii and stage iii, the more rapid the frequency the greater the tension becomes, although the reasons for this are somewhat different in the two stages. It should be kept in mind that the total tension exerted on a tendon at any instant is simply the sum of the tensions being generated by each motor unit at that instant. Some units are contracting, some relaxing and some resting.

To visualize these relations it is necessary to know the rate at which single motoneurons discharge. This rate was measured by Adrian and Bronk, who recorded activity of single motor units through concentric needle electrodes thrust into a muscle. During voluntary contraction the discharge rates of single motoneurons varied between 5 and 50 impulses per second as the contraction increased from light to maximal effort. During postural reflex contraction, Denny-Brown found discharge rates of 5 to 25 impulses per second. It is clear that no significant degree of muscle summation occurs at the lower rates; each unit is producing a series of twitches. Nevertheless, tension grades with frequency. A necessary condition for occurrence of this gradation is that the units contract asynchronously, which they will do because they are recruited at different times

and are activated at different rates. Figure 15 shows how four motor units twitching asynchronously at very low rates sum to produce a relatively smooth, maintained tension on the tendon. Not only will the asynchronized trains of impulses in many motoneurons result in a smooth contraction of the whole muscle, but this contraction will vary according to the average frequency of the twitches in the individual units. Think of the twitch as a quantum of contraction. With more rapid rates of motoneuron discharge the number of units twitching at any one time increases, and their individual forces combine to pull on the tendon.

For the stronger grades of muscular tension the third mechanism comes into play as the frequencies of motoneuron discharge enter the tetanic range. As was seen earlier, as twitches fuse to form a tetanus the tension produced is proportional to the frequency of stimulation up to the fusion frequency. Higher frequencies yield little additional tension. In rapid muscles fusion occurs at about 40 to 50 stimuli per second, which agrees well with the top range of motoneuron discharge during voluntary activity.

NEUROMUSCULAR TRANSMISSION

Events in Neuromuscular Transmission. How a nerve impulse initiates an impulse in a muscle fiber membrane poses a problem not encountered in impulse propagation in either structure. This problem arises from the rapidly changing geometry at the junction of nerve and muscle. If the local circuit current flow of the nerve impulse directly stimulates the muscle fiber membrane, then the nerve fiber must supply a large current in order to depolarize the muscle membrane to threshold. This necessity can be seen from Figures 16 and 17, which show the main structural features of the neuromuscular junction (end-plate region of the muscle). The diameter of the naked axon near its termination is 1 to 2 μ, the diameter of the muscle fiber is about 100 μ. If there were a low-resistance connection between the axoplasm and the sarcoplasm, activity at the nerve terminal would cause local current flow from the inactive muscle membrane. However, the area of muscle membrane that must be depolarized is at least 1000 times larger than the area of the nerve terminal. It is unlikely that the nerve can supply the required current; it is

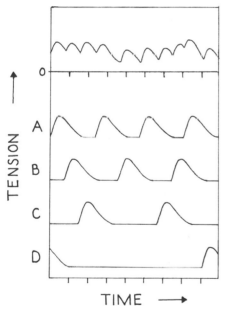

Fig. 15. Summation (top) of tensions developed by four motor units contracting (twitching) asynchronously at different frequencies. Result is a relatively smooth tendon tension. Ordinates, top, tendon tension; A, B, C, D tensions developed by each of four motor units. Abscissa, time (100 millisecond markers). The motor units are stimulated at rates of 4.3, 3.5, 2.4 and 1.1 per second; each produces the same maximum tension. Note that the summed tension is much smoother than that developed by each motor unit.

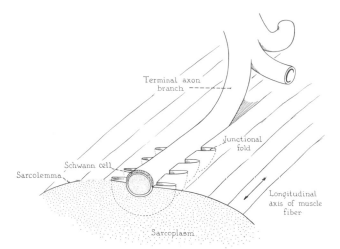

Fig. 16.   End-plate region of the frog. The trough in which the terminal axon branch lies runs parallel to the axis of the muscle fiber. Myelin sheath has ended before terminal branching, leaving only the Schwann cell over the axon. (After Birks, H. E. Huxley and Katz, *J. Physiol.*, 1960, *150*:134–144.)

even more unlikely that there is protoplasmic continuity between nerve and muscle in view of recent electron micrographic studies of the nerve muscle junction (Fig. 17).[6] These considerations, together with earlier physiologic evidence and the highly specialized structure of the nerve terminal and the end-plate membrane, overwhelmingly indicate that neuromuscular transmission is accomplished by means other than local circuit flow, e.g., chemically.

There is an enormous amount of evidence that neuromuscular transmission is mediated by a chemical—acetylcholine (ACh), a methylated quaternary ammonium salt. The sequence of events is as follows: (i) The depolarization of the naked nerve terminal during activity causes the release of a small amount of ACh. (ii) The ACh diffuses across the small gap between the nerve ending and the end-plate and reacts with a *receptor* in the end-plate. (iii) The ACh–receptor complex acts to increase the permeability of the end-plate membrane to cations, specifically to Na^+ and K^+, and is quickly destroyed by the enzyme acetylcholinesterase (AChE), which is localized in high concentrations in the end-plate regions of the membrane. (iv) The membrane potential of the end-plate changes toward zero, no matter what the original potential. (v) If the transmitter action is strong enough, and if the muscle membrane is excitable, the end-plate membrane is depolarized to threshold, and an impulse is propagated away from the end-plate in both directions.

ACETYLCHOLINE LIBERATION.[25, 51]   The depolarization due to the arrival of an impulse at the nerve terminals liberates a minute amount of ACh (about 10^{-17} M.). From studies of the electrical potentials at the end-plate it appears that the ACh is liberated from a large number (200 to 300) of sites in the form of small packets or quanta containing a constant number of ACh molecules. The exact number is unknown but is 1000 to 10,000 molecules per packet, possibly more. This physiologic evidence conforms with biochemical evidence that ACh exists in bound form and with the findings by electron microscopy that the nerve terminals contain many vesicles a few hundred Ångstroms in diameter (Fig. 17). Individual packets are liberated spontaneously at random intervals in the absence of propagated activity in the nerve. During an impulse not all of the ACh liberation sites actually do release a packet of ACh. The number of sites that do release ACh during activity increases directly with the

Fig. 17.   Electron micrographs of transverse and longitudinal sections through the end-plate region of frog muscle fiber, showing relationship between terminal axon and muscle cell. Compare with Figure 16. Axon terminal (AT), Schwann cell (SC), mitochondrion (M), neurolemma (NL), sarcolemma (SL), sarcoplasm (SP), junctional fold (JF), myofilaments (MF), vesicles (V). *Top*, Transverse section through terminal axon branch, muscle fiber and junctional fold. Thus, sarcolemma is seen near neurolemma for only a short distance at left. *Bottom*, Longitudinal section showing relationships between structures involved. Note junctional folds penetrating into the muscle fiber and the existence of a gap between neurolemma and sarcolemma. (From Birks, Huxley, and Katz, *J. Physiol.*, 1960, *150*:134–144.)

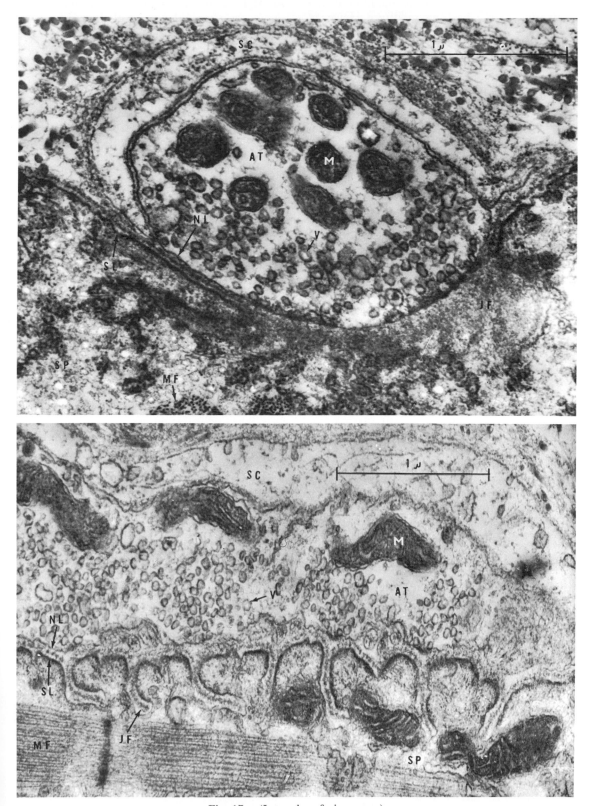

Fig. 17. (Legend on facing page.)

calcium and inversely with the magnesium concentration in the bathing medium. However, the amount of ACh in each packet remains constant over a range of calcium concentrations that changes the total amount of ACh released from near zero to well above normal—indicating that calcium is directly involved in the secretion of the packets of ACh.

END-PLATE RECEPTORS.[25, 51] The muscle end-plates contain two kinds of ACh receptors. One, the receptor proper, combines with ACh to form the complex which leads to end-plate depolarization. The other "receptor" is the enzyme AChE, which inactivates ACh by speeding its hydrolysis to choline and acetate, which are inactive. It is quite possible that these two receptors are part of the same protein molecule, but differential drug effects leave little doubt that there are two sites having different properties. It is probable that the initial receptor–ACh complex is inactive but quickly changes into an active depolarizing form. Simultaneously, ACh is being destroyed by the AChE. The concentration of AChE in the end-plate region is sufficiently high to account for the destruction of the ACh in a few milliseconds, in accord with the calculated duration of transmitter action at the end-plate. It is supposed that both ACh–receptor complexes are in equilibrium with ACh. Therefore, as ACh is hydrolyzed by AChE, more ACh will dissociate from the receptor and, in turn, be hydrolyzed by the AChE. In this way, ACh can exert its transmitter action in the presence of high concentrations of AChE, but only briefly as required to prevent repetitive firing of the muscle fiber. This sequence of events can be diagrammed as shown at the bottom of this page.

During ACh release, part presumably combines with receptor (R) and part with acetylcholinesterase. After release, the ACh combined with receptor (R) dissociates as AChE becomes available after destroying its ACh and, hence, reaction goes from upper right, where all steps are reversible, to lower right where the right hand reaction is irreversible.

Acetylcholine Action at the End-Plate.[51] In their classic analysis of neuromuscular transmission, Fatt and Katz concluded that the action of ACh on the end-plate membrane is to increase its permeability to all free ions in the intracellular and interstitial fluids. However, later evidence indicates that the permeability changes are limited to increases in P_{Na} and P_K to quite large values. Such a change in the properties of the end-plate membrane might result from the creation of a pore through the membrane large enough for these ions to penetrate it rather easily. If Na^+ and K^+ could penetrate this pore with equal ease, then the transmembrane potential near it would go to about zero. Since enough ACh is released by a nerve impulse to produce a large number of such pores, the whole end-plate membrane potential discharges toward zero. However, the duration of the transmitter action is so short that the depolarization process does not reach a steady value. The fall in the potential at the end-plate sets up local circuit flow from adjacent regions, so that the depolarization spreads passively along the muscle membrane. If the depolarization at the end-plate region reaches threshold, an impulse is generated which propagates away from the end-plate in both directions. The end-plate potential (frequently abbreviated e.p.p.) is defined as the potential changes in the neighborhood of the end-plate induced by activation of the ACh receptors which cause the increase in end-plate permeability to Na^+ and K^+. This activation may be induced by means of the ACh released spontaneously from or by activity of the nerve terminals, or by ACh or ACh-like substances applied from an external source.

ANALYSIS OF THE END-PLATE POTENTIAL.[26] Analysis of the e.p.p. is facilitated by adding the blocking agent, curare, to the bathing medium. Curare blocks neuromuscular transmission by reducing the e.p.p. below the threshold of the muscle membrane. This reduction comes about because curare competes with ACh for receptors and forms an inactive complex with them. In consequence, only part of the ACh released by a nerve impulse can combine with receptors to depolarize the end-plate. If the concentration of curare is properly controlled, some ACh–receptor complexes will form, so that the e.p.p. is not abolished and can be studied without inter-

$$\text{ACh release} \rightarrow \text{ACh} \begin{cases} + \text{ R} \rightleftharpoons \text{AChR} \rightleftharpoons \text{AChR}' \text{ (increase in } P_{Na}, P_K). \\ + \text{ AChE} \rightleftharpoons \text{ACh·AChE} \rightarrow \text{Acetate}^- + \text{Choline}^+ + \text{AChE.} \end{cases}$$

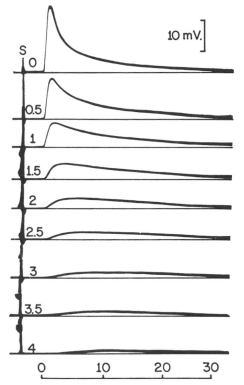

Fig. 18. Transmembrane potential changes produced in a curarized muscle fiber by stimulation of motor nerve to the muscle. *Abscissa,* Time in milliseconds. *Ordinate,* Change in transmembrane potential in millivolts. *S,* Stimulus artefact, signaling time of stimulus to motor nerve. Number by each curve is distance (in mm.) of intracellular recording microelectrode from muscle end-plate. As distance increases, the recorded potential becomes smaller and slower. (From Fatt and Katz, *J. Physiol.,* 1951, *115:*320–370.)

ference by propagated action potentials in the muscle.

If a microelectrode is inserted at the end-plate region in a curarized muscle fiber, a typical monophasic potential change, the e.p.p., is recorded after stimulation of the motor nerve. The size of the e.p.p. depends inversely on curare concentration; the shape of the potential is not affected. That the e.p.p. originates at and is confined to the end-plate region is demonstrated by the recordings in Figure 18. The potentials shown were recorded at successive 0.5 mm. intervals away from the end-plate. It can be seen that the peak height and rise time of the e.p.p. diminish rapidly as the distance increases. Analysis of these records shows that the change in the size and shape of these potentials is accurately in accord with the cable properties of the fiber. These findings lead to

the conclusion that the transmitter action at the end-plate discharges the membrane at that point and that this induced potential change spreads passively in both directions along the muscle fiber membrane.

Anticholinesterases. Many compounds, e.g. prostigmine and di-isopropylfluorophosphate (DFP), inhibit the ability of AChE to hydrolyze ACh. Inhibition of AChE activity at the end-plate by one of these drugs leads, as expected, to a large increase in the size and duration of the e.p.p. A dramatic example of the effect of prostigmine is seen when neuromuscular transmission is blocked by replacing 80 per cent of the sodium chloride in the bathing solution with an equivalent amount of sucrose. The resulting e.p.p. is somewhat slower than the e.p.p. during curarization. Addition of neostigmine to the bath enormously prolongs the e.p.p., as can be seen in Figure 19. The relatively enormous amount of charge displaced from the muscle membrane could not be supplied by current flow from the active nerve terminals, but is a necessary consequence of the ACh theory.

The different ways curare and neostigmine affect the e.p.p. constitute strong evidence that there are two distinct sites of ACh-binding on the end-plate membrane; curare competes with ACh for the receptor and reduces the e.p.p., whereas neostigmine competes with ACh for AChE and increases the e.p.p.[51] The receptor sites for ACh lie on the outside of the membrane; application of ACh, carbaminylcholine

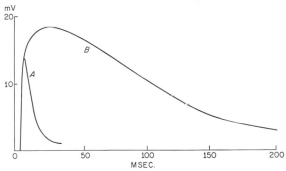

Fig. 19. Effects of an anticholinesterase drug on end-plate potential of single muscle fiber. *Abscissae,* Time in milliseconds. *Ordinates,* Change in transmembrane potential (millivolts) produced by stimulation of motor nerve. *A,* e.p.p. when neuromuscular transmission is blocked after reduction of sodium concentration in bathing medium. *B,* e.p.p. from same fiber after addition of neostigmine to the sodium-deficient bathing medium. (From Fatt and Katz, *J. Physiol.,* 1951, *115:*320–370.)

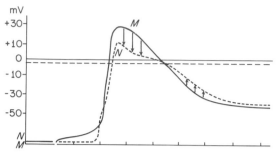

Fig. 20. Action potentials of a single muscle fiber recorded with intracellular electrode in end-plate region. *Abscissa,* Time in milliseconds. *Ordinate,* Transmembrane potential in millivolts. *M,* Action potential recorded at end-plate when muscle is stimulated by electrodes applied directly to it. *N,* Action potential recorded when muscle is stimulated via its motor nerve. Dashed line shows approximate "equilibrium potential" of end-plate membrane in presence of neuromuscular transmitter agent. Arrows indicate how the transmitter action modifies action potential shape. Note reversal in direction of arrows on opposite sides of the dashed "equilibrium potential" line. (From Fatt and Katz, *J. Physiol.,* 1951, *115*:320–370.)

(an ACh-like compound that is hydrolyzed much more slowly), or curare to the inside of the end-plate region has none of the effects on the end-plate that close external application produces.[51]

NEUROMUSCULAR TRANSMISSION.[26]   In an uncurarized muscle the e.p.p. is usually greater than threshold strength, and an action potential arises out of the e.p.p. as it crosses threshold. The threshold potential at the end-plate is the same whether determined by indirect or direct stimulation. However, the shape of the action potential recorded at the end-plate in response to indirect (motor nerve) stimulation differs from the shape of the potential recorded following direct stimulation of the muscle. Figure 20 shows that, in comparison to the directly evoked action potential, the one indirectly evoked is small and rather bizarrely shaped. Close inspection reveals that the changes in the shape of the indirect action potential are always toward a fixed potential slightly below the zero line (arrows). This altered shape is confined to the end-plate region; an action potential recorded a few millimeters away has a normal shape, no matter what the mode of stimulation.

Fatt and Katz interpreted this finding as indicating that the final steady value of the e.p.p. is slightly less than zero and that the membrane resistance of the end-plate is greatly reduced during transmitter activity, which persists with diminishing intensity throughout most of the action potential. Note that time is much more spread out in Figure 20 than it is in Figure 18, and thus that the peak of the e.p.p. occurs about 3 milliseconds after it starts, a time comparable to the duration of the action potential. This persisting resistance change explains the divergence of the indirect end-plate spike toward zero. The reduction in membrane resistance during the rising phase of the action potential is quite large (Chap. 2). The transmitter action must produce a roughly equal additional reduction in resistance at the end-plate because the peak height of the end-plate action potential is considerably reduced.

Other evidence supports the idea that the final steady level of the e.p.p. is near zero. Changes in the end-plate membrane potential produced by applied currents produce proportionate changes in the e.p.p. Additionally, indirect stimuli delivered at various times during the passage of a directly evoked action potential through the end-plate region always produce changes in the potential toward zero. Under normal conditions, sodium ions must carry most of the depolarizing current during transmitter activity, since this is the only ion appreciably out of equilibrium with the steady membrane potential. However, the e.p.p. steady value near zero is below the sodium-ion equilibrium potential, and it must be supposed that potassium ions reduce the amount of depolarization as the membrane potential moves away from the potassium equilibrium potential. Further evidence that potassium permeability is increased during end-plate activity is the finding that the membrane resistance changes when ACh is applied to the end-plate of a muscle depolarized by bathing it in isotonic potassium sulfate.

CARDIAC AND SMOOTH MUSCLE

Classification of Muscle.   There are two general classes of smooth muscle. *Visceral smooth muscle* is found in the walls of the gastrointestinal tract and the genitourinary tract. *Multi-unit* or *motor unit smooth muscle* is found in structures such as the precapillary sphincters, the intrinsic muscles of the eye and the pilo-erector muscles, where direct nervous control is required. Smooth muscle is differentiated from striated muscle histologically by the absence of cross-striations and physiologically by a relative slowness of contraction. Bozler[7] drew a close analogy between the properties of striated and smooth muscle and suggested the following functional classification of muscle:

$$\text{Striated Muscle} \begin{cases} \text{Skeletal} \begin{cases} \text{Many Units} \\ \text{Motor Nerves} \end{cases} \text{Multi-Unit} \\ \\ \text{Cardiac} \begin{cases} \text{Automatic} \\ \text{Syncytial} \end{cases} \text{Visceral} \end{cases} \Big\} \text{Smooth Muscle}$$

The properties of multi-unit smooth muscle with motor nerves are quite similar to those of skeletal muscle; and the properties of cardiac and visceral smooth muscle are quite similar.

Cardiac Muscle. SYNCYTIAL CONDUCTION.[75] One of the most striking features of the heart is that large parts of it contract almost simultaneously. Certainly, the synchronous contraction of the ventricle is necessary for the efficient expulsion of blood. Synchronous contraction or systole could be produced in skeletal muscle by simultaneous activation of all the motor units. However, the heart beats synchronously and spontaneously when completely denervated. Cardiac muscle is thus different from skeletal muscle in being both automatic and a functional syncytium. The term "automatic" refers to the intrinsic ability of a tissue to generate impulses spontaneously and rhythmically, and "functional syncytium" means that the whole tissue acts electrically like a single large cell.

Visceral smooth muscle also has these properties.

As in skeletal muscle, the normal stimulus for contraction of cardiac and smooth muscle is membrane depolarization. In the heart this depolarization is brought about by conducted action potentials; therefore, the synchronous contraction of cardiac muscle arises from its electrical activity. If a microelectrode is inserted into a ventricular cell and the membrane potential is recorded throughout one cycle, the pattern of the recording is the same, save for slight time differences, no matter from which ventricular cell the recording is obtained (Fig. 21*B*). The action potential propagates rapidly throughout the ventricle by local circuit activation; activity in one cardiac cell soon brings adjacent cells into activity. A suprathreshold stimulus applied anywhere in the ventricle initiates activity which spreads throughout the ventricle.

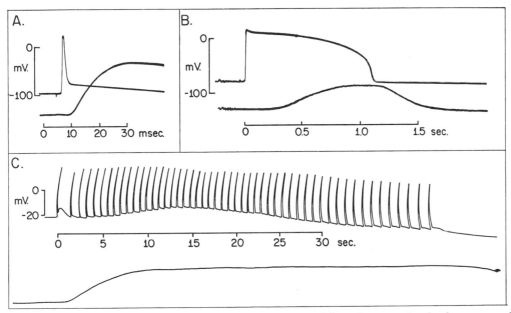

Fig. 21. Simultaneously recorded transmembrane potentials and contraction in three types of muscle. *A,* Isolated frog skeletal muscle fiber. *B,* Whole frog ventricle; action potential recorded from one "cell." *C,* strip of pregnant rat uterus (smooth muscle); action potential recorded from one "cell, spontaneous activity." *Abscissae,* Time in milliseconds (*A*) or seconds (*B* and *C*). *Ordinates,* Upper trace, millivolts; lower trace, arbitrary units of contractile tension. (Part *A* after Hodgkin and Horowicz, *J. Physiol.,* 1957, *136:*17P–18P.)

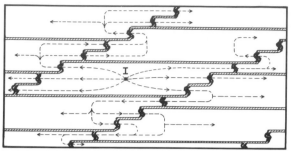

Fig. 22. Simplified and formalized structure of a portion of rat atrial trabecula. Thin straight lines represent regular, excitable cell membranes having high electrical resistance; thickened heavy lines represent intercalated disc membranes or nearby "tight" junctions having low resistance. Each cell is completely surrounded by membrane. Large dot (I) in center indicates location of an intracellular current electrode. Dashed lines with arrowheads indicate major pathways of current flow from the electrode. Current flow through regular membranes into the extracellular fluid is small and is not shown. Intracellular current flow at right angles to the fiber direction follows the zigzag path of least resistance shown largely through the intercalated discs or adjacent low resistance sites. This structure accounts for the spatially nonuniform spread of current. Contractile material is not shown for simplicity. (From Woodbury, *Handbook of physiology, Section 2: Circulation*, vol. I, Hamilton and Dow, eds. Washington, D.C., American Physiological Society, 1962.)

The spread of activity by local circuit flow in a nerve fiber (Chap. 2) was described in terms of a continuous axoplasm with a specific resistivity several orders of magnitude smaller than that of the membrane. In the heart, however, electron micrographs show rather clearly that each cell is surrounded by a distinct membrane, so there is no anatomic continuity of the myoplasm between cells. Yet, equally clearly, activity spreads through cardiac muscle from cell to cell. This is the reason for using the term "functional syncytium." There are specialized regions of "contact" between adjacent cardiac muscle cells, the *intercalated discs*. At the discs, the membranes are close together—about 100 Ångstroms apart—and are greatly folded and interdigitated so that their surface areas are increased. This close approximation and the large area of contact between the surfaces of adjacent cells are both factors which tend to increase the flow of the local currents of an active cell through adjacent inactive cells. Two types of evidence support the idea that flow through low-resistance disks or other low-resistance regions is likely to be the basis of the functional

syncytium: (i) Propagation through cardiac muscle requires the flow of local circuit currents; interruption of this flow by insertion of a high resistance in the circuit blocks conduction.[3] (ii) Current applied via an intracellular electrode in one cell produces in adjacent cells voltage changes of sufficient magnitude to insure depolarization to threshold by an action potential.[76] Additionally, it was found that current spreads as far in the direction of the fibers as it does in the direction perpendicular to the fibers, a further indication that the low resistance regions are in or near the intercalated discs. A possible interpretation of these findings is given by Figure 22.

Two dimensional and three dimensional spread.[76] Activity initiated in one region of the heart spreads in all directions at a velocity depending on the cable and excitable properties of the cells (see Chap. 2). This spread behavior is distinctly different from that of nerve or skeletal muscle fibers. In a nerve fiber the activity travels in one direction, that of the fiber; spread of activity is one dimensional. In syncytial tissues, spread is two or three dimensional. Spread in thin-walled tissues, such as the atrium or the gut wall, is two dimensional; an action potential originating at a point spreads over the surface as a wave.

Such a wave is somewhat analogous to the ripple produced in the surface of a pond by a falling pebble. However, the water wave gradually diminishes in amplitude as it spreads, whereas the electrical wave in tissue is kept constant in amplitude by the excitation of the membrane at each point. In this respect, the electrical wave is more nearly analogous to the wave of "excitation" produced when a lighted match is touched to the center of a sheet of gunpowder spread evenly over a surface. The process of spread is identical in principle. The gunpowder is set afire by the conduction of heat in advance of the burning region; unexcited membrane is "set afire" by the spread of currents in front of the excited area of membrane. The analogy ends there—the membrane presently recovers its excitability. The ventricle, especially the left ventricle, is a thick-walled organ and the spread of excitation is three dimensional. In fact, knowledge of the pathway of the spread of excitation through the ventricle is essential to the understanding of its contributions to the electrocardiogram (Chap. 30). Another way of stating the differences between nerve, atrium and ventricle is that, in nerve, the wave front is a point; in atrium, a line; and in ventricle, a surface.

MEMBRANE POTENTIAL AND CONTRACTION.[75] The action potential of cardiac muscle is usually several hundred milliseconds long. In most circumstances, the contraction time is approximately equal to the duration of the action potential (Fig. 21*B*). This is expected since the available evidence indicates that cardiac muscle contraction, like that of skeletal muscle, is initiated and maintained by calcium release consequent on depolarization and terminated by the sequestering of calcium following repolarization. It is convenient to think of the upstroke of the action potential as "turning on" the contraction and the fast repolarization as turning it off. The long duration of the action potential insures that each contraction is sufficiently prolonged to be maximal; i.e., the tension corresponds to a tetanus in skeletal muscle.

Since the membrane is refractory until repolarization is well advanced, there can be no summation in cardiac muscle. This behavior is consonant with the function of the heart. A strong synchronous contraction is necessary for the efficient ejection of blood from the heart; the contractile properties of cardiac muscle are otherwise much the same as tetanic contractions of skeletal muscle. The length–tension relationships are qualitatively indistinguishable. The mechanical properties of cardiac muscle are described in Chapter 29.

One interesting aspect of cardiac muscle is that the duration of the action potential depends on the heart rate: the faster the rate, the shorter the duration. Over the usual physiologic range, the action potential duration is roughly one-half of the interval between beats. This insures that an increase in heart rate will bring about a maximal increase in cardiac output, because both diastolic filling time and systolic ejection time are reduced. A reduction in the filling time alone would occur if the action potential duration were invariant.

Cardiac action potential. The action potential of cardiac muscle differs from that of nerve or skeletal muscle in its greater duration and in the great variability of duration with rate. The dependence of the rate of rise and the overshoot of the action potential on the external concentration of sodium indicates that the upstroke of the action potential is brought about by a large increase in membrane permeability to sodium.[8, 74] However, the nature of the permeability changes underlying the greatly prolonged period of depolarization—the *plateau phase*—is not known.

Weidmann[73] has shown that total membrane slope resistance is increased during the plateau. This indicates that permeability to sodium is increased and permeability to potassium is reduced during the plateau. A simple explanation[8] of the long duration of the action potential and the dependence of its duration on rate is to suppose that two types of sodium conductance are available (see Chap. 2). The first type of conductance, responsible for the upstroke of the action potential, is initially large, but it is rapidly inactivated (order of milliseconds) following depolarization and just as rapidly activated following repolarization, i.e., like that of squid nerve. The second type, responsible for the plateau, is comparatively small but slowly inactivated (order of seconds) and just as slowly activated following repolarization. After the upstroke of the action potential and the inactivation of the fast sodium conductance, the slowly inactivated sodium conductance, although small, persists. It maintains the membrane potential near zero because the conductance of potassium has fallen, it being assumed that depolarization decreases K^+ conductance rather than increasing it as in squid nerve. As the slowly inactivated sodium conductance decreases, the potential falls slowly until a potential is reached where one or more other conductances begin to change rapidly with membrane voltage. Sodium conductance is "turned off" and potassium conductance is "turned on," so repolarization proceeds with increasing rapidity. Following repolarization, excitability returns with activation of the fast sodium conductance, but an action potential initiated at this time will be short because the slow sodium conductance is only slowly activated. The plateau will occur at a lower voltage, so the potential at which rapid repolarization occurs will be reached more quickly. Trautwein and associates[18] have recently succeeded in making voltage clamp measurements on short segments of Purkinje fibers. Their results are, generally, in agreement with the above hypothesis except that the behavior of potassium ion conductance is dependent on both time and voltage.

AUTOMATICITY OF HEART. Many regions of a syncytial tissue can originate propagating action potentials. However, in the heart there is a region specialized for origination of impulses, the *pacemaker* region in the sino-atrial (S-A) node. The S-A nodal region determines the rate of the heart beat, because its intrinsic rate is faster than those of the atrium and A-V node. An action potential from the S-A node reaches these regions before they have time to develop an intrinsic beat. Pacemaker activity results from special properties of the membrane; action potentials of a pacemaker region are distinctive. The characteristics of a pacemaker cell membrane are such that the membrane potential has no stable value. During diastole, the membrane potential falls slowly toward zero instead of remaining steady as it does in nonpacemaker regions. This slow diastolic depolarization is called the *pacemaker potential* or *prepotential* (see Chap. 10, Fig. 5A).

When the pacemaker potential reaches the threshold voltage, an impulse is generated and propagated away from the pacemaker region in all available directions in the sheet of muscle (Chap. 30). The repolarization process involves a decrease in permeability to sodium and an increase in permeability to potassium, and the membrane voltage approaches the equilibrium potential for potassium. The membrane permeability to sodium during diastole is rather higher in pacemaker tissue than in other tissues; and, as the permeability changes that cause repolarization die out, the potential begins to fall from near the potassium equilibrium potential to a rather low steady value (because of high permeability to sodium).[67] However, this steady value is so low that the potential crosses threshold first and another impulse is initiated. The rate of initiation of impulses depends primarily on the slope of the prepotential. This slope is extremely dependent on the temperature, the ion concentrations and the presence or absence of small concentrations of acetylcholine and epinephrine.

Smooth Muscle. STRUCTURE OF SMOOTH MUSCLE.[62]   The precise alignment of contractile filaments which gives rise to the characteristic cross-striated appearance of skeletal and cardiac muscle is absent in smooth muscle. Nevertheless, the contractile material and mechanism of smooth muscle is much the same as in striated muscle. The typical smooth muscle cell is shaped like a rod, tapering at both ends. Individual cells are typically 4 to 8 μ in diameter in the center and 50 to 200 μ long. Cells are closely packed into long, thin, cylindrical bundles; the thickest part of one fiber lies alongside the tapering parts of its neighbors. There is little extracellular space within these bundles, but between them are large spaces. The bundles are 50 to 100 μ in diameter and branch and coalesce with other bundles every few millimeters. This network of bundles forms into sheets or larger bundles, depending on the function of the tissue.

The cell plasma membrane of smooth muscle differs from that of skeletal muscle; in particular, there are dense thickenings which alternate with thinner regions. The thick regions often coincide with similar regions in adjacent cells. In some smooth muscles, certain membrane regions are greatly convoluted.

The contractile proteins of skeletal muscle—actin, myosin and tropomyosin—have been identified in various types of smooth muscle.[56] However, in comparison with skeletal muscle, the concentrations of the contractile proteins are lower in smooth muscle and the ATP-ase activity is lower and varies differently with pH and with calcium and magnesium ion concentrations.

Myofilaments.[58, 65]   Although thick and thin myofilaments have been observed in some kinds of smooth muscle, they are difficult to demonstrate directly in all; however, other evidence indicates their presence. In relaxed intestinal muscle, the filaments are oriented parallel to one another and with the longitudinal axis of the cell. It is not clear whether these myofilaments originate or terminate at the plasma membrane. The attractive possibility that they may attach to the dense areas of the plasma membrane is weakened by the finding that these dense areas are not found in all smooth muscle cells. Electron microscope studies on molluscan smooth muscle have revealed a more ordered structure of myofilaments:[53] (i) The contractile apparatus contains only two kinds of filaments, thick and thin. (ii) The thin filaments appear to be actin and the thicker filaments are thought to contain myosin and tropomyosin. (iii) These filaments are cross-linked in the same way as in striated muscle. Although there is no conclusive evidence, contraction probably occurs in smooth muscle, as in skeletal, by a relative sliding of two sets of filaments. The muscles are unstriated because the lateral alignment of the filaments is far less regular than in striated muscle.

Syncytium.   Most, if not all, smooth muscle structures can function as an electrical syncytium. There are two kinds of cell-to-cell contact which may provide low resistance intercellular pathways for transmission of excitation. The first is in the relatively large area where the end of one cell makes contact with the midportion of another. Secondly, small "intercellular bridges" (0.1 to 0.5 μ long, 0.2 to 0.7 μ in diameter) between cells have been observed in electron micrographs of some smooth muscle cells.[4] If intercellular protoplasmic contact exists at these "bridges," they would function as effective pathways for the conduction of impulses despite their small size.

Innervation.[11] Smooth muscle is innervated by small diameter (0.1 to 1.7 μ) autonomic postganglionic fibers which are predominantly unmyelinated. These fibers branch extensively in the muscle, forming a fine plexus which is embedded in a Schwann cell syncytium. Small branches of the plexus (2 to 8 fibers) enclosed in one Schwann cell run between muscle cells; the Schwann cells are frequently interrupted where a naked axon comes into close proximity with a muscle cell. In these regions, the axon is loaded with vesicles which are characteristic of presynaptic terminations. There is no evidence of postsynaptic specialization like the end-plate of skeletal muscle. The degree of innervation of smooth muscle appears to depend on its function; the nictitating membrane, iris and arteriolar smooth muscle are heavily innervated, whereas the gut and uterus are lightly innervated. It seems likely that all gradations of innervation occur and that the terms "multiunit" and "visceral" smooth muscle represent the extremes of considerable and little nervous control.

ELECTRICAL ACTIVITY OF VISCERAL MUSCLE.[10] The nature of visceral muscle electrical activity varies from time to time in any one tissue and from tissue to tissue in accordance with the function being performed. Small, slow variations and larger, slow-pacemaker variations with superposed, spikelike or cardiac musclelike action potentials have all been recorded separately and in various combinations. Usually, no "resting" potential exists since the membrane potential is never relatively constant for any period. However, potentials are low, ranging from 30 to 70 mV. and averaging about 50 mV. The small, slow variations in membrane potential are nearly sinusoidal with no regenerative action potentials superposed. The period of oscillation is about 0.5 second. Larger variations of this type become more peaked on the depolarization phase and, if these variations are large enough, threshold is reached (about -30 mV.) and regenerative action potentials are initiated at regular intervals. In some tissues, action potentials are spikes, 0.1 second or less in duration, which may or may not overshoot (Fig. 21*C*), e.g.,

uterus, small intestine. In other tissues—e.g., ureter—action potentials resemble those of cardiac muscle (Fig. 21*B*) but may last many seconds. Presumably the type of action potential depends on the function of the muscle: spikelike in muscles where tension is widely graded and plateau-like where a maximal or tetanic type of contraction is needed. In some circumstances, plateau responses change into spike trains and vice versa, depending on unknown conditions. Action potentials may be initiated by pacemaker activity, by conduction, and by neural, chemical or mechanical stimuli.

Effects of stretch. Stretch depolarizes smooth muscle membrane, and thus may initiate firing or may increase the rate. The response depends strongly upon the rate of application of the stretch; a fast stretch produces a response with a short latency, whereas with a slow stretch the latency is longer and the contractile response more prolonged. Of course, the stretch must depolarize the membrane potential beyond threshold. There is a range of depolarizations, the "firing zone," which produces contractile tension as a result of the generated spike activity. Polarizations on either side of the "firing zone" result in a cessation of firing and a fall in tension.

Syncytial conduction. In cardiac muscle, an impulse originating in any part propagates over that entire part except in abnormal circumstances; the syncytial connections are always effective. In visceral muscle, on the other hand, the syncytial connections are much less efficient; whether or not an impulse spreads from one cell to another depends sensitively on local conditions, particularly on the muscle's tension or length or both and on the concentrations of such substances as acetylcholine, epinephrine and ions in the extracellular medium. Another indication of the low safety factor of syncytial transmission is the finding that individual cells in smooth muscle recover their excitability in 50 to 100 milliseconds following an effective stimulus, while 1 to 5 seconds are required for intercellular impulse conduction to recover. A general pattern of visceral muscle activity is that a number of pacemaker regions generate impulses which spread radially for a short distance and then are blocked. As mentioned above, stretch depolarizes the membrane and, depending on the original conditions, could activate a region as a pacemaker, increase its frequency, or cause depolarization block which could confine activity to a small region. The variations in the efficiency of syncytial conduction with local conditions probably play an important role in coordinating the contractions of visceral muscle so that it performs its different functions. This may account in part for the intrinsic self-regulatory capabilities of this tissue.

Automaticity. Like cardiac muscle, one of the characteristic properties of visceral muscle is intrinsic, rhythmic impulse generation. Unlike normal heart, pacemaker activity is not restricted to a specialized region; rather, the pacemaker focus often shifts from one place to another. Particularly in intestine, various pacemaker regions occur, each with a surrounding area into which its impulses reach. These domains are isolated from each other by regions which temporarily do not conduct. Both the pacemaker regions and the blocked regions shift from time to time. Another difference is that visceral muscle pacemaker activity is much more sensitive to stretch than is cardiac muscle. Indeed, stretch appears to be one of the main determinants of pacemaker activity.

ELECTRICAL ACTIVITY OF MULTI-UNIT MUSCLE.[11] The vas deferens is a multi-unit smooth muscle, heavily innervated by the hypogastric nerve. A single maximal stimulus to the hypogastric nerve produces in every cell of this muscle subthreshold transient depolarization which has many of the characteristics of the end-plate potential (e.p.p.) found in skeletal muscle. These potentials summate and reach threshold at stimulus frequencies of about one per second. These e.p.p.'s have about the same amplitude in each cell but their latencies vary from 20 to 70 milliseconds. This suggests that the bare regions where nerve fibers approximate to muscles are sites of transmitter liberation and that all cells are effectively innervated. The variable latencies are attributed mostly to variations in the diffusion distance between bare nerve and muscle fiber.

The vas deferens is normally quiescent but can be brought into spontaneous, co-ordinated, activity by small doses of norepinephrine; slow pacemaker potentials and propagating spikes are recorded from the muscle cells. Thus, multi-unit muscle can resemble visceral muscle in that both have syncytial interconnections and can be spontaneously active.

EXCITATION–CONTRACTION COUPLING.[10, 16] As in skeletal and cardiac muscle, contractile activity in smooth muscle is initiated by depolarization of the cell membrane and mediated by Ca^{++}. The tension developed when the membrane is completely depolarized by bathing it in a Ringer's solution in which NaCl has been replaced by K_2SO_4 and sucrose is eliminated if the calcium is removed from the bathing solution. Thus, it appears that the calcium ion acts to couple the depolarization of the cell membrane to contraction. The sarcoplasmic reticulum is not well developed but, because of the smallness of cells and the slowness of the mechanical response, calcium ions released at the surface of the cell by depolarization have sufficient time to diffuse into the center of the cell and activate the contractile elements in the interval between the electrical and the mechanical responses.

Contraction is generally initiated by action potentials and not by slow potential changes. In spike-generating muscles a "tetanus" is brought about by a train of spontaneously generated action potentials (Fig. 21C); in such a muscle contractile tension increases with spike frequency. Most long-term active changes in length or tension, called "tone," appear to be due to spike production. However, some types of tone are due mainly to passive properties of the muscle.[50]

MECHANICAL PROPERTIES OF SMOOTH MUSCLE. *Noncontracting muscle.* Visceral musculature in performing its functions undergoes enormous changes in length with comparatively small changes in tension. Bozler[7] found that if a constant load is placed on a strip of smooth muscle, the muscle will, after a rapid initial elongation, continue to elongate at a slower rate until it is increased 50 per cent in length. Furthermore, if a strip of uterine smooth muscle is stretched to a fixed length, the tension, after an initial rise, falls with time to slightly above its initial value. These examples indicate that resistance to stretch in smooth muscle is mainly that of a viscous body with a small elastic component; however, visco-elastic properties vary considerably from tissue to tissue. It is unknown how much of these visco-elastic properties are attributable to the contractile material and how much to the supporting elements. The functional capabilities of a tissue likely depend as much on its passive as on its contractile properties.

Contractile activity.[15, 50] Compared with skeletal muscle, smooth muscle contracts slowly. The duration of the "twitch" of a smooth muscle is 15 to a few hundred times longer than the twitch of a skeletal muscle from the same animal. All phases of contraction are slow. Comparison of Figure 21*A* with 21*C* shows that the contraction time (time to peak tension) is about 30 milliseconds in a frog skeletal muscle twitch compared with several seconds in a tetanus of rat uterus. The active length–tension relationship of smooth muscle is quite similar to that of striated muscle; maximal tension is developed at an optimal length. Developed tension is less for lengths shorter or longer than the optimal length. Characteristically, smooth muscle is capable of developing tensions for long periods of time and with a relatively low rate of energy expenditure. This behavior is probably the result of the low ATP-ase activity; a slow rate of making and breaking the bridges between thick and thin filaments would maintain tension at a low cost in energy consumption, but rate of contraction would be correspondingly reduced.

NEURAL AND HUMORAL CONTROL.[10, 11, 60] Multi-unit muscles are activated both electrically and mechanically by a few stimuli to the motor nerve; visceral smooth muscle is spontaneously active but its level of activity depends on the amount and kind of motor input. Multi-unit muscles ordinarily are not spontaneously active and do not respond to stretch; visceral types are spontaneously active and are stimulated by stretch. Thus, the lack of pre-emptory nervous control over a smooth muscle structure is accompanied to a certain degree by autorhythmicity and self-regulation.

As in skeletal muscle, neuromuscular transmission in smooth muscle is mediated by chemical transmitter substances, two of which are acetylcholine and epinephrine (or norepinephrine). There may be other chemical transmitters or hormones which also act on smooth muscle. Acetylcholine and epinephrine come from cholinergic and adrenergic fibers, respectively. Generally, stimulation of these two types of nerves produces antagonistic effects on smooth muscle. For example, in the rabbit colon stimulation of cholinergic fibers increases the activity whereas stimulation of adrenergic fibers decreases it. This antagonism can be seen more dramatically by observing the effects of the neurotransmitters, acetylcholine and epinephrine (or norepinephrine), on various types of visceral smooth muscle. However, there are exceptions; e.g., in the nictitating membrane of

the cat, stimulation of either cholinergic or adrenergic fibers increases activity. A two-component response is obtained, a "fast" one due to acetylcholine (reduced by acetylcholine-blocking drugs) and a "slow" component due to epinephrine or norepinephrine (reduced by anti-epinephrine drugs).

The mode of action of acetylcholine on smooth muscle is much the same as on skeletal muscle; acetylcholine depolarizes by increasing the permeability of the muscle membrane to sodium, potassium and, possibly, other ions. The amount of depolarization produced by acetylcholine depends upon the initial membrane potential. Acetylcholine can depolarize the membrane only to a value of -15 to -25 mV., so, as the resting potential becomes lower, the depolarizing action of acetylcholine becomes smaller. The mode of action of epinephrine is not known. There are two opposing actions: (i) In those smooth muscle structures activated by epinephrine it depolarizes the membrane by increasing membrane permeability, at least to sodium ions. (ii) There is a delayed hyperpolarization which stops spike generation in part, by increasing the membrane potential. The hyperpolarization is probably secondary to an acceleration of active sodium extrusion.

In addition to the neuronal control of smooth muscle activity, there are humoral or hormonal factors as well. The relative contributions of these various means of control—stretch, neural and hormonal—are not known. Smooth muscle cells are sensitive to the various neural transmitters over their entire surface; skeletal muscle cells are sensitive only at the end-plate. In addition, these transmitters, particularly epinephrine and norepinephrine, are not destroyed rapidly in smooth muscle. Thus, smooth muscle activity may be influenced by circulating transmitter substances, particularly epinephrine and norepinephrine; cholinesterase is a widely occurring enzyme, so the concentration of ACh in blood is usually negligible. Thus, neural transmitters also act as hormones and in this role exert a widespread influence on smooth muscle activity.

The effects of female sex hormones on the activity of uterine smooth muscle are a unique example of hormonal control. Not only does estrogen cause hypertrophy of uterine cells, but it produces an increase in membrane potential. Estrogen increases spontaneous activity and the uterus grows into a structure capable of forceful contractions. In contrast, contractions do not occur in the immature uterus. On the other hand, progesterone decreases activity and blocks contraction. The interplay of these two hormonal actions is important in timing the birth process. Estrogen is necessary to prepare the uterus for activity and progesterone holds it in a quiescent state until the fetus has developed and is ready for delivery.

CLINICAL CORRELATIONS: SKELETAL MUSCLE

Motor Unit Disease. The skeletal muscle motor unit provides a systematic, rational basis for classification of peripheral motor diseases based on the place of attack and the physiologic mechanism disturbed. Diseases attacking each of five points in the motor unit (Fig. 23) would produce different effects. These points are the motoneuron cell body (I), the axon of the motoneuron (II), the neuromuscular junction (III), the muscle membrane (IV), and the contractile machinery of the muscle itself (V).

DESTRUCTION OF CELL BODY OR AXON (I, II). Sudden (acute anterior poliomyelitis) or slow (progressive muscular atrophy) destruction of the motoneuron cell body or sudden destruction of the axon (peripheral nerve injury) produce certain classic signs and other less obvious changes in muscle:

1. Flaccid paralysis: weakness of voluntary movements combined with flaccidity or deficient muscle tone.
2. Absent or hypoactive tendon reflexes.
3. Atrophy and degeneration of muscle.
4. Fibrillation and fasciculation.
5. Altered sensitivity to drugs, especially

acetylcholine, and increased threshold to brief electrical stimuli.

6. Biochemical and histologic changes.

The first of these signs is obviously consequent to a reduction in the number of functioning motor units available for voluntary and reflex response.

Atrophy[1, 2] and degeneration. A change in the volume of a tissue may be due to changes in cell volume, number of cells or both. A decrease in muscle cell volume is called *atrophy;* an increase is *hypertrophy.* An increase in number of cells is *hyperplasia.*

Atrophy in the human results from denervation, disease, old age, cachexia and some myopathies. In all of these situations fiber size is reduced to about 75 per cent of normal. Cross-striations remain until the cells become quite small. In denervation atrophy the changes are more profound and this type of atrophy is distinguished as *degeneration.* A few months or a year after denervation, granularity develops in the sarcoplasm with a loss of myofibrils; finally, only groups of sarcoplasmic nuclei remain in the muscle fiber. Later even these disappear. The changes in disuse atrophy are seldom this severe. Fibrillation is common in some stages of degeneration but is rare in other atrophies. In certain myopathies (progressive muscular dystrophy and polymyositis or dermatomyositis) both atrophy and hypertrophy may be present. The pattern of these changes is haphazard and does not follow the motor unit distribution.

Electromyography (EMG).[52] The proper diagnosis of a disease depends, to a great degree, on the clinical acumen of the physician. However, the small differences between the clinical mani-

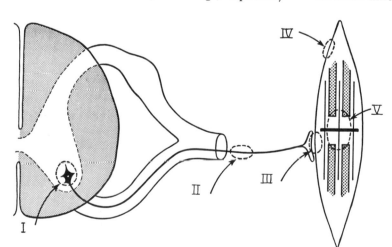

Fig. 23. Diagram representing sites of injury (Roman numerals) in diseases of motor unit.

festations of the various motoneuron diseases sometimes require the aid of various instruments and techniques in the differential diagnosis. The techniques most frequently used involve the following: electromyography, histochemistry, electronic instruments for stimulation and recording of bioelectric and physiologic events, drugs, and the electron microscope to study pathologic changes in ultrastructure. Electromyography will be briefly described here, since it has greatly aided the classification of motoneuron diseases. An electromyogram (EMG) is a recording of electrical activity from a portion of the muscle. This activity can arise from voluntary movement or from direct electrical stimulation or can occur spontaneously in the muscle or nerve. In the clinic, electromyograms are obtained by inserting an electrode about the size of a 24-gauge hypodermic needle into the muscle to be studied. The electrode consists of a wire insulated everywhere but at the tip. The potential of this electrode is the sum of the volume conductor action potentials of surrounding muscle fibers. Thus, most of the electrical activity is from active fibers near the electrode. The other electrode is a large metal plate applied to the skin over an inactive region. In normal muscle, a brief burst of activity (rapid deflections of the pen) is recorded when the electrode is inserted. This is due to action potentials set up in fibers injured by the electrode before depolarization block occurs. There is little or no activity during rest; potentials recorded during contraction are the resultant of the asynchronous discharges of motor units in the electrode's vicinity. Changes in the patterns of activity in disease are helpful in diagnosis (see Fig. 24).

Finer detail may be observed with staggered multilead electrodes[24] or, under certain conditions, intracellular electrodes.[49] With the multilead electrode technique, it is possible to stimulate and record from individual muscle fibers or small groups of fibers and thus to measure absolute refractory periods, absolute irresponsive periods, recovery of excitability and conduction speeds. Intracellular recordings may be informative but are technically difficult.

Fibrillation and fasciculation.[20] In certain motor unit diseases, muscles exhibit small, local, "spontaneous" contractions. Investigations with the EMG have led to the conclusion that one of the common classic neurologic signs—fibrillation—was misnamed. This name suggests that the motor unit discharging spontaneously is the muscle fiber, whereas analysis shows that what was called fibrillation is actually a discharge of a whole motor unit.

Fibrillation, as redefined by Denny-Brown and Pennybacker[20] from electrophysiologic studies, is characterized by 10 to 200 μV. potentials with a duration of 1 to 2 milliseconds. They are irregular and asynchronous, produce no detectable shortening of the muscle, and cannot be observed through the skin. By contrast, the potentials recorded during normal motor unit discharges have an amplitude of 2 to 6 mV. and a duration of 5 to 8 milliseconds. It follows that the unit potential in denervated muscle is the "spontaneous" activation of *single muscle cells* or muscle fibers, and hence properly called fibrillation. The activity reaches a peak

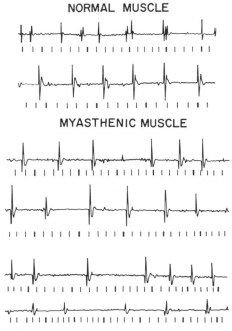

Fig. 24. Electromyographic recordings of motor unit discharge during muscular action in normal and myasthenic persons. Ordinate, voltage, arbitrary units; abscissa, time, 23 milliseconds between marks. Normal muscle: upper trace, two motor units discharging at different frequencies; lower trace, discharges of a single motor unit. Note the uniform amplitude and rate of the single motor unit. Myasthenic muscle: discharges of a single motor unit during continuous muscular action. Upper trace recorded at the start of activity; lower three traces after 40, 80 and 170 seconds of activity respectively. Note sharp decrease in amplitude of the single motor unit during continuous muscular effort without appreciable change in rate. (After Lindsley, *Brain*, 1935, *58*:470–482.)

about eight days after denervation and ceases when reinnervation occurs through nerve regeneration, or, if this fails, ceases when the muscle fibers have degenerated sufficiently. Fibrillation is lessened by curare and increased by prostigmine. That muscle fibers fire in the absence of nerve stimulation is an expression of the denervation sensitivity to acetylcholine, and the stimulus is presumably circulating acetylcholine. This increased sensitivity is explained in part by the finding that a denervated fiber's membrane becomes everywhere sensitive to acetylcholine instead of only at the end-plate.

According to Denny-Brown and Pennybacker's analysis, what was called fibrillation is properly termed *fasciculation*. It is visible through the skin or mucosa and represents a "spontaneous" discharge of motor units. The potential developed by the discharge of a squad of muscle fibers innervated by a single motoneuron would be expected to be greater than a single fiber discharge, since many fibers are involved. It would also be longer, owing to the somewhat asynchronous firing of the fibers. A motor unit discharge could lead to a local response in the muscle only if the fibers composing the squad were adjacent within a fasciculus and not dispersed widely throughout the muscle. This expectation has in fact been realized by histologic investigation. The triggering of the motor unit discharge would appear to lie with the motoneuron cell body. Fasciculation is indicative of lower motor neuron disease attacking the gray column of the spinal cord—amyotrophic lateral sclerosis, progressive muscular atrophy.

In some cases, the origin must be peripheral because procaine block of the motor nerves does not stop fasciculation. Therefore, it may originate at the end-plate of a fiber, be conducted antidromically to the branching point of the motor axon, and, by an "axon reflex," reach all the fibers of a motor unit.

Related to fasciculation is the electromyographic phenomenon of *synchronization*. Potentials 10 to 15 times that developed by a single motor unit are observed in muscles of poliomyelitis patients. The best explanation appears to be that several motor units contract synchronously through some "locking" of the discharge of anterior horn cells. Another possible cause lies in the development of giant motor units when nondegenerated motoneurons sprout and capture (innervate) muscle fibers whose innervation has been destroyed. This kind of synchronization of motor units is to be distinguished from that seen in clonus or tremor and the less definite synchronization in spasticity and rigidity.[39]

Chemical and electrical excitability. The profound effects of denervation suggest that motor innervation exerts a "trophic" influence on muscle which is necessary for the maintenance of the muscle's chemical composition, electrical excitability, chemical sensitivity and metabolic reactions.[66] In addition to atrophy, one of the most striking effects of denervation is the muscle's eventual development of "supersensitivity" to acetylcholine and related substances, becoming 1000 to 100,000 times more sensitive to close intra-arterial injections of acetylcholine. Supersensitivity is apparently due to the enlargement of the ACh sensitive region from the end-plate in normal muscle to the whole fiber surface in the denervated muscle (Chap. 10).

The increased threshold of a denervated muscle to short (ca. 100 microseconds) electrical stimuli results from the fact that they excite intramuscular nerve fibers at lower strengths than they do muscle fibers. This is largely because nerve membrane has much smaller capacity per unit area than muscle membrane. However, this effect is partially counteracted by the larger diameter of the muscle fiber.

MYASTHENIA GRAVIS (III).[2, 70] As one proceeds peripherally in the motor unit, the next critical point is the neuromuscular junction. *Myasthenia gravis* is characterized by muscular weakness and extreme "fatigability" confined to the skeletal muscles but with a predilection for those of the face. Double vision (diplopia), drooping eyelids (ptosis), a toneless voice and difficulty in chewing and swallowing are often present at the initial examination. A repeated movement may initially be strong but becomes progressively weaker. Muscle strength is greatest in the morning and least in the evening.

Figure 24 is an electromyographic record from a normal muscle. The regular rhythm and equal amplitudes indicate that the electrical activity of a single motor unit is being recorded. Sample records taken throughout the course of a continued effort by a patient with myasthenia gravis are shown. Note that the rhythm does not alter, but the spike amplitude soon varies and, eventually, some spikes drop out completely. It follows from the previous discussion of gradation of contraction that the only way a motor unit can be fractionated is by some process occurring in the individual muscle fibers making up the squad. Further evidence that the disorder underlying myasthenia gravis lies in the neuromuscular junction is that the muscle fibers show no histopathologic alteration, respond normally to direct stimulation of the muscle, and are sensitive to drugs. Curare-like drugs aggravate myasthenia; anticholinesterase drugs reduce it and are in fact an effective therapeutic agent.

Physiologically there are four possible mechanisms or "sites" of derangement: (i) a deficient production or liberation of acetylcholine, (ii) an overactive cholinesterase system, (iii) a diminished sensitivity of the muscle end-plate to acetylcholine, and (iv) the circulation of a curare-like substance.

Another possibility is the recent suggestion by Simpson[63] that myasthenia gravis may be an "auto-immune" phenomenon in which the reticulo-endothelial system produces an antibody to end-plate protein. Combination of this antibody with the receptor protein would then reduce the response to endogenous acetylcholine and prevent normal function. This possibility is consistent with the well-known finding that a hyperplastic thymus is found in roughly half of all patients suffering from myasthenia gravis and with recent evidence that suggests an immunologic function for the thymus in the

fetus and newborn. Perhaps myasthenia results from a pathologic change in thymus function.[32]

MYOTONIA (IV).[2] Myotonia is a failure of the muscles to relax normally. In dramatic contrast to myasthenia, myotonic muscles can be contracted promptly and forcefully but cannot be relaxed at will. Further, myotonia is most pronounced after a period of rest and decreases with repeated attempts; the patient's condition is better in the evening than in the morning. A tap anywhere on a myotonic muscle produces a local knot of prolonged contraction.

Because a strain of goats exhibits myotonia,[9] it has been possible to study this sign by electrical methods and isometric myography after stimulation of a sectioned nerve, as in a student laboratory experiment. The delayed relaxation is shown clearly in the myographic record in Figure 25, top. The repetitive electrical discharge is clearly the cause of the prolonged contraction. However, the repetitive discharge cannot be a persistent central discharge because the motor nerve has been sectioned. The response to acetylcholine is prolonged. The delay in relaxation occurs when the muscle is stimulated locally, even after degeneration of the motor nerve. These observations, together with the fact that mechanical or electrical stimulation anywhere on the muscle results in a prolonged electrical discharge and contraction,

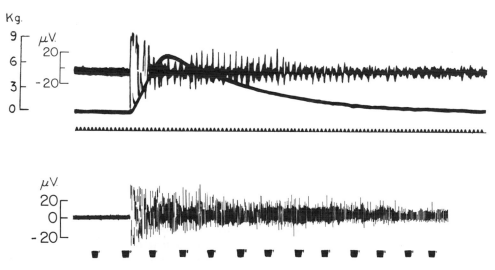

Fig. 25. Upper record: Electrical and contractile activity from a muscle of a myotonic goat in response to a single maximal volley to the motor nerve. Ordinate, voltage (μV.) or tension (kg.); abscissa, time, 10 milliseconds. Note prolonged electrical activity. Lower record: Electromyogram of denervated and curarized leg muscle of myotonic goat. Muscle was stimulated mechanically by a tap. Ordinate, voltage (μV.); abscissa, time, 0.2 second between marks. (After Brown and Harvey, *Brain*, 1939, *62*:341–363.)

even in the denervated, curarized muscle (Fig. 25, bottom), indicate a fault lying in the membrane of the muscle fibers.

DISEASES OF THE CONTRACTILE MECHANISM (v).[2] The fifth site of muscular pathologic disturbance is in the contractile mechanism of the muscle fiber. Progressive muscular dystrophy serves as an example. Nerves and motor nerve endings which appear normal histologically can occur when the muscle fibers are severely degenerated. (For reasons not pertinent to the physiology of muscular contraction, the muscles are greatly enlarged.) The muscle membrane is no doubt also abnormal, sharing in the striking destruction of the core of the muscle fiber; however, the functional status of the membrane is not known. Functionally, the disease is manifested as simple weakness unaccompanied by fibrillation, fasciculation or other evidences of abnormal excitability.

CONTRACTURE. "Contracture" is used clinically to designate a condition of fixed high resistance to passive stretch of a muscle. Contracture may result simply from a fibrosis of the tissue supporting the muscles or, more frequently, the joints. Such a condition may be caused by immobilization of a joint, for example. The term covers a number of unrelated phenomena and should be used in a generic sense, preceded by an appropriate adjective. That some contractures actually result from disorders of the muscle fiber, as opposed to connective tissue elements, is suggested by "myostatic contracture," first described by Moll (see Ref. 61). If the attachments of a muscle are approximated and immobilized or, simply, if the tendon is cut, *innervated* muscle becomes fixed at a shorter length. Muscles maintained at shorter lengths by neural activity—as in spasm induced by tetanus toxin or in spasticity caused by lesions of the descending motor systems—show a similar contracture. After experimental tenotomy, the isometric contraction tension is severely reduced.

"Physiologic contracture" refers to a reversible but prolonged state which lacks some of the features of muscular contraction. The principal difference is that contracture may be local and not accompanied by a propagated action potential. Although myotonia is a prolonged contraction, it is not a contracture. Physiologic contracture may be induced by a number of agents—thermal, electric, mechanical and chemical. It seems probable that some, if not all, of these agents achieve their effects by acting directly upon the contractile mechanism without intermediation of the membrane. However, the mechanisms of both myostatic and physiologic types of contracture cannot be stated with certainty.

Hypertrophy. EXERCISE. It is common knowledge that voluntary muscle increases in size as a result of exercise. This enlargement is an hypertrophy, an increase in the volumes of the individual fibers. Normally, striated muscle fibers do not proliferate by cell division; there is evidence that their number does not increase in the human embryo after 4 to 5 months.

An increase in cross-sectional diameter of a fiber may be due to an increase in sarcoplasm, indicating an increase in metabolic reserves or an increase of the contractile apparatus (myofibrils) or both.

From experiments on running dogs, Marpurgo[54] concluded that exercise hypertrophy results from an increase in the sarcoplasm of the smaller fibers, so that the range of fiber sizes is less. All fibers tend to be large but not larger than the largest fibers in the normal muscle. The size and number of myofibrils did not increase. Denny-Brown *et al.*[19] repeated these experiments with cats, but removed the tendon of the gastrocnemius and related aponeurosis of the plantaris and biceps femoris, leaving only the soleus intact. This treatment results in an almost pure form of isometric exercise for the soleus. After three months, the soleus on the operated side had hypertrophied as a result of a significant increase in the absolute number of myofibrils as well as an increase in sarcoplasm of the smaller fibers. In certain athletic endeavors, the development of maximum cross-sectional diameter of muscle is desired. However, nonisometric exercise increases sarcoplasm but not myofibrils. Since myofibrils are the actual tension-producing machinery of the muscle, a greater degree of force production would occur following their hypertrophy. The sufficient condition for myofibrillar hypertrophy is a contraction of at least two-thirds maximum tetanic tension, a feat of difficulty in animal experimentation and extreme determination in humans.[19] However, even a single daily isometric exercise (2 to 5 seconds) can lead to the same degree of myofibrillar hypertrophy as more prolonged conventional tonic exercises of longer duration repeated several times a day. Increase in muscle size is not the only goal in training;

there appears to be a limitation to size of individual fibers, beyond which the muscles become sensitive to "cramping." In prolonged, heavy exercise the limiting factor is the circulation.

PATHOLOGY. Enlargement of the muscle fiber as a result of disease is found most frequently in myotonia congenita and athetosis (dystonia). The mechanism is not completely understood,[1] but it could be an exercise hypertrophy. In athetosis the healthy portions probably hypertrophy to compensate for the diseased, atrophic portions. In myotonia, the repetitive responses of the muscle membrane to single stimuli could result in exercise hypertrophy.

REFERENCES

1. ADAMS, R. D. *Res. Publ. Ass. nerv. ment. Dis.*, 1960, *38:*318–354.
2. ADAMS, R. D., DENNY-BROWN, D. and PEARSON, C. M. *Diseases of muscle; a study in pathology.* New York, Paul B. Hoeber, 1953.
3. BARR, L. and BERGER, W. *Pflüg. Arch. ges. Physiol.*, 1964, *279:*192–194.
4. BERGMAN, R. A. *Bull. Johns Hopk. Hosp.*, 1958, *102:*195–202.
5. BIANCHI, C. P. and SHANES, A. M. *J. gen. Physiol.*, 1959, *42:*803–815; idem, 1123–1137.
6. BIRKS, R., HUXLEY, H. E. and KATZ, B. *J. Physiol.*, 1960, *150:*134–144.
7. BOZLER, E. *Cold Spr. Harb. Symp.*, 1936, *4:*260–266.
8. BRADY, A. J. and WOODBURY, J. W. *J. Physiol.*, 1960, *154:*385–407.
9. BROWN, G. L. and HARVEY, A. M. *Brain*, 1939, *62:*341–363.
10. BULBRING, E. *Physiol. Rev.*, 1962, *42:*160–174.
11. BURNSTOCK, G. and HOLMAN, M. E., *Ann. Rev. Physiol.*, 1963, *25:*61–90.
12. CARLSON, F. D., *Progr. Biophys.*, 1963, *13:*261–314.
13. CARLSON, F. D., HARDY, D. J. and WILKIE, D. R., *J. gen. Physiol.*, 1963, *46:*851–882.
14. COOPER, S. and ECCLES, J. C. *J. Physiol.*, 1930, *69:*377–385.
15. CSAPO, A. I. *Physiol. Rev.*, 1962, *42:*7–33.
16. DANIEL, E. E., SEHDEV, H. and ROBINSON, K. *Physiol. Rev.*, 1962, *42:*228–260.
17. DAVIES, R. E. *Nature (Lond.)*, 1963, *199:*1068–1074.
18. DECK, K. A. and TRAUTWEIN, W. *Pflüg. Arch. ges. Physiol.*, 1964, *280:*63–80.
19. DENNY-BROWN, D. *Res. Publ. Ass. nerv. ment. Dis.*, 1960, *38:*147–196.
20. DENNY-BROWN, D. and PENNYBACKER, J. B. *Brain*, 1938, *61:*311–334.
21. ECCLES, J. C. and SHERRINGTON, C. S. *Proc. roy. Soc.*, 1930, *B106:*326–357.
22. ELFTMAN, H. *Biol. Symp.*, 1941, *3:*191–209.
23. FALK, G. and FATT, P. *Proc. roy. Soc.*, 1964, *B160:*69–123.
24. FARMER, T. W., BUCHTHAL, F. and ROSENFALCK, P. *Res. Publ. Ass. nerv. ment. Dis.*, 1960, *38:*714–720.
25. FATT, P. *Physiol. Rev.*, 1954, *34:*674–710.
26. FATT, P. and KATZ, B. *J. Physiol.*, 1951, *115:*320–370.
27. *Fed. Proc.*, 1964, *23:*885–939.
28. FENN, W. O. In: *Physical chemistry of cells and tissues*, R. Höber, ed. Philadelphia, Blakiston, 1945.
29. FRANZINI-ARMSTRONG, C. and PORTER, K. R. *Nature (Lond.)*, 1964, *202:*355–357.
30. FREYGANG, W. H., JR., GOLDSTEIN, D. A. and HELLAM, D. C. *J. gen. Physiol.*, 1964, *47:*929–952.
31. GORDON, A. M., HUXLEY, A. F. and JULIAN, F J. *J. Physiol.*, 1964, *171:*28P–30P.
32. HARVEY, A. M. and JOHNS, R. J. *Amer. J. Med.*, 1962, *32:*1–5.
33. HEILBRUNN, L. V. and WIERCINSKI, F. J. *J. cell. comp. Physiol.*, 1947, *29:*15–32.
34. HESS, A. and PILLAR, G. *J. Physiol.*, 1963, *169:*780–798.
35. HILL, A. V. *Proc. roy. Soc.*, 1949, *B136:*399–420.
36. HILL, A. V. *Lancet*, 1951, *261:*947–951.
37. HILL, A. V. *Science*, 1960, *131:*897–903.
38. HODGKIN, A. L. and HOROWICZ, P. *J.Physiol.*, 1960, *153:*370–385.
39. HOEFER, P. F. A. *Res. Publ. Ass. nerv. ment. Dis.*, 1941, *21:*502–528.
40. HUNT, C. C. and KUFFLER, G. W. *J. Physiol.*, 1954, *126:*293–303.
41. HUXLEY, A. F. *Progr. Biophys.*, 1957, *7:*255–318.
42. HUXLEY, A. F. and NIEDERGERKE, R. *J. Physiol.*, 1958, *144:*403–425.
43. HUXLEY, A. F. and TAYLOR, R. E. *J. Physiol.*, 1958, *144:*426–441.
44. HUXLEY, H. E. *J. biophys. biochem. Cytol.*, 1957, *3:*631–648.
45. HUXLEY, H. E. Chap. 7 in *The cell*, vol. IV, J. Brachet and A. E. Mirsky, eds. New York, Academic Press, Inc., 1960.
46. HUXLEY, H. E. *J. molec. Biol.*, 1963, *7:*281–308.
47. HUXLEY, H. E. *Nature (Lond.)*, 1964, *202:*1067–1071.
48. INFANTE, A. A. and DAVIES, R. E. *Biochem. biophys. Res. Commun.*, 1962, *9.*410–415.
49. JOHNS, R. J. *Res. Publ. Ass. nerv. ment. Dis.*, 1960, *38:*704–713.
50. JOHNSON, W. H. *Physiol. Rev.*, 1962, *42:*113–143.
51. KATZ, B. *Proc. roy. Soc.*, 1962, *B155:*455–477.
52. LAMBERT, E. H. *Res. Publ. Ass. nerv. ment. Dis.*, 1960, *38:*247–273.
53. LOWY, J. and HANSON, J. *Physiol. Rev.*, 1962, *42:*34–42.
54. MARPURGO, B. *Virchows Arch. path. Anat.*, 1897, *150:*522–554.
55. NEEDHAM, D. M. Chap. 2 in *The structure and function of muscle*, vol. II, G. H. Bourne, ed. New York, Academic Press, Inc., 1960.
56. NEEDHAM, D. M. *Physiol. Rev.*, 1962, *42:*88–96.
57. PAGE, S. and HUXLEY, H. E. *J. cell Biol.*, 1963, *19:*369–390.
58. PEACHEY, L. D. and PORTER, K. R. *Science*, 1959, *129:*721–722.
59. PODOLSKY, R. J. *J. Physiol.*, 1964, *170:*110–123.
60. PROSSER, C. L. *Physiol. Rev.*, 1962, *42:*193–206.
61. RANSON, S. W. and DIXON, H. H. *Amer. J. Physiol.*, 1928, *86:*312–319.
62. RHODIN, J. A. G. *Physiol. Rev.*, 1962, *42:*48–81.
63. SIMPSON, J. A. *Scot. med. J.*, 1960, *5:*419–436.
64. SZENT-GYÖRGYI, A. *Biol. Bull.*, 1949, *96:*140–161.
65. THAEMERT, J. C. *J. biophys. biochem. Cytol.*, 1959, *6:*67–70.
66. THESLEFF, S. *Physiol. Rev.*, 1960, *40:*734–752.
67. TRAUTWEIN, W. and KASSEBAUM, D. G. *J. gen. Physiol.*, 1961, *45:*317–330.
68. TUNIK, B. and HOLTZER, H. *J. biophys. biochem. Cytol.*, 1961, *11:*67–74.
69. UNIVERSITY OF CALIFORNIA. *Fundamental studies of human*

locomotion and other information relating to design of artificial limbs. Berkeley, 1947, 2 vols.

70. VIETS, H. R. and GAMMON, G. D., eds. *Amer. J. Med.,* 1955, *19:*655–742.

71. WEBER, A., HERZ, R. and REISS, I. *J. gen. Physiol.,* 1963, *46:*679–702.

72. WEBER, H. H. and PORTZEHL, H. *Progr. Biophys.* 1954, *4:*60–111.

73. WEIDMANN, S. *J. Physiol.,* 1951, *115:*227–236.

74. WEIDMANN, S. *J. Physiol.,* 1955, *127:*213–224.

75. WOODBURY, J. W. Chap. 11 in *Handbook of physiology, Section 2, Circulation,* vol. I, W. F. Hamilton and P. Dow, eds. Washington, D. C., American Physiological Society, 1962.

76. WOODBURY, J. W. and CRILL, W. E. In: *Nervous inhibition,* E. Florey, ed. New York, Pergamon Press, Inc., 1961.

REFLEX CONTROL OF SKELETAL AND VISCERAL MUSCULATURE

CHAPTER 6

Spinal Reflexes and Synaptic Transmission

By HARRY D. PATTON

PROPERTIES OF THE SYNAPSE

IN the foregoing chapters attention was focused on the distinctive properties of axons and muscle cells, taken as samples of excitable tissues. Stripped of detail, these properties are *excitability* and *conductivity*. An axon, when excited, responds by generating an action potential, which is then conducted in both directions away from the site of stimulation. Individual excitable cells, no matter what type or how excited, always respond to excitation in this stereotyped fashion; no other response is known. The action potential is thus the only mode of expression available to the nervous system; it is the message carried from sense organ to brain, giving rise to sensation; it is the message relayed from brain and spinal cord to muscle, giving rise to movement. Indeed, all feeling and action are reducible to orderly, sequential, neuronal exchanges of minute quantities of potassium for minute quantities of sodium.

Variety of experience and action results from the channeling of action potentials within the central nervous system and from modulation of action potential discharge patterns. Discharge patterns are initially determined by the properties of sense organs. The messages arriving at the sensory and motor centers of the central nervous system, however, may be quite different from those initiated at the sense organ.

In vertebrates, even the simplest experience and behavior derive from the conduction of action potentials over *chains* of neurons, which are linked together by apposition of the efferent process (axon) of one cell to the cell body or dendrites of another. Such a junction between nerve cells is called a *synapse*. During the latter half of the last century, many histologists argued that the nervous system was a syncytium and that nerve cells were joined together at the synaptic region by protoplasmic extensions between them. We now know, largely from Ramón y Cajal's studies, that neurons are individual units and that the synapse is a region of protoplasmic "contiguity, not continuity." This point is most important because it means that conduction through chains of neurons is discontinuous and, consequently, that the message may be fundamentally altered at each synaptic link. At the synapse, the presynaptic impulse initiates a distinctive process, which may tentatively be called the *transmitter process,* that serves to initiate new action in the post synaptic neuron. The present chapter is primarily concerned with the nature of this transmitter process and its influence on the messages of the central nervous system.

Some of the special properties of synapses may be briefly listed preliminary to a detailed consideration of synaptic function.

1. *Unidirectional conduction.* In contrast to action potentials in a nerve fiber, which are conducted in both directions, action potentials in a neuron chain are conducted in only one direction. For example, action potential messages set up in a dorsal root may be transferred, in the spinal cord, to nerve cells with which the root fibers make synaptic connection, thence to other nerve cells and then, over their axons, to the ventral root. On the other hand, impulses excited in a ventral root, although they traverse the axons and probably part of the perikarya and dendrites of the motoneurons, do not initiate action potentials in the nerve terminals which make synaptic connections with these motoneurons. The synapse is a "one way valve" which determines the direction of transmission.

2. *Repetitive discharge.* A nerve fiber usually responds only once to a single brief stimulus. A single synchronous volley of impulses delivered over a presynaptic path to a neuron often, but not always, evokes a burst or train of spikes in the postsynaptic neuron. The frequency of the postsynaptic discharge usually varies during the burst, but may approach 500 to 1000

impulses a second for short periods. Repetitive discharge is one way in which neural activity is amplified at the synapse.

3. *Failure to transmit faithfully frequencies of presynaptic volleys.* When a nerve fiber is stimulated repetitively, each stimulus elicits one action potential, unless the interval between stimuli is less than the refractory period. Refractoriness is thus the only limitation to faithful signaling of the stimulation frequency. In a chain of neurons, however, the postsynaptic neuron may not respond to each of a series of repetitive presynaptic volleys. For example, if the presynaptic path is stimulated 20 times a second, the postsynaptic neuron may respond only to the first volley reaching it. In general, the longer the chain (i.e., the greater the number of synapses), the less is its capacity to follow imposed frequencies faithfully. Obviously, at such rates of stimulation, frequency-following is not limited by the refractory period of the postsynaptic neuron; for repetitive discharge in response to a single presynaptic volley indicates that the cell is capable of generating impulses at rates up to one every millisecond. Some evidence suggests that high frequency blockage occurs in the fine presynaptic terminals. The special significance of this property of synapses is that temporal patterns of discharge initiated in the presynaptic pathway become significantly altered as they traverse successive synapses in a chain.

4. *Susceptibility to asphyxia, ischemia and depressant drugs.* The synapse is a region of low safety factor, and transmission is easily blocked. A nerve fiber will continue to conduct impulses many minutes after cardiac arrest, but synaptic transmission succumbs much earlier. In general, long chains with multiple synapses are more easily blocked than are shorter, simpler chains. The effectiveness of general anesthetic agents is largely due to the capacity to block synaptic transmission. Reflex movement, sensation and consciousness are abolished, whereas excitability of nerve trunks is little affected, as evidenced by lively muscle contraction when a motor nerve is stimulated directly.

5. *Synaptic delay.* Conduction over axons is continuous and uninterrupted, the rate of conduction being determined by axon diameter. The synaptic transmitter process consumes a finite interval of time. Conduction time over a chain of neurons is therefore greater than the sum of axonal conduction times, a discrepancy which increases with the number of synapses in the chain.

6. *Inhibition.* At some synapses, the consequence of presynaptic activity is not excitation but depression of activity in the postsynaptic neuron. This important property and its mechanism will be discussed in detail below.

ANALYSIS OF SYNAPTIC FUNCTION

The Monosynaptic Reflex.[25]   To study the properties of the synapse it is obviously desirable to select a simple monosynaptic system, i.e., one having only a single synapse. The sympathetic ganglion fulfills this requirement, and for qualitative studies is a satisfactory synaptic model. Quantitatively, however, the peripheral synapses in ganglia are somewhat different from the central synapses in the brain and the spinal cord; for example, the delay at a sympathetic synapse is four to ten times as great as that at a central synapse. Also, one of the important synaptic processes, inhibition, is either poorly developed or lacking in ganglionic synapses. For these reasons, the synapses formed between dorsal root afferent fibers and motoneurons will be used as synaptic models in this discussion.

Figure 1 shows the intramedullary course of dorsal root fibers entering the spinal cord as revealed by silver stains. Some afferent fibers (*a*) plunge without interruption through the gray matter to terminate on motoneurons in the anterior horn (*B*). Such reflex arcs are *monosynaptic*. Other afferent fibers (*b, c*) terminate on neurons in the dorsal and intermediate regions of the gray matter. Although not shown, the axons of these neurons are in turn distributed to other intermediate neurons or to motoneurons to complete the circuit through the spinal cord. Such reflex arcs are *multisynaptic*, and impulses directed through them reach the motoneuron only after transfer through one or more *interneurons*, or *internuncial neurons*, the generic names for cells interposed between primary afferent neurons and the final motoneuron. The difference between monosynaptic and multisynaptic arcs is further clarified by the diagrammatic representation in Figure 2.

Happily, the monosynaptic and multisyn-

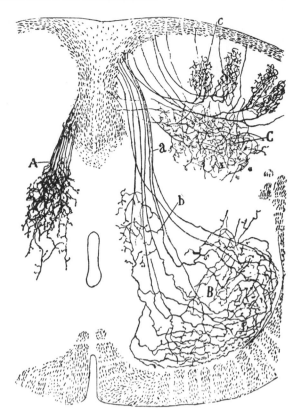

Fig. 1. Distribution of primary afferent collaterals in cross section of spinal cord. On right, collaterals *C* and *c* are distributed to dorsal horn and substantia gelatinosa Rolandi. *a,* Reflexomotor collaterals extending to ventral horn (*B*). *b,* Collaterals to intermediate nucleus of Cajal. On left, dense collaterals (*A*) to intermediate nucleus. (After Cajal, *Histologie du système nerveux,* Paris, Maloine, 1909.)

Fig. 2. Diagram of circumscribed reflex mechanism of Cajal (*left*) showing direct connection between afferent collaterals and motoneurons, and diffuse reflex mechanism of Cajal (*right*) in which an interneuron is intercalated between afferent fibers and motoneurons. (After Cajal, *Histologie du système nerveux,* Paris, Maloine, 1909.)

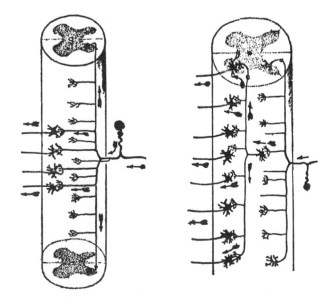

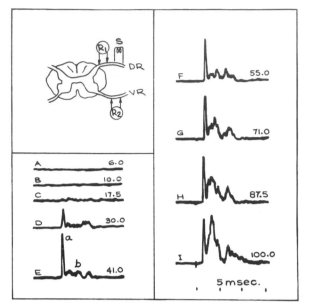

Fig. 3. Spinal reflex discharges elicited by dorsal root shocks of varying intensity. Single shocks were delivered to dorsal root (*DR*) through stimulating electrodes (*S*). Electrodes R_1 recorded dorsal root action potential; electrodes R_2 on ventral root (*VR*) recorded resultant reflex discharge. Traces *A–I* show reflex discharges at R_2 as shock strength was progressively increased. Numbers to right of traces, computed from R_1 recording, indicate number of afferent fibers excited expressed as a percentage of total fiber content of dorsal root. In *E: a*, monosynaptic discharge; *b*, multisynaptic discharges. (After Lloyd, *J. Neurophysiol.*, 1943, 6:111–120.)

aptic arcs can be functionally distinguished. In experiments of the type illustrated in Figure 3, stimulating electrodes (*S*) are placed on a dorsal root near its entrance into the spinal cord, and recording electrodes (R_2) are attached to the proximal portion of the corresponding segmental ventral root to register the emergent reflex discharge. A minimally effective shock to the dorsal root (trace *C*) elicits a small ventral root discharge which begins about 3 milliseconds after the stimulus. As the shock strength is increased (*D–I*), the amplitude of the early synchronous part of the discharge (labeled *a* in trace *E*) increases rapidly to a maximal value (*E*) which is not increased by further increases in shock strength (*F–I*). The later asynchronous part of the discharge (labeled *b* in trace *E*) increases more slowly with increasing stimulus strength, but continues to increase in size after the early discharge has reached a stable amplitude. A reasonable hypothesis is that the early sharp spike reflects a motoneuron discharge re-

flexly elicited through monosynaptic spinal arcs, whereas the later asynchronous waves result from the firing of motoneurons through multisynaptic channels, with consequent repeated synaptic delays.

In point of fact, part of the discrepancy in the latency of the early and the late discharge is attributable to a difference in the sizes of the afferent fibers mediating these discharges, those responsible for the early discharge being larger and hence conducting impulses more rapidly. This difference is suggested by the observation that the early discharge grows most rapidly through a range of stimulus strengths adequate only for low threshold, rapidly conducting, dorsal root fibers; whereas the growth of the later discharges occurs at higher stimulus strengths. The differences in delay due to afferent conduction time are small when conduction distance is minimized by placing the stimulating electrodes close to the cord, and even when appropriate allowances for conduction differences are made, the central delay of the later discharge remains considerably longer than that of the early discharge. Thus, the original hypothesis that the later discharge is conducted over chains more complex than those mediating the early discharge remains plausible.

SYNAPTIC DELAY.[25] To prove that the early discharge is monosynaptic, however, requires an independent measure of the duration of synaptic delay. An approximate value is provided by Renshaw's ingenious experiment shown in Figure 4. Electrodes (*R*) on the ventral root record the motoneuronal discharge elicited by stimulation through electrodes thrust into the intermediate gray matter of the cord in the region occupied only by elements presynaptic to the motoneurons. Weak shocks produce no response (trace *a*). Slightly stronger stimuli (traces *b* and *c*) evoke, after 1.0 millisecond, the response labeled *s*. Upon stronger stimulation, an additional and earlier (0.2 millisecond) discharge, *m*, appears (trace *d*); and, as *m* grows in size with increasing shock strength, the *s* discharge becomes correspondingly smaller (traces *e* and *f*).

The obvious interpretation of this experiment is that the weak shocks excite only the presynaptic elements near the electrodes, and that these elements then synaptically activate the motoneurons, giving rise to the *s* discharge. The latency of the earliest discharge thus elicited includes presynaptic conduction time, one synaptic delay and conduction time from moto-

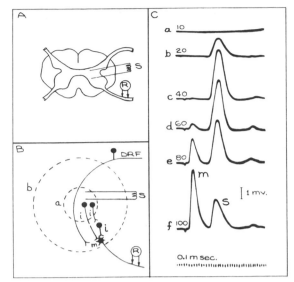

Fig. 4. Measurement of synaptic delay in spinal cord. *A,* Arrangement of stimulating (*S*) and recording (*R*) electrodes. *B,* Diagrammatic interpretation of traces in *C. C,* Responses as stimulus strength (indicated by numbers above traces) was increased. In *B,* only dorsal root fibers (*DRF*) and interneurons (*i*) within dotted circle *a* were excited by weak stimulus; shortest path to *R* therefore included one synapse, and delayed response, marked *s* in *C, b-f,* resulted. With strong stimulus, elements lying within dotted circle *b* were excited; these included some motoneurons (*m*) whose discharge gave rise to *m* in *C, d-f.* Difference in latency between *m* and *s* (about 0.8 millisecond) is approximate duration of synaptic delay. (After Renshaw, *J. Neurophysiol.,* 1940, *3*:373–387.)

neuron cell body to ventral root. With stronger shocks, however, sufficient current spreads to the ventral horn to excite some of the motoneurons directly, giving rise to the earlier *m* discharge (Fig. 4*B*). Because direct excitation renders the motoneurons refractory, the conducted interneuronal impulses find them inexcitable, and hence, as the *m* discharge increases with stronger shocks, the *s* discharge diminishes in amplitude. The latency of the *m* discharge is due to conduction time from motoneuron soma to ventral root recording site. It follows that the difference in latency between the *m* and the *s* discharge provides an estimate of synaptic delay. As measured in this experiment, the delay includes conduction time in the fine presynaptic terminals plus the true synaptic delay, i.e., the interval between the arrival at the motoneuron of a synchronous presynaptic discharge and the depolarization of the motoneuron to the firing level. Because the distances are short, presynaptic conduction time is prob-

ably negligibly small and *m–s* interval thus approximates synaptic delay.

In the experiment illustrated in Figure 4, the *m–s* interval is 0.8 millisecond. In a series of such experiments, the interval varied between 0.7 and 0.9 millisecond.[25] When the cord shock was delivered some 3 milliseconds after a dorsal root volley, the interval diminished to 0.5 to 0.7 millisecond. The central delay in transmission across a single spinal synapse is thus 0.5 to 0.9 millisecond. Comparable delays have been measured in monosynaptic transmission through the oculomotor nucleus, the lateral geniculate body and the cochlear nucleus.

With a measured value for synaptic delay, the hypothesis that the early reflex discharge is monosynaptic can be rigorously tested. Figure 5*b* shows the ventral root discharge evoked by a shock to the corresponding dorsal root; this discharge begins 1.05 milliseconds after the stimulus. The upper trace, labeled *a*, shows the response recorded at the dorsal root entry zone; the latency, 0.30 millisecond (measured to the point where the positive deflection returns to the baseline), gives the conduction time in the dorsal root. Trace *c* shows the ventral root discharge provoked by a shock applied through

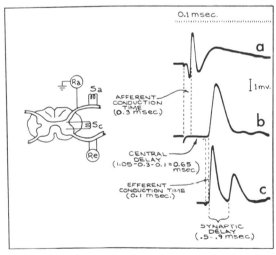

Fig. 5. Demonstration of monosynaptic reflex. Arrangement of stimulating and recording electrodes shown on left. *a,* Response recorded at *Ra* following stimulus at *Sa. b,* Reflex response at *Re* following stimulus at *Sa. c,* Response at *Re* following stimulus at *Sc,* as in Fig. 4. Subtracting afferent conduction time (derived from *a*) and efferent conduction time (from *c*) from latency of reflex in *b* gives central reflex delay of 0.65 millisecond, which falls within range of single synaptic delay derived from *m–s* interval in *c* and in Figure 4. (After Renshaw, *J. Neurophysiol.,* 1940, *3*:373–387.)

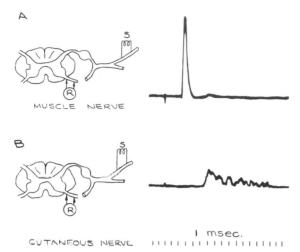

Fig. 6. Reflex responses to afferent volleys of different origin. *A*, Reflex discharge, almost exclusively monosynaptic, elicited by weak afferent volley in gastrocnemius nerve. *B*, Exclusively multisynaptic reflex response elicited by stimulating afferent fibers in sural nerve. (After Lloyd, *J. Neurophysiol.*, 1943, 6:111–120.)

electrodes S_c with sufficient intensity to excite both intermediate presynaptic elements and some motoneurons as in Figure 4*f*. The latency of *m* in *c* (0.10 millisecond) gives the efferent conduction time in the axons. The central delay of the reflex discharge in this experiment is thus $1.05 - 0.30 - 0.10 = 0.65$ millisecond. In other experiments, similarly measured delays ranged from 0.65 to 0.90 millisecond in resting cord, and from 0.5 to 0.7 millisecond when the reflex was conditioned by an antecedent dorsal root volley. Since these delays are too short to permit more than one synaptic delay (0.5–0.9 msec.), it can be concluded that the early reflex discharge is monosynaptic, as initially postulated.

AFFERENT PATH OF THE MONOSYNAPTIC REFLEX. The monosynaptic reflex discharge evoked by stimulation of the dorsal root provides a satisfactory model system for a study of some synaptic properties. For certain experiments, however, the later multisynaptic discharge is an objectionable contaminant. As seen in Figure 3, some multisynaptic activity, in addition to monosynaptic discharge, is evident even with very weak dorsal root shocks, an occurrence suggesting considerable overlap in the sizes (and hence thresholds) of the dorsal root fibers mediating monosynaptic and multisynaptic reflexes. However, as the numbers to the right of the traces indicate, the rates of growth of the two types of reflexes with increasing dorsal root

volleys are quite different. The monosynaptic discharge is maximal when the dorsal root volley is only 41 per cent of maximal. The remaining 59 per cent of the dorsal root fibers, consisting of the smaller diameter group, contribute nothing to the growth of the monosynaptic discharge but contribute heavily to the multisynaptic arcs responsible for the late waves. This sequence suggests that the monosynaptic reflex is mediated exclusively by a restricted group of large afferent fibers, whereas the multisynaptic arcs are fed by smaller fibers.

It has already been mentioned (Chap. 3) that examination of the fiber constitution of "demotored" peripheral nerves, i.e., nerves in which motor axons have degenerated following ventral rhizotomy (root section), indicates that the myelinated afferent fibers of muscle nerves typically fall into three diameter clusters: Group I (12–20 μ), Group II (6–12 μ) and Group III (1–6 μ). The myelinated afferent fibers of cutaneous nerves, on the other hand, fall into two clusters: *alpha* (ca. 6–17 μ) and *delta* (1–6 μ). Both muscle nerves and cutaneous nerves contain, in addition, a large number of unmyelinated afferent fibers (C or Group IV fibers). The striking difference in the two distributions is the relative paucity of large fibers in cutaneous nerves (see Fig. 12, Chap. 3).

The difference in afferent fiber constitution of cutaneous and muscle nerves, coupled with the knowledge that only the largest afferent fibers make monosynaptic connections, suggests that monosynaptic reflexes originate in muscle nerves. Figure 6 shows that this is indeed the case. Both trace *A* and trace *B* were recorded from the first sacral ventral root. In *A*, the stimulus was a shock to the central end of the cut gastrocnemius nerve; in *B*, the afferent volley originated in a cutaneous nerve, the sural. The response to the gastrocnemius afferent volley is almost entirely monosynaptic and can be made completely so by adjusting the stimulus to strengths activating only Group I fibers. On the other hand, the discharge resulting from the sural afferent input is exclusively multisynaptic. Furthermore, systematic investigation using various nerves for afferent input indicates that this finding can be generalized, and that uncontaminated monosynaptic reflexes can be initiated by selectively stimulating Group I afferent fibers of any muscle nerve; when shock strength is increased to values exceeding the thresholds of Group II fibers, multisynaptic discharge also occurs and grows as increasing stimulus strength recruits Group III and IV fibers into the afferent volley. Weak or strong stimulation of cutaneous nerves elicits only multisynaptic reflex discharge.

DISTRIBUTION OF MONOSYNAPTIC DISCHARGE. Experiments of the kind described in the foregoing section establish clearly the afferent origin of monosynaptic reflexes, but do not indicate the peripheral distribution of the reflex discharge, because the recordings are made from the ventral root which supplies many muscles. To determine the "target" muscles of a monosynaptic discharge elicited by stimulating the Group I afferent fibers of a muscle nerve, it is necessary to leave the ventral root intact and place the recording electrode on various peripheral nerves supplying other muscles. When such an experiment is performed, the monosynaptic discharge so prominent in ventral root recordings cannot be detected in any of these peripheral nerves. This finding suggests that the monosynaptic discharge returns only to the muscle from which the afferent volley originates.

That a monosynaptic discharge does, in fact, occupy the efferent fibers of the muscle nerve in which the afferent discharge originates is indicated by the experiment illustrated in Figure 7. To obtain trace *A,* both the stimulating and the recording electrodes were placed on the tibial nerve with all central connections to the spinal cord intact. Stimulation at Group I strength, of course, elicited a compound action potential in the nerve. Because the conduction distance between the stimulating and recording electrodes was small, this compound action potential was fused with the shock artifact (*s*). Later, however, another deflection (*R*) occurred that was clearly of reflex origin, because it was abolished by dorsal rhizotomy (see trace *B*). When allowances for afferent and efferent conduction are made, the reduced central delay of the reflex discharge *R* identifies it as monosynaptic. *The monosynaptic discharge thus returns to— and, except under special conditions, only to—the stimulated muscle nerve.*

The peripheral distribution of a multisynaptic reflex discharge elicited by stimulating Group II, III or IV fibers of muscle nerves or alpha, delta or C fibers of cutaneous nerves is much more diffuse; such discharges can be detected in the motor fibers supplying many muscles in the limb. However, multisynaptic discharges do not indiscriminately activate all limb muscles. Systematic testing reveals that in *the ipsilateral extremity, multisynaptic discharges are distributed almost exclusively to flexor muscles;* extensor muscles receive at best only negligibly slight portions of the multisynaptic discharge. Further details of multisynaptic reflex distribution are given in the next chapter.

Minute Anatomy of the Synapse; Convergence and Divergence. At this juncture, closer scrutiny of the structural organization of spinal synapses is profitable. Figure 8 shows the appearance of fresh, unstained motoneurons isolated from human spinal cord. The cell body (sometimes called the *soma* or *perikaryon*) is usually about 70 μ across, has an irregular polygonal shape, and gives rise to a number of long processes. The initially thick (5 to 10 μ) processes which branch and taper are *dendrites.* Dendrites may extend as far as 1 mm. before breaking up into untraceably small branches. The *axon* originates from the conically shaped *axon hillock,* and in its *initial segment* shows a constriction. Beyond the initial segment, some 50 to 100 μ from the soma, the axon increases in diameter, acquires a myelin sheath, and proceeds from the spinal cord into the ventral root. The axon is distinguishable from the dendrites by its uniform diameter (except for the constriction of the initial segment) and by the scarcity of branches. Some axons give off branches within the spinal cord; they part from the parent fiber

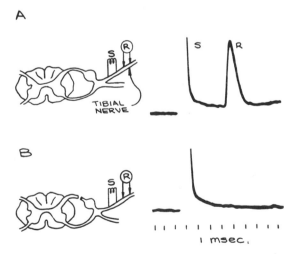

Fig. 7. Experiment proving that monosynaptic reflex discharge occupies efferent axons in nerve from which afferent volley originates. *A,* Responses recorded at *R* on left following weak shock, at *S* on left, to same nerve. *Right, S,* shock artifact and compound action potential of nerve; *R,* monosynaptic reflex discharge. *B,* After dorsal rhizotomy, *R* response is lacking; *R* is therefore reflex. (After Lloyd, *J. Neurophysiol.,* 1943, 6:293–315.)

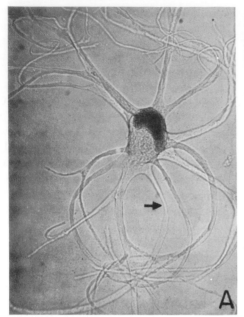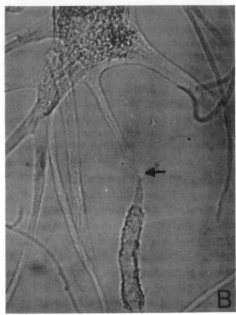

Fig. 8. Isolated human motoneurons. *Arrows* indicate axons; other processes are dendrites. *On right,* initial segment of axon lacks myelin sheath, which begins just distal to axonal constriction marked by arrow. (From Chu, *J. comp. Neurol.*, 1954, *100*:381–414.)

at right angles, curve dorsally into the gray matter and terminate on interneurons. These branches are called *recurrent collaterals* of the axon.

When motoneurons are stained with basic dyes (toluidine blue, thionin, methylene blue), the cytoplasm surrounding the centrally placed, round nucleus is seen to be filled with granules known as *Nissl bodies* or *tigroid bodies*. These structures are said to be absent from the axon hillock and axon, but are seen in the dendrites, at least in the thicker proximal part of their stalks. Nissl bodies are nucleoproteins and undergo dissolution (*chromatalysis*) when the cells are injured as, for example, in amputation of the axon.

In silver-stained preparations of spinal cord, the terminations of presynaptic fibers on motoneurons can be seen (Fig. 9). The terminal branches of the presynaptic fibers are fine and tortuous; they end on both dendrites and soma in small (about 1 μ) round or oval expansions known variously as *synaptic knobs, boutons terminaux* or *end feet*. The soma is particularly richly encrusted with knobs; the dendrites are similarly covered, but the density of knobs diminishes as the dendrite divides into fine terminal branches. It has been estimated that up to 40 per cent of the soma-dendritic membrane is covered with knobs. The axon hillock and the

unmyelinated initial segment of the axon are sparsely supplied with synaptic knobs.

Not all synapses in the central nervous system are characterized by knobs. Fibers terminating on the cells of Clarke's column do so by breaking up into a series of flat plates which are closely applied to soma and dendrites. The fibers of the medial lemniscus terminating in the relay nuclei of the thalamus break up into a rounded bush around the cells. In cerebral cortex presynaptic terminals often establish contact with minute pedunculated excrescences (the dendritic spines) which sprout from the lateral surface of the cylindrical dendritic stalk. The Purkinje cells of the cerebellar cortex receive "basket" endings which encase the soma. These cells also receive the climbing fibers, which run parallel to and in contact with the profusely branched dendritic tree, resembling a vine on a trellis. The climbing fibers and the olfactory glomeruli are examples of *axodendritic synapses* as opposed to *axosomatic* (basket endings) and *axodendrosomatic* synapses (motoneuron, cortical neuron, Clarke's column).

The fine structure of a synaptic knob is shown in the electron micrograph in Figure 10. The junction between the knob and the postsynaptic cell is marked by the arrow. Both the knob and the cell are surrounded by continuous membranes about 50 Å. thick. The knob appears to make a slight indentation in the cell. Between the two membranes there is a clear space about 200 Å. wide; this is the synaptic gap. In addition to nine lamellated mitochondria, the knob contains a profusion of small (about 200 to 600 Å.) round structures, which are called synaptic vesicles. It has been suggested that the vesicles contain chemical substances important in synaptic transmission.

It is well established that the many knobs on a single motoneuron derive from many different parent afferent fibers (Fig. 9). The motoneuron thus constitutes a *final common path* upon which many presynaptic fibers *converge*. There is reason to suppose that many knobs must be activated within a brief period to initiate an impulse in the motoneuron. Firing thus results from the nearly synchronous activity of many afferent fibers converging on the motoneuron; it is doubtful if activity in a single afferent fiber is sufficient to cause postsynaptic discharge.

Considered from the afferent side, the key feature of organization is *divergence*. Each dorsal root fiber breaks into many branches which establish synaptic contact with many postsynaptic cells (Fig. 9). Thus, although no single afferent fiber alone fires a motoneuron, each fiber contributes to the firing of many motoneurons. These basic principles of *convergence* and *divergence* should be kept clearly in mind while reading the following sections.

Facilitation and Occlusion.   The amplitude of the monosynaptic reflex discharge elicited by an afferent volley in Group I fibers in a muscle nerve provides a convenient index of the *number of motoneurons* fired. This is true because the afferent volley is conducted to the motoneurons over a relatively homogeneous pathway with little temporal dispersion, so that the postsynaptic discharge is fairly synchronous. The action potentials of individual fibers in the ven-

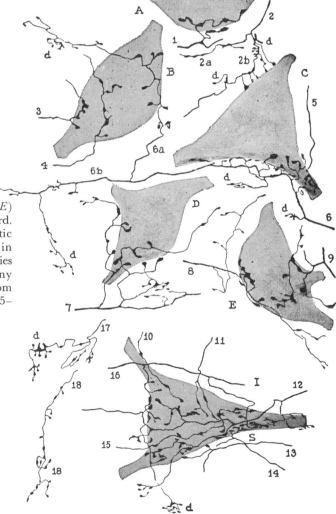

Fig. 9.   Synapses on motoneurons (*A–E*) and on a large interneuron (*I*) of spinal cord. *1* to *18*, Presynaptic fibrils carrying synaptic knobs to the several cells; *d*, synaptic knobs in contact with dendrites. Note that fiber *6* supplies both cell *B* and cell *C*, *divergence*, and that many fibers supply each cell, *convergence*. (From Lorente de Nó, *J. Neurophysiol.*, 1938, *1*.195–206.)

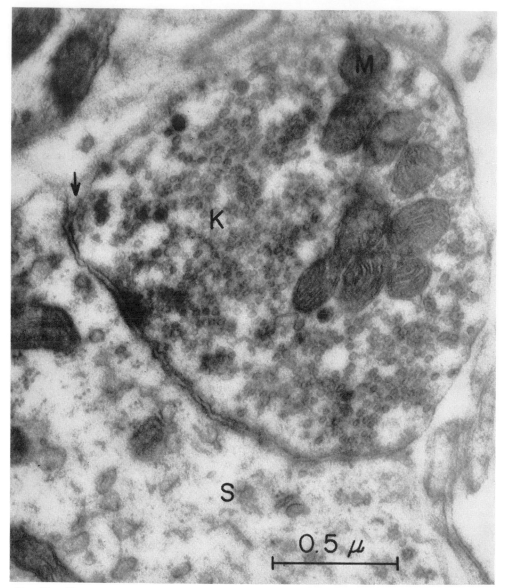

Fig. 10. Electron micrograph of a synapse on a motoneuron. *K,* Synaptic knob containing mitochondria (*M*) and round profiles of many minute synaptic vesicles. *S,* Motoneuron soma. Arrow indicates synaptic gap. × 65,000. (From Palay, *Exp. Cell Res.,* 1958, *Suppl. 5:*275–293.)

tral root are thus approximately added at the recording electrode.* It follows that as stimulus parameters are varied, the excited fraction of the population of motoneurons available to the Group I fibers can be determined simply by measuring the amplitude of the monosynaptic discharge. It has already been shown in Figure 3 that, as the number of excited afferent fibers is increased, the size of the monosynaptic discharge increases, reaching a maximum when approximately one-half of the Group I fibers are recruited.

Reflex amplitude measures only the number of neurons actually *discharged* by the afferent volley. More subtle influences of the afferent volley on motoneurons can be detected by slightly altering the experimental conditions, as in the experiment illustrated in Figure 11*A.* Here, a dorsal root has been divided into two strands, each equipped with a stimulating electrode. A weak stimulus to strand *a* elicits the

---

* With multisynaptic reflexes, the area under the tracing rather than the amplitude represents the number of neurons fired; both wide ranges of afferent conduction times and multiple synaptic delays results in temporal dispersion, so that the discharge of impulses is asynchronous, and therefore individual impulses do not add at the electrode.

small ventral root discharge shown on the left, and a similar stimulus to strand *b* induces the small response shown in the middle trace. Simultaneous stimulation of *a* and *b* produces, on the right, a response which is far greater than the simple sum of the two individual responses. In other words, the number of motoneurons fired by simultaneous activation of strands *a* and *b* is greater than the total number fired by stimulating *a* and *b* separately. An extreme example of this phenomenon is seen when the shocks to *a* and *b* are reduced so that neither delivered alone can cause discharge of motoneurons, but both delivered simultaneously result in a measurable discharge.

The results of this experiment are most simply explained as follows. An afferent volley delivered to a population of motoneurons, a *motoneuron pool*, has varying effects on the individual motoneurons in the pool, these effects being quantitatively dependent upon the density of activated knobs. Some motoneurons receive many knobs from the activated afferent source and are liminally excited; these are said to be in the *discharge zone* of the afferent source. Other motoneurons receive too few knobs from the activated fibers to reduce the motoneuron membrane potential to the firing level. The excitability of these subliminally bombarded motoneurons, however, is increased, a phenomenon known as *facilitation*. These facilitated motoneurons are said to be in the *subliminal fringe* of the afferent source. As a result of the convergence, the subliminal fringes of two afferent sources may have common elements; i.e., some motoneurons may receive a subliminal number of activated knobs from each source. With simultaneous activation of both sources, the excitatory processes may summate, so that some cells in the common subliminal fringes are recruited into the discharge zone. These relationships are shown diagrammatically in Figure 11*B*.

It follows from the foregoing that merely monitoring the ventral root discharge, which indicates the size of the discharge zone only, gives an incomplete picture of the total effect of an afferent volley. The subtle excitability changes which occur in the many cells of the subliminal fringe are detectable only when two afferent volleys are delivered to the motoneurons, as in the experiment shown in Figure 11. The facilitation of the response, i.e., the difference between the response to the combined volleys and the sum of the responses to the two

volleys delivered separately, provides a quantitative measure of the size of the subliminal fringe.

Figure 12 shows diagrammatically the manner in which both discharge zone and subliminal fringe grow as the size of the afferent volley is increased. With weak afferent volleys, no motoneurons discharge, but the facilitation curve shows that considerable numbers of cells are subliminally excited. Indeed, Lloyd's[17] quantitative measurements on monosynaptic reflexes indicate that, when the afferent volley is 7 to 8 per cent of maximum, discharge is just beginning, but the subliminal fringe is already about 30 per cent of maximum. With further increase of afferent volley size, both the subliminal fringe and the discharge zone increase proportionately and reach maxima when the afferent volley is about 40 to 50 per cent of maximum. It should be noted further that no matter how strong the afferent volley, the discharge zone never becomes coextensive with the subliminal fringe. Any afferent volley fractionates its motoneuron pool, discharging only a

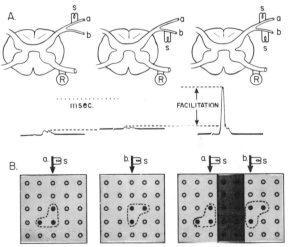

Fig. 11. *A,* Experiment demonstrating facilitation. Dorsal root was split into two strands, *a* and *b.* Weak stimulation of *a* and *b* separately produced reflex responses shown in left and middle traces respectively. Simultaneous weak stimulation of both elicited reflex discharge (trace on right) greater than sum of separate responses.

B, Diagram of mechanism of facilitation. Left and middle figures represent motoneuron pools served by afferent sources *a* and *b* respectively. Each source fires three motoneurons (filled circles enclosed by dotted contours); remaining neurons are subliminally excited. Subliminal fields of *a* and *b* are partially coextensive. When *a* and *b* are simultaneously excited (right), some neurons in common subliminal zones are liminally excited, and eleven rather than six neurons fire.

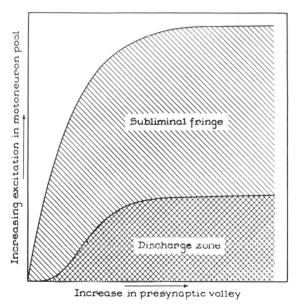

Fig. 12. Semidiagrammatic representation of relative sizes of discharge zone and subliminal fringe as a function of afferent volley strength. (From Lloyd, *J. Neurophysiol.*, 1943, *6*:111–120.)

portion of the total number of motoneurons it serves. The reserve represented by the subliminal fringe is brought into active discharge only when other afferent pathways converging on the same motoneuron pool are activated, providing opportunity for overlap of fringes and summation of subliminal processes.

Because both the subliminal fringe and the discharge zone increase with increased afferent input, it might be expected that when both of two maximal afferent volleys are simultaneously delivered, the discharge zones as well as the subliminal fringes will include common elements, as in Figure 13*B*. If the overlap of the discharge zones is extensive, the response to both volleys delivered simultaneously might be less than the sum of the responses to both volleys delivered individually. That this reduction occurs is shown in Figure 13*A*. The left and middle traces shows the ventral root discharges resulting from maximal stimulation of each of two separated portions of a dorsal root. The trace on the right shows the response to simultaneous maximal stimulation of both branches; the resulting discharge is less than the sum of the separate responses. Such reduction in response, attributable to overlapping of the discharge zones, is called *occlusion*.

TIME COURSE OF FACILITATION.[18] The experiments just described indicate that, although the neurons of the subliminal zone are not fired by

an afferent volley, their excitability is increased. The processes leading to this increased excitability differ only quantitatively from those leading to excitation of cells in the discharge zone. Subliminally excited neurons thus provide a suitable medium for studying the processes that lead to synaptic excitation of neurons.

It is a great advantage if subliminally excited cells can be studied in isolation without the complication of actual firing of cells. One way this isolation can be accomplished is by using very weak afferent volleys (see Fig. 12). A more convenient way of studying subliminally excited motoneurons depends on a peculiarity of the central connections of Group I afferent fibers. As has already been emphasized, a Group I afferent volley can discharge only the *homonymous motoneurons*, i.e., the motoneurons supplying the muscle from which the afferent volley originates. *Heteronymous motoneurons* (those supplying muscles other than the one from

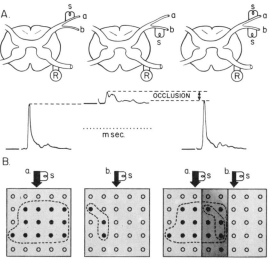

Fig. 13. *A,* Experiment demonstrating occlusion. Dorsal root split into two strands, *a* and *b*. Maximal stimulation of *a* and *b* separately elicited reflex responses shown in left and middle traces. Simultaneous maximal stimulation of strands elicited reflex discharge (right trace) smaller than the sum of separate responses.

B, Diagram of mechanism of occlusion. Left and middle figures represent motoneuron pools served by afferent sources *a* and *b*, respectively. Because the afferent volleys are larger, discharge zones (filled circles enclosed by dotted contours) constitute a greater fraction of total field than in experiment shown in Figure 11*B*. Discharge zones of *a* and *b* overlap. Simultaneous stimulation of *a* and *b* (right) fires only 14 motoneurons rather than expected sum, 16, fired by *a* and *b* separately. Note that one neuron in common subliminal fringe discharged.

which the afferent volley originates) are not fired (except in special circumstances), but conditioning-testing studies indicate that their excitability is altered in a direction which depends upon the relation of their target muscle to the muscle from which the afferent volley originates. For the moment, attention is confined to the motoneurons supplying muscles which are synergistic, i.e., muscles which act on the same joint and in the same way.

An experiment designed to test the influence of an afferent volley arising in a muscle nerve on the motoneurons supplying a synergist of that muscle is illustrated in Figure 14. Stimulating electrodes were situated on the central ends of the cut nerves supplying the two heads of biceps femoris which are, of course, synergistic. Recording electrodes were affixed to the S_1 ventral root. A volley in the larger branch induced the small reflex discharge shown in *A*. A weak Group I volley in the smaller nerve branch evoked no reflex discharge (*B*). (Even if a reflex discharge had occurred, it is known from previous experiments that such discharge occupies only the homonymous motoneurons.) When both nerves were stimulated so that the afferent volleys from the two pathways arrived at the spinal cord simultaneously (*C*), the reflex discharge was greatly increased. It can therefore be concluded that the Group I afferent volley traversing the smaller branch, although not sufficiently strong to fire any motoneurons, produced a subliminal fringe and that this subliminal fringe included the motoneurons supplying the muscle fraction innervated by the larger branch.

From systematic investigations of various muscle nerves, the finding illustrated in Figure 14 can be generalized; i.e., *for any Group I afferent volley, the subliminal fringe includes the heteronymous synergistic motoneurons*.[19] It should be emphasized that this generalization applies only to direct synergists—muscles acting on the same joint and in the same way as the muscle from which the Group I volley originates. Thus, a lateral gastrocnemius Group I volley facilitates the motoneurons supplying the medial gastrocnemius and those supplying the soleus, but has no detectable effect on the excitability of motoneurons innervating the hip or toe muscles.

Heteronymous synergistic motoneurons thus provide a pure pool of subliminally excited cells. By measuring the response of motoneurons to homonymous Group I volleys delivered at various intervals after these motoneurons have been subliminally excited by conditioning volleys in the heteronymous synergistic nerve, it is possible to determine accurately the time course of facilitation.

Figure 15 shows the results of such an experiment in which two branches of the nerve supplying the biceps femoris were used. The conditioning volley was insufficient to elicit a discharge; the test volley delivered to the other branch produced the response seen in traces *A* and *O*. Traces *B* through *N* show how the conditioning volley affects the test response at different conditioning-testing intervals. Facilitation is maximal when the conditioning and testing volleys arrive at the spinal cord at the same time (*B*), but the number of motoneurons responding to the test volley in such pairs of stimuli remains greater than the number responding to the test volley alone (*A* and *O*) for a considerable time after the conditioning volley has reached the spinal cord. The graph in Figure 15 shows the pooled results of seven such experiments. When absolute differences related to individual experiments are eliminated by expressing facilitation as a percentage of maximum facilitation in the particular ex-

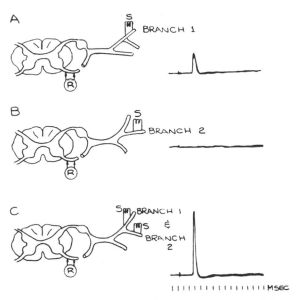

Fig. 14. Facilitation of heteronymous synergistic motoneurons by Group I afferent volley. Two branches of biceps nerve used as afferent paths. *A*, Response elicited by stimulating Branch *1*. *B*, Stimulating Branch 2 elicited no reflex response. *C*, Simultaneous stimulation of branches elicited response larger than control response in *A*. (After Lloyd, *J. Neurophysiol.*, 1946, *9:*421–438.)

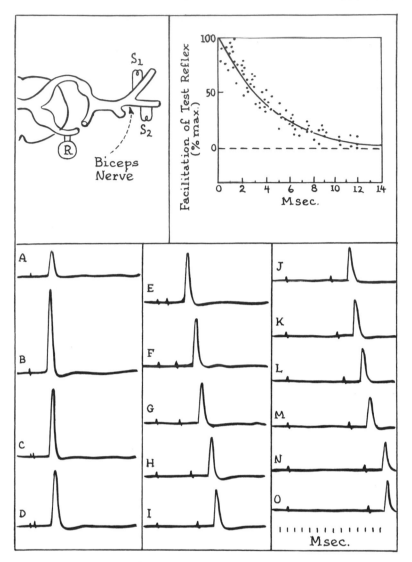

Fig. 15. Time course of facilitation. Group I fibers in two branches of biceps nerve used as afferent paths. Conditioning volley (S_1) applied to one branch elicited no reflex discharge. Test volley (S_2) applied to other branch elicited reflex discharge seen in *A* and *O*. Traces *B–N* show reflex discharges elicited by combined S_1 and S_2 separated by increasing intervals. Graph shows relation between test reflex increase (expressed as percentage of maximal) and conditioning-test interval; data from seven experiments. (After Lloyd, *J. Neurophysiol.*, 1946, *9*:421–438.)

periment, it is clear that the time course of facilitation is remarkably constant. Indeed, the curve shown in Figure 15 can be described mathematically as an exponentially decaying curve which declines to about one-third of its initial value in 4 milliseconds.

The duration of facilitation (or the "central excitatory state" as Sherrington termed it) is of special interest because it outlasts the presynaptic volley as recorded in the dorsal root. The discrepancy implies that between the arrival of the brief presynaptic spike at the knob and the initiation of the postsynaptic spike, some intermediate event of more gradual time course intervenes. Later, evidence will be presented that the presynaptic spike liberates from the knob a chemical transmitter, which diffuses across the narrow synaptic gap to exercise a depolarizing

action on the postsynaptic membrane. The duration of facilitation reflects the time course of action of the transmitter prolonged by the electrical time constant of the postsynaptic membrane. Because of this intermediate step, excitation outlasts the presynaptic spike and the cell stores information—or "remembers" what has happened—for several milliseconds after the spike has decayed.

Inhibition.[18] In the foregoing section it was seen how the use of paired stimuli to different afferent trunks (the "conditioning-testing" technique) can be used to detect subtle changes in neuronal excitability (facilitation) which are not revealed by single stimuli. Further, by varying the interval between conditioning and testing afferent volleys, it was possible to determine the time course of the changes in postsynaptic excitability leading to firing. In the present section, it will be seen that the conditioning-testing technique can also be used to reveal a new and entirely different influence of certain presynaptic fibers on motoneurons, *inhibition*. In inhibition, the afferent volley produces in the postsynaptic neuron a change which reduces its excitability. Inhibition can be detected by testing the responsiveness of neurons to excitatory volleys arriving at various intervals after the neurons have been subjected to an inhibitory volley.

It should be emphasized that mere unresponsiveness of motoneurons following an afferent volley is not adequate proof of inhibition as defined above. For example, when two pathways converge on the same pool of neurons, an *excitatory* volley in one pathway may render the neurons less responsive to a subsequent excitatory volley arriving in the other pathway because of refractoriness or postexcitatory subnormality. Such reduction of response is logically categorized as *occlusion*, although it is sometimes termed "indirect inhibition." True or direct inhibition implies a process that is the opposite of excitation and does not depend on previous discharge of any element in the arc displaying the depressed excitability. The distinction between inhibition and occlusion first became possible when a postconditioning deficit in the responses of monosynaptic arcs was demonstrated, for there, and only there, is it possible to be certain that the conditioning volley has not caused discharge of at least some postsynaptic elements (e.g., interneurons) in the chain.

Excitatory processes (facilitation and/or discharge) result when a pool of motoneurons receives Group I impulses from the muscle supplied by these neurons (homonymous) or from that muscle's synergists (heteronymous synergistic). Motoneurons are inhibited when they receive impulses via Group I afferent fibers originating in muscles antagonistic to the muscle supplied by the neurons (heteronymous antagonistic).[19] Figure 16 shows a typical experiment demonstrating inhibition. Recordings were made from the first sacral ventral root. Traces *A* and *M* show the monosynaptic discharge recorded following an afferent volley set up in Group I afferent fibers originating in the nerve supplying the gastrocnemius. Records *B–L* show the changes in this discharge when

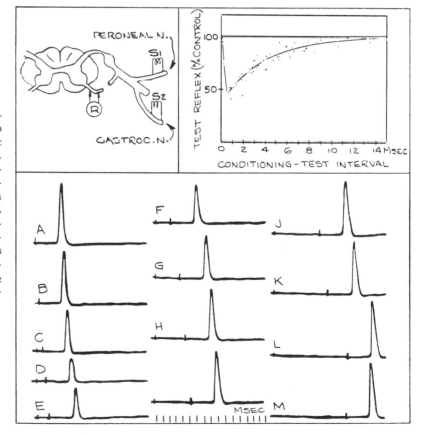

Fig. 16. Time course of inhibition. Group I fibers of two nerves supplying antagonistic muscles used as afferent paths. Weak stimulus S_1 elicited no reflex discharge. Stimulus S_2 elicited monosynaptic reflex seen in traces *A* and *M*. Traces *B–L* show discharges elicited by combined S_1 and S_2 separated by increasing intervals. Graph shows relation between test reflex responses to S_2 at different S_1–S_2 intervals; data from four experiments. (After Lloyd, *J. Neurophysiol.*, 1946, *9*:421–438.)

the test shock to the gastrocnemius nerve was preceded by a conditioning volley in Group I fibers in the deep peroneal nerve which supplies the dorsiflexors of the ankle, i.e., the muscles antagonistic in action to the gastrocnemius. Although no motoneuron discharge was elicited by the weak conditioning shock, it nevertheless greatly reduced the number of neurons discharging to the excitatory test volley.

The graph in Figure 16 shows the time course of inhibition occurring in four different motoneuron pools as a result of conditioning volleys delivered through their respective heteronymous antagonistic pathways. The ordinate shows the percentage decrease in the test reflex discharge when the conditioning inhibitory volley preceded the test excitatory volley by the intervals indicated on the abscissa. The curves indicate that, when conditioning and testing volleys arrive at the spinal cord at the same time (zero on the abscissa), there is little or no inhibitory effect. Inhibition does not reach its maximum until about 0.5 millisecond after the inhibitory volley reaches the spinal cord; thereafter, the process decays exponentially along a time course which is a mirror image of the facilitatory curve seen in Figure 15. Indeed, both the facilitatory and the inhibitory curve decay to $1/e$ in about the same time, 4 milliseconds.

The reason for the delayed (0.5 millisecond) maximum of the inhibitory curve is controversial. Lloyd and Wilson[22] find no evidence of an interneuron interposed in the inhibitory pathway. Eccles,[4] on the other hand, believes that the inhibitory pathway is disynaptic and that the intercalated interneuron accounts for the delay in maximal inhibition. For the present discussion, the question is largely academic and of secondary importance. The important and universally accepted point is: *different presynaptic fibers can exert one of two fundamentally opposite effects on postsynaptic neurons, either facilitation or inhibition.* A neuron receiving a sufficient number of facilitatory impulses within a sufficiently restricted period is excited and discharges an impulse. If a neuron receives a sufficient number of synchronized impulses from inhibitory afferent fibers, its excitability may be so reduced that the neuron no longer responds to excitatory impulses which otherwise are adequate to discharge it.

Facilitation and Inhibition in Multisynaptic Pathways. The two basic synaptic processes of facilitation and inhibition were de-duced from studies of monosynaptic arcs, for reasons already discussed. Similar processes may be presumed to occur at each synapse in more complex neuron chains. It is true that inhibition and occlusion cannot be distinguished clearly in multisynaptic chains, but there is every reason to believe that inhibition rather than occlusion underlies many response deficits in multisynaptic reflexes conditioned by volleys in appropriate afferent channels.

Synaptic processes in multisynaptic arcs differ from those in monosynaptic arcs in two respects: (i) the time course of facilitation and inhibition and (ii) the functional interrelations between the inhibitory and facilitatory pathways.

The time course of reflex facilitation (Fig. 17A) following a single conditioning volley via a multisynaptic path may be much longer than that for a monosynaptic discharge conditioned by a homonymous synergistic volley. Moreover, the development and decay of facilitation via multisynaptic paths is not the smooth and predictable function of time seen in the monosynaptic arc, but rather is typically a varying series of slowly waning maxima and minima. The same characteristics are also obvious in multisynaptic inhibition (Fig. 17B). These characteristics arise not because the fundamental synaptic processes differ in any way, but because the addition of interneurons to the chain increases the time span of motoneuron bombardment by presynaptic impulses. This increase in the duration of bombardment is due partly to the tendency of the interneurons to fire repetitively in response to a single afferent volley.[10, 15, 28] A second reason is that a motoneuron may receive impulses through several chains of various degrees of complexity. Lorente de Nó[23] has classified interneuron chains into two general types: the closed chain and the multiple chain (Fig. 18). In the closed chain (C), collateral branches permit recirculation or reverberation of impulses through the chain, so that bursts of impulses arrive at the motoneurons at intervals determined by the length and complexity of the chain. In the multiple chain (M), sequential activation of parallel chains of interneurons, through collateral branches, results in prolonged bombardment of the motoneurons, the delay in each chain varying with the number of synapses involved. In either instance, the motoneuron is subjected to a variable and asynchronous barrage which prolongs and compli-

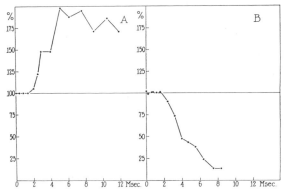

Fig. 17. Facilitation and inhibition through multisynaptic paths. In both experiments the conditioning volley originated in Group II afferent fibers. In *A*, the test reflex was a monosynaptic discharge from a flexor motoneuron pool; in *B*, a monosynaptic discharge from an extensor motoneuron pool. *Ordinates* give size of test reflex discharge, the control size being taken as 100. *Abscissae* show interval between conditioning (Group II) and test (Group I) volleys. (From Lloyd, *Res. Publ. Ass. nerv. ment. Dis.*, 1952, *30*:48–67.)

cates the time course of facilitation and inhibition.

The second difference between multisynaptic and monosynaptic arcs is in the origin and central distribution of their respective inhibitory and facilitatory pathways. Monosynaptic spinal reflexes originate from Group I afferent fibers, found only in muscle nerves. The efferent discharge is *discretely* delivered to the muscle from which the afferent input originated. The same input facilitates motoneurons supplying synergistic muscles and inhibits motoneurons supplying antagonistic muscles. In multisynaptic arcs, the afferent limb is composed of Group II, III, or IV fibers of muscles nerves, or of al-

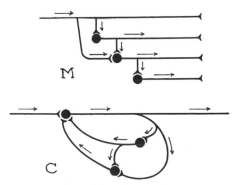

Fig. 18. Plans of the two fundamental types of neuron circuits. *M*, Multiple chain; *C*, closed chain. (After Lorente de Nó, *J. Neurophysiol.*, 1938, *1*:207–244.)

pha, delta or C fibers of cutaneous nerves. Irrespective of origin—cutaneous, subcutaneous, muscular, synovial or periosteal—these afferent fibers have, generally speaking, similar *central connections excitatory to motoneurons supplying ipsilateral flexor muscles and inhibitory to motoneurons innervating ipsilateral extensor muscles.*

Multisynaptic discharges thus occupy efferent pathways that originate from several segments of the spinal cord and that are distributed diffusely to flexor muscles acting at all joints of the extremity. Similarly, the motoneurons supplying extensor muscles acting at all joints of the extremity are inhibited by multisynaptic paths initiated through cutaneous or through Group II, III or IV afferent fibers. The multisynaptic reflex may thus originate from widely dispersed afferent fibers and has *diffuse* central connections involving motoneurons supplying muscles acting at different joints. The monosynaptic reflex has a *discrete* origin in muscle nerves and has *discrete* central connections involving only motoneurons supplying muscles acting at a single joint.

It should not be inferred from the foregoing that multisynaptic discharges are stereotyped. The magnitude of the reflex discharge to the various flexor muscles (as well as the intensity of inhibition of motoneurons supplying the various extensor muscles) varies markedly when the site of afferent stimulation is varied. This property of *local sign*, i.e., variation of efferent discharge pattern with changing locale of afferent origin, is discussed in greater detail in the next chapter.

Reciprocal Innervation. A striking feature of reflex organization is the way in which facilitation and inhibition influence motoneurons reciprocally so that reflexly induced muscular contraction occurs without opposition. Such reciprocal central relations are not confined to the reflex arcs specifically described above, but are found in most reflex arcs, even those influencing smooth muscle, cardiac muscle and glands. The principle of reciprocal innervation may be stated formally as follows: *when the motoneurons supplying a given muscle are reflexly excited by an afferent volley, the motoneurons supplying antagonistic muscles are inhibited by that afferent volley.*

This dual action confers on the afferent volley an especially sensitive and powerful control over the limb reflexes, a control simultaneously initiating muscular contraction of one kind and inhibiting all opposing muscular contraction. These relations for the monosynaptic arc and

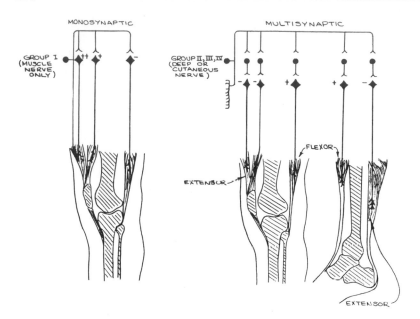

Fig. 19. Reciprocal relations of monosynaptic and multisynaptic reflex arcs. Note that Group I afferent fibers influence only motoneurons supplying muscles acting at a single joint, whereas Group II, III and IV afferent fibers diffusely influence motoneurons supplying muscles acting at several joints.

for the multisynaptic arc are illustrated diagrammatically in Figure 19. It should not be assumed, however, that reflex action lacks flexibility and variability. The diagrams in Figure 19 show the central influences of only a single afferent pathway. In actual fact, each motoneuron receives connections from a host of afferent pathways, and the excitability and behavior of the cell depends at all times upon the relative balance between the excitatory and inhibitory impulses which it receives from these pathways.

It should also be noted that the relationships shown in Figure 19 apply to the motoneurons ipsilateral to the afferent volley. Motoneurons on the contralateral side of the cord are also conditioned by an afferent volley, but generally the effects there are opposite to those found ipsilaterally. Thus, a cutaneous afferent volley excites ipsilateral flexor motoneurons and inhibits ipsilateral extensor motoneurons, but on the contralateral side, the flexor motoneurons are inhibited and the extensor motoneurons excited. This general arrangement of function is called *"double reciprocal innervation"*; it is discussed further in the next chapter.

Intracellular Recording from Motoneurons.[3, 5, 6, 9, 28] Although the technique of recording ventral root discharges emerging from a spinal cord subjected to various afferent volleys serves to demonstrate the basic phenomena of facilitation and inhibition and to delineate their respective time courses, such studies of cell populations or pools are poorly suited to investigation of the intimate mechanisms of excita-

tion and inhibition. For study of such problems, it is desirable to measure directly what happens to the membrane of a motoneuron subjected to excitatory or inhibitory afferent volleys.

Happily, such measurements can be made with ultramicroelectrodes similar to those described in earlier chapters. With electrodes having tip diameters less than 0.5 μ, penetration of the soma membrane can be accomplished without killing the cell, its vitality being evidenced by stable, predictable responses to afferent volleys. Often a cell survives impalement for several hours. The advantage of the technique is that it enables the experimenter to measure the potential across the membrane of a single cell and to observe the voltage changes which result when that cell is subjected to synaptic bombardment over various afferent pathways.

Penetration of spinal cord elements must, of course, be carried out blindly by slowly advancing the electrode through the cord (Fig. 20). Penetration of a membrane is signaled by the abrupt registration of a stable DC potential —the resting membrane potential. It is then necessary to identify the element penetrated. If the element responds to an antidromic ventral root volley with a single spike of invariant latency, it may be presumed that the electrode has lodged in a motoneuron. The identity of the motoneuron is next established by testing its responsiveness to Group I afferent volleys originating in various muscle nerves, since Group I volleys usually fire only their homonymous

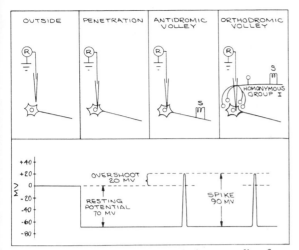

Fig. 20. Diagram of intracellular recording from motoneurons.

motoneurons.* Thus, for example, a penetrated element which responds to antidromic ventral root stimulation and to an orthodromic Group I afferent volley originating in the lateral gastrocnemius nerve may be presumed to be a motoneuron which supplies the lateral gastrocnemius muscle.

Such tests serve to identify the type of element penetrated but do not indicate the part of the cell penetrated—dendrite, soma or axon—because there are no absolute criteria for distinguishing penetration sites.

Action potentials recorded from ultramicroelectrodes in acellular regions (peripheral nerves, dorsal and ventral roots, dorsal columns) usually last about 0.6 millisecond. Intracellularly recorded spikes from spinal gray matter fall into two classes: those having durations of 0.6 millisecond and those with durations of about 1.5 milliseconds. The former probably represent axon spikes; the latter, either soma or dendrite spikes.

MEMBRANE RESTING POTENTIALS OF MOTONEURONS. When a motoneuron is penetrated with a microelectrode, a sustained difference of potential between the internal microelectrode and the external medium is recorded. Sometimes this DC potential increases gradually for the

* It is, of course, also possible to determine the peripheral connection of an impaled motoneuron by antidromically stimulating its axon in the muscle nerve, provided that the ventral root is left intact. Usually, for a variety of reasons, the ventral root is severed, and identification is established by the only slightly less certain method of orthodromic testing.

first few minutes; this phenomenon suggests a sealing of the ruptured membrane around the tip and a consequent decrease in the shunting currents which make the initial potential reading spuriously low. Stable membrane potentials of motoneurons range from 60 to 80 mV., with a mean value of about 70 mV.; they invariably indicate that the inside of the membrane is electronegative to the outside.† The polarity of the resting cell membrane is thus the same as that of the axon membrane, but the magnitude of the polarization usually appears to be somewhat less in the soma membrane. The lower value of the soma membrane potential may reflect continuous subliminal synaptic bombardment, so that the measured potential is not a true "resting" potential; or the lower value may result from injury to the dendritic tree inflicted by the electrode as it approaches the cell body.

Reasoning largely by analogy, one may assume that the mechanisms maintaining the membrane potential in cells and in axons are at least qualitatively the same (see Chap. 2). Unfortunately, with spinal neurons it is not feasible to test this assumption directly by changing the ionic composition of the external medium surrounding the penetrated structure, as has been done with axons. Changes in *intracellular* ion concentrations can be effected by electrophoretic injection of ions through the penetrating electrode;[3] but, unfortunately, the amount of K^+ ion which can be added to the cell sap in this fashion is small compared to the natural high internal K^+ concentration, and the injection has little effect on membrane potential. Attempts to reduce the intracellular concentration of K^+ ion by replacing it with

† The student is here reminded again that it is conventional to use the algebraic signs + or − to indicate the *direction* of membrane polarization. Thus, a membrane potential of − 70 mV. means that the inside of the membrane is 70 mV. negative to the outside. It must be clearly understood that the signs refer only to the direction of polarization, and are not to be taken in the algebraic sense when, for example, the membrane potential changes. Thus a change from − 70 to − 60 mV. is called a decrease, not an increase, in membrane potential, because the absolute voltage across the membrane is decreased, the direction of polarization remaining constant. Similarly, a change from − 70 to − 80 mV. represents an increased membrane potential. Decreases of membrane potential are often referred to as depolarization, increases as hyperpolarization.

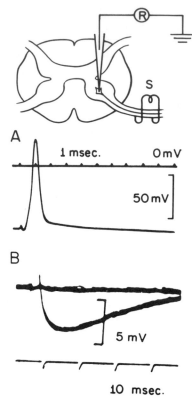

Fig. 21. Intracellularly recorded antidromic action potentials of motoneurons. Diagram shows arrangement of recording (*R*) and stimulating (*S*) electrodes. *A*, Antidromic spike recorded on fast time base and at low amplification. *B*, Antidromic spike recorded on slow time base and at high amplification to show after-hyperpolarization; most of spike was off the screen. Note that during recovery the trace overshoots the resting potential, indicated by horizontal baseline. Figure made by superposing about 20 responses on one negative. (After Eccles, *The neurophysiological basis of mind*, London, Oxford University Press, 1953; and *The physiology of nerve cells*, Baltimore, Johns Hopkins Press, 1957.)

some other injected cation (Na+ or tetramethylammonium) are more effective and produce expected decreases of 10 to 30 mV. in the membrane potential. When Na+ is the replacing ion, the membrane voltage recovers its initial value in several minutes, presumably because the Na+–K+ pump rapidly restores the resting ionic state. Following tetramethylammonium replacement of K+, restitution of the full membrane potential is much slower, presumably because the membrane is only slightly permeable to the tetramethylammonium ion.

The estimated concentrations of Na+, K+ and Cl− ions in the internal and external media of

cat motoneurons are given in Table 1. Also shown are the equilibrium potentials for these ions, computed from the Nernst equation. It should be noted that at a resting membrane potential of − 70 mV., the K+ ion is not at equilibrium (ε_{K+} = − 90 mV.). This inequality presumably occurs because K+ is actively pumped into the cell by some metabolic mechanism, so that the resting membrane never reaches the equilibrium potential of K+.

ACTION POTENTIALS OF MOTONEURONS. The intracellularly recorded action potential of a motoneuron antidromically fired (Fig. 21*A*) usually has an over-all amplitude of 80 to 100 mV. With a resting potential of − 70 mV., the "overshoot" is thus 10 to 30 mV.; in cell bodies, as in axons, the membrane potential is reversed during the action potential. This reversal during action is presumably triggered by an increased permeability to Na+ ions when the membrane potential is reduced to a critical value by the current flow in the axon. The flow of Na+ ions along their steep concentration gradient into the cell establishes a potential across the membrane which approaches that of the Na+ equilibrium potential (+ 60 mV.; see Table 1). The potential does not overshoot to this extent, because the increased Na+ permeability is short-lived and because there follows a period of increased permeability to K+ during which the membrane potential tends to return toward the K+ equilibrium potential of −90 mV. High K+ permeability is persistent. Consequently, after the spike, the membrane becomes hyperpolarized by about 5 mV. (i.e., the membrane potential reaches about − 75 mV.) and does not return to the resting level of − 70 mV. for some 100 milliseconds (Fig. 21*B*).

These concepts are supported by observations on the spike potentials of motoneurons in which the intracellular ionic concentrations have been altered by iontophoretic injection of ions through the intracellular electrode. When,

TABLE 1. *Ionic Concentrations and Computed Equilibrium Potentials of Cat Motoneurons** *

ION	OUTSIDE (mM./l.)	INSIDE (mM./l.)	E(mV.)
Na+	150	ca. 15	ca. +60
K+	5.5	150	−90
Cl−	125	9	−70

* From Eccles.[3]

for example, a current is passed from a Na_2SO_4-filled intracellular electrode to the outside medium, current is largely carried from the electrode to the cell sap by Na^+ ions, whereas the flow outward across the membrane is largely carried by K^+ ions. Thus, intracellular K^+ is replaced by Na^+ ions. It has already been mentioned that such a procedure diminishes the resting potential as a result of depletion of K^+ and consequent increase in the ratio of K^+ outside to K^+ inside the cell. This procedure also causes a reduction in the amplitude and the rate of rise of the action potential, because the added intracellular Na^+ reduces the Na^+ concentration gradient. In addition, when intracellular K^+ is replaced by either Na^+ or tetramethylammonium ions, the after-hyperpolarization is abolished and the decline of the spike is slowed.

If, as suggested by ion injection experiments and by reasoning from analogy with axons, after-hyperpolarization represents a seeking of the K^+ equilibrium potential during the postspike period of high K^+ permeability, no after-hyperpolarization should be observed if the membrane potential is artificially adjusted to equal $\mathcal{E}_{K^+}$. Eccles[3] devised the ingenious technique of adjusting the membrane potential to any desired level by introducing a double-barreled microelectrode into the cell (see drawing in Fig. 22). One barrel of the electrode is used for recording the membrane potential in the conventional fashion. The other barrel is used to pass a brief DC current through the membrane and thus to vary the membrane potential artificially. When the current is passed from the microelectrode outward through the membrane, the membrane potential is decreased, whereas a current passed from the external medium through the membrane into the electrode hyperpolarizes the cell. If the polarizing currents are brief, the membrane potential can be adjusted to any desired level without significantly altering the ion concentrations. Figure 22 illustrates how such variations in membrane potential affect the hyperpolarization following an antidromic spike. As the membrane potential is reduced below the resting level, the afterpotential increases in amplitude, whereas artificial hyperpolarization decreases the afterpotential.

The relationship between the membrane potential and after-hyperpolarization is shown graphically in Figure 22. It usually is impractical to hyperpolarize the cell sufficiently to reduce the after-hyperpolarization to zero, because at such high membrane potentials the impulse may fail to invade the cell. However, it can be seen that the points fit reasonably well onto a straight line which, by extrapolation, intersects the abscissa at a membrane potential of about 90 mV. Intersection at this point means that K^+ exchange, which is presumably responsible for postspike hyperpolarization, is "satisfied," or in a steady state only when the membrane potential is -90 mV., or about 20 mV. greater than the resting level. Calculated from the Nernst equation with the assumption of an external K^+ concentration of 5.5 mM. per liter and $\mathcal{E}_{K^+} = -90$ mV., the internal K^+ concentration must be about 150 mM. per liter, or approximately twice that required to maintain the observed resting membrane potential of -70 mV. The internal K^+ concentration is unexpectedly high because K^+ is pumped into the cell against its concentration gradient by some active metabolic process. There is reason to believe that the mechanism pumping K^+ into the cell is linked to that pumping Na^+ out (see Chap. 1).

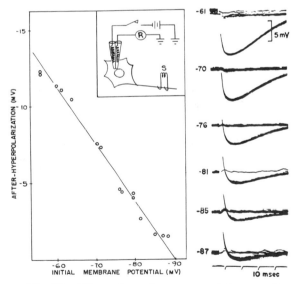

Fig. 22. Effect of membrane potential on amplitude of after-hyperpolarization. Traces show after-hyperpolarization recorded at different membrane potentials established by passing current through polarizing barrel of double-barreled microelectrode. Numbers to left of traces give membrane potential. Graph indicates that after-hyperpolarization is lacking at membrane potential of 90 mV. (After Eccles, *The physiology of nerve cells,* Baltimore, Johns Hopkins Press, 1957.)

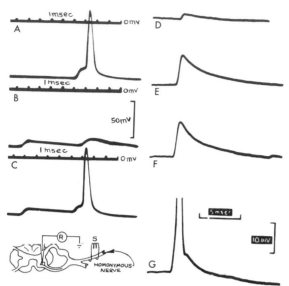

Fig. 23. Intracellularly recorded responses of motoneurons to homonymous Group I afferent volleys. *A*, Response to barely liminal volley. *B*, Response to two subliminal volleys. *C*, Same as *B* except that interval between volleys is reduced so that the second EPSP sums with first and discharges cell. *D–G*, Responses of another cell to afferent volleys of increasing intensity. In *G* the EPSP reaches threshold and the cell discharges. (After Eccles, *The neurophysiological basis of mind*, London, Oxford University Press, 1953.)

The origin of motoneuron spikes.[3, 12]   The rising limb of the motoneuron spike typically displays a slight notch when the depolarization has proceeded to about 30 to 40 mV. This notch is a constant feature if the spike is generated by an antidromic volley, by a presynaptic volley, or by a depolarizing current passed directly through the membrane via one barrel of a double-barreled electrode.

Analysis indicates that the notch reflects the spread of depolarization from a low threshold portion of the cell to a high threshold portion. When the cell is depressed, e.g., during recovery from an antecedent discharge, the spike often does not reach its full size of 80 to 100 mV., but declines from a peak of about 30 to 40 mV. above the resting level. In other words, in the depressed cell the spike amplitude is about equal to, or slightly less than, that of the notch seen in full-sized spikes of the undepressed cell. In antidromically elicited spikes, it can be seen that the portion of the membrane giving rise to the small spike is triggered when the membrane is depolarized by about 10 mV. For various reasons, it is believed that the small, low threshold spike (called the A spike by Fuortes *et al.*[12]) originates in the region of the axon hillock or initial segment of the axon. The higher threshold B spike seems to originate in the soma and/or dendrites. Eccles[3] assumed that the low threshold small spike originates in the initial segment of the axon, and he called it the "IS spike." The high threshold spike he labeled

the "SD spike" because he believed that it originates in the soma and dendrites. In view of uncertainties regarding the exact origin of the two components, the noncommittal designations "A" and "B" are preferable. Fuortes *et al.*[12] have shown that an orthodromically elicited A spike is all that is necessary to generate a full-blown spike in the axon; hence, effective synaptic transmission need involve only a fraction of the total postsynaptic membrane.

SYNAPTIC EXCITATION; THE EPSP.   Figure 23*A* shows an action potential recorded intracellularly from a motoneuron subjected to a liminal homonymous Group I afferent volley. Prior to the onset of the spike, a small depolarization appears; when this reaches about 10 mV., the spike is generated. A prepotential of this type is consistently observed in neurons subjected to excitatory presynaptic volleys, and is believed to reflect the pre-excitatory change induced in the membrane by the excitatory volley. For this reason, the prepotential is called the excitatory postsynaptic potential, or EPSP.[3]

To study the full time course of the EPSP, it is convenient to avoid firing the cell, because the spike obscures all but the rising phase of the EPSP. Firing can be prevented by reducing the size of the afferent volley until the induced EPSP is too small to initiate a spike, or, in other words, by recording from the cell when it is in the subliminal fringe rather than in the discharge zone.* Examples are shown in Figure 23*D*, *E* and *F*. The EPSP begins about 0.5 millisecond after the primary afferent volley enters the spinal cord, rises to a summit in 1.0 to 1.5 milliseconds after being initiated, and then declines slowly along an approximately exponential time course with a time constant of slightly more than 4 milliseconds. It is significant that the time course of the decay of the EPSP is of the same order as that of the facilitation curve determined by the conditioning-testing method applied to motoneuron populations.

Figure 23*D*, *E* and *F* shows another important characteristic of the EPSP—that it is a graded process capable of summation. In contradistinction to the size of the propagated spike, which is "all-or-nothing," the size of the

---

* A convenient method for studying EPSP without the complication of superimposed spikes is to deliver the Group I volley over the heteronymous synergistic pathway. Such volleys produce an EPSP which is qualitatively indistinguishable from, but smaller than, the EPSP produced by subliminal postsynaptic volley via the homonymous pathway.

EPSP is a direct function of volley size. Moreover, when two subliminal volleys are delivered within a time interval less than the EPSP decay time, as in Figure 23*B* and *C,* the second EPSP may sum with the "tail" of the first EPSP and cause sufficient depolarization (about 13 mV. in this instance) to discharge the neuron. The behavior of the EPSP thus parallels closely the process of facilitation and may be presumed to be the electrical manifestation of that process.

When the membrane potential is artificially altered by passing brief polarizing currents through an intracellular electrode, the EPSP induced by an excitatory volley displays a marked alteration in amplitude and configuration. As the membrane potential is decreased, both the amplitude and the rate of rise of the EPSP diminish until, when the membrane potential is artificially set at about 0 mV., the excitatory volley produces no change in membrane potential. When the polarizing current is such that it reverses the membrane potential (i.e., makes the outside of the cell negative to the inside), the EPSP is reversed in sign. Thus, the process underlying the EPSP seems to be one which is in equilibrium at about 0 mV.; when the membrane potential is above or below this value, an excitatory volley makes the membrane seek this equilibrium value. In the normal cell, of course, the effect is depolarization.

For a number of reasons, it seems likely that excitatory impulses cause a nonspecific increase in permeability to all ions. For example, injection of various ions into the cell has little or no effect on the amplitude and time courses of the EPSP. These data are best explained by assuming that the excitatory impulses initiate a transmitter process which "short-circuits"* the postsynaptic membrane beneath the synaptic knobs, permitting ions to flow along their concentration gradients and thus reduce the membrane potential. The extent of the depolarization depends on the number of "short circuits" produced, and this number in turn depends on the number of activated synaptic knobs. If the EPSP reduces the membrane po-

tential by about 10 mV. (i.e., to about -60 mV.), the threshold is reached, and the membrane becomes specifically highly permeable—first to Na^+ and then to K^+ ions—and a propagated spike is generated.

THE SYNAPTIC EXCITATORY TRANSMITTER.[24] It will be recognized that the EPSP is very similar to the end-plate potential recorded at motor end-plates when motor fibers are excited. The end-plate potential results from the liberation of a chemical transmitter agent, presumably acetylcholine. It is almost certain that excitatory synaptic knobs also liberate a chemical transmitter which renders the subjacent postsynaptic membrane highly permeable to all ions, just as the neuromuscular transmitter renders the end-plate permeable to cations. Unfortunately, the identity of the central excitatory transmitter is not known; it may be that more than one such substance exists. Although there is some reason to believe that acetylcholine is the excitatory transmitter at some spinal synapses, it seems unlikely that acetylcholine is the transmitter between dorsal root afferents and motoneurons, because analysis indicates that dorsal root fibers contain very little acetylcholine and choline-acetylase (an enzyme which, in the presence of ATP, acetylates choline). A full discussion of the efforts to identify transmitter agents at various synaptic junctions is given in monographs by Eccles[3, 6] and by McLennan.[24]

A commonly proposed hypothesis is that the numerous vesicles seen in electron micrographs of synaptic knobs comprise packets of preformed transmitter. Further, the action potential of the knob (or of the fine terminal fiber from which it derives) is supposed somehow to trigger rupture of vesicles through the membrane, thus releasing transmitter into the narrow synaptic cleft whence it reaches the postsynaptic membrane by diffusion. Intimate details of the electrosecretory coupling mechanism and of the synthesis, storage and release of transmitter are unfortunately lacking. However, there is evidence that the effectiveness of a presynaptic spike in liberating transmitter varies with (a) the amplitude of the presynaptic spike,[14, 26] and (b) the concentrations of Ca^{++} and Mg^{++} in extracellular fluid.[14, 26]

The relation between presynaptic spike size and transmitter release can be demonstrated directly in the giant synapse of the squid stellate ganglion, an axo-axonal synapse in which both

---

* The term "short-circuit" is used here in a relative sense. Computations indicate that, with maximal presynaptic action, the total membrane resistance drops from about 8×10^5 ohms to as low as 5×10^5 ohms. This latter resistance is composed of many higher resistances in parallel, the resistances of the patches of membrane under activated and nonactivated knobs.[3]

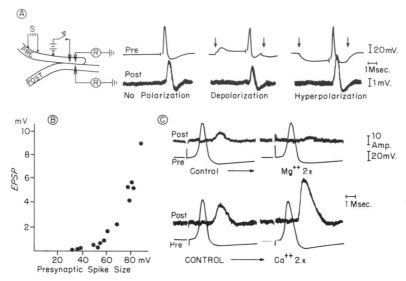

Fig. 24. Influence of presynaptic membrane potential and of ions on transmitter efficacy of presynaptic spike in squid giant synapse. *A,* Diagram at left shows location of stimulating, recording and polarizing electrodes. In middle and right traces the membrane potential was artificially altered by polarizing currents passed during the period between arrows. Depolarization (middle) diminished spike and EPSP, hyperpolarization (right) produced opposite effects. *B,* Graph of relation between presynaptic spike and EPSP amplitudes. *C,* Upper traces, increased Mg++ concentration reduced EPSP without altering presynaptic spike size. Lower traces, increased Ca++ concentration increased EPSP without altering spike size. (After Takeuchi and Takeuchi, *J. gen. Physiol.,* 1962, *45:*1181–1193.)

the pre- and postsynaptic fibers are sufficiently large to permit intracellular recording at the site of synaptic contact. In the experiment illustrated in Figure 24*A*, the presynaptic fiber was impaled with two electrodes, one being used to record the presynaptic spike initiated by a shock at *S*, the other, connected to a battery circuit, serving as a means of artificially adjusting the membrane potential. A single electrode inserted into the postsynaptic fiber recorded the EPSP, the amplitude of which, under the conditions of the experiment, measured the amount of transmitter released. When the presynaptic fiber was depolarized, the over-all amplitude of the presynaptic spike was correspondingly reduced and the EPSP was smaller. Conversely, hyperpolarization of the presynaptic ending resulted in increased amplitude of presynaptic spike and of EPSP. Figure 24*B* shows graphically the variation of EPSP (transmitter release) with variations of spike amplitude.

The relationship between presynaptic spike amplitude and transmitter release explains the phenomenon of *post-tetanic potentiation* of spinal reflexes in intact mammals.[7, 20, 27] The amplitude of monosynaptic reflex discharge to single-shock stimulation of a dorsal root is enormously increased following a brief period of high frequency stimulation of the dorsal root. Post-tetanic reflex discharges may attain amplitudes five or six times the control size and some degree of potentiation may last for as long as five minutes. In Chapter 3 it was pointed out that high frequency repetitive stimulation of a nerve trunk results in a prolonged positive after-potential or hyperpolarization of the tetanized fibers (see Chap. 3, Fig. 9). It might, therefore, be expected that following a dorsal root tetanus, the presynaptic terminals within the spinal cord would become similarly hyperpolarized and that spikes generated in such hyperpolarized fibers would be correspondingly increased in amplitude. Even a small increase in the amount of transmitter released from the synaptic knobs of hyperpolarized fibers causes a large increase in the numbers of motoneurons discharged by recruiting into the discharge zone many cells from the subliminal fringe. Lloyd[20] showed that, following tetanization, the compound action potential recorded from the dorsal root undergoes a slight increase in size, the increase running a time course similar to that of post-tetanic potentiation of reflex discharge. Also, spike potentials recorded intracellularly from single presynaptic fibers within the spinal cord (presumably near their terminal ends) increase in amplitude following a conditioning tetanus.[7]

A pathway potentiated by tetanization recruits into the discharge zone neurons which are normally in the subliminal fringe. It has been stressed that a Group I afferent volley normally facilitates but does not fire its heteronymous synergistic motoneurons. After Group I afferent fibers have been tetanized, they may discharge not only homonymous motoneurons, as usual, but also some heteronymous synergistic motoneurons.[21] Such "cross-firing" substantiates the concept that the state of motoneurons in the subliminal fringe differs only quantitatively and not qualitatively from that of neurons in the discharge zone.

The roles of Ca^{++} and Mg^{++} in transmitter release are indicated by the experiment illustrated in Figure 24C. Increasing Ca^{++} concentration in the bathing medium greatly increased the postsynaptic response to a presynaptic spike, whereas increasing Mg^{++} concentration produced the opposite result. These effects were not due to alterations in presynaptic spike amplitude, for, with the concentrations employed, the presynaptic spike was unaltered. Because of its blocking action on transmitter release, Mg^{++} is an effective anesthetic agent; the block can be rapidly reversed by injecting Ca^{++}.

CENTRAL SYNAPTIC INHIBITION; THE IPSP. When a resting motoneuron is subjected to an inhibitory volley of impulses delivered over its heteronymous antagonistic pathway, the membrane often undergoes a transient hyperpolarization, as shown in Figure 25. The change in membrane potential which follows a synaptic inhibitory volley is called the inhibitory postsynaptic potential, or IPSP.[3] The IPSP, like the EPSP, is a graded nonpropagated response of the postsynaptic cell to presynaptic activation. The IPSP usually begins 1.25 to 1.5 milliseconds after the primary afferent volley enters the spinal cord, reaches a summit in 1.5 to 2.0 milliseconds, and decays with a time constant of about 3 milliseconds. In cells with normal resting membrane potentials of about 70 mV., the amplitude of the IPSP rarely exceeds 5 mV. (In other words, the membrane potential may rise to as much as 75 mV. following an inhibitory afferent volley.) During the IPSP, the responsiveness of the cell to excitatory volleys is diminished. This decreased responsiveness is partly

due to hyperpolarization of the membrane during the IPSP, but as will be seen below, postsynaptic hyperpolarization does not fully account for the effectiveness of an inhibitory volley.

Unlike the EPSP, which is little affected by ion injections, the IPSP is markedly altered by injections which alter the internal Cl^- or K^+ concentration. Injection of Cl^- ions, for example, converts the hyperpolarizing IPSP into a depolarizing potential; indeed, following injection of Cl^- ions, a normally inhibitory volley may cause sufficient depolarization to fire the cell. Similarly, depleting intracellular K^+ by replacement with Na^+ or tetramethylammonium ions also converts the IPSP to a depolarizing response. These observations suggest that the inhibitory process exerts its effect by altering the permeability of the membrane to the small ions K^+ and Cl^-.

It will be recalled that the equilibrium potential for K^+ is about -90 mV.; the Cl^- ion appears to be at equilibrium at a resting membrane potential of -70 mV. Consequently, it might be expected that, if the inhibitory process selectively increases membrane permeability to small ions (K^+ and Cl^-), the membrane potential would seek a value midway between the

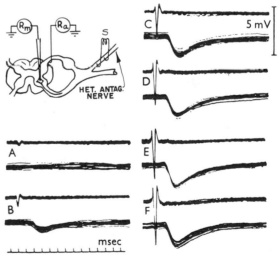

Fig. 25. Intracellularly recorded inhibitory postsynaptic potentials (IPSP). Responses recorded from biceps semitendinosus motoneuron following Group I afferent volley through quadriceps nerve (heteronymous antagonistic path). Traces *A–F* show afferent volley (upper trace) and intracellular response (lower trace) as stimulus strength was progressively increased. Each record formed by superimposing several traces. (After Eccles, *The physiology of nerve cells*, Baltimore, Johns Hopkins Press, 1957.)

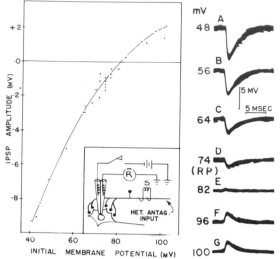

Fig. 26. Effect of membrane potential on IPSP. Traces show intracellularly recorded IPSP elicited by heteronymous antagonistic Group I afferent volley as membrane potential was artificially varied by polarizing electrode. Numbers to left of trace indicate membrane potential; *RP*, resting potential. Graph shows that IPSP is a hyperpolarizing response at membrane potentials less than 80 mV., but becomes a depolarizing response when membrane potential exceeds 80 mV. (After Eccles, *The physiology of nerve cells*, Baltimore, Johns Hopkins Press, 1957.)

respective equilibrium potentials of these two ions. As shown in Figure 26, when the membrane potential is artificially set at -80 mV., the inhibitory volley produces no detectable IPSP. When the membrane potential is less than 80 mV., the IPSP is a hyperpolarizing response; when the membrane potential is greater than 80 mV., the IPSP is a depolarizing response. These experimental findings are thus compatible with the hypothesis that inhibitory impulses increase K^+ and Cl^- permeability and tend to drive the membrane potential toward -80 mV. (i.e., the mean of the Cl^- and K^+ equilibrium potentials).

In neurons with a normal resting potential and internal ionic composition, the IPSP is hyperpolarizing. However, an inhibitory volley depresses the motoneuron even when the IPSP is of the depolarizing type, e.g., when the IPSP is elicited in a cell artificially hyperpolarized by a polarizing current. It follows therefore that mere hyperpolarization is not the sole cause of inhibitory depression. Rather, it appears that the temporary stabilization of the membrane near the equilibrium potential for the IPSP (-80 mV.) makes it difficult to depolarize the membrane to the level (about -60 mV.) required to initiate an increase in Na^+ permeability.

THE INHIBITORY TRANSMITTER.[24]   It may be assumed that the difference between excitatory and inhibitory nerve fibers is in the chemical transmitters which they liberate. The excitatory transmitter causes a nonspecific increase in permeability to all ions, whereas the inhibitory transmitter causes a specific increased permeability to small ions, of which Cl^- and K^+ are the important naturally occurring species. On certain crustacean neurons gamma aminobutyric acid (GABA), which can be isolated from nerve tissue, mimics the action of an inhibitory volley.[16] The inhibitory transmitter agent at mammalian spinal synapses has not yet been identified.

The mechanisms underlying release of inhibitory transmitter are no better understood than those regulating release of excitatory transmitter. Inhibition, like excitation, displays post-tetanic potentiation;[20] it may, therefore, be concluded that, in both, transmitter release from knobs is quantitatively related to the amplitude of the triggering presynaptic spike. In some spinal reflex arcs strychnine[1] and tetanus toxin[2] diminish or even abolish the effectiveness of inhibitory volleys; the convulsive effect of these substances may be partly due to this property. It is not clear whether strychnine and tetanus toxin block release of transmitter from presynaptic terminals or whether they render the postsynaptic membrane insensitive to it.

PRESYNAPTIC INHIBITION.   Frank and Fuortes[8, 11] were the first to observe that some motoneurons subjected to inhibitory volleys showed no hyperpolarizing IPSP and no change in threshold to direct stimulation through a microelectrode. Nevertheless, such an inhibitory volley reduced by as much as 50 per cent the EPSP generated by an excitatory volley (Fig. 27). In such instances inhibition is *presynaptic;* i.e., the inhibitory volley in some manner either blocks presynaptic excitatory impulses or reduces their transmitter-releasing potency.

Eccles[5, 6] postulates that presynaptic inhibitory fibers terminate not on postsynaptic cells but on presynaptic excitatory knobs, which they depolarize. It has already been pointed out that lowering the membrane potential of a presynaptic fiber reduces the amplitude of its spike, making it less effective in liberating transmitter. According to this view then, the presynaptic inhibitory fibers act by limiting the amount of transmitter released from activated excitatory knobs. The following evidence is presented in support of the hypothesis: (i) Repetitive stimulation of presynaptic inhibitory pathways produces a prolonged depolarization of intramedullary presynaptic excitatory fibers measurable with intracellular electrodes. (ii) Potential changes of durations fitting the time course of presynaptic inhibition can be recorded from the dorsal roots, cord dorsum, and the gray matter following repetitive stimulation of presynaptic inhibitory pathways; the polarity and magnitude of these potentials recorded at different sites are consistent with the hypothesis that they derive from prolonged depolarization of presynaptic endings in the ventral horn gray. (iii) The electrical excitability of presynaptic terminals can be gauged by measuring the amplitude of the antidromic compound action potential of the dorsal root elicited by a shock delivered through an electrode thrust into the region of the presynaptic terminals in the ventral horn gray.[27] After conditioning tetani are delivered through presynaptic inhibitory pathways, the antidromic dorsal root spike to a standard test intramedullary shock increases, suggesting increased excitability of the presynaptic terminals, a finding consistent with the hypothesis that the tested terminals are depolarized.[5, 6] (iv) Electron micrographs of synaptic regions indicate that where knobs are densely clustered their borders often are in intimate contact and at some of these junction sites the closely apposed membranes show thickening and increased density, a presumed morphological sign of a transmission site.[13]

Summary of Synaptic Mechanisms. It is now possible to reconstruct in some detail what changes occur in the spinal cord when a Group I afferent volley is directed into it (Fig. 28). At the homonymous synapses, the volley liberates a transmitter which increases permeability to all ions and permits the voltage across the membrane to run down. In some cells, many short circuits will occur because the cells receive many active synaptic knobs. In these cells, when the depolarization reaches about 10 mV. less than the resting membrane potential, there is a sudden large increase in Na+ permeability, so that the membrane potential shifts rapidly toward the Na+ equilibrium potential; hence, the potential across the membrane reverses. Following in the wake of high Na+ permeability, K+ permeability increases, driving the membrane potential back towards the K+ equilibrium potential of −90 mV. As the K+ permeability wanes, the membrane potential returns to the resting level of about −70 mV.

Other homonymous motoneurons and also the heteronymous synergistic motoneurons receive fewer active knobs and are consequently in the subliminal fringe of the excitatory volley.

In such motoneurons the short-circuiting action of the excitatory impulses is insufficient to reduce the membrane potential to the critical level required to activate the increase in permeability to Na+. Consequently, these cells do not discharge, but during the time course of the EPSP their excitability is increased.

Finally, the volley exerts an effect on the heteronymous antagonistic motoneuron pool. Here, the presynaptic impulses cause the release of an inhibitory transmitter which increases the permeability to K+ and Cl− ions. Consequently, the membrane potential is driven toward −80 mV. and the excitability of the cell is diminished. In addition, inhibitory volleys may block excitatory impulses in presynaptic fibers (presynaptic inhibition).

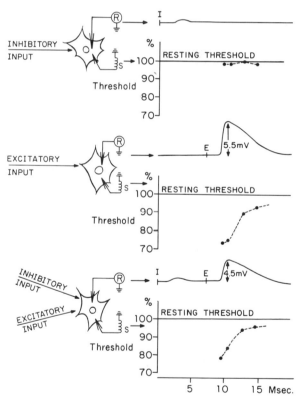

Fig. 27. Presynaptic inhibition in a spinal motoneuron. Sketches show intracellular recording electrode and intracellular stimulating electrode used to determine electrical threshold of motoneuron membrane. *Upper,* Inhibitory input alone caused no significant alteration of either membrane potential or threshold. *Middle,* Excitatory input alone depolarized motoneuron (EPSP) and decreased threshold. *Lower,* Inhibitory input preceded excitatory input; both amplitude of EPSP and its effectiveness in lowering threshold were diminished. (After Frank, *I.R.E. Trans. Med. Electron.,* 1959, *ME–6:85–88.*)

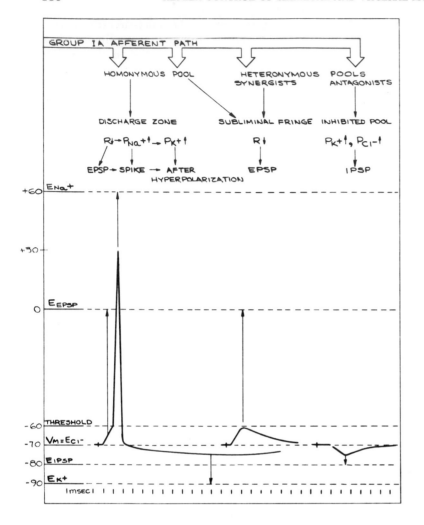

Fig. 28. Summary diagram of monosynaptic connections and events. *Upper,* Functional connections of Group I afferent fibers and permeability changes which they exert on various motoneuron pools; *R,* membrane resistance; *P,* permeability. *Lower,* Intracellularly recorded responses and equilibrium potentials (*E*) toward which each process tends to drive membrane potential; *Vm,* resting membrane potential.

REFERENCES

1. BRADLEY, K., EASTON, D. M. and ECCLES, J. C. *J. Physiol.,* 1953, *122:*474–488.
2. BROOKS, V. B., CURTIS, D. R. and ECCLES, J. C. *J. Physiol.,* 1957, *135:*655–672.
3. ECCLES, J. C. *The physiology of nerve cells.* Baltimore, Johns Hopkins Press, 1957.
4. ECCLES, J. C. In: *Nervous inhibition.* E. Florey, ed. New York, Pergamon Press. 1961.
5. ECCLES, J. C. *Ergebn. Physiol.,* 1961, *51:*299–430.
6. ECCLES, J. C. *The physiology of synapses.* Berlin, Springer, 1964.
7. ECCLES, J. C. and KRNJEVIĆ, K. *J. Physiol.,* 1959, *149:*250–276.
8. FRANK, K. *I.R.E. Trans. Med. Electron.,* 1959, *ME–6:*85–88.
9. FRANK, K. and FUORTES, M. G. F. *J. Physiol.,* 1955, *130:*625–654.
10. FRANK, K. and FUORTES, M. G. F. *J. Physiol.,* 1956, *131:*424–435.
11. FRANK, K. and FUORTES, M. G. F. *Fed. Proc.,* 1957, *16:*39–40.
12. FUORTES, M. G. F., FRANK, K. and BECKER, M. C. *J. gen. Physiol.,* 1957, *40:*736–752.
13. GRAY, E. G. *Nature (Lond.),* 1962, *193:*82–83.
14. HAGIWARA, S. and TASAKI, I. *J. Physiol.,* 1958, *143:*114–137.
15. HUNT, C. C. and KUNO, M. *J. Physiol.,* 1959, *147:*346–363.
16. KUFFLER, S. W. and EDWARDS, C. *J. Neurophysiol.,* 1958, *21:*589–610.
17. LLOYD, D. P. C. *Yale J. Biol. Med.,* 1945, *18:*117–121.
18. LLOYD, D. P. C. *J. Neurophysiol.,* 1946, *9:*421–438.
19. LLOYD, D. P. C. *J. Neurophysiol.,* 1946, *9:*439–444.
20. LLOYD, D. P. C. *J. gen. Physiol.,* 1949, *33:*147–170.
21. LLOYD, D. P. C., HUNT, C. C. and McINTYRE, A. K. *J. gen. Physiol.,* 1955, *38:*307–317.
22. LLOYD, D. P. C. and WILSON, V. J. *J. gen. Physiol.,* 1959, 1219 1231.
23. LORENTE DE NÓ, R. *J. Neurophysiol.,* 1938, *1:*207–244.
24. McLENNAN, H. *Synaptic transmission.* Philadelphia, W. B. Saunders Co., 1963.
25. RENSHAW, B. *J. Neurophysiol.,* 1940, *3:*373–387.
26. TAKEUCHI, A. and TAKEUCHI, N. *J. gen. Physiol.,* 1962, *45:*1181–1193.
27. WALL, P. D. and JOHNSON, A. R. *J. Neurophysiol.,* 1958, *21:*148–158.
28. WOODBURY, J. W. and PATTON, H. D. *Cold Spr. Harb. Symp. Quant. Biol.,* 1952, *17:*185–188.

CHAPTER 7

Reflex Regulation of Movement and Posture

By HARRY D. PATTON

IN the previous chapter some simple reflex arcs were analyzed for the purpose of elucidating the principles of synaptic transmission. In the present chapter the *functional* role of spinal reflexes in the coordination of posture and phasic motor activity will be considered. It should be emphasized from the outset that, in assessing the function of reflex arcs in intact animals, certain experimental procedures allowable in analysis of synaptic mechanisms are excluded or, at best, must be used with reservation. For example, in the experiments described in Chapter 6, reflex discharges were commonly elicited by applying electric shocks to appropriate bundles of afferent fibers. Such stimulation excites many afferent fibers in synchrony, so that the spinal motoneurons receive a relatively brief-acting "packet" of impulses.

In studies of synapses synchronous bombardment of motoneurons is both advantageous and defensible because it allows accurate measurement of the time course of synaptic events. In nature, however, reflex action originates at the receptor organs, and the afferent inputs to the motoneurons are rarely synchronous because the receptors fire repetitively and out of phase with one another. An even more serious drawback to stimulation of a nerve trunk is that afferent fibers of different functional species may be excited in unnatural concert, since the correlation between fiber size (and hence threshold) and functional species is not absolute. For example, even the Group I afferent fibers of muscle nerves are not functionally homogeneous (see below). Therefore, in the present chapter, attention will be focused primarily on experiments in which reflexes are elicited by natural stimulation of the receptors.

Also, in evaluation of the functional significance of reflexes, emphasis is placed on observations made while reflex arcs are as nearly intact and uninfluenced by drugs as humane requirements to avoid causing pain permit. The study of reflexes in the truly "natural state" is impossible, for the uncertainty principle applies equally to physiologic and physical systems. However, many procedures (e.g., root sections, deep anesthesia) necessary for learning basic properties of reflex *components* can and must be avoided in studying the properties of the whole *system*. Stated in another way, the goal of this chapter is to present a *synthetic* rather than a purely *analytical* picture of reflex function by emphasizing the behavior of freely interacting components of the reflex arc rather than their behavior in controlled isolation.

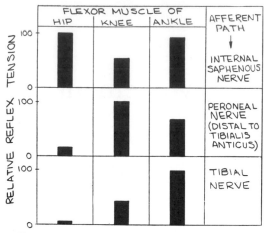

Fig. 1. Local sign in the flexion reflex. Bars indicate relative reflex tensions developed in three flexor muscles as a result of stimulation of each of three nerves (afferent paths) serving sensory endings in different portions of hindlimb. Each path activated all three muscles, but relative participation of the muscles in the reflex movement varied with afferent path. (After Creed and Sherrington, *Proc. roy. Soc.,* 1926, *B100*:258–267.)

The Flexion Reflex and Crossed Extension.[38]

A convenient preparation for the study of spinal reflex patterns is an animal in which the spinal cord has been permanently transected above the lumbosacral enlargement—a "spinal animal."* Segments below the level of the transection are, of course, insensate, and hence the reflex patterns of these segments may be freely studied without the use of anesthetic drugs. In such a preparation, stimulation of the skin or deep structures of the hindlimbs, for example, elicits a variety of movements and postures which must be mediated solely by spinal reflex arcs, because the lower cord has been isolated from supraspinal structures by the transection. Two spinal reflex patterns are particularly prominent—the *flexion reflex* and the *tendon jerk.*

The flexion reflex is elicited by noxious stimulation (pinching, burning, strong electrical stimulation), particularly of the skin, although similar stimulation of deep structures after removal or denervation of the skin is also effective. The reflex response consists of contraction of the *ipsilateral* flexor muscles at the ankle, knee and hip so that the whole limb is with-

* In acute experiments the spinal cord is sometimes transected at C_1, and the animal is maintained by artificial respiration. Such an animal is referred to as a "high spinal" or "decapitate" preparation.

drawn from the noxious stimulus. Palpation of the muscles reveals that, as the flexor muscles contract, the extensor muscles relax, an event suggesting that the extensor motoneurons are inhibited. Thus, the afferent fibers subserving the flexion reflex make *reciprocal* connections (see Chap. 6) with the ipsilateral motoneurons, so that flexor withdrawal of the limb is not impeded by simultaneous contraction of the antagonistic extensor muscles. Because the adequate stimulus for eliciting the flexion reflex is one which is harmful to the tissues, Sherrington[38] called it a *nociceptive* reflex, and, because the reflex contraction results in removal of the extremity from the damaging stimulus, he looked upon the flexion reflex as protective.

Reflex withdrawal of the stimulated limb is associated with contraction of the extensor muscles and relaxation of the flexor muscles of the corresponding contralateral extremity. This contralateral component is known as the *crossed extension reflex.* The crossed extension reflex is not a separate reflex but is accessory to, or a part of, the nociceptive flexion reflex. The afferent fibers subserving the flexion reflex send to the opposite side of the spinal cord collateral branches which have reciprocal connections opposite those in the ipsilateral spinal cord. This arrangement is known as *double reciprocal innervation.* The crossed extension reflex supports the weight of the body when the ipsilateral limb flexes.

Often when the noxious stimulus is prolonged, the crossed extension reflex is not sustained, but gives way to a rhythmically alternating stepping movement. In Sherrington's words, "The irritated foot is withdrawn from harm and the other legs run away."

Prominent features of the flexion reflex are its broad receptive field and its wide sphere of action on muscles. Generally speaking, noxious stimulation anywhere on the distal portion of the limb causes reflex contraction of the flexor muscles at all joints in the limb. The pattern of contraction, however, is not stereotyped, for the relative strength of the contractions of various muscles varies with the site of stimulation. Figure 1 shows the relative participation of three flexor muscles in reflex limb movement elicited by electrical stimulation of three different afferent nerves supplying sensory fibers to different regions of the limb. It can be seen that each of the three afferent nerves drives the motoneurons of each muscle, but in quantitatively different combinations. Such data indicate that the nature of the limb movement and the final position of the limb vary, depending on the site of harmful stimulation. Such dependence of the reflex pattern on the origin of the afferent input is called *local sign*. Because of local sign, effective and appropriate withdrawal of the limb occurs irrespective of the site of injury.

Local sign is even more evident when the reflex is elicited by natural noxious stimulation of the skin rather than by electrical stimulation of nerve trunks. For example, pinching the skin on the proximal portion of the limb may elicit reflex patterns which depart from the standard ipsilateral flexion-crossed extension pattern, giving rise to bilateral flexion (dorsolateral surface of the thigh) or to bilateral extension (ventromedial surface of the thigh).[30] Effects of pinching the skin even on the distal portion of the limb are variable depending on the site of stimulation. For example, the motoneurons supplying an individual flexor muscle may be inhibited, rather than excited, if the skin overlying an antagonistic extensor muscle is pinched.[10]

AFFERENT PATH AND SYNAPTIC ORGANIZATION OF THE FLEXION REFLEX. Several features of the flexion reflex are strongly reminiscent of the multisynaptic discharges (see Chap. 6) elicited by electrical stimulation of cutaneous fibers and of deep afferent fibers less than 12 μ in diameter (Groups II, III, and IV) which form the afferent limb of polysynaptic reflexes. (i) The broad receptive field including deep structures as well as the cutaneous surface of the limb agrees with the ubiquitous distribution of afferent fibers which feed polysynaptic reflex arcs. (ii) The channeling of the reflex discharge exclusively into ipsilateral flexor muscles, with concomitant inhibition of ipsilateral extensor motoneurons, is also typical of multisynaptic arcs. The diffuse distribution of the efferent discharge, involving reciprocal action at all joints of the extremity, too, is peculiar to multisynaptic arcs and in striking contrast to the discrete distribution of monosynaptic discharges (cf., Fig. 19, Chap. 6). (iii) The flexion reflex typically displays *afterdischarge* (i.e., the contraction outlasts the stimulus), which is expected in multisynaptic systems where recirculation of impulses through interneuron circuits permits sustained motoneuron bombardment after the primary afferent volley has ceased. (iv) Finally, the

noxious or harmful nature of the adequate stimulus for the flexion reflex agrees with evidence indicating that many of the unmyelinated and small myelinated fibers supply the plexuses of free nerve endings which are sensitive to noxious or painful stimuli (see Chap. 14). There can be little doubt that the nociceptive reflex utilizes multisynaptic arcs having Group III (or delta) and IV fibers for their afferent limbs.

Cutaneous Alpha and Group II Reflexes. The functional significance of the Group II and of cutaneous alpha afferent fibers which mediate a multisynaptic reflex discharge to ipsilateral flexor muscles is not entirely clear, since there is no reason to suspect that the endings which these fibers supply are nociceptive. The Group II afferent fibers found in muscle nerves originate in the secondary or flower spray endings of the muscle spindles, which are sensitive to muscle stretch (see below). Alpha fibers of cutaneous nerves principally supply touch-sensitive or pressure-sensitive endings.[16]

Although excitation of alpha fibers elicits an ipsilateral flexion reflex, the crossed connections of these fibers differ from those of delta, Group III and Group IV fibers, which in addition mediate a crossed extension reflex. Electrical stimulation of alpha fibers facilitates contralateral flexor motoneurons and either does not affect or inhibits contralateral extensor motoneurons.[31] In other words, these fibers appear to mediate a bilateral flexion reflex of unknown functional significance. The crossed connections of Group II fibers are complex and vary with the muscle of origin.[32]

Other Polysynaptic Reflexes. In spinal preparations light pressure or stretch applied between the toe-pads elicits extension of the limb; this is called the *extensor thrust reflex*. The afferent fibers traverse the plantar nerves, but electrical stimulation of these nerves elicits only flexion and crossed extension, a finding that emphasizes the extent to which reflex patterns may be concealed when unnatural stimulation of whole nerve trunks is employed to trigger reflex action. The extensor thrust presumably plays a role in reflex standing or walking.

Rhythmically alternating, stepping movements of the hindlimbs can sometimes be initiated in the chronic spinal dog by tactile stimulation of the foot pad or, more consistently, by suspending the animal erect off the ground so that gravity imparts a stretch on the hip ex-

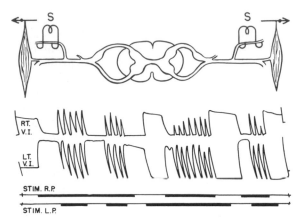

Fig. 2. Production of rhythmic reflexes (stepping by concurrent stimulation of right and left peroneal nerves. Diagram at top represents experimental arrangement. Upper two traces are myographic records of tension in right (*RT.*) and left (*LT.*) vastus intermedius muscles (knee extensors). Lower two traces signal repetitive stimulation of afferent fibers of right (*R.P.*) and left peroneal (*L.P.*) nerves. Note rhythmic alternation of muscle contraction during concurrent stimulation of the two nerves. (After Creed *et al., Reflex activity of the spinal cord,* Oxford, Clarendon Press, 1932.)

tensors. Since both the touch-pressure receptors of the feet and the stretch-sensitive spindle endings in the hip muscles are in a position to be alternately excited by normal stepping, it is tempting to assume that stepping is maintained by rhythmic variation of input from these receptors.

The mechanism of stepping, however, is complex. Sherrington found that denervation of the tactile receptors by section of all the cutaneous nerves of the leg impaired walking in the cat so little that an animal was able to walk accurately on a horizontal ladder. Moreover, rhythmically alternating stepping may be induced experimentally by simultaneous repetitive stimulation of afferent fibers originating in each of the hindlimbs. Figure 2 shows the results of an experiment in which the tensions in the right and left vastus intermedius muscles (knee extensors) were recorded during afferent stimulation of one or both peroneal nerves. When only one nerve was stimulated, the ipsilateral extensor muscle relaxed and its contralateral counterpart contracted. When both nerves were stimulated concurrently at equal intensities, rhythmically alternating contraction and relaxation of the two muscles occurred and persisted as long as the concurrent stimulation lasted. In this instance, the input to the two halves of the

cord is equal and nonperiodic. Further, such rhythmically alternating contractions of symmetrical muscles can be initiated after complete deafferentation of the limb. The mechanism for rhythmic alternation must therefore be a "built-in" feature of the spinal cord capable of operating in the absence of alternating afferent input such as that which stepping presumably initiates in the cutaneous and deep receptors.

The Tendon Jerk. Another easily elicited spinal reflex, and one of great importance to the neurologist, is the tendon jerk. One can elicit this reflex in almost any muscle by sharply tapping either the muscle or the tendon, thus imparting a brief stretch to the muscle. The reflex response consists of a twitchlike contraction of the stretched muscle. The neurologist most commonly elicits these reflexes in the extensor muscles of the leg—e.g., quadriceps (knee jerk or patellar reflex) and triceps surae (ankle jerk or Achilles reflex)*—but flexor muscles show similar jerk responses to brief stretch (pluck reflexes). In the arm, the biceps, triceps and pectoral muscles are common test sites; in the face, tapping the lower jaw produces a "jaw jerk" of the masseter muscle.

Tendon jerks are characterized by short latency and absence of afterdischarge. Indeed, the quadriceps jerk has such a brief latency (19 to 24 milliseconds in man) that for many years its reflex nature was questioned; but Sherrington's[35] demonstration that the quadriceps jerk of experimental animals is subject to central inhibition and is abolished by dorsal or ventral

---

* Although deeply ingrained in medical jargon, the terms "knee" and "ankle" jerk should be dropped in favor of the more descriptive terms "quadriceps" and "triceps surae" jerk, respectively.

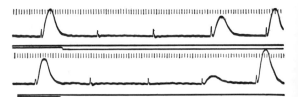

Fig. 3. Inhibition of knee jerk in spinal cat. Myographic recording from quadriceps muscle; tendon taps delivered at three per sec. Sharp upward deflections record tendon taps; subsequent larger deflections represent jerk reflex contractions. Signal at bottom of each record indicates time of delivery of a single shock to an ipsilateral afferent nerve trunk. Time scale: 20 milliseconds. (From Ballif *et al., Proc. roy. Soc.,* 1925, *B98:*589–607.)

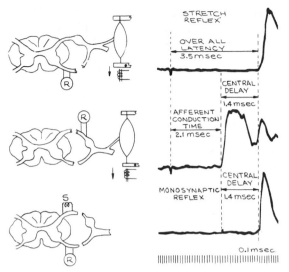

Fig. 4. Lloyd's experiment proving the monosynaptic nature of the stretch reflex. *Upper trace,* Reflex discharge recorded from ventral root following brief muscle stretch. *Middle trace,* Afferent discharge recorded from dorsal root following muscle stretch. *Lower trace,* Monosynaptic discharge recorded from ventral root following weak shock to dorsal root. The latency of the monosynaptic discharge is the same as the central delay of the stretch-induced discharge (over-all latency minus afferent conduction time). (After Lloyd, *J. Neurophysiol.,* 1943, *6*:317–326.)

rhizotomy clearly established the tendon jerk as a reflex. The short latency and the absence of afterdischarge suggest that tendon jerks are mediated by rapidly conducting monosynaptic pathways. Other similarities between the tendon jerk and the monosynaptic reflex discharge elicited by electrical stimulation of Group I afferent fibers are: (i) Both reflect into, and only into, the muscle or muscle fraction from which the afferent activity arises. (ii) Both reflexes, when initiated in extensor muscles, are inhibited by strong stimulation of cutaneous afferent trunks. The effect of a single inhibitory volley persists for periods as long as 1 second (Fig. 3). (iii) Both reflexes are inhibited by Group I afferent volleys initiated in nerves supplying antagonistic muscles, and in both the inhibitory input arises only from *direct* antagonists; afferent input from muscles acting at joints other than the one at which the test muscle works is ineffective. The jerk reflex of the quadriceps is also inhibited by stretching or kneading its antagonists, the hamstring muscles.[35]

The close similarity between tendon jerks and electrically evoked monosynaptic discharges is strong presumptive evidence that tendon

jerks are mediated by reflex arcs of two neurons responding to impulses originating in afferent fibers of Group I size. Lloyd's[25] experiments provide conclusive evidence that this is so. Brief stretches comparable to those imposed by tapping the tendon were applied to a muscle by a solenoid attached to its tendon. Stretch-induced afferent discharges, recorded from appropriate dorsal roots, had conduction velocities in the Group I range (about 116 m./sec.), indicating that muscle stretch excites receptors innervated by the largest and most rapidly conducting afferent fibers. Ventral root reflex discharges resulting from brief muscle stretch had the same central delay as monosynaptic discharges elicited by electrical stimulation of Group I afferent fibers (Fig. 4).

In man, Magladery *et al.*[26] have shown that it is possible to excite selectively the large-diameter afferent fibers by using weak shocks delivered through electrodes placed on the skin over mixed nerves. Recording electrodes inserted into the lumbar vertebral canal register two major deflections in response to such stimulation; the earlier appears to represent the afferent volley traversing the dorsal roots, whereas the later deflection represents the reflex discharge over the ventral roots (Fig. 5). The interval between the two deflections is thus a

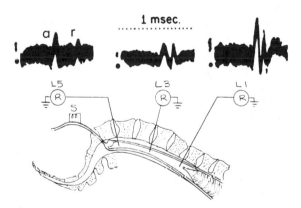

Fig. 5. Monosynaptic reflexes in man. Weak shocks to posterior tibial nerve excite large afferent fibers but not efferent fibers. Electrodes inserted into vertebral canal at levels shown recorded activity in the spinal roots as seen in the traces above (each record consists of several superimposed traces). Deflection *a* is afferent volley in dorsal roots; *r* is reflex efferent volley in ventral roots. Interval between deflections measures central delay plus variable root conduction time. At L_1 the interval was 1.5 milliseconds. Estimated root conduction time (dorsal plus ventral) was 0.6 millisecond, leaving a central delay of 0.9 millisecond. (After Magladery *et al.,* *Res. Publ. Ass. nerv. ment. Dis.,* 1952, *30*:118–151.)

measure of the time required for transmission through the roots central to the intrathecal electrode plus the delay in the spinal cord. With the recording electrode at L_1 (the termination of the cord in man), this delay was 1.5 milliseconds. If a reasonable allowance of 0.3 millisecond is made for conduction in each root, the cord delay is reduced to about 0.9 millisecond, which allows only a single synaptic delay. When the reflex muscular response to nerve stimulation is monitored electromyographically, the over-all latency is 19 to 24 milliseconds; this is also approximately the latency of the contraction elicited by tendon tap.[11] In both man and experimental animals, therefore, it is clearly established that the tendon jerk is mediated by a rapidly conducting monosynaptic arc.

The Stretch or Myotatic Reflex.[23, 24] The functional significance of the flexion reflex as a protective mechanism is obvious. In contrast, the significance of the tendon jerk is, at first thought, obscure. What can be the functional utility of a reflex that causes a muscle to twitch when its tendon is sharply rapped? The obscurity arises largely from the abnormal way in which the tendon jerk is elicited. It has already been suggested, and will be further proved below, that the adequate stimulus for the reflex mechanism mediating the tendon jerk is *stretch of the muscle*. Tapping the tendon or belly of the muscle to elicit the tendon jerk stretches the muscle between its points of origin and insertion only very briefly. The stretch-sensitive receptors in the muscle are excited synchronously, and, since the afferent pathway is relatively homogeneous in fiber diameter and conduction velocity, the afferent impulses arrive at the spinal cord as a rather synchronous volley. As a result, the motoneurons respond with little temporal dispersion, setting up in the motor nerve a synchronous discharge to which the muscle responds with a brief twitch much like the response of the muscle to a single electric shock to its motor nerve.

Normally, however, the stretches imposed on muscles are of a different nature. Indeed, except possibly for landing from a leap or jumping on a pogostick, it is unlikely that muscles are ever subjected to the sudden brief stretches that the neurologist commonly employs in eliciting a jerk reflex. Natural stretches are usually imposed on muscles by the action of gravity. Thus, during standing, the quadriceps muscle is subjected to stretch because the knee tends to bend in accordance with gravitational pull. The resultant afferent discharge is highly asynchronous, because such a sustained stretch causes many stretch receptors to fire repetitively at frequencies which are determined by the thresholds of individual receptors and by the amount of stretch. Consequently, the motoneurons receive a prolonged asynchronous bombardment, and they discharge impulses with corresponding asynchrony. The result is a smooth, sustained contraction of the stretched muscle, so that the upright position is automatically maintained despite the action of gravity. When viewed in this light, the stretch reflex, of which the tendon jerk is a fractional and somewhat artificial manifestation, clearly is significant as a *mechanism for upright posture or standing*.

The role of the stretch reflex in posture was first appreciated by Sherrington[36] as a result of his observations on animals subjected to transection of the brain stem at the midcollicular level. In such *decerebrate* preparations the limbs assume a posture of rigid extension, the head and tail are held erect, and the jaw is tightly closed by tonic contraction of the masseter muscle. Although the animal executes no voluntary movements, it will, when placed upon its feet, stand in a rigid, immobile exaggeration of the normal upright posture. Sherrington[39] rightly surmised that such decerebrate rigidity resulted from overactivity of a spinal reflex mechanism that normally maintains upright posture. The overactivity results from interruption by the lesion of certain descending pathways (described in Chapter 9) which exert an inhibitory influence on the segmental spinal reflex.

Sherrington proved his hypothesis that decerebrate rigidity is a spinal reflex by demonstrating that division of the dorsal roots supplying a rigid limb abolishes its rigidity.[36] He next attempted to determine the origin of the requisite afferent inflow from the limb.[40] Section of cutaneous-nerves, or even skinning the legs and feet, did not alter the rigid state, findings indicating that the essential receptors are not cutaneous. Furthermore, when the joint was flexed after the tendons of its controlling muscles were cut, the freed muscles did not contract. This observation indicated that the receptors are not located in the joints. When, however, the tenotomized muscle was stretched by a sustained pull on the severed tendon, the muscle contracted and offered palpable resistance to stretch. By the process of exclusion,

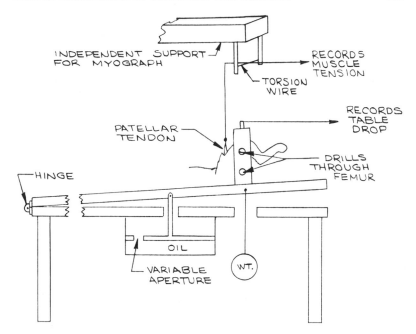

Fig. 6. Diagram of "fall table" similar to that used by Sherrington to demonstrate the stretch reflex.

Sherrington thus deduced that the receptors lie in the muscle itself and, further, that the adequate stimulus for the receptors is stretch of the muscle. Many sensory receptors, such as the retina, the ear and the tactile endings, are acted upon by agents of the external world. The stretch receptors of muscle, however, are excited by events occurring in the muscles themselves; the body itself acts as the stimulus to its own receptors. For this reason, Sherrington[40] termed the muscle stretch receptors *proprioceptors.*

To study the stretch reflex quantitatively, Sherrington constructed an ingenious device known as the "fall table,"[23, 24] the important feature of which was a top which could be lowered for measured distances at various rates (Fig. 6). The leg of an experimental animal was fixed rigidly to a stand on the table by means of drills passed through the bones of the leg. A muscle of the fixed leg was then dissected free and attached to a myograph mounted on a stand independent of the movable table top. Then, when the table top was lowered, the tension developing in the muscle in response to its elongation could be recorded. Figure 7 shows the results of such an experiment. The dotted line *T* indicates the extent of the table displacement; the heavy line *M* shows the tension developed in the muscle. Elongation of the muscle by only 8 mm. produced a sustained tension, initially amounting to 3.5 kg. and then decreasing to a stable plateau value of about 3.0 kg. Some of this tension was, of course, attributable

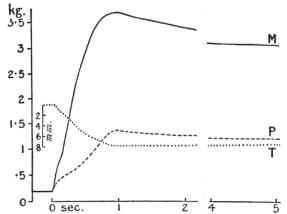

Fig. 7. Stretch or myotatic reflex of cat demonstrated with "fall table." *M,* Tension developed in innervated quadriceps muscle. *T,* Relative elevation of table, which was dropped 8 mm. *P,* Passive elastic tension developed by similar stretch after denervation of the muscle. Tension difference (*M* − *P*) represents active reflex tension. (From Liddell and Sherrington, *Proc. roy. Soc.,* 1924, *B96:*212–242.)

to the elastic properties of the muscle, but this moiety could be quantitatively determined by repeating the stretch after denervation of the muscle (dashed line *P*). The difference between curves *M* and *P* (about 1.8 kg. at the plateau) represents the *reflex* contractile tension developed in the muscle by stretch.

The same experimental arrangement can also be used to show that the stretch reflex is subject to inhibition. Figure 8 illustrates inhibition of the stretch reflex in a knee extensor in-

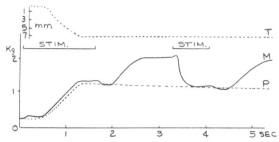

Fig. 8. Inhibition of stretch reflex in an extensor muscle by stimulation of an ipsilateral cutaneous nerve (afferent). *M, P* and *T* as in Fig. 7. During stimulation of cutaneous nerve, tension in innervated muscle was approximately the same as that in denervated muscle; in absence of inhibitory stimulation reflex tension of about 1 kg. (*M − P*) slowly developed. (After Liddell and Sherrington, *Proc. roy. Soc.,* 1924, *B96:*212–242.)

duced by repetitive stimulation of an ipsilateral cutaneous nerve trunk. This effect is comparable to inhibition of the knee jerk (Fig. 3) and of the monosynaptic discharge (Fig. 17, Chap. 6) induced by electrical stimulation of cutaneous afferent fibers. Figure 9 shows inhibition of a stretch reflex in an extensor muscle brought about by a physiologic stimulus—stretching of an antagonistic flexor muscle. The result is reminiscent of the inhibition of a monosynaptic discharge by stimuli traversing the heteronymous antagonistic Group I pathway (Fig. 16, Chap. 6).

Sherrington's experiments thus proved conclusively the existence of a reflex mechanism for posture and for skeletal muscle tone. By *tone* is meant the resistance of a muscle to passive elongation or stretch. When the stretch reflex arc is interrupted or when the descending central pathways facilitating the stretch reflex are severed, the muscle becomes flaccid or hypotonic, and offers little resistance to stretch. On the other hand, when central structures inhibitory to the stretch reflex are removed, as in the decerebrate preparation, the muscles are hypertonic and resist elongation so actively that passive flexion of the joint meets with marked resistance.

In man, such hypertonic stretch reflexes are commonly encountered following chronic lesions of the internal capsule, and the affected limb is said to be *spastic.* In both spasticity and decerebrate rigidity, the hypertonus is confined to the antigravity muscles, or physiologic extensors. In spastic man and monkey, passive flexion of a joint resulting in stretch of extensor

muscles at the ankle, knee or hip meets active resistance, but passive extension of these joints is accomplished without opposition. In the arm, resistance is most prominently displayed in the anatomic flexor muscles, for these are the muscles which counteract the forces of gravity. In the sloth, which habitually counteracts gravity with flexor muscles while hanging upside down from branches, decerebration produces a flexor rigidity. In quadrupeds that normally maintain upright posture (cat, dog), decerebrate rigidity principally affects the extensor muscles of both the front and the back legs. Indeed, in the decerebrate cat, a sustained stretch reflex from hindlimb flexor muscles cannot be elicited by the fall table technique. The flexor muscles respond readily to the synchronous volley elicited by a tap on the tendon (pluck reflex), but do not give sustained reflex contractions in response to the asynchronous afferent bombardment provided by the sustained stretches imposed by the fall table. It seems likely that the selective distribution of hypertonus to the antigravity muscles in the decerebrate and spastic states reflects the reciprocal connections of the descending pathways maintaining the hyperexcitable state, since the segmental mechanism for stretch reflexes appears to be as well developed in flexor as in extensor muscles.

Since the jerk reflex and the static stretch reflex utilize exactly the same pathways, it may seem strange that flexor muscles display the former but not the latter. The differentiation results from the nature of the stimulus, the opportunities for effective summation at the motoneuron pool being far greater with synchro-

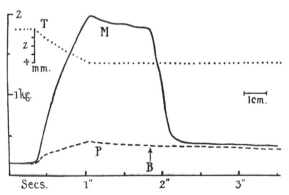

Fig. 9. Inhibition of stretch reflex in extensor muscle (quadriceps) by stretch of antagonistic flexor muscle (biceps femoris). *M, P* and *T* as in Fig. 7. At arrow (*B*) a 4 mm. stretch was applied to biceps femoris inhibiting quadriceps so that tension fell to that of paralyzed muscle. (From Liddell and Sherrington, *Proc. roy. Soc.,* 1925, *B97:*267–283.)

nous (tendon tap) than with asynchronous (slow stretch) inputs. In fact, synchronous inputs are so effective that a relatively severe reflex depression may not be obvious from tests of the tendon jerks alone. For example, after spinal transection in the cat, the lower extremities become flaccid and never again display a sustained stretch reflex;[27] but tendon jerks, although their nature is somewhat altered, are easily elicited. The tendon jerk taken alone is a gross and blunt diagnostic tool.

Receptors in Muscle and Tendon.[2,4] Sherrington's studies of the stretch reflex implicated a stretch-sensitive receptor located in either the muscle or the tendon. Muscles and tendons are supplied with a variety of receptors—free nerve endings, encapsulated pacinian corpuscles, etc. —but with regard to postural reflexes, attention focuses principally on the *Golgi tendon organ* and the *muscle spindle*. The tendon organ is found in the tendons of all mammalian muscles, close to their muscular origins. The organ consists of a number of tendon fasciculi enclosed in a fusiform or cylindrical fibrous capsule which is penetrated by one or two myelinated nerve fibers (Fig. 10). After entering the capsule, the fibers break up into smaller and smaller branches, lose their myelin sheaths, and terminate in a rich arborization in the tendon bundle. Tension on the tendon distorts or displaces these endings and constitutes the adequate stimulus for receptor discharge. Because of its location in the tendon, the tendon organ is equally susceptible to, and does not distinguish between, mechanical stretch applied by a passive pull on the muscle and that applied by active muscular contraction, both being actions which exert tension on the tendon. The Golgi tendon organ is, as Fulton and Pi-Suñer[8] first emphasized, in "series" with the muscle (Fig. 11*B*).

The muscle spindle[2] is located within the muscle itself, and consists of a bundle of two to ten thin specialized muscle fibers (*intrafusal fibers*) surrounded by a connective tissue capsule which attaches (at its ends) to the endomysium

of the regular or *extrafusal* muscle fibers, to the tendon, or to perimysial connective tissue (Fig. 12). The long, slender ends of the intrafusal fibers are striated and contractile, whereas the central or equatorial region, which is somewhat expanded and filled with nuclei, is unstriated and probably noncontractile. In this *nuclear bag* region of the spindle, and for a short distance on either side where nuclei are arranged in a central core (*myotube region*), the connective tissue capsule is separated from the intrafusal fibers by a lymph space traversed by delicate septa and nerve fibers. The latter are of three major types:[2] (i) Large (8 to 12 μ)* myelinated afferent fibers which, after entering the capsule, branch, lose their myelin, and end in helical terminals that encircle the nuclear bag region of the intrafusal fibers. These endings are variously known as *annulospiral, primary* or *nuclear bag endings*. (ii) Smaller (6 to 9 μ) myelinated afferent fibers end in coils, rings or varicosities in the myotube regions on one or both sides of the nuclear bag endings. These are called *flower spray, secondary* or *myotube endings*. Some spindles lack myotube endings. Both the myotube and the nuclear bag endings degenerate after section of the dorsal roots. (iii) Small (3 to 7 μ) myelinated efferent fibers terminate in end-plates situated on the striated poles of the intrafusal fibers. These fibers are known to be motor, because they degenerate following ventral rhizotomy but not after dorsal root section. According to Barker,[2] both poles of the intrafusal fibers receive motor innervation. The functional significance of these *fusimotor fibers* or *gamma efferents* is discussed later in this chapter.

In addition to these three main types of fibers, muscle spindles receive a varying number of fine (0.5 μ) fibers, some of which appear

---

* The fiber diameters quoted here are measurements of the axons close to the spindle where they may well be smaller than the parent axons in the main nerve trunk.

Fig. 10. Golgi tendon organ. At left, muscle fibers (*m*) end in tendon bundles (*t*) that extend to right near the junction of muscle and tendon. Two nerve fibers (*n*) pass to tendon and branch profusely between and around the tendon bundles forming the end organ (*G*).

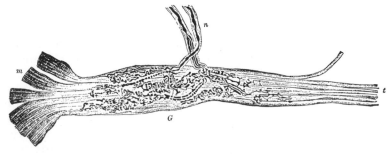

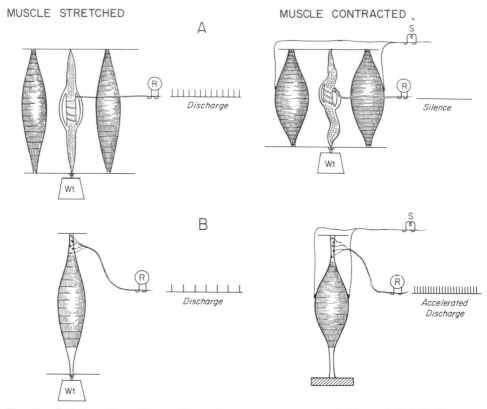

Fig. 11. Relation of muscle spindles and tendon organs to muscle fibers. *A,* Spindle is arranged "in parallel" with muscle fibers so that muscle contraction slackens tension on spindle. *B,* Tendon organ is arranged "in series" with muscle fibers so that both passive and active contraction of muscle cause receptor to discharge.

to be the sympathetic motor nerves for the vasculature of the spindles; others, which are afferent, ramify in the capsule as free nerve endings and probably mediate pain sensation.

From a study of teased stained spindles, Boyd[4] finds that intrafusal fibers are of two types distinguishable on the basis of structure, rate of atrophy following ventral root section, and type of innervation. *Nuclear bag fibers,* usually about two to a spindle, are relatively large (25 μ diameter) and long (7 to 8 mm.), stretching the full length of the spindle. In the equatorial region they have a prominent nuclear bag and, in the polar regions, a large number of myofibrils uniformly distributed in scant sarcoplasm. They degenerate slowly following ventral root section. *Nuclear chain fibers* are more numerous (usually 4 to 5 per spindle), smaller (12 μ diameter) and shorter (4 mm.); their ends attach to the surface of the nuclear bag fibers. In the equatorial region they display a single chain of nuclei, whence they derive their name. Myofibrils are less numerous and more variable in size and distribution than in nuclear bag fibers. They degenerate promptly following ventral rhizotomy.

Primary endings are distributed to both nuclear chain and nuclear bag fibers, but secondary endings are principally on nuclear chain fibers. Motor innervation of the two types of fiber also differs. Nuclear bag

fibers have 1 to 6 discrete end-plates at the extreme poles; these are supplied by the larger (2.5 to 4.5 μ) fusimotor terminals. Nuclear chain fibers are innervated by smaller (1 to 2 μ) fusimotor fibers which terminate all along the surfaces (except at the site of the primary ending) in a fine, complicated network lacking discrete end-plates.

To return to the afferent endings of the spindle, both the myotube and the nuclear bag endings are so arranged that they can easily be mechanically distorted by stretch of the muscle. However, unlike the Golgi tendon organ, the muscle spindle is arranged in "parallel" with the extrafusal fibers, so that contraction of the extrafusal fibers tends to remove spindle tension induced by external stretch (Fig. 11*A*). In the next section it will be pointed out that this feature permits experimental distinction between spindle endings and Golgi tendon endings merely by observation of the effect of muscle contraction on a stretch-evoked discharge recorded from their parent axons. It should also be noted, however, that if the intrafusal fibers are made to contract by action of the small motor nerve fibers supplying the two contractile poles, the noncontractile nuclear bag region is put under a tension which constitutes a mechanical stimulus to the nuclear bag and myotube endings equivalent to passive stretch of the whole muscle.

DISCHARGE PROPERTIES OF STRETCH RECEPTORS.[28] The discharge properties of stretch receptors can be studied by recording from their parent axons during muscle stretch. If activity in a whole nerve trunk is recorded, the tracing shows only a chaotic flare of spike-like activity during muscle stretch, because the stimulus excites many end organs which fire out of phase with one another. Such records are usually too complex for analysis. Records satisfactory for analysis can be obtained by isolating one or, at most, a few axons supplying active receptors. Such "single unit" analysis of stretch receptors was first accomplished by Adrian and Zotterman[1] in 1926. They chose to study certain small muscles in the frog which have only a few stretch receptors. By successively paring off bits of the muscle, Adrian and Zotterman were able to whittle away all but one stretch receptor, the activity of which could be recorded in the nerve trunk supplying the muscle. In larger mammalian muscles, this technique for reducing the number of receptors is unsatisfactory, owing to the extensive injury incurred by the drastic carving of the muscle. Matthews[28] obtained the first successful recordings from stretch receptors in cats by subdividing the nerve trunk into small bundles until he isolated a strand containing only one axon which fired in response to muscle stretch. Successful isolation of a single stretch-sensitive unit is recognized by the occurrence during muscle stretch of rhythmically recurring, all-or-nothing spikes of constant amplitude and configuration. Stretch-sensitive units may also be isolated from the dorsal roots, where the rootlets are easily divided into strands. Another satisfactory method,[41] which eliminates the necessity for nerve teasing, is intracellular recording with an ultramicroelectrode in the nerve trunk, the dorsal root or the dorsal column, for an intracellular electrode is not appreciably affected by activity in adjacent fibers.

All stretch-sensitive units have properties in common. All respond to stretch with a regular rhythmic discharge of impulses. The rate of firing is somewhat higher during and immediately after the imposition of stretch, but the discharge rate rapidly reaches a relatively steady level,

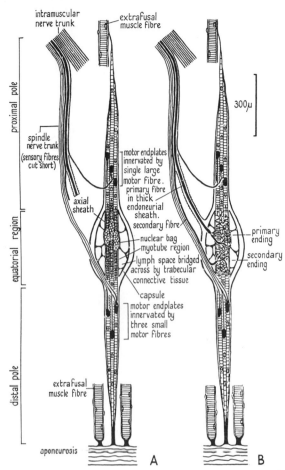

Fig. 12. The muscle spindle and its nerves. *A* shows only the motor fibers (fusimotor fibers) innervating the intrafusal fibers; *B* shows in addition the afferent fibers and their termination in the equatorial or "nuclear bag" region. (From Barker, *Quart. J. micr. Sci.,* 1948, *89*:143–186.)

which is maintained for hours if the muscle stretch is held constant. When the tension on the muscle is increased, the number of impulses per unit time increases, but not in a linear fashion. The firing rate is approximately directly proportional to the log of the applied muscle tension.* *Discharge frequency is thus one way by which the receptor signals intensity of stimulus to the central nervous system* (see Chap. 4).

If the monitored strand of fibers contains several axons supplying stretch receptors, another correlate of intensity becomes evident. *As stimulus intensity is increased, the number of units re-*

---

* This relationship holds only within a limited range of applied tensions. At high tensions, the response falls short of the expected proportionality. Moreover, for different receptors, the slopes of the curves relating discharge rate to log tension are different.

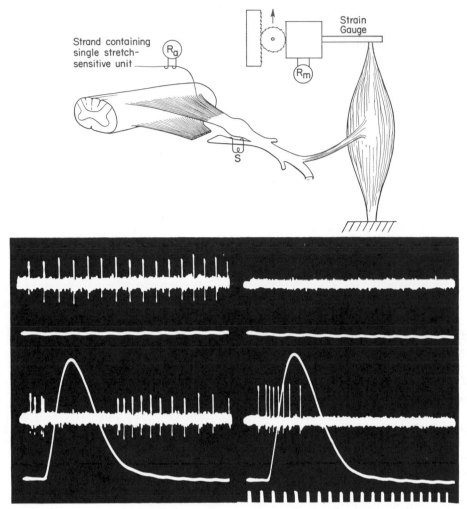

Fig. 13. Behavior of spindle (A type) and tendon organ (B type) receptors during muscle stretch and muscle contraction. In the tracings the thick line is record from dorsal root strand (R_a in diagram); the thin line is record of muscle tension (R_m) in diagram. *Left,* A type discharge from spindle receptor. In upper record, moderate sustained stretch of muscle induced by moving tension recorder upward elicited regular rhythmic discharge of receptor. In lower record, discharge ceased during muscle twitch induced by single shock to ventral root at S in diagram. *Right,* B type discharge from tendon receptor. In upper trace, moderate muscle stretch failed to discharge high-threshold tendon organ. In lower trace, discharge occurred during muscle twitch. (Records provided by Dr. C. C. Hunt.)

sponding increases. The thresholds of stretch receptors are distributed in accordance with a normal frequency curve, so that an increase in the intensity of the stimulus, i.e., muscle stretch, recruits additional units.* Each of these receptors fires at a frequency which is determined by the extent to which the stimulus exceeds the

threshold of the individual receptor. These two intensity-signaling variables—number of active units and frequency of unit discharge—account for the grading of reflex response to various degrees of stretch. It has already been pointed out in Chapter 4 that these properties are also found in other receptors.

Of more interest for the present discussion are the unique properties of different stretch receptors. Matthews[28] found that the stretch-sensitive receptors of muscle can be divided into two general types, designated A and B, which differ

---

*Receptor variation in threshold is due partly to true variance in sensitivity to stretch and partly to variance in location in the muscle, some receptors bearing more of the brunt of muscle stretch than others.

principally in their behavior during active muscle contraction. Units of the A type typically have a low threshold to muscle stretch, 1 to 2 grams of tension often being sufficient to evoke a sustained rhythmic discharge. If, during such a stretch-evoked sustained discharge, a twitch contraction of the stretched muscle is elicited by a single shock to the ventral root, the discharge *ceases* during the twitch (Fig. 13, *left*). The A receptor thus behaves as if it were in "parallel" with the contractile extrafusal fibers, so that contraction, by shortening* the muscle, removes the tension from the receptors (Fig. 11*A*). It will be recalled that the muscle spindle is anatomically arranged in parallel with the muscle fibers. In addition, the position of a unit under observation can be roughly localized by pressing on the muscle with a glass rod while the muscle is stretched, for such local mechanical distortion excites the receptors. Local warming, which accelerates the discharge of a firing unit, also serves to localize the unit. In these ways, Matthews[28] found that receptors of the A type lie in the belly of the muscle or near its top insertion, but never in the tendon. For these reasons, it seems almost certain that units of the A type are spindle endings.

In contrast to the A type or spindle ending, the units which Matthews labeled B consistently display *accelerated firing* during muscle contraction (Fig. 13, *right*). Another difference is that B receptors have relatively high thresholds to muscle stretch, usually requiring tensions of 100 to 200 grams or more for sustained firing. Consequently, when the tension on the muscle is slight but adequate to excite A endings, the B endings may not fire unless the muscle is caused to contract. Upon contraction of the muscle, a burst of spikes occurs during the twitch. The behavior of B units therefore is that of receptors arranged in "series" with the muscle, and anatomically the Golgi tendon organ fulfills this requirement. Further, Matthews found by local probing and warming that B units are located either in the tendon or in the musculotendinous junction where the Golgi tendon organ is found histologically.

The presence or absence of a silent period in unit discharge during muscle contraction can

thus be used experimentally to distinguish between spindle endings and tendon receptors. The strength of the contraction-producing stimulus to the ventral root is important, however. In A receptors, a single shock to the ventral root adequate to cause only a submaximal or, at most, a maximal isometric muscle twitch results in cessation of discharge during the twitch. If, however, the shocks are supramaximal (i.e., more intense than is required for development of maximal contractile tension), and particularly if they are delivered repetitively, the rate of discharge of the A unit may increase during contraction of the muscle. In other words, when the motor fibers are stimulated supramaximally, the A unit behaves as if it were in series with the muscle. As will be shown later, such stimulation activates the small, high threshold fusimotor fibers that are distributed exclusively to the intrafusal muscle fibers. The resulting contraction of intrafusal muscle fibers does not add detectably to the total muscle tension but markedly influences the spindle endings, because they are in series with the intrafusal fibers, so that contraction of the two poles of the intrafusal fibers takes up slack in the spindle caused by extrafusal contraction and puts the spindle endings under tension.†

AFFERENT FIBERS SUPPLYING STRETCH RECEPTORS. As just described, the differential behavior of receptors during muscle contraction permits recognition of spindle and tendon endings. Once a unit has been isolated and classified, its conduction velocity can be measured; in turn, the diameter of the axon supplying it can be estimated, for the axon diameter in microns is linearly related to the conduction rate in meters per second, the ratio being 6 : 1 (cf. Chap. 3). Hunt[14] isolated and classified several hundred stretch-sensitive units from cat soleus

---

* Discharges of A units cease during muscle contraction even when the twitch is isometric, presumably because the tendon is somewhat elastic so that even under isometric recording conditions some internal shortening occurs during a twitch.

† Hunt and Kuffler[15] point out that A units may occasionally discharge during contractions set up by motor volleys too weak to excite fusimotor fibers, especially if the contraction occurs under rigidly isometric conditions and when the initial tension on the muscle is high. Such deviant responses are thought to be due to some unusual distribution of tension within the muscle that increases the amount of stretch deformation on some spindle endings. By varying the conditions, the experimenter can always demonstrate the silent period of such elements, so that there is never serious difficulty in distinguishing them from B endings, which show accelerated discharge during contraction under all conditions.

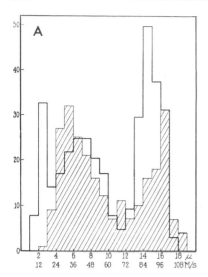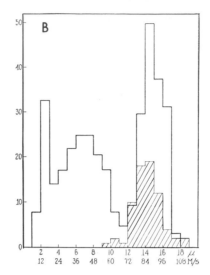

Fig. 14. Diameter distribution of afferent fibers supplying muscle spindles (*A*) and tendon organs (*B*). Heavy line in each graph plots diameter distribution of myelinated afferent fibers as determined histologically. Hatched area plots distribution of fibers supplying muscle spindles in *A* and tendon organs in *B* as determined by physiologic testing. *Ordinates,* Number of fibers in each 1 μ category. *Abscissae,* Diameter in μ and conduction rate in m. per sec. (After Hunt, *J. gen. Physiol.,* 1954, *38:*117–131.)

and gastrocnemius muscles by painstakingly dissecting and sampling the dorsal roots. The conduction rate in the axon was determined by electrically exciting the nerve trunk and measuring conduction time and distance to the dorsal root. The diameter was then computed by dividing the conduction rate by 6.

Figure 14*A* shows the distribution of computed axon diameters for spindle (A) endings of soleus muscle superposed on the afferent fiber distribution of the soleus nerve as determined histologically. Spindle endings fall into a bimodal distribution accounting for approximately half of the Group I fibers (12 to 20 μ) and for virtually all of the Group II fibers (4 to 12 μ) in the nerve. Because the fibers supplying the annulospiral or nuclear bag endings appear to be larger than those supplying the secondary or myotube endings, it is logical to conclude that Group I fibers supplying A receptors (hereafter called *Group IA fibers*) supply annulospiral endings, whereas the Group II fibers of the muscle nerve probably supply myotube or secondary endings. Recently ingenious techniques have been devised whereby the behavior of primary and secondary endings of the same muscle spindle can be simultaneously studied.[3] Apart from conduction rate, only small distinction can be made between annulospiral endings innervated by Group IA fibers and myotube endings innervated by Group II fibers. Both display silent periods during muscle contraction and both are accelerated by fusimotor stimulation. Myotube endings have slightly higher thresholds to stretch than do annulospiral endings, but the difference is slight (about 19:3 grams).

Figure 14*B* shows the diameter distribution of axons supplying endings of the B type (Golgi tendon organ). The distribution is unimodal and essentially confined to the Group I diameter range (>12 μ). *Group I fibers supplying B endings are called IB fibers.* Tendon endings supplied by Group IB fibers not only differ markedly from spindle endings in their response to muscle contraction (acceleration versus silent period), but also have significantly higher thresholds to stretch (100 to 200 grams). Furthermore, tendon endings are completely uninfluenced by stimulation of fusimotor fibers.

Together, the Group IA fibers supplying annulospiral spindle endings and the Group IB fibers supplying Golgi tendon organs account satisfactorily for the entire Group I population of the nerve. The entire Group II population appears to be devoted to spindle endings, presumably those of the myotube or secondary type.

Stretch Reflex Receptor. A question now arises: Which of the three nerve endings in muscle subserves the stretch reflex? The secondary endings of the spindle, innervated by Group II afferent fibers, may be eliminated. The reflex pattern elicited by exciting Group II fibers, whether of spindle or cutaneous origin, is that of the multisynaptic flexion reflex, whereas the stretch reflex is a monosynaptic arc served by Group I afferent fibers. Both the annulospiral spindle endings and the Golgi tendon organ, however, are innervated by Group I fibers, and hence are equally likely candidates.

It is generally believed (but admittedly largely on the basis of indirect evidence) that the annulospiral rather than the tendon endings are the receptors for the myotatic reflex. The low threshold to muscle stretch of the annulospiral endings, as opposed to the very high thresholds of tendon organs, is a suggestive datum, since the stretch reflex is elicited by exceedingly minute stretches. Secondly, selectively eliminating tendon organs by locally anesthetizing or resecting the tendon does not abolish the stretch reflex or tendon jerk. Finally, on the electrical record of a muscle engaged in a tendon jerk, the initial synchronous burst of activity which slightly precedes the onset of mechanical contraction is followed by a period of electrical silence which coincides with the reflex shortening of the muscle and which ends coincident with relaxation of the muscle. This *silent period* during the tendon jerk probably results partly from cessation of the excitatory afferent input from the receptors during muscle shortening, an interpretation which accords well with the properties of spindle endings but not with those of tendon organs.

Although this interpretation is probably partly correct, the genesis of the silent period is more complex. Denny-Brown[7] found that the silent period involved not only the muscle engaged in the jerk but also the tonic electrical activity of other muscles which are not participating in the jerk. He suggested that, during the silent period, there occurs not only withdrawal of excitatory input but also initiation of an active inhibitory input which affects both the motoneurons supplying the stretched muscle and those innervating adjacent muscles.*

There are at least two possible sources for this inhibition. One of these is the recurrent collaterals described by Cajal and by Renshaw. Before emerging in the ventral root, many motor axons give off recurrent collaterals which terminate on interneurons situated in the ventromedial region of the ventral horn.[34] These interneurons, sometimes called "Renshaw cells" after their discoverer, make inhibitory connections with the motoneurons.[33] A synchronous

reflex discharge, such as that elicited by tendon tap, is thus directed not only over the motor axons to the muscle but also, through the recurrent collaterals, to the Renshaw cells, which in turn deliver a high frequency burst of inhibitory impulses to the motoneurons.

The other, and probably more important, source of inhibition accounting for the silent period is the Group IB fibers supplying the tendon organs. Before this pathway is described, it may be pointed out that the implication of tendon organs and Group IB fibers in a proprioceptive arc inhibitory to the homonymous motoneurons is, by exclusion, a further and compelling reason for believing that the Group IA fibers supplying the annulospiral spindle endings constitute the afferent limb of the stretch reflex.

The Clasp Knife Reflex; Autogenic Inhibition. When one attempts to flex forcibly the rigid limb of a decerebrate preparation, resistance is encountered as soon as the muscle is stretched and increases throughout the initial part of the bending. This resistance is, of course, due to the hyperactive reflex contraction of the muscle in response to stretch. If flexion be forcibly carried farther, a point is reached at which all resistance to additional flexion seems to melt and the previously rigid limb collapses readily. Because the action is one which permits the stretched muscle to elongate freely, it is appropriately called a *lengthening reaction*. Also, because the resistance of the limb resembles that of a spring-loaded folding knife blade, this phenomenon is often called the "clasp knife" reaction. A similar phenomenon is regularly observed in human patients with spasticity, in whom the reaction is often best elicited by rapidly and forcibly flexing the spastic limb. Under these conditions, the clasp knife reaction is manifested by a "catch and give" in the resistance, i.e., the muscle first resists, then relaxes. In either instance, it appears that excessive (or rapid) stretch of the muscle brings into play some new influence which temporarily or permanently annuls the stretch reflex and allows the muscle to be lengthened with little or no tonic resistance.

Strong stretch of an extensor muscle also abolishes or diminishes the reflex contraction of that muscle brought about by means other than stretch. For example, when an extensor muscle is reflexly contracting in response to stimulation of a contralateral cutaneous nerve (crossed extension reflex) and the muscle is forcibly

---

* Electrical silence in direct synergists of the stretched muscle might be explained on the basis of withdrawal of excitation. The silent period, however, has a much wider distribution in limb muscles and may actually be observed in muscles which operate on joints different from that governed by the stretched muscle. Since there are no known excitatory monosynaptic connections between muscles acting at different joints, some process other than withdrawal of excitatory input must be postulated.

stretched, it may suddenly give and lengthen without resistance.

Sherrington[37] demonstrated that the clasp knife phenomenon is reflex in nature and dependent upon stretch of the muscle. When the clasp knife reaction is elicited, not only does the stretched extensor muscle relax but its antagonists (flexors) contract. Often there is a concomitant contraction of the extensor muscles of the contralateral limb (*Phillipson's reflex*) indicating doubly reciprocal connections of the responsible afferent pathways. The clasp knife reflex can be elicited in a muscle after all other muscles and structures of the limb have been denervated. When deafferented by appropriate dorsal rhizotomy, the stretched muscle, of course, becomes flaccid, and there is no tone against which to test for the clasp knife reflex. The deafferented muscle can, however, still be activated reflexly by stimulation of a contralateral cutaneous nerve (crossed extension reflex); strongly stretching the deafferented muscle does not abolish such a crossed reflex contraction as it does in the intact preparation.

These observations indicate that, in addition to the classic stretch reflex already described, there exists a proprioceptive stretch reflex arc of relatively high threshold which inhibits its homonymous motoneurons. Such inhibition, mediated by afferent fibers from a stretched muscle and acting on motoneurons supplying the stretched muscle, is known as *autogenic inhibition*. It follows that during muscle stretch the motoneurons supplying the stretched muscles are bombarded by impulses delivered over two competing pathways, one excitatory and the other inhibitory. The output of the motoneuron pool depends upon the balance between the two antagonistic inputs. With excessive stretch, the high threshold inhibitory pathway becomes an increasingly potent determinant and eventually dominates the motoneuron pool. Functionally the inhibitory pathway serves to *protect the muscle from overload* by preventing damaging contraction against strong stretching forces.

The influence of autogenic inhibition is detectable at degrees of stretch less than that required to annul the stretch reflex completely. For example, Sherrington[6] noted in fall table experiments that the reflex contraction elicited by small or moderate muscle stretch (2 per cent increase in length) was maintained at a steady level for half an hour or longer. When the stretch imposed on the same muscle was greater (4 to 5 per cent increase in length), the reflex contraction often faded in 5 to 10 minutes.

THE GOLGI TENDON ORGAN AND AUTOGENIC INHIBITION. There are a number of indications that Group IB fibers innervating the Golgi tendon organ constitute the afferent limb of the clasp knife reflex. The tendon organs are, of course, sensitive to stretch, which is the adequate stimulus for the clasp knife reflex. The relatively high threshold of the tendon organ to stretch accords well with the observation that the clasp knife reflex dominates the motoneurons only when muscle stretch is extreme.

McCouch *et al.*[29] showed that the quadriceps jerk could be inhibited by local electrical stimulation of the tendon or the musculotendinous junction of the vastus intermedius muscle, but not by similar stimulation of the muscle belly. Further indication that the tendon organ feeds a reflex arc inhibitory to the homonymous motoneurons derives from the experiments by Hunt[13] and by Granit.[9] They found that tetanic contraction of a muscle induced by repetitive stimulation of the distal end of the cut ventral root inhibited a monosynaptic reflex discharge set up by stimulation of the Group I afferent fibers from the muscle. Since during muscle contraction the spindle discharge ceases and the tendon-organ discharge is accelerated, it seems reasonable to ascribe this inhibition to activation of the tendon organs.

In man Libet *et al.*[22] found that the electromyographic response of tibialis anticus during voluntary contraction was 50 per cent less when the muscle was in a stretched position (ankle ventroflexed) than when it was at short length (ankle dorsiflexed). The finding is consistent with the interpretation that extreme stretch of the muscle, by exciting tendon receptors, provides an inhibitory input to the homonymous motoneurons making them less accessible to the excitatory impulses in descending pathways underlying voluntary contraction. In accordance with this interpretation, it was found that electromyographic amplitude was independent of muscle length when the tendon was infiltrated with procaine.

CENTRAL CONNECTIONS OF GROUP IB FIBERS. The evidence discussed in the previous section strongly implicates the Golgi tendon organs, and the Group IB fibers which supply them as the afferent limb of the clasp knife reflex. To study the central connections of the clasp knife reflex it is desirable to depart from the method of natural stimulation and resort to the conditioning-testing technique, using Group IB fibers for the conditioning pathway. A difficulty is encountered here, however, because Group IB and IA fibers are of the same or only slightly different diameters and electrical thresholds,* so that selective stimulation of IB fibers apart from IA fibers is difficult.

Despite this technical handicap, Laporte and Lloyd[20] were able to distinguish between the effects on motoneurons occasioned by afferent volleys conducted in Group IA fibers and those resulting from activation of Group IB fibers. This distinction is possible because, as will be developed below, the Group IB fibers have interposed between their presynaptic endings and the motoneuron a single interneuron. In other words, the clasp knife reflex mediated by Group IB fibers is a *disynaptic reflex arc*, whereas the myotatic reflex mediated by Group IA fibers is, of course, monosynaptic. In the monosynaptic pathway the threshold for influence upon the motoneurons is that of the Group IA fibers exerting the influence. In the disynaptic pathway, the threshold for influence upon the final elements, the motoneurons, depends not only upon the threshold of the Group IB fibers but also upon the response threshold of the intermediary elements, the interneurons. For this reason, although Group IA and IB fibers have similar thresholds, the conditioning volleys required to exert detectable influence upon the motoneurons via the Group IB fibers are somewhat greater than those required to demonstrate excitatory conditioning through the simpler monosynaptic pathway fed by Group IA afferent fibers.

Figure 15 shows the effect of conditioning a monosynaptic test reflex of the plantaris muscle by volleys of varied intensity delivered over the nerve supplying the synergistic muscle flexor longus digitorum. With a feeble conditioning volley, the monosynaptic facilitation curve (*closed circles*) typical of Group IA fibers was obtained. When the intensity of the conditioning volley was increased (*open circles*), the

* The threshold of axons to electrical stimulation should not be confused with the threshold of the reflex to natural stimulation via the appropriate sense organs. Thus, Group IA and IB fibers are equally accessible to electrical stimulation of the nerve trunk, but the spindle endings supplied by Group IA fibers are far more sensitive to natural stimulation (stretch) than are the tendon organs innervated by Group IB fibers.

earliest part of the curve was unaltered, but, when the interval between the conditioning and the test volley was 0.5 to 0.6 millisecond, the smooth decay of the facilitation curve was interrupted by the sudden onset of an inhibitory process, and the test response was reduced far below the control level. The 0.5 to 0.6 millisecond delay in the onset of the inhibitory action was constant irrespective of the length of the afferent pathway, and therefore cannot be explained by assuming that the inhibitory impulses traverse a more slowly conducting system of fibers than that responsible for facilitation. Rather, the delay must be due to an intercalated interneuron.

The third curve of Figure 15 (*crosses*) was obtained when the conditioning volley was so increased that it activated Group II as well as Group I afferent fibers. A second phase of inhibition appeared at a conditioning-test interval of about 2 milliseconds, clearly reflecting the delays resulting from the multisynaptic organization of Group II-fed reflex arcs.

When the Group IB disynaptic linkages of

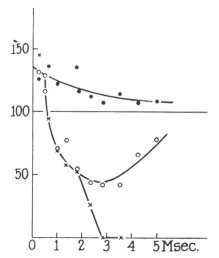

Fig. 15. Reflex conditioning of motoneurons by three intensities of afferent volley delivered over the heteronymous synergistic pathway. With weak Group I conditioning volleys the expected curve of facilitation was obtained (*filled circles*). When the intensity of the conditioning volley was slightly increased, the facilitation curve was interrupted at a conditioning-testing interval of 0.5 millisecond by a phase of inhibition (*open circles*). An additional increase in conditioning volley strength sufficient to activate Group II fibers (*crosses*) added a still later and more profound phase of inhibition beginning at a conditioning-testing interval of 2 milliseconds. (From Laporte and Lloyd, *Amer. J. Physiol.*, 1952, *169*:609–621.)

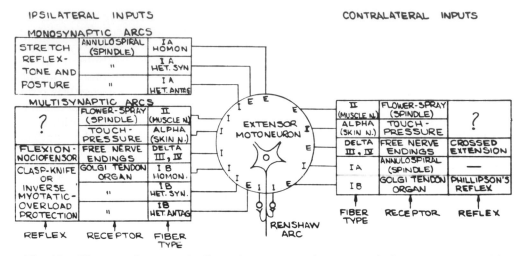

Fig. 16. Diagram of segmental afferent inputs converging on a typical motoneuron supplying an extensor muscle. The influence of each input is indicated as excitatory (*E*) or inhibitory (*I*).

various muscles are systematically studied, the following generalizations are reached. Group IB fibers form disynaptic inhibitory linkages with their homonymous motoneurons and with the motoneurons supplying synergists of the muscle from which they arise. On the other hand, Group IB volleys facilitate, through disynaptic linkages, the motoneurons supplying muscles antagonistic to those from which the afferent volley originates. In other words, the reciprocal connections of Group IB are just the opposite of those typical of Group IA fibers. For this reason, the clasp knife reflex is sometimes referred to as the *inverse myotatic reflex*. The reciprocal connections of the Group IB fibers, however, are somewhat more diffuse than those of the monosynaptic arcs arising in Group IA fibers, for the former may exert, through disynaptic linkages, inhibitory influences on motoneurons supplying muscles which are not direct antagonists of the muscle of origin. For example, a Group IB afferent volley set up in the quadriceps (knee extensor) nerve inhibits, through the disynaptic pathway, the motoneurons supplying the triceps surae (ankle extensor). This phenomenon is in marked contrast to the connections of Group IA fibers which are confined to the motoneurons supplying muscles acting around a single joint.

Summary of Reflex Pathways. At this juncture it is profitable to examine as a whole the segmental afferent inputs to a typical spinal motoneuron. Figure 16 summarizes diagrammatically the various pathways which play upon a spinal motoneuron supplying an extensor muscle. A corresponding diagram of the inputs to a flexor motoneuron would be identical, except that the influence of the multisynaptic paths fed by cutaneous and by Group II, III and IV fibers would be reversed. The striking feature of Figure 16 is the multiplicity of pathways which converge on the final common pathway, the motoneuron. In point of fact, Figure 16 gives but a limited picture of this convergence, for only the segmental inputs are shown. Omitted (for discussion in Chap. 9) are the numerous pathways which arise from other spinal segments and from supraspinal structures and which terminate directly or indirectly upon the motoneuron. Each neuron is thus subjected to a multitude of influences, some reinforcing and some antagonistic, and the balance of these influences at any time determines the membrane potential and hence the excitability of the cell. The motoneuron, the final common path of the arc, thus integrates the messages which impinge upon it.

A persistent problem in neurophysiology has been the apparent hopelessness of explaining complex behavior in terms of what, in axons, appears to be a stereotyped inflexible response —the action potential. Now it can be seen that the system as diagrammed in Figure 16 is a highly flexible machine in which shifts in the intensity and source of afferent bombardment arising from numerous different receptors may alter drastically the participation of the different motoneurons and their subservient muscles in reflex action and thus give rise to an infinite variety of behavioral patterns.

The Fusimotor Fibers and Spindle Regulation.[18, 19, 21]   In the preceding sections, attention was focused on the influence exerted by various receptor organs upon the motoneurons. To complete the picture, it is now profitable to consider the influence exerted by certain motoneurons upon a receptor, the muscle spindle. It has already been mentioned that the intrafusal fibers of the muscle spindle receive a motor innervation that typically supplies both contractile poles of the fiber. It is easy to visualize how activation of the fusimotor fibers by inducing polar contraction of the intrafusal fibers might put the noncontractile nuclear bag region under tension and thus produce in the receptor endings a mechanical distortion indistinguishable from that occasioned by passive stretch of the whole muscle. In this way, the fusimotor fibers may initiate spindle discharge in the absence of external stretch or, in the presence of stretch, so increase the sensitivity of the spindle that the frequency of afferent discharge is markedly increased. The fusimotor system thus serves as a biasing mechanism regulating the sensitivity of the receptor.

That the fusimotor fibers constitute a specialized efferent pathway distinguishable from that supplying the extrafusal muscle fibers was first proposed by Leksell.[21] Examination of the myelinated fiber spectrum of a ventral root or of a muscle nerve deafferented by degenerative dorsal rhizotomy reveals that the efferent fibers fall into two distinct size categories (Fig. 17). One group, constituting about 70 per cent of the total, ranges in diameter from about 8 to 13 μ, and thus falls approximately in the A-alpha classification of Gasser. The remaining 30 per cent of the myelinated motor fibers, ranging from about 3 to 8 μ in diameter with a peak cluster at 5 μ, are designated gamma efferents.* The absence of overlap between the two groups makes them relatively easy to distinguish. Figure 17 shows action potentials recorded from the gastrocnemius nerve following stimulation of the S_2 ventral root. In the upper trace, the stimulus was just maximal for the large low threshold alpha fibers. The lower figure shows a trace taken when the stimulus strength was increased sufficiently to recruit the smaller

gamma fibers. The peak conduction velocity of the first deflection was 76 m. per second; that for smaller and later deflection was 27 m. per second. The computed fiber diameters corresponding to these velocities are about 13 μ and 5 μ, respectively—values which agree satisfactorily with the histologic data.

Leksell noted that, when the muscle nerve was stimulated with graded shocks, twitch tension of the muscle was directly related to shock strength only until the alpha spike reached full size; further increase in shock strength caused no further increment in muscle tension, even though such strong shocks resulted in the appearance and growth of the gamma spike. In other words, the gamma fibers appeared to contribute nothing to contractile tension. This conclusion can be tested in another way. When pressure is applied to a nerve trunk, the larger fibers are blocked before the smaller ones are. Leksell found that when the alpha fibers were thus differentially blocked, stimulation central to the block produced little or no contractile response in the muscle, even though electrical recording from the nerve trunk distal to the block showed that conduction in the small gamma fibers was unaltered. It may therefore be concluded that the gamma fibers constitute a discrete efferent system innervating some structure in the muscle other than the ordinary tension-producing extrafusal muscle fibers.

It is now clear that the gamma efferent fibers are distributed *exclusively* to the spindle intra-

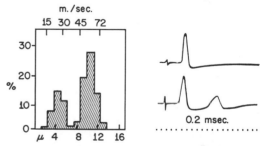

Fig. 17. Diameter spectrum and compound action potential of motor fibers supplying soleus. *Left,* Note distinct bimodal distribution of fiber diameters. Velocity spectrum shown on upper ordinates. *Right upper trace,* Compound action potential elicited by stimulus just maximal for large-diameter, rapidly conducting fibers. *Right lower trace,* Stronger stimulus elicited a second deflection ascribable to activity in the small slowly-conducting fibers. (Histologic data after Eccles and Sherrington, *Proc. roy. Soc.,* 1930, *B106*:326–357; electrical data after Kuffler *et al., J. Neurophysiol.,* 1951, *14*:28–54.)

---

* In some deafferented muscle nerves the gamma cluster is divisible into two subclusters: gamma$_1$ (4 to 8 μ) and gamma$_2$ (1 to 4 μ). The larger fibers are said to innervate nuclear bag fibers; the smaller, nuclear chain fibers.[5]

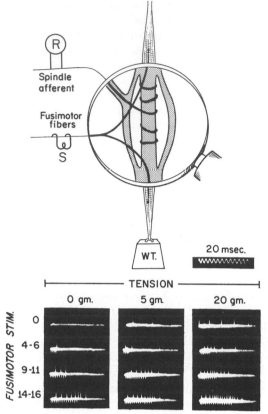

Fig. 18. Effects of tension and fusimotor stimulation on discharge rate of spindle ending. Upward deflections in traces are action potentials of a single isolated spindle afferent fiber. Small deflections below the baseline in some records are shock artifacts produced by stimulating fusimotor fibers. Note that discharge rate depends on both passive tension and fusimotor activity. (After Kuffler *et al.*, *J. Neurophysiol.*, 1951, *14*:29–54.)

fusal fibers, hence the term "fusimotor fibers."[17] Fusimotor activation causes contractions of the intrafusal fibers that are too feeble to add significantly to the total muscle tension but are sufficient to affect profoundly the afferent discharge of the spindle. This effect was demonstrated by Leksell, but more precisely by Kuffler *et al.*,[19] who dissected out for stimulation single fusimotor fibers in the ventral root. Figure 18 shows the effect of fusimotor activity on a single stretch receptor subjected to varying degrees of stretch. At each level of passive stretch the frequency of afferent discharge was accelerated by fusimotor stimulation, and the degree of acceleration increased with the number of fusimotor volleys delivered to the spindle. It is clear therefore that the afferent discharge of the spindle depends not only upon stretch

but also upon the number of impulses reaching the spindle via the fusimotor fibers. Each spindle receives up to fifteen such fusimotor fibers, which provide a precise mechanism for grading through a considerable range the sensitivity of the receptor to stretch. Also, each individual fusimotor fiber, by branching, participates in the innervation of several spindles, and can thus influence the discharge in a number of afferent fibers from different spindles.

It has already been mentioned that spindle receptors cease firing during muscle contraction. This pause comes about because the intrafusal fibers are arranged in parallel with the extrafusal fibers, so that shortening of the latter removes tension from the spindle. If, however, there is concomitant activation of the fusimotor system sufficient to take up the slack in the intrafusal fibers, the spindle endings may continue to discharge even during contraction. Figure 19 illustrates an experimental demonstration of this phenomenon. The upper trace shows the regular rhythmic firing of an A spindle receptor in response to a maintained 15 gram stretch on the muscle. In the middle trace, the muscle was caused to contract by stimulation of a portion of the ventral root containing only alpha efferent fibers; during the contraction, the spindle discharge ceased. For the bottom tracing, this same sequence was repeated, except that, in addition, a single fusimotor fiber supplying the spindle was stimulated nine times during the early part of the contraction. As a result of fusimotor stimulation, spindle discharge continued throughout the contraction. It may be inferred from such experiments that, in the intact animal, spindle behavior during muscular contraction is determined by the amount of fusimotor activity as well as by the extent of muscle shortening.

REFLEX ACTIVITY OF THE FUSIMOTOR SYSTEM. The discovery of the fusimotor system necessitates reconsideration of the mechanism of the stretch reflex. It will be recognized that the stretch reflex system in the intact animal is composed of a "peripheral loop" of nerve fibers, represented diagrammatically in Figure 20. On the motor side of the loop are the alpha and gamma fibers, both of which influence in unique ways the discharge behavior of the spindle receptors. On the afferent side of the loop, various receptors play back upon and reflexly influence the discharge of both the alpha and gamma systems. It follows that investigations involving the common experimental procedure of dividing ventral or dorsal roots may yield accurate information about the properties of the individual components of the stretch reflex system, e.g., the spindle receptors; but, because the loop is broken, such experiments give a rather distorted picture of the behavior of these components in the intact animal. A measure of this distortion is illustrated in Figure 21, which, in traces *A* and *B,* shows the discharge of a single spindle receptor in a preparation in which the loop was left almost entirely intact. This preparation was accomplished by cutting only a negligibly tiny strand of the dorsal root to sample spindle activity, leaving intact the remainder of the dorsal root and all of the ventral root. Even with the muscle slack and under no measurable stretch, the receptor

discharged a continuous barrage of impulses. When the muscle was stretched, the discharge of the receptor accelerated, but the firing during both the slack and the stretch state was irregular and tended to occur in bursts of varying frequencies. Traces *C* and *D* show the behavior of the same preparation after the loop was interrupted by ventral root section. In the slack state, the spindle was silent. During stretch, the receptor responded with a regularly recurring discharge of impulses quite unlike that in *A* and *B*. Such experiments suggest that, in the intact animal, the fusimotor system maintains a tonic discharge which fluctuates in magnitude as the afferent input to the fusimotoneurons varies.

This "resting" tonic discharge of fusimotoneurons has been studied by Hunt,[12, 17] who dissected out small strands of gamma efferent

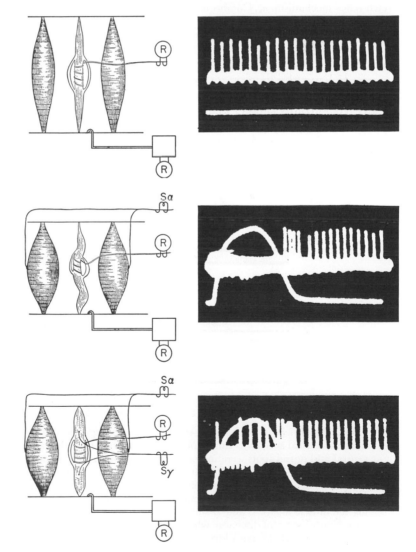

Fig. 19. Effect of fusimotor stimulation on the silent period in spindle discharge during muscle contraction. Thick line in traces, record from spindle afferent fiber; thin line, tension of muscle. *Upper trace,* Sustained tension (15 grams) elicits rhythmic firing of receptor. *Middle trace,* Discharge ceases during muscle twitch because spindles are relieved from stretch. *Lower trace,* Fusimotor stimulation (indicated by shock artifacts extending beneath baseline) takes up "slack" in spindle and permits sustained discharge even during muscle contraction. (After Hunt and Kuffler, *J. Physiol.*, 1951, *113*:298–315.)

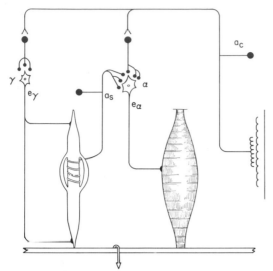

Fig. 20. Diagram of the "peripheral loop" of the stretch reflex mechanism. a_c, Cutaneous afferent path; a_s, spindle afferent path; e_α and e_γ, alpha and gamma (fusimotor) efferent pathways respectively.

with the limb in a neutral position, many fusimotoneurons are silent, while others maintain a continuous but irregular discharge at frequencies of 10 to 60 per second. That this discharge is highly dependent on segmental afferent inflow is suggested by Hunt's finding that the discharge was abolished by bilateral section of the lumbosacral dorsal roots.*

Various stimuli to the limbs reflexly alter the fusimotor discharge.[12, 17] In this respect cutaneous stimuli are especially effective, light touch, pressure or pin prick causing prominent changes in the discharge frequency of tonically firing units and sometimes driving a resting unit into activity. Generally speaking, such stimuli, particularly when applied to the foot, increase the fusimotor discharge to the ipsilateral flexor muscles but diminish the discharge to ipsilateral extensors. On the side opposite the stimulus, the extensor muscles receive increased fusimotor discharge, whereas the discharge to the flexors is diminished. Thus, in the flexion and crossed extension reflexes, the gamma and alpha motoneurons are affected alike. This arrangement probably acts to compensate for the

* Other experiments, to be discussed in Chapter 9, indicate that tracts descending from supraspinal structures also influence fusimotor discharge.

fibers from ventral roots or muscle nerves, taking care to leave the loop intact except for the small sampling strand. Fusimotor spikes are usually recognizably smaller in amplitude than alpha fiber spikes and are thus easily distinguished. In the spinal or decerebrate animal

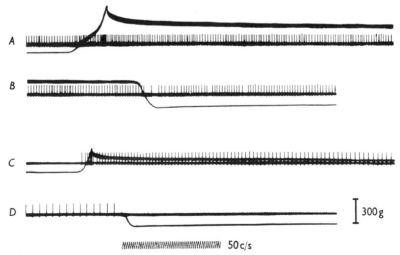

Fig. 21. Effect of ventral root section on muscle spindle response to muscle stretch. Trace with spikes, electrical activity of single spindle afferent fiber; smooth trace, muscle tension. In *A* and *B* both ventral and dorsal roots were intact except for small strand of dorsal root dissected to sample spindle response. At the beginning in *A*, although the muscle was slack, the unit discharged with an irregular rhythm. When the muscle was stretched 10 mm. as indicated by rise of tension, discharge was moderately accelerated but rhythm remained irregular. *B* is a continuation of *A* showing effect of slackening the muscle again. *C* and *D* show response of same unit to 10 mm. stretch after section of ventral root. Note absence of discharge when muscle was slack and regular rhythmic nature of discharge during muscle stretch. (From Eldred *et al.*, *J. Physiol.*, 1953, *122*:498–523.)

reduction of spindle discharge which might otherwise occur when the reflexly contracting flexor muscle shortens. Fusimotor activity thus provides a mechanism for maintaining a sensory message from the spindles proportional to the amount of external stretch even under changing conditions of muscle contraction.

The distribution of reflexly evoked fusimotor discharge, however, is not stereotyped. Cutaneous stimuli, particularly to proximal portions of the limb, may elicit patterns of fusimotor distribution which do not parallel the flexion and crossed extension patterns. Furthermore, the pattern varies with change in the site of stimulation. For example, the fusimotor discharge to the knee extensor, the quadriceps, in accordance with the flexion reflex pattern, is inhibited by touching or squeezing the ipsilateral foot, but the effect of similar stimulation of the skin on the thigh varies with the locus of stimulation. Touching the skin overlying the quadriceps increases fusimotor discharge to this muscle, whereas touching or squeezing the skin overlying its antagonists, the flexor hamstring muscles, inhibits tonic fusimotor discharge to the quadriceps. The fusimotor arcs, like the flexion reflex, thus display local sign.

Electrical stimulation of cutaneous nerves also markedly influences fusimotoneurons, but the effect varies so much with the afferent trunk employed and with the fusimotoneuron sampled that no generalizations are readily apparent. The unnatural electrical activation of functionally heterogeneous afferent fibers may obscure orderly functional patterns. Electrical stimulation, however, has the advantage that the temporal properties of fusimotor arcs can be determined. Measured central delays are in excess of 2 milliseconds, a fact suggesting that afferent fibers connect to fusimotoneurons through one or more interneurons.[17]

Deep receptors also influence fusimotoneuron activity but, in general, somewhat less prominently than cutaneous receptors do. The stretch receptors of muscle and tendon appear to influence the fusimotoneurons little or not at all.[17] Although muscle stretch sometimes inhibits fusimotor discharge to the stretched muscle,[12] there is reason to doubt that the responsible receptors are muscle spindles or tendon organs. The afferent fibers mediating this inhibition do not reach the spinal cord through the muscle nerve as do the Group IA and IB fibers supplying spindles and tendon organs.

Moreover, electrical stimulation of muscle nerves at intensities adequate only for Group I fibers does not influence fusimotoneurons. It therefore seems that the receptors responsible for fusimotor inhibition during muscle stretch are neither the spindle nor the tendon organs.

In closing it may be stated that, in the present state of knowledge, the physiologic significance of the fusimotor system is not completely clear. It is obvious that the gamma fibers are potentially powerful regulators of spindle function and hence of reflex function. The full measure of their significance in posture and movement cannot be assessed until the conditions governing their activation are further clarified.

CLINICAL SIGNIFICANCE OF REFLEXES

Examination of reflex status is a standard and valuable clinical diagnostic procedure. Clinically, reflexes are categorized as either *deep* or *superficial.* By "deep reflexes"* is meant all stretch or myotatic reflexes of the phasic or "jerk" type, i.e., those elicited by a sharp tap on the appropriate tendon or muscle to induce brief stretch of the muscle. Detailed lists of the commonly tested deep reflexes and the spinal segments which subserve them can be found in textbooks of neurology. The same type of neural arcs may be tested in the limbs and jaw by gauging the resistance to passive movement of the member; this is a test of *muscle tone* which, like the jerk, depends on the stretch reflex arc. An important difference between this test and the elicitation of jerk reflexes is the nature of the afferent discharge. With slow stretch (passive movement) it is asynchronous and prolonged (static stretch reflex), and with brief stretches (tapping) it is synchronous and of short duration. The *superficial* or *cutaneous* reflexes are withdrawal reflexes elicited by noxious or tactile

---

* Deep reflexes are also sometimes inappropriately called "periosteal" reflexes, because neurologists once quite mistakenly believed that the receptive elements were in the periosteum. The term "tendon" reflex, also commonly used interchangeably with "deep" reflexes, is unfortunate, because the receptors are, of course, in the muscle rather than in the tendon and because the jerk reflexes can be elicited by tapping the muscle directly as readily as by tapping the tendon. The clasp knife or inverse myotatic reflex is properly a tendon reflex.

stimulation of the skin, and display the same general properties as the nociceptive flexion reflex described above. Examples are the plantar reflex (plantar flexion of the toes when the sole of the foot is stroked or scratched), the cremasteric reflex (elevation of the testicle when the inner and upper surface of the ipsilateral thigh is lightly scratched), and the abdominal reflex (contraction of the abdominal musculature when the overlying skin is stroked with a dull pin).

Diseases of the nervous system may affect reflexes in one of three ways: (i) the reflexes may be hypoactive or absent, (ii) the reflexes may be hyperactive, or (iii) the pattern of reflex response to a standard stimulus may change to a new one (the so-called "pathologic reflexes"). In evaluating reflexes in man it should be remembered that the motoneurons are subject to a multitude of influences which vary in intensity from patient to patient and in the same patient from time to time. Patients under strong emotional stress may temporarily display brisk myotatic reflexes suggestive of hyperactivity. It is not unlikely that anxiety and tension are associated with increased fusimotor activity.

On the other hand, in a thoroughly relaxed patient the quadriceps jerk, through lack of descending facilitation, is sometimes difficult to elicit. This difficulty may arise because the muscle is sufficiently slack that the tap fails to impart much stretch to the muscle. Spuriously weak reflexes may also occur in older patients in whom structural changes in the muscle and the tendon permit slack in the system. In such instances, myotatic responses can often be elicited by tapping the muscle rather than the tendon, since stretch receptors are sensitive to deformation resulting from tapping the muscle even though little stretch is imparted to the muscle as a whole. Responses so elicited are usually more localized than those induced by tendon tap, because the stimulus affects only a part of the receptive field of the muscle. Even in the absence of such relaxation, the knee jerk is difficult to elicit in some subjects in whom there is no reason to suspect neurologic disease.

It follows from all these considerations that evaluation of reflex performance requires a judicious and cautious approach. If the reflexes appear either equally depressed or equally hyperactive at all levels, repeated examinations, preferably over a considerable period and in a variety of environmental circumstances, may be required to distinguish the spurious from the significant. When the reflex aberrations are asymmetrical— occurring, for example, in one limb and not in another, or on only one side of the body— the examiner is on safer ground, because one part of the body then serves as a control for the others.

Hyporeflexia. It is obvious from the preceding discussion that any process which interrupts or depresses conduction through any part of the reflex arc results in hypoactivity of that reflex in proportion to the severity of damage. The lesion may be in the afferent pathway, as in tabes dorsalis, in which the pathologic process begins in the dorsal root ganglia; or the lesions may affect the efferent limb. Disruption of this portion may result from disease in the gray matter causing injury to the motoneurons, as in anterior poliomyelitis. Disease of nerve trunks commonly affects both the afferent and the efferent limb of a reflex arc; examples are the several varieties of polyneuritis and herniated intervertebral discs or tumors which compress both dorsal and ventral roots in their course through the vertebral canal. Finally, disturbances, such as myasthenia gravis, which interfere with neuromuscular transmission may result in depression or lack of reflexes.

Depressed reflexes, however, do not always indicate an interruption of the segmental arc. It has been mentioned that motoneuron excitability is conditioned by pathways descending the cord from more cephalic spinal and suprasegmental levels as well as by segmental inflows. Even though the segmental arcs are intact after these descending pathways are interrupted by transection of the cord, the reflex responses are severely depressed (spinal shock) in regions innervated by the decentralized spinal segments. With passage of time, some reflexes return (particularly the flexion reflex patterns of the extremities, which may actually become troublesomely hyperactive), but the static stretch reflex often remains permanently depressed. Similarly, cerebellar lesions, by destroying neurons which feed into descending tracts facilitatory to the motoneurons, result in hypoactive stretch reflexes.

Hyperreflexia. Hyperactivity of deep reflexes sometimes results from inflammatory lesions involving the segmental arc, e.g., during the early stages of the intervertebral disc syndrome or of polyneuritis. Persistently hyperactive deep reflexes, however, almost always indicate destruction of descending tracts inhibitory to the segmental stretch reflex mechanism, as in spastic hemiplegia following infarction (from hemorrhage, etc.) in the internal capsule. In this instance, myotatic hyperreflexia is indicated by increased briskness and amplitude of deep reflexes and by increased resistance to passive flexion at the joints (spasticity). In addition, the peripheral distribution of stretch reflex discharge is often increased owing to the occurrence of "crossfiring."

It has already been emphasized that, normally, the stretch reflex discharge returns only to the muscle stretched. When motoneuron excitability is increased (see p. 177), the afferent volley may fire motoneurons that normally are only facilitated (crossfiring). In spasticity, crossfiring is exemplified by *Hoffman's reflex* in which flicking the terminal phalanx of the middle finger results in twitchlike flexion in the other fingers and in adduction and flexion of the thumb. Such a broad field of reflex action resulting from brief stretch of the flexor muscles of one finger joint manifests myotatic hyperactivity.

Another important sign of hyperreflexia, often associated with spasticity, is *clonus*. Clonus occurs when the asynchrony of the motoneuron discharge in a stretch reflex is lost. There then ensues a series of regularly repeated, jerklike contractions superimposed upon a tonic contraction. In the hyperreflexic patient, clonus may be initiated by putting the muscle under moderate but sustained stretch and then tapping the tendon. A jerk response, of course, results; but it is followed by a succession of jerks which continue for a considerable time if the steady stretch is maintained. Figure 22 presents a myograph tracing of a clonic response in a decerebrate cat; the accompanying electromyogram shows that each wavelet of contraction is preceded by a muscle action potential, indicating that the motoneurons are discharging in periodic synchronous bursts. The simplest explanation of clonus is based on the "in parallel" behavior of the stretch receptor. The tap on the tendon initiates a synchronous volley of afferent impulses which fire the motoneurons in concert, causing a jerk contraction. This contraction relieves the spindles of the tension imposed by the sustained stretch, so that they cease firing and the afferent drive to the motoneurons ceases. As a consequence, the muscle relaxes and the spindles are thereby again put under tension which

initiates an afferent volley that again fires the motoneurons so that the sequence is repeated. Even in a healthy subject a slight tendency toward oscillation during a jerk contraction may be observed. If the muscle is under passive tension prior to the tapping of the tendon, the electromyogram displays an asynchronous discharge which indicates that motor units are reflexly firing in response to the sustained stretch. When the tendon is tapped, the electromyogram displays a large synchronous discharge just preceding the muscle contraction, but during the development of contractile tension the asynchronous discharge is in abeyance—the "silent period" already described. As the muscle relaxes and the spindles are again put under tension, firing of motor units resumes and relaxation of the muscle is delayed. Indeed, a second small contraction, the myotatic appendage, may appear on the tension record. When the motoneurons are hyperexcitable, as in spasticity, a series of myotatic appendages appear, constituting clonus which may persist for minutes. Sustained clonus is always a manifestation of hyperreflexia indicating damage within the central nervous system.

Pathologic Reflexes. These are reflex responses which do not occur in the normal person. In a sense, the Hoffman reflex is a pathologic reflex. A better example is the *Babinski sign* or reflex. In the normal adult, stroking the sole

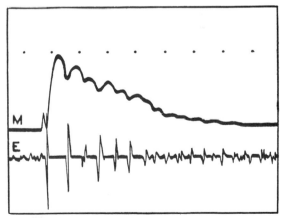

Fig. 22. Clonus. Electrical (*E*) and mechanical (*M*) records of quadriceps muscle. A slight stretch previously applied produced a tonic reflex discharge to the muscle, as indicated by the asynchronous waves in *E*. A tap to the tendon indicated by the first sharp deflection in *M*, elicited a brisk jerk reflex followed by a typical clonic discharge evident in both *M* and *B*. Time above, 100 milliseconds. (After Denny-Brown, *Proc. roy. Soc.,* 1929, *B104*:252–301.)

of the foot causes plantar flexion of the toes; this is the plantar flexion reflex. In certain diseases of the central nervous system, however, the response to plantar stimulation (particularly along the lateral surface and the ball of the foot) is dorsiflexion of the great toe, often accompanied by fanning of the other toes. The Babinski reflex is part of the generalized flexion reflex pattern and is accompanied by flexor contraction at other joints of the limb; the significant deviation in the Babinski reflex is the aberrant pattern. In adults, presence of the Babinski reflex is always a sign of disease, but this pattern is normal in infants, particularly when they are asleep. The Babinski reflex is commonly believed to indicate interruption of the pyramidal tract (see Chap. 12).

Deductions from Examination of Reflexes. In summary, it may be pointed out that the examination of reflexes provides several kinds of information to the thoughtful physician. *First,* unilateral aberration of reflex performance provides a basis for identifying the *side* affected by the disease process. *Second,* the distribution of reflex aberrations along the longitudinal axis of the body often betrays the *segmental level* of the lesion. *Third,* once a segmental defect is established, attention may be turned to identifying the *defective component* in the arc. Loss of reflex accompanied by loss of sensation but without voluntary motor weakness implies injury to the afferent limb. Loss of reflex without sensory defect but with muscular weakness, atrophy, fibrillation or fasciculation suggests injury to the efferent limb. *Fourth,* examination of segmental reflexes often reveals disturbances of *more distant structures* which influence the segmental arcs. Thus, disease of descending pathways inhibitory to the segmental reflex mechanism is brought to the physician's attention by hyperreflexia, as in spasticity.

REFERENCES

1. ADRIAN, E. D. and ZOTTERMAN, Y. *J. Physiol.,* 1926, *61:* 151–171.
2. BARKER, D. *Quart. J. micr. Sci.,* 1948, *89:*143–186.
3. BESSOU, P. and LAPORTE, Y. Pp. 105–119 in *Symposium on muscle receptors,* D. Barker, ed., Hong Kong, Hong Kong University Press, 1962.
4. BOYD, I. A. *Phil. Trans.,* 1962, *B245:*81–136.
5. BOYD, I. A. and DAVEY, M. R. Pp. 191–198 in *Symposium on muscle receptors,* D. Barker, ed., Hong Kong, Hong Kong University Press, 1962.
6. CREED, R. S., DENNY-BROWN, D., ECCLES, J. C., LIDDELL, E. G. T. and SHERRINGTON, C. S. *Reflex activity of the spinal cord.* London, Oxford University Press, 1932.
7. DENNY-BROWN, D. *Proc. roy. Soc.,* 1928, *B103:*321–336.
8. FULTON, J. F. and PI SUÑER, J. *Amer. J. Physiol.,* 1928, *83:* 554–562.
9. GRANIT, R. *J. Neurophysiol.,* 1950, *13:*351–372.
10. HAGBARTH, K. E., *Acta physiol. scand.,* 1952, *26*(Suppl. 94):1–58.
11. HOFFMANN, P. *Arch. Anat. Physiol. (Lpz.), Anat. Abt.,* 1910, 223–246, 1 pl.
12. HUNT, C. C. *J. Physiol.,* 1951, *115:*456–469.
13. HUNT, C. C. *J. Physiol.,* 1952, *117:*359–379.
14. HUNT, C. C. *J. gen. Physiol.,* 1954, *38:*117–131.
15. HUNT, C. C. and KUFFLER, S. W. *J. Physiol.,* 1951, *113:* 298–315.
16. HUNT, C. C. and McINTYRE, A. K. *J. Physiol.,* 1960, *153:* 88–98.
17. HUNT, C. C. and PAINTAL, A. S. *J. Physiol.,* 1958, *143:* 195–212.
18. KUFFLER, S. W. and HUNT, C. C. *Res. Publ. Ass. nerv. ment. Dis.,* 1952, *30:*24–47.
19. KUFFLER, S. W., HUNT, C. C. and QUILLIAM, J. P. *J. Neurophysiol.,* 1951, *14:*29–54.
20. LAPORTE, Y. and LLOYD, D. P. C. *Amer. J. Physiol.,* 1952, *169:*609–621.
21. LEKSELL, L. *Acta physiol. scand.,* 1945, *10*(Suppl. 31): 1–84.
22. LIBET, B., FEINSTEIN, B. and WRIGHT, E. B., JR. *Electroenceph. clin. Neurophysiol.,* 1959, *11:*129–140.
23. LIDDELL, E. G. T. and SHERRINGTON, C. S. *Proc. roy. Soc.,* 1924, *B96:*212–242.
24. LIDDELL, E. G. T. and SHERRINGTON, C. S. *Proc. roy. Soc.,* 1925, *B97:*267–283.
25. LLOYD, D. P. C. *J. Neurophysiol.,* 1943, *6:*317–326.
26. MAGLADERY, J. W., PARK, A. M., PORTER, W. E. and TEASDALL, R. D. *Res. Publ. Ass. nerv. ment. Dis.,* 1952, *30:*118–151.
27. MATTHES, K. and RUCH, T. C. *Quart. J. exper. Physiol.,* 1932, *22:*221–231.
28. MATTHEWS, B. H. C. *J. Physiol.,* 1933, *78:*1–53.
29. McCOUCH, G. P., DEERING, I. D. and STEWART, W. B. *J. Neurophysiol.,* 1950, *13:*343–350.
30. MEGIRIAN, D. *J. Neurophysiol.,* 1962, *25:*127–137.
31. PERL, E. R. *Amer. J. Physiol.,* 1957, *188:*609–615.
32. PERL, E. R. *J. Neurophysiol.,* 1958, *21:*101–112.
33. RENSHAW, B. *J. Neurophysiol.,* 1941; *4:*167–183.
34. RENSHAW, B. *J. Neurophysiol.,* 1946, *9:*191–204.
35. SHERRINGTON, C. S. *Proc. roy. Soc.,* 1893, *52:*556–564.
36. SHERRINGTON, C. S. *J. Physiol.,* 1898, *22:*319–332.
37. SHERRINGTON, C. S. *Quart. J. exp. Physiol.,* 1909, *2:*109–156.
38. SHERRINGTON, C. S. *J. Physiol.,* 1910, *40:*28–121.
39. SHERRINGTON, C. S. *Brain,* 1915, *38:*191–234
40. SHERRINGTON, C. S. *Nature (Lond.),* 1924, *113:*732, 892–894, 929–932.
41. WOODBURY, J. W. and PATTON, H. D. *Cold Spr. Harb. Symp. quant. Biol.,* 1952, *17:*185–188.

CHAPTER 8

Transection of the Human Spinal Cord: The Nature of Higher Control

By THEODORE C. RUCH

THE principles of reflex action outlined in earlier chapters are applied clinically in dealing with destructive diseases and mechanical injury of the spinal cord. Such injuries are especially common during war. During World War I, spinal transection meant early death; during World War II, however, the prognosis for patients with spinal paraplegia was radically altered. Through application of physiologic principles, many of these men have been rehabilitated and are now self-reliant citizens.

When the spinal cord is severed, all muscles innervated from segments below the transection become paralyzed (paraplegic), and the skin and other tissues are anesthetic. Voluntary motion and sensation are abolished and never recover. Reflexes, although initially abolished, do recover to some degree, and some become overactive. This chapter will be concerned with the higher control of reflex action; sensory changes from complete and partial spinal cord section are discussed in Chapter 15.

CONSEQUENCES OF SPINAL TRANSECTION

Spinal Shock. The disappearance of reflexes was designated "spinal shock" some 100 years ago by Marshall Hall,[13] and the term, despite its inappropriateness, is still used. Spinal shock is not related to surgical shock or to spinal concussion, which results from physical shock to the spinal cord. As Sherrington[31] proved, spinal shock will occur when the cord is functionally sectioned atraumatically, as by cooling or by injection of procaine. If reflexes of segments below a transection have returned, another section just below the first produces no shock effect. In short, it is the *fact* of cord section —not the *act* of transection—which produces spinal shock. The alternative terms are *post-transectional areflexia* or *hyporeflexia*. The state of increased reflex excitability which may supervene can be called *post-transectional hyperreflexia*. A phenomenon following a brain lesion comparable to spinal shock is *diaschisis* (von Monakow).

Areflexia and hyporeflexia. The most conspicuous sign of spinal shock in man and other primates is the suppression of all reflexes, both skeletal and visceral, below the transection. This suppression is usually complete during the first two weeks after the injury. Before the first World War it was believed that the reflexes were permanently abolished, this belief having arisen because intercurrent infections of the bladder or other structures reduced the excitability of the spinal cord. Then, Head and Riddoch[14] proved that some paraplegic patients could be maintained indefinitely by fastidious nursing care, and that in such patients spinal reflexes began to return after two to three weeks. Since World War II, Freeman[5] and others[19] have found that reflexes may reappear within two to three days after the accident.

Return of Reflexes and Hyperreflexia.
Flexion reflex and the Babinski sign. Contrary to early studies, withdrawal movements in response to plantar stimulation (rather than the knee jerk) are the first reflexes to emerge from the period of areflexia; anal and genital reflexes also recover early. As the withdrawal reflex becomes more brisk, the toes (especially the great toe) tend to become extended upward during the response (the sign of Babinski[9]). In the course of the third and fourth weeks following the injury, the withdrawal response becomes more vigorous, and the zone from which it can be elicited spreads up the inner side of the leg, the knee and the hip. The withdrawal response is brought about mainly by strong contraction of the hamstring muscles of the thigh.

Mass reflex. Several months after spinal transection, the withdrawal reflexes tend to become exaggerated and spread to the visceral autonomic outflow. Thus, if the plantar surface of the foot is vigorously scratched, both extremities may withdraw violently, the patient may sweat profusely, and both the bladder and the rectum may contract. This widespread reflex activation of the musculature in spinal man is referred to as the "mass reflex."[14] Mass reflexes may be evoked unintentionally and, at times, they appear to develop spontaneously without obvious stimulation. Flexor reflex contractions with or without autonomic concomitants are very disturbing to the patient, since they interfere with his sleep and rest.

Extensor reflexes. During the first weeks after a spinal transection, the lower extremities are flaccid: they are limp and do not resist manipulation. Even after the withdrawal reflexes have returned, the limbs usually are still flaccid except when exhibiting flexor spasms. Some months after spinal transection, if there are no complications, a slight degree of extensor posture usually develops, but the extremities seldom become strongly spastic, as in hemiplegia. Strong extensor spasticity occurring soon after the transection generally indicates that the spinal cord is not completely severed and that some degree of functional recovery can be anticipated. However, patients with surgically verified spinal transections may reach a stage in which the tendon reflexes are hyperactive as judged by decreased threshold and clonus. Stretch reflexes and positive supporting reactions sufficiently sustained to permit momentary support of the body have been reported. The lower extremities show both ipsilateral and crossed extension reflexes, but extreme resistance of the extensors to passive stretch is seldom found in spinal man.[18]

Autonomic reflexes. Surprisingly, autonomic reflexes are even more completely suppressed in spinal shock than are somatic reactions. During the first month or two the skin is completely dry, sweating having been wholly abolished, and the skin may be warm and pink owing to separation of the autonomic outflow innervating it from the descending vasoconstrictor impulses. In monkeys, sweating generally does not appear until the third month. In the later stages, this sweating may be so excessive that the patient's clothing and bed linen are constantly wet.[5, 10]

Of the autonomic reflexes, those of the bladder are most important to the patient; these are described in full in Chapter 51.

Completeness of Spinal Transection. In civil life complete spinal transections fortunately are rare. Much more common are partial injuries, and it is important to be able to distinguish between an incomplete and a total transection. Broadly speaking, incomplete transections are marked by an early return of extensor reflexes and are eventually associated with spasticity and great reflex hyperactivity. A patient with a cervical dislocation who appears completely paralyzed below the level of dislocation but who nevertheless exhibits extensor reflexes has an incompletely divided cord, and he has a good possibility of functional recovery if the dislocation can be reduced. Often a patient shows flaccidity and areflexia shortly after the injury but later develops spasticity and active reflexes.

A spinal transection represents the sudden withdrawal of the many excitatory and inhibitory influences which play upon the spinal reflex arcs. A partial interruption of the spinal cord disrupts some but not all of the descending pathways. Since these pathways originate at different levels of the neural axis, transection at higher levels will interrupt some of them and not others. To obtain a complete view of the nature of higher control and the clinical syndromes resulting from destructive lesions of the nervous system, it is necessary to consider the same topic at each level of transection.

NATURE OF HIGHER CONTROL

Spinal transection suddenly interrupts all descending pathways which control spinal reflexes by facilitation and inhibition. The results are necessarily complex. The nature of higher control is the subject of several of the following chapters, but it cannot be fully understood until sections at higher levels interrupting only a few descending pathways are studied.

It might be thought that stretch reflexes, for example, disappear in the higher animal because they have, in course of evolution, been long-circuited through the brain. That these reflexes in higher animals are served by monosynaptic spinal reflex arcs has been proved by Magladery.[24] It is generally conceded that spinal shock results from sudden interruption of control normally exerted on spinal centers by forebrain structures. In the course of evolution, the forebrain has come to dominate lower midbrain and spinal centers more and more, the domination being most complete in man and other higher primates. This evolutionary process is generally referred to as "encephalization." The degree of spinal shock reflects the degree to which a given spinal reflex depends on the brain for facilitation of the segmental afferent input. Generally, the dependence becomes greater as the primate series is ascended, but exceptions do occur. For example, the reflexes of the semiprehensile hind foot of the chimpanzee may be more profoundly disturbed than those of the human foot after spinal transection.

The depression of reflexes comes about because, as will be brought out many times in subsequent chapters, descending pathways converge and summate with the segmental afferent input. Presumably, these descending tracts are discharging continuously, subliminally exciting the motoneurons and keeping many near the point of discharge.[21] As a result, a local afferent volley which has few motoneurons in its discharge zone is able to discharge many neurons lying in its subliminal fringe. If the flow of descending impulses is terminated, the reflex shrinks to its original discharge. This recession explains much of the areflexia and hyporeflexia which follow spinal transection.

Fulton[7] has pointed out that another mechanism may be operative. In addition to or instead of withdrawing facilitation from anterior horn cells, withdrawal of descending impulses might remove an inhibitory influence acting upon the interneurons of an antagonistic reflex arc, necessarily a multisynaptic one. An afferent volley in this arc, e.g., for a flexion reflex, would traverse the uninhibited interneurons with less reduction and would inhibit the motoneurons of the antagonistic extensor reflex. Thus, the flexion reflex should be, and is, augmented while the extensor reflex is inhibited. In passive flexion of a joint to test an extensor stretch reflex, the mere manipulation might prevent one's feeling the weak but recovering stretch reflex.

Ballif *et al.*[1] demonstrated myographically that the knee jerk of a spinal animal, though strong, is inhibited for several seconds by a single ipsilateral stimulus, whereas the knee jerk of a decerebrate animal is inhibited for only a tenth of a second. It is apparent that it is extremely difficult to distinguish between inhibition and lessening of facilitation as mechanisms of spinal shock, and probably both contribute. One of the complexities of the nervous system is that the higher centers can control a spinal reflex by exerting their influence (i) on the motoneurons (ii) on the internuncial neurons of the reflex arc and (iii) on the γ motoneurons which set the sensitivity of the stretch afferent organs and (iv) a combination of the preceding.

Site of Spinal Shock. The immediate change which motoneurons and some interneurons undergo when the spinal cord of a decerebrate animal is sectioned has been shown directly by recording intracellularly at L 5 while the spinal cord was blocked by cooling at Th 10.[2] At each cold block (Fig. 1), most of the cells proved by antidromic firing to be motoneurons underwent a hyperpolarization of from 2 to 6 mV. (mean 3.6 ± 2 mV.). This was reversible by rewarming. These experiments prove that acute spinal shock is evident at the motoneuron as a steady membrane charge but do not establish whether the hyperpolarization derives from withdrawal of facilitation or from increase in tonic inhibition and whether its source is supraspinal or segmental.

In Chapter 9 a strong supraspinal influence on the γ efferent fibers and, hence on the excitability of the stretch afferents will be documented. Some of the depression of the stretch

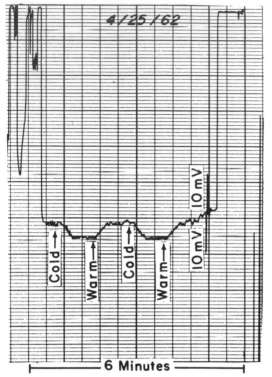

Fig. 1. Intracellular recording from a lumbar motoneuron during alternate cold block and rewarming of the spinal cord in the thoracic region. Large drop in the transmembranal polarization signals penetration of cell. Vertical line at right is the calibration. (After Barnes, Joynt and Schottelius, *Amer. J. Physiol.*, 1962, *203:*1113–1116.)

reflex after spinal transection could result from a reduction in γ efferent discharge. In man, ipsilateral extension jerk elicited by nerve stimulation suffers less than activation of the same muscle by a tendon tap, a difference ascribable to reduced sensitivity of the muscle spindle.[34]

However, in the monkey there is no clear evidence of a reduced γ efferent discharge after spinal transection.[15]

The converse question is: Do hyperactive tendon reflexes after recovery from spinal shock represent heightened fusimotor discharge and resultant increased muscle spindle sensitivity? Meltzer *et al.*[27] could find no increase in the afferent impulses coming from the muscle nerve on the side of a spinal cord hemisection though the ankle jerk was increased 1.5 to 15 times that recorded on the less active side. This activity was therefore ascribed to increased α motoneuron excitability.

The strong inhibitory effects of descending pathway on the γ efferent neurons documented by brain stimulation have yet to be

clearly demonstrated by experiments involving transection.

Release of Function. When reflexes below a transection become stronger and more easily elicited, "release of function"* is said to have occurred. The simplest example of release of function is provided by the consideration of what happens to the flexion reflex when the spinal cord of the decerebrate cat is sectioned in the midthoracic region.[29] As will be discussed in greater detail in Chapter 9, a decerebrate cat is a reduced system in which the only descending pathways still affecting the reflex arcs are the vestibulospinal and reticulospinal tracts from the medulla oblongata. What occurs on transection—by surgery, cooling or procaine injection—is a prompt and marked *decrease* in the excitability of stretch and other extensor reflexes and an *increase* in the excitability of the flexion reflex. In other words, the two classes of reflexes are oppositely affected, and the simplest conclusion is that the descending pathways innervate two classes of motoneurons reciprocally. There is the same advantage to reciprocal innervation from the descending pathways as there is to such innervation by the local afferent inputs.

Further evidence of reciprocal effects of spinal transection is seen in the reflex changes in the forelimbs following midthoracic transection in a decerebrate cat. These changes, termed the Schiff–Sherrington phenomenon, are, as indicated in Figure 2, a striking augmentation of the stretch reflex and a decrease in the size of the flexion reflex to equal stimuli. The former is clearly observable without instrumental recording as an increased stiffening of the forelimbs. (The changes are opposite in homologous muscles of the forelimb and hindlimb, and while this must have meaning, the reciprocal changes between flexors and extensors constitute the significant point.)

The diminution of reflexes in these experiments illustrates *spinal shock* resulting from withdrawal of facilitation; the augmentation of reflexes illustrates *release of function* resulting from withdrawal of inhibition. These two phenomena always occur together and are manifestations of a reciprocal relationship of descending pathways to extensor and flexor spinal motoneurons. Descending pathways other than the

---

* Release of function was first recognized in 1833 by Marshall Hall,[12] who also was the first to describe spinal shock clearly.

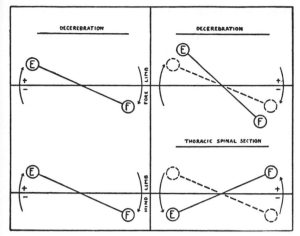

Fig. 2. A schematic diagram of the reciprocal effect of thoracic transection of the spinal cord upon the reflex activity of fore and hind limbs of the decerebrate preparation. *E* and *F* are the extensor and flexor motoneurons. The ordinates are reflex excitability and indicate merely decrease and increase and not absolute amount of change in reflex excitability. (From Ruch and Watts, *Amer. J. Physiol.*, 1934, *110:*362–375.)

vestibulospinal tract act in the same reciprocal fashion but vary in sign, so that a spinal transection which interrupts many descending pathways at once can have quite complex effects. Nevertheless, the effects of transecting lesions, and of certain large brain lesions, can best be interpreted in terms of a kind of algebra of the nervous system in which positive and negative quantities are summated. (For examples, see Chap. 51.)

Synaptic Basis of Release Phenomena. Since the myographic demonstration of the Schiff–Sherrington phenomenon[29] the stretch reflex of the forelimb extensor muscle (triceps) has become a model for investigating release of function, especially by the Italian neurophysiologists, Stella, Cardin, and Moruzzi (see Pompeiano[28]). Even in the reduced nervous system represented by the decerebrate animal they have identified three powerful sources of tonic inhibition of the forelimb stretch reflex—(i) ascending inhibition revealed by postbrachial transection (Schiff–Sherrington phenomenon), (ii) cerebellar inhibition manifested by increase of extensor tone after cerebellectomy or bilateral destruction of the fastigial nuclei of the cerebellum, and (iii) crossed inhibition originating in the proprioceptors of the opposite limb revealed by deafferentation.

The motoneurons' excitability at any one time is the sum of many inhibitory and many facilitatory influences. The motoneuron effects an algebraic summation of the "plus and minus" inputs. One example of the way the excitability of a reflex can be manipulated up and down is seen in Figure 2. More examples of the "algebra of higher control" will be encountered in subsequent chapters, e.g., Chapter 51.

At the synaptic level release of function presents much the same alternatives as does acute spinal shock. Is the effect a direct disinhibition of α motoneurons or an indirect one by way of disinhibiting γ motoneurons? Is the effect on the motoneurons or upon inhibitory internuncial neurons, or is it by blocking some impinging excitation? The first question can be answered in favor of direct effect (Fig. 3). Pompeiano[28]

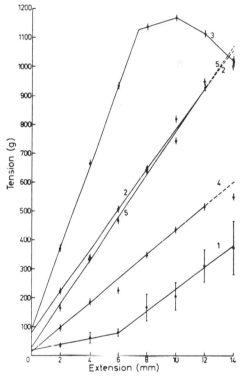

Fig. 3. Initial limb of the stretch reflex recorded from a forearm extensor muscle (caput longis of triceps brachii) after various neural sections. 1. Average value and range of three stretch reflexes in the *precollicular* decerebrate animal; 2. after postbrachial transection of the spinal cord; 3. after deafferentation of the contralateral forelimb C_6 to Th_2; 4. after deafferentation of ipsilateral forelimb; 5. after complete cerebellectomy. Duration of stretch was 13.1 sec. Record 4 is a pseudostretch reflex representing the increased tension and is due to effect of muscle length on the increased muscular contraction caused by the α motor neuron discharge. (From Pompeiano, *Arch. ital. Biol.*, 1960, *98:* 92–117.)

has shown that if enough inhibitory influences are removed by contralateral deafferentation and postbrachial transection the triceps muscle exhibits tone, even after it is also deafferented. Now if the cerebellum is removed, a large increase in tone occurs which must be independent of the muscles' γ loop interrupted by deafferentation. A similar demonstration has been made for ascending inhibition.

Terzuolo[33] reached the same conclusion by recording monosynaptic reflex discharge intracellularly in extensor neurons during inhibition produced by stimulation of the bulbar reticular system. The fact that inhibitory slowing occurs when the γ loop is rendered ineffective by anterior root section indicates an action on the α motoneurons as do increases in membrane potential ranging from 1.5 to 10.5 mV. (mode 1.5 to 3.5 mV.). Although the inhibitory effect of reticular stimulation is established to be on the motoneurons, it might be either a direct inhibitory bombardment or a blocking of impinging excitatory impulses or both. Analyses of the synaptic phenomenon have indicated a direct postsynaptic inhibition.

Mechanisms of Recovery.   The question now arises: Is spinal shock more than mere withdrawal of facilitation and inhibition? Withdrawal of descending influences explains adequately the decrease or release of spinal reflexes. However, there is considerable recovery from the depression of reflexes, and this requires exploration. Why recovery should occur is a puzzle, but clues to a solution are offered by the following experiment.

The effects of interrupting all the descending pathways suddenly are much more profound than those of a gradual interruption. McCouch and Fulton[9, 26] removed the motor cortex of one cerebral hemisphere and noted a depression of reflexes in the contralateral limbs (the corticospinal pathway is crossed). After the reflexes had recovered, the spinal cord was sectioned. The reflexes in the limb contralateral to the brain lesion were only moderately depressed, whereas the spinal shock was profound in the previously normal extremity. The two-stage removal of descending influences had exerted less effect than did the one-stage removal. (For a somewhat similar demonstration, see Chap. 12.) These experiments show that cerebral lesions can depress spinal reflexes. Kempinsky[16] has recently demonstrated what von Monakow deduced from clinical observations and termed diaschisis—that cerebral lesions will depress the electrical activity in a remote region with which the damaged area is neuronally connected. This "cerebral shock" or diaschisis will be discussed again in Chapter 12. It is theoretically significant that a depression of excitability of motoneurons also follows dorsal root section and that this period of depression is followed by one of increased excitability.[33]

One theory of spinal shock holds that the sudden withdrawal of facilitation decreases the excitability of spinal motoneurons and interneurons more than would be accounted for by the mere withdrawal of excitatory background. In the monkey, depression of reflexes increases for an hour or two after spinal section. Recovery of function is in part interpreted as a return to normal from the "S state" or "shock state" of the neurons. The S state is hypothetical but can be supported by analogy: in certain situations, interruption of axons can cause the cell bodies on which they terminate to undergo microscopically visible disorganization (transneuronal degeneration); degeneration of the muscle cell as a consequence of a sectioning of its motor nerve has already been pointed out. If these transjunctional changes can proceed to the point of visible degeneration, it is not inconceivable that interference with descending fibers terminating on spinal motoneurons can cause changes in them which are not visible under the microscope but which are manifest in a decreased synaptic excitability.

There is good reason to believe that spinal reflex arcs subsequently attain a level of excitability which is more than a return to normal from a hypothetical S state. In part, this hyperactivity reflects a release of function when, as is usually the case, inhibitory as well as excitatory pathways are interrupted by a lesion. Release of function would not be apparent until the S factor had disappeared. But this perhaps does not explain the protracted, month-long increase in excitability following the initial state of depression.

Convincing evidence has been adduced that motoneurons partially denervated by spinal transection[3] or posterior root section[4] become highly sensitive to chemical agents (see law of denervation, Chap. 10). If chemical substances of this kind are present in the synaptic region, they might influence the excitability of motoneurons irrespective of whether neurohumors are involved in transmission at central synapses.

McCouch and his co-workers[26] have described another mechanism which would account for a progressive increase in the excitability of reflex arcs below a spinal transection. These investigators have furnished anatomic and electrophysiologic evidence that, subsequent to spinal transection, the local posterior root fibers sprout new collaterals and produce more synaptic connections with motoneurons and interneurons.[22] This increase in connections would, for reasons already familiar (Chap. 6), increase the magnitude of a reflex response to the same peripheral stimulation. (An analogous sprouting of teledendrons of sensory neurons into denervated skin is described in Chapter 15.)

In patients suffering from neurologic disorders, the "spontaneous" recovery of function can be a difficulty, as in the disturbing flexor spasms of paraplegia; or it can be the sole hope for improvement of the patient, as in hemiplegia. Despite the latter fact, the problem of analyzing the basic mechanism of *shock* and *recovery of function* has been largely left to the future.

HIGHER CENTRAL CONTROL OF AFFERENT INPUT[23]

Within the past decade it has been discovered that descending tracts from the brain influence not only motor neurons but also the γ neurons which regulate sensitivity of the muscle spindle. These receptors make no known contribution to the sensory processes of the cerebral cortex, so that fusimotor control has motor rather than sensory significance. However, central control of the auditory end-organ sensitivity has been demonstrated. Further, higher control is exerted on the first synapse of the somatosensory system, i.e., the synapse between the peripheral afferent neuron with the second order neuron which crosses the spinal cord to ascend in the lateral and ventral white columns to the thalamus and on to the cerebral cortex. In the fundamental observation Hagbarth and Kerr[11] noted that stimulation of the reticular substance of the brain stem, whether inhibitory or facilitatory to motor activity, diminished and sometimes abolished conduction from first to second order neurons. The afferent fibers which enter the spinal cord to ascend in the posterior columns were partially blocked at their first

synapse in the medulla oblongata. These observations have been confirmed and elaborated; many brain structures exert control of the first synapse in ascending systems.

The significance of this higher control of ascending pathways is puzzling. Most surprisingly, the controls are exerted mainly by what have been considered motor areas or tracts or both, including what has been considered the highest motor tract of all—the pyramidal or corticospinal tract.

In general, the influences of descending pathways on ascending pathways tend to be inhibitory. For sensation this could be a mechanism of attention, a gating of the afferent inflow, a selection of stimuli by an active rather than a passive brain. These systems are involved in the process of "habituation" by which repeated sensory impulses lose the ability to gain access to the higher levels of the nervous system (Chap. 24). But why should a "classical"* motor tract, the pyramidal, determine transmission in the classical sensory tract? Does this make it a part of the sensory apparatus? Certainly this whole development breaks down the distinction between "sensory" and "motor" as two sequential causally related events. The significance of the descending influences on the transmission through ascending pathways which serve sensation (and the control of movement) must be considered in connection with each brain structure. Because there is no clear indication of the significance of these descending pathways to sensation, they will be discussed mainly in relation to "motor" structures and function.

---

* "Classical" means something believed for a long time (and now commencing to be considered "not the whole story" or even to be doubted).

REFERENCES

1. BALLIF L., FULTON, J. F. and LIDDELL, E. G. T. *Proc. roy. Soc.,* 1925, *B98*:589–607.
2. BARNES, C. D., JOYNT, R. J. and SCHOTTELIUS, B. A. *Amer. J. Physiol.,* 1962, *203*:1113–1116.
3. CANNON, W. B. and HAIMOVICI, H. *Amer. J. Physiol.,* 1939, *126*:731–740.
4. DRAKE, C. G. and STAVRAKY, G. W. *J. Neurophysiol.,* 1948, *11*:229–238.
5. FREEMAN, L. W. *J. Amer. Med. Ass.,* 1949, *140*:949–958, 1015–1022.
6. FRENCH, J. D. and PORTER, R. W., eds. *Basic research in paraplegia.* Springfield, Ill., Charles C Thomas, 1962.
7. FULTON, J. F. *Muscular contraction and the reflex control of movement.* Baltimore, Williams & Wilkins, 1926.

8. FULTON, J. F. and KELLER, A. D. *The sign of Babinski: A study of the evolution of cortical dominance.* Springfield, Ill., Charles C Thomas, 1932.

9. FULTON, J. F. and McCOUCH, G. P. *J. nerv. ment. Dis.,* 1937, *86:*125–146.

10. GUTTMAN, L. and WHITTERIDGE, D. *Brain,* 1947, *70:*361–404.

11. HAGBARTH, K. E. and KERR, D. I. B. *J. Neurophysiol.,* 1954, *17:*295–307.

12. HALL, M. *Phil. Trans.,* 1833, 635–665.

13. HALL, M. *Synopsis of the diastaltic nervous system; or the system of the spinal marrow; and its reflex arcs.* London, J. Mallett, 1850.

14. HEAD, H. and RIDDOCH, G. *Brain,* 1917, *40:*188–263.

15. HUNT, R. S., MELTZER, G. E. and LANDAU, W. M. *Arch. Neurol. (Chic.),* 1963, *9:*120–126.

16. KEMPINSKY, W. H. *Arch. Neurol. Psychiat. (Chic.),* 1958, *79:*376–389.

17. KUHN, R. A. *Brain,* 1950, *73:*1–51.

18. KUHN, R. A. and MACHT, M. B. *Bull. Johns Hopk. Hosp.,* 1949, *84:*43–75.

19. KUHN, W. G., JR. *J. Neurosurgery,* 1947, *4:*40–68.

20. LANDAU, W. M. and CLARE, M. H. *Arch. Neurol. (Chic.),* 1964, *10:*117–122.

21. LIDDELL, E. G. *Brain,* 1934, *57:*386–400.

22. LIU, C.-N. and CHAMBERS, W. W. *Arch. Neurol. Psychiat. (Chic.),* 1958, *79:*46–61.

23. LIVINGSTON, R. B. Chap. 31 in *Handbook of physiology; Section 1: Neurophysiology,* vol. 1, J. Field, ed., Washington, D. C., American Physiological Society, 1959.

24. MAGLADERY, J. W., PARK, A. M., PORTER, W. E. and TEASDALL, R. D. *Res. Publ. Ass. nerv. ment. Dis.,* 1952, *30:*118–151.

25. McCOUCH, G. P. *Amer. J. Physiol.,* 1924, *71:*137–152.

26. McCOUCH, G. P. and LIU, C. Y. *J. Neurophysiol.,* 1958, *21:*205–216.

27. MELTZER, G. E., HUNT, R. S. and LANDAU, W. M. *Arch. Neurol. (Chic.),* 1963, *9:*133–136.

28. POMPEIANO, O. *Arch. ital. Biol.,* 1960, *98:*92–117.

29. RUCH, T. C. and WATTS, J. W. *Amer. J. Physiol.,* 1934, *110:*362–375.

30. SAHS, A. L. and FULTON, J. F. *J. Neurophysiol.,* 1940, *3:*258–268.

31. SHERRINGTON, C. S. *The integrative action of the nervous system.* New Haven, Conn. Yale University Press, 1906.

32. TEASDALL, R. D. and STAVRAKY, G. W. *J. Neurophysiol.,* 1953, *16:*367–375.

33. TERZUOLO, C. *J. Neurophysiol.,* 1964, *27:*578–591.

34. WEAVER, R. A., LANDAU, W. M. and HIGGINS, J. F. *Arch. Neurol. (Chic.),* 1963, *9:*127–132.

CHAPTER 9

Pontobulbar Control of Posture and Orientation in Space

By THEODORE C. RUCH

ALTHOUGH stretch reflexes are present in the chronic spinal animal, including spinal man, they are poorly sustained. For example, the knee jerk may be brisk, but a protracted stretch of the quadriceps muscles does not give rise to a persistent reflex contraction. In contrast, when the midbrain is so sectioned that the pons and medulla oblongata are left intact and connected with the spinal cord through their descending pathways, the stretch reflexes become hyperactive, *decerebrate rigidity* (Fig. 1 and Chap. 7). The myotatic reflex, which is the basis of decerebrate rigidity, has already been discussed; there remains the question of the higher control of these spinal reflexes. This question is of particular interest because decerebrate rigidity in animals resembles the spasticity associated with hemiplegia in man, a most common neurologic disorder.

Historical Note. Decerebrate rigidity was first clearly described by Sherrington in a paper published in 1898.[19] He noted that, shortly after brain stem sectioning, extensor posture became exaggerated, affecting the four extremities and the neck and tail. He argued that, since this state persisted indefinitely, it could not result from irritation incident to the cut and must therefore be looked upon as a "release" of the lower brain stem from control normally exercised by higher centers in the forebrain. His analysis of the condition is one of the classics of physiology.

In analyzing decerebrate rigidity, Sherrington first asked what forebrain areas must be destroyed to release the rigidity. He reasoned that exclusion of the pyramidal tracts was not responsible, because semisection at the level of the corpora quadrigemina caused the rigidity to appear on the *ipsilateral* side, whereas the pyramidal pathways cross below this level. Sher-

Fig. 1. Cat in decerebrate rigidity. Note hyper-extended posture of neck, arching of back (opisthotonos) and extension of tail. Sherrington described the total pattern as "an exaggerated caricature of reflex standing." (From Pollock and Davis, *J. comp. Neurol.*, 1930, *50*:377–411.)

rington concluded that decerebrate rigidity must result from interruption of extrapyramidal projections from some part of the forebrain. Subsequent chapters show that descending systems from the cerebral cortex, the basal ganglia and the cerebellum are involved. It suffices now that impulses in these paths funnel into the structures of the lower brain stem (reticular formation) which will be described in this chapter.

The second question is what brain stem nuclei maintain the rigidity by facilitating the spinal myotatic reflex arcs. The vestibular nuclei are certainly involved (not the red nuclei, as was once supposed),[16] and the lateral reticular formation has been implicated.

RETICULAR FORMATION AND THE STRETCH REFLEX[9]

According to Brodal,[5] "reticular formation" as used by anatomists comprises those areas of the brain stem which are made up of "diffuse aggregations of cells of different types and sizes, separated by a wealth of fibers travelling in all directions. Circumscribed groups of cells, such as the red nucleus or the facial nucleus, formed of relatively closely packed units of a more or less uniform size and type, are not considered to be part of the reticular formation, which forms, so to speak, a sort of matrix in which the 'specific' nuclei and the more conspicuous tracts, e.g., the medial longitudinal fasciculus, are imbedded." Some nuclei with a reticular structure have received names and tend to be excluded when physiologists use the phrase. Finally, the

trend anatomically is to break up the reticular formation into fairly circumscribed cellular areas which can be referred to as nuclei.

The functions of the reticular formation remained obscure for many years. In 1946, Magoun and Rhines[15] reported that stimulation of the reticular substance lying ventromedially in the caudal part of the bulb inhibited the knee jerk, decerebrate rigidity, and movement resulting from stimulation of the motor area of the cerebral cortex. With stimuli of ordinary intensity the inhibitory effect was bilateral, but with weak stimuli it was mainly ipsilateral. These investigators also described a facilitatory region which lay more laterally in the reticular formation and was considerably more extensive, running upward into the midbrain tegmentum, the central gray matter and the subthalamus (Fig. 2).[18] Stimulation of these regions facilitated the knee jerk and augmented the responses to stimulation of the motor area.

At first sight, these reticular areas and their reticulospinal tracts provided an exceedingly simple explanation of decerebrate rigidity and the higher control of posture that was not unlike the action of the brake and accelerator on a car. The reticular facilitatory area was considered to provide a supraspinal facilitation maintaining rigidity. The reticular inhibitory area was believed to be deprived of its input from the cerebellar and cerebral cortex, and hence functionless. However, further analysis revealed that, as previously believed, the vestibulospinal tract also facilitates stretch reflexes. Furthermore, as described in Chapter 7, the net

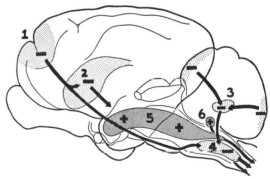

Fig. 2. Reconstruction of cat's brain showing inhibitory and facilitatory systems concerned in spasticity. Inhibitory pathways are: *1*, corticobulboreticular; *2*, caudatospinal; *3*, cerebelloreticular; and *4*, reticulospinal. Facilitatory pathways are: *5*, reticulospinal and *6*, vestibulospinal. (From Lindsley *et al., J. Neurophysiol.*, 1949, *12*:197–216.)

effect of bulbospinal descending pathways in the decerebrate preparation is facilitatory to extensor reflexes and inhibitory to flexor reflexes. If the lateral reticular area were purely facilitatory, loss of its influence could not explain the changes in reflex activity following spinal transection in a decerebrate preparation, because there is a reciprocal decrease of the stretch reflex excitability and increase of flexor reflex excitability.

Further experimentation by Sprague and Chambers[20] has removed this objection by showing that the purely inhibitory and purely excitatory effects of reticular stimulation described by Magoun and Rhines are the exception, not the rule. Generalized inhibition is uncommon in decerebrate cats, and it never occurs in unanesthetized intact cats stimulated through implanted electrodes. Rather, the effect is reciprocal—extensor inhibition-flexor contraction and vice versa—in a given limb. Thus, the reticulospinal tract obeys Sherrington's law of reciprocal innervation.* Threshold stimulation near the midline (the inhibitory area of Magoun and Rhines) tends to inhibit extensor tonus and to cause flexor contraction. Lateral stimulation (the facilitatory area of Magoun and Rhines) tends to facilitate decerebrate rigidity and inhibit flexion. (Reciprocal effects on the opposite limbs are also the rule.)

Gernandt and Thulin[8] recorded monosynaptic and multisynaptic ventral root reflex discharge while stimulating the reticular substance. They found definite reciprocal effects, especially from the medial reticular area. Moving the stimulating electrode position only 0.1 mm. might change the response to the reverse reciprocal effect. Often, an inhibitory or facilitatory effect which was strong at first decayed even though the stimulation was continued. Such decaying responses were followed by a postexcitatory rebound of opposite sign—typical of stimulation of a "mixed" structure. Since Magoun and Rhines originally investigated extensor reflexes extensively and nociceptive flexion reflexes very little, it is quite apparent how the idea of a purely facilitatory and a purely inhibitory area in the reticular formation could

* Should this prove otherwise, it would be profitable to think of possible nonpostural functions for this system, where nonreciprocal effects would be meaningful. Thus it is possible that the descending reticular system is concerned with awakening the animal or putting it to sleep, as is the ascending aspect of this system (Chap. 23).

arise. In the light of the subsequent work by Sprague and Chambers and others, it would be appropriate to refer to the "bulbar reticular extensor inhibitory area" and the "lateral reticular extensor facilitatory area."

Alpha and Gamma Mechanisms of Higher Control. In considering the influence of various brain centers on myotatic reflexes and tonus, one must think of two ways in which such reflexes can be influenced: (i) by facilitation or inhibition of the large α motoneurons which innervate the majority of muscle fibers; (ii) by facilitation or inhibition of the small γ motoneurons which cause contraction of the intrafusal fibers of the muscle spindles, thereby increasing the rate of spindle firing, which in turn influences the amount of the α motoneuron firing that underlies extensor tonus. The reticular system apparently acts mainly through the γ efferents. Since the spindle discharge is only mildly inhibitory to the flexion reflex, the reticular system will affect chiefly extensor myotatic reflexes. This helps us understand how the lateral reticular areas could appear to be purely facilitatory.

Granit and Kaada[10] attached an extensor muscle to a sensitive myograph; a cut-down dorsal root filament, containing a Group I fiber from a muscle spindle in the muscle was placed on recording electrodes. When a point in the brain was stimulated, they could learn: (i) whether the muscle spindle firing was decreased or increased; (ii) whether there was any change in muscle contraction which might account for the change in spindle activity through slackening the muscle spindles. Weak stimulation of the pontile and mesencephalic ("facilitatory") reticular areas augmented the spindle discharge without causing a change in muscle tension.

In similar experiments, the bulbar region, from which Magoun and Rhines obtained inhibition of the knee jerk and decerebrate rigidity, was stimulated. The rate of spindle discharge was dramatically reduced as the result of γ efferent inhibition. An example of such an experiment is shown in Figure 3. Many of the cerebellar and cerebral structures which affect posture do so via the γ efferent system and presumably through the reticular areas. Other descending impulses may act upon the α motoneurons; e.g., elimination of the anterior cerebellum augments decerebrate rigidity although simultaneously paralyzing the γ efferent system.[6] This effect must be exerted directly upon the α motoneurons, probably by the vestibulospinal tract.

Input to Reticular and Nuclear Structures. If, as pointed out above, the lower brain stem gives rise to descending axons inhibitory as well

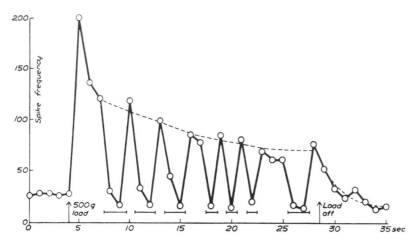

Fig. 3. Discharge frequency of a single fiber from a muscle spindle loaded with 500 grams. The bulboreticular inhibitory system was stimulated intermittently as shown by the lines below the curve. Note accompanying decrease in rate of spindle discharge. (From Granit and Kaada, *Acta physiol. scand.,* 1953, *27*:130–160.)

as excitatory to myotatic reflexes, why are myotatic reflexes hyperactive after decerebration? More specifically, why does the facilitatory pathway remain active while the inhibitory pathway is no longer functional? The reason is that the extensor inhibitory reticular system is dependent for its activity on impulses descending from higher centers (cerebral and cerebellar cortex). In contrast, vestibulospinal pathways facilitating extensors are activated through the labyrinth, and the reticular extensor facilitatory system receives impulses from the ascending afferent systems, including those originating in the muscles. A midbrain transection would remove the input into the reticular inhibitory system, thus leaving the innervated facilitatory system unopposed and the extensor reflexes overactive.

Summary. The brain stem is the origin of descending pathways, vestibular and reticular, that facilitate myotatic reflexes of extensor muscles (and inhibit nociceptive flexor reflexes), so that hypertonus (exaggerated standing) occurs when the effects of this system are unopposed by descending inhibition of myotatic reflexes (and facilitation of flexor reflexes). The actions on stretch reflexes are by two routes: (i) gamma efferent fibers innervating intrafusal fibers, and (ii) alpha motoneurons innervating the ordinary extrafusal motor fibers.

POSTURAL REFLEXES
(STATIC REACTIONS)

Postural reactions, sometimes designated "attitudinal" reflexes,[12, 13] are of three types: (i) local static reactions, (ii) segmental static reactions, and (iii) general static reactions, which include the tonic neck and labyrinthine reflexes. These terms were used by Magnus in his famous book *Körperstellung* (body posture). Some of the underlying reflexes have already been discussed under other names. All are proprioceptive in nature, the local static reactions stemming primarily from gravitational stimuli, segmental reactions arising from the effects of movement of one extremity on the opposite extremity, and general static reactions arising from the actual position of the head in space. Acceleratory reactions, e.g., postrotational nystagmus, are initiated by the semicircular canals and are distinct from the tonic labyrinthine reactions, which are independent of movement or acceleration.

The afferent sources of stimulation are as follows: (i) static reactions originate in the muscles themselves; (ii) segmental reactions develop as a result of afferents from one muscle acting upon fellow muscles of the same segment on the opposite side; and (iii) neck and labyrinthine reactions stem from receptors in the membranous labyrinth (the otolith) and in the neck muscles. Transecting the neural axis of an experimental animal and testing for the presence of the static reactions reveals the general site of the neural structures subserving them.

Spinal Animal. The basic pattern of the local and segmental static reflexes is to be found in the spinal animal. The stretch reflex—the most prominent of the *local static reactions*—is elicitable, though not strongly developed. The crossed extensor reflex may also be obtained, its presence indicating that *segmental static reactions* are also laid down at the spinal level. General static reactions are also seen. When a crossed extensor reflex is obtained in the high spinal preparation, the ipsilateral forelimb also extends. This reaction pattern tends to keep the animal from toppling over and is also a part of the quadrupedal pattern of movement involved in forward locomotion.

Low Decerebrate Animal (Bulbospinal Preparation).* All three types of static reactions are well developed in the decerebrate animal.

LOCAL STATIC REACTIONS. Local static reactions are most conspicuously developed in the extremities, and they have to do primarily with stance—the fixed standing posture that prevents collapse of the extremity under force of gravity. Sir Thomas Browne wrote (1646):

"For station is properly no rest, but one kinde of motion, relating unto that which Physitians (from Galen) doe name extensive or tonicall, that is an extension of the muscles and organs of motion maintaining the body at length or in its proper figure, wherein although it seem to be immoved is nevertheless [not] without all motion, for in this position the muscles are sensibly extended, and labour to support the body, which permitted unto its proper gravity would suddenly subside and fall unto the earth, as it happeneth in sleep, diseases and death; from which occult action and invisible motion of the muscles in station (as Galen declareth) proceed more offensive lassitudes then from ambulation."†

Magnus put the problem of the local static reaction as follows:[13]

"A movable limb is at times used as an *instrument* for very different purposes (such as scraping, scratching, fighting, etc.), and moves freely in all joints, whereas at other times it is transformed into a stiff and strong *pillar,* which gives the impression of being one solid column, able to carry the weight of the body. Experiments have shown that this is accomplished by a series of local static reflexes."

In becoming pillar-like, joints must become fixed; this involves simultaneous contraction of opposing muscle groups. The stretch reflex, which is at the basis of the antigravity response, is not of itself sufficient to fix a given joint: opposing muscles must contract simultaneously to ensure fixation of the joint but must relax re-

* Preparations made by transecting the neural axis can be designated by the level of the decerebrating transection or by the highest brain stem level maintaining connection with the spinal reflex arcs, e.g., bulbospinal.

† *Enquiries into vulgar and common errors,* 1646, Book 3, Chap. I. Of the Elephant, p. 105.

ciprocally when position of the extremity is changed even slightly.

The basis of this coordinated response involving the entire musculature of an extremity was discovered by Magnus in a decerebellated dog. Here the already exaggerated stretch reflexes are still more pronounced when the pads of the feet are lightly touched. The extremity in these circumstances follows one's finger as if it were a magnet. Although now designated the "positive supporting reaction," the response when first described was termed the "magnet reaction." Close analysis revealed that the reaction starts from a touch stimulus to the skin of the toe pad, i.e., *exteroceptive* stimulus; this, however, is followed by a *proprioceptive* stimulus, i.e., stretch of the interosseus muscles by separation of the toe pads. When the skin of the foot was anesthetized, the exteroceptive phase was abolished, but as soon as the toe pads became separated, the proprioceptive stimulus promptly initiated the response. Once the extremities encountered active resistance, other muscles were stretched, and they in turn reinforced the reaction initiated from the skin and small muscles of the toe pads. The reaction itself transforms the extremity from a flexible and toneless state into a supporting member having the stiffness of a rigid pillar. Although present in normal animals and in man, the reaction is more readily demonstrated in a decerebrate preparation in which all of the static reactions are released and exaggerated.

SEGMENTAL STATIC REACTIONS. The crossed extension reflex is one of the classic reactions of decerebrate animals. One must also recognize intersegmental static reactions. For example, when a hindlimb is caused to extend either through the positive supporting reaction or from a crossed extension reflex, the opposite forelimb also extends, thus demonstrating the influence of the lumbar segments upon the cervical. The same pattern also occurs in reverse—the extension of one forelimb is accompanied automatically by the extension of the opposite hindlimb, all of which is a pattern essential for quadrupedal standing as well as for locomotion.

GENERAL STATIC REACTIONS. Once an animal succeeds in standing, his stance can be modified in accordance with the needs of a given situation. If, for example, a cat lifts its head to look up to a shelf, both forelimbs become automatically extended; if it tries to look under a sofa, both forelimbs become flexed. The general static reactions are due in part to the influence of one muscle group upon muscle groups in other segments, but they are also modified by the tonic neck and labyrinthine reflexes.

Tonic neck reflexes.   In order to differentiate neck from labyrinthine reflexes, both labyrinths must be destroyed and sources of stimulation for the static reactions removed, so that only the influence of the neck muscles will be observed when the neck is turned. Rotation of the jaw to the right in such a preparation causes prompt increase in the extensor posture of both limbs on the right side and relaxation of the limbs on the other side. Dorsal flexion of the head of non-hopping animals causes extension of both forelimbs and relaxation of the hindlimbs (cat looking up to shelf); ventral flexion of the head causes relaxation of both forelimbs and extension of the hindlimbs (cat looking under sofa).

These reactions are obviously purposeful. If a cat walking forward in a straight line hears a mouse to its right, mere turning of the head to the right causes the extremities on that side to become extended, and the cat is automatically prepared for a quick takeoff with its left foot. Clear-cut utility is also seen in extension and flexion of the forelimbs when the gaze is directed upward and downward, respectively. Section of the dorsal nerve roots in the anterior cervical region abolishes these reactions. These reactions are prominent in decerebrate cats and have also been clearly demonstrated in labyrinthectomized monkeys following bilateral removal of the motor and premotor areas.

Tonic labyrinthine reflexes.   The tonic neck and labyrinthine reactions can be separated by severing bilaterally the upper four cervical sensory roots. The labyrinth itself has two distinct mechanisms, one the otolith and the other the semicircular canals. The static labyrinthine reactions are probably mediated by the otolith, and the reactions to angular acceleration appear to stem primarily from the semicircular canals, but a clear-cut distinction between the functions of the two end organs has never been achieved. The static labyrinthine reactions manifest themselves through changes in resting posture brought about by alterations of the animal's position. When the animal is placed on its back, i.e., in a horizontal supine position, the extremities are maximally extended. Extension is minimal when the animal is prone with its snout tilted 45 degrees to the horizontal plane.

This behavior is contrary to expectation, and its rationale must yet be worked out.

The low decerebrate animal never rights himself, stands or walks spontaneously. That this is not due to "shock" but rather to the loss of the necessary neural apparatus was proved by Bard and Macht,[3] who maintained bulbospinal animals for as long as 40 days without observing the spontaneous head or body righting shown by high decerebrate preparations.

High Decerebrate Animal (Midbrain and Thalamic Preparations).   The neural apparatus essential for the reactions described below appears to lie in the midbrain, since the reactions are seen if the neural axis is transected just above the red nucleus and the animal is kept alive and in good condition for one or two weeks. If the transection is even higher, yielding a thalamic or decorticate preparation, righting, standing and walking are seen immediately after the operation, and the adjustments are generally brisker and more powerful. The structures lying between the red nucleus and the cerebral cortex apparently facilitate the function of the structures which execute rigidity and walking.

RIGHTING REFLEXES.   The second category of general static reactions are the so-called righting reflexes. Once toppled over, the low decerebrate animal exhibits no tendency to regain the upright position. Cats and dogs exhibit no decerebrate rigidity when the midbrain is intact. When the animal is placed on its side, it tends first to right its head and then its body. Through a series of such maneuvers the animal may achieve an upright position, standing essentially normally on all four limbs. The midbrain primate (Fig. 4) shows a similar tendency,

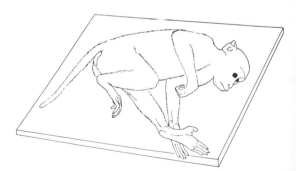

Fig. 4.   Thalamic reflex posture in decorticate monkey. Note the lowermost extremities are extended and the uppermost flexed. (From Bieber and Fulton, *Arch. Neurol. Psychiat.* (*Chic.*), 1938, *39*:433–454.)

but is unable actually to stand, even though some of the righting reflexes described below are present. The primate differs from the dog or the cat in greater encephalization of motor function in the forebrain.

The classic righting reflex can be demonstrated in the intact cat by dropping it blindfolded with its legs pointed upward. The cat turns with almost incredible speed and lights deftly on all fours. Magnus[12] noted that in every case a rotation of the head initiates the turn. This rotation he considered due to labyrinthine righting reflexes. Rotation of the upper body follows to align it with the head. This Magnus ascribed to neck righting reflexes. These two reactions are followed by rotation of the lower body, completing the turn. Rademaker and Ter Braak[17] have analyzed the muscular movements employed in turning. After its labyrinths have been destroyed, a blindfolded cat fails entirely to turn when dropped, and plummets to the floor on its back. It is not yet clear which part of the labyrinth is responsible for the reaction, but most investigators believe the utricle to be the primary receptor.

The reflexes responsible for the righting tendency have been separated into five principal groups. The reactions are sequential, as are those involved in swallowing.

Labyrinthine righting reflexes. If all the sensory channels contributing to the righting reflex are obliterated, the animal lies on its side, disoriented, and makes no attempt to bring its head or body into the horizontal position. This "zero" condition is accomplished if both labyrinths are destroyed, the animal is blindfolded, the upper cervical sensory nerve roots are cut, and a weight is applied to the upper surface of the animal's body. If, however, one of these sensory fields is left intact, its contribution can be analyzed. If an animal is blindfolded but its labyrinth is still intact, the head assumes the horizontal position irrespective of the position of the remainder of the body, i.e., the head is given orientation in space. This reaction, like that of a tonic labyrinthine response, disappears if the otoliths are destroyed. The reaction is thus static, having nothing to do with acceleratory responses. The labyrinthine righting reactions are undoubtedly primary and take the lead, as it were, in bringing the body as a whole into the upright position.

Body-on-head righting reflexes. If a labyrinthectomized animal is blindfolded and is placed in the lateral position on a table, the head also tends to right itself. The reaction can be inhibited by placing a weighted board on the animal's upper surface. The reaction thus is due to asymmetrical stimulation of the receptors of the body surface. These reactions are seen in a thalamic primate as well as in the cat and dog.

Neck righting reflexes. Once the neck has been turned in response to the labyrinthine and body-on-head righting reflexes, the neck muscle proprioceptors become stimulated, and the body itself then tends to be brought into a horizontal position following the head. This response likewise is seen in the primate and is accompanied by a grasping reflex presently to be described.

Body righting reflexes acting on body. If the head and shoulders are held in the lateral position, the hindquarters tend to assume the horizontal position independently of the forward segments. This reaction can be inhibited by applying weight to the animal's upper surface.

Optical righting reflexes. In the normal animal the eyes contribute to the righting reactions, but since the occipital lobes are absent in the thalamic preparation, visual data play no part in midbrain righting. If the labyrinths and neck muscles are denervated and the animal is dropped with its eyes open, righting still occurs, but this reaction fails if such a preparation is blindfolded. The optical cues are particularly important in the primates, for optical righting can still be demonstrated in monkeys after their motor and premotor areas have been completely removed bilaterally (Chap. 12).

Grasp reflex. The thalamic primate (unlike the cat and dog) has an abnormal distribution of postural reflexes. When the animal is in the lateral position, the lowermost extremities are vigorously extended and the uppermost extremities are flexed (Fig. 4). The uppermost extremities, furthermore, exhibit an involuntary grasp reflex. When the animal is turned to the opposite side, the thalamic reflex pattern is reversed; the extremities previously extended now become flexed and also show a grasp reflex which was previously absent. The grasp reflex seems to be a general static reaction[4] and is well known to clinical neurologists in a slightly modified form termed "forced grasping."

Postural Reactions Depending upon Cerebral and Cerebellar Cortex. Two groups of reactions important to the postural mechanism clearly depend upon the integrity of the cere-

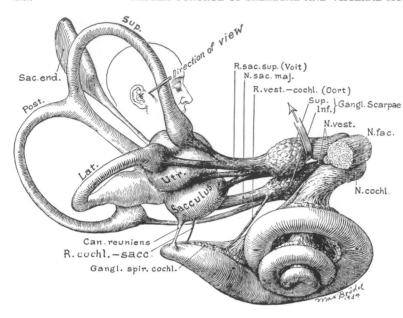

Fig. 5. Structural relations of innervation of human labyrinth. Note orientation of the three nerves supplying the macula sacculi—also Oort's nerve, passing through the cochlea. (From Hardy, *Anat. Rec.*, 1935, *59*:403–418.)

bral cortex[2] and the cerebellum.[20] These are the placing and the hopping reactions.

PLACING REACTIONS. The placing reactions ensure that the foot shall be in a position suitable for normal standing and normal locomotion. These reactions are of two types, visual and nonvisual. When an animal is lowered toward a visible supporting surface, the forelimbs are put down, so that, without further adjustment, the limbs are in a position to support the weight of the body. When the animal is blindfolded, a similar reaction occurs as a result of a combination of exteroceptive and proprioceptive stimuli.[2] (Contact placing, which occurs when the foot touches an object, is described in Chapter 14.)

HOPPING REACTIONS. Hopping reactions are evoked when the body is displaced in a horizontal direction; these maintain the animal in a normal standing posture. If an animal is held so that it stands on one leg and its body is then moved sideways, the leg hops in the direction of the displacement, so that the leg remains more or less under the body. Rademaker has pointed out that the reaction is due to stretching of the muscles and probably is little affected by exteroceptive stimuli.

LABYRINTHINE ACCELERATING REFLEXES

Although technically an organ of special sense, the labyrinth gives rise to reflexes which orient the body in space and which hence are allied to postural reflexes. The labyrinth, often referred to as the vestibular organ, is made up of two principal parts: the semicircular canals and the otolith organs (saccule and utricle), as seen in Figure 5.

Position and structure of labyrinth. The membranous semicircular canals lie within the bony labyrinth. These canals contain endolymph which communicates through fine openings with the endolymph in the utricle. The canals lie in three planes that are, approximately at least, at right angles to the mesial or sagittal plane of the body, and each of the vertical canals makes an angle of about 45 degrees with this mesial plane. The plane of each anterior canal is parallel to that of the posterior or inferior vertical canal of the opposite side of the head, as represented in Figure 6. At one end of each canal, near its junction with the utricle, is the swelling known as the ampulla. Within the ampulla lies the crista acustica, containing hair cells which communicate with the nerve fibers and which therefore are considered to be the receptors of the organ. Sitting astride the hair cells and crista is a gelatinous partition known as the cupula, which rises like a swinging door to the roof of the ampulla, filling the whole cross section of this structure. Once considered a fixation artefact, the cupula is now known to be a real structure of functional importance. It responds in a highly damped fashion to hydrostatic forces acting upon it through the endolymph. The nerve fibers distributed to the hair cells pass into the vestibular branch of the VIIIth nerve.

Function of the Semicircular Canals. The work of Flourens and of the investigators who followed him* made it evident that a primary function of the semicircular canals is to register movement of the body in space; expressed more precisely, the vestibular organ responds to any *change in the rate of movement,* i.e., to acceleration or deceleration. In fast aircraft, for example, very intense acceleratory forces may develop, particularly in the "pull-out" from a dive or in a close turn. In these circumstances the semicircular canals may be so profoundly stimulated that the pilot becomes completely disoriented in space, especially if he should inadvertently turn his head during the high acceleration (Coriolis effect).†

Acceleratory reflexes may be described under two headings: (i) linear acceleration and (ii) angular acceleration.

ACCELERATORY REFLEXES.   *Linear acceleration.* If a blindfolded cat is suddenly lowered through the air with its head down, its forelegs become extended and its toes spread (vestibular placing reaction). This is the normal response to linear acceleration. The obvious purpose of the reaction is to facilitate landing after a jump from a high place.

Angular acceleration and nystagmus.   During rapid rotation around the vertical axis of the body, a series of reactions affect the muscles of the eyes, neck, limbs and trunk. As the head turns, the eyes turn slowly in the *opposite* direction in order to maintain the gaze at a fixed point and to maintain visual contact with the environment. But, as the body turns farther, the eyes swing rapidly in the direction of the rotation and fix upon a new point, which is held in view as the eyes again move slowly and the rotation continues. This alternate movement of the eyes—a quick refixation phase followed by a slow fixation deviation—is termed *nystagmus.* The direction of the nystagmus is designated clinically by the direction of its quick phase.

When rotation continues for a time at a constant rate, the nystagmus disappears, indicating that acceleration is the stimulus for the response rather than continuous motion. If the acceleration is suddenly stopped, the involuntary eye movements commence once again, but in the opposite direction; i.e., *in postrotational nys-*

tagmus the direction of the quick phase is the opposite of the direction of the preceding acceleration (and of the quick phase during rotation). Combining this rule with a knowledge of the physiologic significance of the eye movements makes it unnecessary to remember the direction of the initial nystagmus. During rotation, the eyes move slowly in the direction opposite that of rotation in order to maintain fixation, and the quick or refixation movement is in the *same direction as the rotation.* Therefore, in postrotational nystagmus the quick phase is opposite to the direction of the prior rotation.

Nystagmus may be horizontal, vertical or rotatory in direction, since the particular response depends upon which semicircular canals or groups of canals are stimulated, i.e., upon the direction of the acceleration. If the head is bent forward at an angle of 30 degrees, the horizontal semicircular canals are in the plane of rotation about the vertical axis of the body and they become responsible for the nystagmus caused by the rotation.

Nystagmus induced by rotation or, more often, by irrigation of the ear with cold water is a clinical test of labyrinthine function. Nystagmus may occur "spontaneously" after a variety of lesions affecting the sense organs or the neural pathways connecting the labyrinth with the motor nuclei innervating the eye muscles. Such nystagmus is of great aid in localizing lesions of the brain.

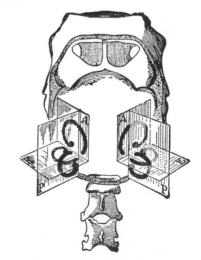

Fig. 6.   Position of semicircular canals in birds. The three canals lie in planes at right angles to one another. External or horizontal canals (*E*) on the two sides lie in same plane. Anterior canal of one side (*A*) lies in a plane parallel to that of the posterior canal (*P*) of the other side.

---

* The literature on the semicircular canals and the vestibule is very extensive. The principal bibliography may be obtained from the works by Camis,[6] and by McNalley and Stuart.[11]

†Coriolis, G. G. *Traité de la mécanique des corps solides et de calcul de l'effet des machines,* Paris, 1829.

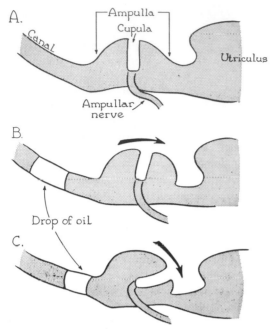

Fig. 7. Ampulla and semicircular canal of living fish (pike) before and during angular acceleration. *A*, Normal relations of ampulla, cupula and utriculus in semicircular canal. In *B*, a drop of oil has been inserted in canal. Note in *C* that cupula, nearly vertical in *B*, bends toward utricle as result of flow of endolymph into ampulla. (After Dohlman, *Proc. Roy. Soc. Med.,* 1935, *28*:1371–1380.)

Mechanism of stimulation of the canals. If the fluid in the semicircular canals moves, the mechanisms for stimulation of the hair cells during and after rotation are easily visualized. While the small diameter of the membranous canals and the consequent capillary forces and frictional resistances argue against fluid movements, direct visualization indicates that movement actually occurs—at least in the semicircular canals of fish. Steinhausen[21] devised an ingenious method of visualizing the semicircular canals in the living animal through the use of dyes, and Dohlman[7] succeeded in introducing a drop of oil into the canal so that he could follow the movement of the endolymph during angular acceleration.

Steinhausen found that the cupula (Fig. 7) bends over toward the utricle when endolymph moves into the ampulla and slowly returns to its resting position after the acceleration stops.

The relations of the canal to the ampullar nerve, the crista and the cupula are shown in Figure 7*A*. In Figure 7*B* one sees a semicircular canal at rest with a drop of oil in the lumen of the canal. In Figure 7*C* the same canal is shown during angular acceleration; the oil droplet has moved forward, and the cupula is bent over through an angle of some 30 degrees. Dohlman points out that, when the rates of displacement and return of the cupula are actually determined, they coincide precisely with the duration of nystagmus during the acceleration and with that of the postrotational nystagmus which follows. To quote:

"The cupula deviates during, perhaps, the first, or possibly also the second, revolution as long as the rotation is accelerated. On reaching a constant speed the rotation no longer affects the fluid or the cupula in any way. The deviation of the cupula is now, however, gradually diminished by its elasticity; and after about half a minute it has returned to the original position. It is to be expected that the nystagmus *during rotation* should cease when the cupula resumes its normal position, and it does, as Buys showed by nystagmographic registration several years ago.

"When rotation stops we again have, as a result of the effect of retardation on the endolymph, a deviation of the cupula, this time in the opposite direction. A post-rotational nystagmus occurs, and lasts as long as the cupula needs to return once more, through its elasticity, to its starting position. This explains why a post-rotatory nystagmus does not occur until after a longer continued rotation. And it explains why we must have a rotational time of about 20 seconds to obtain the longest nystagmus for any rotational speed. For the cupula has by that time regained its initial position by its elasticity, so that it might be ready for the maximal displacement in the opposite direction through the inertia of the endolymph when the rotation ceases. So the nystagmus *during* rotation, like the *post-rotational* nystagmus, is a consequence of the deviation of the cupula; and its duration depends on the time the cupula requires to reassume its normal position."[7]

In human subjects in whom the membranous labyrinth had been opened to expose the horizontal canal to mechanical stimulation, suddenly applied pressure caused a horizontal nystagmus lasting about 20 seconds.[7]

CLINICAL CORRELATIONS: CALORIC REACTIONS. In 1908, the Swedish neurologist Robert Bárány[1] found that irrigating the external auditory canal with water cooler than body temperature produced about a minute later a nystagmus of variable characteristics depending on the position of the head in space. This procedure has become a useful, if somewhat uncomfortable, clinical test of labyrinthine function, largely replacing the rotation test. Various theories have been proposed to explain the mechanism of caloric nystagmus, and that postulating convection currents appears to be the most satisfactory. During caloric stimulation, the endolymph within the canal is gradually cooled at the point nearest the auditory meatus. This focal chilling causes the endolymph to flow, thus leading to a deviation of the cupula caused by the convection currents. The difference between the two forms of stimulation—rotational and caloric—lies in this: rotation suddenly stimulates both labyrinths, whereas in the caloric test there is a gradual stimulation of only one labyrinth. Thus, caloric stimulation permits the neurologist to determine which labyrinth is affected and to estimate from the duration of the nystagmus the degree of impairment.

Abnormal paroxysmal stimulation of the semicircular canals or of the nerves which innervate them also occurs, the classic syndrome being the one described in the nineteenth century by the French neurologist Menière. Characteristically, the afflicted patient experiences buzzing in the ear (tinnitus), hearing loss and attacks of dizziness during which he is thrown to the ground. Failure or sluggishness of the nystagmic response to caloric stimulation is diagnostic and also indicates that the disturbance destroys function as well as stimulating it. Section of the VIIIth nerve on the affected side relieves the dizziness and improves hearing, because the normal ear hears better when the buzzing in the other ear has ended.

Utricle and Saccule.   In summarizing the vast and conflicting literature concerning the discrete functions of the various parts of the labyrinth, McNalley and Stuart[11] drew attention to the work of Ross, who succeeded in recording action currents from individual fibers of the vestibular nerve. He found that the labyrinthine receptors can be divided into three groups, those responding to slow mechanical vibration, those responding to tilting movements (linear acceleration) and those responding to rotatory movements. The semicircular canals are stimulated quite clearly by rotatory movements and probably not by gravity per se;

the cupula projection from the floor of the ampulla would not respond to an increased gravitational force. The otolith organ in the utricle responds to both linear acceleration and tilting; and, in frogs, destruction of the utricle without encroachment upon the semicircular canals has abolished the normal response to linear acceleration and tilting.

Evidence concerning the function of the *saccule* is also conflicting, but it is currently believed to be associated with reception of slow vibrational stimuli rather than being an essential part of the vestibular mechanism.[11]

REFERENCES

1. BÁRÁNY, R. *Med. Klinik*, 1908, *4*:1903–1905.
2. BARD, P. *Harvey Lect.*, 1937–38, *33*:143–169.
3. BARD, P. and MACHT, M. B. In: *Ciba Foundation Symposium on the neurological basis of behaviour*, G. E. W. WOLSTENHOLME and C. M. O'CONNOR, eds. Boston, Little, Brown and Co., 1958.
4. BIEBER, I. and FULTON, J. F. *Arch. Neurol. Psychiat. (Chic.)*, 1938, *39*:433–454.
5. BRODAL, A. *The reticular formation of the brain stem. Anatomical aspects and functional correlations.* London, Oliver and Boyd, 1957.
6. CAMIS, M. *The physiology of the vestibular apparatus*, trans. by R. S. CREED. London, Oxford University Press, 1930.
7. DOHLMAN, G. *Proc. roy. Soc. Med.*, 1935, *28*:1371–1380.
8. GERNANDT, B. E. and THULIN, C. A. *J. Neurophysiol.*, 1955, *18*:113–129.
9. GRANIT, R., HOLMGREN, B. and MERTON, P. A. *J. Physiol.*, 1955, *130*:213–224.
10. GRANIT, R. and KAADA, B. *Acta physiol. scand.*, 1953, *27*:130–160.
11. McNALLEY, W. J. and STUART, E. A. *War Med. (Chic.)*, 1942, *2*:683–771.
12. MAGNUS, R. *Körperstellung.* Berlin, J. Springer, 1924.
13. MAGNUS, R. *Lancet*, 1926, *2*:531–536; 585–588.
14. MAGOUN, H. W. *Physiol. Rev.*, 1950, *30*:459–474.
15. MAGOUN, H. W. and RHINES, R. *J. Neurophysiol.*, 1946, *9*:165–171.
16. RADEMAKER, G. G. J. *Das Stehn.* Berlin, J. Springer, 1931.
17. RADEMAKER, G. G. J. and TER BRAAK, J. W. G. *Acta otolaryng. (Stockh.)*, 1936, *23*:313 343.
18. RHINES, R. and MAGOUN, H. W. *J. Neurophysiol.*, 1946, *9*:219–229.
19. SHERRINGTON, C. S. *J. Physiol.*, 1898, *22*:319–332.
20. SPRAGUE, J. M. and CHAMBERS, W. W. *Amer. J. Physiol.*, 1954, *176*:52–64.
21. STEINHAUSEN, W. *Z. Hals-, Nas. u. Ohrenheilk.*, 1931, *29*:211–216.

CHAPTER 10

The Autonomic Nervous System

By HARRY D. PATTON

IN the foregoing chapters attention was focused on reflex systems in which the effector organ is skeletal muscle and the response is skeletal movement. Such reflex arcs are termed *somatic reflexes*. Smooth muscle, glands and the conducting tissue of the heart also receive motor nerve supplies which, when reflexly activated, alter the functional state of the innervated organ; such reflexes are termed *autonomic reflexes*.

Autonomic nerve discharge to smooth muscles and glands has an important role in visceral and glandular responses to environmental changes; for example, reflex alteration of arteriolar diameter, mediated over autonomic motor fibers supplying vascular smooth muscle, is at least partly responsible for the shifting of blood from one vascular bed to another in accordance with physiologic demand. Similarly, although not initiating the beat of the heart, reflex discharges over the autonomic nerves sup-

plying the cardiac pacemaker modulate and regulate the rate of beating, so that the varying demands upon the pumping system are automatically met. Numerous examples of the regulation of visceral and glandular structures by autonomic reflex arcs will be encountered in subsequent chapters. This chapter is concerned with the general properties and organization of the autonomic nervous system.

The distinction between autonomic and somatic motor outflows is based on both anatomic and functional grounds. Before entrance upon a detailed description of the autonomic system, a brief account of its unique and distinctive properties is appropriate. Anatomically the autonomic outflow differs from the somatic outflow in the location of the motoneuron soma. In the somatic division, the cell bodies of the motoneurons are located exclusively within the central nervous system, in the anterior spinal

226

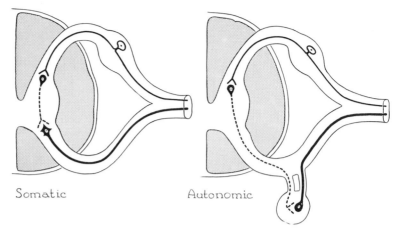

Fig. 1. Diagram illustrating a somatic reflex arc (*left*) and an autonomic reflex arc (*right*).

Somatic

Autonomic

horns or in the motor nuclei of cranial nerves in the brain stem. With one exception, the adrenal medulla, smooth muscle and glands receive direct motor innervation from cell bodies situated in ganglia outside the central nervous system. Thus the typical autonomic reflex chain contains one synaptic junction between the outflow from the central nervous system and the effector organ.

The centrally located penultimate neuron whose axon feeds the ganglion is appropriately termed the *preganglionic neuron;* its axon is typically myelinated and displays the distinctive properties of B fibers (see Chap. 3). The ultimate neuron, originating in the ganglion, is called, somewhat less appropriately, the *postganglionic neuron;* its axon is unmyelinated and displays the distinctive properties described in Chapter 3 under the heading "s.C. fibers." Figure 1 contrasts diagrammatically somatic and autonomic reflex arcs. It should be noted that the afferent sides of these arcs are indistinguishable; indeed, one and the same afferent pathway may feed both autonomic and somatic outflows. The preganglionic neuron may be considered the homologue of the interneuron of somatic arcs. Just as the interneuron, by its numerous intersegmental connections with motoneurons, tends to cause diffuse efferent discharge over several spinal segments, so the preganglionic neuron, by connection with several ganglia, may distribute the postganglionic efferent discharge.

A second fundamental difference between autonomic and somatic reflex arcs lies in the site at which inhibition occurs. In somatic arcs, inhibition is exerted by one neuron upon another, but never by a nerve cell upon an effector (muscle) cell. Relaxation of a skeletal muscle is accomplished by inhibition within the spinal cord of the motoneurons which excite it. This is *central inhibition*. In autonomic reflex arcs, presynaptic fibers may inhibit preganglionic neurons, but, in addition, some autonomic postganglionic fibers inhibit the action of the effector organs which they innervate. The best documented example of such *peripheral* or *neuroeffector inhibition* is the action of vagal impulses upon the heart—the excitability of the pacemaker is so diminished that the heart rate declines. Intense vagal stimulation may result in temporary cardiac standstill.

ORGANIZATION OF AUTONOMIC OUTFLOW

It is convenient to divide the autonomic outflow into two divisions distinguished by the location of their preganglionic cell bodies. The *sympathetic* or *thoracolumbar division* originates from preganglionic neurons in the thoracic and upper lumbar spinal segments, and its axons leave the spinal cord via the corresponding ventral roots. The *parasympathetic* or *craniosacral division* originates from preganglionic neurons in certain cranial nerve nuclei and in the second, third and fourth sacral segments of the spinal cord. The cranial outflow leaves the brain with the appropriate cranial nerves, and the sacral parasympathetic outflow emerges over the S_2, S_3 and S_4 ventral roots.

Sympathetic or Thoracolumbar Outflow. The cell bodies of the preganglionic neurons are found in the intermediolateral gray matter of spinal segments T_1 to L_2 or L_3; the axons of these neurons emerge in the corresponding ventral roots and enter the spinal nerve, where they part from the somatic motor fibers via the *white ramus communicans* to reach the paravertebral sympathetic ganglion chain.

This chain contains one ganglion for each segmental nerve, except in the cervical region where individual ganglia become variably fused to form two or three ganglia—the superior, middle and inferior cervical ganglia. The superior ganglion is the largest and gives rise to the postganglionic sympathetic supply to the head. The inferior ganglion is often fused with the first thoracic ganglion into a dumbbell-shaped structure called the "stellate" ganglion. The remaining thoracic, lumbar and sacral ganglia are variable, small and segmentally arranged.

On entering the ganglionic chain a preganglionic fiber may pursue one of three courses:

(i) It may pass up or down the chain to establish synaptic connections with postganglionic neurons in ganglia belonging to more superior or inferior segments. In this way ganglia of cervical, lower lumbar and sacral segments lacking white rami receive input from the spinal cord. The fibers connecting the ganglia in the chain are largely composed of preganglionic fibers following this course. Each such fiber connects with many postganglionic cells situated in several ganglia; a single white ramus may connect with as many as eight or nine segmental ganglia. Consequently, a discharge of discrete central origin is spread diffusely over several segments in a manner reminiscent of the multisegmental discharge of somatic arcs which contain one or more spinal interneurons. The axons of the postganglionic cells in the paravertebral chain pass through the *gray ramus communicans* to enter the corresponding segmental nerve, where they reach the autonomic effectors of the skin and subcutaneous structures (cutaneous and deep blood vessels, sweat glands, pilomotor smooth muscle). *Each spinal nerve receives a gray ramus from its corresponding ganglion.* In addition to their projections through the gray rami, the cervical and thoracic ganglia send postganglionic bundles to the structures of the thoracic cavity, notably the heart (cardiac accelerator nerves).

(ii) The preganglionic fibers may pass without interruption through the chain into the splanchnic nerves to reach the celiac or other ganglia lying in the prevertebral sympathetic plexus, which invests the abdominal aorta and its major branches down to the iliac arteries. The postganglionic neurons of the prevertebral plexus supply fibers to the smooth muscle of the abdomial and pelvic viscera, to the glands of the gut, to the blood vessels of the abdominal viscera, etc.

(iii) Some preganglionic fibers of the splanchnic nerve directly innervate the secretory cells of the adrenal medulla. The adrenal medulla is the only sympathetic effector organ known to be directly innervated by preganglionic fibers.

Parasympathetic or Craniosacral Outflow. The cranial portion of the parasympathetic outflow originates from preganglionic neurons situated in brain stem nuclei of cranial nerves III, VII, IX and X. The axons of these neurons travel with these nerves to supply postganglionic neurons in ganglia within or near the thoracic and abdominal viscera. The sacral parasympathetic outflow arises from preganglionic neurons, mostly in the third and fourth sacral spinal segments but sometimes also in the second and fifth. The axons of these neurons emerge with the corresponding ventral roots, but separate from the somatic efferent fibers to form the *nervi erigentes,* or pelvic nerves, which supply postganglionic neurons innervating the genitalia and the autonomic effectors of the pelvic cavity. The parasympathetic ganglia containing the postganglionic neurons are usually situated in or near the organ innervated. Unlike the sympathetic ganglionic system, the parasympathetic system contains few or no interconnections between ganglia. Consequently, parasympathetic discharge is more discrete than sympathetic discharge.

AUTONOMIC INNERVATION OF VARIOUS STRUCTURES

The autonomic innervation of some important visceral structures may now be summarized (see also Figure 2). More detailed accounts appear in the monographs by White *et al.,*[16] Kuntz[8] and Mitchell. [11, 12]

LACRIMAL GLANDS

PARASYMPATHETIC. *Preganglionic neurons* originate in the superior salivatory nucleus; axons pass with the VIIth nerve, the nervus intermedius, and the greater superficial petrosal and vidian nerves to reach *postganglionic neurons* in the sphenopalatine ganglion. Their axons pass in the maxillary division of the Vth nerve to the lacrimal glands. *Function:* Vasodilation and secretion.

SYMPATHETIC. *Preganglionic neurons* originate in the intermediolateral cell column of the upper thoracic spinal segments; axons ascend the sympathetic chain to reach *postganglionic neurons* in the superior cervical ganglion. Their axons ascend in the carotid plexus, the deep petrosal and vidian nerves, and the maxillary division of the Vth nerve to the glands. *Function:* Vasoconstriction.

EYE

PARASYMPATHETIC. *Preganglionic neurons* originate in oculomotor nucleus; axons travel in the oculomotor nerve to reach *postganglionic neurons* in the ciliary ganglion. Their axons traverse the short ciliary nerve to reach the ciliary muscle and the constrictor muscle of the iris. *Function:* Pupillary constriction (miosis), accommodation for near vision.*

SYMPATHETIC. *Preganglionic neurons* originate in upper thoracic segments; axons ascend the sympathetic chain to reach *postganglionic neurons* in the superior cervical ganglion. Their axons pass via the carotid plexus and the ophthalmic division of the Vth nerve to the dilator muscles of the iris, the smooth muscle of the levator palpebrae superioris, the radial fibers of the ciliary muscle and the blood vessels of the retina, orbit, and conjunctiva. In lower mammals, e.g., the cat, fibers also supply the nictitating membrane. *Function:* Pupillary dilation (mydriasis), vasoconstriction, elevation of the lid and accommodation for far vision.*

SALIVARY GLANDS

PARASYMPATHETIC. *Preganglionic neurons* of outflow to submaxillary and sublingual glands originate in the superior salivatory nucleus; those of the outflow to the parotid glands originate in the inferior salivatory nucleus. From the former, axons pass in the facial nerve and through the chorda tympani to the submaxillary and sublingual ganglia. Axons from the inferior salivatory nucleus pass via the tympani branch of the IXth nerve to the lesser superficial petrosal nerve and thence to the otic ganglion. Axons of the *postganglionic neurons* pass from the submaxillary and sublingual ganglia to their respective glands and from the otic ganglion via the auriculotemporal branch of the Vth nerve to the parotid gland. *Function:* Vasodilation and secretion.

*During accommodations for near vision the circular fibers of the ciliary muscle contract in response to the parasympathetic innervation. This action releases the tension on the suspensory ligament, permitting the anterior surface of the lens to bulge and thus assume a more nearly spherical shape. During accommodation for far vision not only do the circular fibers of the ciliary muscle relax, but the radial fibers innervated by sympathetic fibers contract. Both actions increase the tension on the suspensory ligament and thus flatten the lens.[13]

SYMPATHETIC. *Preganglionic neurons* originate in upper thoracic segments; axons ascend the chain to reach *postganglionic neurons* in the superior cervical ganglion. Their axons run along the external carotid and external maxillary arteries. *Function:* Vasoconstriction and secretion.

HEART[12]

PARASYMPATHETIC. *Preganglionic neurons* originate in the dorsal motor nucleus of the vagus; axons pass through the vagal trunk to reach *postganglionic neurons* in ganglia found in the cardiac plexus and in the walls of the atria. Distribution of the endings is disputed, but they probably reach the coronary vessels, atrial musculature, sino-atrial node and conduction tissue. *Function:* Cardiac deceleration and perhaps coronary constriction.

SYMPATHETIC. *Preganglionic neurons* originate in the intermediolateral column of the upper four or five thoracic spinal segments; axons pass with the corresponding ventral roots and white rami to the sympathetic chain to reach *postganglionic neurons* in the upper four or five thoracic ganglia and in the cervical ganglia. Axons from the cervical ganglia form the superior, middle and inferior cardiac nerves which run to the cardiac plexus, where they are joined by varying numbers of thoracic cardiac nerves from the thoracic ganglia. Some postganglionic neurons arise in ganglia along the course of the cardiac nerves and in the cardiac plexus, and receive their input from preganglionic fibers which run through the chain without synaptic interruption. Distribution of terminals is disputed, but probably extends to coronary vessels, the pacemaker, the conduction system and both the atrial and the ventricular myocardium. *Function:* Cardiac acceleration and perhaps coronary dilation.

LUNGS

PARASYMPATHETIC AND SYMPATHETIC. Origins of innervation are similar to those for the heart except that the sympathetic preganglionic portion originates in the T_2–T_6 segments. Both parasympathetic and sympathetic fibers enter the pulmonary plexus, in which the parasympathetic ganglia are embedded. Parasympathetic fibers of both supplies terminate in bronchi and blood vessels. *Function:* The parasympathetic impulses constrict and the sympathetic dilate the bronchi. Despite demonstrable vascular endings, there is little evidence of significant vasomotor regulation of pulmonary vessels.

ESOPHAGUS

PARASYMPATHETIC. Supplied by branches of the vagi. *Function:* Contraction of smooth muscle.

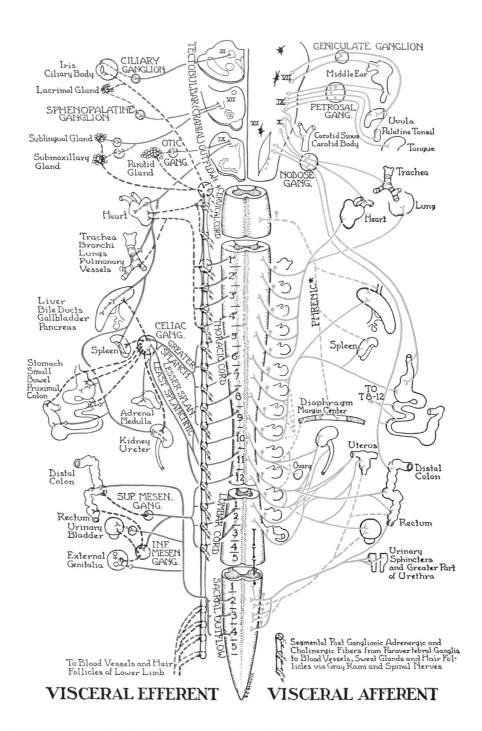

VISCERAL EFFERENT   **VISCERAL AFFERENT**

Fig. 2. Afferent and efferent innervation of visceral structures. Blue, cholinergic neurons; red, adrenergic neurons; solid lines, efferent preganglionic fibers; broken lines, efferent postganglionic fibers. Afferent fibers from diaphragm are drawn in broken lines to emphasize that it is a somatic structure even though it lies in the visceral cavity.

ABDOMINAL VISCERA, GLANDS AND VESSELS

Parasympathetic. Vagal *preganglionic* fibers traverse the prevertebral plexus without interruption to reach *postganglionic neurons* in the intrinsic plexus of the visceral organ. *Function:* Stimulation of peristalsis and gastrointestinal secretion.

Sympathetic. *Preganglionic neurons* originate in the lower seven or eight thoracic segments and the upper lumbar segments; axons run via the splanchnic nerves to reach the *postganglionic neurons* in the prevertebral ganglionic plexus. Postganglionic endings are supplied to the visceral blood vessels and the smooth muscle of the viscera. Innervation of the adrenal medulla is preganglionic. *Function:* Vasoconstriction and inhibition of peristalsis; secretion in adrenal medulla; sympathetic supply to the liver causes glycogenolysis.

PELVIC VISCERA

Parasympathetic. *Preganglionic neurons* originate in the second, third and fourth sacral segments; axons form nervi erigentes which reach ganglia in the walls of the organs innervated. *Postganglionic neurons* supply the uterus, tubes, testes, erectile tissue, sigmoid colon, rectum and bladder. *Function:* Contraction of bladder (see Chap. 51) and lower colon; erection; the significance of uterine innervation is unknown.

Sympathetic. The origin and path of *preganglionic neurons* are the same as those for innervation of abdominal viscera. *Postganglionic axons* run in the hypogastric nerves to the blood vessels, lower colon and rectum, and seminal vesicles. *Function:* Contraction of internal vesical sphincter (see Chap. 51); vasoconstriction; ejaculation of semen; inhibition of peristalsis in lower colon and rectum.

PERIPHERAL VESSELS AND
CUTANEOUS EFFECTORS

Sympathetic. These structures receive only sympathetic innervation by *postganglionic* fibers with cell bodies in the ganglion chain. Their axons join the segmental nerves via the gray rami, to be distributed to the skin and deep vessels. *Function:* Vasoconstriction in both cutaneous and deep vessels (existence of an additional system of vasodilator fibers to the vessels of muscle has been postulated from indirect evidence[4]); secretion in sweat glands; excitation of pilomotor muscles.

It will be noted from the foregoing account that some autonomic effectors (e.g., heart, coronary vessels, gut, salivary glands) receive dual innervation, and that others (e.g., adrenal medulla, sweat glands, pilomotor muscles, many vascular beds including those of skin and muscle) receive only sympathetic innervation.

In dually innervated systems, impulses in the two nerve supplies may act antagonistically. For example, parasympathetic impulses decelerate the heart, whereas sympathetic impulses accelerate it. In the gut, the roles of the two innervations are reversed, the sympathetic being inhibitory and the parasympathetic excitatory. In the iris both the parasympathetic and the sympathetic innervation are excitatory to their respective effector organs, but these (the circular and radial muscles) act antagonistically in regulating the diameter of the pupil. At any time, the functional state of the organ receiving antagonistic innervation depends on the balance between the tonic (continuous) discharges delivered over the two sets of nerves. Tonic discharge is regulated by reflex afferent pathways, which generally connect reciprocally with the preganglionic neurons of the two systems, so that the inhibitory discharge is increased when the excitatory discharge increases, and vice versa. Such dual innervations provide for sensitive regulation, a small afferent input being sufficient to produce pronounced functional changes in the organ.

In still other effectors receiving dual innervation, the two supplies act in synergy. One example is regulation of the secretory cell of the salivary gland. Both sympathetic and parasympathetic impulses stimulate secretion, but the respective secretions differ in composition. This difference does not, as was once thought, reflect the existence of two kinds of salivary cells; it is now clear that an individual gland cell receives secretory innervation from both sympathetic and parasympathetic supplies.[10] Regulation of effector systems receiving a single innervation is accomplished through modulation of the tonic excitatory efferent discharge.

GENERAL PRINCIPLES OF AUTONOMIC REGULATION

The many other names for the autonomic nervous system—"visceral," "involuntary," etc. —indicate that it subserves functions different from those mediated by somatic nerves. The autonomic system innervates smooth muscle, cardiac muscle and glands; the components of this system are the regulators concerned with emergency mechanisms, with repair and with the preservation of a constant internal environment. The somatic nerves, on the other hand, control striated muscle and relate the organism to its external environment. When somatic nerves are severed, the muscles they innervate degenerate. Such degeneration usually does not follow section of autonomic nerves. When deprived of autonomic innervation, the organs remain morphologically and physiologically intact, and often function autonomously to a degree.

Claude Bernard pointed out that the blood and lymph which bathe the cells of organisms constitute the *milieu interne,* or internal environment. This internal environment, a product of the organism and controlled by it, was termed the *fluid-matrix* by Walter Cannon, who expressed the belief that the organism's freedom from disturbance "in spite of extensive changes in the outer world, has been brought about by mechanisms, which maintain uniformity of the fluid-matrix." This concept of the steady states maintained in the internal environment, or fluid matrix, and of the importance of constancy of this matrix for continuous efficient action of the organism, ultimately became known as Cannon's doctrine of *homeostasis.*

An animal lacking homeostatic mechanisms must limit its activities or restrict its environment to achieve protection. For example, the frog, which has no temperature-regulating mechanism, must live in the depths of a pond during the winter to survive the cold. In contrast, many mammals can venture out in winter because their body temperature is "thermostatically" regulated to a constant level by autonomic reflex arcs which appropriately vary the diameter of the cutaneous blood vessels (through which heat is lost to the environment), the activity of the pilomotor muscles and sweat glands, and the secretion of the calorigenic product of the adrenal medulla, epinephrine. Another example of homeostasis is the maintenance of arterial blood pressure at relatively constant levels by afferent discharge of the pressoreceptors in the aortic arch and the carotid sinus. These receptors continuously monitor the arterial pressure and, through appropriate reflex connections, alter the tonic autonomic discharge controlling both the heart rate and the diameter of the arterioles.

Junctional Transmission in the Autonomic Nervous System.[1]   Figure 3 shows semidiagrammatically the results of two experiments which emphasize a fundamental contrast be-

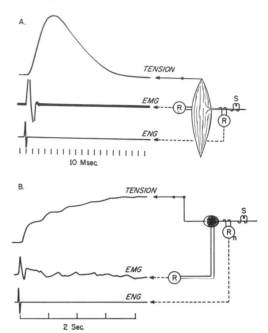

Fig. 3. Neuromuscular transmission in somatic and autonomic effector systems. *A,* Simultaneously recorded electroneurogram, electromyogram and mechanical response of skeletal nerve muscle preparation following single shock to motor nerve. *B,* Simultaneously recorded electroneurogram, electromyogram and mechanical response of nictitating membrane following single shock to postganglionic motor nerve. Note difference in time scales. (Partly after Eccles and Magladery, *J. Physiol.,* 1937, *90:*31–99.)

tween neuromuscular transmission in the somatic and in the autonomic nervous systems. The record in *A* shows the nerve action potential, the muscle action potential and the muscle tension of a skeletal muscle following a single shock to its motor nerve. Each nerve fiber in the trunk responds to the stimulus with a single brief action potential; the resultant compound potential, recorded close to the neuromuscular junction, is brief. Shortly thereafter the action potential of the muscle is recorded as a brief solitary event followed closely by the muscle twitch which is recorded as a change in muscular tension. The arrangement of stimulating and recording electrodes to obtain Figure 3*B* is similar; but the muscle is the smooth muscle of a cat's nictitating membrane, which is supplied by a motor nerve composed of sympathetic axons (from the superior cervical ganglion). As in the somatic motor nerve, the nerve action potential is brief and solitary, but the electromyogram shows a series of somewhat asynchronous deflections, which persist long after the nerve fibers have repolarized. The tension record shows, further, that each muscle action potential is associated with increments of contraction, so that the resulting tension curve is prolonged and bumpy, resembling an unfused tetanus of skeletal muscle.

Persistence of electrical and mechanical activity long beyond the duration of the excitatory nerve impulses is typical of autonomic neuroeffectors and persuasively suggests that the nerve exerts its action on effectors by liberating a chemical transmitter agent which remains and continues to act on the effector after the nerve action has ceased. Observations of this sort led to the theory of humoral transmitters. It has been pointed out that somatic neuromuscular transmission is also accomplished by the liberation of a chemical transmitter (probably acetylcholine) which depolarizes the end-plate, but that transmitter is destroyed rapidly and its action is brief. At autonomic junctions the slow destruction and prolonged action of the transmitter make the chemical nature of transmission much more immediately obvious.

Cholinergic Fibers. Humoral transmission in an autonomic neuroeffector system was first clearly demonstrated by Otto Loewi.[9] Because cardiac inhibition resulting from vagal stimulation far outlasts the period of nerve stimulation, Loewi suspected a humoral transmitter. In the experiment illustrated in Figure 4 fluid perfusing a donor frog heart (*D*) was used to perfuse a second, recipient heart (*R*). When the vagus nerve supplying heart *D* was stimulated, cardiac arrest occurred; shortly thereafter heart *R* also stopped beating, an event implicating an inhibitory chemical agent liberated into the perfusion fluid at the vagal endings in heart *D* and then carried to heart *R*. Loewi noncommittally termed the vagal inhibitory transmitter *Vagusstoff*.

Identification of Loewi's *Vagusstoff* followed from Dale's studies[3] on the pharmacologic actions of choline and its esters. He noted that the acetyl ester of choline is *parasympathomimetic*, i.e., when injected into the blood stream, acetylcholine acts upon autonomic effectors, including the heart, in a manner similar to or mimicking the action exerted on these effectors by their respective parasympathetic nerves. The drug atropine blocks the action of acetylcholine on smooth muscle and similarly blocks the action of parasympathetic nerves on their effec-

tors. The drug eserine, on the other hand, potentiates the action of acetylcholine by inactivating the enzyme cholinesterase, which splits acetylcholine into the relatively inert choline and acetic acid. Eserine also potentiates the effect of parasympathetic nerve stimulation. Such observations provided presumptive evidence that Loewi's *Vagusstoff*—as well as the transmitter at all other parasympathetic postganglionic endings—is either acetylcholine or a closely related substance.

Subsequent investigations have revealed that acetylcholine is also the transmitter agent liberated by autonomic preganglionic fibers, sympathetic as well as parasympathetic. The brief action of the transmitter in ganglia (and at the somatic neuromuscular junction) results from high concentrations of cholinesterase at these sites, so that the liberated transmitter is destroyed within the refractory period of the postjunctional cell.

Nerves which liberate an acetylcholine-like transmitter are called *cholinergic fibers*. In summary, these include somatic motor fibers, all autonomic preganglionic fibers and all parasympathetic postganglionic fibers. In addition, the sympathetic postganglionic fibers supplying sweat glands are also cholinergic (see below).

Sympathetic Postganglionic Mediators. It has already been pointed out that there is reason to suspect that sympathetic postganglionic endings liberate a humoral transmitter which is destroyed relatively slowly and which may act to prolong depolarization in sympathetic effectors. The proof that sympathetic nerve endings liberate a humoral agent under physiologic conditions was first provided by Cannon and his asso-

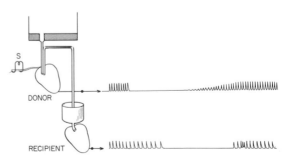

Fig. 4. Loewi's experiment demonstrating humoral mechanism of vagal inhibition of heart. Stimulation of vagus supplying donor heart released chemical inhibitory mediator which not only arrested donor heart but, after diffusion into perfusion fluid, also arrested recipient heart. (After Bain, *Quart. J. exp. Physiol.*, 1932, *22*:269–274.)

ciates when they analyzed the mechanism of the cardiac acceleration which accompanies exercise and emotional excitement. Even after the heart was completely denervated by severing of the vagi and the cardiac accelerator nerves, these investigators observed that struggling, excitement or physical exercise induced a prompt (one minute) increase in heart rate of 80 to 100 beats per minute. Such acceleration results partly from the liberation into the circulation of epinephrine by the adrenal medulla. However, adrenal secretion does not entirely account for the response. Cannon found that, after the adrenals were removed or denervated, a moderate (25 to 30 beats per minute) but delayed (three minutes) increase in heart rate followed emotional excitement. Delayed emotional tachycardia persisted in animals subjected to hypophysectomy and bilateral abdominal and cervical sympathectomy. However, complete removal of the abdominal and thoracic sympathetic chains abolished the response.

These experiments implicated an extra-adrenal humoral agent released into the blood stream during exercise or excitement and capable of exerting a sympathetic-like (acceleratory) influence on the heart. Derivation of this substance from sympathetic nerve endings was indicated by experiments in which sympathetic nerves were stimulated electrically. When injected into the blood stream, perfusates of organs collected during stimulation of their sympathetic nerves caused cardiac acceleration and increased blood pressure. Years earlier, Elliott had presciently observed that epinephrine, the secretion of the adrenal medulla, is a *sympathomimetic agent;* i.e., it mimics the action of sympathetic postganglionic stimulation. Although the actions of the sympathetic mediator and of epinephrine were very similar, there were some differences, and Cannon cautiously termed the mediator *sympathin.* It is now known that both the adrenal medulla and the sympathetic postganglionic endings secrete at least two catechol amines—epinephrine and norepinephrine. Although closely related structurally, these two substances do not invariably exert identical actions on effector organs; a full catalogue of their pharmacologic properties can be found in textbooks of pharmacology or in von Euler's monograph.[5] The proportions of epinephrine and norepinephrine secreted appear to vary from nerve to nerve, but norepinephrine is the major

sympathetic postganglionic mediator and probably corresponds to Cannon's sympathin. Adrenal medullary secretion, on the other hand, appears to be principally epinephrine, at least in man.

Nerve fibers secreting epinephrine and/or norepinephrine are called *adrenergic fibers.* Most sympathetic postganglionic fibers are adrenergic. A notable exception is the sympathetic postganglionic innervation of the sweat glands, which is cholinergic and readily blocked by atropine. Other sympathetic postganglionic cholinergic systems have been postulated but are not so well documented.

In passing it may be noted that the discovery of the adrenergic nature of sympathetic postganglionic fibers renders less anomalous the absence of a peripheral synapse in the adrenal medullary innervation. Indeed, the adrenal medullary cells and the sympathetic postganglionic neurons are very similar, since they secrete the same substance and derive from the same embryologic tissues.

Effect of Autonomic Nerve Impulses on Membrane Potentials of Postjunctional Cells.[7] The technique of intracellular recording, so fruitful in studying junctional transmission at muscle end-plates and central synapses, has had limited application to the study of autonomic transmission, principally because the effector cells are generally small and hence tolerate penetration poorly. An exception is cardiac tissue, from which satisfactory intracellular recordings can be obtained. However, a special problem is created when movement of the spontaneously beating heart dislodges the electrode. This accident can be avoided by the ingenious "dangle electrode" technique devised by Woodbury and Brady,[17] who mounted the electrode on a fine flexible wire. Once inside the fiber, the electrode rides freely with the fiber's contractions.

In the spontaneously beating heart, the beat originates in the sinoatrial node, a small nodule of specialized tissue in the wall of the right atrium (see Chaps. 29 and 30). Intracellular recordings from this tissue show rhythmically recurring slow depolarizations (the "pacemaker" potential). When depolarization proceeds to threshold, an action potential is generated (Fig. 5A). No pacemaker potential is seen in recordings from atrial fibers (Fig. 5B). The cause of the pacemaker depolarization is not settled. It

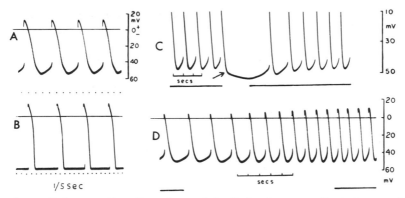

Fig. 5. Intracellular recordings from frog atrial cells beating normally during vagal inhibition and during sympathetic acceleration. *A*, Record from pacemaker cell in normally beating heart; note pacemaker potential (slow depolarization preceding each beat). *B*, Record from atrial fiber in normally beating heart; note absence of pacemaker potential (flat baseline preceding spike). *C*, Records from pacemaker cell during vagal stimulation; gain is high so that peaks of action potentials and zero reference lines are not shown. During vagal stimulation, indicated by break in bottom line, cell becomes hyperpolarized and pacemaker potentials and spikes are in abeyance. Note decreased slope of pacemaker potential in first two beats after recovery. *D*, Records from pacemaker cell during sympathetic stimulation, indicated by break in bottom line. Slope of pacemaker potential increases and rate accelerates. (From Hutter and Trautwein, *J. gen. Physiol.*, 1956, *39*:715–733.)

probably results from a gradual decrease of K^+ permeability during diastole superimposed on a relatively high Na^+ permeability.[14]

Figure 5*C* shows intracellular recordings from pacemaker tissue before, during and after vagal stimulation. During the stimulation period the membrane became hyperpolarized, and the rhythmically recurring depolarizations were abolished. With cessation of vagal stimulation, the pacemaker cell slowly depolarized as the transmitter was destroyed, until threshold was reached and an action potential was generated. During the first few beats, the rate of rise of the pacemaker potential was slow, so that the heart rate remained depressed; also, the duration of the action potential was curtailed. In subsequent beats, the recorded potentials gradually resumed the prestimulation configuration.

It is likely that hyperpolarization during vagal stimulation reflects an increased permeability of the pacemaker membrane to K^+ so that the membrane potential is driven toward the K^+ equilibrium potential. In accord with this hypothesis, acetylcholine increases total membrane conductance[15] and increases K^+ fluxes[6] in atrial pacemaker cells. Also in accord with this interpretation is the shortening of the action potential during vagal inhibitory action (note the first spike after the period of arrest in Fig. 5*C*). This shortening is a manifestation of rapid repolarization which, in pacemaker tissue, as in

nerve and skeletal muscle cells, is the consequence of increased permeability of the membrane to K^+. It will be readily recognized that the action of the vagal transmitter, presumably acetylcholine, is quite different from the action of acetylcholine on the motor end-plate. The discrepancy emphasizes the extremely varied responses of different tissues to a chemical agent.

Figure 5*D* shows the effect of sympathetic stimulation on potentials recorded intracellularly from a pacemaker cell. The firing level remains constant, but the slope of the pacemaker potential increases. As a result, the threshold voltage is reached more rapidly, and the rate of firing increases accordingly. Simultaneously, the "overshoot" of the spike increases, so that the over-all amplitude of the action potential is greater. These events are satisfactorily explained if it is assumed that the sympathetic transmitter increases the permeability of the pacemaker membrane to Na^+ ions and thus permits more rapid depolarization to the firing level and a closer approximation during the spike to the Na^+ equilibrium potential.

DENERVATION HYPERSENSITIVITY[2]

When an autonomic effector is denervated, it becomes increasingly sensitive to chemical agents. This sensitivity is most pronounced

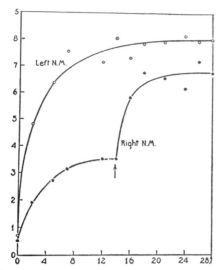

Fig. 6. Contractile responses of denervated nictitating membrane to epinephrine. *Ordinates,* Amplitude of isotonic contraction (cm.) in response to 10 μg. of epinephrine. *Abscissa,* Days after initial denervation. At day 0, left membrane denervated postganglionically, right membrane denervated preganglionically. At day 14 (*arrow*), right membrane denervated postganglionically. (From Hampel, *Amer. J. Physiol.,* 1935, *111*:611–621.)

when the organ is directly denervated by section of its *postganglionic* nerves (Cannon's law of denervation). Such denervation hypersensitivity was first described by Budge, who produced Horner's syndrome in rabbits. *Horner's syndrome,* which results from interruption of the sympathetic supply to the face, consists of pupillary constriction (miosis), drooping of the eyelid (ptosis), and flushing of the face owing to loss of vasoconstrictor tone.

Since the postganglionic sympathetic supply to the face originates in the superior cervical ganglion, which receives a preganglionic sympathetic input from the fibers ascending the cervical chain, Horner's syndrome may be experimentally produced either by dividing the cervical chain to interrupt the preganglionic fibers, or by a transection of the postganglionic fibers emerging from the ganglion. Budge found that, when a preganglionic section on one side and a postganglionic section on the other were performed, the resultant Horner's syndrome was initially symmetrical bilaterally. With the passage of time, however, the pupil on the side of the postganglionic denervation was larger than the one on the preganglionically denervated side, and the discrepancy was intensified when

the animal was frightened or subjected to emotional excitement. Budge could not explain the phenomenon of the paradoxical pupil; but it is now known that denervation hypersensitivity to circulating epinephrine (released into the blood stream during emotional excitement) accounts for the paradoxical pupil as well as for a number of similar phenomena in other denervated organs.

Even skeletal muscle displays the phenomenon of denervation hypersensitivity. Following section of the motor nerve, the muscle fiber membranes become hypersensitive to acetylcholine. Fibrillation in denervated skeletal muscle presumably results from the depolarization of hypersensitive end plates by minute quantities of circulating acetylcholine or other excitatory chemical substances.

A quantitative study of denervation hypersensitivity is illustrated in Figure 6. The response of the nictitating membrane to a standard dose of epinephrine was measured on successive days following postganglionic denervation on the right side. Both nictitating membranes underwent a gradually increased sensitivity to epinephrine, as evidenced by the amplified responses, but the sensitivity was much more prominent in the membrane postganglionically denervated. On the 14th day the right superior cervical ganglion was removed, and the sensitivity of the related membrane increased, approaching that displayed by the left membrane. If denervation is caused by crushing of the nerves, so that they may regenerate, hypersensitivity occurs but wanes as the regenerating fibers re-establish connections with the muscle cells.

The mechanism of denervation hypersensitivity is not understood. It is probably partly attributable to the demonstrable disappearance from the denervated structure of the enzymes which normally inactivate the transmitter (cholinesterase or monoamine oxidase). This explanation is at best only partial because the increased sensitivity is not specific; the denervated nictitating membrane becomes hypersensitive not only to epinephrine but also to acetylcholine, pilocarpine, calcium, potassium, arterenol, tyramine and several nonphenolic aromatic amines.

Surgery of the Autonomic Nervous System and Denervation Hypersensitivity. To conclude this chapter, an example may be given of the application of the functional and anatomic principles outlined above to a practical clinical problem. To relieve any of a number of disorders, the therapeutic procedure is surgical interruption of the autonomic nerve supply to the diseased organ. The signs of these diseases and the appropriate surgical procedures are discussed in detail by White *et al.*,[16] but for present purposes a single disease may be considered.

Raynaud's disease is a peripheral vascular disease in which there are painful paroxysms of cutaneous vasospasm (usually in the fingers or toes) so intense that gangrene may result. The paroxysms are often precipitated by exposure to cold or by emotional stress. While it is not certain that the vasospasm results from excessive sympathetic discharge, sympathectomy of the affected regions is nevertheless a rational procedure, since impulses in sympathetic fibers regulate vasoconstriction of cutaneous vessels and since interruption of these fibers increases blood flow through the skin.*

The vasoconstrictor pathway to the hand originates in preganglionic neurons situated in spinal segments T_2 to T_7; most of the postganglionic cell bodies are in the stellate ganglion, although a varying small number lie in the second and third thoracic ganglion. The hand can thus be sympathectomized by removal of the stellate, T_2 and T_3 ganglia. This operation has the defect of producing a Horner's syndrome, since the preganglionic fibers ascending the chain to the superior cervical ganglion are interrupted. A more serious objection is that the sympathectomy of the hand is postganglionic, and the denervated vessels become so sensitive to epinephrine that cold exposure or emotional stress (both of which increase adrenal medullary secretion) may precipitate vasospastic attacks

* In chronic Raynaud's disease anatomic changes in the vessels eventually prevent dilation even in the absence of vasoconstrictor nerves. In such cases sympathectomy is of no value. A standard procedure is to perform a diagnostic procaine block of the stellate ganglion. If this procedure does not cause increased blood flow to the hand, as indicated by a rise in skin temperature, surgery is not recommended.

even more severe than those occurring before operation.

A much more successful procedure is preganglionic sympathectomy. The sympathetic chain is divided between the third and fourth ganglia; this interrupts preganglionic fibers originating in segments T_4 to T_7 and ascending the chain. To interrupt the fibers originating in the T_2 to T_3 segments, the segmental nerves are cut at a point central to the entry of the postganglionic fibers via the gray rami. Not only are the consequences of denervation hypersensitivity thus avoided, but Horner's syndrome does not occur because preganglionic fibers passing from the T_1 segment to the superior cervical ganglion are intact.

REFERENCES

1. CANNON, W. B. and ROSENBLUETH, A. *Autonomic neuro-effector system.* New York, Macmillan, 1937.
2. CANNON, W. B. and ROSENBLUETH, A. *The supersensitivity of denervated structures.* New York, Macmillan, 1949.
3. DALE, H. H. *J. Pharmacol.* 1914, 6:147–190.
4. ELIASSON, S., LINDGREN, P. and UVNÄS, B. *Acta physiol. scand.,* 1952, 27:18–37.
5. VON EULER, U. S. *Noradrenaline.* Springfield, Ill., Charles C Thomas, 1955.
6. HUTTER, O. F. In: *Nervous inhibition.* E. Florey, ed. New York, Pergamon Press, 1961.
7. HUTTER, O. F. and TRAUTWEIN, W. *J. gen. Physiol.,* 1956, 39:715–733.
8. KUNTZ, A. *The autonomic nervous system.* Philadelphia, Lea and Febiger, 1953.
9. LOEWI, O. *Pflüg. Arch. ges. Physiol.,* 1921, 189:239–242.
10. LUNDBERG, A. *Acta physiol. scand.,* 1957, 40:21–34.
11. MITCHELL, G. A. G. *Anatomy of the autonomic nervous system.* Edinburgh, E. and S. Livingstone Ltd., 1953.
12. MITCHELL, G. A. G. *Cardiovascular innervation.* Edinburgh, E. and S. Livingstone Ltd., 1956.
13. MORGAN, M. W., JR., OLMSTEAD, J. M. D. and WATROUS, W. G. *Amer. J. Physiol.,* 1940, 128:588–591.
14. TRAUTWEIN, W. and KASSEBAUM, D. G. *J. gen. Physiol.,* 1961, 45:317–330.
15. TRAUTWEIN, W., KUFFLER, S. W. and EDWARDS, C. *J. gen. Physiol.,* 1956, 40:135–145.
16. WHITE, J. C., SMITHWICK, R. H. and SIMEONE, F. A. *The autonomic nervous system.* New York, Macmillan, 1952.
17. WOODBURY, J. W. and BRADY, A. J. *Science,* 1956, 123:100–101.

CHAPTER 11

Higher Control of Autonomic Outflows: The Hypothalamus

By HARRY D. PATTON

INTRODUCTION

In the previous chapter it was pointed out that visceral organs, glands and blood vessels—structures important in the maintenance of a constant internal environment (homeostasis)—are regulated by the autonomic nervous system. The preganglionic autonomic neurons are maintained in a continuous but quantitatively variable state of activity by a host of inputs. Some of these inputs are segmental in origin (dorsal roots); others originate in supraspinal structures and descend the neural axis to reach the levels of autonomic outflow.

Some idea of the relative role of supraspinal as contrasted to segmental control of the spinal autonomic outflows (sympathetic and sacral parasympathetic) can be obtained by studying autonomic reflexes in animals subjected to transection of the neural axis at different levels. After the spinal cord is transected above the level of T_1, for example, the spinal autonomic outflows are regulated solely by segmental inputs. The immediate consequence of such a transection is profound depression of all autonomic reflexes,[57] paralleling the depression of somatic reflexes

(spinal shock). Blood pressure drops precipitously, owing to a decrease in the sympathetic discharge to the visceral vascular bed and a consequent diminution in the peripheral resistance to flow.* Temperature regulation is lacking, sweating is absent, and the body temperature changes toward that of the environment. The bladder and bowel are paralyzed, and sexual reflexes (erection and ejaculation) are lacking.

After several weeks spinal shock wanes and the segmental autonomic reflexes reappear. The blood pressure rises from the low levels typical of the spinal shock period and fluctuates in response to noxious stimulation of the skin. (Permanently lacking, however, is the adaptive vasoconstriction which normally prevents gravitational hypotension when the body is moved from a horizontal to a vertical position, because the spinal pathways which connect the pressure-monitoring receptors in the aortic arch and the carotid sinus with the sympathetic outflows are severed.) At the same time vestiges of temperature regulatory mechanisms reappear; sweating returns, and noxious stimulation of the skin may

* Regulation of heart rate remains because it is governed largely by vagal impulses.

238

elicit troublesomely profuse sweating. Immersion of one extremity in cold water induces vasoconstriction in the contralateral limb, and, conversely, heating one limb is followed by vasodilatation in the other. Nevertheless, even after long recovery periods, temperature regulation remains sluggish, and the smoothly coordinated adjustments of blood vessels, sweat glands, pilomotor muscles and skeletal muscles which make the normal mammalian body temperature independent of environmental temperature are never recovered. Similarly, micturition, defecation and sexual reflexes return and can be elicited by stimulation of the skin of the thigh or genitalia. Micturition in the paraplegic, however, often fails to evacuate the bladder completely. Even ignoring the acute effects of spinal shock, we may conclude that autonomic reflex arcs are highly dependent on supraspinal inputs.

The contribution of medullary structures to the regulation of autonomic reflexes may be inferred from studies on decerebrate preparations in which the brain stem is sectioned at the intercollicular level. Such preparations rarely survive more than a few weeks (and then only with most exacting postoperative care), so that only the acute effects of interruption of suprabulbar pathways can be studied.* The status of autonomic reflexes in such preparations resembles in general that in the spinal preparation. Temperature regulation is lacking, and body temperature fluctuates with environmental temperature. A major difference, however, is that arterial blood pressure is maintained rather well in the decerebrate preparation in contrast to the profound hypotension of the spinal animal. Moreover, both the heart and the visceral vessels respond appropriately to postural changes, so that perfusion pressure remains constant despite changes of the position of the body in space. Retention of these responses is due to the retention of the medullary vasomotor and cardioregulatory centers and their afferent inputs via the IXth (carotid sinus) and Xth (aortic arch) cranial nerves (see Chap. 34). The threshold for the micturition reflex is decreased in the decerebrate cat, an example of release of reflex function from supracollicular inhibition. The

released center, however, is in the pons, not the medulla (see Chap. 51).

Finally, if the test section is made at a higher level by removal of the cerebral cortex, residual autonomic function gives some indication of the relative participation of supracollicular brain stem structures in the regulation of autonomic function. Cats and dogs survive decortication surprisingly well and can be kept in good health for long periods. Blood pressure is well maintained, temperature regulation is normal, and the bladder, bowel and sexual functions are essentially those of the intact animal.

The full measure of autonomic reactivity in the decorticate preparation is seen when a mildly noxious stimulus such as lightly pinching the skin is applied. Such stimulation evokes a paroxysm of behavior which, because it stimulates rage, was named "sham rage" by Cannon and Bard. Sham rage is a coordinated reaction pattern with many components mediated by autonomic (principally sympathetic) outflows. Thus, in addition to somatic attitudes of anger (arching of back, spitting, snarling and protrusion of claws), the decorticate animal provoked into sham rage displays piloerection, pupillary dilation, tachycardia and elevated blood pressure. In striking contrast, the decerebrate preparation never shows such explosive behavior.†

The full significance of sham rage is discussed in Chapter 26; for now it need only be emphasized that the presence of sham rage in the decorticate preparation and its absence in the decerebrate preparation indicate that structures lying between the cortex and midbrain influence powerfuly, via descending connections, the lower brain stem and spinal autonomic centers. Moreover, this control is well integrated, so that discharges over both autonomic and somatic pathways are blended into an effective behavioral pattern. This integrative center lies in the hypothalamus.

Prior to and since the discovery of its role in sham rage, the hypothalamus has been subjected to focal lesions and focal stimulation. The results of these experiments indicate that the different areas in the hypothalamus are impor-

---

* "Chronic" decerebrate preparations which will survive a month or more can be obtained if the hypophysis and a small isolated island of the overlying hypothalamus are left intact.[7]

† In response to strong nociceptive stimuli, chronic decerebrate cats show some fragments of affective behavior, e.g., vocalization, protrusion of claws, running movements and acceleration of pulse and respiration. The responses are poorly coordinated, and the threshold for evoking them is high.[7]

tant portions of many of the visceral regulatory mechanisms which maintain the constancy of the internal environment. The remainder of this chapter is devoted to a résumé of these functions.

ANATOMIC ORGANIZATION OF THE HYPOTHALAMUS

The hypothalamus (Fig. 1) consists of those structures in the walls and floor of the third ventricle extending from a position slightly rostral to the optic chiasm caudally to the mammillary bodies. Dorsally the thalamus and subthalamus bound the hypothalamus. On its ventral surface it is connected to the hypophysis by a strand of fine nerve fibers originating in hypothalamic nuclei and running via the median eminence and infundibular stalk into the posterior lobe of the hypophysis. Much of the substance of the hypothalamus is composed of small diffusely arranged cells not clearly segregated into nuclear groups. Nevertheless, the following regions and nuclei, some more clearly delimited than others, can be defined: (i) anterior region, including the preoptic, supraoptic and paraventricular nuclei; (ii) middle region, including the tuberal nuclei and the lateral nuclear masses; and (iii) the posterior region, including the posterior hypothalamic nuclei and the mammillary nuclei.

Many afferent pathways lead into the hypothalamus; they include: (i) the *medial forebrain bundle*, which originates in the ventromedial areas of the rhinencephalon and is distributed to the preoptic region and the lateral hypothalamic and lateral mammillary nuclei; (ii) the *fornix,* which connects the hippocampus with the mammillary nuclei; (iii) the *stria terminalis,* which connect the amygdaloid nuclei with the preoptic and anterior hypothalamic regions; (iv) the *mammillary peduncle,* which feeds impulses ascending from spinal and tegmental structures into the lateral mammillary nucleus; and (v) numerous other, less well defined pathways connecting the hypothalamus with the frontal cortex, the globus pallidus and the thalamus. Branches from the optic tract ending in the supraoptic and ventromedial nuclei have also been described and implicated in the retinal regulation of hypothalamic and hypophysial function.

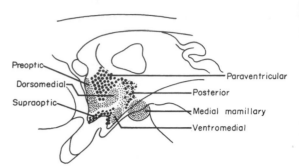

Fig. 1. Hypothalamic nuclei projected on the wall of the third ventricle. (From Peele, *The neuroanatomical basis for clinical neurology,* New York, McGraw-Hill, 1954.)

The efferent pathways include: (i) The *mammillothalamic tract of Vicq d'Azyr.* This pathway links the medial mammillary nucleus with the anterior thalamic nuclei which project to the cortex of the cingular gyrus. (ii) The *mammillotegmental tract* runs from the medial mammillary nuclei to the lateral and medial reticular structures in the tegmentum. (iii) The *periventricular system* arises mainly in the supraoptic, posterior and tuberal nuclei and descends in periventricular gray matter. Some fibers in this system terminate in the dorsomedial thalamic nucleus; others supply the midbrain tegmental reticular nuclei; but most pass into the dorsal longitudinal fasciculus. It is believed that this tract supplies brain stem parasympathetic nuclei and also, through relays, the spinal sympathetic preganglionic neurons. There is also evidence for a dorsolaterally placed descending tract leading from the hypothalamus to spinal levels. (iv) The *hypothalamico-hypophysial* tract leads from the supraoptic nuclei into the posterior lobe of the hypophysis. Some of the fibers originate from the paraventricular nuclei. The role of this tract in regulating water metabolism is discussed later. Fiber tracts leading into the posterior lobe from the tuberal nuclei have also been described.

REGULATION OF BODY TEMPERATURE[59]

It has already been pointed out that experimental animals subjected to transection of the brain stem below the level of the hypothalamus become poikilothermic. The thermoregulatory function of the hypothalamus is even more clearly indicated when discrete portions of the hypothalamus are destroyed experimentally in otherwise intact animals.

Discrete destruction or stimulation of the hypothalamus (or any other subcortical structure) is accomplished with the aid of the stereotaxic apparatus invented by Horsley and Clarke. This consists of an electrode carrier framework which is firmly attached to the animal's head by bars in the ears and clamps fitting against the upper jaw and the inferior orbital ridge. The framework on which the electrode carrier moves is calibrated in millimeters in all three planes of movement: anteroposterior, lateral and vertical. To calibrate the instrument for a given species, wires are introduced into the brain at measured coordinates in each of the three planes. The animal is then sacrificed and serial brain sections are prepared. Measurement on the sections from the distance between the holes made by the reference wires and any subcortical structure yields coordinates for the structure. Using these coordinates one can accurately introduce the uninsulated tip of an insulated electrode into the desired structure with only minimal damage to those overlying it. Stimulation can then be carried out by conventional methods. To produce a lesion a direct current is passed through the electrode tip (positive) through the brain and out through a diffuse electrode (negative) applied to the skin. The high current density at the small uninsulated tip of the electrode causes local electrolytic destruction of tissue in the surrounding region. The size of the lesion varies with current intensity and duration.

The influence of discrete hypothalamic lesions on temperature regulation varies with their location. Lesions in the rostral hypothalamus (level of optic chiasm and anterior commissure), particularly in its lateral reaches, render an animal incapable of regulating its temperature in a warm environment, although it may maintain a normal body temperature in a cold environment. Indeed, so profound is the deficit following rostral hypothalamic destruction that death from hyperthermia often results if the animal is kept at room temperature. Similarly, hyperthermia in man and inability to withstand warm environments have been described as following anterior hypothalamic lesions due to tumors or infarcts.[18, 65] The disturbances are traceable to inadequate operation of the heat loss mechanisms which normally are activated by exposure to a warm environment. In man these are principally cutaneous vasodilatation, which increases radiation of heat to the environment, and sweating, which lowers body temperature by evaporative cooling. In furry animals such as the dog and cat, panting is an important means of heat loss. Following rostral hypothalamic destruction these adaptive changes do not occur when the environmental temperature is elevated, so body temperature rises.

When lesions are placed in the caudal hypothalamus dorsolateral to the mammillary bodies, the animal's ability to maintain normal body temperature in either a warm or a cold environment is seriously impaired; such preparations are essentially poikilothermic. It is probable that the heat loss mechanisms fail in such animals because the lesions interrupt the pathways descending from the rostrally located *heat loss centers,* and that the failure to regulate against cold results from destruction of a caudally located *heat production and conservation center.* In normal animals, exposure to cold elicits cutaneous vasoconstriction, shivering, piloerection and increased epinephrine secretion—all mechanisms which tend to increase the heat content of the body and prevent excessive cooling. Epinephrine and shivering act by increasing metabolism and thus heat production, whereas piloerection* and vasoconstriction conserve body heat by increasing the surface insulation. Following posterior hypothalamic lesions these adaptive mechanisms are defective, and in cold the body temperature inclines toward environmental temperature.

In exceptional instances regulation against heat and cold may be dissociated following posterior hypothalamic lesions. An example is illustrated in Figure 2. In contrast to the intact dog (*46*), which shivered vigorously and maintained normal body temperature when exposed to cold, dog *28* with posterior hypothalamic lesions failed to shiver and suffered profound hypothermia (*left graph*). When exposed to a warm environment, however, dog *28* panted and showed only slightly elevated body temperature, in contrast to dog *72-D* with rostral hypothalamic lesions. The latter animal became markedly hyperthermic without panting after only brief exposure to a warm environment (*right graph*).

The role of hypothalamic structures in initiating thermoregulatory responses is also demon-

---

* The fluffing of body hair to trap an insulating layer of stationary air is an important means of heat conservation in furry animals. In man piloerection has no thermoregulatory importance but persists vestigially in the form of "goose bumps."

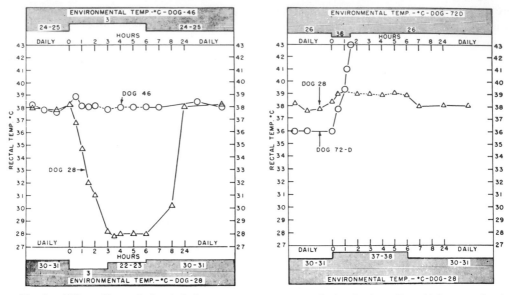

Fig. 2.   Effect of hypothalamic lesions on temperature regulation in dogs. Dog *46,* intact animal; dog *28,* posterior hypothalamic lesions; dog *72D,* rostral hypothalamic lesions. Dotted lines joining points indicate, on left, shivering; on right, panting. (From Keller. *Phys. Therap. Rev.,*1950, *30*:511–519.)

strated by stimulation experiments. In un-anesthetized animals electrical stimulation through electrodes permanently implanted in the rostral hypothalamus (level of optic chiasm and anterior commissure) causes panting and cutaneous vasodilation with a resultant drop in body temperature, particularly when the animal is in a cold environment.[4] Cold-induced shivering is inhibited by rostral hypothalamic stimulation, but exposure to cold increases the electrical threshold for inducing panting and vasodilation. These latter observations suggest reciprocal connections between the heat loss and heat production centers. On the other hand, stimulation of the posterior hypothalamus (in the tuberal region between the fornix and the mammillothalamic tract) induces a muscular tremor resembling shivering.[10]

It is thus apparent that the hypothalamus contains two opposing thermoregulatory centers which by their descending connections bring about coordinated and integrated neural discharges to structures involved in maintaining a constant body temperature. In the intact animal these two centers operate reciprocally. When environmental temperature increases and body temperature begins to rise, the anteriorly located heat loss centers are activated and overheating is prevented. Similarly, low environmental temperatures activate the pos-

teriorly placed heat conservation and production center, and the resultant shivering, pilo-erection, vasconstriction and epinephrine secretion combat excessive cooling of the body. The hypothalamic centers have been likened to a thermostat which operates automatically to prevent large fluctuations of body temperature.

A thermostat requires a receptive mechanism to sample the temperature as well as an executive mechanism to bring about the appropriate regulation. For the hypothalamic thermostat two receptive mechanisms are available: (i) cutaneous thermoreceptors, which vary their rate of firing with changes in skin temperature and which presumably feed impulses into the hypothalamic thermoregulatory centers; and (ii) centrally located thermodetectors, which respond to changes in internal, particularly intracranial, temperature. The properties of cutaneous thermoreceptors are described in detail in Chapter 14. Thermoreceptors are classified as warmth or cold receptors according to the range of temperatures which cause them to discharge. The messages from thermoreceptors are presumed to reach the hypothalamic thermoregulatory centers, where they initiate the appropriate reciprocal actions—i.e., impulses initiated in cold receptors excite the caudally located heat production and conservation center and inhibit the rostrally located heat loss center; impulses from warmth receptors have the reverse action on the hypothalamic centers. In addition, the messages from thermoreceptors presumably feed into other ascending pathways to thalamus and cortex and constitute in part the basis of conscious sensation of temperature, which provides a cue for complex adaptive behavior, such as seeking a more comfortable environment (shelter, shade, etc.).

The existence of centrally located thermodetectors is also well documented. Warming the carotid blood entering the head induces sweating, panting and vasodilation, even though skin temperature (except on the head) is not altered by the procedure. Similarly, cooling the carotid blood induces vasoconstriction, piloerection and shivering. That the thermosensitive regions are contained in the hypothalamus (and indeed are coextensive with the thermoregulatory centers) is indicated by experiments[22, 23, 42] in which local heating of the rostral hypothalamus by diathermy induced sweating, panting and vasodilation. Such local heating does not directly affect skin or body temperature; indeed, inappropriate panting and sweating could be induced by heating the hypothalamus when the body temperature was subnormal (35° C.).

Nakayama *et al.*[50] explored the rostral hypothalamus of cats with microelectrodes. About 20 per cent of the units isolated in the midline rostral to the anterior commissure increased their discharge rates when the adjacent hypothalamus was locally heated by radio frequency currents or by circulating warm water through an implanted electrode (Fig. 3). Within this

region no cold-sensitive units were found. It seems clear, therefore, that some of the hypothalamic neurons are directly sensitive to temperature and thus vary in activity in accordance with the temperature of the blood perfusing them.

The relative roles of the cutaneous receptors (sensitive to skin temperature) and the central thermodetectors (sensitive to body core temperature) in initiating and controlling thermoregulatory functions are not entirely clear.[9, 40] Magoun *et al.*[42] found it necessary to elevate hypothalamic temperature to feverish levels (104.5° to 109° F.) to elicit panting and sweating, a fact which suggested that the central receptors constitute a rather crude protective mechanism. Recent studies with more refined techniques[1] suggest that the hypothalamic thermodetectors are much more sensitive than previously supposed. Cooling the anterior hypothalamus only 0.5 to 1.0°C. by passing chilled water through an implanted thermode elicited detectable drops of skin temperature (vasoconstriction) and increases in rectal temperature and rate of oxygen consumption; warming the hypothalamus by similar amounts elicited even more pronounced increases of skin temperature (vasodilation) and decreases in rectal temperature and metabolic rate. Data on human subjects suggest that sweat secretion is related more closely to core temperature than to skin temperature.[9] Studies by Carlson[16] indicate that both cutaneous and central receptors are involved in the activation of shivering induced by cold exposure.

Fig. 3. Extracellular recording from hypothalamic thermodetector cell. *Left,* Preoptic unit (upper) and respiratory (lower) responses to local heating of the anterior hypothalamus with radio-frequency current. *Right,* graphic representation of data from the same experiment. Open circles = frequency of unit discharge; closed circles = respiratory rate. (From Nakayama *et al., Amer. J. Physiol.*, 1963, *204:*1122–1126.)

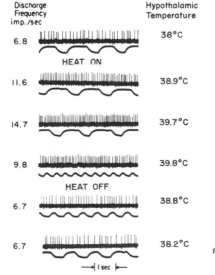

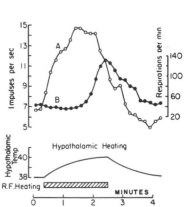

Behavioral studies indicate that central thermodetectors not only are important in simple reflex thermal adjustments but also regulate complex behavioral responses to altered environmental temperatures (see Chap. 25).

REGULATION OF WATER BALANCE[21]

It was mentioned above that a prominent tract of unmyelinated fibers originates from cells in the supraoptic and paraventricular nuclei and traverses the median eminence and pituitary stalk to terminate in the posterior lobe of the hypophysis. This hypothalamico-hypophysial tract is essential to the formation and release of posterior hypophysial hormones, the most important of which is the *antidiuretic hormone* (ADH). Its function is described in detail in Chapters 44 and 45. Briefly, ADH promotes reabsorption of water from renal tubular fluid into the blood stream and thus limits the amount of water lost from body stores to the urine. Other things being equal, urinary volume is inversely related to the amount of ADH in the blood reaching the kidney. Secretion of ADH is dependent on the integrity of the hypothalamico-hypophysial tract. Injury to the system at the supraoptic nuclear level or to its course through the median eminence and hypophysial stalk, or destruction of the posterior hypophysis itself, causes *diabetes insipidus*, in which excessive volumes of dilute urine are secreted (polyuria). The excessive urinary water loss (up to 20 liters a day in man) results in excessive thirst and ingestion of large quantities of water (polydipsia); the victim is a veritable aqueduct and spends most of his waking hours dashing from water fountain to water closet and back again.

The dependence of ADH secretion on the hypothalamico-hypophysial system has also been demonstrated by stimulation experiments. In rabbits, Harris[32] found that electrical stimulation through electrodes permanently implanted in the tract caused ADH secretion sufficient to block the diuresis induced by a previously administered oral water load.

Neurosecretion.[51] In most neurally regulated secretory systems (e.g., salivary glands, sweat glands, adrenal medulla) nerve fibers terminate on gland cells; nerve impulses initiate the secretory process in the gland cells. The neurohypophysis is an exception to this arrangement. Apart from supporting elements, the posterior lobe is relatively cell-free and its mass is largely composed of terminations of the hypothalamico-hypophysial tract. In some species, the terminal fibers are arranged in parallel rows in close relation to highly vascular connective tissue trabeculae.[11]

The fibers of the hypothalamico-hypophysial tract thus appear to innervate no particular structure but terminate blindly near blood vessels. This perplexing situation has been clarified by Bargmann's discovery[8] that chrome hematoxylin (Gomori stain) applied to sections of posterior hypophysis stains selectively dense intracellular granules which are presumed to comprise either the secretory product of the neurohypophysis or a ground substance to which the active hormone is attached. The material is found in high concentration surrounding the nerve terminals in the neural lobe but also along the entire extent of the hypothalamico-hypophysial tract and within the cells of the supraoptic and paraventricular nuclei. Electron micrographs reveal that the granules are surrounded by a plasma membrane; the nerve terminals in the posterior lobe contain, in addition to secretory granules, many vesicles similar to those found elsewhere in presynaptic fibers.[27] Water deprivation, which is known to increase the secretion of ADH (see below), causes a reduction in the amount of Gomoristainable material present, particularly in the neurohypophysis but also in the supraoptic and paraventricular cell bodies. It is therefore suggested that the paraventricular and supraoptic nuclei are composed of *neurosecretory* cells capable of elaborating ADH, which then diffuses down in the axons to the terminals to be stored in the posterior hypophysis. Unitary recordings, both extracellular[15] and intracellular,[39] from neurosecretory cells reveal that they are electrically excitable; indeed, their properties do not differ strikingly from those of other neurons. The exact relation of the electrical activity of these cells to the formation and release of ADH is not yet clear.

Regulation of ADH Secretion. Renal excretion of water is closely related to body stores of water. Ingestion of large quantities of water leads to a prompt reduction of tubular reabsorption of water and consequent diuresis. On the other hand, water deprivation leads to accelerated water reabsorption and a scant, concentrated urine. This homeostatic regulation tending to maintain constant water stores and osmotic pressure of blood is achieved by variations in the secretion of ADH in accordance with the blood osmotic pressure. Intracarotid injection of hypertonic solutions stimulates the release of ADH, so that more water is reabsorbed by the kidney. When carotid blood is made hypotonic, ADH secretion declines and diuresis results. These changes are abolished when the internal carotid artery is ligated. Somewhere within the cranial cavity, therefore, cells exist (possibly those of the supraoptic and paraventricular nuclei) which are *osmoreceptors* and which comprise a mechanism for automatic regulation of ADH secretion and hence water excretion in accordance with bodily needs.[63]

However, there may exist mechanisms other than osmoreceptors for regulating ADH secretion. Reduction of total extracellular volume, e.g., by hemorrhage, increases ADH levels and induces oliguria. Conversely, expansion of extracellular volume by transfusing isotonic solutions leads to diuresis. These facts have led to the postulation of "volume receptors" which respond to increased plasma volume and reflexly inhibit ADH secretion. Several possible sites for the hypothetical volume receptors have been suggested; a full discussion of the problem is given in Chapter 45.

Water Intake. In view of the important role of the hypothalamus in regulating water output, it is perhaps not surprising that it also plays a part in the regulation of water intake. Such a function is indicated by the experiments of Andersson and McCann,[5] who stimulated the hypothalamus of goats through permanently implanted electrodes. Stimulating the region between the columns of the fornix and the mammillothalamic tract induced polydipsic drinking sufficient to cause overhydration up to 40 per cent of the body weight and to cause dilution of renal fluid and polyuria. Microinjections of hypertonic saline in the same regions also induced polydipsia, a response suggesting (but not proving) that the responsible neurons (like the hypothalamico-hypophysial osmoreceptors) are sensitive to the osmotic pressure of the body fluids.

OXYTOCIN SECRETION

In addition to ADH the posterior pituitary elaborates a hormone, oxytocin, which causes (i) powerful contraction of the gravid or estrous uterus and (ii) ejection of milk from the lactating mammary gland. Electrical stimulation of the supraoptic hypophysial tract causes liberation of oxytocin as measured by the responses of both the estrous uterus and the lactating mammary gland.[17, 32] The natural stimuli which trigger release of oxytocin are not entirely clear. In the case of lactation the sensory irritation of the nipples incident to sucking probably constitutes the adequate stimulus. Whether oxytocin is involved in the initiation of spontaneous labor is controversial; in any event, there is no conclusive evidence that the hormone is released at term.

REGULATION OF ADENOHYPOPHYSIAL FUNCTION [33, 34]

Although it is well established that the posterior lobe of the hypophysis receives nerve fibers from the hypothalamus, repeated investigations have failed to demonstrate convincingly that the anterior hypophysial lobe is similarly innervated. Nevertheless, there is considerable evidence that the central nervous system, particularly the hypothalamus, plays some part in the government of adenohypophysial secretion. Since there are no direct neural connections which might mediate this control, it is postulated that certain hypothalamic cell groups elaborate chemical mediators which, reaching the adenohypophysis via the blood stream, stimulate the production and release of hormones. Such hypothalamic cells are thus neurosecretory cells.

Hypothalamico-hypophysial Portal System.[28] Although the hypothalamus and adenohypophysis are not neurally connected, they are connected by a special vascular system which is thought to transmit humoral agents from the hypothalamus to the pituitary. The internal carotid and posterior communicating arteries form a rich vascular plexus over the surface of the median eminence. From this plexus arise myriads of capillary loops which arch up into median eminence, where they are closely related to neurosecretory axons. The capillary loops then coalesce into larger trunks which pass down the hypophysial stalk and drain into the sinusoids of the adenohypophysis. Other branches of the internal carotids penetrate the hypophysis more directly.

Harris[32, 34] believes that a vascular connection with the hypothalamus is essential to the secretory functions of the hypophysis. Severing the pituitary stalk (and consequently the portal vessel) has no permanent effect on adenohypophysial function.[61] According to Harris, it recovers because the severed portal vessels rapidly regenerate. If, however, regeneration is prevented by inserting a paper barrier between the base of the brain and the decentralized hypophysis, or if the gland is transplanted to a remote site, signs of pituitary deficiency ensue (cessation of growth and gonadal, adrenocortical and thyroid atrophy). The interpretation is that such hypophysial transplants, although histologically intact, fail to function because they have lost the direct vascular "pipeline" from the hypothalamic neurosecretory centers.

Adrenocorticotrophic Hormone. Secretion of adrenocortical hormones (with the exception of aldosterone) is entirely regulated by the adrenocorticotrophic hormone (ACTH) secreted by the adenohypophysis (see Chap. 59). Secretion of ACTH with consequent activation of the adrenal cortex may be initiated by a wide variety of seemingly unrelated physiologic and pharmacologic stimuli which are collectively called "biologic stresses." Examples of stresses which activate the pituitary-adrenal axis are exposure to extremes of heat or cold, anoxia, hemorrhage, pain, bacterial toxins, histamine and anesthetic agents. Pituitary-adrenal responsiveness to such stresses is not altered by section of the pituitary stalk,[61] but is abolished by lesions of the median eminence or of the posterior hypothalamus.[30, 47] It is therefore postulated that stress situations induced either by afferent neural input or (in the case of chemical stresses) by direct action stimulate neurosecretory hypothalamic cells to secrete a humoral substance, corticotrophin releasing factor (CRF). CRF is carried by the portal vessels to the hypophysis, where it stimulates secretion of ACTH which, in turn, stimulates adrenocortical secretion.

Additional evidence implicating hypothalamic structures in the regulation of ACTH secretion is provided by experiments involving electrical stimulation of the hypothalamus through implanted electrodes in unanesthetized animals. Stimulation in the tuberal and posterior hypothalamic regions activates the pituitary-adrenal system.[30] Also, extracts prepared from hypothalamic tissue stimulate secretion of ACTH by pituitary cells grown in tissue culture.[31] Although such experiments indicate that the hypothalamus participates in the regulation of ACTH secretion, other mechanisms have been proposed; these are discussed in Chapter 59.

Gonadotrophin Secretion[20] (see Chaps. 62 and 63). Numerous observations suggest neural regulation of pituitary gonadotrophin secretion. In many birds and mammals the sexual cycle may be altered by varying the exposure of the animal to light. For example, a midwinter estrus in the ferret, which normally breeds in the spring, can be induced by exposing the animal to light. Such disturbances in seasonal sexual cycles depend on the visual pathways; ferrets blinded by section of the optic nerve do not have estrus cycles even when exposed to light. Light-induced estrus also fails to occur in ferrets with transected hypophysial stalks. According to Donavan and Harris[19] interruption of the hypothalamico-hypophysial portal system and prevention of vascular regeneration is critical, but this statement has been contested.[62]

Cats and rabbits normally ovulate only after coitus. In estrous cats stimulation of the hypothalamus in the vicinity of the ventromedial nuclei elicits ovulation, and lesions in the ventromedial tuberal region block coitus-induced ovulation.[58]

Thyrotrophin Secretion. Hypothalamic lesions between the levels of the paraventricular nuclei and the median eminence prevent the thyroid hypertrophy which normally results from administration of phenylthiourea.[12, 29] This compound blocks the synthesis of thyroid hormone. The resultant diminution of circulating thyroid hormone stimulates secretion of thyrotrophin, which causes the thyroid gland, although hormonally nonfunctional, to enlarge (see Chap. 60). The effectiveness of hypothalamic lesions in preventing phenylthiourea-induced goiter suggests that the lowered thyroxin blood levels act on neurosecretory cells in the hypothalamus. The latter cells presumably liberate an agent which reaches the hypophysis via the portal vessels and stimulates secretion of thyrotrophin. Conversely, when the thyroxin concentration of fluids bathing the hypothalamus is increased by local intrahypothalamic injection of thyroxin, the neurosecretory elements are depressed, and thyrotrophin secretion diminishes.[64]

Prolactin Secretion. It is well known to the dairyman as well as to the physiologist that maintenance of lactation depends on continued suckling or milking. The breasts of lactating rats undergo involution if the young are allowed to suckle only breasts rendered anesthetic by spinal transection; if suckling of breasts above the level of the transection is permitted, lactation persists.[37] Furthermore, the mammary involution which normally occurs when the litter is removed from a lactating rat can be prevented by the satanic procedure of painting the nipples with turpentine; the irritation thus produced serves as an adequate substitute for that produced by suckling.[36]

The role of the hypothalamus in the regulation of prolactin secretion is difficult to assess. Lactation involves three different hormonal mechanisms: (i) ovarian hormones, regulated by the pituitary gonadotrophins, develop and maintain the secretory tissue and duct systems; (ii) prolactin stimulates milk secretion; and (iii) oxytocin from the posterior pituitary regulates the ejection of milk. Disturbances of lactation following central neural lesions are therefore hard to analyze.

Growth Hormone Secretion. Little is known about the regulation of the secretion of somatotrophin or growth hormone. Growth is usually impaired when the pituitary is transplanted to remote sites, but whether this disorder is due to loss of the vascular connections with the hypothalamus or to other factors is not clear. Recently Bach *et al.*[6] have reported that kittens subjected to lesions of the paraventricular nucleus fail to grow and that the defect can be corrected by administering growth hormone. The hypophysis of the stunted animals showed extensive loss of acidophil cells, which are believed to be the source of growth hormone.

The physiologic stimuli to growth hormone secretion are not known. Using recently developed methods for assaying blood levels of growth hormone, two groups of investigators[38, 53] find that hypoglycemia is a potent stimulus to somatotrophin secretion. The effect is independent of insulin, glucagon and epinephrine. It is not known whether hypoglycemia acts directly on the hypophysis or indirectly through some neural structure (e.g., the paraventricular nucleus) to trigger somatotrophin release.

REGULATION OF FOOD INTAKE[14]

Hetherington and Ranson[35] first demonstrated that animals subjected to small bilateral lesions of the ventromedial hypothalamic nucleus become obese. Careful measurements indicate that the obesity results from increase in food intake, often threefold (Fig. 4). Gastrectomy does not prevent the development of

hypothalamic hyperphagia and obesity; thus there is no evidence that increased afferent input from the gastrointestinal tract drives the animals to increase their food intake. Indeed, behavioral experiments[48] suggest that the animals that were operated upon have no increased food drive and will not work as hard as normal animals for a food reward. For this reason it has been postulated that the ventromedial nucleus is concerned with *satiety* rather than with the initiation of feeding. In other words, the hyperphagic animal doesn't know when to stop eating.

When bilateral lesions are made in the lateral hypothalamus, anorexia results and the animals may die of starvation unless force fed.[2] If, rather than being destroyed, this same region is stimulated through implanted electrodes, food intake increases strikingly (Fig. 5). The lateral hypothalamic region is therefore termed a *feeding center.*

The rather precise adjustment of food intake to energy expenditure and the maintenance of relatively constant body weight thus appears to depend upon the balanced operation of the hypothalamic feeding and satiety centers. Of

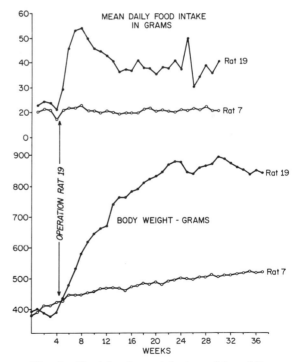

Fig. 4. Food intake and body weight of littermate rats. In rat 19 the ventromedial nucleus of the hypothalamus was electrolytically destroyed at the fourth week.

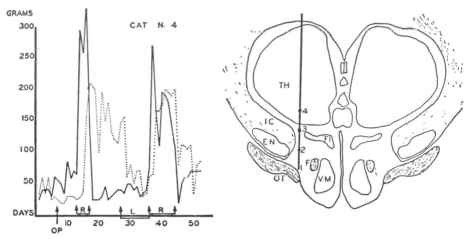

Fig. 5. Effect of stimulating feeding center on food intake in cat. *Solid lines,* meat intake; *dotted lines,* milk intake. *OP,* Implantation of electrodes; *R,* daily stimulation at a point between *2* and *3* in section with marked increase in food intake; *I,* stimulation of a point 2 mm. posterior; 1.5 mm. inferior, and 0.5 mm. lateral to *R* with no effect on food intake. (From Delgado and Anand, *Amer. J. Physiol.,* 1953, *172:*162–168.)

the two, the laterally placed feeding center appears to be dominant, since destruction of both the feeding and the satiety centers results in anorexia and weight loss. Further consideration of the role of the hypothalamic centers in regulating food intake resolves into two questions: what are the efferent connections of the centers and what are the afferent inputs which "inform" the centers of the energy stores of the body? Concerning the first question, little is known except that probably both centers give rise to descending tracts which connect with the cranial and spinal nuclei involved in the complex behavior of seeking and ingesting food. Hyperphagia has been produced by lesions caudal to the hypothalamus in the rostral mesencephalic tegmentum; such lesions presumably interrupt descending pathways from the satiety center. Two additional areas concerned with eating were disclosed by stimulation experiments, one in the premammillary region and one in the mammillary region.[54] In goats, Larsson[41] induced polyphagia by electrical stimulation in the medulla near the dorsal motor nucleus of the vagus; this region might be supposed to receive fibers from the hypothalamic feeding center.

The way in which the hypothalamic centers are activated, although a subject of much speculation, is obscure. Two theories have been advanced. One, proposed by Brobeck,[13] may be termed the *thermostat theory.* Briefly, this theory assumes that the feeding and satiety centers, like the thermoregulatory centers, are sensitive to body temperature; decrease in body temperature is supposed to activate the feeding center and depress the satiety center, whereas increased temperature acts on the centers in the opposite sense. Ingestion of food by increasing heat production [the so-called specific dynamic action (SDA)] leads to satiety, whereas the cooling of the body as heat is dissipated activates the feeding center. The SDA varies with composition of the diet; Strominger and Brobeck[60] found that rats ingest various diets not in proportion to either bulk or total caloric content but rather in proportion to the SDA.

The second theory is the *glucostat* theory, proposed by Mayer.[45] According to this theory, the hypothalamic centers are sensitive to blood glucose levels: hypoglycemia is supposed to excite the feeding center and inhibit the satiety center, whereas hyperglycemia has the reverse actions. In support of this theory, Anand *et al.*[3] found that hypoglycemia decreased electrical activity recorded through electrodes implanted in the ventromedial ("satiety") nucleus and slightly increased the activity recorded from the lateral ("feeding") center. Hyperglycemia resulted in opposite changes in the activity of the two regions. To explain the paradoxical polyphagia of diabetes mellitus (in which, of course, the blood sugar level is high), Mayer suggests that, in the absence of insulin, the failure of sugar to penetrate the receptor cells "tricks" them into behaving as if the blood sugar were actually low. A difficulty with this explanation is that brain cells, unlike cells of other tissues, apparently do not suffer alterations of glucose transport and utilization even in the absence of insulin.

Obesity is induced in mice by gold thioglucose, which destroys cells in the ventromedial nucleus. Other gold-thio compounds, many closely related to gold thioglucose and equally toxic, are ineffective. Mayer and Marshall[46] suggest that the affinity of glucoreceptors in the ventromedial nucleus for the glucose moiety of gold thioglucose causes them to accumulate damagingly high quantities of gold.

REGULATION OF GASTRIC ACID SECRETION

It has been mentioned above that hypothalamic hyperphagia is a disturbance of feeding behavior and does not appear to be directly related to alterations in gastrointestinal function. Nevertheless, the hypothalamus does appear to be involved in gastric secretory activity. According to Porter *et al.*,[24, 52] electrical stimulation of the rostral hypothalamus at the level of the optic chiasm induces a prompt increase in secretion of gastric acid indicated by a drop in pH which reaches maximum in about one hour. The

efferent pathway is the vagus nerve, for vagotomy abolishes the response (Fig. 6, *left*). Stimulation of the posterior (tuberal or mammillary) hypothalamus induces a much more delayed gastric acid secretion which is not maximal until three hours after stimulation. This latter secretory response is not influenced by vagotomy but disappears after bilateral adrenalectomy. It is therefore postulated that the hypothalamus is involved in two gastric secretory mechanisms—one neural (vagus) and the other humoral—acting through the adenohypophysis and the adrenal cortex. Insulin-induced hypoglycemia, a strong stimulus to gastric acid secretion, appears to act through both the neural and the humoral channels. Thus lowered blood sugar initiates, via the hypothalamus, not only food-seeking behavior (according to the glucostat theory) but also the secretion of gastric acid to prepare the stomach for the reception of food.

Overactivity of the hypothalamic secretory mechanism leads to injury of the stomach. In monkeys prolonged hypothalamic stimulation (two to four times daily for four to ten weeks) through implanted electrodes often leads to gastric hemorrhage and ulceration.[25] It has long been known that gastric hyperacidity and peptic ulcers occur more frequently in patients under chronic emotional stress; indeed, these abnormalities may be induced in experimental animals by subjecting them repeatedly to conflict

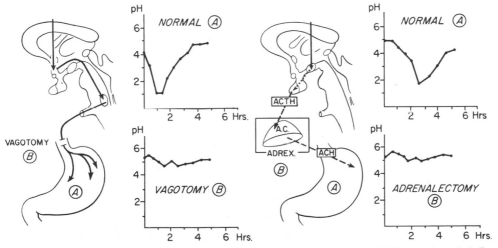

Fig. 6. Diagram of neural and humoral mechanisms regulating gastric HCl secretion. *Left*, Rostral hypothalamic stimulation causes prompt acid secretion (indicated by decreased pH in curve A); response is abolished by vagotomy (curve B). *Right*, Stimulation of posterior hypothalamus causes delayed acid secretion (curve A). Response is not altered by vagotomy but is abolished by adrenalectomy (curve B). (From French *et al.*, *Surgery*, 1953, *34*:621–632.)

situations. Peptic ulcer is therefore often described as a "psychosomatic disorder." In view of the known role of the hypothalamus in elaborating emotional behavior and in regulating gastric secretory mechanisms, it may be suggested that peptic ulcer is more aptly described as a "hypothalamosomatic disorder."

CARDIOVASCULAR REGULATION IN FEAR, ANGER AND EXERCISE

It has been observed repeatedly in experiments on anesthetized animals that electrical stimulation at various hypothalamic sites induces marked alterations in the cardiovascular system, e.g., changes in blood pressure and heart rate. The significance of these changes is not easy to evaluate in anesthetized or restrained preparations in which the behavior of the animal is suppressed. When Hess developed the technique of permanently implanting stimulating electrodes in the brain it became possible to observe the effects of hypothalamic stimulation on unanesthetized and unrestrained animals. As described in more detail in Chapter 35, such experiments indicate that the hypothalamus plays an important role in the elaboration of emotional or affective behavior. Stimulation at some hypothalamic foci elicits behavior which mimics that displayed by an animal subjected to a threatening situation and which might therefore be called the behavioral pattern of fear. Stimulation at other sites elicits aggressive reactions similar to those displayed by animals angered by natural stimuli or situations.[49] In both fear and anger, changes in heart rate and blood pressure are constantly occurring accompaniments of the total behavioral picture; along with the onset of "fight or flight," to use Cannon's expression, there are concomitant automatic adjustments of the cardiovascular system to support the increased demands for oxygen attending combat or hasty retreat. The cardiovascular changes observed in anesthetized animals during hypothalamic stimulation appear therefore to represent isolated fragments of a total behavioral pattern which is readily recognizable only in the unanesthetized and unrestrained preparation.

Adaptive cardiovascular adjustment occurs, however, in situations other than those eliciting fear or anger. Simple muscular exercise, no matter how motivated, is accompanied by prompt adaptive changes in the heart and vascular tree. Using a variety of ingeniously devised recording instruments which are attached permanently to the heart and great vessels, Rushmer[55] and his colleagues succeeded in monitoring in intact, unanesthetized dogs the cardiovascular response to exercise (walking on a treadmill). Electrical stimulation of the diencephalon in the region of the fields of Forel induces cardiovascular changes which mimic to a remarkable degree those induced in intact dogs by exercise. When bilateral lesions are inflicted on these same regions (Fig. 3, Chap. 35), exercise no longer elicits the cardiovascular adjustments seen in intact dogs.[56]

Pulmonary Edema.[26, 43, 44] An observation which documents dramatically the vital function of the hypothalamus is that lesions in the preoptic region lead to lung edema and hemorrhage. The edema often develops with an explosive suddenness within one to 24 hours after induction of the lesions and results in the rapid asphyxial death of the animal. Hypothalamic lung edema is apparently a release phenomenon, for caudal hypothalamic lesions, spinal transection or splanchnic nerve sections protects the animals from the effects of preoptic lesions. It has been suggested that the released hypothalamic centers normally regulate the capacity of the systemic venous reservoirs. After destruction of the preoptic region, the unfettered activity of the caudally located centers may result in constriction of venous reservoirs so that an excess volume of blood is dumped into the pulmonary circuit, causing lung hemorrhage and edema.

REFERENCES

1. ADAMS, T. *J. appl. Physiol.*, 1963, *18*:772–777.
2. ANAND, B. K. and BROBECK, J. R. *Yale J. Biol. Med.*, 1951, *24*:123–140.
3. ANAND, B. K., DUA S. and SINGH, B. *Electroenceph. clin. Neurophysiol.*, 1961, *13*:54–59.
4. ANDERSSON, B., GRANT, R. and LARSSON, S. *Acta physiol. scand.*, 1956, *37*:261–280.
5. ANDERSSON, B. and McCANN, S. M. *Acta physiol. scand.*, 1955, *33*:333–346.
6. BACH, L. M. N., O'BRIEN, C. P. and COOPER, G. P. *Prog. Brain Res.*, 1964, *5*:114–126.
7. BARD, P. and MACHT, M. B. Pp. 55–75 in *Ciba Foundation symposium on neurological basis of behavior*, G. E. W. WOLSTENHOLME and C. M. O'CONNER, eds. Boston, Little, Brown and Co., 1958.
8. BARGMANN, W. *Z. Zellforsch.*, 1949, *34*:610–634.
9. BENZINGER, T. H. *Proc. nat. Acad. Sci. (Wash.)*, 1959, *45*:645–659.

10. BIRZIS, L. and HEMINGWAY, A. *J. Neurophysiol.*, 1957, *20*:91–99.
11. BODIAN, D. *Bull. Johns Hopk. Hosp.*, 1951, *89*:354–376.
12. BOGDANOVE, E. M. and HALMI, N. S. *Endocrinology*, 1953, *53*:274–292.
13. BROBECK, J. R. *Yale J. Biol. Med.*, 1957, *29*:565–574.
14. BROBECK, J. R. Chap. 47 in *Handbook of physiology, Section 1: Neurophysiology*, vol. 2, J. Field, ed. Washington, D.C., American Physiological Society, 1960.
15. BROOKS, C. McC., USHIYAMA, J. and LANGE, G. *Amer. J. Physiol.*, 1962, *202*:487–490.
16. CARLSON, L. D. *Proc. Soc. exp. Biol. (N. Y.)*, 1954, *85*:303–305.
17. CROSS, B. A. and HARRIS, G. W. *J. Endocrin.*, 1952, *8*:148–161.
18. DAVISON, C. *Res. Publ. Ass. nerv. ment. Dis.*, 1940, *20*:774–823.
19. DONAVAN, B. T. and HARRIS, G. W. *Nature (Lond.)*, 1954, *174*:503–504.
20. EVERETT, J. W. *Physiol. Rev.*, 1964, *44*:373–431.
21. FISHER, C., INGRAM, W. R. and RANSON, S. W. *Diabetes insipidus and the neuro-hormonal control of water balance: a contribution to the structure and function of the hypthalamico-hypophyseal system*. Ann Arbor, Mich., Edwards Brothers, 1938.
22. FOLKOW, B., STRÖM, G. and UVNÄS, B. *Acta physiol. scand.*, 1949, *17*:317–326.
23. FOLKOW, B., STRÖM, G. and UVNÄS, B. *Acta physiol. scand.*, 1949, *17*:327–338.
24. FRENCH, J. D., LONGMIRE, R. L., PORTER, R. W. and MOVIUS, H. J. *Surgery*, 1953, *34*:621 632.
25. FRENCH, J. D., PORTER, R. W., CAVANAUGH, E. B. and LONGMIRE, R. L. *Arch Neurol. Psychiat. (Chic.)*, 1954, *72*:267–281.
26. GAMBLE, J. E. and PATTON, H. D. *Amer. J. Physiol.*, 1953, *172*:623–631.
27. GERSHENFELD, H. M., TREMEZZANI, J. H. and DE ROBERTIS, E. *Endocrinology*, 1960, *66*:741–762.
28. GREEN, J. D. and HARRIS, G. W. *J. Endocrin.*, 1947, *5*:136–146.
29. GREER, M. A. *J. clin. Endocrin.*, 1952, *12*:1259–1268.
30. DE GROOT, J. and HARRIS, G. W. *J. Physiol.*, 1950, *111*:335–346.
31. GUILLEMIN, R., HEARN, W. R., CHEEK, W. R. and HOUSHOLDER, D. E. *Endocrinology*, 1957, *60*:488–506.
32. HARRIS, G. W. *Phil. Trans.*, 1947, *B232*:385–441.
33. HARRIS, G. W. *Neural control of the pituitary gland*. London, Edward Arnold Ltd., 1955.
34. HARRIS, G. W. Chap. 39 in *Handbook of physiology, Section 1: Neurophysiology*, vol. 2, J. Field, ed., Washington, D.C., American Physiological Society, 1960.
35. HETHERINGTON, A. W. and RANSON, S. W. *Anat. Rec.*, 1940, *78*:149–172.
36. HOOKER, C. W. and WILLIAMS, W. L. *Yale J. Biol. Med.*, 1940, *12*:559–564.
37. INGELBRECHT, P. C. R. *Soc. Biol. (Paris)*, 1935, *120*:1369–1371.
38. JANSZ, A., DOORENBOS, H. and REITSMA, W. D. *Lancet*, 1963, *1*:250–251.
39. KANDEL, E. R. *J. gen. Physiol.*, 1964, *47*:691–717.
40. KERSLAKE, D. McK. *J. Physiol.*, 1955, *127*:280–296.
41. LARSSON, S. *Acta physiol. scand.*, 1954, *32*(suppl. 115):1–63.
42. MAGOUN, H. W., HARRISON, F., BROBECK, J. R. and RANSON, S. W. *J. Neurophysiol.*, 1938, *1*:101–114.
43. MAIRE, F. W. and PATTON, H. D. *Amer. J. Physiol.*, 1956, *184*:345–350.
44. MAIRE, F. W. and PATTON, H. D. *Amer. J. Physiol.*, 1956, *184*:351–355.
45. MAYER, J. *Physiol. Rev.*, 1953, *33*:472–508.
46. MAYER, J. and MARSHALL, N. B. *Nature (Lond.)*, 1956, *178*:1399–1400.
47. McCANN, S. M. and BROBECK, J. R. *Proc. Soc. exp. Biol. (N. Y.)*, 1954, *87*:318–324.
48. MILLER, N. E., BAILEY, C. J. and STEVENSON, J. A. F. *Science*, 1950, *112*:256–259.
49. NAKAO, H. *Amer. J. Physiol.*, 1958, *194*:411–418.
50. NAKAYAMA, T., HAMMEL, H. T., HARDY, J. D. and EISENMAN, J. S. *Amer. J. Physiol.*, 1963, *204*:1122–1126.
51. ORTMANN, R. Chap. 40 in *Handbook of physiology, Section 1: Neurophysiology*, vol. 2, J. Field, ed., Washington, D.C., American Physiological Society, 1960.
52. PORTER, R. W., MOVIUS, H. J. and FRENCH, J. D. *Surgery*, 1953, *33*:875–880.
53. ROTH, J., GLICK, S. M., YALOW, R. S. and BERSON, S. A. *Science*, 1963, *140*:987–988.
54. RUCH, T. C., MAIRE, F. W. and PATTON, H. D. *Abstr. Comm., Congr. int. Physiol.*, 1956, *20*:788.
55. RUSHMER, R. F. *Cardiac diagnosis, a physiologic approach*. Philadelphia, W. B. Saunders, 1955.
56. RUSHMER, R. F. and SMITH, O. A., JR. *Physiol. Rev.*, 1959, *39*:41–68.
57. SAHS, A. L. and FULTON, J. F. *J. Neurophysiol.*, 1940, *3*:258–268.
58. SAWYER, C. H. Pp. 164–174 in *Physiological triggers and discontinuous rate processes*, T. H. BULLOCK, ed. Washington, D.C., American Physiological Society, 1957.
59. STRÖM, G. Chap. 46 in *Handbook of physiology, Section 1: Neurophysiology*, vol. 2, J. Field, ed., Washington, D.C., American Physiological Society, 1960.
60. STROMINGER, J. L. and BROBECK, J. R. *Yale J. Biol. Med.*, 1953, *25*:383–390.
61. TANG, P. C. and PATTON, H. D. *Endocrinology*, 1951, *49*:86–98.
62. THOMPSON, A. P. D. and ZUCKERMAN, S. *Proc. roy. Soc.*, 1954, *B142*:437–451.
63. VERNEY, E. B. *Proc. roy. Soc.*, 1947, *B135*:25–105.
64. YAMADA, T. and GREER, M. A. *Endocrinology*, 1959, *64*:559–566.
65. ZIMMERMAN, H. M. *Res. Publ. Ass. nerv. ment. Dis.*, 1940, *20*:824–840.

CHAPTER 12

The Cerebral Cortex: Its Structure and Motor Functions

By THEODORE C. RUCH

Since antiquity, the cerebral hemispheres have been looked upon as the organ of intelligence and conscious sensation. Consequently, the structure of this region of the brain has long aroused curiosity. Ancient writers, and even those of the Renaissance, speculated widely about the localization of consciousness. Some placed the "psyche" in the cerebral ventricles; others drew diagrams suggesting precise localization of various mental faculties in different regions of the forebrain. Neurologists of the seventeenth century, such as Willis and Vieussens, carried out experiments which indicated that the brain substance, not the ventricles, is the seat of consciousness. Willis, moreover, proclaimed the cerebrum the seat of volitional movements and the cerebellum the source of involuntary movements; he also described the gross structure and blood supply of the brain in detail.

Historical note.[21] Use of the microscope came late in the analysis of the structural organization of the nervous system. The story actually began in February 1776, when an Italian medical student, Francesco Gennari, observed the well defined white line which indicates special structural organization of the occipital lobes of the brain; this line is now recognized as a primary landmark within the so-called visual cortex. In 1840, the French psychiatrist J.-P. Baillarger[24] found macroscopically that six discrete layers can be identified in most areas when thin sections of human cerebral cortex are placed between two plates of glass, but that the relative width of a given layer varies widely from one region to another. He also established that Gennari's white line extends into other cortical areas and corresponds to his own "external band."

In the early part of the present century improved staining methods were brought to bear upon the cortical histology of man and other primates, and this is still a subject of active investigation. This study has taken two main directions: (i) cytoarchitecture and myeloarchitecture, i.e., the cellular and fiber make-up of various cortical areas (Campbell,[12] Brodmann,[8] C. and O. Vogt,[71] and von Economo and Koskinas[19]); and (ii) dendritic and axonic ramifications as studied with silver impregnation methods by Ramón y Cajal[55] and, more recently, by Lorente de Nó[42] and Sholl.[59] Further insight into cortical function has been gained by investigating thalamocortical projections to specific regions and efferent projections from them. Collectively, these studies provide an anatomic framework with which functional studies—ablation, stimulation and the recording of evoked potentials—can be correlated.

STRUCTURE

Through studies of cytoarchitecture (cellular) and myeloarchitecture (dendritic and axonal), the neocortex, as opposed to the archicortex, has been subdivided into areas of specific structure in the belief that structural differences bespeak differences in function. Within each area, the cortex is divided into six more or less distinct layers. The stratification is based on the presence of specific types of cells peculiar to each layer.

The four main types of cells are:

(i) Cells with descending axons, often reaching the white substance, to be continued by a projection or association axon.

(ii) Cells with short axons ramified near the cell body, often within its area of dendritic ramification.

(iii) Cells with ascending axons ramified in one or several cortical layers.

(iv) Cells with horizontal axons.

The six recognized layers are:

I. The molecular or superficial plexiform layer. This layer lies immediately beneath the pia mater and is about 0.25 mm. thick; it is sparsely populated with nerve cell bodies,[59] and is made up of dendrites and axons from neurons lying deeper in the cortex.

II. The external granular layer, or the layer of small pyramidal cells. This layer contains many pyramidal cells, those nearer the lower boundary generally being larger than those above. The apices of these cells are directed toward the external surface. The apical dendrites terminate in the molecular layer and form the basis of intracortical association; the axon arising from the basal side of the cell passes inward to constitute one of the fibers of the medullary portion of the cerebrum. The other cells in this layer belong to the short axon group (Golgi type II or granule cells). This thick lamina of cells is sometimes subdivided into three layers of small, medium and large pyramidal cells.

III. The external pyramidal layer, a layer of larger pyramidal cells. This layer is sometimes difficult to distinguish from layer II.

IV. The internal granular or stellate layer. This layer is composed of many small multipolar cells with short branching axons. These latter are Golgi type II cells and receive endings of specific thalamic afferents to the sensory cortex.

V. The deep layer of large pyramidal cells. Here lie large or medium-sized pyramidal cells, similar in form to those in layer II, with axons which pass into the medulla or white matter of the cerebrum.

VI. The layer of fusiform or spindle-shaped cells. Layer VI consists of cells whose form is more irregular than that of the pyramidal cells. The axons of these irregularly shaped cells pass into the medullary portion of the cerebrum, and their dendrites stretch externally into the layers of pyramidal cells. This layer also contains some Golgi type II cells.

Physiologic Deductions from the Histology of the Cortex. Ramón y Cajal[55] stressed some anatomic features leading to physiologic generalizations. One to which we have returned is that every part of the cortex receives incoming impulses and gives rise to outgoing impulses; every part of the cortex is, therefore, both the terminal of an afferent path and the beginning of an efferent path. In other words, a cortical point is a reflex center of greater or lesser complexity. Second, there are provisions for the spread of impulses both horizontally through the gray matter and also along association fibers running through the white matter. Thus, efferent discharges from one part of the cortex can be aroused by impulses coming to it from other cortical areas. A given area, in addition to discharging caudally over its own efferents, may transmit impulses to another area and discharge over the latter's efferents. Third, all parts of the neocortex are described as having or departing from a basic structure.

Although the size, shape and density of cell bodies in the cerebral cortex are useful in cytoarchitectural mapping, they offer few clues to function. Study of the plexuses of dendritic and axonal branches that cut across cortical cell layers and determine the synaptic connections through which nerve impulses are transmitted is more useful to physiology.

Layer IV of the cortex is a receptive layer, since the *specific thalamocortical afferents* mainly end there in a compact axon brush; but other layers are also receptive. The *nonspecific thalamocortical afferents* begin to give off horizontal collaterals while still in the white matter; these turn and ascend through the cortex to the outermost layer, ending in terminal branches which

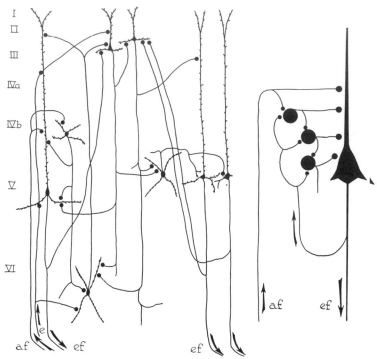

Fig. 1. Diagram of some intracortical neuron chains. Note that few dendrites and axonal branches have been included. Synaptic junctions are indicated by thickening of axon. *af,* Axon entering cortex; *ef,* axon leaving cortex; *e,* axon of intra-areal cortical association cell whose cell body lies in sixth layer, outside picture. Diagram at right is a simplification of diagram at left. Afferent fiber activates large pyramidal cell, which is origin of efferent fiber and also of a system of cortical internuncial cells; recurrent collateral of *ef* delivers impulses again to internuncial system. This diagram exemplifies the broad plan upon which the cerebral cortex is organized. Roman numerals at left indicate cortical layers. (After Lorente de Nó in Fulton, *Physiology of the nervous system,* 3rd ed. New York, Oxford University Press, 1949.)

also run horizontally. Because of the dual system of branching, the nonspecific afferents terminate in blocks of cortex. Axons linking area to area, or cortex to cortex, are now also thought to terminate in several layers.

The fifth and sixth layers are the main efferent layers. They contain the cell bodies of axons which enter the pyramidal tract. The apical dendrites of the cells in these layers ascend, giving off collaterals, but the basal dendrites may spread laterally or obliquely downward, presenting a much greater area for synaptic contact than the cell body itself. Callosal and association efferent fibers also originate in the deep layers, V and VI.

An impulse traversing one cortical afferent may pass directly or monosynaptically to a cortical efferent, but, through collaterals and cortical cells with short dendrites and axons (cortical internuncials), cortical afferents can effect multisynaptic connection with the efferent neuron, as shown in Figure 1. Moreover, through the recurrent collaterals of cortical ef-

ferents ending on other neurons of the same type, circular chains capable of re-excitation or "reverberation" are formed, an anatomic formation which has important physiologic implications.

Altogether, the cerebral cortex reduced to its absolute skeleton is not unlike the spinal cord. As said by Lorente de Nó,[42] cortical neuron chains "are in no way different from chains of internuncial neurons in any part of the central nervous system." He also points out that, from mouse to man, cortical cells with short axons increase in number more than cells with long ascending or descending axons.

Cajal was first to point out that the large number of cells with short axons was the anatomic expression of the delicacy of function of the brain of man. It is now known that synaptic transmission demands the summation of impulses under strict conditions, and it is evident that the more heterogeneous the origin of the synapses on the cells with descending axons, the more rigid become the conditions for threshold stimulation, and the more accurate the selection of the paths through which the impulses may be conducted. The reduction of the number of cells with short axons, without essential modification of the long links in the chains of cortical neurons, makes the cortex of the mouse the "skeleton" for the human cortex.[31]

Electrophysiologists,[1] by using microelectrodes which can record from single cells throughout the depth of the cortex, have developed a physiology of the cortex comparable to the histologic studies of the cortex made with silver stains. This development brings closer an understanding of cortical function.

CYTOARCHITECTURAL MAPS. Although cytoarchitectural maps offer few clues to function, major differences between cytoarchitectural fields have been given functional significance. However, every small cytoarchitectural difference does not imply a functional difference nor does each function require a unique cytoarchitecture. Some students of cytoarchitecture have overzealously divided the cortical layers into more and more sublayers and the cortical areas into smaller and smaller subareas. Many of these proposed divisions, almost always based on subjective and nonquantitative criteria, have not been verified by other observers looking at the same sections. Many cytoarchitectural boundaries are not constant from animal to animal, and variations often result from distortions produced mechanically by the cortical folds, which notoriously differ from brain to brain

within a species. It is interesting that the revolt against excessive parcellation was initiated by two psychologists[34] rather than by neuroanatomists.

Experiments on the cerebral cortex are often described in terms of fissures, sulci, gyri and lobes. The fissural pattern for the rhesus monkey, a common laboratory animal, is shown in Figure 2. It can be seen that the simian brain is basically similar to the human, but much simpler. Cytoarchitectural maps also provide a language in which to describe the cortex, a language that is often more compact than description in terms of fissures and convolutions. It is virtually impossible to follow present and past experimental literature based on the monkey without knowledge of Brodmann's map. This map, as modified by the Vogts,[71] and another produced by von Bonin and Bailey[6] are reproduced for reference in Figure 3.*

* In this map the initial letter is drawn from the name of the lobe. The numbers used by Brodmann and others can be remembered more easily if the way they were assigned is understood. His monkey brain was cut horizontally, so the precentral and postcentral regions appeared in the first few sections. These received the low numbers (1–8) as different cytoarchitecture was encountered. It will be noticed that the numbers jump from front to back. The next important group of numbers (9–12) is frontal; 17–19 are occipital; 20–22 are in the temporal lobe in the order of their appearance in serial horizontal sections.

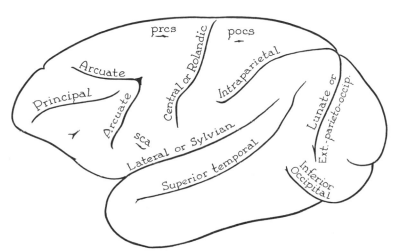

Fig. 2. Dorsolateral view of the left cerebral hemisphere of *Macaca mulatta* showing pattern and names of sulci. Note following differences from human brain: (i) fewer and less complex sulci, (ii) smaller prefrontal lobe, (iii) ascending course of intraparietal, lateral and superior temporal fissures (also lesser development of posterior parietal region), (iv) lesser development of the superior precentral (*prcs*) and postcentral (*pocs*) sulci. Sulcus subcentralis anterior (*SCA*) may correspond to the human inferior precentral sulcus. (After von Bonin and Bailey. *The neocortex of* Macaca mulatta. Urbana, University of Illinois Press, 1947.)

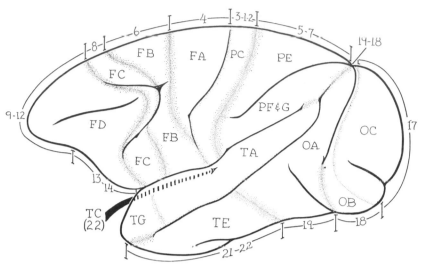

Fig. 3. Cytoarchitectural map of monkey brain relating terminology of Brodmann (*numbers*) to that of von Bonin and Bailey (*letters*). The areas and the relation of the designations are only approximate.

In the interpretation of such maps it should be realized that the boundaries are not sharp; instead, one type of cortex blends into another. The Brodmann terminology can be modified to encompass modern studies. The expression "areas 3–1–2" may be retained, even though the differences between 3 and 1 may not be real and 2 is nonexistent. Similarly, use of "areas 9–12" reflects skepticism of the significance of the subareal differences but describes a region for which there is no other generally accepted term, since some object to the word "prefrontal." In the description below, the letters signify von Bonin and Bailey's terminology. The numbers are those of Brodmann, occasionally modified. Some of the areas concerned with motor function will be discussed in detail; others will be described in later chapters.

FA (*area 4*) is agranular cortex beginning in the depth of the central fissure and extending up its anterior bank onto the free surface of the precentral gyrus. Here the gray matter is thick (3.5 to 5.0 mm.); the presence of the giant pyramidal cells of Betz in the fifth layer constitutes the major basis for determining the anterior border. Since the size necessary to qualify a cell as a Betz cell is not agreed upon, the forward boundary is not definitely established.

FB, together with *FA,* corresponds roughly to Brodmann's *area 6,* although the posterior boundary, as noted, fluctuates markedly. In this area, the cortex is still thick and agranular but lacks giant pyramidal (Betz) cells in the fifth layer.

FC, corresponding to *area 8* as modified since Brodmann, is a transitional band with a poorly developed internal granular layer; it extends around the frontal pole. On the lateral surface, *FC* is largely buried in the two limbs of the V formed by the arcuate fissure, but issues from it laterally. The remainder of the frontal lobe (*FD* or *area 9–12*) is quite uniform in structure, except for an area around the posterior end of the principal fissure.

PB lies almost entirely buried in the depth of the central fissure and is easily recognized. Like other primary sensory areas, *PB* is koniocortex ("dusty cortex," referring to its highly granular nature). *PC,* occupying the free face of the postcentral gyrus, loses the excessive granulation and becomes homotypical; i.e., all six layers are present and none is "overdeveloped." Since area 2 has been shown by von Bonin and Bailey to be nonexistent, the posterior boundary of area *PC* lies somewhat anterior to the superior postcentral fissure. The two terminologies can be made congruent by speaking of *Brodmann areas 3 and 1.*

The remaining areas which figure prominently in discussion of motor function are the two concentric bands surrounding the large and easily identified striate area (the primary visual area), which in monkeys, unlike the situation in man, extends over the free surface of the occipital lobe. The transition from *OC* or *area 17* is sharp, *OB* or *area 18* being homotypical and marked by the presence of very large cells in the third layer. The boundaries between *OB* and *OA* and between *OA* and the parietal lobe are not sharp, and cytoarchitectural analysis is made difficult by the deep fissures in the region. The Vogts and von Bonin and Bailey agree in restricting area 17 mainly to the posterior wall of the lunate sulcus. The general region can be termed *area 18–19* without neglect of major cytoarchitectural criteria.

Corticospinal or Pyramidal Tract.[51]   By definition, the pyramidal tract consists of those fibers which originate in the cerebral cortex and pass to the spinal cord through the medullary pyramids.* It is only accidental and incidental that some of the tract originates in large, conspicuous, pyramid-shaped cells such as the Betz cells. The term "pyramidal tract" in no way implies fibers originating from such cells; in fact, the tract was named before the shape of the cells of origin was known.† Fibers from the cortex to the cranial motor nerve nuclei are functionally similar to those going to spinal segments. Although such fibers obviously do not pass through the pyramids, they should not be confused with those termed extrapyramidal fibers. Some corticobulbar fibers end on intercalated nuclei and are difficult to separate morphologically or experimentally from those that end more directly on the motor nerve nuclei.

It is now believed that all or most of the fibers in the pyramids arise from the cerebral cortex; degeneration in the pyramids is said to be complete after decortication.[47] That the pyramidal tract arises solely in the giant Betz cells is a misconception; the tract also arises from small cells distributed through the third to the sixth layer. In man, the motor area of each hemisphere contains approximately 34,000 Betz cells, enough to account for the 2 per cent of fibers with large diameters ranging from 11μ to 20μ, but not nearly enough to account for the one million axons in each medullary pyramid. Figure 4 shows the distribution of the diameters of the myelinated fibers which constitute the major portion of the pyramidal tract.[35] The remaining fibers in the tract are unmyelinated and recently[16] were estimated to constitute 6 per cent of it. Little is known of their origin and function.

Although many pyramidal tract fibers originate in the primary motor sector (area 4), that the pyramidal tract originates exclusively there is also a misconception. The proportion of fibers originating from the monkey's precentral gyrus

*Although recent anatomic evidence that the pyramids may contain ascending fibers has not been contradicted, functional evidence thought to indicate their existence has been thoroughly disproved.[49]

†Some fibers in the pyramids give collaterals to the pontine nuclei and possibly to the reticular formation of the medulla. Should these collaterals reach the cord without synapse they would be corticospinal but not pyramidal. Further, because of this collateralization, it is possible that the distinction between pyramidal and extrapyramidal fibers has been overdrawn.

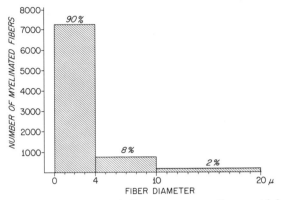

Fig. 4. Myelinated fiber spectrum of pyramidal tract. (After Lassek. *J. comp. Neurol.*, 1942, *76:*217–225.)

by the most recent and careful estimates[57] is 31 per cent and that from area 6, contrary to many previous estimates is nearly as large, 29 per cent (Fig. 5). The remainder, 40 per cent, arises from the postcentral gyrus and the posterior parietal lobe. The prefrontal occipital and temporal lobes are now not thought to give origin to any fibers passing through the pyramids. Earlier estimates ascribed a significant share of fibers to these areas because motor and sensory cortical lesions left some 40 per cent of fibers undegenerated. Recent studies indicate that axonal degeneration and disappearance require not a few weeks but a year. Axons late to disappear were ascribed to origins other than the motor and sensory areas.

Extrapyramidal Projections from the Cortex. Overlapping with pyramidal tract projections in respect to point of origin are projections to a wide range of subcortical structures including the brain stem reticular formation (Table 1, Chap. 13). Through these structures impulses eventually reach the segmental level in the spinal cord and can both *effect* and *affect* movement. Extrapyramidal pathways from the cortex to the spinal cord differ from the pyramidal or corticospinal system in two ways: (i) the chains of neurons are synaptically interrupted in the basal ganglia or in the brain stem nuclei or reticular formation; and (ii) by definition, the pathways do not pass through the medullary pyramids. These systems of neurons can be termed the "cortically originating extrapyramidal system," which can be abbreviated "COEPS." Since the extrapyramidal system also receives subcortical inputs, COEPS is not a synonym for "extrapyramidal system,"

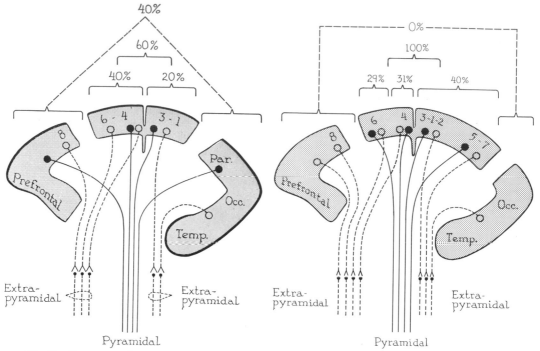

Fig. 5. Summary diagram showing older (left) and newer (right) views of the origins of pyramidal and extrapyramidal systems influencing spinal motoneurons. Note overlapping resulting from extrapyramidal systems originating from sensorimotor areas. Quantitative estimates and other details will vary, depending on technique used. (*Left,* based on data from Lassek,[35] Mettler[47] and others; *right,* based on Russell and De Myer.[57])

but refers to that portion of it which originates in the cerebral cortex. The major COEPS pathways may be summarized as follows.

Corticostriatal and corticopallidal. The existence of a corticostriatal system had long been suspected but could not be demonstrated by the usual degeneration techniques.* Glees,[27] using a silver stain, has observed an unmyelinated corticocaudate and corticoputamen projection in cat and monkey. Dusser de Barenne and his coworkers applied strychnine to the cortex in monkeys and recorded strychnine spikes† in the caudate nucleus. Impulses originating in the cortex can reach the pallidum by way of the putamen or by

*A discrete area of cortical tissue is ablated. Some time later, the animal is sacrificed, and lower neural structures are stained and studied histologically for degenerated fibers.

†Strychnine causes a large number of neurons to synchronize their discharges. The result is periodic spikes at the terminus of the neurons in another part of the cortex or in a subcortical nucleus. Since the spikes suffer temporal dispersion at the first synapse, the recording of a spike means a direct connection between the recording and strychninized points. "Strychnine neuronography" is a useful tool for functional anatomy.

direct pathways. Glees traced fibers from area 6 to the external segment of the globus pallidus. From the basal ganglia, impulses can be relayed along the lenticular fasciculus and the ansa lenticularis; and, after traversing a synapse in the field of Forel, the impulses reach the midline tegmentum. A more direct projection from areas 4 and 6 enters the midbrain nuclei including the red nucleus.

Corticothalamic. In general, a specific cortical area sends fibers to the thalamic nucleus from which it receives fibers. This reciprocal arrangement occurs in the motor cortex as well as in the sensory and the association cortex.

Corticoreticular. Rossi and Brodal,[56] using a silver method, found that corticoreticular fibers originate from much of the cerebral cortex but mainly from the sensorimotor region, particularly the motor area. These fibers end predominantly in the pontine reticulum and in the medulla dorsal to the inferior olive. The projection is bilateral and poorly, if at all, organized somatotopically. The terminations of this projection are in the regions from which the reticulospinal tracts originate, providing an extrapyramidal connection of the cortex with spinal motoneurons. Several investigators[2, 3] have shown that single reticular units can be activated by cortical stimulation; the latency (2 to 6 milliseconds) of the response suggests that the connection is a direct corticoreticular neuron.

Some of these connections may be effected by collaterals from the pyramidal tract.

Corticopontine. Each of the four major lobes of the brain projects to the pons, the frontopontine tract being the largest projection. It arises equally from areas 4 and 6. Besides conveying impulses to the cerebellum, this important tract in primates is thought to give off collaterals to midbrain structures, e.g., the substantia nigra. According to Cajal, some corticopontine fibers are actually collaterals of corticospinal fibers.

The COEPS provides not only multisynaptic pathways to the spinal cord but also recurrent or "feedback" pathways from the cortex that pass through the subcortical structures to return to the cortex. There are at least three such potential pathways from the cortex: (i) via the cortico-ponto-cerebellar tract and returning via the dentatothalamo-cortical pathway; (ii) via collaterals from the corticopontine tract and from direct corticospinal fibers to the substantia nigra and thence via nigrostriatal fibers to join the loop described next; and (iii) via cortico-striatal-pallidal projections, thence via the anteroventral nucleus of the thalamus and its projections to the motor areas.

MOTOR FUNCTIONS

Pyramidal Tract. A single point in the motor area of the cortex can be stimulated and the resulting discharge in the pyramidal tract recorded from any point along its course— from the interneurons of the spinal cord, from the motor roots and nerves, or from the muscles. In fact, a point on the motor cortex and the pyramidal fibers to which it gives rise can be treated like the afferent limb of a reflex arc and subjected to the same kind of analysis. Stimulations of two cortical points can be interacted like stimulations of two afferent nerves.

D AND I RESPONSES. The first question to be asked is, what is stimulated when electrodes are applied to the cortical surface of the motor area? The cells of origin of the pyramidal tract? The intracortical neurons which end on these cells? Because too many stages intervene, the response of a muscle or even of a nerve to stimulation of the motor cortex will obviously not give much information.

Patton and Amassian[50, 51] inserted a record-

ing microelectrode into the bulbar pyramid or the pyramidal tract of the cervical spinal cord and stimulated the motor cortex. In the records so obtained (Fig. 6), the first deflection (D wave) is a stable, short-latency (0.7 millisecond), short-duration, positive wave. This wave is followed by a series of positive, irregular or imperfectly rhythmic waves beginning after a longer time (2.0 to 2.5 milliseconds) and lasting for many milliseconds. The first wave was termed the D wave because analysis indicated that it appeared when the electric current excited *directly* the cells giving rise to the pyramidal tract axons. The later deflections were termed the I waves because analysis showed that they were caused by indirect excitation of pyramidal tract neurons. The longer latency of the I waves was accounted for by the time consumed in traversing chains of intracortical neurons.

The experiments leading to this conclusion illustrate how a neurophysiologic analysis can be made. Briefly, the D wave relative to the I waves was more resistant to anesthesia, anoxia, etc.; had a shorter recovery cycle; and persisted when the cortex was removed and the underlying white matter was stimu-

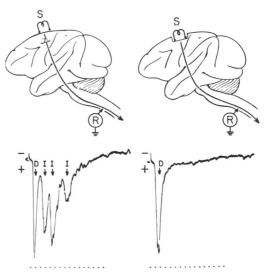

Fig. 6. Pyramidal tract responses to stimulation of motor cortex (*left*) and white matter (*right*) in monkey. Recording electrode in lateral column of spinal cord at C_1. Downward deflection indicates positivity at electrode in pyramidal tract. Time, 1 millisecond. *D* and *I* waves are labeled. (After Patton and Amassian, Chap. 34 in *Handbook of physiology, Section I, Neurophysiology,* vol. 2, J. Field, ed. Washington, D. C., American Physiological Society, 1960.)

lated (Fig. 6). In "penetration experiments," the I waves appeared only when the tip of the stimulating electrode was within the cortex. Further, when the stimulating electrode was moved rostrally, the D wave disappeared, but the I wave persisted for some distance. This observation will help in resolving some of the controversial aspects of localization in the motor cortex.

RATES OF CONDUCTION. In general, the pyramidal axons are small, less than 2 per cent being of Group I diameter (11 to 22 μ). Maximal conduction velocity in the spinal portion of the tract is, according to Lloyd[41] and Bernhard *et al.*,[5] 60 to 70 meters per second. This difference in velocity suggests that the axons between the cortex and the pyramid are larger than those below the pyramids, the fibers becoming attenuated by collateralization in the spinal cord.

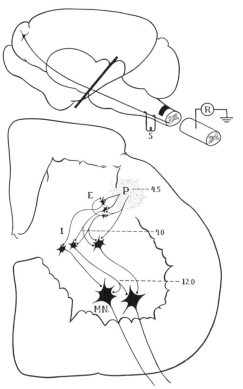

Fig. 7. Diagram of Lloyd's experiment on activation of spinal nuclei by pyramidal tract discharge. Upper drawing shows positions of stimulating and recording electrodes and of brain ablations to rule out nonpyramidal conduction. Time noted at each level is first detectable facilitation of nuclear neurons. Subtraction gives nuclear delay in *previous nucleus. P,* Pyramidal tract; *E,* external basilar cells; *I,* intermediate nucleus of Cajal; *MN,* motoneuron. (After Lloyd. *J. Neurophysiol.,* 1941, *4:*525–546.)

SPINAL STAGE OF PYRAMIDAL SYSTEM FUNCTION. Knowledge of how the interneurons and motoneurons of the spinal cord are excited is necessary to a complete picture of pyramidal tract activity. In the cat, Lloyd[41] used microelectrodes to record from the nuclear groups of the spinal gray matter while he stimulated the bulbar pyramids (Fig. 7). (All of the medulla except the pyramids had been sectioned below the stimulating electrodes to prevent activation of descending fibers in the extrapyramidal system, and a midcollicular decerebration had been performed to prevent impulses from ascending in sensory tracts and activating the pyramidal tract at the cerebral cortex.)

In view of the great power and promptness of voluntary contractions in intact animals, Lloyd's study revealed a surprising amount of "inertia" in the spinal stage of pyramidal tract function. A single shock discharged only the cells of the external basilar nucleus, which lies in the gray matter just deep to the pyramidal tract fibers. The pyramidal volley arrived 4.5 milliseconds after the pyramids were stimulated and almost immediately discharged a few external basilar cells. This latency largely represents conduction time in the tract. To cause the intermediate nucleus of Cajal to discharge, repeated stimulation was required. By testing the excitability of this nucleus with spinal volleys, Lloyd showed that a nuclear delay of 4.5 milliseconds passed before the external basilar nucleus discharged into the intermediate nucleus. Another 3 milliseconds elapsed before the motoneurons were facilitated, a finding indicating another nuclear delay in the intermediate nucleus. As the repeated stimuli continued, the latency between arrival of an impulse at the spinal segment and motoneuron facilitation was reduced to 1.0 millisecond.

From these studies it can be concluded that two systems of interneurons are involved, one at the cortical stage and one at the spinal stage of pyramidal tract activation. Movements elicited by cortical stimulation will therefore have properties similar to those which interneurons lend to spinal reflex action, and the following phenomena could also be predicted on this basis.

Excitable Properties of the Motor Cortex and Its Efferent Pathways (Pyramidal and Extrapyramidal). **RECIPROCAL INNERVATION.** In 1889, Sherrington demonstrated that, given a background of reflex muscular contraction, stimulation of a cortical point* might excite flexor motoneurons and inhibit the antagonistic extensor motoneurons—a "flexor point." Conversely, stimulation of a neighboring point might excite the extensor motoneurons and inhibit the antagonistic flexor motoneurons—an "extensor point." The site of the inhibition is in the spinal cord, because the same phenomenon has been demonstrated by stimulating the white matter underlying flexor and extensor points. That reciprocal innervation of muscles by the pyramidal tract has been questioned is understandable because: (i) the flexor and extensor points may overlap somewhat; and (ii) intracortical neurons may spread impulses from one point to another, both giving co-contraction of flexors and extensors.

LATENCY. The latency of cortically induced movements in response to a repetitive stimulus (summation time) may be as long as several seconds, during which time more than 100 volleys pass down the pyramidal tract. In contrast, man can initiate a voluntary response to a signal in less than one fifth of a second. Analytical studies indicate conduction times and nuclear delays in the spinal interneurons measured in milliseconds. Such long latencies of movement in response to cortical stimulation, then, must represent an interaction of excitatory and inhibitory effects resulting from a mixed stimulation of what may be loosely termed "extensor" exciting and "flexor" exciting pyramidal tract fibers.

AFTERDISCHARGE. The movement induced by stimulation of the motor cortex often continues long after the cessation of the stimulation. This afterdischarge is at first sustained ("tonic") and then becomes a series of rhythmic contractions ("clonic"). The same sequence of events is seen in epileptic seizures of the Jacksonian type. Experimentally induced epilepsy is best ascribed to cortical interneurons acting in closed or self-reexciting circuits.

FACILITATION.[18] Bubnoff and Heidenhain[10] recognized that stimulation of one point on the cortex can facilitate (or inhibit) the response of another point. Facilitation is manifested by a greater response to a cortical testing shock

*A cortical point is not a physiologic, anatomic or physical entity, but is simply the point at which electrodes are placed. The current may, for example, excite neurons at a distance from the "point."

when it is preceded by a cortical conditioning shock than when it is given alone. In fact, stimulation of one point may not merely facilitate but actually may discharge pyramidal tract fibers originating from another cortical point. For example, stimulation of neurons in area 6 may cause neurons in area 4 to discharge. Both intracortical spread and arcuate association fibers are involved in this activation. When the discharge of a stimulated area into another falls short of causing the latter to discharge, facilitation occurs. The duration of facilitation in this system is measured in seconds, 13 seconds being a typical figure. Facilitative interaction also occurs at the spinal interneuron pool, and activity at this level as well as at the cortex is important in the interpretation of cortical localization experiments.

EXTINCTION.[18] At intervals longer than those required to demonstrate facilitation, and especially with pulses of long duration, the response to a testing stimulus may be *smaller* when the stimulus follows a conditioning stimulus than when it is delivered alone. Dusser de Barenne and McCulloch[18] called this phenomenon "extinction" to give it a name not limited to a specific mechanism. The unresponsiveness is cortical, not spinal, and is local, becoming progressively less apparent if the electrodes delivering the testing shocks are moved a few millimeters from the conditioning electrodes. *Extinction* was defined as a diminution or absence of response to stimulation of a motor focus following antecedent stimulation of the *same* focus. *Inhibition* is also a diminution or absence of an expected response, but is manifest when the testing stimulus has been preceded by stimulation of *another* cortical point, one from which an antagonistic response may be elicited. Because Betz cells serving antagonistic muscles may not be totally separate, this distinction is not sufficient. In fact, the relationship of extinction to inhibition, suppression, voltage drifts and pH changes in the cerebral cortex is not entirely clear, and whether extinction exists at all has been questioned.[51]

LABILITY.[9] With facilitation, inhibition and extinction resulting from cortical stimulation, it could be anticipated that the motor cortex exhibits a certain lability of response. Not all intensities and frequencies of stimulation give the same result, and apparently identical stimuli do not give identical responses. The names given various manifestations of this "instability of the cortical point"[9] need not concern us. One manifestation of lability is explicable by the immediate history of the point stimulated (intracortical facilitation); another is a change in response as the parameters of the stimulus are changed.

Lilly et al.[40] varied and monitored the pulse duration, amplitude and frequency of cortical stimulation. (i) Combinations of amplitude and duration constituted an intermediate range which excited efferent cells; (ii) stimuli in a second range of durations and amplitude excited both cells and efferent fibers in the white matter; and (iii) strong unidirectional pulses of long duration destroyed cells and, eventually, fibers in the immediate vicinity of the stimulating electrode. (This damage is avoided by using Lilly's reverse pulse stimulator.) It follows that, if stimuli of different parameters excite different structures and if some stimuli injure fibers, quite different results may be obtained by different investigators, or by the same investigator during successive stimulations of the cerebral cortex.

SPREADING DEPRESSION.   Electrical, mechanical or chemical stimuli applied to the cerebral cortex were observed by Leão[37] to cause a slowly expanding depression of its spontaneous electrical activity. This depression spreads over the cortex at a rate of 2 to 3 mm. per minute and persists at any one point for two to six minutes. It is also manifested by a decreased cortical excitability to stimulation, a slow change in the steady potential, vascular dilatation and an increase in the electrical resistance of the cortex.[70]

Spreading depression is a marked phenomenon in the rabbit, but it is more capricious in the cat and monkey. Marshall[45, 46] has shown that such depression is an important experimental artifact caused by dehydration and cooling of the cerebral cortex when it is widely exposed. The depression can be prevented by protecting the cortex with mineral oil, or it can be induced by dehydrating the animal by means of an intravenous administration of sucrose. Marshall's analysis suggests that spreading depression is a phenomenon of the pathologic cortex. Spreading depression is significant as a source of error in experiments on the cerebral cortex and may play some role in the general cortical depression that follows epileptic seizures.

Prior to Marshall's analysis, it was believed that stimulation of specific bands of the cerebral cortex (running mediolaterally) gave rise

to a widespread diminution of electrical activity and excitability. This phenomenon was given the name "suppression" and was thought to be mediated by circuits passing through the basal ganglia and returning to the cerebral cortex. Experiments by Marshall[45] and by Sloan and Jasper[60] indicate that this suppression is the same as the spreading depression of Leão and that it can be initiated from any point on the cortex, not specifically from the so-called suppressor bands.

Somatotopic Organization of the Motor Cortex.   That different parts of the body move when different parts of the precentral gyrus are stimulated has been known for nearly a century, but the nature and detail of this somatotopic representation are still subjects of experiment and controversy. "Representation of the body," "somatotopic organization" and "topographic organization" are synonyms. All mean that the cortical cells which give rise to the descending fibers activating different muscle groups lie in broadly the same relation to one another as do the muscles in the body. On the other hand, according to some authors, movements rather than muscles are represented.

Figure 8 shows the sequence of motor representation expressed in terms of body structures. The body parts are represented "upside down," with the leg area medial, the face area lateral, and the arm area lying between. In man, much of the leg area is buried in the medial longitudinal fissure, and much of the primary motor area for the arm and face lies buried on the anterior wall of the central fissure. In the monkey, more of the motor area lies on the free surface.

An important functional deduction can be made from the amount of cortical space devoted to a given part of the body. The lips and tongue, which are highly mobile and capable of finely graded movement, have larger cortical spaces devoted to them than do the less mobile fingers. The finger and hand areas of the cortex are much greater than the total of those governing the movements of all the other arm muscles. This arrangement suggests that finely graded movements are obtained by the simplest of all methods—the provision of a larger number of efferent neurons. Since the efferent cells, especially the Betz cells, occur in clusters, it is probably not only the number of cells but also the number of interspersed intracortical neurons that determines the variety of movement of which the hand or tongue is capable. In either case, cortical space is required. In view of these considerations, it should not be surprising that the degree of paralysis caused by equal-sized lesions in the motor areas is greater and more persistent in the hand than in the shoulder.

The history of the discovery that movement can be elicited by cortical stimulation is informative because it illustrates how careful clinical observation and astute deductions can interact with the more analytical and controlled animal experiments. In 1870, Hughlings Jackson, the great physiologically minded neurologist, postulated the existence of a somatotopically organized motor area from his observations of the epileptic seizures which originate in that area and now bear his name. In a given patient, a seizure might start in the lips, spread to the face, then to the arm, and then to the leg (the "march of epilepsy"). Hughlings Jackson[31] reasoned that there must exist, somewhere in the brain, structures having a concern with the lip, and further, that the remainder of the musculature must be represented there in an orderly fashion, accounting for the successive and orderly involvement during the epileptic discharge. Independently and experimentally, Fritsch and Hitzig[20] discovered the electrical excitability of the motor cortex in the dog and the monkey, mapped areas for the face, the arm and the leg, and demonstrated

some evidence of localization of even smaller body parts.

The trend in both animal and human experiments has been from localization in terms of region (face, arm, leg) to movements of joints and digits, culminating in the suggestion (Marion Hines) that single muscles may be separately represented in the motor cortex. Hughlings Jackson and others following him[74, 75] have expressed the opposite view. Impressed by the fact that a patient can recover the use of a limb after destruction of cortical representation of that limb previously defined by stimulation, they have favored the idea of a widespread overlapping of the representation of muscle groups. Sherrington generalized that the cerebral cortex "thinks" in terms of movements, not muscles; and this view has been found persuasive, particularly by British neurologists and neurophysiologists.

EVIDENCE FROM SINGLE MUSCLE RECORDING. Responses of an individual muscle or its nerve to systematic stimulation of the motor cortex have been studied in efforts to resolve the question.

Just which muscles at a given joint respond to cortical stimulation is difficult to discern with the naked

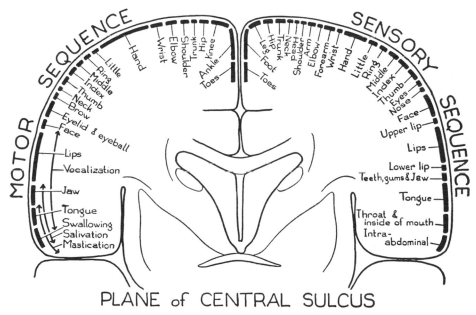

PLANE of CENTRAL SULCUS

Fig. 8. Diagrammatic representation of sensory and motor sequences as mapped by threshold stimulation of cerebral cortex in man. Length of bars indicates in general way extent of cortical areas devoted to each structure in average patient. This is subject to considerable variation, however. (From Rasmussen and Penfield, *Fed. Proc.*, 1947, 6:452–460.)

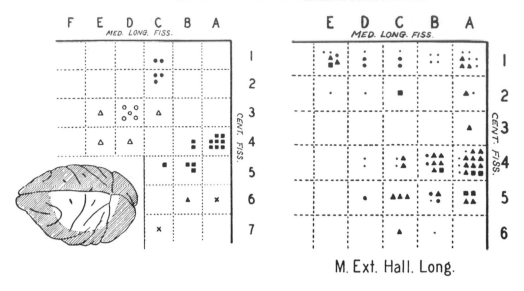

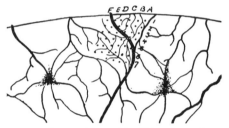

- M. Extensor Digitorum Longus (EDL)
- M. Extensor Hallucis Longus (EHL)
- M. Tibialis Anticus (TA)
- M. Abductor Hallucis Longus (AHL)
- M. Flexor Digitorum Longus (FDL)
- M. Tibialis Posticus (TP)

Fig. 9.　Muscle responses from stimulation of motor cortex. *Lower right,* grid of blood vessels and stimulated points. Broad dark line is caused by vein leaving central fissure to enter longitudinal sinus. Above are two maps of this small cortical area that are related to brain diagram by letters and numbers. *Upper left* shows points from which response was obtained in single foot or ankle muscle. Note that such "solitary" responses cluster. *Upper right* shows points from which extensor hallucis longus was activated. Note, however, that in region *AB45* responses were of short latency; large squares, 0–1.00 second; large triangles 1.01–2.00 seconds. Small circles represent latencies of 2.01–3.00 seconds, and dots, latencies of 3.01 seconds or longer. Responses of several muscles were obtained from *Row 1 A–E,* possibly owing to proximity to supplementary motor area. (From Chang *et al. J. Neurophysiol.,* 1947, *10*:39–56.)

eye. Using monkeys, Chang *et al.*[14] isolated the tendons of 13 muscles acting over the ankle and attached them, eight at a time, to myographs. Part of the foot area in the motor cortex was divided into millimeter squares and systematically stimulated. The response produced in each muscle by a given stimulus was recorded on a two-dimensional plot for that muscle in the space corresponding to the cortical point stimulated. Three major results were obtained: (i) Occasionally, only one of eight muscle responded, and the points for such "solitary responses" by a given muscle always fell in a cluster (Fig. 9, *left*). (ii) When the responses of each muscle were classified according to latency, those with the shortest latency clustered on contiguous points, whereas the points that yielded intermediate and long-latency responses tended to form surrounding rings (Fig. 9, *right*). (iii) When the responses of any two muscles were graded and repre-

sented on the cortical map as greater or less than the other muscle responses, a similar clustering was observed (Fig. 10).

The latency study has been conducted in another way by Bernhard and Bohm,[4] who recorded the latency of impulses in a muscle nerve and correlated it with the point stimulated on the motor cortex (Fig. 11). Again, the lines representing given latencies formed concentric rings. Thus, a given muscle can be thrown into contraction from a fairly wide area of the motor cortex, but into strong short-latency contraction only from a narrow focus.

Both of these studies lead to the concept that Betz and other corticofugal cells activating the motoneuron pool for a given muscle are topographically closely related to one another in the

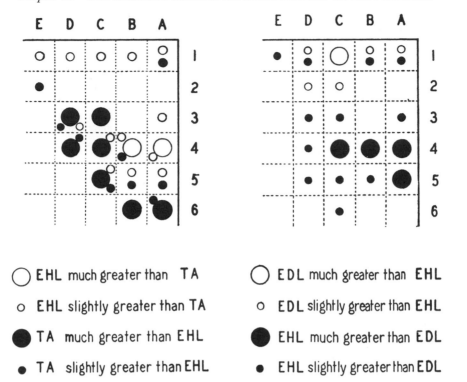

Fig. 10. Foci and fields of muscle representation determined by relative strengths of contraction in pairs of muscle to same cortical stimulation. Note that extensor hallucis longus (*EHL*) contractions relative to extensor digitorum longus (*EDL*) contractions were greatest in *4 ABC* and adjoining *5A*, establishing a focus. In the surrounding squares, relative strength of *EDL* contractions was less, establishing a field. Responses of *EDL* exceeded *EHL* only for points in rows *1* and *2*. Note in diagram at left that extensor hallucis longus (*EHL*) and tibialis anticus (*TA*), which in monkeys are slips of the same muscle, are spatially less differentiated than *EDL* and *EHL*. Compare this map with Figs. 9 and 11. (From Chang *et al.*, *J. Neurophysiol.*, 1947, *10*:39–56.)

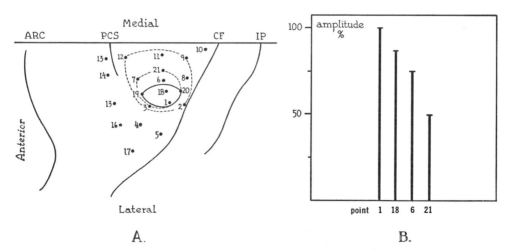

Fig. 11. *A,* Latency (summation time) for monosynaptic activation of triceps motoneurons from different points on left motor cortex, 1 second for inner circle, 3 seconds for next (*dashed*), and 7 seconds for outer circle. Note closeness of isotemp lines inferiorly, suggesting sharp boundary between arm and face. This diagram confirms experiment shown in Figs. 9 and 10. *B,* Amplitudes of monosynaptic discharge from points in a line running vertically through field for triceps. (After Bernhard and Bohm, *Arch. Neurol. Psychiat. (Chic.),* 1954, *72*:473–502.)

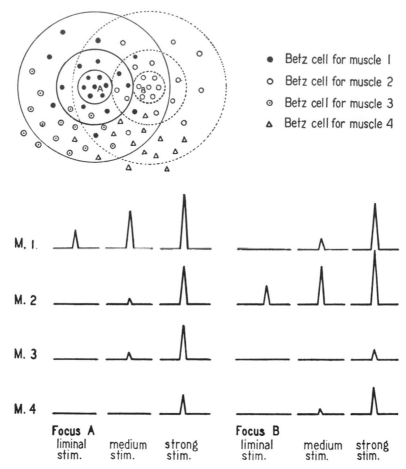

Fig. 12. Diagrammatic representation of hypothetical distribution of Betz and other cells of fifth and sixth layers for individual muscles. A cell group for each muscle has a focal distribution and an overlapping fringe. Each symbol stands for a Betz cell; large concentric circles are spheres of excitation. Expected contraction of muscles to cortical stimulation at different strengths is shown by myograms drawn in lower part of figure, in which magnitude of contraction is determined by number of Betz cells involved in sphere of excitation. Scale is in millimeters; zones *A* and *B* represent about 4 to 8 mm.[2] (From Chang *et al., J. Neurophysiol.,* 1947, *10:*39–56.)

motor cortex.* In fact, as shown in Figure 12, there appears to be a focus of neurons surrounded by a field for each muscle. The foci for two muscles never overlap, although the field for one muscle may overlap the field and even the focus for another.

For several reasons, the size of the focus and the field for a given muscle, and the degree of overlapping with other muscles, are probably even more restricted than Figures 8 to 11 suggest. Extrapyramidal projections from area 4 and any collateralization of the pyramidal tract axons would obscure a tight grouping of the Betz cells concerned with a given muscle. Further,

* It is remarkable that the axons in the peduncle, the pyramids and the spinal cord are not so related but are considerably intermixed.

transcortical spread of the stimulating current or nerve impulses in intracortical neurons would also obscure discrete localization. That currents of threshold strength can activate neurons 4 mm. away from the electrodes has been proved by Phillips,[54] who used a single cortical unit technique.

EVIDENCE FROM PYRAMIDAL TRACT RECORDING. The common result of cortical stimulation at a single point, especially with strong, long-duration pulses delivered through unipolar electrodes, or with any type of stimulus in an unanesthetized animal, is activation of several muscles, producing a movement of one or more joints. The basic and controversial question is whether this finding means that the motor cortex integrates the activities of various muscles into movements by re-representing the muscle many times and diffusely, contrary to the picture presented above.

The experiments on the D and I waves of the pyramidal tract discharge appear to resolve the controversy and, more important, to explain how the motor cortex organizes the contractions of individual muscles into a pattern which constitutes a skilled coordinated voluntary movement. After location of the point on the cortex giving a large D wave in the axons near the microelectrode tip in the pyramidal tract, the stimulating electrodes were moved several millimeters away from this cortical point until the D response disappeared. A threshold stimulus now elicited only I waves over the intracortical neurons, a D wave occurring only if the intensity was so high that the stimulus spread electrically to the cell body of the primary motor area. A stimulus near threshold can therefore indirectly excite a cell body at a distance of several millimeters.

The conclusion can be drawn that the cells of origin of the corticofugal pathways are highly organized topographically; that the neurons connected ultimately with a given muscle are grouped closely together in the cortex. Thus, the motor cortex is organized in terms of muscles. By definition, the motor cortex thinks in terms of movements, since it produces movement. But the organization of different movements is accomplished, not in the arrangement of Betz and other cells in the deep layers, but in the manifold connections of intracortical neurons with such cells. The neuropil of the cortex thinks in terms of movements, and the controversy over cortical localization can be traced to neurophysiologists' thinking in terms of a morphologically complex structure —the motor cortex—rather than in terms of its various cellular components—single units or classes of like neurons.

EXTENT OF PRIMARY MOTOR AREA.   That the mediolateral dimension of the precentral gyrus represents the cephalocaudad dimension of the animal has been known since 1870. By contrast, how the anteroposterior dimension is utilized and what constitutes the forward border of the motor area are still somewhat uncertain. The latter has, in fact, been shifted forward and backward, like the boundaries of some countries. If the mediolateral dimension represents the cephalocaudad dimension of the animal, it is logical that the axial and appendicular dimension should be represented in the remaining anteroposterior dimension of the motor area; and, in fact, this is the most recent view.

In the simunculus based on Woolsey's experiments (Fig. 13), the areas of representation of the fingers, toes, lips and tongue are mainly buried in the central fissure, and the successively more proximal musculature is represented more anteriorly in orderly sequence. The threshold for movement rises and is higher for the axial than for the apical musculature. Note the position of the superior precentral sulcus or "dimple," which corresponds roughly to the anterior border of the motor area by certain cytoarchitectural and functional studies. If the simunculus in Figure 13 is correct, the axial musculature is represented in Brodmann's area 6, which has not previously been considered part of the body representation. In the light of recent experiments on unipolar versus bipolar stimulation, it is possible that Woolsey's studies place the forward boundary too far rostral. That such an expanse of cortex is needed to manage the proximal musculature is improbable.

Other Cortical Motor Areas.   With appropriate electrical stimulation, movements can be induced by activating areas other than the primary motor area. In fact, experiments on unanesthetized animals indicate that this is true of virtually the whole of the convexity of the cerebral hemispheres.[39] For each area and type of movement, the question arises whether (or in what degree) the responses from a given point are due to (i) physical spread of current, (ii) spread of impulses over intracortical and intercortical fibers to the primary motor areas, (iii) activation of extrapyramidal fibers (COEPS) originating at the stimulated point, or (iv) activation of pyramidal tract fibers (or equivalent corticobulbar fibers going to the cranial motor nuclei), since, as we have seen, much of the pyramidal tract originates outside the primary motor area.

Whether the first two factors are operative is frequently learned by ablating the primary motor area or by cutting between it and a stimulated area. The consensus is that pyramidal tract efferents are concentrated near the central fissure, and that their concentration diminishes in passing forward. Conversely, the precentral gyrus contributes some fibers to the extrapyramidal system, and this contribution increases in passing forward into areas 6 and 8. With these differences in the kind of efferent projection comes a difference in the kind of movement that results. Tower[66] and Marion

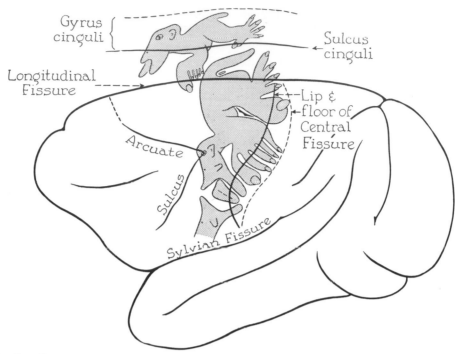

Fig. 13. Somatotopic organization of primary and supplementary motor areas. Note that central and longitudinal fissures are shown "opened out" with dotted line representing floor of a fissure and solid line lip of fissure on brain surface. At bottom of figure is an ipsilateral face area. In bay formed by foot, hand and abdomen is precentral dimple, the anterior border of area 4 (cf. Fig. 2). Much of the primary simunculus and virtually all of supplementary area falls in area 6. (After Woolsey *et al., Res. Publ. Ass. nerv. ment. Dis.,* 1952, *30:*238–264.)

Hines showed that the primary motor area is to some degree the cortical origin of the extra-pyramidal system. They sectioned the pyramids of cats, monkeys and chimpanzees, and found that not all ability to move was lost. Although movement lost the delicacy, accuracy and variety that are embodied in the phrase "skilled movement," certain gross movements, such as clutching and climbing, were retained. Moreover, stimulation of the precentral gyrus subsequent to section of the pyramids gave rise to such movements, but not to movements of single muscles or single joints.

However, a recent study emphasizes the lack of change in the type of movement elicited from the motor area after pyramid section[7] except for a threshold change. Experience with the degree of recovery of motor skills by patients after pedunculotomy causes Bucy[11] and others to believe the distinction between COEPS and the pyramidal tract has been overemphasized. The rapidity of conduction over COEPS pathways, the slowness of conduction in some pyramidal tract fibers, the relative

weakness of pyramidal tract effects on spinal mechanisms, and the comparative anatomy of the pyramidal tract tend to play down its role in voluntary movement and suggest some function beyond the activation of motoneuron discharge.[64]

That the corticospinal tract is not the sole agent of volitional skilled movement is true in man as well as in monkeys. The pyramids have not been sectioned surgically, but the corticospinal fibers (along with some extrapyramidal fibers) have been interrupted, occasionally bilaterally, in the cerebral peduncle and in the posterolateral region of the spinal cord. The resulting paralysis has been surprisingly slight and the ultimate recovery surprisingly great. For example, after a posterolateral cordotomy, a patient was still able to play a Beethoven piano concerto. Clearly, the role of the COEPS in the execution of movement is considerable and should be examined in detail. However, as pointed out, it is not always possible to decide whether a given response is executed over the extrapyramidal or the "extraprecentral pyramidal" system. By this latter term is meant pyramidal tract fibers arising elsewhere than in the classic cortical motor area.

SECOND MOTOR AREA.   A small motor area in the lateral prolongation of the precentral gyrus onto the lip of the sylvian fissure has been described. The body is represented in reverse order to the representation in the precentral gyrus. Discovered by Sugar *et al.*,[63] the existence of the area has been confirmed[36] but little is known of its function. According to Lauer[36] and Woolsey *et al.*,[77] the area immediately below the main motor representation is an ipsilateral motor face area. This finding correlates with our knowledge that the facial musculature tends to escape paralysis when cortical or capsular lesions are restricted to one side of the brain.

SUPPLEMENTARY MOTOR AREA.[53, 77]   In both monkey and man the musculature is represented a third time in the cortex. This representation (Fig. 13), constituting the *supplementary motor area,* is shown in Figure 13 as originally described by Woolsey[77] and in Figure 14 as described by Hughes and Mazurowski[29] from experiments on unanesthetized monkeys. In the latter, the representation occupies the mesial extent of area 6 and the cingular gyrus; it extends forward on the mesial surface of the prefrontal lobe and is bilateral with the ipsilateral representation in the cingular gyrus. The movements from the head region are often "meaningful acts," such as yawning, vocalization or coordinated movements of head and eyes. Also found in the unanesthetized animals is a purely ipsilateral, higher threshold, mirror image (foot-to-foot and tail-to-tail) representation posterior to the projection of the central fissure onto the mesial surface.

In contrast with the primary motor area, the thresholds are higher and more affected by anesthesia, and the responses are in the nature of the assuming and holding of a limb posture rather than quick phasic movements like those induced by precentral stimulation. The postures are often held many seconds after the stimulus has ceased. The responses are often bilateral, and one stimulation tends to facilitate the next.

While the anterior supplementary area gives rise to fibers projecting widely to the frontal and precentral cortex, those reaching the primary motor areas of the same and opposite hemispheres constitute the main projection.

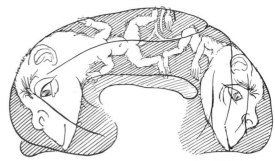

Fig. 14.   Anterior (left) and posterior (right) motor simiusculi obtained by stimulation through implanted electrodes in unanesthetized monkeys. Note in top middle of diagram the separate foot and tail areas which are undoubtedly part of the primary motor area on the lateral surface. (From Hughes and Mazurowski, *Electroenceph. clin. Neurophysiol.,* 1962, *14:*477–485)

However, the supplementary area can act independently and in the absence of these connections. Contrary to some reports, it does not contribute fibers to the pyramidal tract, but rather has extensive connections with brain stem structures, inducing motor effects via the extrapyramidal motor system.[17a] Comparable analysis of the posterior supplementary area has been made. The postural nature of the movements, the long after-action and facilitation, and the tendency of widespread areas of musculature to be involved—all are properties associated in reflex action with multisynaptic connections and are to be expected of an area connected with the motoneurons through the extrapyramidal system.

Other Supplementary Areas.   An experiment on unanesthetized monkeys was devised to learn the total extent of the free cortical surface which yields movements upon electrical stimulation.[39] As seen in Figure 15, nearly all of the lateral surface of the cerebral cortex was stimulated through as many as 610 implanted electrodes. Most of the cortex was excitable at about the same threshold, but the type of movement varied from region to region.

All regions of the cerebral cortex giving rise to movement on stimulation were termed supplementary motor areas by Crosby.[15] Movements obtained by stimulating the postcentral gyrus are mainly effected through the precentral motor area. A posterior parietal supplementary motor area discharges partly through the pyramidal systems and partly through the extrapyramidal system. The temporal lobe contains two supplementary motor

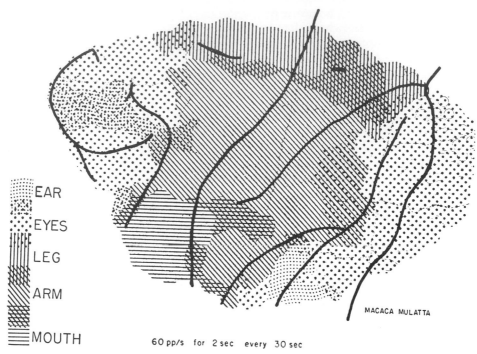

EAR

EYES

LEG

ARM

MOUTH

MACACA MULATTA

60 pp/s for 2 sec every 30 sec

Fig. 15. Map of movements elicited at threshold from cortex of unanesthetized monkey. All of 610 electrodes used yielded same kind of response at about same threshold. Movements elicited by stimulating a given receiving area were appropriate to the corresponding sensation; i.e., eyes and head moved from stimulation of visual areas, ear from acoustic area, somatic musculature from tactile area. To identify fissures compare with Fig. 2. (From Lilly in *Biological and biochemical bases of behavior,* Harlow and Woolsey, eds. Madison, University of Wisconsin Press, 1958.)

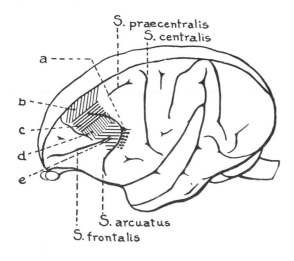

S. praecentralis
S. centralis

a

b

c

d

e

S. arcuatus
S. frontalis

Fig. 16. Subdivisions of frontal eye field and area yielding closure of eyes in monkey (*Macaca mulatta*). Designations: *a,* closure of eyes; *b,* pupillary dilatation; *c,* "awakening"; *d,* conjugate deviation to opposite side; *e,* nystagmus to opposite side. (From Smith, in Bucy, *The precentral motor cortex.* Urbana, University of Illinois Press, 1944.)

areas, one in the lateral region and one in the temporal portion of the preoccipital field. Both regions remain excitable after damage to the primary motor area. They tend to provoke ipsilateral as well as contralateral movements, especially in the facial musculature, the movements on both sides being gross rather than fine.

EYE MOVEMENTS.[62] Stimulation of area 8 in both man and animals causes responses of the musculature of the orbit and the lacrimal glands. The eyes sweep together (conjugate deviation) so that they often "look away from the stimulating electrodes." Ablation results in lateral deviation of the eyes so that they look toward the side of the lesion and cannot voluntarily move in the opposite direction. Movements obliquely upward and downward also occur, as shown in Figure 16. Fibers from these areas have been traced either directly to the eye nuclei or to coordinating nuclei which distribute impulses to the motor nuclei for the eye. According to Woolsey *et al.*[77] and Crosby,[15] a part of the frontal eye fields is included in the primary motor area representation.

It is significant that autonomic motor responses (lacrimation and pupillary dilatation or constriction) are obtained from foci closely adjacent to, and sometimes overlapping, the foci giving rise to motor effects on the eye musculature. Similar but generally weaker responses of the eye are obtained by stimulating areas 18 and 19 of the occipital lobe. Conjugate deviations elicited by stimulating area 17, the primary visual cortex, are perhaps to be viewed as sensorimotor responses of fixation.

ADVERSIVE MOVEMENTS. In man, a sustained lateral movement of the eyes and twisting of the neck and upper trunk may constitute an epileptic seizure. Such *adversive seizures* are usually caused by a discharging focus in the general region separating the motor areas from the prefrontal lobe. The exact relationship of this region to the eye fields (area 8), to the forward-lying representation of the axial musculature in the monkey,[77] and to the supplementary motor area is not clear. However, it seems that a broad area, encompassing the anterior part of area 6 and the posterior portion of the prefrontal lobe including area 8, constitutes an extrapyramidal adversive field. It lies in proximity to the pyramidal field for the axial musculature.[77] In patients, Penfield and Jasper[52] observed adversion traceable to a region still farther forward and medial. Their patients, however, were not aware of an epileptic discharge. Adversive movements elicited by stimulation of area 22 of the temporal lobe also have been described.

Use of the term "adversive movements" to describe seizures and experimentally elicited movements does not clearly convey their direction or physiologic significance. The term "orientational movements" may be substituted. Visual and somatosensory impulses initiated externally from the right side pass into the left hemisphere. If such impulses elicited adversive movements by way of area 8, the eyes and the body would twist to the right and thus would be oriented toward the external stimulus. Adversive or orientational movements may therefore be a part of the motor aspect of attention.

AUTONOMIC REACTIONS.[32] In addition to the autonomic effects of stimulation of the eye fields, there are autonomic reactions to stimulation anterior to the motor area in area 6 or in the premotor area. These are true responses, not nociceptive reflexes activated by stimulation of pain afferents associated with cerebral blood vessels.[73] The arrangement of points yielding autonomic responses coincides closely with the distribution of somatic motor foci. Vasomotor reactions in arms and legs can be obtained by stimulating points on the premotor area opposite the arm and leg areas, respectively. These changes may be associated with fluctuations in the systolic blood pressure and the heart rate. Vasopressor points are usually discrete and separable from vasodepressor points, but their spatial relation varies from animal to animal, and they are highly susceptible to changes in the type of anesthetic used and in the depth of anesthesia. This cortical representation of autonomic function has been confirmed by ablation studies, and aids in explaining autonomic changes often observed in clinical cases of hemiplegia.

CORTICAL EFFECTS ON ASCENDING SYSTEMS

There are two general ways in which the cerebral cortex can influence the afferent input to the brain: (i) by way of the γ efferent motoneurons or fusimotor fibers which contract the intrafusal muscle fibers of the muscle spindle, thereby increasing the discharge of Group IA impulses, and (ii) by acting upon a synapse of an ascending system.

Stimulation of the motor area, unlike stimulation of the reticular area (Chaps. 8 and 9) usually increases the rate of fusimotor discharge although depression can occur.[48] The rate changes are large, e.g., from a resting rate of 10 per second to 60 per second when the cortex is stimulated. The postcentral gyrus activates fusimotor neurons independently of the precentral gyrus; this is not evidence of a control of sensory significance because the postcentral gyrus is a motor area as well as a sensory area.

Cortical maps of fusimotor responses resemble closely the classic maps of movement and muscle representation. The γ motoneurons have discrete areas of cortical representation about like those of α motoneurons (5.0 to 9.5 sq. mm.), and often the two types of motoneurons in a given filament of the ventral root are activated from the same cortical region (Fig. 17). This close tie at the cortex, like that occur-

FOCAL AREAS OF L₄ SPINAL MOTORNEURONES
AS DETERMINED BY ELECTRICAL STIMULATION OF CORTEX

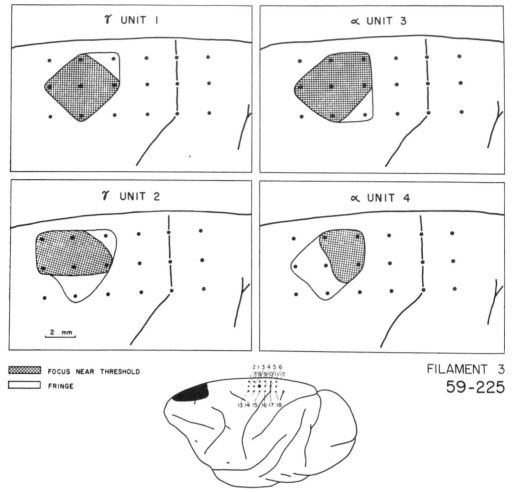

Fig. 17. Maps showing cortical areas from which gamma (left) and alpha (right) motoneurons of a single ventral root filament were caused to discharge. Note similarity in size and position of the excitable field for α and γ motoneurons. (From Mortimer and Akert, *Amer. J. phys. Med.*, 1961, *40:* 228–248.)

ring in the extensor muscles (Chap. 7), suggests that a detailed control function rather than a global facilitatory action is executed through the fusimotor system. Furthermore, there exists the temporal coincidence requisite for fusimotor discharge to affect α motoneuron discharge. In fact, in spontaneous movements γ preceded α motoneuron discharge by more than a second (Fig. 18). As pointed out in Chapter 8, the cortical control of spindle discharge is more probably significant to the control of movement than of sensation. While an increasing number of corticospinal tract axons terminate on the α motoneurons in primates, as Mortimer and Akert point out,[48] the fact of cortical control of the fusimotor system adds a second mechanism—the spindle—to share with the α motoneurons the shaping of the discharge which causes the muscle to contract. The discovery of a new neural mechanism invites speculation in respect to functional significance, but as yet there is little to go on. At this stage it suffices to say that, if a cortically induced movement were not preceded or accompanied by fusimotor activity, the stretch afferent might cease firing as the muscle shortened. Thus there could be little flow of information over Group IA fibers to the cerebellum or to α motoneurons.

A projection from the motor areas of the cerebral cortex to the nucleus of the posterior columns (N. cuneatus and gracilis) has been known since the beginning of the century. It was "rediscovered" and documented in detail in 1957 by three different anatomists.[13, 33, 72] A reticular inhibition of the gracilis nucleus was demonstrated electrophysiologically at about the same time. Magni *et al.*[43] have shown a direct pyramidal tract effect on these nuclei, i.e., not by way of collaterals from the pyramidal tract fibers to the reticular formation. Pyramidal tract stimulation induced a postsynaptic response in the gracile neurons and diminished the response evoked by somatic nerve stimulation supposedly by occlusion rather than by inhibition.

Towe and Jabbur,[65] recording from single units in the nuclei of the posterior columns, showed that 60 per cent of the units in the cuneate nucleus, as judged by its response to cutaneous stimulation, were depressed and 30 per cent were excited; the depression is direct rather than occlusive, and latency studies suggest that it might be exerted by collaterals from the pyramidal tract to the reticular formation. Both depression and excitation are produced by the pyramidal tract because both are retained by sectioning all of the brain stem except the pyramidal tract.[30] Conversely, when the pyramidal tract is sectioned, all facilitations and all but a weak inhibition disappear—the latter supposedly because of an extrapyramidal system.

It is significant that about half of the neurons in the dorsal column nuclei can be *discharged* by cortical stimulation via the pyramidal tract. This does not fit into any simple concept of gating a sensory input. It is further significant that the effect of cortical stimulation comes from the more restricted origin of the pyramidal tract as defined by recent studies (Fig. 5, right). This indicates that the intervention of the cortex on conduction over ascending systems is significant to movement rather than conscious sensation. No hypothesis relating the excitatory effects to sensation has been formulated, whereas a positive feedback to the cerebral cortex has been postulated in the execution of voluntary movements (see Chap. 13).

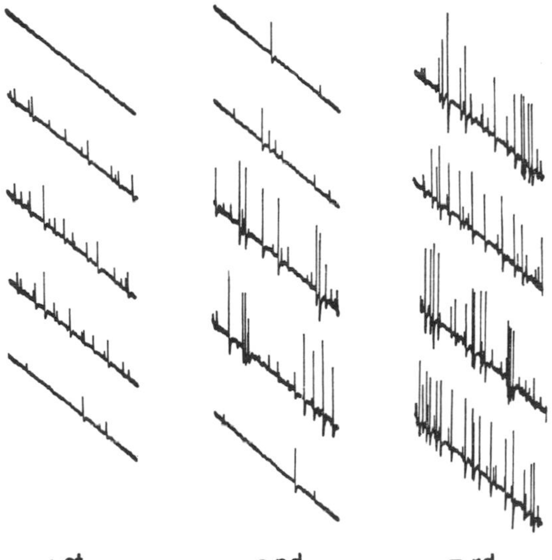

| st   2 nd   3 rd

Fig. 18. Selected sweeps of unit activity recorded from a ventral root filament of L$_7$ during three consecutive "spontaneous" (nonevoked) movements labeled 1st, 2nd and 3rd. The filament was quiescent prior to the first movement. Small fusimotor discharges preceded by 1.2 seconds the first α motoneuron discharge (seen in the third sweep at left). Note recruitment of α motoneurons in second and third movement. Sweep speed is 100 milliseconds. (From Mortimer and Akert, *Amer. J. phys, Med.*, 1961, *40*:228–248.)

CLINICAL PHYSIOLOGY OF THE MOTOR SYSTEMS

Investigation of the motor systems based on regional cortical ablations, principally by Fulton and Kennard,[22, 26] and on section of the medullary pyramids by Tower[66] and by Hines have profoundly altered the interpretation of such common clinical disorders as *hemiplegia*. Neurologists and neuropathologists were handicapped in learning the neuroanatomic basis of the signs making up hemiplegia because capsular lesions simultaneously and inevitably damage both the pyramidal and the COEP systems. In fact, the same is true of all other naturally occurring damage to the corticospinal neurons in the cortex, brain stem or spinal cord. That all of the signs of hemiplegia should have been ascribed to disruption of the pyramidal tract is an understandable error, but neurophysiologic analysis has now shown that many classic signs of pyramidal tract damage are in fact caused by damage to the extrapyramidal system.

Neurologists confronted with paralysis of voluntary movement ask first: Is this a disease or disturbance of the lower motoneurons—in modern language, motoneuron disease? Or is

Disease of Upper Motor Neurons
(*Syndromes Involving Spastic Paralysis*)

I. *Movement*
   1. Paralysis — Absence of voluntary movement.
   2. Paresis — Weakness of voluntary movement or deficient motor power.

II. *Postural reflexes*
   1. Spasticity — Resistance to passive movement of a joint, strongest in flexors of arms and extensors of leg. Fundamentally a stretch or myotatic reflex, the mounting resistance to increased force terminating in a collapse of the resistance (lengthening or "claspknife" reaction), distinguishes spasticity from *rigidity*. Spasticity is an example of "release of function."

   2. Exaggerated deep reflexes
      Tonic tendon jerk, etc. — Threshold of deep reflexes is low, and presence of myotatic appendage causes "dead beat" rather than pendular termination.

      Clonus — A rhythmic series of contractions following the knee or ankle jerks; also elicited by an abruptly applied but sustained passive stretch of extensors.

      Rossolimo's reflex (toes)
      Hoffmann's sign (fingers) — Sudden release of fingers (or toes) after bending them downward causes them to spring backward, stretching the physiologic extensors and causing a brief, smart contraction in all digits. Spasticity and alteration of deep reflexes are fundamentally the same phenomenon, differing only in the way the stretch reflex is elicited.

III. *Other reflexes*
   1. Babinski sign present*
      (Loss of plantar flexion) — Normal adult reflex response to scratching sole is downward or plantar flexion of toes. Babinski sign is an upward or dorsiflexion, especially of great toe, with or without fanning. It is caused by contraction of physiologic flexors and is often combined with flexor contraction at knee and hip.

   2. Abdominal and cremasteric reflexes absent — Contraction of abdominal muscles and retraction of testicle to stroking of abdomen and inner side of thigh, respectively, do not occur.

IV. *Muscle*
   1. No atrophy of degeneration
   2. No electrical reaction of degeneration
   3. No fasciculation or fibrillation
   4. No contracture — The absence of these signs plus the spasticity, etc., distinguish hemiplegia from flaccid paralysis of motoneuron disease; any atrophy is due to disuse and any contracture to holding limb in fixed position. (see Chap. 5 for details.)

* A clinical nicety is never to speak of a "positive Babinski sign"—a tautology.

it a disturbance of the descending motor tracts —upper motor neuron disease?* Preliminary to an analysis of the clinical syndromes, such as hemiplegia, which are characterized by spastic paralysis, their components may be presented in outline under four categories.

Experimental Analysis. The need to abandon the idea that all elements of the syndrome resulting from lesions at the upper motor levels could be ascribed to interruption of the pyramidal tract became apparent from the critical experiments by Fulton and his colleagues.[22, 23, 25, 26] They have proved that neither the paralysis (see below) nor the reflex changes of hemiplegia can be ascribed solely to damage to the pyramidal tract. These workers removed area 4 in monkeys and chimpanzees, extensively damaging the pyramidal tract while creating relatively little interference

*If the paralysis is manifest in the facial musculature, the equivalent of upper motor neuron disease is supranuclear disease.

with COEPS. *Flaccidity rather than spasticity ensued.* Neither exaggerated deep reflexes nor clonus was in evidence. Although some digital spasticity occasionally occurred several weeks later,[17] it need not have been caused by failure of pyramidal tract function, because even area 4 gives rise to some extrapyramidal fibers.

In additional experiments, Fulton proved further that interruption of COEP fibers is responsible for the spasticity of hemiplegia. Bilateral ablations which included area 6 as well as area 4 caused, in addition to a more profound and enduring paralysis, a typical spasticity and exaggeration of the deep reflexes. In the chimpanzee, these included Rossolimo's and Hoffmann's signs. Toe fanning was added to the Babinski sign, which had followed removal of area 4. The question has recently been raised whether this increased spasticity is due to interference with all of the anterior portions of the motor area or only with its most medial part, the supplementary motor area.[67, 68] Whichever is the case, "pyramidal tract disease" and "upper motor neuron disease" are not synonymous, and the cortically originating portion of the extrapyramidal system must be taken into account in understanding hemiplegia.

As pointed out above, the pyramidal tract consists of those fibers which originate in the cortex and pass to the spinal cord through the medullary pyramids. Therefore, the conclusive experiment is to section the medullary pyramids. The ensuing disturbances throw light on pyramidal tract function; hence, the other clinical signs reflect the functions of the extrapyramidal system.

Pyramidotomy was performed by Tower[66] on monkeys and by Hines[28] on a chimpanzee. The results fully confirmed the cortical ablation experiments. Spasticity was neither an early nor a late consequence of the pyramidal interruption. In the monkeys, there was a definite flaccidity, and in the chimpanzee, a slighter flaccidity. The Babinski sign (in the chimpanzee) and the loss of abdominal reflexes remained as the true pyramidal tract signs. (The status of the cremasteric reflex must be assumed, since the chimpanzee subjected to pyramidotomy was a lady!) Forced grasping, induced by stretching the physiologic extensors of the digits, resulted in a strong plantar flexion that was severe enough to cause an animal to get "hung up" through inability to release its grip on the cage bars.

As pointed out above, interference with the pyramidal tract at all levels from the cerebral cortex to the spinal cord (except at the pyra-

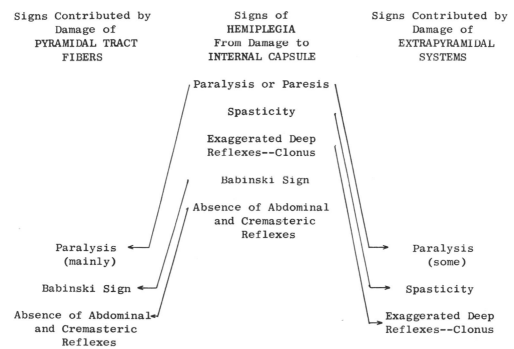

Fig. 19. Contributions of pyramidal tract and extrapyramidal systems to syndrome resulting from damage to internal capsule in man.

mids, which are rarely if ever selectively disrupted by pathologic processes) necessarily involves simultaneous interference with the pyramidal tract and the COEPS. In the light of these experiments, the respective contributions of the pyramidal and COEP systems are those shown in Figure 19.

Much of what is known of the extrapyramidal system has been deduced by subtracting proved pyramidal tract signs from the total and ascribing what is left to the extrapyramidal system. This method may have to be qualified. There is anatomic evidence that corticospinal fibers give off collaterals before reaching the the pyramids. These collaterals enter the pontine nuclei and probably the medial reticular formation, *potentially* reaching descending pathways and exerting an effect on extensor reflexes that is opposite (i.e., inhibitory) to that of the parent corticospinal tract of fibers.

Fulton's and Tower's reinterpretations of corticospinal function afford an explanation, previously lacking, for a typical feature of hemiplegia. The immediate results of disruption of the internal capsule are flaccidity and a reduction in deep reflexes, both of which persist for a varying number of days and gradually give way to the spasticity typical of chronic hemiplegia. Transitory areflexia or hyporeflexia implies the withdrawal of a descending facilitatory influence on segmental neurons. Since the pyramidal tract was traditionally assigned an inhibitory relationship to the segmental postural reflexes, its interruption could not logically underlie the initial flaccidity. However, if in man (as in the monkey) the pyramidal tract is facilitatory to extensor reflexes, the initial flaccidity can be ascribed to its interruption.

Whether in man it is necessary to abandon the idea that the pyramidal tract is the sole servant of voluntary activity cannot be answered with certainty, since neither nature nor the neurosurgeon has selectively sectioned the pyramids. In most clinical studies it is necessary to lump the extrapyramidal systems with the pyramidal systems that originate elsewhere than from the primary motor area. It suffices to say that, in man, section of the cord sector containing the pyramidal tracts, or of the middle two-thirds of the cerebral peduncle containing corticospinal fibers, produces much less interference with volitional movement than does a capsular lesion. The conclusion is that, in man

as in animals, the corticospinal tract from the primary motor area, the corticospinal fibers originating elsewhere in the cortex, and the COEPS work together to produce skilled voluntary movements. This concept is helpful in the interpretation of the recovery of voluntary power after lesions of the motor system.

Recovery of Voluntary Power. Explanation of the recovery of voluntary power that occurs after lesions in the cortical arm or leg area has always presented a problem. In fact, the degree of recovery possible when supposedly all of the cortical arm area is destroyed has led some clinicians to form the view that the arm is represented throughout the length of the precentral gyrus. Such an assumption is no longer necessary now that it is known that: (i) the corticospinal tract originates in substantial degree from areas outside the primary motor area, and (ii) the COEPS supports some voluntary movement. In addition, the amount and complexity of voluntary activity that can be supported by subcortical motor centers have been underestimated in both the monkey[69] and in man, for reasons given below.

Several factors affect the duration and ultimate degree of paralysis. (i) *Extent of cortex removed.* In monkeys, removal of area 6 including the supplementary motor area adds to the depth and duration of voluntary paralysis. Bilateral removal of areas 4 and 6 is more paralyzing than a comparable unilateral lesion. Similarly, retention of one area 6 leaves an animal significant useful movement.* If the parietal lobe, which gives rise to pyramidal tract fibers, is removed, there is a further deficit, only in part attributable to interference with somatic sensation. (ii) *Time between operations.* If bilateral removal of areas 4 and 6—an operation reducing a monkey's motor status virtually to that of a complete decorticate animal—is performed in stages with a long period elapsing between stages, a surprising amount of voluntary ability is recaptured. (iii) *Phylogenetic position.* Clinical signs following isolated ablation of area 4 increase in severity as the primate scale is ascended. Lemurs and New World monkeys exhibit less deficit than do the mangabeys and

---

*Whether this is an argument for the motor capacity of COEPS or of corticospinal fibers is not entirely clear, since the anatomic and electrophysiologic evidence in respect to the origin of fibers in area 6 is conflicting, as is the evidence in respect to the border of the primary motor area.

macaques, and the chimpanzees exhibit a greater deficit. Motor functions are more highly encephalized (actually "corticalized") in the animals with more highly developed brains. (iv) *Age.* If the removal of areas 4 and 6 is carried out in an infant, the animal is at first little affected by the procedure, a condition which correlates with the late myelination of the pyramidal tract. Serious motor deficits begin to appear as the animal matures, but it may never become as gravely affected as an animal undergoing the ablation as an adult. (v) *Postoperative care.* When small cortical areas are removed in serial operations, passive exercise to prevent contractures and nursing care to prevent bedsores, wasting, etc.,[69] are important factors in recovery. (vi) *Retraining.* The amount of forced usage of the paretic extremity. (vii) *Time after operation.* Given (v) and (vi) above, recovery continues over a much longer postoperative period than is observed in most experiments.

MECHANISMS OF RECOVERY. Even though recovery of function is the first concern of the patient and should be the concern of the neurologist, little research has been devoted to this subject. Definite explanations of the recovery mechanisms cannot be given. One factor is embraced in the term "neighborhood symptoms." Whether the cause of the disorder is a vascular accident or a meticulous surgical ablation, some reversible damage—trauma, dehydration, edema, venous occlusion, free blood, etc.—is done to cortical areas or tracts neighboring on the areas completely destroyed. As these transient lesions abate, what remains functions at more normal levels, and the paresis shrinks in severity and in distribution over the musculature.

Since motor skills can be improved by learning, it is reasonable to believe that usage and training can increase the level at which the undamaged apparatus can perform. This is termed "compensation." That tracts or cortical areas which have previously not controlled a given muscle do so after a lesion—as implied by the term "vicariation"—is exceedingly doubtful. However, performance of the same act with a different set of muscles is a commonplace phenomenon.

The sequence of events—areflexia, hyporeflexia and ultimate hyperreflexia—is typical of both capsular hemiplegia and spinal transection. The hyperreflexia (spasticity) is interpretable as *release of function*, i.e., release from inhibition by a descending pathway. The problem is why this release is not immediately manifest. Release phenomena are manifest within seconds in certain experimental situations, e.g., decerebrate rigidity or the *increase* in the excitability of the hindlimb flexion reflex following spinal transection in a decerebrate preparation. In both instances, no major facilitatory tract is removed by the transection. In primary transection of the spinal cord or in capsular hemiplegia, descending facilitatory tracts as well as inhibitory ones are removed. According to one interpretation, interruption of facilitatory pathways causes some change in the motoneuron's excitability, thus preventing any manifestation of the withdrawal of inhibition until the motoneuron has recovered excitability.

What is Released? Spasticity is a release phenomenon. Two questions must be asked about any release phenomenon. What structures must be damaged to effect the release, and what structures are released? In respect to spasticity and other signs of hemiplegia, the first of these questions has been answered in this chapter. The importance of the second question was first stressed by the philosophical neurologist Hughlings Jackson, who pointed out that a negative event (a lesion) cannot cause a positive event (a phenomenon such as spasticity). Except when irritative, a lesion can be only an antecedent circumstance; the direct *cause* or underlying mechanism of the overactivity must be the structures remaining functional. Releasing the brake of an automobile does not cause the car to go forward; it is the motor which does that. Magoun and Rhines[44] have expressed Hughlings Jackson's idea in a homely fashion, likening the motor systems to a jack-in-the-box. The motor cortex is the lid—but what is the spring that makes the jack jump out of the box?

At first sight, the segmental stretch reflex might seem to be the thing which is released. However, in the higher primates including man, spinal reflexes in themselves are not very strong, or they would not be depressed after spinal transection. For spasticity to develop, some facilitatory tract from the brain stem must remain functional. Just what tract or tracts are responsible is discussed in detail in the next chapter, but they may be previewed briefly as follows. One such tract is the vestibulospinal tract, but it may not be as important in primates as it is in the cat or dog. The second possibility is the reticulospinal tracts descending from the lateral reticular facilitatory area, described by Magoun and Rhines.[44] As will be discussed more fully, the reticular system may be involved in both the maintenance and the release of stretch reflexes. Impulses have been traced by strychnine neuronography from the anterior portion of the motor areas to the bulbar reticular inhibitory area, whence inhibition of the stretch reflexes is exerted by the reticulospinal tracts. Some such fibers may go from the cortex to the caudate nucleus and hence, through poorly defined pathways, to the bulbar reticular inhibitory area. Both of these pathways require verification before they can be fully accepted as the source of the impulses involved in the production of spasticity.

REFERENCES

1. AMASSIAN, V. E. *Electroenceph. clin. Neurophysiol.*, 1953, *5:* 415–438.
2. AMASSIAN, V. E. and DeVITO, R. *J. Neurophysiol.*, 1954, *17:*575–603.
3. v. BAUMGARTEN, R., MOLLICA, A. and MORUZZI, G. *Pflüg. Arch. ges. Physiol.*, 1954, *259:*56–78.
4. BERNHARD, C. G. and BOHM, E. *Arch. Neurol. Psychiat. (Chic.)*, 1954, *72:*473–502.
5. BERNHARD, C. G., BOHM, E. and PETERSEN, I. *Acta physiol. scand.*, 1954, *29* (Suppl. 106): 79–105.
6. von BONIN, G. and BAILEY, P. *The neocortex of* Macaca mulatta. Urbana, University of Illinois Press, 1947.
7. BRINDLEY, G. S. and LEWIS, R. P. *J. Physiol.*, 1964, *170:* 25P–26P.
8. BRODMANN, K. *Vergleichende Lokalisationslehre der Grosshirnrinde in Prinzipien dargestellt auf Grund des Zellenbaues.* Leipzig, J. A. Barth, 1909.
9. BROWN, T. GRAHAM, and SHERRINGTON, C. S. *Proc. roy. Soc.*, 1912, *B85:*250–277.
10. BUBNOFF, N. and HEIDENHAIN, R. Chap. 7 in *The precentral motor cortex*, 2d ed., P. C. BUCY, ed. Urbana, University of Illinois Press, 1949.
11. BUCY, P. C. *Brain*, 1957, *80:*376–392.
12. CAMPBELL, A. W. *Histological studies on the localisation of cerebral function.* Cambridge, Cambridge University Press, 1905.
13. CHAMBERS, W. W. and LIU, C-N. *J. comp. Neurol.*, 1957, *108:*23–55.
14. CHANG, H.-T., RUCH, T. C. and WARD, A. A., JR. *J. Neurophysiol.*, 1947, *10:*39–56
15. CROSBY, E. C. In: *Progr. Neurobiol. Proc. 1st. Int. Meet. Neurobiologists.* Amsterdam, Elsevier, 1956.
16. DeMYER, W. *Neurology*, 1959, *9:*42–47.
17. DENNY-BROWN, D. and BOTTERELL, E. H. *Res. Publ. Ass. nerv. ment. Dis.*, 1948, *27:*235–345.
17a. DeVITO, J. L. and SMITH, O. A. *J. comp. Neurol.*, 1959, *111:*261–278.
18. DUSSER DE BARENNE, J. G. and McCULLOCH, W. S. *J. Neurophysiol.*, 1939, *2:*319–355.
19. von ECONOMO, C. and KOSKINAS, G. N. *Die Cytoarchitektonik der Grosshirnrinde der erwachsenen Menschen.* Berlin, J. Springer, 1925.

20. FRITSCH, G. and HITZIG, E. *Arch. Anat. Physiol. (Lpz.)*, 1870, *37:*300–332.
21. FULTON, J. F. *Bull. Hist. Med.*, 1937, *5:*895–913.
22. FULTON, J. F. *Functional localization in the frontal lobes and cerebellum.* Oxford, Clarendon Press, 1949.
23. FULTON, J. F. *Physiology of the nervous system.* 3d ed. New York, Oxford University Press, 1949.
24. FULTON, J. F. *Gesnerus*, 1951, *8:*85–91.
25. FULTON, J. F., JACOBSEN, C. F. and KENNARD, M. A. *Brain*, 1932, *55:*524–536.
26. FULTON, J. F. and KENNARD, M. A. *Res. Publ. Ass. nerv. ment. Dis.*, 1934, *13:*158–210.
27. GLEES, P. *J. Anat. (Lond.)*, 1944, *78:*47–51.
28. HINES, M. *Biol. Rev.*, 1943, *18,* 1–31.
29. HUGHES, J. R. and MAZUROWSKI, J. A. *Electroenceph. clin. Neurophysiol.*, 1962, *14:*477–485.
30. JABBUR, S. J. and TOWE, A. L. *J. Neurophysiol.*, 1961, *24:* 499–509.
31. JACKSON, J. HUGHLINGS. *Selected writings of John Hughlings Jackson.* J. Taylor, ed. New York, Basic Books, Inc., 1956, 2 vols.
32. KENNARD, M. A. Chap. 9 in *The precentral motor cortex*, 2d ed., P. C. Bucy, ed. Urbana, University of Illinois Press, 1949.
33. KUYPERS, H. G. J. M. and TUERK, J. D. *J. Anat. (Lond.)*, 1964, *98:*143–162.
34. LASHLEY, K. S. and CLARK, G. *J. comp. Neurol.*, 1946, *85:* 223–305.
35. LASSEK, A. M. *J. comp. Neurol.*, 1942, *76:*217–225.
36. LAUER, E. W. *J. Neurophysiol.*, 1952, *15:*1–4.
37. LEÃO, A. A. P. *J. Neurophysiol.*, 1944, *7:*359–390, 391–396; *ibid.*, 1947, *10:*409–414.
38. LEVIN, P. M. Chap. 5 in *The precentral motor cortex*, 2d ed., P. C. Bucy, ed. Urbana, University of Illinois Press, 1949.
39. LILLY, J. C. In: *Biological and biochemical bases of behavior,* H. F. Harlow and C. N. Woolsey, eds. Madison, University of Wisconsin Press, 1958.
40. LILLY, J. C., AUSTIN, G. M. and CHAMBERS, W. W. *J. Neurophysiol.*, 1952, *15:*319–341.
41. LLOYD, D. P. C. *J. Neurophysiol.*, 1941, *4:*184–190.
42. LORENTE DE NÓ, R. In: *Physiology of the nervous system,* 3d ed., J. F. Fulton, ed. New York, Oxford University Press, 1949.
43. MAGNI, F., MELZACK, R., MORUZZI, G. and SMITH, C. J. *Arch. ital. Biol.*, 1959, *97:*357–377.
44. MAGOUN, H. W. and RHINES, R. *Spasticity: The stretch-reflex and extrapyramidal systems.* Springfield, Ill., Charles C Thomas, 1947.
45. MARSHALL, W. H. *Electroenceph. clin. Neurophysiol.*, 1950, *2:*177–185.
46. MARSHALL, W. H. and ESSIG, C. F. *J. Neurophysiol.*, 1951, *14:*265–273.
47. METTLER, F. A. *Proc. Soc. exp. Biol. (N. Y.)*, 1944, *57:*111–113.
48. MORTIMER, E. M. and AKERT, K. *Amer. J. phys. Med.*, 1961, *40:*228–248.
49. PATTON, H. D. and AMASSIAN, V. E. *Amer. J. Physiol.*, 1955, *183:*650.
50. PATTON, H. D. and AMASSIAN, V. E. *J. Neurophysiol.*, 1954, *17:*345–363.
51. PATTON, H. D. and AMASSIAN, V. E. Chap. 35 in *Handbook of physiology, Section 1, Neurophysiology,* vol. 2, H. W. Magoun, ed. Washington, D. C., American Physiological Society, 1960.
52. PENFIELD, W. and JASPER, H. *Epilepsy and the functional anatomy of the human brain.* Boston, Little, Brown & Co., 1954.
53. PENFIELD, W. and WELCH, K. *Arch. Neurol. Psychiat. (Chic.)*, 1951, *66:*289–317.

54. PHILLIPS, C. G. *Quart. J. exp. Physiol.,* 1956, *41:*58–69.
55. RAMÓN Y CAJAL, S. *Proc. roy. Soc.,* 1894, *55:*444–468.
56. ROSSI, G. F. and BRODAL, A. *J. Anat. (Lond.),* 1956, *90:* 42–62.
57. RUSSELL, J. R. and DEMYER, W. *Neurology,* 1961, *11:* 96–108.
58. SHERRINGTON, C. S. *J. Physiol.,* 1889, *10:*429–432.
59. SHOLL, D. A. *The organization of the cerebral cortex.* London, Methuen & Co., 1956.
60. SLOAN, N. and JASPER, H. H. *Electroenceph. clin. Neurophysiol.,* 1950, *2:*59–78.
61. SMITH, O. A., JR., and DEVITO, J. L. *Fed. Proc.,* 1958, *17:* 35, 151.
62. SMITH, W. K. Chap. 12 in *The precentral motor cortex,* 2d ed., P. C. Bucy, ed. Urbana, University of Illinois Press, 1949.
63. SUGAR, O., CHUSID, J. G. and FRENCH, J. D. *J. Neuropath.,* 1948, *7:*182–189.
64. TOWE, A. L. Unpublished observations.
65. TOWE, A. L. and JABBUR, S. J. *J. Neurophysiol.,* 1961, *24:* 488–498.
66. TOWER, S. S. Chap. 6 in *The precentral motor cortex,* 2d ed.,

P. C. Bucy, ed. Urbana, University of Illinois Press, 1949.
67. TRAVIS, A. M. *Brain,* 1955, *78:*155–173.
68. TRAVIS, A. M. *Brain,* 1955, *78:*174–198.
69. TRAVIS, A. M. and WOOLSEY, C. N. *Amer. J. phys. Med.,* 1956, *35:*273–310.
70. VAN HARREVELD, A. and OCHS, S. *Amer. J. Physiol.,* 1957, *189:*159–166.
71. VOGT, C. and VOGT, O. *J. Psychol. Neurol. (Lpz.),* 1919, *25:*279–461.
72. WALBERG, F. *Brain,* 1957, *80:*273–287.
73. WALL, P. D. and PRIBRAM, K. H. *J. Neurophysiol.,* 1950, *13:*409–412.
74. WALSHE, F. M. R. *Brain,* 1942, *65:*409–461.
75. WALSHE, F. M. R. *Brain,* 1943, *66:*104–139.
76. WOOLSEY, C. N. In: *Biological and biochemical bases of behavior.* H. F. Harlow and C. N. Woolsey, eds. Madison, University of Wisconsin Press, 1958.
77. WOOLSEY, C. N., SETTLAGE, P. H., MEYER, D. R., SENCER, W., PINTO-HAMUY, T. and TRAVIS, A. M. *Res. Publ. Ass. nerv. ment. Dis.,* 1952, *30:*238–264.

CHAPTER 13

Basal Ganglia and Cerebellum

By THEODORE C. RUCH

MOTOR FUNCTIONS OF THE BASAL GANGLIA

THE basal ganglia are involved in the control of movement and posture, since abnormal spontaneous movement results from lesions of these ganglia in man. The abnormal functions attendant upon such lesions are well known clinically, but the normal function of the basal ganglia is difficult to visualize. The conventional experimental methods of ablation, stimulation and degeneration in animals have provided tantalizing clues but little definitive information. Certain of the basal ganglia have functions which cannot be classified as motor. These functions will be discussed elsewhere.

Anatomic Considerations. By "basal ganglia" is meant all subcortical motor nuclei of the forebrain including the caudate nucleus, the putamen and the globus pallidus. They discharge to such structures as the corpus Luysi (subthalamic nucleus), the substantia nigra, the red nucleus and the reticular formation in the brain stem, as shown in Table 1. Modern authors include these brain stem structures among the basal ganglia. The caudate nucleus and the putamen, although separated by the internal capsule, are phylogenetically related and are known morphologically as the striatum. Although the putamen and the globus pallidus have been joined under the term "lenticular nucleus," this grouping is not meaningful. It is, however, meaningful to divide the pallidum into a medial (internal) and a lateral (external) portion. The external portion is, in a sense, afferent, since it receives fibers from other structures including the thalamus and the cerebral cortex. These connections are arranged to form a circuit: motor cortex–pallidum–thalamus–motor cortex. The internal division sends a large projection via the ansa and the fasciculus lenticularis to the lateroventral nucleus of the thalamus, which projects to the cerebral cortex. The pallidum also has descending connections with the subthalamic nucleus.

Lying deep to the cerebral cortex and lateral to the cerebral ventricles, the basal ganglia are the highest motor center in birds and lower forms, which possess little cerebral cortex. In these species these nuclei preside over a motor apparatus capable of producing such highly skilled movements as flying. Consistently, the

TABLE 1. *Connections of the Basal Ganglia (after Jung and Hassler[12])*

CORTICOSTRIONIGRAL

prefrontal cortex (9–12) → caudate → ventral surface internal capsule → substantia nigra (pars anterior)

[area 6, parietal and temporal lobe → internal putamen → pallidum → substantia nigra (pars posterior)

centre median → putamen

STRIOPALLIDORETICULAR

putamen & caudate → external pallidum

interstitialis nuc. → external pallidum

intralaminar nuc.
ascending reticular via thalamus
spinothalamic
medial lemniscus

H₂ of Forel
fasciculus lenticularis → ventromedial hypothalamic nuc.

subthalamic nuc.

red nuc. → pars parvicellularis → midbrain tegmentum → inferior olives → reticulospinal

red nuc. → pars magnocellularis → rubrospinal tract

STRIOPALLIDOCORTICAL

putamen & caudate → external pallidum → internal pallidum

fasciculus thalamicus (H₁ of Forel)
nucleus ventralis anterior

nucleus ventralis lateralis (anterior part)

motor areas 4, 6

red nucleus → nucleus ventralis lateralis

dentate nucleus magnocellular part → red nucleus

cerebellar cortex → dentate nucleus

Pyramidal tract

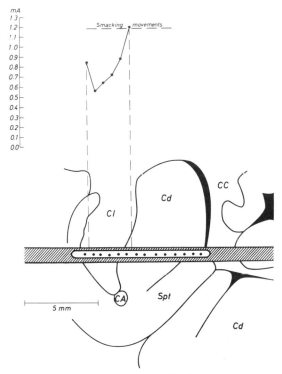

Fig. 1. Threshold for "arrest" of a learned movement from electrical stimulation of the internal capsule and caudate nucleus through a 14-lead implanted electrode (horizontal). Threshold is given on the ordinates. Points deeper within the caudate nucleus, Cd, produced arrest but also produced facial movements typical of stimulating the septal region, Spt., suggesting that arrest was also caused by spread of current. CI is internal capsule, CA is the anterior commissure. (From Laursen, *Acta physiol. scand.*, 1962, *54*:185–190.)

basal ganglia receive fibers from the intralaminar nuclei, the centromedian nuclei and the smaller midline nuclei. These fibers complete a potential subcortical connection of the ascending afferent systems with the basal ganglia. However, this system is not necessarily motor in function. With the development of a whole new apparatus for the control of movement—the cerebral cortex—the evolutionary fate of the basal ganglia becomes an intriguing question.

Motor Responses.[7, 21]   The results of early attempts to elicit movement by stimulation of the basal ganglia were mainly negative, and the apparent exceptions actually reflected spread of current to the internal capsule.

In recent experiments stimulation through implanted electrodes in unanesthetized cats left multineuron pathways not depressed and permitted weaker, nonspreading stimuli to be

used. Limb flexion was caused by spread of movement to the internal capsule.[15] Lipsmacking, salivation and swallowing were traced to the adjacent septal region.

Contraversive head and eye movements—i.e., looking away from the side of stimulation—and, with stronger stimulation, running in a circle away from the side of stimulation appear to be the only verified results of caudate stimulation.[7, 15] These have a long latency, are subject to and look like the similar movements of a normal cat, suggesting that the caudate nucleus functions at a high level of integration.

INHIBITORY EFFECTS.   If the responsiveness of the basal ganglia is examined against a background of either posture or movements concurrently induced by stimulation of the cerebral cortex, stimulation of the caudate nucleus and the globus pallidus causes inhibition (Fig. 1). Motor reactions initiated by the cerebral cortex "melt away" when even a weak stimulus is delivered to the caudate nucleus.[17, 22] Pallidal stimulation likewise does not induce movement but interrupts a cortically induced movement, thus causing the limb to be held in space.

This sudden inhibition of movement was seen by Laursen[15] but it was due to stimulation of fibers in the internal capsule rather than the caudate nucleus. Laursen trained animals to cross a hurdle in a two-compartment box and could freeze them in any position while crossing. This inhibition was obtained at lowest threshold from the internal capsule; from the caudate nucleus, it was obtained only at strengths causing signs of septal stimulation (Fig. 1), i.e., strong enough to spread to the internal capsule as well.

It is probable that cortically originating fibers give collaterals to the caudate nucleus. A strong immediate arrest of movement from capsular stimulation and weak and delayed arrest from caudate stimulation might be expected. Arrest of movement is also seen from stimulation of the thalamus and the amygdala. Anesthesia may favor the inhibitory and "holding" responses; they were not seen following stimulation of the striopallidum in unanesthetized cats by Forman and Ward.[7]

ACTIVATION BY MOTOR CORTEX.   There is some evidence that the basal ganglia are activated by strychnine stimulation of the motor cortex.[5] An anatomic projection from the cortex to the caudate nucleus—a projection which could account for this activation—has been described by Glees.[8] There are also anatomic connections through which the caudate nucleus, when activated, could discharge to the globus pallidus, which in turn is connected with the part of the thalamus that projects to area 4 of the cerebral cortex. Whether this circuit is in fact the route through which the stimulated caudate inhibits movements induced by the cortex has not been proved by critical studies of single unit discharge in the pyramidal tract (see Chap. 12). Much of the functional evidence for the existence of this circuit is based on suppression of the electrical activity of the cortex, a phenomenon of doubtful status (see Chap. 12). Since inhibition is stronger from capsular than from caudate or pallidal stimulation, an effect downstream is suggested. This could be a return loop from the midbrain to the motor cortex or an interaction at the spinal level.

Experimental Lesions. RELATION TO MOVEMENT. Whether the striatum has any function independent of the cortex has been doubted by most investigators,[21] and this is consistent with inability to elicit movement by stimulating the caudate nucleus and putamen.

Cats with neocortex removed were compared with others having, in addition, the striatum removed (so called thalamic cats) so that the independent functions of the striatum could be assessed.[24] Changes on the behavioral level rather than added paresis were noted. Striatal cats groomed themselves, groomed other cats, ate spontaneously, were active and exhibited sex behavior. Cats without neocortex and striatum lacked these abilities, although the component parts of the activity could be elicited. The striatum thus appears to be involved in ordering the component parts of complex movement. As pointed out below, the basal ganglia must participate in movement, since, in man, abnormal spontaneous movements are modified by lesions damaging these ganglia.[6]

Although in themselves of little effect, lesions of the basal ganglia proper combined with lesions of the anterior portions of the motor areas in monkeys and apes induce disturbances of movement reminiscent of those seen in man.[13, 14] This suggests (i) that the basal ganglia in some way modulate the activity of the primary motor areas, either by direct action on them or by convergence at lower levels, and (ii) that the anterior motor areas and the basal ganglia act synergistically, but independently, to modulate the discharges from the primary motor area.

RELATION TO POSTURE. In Chapter 12 was described a cortex–caudate–reticular mechanism, the interruption of which causes spasticity. This mechanism is part of the cortically originating extrapyramidal system (COEPS). However, the disturbance of postural reflexes occurring in the most common disease of the basal ganglia is clinically termed *rigidity*, and differs from spasticity in its properties and, presumably, in its cause. The actual disturbances of posture and movement resulting from damage to the basal ganglia are best discussed from clinical information.

In recent years the classic consequences of prefrontal lobe lesions at the behavioral level— "hyperactivity" and "recent memory"—have also been ascribed to the caudate nucleus (see Chap. 23). If the evidence is taken at face value, the role of the caudate nucleus encompasses what might be considered most primitive movement—turning of eyes and head and circling—to intellectual functions. If the difficulty of separating caudate function anatomically and physiologically from surrounding and overlying structures is so great, the allocation of role to the other nuclei of the basal ganglia cramped close to one another and interlaced with ascending and descending pathways is understandably greater and our knowledge correspondingly more fragmentary and speculative. For this reason experimental knowledge will be presented in connection with clinical syndromes.

Pathophysiology of Basal Ganglia in Man. The abnormalities resulting from damage to the basal ganglia are more outspoken and more easily examined in man than in experimental animals. Unfortunately, lesions of the human basal ganglia are mainly produced by diffuse pathologic processes, so that clinical cases tell little of functional localization. (The areas of greatest or most common damage may simply be those most easily damaged by the specific agent, not those responsible for the syndrome.) Presumably, the various ganglia do not all have similar functions, because there are two groups of disorders that contrast with one another in many ways.

ATHETOSIS, CHOREA, BALLISMUS. This group of disorders is a spectrum of dyskinesias or abnormal movements having many points of similarity; athetosis and chorea often occur together. These dyskinesias have in common marked—even violent—voluntary-like movement with *no typical changes in muscle tonus*.* Paradoxically, these movements are involuntary, i.e., not willed by the patient and beyond his control.

In *chorea*, meaning "dance," a wide variety of rapidly performed, jerky, but well coordinated movements occur ceaselessly. They are not willed by the patient and serve no purpose. Their coordinated, purposive look led Hughlings Jackson to speak of "some method in their madness."

In *athetosis*, the limbs indulge in ceaseless, slow, sinuous, writhing movements which are especially severe in the hand and are involuntary. They are reminiscent of certain oriental dances and bear less resemblance to coordinated voluntary movements than do those of chorea; antagonistic muscles may contract simultaneously. The brain damage is said to be greatest in the striatum.

In *ballismus*, the movements are violent and flinging (ballistic) and are caused by contractions of the proximal limb muscles. If the movements are confined to one-half of the body, as is commonly the case, the condition is called *hemiballismus*.

Clinical and neuropathologic observations, animal experiments and neurosurgical attempts to relieve chorea and athetosis have not yielded any consistent picture of the underlying mechanism of these diseases and what lesions produce them. There is some evidence that human athetosis is relieved by lesions of the premotor area and of the anterior columns of the spinal cord. Bucy[2, 3] has suggested that athetosis represents an abnormal discharge over the COEPS.

Perhaps the clearest production of involuntary movement is shown by monkeys (but not cats) in which the subthalamic nucleus of Luysi is partially destroyed.[29] Clinically, lesions in this nucleus are believed to cause hemiballismus. However, the involuntary movements (hyperkinesis) obtained in monkeys are of the choreic type; i.e., they occur in irregular sequences of movement varying in amplitude and duration. Sometimes the movement is slower and more sinuous (athetoid) and only occasionally is it the repetitive, flinging, ballistic type. The latter is the type associated with pathologic disturbance of this nucleus in man. As in man, the hyperkinesis does not occur if

*In the contrasting disease, parkinsonism, tonus is severely disturbed, and involuntary movements are generally less conspicuous.

nearby structures are damaged, e.g., the internal pallidum, fasciculus lenticularis (H_2) and thalamicus (H_1) or the internal capsule. The subthalamic nuclei have ascending connections with the internal pallidum and could affect corticospinal and COEPS discharge by way of the ventrolateral thalamic nucleus. The descending efferents are thought to be rubrospinal. The spinal pathway mediating the abnormal movements following experimental lesions of N. subthalamicus has been narrowed down to the posterolateral columns of the spinal cord deep to the dorsal spinocerebellar tract.[4] Lesions here abolished choreiform movements, which failed to return with partial recovery of voluntary movement. The movements are probably executed over the corticospinal tracts but the rubrospinal and pontine reticular spinal tracts passing through this region of the spinal cord must also be suspected. However, lesions of the red nucleus do not abolish N. subthalamicus hyperkinesis, whereas cortical intervention does. For this category of involuntary movement, the point of interaction between the extrapyramidal system and the pyramidal system appears to be the cortical motor areas.

PARKINSON'S DISEASE (PARALYSIS AGITANS). As the second part of the formal name suggests, paralysis agitans is, like the previous group, often marked by an involuntary movement—in this case a *tremor*. Unlike athetosis, chorea and ballismus, Parkinson's disease results in a definite and disabling reduction in voluntary and associated movements (poverty of movement) and also in a definite disturbance in the postural sphere, *rigidity*. Observations on Parkinsons's disease and related animal experiments can be taken as exemplifying two important clinical signs, rigidity and tremor. The pallidum and the substantia nigra are often said to be the most consistent sites of damage in this syndrome. However, there is good reason to believe that the lesions in the pallidum are not the responsible ones.

Although nearly a century and a half have elapsed since Parkinson described the syndrome, none of its three major components can yet be clearly explained in terms of mechanism or responsible neural structure. Since the major components tend to occur in different proportions in different patients, and since the brain damage is diffuse, it is presumed that several structures may be involved.

Poverty of movement. Parkinson's disease contrasts with chorea and athetosis in that initiation of voluntary movement is difficult and there is a resultant immobility. Absent are the small restless movements, the play of emotional expression on the face, and the movements associated with intentional movements, such as arm-swinging during walking seen in normal persons. Despite the formal name for the condition, there is no real paralysis, and in this fact, as well as in the type of tonus change, Parkinson's disease differs from spastic paralysis resulting from capsular lesions. Magoun and Rhines[16] ascribe the poverty of movement to interference with the descending reticular facilitatory system; however, such interference might be expected to induce accompanying flaccidity rather than rigidity. Some think that movement is damped by the rigidity, since movement improved in amplitude, speed and endurance when injection of procaine hydrochloride into the muscles had caused them to become flaccid.[28] However, the tendency for hypokinesia and rigidity to occur in different proportions in different patients suggests that rigidity is not the sole basis for the poverty of movement.

Rigidity. In Chapter 12 rigidity was distinguished from spasticity. A rigid limb affords resistance throughout the entire extent of a passive movement. The resistance does not develop suddenly, does not mount with the application of additional force, and does not collapse terminally in a lengthening reaction. Sometimes, however, the response to passive movement is a series of catches and gives—so-called "cogwheel" rigidity. The rigidity is manifest in both extensor and flexor muscles, being stronger in the latter. To the examiner the resistance has a

dead, leadlike feel, as opposed to the live vibrant resistance felt in the spastic limb. The rigid limb therefore exhibits a more marked plasticity than does a spastic limb. The rigidity of extrapyramidal disease is dependent upon the integrity of the myotatic reflexes; it disappears in muscles deprived of afferent innervation by posterior root section.[18] However, the tendon reflexes are not exaggerated or marked by clonus. It is interesting that Jendrassick's maneuver (clenching of hands), used to bring out or enhance a weak tendon jerk, does not affect such reflexes in Parkinson's disease (Fig. 2). In all these respects, the rigidity resulting from extrapyramidal lesions at the level of the basal ganglia differs from the spasticity caused by interference with the COEPS.

Section of the pyramidal tract at the spinal level in Parkinson's disease does not augment rigidity but rather decreases it slightly.[20] Thus interruption of the pyramidal tract appears to cause neither rigidity nor spasticity. Contrary to expectation from results of animal experiments, in man section of the efferent outflow from the pallidum (ansa lenticularis) or destruction of the medial pallidum itself may virtually abolish rigidity.[6] Moreover, surgical destruction of the lateroventral nucleus, which receives impulses from the pallidum and projects to areas 4 and 6 of the cerebral cortex, also may abolish rigidity. It thus seems that the globus pallidus should not be considered a structure which, when damaged, releases the mechanisms underlying rigidity; rather it should be considered contributory to the mechanism underlying rigidity. It is not clear how this system of fibers operates in the intact animal—whether through the midbrain motor nuclei or by influencing descending pathways

Fig. 2. Electromyograms of deep reflex jerks in biceps brachii in a case of hemiparkinsonism. Left side of records shows size of reflex before reinforcement by hand-clasping; right side shows reflex during hand-clasping. The reflex in limb exhibiting parkinsonism is unchanged by reinforcement. (After Hassler, *Dtsch. Z. Nervenheilk.,* 1956, *175:*233–258.)

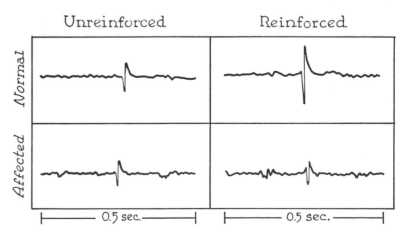

(COEPS) at the level of the cerebral cortex. Hassler,[10] who ascribes the Parkinson syndrome to destruction of the substantia nigra, suggests that loss of *ascending* collaterals from the nigra to the pallidum permits overactivity in the pallidothalamic system of neurons. As with spasticity and decerebrate rigidity, descending influences may cause the rigidity of Parkinson's disease by acting upon the alpha motoneurons or upon the fusimotor fibers. Marked inhibition of spindle discharge follows stimulation of the lateroventral nucleus of the thalamus; this effect is exerted through the cerebral cortex.[27] This finding cannot be correlated in any simple way to the demonstrated effects of lateroventral thalamic lesions on Parkinson's disease.

Tremor. The tremor, which is initially most obvious distally in the limb, is fine, highly regular and rapid (four to eight cycles per second). It occurs during rest and stops when the limbs are used voluntarily. It is therefore variously termed "tremor of rest" or "static tremor." Electromyography shows that antagonistic muscles are alternately activated and that the rate is surprisingly constant over long periods in a given muscle group. Both in its sinusoidal regularity and its occurrence at rest, the tremor of Parkinson's disease contrasts with the intentional tremor of cerebellar disease (see below). In the later stages of the disease, which is rather common in people who contracted influenza during World War I, the tremor becomes more

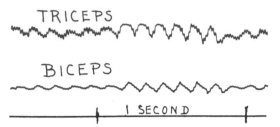

Fig. 4. Synchronous electromyograms of triceps and biceps in a monkey exhibiting tremor consequent to ventrolateral midbrain lesion. Note alternating contraction in antagonistic muscles. (From Ward *et al.*, *J. Neurophysiol.*, 1948, *11*:317–330.)

violent, shaking the whole body and thus greatly disturbing and exhausting the patient.

Production and control of tremor. Pathologic or neurosurgical damage to the motor areas,[2] the internal capsule, the cerebral peduncle (Fig. 3)[3] or the posterolateral region of the spinal cord[19, 20] abolishes or diminishes tremor, at least transiently. The relationship is well established, but different authors interpret it quite differently. Bucy,[2] for example, considered the tremor to result from an oscillatory continuous discharge of the pyramidal tract unmodulated by a cortex-to-cortex circuit through the basal ganglia, the oscillating discharge being superseded by impulses mediating smooth movement when the pyramidal tract is involved in voluntary movement. However, no experimental lesion of the striopallidum link in the modulating circuit has ever produced a static tremor. On the other hand, Ward[25, 26] and others[9, 22] have produced a Parkinson-like tremor in monkeys by placing lesions in the ventrolateral midbrain reticular area between the red nucleus and the substantia nigra. The tremor is about eight cycles per second, and antagonistic muscles contract alternately (Fig. 4). As seen in Figure 5, the tremor, as in Parkinson's disease, disappears upon voluntary movement and tends to be increased during emotional excitement; it disappears during sleep. Other signs of Parkinson's disease were masked facies, sluggish movements and rigidity. On the basis of these experiments, Ward postulates that the lesion giving rise to the tremor of clinical Parkinson's disease lies in the mesencephalic tegmentum. Effective lesions in the ventrolateral midbrain have included the substantia nigra in some series[9] and the anterior fibers of the brachium conjunctivum destined for the

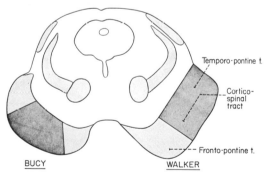

Fig. 3. Cross sections through the human midbrain. On right is shown a pedunculotomy performed by Walker and on the left one performed by Bucy. Involuntary movements were greatly diminished and recovery of voluntary power included independent movements of fingers in Bucy's case. (After Bucy, Chap. 11 in *Pathogenesis and treatment of parkinsonism*, W. S. Fields, ed. Springfield, Ill., Charles C Thomas, 1958.)

MOVEMENT DISORDER – MONKEY

Effect of Voluntary Movement on Tremor at Rest

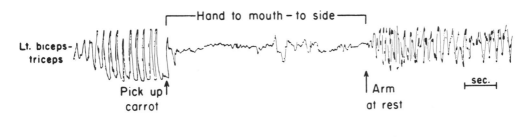

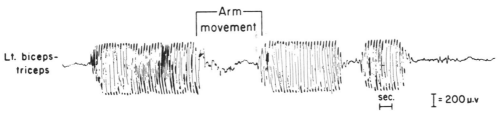

Fig. 5. Electromyographic records of arm tremor in monkey with bilateral lesions of ventromedial midbrain region. Note absence of tremor while a carrot is grasped and placed in mouth, and while arm is being returned to animal's side. (From Schreiner *et al.,* in *Pathogenesis and treatment of parkinsonism,* W. S. Fields, ed., Springfield, Ill., Charles C Thomas, 1958.)

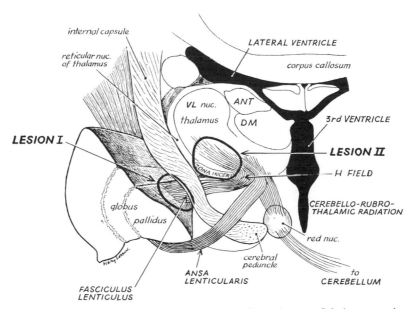

Fig. 6. Diagram in three dimensions of the basal ganglia and some of their connections, showing the sites of operation for relief of parkinsonism. Lesion I, originally used by Cooper, consisted of interrupting pallidothalamic connections. This lesion is less effective in respect to tremor than Lesion II in the gateway of pallidal and cerebellar pathways to the ventrolateral nucleus of the thalamus. (From Lin, Okumura and Cooper, *Electroenceph. clin. Neurophysiol.,* 1961, *13*:631–634.)

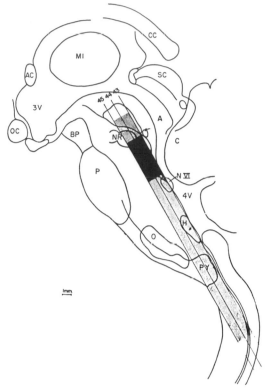

Fig. 7. Sagittal section through brain stem showing tremorogenic zone demarcated by electrical stimulation. Black area between Horsley-Clarke coordinates 43 and 45 yields tremor most consistently. Pertinent abbreviations are: *NR*, nucleus ruber; *VI*, nucleus of abducens nerve; *H,* nucleus of hypoglossal nerve; *O,* inferior olive; *PY*, pyramids. (From Jenkner and Ward, *Arch. Neurol. Psychiat. (Chic.)*, 1953, *70*:489–502.)

thalamus and pallidum in most. Although interruption of these fibers can produce resting tremor and may be contributory, it is not necessary for the production of tremor.

Since, according to Hughlings Jackson's principle, the tissue destroyed cannot directly cause an overactivity (tremor), Ward concluded that the lesion, by interrupting descending pathways, has permitted some lower brain stem mechanism to oscillate. The oscillatory discharge is, by exclusion of major descending systems, in the reticulospinal tract. Stimulation of the reticular substance below the level of the lesion causes rapid oscillatory movements (15 to 25 per second).[11] As seen in Figure 7, the region yielding this tremor is the medial reticular substance lying between the red nucleus and the VIth cranial nerve. Presumably, impulses inhibiting these tremorogenic neurons come from higher levels and funnel through the ventrolateral midbrain area—perhaps from

the substantia nigra, but this assumption has not yet been verified. The role of the pyramidal tract is envisioned as the supplying of a facilitatory, nonoscillatory background which is necessary for tremor just as a tonic background is favorable to clonus. Stimulation of other regions besides the reticular core causes tremor, e.g., brachium conjunctivum, nucleus ruber and amygdala.[1]

A search for single units discharging synchronously with the tremor revealed none in the reticular formation, in contrast with 15 per cent of cells synchronously discharging recorded from the sensorimotor area of the cortex.[9] Chlorpromazine produces static tremor, but, judging from neuropathologic lesions it causes, its action is too wide to have localizing value. However, the tremor produced by drugs or lesions and stimulation of the reticular system is abolished by decerebration.[1] Thus levels above the midbrain may be necessary for tremorogenesis either independently or by way of the reticular formation. Since sleep inhibits tremor, it is worthy of note that ascending reticular impulses may produce a nonspecific activation of brain structures favorable for tremor.

Abolition of tremor by damage to the projections from the cortical motor areas as a consequence of a stroke causing hemiplegia was known by Parkinson himself. Neurosurgical interference with the motor areas,[1] internal capsule, cerebral peduncle (Fig. 3), or the posterolateral column of the spinal cord abolishes or diminishes tremors whereas the paresis lasts. Further insight into tremor again has come from clinical observations.

The substantia nigra and the globus pallidus are usually considered the most common sites of damage resulting in paralysis agitans, but, quite empirically, it was learned by Cooper in 1952 (see Ref. 4 and Fig. 6) that destruction in the region of the globus pallidus decreases both tremor and rigidity, and restores mobility to many patients with Parkinson's disease. Destruction of the ansa lenticularis or the ventrolateral nucleus of the thalamus (Fig. 6) has proved even more effective. Experimental Parkinson's disease from midbrain lesions is also relieved by pallidectomy.[22]

The sites of the operations which reduce tremor, rigidity and hypokinesis are on a known neural loop: motor areas → putamen → pallidum → ventrolateral nucleus of the thalamus

→ motor areas. Into this feed contributions from the brachium conjunctivum, nigra-pallidal fibers and possibly parallel fibers from the ventrolateral reticular formation. Lesions at all these three input sites are suspected of causing tremor. Interruption of the loop or of the pyramidal tract—an offshoot from it— relieves the tremor. Thus, a second hypothesis of tremor is that an oscillation of a feedback system occurs when not driven by the cortex or by cerebellar, nigral or reticular inputs. It would be necessary to think of the input outside the loop as inhibitory since high gain in a feedback system causes oscillation.

A reverberating circuit, of which cortex-to-cortex might be a complex example, is one means of producing an oscillation. Sensory motor unit discharge in phase with the tremor lends some support to this idea. Oscillation can also be produced by subjecting spinal motor neurons to evenly balanced excitation of flexor and extensor neurons, much like the teeter board analogy that will be used to explain rhythmic respiration (Chap. 41). A strong bias, as represented by decerebrate rigidity, should be unfavorable to this kind of oscillator—and is—but so should the rigidity of parkinsonism.

Another familiar oscillation occurs when there is a strong bias rhythmically interrupted, as in clonus.

Parkinsonian tremor presents a bewildering series of paradoxes and uncertainties, to which can be added the empirical fact that atropine-like compounds relieve Parkinson's disease, an action suggesting that excessive acetylcholine or acetylcholine-sensitivity may be involved. However, acetylcholine mediation of synaptic transmission in the brain has never been proved.

It is paradoxical that destruction of the very structures showing maximum pathologic alterations in Parkinson's disease often lessens the disability. This paradox could be resolved by the possible (but unpopular and unsubstantiated) hypothesis that the circuit consisting of the globus pallidus, the ansa lenticularis and the ventrolateral thalamus is the site of a discharging lesion. Such a discharge might act on the cerebral cortex or upon the brain stem tegmentum. To account for a symptom-free interval of as long as 30 years, and to account for the efficacy of anticholinesterase drugs on the basis of degeneration hypersensitivity, it is necessary to postulate further that an irritative-destructive process begins long after the original influenzal infection. In short, although the disappearance or reduction of tremor by pallidectomy

does not establish the pallidum as the site of the discharging oscillatory lesion, the possibility that this is the case must be considered.

CEREBELLUM

Orientation. The cerebellum, like the cerebral hemispheres, is a suprasegmental structure, but it has no long, direct pathway to the spinal cord comparable to the pyramidal tract. Thus, the cerebellum can influence motoneurons only through its connections with the motor systems of the brain stem and with the cerebral cortex. It is therefore not surprising to find that the cerebellum does not execute detailed movements;* none disappears when it is extirpated. Its chief function lies in the *control* or regulation of movement, especially voluntary skilled movements, but also such brain stem functions as walking. The cerebellum also regulates posture and tonus; it must also regulate visceral activities, since many of them are altered by cerebellar stimulation or ablation.[43]

Consistent with widespread regulation or control is the cerebellum's richness of efferent and afferent connections,[57] as seen in Figure 8.

*Cerebellar stimulation does produce coordinated rotations of the head or flexions and extensions involving the whole limb. Such stimulation also facilitates and inhibits movements. The distinction between a strong facilitation and a weak movement is not great. The above distinction may therefore be more conventional than real. In fact, Sprague and Chambers[61] found that contact placing reactions are lost after cerebellectomy.

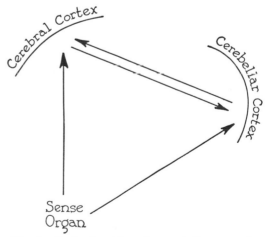

Fig. 8. Basic plan of cerebrocerebellar control system. Arrows indicate the pathways of impulse conduction, not neurons.

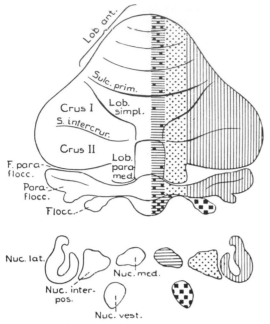

Fig. 9. Diagram of primate corticonuclear zones. Note that medial or vermal zone of cerebellum (*horizontal lines*) projects to nucleus medialis, i.e., fastigial nucleus, and to the vestibular nuclei; intermediate or paravermal zone (*stipple*) projects to nucleus interpositus; and lateral zone (*vertical lines*) projects to nucleus lateralis or dentate nucleus. (From Jansen and Brodal, *Avh. norske VidenskAkad., Kl. I,* 1942, No. 3.)

It is reciprocally connected* with the cerebral motor and sensory areas.[48, 50, 57] It projects to the brain stem structures giving rise to descending motor pathways. Control requires information. Functional studies indicate that the cerebellum receives an afferent input not solely from the proprioceptive and vestibular systems, but from many sensory systems, including those for vision and audition.[59] Certain areas of the cerebellar cortex are somatotopically organized, although not in the detail found in the cerebral

*"Reciprocal connection," not to be confused with "reciprocal innervation," means that A sends fibers to B and B sends fibers to A.

cortex. Furthermore, there is evidence of functional localization reflecting differences in the efferent and afferent projections; however, thought on this matter is now in a state of flux.

Anatomic Organization. The cerebellum, like the cerebrum, consists of a cortex and deep nuclei. Unlike the cerebral cortex, the three-layered cortex of the cerebellum has a uniform structure showing no cytoarchitectural subdivisions. The efferent cells of the cerebellar cortex, the Purkinje cells, send their axons to the deep nuclei in such a manner that the cerebellum can be divided into longitudinal corticonuclear zones (Table 2 and Fig. 9). The efferent path is then continued by neurons of these nuclei, the axons leaving the cerebellum via the inferior and superior peduncles to reach various nuclei of the thalamus, midbrain and medulla.[38] Some cortical areas also project directly to the vestibular nuclei of the medulla (Fig. 9). The corticonuclear zones were delimited anatomically by Jansen and Brodal,[51] and this description was modified recently by Cohen *et al.*[38] The functional significance of these zones has been stressed by Chambers and Sprague.[37] This way of dividing the cerebellum may be termed the longitudinal or zonal, in contrast to the transverse or lobular division.

The afferent pathways to the cerebellum terminate chiefly in the cortex (the granule and Purkinje cell layers) and to a lesser extent in the deep nuclei. The regions of termination of the various afferent pathways are shown in Figure 10, in which the lobular organization of the cerebellum is illustrated. Although knowledge of afferent projections has influenced the concept of a lobular organization, this concept is based to a greater extent on comparative anatomy and embryology.†[41, 42, 43, 53]

Knowledge of the connections of the cerebellum is essential for the understanding of its functional organization. Comparative anatomy

†The afferent pathways can also be related satisfactorily to the longitudinal corticonuclear zones.

TABLE 2. *Corticonuclear Zones of the Cerebellum*

Medial zone	Vermal cortex	Fastigial nuclei
Intermediate zone	Paravermal cortex (incl. paramedianus?)	Interpositus or intermediate nuclei‡
Lateral zone	Hemispheric cortex lobulus ansiformis and parafloccules	Dentate nucleus

‡ Globosus and emboliformis nuclei of man.

and embryology have demonstrated that the cerebellum has two major divisions separated by the posterolateral fissure—the flocculonodular lobe and the corpus cerebelli. Phylogenetically, the flocculonodular lobe develops early, and it receives its connections chiefly from the vestibular system. This lobe is relatively the same in various animals and is sometimes called the *archicerebellum*. The corpus or body of the cerebellum first appears as a medial (vermal) area consisting of a cortex and deep nuclei, which are presumably the homologue of the fastigial nuclei. This area, the *paleocerebellum*, is connected primarily with the vestibular mechanism and the proprioceptors and exteroceptors of the body and head. In mammals the paleocerebellum also receives corticopontile connections. The body of the cerebellum shows great development, especially in its lateral parts (*neocerebellum*), which consist of intermediate and lateral areas with their respective nuclei (Fig. 10). The lateral area receives its chief connections from the cerebral cortex via the pontine nuclei and additional connections from the upper brain stem via the inferior olive. The intermediate area shares the afferent connections of the lateral area and many of those of the vermis. These connections are the ventral

and dorsal spinothalamic tracts, the tectocerebellar tracts and the connections with the trigeminal and other sensory systems innervating the face.

The flocculonodular lobe projects back to the vestibular nuclei. The vermal area of the corpus cerebelli projects to the same vestibular nuclei, to the reticular formation of the medulla, and to the pons, midbrain and thalamus. The lateral and intermediate areas project to the reticular formation of the midbrain and to the red nucleus and the thalamus. Thus all areas of the cerebellum except the flocculonodular lobe project to the origin of the pyramidal and extrapyramidal systems in the cerebral cortex via the ventral thalamic nuclei. All cerebellar areas likewise send projections to the subcortical extrapyramidal systems, that from the vermal area going chiefly to the medulla (reticulospinal paths).

The concept of lobular parcellation now seems inadequate in the light of some of the newer information on afferent and efferent somatotopic organization. For example, the representation of the body surface extends behind the fissura prima into the declive and the simplex lobule; moreover, a second spinothalamic projection area exists, and there is a

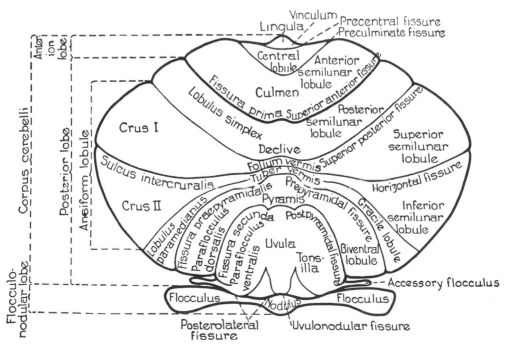

Fig. 10. Diagram of primate cerebellar cortex to summarize various terminologies, based principally on lobes and afferent projections to cerebellar areas (*right*). (From Larsell, *Anatomy of the nervous system*, 2d ed. New York, Appleton-Century-Crofts, 1951.)

representation of the body surface in the posterior part of the posterior lobe. Under the system of lobular division, the anterior lobe—that part of the corpus cerebelli rostral to the primary fissure—has often been treated as a unit. In primates, however, this lobe consists of three zones—vermal, intermediate and lateral— each having different fiber connections and functions. Such a subdivision exists in the posterior lobe, lying between the primary and posterolateral fissures. In each instance, the lateral (and probably the intermediate) area should be referred to as the hemisphere. Even the flocculonodular lobe is subdivided into a vermal portion, the nodulus, and a lateral portion, the flocculi.

FUNCTIONAL ANATOMY OF THE CEREBELLUM

Localization and Projection. If the cerebellar cortex is explored, millimeter by millimeter, with a recording electrode while a point on the skin is touched, a cerebellar point will be found at which the so-called evoked potential is maximal (see Chaps. 15 and 23). Stimulation of an adjacent point on the skin evokes a maximal potential at an adjacent point on the cortex. In this fashion, a *somatotopic* map of the cerebellar cortex has been produced, and the cortex is said to be somatotopically or topographically organized. Elicitation of movements by cerebellar stimulation has confirmed such maps. If the evoked potential technique is applied to the cerebral and the cerebellar cortex, recording from one while stimulating the other (and then reversing the procedure) reveals many specific connections between them.

MULTIPLICITY OF INPUTS. By varying the type of stimulus to the body, or by stimulating different sense organs such as the eye or the ear, one can determine the kind of sensory input received by a central area. Until 1942, when Snider and Stowell[59] performed experiments of this type, the afferent input into the cerebellum was thought to be exclusively vestibular and proprioceptive. These workers demonstrated that tactual, visual, auditory and even visceral impulses reach the cerebellar cortex. Subsequently it was learned that the portion of the cerebellar cortex responding to peripheral stimulation is reciprocally connected with the cerebral cortical area which responds to the same type of stimuli. Thus the vermal and intermediate parts of the anterior

lobe, which receives somesthetic input, are connected with the postcentral gyrus, the somatosensory area of the cerebral cortex; the cerebellar visual area (vermis of the posterior lobe) is interconnected with the cerebral cortical visual area; etc. Finally, after it was discovered that the cerebral cortex contains two somatosensory areas (see Chap. 15), the classic postcentral one (somatic area I) was found to be interconnected with the anterior projection field of the spinocerebellar tract in the anterior lobe and the second (somatic area II) with the posterior or paramedian projection of the spinocerebellar tracts.[47]

Beginning with Adrian's work[30] in 1943, demonstrations of a comparable reciprocal connection—cerebellum to cerebral cortex and vice versa—between all zones of the anterior lobe and the motor areas of the cerebral cortex became available. All these experiments also revealed an element of topographic organization.

One role of the cerebral-cerebellar connection has recently been disclosed. When the major somatic sensory pathways to the *cerebral* cortex are functionally intact, the evoked potential in cerebellar cortex elicited from cutaneous stimulation is very large. Section of the dorsal columns, medial lemniscus and cerebral peduncles or lesions of the N. ventralis posterior lateralis reduce the cerebellar-evoked potential. There must be, therefore, a loop that conducts impulses from the somatosensory pathways, through cerebral cortex to cerebellar cortex, employing the reciprocal element connecting the two cortices. Thus, the cerebellum has a direct (spinocerebellar) and an indirect posterior column to cerebral cortex pathway from the skin (Kennedy and Grimm, unpublished).

To summarize: (i) The cerebellum receives afferent inputs other than vestibular and proprioceptive. (ii) The anterior lobe is reciprocally connected with somatosensory area I of the cerebral cortex. (iii) The posterior lobe (paramedian lobule) is reciprocally connected with the second somatosensory cortex. (iv) The motor area of the cerebral cortex and the entire anterior lobe are reciprocally connected. (v) In all these areas there is considerable somatotopic organization. The general plan of reciprocal connections can be diagrammed as in Figure 8.

It can be deduced from this information that

the cerebellum (since it has an input from ex-teroceptors) is concerned with adjustments of the body to the external world as well as to the internal proprioceptive world. Secondly, the cerebral motor cortex and the cerebellum must work closely together in effecting and controlling movements.

Somatotopic Organization. Evidence of a somatotopic organization of the cerebellar cortex comes from electrophysiologic studies of afferent inputs and stimulation of the cerebellar cortex and anatomic studies of the projections of the spinocerebellar tracts. This organization is, however, relative rather than absolute.* The body surface of the cat is projected into its anterior cerebellum, so that the tail is predominantly "localized" in the lingula, the hindleg in the simplex. Furthermore, the axial portions of the animal are represented along the midline in the vermis, and the apical portions more laterally, in the intermediate cortex. Similarly, as shown in Figure 11, the tail areas in the somatosensory and motor areas of the cerebral cortex are reciprocally connected with the lingula—and so on through the cerebral and cerebellar areas for the hindlimb, forelimb and neck–face. In the second representation of the body surface, found in the posterior part of the corpus cerebelli, there is also a topographic localization.

FUNCTIONS OF THE CEREBELLUM

Equilibration. Since part of the cerebellum developed from the vestibular structures of the medulla oblongata, it is not surprising that regulation of the mechanism underlying upright posture is a cerebellar function. One such mechanism is equilibration, or balancing, and its regulation is served mainly by the flocculonodular lobe.

FLOCCULONODULAR LOBE. The disturbances resulting from ablation of this lobe reflect its vestibular afferent and efferent connections. Dow[40] performed isolated ablations in this area

---

* In electrophysiologic mapping experiments conducted on *un*anesthetized cats by Combs,[39] stimulation of a point on the skin or of a cutaneous nerve resulted in bilateral activation of all folia of the vermal and intermediate anterior lobe. For reasons which will be brought out in the discussion of similar experiments on the cerebral cortex, this finding is not incompatible with the existence of a focus of representation as revealed in experiments involving use of barbiturate anesthetics.

and observed conspicuous disturbances of equilibrium without either changes in the basic postural reflexes or difficulties in volitional movements. After such a lesion, a monkey can feed itself manually without tremor or deviation of the hands, but it is unable to stand, even on a broad base, without swaying and falling. For this reason, the monkey generally sits, propping itself up in a corner to secure support from two sides of the cage or maintaining equilibrium by clutching the cage wall or floor. The syndrome is therefore one of *disequilibration*. The vestibular concern of the flocculonodular lobe is further documented by the fact that development of motion sickness in dogs is prevented by ablation of this area but not by removal of any other in either the cerebellar or cerebral cortex.[64, 65]

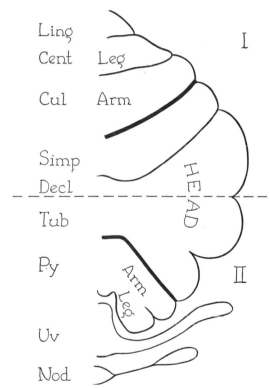

Fig. 11. Summary diagram showing somatotopic organization of cerebellar cortex and nature of cerebrocerebellar relationships. The latter are indicated by the Roman numerals (referring to cerebral somatosensory areas) and horizontal dashed line. For meaning of abbreviations, see Fig. 10. Much of data obtained on cats and extrapolated to primate cerebellum. Representation in paramedian lobule, behind lower heavy line indicating prepyramidal fissure, is bilateral. (After Hampson *et al., Res. Publ. Ass. nerv. ment. Dis.,* 1952, 30:299–316.)

OTHER CEREBELLAR AREAS REGULATING STAND-
ING. The stretch reflexes are the raw materials
of standing, but these basic reflexes must be
controlled. Equilibration is only one phase of
this control, the phase in which the vestibular
system is important. Vision, too, is a factor, as
can be quickly learned by standing on one foot
and comparing the amount of swaying with
the eyes closed and with them open. Proprioception is another factor, since interruption of
spinal proprioceptive pathways, as in locomotor
ataxia, makes standing without swaying difficult, especially when the eyes are closed (Rom-
berg's sign).

Although the flocculonodular lobe is unquestionably important in equilibration, it is not
the only cerebellar structure regulating standing. Recent evidence suggests that the medial
zone of the vermis throughout the whole of the
cerebellum is concerned with standing. Chambers and Sprague[36] found that lesions confined
to the anterior zone of the vermal area produce
difficulties in standing like those caused by posterior (medial) vermal lesions affecting the
nodular area. Since the medial vermal cortex
projects to the fastigial nucleus, which in turn
sends many fibers to and receives many fibers
from the vestibular nucleus of the medulla oblongata, this finding is anatomically reasonable. Furthermore, the spinocerebellar tract,
carrying proprioceptive and tactual impulses
from the body, projects heavily to the anterior
portion of the vermis. Such sensory impulses
would be helpful in maintaining equilibrium.
Finally, visual and auditory impulses are projected to the vermal structures, centering on
the declive, the folium and the tuber vermis.[52, 59] It may be predicted that one function
of this projection will prove to be the visual element in the maintenance of the body's orientation in space.

In summary, standing—whether on two legs
or four—depends upon three afferent inputs:
vestibular, somesthetic and visual. All these are
heavily represented in the most medial vermal
regions of the cerebellar cortex that control the
musculature of the entire body. The higher
control of equilibration and standing seems to
be served by the medial vermal region of the
corpus cerebelli and by the flocculonodular
lobe.

Tonus. More fundamental to standing than
equilibration is the control of the myotatic reflexes. As discussed in Chapter 6, these include
two-neuron-arc spinal reflexes regulated by impulses descending from the vestibular nuclei
and from the brain stem reticular system. Normally, such reflexes serve to prevent collapse of
the joints by the pull of gravity. A decerebrate
animal, in which descending influences from
the cerebellum and cerebrum are interrupted,
can stand, but its legs must be adjusted under
it. If pushed slightly from the side, the animal
does not adjust the strength of its extensor reflexes sufficiently to prevent toppling. The intact animal has a greater capacity for promptly
adjusting its muscular contractions to the vicis-
situdes of gravitational forces. The cerebellum
is concerned with reflex tonus of the musculature and presumably functions to control that
tonus.

Inhibition of extensor tonus is the predominant effect of threshold stimulation of the medial anterior lobe. This inhibition of rigidity is
especially evident when the vermal area of the
anterior lobe of a decerebrate cat is stimulated.
Consistently, when decerebration is combined
with ablation of this lobe, as in the anemic
method of decerebration,[54] the release of extensor myotatic reflexes is greater than that
following simple transcollicular decerebration.
These effects in decerebrate animals prove also
that much of the postural influence of the medial anterior lobe is exerted on the brain stem
—understandable since the major outflow from
the lobe is the fastigiobulbar tract to the vestibular and reticular nuclei of the medulla.
There is little doubt that the loss of the anterior
lobes is responsible for the extensor spasm, the
opisthotonos and the hyperactive positive supporting reaction seen during the *initial* stages
after decerebellation. However, in the dog and
cat, the medial anterior lobe is not purely inhibitory to extensors, but usually activates the
flexors reciprocally. Moreover, after stimulation of the lobe has ceased, a contrary effect
often appears—contraction of extensor muscles
and inhibition of flexor motoneurons. The response obtained depends somewhat on the parameters of the stimulus. This and the rebound
phenomena indicate that the anterior cerebellum contains oppositely acting components,
each of which acts reciprocally on flexor and
extensor motoneurons.

The release of extensor reflexes is greater and
more enduring in the pigeon than in the dog or
cat, and is less in the monkey than in the cat.
In man, a medial anterior lobe syndrome de-

noted by release of extensor reflexes has never been identified. All these facts lead to the conclusion that the extensor-inhibiting postural function of the medial anterior lobe has changed during phylogeny.

A factor in the complex effects of ablation of the anterior lobe was disclosed by Sprague and Chambers[60] when they destroyed only one fastigial nucleus, the main outflow from the anterior lobe (and from the remainder of the vermis). Whereas bilateral nuclear lesions have effects similar to those of an ablation of the anterior lobe, destruction of one fastigial nucleus causes spasticity in the contralateral extensor muscles and in the flexor muscles of the ipsilateral limbs. Another complicating observation was that lesions of the vermian cortex of the anterior lobe exert effects opposite to those of lesions of the underlying fastigial nucleus. The cortex presumably inhibits the nucleus, which, in turn, is inhibitory to contralateral extensors and ipsilateral flexors. With the cerebellum, as with many other structures, what is seen on stimulation or ablation reflects the predominant rather than the *sole* function of the structure.

Suprasegmental influences on myotatic reflexes can be exerted on either the alpha motoneurons or the gamma fusimotor neurons. The cerebellum acts through both avenues. Granit and Kaada[46] have shown that the afferent discharge from a muscle spindle is *decreased* by stimulation of the vermal portion of the anterior lobe, an action which would decrease muscle tonus. This finding corresponds to the known predominant effect (inhibition) of such stimulation on myotatic reflexes. Stimulation of the intermediate portion of the anterior lobe increased the spindle discharge, a finding which correlates with studies described later in this chapter. The tonus changes exerted through gamma efferents occurred at a lower threshold of anterior cerebellar stimulation than did direct effects upon alpha motoneurons. However, the anterior cerebellum also acts upon alpha motoneurons. Functional ablation of it by cooling resulted in extensor hypertonus without increased gamma efferent discharge. Knowledge of the higher control of tonus via the gamma efferent is a new development which may in the future explain some of the puzzling features of abnormal tonus states (Chap. 6).[43]

One hypothesis to account for the severe *hypo*tonia seen in clinical cases of cerebellar damage is that hypotonia is caused by injury to the lateral corticonuclear zone of the whole cerebellum. Since these areas are developed progressively in primates, including man, this theory might explain why hypotonia rather than hypertonia is typical of the human cerebellar syndrome. Unfortunately, lesions in experimental animals have rarely been confined to the lateral zone but have included portions of the medial and intermediate zones, and thus an element of extensor reflex release has been introduced.

It is not certain whether lesions confined to the lateral portion of the cerebellum in the dog or cat result in hypotonia after the initial stage of hypertonus.[32, 37] Hypotonia is much more marked in the primate. After unilateral cerebellar ablations sparing the anterior vermis and the fastigial nucleus in baboons, Botterell and Fulton[31] observed hypotonia, which was more severe and enduring when the dentate nucleus was damaged.

The lateral and intermediate portions of the cerebellum, unlike the vermis, do not project to the reticular and vestibular areas of the brain stem known to be concerned with facilitating and inhibiting the basic, spinal, myotatic reflexes. How, then, can these cerebellar areas influence muscular tonus?

The efferent projection of the lateral lobes of the cerebellum is to the dentate nucleus, from which fibers pass to the thalamus, some with a synapse in the red nucleus (Fig. 12). At this point, an influence on posture could be exerted by way of the rubrospinal tracts or the neighboring descending systems of the reticular facilitatory area. A synapse in the lateroventral nucleus of the thalamus interrupts the ascending pathways to the cerebral cortex. Fibers from this nucleus project to the motor areas of the motor cortex. Physiologic experiments teach that the pyramidal tract arising in the motor area is facilitatory to the extensor monosynaptic reflex arcs serving stretch reflexes. It is reasonable to assume that the fibers reaching the cerebral cortex from the lateral cerebellum provide the input drive for this tonic pyramidal influence on extensor reflexes. If this drive were eliminated by a lateral cerebellar lesion, the effect would be hypotonia.

It would be going too far to ascribe the hypotonia of the human cerebellar syndrome entirely to injury to the lateral hemispheres, since the more medial cerebellar regions connect with the motor area through the fastigial and interpositus nuclei as well as with the brain

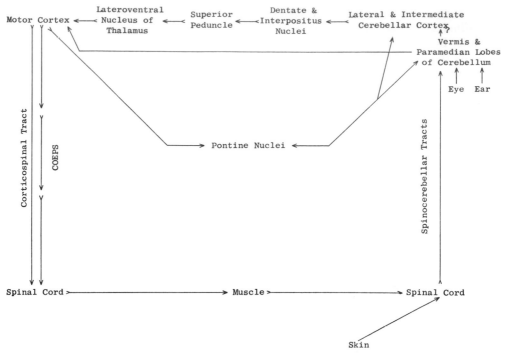

Fig. 12. Feedback loops from and to motor cortex. Long loop involves a return of proprioceptive information from muscle to motor cortex by way of cerebellum. This loop assumes existence of connections between paleocerebellum and neocerebellum. A second potential loop is shorter and entirely within brain. It may or may not receive information from periphery, depending on connection of neocerebellum with vermis and paramedian lobes, which receive proprioceptive and exteroceptive sensory information. Note that short loop is informed of events in periphery only if there are connections between the medial and the more lateral cerebellar regions. Also note that arrow connecting vermis and paramedian lobe is questioned. This pathway is known functionally but not anatomically.

stem. However, the influence of the medial cortex upon pyramidal tract discharge seems to be mainly inhibitory,[38, 61] and the net effect exerted through the brain stem connection is inhibitory to extensor tonus. Damage to either system would not produce hypotonia. Altogether, it is probable that damage in the greatly expanded lateral hemisphere is responsible for the hypotonia consequent to cerebellar injury in man.

Control of Volitional Movements. Because these controls are displayed best in man when cerebellar disease has disrupted them, the detailed descriptions may be deferred. It suffices to say that the signs of such defects are errors in the rate, range, force and direction of volitional movements (ataxia) and coarse, irregular oscillations, especially at the termination of a movement.

Anatomic considerations strongly suggest that the lateral and paravermal zones of the cerebellum are particularly concerned with the control of voluntary movement of the limbs.

The lateral zone has developed commensurate with manipulatory ability in the primate series, and the afferent and efferent connections of these lobes form a cerebello-cerebellar circle. However, the paravermal cortex also projects to the motor cortex via the interpositus nucleus and, unlike the lateral zone, is somatotopically highly organized. The most recent evidence from animal experiments indicates that ablation of the paravermal cortex induces ataxic movement; the influence of the more lateral region is less clearly established—a situation which may mean simply that the influence is more subtle. Paradoxically, lesions of the dentate nucleus, through which the lateral cortex exerts its influence, produce the most striking effects on volitional activity.[31, 45] Regardless of the relative roles of the lateral and the paravermal cortex, it is clear that they, together, control voluntary movement through the projections ultimately reaching the cortex, whereas the midline structures influence mainly the basic postural reflexes.

Before the ways in which the cerebellum and the cerebral cortex interact in the control of voluntary movement are discussed in detail the manifestations of cerebellar disease in man should be examined. Not only are certain disturbances more pronounced in man than in animals, but the examination of movement can be more detailed and enlightening in man than in experimental animals. However, it should be remembered that knowledge of which cerebellar regions have been destroyed or damaged is less certain.

Clinical Correlations. DISTURBANCES OF GAIT AND STATION. A specific type of tumor (medulloblastoma) occurring in young children induces disorders almost exactly like those which Dow[40] produced in monkeys by ablating portions of the flocculonodular lobe. Arising from the roof of the fourth ventricle, often at the base of the nodulus, these tumors produce few obvious signs of incoordination of movement as long as the child lies in bed. However, he is unable to balance and walk. Disturbances of gait and station, unaccompanied by hypotonia, also occur when the more anterior vermal region is affected by tumor or degeneration. Such cases are rare. In fact, as a result of the sheltered position of the anterior and flocculonodular lobes and their proximity to vital brain stem structures, the usual case of cerebellar disease probably reflects mainly damage to the cerebellum as a whole.

DISTURBANCES OF TONUS. The common procedure of passive flexion or extension of a joint, or simply shaking a limb, is generally used to demonstrate disorders of tonus. A *pendular knee jerk* is a manifestation of hypotonia. Through default of the myotatic appendage, the limb is not lowered but falls as an inert body does, and swings back and forth (Fig. 13). Failure of the antagonistic flexors to respond with a stretch reflex as the leg passes the midposition is also

a factor. The mechanism of cerebellar hypotonia is not known with certainty. As pointed out earlier, the neocerebellum is connected with the motor areas of the cerebral cortex and can facilitate their action. From the Fulton–Tower–Hines analysis of pyramidal tract function, default of the cerebellar discharge to the motor cortex could, like interruption of the pyramidal tract, result in flaccidity. Default of the cerebellar connection with the upper brain stem, which contains the reticular facilitatory area, is another possibility.

DISTURBANCES OF VOLUNTARY MOVEMENT.[49, 50] Deficiencies in force (asthenia), rate, direction (dysmetria) and steadiness (tremor) of movement are typical effects of cerebellar lesions on volitional movement. Starting, stopping and changing the direction of motion are especially disturbed.

The weakness of voluntary movements is not accompanied by loss of any specific movement, and, although severe subjectively, it is not easily demonstrable objectively. This *asthenia* is explicable by the hypothesis that the cerebellum facilitates the motor cortex. As with many cerebellar signs, the facilitation could be at the segmental level by way of the cerebellar connections with the brain stem.

In patients with cerebellar lesions, simple movements are slow to start (Fig. 14), a condition presumably reflecting the lack of facilitation. Figure 14 also shows that movements are slow to stop, so that hypermetria—overshooting the mark—occurs in a finger-to-nose test. (However, the finger can also undershoot—hypometria.) The rebound phenomenon, i.e., inability to restrain an arm exerting tension when it is suddenly released by the examiner, is a failure to stop a willed muscular contraction

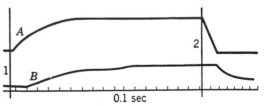

Fig. 14. Myograms of voluntary contraction by a patient with unilateral cerebellar lesion. *A*, normal; *B*, affected hand. Vertical lines *1* and *2* mark signals to start and stop gripping. Note slower start, weaker contraction, and delayed relaxation in the lower record. (From Ruch, Chap. 5 in *Handbook of experimental psychology*, S. S. Stevens, ed. New York, Wiley, 1951.)

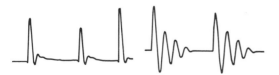

Fig. 13. Excursion of leg in knee jerk in normal person (*left*) and in patient with cerebellar lesion (*right*). Note that in three knee jerks at left leg falls "deadbeat," whereas in two knee jerks at right leg oscillates after initial upright excursion due to the knee jerk itself. (From Holmes, *Lancet*, 1922, *202*:1177–1182.)

NORMAL
ARM

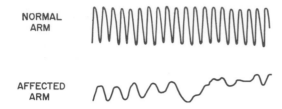

AFFECTED
ARM

Fig. 15. Tracings of rapidly alternating supination and pronation of arms illustrating adiadochokinesis. By contrast with normal arm, affected arm even initially made slow, low-amplitude movements, which rapidly deteriorated further. (From Holmes, *Lancet*, 1922, *203*:59–65.)

quickly. As shown in Figure 15, a patient with cerebellar disease is unable to perform alternating movements (supination and pronation of forearms) rapidly and with equal excursions (adiadochokinesis). This sign again reflects a defect in starting and stopping a movement.

A cerebellar tremor is "intentional" (i.e., occurs during voluntary movement rather than rest), terminal (most marked at the end of a movement), and coarse and irregular, as seen in Figure 16. In all these respects, cerebellar tremor contrasts so greatly with the regular oscillatory tremor of rest seen in Parkinson's disease that "tremor" may be a poor term. The term "ataxic tremor" is descriptive.[34] In visualizing the cerebellar tremor, one can imagine the arm drifting from the intended path and being corrected too late and too vigorously, so that the hand overcorrects and then overshoots the intended path. This overcorrection continues through slowness in stopping a movement and in initiating a return toward the course. As this sequence is repeated, the result is an irregular tremor which mounts in severity as the

movement progresses. The whole appearance somewhat resembles the first attempt to steer a boat. There are also typical disturbances in speaking, writing, standing and walking, but they present no new features.

The effort of neurophysiologists is to reduce the many manifestations of cerebellar disease to one or two basic defects. A unitary explanation of cerebellar symptoms must take into account the cerebellocerebral relationships.

Cerebellocerebral Relationships. The principal fact is the one we started with. The cerebral cortex cannot execute coordinated movements without help. This is true even though the cerebral cortex has at its disposal rich information from proprioceptors and exteroceptors. Although the cerebellum also has rich somatosensory inputs, it is presumed to contribute to cortically induced movement something over and beyond sensory information. It is surely significant that the cerebellum is reciprocally linked with the cerebral motor cortex, the connections potentially forming a loop.

It has long been known that stimulation of the neocerebellum can make the motor cortex more excitable,[55] and that some of this effect is exerted through connections between the two structures rather than by convergence on the reticular substance or spinal levels. Electroencephalographic waves are augmented. Surprisingly, the influence of the midline paleocerebellar areas on corticomotor excitability is better documented.[43] These areas have a topographic organization, and their influence on the motor cortex, like their influence on the limb reflexes, is often *inhibitory* but can be facilitatory. Snider and Magoun[58] have found facilitatory areas lying just lateral to the vermis

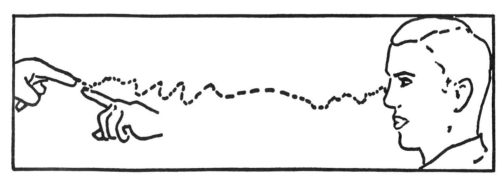

Fig. 16. Record of tremulous movement obtained by having patient move his finger from his nose to touch the finger of the examiner, represented at the left. Note irregularity and coarseness of tremor and that it is most marked near termination of the movement. (From Ruch, Chap. 5 in *Handbook of experimental psychology,* S. S. Stevens, ed. New York, Wiley, 1951.)

in the anterior lobe and the paramedian lobule. The occurrence of inhibitory or occlusive interaction in the cerebral cortex has been shown by recording from the pyramidal tract while interacting cerebellar and motor area stimulation.[63] It is clear that the cerebellum exerts both facilitatory and inhibitory influences on movement initiated by the cerebral motor cortex. This helps us to understand why the clinical manifestations of cerebellar injury present contrary elements—slowness to start and overshoot.

Altogether, the available data on the functioning of reciprocal cerebellocerebral connections does not permit more than speculation. Since the function of the neocerebellum is the control of discrete limb movement, and since control systems developed in engineering often employ a feedback loop, considerable *a priori* significance is attached to the potential neural loop afforded by the reciprocal cerebellocerebral connections. Wiener [66] and others[44] have commented on the similarity between servomechanisms and the neural control of movements. This parallel is illustrated in Figure 17.

A command to take a new position activates a motor which effects the movement to a degree dependent upon the difference between the present position and the desired position. A signal from the response is returned to the comparator, where present position is again related to intended position and a new order is issued to the power source. Thus the error, i.e., difference between present and intended position, is progressively reduced. Such systems are subject to overshoot and oscillation in making rapid transients if underdamped, or to a sluggish response if overdamped. Unfortunately for the sake of simple analogy, the signs of cerebellar disease appear to be overdamping at the initiation of movement and underdamping at its end.

The cerebellum might serve as a comparator, comparing the order from the cortex with the resulting limb position; however, the cerebral cortex itself, with its extensive exteroceptors, would be a more logical candidate for the task of comparing the goal with the present position. Perhaps the cerebellum should be considered analogous to the feedback stabilizing or controlling network, which determines whether the system is too slow in its control or is prone to oscillation.

It has been suggested[56] that the motor cortex is handicapped in planning movements in time because nerve impulses cannot be stored to be discharged after a fixed delay. However, if the motor cortex discharged in a circular pathway involving the cerebellum, a programming of movement in time might be possible. The cerebellum might provide an accelerating or facili-

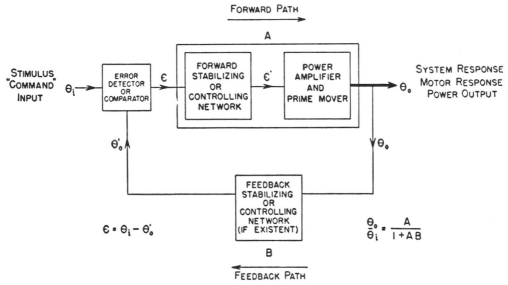

Fig. 17. Diagram illustrating the analogies between a physiologic control system and the basic elements of a servosystem. The "command" is a low energy input such as the sight of an object. The forward path might represent the corticospinal pathways. Θ reflects achieved movement, which is compared with intent of stimulus, and a modified order goes over the forward path. (From Frank *et al., Ann. N. Y. Acad. Sci.,* 1948, *50:*187–277.)

tating mechanism to impart velocity without overshoot. Default of such a function would account for the slowness of movements to start in a patient with cerebellar disease (Fig. 13). A programming circuit with the correct delay characteristics would be helpful in decelerating movement to prevent overshoot or a jerky stop. Movements so roughed in could be further refined by afferent sensory reports, either via the cerebellum or to the cerebral cortex by way of the spinothalamocortical fibers. Whatever its resemblance to servomechanisms, the cerebellum has the requisite facilitatory and inhibitory relationship to the motor cortex and to the brain stem mechanisms to aid both systems in starting and stopping movements in the manner necessary to effective, well directed movement.

REFERENCES

BASAL GANGLIA

1. ARONSON, N. I., BECKER, B. E. and McGOVERN, W. A. *Confin. neurol. (Basel)*, 1962, *22*:397–429.
2. BUCY, P. C. Chap. 15 in *Precentral motor cortex*, 2d ed. Urbana, Ill., University of Illinois Press, 1949.
3. BUCY, P. C. Chap. 11 in *Pathogenesis and treatment of parkinsonism*, W. S. FIELDS, ed. Springfield, Ill., Charles C Thomas, 1958.
4. CARPENTER, M. B., CORRELL, J. W. and HINMAN, A. *J. Neurophysiol.*, 1960, *23*:288–304.
5. DUSSER DE BARENNE, J. G. and McCULLOCH, W. S. *J. Neurophysiol.*, 1941, *4*:311–323.
6. FIELDS, W. S. *Pathogenesis and treatment of parkinsonism.* Springfield, Ill., Charles C Thomas, 1958.
7. FORMAN, D. and WARD, J. W. *J. Neurophysiol.*, 1957, *20*: 230–244.
8. GLEES, P. *J. Anat. (Lond.)*, 1944, *78*:47–51.
9. GYBELS, J. M. *The neural mechanism of Parkinsonian tremor.* Brussels, Editions arscia, S.A., 1963.
10. HASSLER, R. *Dtsch. Z. Nervenheilk.*, 1956, *175*:233–258.
11. JENKNER, F. L. and WARD, A. *Arch. Neurol. Psychiat. (Chic.)*, 1953, *70*:489–502.
12. JUNG, R. and HASSLER, R. Chap. 35 in *Handbook of physiology; Section I, neurophysiology*, vol. 2, J. FIELD, ed. Washington, D. C., American Physiological Society, 1960.
13. KENNARD, M. A. *J. Neurophysiol.*, 1944, *7*:127–148.
14. KENNARD, M. A. and FULTON, J. F. *Res. Publ. Ass. nerv. ment. Dis.*, 1942, *21*:228–245.
15. LAURSEN, A. M. *Acta physiol. scand.*, 1962, *54*:175–184; 185–190.
16. MAGOUN, H. W. and RHINES, R. *Spasticity: The stretch-reflex and extrapyramidal systems.* Springfield, Ill., Charles C Thomas, 1947.
17. METTLER, F. A., ADES, H. W., LIPMAN, E. and CULLER, E. A. *Arch. Neurol. Psychiat. (Chic.)*, 1939, *41*:984–995.
18. POLLOCK, L. J. and DAVIS, L. *Arch. Neurol. Psychiat. (Chic.)*, 1930, *23*:303–319.

19. PUTNAM, T. J. *Arch. Neurol. Psychiat. (Chic.)*, 1940, *44*:950–976.
20. PUTNAM, T. J. and HERZ, E. *Arch. Neurol. Psychiat. (Chic.)*, 1950, *63*:357–366.
21. RIOCH, D. McK. and BRENNER, C. *J. comp. Neurol.*, 1938, *68*:491–507.
22. SCHREINER, L. Chap. 5 in *Pathogenesis and treatment of Parkinsonism*, W. S. FIELDS, ed. Springfield, Ill., Charles C Thomas, 1958.
23. TOWER, S. S. *Brain*, 1935, *58*:238–255.
24. WANG, G. H. and AKERT, K. *Arch. ital. Biol.*, 1962, *100*: 48–85.
25. WARD, A. A. Chap. 4 in *Pathogenesis and treatment of Parkinsonism*, W. S. FIELDS, ed. Springfield, Ill., Charles C Thomas, 1958.
26. WARD, A. A., JR., McCULLOCH, W. S. and MAGOUN, H. W. *J. Neurophysiol.*, 1948, *11*:317–330.
27. WARD, A. A. and STERN, J. Personal communication.
28. WALSHE, F. M. R. *Brain*, 1924, *47*:159–177.
29. WHITTIER, J. R. and METTLER, F. A. *J. comp. Neurol.*, 1949, *90*:319–372.

CEREBELLUM

30. ADRIAN, E. D. *Brain*, 1943, *66*:289–315.
31. BOTTERELL, E. H. and FULTON, J. F. *J. comp. Neurol.*, 1938, *69*:63–87.
32. BREMER, F. *Arch. int. Physiol.*, 1922, *19*:189–226.
33. BROOKHARDT, J. M. Chap. 51 in *Handbook of Physiology; Section I, neurophysiology*, vol. 2, J. FIELD, ed. Washington, D. C., American Physiological Society, 1961.
34. CARREA, R. M. E. and METTLER, F. A. *J. comp. Neurol.*, 1947, *87*:169–288.
35. CASEY, K. L. and TOWE, A. L. *J. Physiol.*, 1961, *158*:399–410.
36. CHAMBERS, W. W. and SPRAGUE, J. M. *J. comp. Neurol.*, 1955, *103*:105–129.
37. CHAMBERS, W. W. and SPRAGUE, J. M. *Arch. Neurol. Psychiat. (Chic.)*, 1955, *74*:653–680.
38. COHEN, D., CHAMBERS, W. W. and SPRAGUE, J. M. *J. comp. Neurol.*, 1958, *109*:233–266.
39. COMBS, C. M. *J. Neurophysiol.*, 1954, *17*:123–143.
40. DOW, R. S. *Arch. Neurol. Psychiat. (Chic.)*, 1938, *40*:500–520.
41. DOW, R. S. *Biol. Rev.*, 1942, *17*:179–220.
42. DOW, R. S. *J. Neurophysiol.*, 1942, *5*:121–136.
43. DOW, R. S. and MORUZZI, G. *The physiology and pathology of the cerebellum.* Minneapolis, University of Minnesota Press, 1958.
44. FRANK, L. K., HUTCHINSON, G. E., LIVINGSTON, W. K., McCULLOCH, W. S. and WIENER, N. *Ann. N. Y. Acad. Sci.*, 1948, *50*:187–278.
45. FULTON, J. F. *Functional localization in the frontal lobes and cerebellum.* Oxford, Clarendon Press, 1949.
46. GRANIT, R. and KAADA, B. R. *Acta physiol. scand.*, 1952, *27*:130–160.
47. HAMPSON, J. L. *J. Neurophysiol.*, 1949, *12*:37–50.
48. HENNEMAN, E., COOKE, P. M. and SNIDER, R. S. *Res. Publ. Ass. nerv. ment. Dis.*, 1952, *30*:317–333.
49. HOLMES, G. *Lancet*, 1922, *202*:1177–1182, 1231–1237; *203*:59–65, 111–115.
50. HOLMES, G. *Brain*, 1939, *62*:1–30.
51. JANSEN, J. and BRODAL, A. *Avh. norske VidenskAkad., Kl. I*, 1942, No. 3.
52. KOELLA, W. P. *J. Neurophysiol.*, 1959, *22*:61–77.
53. LARSELL, O. *Arch. Neurol. Psychiat. (Chic.)*, 1937, *38*:580–607.
54. POLLOCK, L. J. and DAVIS, L. *Brain*, 1927, *50*:277–312.

55. Rossi, G. *Arch. Fisiol.*, 1912, *10*:389–399.
56. Ruch, T. C. Chap. 5 in *Handbook of experimental psychology*, S. S. Stevens, ed. New York, John Wiley & Sons, 1951.
57. Snider, R. S. *Arch. Neurol. Psychiat. (Chic.)*, 1950, *64*:196–219.
58. Snider, R. S. and Magoun, H. W. *J. Neurophysiol.*, 1949, *12*:335–345.
59. Snider, R. S. and Stowell, A. *J. Neurophysiol.*, 1944, *7*:331–357.
60. Sprague, J. M. and Chambers, W. W. *J. Neurophysiol.*, 1953, *16*:451–463.
61. Sprague, J. M. and Chambers, W. W. *Arch. ital. Biol.*, 1959, *97*:68–88.
62. Thomas, D. M., Kaufman, R. P., Sprague, J. M. and Chambers, W. W. *J. Anat. (Lond.)*, 1956, *90*:371–385.
63. Towe, A. L. and Casey, K. L. *Physiologist*, 1959, *2*:22.
64. Tyler, D. B. and Bard, P. *Physiol. Rev.*, 1949, *29*:311–369.
65. Wang, S. C. and Chinn, H. I. *Amer. J. Physiol.*, 1956, *185*:617–623.
66. Wiener, N. *Cybernetics or control and communication in the animal and the machine.* New York, John Wiley & Sons, 1948.

SENSORY FUNCTIONS OF THE NERVOUS SYSTEM

CHAPTER 14

Somatic Sensation

By THEODORE C. RUCH

INTRODUCTION

ALL knowledge comes to us through our sense organs. Our simplest motor acts are initiated through sense organs; our most complex ones are controlled by means of them. Pain is a matter of immediate interest in many clinical conditions, and testing other forms of somatic sensation is a considerable part of the neurologic examination. In the next chapter it will become clear that the distinction between sensation and perception is a valuable clue to the level of nervous system damage. Under the broad heading of sensation come complex phenomena which are immensely important to the individual experiencing them: hunger, nausea, vertigo, sexual sensations, feelings of fatigue, and a host of ill-defined discomforts originating in the deeper structures of the body. Many of these have only recently become the object of physiologic inquiry.

Sensation, Perception and Affect. A sensation has several parameters (dimensions) or attributes. The first of these is *quality*, the subjective difference which enables us to name sensations—warmth, cold, taste, etc. A sensory modality* or simply a "sense" often includes submodalities which may or may not blend into one another. Thus, red and green are submodalities of vision, and sweet and sour, of taste. Submodalities are unlike enough subjectively so that we give them different names. At each level from the sense organ to the cerebral cortex neurophysiologists seek to discover func-

---

* Modality is a traditional word of obscure meaning which is not greatly clarified by the dictionary. Perhaps the simplest synonym for "a modality of sensation" is simply "a kind of sensation."

tional and structural mechanisms underlying modalities and submodalities of sensation.

Intensity is obviously a fundamental parameter of sensation; without some finite strength of the stimulus, the subjective threshold is not exceeded and no sensation occurs.

Locus is a third basic parameter. A sensation appears to come from some part of the body or the external world (*projection,* see p. 315). How the brain can know locus is one of the problems that neurophysiologists are intensely investigating.

Pure sensation is an abstraction and probably occurs only the first time a baby experiences that sensation. Thereafter past experience, the blending of sensations, the comparison of one sensation with another, etc., transform sensation into perception: The fusion of cold and pressure yields a perception of wetness. A perception may involve simply a temporal pattern of a single modality.

The comparison of two stimuli simultaneously or successively presented in respect to intensity, quality or position is in psychological parlance a *judgment,* or in physiologic and clinical parlance a *discrimination.* The discrimination of spatial aspects of a stimulus, its location, size, shape, etc., is particularly important in clinical neurologic diagnosis and is discussed at length in this and the next chapter.

Finally, the subjective response to afferent impulses has another aspect. Besides the quality, intensity and locus of a sensation or perception, we feel that some sensations are pleasant, others unpleasant. Technically this aspect of sensation is known as *affect.* In certain neurologic disorders, the affect becomes more intense and the quality of sensation less vivid, suggesting different brain mechanisms for the two phenomena.

The preceding paragraphs are diagrammed in Figure 1.

In broad outline, knowledge of our environment involves: (i) the sensor–transducer function of the peripheral terminals of a sensory neuron, (ii) conduction along nerves and central tracts and transformation of signals at at least two synaptic stations, and (iii) appreciation of the quality, intensity, locus and affective quality of the stimulus and the combination of these data into recognition of the object. As pointed out in Chapter 4, the sense organs of the skin through the phenomenon of the adequate stimulus (or, better stated, because of the

property of differential sensitivity) analyze the energy flux between the environment and the skin. Nerve impulses carry this information to the cerebral cortex.

Determination and Classification of Sensory Modalities. Touch was, until nearly this century, treated as a single, unitary sense which appreciated many aspects of the stimulus object.[3] Thus, warmth or coldness, pressure, etc., were thought of as subqualities of the single sense of "feeling" or "touch." About 1890, it was discovered that the skin is not everywhere uniformly sensitive to all aspects of a stimulating object. If the skin is marked off in millimeter squares and systematically explored with very small objects—blunt (pressure), sharp (pain), warm and cold—it is found that some spots give rise to sensations of warmth but not of cold or pain, while others respond only to a cold stimulus and with a sensation of coldness; still other areas respond only with sensations of pressure or pain. Cutaneous sensibility is therefore *punctiform* or pointlike in its distribution. This was one of the fundamental experiments in the physiology of sensation. On the basis of such experiments, touch was easily divided into several separate senses—pressure or touch, warmth and cold.

The senses and sensory receptors are classified in several ways, all of which are useful. Since parts of each system are in common use, it is well to become familiar with all.

Sherrington's classification.[31] This classification of receptors is much used in physiologic literature and is based on the source of the stimulus and the location of the receptor. The proprioceptors, found in muscles, tendons and

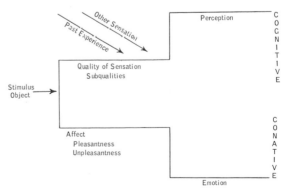

Fig. 1. Diagram of two aspects of the subjective consequences of a stimulus at two levels of psychological (or neural) complexity. Judgment is another step above perception.

joints, and in the labyrinth, give information concerning the movements and position of the body in space. The exteroceptors, of the skin, give information on changes in the immediate external environment. The interoceptors transmit impulses from the visceral organs. The teleceptors, or distance receptors, inform us of changes in the more remote environment, and are the sense organs of the eyes, ears and nose. (By usage, labyrinthine receptors are often not included in the proprioceptive group.)

Clinical classification of sensation. The clinical classification of sensation is strongly influenced by anatomy. The following list shows how the modalities of sensation are designated by clinicians; in the right-hand column a sample term to illustrate clinical terminology of the sensation and its disturbances is given.

I. *Special senses* served by the cranial nerves
  1. Vision................Hemianopia
  2. Audition...............None
  3. Taste..................Ageusia
  4. Olfaction..............Anosmia
  5. Vestibular ....None

II. *Superficial or cutaneous sensations* served by the cutaneous branches of spinal and certain cranial nerves
  1. Touch–pressure.........Hypesthesia
  2. Warmth.............⎱
  3. Cold................⎰Hypothermesthesia
  4. Pain ....Hyperalgesia

III. *Deep sensations* served by muscular branches of spinal nerves and certain cranial nerves
  1. Muscle, tendon, and joint sensibility, or position sense.................Bathesthesia
  2. (Deep pain)
  3. (Deep pressure)

IV. *Visceral sensations* served by fibers traversing the autonomic nervous system
  1. Organic sensation, e.g., hunger, nausea, etc.
  2. Visceral pain

The parentheses indicate that the position of deep pain and pressure in the scheme is anomalous. Thus, the phrase "deep sensation," as ordinarily used, does not include muscular pain and sometimes does not include deep pressure.

Other classifications. Sensory receptors are sometimes designated by the agent which most easily stimulates them, e.g., chemoreceptors, mechanoreceptors, etc. The term *nociceptors* was applied to pain receptors by Sherrington because they respond to a variety of stimuli which have in common the property of being noxious or damaging to the tissues. Finally, a useful dichotomy applicable to both motor and sensory phenomena is *somatic* and *visceral* for sensations arising in structures derived from the somatopleura and visceropleura, respectively. Somatic sensation (or *somesthesia*)

is a convenient name for superficial and deep sensation together.

Adequate Stimulus (Differential Sensitivity or Specificity). Traditionally, physiologists speak of the *law of the adequate stimulus* to describe the fact that sense organs typically have a low threshold for one form of energy though may be stimulated by other forms if sufficiently strong (Chap. 4). The use of the word "law" in this connection is unfortunate since, sometimes it is biologically useful to have a narrow band pass filter and for other biological functions a wide band pass, or funnel-like sensitivity may be desirable. It is therefore pertinent to inquire of each receptor the degree of specificity of its response to the energy spectrum. Some cutaneous sense organs are quite specific, others less so, but the truly nonspecific ending postulated as the end organ serving pain has escaped electrophysiologic verification.

It is important to make the distinction between the sense organ's sensitivity to various modes or intensity of energy and the ultimate ending and psychological effect in the brain. Also important is the distinction between physiologic and anatomic specificity of sense organs.

Whatever the mechanism of specificity, most sense organs respond differently to different forms of energy, analyzing the complex energy pattern of the external world, and translate them into a pattern of nerve impulses which are combined in the cerebral cortex to give an analog of the external world.

"Specific Nerve Energies" (Nonspecific Sense Organ Discharge). Complementary to the principle of the adequate stimulus is another law enunciated by Johannes Müller,[26] known as the "doctrine of specific nerve energies." Although a sense organ can be stimulated by other than its adequate stimulus, and a sensory system can be stimulated centrally, the *response* is of the same subjective quality regardless of *kind* of physical stimulus. Thus, the excitation of the visual system whether by pressure on the eye, by electrical stimulation or by irritative stimulation of the visual pathway (by a pathologic process) gives rise to *visual* sensation only. Müller's principle implies that the modality or submodality of sensation depends upon *what* end organ or *what* nerve fiber is stimulated and not upon what energy stimulated them. The phrase "specific nerve energy" was an unfortunate choice to convey the idea of a nonspecific sense organ discharge. Actually Müller favored the idea that the subjective quality distinguishing one sense modality from another or simply "modality specificity" is determined centrally, a concept subsequently supported by the elicitation of visual sensation by stimulation of the cortical visual area in conscious human patients and of somatic sensation by stimulation of the cortical somatosensory area. Müller's law is broadly analogous to a "place theory" in the language applied to the auditory system (see Chap. 18).

Coding and Pattern Theories. In contrast to the idea of specifically sensitive endings and private lines (fiber coding) to specific cortical loci is a growing belief by some that spatial pattern of fibers and temporal (frequency) patterns determine *quality* of sensation. Weddell,[35, 36] who has demonstrated the profuse division and interdigitation of the originating branches of single axons and the absence of morphologic specialization of receptors in hairy skin and the artifactual nature of some complex endings in nonhairy regions, is the chief exponent of this point of view. Certainly some cutaneous sense organs are sensitive to more than one kind of energy; i.e., they are partially nonspecific. Weddell argues that all cutaneous organs could be nonspecific and by firing in different frequency or temporal patterns and in varying combinations with the endings of interdigitating axons could convey information of quality and locus to the brain, making unnecessary the concept of specific sense organs.

The simplest modality coding would be the firing of sense organs at different impulse frequencies in response to different energies. If these frequencies were preserved in ascending to the brain, they could be given different subjective interpretations. This would require only that the axon form a synaptic connection with a second order neuron that could respond only to a high frequency discharge and another that would respond only to a low frequency discharge. Such coding usurps the dimension usually allocated to intensity signaling. The specificity of end organs will be discussed in more detail later in this chapter.

Intensity. The discharge from a field of sense organs is a quantity, the number of afferent axons times the frequency of firing. The latter, in turn, is proportional to the log of the stimulus strength. The importance of these two factors is different in rapidly adapting sense organs and those which maintain a plateau discharge. Gray[11] points out that the most sensitive and rapidly adapting mechanoreceptors in cat's pad may fire only once to an impact, which precludes frequency coding. In multifiber preparations there is a continuous relation between the number of fibers contributing to the action potential and the skin displacement by the stimulator. Fifty fibers were fired by a 20 μ displacement at a single point on the pad. The interdigitation of terminals (multiple innervation of a single spot) seems to be the means by which the strength of a stimulus to rapidly adapting fibers can be coded.

Conversely, in sense organs capable of yielding a steady discharge, frequency is available for coding the strength of stimulus, and the frequency is the log of the stimulus strength.

In passing through the synaptic junctions of the somatosensory pathways the logarithmic relationship of intensity to frequency is changed to a power function according to Mountcastle *et al.*,[25] who have measured the relationship between joint angle of a cat's limb and the firing rate of single cell in the thalamic nucleus which receives impulses from the deep-lying receptors. This finding correlates with some twenty years of research by psychologists on the relation between stimulus and sensation. Stevens and his co-workers[32] have amassed overwhelming evidence that the magnitude of sensation relates to intensity of stimulation not as a log function but as a power function:

$$\Psi = K\,\Phi^2$$

in which psychological magnitude (Ψ) is a constant times some power of the magnitude (Φ) of the physical stimulus. This is a rather unusual relationship between input and output in contrast to the law of diminishing returns represented by a logarithmic relationship. It is, however, extensively demonstrated, as seen in the next chapter.

Neurohistology of Cutaneous Sensation.[12, 24, 35, 36, 37] Hairy skin contains only fine free nerve endings and nerve baskets about the roots of the hair, and together these must serve touch, cold and warmth, once thought to be served by specialized encapsulated endings of various sorts. No encapsulated endings of any kind are found in hairy skin and the same is true of the cornea, which clearly is sensitive to both touch as well as pain.[23] Glabrous skin, such as the lips and finger tips, does contain in addition to free nerve endings encapsulated end-organs and "organized" endings made up of whorls of unmyelinated terminal fibers. That differential sensitivity is based on morphologic differentiation is now in doubt (i) because glabrous and adjacent hairy skin do not differ greatly in sensitivity and (ii) because the specialized endings do not, as once thought, fall into four morphologic categories corresponding to the four cutaneous senses, but present many gradations. Unencapsulated nerve endings connected with C-fibers can be specifically and exquisitely sensitive to cold, warmth and touch. Functions ascribed to the capsule of an end-organ where it exists are now viewed quite differently. For example, the capsule of the pacinian corpuscle may not give the sensory ending specificity and sensitivity, as once thought, but rather protection from strong stimuli.

A free nerve ending is formed by the repeated dichotomizing of an axis cylinder, which loses its medullary sheath, but not the sheath of Schwann until the very end. The fine naked branches of the axis cylinder ramify among the cells of the deeper layers of the epidermis; other free nerve endings are found subepidermally. Knowledge of these terminations comes from intravital staining with methylene blue. The free nerve endings are not disposed in the skin like trees in the forest with trunks widely separated and branches touching; instead, the arrangement is pseudoplexiform. The ramifications of a parent axon are said to interconnect and form a true nerve net. Nets derived from different parent axons overlap, interdigitate, but do not form a syncytium; i.e., they are not interconnected protoplasmically. Nerve fibers from the superficial plexus branch repeatedly over a wide area and end in fine, unmyelinated, beaded terminals disposed beneath and among the cells of the deeper layers of the epidermis. The type of ending associated with hairs exhibits a similar interdigitating pattern. An afferent axon may serve 100 hairs scattered over several square centimeters of skin and, conversely, a single hair is served by 2 to 20 axons. More organized receptors in hairless skin also receive multiple innervation.

The ramifications of an axon can be followed to some degree histologically, but electrophysiologic studies are more certain.

Receptive Fields. Tower[33] in 1940 first mapped the *receptive field* of a single afferent axon. A single fiber of a long ciliary nerve was discharged by stimuli applied over an area forming roughly a quadrant of the cornea and the adjacent sclera and conjunctiva. The receptive fields for different axons varied between 50 and 200 sq. mm. The branches of a single axon can be followed anatomically over areas of this size.[35] Within this field there were, of course, silent points, and stimulation of these would sometimes cause a different sensory fiber to discharge.

The receptive field of a single afferent fiber for light brushing of the skin of the cat's leg varied between 2 by 2 mm. to 18 by 10 mm.[34] Single axons (3 to 11 μ) connected with an ending sensitive to pin prick but not light touch yield larger zones, 3 by 3 mm. on foot pad and ten times larger on hairy areas. In all cases the receptive field was round or oval (with the long axis running down the leg), and was never irregular or patchy. A receptive field for the axon, as Tower first showed, is not uniformly sensitive but exhibits a spatial gradient. In passing from the center to the periphery, the threshold is higher, the latency is longer by as much as 5 milliseconds, and the discharge less prolonged. The ending studied was rapidly adapting and connected with axons conducting at the average rate of about 75 meters per second.

The receptive field gradient obtained for unmyelinated fibers whose endings respond to weak mechanical stimulation and yield a steady discharge is even more striking. The latency at the center of the field was 15 to 35 milliseconds and at the periphery 270 milliseconds. Presumably some type of summation between branches of axons underlies the receptive field gradient, but the mechanism of such summation is unknown. For the possible significance of the response gradient in localization of a stimulus see the next chapter.

The size of the receptive field is an additional method for categorizing different kinds of sensory inputs.

Free Nerve Endings Associated with C-Fibers.[7, 8, 21] The free nerve endings—unassociated with hair follicles—and their small unmyelinated C-fibers, once considered to respond only to strong damaging stimuli and to subserve pain, play a much greater potential role in sensation. This was first shown by Douglas and Ritchie in an experiment in which the impulses in large-diameter, low-threshold fibers are caused to collide, leaving a C-fiber volley to reach the recording electrodes (see Fig. 2 for explanation). By this method it was proved that the endings of many C-fibers in skin nerves respond to stimuli of the most innocuous character, e.g., brushing the skin with absorbent cotton. At somewhat greater pressure with the cotton swab a second, slower C-wave occurs. Similarly, temperature decreases of 3 °C. caused a C-fiber discharge and a fall of 10 °C., less intense than a painful cold stimulus, activated three-quarters of the C-fibers. Knowledge of the C-fiber ending's behavior was increased by studying single axons from them electrophysiologically. Iggo[21] succeeded in recording from single C-axons (conducting at 0.6 to 1.4 meters per second) by incredibly skillful "cutting down" techniques. In agreement with the results of Douglas and Ritchie, levels of stimulation far less than those which would be expected to arouse pain induced impulses in C-fibers. All C-fibers cannot, therefore, subserve

pain; some are clearly cold (and others warm) fibers, judged by the criteria of threshold and specificity.[23]

Some single C-fibers responded to more than one form of energy, again at levels not likely to produce pain and considerably below those responses in myelinated fibers for energies other than the adequate stimulus. In fact, the requisite stimulus intensity was little below that of the specific receptor served by large unmyelinated fibers. In contrast to A-fibers, C-fibers have slow firing rates and tend to respond for long periods after cessation of the stimulus (after discharge). While most C-fiber endings responded to some kind of innocuous stimuli, such as slight hair displacement or light pressure on the skin, some responded only to strong (? painful) stimuli.

It is, of course, not known from animal experiments whether the C-fiber equipped with wide band-pass endings transmits impulses to the brain resulting in conscious sensation. However, there is presumptive evidence that it does.

SOMATIC SENSES

Temperature Senses.[38] Rather than a single temperature sense there are two: one for cold and one for warmth. Three pieces of evidence support this statement: (i) The skin contains receptors which fire more rapidly as the temperature increases and others which fire more rapidly as the temperature decreases. (ii) There is a clear subjective difference between warmth and cold. (iii) Temperature sensibility is distributed in a punctate or "spotty" fashion. When the skin is explored millimeter by millimeter, spots (or more accurately, small areas) are found which respond only with a sensation of cold (Fig. 3). Other spots, fewer in number, respond only to warmth, and the intervening areas are sensitive to neither. On the forearm, cold spots average about 13 to 15 per square centimeter and warm spots only one or two per square centimeter. It was once believed that beneath each type of spot lay a distinctive type of end-organ. Failure to prove this by mapping spots and identifying histologically an underlying sense organ early cast doubt on the morphologic specificity of sense organs. Thus, the areal nature of the cold and warm spots suggested that a highly branching fiber or group of fibers serves the temperature receptors. It has

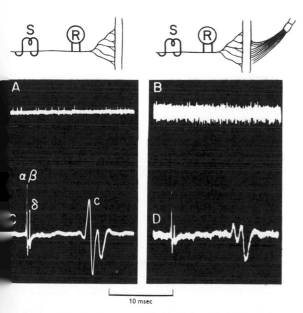

Fig. 2. Action potentials of myelinated and unmyelinated fibers of a sensory nerve twig before (*A*) and after (*B*) skin was stroked with cotton gauze. In *C* and *D* the unit nerve impulses seen in *A* and *B* have been shunted out so that the C wave is emphasized and the alpha, beta and delta waves (seen at left of each record) are reduced; also an antidromic volley was sent down the nerve to collide with the impulses in it. Note that the C wave of the antidromic volley in *C* is greatly reduced by collision after stroking. (After Douglas and Ritchie. *J. Physiol.*, 1957, *139*:385–399.)

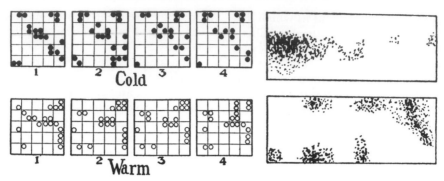

Fig. 3. Maps of thermal sensitivity of skin. *Left:* Results of four successive mappings (left to right) of same area on upper arm. Each small square equals 4 mm.² Observe high degree of similarity in independent mappings and that sensitive spots occur in groups. (From Dallenbach, *Amer. J. Psychol.,* 1927, *39:*402–427.) *Right:* Maps of distribution of sensibility to cold in 12 mappings of an area on volar surface of forearm. Each rectangle corresponds to area on skin 4 by 10 mm., and each represents a different subject. Subjects were permitted to report neutral and three degrees of coldness. Score for each point is crudely given by depth of shading. (From Jenkins, *J. exp. Psychol.,* 1939, *25:*373–388.)

since been proved that "with one exception, a mechanoreceptor," only free nerve endings are found in the spaces between hair shafts.

Whether there is a morphologically specialized temperature ending even in hairless skin and mucous membranes is also doubtful. The

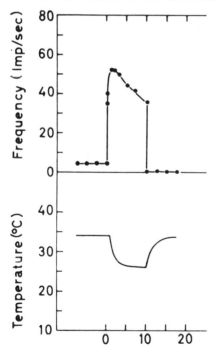

Fig. 4. Frequency of discharge of a single "cold fiber" (upper) in man and the cutaneous temperature (lower), both plotted against time in seconds. Note that the response has a much higher frequency to a smaller temperature change than in the next figure. (From Hensel and Bosman, *J. Neurophysiol.,* 1960, *23:* 564–568.)

strongest evidence for a specialized cold ending, Krause's end bulb, has been disproved. (The evidence for the warmth ending of Ruffini was never strong.) What were long thought to be Krause's end bulbs in the conjunctivum are seen in number only in older persons and are believed by Weddell[35] to be regenerating fibers which have met an obstruction, proliferated and twisted to form so called *sterile end bulbs* like those found in the proximal stumps of divided nerves. It appears certain that in hairless skin no encapsulated or specialized organs exist. However, it must be remembered that *the absence of a microscopic anatomic specificity does not disprove functional specificity.* For example, the threshold energy for warmth sensation is one-thousandth of that for heat-induced pain, though both are served by free nerve endings.

Some skin receptors served by myelinated fibers are sensitive only to cooling—the classic cold receptor (Fig. 4). In man,[17] as in the cat, they respond to lowered temperature with a large increase in firing rate, specifically in man an increase of 45 impulses per second in response to a 10°C. temperature drop. Another and perhaps more numerous group exhibit both mechanical and temperature sensibility (Fig. 5). They are, however, only weakly responsive to cooling, the discharge increase being about one-ninth that of a specific cold receptor. Because they respond vigorously to pressure, they can be classed as mechanoreceptors with some cold receptive ability. They differ from other mechanoreceptors by firing spontaneously at neutral skin temperature in the absence of

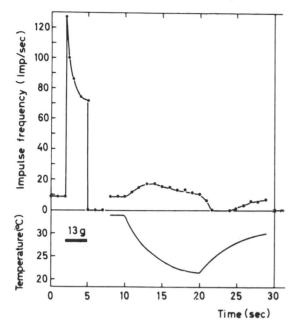

Fig. 5. A plot of discharge frequency of a non-specific, mechanothermal sensitive sense organ in man. Contrast the high frequency response to pressure (13 g) left to the low frequency discharge to large drop in temperature (nearly 20° C.) at the right. (From Hensel and Bosman, *J. Neurophysiol.*, 1960, *23*:564–568.)

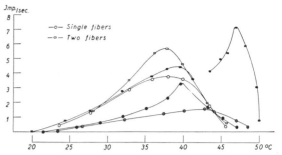

Fig. 6. Graphs showing relation between frequency of discharge and temperature for different single and dual warm fiber preparations. Steady discharge after adaptation has occurred is graphed. An occasional fiber (one in 13) had a maximum above 45° C. and was undoubtedly a heat fiber. (From Dodt and Zotterman, *Acta physiol. scand.*, 1952, *26*:345–357.)

known mechanical stimulation. Their role in sensation is unknown. Their existence may explain why a cold object resting on the palm of the hand seems heavier than a warm one of the same size and weight (Weber's illusion).

The less numerous warmth fiber has not yet been identified electrophysiologically in man but has been in animals (see Fig. 6). Moreover, a "heat" receptor has been discovered by Iggo. It is excitable by radiant heat. As seen in Figure 6, it starts firing in the range at which the warmth fibers are decreasing their firing rate and above that at which tissue damage starts. Figure 7 shows increased frequencies of response with high temperature. It is sufficiently heat specific to demarcate it from the postulated nonspecific nociceptive receptor. It may, however, contribute to a subjective pain response as well as serve thermal sensibility, which persists after blocking of myelinated fibers.

In the cat, dog and rat highly sensitive cold and warm fibers conducting with C-fiber velocity are abundant. Responses to a temperature decrease of 0.3° C. have been detected in single fiber preparations and three-quarters of C-fibers respond at 10° C. A "cold" C-fiber can main-

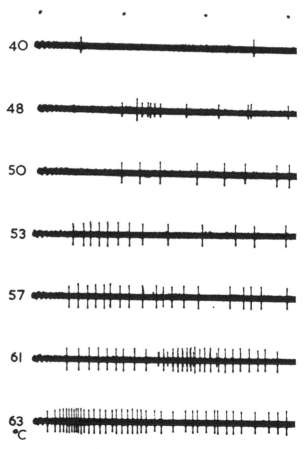

Fig. 7. Responses in a C-fiber (1 meter per second conduction velocity) when a heated brass rod was applied to the skin. The discharge at 40° and 48° C. save one are from a nearby mechanoreceptor; the rod alone did not stimulate the "heat" receptor. The dots at the top give time in seconds. (From Iggo, *Quart. J. exp. Physiol.*, 1959, *44*:362–370.)

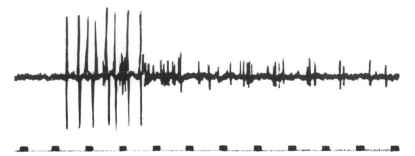

Fig. 8. Oscillographic record from a "cut-down" lingual nerve showing a volley of large fiber potentials (touch) and of small fiber potentials (cold). Stimulus was a current of air strong enough to deform surface of tongue visibly. (From Zotterman, *Skand. Arch. Physiol.,* 1936, 75:105–120.)

tain steady firing at a temperature as high as 38°C.[22] However, in the monkey, which is expected to be more like man, only a few such fibers are found (Iggo[22]). Fibers highly cold-sensitive (0.5° C. threshold) conduct at rates of 3.6 to 15 meters per second and hence are among the smallest myelinated fibers. They maintain a discharge in response to a sustained temperature drop and are not stimulated by the usual mechanical stimuli. They originate in a single, restricted spot on the skin and have a small receptive field measuring 0.25 to 0.6 sq. mm.

These experiments agree with nerve-block experiments on man showing that most, though not all, impulses underlying thermal sensation are conducted in myelinated fibers.

Contrary to past teachings, there are no morphologically specialized endings for thermal receptors either in smooth or hairy skin. Regardless of the lack of morphologic specificity, physiologically specific receptors have been found for which the adequate stimulus is: cold but not warmth or heat, warmth but not cold or heat, or heat alone. However, a receptor which responds strongly to pressure and weakly to cold is fairly commonly encountered in man. Extrapolation from experiments on the monkey suggests that C-fiber involvement in combined thermal and mechanical sensitivity is not a major factor in man.

The adequate stimulus for both warmth and cold is heat. Cold is not a positive quantity, and temperature does not have the dimension of energy. The threshold stimulus for cold receptors is a fall in temperature at the rate of 0.004°C. per second and, for warmth receptors, a rise of 0.001°C. per second, both continuing for three seconds.[22] The thermal sense organs record not the temperature of objects, but the temperature of the skin at the depth at which the receptors are situated. Hence they are stimulated by internal heat as well as by the

heat of the environment. The patient with Raynaud's disease who experiences a vasospasm in the fingers complains bitterly of the cold even in a warm room. A metal object and a wooden object of the same temperature do not seem equally cold to the touch because the metal object conducts heat from the skin more readily. A most important factor is the temperature of the skin. Objects having a temperature close to the physiologic zero, i.e., the temperature of the skin, elicit neither warmth nor cold sensations. On the other hand, even warm air falling on the warmer skin during fever arouses distressing sensations of cold. Since thermal sense organs play a role in the regulation of body temperature, it is important to know the exact nature of the temperature stimulus.

Hensel and Zotterman[38] recorded "cold" impulses from the lingual nerve along with the surface and intracutaneous temperature of the tongue during cooling with cold water (Fig. 8). A drop in water temperature from 37° to 13°C. caused a maximum discharge within one to two seconds which fell exponentially to a plateau rate of 25 impulses per second in about 70 seconds, at which time the temperature at the level of the receptor was no longer changing. Such steady discharges were recorded after 70 minutes of cooling. Thus, while temperature change is a powerful stimulus to the rapidly adapting cold receptor, it is not a necessary condition for stimulation, since discharge to steadily maintained cooling occurred. The actual stimulus therefore is either a temperature gradient (energy flow) from within out or the absolute temperature. The latter would imply that excitation depends on some internal physiologic process, such as a chemical reaction, inversely dependent on temperature. The direction of temperature gradient and heat flow is of no importance. From experiments comparing responses from one surface of the tongue when comparable gradients from within out were maintained during cooling of first the upper and then the lower surface, Hensel and Zotterman[38] concluded that temperature *per se* rather than a temperature gradient is the actual stimulus to the cold receptor. By combining frequency of firing and recruitment, as few as ten cold fibers can show a linear relation of impulses per second to temperature between 38° and 27° C.[38]

Touch–Pressure. Touch is one of the four fundamental cutaneous sense modalities. Whether touch forms a single sense modality, like warmth or cold, or whether there are subqualities, served by distinct neural mechanisms, is uncertain. That there are several functional types of mechanoreceptors is certain.

The existence of at least two physiologically specific mechanoreceptors was first proved by Adrian and Zotterman[1] by recording action potentials from single cutaneous fibers while stimulating the skin. One receptor was rapidly adapting, the discharge lasting only 0.2 second to a sustained touch, and the second was slowly adapting, maintaining after an initial period of rapid adaptation, a sustained discharge for many seconds. It is now possible to describe these receptors from similar studies conducted on monkey skin, both hairy and glabrous, and from heroic experiments on man.

The rapidly adapting receptors which fire only while the skin is being touched or a hair is being bent have a low threshold (5 to 20 mg. tested by von Frey hairs), are connected with myelinated fibers (2 to 8 μ from hairy skin and 6 to 11 μ from smooth skin) and have large receptive fields, 1.5 to 5 sq. cm. at threshold. In man, bending a hair by 5°, which is the sensory threshold, may elicit only one impulse. Some receptors are temperature-sensitive, but they give only three to five responses to a large and rapid decrease of the skin's temperature and are therefore classed as mechanoceptors. The rapidly adapting fibers from smooth skin have higher thresholds and are unaffected by temperature.

The second touch receptor discovered by Adrian and Zotterman has been found in man.[17] After an initial period of rapid adaptation, it maintains a steady discharge with little further decrease in frequency. The plateau frequency is related to amount of pressure and attains rates as high as 330 impulses per second. The pressure which will just discharge the end-organ is in the same range as the sensory threshold of the same region. The receptor does not fire spontaneously or in response to cooling and its steady response to pressure is unaffected by temperature. It has a spotlike receptive field of about 1 to 2 mm. in diameter in hairy and adjacent nonhairy skin. In the monkey, Iggo[22] finds a receptor similar in its spotlike distribution and firing characteristic. Its afferent fibers are large, in the 6 to 9 μ range. It is a specific mechanoreceptor. In the cat, 64 of 77 fibers examined were fired either from one or from two spots, the spots being usually within 1 to 5 mm. of each other even when a cluster of 3 to 8 spots fired a single axon.[20]

A nonspecific skin receptor of man[17] differs by being sensitive to cooling as well as to pressure, by discharging spontaneously at a low rate (one impulse per second) and having a maximal discharge rate which is a fraction of that attained by the specific touch receptor. In the monkey[22] this receptor has fieldlike distribution leading to afferent fibers 5 to 13 μ in diameter. Receptors with a fieldlike distribution found in glabrous skin are similar except that the threshold is higher by 5 to 20 times.

The sensory response to these nonspecific receptors is thought to be a touch–pressure sensation. While the functional significance of sensitivity to both cold and pressure is not known, it is suggestive that impulses arising from such receptors appear to enter ascending sensory systems having characteristics which can be broadly termed "nonspecific."

Pain. The sensory mechanism for pain is in many ways unique. The sensory end-organs for pain are spread through virtually all of the tissues of the body, so that three kinds of pain are recognized and designated: (i) superficial or cutaneous pain; (ii) deep pain from muscles, tendons, joints, and fascia; and (iii) visceral pain. The first two together form somatic pain. The pain endings are unique also in exhibiting only to a limited degree the phenomenon of the adequate stimulus. Several kinds of energy are adequate to elicit pain—electrical, mechanical, extremes of heat and cold, and a wide variety of chemical stimuli. The pain ending therefore is not specialized to react to a single form of energy, but reacts to extreme degrees of several kinds of stimulation. Sherrington pointed out that the property common to all stimuli adequate to excite pain endings is the threat of damage to the tissues. Hardy *et al.*[13] have proved this quantitatively for heat energy. Thus, increasing degrees of heat first stimulate warmth endings and then, at 44.9°C., commence to stimulate pain endings. At about 44° to 45°C., irreversible damage to the skin, demonstrable histologically, occurs, and accompanying release of chemical substances such as

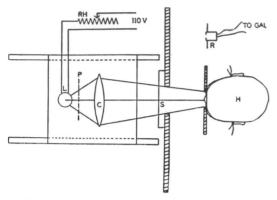

Fig. 9. Radiant energy apparatus for measuring warmth and pain sensibility. Light from 1000 watt lamp, *L,* is focused by condensing lens, *C,* through fixed aperture of 3.5 sq. mm. on forehead of subject, which is blacked by India ink. Intensity of radiation is controlled by means of rheostat, *RH,* and duration by shutter, *P,* which automatically limits exposure to 3 seconds. Shutter, *S,* is hand-operated. (From Hardy *et al., J. clin. Invest.,* 1940, *19*:649–657.)

histamine is expected. One explanation of the wide stimulus spectrum of the pain end-organ is that various noxious stimuli release a chemical substance in the skin and that this substance stimulates the end-organs. The evidence for this will be presented in the next chapter under the heading *Hyperalgesia.*

In Sherrington's classification of the senses, pain was termed *nociceptive,* meaning sensitive to noxious agents. The function of the pain sense is protective, whereas the other modalities of sensation are primarily informative or gnostic. Other differences are that pain is unpleasant or, in other words, possesses a considerable *affect;* that pain leads to more precipitate action; and, finally, that certain types of pain tend to radiate and to be poorly localized.

Because pain is so unlike other forms of sensation, it was long considered not a separate form of sensation but rather a response elicited by intense stimulation of other kinds of sensory end-organs. This overstimulation or intensive theory is refuted by considerable evidence, including the fact that stimulation of certain areas causes only pain. That overstimulation of touch and pressure organs does not cause pain was proved by Cattell and Hoagland.[5] Intense stimulation of an end-organ increases the frequency of its discharge. Stimulating the skin of a frog with puffs of air at a high frequency produced high rates of discharge (300 per second). When such stimuli were applied to an unanesthetized frog, it exhibited no sign of pain.

MEASUREMENT OF PAIN SENSIBILITY. For purposes of clinical examination, pain is elicited by pricking the skin with a pin or needle. The subject reports whether the pricks "feel" different on the two sides of the body, or he is asked to distinguish between the point and the head of a pin. Thresholds can be determined more quantitatively with a thistle glued to a von Frey hair (see below). In such tests touch receptors are stimulated along with the pain receptors, and the results are not sufficiently quantitative.

Hardy *et al.*[15] employed radiant heat (Fig. 9) in increasing intensities to obtain a threshold for pain. If precautions are taken to ensure that skin temperature is stabilized, or its variations corrected for, thresholds of a single individual are remarkably invariable. As with cold sensation, pain from radiant heat seems to depend on actual skin temperature and not on the rate of change. In contrast with other sensory channels, the threshold is not dependent on size of area stimulated. Spatial summation between fibers supplying a given area, or between the branches of a single fiber, apparently does not occur. Hardy *et al.*[16] found that they could discriminate only 21 steps (j.n.d.) between threshold and maximum pain, and the range of energy was little more than 2:1. The grossness of the j.n.d. is experimental justification for speaking of pain as a nondiscriminative modality of sensation.

Visceral pain, deep pain and special forms of pain are discussed in Chapter 16.

For many decades the nociceptive receptor was thought to be a free nerve ending responsive to several forms of energy if sufficiently strong and connected with unmyelinated or the smallest unmyelinated axons. Despite the ability to record from such axons in cutaneous nerve it has not been possible to identify electrophysiologically a pain ending responsive to a variety of stimuli and *only* at strong intensities. Among the endings innervated by C-fibers are some that have the required high threshold such as the so-called "hot" fibers or those sensitive only to pricking or squeezing the skin but not to light touch. An occasional fiber is found which is sensitive to both extreme cold and heat. However, all these are too modality-specific to qualify as the hypothetical wide band-pass pain receptor. The free nerve endings connected with C-fibers, so abundant and so suited to reception of noxious stimuli of several kinds have other occupations (touch, warmth, cold reception) and can no longer be associated exclusively with pain. Pain is a sensory modality in search of a sense organ.

Deep Sensibility. Although one gives it little thought, a person with closed eyes knows the direction of a movement, active or passive, and is aware of the position of his arms and legs. It was not until 1826 that Charles Bell[3] explicitly described the "sixth" sense—muscle sense. "For example," he said, "between the brain and the muscles, there is a circle of nerves; one nerve conveys the influence from the brain to the muscle; the other gives the sense of the condition of the muscle to the brain." The forms of deep sensibility exclusive of pain and deep pressure are known by several synonyms, all of which are in common use: muscle sense or, more completely, muscle, tendon and joint sensibility; kinesthesia (Bastian); proprioception (Sherrington); and, operationally and clinically, position sense and the appreciation of passive movement (Head). Some, for inadequate semantic reasons, prefer kinesthesia (sense of movement) to proprioception (or self knowledge) because the receptors from joints seem more important to cortical awareness of passive movement of the limb or the position in space than are the muscle receptors, originally implicated by Goldscheider.

Four types of sense organs are found in muscles, tendons and joints: (i) the muscle spindle; (ii) the Golgi tendon organ; (iii) the joint organs, the pacinian corpuscle, etc.; and (iv) free nerve endings. The analysis previously presented suggests that muscle, tendon and joint receptors as a group record three aspects of the state of the muscle: active contraction, passive stretch (length of fiber) and tension, whether produced by passive stretch or active contraction.

Browne *et al.*[4] found that application of procaine to the joint capsule ends the appreciation of passive movement of the metatarsal-phalangeal joint and appreciation of the position of the great toe in space. Significant clinically is the fact that some normal subjects appreciated only very large displacements (10 to 30 degrees). Impairment of the appreciation of passive movement, whether occurring naturally or induced by application of procaine to the capsule, was not associated with any defect in appreciation of active movement. The former function is capsular; the latter is muscular or tendinous. The joint capsule contains end-organs of the nonadapting type which vary the discharge rate according to joint position.

THE NEUROLOGIC EXAMINATION OF SENSATION

So far, sensory function has been discussed mainly from a biologic point of view with brief mention of how it is examined clinically. In the following pages are described normal psychological processes of a higher order, relating them to the sensory examination of neurologic patients.

Clinical Examination of Deep Sensibility. Deep pressure and deep pain are elicited by firm, massive pressure over muscles or tendons. Muscles and tendons possess an exquisite pain sensibility; this is discussed in a subsequent chapter.

The "appreciation of passive movement" of a single joint is commonly tested in the neurologic examination. If a finger or toe is grasped by the side (to minimize cues from pressure) and moved up or down, a patient with normal sensibility states the direction of quite small angular displacements. A roughly quantitative estimate of the threshold can thus be obtained.

The "sense of position" is tested in a variety of ways. A limb is placed in an unusual position and the patient, with eyes closed, is asked to duplicate the posture with his other limb. Another maneuver—the finger-to-finger test—consists of passively moving the arm to be tested and bringing it to rest with finger extended. The patient is then asked to touch the extended forefinger with the forefinger of the other hand. By interposing a piece of cardboard between the two fingers and marking their positions, a quantitative estimate of the error can be obtained. Recently, another method for quantitation of position sense was described by Cohen[6] (Fig 10). In animals something akin to the sense of position is tested by determining whether a false or abnormal position—not extreme enough to be painful—is corrected, a test which is valid only when motor ability is normal. A similar procedure applicable to animals is the "proprioceptive placing" reaction (Chap. 9).

The appreciation of muscle tension is studied by determining the ability to detect difference in weight of objects by lifting them. Two weights are usually presented, and the subject is asked to state which is the heavier. This classic laboratory procedure in psychology has proved useful in studying neurologic patients and has been adapted to monkeys and chimpanzees in the study of cortical localization of sensory functions.

Vibratory Sensibility. The appreciation of vibration, or pallesthesia, is tested crudely by placing the base of a vibrating tuning fork upon the skin. A thrill or feeling of vibration is normally experienced, but only a sense of continuous contact is felt in the presence of certain neurologic lesions. Electrically driven vibratory devices yield thresholds in terms of the just perceptible amplitude of vibration. The greatest sensibility occurs at 200 to 400 cycles per second and can be as low as 0.064 μ displacement.[29] Vibratory sensibility is often erroneously considered a separate sense modality rather than a special excitation of the sense organs for pressure and possibly proprioception. Because application of the fork over bone intensifies the stimulus in a purely mechanical fashion, vibratory sensation has been mistakenly called "osseous sensation." The lowest threshold is found not over bone but on the finger tips. Vibratory sensibility has a punctate distribution with vibration-sensitive spots corresponding to pressure-sensitive spots. Deep sense organs are also involved. In fact, the deep-lying pacinian corpuscle is especially suited for the detection of vibration, following one-for-one in the range from 150 to above 700 cycles per second, rates at which no other somatic end-organ can follow.[19] (The pa-

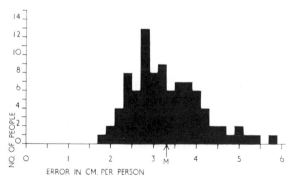

Fig. 10. Accuracy of position sense in 91 normal young adults. Subjects touched with forefinger a reference point on a target at arm's length. After closing eyes and returning arm to side, subjects attempted to touch the point again. Test was repeated until 48 different points were tried. *Abscissa,* mean error on 48 points. (From Cohen, *J. Neurophysiol.,* 1958, *21*:550–562.)

cinian corpuscle cannot follow below 150 because of its rapid adaptation.) The presence of pacinian corpuscles in interosseous membranes and other structures related to bone may contribute to making regions over bone especially sensitive to vibration.

Vibratory sensibility is certainly not a separate sense. It is certainly not bone sensibility, nor does it seem to be associated exclusively with either deep or superficial pressure receptors. Vibratory sensibility is a perception of a temporal pattern of pressures, somewhat like the flicker phenomenon in vision (Chap. 20). This interpretation is supported by the behavior of vibratory sensibility in various clinical neurologic conditions.

The underlying impulses must be conducted in the posterior columns of the spinal cord since defective vibratory appreciation is typical of spinal cord lesions but surgical section of the anterolateral columns leaves it unimpaired. If spinal cord damage is sufficient to affect position sense, vibratory appreciation is always affected. In contrast, lesions of the cerebral cortex rarely affect vibratory sensibility unless they penetrate deeply; in such cases damage to the thalamus may be responsible (Fig. 11). Though not subject to any simple explanation, this difference in vulnerability of vibratory sensitivity at the spinal and cerebral levels makes vibratory sensibility helpful in clinical diagnosis.

The vibratory sensibility changes with age, beginning to diminish at or just about fifty years. It is an accurate indicator of sensory loss in diabetes and pernicious anemia.

Localization or Topognosis.[3] Every somatic sensation has in addition to its quality and its intensity a localization upon the body surface. The accuracy of localization has been extensively investigated in both normal persons and neurologic patients. Weber (1852) touched the skin with a pointer dipped in powdered charcoal to mark the point stimulated; the subject, with his eyes closed throughout, tried to touch the same spot with another pointer. The measured discrepancy between the two marks gave the error of localization, which was found to vary greatly in different regions of the body surface.

Usually only localization of light pressure is tested clinically; it is sometimes forgotten that all sensations can be localized, though with quite different accuracy. (The explanation for this will be given in the next chapter.) Localiza-

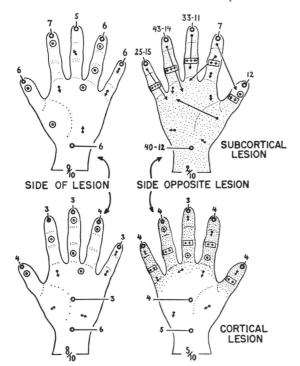

Fig. 11. Example of Fox's chart used for recording sensory examination of neurologic patients with subcortical (*upper*) and cortical lesions (*lower*). Degree of loss of position sense in phalangeal joint is indicated by +, + + and + + +; accurate localization of point touched is designated by circle and dot; displacement of an erroneous localization is indicated by arrow. Areas of hypesthesia are indicated by stipple. Fraction at wrist is a measure of stereognosis and shows number of successfully identified objects in series of ten presenting increasing difficulty. Numbers connected by line with heavy circle give threshold of vibration in arbitrary unit at point indicated; a large number signifies large amplitude of vibration. (After Fox and Klemperer, *Arch. Neurol. Psychiat.* (*Chic.*), 1942, *48:*622–645.)

tion may be severely impaired by damage to central pathways when mere awareness of the stimulation is preserved. Testing topognosis is, therefore, part of the neurologic examination (Fig. 11).

Projection of Sensation. This is a phenomenon related to localization.* The ultimate event in the sensory process occurs in the brain, but in no case are we aware of this. On the contrary, our sensations are projected either to the

*The distinction between projection and localization is that the former has more to do with the envelope or layer, external or internal, from which a sensation appears to come. Localization has more to do with where on these envelopes the sensation is localized (see Chap. 16).

external world or to some peripheral organ in the body, i.e., to the place where experience has taught us that the acting stimulus arises. Sound seems to come from the bell, light from the lamp, etc. Pain, muscle sense, labyrinthine sensations, hunger, thirst, sexual sense, etc., are projected to the interior of the body. The temperature senses may be projected either to the air or to the skin, according to circumstances.

An aspect of sensation important to clinical neurology and which deserves to be called the *law of projection* is that stimulation of sensory pathways at any point central to the sense organ gives rise to a sensation which is projected to the periphery and not to the point of stimulation.

Numerous examples of this law can be cited. An amputee may experience projected sensations so elaborate that they amount to a feeling that the limb is still present and executing movements, often painful—the phenomenon of"phantom limb." Irritation of a dorsal spinal root by a ruptured intervertebral disc of the fifth lumbar segment often gives rise to a sensation of pain over the buttock and down the back of the thigh, which is the region innervated by the affected root. Stimulation of the cerebral cortex in conscious human patients at the time of intracranial operation gives rise to sensations which appear to come not from the head but from the skin of some part of the body. In all these cases the cerebral cortex interprets the nerve impulses as though they had come from the sense organ. For further implications of the phenomenon of projection, see the section on referred pain (Chap. 16).

Two Point Sensibility. If the blunt points of a compass are applied simultaneously to the skin with sufficient distance between them, they are perceived as two separate points of contact. If the points are brought progressively closer together in successive applications, they eventually give rise to a sensation of a single point applied to the skin. The smallest distance between points at which they are still perceived as two separate contacts is the *two point threshold.* A two point threshold can be determined for all forms of sensation, but only thresholds for light pressure and occasionally pain (prick) are tested clinically. The two point threshold is a smaller distance for touches than for warmth or cold stimuli. The ability of the skin to resolve two points is only one three-thousandths of that of the eye. Regional differences are pronounced (Fig. 12) and broadly parallel the accuracy of localization. They do not, however, parallel regional variations in the intensity threshold. In

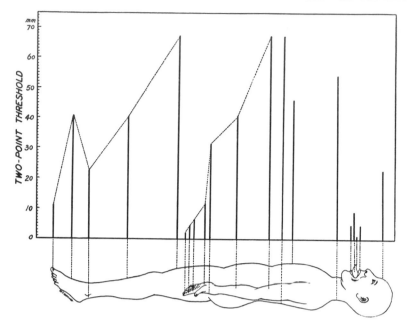

Fig. 12. Regional variation in two point threshold for touch. Length of vertical lines is approximately equal to magnitude of two point threshold. (Data from Weber cited by Sherrington in Schäfer, *Text-book of physiology.* Edinburgh, Young J. Pentland, 1900.)

the neurologic examination corresponding areas on both sides of the body must be tested.

Size, Shape, Figure Writing, Etc. The ability of the cutaneous and proprioceptive sensory systems to appreciate the spatial aspect of objects is demonstrable by a variety of simple maneuvers. Objects of graded size, such as coins, placed successively in the hand are discriminated. The direction and length of a line drawn upon the skin are recognized. Touch and pressure are mainly responsible for such discrimination. Geometric patterns of warmth produced without contact (radiation) are virtually unrecognizable. Perhaps the most convenient test of the spatial aspect of skin sensibility is the "figure writing" test introduced by Foerster. While the patient's eyes are closed, numerals between 0 and 9 are written on his palm or another smooth surface of his body with a blunt, pointed object, using a slow, even movement. Although mistakes are rarely made by a normal person after the first few trials, certain neurologic patients do little better than chance. The manner of recording the observation is as follows:

As written	1	2	7	4	8	6	9	5	3	0
As reported	1	2	6	3–2	6	6	1	7	7	0

Figure writing, left hand. J. P., a white youth aged 18. Tests were conducted subsequent to a right occipital craniotomy which disclosed an aneurysm of the posterior cerebral artery with a hemorrhagic cyst in the anterior portion of the occipital lobe. The resection included the midportion of the posterior parietal lobe.

STEREOGNOSIS. The appreciation of the form of three-dimensional objects by palpation without the aid of vision is termed *stereognosis* or the knowledge of (geometric) solids. A key, a coin or a pencil may serve as a test object— "recognition of common objects." A series of standardized objects or geometric forms of graded difficulty, as employed by Fox (Fig. 11), is desirable because it allows a rough quantitative statement of ability. Stereognosis is not a "sense" despite the common clinical usage. It is a complex perception or concept based upon the synthesis of the several modalities of somatic sensation.

Touch and kinesthesis perhaps yield the most information, but all senses may be involved. For example, the roundness of a cyclinder is recognized by the even pressure on the pulp of the fingers when it is rolled, kinesthetic sense giving information on the diameter and weight of the object. It is soon appreciated that the object rolls in one direction but not the other. As the finger slides along the smooth surface, an end is discovered which proves to be a flat, smooth surface, the circular border of which confirms the original impression. And when the identical impression is gained from the opposite end, the data are synthesized into the conclusion that the object is a cylinder. Additional data with regard to smoothness and temperature complete its recognition as a metal cylinder.

It is not difficult to understand how stereognosis becomes defective when either tactual or kinesthetic sense is blunted, although one can partly substitute for the other. This situation is more properly termed stereoanesthesia. After lesions of the posterior parietal lobe, stereognosis seems to be affected out of proportion to the deficit in the basic sensations—so-called pure astereognosis. At some point difficult to define, disturbances of the higher levels of sensation merge into agnosia and aphasia (see Chap. 23).

REFERENCES

1. ADRIAN, E. D. *The basis of sensation.* London, Christophers, 1928.
2. BELL, C. *Phil. Trans.,* 1826, Pt. 2, pp. 163–173.
3. BORING, E. G. *Sensation and perception in the history of experimental psychology.* New York, D. Appleton-Century Co., 1942.
4. BROWNE, K., LEE, L. and RING, P. A. *J. Physiol.,* 1954, *126*:448–458
5. CATTELL, McK. and HOAGLAND, H. *J. Physiol.,* 1931, *72:* 392–404.
6. COHEN, L. A. *J. Neurophysiol.,* 1958, *21*:550–562.
7. DOUGLAS, W. W. and RITCHIE, J. M. *Physiol. Rev.,* 1962, *42*:297–334.
8. DOUGLAS, W. W., RITCHIE, J. M. and STRAUB, R. W. *J. Physiol.,* 1960, *150*:266–268.
9. FIELD, J., ed. *Handbook of physiology; Section I: Neurophysiology,* vol. 1. Washington, D.C., American Physiological Society, 1959.
10. GELDARD, F. A. *The human senses.* New York, John Wiley & Sons, 1953.
11. GRAY, J. In: *Biological receptor mechanisms.* Cambridge, The University Press, 1962.
12. HAGEN, E., KNOCHE, H. SINCLAIR, D. C. and WEDDELL, G. *Proc. roy. Soc.,* 1953, *B141:*279–287.
13. HARDY, J. D., GOODELL, H. and WOLFF, H. G. *Science,* 1951, *114*:149–150.
14. HARDY, J. D. and OPPEL, T. W. *J. clin. Invest.,* 1937, *16:* 533–540.
15. HARDY, J. D., WOLFF, H. G. and GOODELL, H. *J. clin. Invest.,* 1940, *19*:649–657.
16. HARDY, J. D., WOLFF, H. G. and GOODELL, H. *J. clin. Invest.,* 1947, *26*:1152–1158.
17. HENSEL, H. and BOSMAN, K. K. A. *J. Neurophysiol.,* 1960, *23*:564–568.
18. HENSEL, H., IGGO, A. and WITT, I. *J. Physiol.,* 1960, *153:* 113–126.
19. HUNT, C. C. *J. Physiol.,* 1961, *155*:175–186.
20. HUNT, C. C. and McINTYRE, A. K. *J. Physiol.,* 1960, *153*:88–98; 99–112.
21. IGGO, A. *Quart. J. exp. Physiol.,* 1959, *44*:362–370.
22. IGGO, A. *Acta neurovegetativa,* 1962, *24*:225–240.
23. IRIUCHIJIMA, J. and ZOTTERMAN, Y. *Acta physiol. scand.,* 1960, *49*:267–268.
24. LELE, P. P. and WEDDELL, G. *Brain,* 1956, *79*:119–154.
25. MOUNTCASTLE, V. B., POGGIO, G. F. and WERNER, G. *J. Neurophysiol.,* 1963, *26*:775–806.
26. MÜLLER, J. *Handbuch der Physiologie des Menschen für Vorlesungen,* Coblenz, J. Holscher, 1834–1840, 2 vols. Translated selections in: Rand, B. *The classical psychologists.* Boston, Houghton Mifflin, 1912.
27. OPPENHEIMER, D. R., PALMER, E. and WEDDELL, C. *J. Anat. (Lond.),* 1958, *92*:321–352.
28. PERL, E. R. *Ann. Rev. Physiol.,* 1963, *25*:459–492.
29. PLUMB, C. S. and MEIGS, J. W. *Arch. gen. Psychiat.,* 1961, *14*:611–614.
30. ROSENBLITH, W. A., ed. *Sensory communication.* New York, John Wiley & Sons, 1961.
31. SHERRINGTON, C. S. *The integrative action of the nervous system.* New Haven, Yale University Press, 1906.
32. STEVENS, S. S. See Rosenblith, No. 30.
33. TOWER, S. S. *J. Neurophysiol.,* 1940, *3*:486–500.
34. WALL, P. D. *J. Neurophysiol.,* 1960, *23*:197–210.
35. WEDDELL, G. In: Brazier, ed. *Brain and behavior,* Vol. I, Washington, D.C. American Institute of Biological Sciences, 1961.
36. WEDDELL, G. See Rosenblith, No. 30.
37. ZANDER, E. and WEDDELL, G. *J. Anat. (Lond.),* 1951, *85:* 68–93.
38. ZOTTERMAN, Y. Chap. 18 in *Handbook of physiology. Section 1. Neurophysiology,* Vol. 1, J. FIELD, ed. Baltimore, Williams & Wilkins, 1959.

CHAPTER 15

Neural Basis of Somatic Sensation

By THEODORE C. RUCH

CHAPTER 14 described the stimuli and physiologic characteristics of the sense organs and the end results of somatic sensation: perception and affect; this chapter takes up the sensory pathways in sequence, beginning with the peripheral nerve trunk and ending with the thalamic and cortical organization.

The clinical examination for neurologic diseases involves two questions: which sensory functions are lost? and, equally important, which are retained? What is lost and what is retained is called a *dissociation of sensation*. Pathologic lesions at each level of the nervous system produce characteristic dissociations. From a knowledge of these dissociations the level and location of a lesion are deduced. Four kinds of dissociation are taken into account: (i)

topographic dissociations, in which certain regions of the body show altered sensitivity and other regions remain normal; (ii) *modality dissociations,* in which one or a group of sensations are lost or impaired while others are preserved; (iii) an *affect-quality dissociation,* in which the affect is exaggerated; and (iv) *dissociations of levels of sensation,* in which the more complex sensory functions, e.g., perception, are lost but the simpler ones are retained.

PERIPHERAL NERVE AND SPINAL ROOTS

A "peripheral nerve field" is the area of skin supplied by one cutaneous nerve. Charts showing the fields for the major cutaneous nerves are used clinically to record the distribution of sensory disturbances. Not shown on such charts, however, is the overlap between peripheral nerve fields. Each major nerve field has a central zone of skin, the *autonomous zone,*[71] innervated *only* by the parent nerve and, therefore, completely anesthetic when the nerve is sectioned. Between this zone and the surrounding fully innervated skin is the *intermediate zone* of overlap, where sensation is now served only by branches from neighboring nerves. The sensation elicited by stimulation in this zone of overlap has three abnormal aspects: (i) sensory dissociation, only pain and possibly pressure being appreciated; (ii) hypesthesia, responses to light pressure stimuli showing a gradual transition from anesthesia to normal threshold; and (iii) hyperpathia, pain sensations being abnormally unpleasant.

After nerve section, sensibility is recovered by a remarkable circumferential shrinkage of the anesthetic area, i.e., the intermediate zone extends day by day into the anesthetic area. This shrinkage starts within the first few days after nerve section, long before regenerating fibers could possibly reach the skin. Pollock[50] reasoned that the shrinkage is due to an ingrowth of fibers from the adjacent peripheral nerve fields, because the recovery was not lost after a resectioning of the regenerating nerve. Weddell *et al.*[71] have demonstrated by intravital staining that unmyelinated fibers do grow out from the intermediate into the autonomous zone.

Shortly after nerve section, pain (and, to some degree, touch sensibility) elicited from the intermediate area is qualitatively altered. Although a stronger stimulus is needed to arouse sensations of pain (hypalgesia), once the threshold is exceeded the pain is peculiarly strong and unpleasant (hyperpathia). This phase passes, but at about the time the sensation served by the regenerating nerve returns to the anesthetic area, the abnormal pain responses tend to reappear.

Epicritic and protopathic sensibility.[10, 20, 67, 70] Head grouped the abnormal sensations found in the intermediate zone, in the autonomous zone during later stages of nerve regeneration, and in regions of special sensitivity, e.g., glans penis, under the name *protopathic sensibility;* and for it he postulated a special set of fibers having a wide peripheral nerve field and quick regeneration. He also postulated a second set of fibers for each modality to carry out fine intensity and spatial discriminations e.g., serving two-point threshold; for these he coined *epicritic sensibility.* The more highly evolved epicritic system was believed to inhibit the phylogenetically older protopathic system, except when absent, as after nerve section.

Few now accept Head's theory. Some of his observations were in error and others have different explanations, e.g., the thinning out of fibers in the intermediate zone. Nevertheless, the terms are still used by clinical neurologists. Perhaps, in a very broad sense, the terms can be used to characterize two kinds of sense organs and sensory pathways with different physiologic properties.

Dermatomes.[23, 24, 27, 59] The area of skin supplied with afferent fibers by a single posterior root is a *dermatome.* Because the dermatomes are important to clinical neurology, they have been mapped repeatedly (Fig. 1). Such charts, which are used in recording the results of a sensory examination, show the dermatomes as contiguous fields. Actually the dermatomes of adjacent roots overlap greatly, so that always two and sometimes three roots supply a single point on the skin. The dermatomes are therefore considerably larger than those shown on most clinical charts. The size of a dermatome is somewhat smaller for pain than for temperature and smaller for temperature than for touch, which is just the reverse of the dissociation in the border surrounding a peripheral nerve injury. Dermatomes, or *sensory root fields,* must not be confused with peripheral nerve fields. The two are quite different in shape, and often the fibers of one dermatome are conducted to the spinal cord in two peripheral nerves.

The dermatomes cannot be demarcated by sectioning a single posterior root and mapping the resulting area of anesthesia, since, owing to overlap, none may be found. The classic method for mapping dermatomes is that of *remaining sensibility.* Sherrington sectioned three roots above and three below the intact root to be studied, producing an island of sensitivity in a sea of anesthesia. Mapping the hyperesthesia induced in the skin surface by injection of 5 per cent saline solution into the interspinous ligaments[27] is another method of dermatomal mapping. Finally, mapping zones of hypesthesia produced by pressure on posterior roots has yielded results at variance with those obtained by the classic procedure.[23, 24]

According to Sherrington,[59] dermatomes are the distorted remnants of what was originally an orderly metameric arrangement that has survived with clarity only in the trunk. There, the dermatomes consist of a series of 12 narrow (overlapping) bands running from the vertebral column to the midventral line. The bands slope downward as they pass around the body to the ventral surface, because, as a result of his upright posture, man's front has blossomed while his back has regressed. In the limbs, the segmental organization is less clear because a number of metameres have been combined to form the limb. The apparent complexity of the dermatomes is clarified if man is placed in the

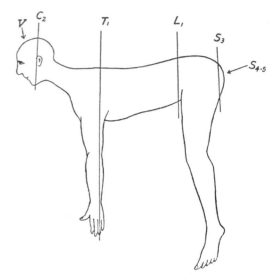

Fig. 2. Key dermatomal boundaries in man in quadruped position. First spinal dermatome is shown as C_2 because first cervical segment lacks posterior root. (After Monrad-Krohn, *The clinical examination of the nervous system*, 3rd ed., London, H. K. Lewis, 1926.)

posture of his forebears as in Figure 2, which brings out the neurologically important fact that the perianal region—once ornamented by a tail—and not the foot is the most caudal part of the body and hence is innervated by the lowermost posterior roots.

According to Sherrington's observation, the dermatomes of the arms, when viewed from the side, are "rays" which originate at a mid-dorsal line, as brought out in Figure 3, and terminate in the midventral line. Thus, the dermatomes, as the name suggests, are not bands but cuts or slices. In the arm, a dermatome consists of the surface of a wedge which passes through the arm in the same plane as, but diverging from, the plane established by the mid-dorsal and midventral line of the limb from which the dermatome takes origin. For example, the same dermatome includes the back and front of the middle finger. Dermatomes anterior to the mid-dorsal and the midventral plane are *preaxial;* those posterior are *postaxial.*

Keegan and Garnett[24] present a different kind of dermatomal map based upon the distribution of dermal hypesthesia caused by nucleus pulposus material extruding from a ruptured intervertebral disc and pressing on individual posterior roots. In this map (Fig. 3), the dermatome extends as a band from the backbone down the arm or leg to its tip, and this pattern is repeated serially much as on the trunk. It is surprising that a difference of opinion exists on such a fundamental matter as the shape of the dermatomes.

The dermatomal pattern is significant in several ways to both clinical medicine and physiology: (i) in distinguishing peripheral nerve injury from root in-

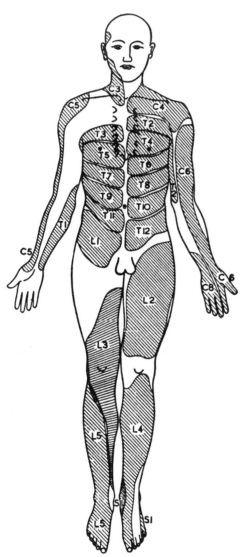

Fig. 1. Dermatomes of man determined by method of "remaining sensibility." Half the dermatomes are shown on left and remainder on right in order to display the overlap. (Data of Foerster, *Brain,* 1933, *56:*1–39, redrawn by Lewis, *Pain,* New York, Macmillan, 1942.)

jury; (ii) in localizing the level of spinal cord injury; (iii) in determining the levels for root sections or cordotomy for relief of pain; (iv) in treating herpes zoster, which is often distributed on the skin according to dermatomes; (v) in recognizing the origin of visceral pain, which is often referred to a dermatome; and (vi) in studying the lamination of spinal tracts and the projection of the body surface upon the cerebral cortex (see below).

Conduction of Sensory Nerve Impulses. With the discovery that afferent nerve axons fall into several groups of different fiber size and conduction rates, attempts were made to associate modality of sensation with fiber groups. The order of failure of different sensory modalities during cocaine and ischemic nerve block was studied. These attempts, with one exception, have been in a sense unsuccessful because of the high degree of overlap. However, the early observations in which pain was associated with small myelinated delta fibers and the even smaller unmyelinated C fibers have been of considerable importance in understanding clinical pain phenomena.

Double Pain Response.[27, 47, 51] Evidence for the existence of a fast and a slow system of pain fibers comes from several sources: (i) *Psy-chologic studies*. Several investigators have described under the names *double pain, delayed pain, echo pain* or *first* and *second pain* the fact that the pain sensation from a brief stimulus is often experienced as two pulses or peaks of pain. You can demonstrate this for yourself by flicking the dorsum of a finger against a light bulb. (ii) *Latency studies*. If the two pain pulses are due to rapidly and slowly conducting fibers, the interval between pulses should be greater when stimuli are applied to the distal end of an extremity than when they are applied to the proximal end. They are,[27] and the delays are compatible with the difference between C and delta rates of conduction. During asphyxial block, the reaction time to second pain remains unchanged for 36 minutes while first pain fails or appears after a prolonged latency after 18 to 24 minutes.[59a]

CLINICAL CORRELATIONS. *Tabes dorsalis and peripheral neuropathy.*[62] Neurosyphilitic damage to the posterior roots may result in loss of touch, proprioception, etc., without destroying pain. However, such pain is often felt after a delay of 1 or 2 seconds and may well be especially disagreeable—hyperpathic. This was not understood until the existence of the "slow" pain fibers was discovered. The latencies of the pain re-

Fig. 3. Diagrams of monkey and man contrasting two concepts of the cervical dermatomes. According to Sherrington, the dermatomes converge on a mid-ventral and mid-dorsal line (not shown). Note also the overlap. Human dermatomes as determined by hypesthesia resulting from a ruptured intervertebral disc begin at midline of chest and back (not shown). This is not a species difference since Foerster's diagram of man resembles that of the monkey; both were obtained by the same method. (After Sherrington, *Phil. Trans.*, 1898, *B190*:45–186; and Keegan and Garnett, *Anat. Rec.*, 1948, *102*:409–437.)

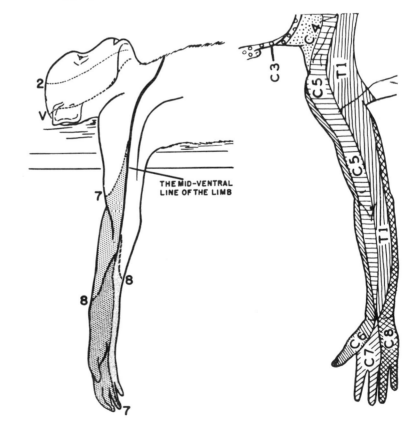

THE MID-VENTRAL LINE OF THE LIMB

sponse in most tabetic patients and of *second* pain in normal persons are approximately the same.[47] Further, the delay in the pain response in the tabetic patient is about 1 second after stimulation of the knee, but nearly 2 seconds after stimulation of the toes. That light touch, position sense and vibratory sensibility are affected early in both tabes dorsalis and nutritional neuropathy is explicable on the grounds that the impulses mediating these sensory functions travel in fast-conducting fibers of the A group while pain impulses are conducted in fibers of small diameter. Pain fibers in tabes also seem to fire spontaneously, causing tabetic crises, as though the pathologic factor which is progressively killing fibers causes bursts of impulses to be generated in the ones remaining viable.

Hyperpathia.[62, 63]   Dissociations of pain from other modalities are often associated with a qualitative change in pain, its disagreeableness (affect) being heightened—the phenomenon of *hyperpathia* or *dysesthesia.* From time to time it is suggested that the unmyelinated fibers serve a kind of pain different from the more rapid one. One can easily verify for himself that the qualities of the two flashes of pain elicited from normally innervated skin are similar if not identical, although the second tends to be more prolonged. Hyperpathia tends to occur when pain sensibility persists after the other modalities of sensation are blocked (nerve ischemia, tabes,[62] neuropathy,[63] nerve degeneration). Head, as noted earlier, postulated a central inhibitory interaction between pain and other modalities of sensation. However, Landau and Bishop[25] believe, from experiments involving asphyxial nerve block, that the slow pain impulses (C fibers) give rise to dull, burning, disagreeable pain when not preceded by the delta pain impulses.

SENSORY PATHWAYS OF THE SPINAL CORD

The axons of afferent neurons, on entering the spinal cord, may (i) connect with spinocerebellar neurons; (ii) without synaptic interruption or crossing, ascend in the ipsilateral posterior column to the medulla; or (iii) synapse with a neuron which sends an axon across the spinal cord to ascend in the contralateral anterolateral region of the cord. Of the various somatic and visceral modalities of sensation, some are conveyed exclusively in the posterior columns, others in the anterolateral columns, and still others in both pathways. The possibil-

ity of a third pathway is discussed later in the chapter.

Anterolateral Tracts.[*18, 22, 65, 69, 72]   Impulses conducted in the anterolateral tracts subserve the following kinds of sensation and perception:

Partially anterolateral:
1. Pressure and touch

Exclusively anterolateral:
1. Pain from skin, muscles, tendons, joints and viscera
2. Warmth
3. Cold
4. Sexual sensations
5. Tickle, itch and feelings of muscular fatigue

Upon entering the spinal cord, sensory fibers are regrouped so that (i) the fibers for cutaneous and deep sensibility are no longer separate and (ii) the fibers serving the same quality of sensation are sorted out and grouped together. Thus, pain fibers from cutaneous, muscular and visceral nerves are collected together in the anterolateral tract, and the muscle sense impulses from the deep branches pass into the posterior columns. Both temperature senses go together.

Several of these modalities of sensation inform us of the body's condition; this is in part true even of thermal sensation. Phylogenetically, the anterolateral tracts represent an ancient system of fibers concerned with "self-reception" and little with the external world. However, this aspect should not be overemphasized since some of the ascending fibers are not only truly spinothalamic but also are connected with the cerebral cortex and do convey information about the external world (see below).

Functional anatomic details—origin and decussation. Each posterior root branches into a fan of rootlets which enter the spinal cord. At the point of entry, the fibers of each filament sort out according to size. The *medial division* contains the large myelinated fibers which, instead of entering the posterior horn, swing across its tip to enter the posterior columns (Fig. 4). The unmyelinated and small myelinated fibers are grouped into a *lateral division* which swings laterally and, bifurcating, forms the tract of Lissauer (*dorsolateral fasciculus*) at the tip of the posterior horn. This is not really a tract since the fibers ascend only one to three segments before terminating in the substantia gelatinosa Rolandi, a cell column capping the poste-

* This term is preferable to "spinothalamic tract" since our knowledge is based on cord sectioning which also severs the many other tracts in the area.

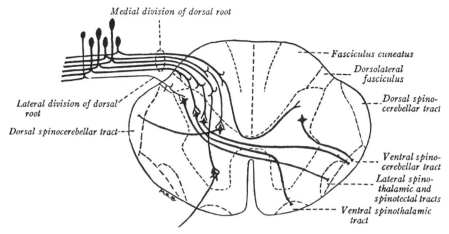

Medial division of dorsal root

Fasciculus cuneatus

Dorsolateral fasciculus

Dorsal spino-cerebellar tract

Lateral division of dorsal root

Dorsal spinocerebellar tract

Ventral spino-cerebellar tract

Lateral spino-thalamic and spinotectal tracts

Ventral spinothalamic tract

Fig. 4. Schematic cross section of spinal cord showing destination of fibers of medial and lateral divisions of dorsal root and position of ascending tracts. (From Ranson and Clark, *Anatomy of the nervous system*, Philadelphia, W. B. Saunders Co., 1959.)

rior horn. This column is named for its discoverer and for its seemingly uniform texture (due to the smallness of the cell bodies and the absence of large myelinated fibers traversing it) (see Fig. 5). The axons of its fine cells cross the cord and ascend in the lateral spinothalamic tract or other tracts in this region.

Some fibers of the medial division terminate, either immediately or after ascending several segments, upon large pericornual cells in the posterior horn. The axons of these cells decussate in the ventral gray commissure to ascend in the ventral portion of the anterolateral column (ventral spinothalamic tract). This scheme may be too rigid; both divisions of the posterior root probably contribute to both the lateral and the ventral spinothalamic tract.

Clinical correlations: Syringomyelia. The proximity of the anterior gray commissure to the central canal makes the decussating fibers liable to interruption by a widening of the central canal (syringomyelia). This produces a clinical syndrome consisting of loss of pain and of warmth and cold sensations on *both sides* of the body at the level of the segments affected. Touch, pressure and deep sensibility are not affected. Syringomyelia is, therefore, a good example of modality dissociation.

LAMINATION. The ascending tracts of the anterolateral region (spinobulbar, spinotectal and spinothalamic) are laminated. This means that the contributions of successive dermatomes form more or less distinct layers or laminae of fibers. A tract so arranged is said to be "topographically organized." The lamination is in

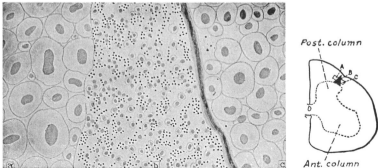

Post. column

Ant. column

Fig. 5. Silver stained cross-section through white matter at tip of dorsal horn of spinal cord as shown in insert at the right. *a,* In the slide are the large fibers of the medial division of dorsal root after entering fasciculus cuneatus. *b,* Unmyelinated fibers appearing as fine dots and fine myelinated fibers of lateral division after entering fasciculus dorsolateralis (Lissauer). *c,* Second order fibers of dorsospinocerebellar tract. (From Ranson and Clark, *Anatomy of the nervous system*, Philadelphia, W. B. Saunders Co., 1959.)

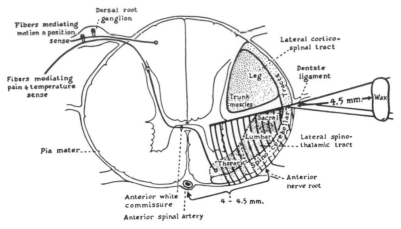

Thoracic II.

Fig. 6. Diagram illustrating cordotomy. Cross section of spinal cord shows lamination of spinothalamic tract, position of pyramidal tract in relation to it, and presence of other tracts in lower quadrant. A piece of bone wax is mounted 4.5 mm. from tip of knife as a depth gauge. Heavy curved lines in ventral quadrant indicate sweep of knife. Note that a desire to spare lateral corticospinal tract would result in sparing of sacral dermatomes. (From Kahn and Rand, *J. Neurosurg.*, 1952, *9*:611–619.)

the form of imperfect annular rings with the fibers from the most caudal regions lying superficially because the long fibers from sacral segments are pushed outward by the accretion of crossing fibers at each successive segment (Fig. 4). Some other influence pushes the longer sacral fibers laterally and dorsally away from the margin of the ventral horn where they originally lay. This results in the arrangement seen in Figure 6. The physiologic significance of such lamination is the preservation of the topographic organization of fibers whereby the dermatomes of the body surface may ultimately be projected onto the cortical sensory areas.

Clinical correlations: Cordotomy.[22, 65, 72] Lamination explains certain features of the symptoms produced by spinal cord tumors. Extramedullary tumors, those originating outside the spinal cord, tend to cause hypalgesia in the caudal dermatomes first, because the pressure from the outside blocks first the peripherally lying fibers from the sacral segments. As the cord is pressed further, the sensory border creeps up. Intramedullary tumors, on the other hand, may leave a characteristic region of intact sensibility in the anogenital region because they spare the peripherally lying fibers derived from the lowest sacral roots.

The separation of sensory impulses to travel in the anterolateral and posterior columns of the spinal cord allows surgical interruption of the pain pathway without production of a disabling anesthesia and ataxia. As shown in Figure 6, a small knife is inserted into the spinal cord just below the dentate ligament and pyramidal tract and is drawn downward through the

anterolateral columns. Such anterolateral cordotomies are performed to relieve unbearable pain not tractable to medical control. The operation is effective for superficial, deep and visceral pain, although, for the last, bilateral operations are required. Despite the fact that the ventral spinocerebellar and various descending motor tracts—vestibulospinal, tectospinal, ventral corticospinal tracts, etc.—are partially sectioned, little motor disturbance is apparent. Bilateral cordotomy rarely interferes permanently with bladder function or with sensations of bladder fullness. However, sensations of the sexual orgasm are usually lost.

Posterior White Columns.[18, 60] These columns (more correctly funiculi), lying between the posterior horns, are formed by the ascending and descending branches of the fibers making up the medial division of the posterior horns. Some of the ascending fibers reach the medulla before synaptic interruption; others transmit impulses to the second order neurons which form well defined ascending tracts passing to the cerebellum. By collaterals, impulses also reach the motoneurons and possibly the propriospinal system.

The sensory functions of the posterior columns are known from the study of residual sensation in patients subjected to anterolateral cordotomy for relief of pain. In some of these operations, the ventral region of the spinal cord near the midline has been intentionally included; the most posterior segment of the funiculus is spared because it contains the pyramidal tract.

The sensory impulses conducted in the posterior columns serve the functions listed below. Note that the list includes processes of a perceptual nature, some of which involve more than one modality of posterior column sensibility. A clinical or laboratory test of each sensory or perceptual function, described in Chapter 14, is also mentioned.

A. Muscle, tendon and and joint sensibility (proprioception, kinesthesia)
　　1. Passive movement—threshold angular movement for appreciation that movement has occurred
　　2. Threshold of tension—discrimination of lifted weights
　　3. Position of limb in space—finger-to-finger test
B. Touch and pressure
　　1. Light touch—absorbent cotton
　　2. Light pressure—von Frey hairs
　　3. Massive pressure—weight discrimination with supported hand
C. Perceptual functions
　　1. Topognosis or localization—spot finding test
　　2. Two-point discrimination—compass test
　　3. Spatial functions—figure writing
　　4. Appreciation of vibration—tuning fork test or pallesthesiometer
　　5. Stereognosis—recognition of common objects by palpation

The sensations served by the posterior columns are gnostic,* discriminative, "epicritic" and spatial. They give knowledge of the position of the limbs in space and knowledge of objects making up the external world. For this knowledge, fine discrimination of the weight, size and texture of objects handled is required. However, intensity, spatial and temporal discriminations are not exclusively the attributes of posterior column sensibility; nor are there some fibers serving localization and others serving intensity discrimination. These are functions common to all forms of sensation. But the sensory axons of the posterior column have modality-specific receptors and small receptive fields, and are topographically organized so they perform such functions as localization, resolution of two stimuli or discrimination of intensity very accurately.†

*From "gnosis" meaning "knowledge."

†Note that one should not speak of a "sensation," much less a "two-point threshold," ascending the posterior columns.

About touch, two views are held: (i) The anterolateral pathway is functionally equivalent to the posterior column pathway, or (ii) the posterior column system, phylogenetically newer, is capable of a higher degree of perceptual function. After anterolateral cordotomy, including all of the ventral region, the disturbance of perceptual proprioceptive and tactual function (localization, two-point discrimination and figure writing) is minimal,[18] but the threshold for light pressure is markedly elevated.[73] The posterior columns are rarely sectioned surgically, but experiments on animals suggest that the spinothalamic tract may serve more perceptual function than previously suspected. On the other hand, current electrophysiologic and anatomic studies are revealing many details consistent with the characterization of the posterior column system as providing the brain with knowledge of the external world and the anterolateral system as providing information about the state of the organism itself.

SENSORY SYSTEMS OF THE BRAINSTEM

At the upper border of the medulla oblongata, impulses derived from the fifth and other mixed cranial nerves are added to the ascending sensory systems. Here, the ascending systems undergo some rearrangement.

Trigeminal Nerve. Pain, temperature and touch-pressure sensibility of the face and buccal cavity are served by trigeminal neurons. Their cell bodies are located in the semilunar (gasserian) ganglion and their central processes enter the pons. Approximately half of the fibers of large diameter bifurcate, giving one branch to the main sensory nucleus located in the pons and one branch to the elongated spinal nucleus which extends through the medulla to meet the substantia gelatinosa Rolandi. The other half of the large fibers connect only with the main nucleus. All but a few of the fine fibers connect only with the spinal nucleus. Pain and temperature impulses pass exclusively by way of the spinal nucleus. Harrison and Corbin[19] recorded tactual impulses from the spinal tract of the trigeminal nerve. As in the spinal cord, a small and functionally unimportant component of the touch-pressure system pursues the same course as the impulses for pain and temperature.

TABLE 1. *Sensory Connections of Spinal and Cranial Nerves*

SPINAL NERVE	TRIGEMINAL NERVE	FACIAL, GLOSSOPHARYNGEAL AND VAGUS NERVES
Lateral division		
Tract of Lissauer	Descending fibers	Tractus solitarius
Substantia gelatinosa Rolandi	Spinal nucleus	Nucleus of tractus solitarius
Spinothalamic tract	Ventral secondary tract	Unknown
Medial division		
Posterior columns	Ascending fibers	
Nn. gracilis and cuneatus	Main sensory nucleus	
Medial lemniscus	Dorsal secondary tract	

The proprioceptive innervation of the striate muscles of the face and the orbit has long been a neurologic puzzle. Recent studies suggest that the mesencephalic extension of the trigeminal nucleus contains the cells of origin for afferent fibers coming from the muscles of mastication (which also receive motor fibers from the trigeminal nerve). If so, this is the one known instance in which cell bodies of afferent neurons are found *within* the substance of the central nervous system. Although proprioceptive end-organs have been demonstrated in eye muscles,

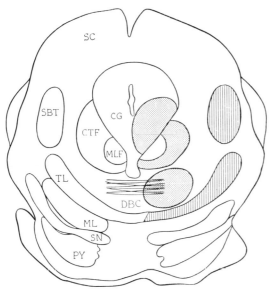

Fig. 7. Brainstem areas conducting impulses from tooth pulp. Vertically lined areas are the classic pain pathways, the spinobulbothalamic tract (*SBT*) and the trigeminal lemniscus (*TL*) adjacent to the medial lemniscus (*ML*). Dotted areas are three additional regions from which tooth pulp impulses were recorded: one in the central gray (*CG*), one in the central tegmental fasciculus (*CTF*), and one in the reticular substance lateral to decussation of the brachium conjunctivum. Section is at the level of the superior colliculi (*SC*). (After Melzack, Stotler and Livingston, *J. Neurophysiol.*, 1958, *21*:353–367.)

the location of cells or origin of the fibers supplying them is unknown.

SECOND ORDER NEURONS.[28, 33, 69] As shown in Table 1, the second order neurons carrying somatosensory impulses ascend by way of the medial lemniscus and the dorsal secondary trigeminal tract, and the spinothalamic and ventral secondary trigeminal tract. These are joined by other, less well worked out systems of secondary neurons from the vagus, etc., and all terminate in the thalamus. In addition to these well organized tracts, there are others which are less well organized. When impulses from the teeth were traced through the brain stem, electrical activity was recorded from no less than five areas (Fig. 7).[33] Three of these lie within the reticular area.

Clinical correlations: Trigeminal neuralgia. This consists of paroxysmal attacks of excruciating pain projected to an area innervated by one or more divisions of the trigeminal nerve. Vasomotor and secretory disturbances may accompany the pain; the facial musculature undergoes clonic contractions—hence the common name *tic douloureux.* The area of skin affected is often apparently hyperesthetic and hyperalgesic, but measurements of threshold indicate a *decreased sensitivity,* suggesting a central overresponse rather than true hyperesthesia. In cases of severe trigeminal neuralgia, the trigeminal neurons are severed central to the ganglion (retrogasserian neurectomy) to avoid regeneration. Although effective, this operation sacrifices touch sensitivity, which results in an unpleasant feeling of numbness over the face, and keratitic changes in the cornea due to loss of protective pain reflexes may ensue.

THALAMOCORTICAL SYSTEMS

All sensory tracts except the olfactory are interrupted by a synapse in the thalamus of the diencephalon before proceeding to the cerebral cortex. The thalamus is therefore the gateway to the cerebral cortex through which passes most information gained from the external world and from our bodies.

From anatomic, electrophysiologic and behavioral techniques combined with surgery, three kinds of pathways to the cerebral cortex have been demarcated. These are potentially but not necessarily sensory pathways. They are as follows: (i) the classic somatosensory pathways—the posterior column and *true* spinothalamic systems—which traverse relay nuclei and end in the primary areas of the cerebral cortex, (ii) "by-passing" tracts sometimes derived from relay nuclei but often traversing other thalamic nuclei and ending adjacent to classic cortical sensory areas, and (iii) multineuron pathways (or collaterals from the above) which synapse before reaching the thalamus, sometimes more than once, and employ different thalamic nuclei than (i) and (ii) above; they may or may not reach the cerebral cortex. These latter pathways are often revealed only by silver stains for degenerating axons.

Classic Somatic Sensory Pathways via Relay Nuclei.[13, 53, 68]   These fall into three groups: (i) axons passing up the posterior columns to synapse in the nuclei of gracilis and cuneatus with second order fibers that enter the medial lemniscus, (ii) axons originating at the spinal level and passing uninterrupted to the thalamus—the "true spinothalamic tract," and (iii) the homologous elements added to this system from the trigeminal nerve (see Table 1). The course of these pathways, which consist primarily of myelinated fibers, has been determined by placing lesions in the spinal cord or in the gracile or cuneate nuclei and tracing, with the Marchi method, the resulting degeneration of myelin.

All of these fibers end in the posterior ventral portion of the nuclear masses lateral to the internal medullary lamina. Those areas receiving impulses from the face end medially in a nucleus appropriately called n. ventralis posteromedialis (or for its shape, the "arcuate" nucleus [see Fig. 8]). The second order fibers receiving impulses from the body end more laterally in the n. ventralis posterolateralis. A tendency for the spinothalamic fibers to end slightly more posteriorly has been described, but there is virtual fusion of the two systems (and hence, of modalities). By contrast, the contributions from various parts of the body tend to remain distinct, i.e., the posteroventral nuclei have a topographic organization. This is

shown by cutting the spinal cord at various levels and identifying the distribution of Marchi degeneration in the thalamus. In a spider monkey (Fig. 8), which has a prehensile tail (a fifth hand), successive groups of dermatomes between the caudal segments and the cervical ones are represented in a lateral-to-medial sequence in n. ventralis posterolateralis; the sequence is completed by the face representation still more medially. An even finer topographic organization was proved by Mountcastle and Henneman,[38, 39] who searched the thalamus in half-millimeter steps for electrical activity during stimulation of points on the body surface. They obtained a finely detailed map of the thalamus with the head posteromedial, the tail anterolateral, the back superior and the feet inferior. In short, the body surface is *projected* onto the thalamus, specifically onto the posteroventral nucleus.

Projection in the nervous system is roughly analogous to the projection of a lantern slide, nerve fibers taking the place of light "rays." There is considerable distortion. Certain parts of the body are "blown up"

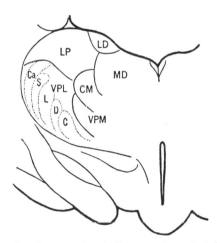

Fig. 8.   Cross-sectional diagram through left half of thalamus, showing areas of nucleus ventralis posterolateralis (*VPL*) in which spinothalamic tract fibers from different levels of spinal cord terminate. From Marchi degeneration studies on monkey with prehensile tail. Comma-shaped areas enclosed in fine dots show termination of spinothalamic tract fibers. Order of termination from lateral to medial is: *Ca,* caudal; *S,* sacral; *L,* lumbar; *D,* thoracic; *C,* cervical. For abbreviation of thalamic nuclei see legend of Fig. 10. Note that degeneration was not found in nucleus ventralis posteromedialis (*VPM*), "face" and "taste" nucleus. (After Chang and Ruch, *J. Anat. (Lond.),* 1947, *81:* 140–149.)

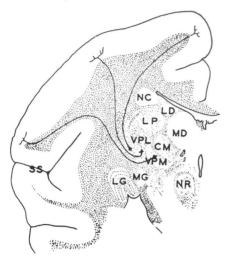

Fig. 9. Schematic frontal section through thalamus and postcentral gyrus of cerebral cortex to show topographic arrangement of projection fibers from posteroventral nuclei. Nucleus ventralis posteromedialis (*VPM*) projects to inferior end of postcentral gyrus near sylvian fissure (*SS*), whereas nucleus ventralis posterolateralis (*VPL*) projects to middle and superior thirds of postcentral gyrus. (From Walker, *The primate thalamus,* Chicago, University of Chicago Press, 1938.)

or enlarged, an arrangement which is functionally significant (see below). The essential feature of a topographically organized system is that the spatial relations existing peripherally are preserved. A detailed organization is often described as a "point-to-point" projection, i.e., a point on the body surface is projected to a point on the thalamus or cortex. A point in this case should be considered a point of maximal electrical response.

The topographic organization manifested in the thalamic terminations of sensory systems is preserved in the thalamocortical projections but is inverted from side to side (Fig. 9). The medially situated arcuate nucleus (VPM), receiving impulses from the face, projects laterally near the sylvian fissure. The lateral part of the posterolateral nucleus (VPL), receiving impulses from the leg, projects near the midline. The projection of impulses from the arm is intermediate in both thalamus and cortex. Thus, the body surface is projected upon the postcentral gyrus with its spatial relations preserved; the lateromedial relationship is opposite in the thalamus and cortex. This information was gained by truncating the axons of thalamocortical projection fibers by a restricted lesion of the cortex and observing the "retrograde degeneration reaction"—chromatolysis, eccentric placement of the nucleus and blurring of the

cell outline. In most thalamocortical neurons this goes on to complete degeneration, disappearance and gliosis. Thalamic nuclei receiving input *directly* from the great ascending system and sending output to the cerebral cortex are termed *relay nuclei*.[59] For other thalamic nuclei and their connections refer to Figure 10.

Ipsilateral nature of projections. All of the cortical projection from one half of the thalamus passes to the cerebral cortex on the same side; none crosses in the corpus callosum to the opposite cortex. Thus, any representation of one lateral half of the body surface in the ipsilateral cortex must come about because some fibers either do not cross at levels below the thalamus or cross twice, once at a spinal level and once at a brain stem level. A slight ipsilateral projection to the relay nuclei has been demonstrated electrically.[39] Other systems discussed below have a large ipsilateral component.

EVOKED POTENTIAL MAPPING OF SENSORY CORTEX.[53, 77] Recording action currents evoked in the postcentral gyrus of the cerebral cortex by cutaneous stimulation reveals a detailed *dermatomal* projection.[77] Tactual stimulations were applied to the skin, and a recording electrode connected to an oscilloscope was moved systematically over the cortex in millimeter steps. Maximal *evoked* potentials* in response to stimulation occurred in the areas receiving projection fibers from the posteroventral nucleus, cytoarchitectural areas 3, 1 and 2. Short latency potentials with clear topographic localization were recorded from areas 4 and 6. Electrical responses were confined to the contralateral cortex, except that stimulation of the face gave rise to ipsilateral cortical responses as well.

The main conclusion reached from these experiments was that "the parts of contralateral body surface are represented in an orderly sequence. In the case of the lower extremity this sequence clearly reflects the metameric origin of the dermatomes; the arrangement is in the order of spinal innervation, not in the order—hip, thigh, knee, leg, ankle, foot, toes." Thus, the order may be termed "dermatomal" or "metameric," as opposed to "regional," the

*Cortical potentials induced by stimulation of endorgans or afferent pathways are, by convention, termed *evoked potentials.* The earliest response is surface-positive and brief in latency and duration. Later waves will be discussed in a subsequent chapter. *Evoked potentials* are sometimes called *slow potentials* to distinguish them from spike-like potentials from single cortical units (*fast potentials*).

term "segmental" being ambiguous. The dermatomal law is borne out by the fact that a fast fiber component of the splanchnic nerve reaches the trunk area of the cortex, the region which had been predicted on the basis of the segments at which the splanchnic nerve impulses enter the spinal cord. The observation also suggests that one should speak of the "somatovisceral" area rather than of simply the "somatosensory" area.[1, 2, 3]

Another result has been to demonstrate that the extent of cortical area devoted to a given region parallels the tactual acuity and innervation density of the region. Thus, a wider strip is devoted to the distal than to the proximal portions of the limbs or to the trunk dermatomes. Representation of T_{1-12}, dermatomes for the chest and abdomen, is compressed into a cortical strip only 2.5 mm. wide. In contrast, the cortical area for the thumb and forefinger dermatome (C_8) is several times larger.

The large numbers of sense organs and cortical neurons devoted to the relatively small skin areas of thumb and fingers underlie the low two-point threshold and small error of localization of stimuli in those regions, and topographic organization of thalamocortical projections explains why a cortical lesion may, for example, affect the arm but spare the leg. However, although such organization is clinically important, is there sufficient point-to-point representation of the body surface on the cortex *physiologically* to contribute the neural substrate for topognosis and two-point discrimination?

Somatic area II.[76] The sensory representation of the body in the postcentral gyrus is duplicated in reverse order, i.e., face, arm, leg, in passing from the foot of the postcentral gyrus to the bottom of the sylvian fissure. This so-called "somatic area II" is less well organized topographically and the evoked potentials are of longer latency and more susceptible to anes-

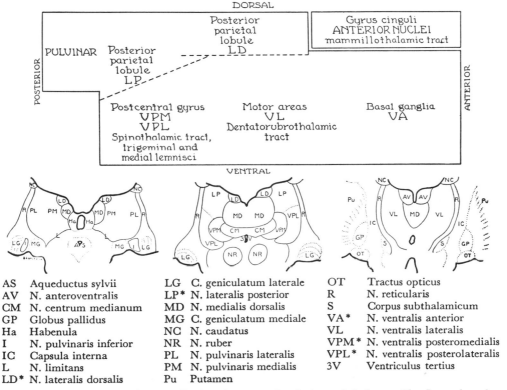

AS	Aqueductus sylvii	LG	C. geniculatum laterale	OT	Tractus opticus
AV	N. anteroventralis	LP*	N. lateralis posterior	R	N. reticularis
CM	N. centrum medianum	MD	N. medialis dorsalis	S	Corpus subthalamicum
GP	Globus pallidus	MG	C. geniculatum mediale	VA*	N. ventralis anterior
Ha	Habenula	NC	N. caudatus	VL	N. ventralis lateralis
I	N. pulvinaris inferior	NR	N. ruber	VPM*	N. ventralis posteromedialis
IC	Capsula interna	PL	N. pulvinaris lateralis	VPL*	N. ventralis posterolateralis
L	N. limitans	PM	N. pulvinaris medialis	3V	Ventriculus tertius
LD*	N. lateralis dorsalis	Pu	Putamen		

Fig. 10. Correlation of longitudinal and cross-sectional views of thalamus. *Top:* Lateral nuclear mass of macaque thalamus in schematic parasagittal section. Cortical projection is given above abbreviation; afferent connection, below it. (Data from Walker, *The primate thalamus*, Chicago, University of Chicago Press, 1938, and after Ranson, *Anatomy of the nervous system*, 1943.) *Bottom:* Cross sections of chimpanzee thalamus at three levels—*left*, posterior; *middle*, midthalamus; *right*, anterior. (From Fulton, *Physiology of the nervous system*, 3d ed., New York, Oxford University Press, 1949.)

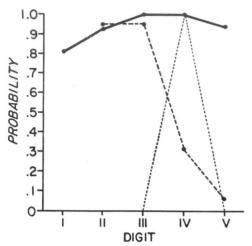

Fig. 11. Size of the field from which three different cortical units could be fired. *Solid line,* unit with a large receptive field; *dotted line,* unit with receptive field confined to one finger; *dashed line,* unit with large field, showing rapid decline of discharge probability near edge of field. (From Towe and Amassian, *J. Neurophysiol.,* 1958, *21:*292–311.)

thesia than those in the postcentral gyrus. Here, ipsilateral as well as contralateral cutaneous stimulation evokes potentials, and the second area may be more important in lower animals than in primates. Ablation experiments leave the function of somatic II in doubt.[43] With the discovery of an additional sensory area, the classic primary area is now often termed somatic area I or simply somatic I.

RECEPTIVE ZONE OF THALAMIC AND CORTICAL NEURONS.[36, 53] There is considerable divergence within the sensory pathway so that the receptors at a single spot on the skin will excite many cells in the postcentral gyrus, especially in the unanesthetized animal. This divergence is orderly, however, and a single postcentral neuron has a homogeneous receptive field rather than a mosaic of skin patches from which it can be excited. The fields tend to be round on the hand or foot and elliptical on the arm or leg with the long axis of the field running parallel to the extremity.[51] They are quite large, even on the hand, where they average about 3 sq. cm. in area; on the shoulder (monkey), they average about 25 sq. cm. and are still larger on the back. These figures are calculated to be 15 to 100 times the area of the receptive field for a second order neuron.[36] As in the periphery, the neuron is maximally excited when the stimulus falls in the center of the receptive field and the number of discharges decreases as the stimulus

is moved toward the edges of the field; the firing probability decreases and the latency becomes longer.[36, 66] Thus, we see that progressively in the central pathway, as in the periphery, canalization has been eschewed in favor of divergence.

This brings out another property of synapses in the sensory system—a tendency to fire in trains of impulses in response to a single volley input. This tendency was shown by Amassian and DeVito[6] to be established at the first synapse, i.e., in the cuneate nucleus, but it is characteristic of the thalamus and the cerebral cortex as well. Characteristic, also, is lability of latency as a function of stimulus intensity applied to the input.

Towe and Amassian[66] have found in somatic area I a few cortical units with large receptive fields, e.g., a cortical neuron almost equally responsive to stimulation of all the five digits (Fig. 11). Such large receptive fields may belong to the spinothalamic system and smaller ones to the posterior column–medial lemniscal system.

By-pass Systems.   Ablation of the cerebral cortex immediately in front of and behind the postcentral gyrus produces retrograde degeneration in nuclei other than the classic relay nuclei (VPM and VPL).[13, 59] The nucleus projecting to motor areas of the procentral gyrus (strongly to area 4 and weakly to area 6, as seen in Figures 10 and 12) is the n. ventralis lateralis,* which lies just anterior to the relay nuclei. The spinal input to this nucleus is relayed through the cerebellum via the dentatorubrothalamic tract. It would be easy to dismiss a system ending in a motor area as being concerned not with conscious sensation, but with the control of movement; however, evidence for a discriminative sensory function of this area will be presented below.

Evoked surface-positive responses to peripheral stimulation, recorded from the precentral gyrus of monkeys, were found to have about the same latency as postcentral responses.[57] Malis et al.[29] proved that this activity is not "relayed" from the postcentral gyrus since it persisted after gyrectomy. The electrophysiologic evidence proving whether this system is sensory or simply afferent is incomplete. Does the rapid con-

*This nucleus is a relay nucleus in Walker's classification but is considered a part of a by-pass system because of the afferent input and cortical projection.

duction in the spinocerebellar fibers make up for a delay in cerebellar detour? Are there other pathways to the motor area (see below)? Does the rapidity of Betz cell discharge after a stimulus to the projections of the lateroventral input mean that this system controls Betz discharge and is unrelated to sensation? Other evidence is necessary to answer these questions.

A second subset of somatosensory projections to the cerebral cortex apart from the projection of the relay nuclei to the primary sensory area has been disclosed from lesions placed *behind* the precentral gyrus in the posterior parietal lobe (areas 5 and 7). In this case, retrograde degeneration was found in the n. lateralis dorsalis and n. lateralis posterior and in the pulvinar, all of which are lateral to the internal medullary lamina and posterior to the n. ventralis lateralis. The nn. lateralis posterior (Fig. 12) and dorsalis project to areas 5 and 7. The pulvinar projects more posteriorly. Comparison of Figures 10 and 12 shows that the anterior-posterior relation of these projections is the same in the thalamus and cortex. Walker's[68] interpretation was that these nuclei receive afferent input from the relay nuclei. It is now known that some posterior thalamic nuclei receive input *directly* from both the anterolateral and the posterior column spinal pathways (see below). It will be seen that these posterior parietal areas are concerned with discriminative function, just as is the postcentral gyrus.

NONLEMNISCAL, NONSPINOTHALAMIC RELAY PATHWAYS.[11, 31, 32] In the last century, Sherrington and others observed that the pathways of the anterolateral column, while ascending the spinal cord and brainstem, not only acquire fibers but also lose them. In the cat, this loss of fibers is so great that few anterolateral fibers ever reach the thalamus directly. In monkeys and man, however, there is a substantial classic spinothalamic tract, i.e., fibers coursing without interruption to relay nuclei and eventually to somatic area I. Until recently, "spinothalamic" and "anterolateral columns" were often equated and other ascending systems in these columns were ignored. The extent and termination of anterolateral pathways is now more fully appreciated because of the development of the Nauta stain for degenerating axons.

Many anterolateral fibers terminate in the brainstem, raising the question of whether they serve brainstem control of reflexes or continue on to the thalamus and cortex; if they continue on, do they perform any sensory function and, if so, what kind? Because these fibers are in a sense a new territory of neurophysiology, they will be described without regard to sensory function. Quite possibly, within this system lies the answer to the question of the affective aspect of sensation as exemplified by pain. Unthinkingly, pain has been identified with the spinothalamic tract to the extent that many

Fig. 12. Diagram of connections and projections of main thalamic nuclei. Geniculate bodies and nuclei with purely subcortical connection are not shown. Details of connections indicated by dotted lines are not known. Numbers along cerebral cortex designate Brodmann areas. Recently described connections of the spinothalamic tract with the cerebral cortex by way of the posterior group of nuclei (see page 332) are not included. (Based upon Walker and LeGros Clark. From Ruch, Kasdon and Walker, unpublished.)

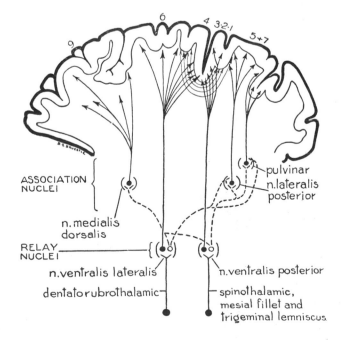

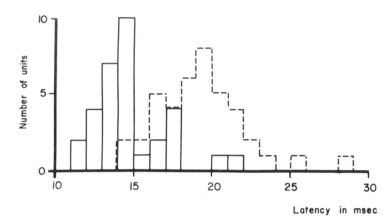

HINDFOOT

Fig. 13. Histogram of mean latencies for discharge of single units in somatosensory area II. Solid line, posterolateral tract intact; dashed lines, comparable data for dorsal column pathway. In both pathways units with small receptive fields were tested. (From Andersson, *Acta physiol. scand.*, 1962, *56*:Supplement 194.)

other components of the anterolateral column system which have different endings in the brainstem have been ignored. Mehler et al.[32] and Bowsher,[11] applying the Nauta technique to monkeys, describe the *anterolateral* (as opposed to the spinothalamic) system as follows:

Spinobulbar pathways. Many anterolateral fibers terminate in or give collaterals to the lateral reticular nucleus and to the medial reticular formation. Some of these are collaterals from spinothalamic axons ascending to the thalamus. Also, an independent spinoreticular tract terminating most strongly in the medial reticular "core" is probable.

Spinomesencephalic system. In man and monkey, axons from the anterolateral columns terminate in the mesencephalon, specifically in the deep layers of the superior colliculus (spinotectal fibers) and in the adjacent lateral aspect of the central gray substance; both pathways have been implicated in pain.

Spinoposterothalamic pathway. At the junction of the mesencephalon and the diencephalon, a group of fibers from the anterolateral columns splits off as it passes just medial to the medial geniculate body, terminating in the pars magnocellularis of that body and in the supragenic-ulate nucleus. Thus, some components relay in nuclei other than the classic ventral posterior relay nuclei. Some fibers from the medial lemniscus also end here.[11]

Spinal connections to medial nuclei. Another component splits off from the spinothalamic tract and pursues a medial course to synapse in the rather ill-defined nuclei making up the intralaminar group. According to Bowsher,[11] these fibers end in nn. parafascicularis and cen-

tralis lateralis but not in the large, easily identified center median or any other intralaminar nucleus. This pathway, preponderant in primitive mammals, has been termed the "paleospinal" pathway by Bishop[9] to distinguish it from the "true" or "classic" spinothalamic pathway that terminates more laterally in relay nuclei along with the spinothalamic tract. The later pathway he terms the "neospinal-thalamic" tract, which, by convention, is what is meant when one speaks of the spinothalamic pathway without any modifier. The systems described above as synapsing elsewhere than in nn. ventralis posteromedialis and lateralis are "spinothalamic" but are not ordinarily included when one speaks of the spinothalamic tract, and they have different functional properties. The above description is based on the degeneration seen in the medial thalamus following interruption of the anterolateral columns of the spinal cord; to these must be added systems which synapse in the brain stem and continue on to thalamic areas which may or may not transmit impulses directly or indirectly to the cerebral cortex.

The multisynaptic and direct paleospino-thalamic systems ending in the intralaminar nuclei will be discussed in Chapter 22.

Soon after introducing in this country the technique of single cortical neuron analysis of somatosensory function, Amassian discovered a somatosensory projection to an association area in the cat.[4] The same single unit was found to respond to large areas of the body surface, two legs or perhaps all four legs, and to more than one modality. This contrasts with the modality-specific cells of the postcentral gyrus.

In 1957, Whitlock and Perl[46, 74] discovered in the cat and monkey that peripheral stimuli evoke potentials in the magnocellular portion of the medial geniculate body when both posterior columns and one lateral column are sectioned. Natural stimuli such as a transient mechanical stimulus or a strong stimulus of almost any kind were also effective in evoking a response.[46] Responses also could be recorded somewhat posteriorly in adjoining tissue. Since posterior thalamic neurons have large, bilateral and often patchy receptive fields,[48] no topographic organization could be established. The same cell in this general posterior region responded to a wide variety of stimuli, including different somatic (though not joint movement) and auditory stimuli. They are neither "space-specific" nor "modality-specific." There is little reason to associate this region especially with pain, as Poggio and Mountcastle[48] have attempted. Much anatomic and physiologic evidence, of which only a part concerns us now, leads to the conclusion that the whole posterior region of the thalamus receives a wide variety of sensory inputs and projects to the "association areas" lying between the somesthetic, visual and auditory areas of the cerebral cortex.

It is concluded, therefore, that the posterior region of the thalamus contains two by-pass systems. One is indirect by way of relay nuclei to by-pass nuclei and is probably more heavily a posterior than an anterior column system. (Fig. 12). The second system involves posterior nuclei only and receives more anterolateral than posterior column impulses.

Other Ascending Systems. Recent studies indicate the existence of a third sensory system which ascends in the *lateral columns* immediately adjacent to the posterior horn. This system, unlike the nearby dorsal spinocerebellar system, is not destined for the cerebellum but reaches somatic areas I and II. It is called the postero-lateral tract or Morin's tract after its discoverer. Some axons in the region are ipsilaterally and monosynaptically excited and have restricted receptive fields. They respond specifically to light touch but not to stimulation of muscle nerves. Another group responds broadly in respect to place and modality. Both groups relay in the lateral cervical nucleus and terminate in sensory area I and sensory area II. Those with restricted fields have a latency shorter than the posterior column systems, as shown in Figure 13. Mark and Steiner[30] have identified a rapidly conducting system of fibers to the cerebral cortex which appear to run in the posterolateral position in the cord.

Kennedy and Towe[26] have recently discovered a fast pathway to the cat's motor and sensory cortex. This pathway conducts from bulb to cortex in 1.5 milliseconds (including one synapse), which is considerably more rapid

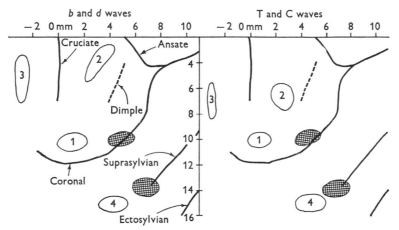

Fig. 14. Foci of maximal cortical response from the fast lemniscal system (cross hatching) demonstrated in two ways—ipsilateral ventral bulbar (left) and contralateral forepaw stimulation (right). The response in Somatic Area I is centered on the coronal sulcus and that in Somatic Area II on the suprasylvian. The numbered regions are maximal zones for slower lemniscal components. The *b* wave from ventral bulbar stimulation and the T wave potential evoked by peripheral stimuli are clearly the same and differ from the later *d* and C wave associated with slow lemniscal elements. (From Morse and Towe, *J. Physiol.*, 1964, *171*:231–246.)

than other fibers in the medial lemniscus. Morse and Towe[34a] have shown that this pathway traverses the posterior columns, the rostral part of the cuneate nucleus, probably the posteroventral nucleus of the thalamus and projects caudolaterally to somatosensory areas I and II (Fig. 14). The fast lemniscal system is believed to convey touch impulses and the slow lemniscal system impulses from hair stimulation. This type of modality separation is different from that suggested by other investigators.

The fast posterolateral and the fast lemniscal pathways do not appear to be parts of the same system.

CORTICAL FUNCTION IN SENSATION

Anatomic and electrophysiologic studies give detailed knowledge of topographic organization of sensory systems and of what kind of sensory end-organ sends impulses to what region of the cortex, and experiments depending on human or animal behavior in a sense validate deductions from electrophysiology.

Electrical Stimulation.[44]   The cortical sensory area was stimulated electrically in conscious patients by Cushing in 1909 and later by Foerster and by Penfield.[44] Stimulation of the area for the foot gives rise to sensations which seem to come from the foot; stimulation near the face area causes sensations localized to the face (see the *law of projection*). Sensations can often be elicited by stimulating the motor areas of the precentral gyrus even though the postcentral gyrus has been ablated, and these sen-

sations are similar in quality to those elicited by stimulation of the postcentral gyrus. Ease of elicitation correlates well with the density of thalamocortical projection fibers. Sensations of the spinothalamic category—pain, warmth and cold—are rarely reported, the usual responses being a sense of numbness, tingling and, especially, a sensation of movement unaccompanied by actual movement. The sensations are not clearly formed, but the same is true of those aroused by stimulation of a sensory nerve. No evidence of zonal localization of modalities has been obtained.

Ablation Experiments.   Through special techniques developed by psychologists, an animal's sensory status after a cortical ablation can be inferred from his overt behavior (see Chap. 24). The ability to discriminate weight, roughness and geometric forms after the formation of various cortical lesions has been studied[56] objectively and quantitatively. Ablation of the postcentral gyrus (areas 3–1) reduces ability to discriminate roughness and weight in the chimpanzee (Fig. 15) and, to a lesser degree, in the monkey. Significantly, a parietal lobectomy (areas 5 and 7) interferes much more with the ability to discriminate weight and roughness than does ablation of the postcentral gyrus. Obviously, the posterior parietal lobule does not depend solely upon sensory impulses related through the short association fibers from the postcentral gyrus. Besides the direct pathway between relay nuclei and areas 3–1 (Fig. 12), there is growing evidence for the anatomic substrate demanded by these experiments, namely "by-pass" systems by which impulses from the

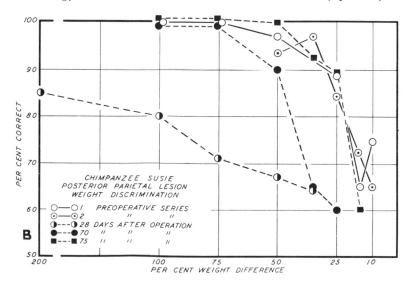

Fig. 15. Discrimination of lifted weights before and after ablation of the posterior parietal lobule contralateral to the arm tested, secondary to ipsilateral parietal lobectomy. Note the decreased ability shown in the first postoperative series. The improvement between the second and the third postoperative curve (filled circles and squares) is due to retraining, the lapse of time being insignificant. (From Ruch, Fulton and German, *Arch. Neurol. Psychiat.*, (*Chic.*), 1938, *39*:919–937.)

ascending sensory systems reach the cortex. As indicated above, fibers pass from relay nuclei via posterior thalamic nuclei to areas 5 and 7. Others by-pass the relay nuclei entirely; e.g., the anterolateral and posterior column systems synapse directly in the posterior thalamic region. The possibility that the spinothalamic components to the posterior thalamic nuclei are involved in weight discriminations becomes more likely because posterior column section, although interfering seriously with the discrimination of weights at first, has little permanent effect.[17] The anterolateral or the posterolateral tracts must support this recovery of function.

It may be concluded from much recent anatomic and physiologic investigation that the conventional pathway, from the thalamus to sensory area to the posterior-lying "association" area, is not the only course open to sensory impulses (see also Chap. 21). These and parallel experiments on auditory systems have led to the abandonment of the idea of "association areas" (Chap. 23).

Ablation of the parietal lobe also does not end ability to discriminate weights or roughness, except transiently. After an extensive lapse of time and retraining, impairment in ability to discriminate small differences in weight is all that remains. When discovered, the second somatic area was naturally suspected of underlying the recovery of discrimination function after parietal lobectomy. This was not borne out by later experimentation.[24a, 43] Although precentral lesions do not have great effects alone, when combined with extensive postcentral lesions they appear to increase the impairment.[24a] Further, indirect lines of evidence suggest that the so-called "motor areas" may serve discriminative functions and are, in fact, sensorimotor areas. For example, section of the medial lemniscus and spinothalamic tract in the midbrain leaves some weight discrimination and other proprioceptive functions.[60] When the lesion includes the dentatorubrothalamic tract, the impairment is much greater. However, as noted earlier, posterior column section in the monkey fails to abolish weight discrimination permanently. This result of posterior column section in the cervical region would seem to minimize the importance of the cerebellar "bypass" because the fibers from the arm to the dorsospinal cerebellar pathway run in the posterior column up to the medulla (external cuneate nucleus) and therefore would be sec-

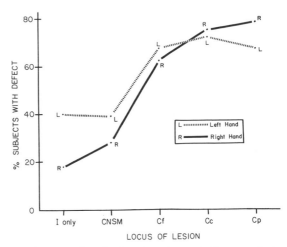

Fig. 16. Graph showing that missile wounds in the contralateral precentral (C_f), postcentral (C_c), and the posterior parietal (C_p) sectors cause sensory defects in about the same number of patients. I, lesions of the ipsilateral side only; CNSM, lesions sparing contralateral C_f, C_c, and C_p. (From Semmes *et al.*, *Somatosensory changes after penetrating brain wounds in man*. Cambridge, Mass., Harvard University Press, 1960.)

tioned. The posterolateral and anterolateral pathway systems may be involved. If so, their strong ipsilateral component may provide bilateral discrimination of weight and roughness. That in man, the three sectors—precentral, postcentral and posterior parietal lobule—are involved in sensation is shown in Figure 16, where it can be seen that penetrating wounds in the three regions produced somatosensory disturbances in about the same percentage of cases.[58]

Clinical Studies: Cortical Function in Man.[20, 21, 44, 56, 58, 70] The status of sensation can be learned in much greater detail in man than in animals, especially when refined, quantitative methods borrowed from the psychologists are used, as by Head[20] and more recently by Semmes et al.[58] However, interpretation may be confused by increased intracranial pressure, lesions which do not respect cytoarchitectural zones, lack of histologic verification of the lesion, especially when it is progressive, unconscious selection of cases, and failure to include control patients. Studies in man often show only the *kind* of sensory function carried on by the cerebral cortex and leave unanswered many of the questions on cortical localization and the "corticalization" of sensory functions.

Cortical lesions do not produce anesthesia

for any modality of sensation except as a transitory phenomenon. Persisting anesthesia implies subcortical damage, as shown in Figure 11 of the previous chapter, because the thalamus subserves sensation; deep lesions are more effective because they may injure the thalamus or because they interrupt projection fibers to a larger area of cortex. Cortical lesions are manifested by an increase in the threshold for elicitation of sensation, and in severe cases only the fact and kind of stimulation can be recognized. The modalities of sensation are not equally affected. Pain recovers most quickly and almost completely; pressure, warmth and cold recover next. Light touch and proprioceptive sensation are most severely and permanently damaged. Discrimination of intensity is subnormal for all modalities.

Perceptions having a strong spatial element—topognosis, two-point discrimination, figure writing and stereognosis—are especially affected by cortical lesions, and deficiencies in them may well be the first sign of damage to the parietal region. On the other hand, perception of temporal patterns (vibratory sensibility) is relatively little influenced by cortical lesions unless they extend into the white matter (Chap. 14, Fig. 11). Tactual and proprioceptive sensations, and the perceptions built upon them, are affected in much the same way by parietal and posterior column lesions. This is not true of vibratory sensibility, which is greatly blunted by posterior column lesions but not by cortical lesions. The defects of stereognosis represent more than the default of a necessary sensory channel. They occur, especially from parietal lesions, in a marked degree when sensation is not greatly disturbed. If sensation is disturbed, the term to use is "astereognosis through anesthesia," or "stereoanesthesia."

Because spatial and discriminative functions are severely damaged by cortical lesions, Head and others have given the impression that sensation has a thalamic and perception a cortical representation. Intensity and spatial functions have even been assigned different areas in the parietal lobes. To separate sensation and perception is not in accord with modern psychologic teaching or with the close interrelation between the thalamus and cerebral cortex. Apparently the discrimination of fine spatial functions and of differences in intensity requires a multitude of neurons arranged in dense, spatially organized fields. The cortex possesses such fields and the thalamus does not. Why else do regions with a high degree of spatial discriminative ability, e.g., the forefinger or the fovea of

the retina, have a wide expanse of the cortex devoted to them? Thus, even if the thalamus is capable of some form of sensation, it apparently does not possess the extensive apparatus necessary for fine discrimination and accurate localization, since only very few functional cells are left when the cortex is removed. Crude sensation of the type ascribed to the thalamus is "crude" in the sense that it is poorly located and capable only of coarse discrimination. Here, as in the discussion of epicritic and protopathic sensation, the same facts are open to two theories, one assuming qualitative difference and a different neural substrate, the other stressing quantitative and topographic differences in the neuronal organization of tracts and projection fields.

It is possible to argue that lamination and topographic organization at the thalamus and cortex represent mere engineering conveniences and are not functionally significant. Two facts would support this belief. The posterior parietal lobe is poorly organized topographically; yet damage to it can interfere with spatial discriminations, even though the highly organized apparatus of the postcentral gyrus remains intact. Moreover, the single cortical unit technique applied to the association area of a cat under chloralose anesthesia (a cortical excitant) shows that the same cell in the somatic association area can be fired from all four limbs and from superficial, deep and visceral nerves.[4] Topographic organization appears to be progressively less in ascending through the various levels of the nervous system. Some of the modern speculation based upon work of communication engineers suggests that this very dispersal rather than canalization may make more accurate discriminations possible. This question will be treated in detail below.

NEURAL BASIS OF SPECIFIC SENSORY FUNCTIONS

In the preceding chapters the dimensions of a sensation—e.g., quality and intensity, the nature of perception and judgment, and the connative (affective) aspects—were defined and clinical tests were described. The neural pathways for somatic sensation as known from anatomy and electrophysiology have been described; in this section, the neural basis for various aspects of sensation will be discussed.

Quality. The ability to experience the several modalities of sensation is subjective so that knowledge of the role of the thalamus and cortex depends on clinical studies. Even studies of the hemidecorticate man do not give a clear answer because sensation may be served by ipsilateral pathways to the intact cortex. Thus, in the side of the face contralateral to an hemispherectomy, touch and pinpricks are quite well appreciated (and to some degree localized), but over the body all forms of sensation are lost except the appreciation of heavy touches and pinpricks. Loss of a hemisphere including the thalamus leaves some pain sensibility. Lesions less in extent than a hemispherectomy leave appreciation of the kind of stimulation (quality) intact while interfering with other aspects of the sensation such as localization. Thus, pain conventionally considered a thalamic function could be due either to the ipsilateral pathways to the intact hemisphere or to midbrain.

Pain and Affect. Neither pain nor affect is a single, simple thing. Pain varies from the bright, localized, mildly unpleasant experience of a pinprick to insufferable, excruciating perversion of pain and affect, better described as suffering rather than pain. An understanding of the pain-hyperpathia-suffering continuum spans the distance between the oldest, most primitive remnants in the nervous system to the frontal lobe, which has undergone perhaps the greatest phylogenetic development of any part of the brain. A guiding principle in understanding pain goes back to Hughlings Jackson, Henry Head and C. J. Herrick. According to this principle, when evolution builds a new story on the nervous system it never quite abandons the older ones but merely conceals them by an inhibitory overlay until disease comes along and allows the primitive mechanism free play. Livingston[28] has likened the physician's approach to pain to a chess game; if so, the opponent is often an ancestral ghost. The evolutionary approach to pain was ably developed by Bishop,[9] and much of a second guiding principle to understanding pain is based on his work and that of Collins.[14, 15] This principle may be stated as follows: Fiber size is not only related to the evolutionary development of a sensory system but also is maintained from the periphery throughout the sensory system.

Bilateral anterolateral cordotomy may control pain completely (but often does not control perversion of pain). Therefore, it would appear that the posterolateral spinal pathway is not concerned with pain, a view consistent with its

rapid conduction rate. By contrast, mesencephalic spinothalamic tractotomy has been unsuccessful. Cutting the spinothalamic tract at this site would leave open the fine-fibered spinobulbar reticular pathway described earlier. The pain remaining is especially unpleasant and is described as the causalgic or "burning" type.[9] Because this pathway is multisynaptic to the site of thalamic synapse it is somewhat difficult to determine, but the strong development of the medial reticular system suggests a medial location. At the midbrain level pain impulses from the feet are carried in the central gray and in the spinothalamic tract. Section of each separately abolishes pain for a few days, so there are two pathways for pain.[33] Electrodes have been implanted in each of the two pathways in cats and connected with different lever-switches under the animals' control. Stimulation through either pathway causes unmistakable signs of pain and the cats quickly learn to open whichever circuit the experimenter has closed; i.e., a subjective discrimination must have taken place. The two pathways must therefore serve two kinds of pain sensation.

That a component of the anterolateral pathway terminates in the tectum of the midbrain lends substance to several observations linking it with pain. Painlike responses to skin stimulation are retained when a lesion is placed just below the thalamus.[69] Stimulation in the tectal region in man causes subjective pain sensation, and the objective signs from similar experiments in animals persist after destruction of the posteroventral thalamus.[61]

Head[20] believed that affect was served by a midline structure of the thalamus. The medial coursing multisynaptic pathways discussed would, from their anatomic position near or in the central gray substance reach the medial thalamic structures. Another significant group of fibers split off from the classic spinothalamic tract just as it enters the thalamus and takes a medial course terminating in the intralaminar nuclei. Attempts[48] to implicate a pathway through the posterior thalamic nuclei and sensory area II in nociception have less force than the more direct experiments of Perl and Whitlock,[46] which show that impulses from gentle cutaneous stimulation reach this region.

Pain is only slightly and transiently affected by cortical lesions, and clear-cut pain experiences are not elicited by stimulating the human cerebral cortex. In contrast to stimulation of the spinothalamic tract or the lateral nuclear mass of the thalamus, stimulation of the sensorimotor cortex will not motivate behavior, as will peripherally induced pain.[16]

Clinical correlations: Thalamic syndrome. In a classic "thalamic syndrome," spontaneous pain and subjective over-response to pleasant and unpleasant stimuli are prominent features. This syndrome is usually caused by occlusion of a small blood vessel (thalamogeniculate branch of the posterior cerebral artery) which supplies the posterolateral portion of the lateral nuclear mass of the thalamus.

The syndrome consists of unilateral symptoms:[68] (i) fleeting hemiplegia or hemiparesis, (ii) sensory disturbances of the cortical type, and (iii) over-response or hyperpathia. Attacks of "spontaneous" or central pain of a severe, agonizing nature are common. Pinprick or strong stimulation produces an intensely disagreeable, irradiating, diffuse sensation which is quite intolerable. One of Head's patients, a clergyman, complained that his trousers produced such disagreeable sensations that he was forced to remove them! Pleasantness of a sensation is also magnified, and emotional responses to music give rise to excessive "feelings" on one side of the body! Sensory over-response differs from hyperesthesia because the threshold is often elevated, but once it is attained the experience is overly intense. Little definite can be said about the thalamic syndrome. Spontaneous pain and over-response have in common with the hyperpathia produced by disturbances at lower levels a reduction of touch and deep sensibility paralleled by a heightened response to painful stimuli. Perhaps all have a common explanation in the hypothesis that affective activity of the midline nuclei is normally held in check when the ventral posterior nucleus is activated.

Neural Basis of Intensity Appreciation. From psychological experiments in which the differences between small weights were estimated by lifting them, Weber discovered in the nineteenth century that the smallest discriminable difference (just noticeable difference, j.n.d.) is a constant fraction of the weights themselves, the so-called "Weber fraction." This fraction is approximately 1/30; i.e., 31 grams is discriminated from 30, 62 grams from 60, and so on. This is usually stated as $\Delta I/I = C$, in which ΔI means a just discriminable increment of intensity.

Fechner's name is linked to Weber's because by mathematical manipulation he derived a relationship between stimulus and sensation. By assuming that discriminable increments are equal units of sensation, he derived the Weber-Fechner law:

$$\text{Sensation} = \text{K} \log \text{I} + \text{C}$$

Although a logarithm function describes the relationship between stimulus intensity and frequency of sense organ discharge (see Chap. 4), it does not apply to sensation when measured in other ways nor to the frequency of response of thalamic and cortical neurons.

The measurement of sensation—psychophysics—is performed by means of three procedures:

1. *Discriminability scales* are scales of equal (just noticeable) differences.

2. *Category scales* are obtained, for example, by assigning a series of tones to a given number of equally spaced categories.

3. *Magnitude scales* are exemplified by the method of "magnitude estimation." The observer simply assigns a number to the intensity of his subjective impression relative to a standard. This is a ratio scale like the decibel scale used in expressing sound intensities.

The different results yielded by these three methods are shown in Figure 17. The j.n.d. scale approximates a logarithmic function and the magnitude scale is a power function which approximates a straight line because its exponent value is nearly one (0.95). The method of magnitude estimation has been applied to a large number of sensory processes, each time yielding a power function though of a variable magnitude.

Plotted on log-log coordinates, the power function becomes a straight line whether the

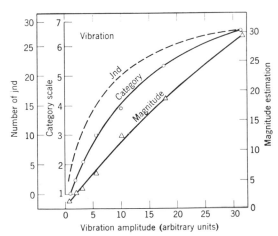

Fig. 17. Three psychophysical methods quantifying apparent intensity of the amplitude of a vibration applied to the finger tip. Note that the axes of the graph are linear. (From Stevens, In: *Sensory communication.* W. A. Rosenblith, ed., New York, John Wiley & Sons, 1961.)

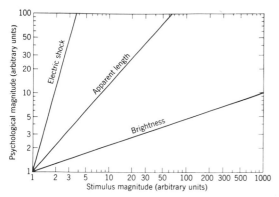

Fig. 18. The results of magnitude estimation for three sensory functions plotted on log-log coordinates. The slope of the line corresponds to the exponent of the power function relating psychological to physical magnitude. (From Stevens, In: *Sensory communication.* W. A. Rosenblith, ed., New York, John Wiley & Sons, 1961.)

exponent is less or more than one (Fig. 18). This permits easy comparison of the effect of, say, doubling stimulus intensity on subjective response for any number of stimuli.

Data gained by such a subjective procedure as assigning a number to the strength of a sensation naturally cause skepticism. However, the validity of the data is shown by several experiments, e.g., cross-modality comparisons. If a subject is asked to equate throughout the intensity series the loudness of a noise with the amplitude of a tactual vibration, the relationship between the two modalities is linear (Fig. 19). The slope of the line is close to that predicted from the ratios of exponents of the loudness and vibration function.

Another cross-modality comparison is *ratio matching.* The subject may be asked to adjust one loudness to another so that they bear the same relation to each other as two presented brightnesses bear to each other, i.e., C is to D as A is to B. If both energies are plotted relative to threshold, i.e., using a decibel scale for light as well as sound, the relationship is indicated by an approximately 45° line, showing nearly perfect cross-modality matching.

In another remarkable experiment the subject is asked to squeeze a hand dynamometer in proportion to loudness of a noise. When the force of the grip is plotted against loudness a straight line results. In fact, when grip is scaled against different sensory stimulation, the obtained exponent agrees well with the predicted exponent.

Parenthetically, it is worth knowing that functions far removed from sensation lend themselves to scaling procedures. For example, a group of students asked to apply a number to the seriousness of various kinds of juvenile delinquency produced a scale which agreed well with a similar one produced by judges of the juvenile court.

In summary, the relationship between physical energy and sensation seems best described not by a logarithmic function as in the Weber-Fechner law, but by a power function of a ratio of a given response to threshold. In a nicely mnemonic equation, Steven's law states

$$\Psi = K (\Phi - \Phi_\theta)^n$$

The psychological magnitude *psi* is related to a power of the magnitude of the physical stimulus *phi* less the threshold effective stimulus. The magnitude range of the exponent *n* for natural environmental stimuli has ranged between 0.33 for visual brightness and 1.6 for warmth; for electrical stimulation, 3.5.

Psychologic and physiologic correlation. The discharge frequency of a thalamic or cortical neuron is held to be an analog of stimulus intensity. The nature of this relationship—logarithmic versus a power function—can be determined and tested quantitatively most nearly ideally by using joint receptors. The frequency of impulses from these receptors returns, after an accelerated discharge during and just after joint movement, to an almost steady state

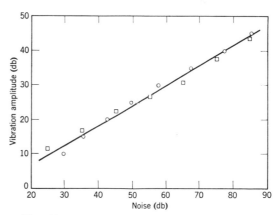

Fig. 19. Equal sensation functions obtained by adjusting loudness to match tactual vibration (circles) and vice versa (squares). Note that the stimuli are expressed on a logarithmic (decibel) scale. (From Stevens, In: *Sensory communication.* W. A. Rosenblith, ed., New York, John Wiley & Sons, 1961.)

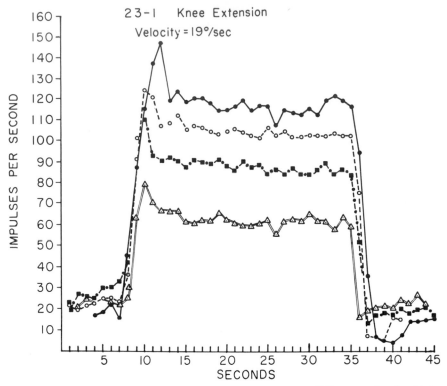

Fig. 20.   The response frequency of a single thalamic neuron to different maintained joint angles reached by a constant velocity of joint rotation. Movement toward extension started at the 7th second, those toward flexion at the 35th second. (From Mountcastle, Poggio and Werner, *J. Neurophysiol.*, 1963, *26*:807–834.)

which is independent of the velocity of the previous movement (Fig. 20).

When the frequencies of response in certain thalamic cells for different joint angles are plotted in the same way as the psychophysiologic data in Figure 18, a similar straight line relationship is found (Fig. 21).

There is here a very close correlation between a psychologic (magnitude estimation) and a physiologic measurement (frequency of thalamic neuron response) of the central analogs of stimulus intensity. Not only are they both power functions, but the size of the exponent for joint position (average 0.7) falls in the same range as mechanoreception studied psychologically, 1.0. This is perhaps the most successful cross-correlation between electrical events and psychologic phenomena yet achieved.

Neural Basis of Localization and Two-point Discrimination.   Weber assumed that the two-point threshold for a given region was fixed by the size of the skin area to which terminals of a single nerve fiber are distributed (so-called Weber's sensory circles). When one unexcited

sensory brush remained between the two on which the compass rested, the points were, according to Weber, appreciated as two. The size of cutaneous receptive fields is to some degree correlated with the size of the two-point threshold in the same region. But Weber's notion of two excited receptors and an intervening unexcited one, each with a private path to the cerebral cortex, is now recognized to be incorrect. The ramifications within the skin of a single posterior root fiber do not occupy discrete areas but overlap. It is implicit in Weber's concept that the three neurons making up the sensory pathway from receptor to sensory cortex constitute a simple chain having no cross-connections with other chains at the synaptic levels. Even in the most highly organized somatosensory system each peripheral axon excites a large number of cortical cells and this divergence occurs at each synaptic station, as shown in Figure 22. There being no point-to-point projection, maxima may be discriminated. One factor sharpening these peaks is a peripheral axon's greater frequency of firing from the center of its receptive field than from the periphery (lower left). The same is true of the much larger receptive field of a cortical neuron. That inhibition of a cortical unit can follow a volley to a somatosensory input which does not itself fire that unit was first clearly demonstrated by Towe and Amassian[66] in 1955 (see Fig. 23). This established the existence of a true inhibition not due to neuron sharing. As in the auditory and visual systems, an excitatory receptive field is surrounded by an inhibitory one. However, inhibitory fields of postcentral neurons are even larger than the excitatory fields and can include the whole area from elbow to wrist.[51] A highly suggestive observation is that adjacent or nearby cells often act reciprocally—one excited, the other inhibited. It is difficult to visualize the summation of excitatory fields and inhibitory surrounds of overlapping receptive fields of such large dimensions as giving sharp peaks. The problem of the two-point threshold is much the same as that of visual acuity, in which a start has been made on understanding spatial discrimination.

Amassian[5] attaches great weight to the fact that at each synapse sensory units, unlike motoneurons, tend to fire in bursts or trains of impulses. This is true of the posterior column as well as of the anterolateral system. Possibly, the temporal features of cortical activity play a role in "coding" the locus of a stimulus over and above the intensity information conveyed by frequency. In any case, a complete explanation of cortical function must include an explanation of the propensity of afferent neurons to fire repetitively. Amassian further points out that tactual acuity (discrimination of grades of sandpaper) carried out in the absence of the postcentral gyrus casts doubt on the dependence of acuity on topographic organization. He concludes from a detailed review that "At present, it appears unlikely that discriminative abilities are any more dependent on topographically organized cortex than they are on nontopographically organized cortex.... It is most unlikely that two portions of the body stimulated at various intensities could induce an identical temporal pattern of activity in a population of

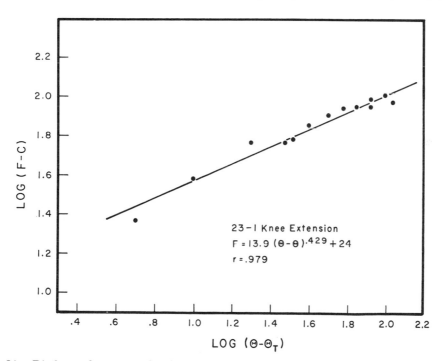

Fig. 21. Discharge frequency of a thalamic neuron plotted against joint angle. Frequency was obtained after the discharge had reached steady state. The same transformation used by Stevens was used here: subtraction of spontaneous rate (C) from obtained frequency (F), subtraction of threshold angle Θ from each angle plotted, and conversion of the stimulus continuum to a ratio scale. Both Θ variables are expressed on a log-log scale as in Figure 19. The Pearson coefficient of correlation of .979 indicates how well the straight line fits the data. (From Mountcastle, Poggio and Werner, *J. Neurophysiol.*, 1963, *26:* 807–834.)

central neurons. The major problems facing such studies are to identify those particular relationships between unit responses of different neurons which persist in the face of a change in stimulus intensity and to prove that such a pattern of activity engenders specific responses of the organism. The need for a statistical interpretation became apparent when it was discovered that stimulation of a given set of fibers led to discharge of neurons A.B.C., etc., with probabilities P_a, P_b, P_c, etc."

The paradox of the nervous system is that in ascending the sensory pathways both di-

mensions of a sensory input have remained relatively unrestricted in space (overlap, divergence–convergence) and time (repetitive firing); at least the former is greater in cortical than in subcortical levels and in the newer "association" than in the older primary sensory areas.

The optimists can argue that even the human brain has just taken the first step toward a one-to-one relationship between points and points on the cortex in the posterior column system and has a great evolutionary future before it. Others, however, including communica-

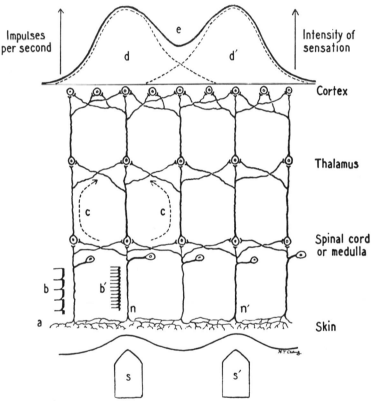

Fig. 22. Schematic diagram illustrating some neural factors involved in localization and in discrimination of two points; s and s' are the points of compass used in determining a two point threshold; a is plexus of interlocking terminals; b and b' show rate of discharge from sensory neuron stimulated at periphery of terminal brush and second neuron stimulated at center of its distribution. Arrows c illustrate that tendency of excitation to spread in first synaptic layer results in intensification by facilitation of core neuron in next synaptic layer; d and d' represent graphically frequency of corticopetal impulses arriving upon (and hence activity of) each cortical cell when due to s and s' respectively; e represents summed activity pattern; d, d' and e are termed *modal excitation fields.* In the diagram an attempt has been made to combine the views of Weber, Bernstein, Lorente de Nó, Tower, and Marshall and Talbot but not the surround inhibition of Towe and Amassian, Mountcastle and Powell and others.

*In a frequency curve in which classes are arranged along the abscissae from small to large and the number falling within each class is graphed, the mode is that class which contains the largest number of frequencies or members.

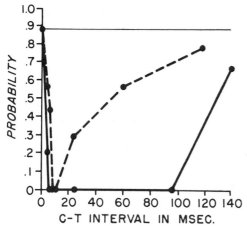

Fig. 23. Demonstration of inhibition by conditioning—test shocks applied to the digits showing that inhibition decreases with greater spatial separation on the skin. Note that stimulation of the middle finger, which almost never failed to cause firing, fails to fire for nearly 100 msec. (solid line) when preceded by a shock to the index finger. Stimulation of the thumb caused shorter-lasting inhibition. Probability of stimulation of thumb or index finger firing the unit was nearly zero. (From Towe and Amassian, *J. Neurophysiol.*, 1958, *21:* 292-311.)

tion engineers, see virtues in the "sloppiness" of the nervous system. Certainly the engineers faced with the problem of conveying the maximum amount of information over the minimum number of lines quickly abandoned the door bell model.

Much ingenious experimentation and sophisticated thinking will be required before we learn what, if anything, is gained by the lack of spatial and temporal constraint in sensory pathways.

REFERENCES

1. AMASSIAN, V. E. *J. Neurophysiol.*, 1951, *14:*433–444.
2. AMASSIAN, V. E., *J. Neurophysiol.*, 1951, *14:*445–460.
3. AMASSIAN, V. E. *Res. Publ. Ass. nerv. ment. Dis.*, 1952, *30:* 371–402.
4. AMASSIAN, V. E. *J. Neurophysiol.*, 1954, *17:*39–58.
5. AMASSIAN, V. E. *Int. Rev. Neurobiol.*, 1961, *3:*67–136.
6. AMASSIAN, V. E. and DEVITO, R. V. *J. Neurophysiol.*, 1954, *17:*575–603.
7. ANDERSON, J. A. *Acta physiol. scand.*, 1962, *56:* Suppl. 194.
8. V. BEKESY, G. *J. acoust. Soc. Amer.*, 1957, *29:*1059–1069; *ibid.*, 1958, *30:*399–412.
9. BISHOP, G. H. Chap. 5 in *Neural physiopathology.* R. G. Grenell, ed. New York, Harper & Row, 1962.
10. BORING, E. G. *Sensation and perception in the history of experimental psychology.* New York, D. Appleton-Century Co., 1942.
11. BOWSHER, D. *J. comp. Neurol.*, 1961, *117:*213–222.
12. BROOKHART, J. M., LIVINGSTON, W. K. and HAUGEN, F. P. *J. Neurophysiol.*, 1953, *16:*634–642.
13. CLARK, W. E. LEG. and BOGGON, R. H. *Phil. Trans.*, 1935, *B224:*313–359.
14. COLLINS, W. F. and RANDT, C. T. *J. Neurophysiol.*, 1958, *21:*345–352.
15. COLLINS, W. F., NULSEN, F. E. and RANDT, C. T. *Arch. Neurol. (Chic.)*, 1960, *3:*381–385.
16. DELGADO, J. M. R., ROBERTS, W. W. and MILLER, N. E. *Amer. J. Physiol.*, 1954, *179:*587–593.
17. DEVITO, J. L., RUCH, T. C. and PATTON, H. D. *Indian J. Physiol. Pharmacol.*, 1964, *8:*117–126.
18. FOERSTER, O. *Bumke u. Foersters Handb. Neurol.*, 1936, *5:*1–403.
19. HARRISON, F. and CORBIN, K. B. *J. Neurophysiol.*, 1942, *5:* 465–482.
20. HEAD, H. *Studies in neurology.* London, Oxford University Press, 1920.
21. HOLMES, G. *Brain*, 1927, *50:*413–427.
22. HYNDMAN, O. R. and WOLKIN, J. *Arch. Neurol. Psychiat. (Chic.)*, 1943, *50:*129–148.
23. KEEGAN, J. J. *Arch. Neurol. Psychiat. (Chic.)*, 1943, *50:*67–83.
24. KEEGAN, J. J. and GARNETT, F. D. *Anat. Rec.*, 1948, *102:* 409–437.
24a. KRUGER, L. and PORTER, P. *J. comp. Neurol.*, 1958, *109:* 439–467.
25. LANDAU, W. and BISHOP, G. H. *Arch. Neurol. Psychiat. (Chic.)* 1953, *69:*490–504.
26. KENNEDY, T. T. and TOWE, A. L. *J. Physiol.*, 1962, *160:* 535–547.
27. LEWIS, T. *Pain.* New York, Macmillan, 1942.
28. LIVINGSTON, W. K. In *Basic research in paraplegia.* J. D. French and R. W. Porter, eds., Springfield, Ill., Charles C Thomas, 1962.
29. MALIS, L. I., PRIBRAM, K. H. and KRUGER, L. *J. Neurophysiol.*, 1953, *16:*161–167.
30. MARK, R. F. and STEINER, J. *J. Physiol.*, 1958, *142:*544–562.
31. MEHLER, W. R. In *Basic research in paraplegia.* J. D. French and R. W. Porter, eds., Springfield, Ill., Charles C Thomas, 1962.
32. MEHLER, W. R., FEFERMAN, M. E. and NAUTA, W. J. H. *Brain*, 1960, *83:*718–750.
33. MELZACK, R., STOTLER, W. and LIVINGSTON, W. K. *J. Neurophysiol.*, 1958, *21:*353–367.
34. MORIN, F. *Amer. J. Physiol.*, 1955, *183:*245–252.
34a. MORSE, R. W. and TOWE, A. L. *J. Physiol.*, 1964, *171:* 231–246.
35. MOUNTCASTLE, V. B. *J. Neurophysiol.*, 1957, *20:*408–434.
36. MOUNTCASTLE, V. B. Chap. 22 in *Sensory communication.* W. A. Rosenblith, ed., New York, John Wiley & Sons, 1961.
37. MOUNTCASTLE, V. B., COVIAN, M. R. and HARRISON, C. R. *Res. Publ. Ass. nerv. ment. Dis.*, 1952, *30:*339–370.
38. MOUNTCASTLE, V. B. and HENNEMAN, E. *J. Neurophysiol.*, 1949, *12:*85–100.
39. MOUNTCASTLE, V. B. and HENNEMAN, E. *J. comp. Neurol.*, 1952, *97:*409–439.
40. MOUNTCASTLE, V. B., POGGIO, G. F. and WERNER, G. *J. Neurophysiol.*, 1963, *26:*807–834.
41. MOUNTCASTLE, V. B. and POWELL, T. P. S. *Bull. Johns Hopk. Hosp.* 1959, *105:*173–200, *idem*, 201–232.
42. NORRSELL, V. and VOORHOEVE, P. *Acta physiol. scand.*, 1962, *54:*9–17.
43. ORBACH, J. and CHOW, K. L. *J. Neurophysiol.*, 1959, *22:* 195–203.

44. PENFIELD, W. and RASMUSSEN, A. T. *The cerebral cortex in man: a clinical study of localization of function.* New York, Macmillan, 1950.

45. PERL, E. R. *Ann. Rev. Physiol.*, 1963, *25:*459–492.

46. PERL, E. R. and WHITLOCK, D. G. *Exp. Neurol.*, 1961, *3:* 256–296.

47. POCHIN, E. E. *Clin. Sci.,* 1938, *3:*191–196.

48. POGGIO, G. F. and MOUNTCASTLE, V. B. *Bull. Johns Hopk. Hosp.,* 1960, *106:*266–316.

49. POGGIO, G. F. and MOUNTCASTLE, V. B. *J. Neurophysiol.,* 1963, *26:*775–806.

50. POLLOCK, L. J. *J. comp. Neurol.,* 1920, *32:*357–378.

51. POWELL, T. P. S. and MOUNTCASTLE, V. B. *Bull. Johns Hopk. Hosp.,* 1959, *105:*133–162.

52. RANSON, S. W., DROEGEMUELLER, W. H., DAVENPORT, H. K. and FISHER, C. *Res. Publ. Ass. nerv. ment. Dis.,* 1935, *15:*3–34.

53. ROSE, J. E. and MOUNTCASTLE, V. B. Chap. 17 in *Handbook of physiology. Section 1. Neurophysiology,* vol. 1, J. Field, ed. Washington, D. C., American Physiological Society, 1959.

54. RUCH, T. C. Chap. 19 in *Physiology of the nervous system,* 3d ed., J. F. Fulton, ed. New York, Oxford University Press, 1949.

55. RUCH, T. C. Chap. 4 in *Handbook of experimental psychology,* S. S. Stevens, ed., New York, John Wiley & Sons, 1951.

56. RUCH, T. C., FULTON, J. F., and GERMAN, W. J. *Arch. Neurol. Psychiat. (Chic.),* 1938, *39:*919–937.

57. RUCH, T. C., PATTON, H. D. and AMASSIAN, V. E. *Res. Publ. Ass. nerv. ment. Dis.,* 1952, *30:*403–429.

58. SEMMES, J., WEINSTEIN, S., GHENT, L. and TEÛBER, H.-L. *Somatosensory changes after penetrating brain wounds in man.* Cambridge, Mass., Harvard University Press, 1960.

59. SHERRINGTON, C. S. *Phil. Trans.,* 1898, *B190:*45–186.

59a. SINCLAIR, D. C. and STOKES, B. A. R. *Brain,* 1964, *87:* 609–618.

60. SJÖQVIST, O. and WEINSTEIN, E. A. *J. Neurophysiol.,* 1942, *5:*69–74.

61. SPIEGEL, E. A., KLETZKIN, M. and SZEKELY, E. G. *J. Neuropath. exp. Neurol.,* 1954, *13:*212–220.

62. STEIN, M. H. and WORTIS, H. *Arch. Neurol. Psychiat. (Chic.),* 1941, *46:*471–476.

63. STEIN, M. H., WORTIS, H. and JOLLIFFE, N. *Arch. Neurol. Psychiat. (Chic.),* 1941, *46:*464–470.

64. STEVENS, S. S. Chap. 1 in *Sensory communication.* W. B. Rosenblith, ed. New York, John Wiley & Sons, 1961.

65. SWEET, W. H. Chap. 19 in *Handbook of physiology, Section 1.* vol. 1. J. Field, ed. Washington, D. C. American Physiological Society, 1959.

66. TOWE, A. L. and AMASSIAN, V. E. *J. Neurophysiol.,* 1958, *21:*292–311.

67. TROTTER, W. and DAVIES, H. M. *J. Psychol. Neurol. (Lpz.),* 1913, *20,* Erganzungsheft *2:*102–150.

68. WALKER, A. E. *The primate thalamus.* Chicago, University of Chicago Press, 1938.

69. WALKER, A. E. *Res. Publ. Ass. nerv. ment. Dis.,* 1943, *23:*63–85.

70. WALSHE, F. M. R. *Brain,* 1942, *65:*48–112.

71. WEDDELL, G., GUTTMANN, L. and GUTMANN, E. *J. Neurol. Psychiat.,* 1941, *N.S. 4:*206–225.

72. WHITE, J. C. and SWEET, W. H. *Pain. Its mechanisms and neurosurgical control.* Springfield, Ill., Charles C Thomas, 1955.

73. WHITE, J. C., SWEET, W. H., HAWKINS, R. and NILGES, R. G. *Brain,* 1950, *73:*346–367.

74. WHITLOCK, D. G. and PERL, E. R. *J. Neurophysiol.,* 1959, *22:*133–148.

75. WHITLOCK, D. G. and PERL, E. R. *Exp. Neurol.,* 1961, *3:* 240–255.

76. WOOLSEY, C. N. and FAIRMAN, D. *Surgery,* 1946, *19:*684–702.

77. WOOLSEY, C. N., MARSHALL, W. H. and BARD, P. *Bull. Johns Hopk. Hosp.,* 1942, *70:*399–441.

78. ZOTTERMAN, Y. *J. Physiol.,* 1939, *95:*1–28.

CHAPTER 16

Pathophysiology of Pain

By THEODORE C. RUCH

IN the previous two chapters the pathologic physiology of pain as seen in disturbances of the nervous system has been stressed. The present chapter will deal with the pain arising from pathologic processes at the periphery: visceral pain, muscle and joint pain and cutaneous hyperalgesia. In a sense, all pain is pathologic, but these forms of pain are especially so. This chapter will also deal with the physiologic mechanisms involved in psychosomatic pain states.

Characteristics of Pain. Pain is often described as pricking, stabbing, tearing, stinging, burning or throbbing. These descriptions reflect the duration of the sensation or identify it with an agent which has caused such pain in the past. Many agents (needle prick, pinching, traction on a hair, heat, electric current, etc.) cause indistinguishable "pricking" pains when briefly and focally applied.[28] The same stimuli prolonged cause a "burning" pain, even though heat is not involved. What Lewis[28] called the time–intensity curve of pain makes pains seem different and often suggests a possible origin. A needle prick produces a flash of pain. The impact of the pulse wave over sensi-

tive pain organs will cause a throbbing pain, etc. Figure 1 gives additional examples.

Sharp pain elicited from the skin is called "bright." Heavy, diffuse, aching pain from the deeper layer of the skin or the subjacent receptors, as is elicited by sustained pinching of the web between the fingers, is called "dull." The autonomic responses to deep and visceral pain—sweating, nausea, fall in blood pressure causing pain to be sickening—differ from those

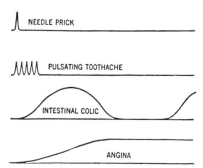

Fig. 1. Time-intensity curves of some common forms of pain. (From Lewis, *Pain,* New York, Macmillan, 1952.)

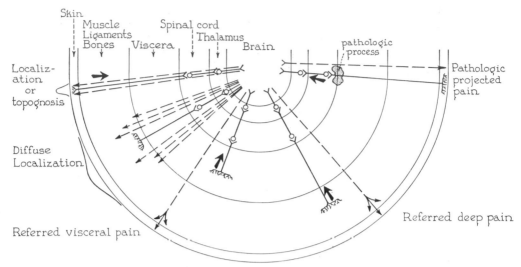

Fig. 2. Highly schematic representation of the projection of pain to points distant from the actual stimulation. Note that the place from which the pain seems to come (projection) may be incorrect in respect to two dimensions, depth and distance.

to cutaneous pain. Thus, pain is a protean phenomenon differing in quality and time course, depending on how it is elicited.

Localization, Projection and Reference of Pain. These words are related but should not be used indiscriminately. The basic concept is *projection* (see Chap. 14), a psychologic process which makes sensation seem to come from some layer of the body or from the external world. *Localization* (topognosis) reflects slight random errors in the projection of the sensation to the skin (Fig. 2). The clarity and extent of the projection can vary. Deep and visceral pain are often described as diffuse and poorly localized. *Projected pathologic pain* accurately describes the fact that impulses set up anywhere along the pain pathway from nerve to cortex give rise to a sensation projected to the peripheral region served by the end-organs of that pathway. Thus, the pain from a ruptured intervertebral disk is projected, not referred. (Note that it is the stimulus that is pathologic; the projection is normal, the brain merely having been tricked.) *Referred pain* is pain projected to an area distant from and usually superficial to the point of end-organ stimulation. Referred pain can be described as a systematic error in the projection of pain; examples will be given below.

CUTANEOUS HYPERALGESIA

In many pathologic states of the skin, light innocuous contacts not normally painful, such as friction from clothes, arouse pain. Often the pain is an especially intense, unpleasant, burning sensation which is diffuse, poorly localized or prolonged. This condition, called *hyperalgesia*, can be caused by a large number of agents (heat, abrasions, ultraviolet light, freezing, etc.). Two forms of hyperalgesia appear to exist. In *local* or *primary hyperalgesia*, the threshold is lowered; the response is intense, often burning in character, is accompanied by vasodilation (reddening) and extends beyond the area of damage, though not so far as in *secondary hyperalgesia*. In secondary hyperalgesia the threshold is actually elevated, but the response, once it occurs, is unpleasant. The zone of secondary hyperalgesia extends beyond the injured area and the surrounding zone of vasodilation. Secondary hyperalgesia is akin to referred pain.

Primary Hyperalgesia. Although it is common experience that some time after an injury the skin becomes reddened and hypersensitive to pain, it was not until 1933 that a major study of this phenomenon was conducted.[29] Pain resulting from brief stimulation of a hyperalgesic area has a burning quality. It is translated into actual pain when the area is heated. Cooling reduces the hyperalgesia.

Because the hyperalgesic state develops after a painless interval, Lewis and Hess[29] reasoned that it is not caused by persisting damage of nerve endings dating from the trauma. Echlin and Propper[15] demonstrated a sense organ basis for hyperalgesia. They applied equal stimuli to intact and scraped frog skin and recorded from

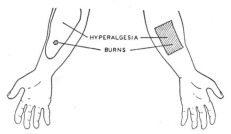

Fig. 3. Arm to right illustrates primary hyperalgesia confined to area of lesion; arm to left, secondary hyperalgesia extending well beyond burn. (From Hardy *et al., J. clin. Invest.,* 1950, *29:*115–140.)

the cutaneous nerves. After scraping, the stimulus elicited more of the slowly conducted impulses typical of pain, and the threshold was lower. In minor injuries, hyperalgesia is confined to the traumatized area (Fig. 3), but, with greater injury, it gradually spreads out somewhat, especially along lymphatic channels. This pattern would result from the diffusion of a substance which causes both pain and vasodilatation, part of the inflammation process. Histamine is such a substance. Lewis and Hess[29] believed that some other, unidentified, substance is involved, because hyperalgesia is not combined with itching, the main response to histamine injected intradermally.

Primary hyperalgesia caused by the local release of chemical substances from damaged cells and coincident with the area of damage (and the wheal) may be termed *local primary hyperalgesia* in contrast with what may be termed *circumferential hyperalgesia.** In the former, the peripheral nerves are involved only in transmitting pain impulses to the central nervous

* Considerable confusion in terminology has arisen because two terms, "primary hyperalgesia" and "secondary hyperalgesia," have been used to describe three events. In the light of new evidence we are adding a subclass to primary hyperalgesia— "circumferential hyperalgesia"—rather than treat this phenomenon as an alternate mechanism of secondary hyperalgesia as in the previous edition of this book.

system; in the latter, they cause the release of a "pain substance."

Surrounding an injury, there appears after some delay an area of vasodilatation called the "flare" (Chap. 32).

Early work which shows that the flare is mediated by fibers with cell bodies in the dorsal root ganglion has been reconfirmed in man.[12] The flare persists indefinitely after section central to the ganglion, and for a time after section peripheral to the ganglion, and then progressively disappears as the sensory fibers degenerate. Flare and vasodilatation from posterior root stimulation are ascribed to the release of a chemical substance. In the flare, this release is supposedly based on an axon reflex, some of the widely branching terminal axons being sensory and some motor, the latter releasing a mediator in the vicinity of blood vessels, causing vasodilatation and sensitizing neighboring sense organs. (However, the possibility that the chemical substance is a chemical interposed between strong, tissue-damaging stimulation and sensory ending discharge which is released by backfiring into the receptive terminals, has never been disproved.)

A necessary link in the chain of evidence is that the substance released by antidromic stimulation will lower the threshold to noxious stimuli. This has been shown in two ways.

Habgood has demonstrated release of a chemical substance by antidromic stimulation of frog's cutaneous nerve. He arranged two pieces of frog skin, each with a cutaneous nerve attached, in such a way that their undersides were in contact and the two nerves were available for stimulation and recording (Fig. 4). When one nerve was stimulated antidromically, the dromic discharge caused in the other nerve by a standard stimulus applied to its piece of skin was increased (sensitization). Often actual discharge was produced in the second nerve (induced discharge). Sensitization and induced discharge also occurred during stimulation and recording from adjacent nerve twigs. Pharmacologic analysis suggested that histamine (not acetylcholine) was the chemical agent involved.

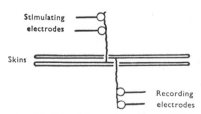
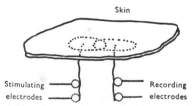

Fig. 4. Double skin preparation (*left*) and double nerve preparation (*right*) used to prove the release of a chemical by antidromic stimulation of a cutaneous nerve. (From Habgood, *J. Physiol.,* 1950, *111:*195–213.)

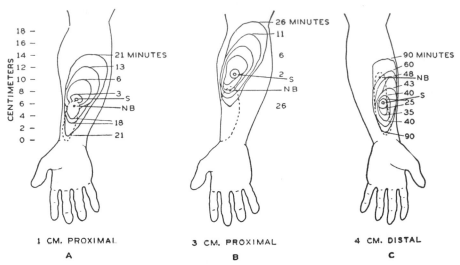

Fig. 5. Development of secondary hyperalgesia as shown by concentric solid lines when a cutaneous nerve is stimulated at point *S* proximal (*A, B*) and distal (*C*) to a nerve block (*NB*). Broken line marks area of anesthesia supposedly due to nerve damage. Figures give rate of development and spread of hyperalgesia. (From Hardy *et al., J. clin. Invest.,* 1950, *29:*115–140.)

Chapman *et al.*[12] perfused and collected fluid from the skin through two hypodermic needles during vasodilatation evoked by noxious stimulation of the skin. The perfusate obtained at a distance 4 cm. from the point of stimulation was reinjected into normal skin and produced a wheal, flare and pain of a burning quality. This strongly supports a humoral interpretation of circumferential hyperalgesia.

While histamine has the requisite vasodilating and pain-producing abilities and has been considered the mediator of hyperalgesia, the experiments of Chapman *et al.*[12] point to a polypeptide similar to bradykinin.

Bioassay (rat duodenum, uterus and blood pressure) indicated this similarity (but not identity) to oxytocin and to vasodilator polypeptides, bradykinin and others. For this reason the substance has been termed "neurokinin." Neurokinin was obtained from perfusate collected beneath a thermal injury, and from the dermatome of a cut posterior root stimulated at its peripheral end. Neurokinin was not produced from noxious stimulation in an area of skin denervated by nerve section, but was in the dermatome of the posterior root, sectioned a year previously. Though obtainable in the region of noxious stimuli immediately after extirpation of the ganglion, it gradually disappeared from the perfusate accompanied by a step-by-step decrease in the size of the flare until both disappeared in about 10 days. Thus, the re-

covery of neurokinin was affected by a variety of procedures in exactly the same way as the flare, which is compatible with the neurokinin being responsible for the flare and hyperalgesia.

Secondary Hyperalgesia. Prolonged electrical stimulation causes, after a painless interval, hyperalgesia extending two or three inches beyond the point of stimulation (Fig. 3). The main characteristics distinguishing secondary from primary hyperalgesia are: (i) The painful area extends far beyond the borders of the irritation and beyond the area of vasodilatation into normal-appearing skin. (ii) The secondary form never lasts more than 48 hours, whereas primary hyperalgesia may last for days. (iii) The threshold only seems lower in secondary hyperalgesia because the subjective response is greatly augmented.[18] (iv) Secondary hyperalgesia extends beyond the area of flush (erythema), but the pain and vascular phenomena in primary hyperalgesia are usually coincident, at least initially.

Hardy *et al.*[19] stimulated a nerve *proximal* to a procaine block. They obtained hyperalgesia mostly proximal to the block (Fig. 5). Repeated pinpricks within the hyperalgesic area caused its borders to shrink, an occurrence suggestive of central inhibition. After the pricking was stopped, the zone expanded again. Hardy and his co-workers concluded therefore that secondary hyperalgesia occurs because a barrage of impulses from the injured area facilitates centrally the afferent pathways from adjacent skin areas. They postulated an interneuronal system between first-order pain neurons and spinothalamic tract fibers. However, this system has not been proved anatomically or physiologically. It is unwise to postulate a set of fibers to explain each physiologic phenomenon, and dichotomizing of first-order neurons would seem to make such interneurons unnecessary. Quite possibly hyperalgesia is explicable along the same lines as referred pain, discussed in detail below (see Fig. 13). Also, the point of interaction may well lie in the thalamus or cortex rather than in the spinal cord.

Itch. Itching rivals pain in the amount of discomfort it causes. According to Rothman,[39] it is a temporal pattern of pain which tends to follow stimuli as an afteraction. Bishop[6] induced it with repeated shocks by "sparking" from electrodes not quite touching the skin, each stimulus being too weak to be felt by itself. As shown in Figure 6, itch is distributed in a punctate fashion; this is true of chemically induced itch[40] as well as of that induced by electrical and mechanical stimulation.[2, 6, 7, 41] In sensory dissociations resulting from neurologic lesions or operations, pain and itching are lost together.

Itching disappears entirely in cases of complete analgesia, but is not affected in cases of touch anesthesia.[5] According to Zotterman,[54] the impulses underlying itching are conducted in C fibers, since only these continue to discharge in the afterstimulation period when itching occurs. The latent period for itch following mechanical stimulation is consistent with this view.[42] However, C-fiber conduction rates no longer identify an afferent input with pain.

Some itching is explained by the release of a chemical substance, perhaps histamine, which stimulates nerve endings. Histamine injected into the skin certainly causes intense itching, and histamine is liberated into the skin by the types of injury which cause itching (mechanical damage, electrical stimulation, sunburn, etc.). On the other hand, as the concentration of intradermally injected histamine is reduced, itch disappears before reddening and whealing, and yet in pruritus, violent itching occurs without visible skin change.[2] Arthur[2] and Shelley[40, 41] argue that, unlike histamine, a proteinase produces a prompt and sustained itching without evident whealing or other gross tissue damage. More than two substances may be required to explain the itch in various pathologic states of the skin.

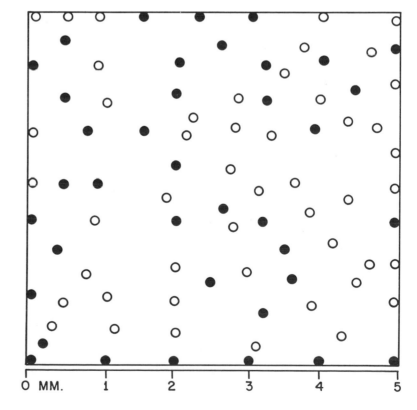

Fig. 6. Map of itch points on flexor surface of wrist. *Solid circles,* Points at which itching was reported. *Unfilled circles,* Sites at which itching was not experienced. Stimulus, 5 millisecond square-wave pulses; rate, 25 impulses per second; intensity, 1.5 V. (After Shelley and Arthur. *Arch. Derm. (Chic.),* 1957, *76:*296–323.)

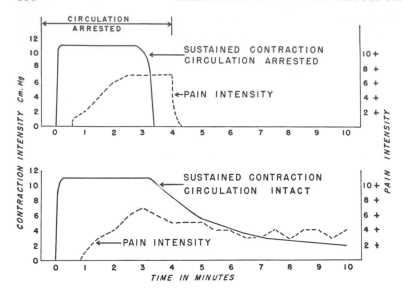

Fig. 7. Time course of sustained muscle contraction and resulting pain with arrested and intact circulation. In both experiments contraction was maintained as long as possible. (From Dorpat, *Mechanisms of muscle pain,* M.D. thesis. University of Washington School of Medicine, 1952.)

DEEP PAIN

The impulses underlying deep pain originate in muscles, tendons and joints, and, with occasional exceptions, traverse the muscle branches of mixed nerves. The quality of deep pain is dull, aching or boring. It seems to come from below the skin, but is difficult to localize, for it tends to radiate. Deep pain is accompanied by a definite autonomic response and is especially disagreeable, even sickening. The deep structures vary in sensitivity. According to Inman and Saunders,[23] the periosteum has the lowest threshold to irritating chemicals, followed in order of ascending threshold by ligaments, fibrous capsules of joints, tendons, fascia and the body of muscle. Feindel *et al.*[16] applied the methylene blue staining technique to deep pain fiber plexuses. Fine, beaded, naked fibers like those in skin form networks of varying density, being sparsest in connective tissue septa of muscles, denser in fascia, and still denser in periosteum. The density of innervation, then, seems to agree with the sensitivity of the structures.

Adequate Stimuli for Deep Pain. Mechanical forces excite deep pain endings. After trauma or infection these become so sensitive that the slightest touch or movement may be distressing. The endings are also sensitive to chemicals used experimentally or occurring in the body. Prolonged, continuous contraction of muscles, as in holding surgical retractors, causes muscles to ache and become sore. Rhythmic contraction, as in walking, or sustained contrac-

tion interrupted at frequent intervals causes no pain unless the muscle is ischemic. The pain which results from activity of ischemic muscle is called angina if it occurs in the heart and intermittent claudication if it occurs in the leg.*

Lewis' experimental analysis[28] of muscle pain is one of the classics in human physiology. It illustrates how much can be accomplished with minimal equipment but with close observation and reasoning. He had a subject grip an ergograph at the rate of once each second. When the circulation to the forearm was arrested by an inflated sphygmomanometer cuff around the upper arm, the standard exercise caused pain within 24 to 45 seconds which became severe in 60 to 90 seconds. Muscle tension is not the direct cause of such pain, because the pain is continuous while the contractions are intermittent. Under standard conditions, the time of onset of pain is remarkably constant, as is the onset of claudication in a patient. In ergographic experiments, Park and Rodbard[35] found the severity of pain to be exactly related to the amount of work, i.e., the product of the number of contractions times the square root of the load and the cube root of duration. When exercise is stopped but occlusion is continued, the pain continues undiminished (Fig. 7). When blood is readmitted to the limb, the pain disappears within a few seconds. Since the pain stimulus

* "Angina," a Latin word, refers to the sense of suffocating contraction which accompanies the pain from the heart. "Claudication" refers to the limping which accompanies the pain.

appears to be "stored up," Lewis and his co-workers concluded that the stimulus is a chemical substance arising out of the contraction process.

This substance seems to be eliminated from the muscle by metabolism rather than by being washed out in the blood. Intact circulation does not prevent the development of pain in muscles during sustained contraction (Fig. 7) or during rhythmic contraction when the blood is insufficiently oxygenated. However, oxygen lack in itself is probably not the direct and sufficient pain stimulus.

Lewis termed the hypothetical metabolite "factor P." It seems to be a normal product of muscle metabolism in both the resting and active states and to stimulate the pain endings only when it accumulates in fairly large quantities. Exercise facilitates this accumulation because it induces greater metabolic activity and thus greater release of factor P. For example, if a muscle with an occluded blood supply is exercised, but not to the point of pain, continued arrest of circulation to the resting muscle will eventually cause pain.[33] Cessation of pain requires only that the concentration of factor P be reduced below the critical threshold level, not that it be completely removed from the muscle. If a muscle performs measured work until pain starts and is rested only until pain stops before the experiment is repeated, the time to onset of pain is much shorter for the second trial.[28] This means that the factor P produced during the second trial is added to an accumulation remaining from the first trial, even though pain induced by the first trial had stopped.

Of the many agents which may constitute factor P (anoxia, pH changes, lactic acid, potassium, histamine) lactic acid or any of the intermediary substances of the Krebs cycle can be ruled out since subjects with hereditary absence of muscle phosphorylase (McArdle's syndrome) experience severe pain on exercise of ischemic muscles. Potassium, in the opinion of Dorpat,[14] is most likely the one. Both activity and ischemia release potassium from the muscle fiber, and intra-arterial injection of it provokes a severe pain in muscle resembling ischemic muscle pain. However, the same is true of intra-arterial injection of 1 to 2 μgm. of bradykinin, the site of pain stimulation supposedly being the free branching terminal of perivascular nerves around capillaries.

The pain-inducing nature of sustained muscle contraction is particularly important because many pains and aches in organic disease and anxiety states result from it. The underlying mechanism is probably diminished blood flow caused by compression of blood vessels within the muscles.[14] Muscle temperature *decreases* momentarily at the beginning of exercise, probably because the blood, which is warmer than the arm, is prevented from entering it.

Causes of sustained muscle contraction. Sustained contractions of skeletal muscle likely to cause pain may arise from higher centers or from reflexes of somatic or visceral afferents. Such reflexes are important (i) as diagnostic signs (Kernig's sign, stiff neck of meningeal irritation, abdominal rigidity of appendicitis), and (ii) as secondary sources of pain and discomfort.

Nociceptive impulses experimentally induced from a restricted focus in the head often give rise to a pain confined and fairly well localized to the traumatized focus, and also to a second, more generalized, pain ("headache"). According to the following analysis, the second pain results from tension of the neck muscles.[42] A single injection of 0.6 ml. of 6 per cent saline solution into the right temporal muscle caused intense local pain accompanied by sweating, salivation, lacrimation, nausea and contraction of the temporal and neck muscles. However, it caused no discomfort in the neck. Additional injections were made before temporal muscle pain had subsided. Pain in the neck began after the second injection and increased with each subsequent injection. At the end of 40 minutes, the neck pain was rated at nearly half the intensity of the local pain. With other stimuli—an irritating substance injected into the conjunctival sac or excessive activity of the external ocular muscle to overcome a tendency to double vision caused by a vertical prism set before one eye—the neck pain outlasted and, in the latter case, exceeded the local (frontal) pain (Fig. 8). The neck pain was promptly relieved by massage. It is not known how much the building up of the reflex muscle contraction is due to a change in the interneuron pools of the spinal cord, since no clear experimental demonstration of such long-lasting facilitatory effects has been made. The muscle contraction may be due to a vicious circle: deep pain→sustained reflex contraction→deep pain→reflex contraction→ etc. The success of such single procedures as osteopathic treatments, ethyl chloride sprays and procaine hydrochloride injection of trigger zones may depend on the breaking of the circle.

Muscle pain in anxiety states. Headache associated with a mild emotional disturbance such as that caused by an uncongenial job was found to be accompanied by tension of the neck and scalp muscles which disappeared along with the pain after psychiatric and drug therapy.[12] According to Holmes and Wolff,[21] in many instances of backache local dysfunction is minimal and mus-

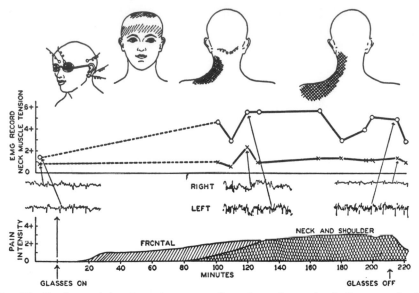

Fig. 8. Distribution and time intensity course of muscle tension and pain from sustained contraction of external ocular muscle induced by vertical prism in front of left eye. Note neck pain and muscle tension, middle record, is on this side. Dips in upper EMG record are due to involuntary movements of head and neck. (From Simons *et al., Res. Publ. Ass. nerv. ment. Dis.,* 1943, *23*:228–244.)

cle tension produced by emotional tension is the cause of *secondary pain* in the back. Muscle tension could readily be induced by provoking hostility in the patient and relieved by appropriate psychiatric treatment. Thus, the sustained muscle contraction which causes pain reduces down to a familiar pattern representing a segmental reflex discharge and facilitation of this reflex from the brain.

Referred Muscle Pain. By a mechanism entirely different from that operating in secondary pain, the stimuli arising from a restricted focus in muscle can give rise to pain which ap-

pears to come from points distant from the point of stimulation. In short, muscle pain shows the phenomenon of referred pain in the same way as visceral pain does (see below). Lewis and Kellgren[30] injected small quantities of 5 per cent saline solution, which is highly irritating, into deep structures. Localization of the resulting pain was fairly accurate when injections were made into fascia or tendons lying near the surface and into the periosteum of superficial bones such as the tibia. Pain from the same kinds of deeply situated structures,[25] and also pain from the belly of a muscle, were diffuse and often

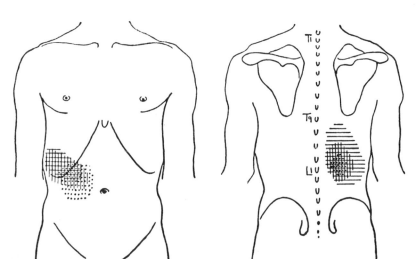

Fig. 9. Reference of deep pain elicited by injections of hypertonic saline into three muscles supplied with pain fibers from T_9: multifidus muscle (*horizontal lines*), intercostals (*vertical lines*) and rectus abdominis (*dots*). (From Kellgren, *Clin. Sci.,* 1938, *3*:175–190.)

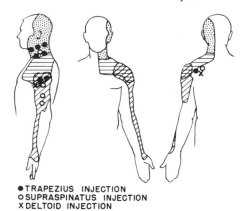

● TRAPEZIUS INJECTION
○ SUPRASPINATUS INJECTION
✕ DELTOID INJECTION

Fig. 10. Sites of cutaneous hyperalgesia resulting from injecting 5 per cent sodium chloride solution into muscles. Points of hypersensitivity to radiant heat (Hardy–Wolff apparatus) resulting from injecting into a given muscle are shown by location of the symbols for each muscle. Dermatome C_3 dots, C_4 horizontal lines, C_5 diagonal lines. (From Klingon and Jeffreys, *Neurol. (Minneap.)*, 1958, *8*:272–276.)

were referred to a distant area of the skin surface in a regular, reproducible fashion (Fig. 9). Deep somatic pain was referred to the dermatomes supplied by the posterior roots which conduct pain impulses from the muscle stimulated. Pain from the muscle itself is initially diffuse and tends to shrink down to a small area of pain and muscle tenderness related to the origin and insertion of the muscles rather than the point of saline injection. The referred pain for deep muscle stimulation is accompanied by rigidity and tenderness of muscles, and the skin may become hyperesthetic. Such points of cutaneous hypersensitivity occur on the arm and neck when the deep muscles of the back of the shoulder are stimulated (Fig. 10). However, as in referred pain the impulses from the cutaneous hyperalgesic point and from the muscles stimulated enter the spinal cord by the same posterior root.

VISCERAL AND REFERRED PAIN

Neuroanatomists, following Langley, define the sympathetic nervous system as an efferent system. Langley was fully aware that sympathetic nerves and the white rami carry sensory fibers from the viscera. He chose to "rule them out" by definition because, except in origin, they resemble ordinary somatic afferents, whereas the sympathetic efferents are distin-

guished from somatic efferents by a peripheral synapse. Because so much autonomic surgery is performed to control pain, the modern tendency is to alter Langley's definition and to speak of "sympathetic," "autonomic" or, better still, *"visceral" afferents*. Pain impulses arising within the abdominal and thoracic cavities may reach the central nervous system by three channels: (i) the parasympathetic nerves, (ii) the sympathetic nerves, and (iii) the somatic nerves innervating the body wall and the diaphragm. The last of these channels makes visceral sensation a somewhat larger question than autonomic afferent innervation.

Visceral Pain.[28, 33, 48, 49] It is noted by surgeons operating with local anesthesia that visceral organs can be handled and even cut, crushed or burned without causing sensation, as long as traction on the mesentery and stimulation of the body wall are avoided. And it is true that the viscera are sparsely innervated. However, Kinsella[26] has shown that a broad, firm, manual pressure on the appendix elicits pain when restricted stimuli affecting only a few fibers of the sparse innervation are ineffective. If account is taken of the principle of the adequate stimulus and the fact that pathologic states may lower the threshold of pain fibers, the viscera are unquestionably sensitive. The viscera are not normally exposed to the forms of stimulation that are adequate for skin receptors and therefore have not evolved sensitivity to them. The adequate stimuli for visceral afferents are those arising from their own environment and especially from their own activities and pathologic states. Such adequate stimuli include: (i) sudden distension against resistance; (ii) spasms or strong contractions, especially when accompanied by ischemia; (iii) chemical irritants; and (iv) mechanical stimulation, especially when the organ is hyperemic (stomach). The pain from such stimulation is not, as is often stated, due to traction on the mesentery. Normal contractions and relaxations of visceral organs apparently do not discharge pain fibers, although normal activities may become painful when the blood supply is inadequate.

Most visceral reflexes and organic sensations are served by afferents in the parasympathetic nerves (see Chap. 17), but *impulses serving visceral pain are conducted mainly in the sympathetic nerves*. The major exceptions to this rule, given in detail below, lie in the pelvic regions and in the esophagus and trachea. Because sympathetic nerves

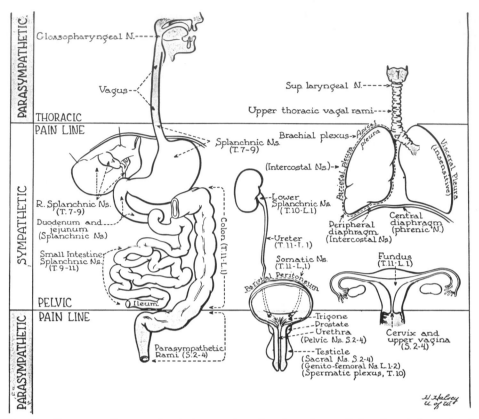

Fig. 11. Summary diagram of pain innervation of various viscera. Pain afferents from structures between thoracic and pelvic pain lines traverse sympathetic nerves, and structures above and below these lines traverse parasympathetic nerves. (Data from White, *Res. Publ. Ass. nerv. ment. Dis.,* 1943, *23.*373–390.)

are not essential for visceral regulatory reflexes, sympathectomy for the relief of pain does not produce serious visceral dysfunction.

Pain pathways can be interrupted at several points, as can be seen by tracing a typical pathway from an abdominal organ. The axons of free nerve endings in the walls of a viscus follow the artery to the abdominal aorta, where they traverse the collateral ganglia without synapse and enter the splanchnic nerve. The ganglion of the sympathetic chain is entered and traversed, again without synapse; and, by way of the white ramus, the fibers reach the spinal nerve close to the spinal ganglia. The cell body of the viscerosensory fiber is situated in the spinal ganglion, and the central process enters the spinal cord by way of the dorsal root. There it forms reflex connections with somatic motoneurons and preganglionic fibers and ascending connections with the neurons of the spinothalamic tract. A visceral organ can therefore be denervated of pain fibers by (i) stripping the artery supplying it (periarterial neurectomy), (ii) removal or alcohol injection of the sympathetic chain of ganglia at appropriate levels, (iii) rhizotomy of several posterior roots, and (iv) section of the spinothalamic tract (cordotomy). Impulses from a

single visceral organ enter the spinal cord by several roots, necessitating extensive root sections. Cordotomy is often the operation of choice because somatic as well as visceral structures are frequently involved.

Visceral pain fibers are not confined to the sympathetic nerves. Many pain impulses reach the spinal cord via the pelvic nerve; others reach the brain stem via the vagus nerve. Sympathetic surgery for the relief of hypertension permits study of this question in man (Fig. 11). Below an imaginary line, which may be termed the *pelvic pain line,* pain impulses from the bladder neck, prostate, urethra, uterine cervix and the lower end of the colon are conducted to the spinal cord by way of the parasympathetic pelvic nerve. This explains why hypogastric neurectomy fails to relieve bladder pain. Note that the portions of the urogenital system falling above this line (bladder fundus, kidney, ureters, ovaries, fallopian tubes, uterus and testes) are served with pain afferents by way of sympathetic nerves. (The testes have migrated below the pelvic pain line, carrying with them a sympathetic innervation derived from the tenth thoracic cord segment.) Above the pelvic pain line, the pain fibers from the abdominal and most of the thoracic viscera pursue sympathetic nerves, although they have equal opportunity to join the vagus nerve.

It has long been taught that no visceral pain impulses are conducted in the vagus. By means of implanted electrodes, Bradford Cannon[10] stimulated the vagus in cats below the recurrent laryngeal branches. No pain responses were observed. However, other observations[17, 46, 51] suggest that a "thoracic pain line" may be drawn, with the esophagus and trachea giving fibers to the vagus nerve. Finally, it is to be noted that somatic nerves are also concerned with innervation of the visceral cavities.

Impulses arising in visceral structures may give rise to pain localized to more superficial structures of the body, often those at a considerable distance from the disturbed organ. Such pain is said to be *referred*. Why visceral pain is referred is not known, but what determines where the pain is referred is known. Pain is referred to the dermatomes supplied by the posterior roots through which the visceral afferent impulses reach the spinal cord. This may be called the "dermatomal rule." Thus, referred pain from the heart (angina pectoris) seems to come from the chest and from a thin strip along the inner aspect of the upper arm. The highest root carrying pain fibers from the heart is the first thoracic posterior root, and the upper border of the corresponding dermatome extends out along the inner aspect of the arm.

Pain is only one of four associated signs of visceral disease. Irritation of the viscera by a pathologic process is manifested in four ways: (i) pain; (ii) hyperalgesia, hyperesthesia or tenderness; (iii) autonomic reflexes—sweating, piloerection or vasomotor changes; (iv) somatic reflexes, muscular rigidity.

Types of Pain from Viscera. Two main types of "visceral" pain must be recognized: (i) quasivisceral pain aroused by stimulation of the inner surfaces of the body wall, and (ii) pain actually arising from the viscera. Either type may be unreferred or referred. Quasivisceral pain is an important factor in visceral disease. Spread of inflammation, exudation, pressure, friction or an invasion of the body wall by a pathologic process causes pain impulses which reach the spinal cord via the somatic nerves supplying the walls of the visceral cavities. Moreover, the thoracic and abdominal cavities are deeply penetrated by a somatic nerve—the phrenic—in which one fiber in three is sensory and many are unmyelinated. Table 1 summarizes the role of the somatic afferent fibers.

Unreferred parietal pain. Capps and Coleman[11] studied this kind of pain in conscious patients. Taking advantage of the space for maneuvering afforded by collections of exudate in the body cavities, these workers stimulated various internal structures. A wire was passed into the space by means of a trocar, and pressure or friction was applied to visceral and parietal structures. The peritoneum was insensitive to this kind of stimulus, but stimulation of the inner body wall caused a sharply localized pain. This pain seemed to come from the body wall over the site of stimulation, presumably because one posterior root innervates superimposed areas on the internal and external surface of the body wall. The lower right quadrant pain in the second stage of appendicitis falls in this category.

Referred parietal pain. Experimental stimulation of the margin of the diaphragm, innervated by the lower six intercostal nerves, was referred to the anterior abdominal wall, which is innervated by the same thoracic nerves (Fig. 12, *right*). Pain from stimulation of the central zone of the diaphragmatic pleura or peritoneum was invariably referred to the point of the shoulder and neck (Fig. 12, *left*). This reference is well recognized clinically. Thus, impulses ascending the phrenic nerve and entering the spinal cord via C_{3-4} are referred to the dermatomes of these roots.[20] Because the diaphragm has migrated caudally, carrying its nerve supply with it, the discrepancy between the points of origin and of reference is dramatic.

Referred visceral pain. Unlike referred somatic

TABLE 1. *Role of Somatic Afferent Fibers in Sensibility of Visceral Cavities*

Somatic afferent fibers	Phrenic nerve	Central zone of diaphragm Portions of pericardium Biliary tract
	Thoracic and upper lumbar spinal nerves	Parietal pleura Parietal peritoneum Borders of diaphragm Roots of mesentery

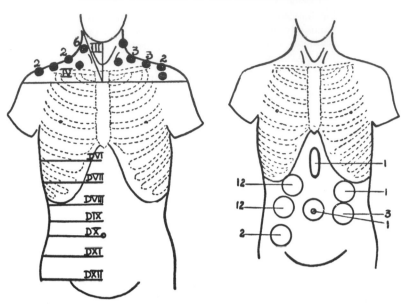

Fig. 12. Superficial reference of pain from diaphragm. *Left:* Reference of pain from stimulating *central zone* of diaphragm. Black dots and attached numbers represent position and frequency of reference in a series of observations. Pain is also referred to corresponding territory on dorsal surface of neck and shoulders (not shown). Roman numerals identify 3rd and 4th cervical and 6th to 12th thoracic dermatomes (*D*). *Right:* Reference of pain from visceral disease affecting *margins* of diaphragm. Circles represent points of reference, numbers the frequency of reference; in two cases pain was referred to back. Margins of diaphragm are innervated by lower six thoracic posterior roots. Compare their cutaneous distribution shown in figure at left with zones of reference shown in figure at right. (From Capps and Coleman, *An experimental and clinical study of pain in the pleura, pericardium and peritoneum.* New York, Macmillan, 1932.)

pain, this type of pain results from impulses arising in the viscera and conducted over visceral nerves, usually sympathetic. Frequently, the pain seems to come from the superficial layers of the body, often at a considerable distance from the diseased organ. Despite the error of reference, the localization may be quite definite, and its apparent location obeys the dermatomal rule. Angina pectoris and the pain from myocardial infarction are perhaps the classic examples of a referred visceral pain. The pain from a renal stone descending the ureter does not move but has a fixed reference (to the groin although the upper end of the ureter is beneath the last rib). An inflated balloon in the gut, which embryologically is a midline structure, gives rise to pain which has the same reference whether the stimulated portion of the gut is on the left or right side of the body. Stimulation of the central end of the splanchnic nerve in conscious patients gives rise to referred pain.[47] There seems little justification for Morley's contention[34] that pain from the viscera is referred only when the body wall is involved.

Unreferred visceral pain (splanchnic pain). In anginal pain there is, in addition to the superficially referred pain, a deep, substernal, agonizing component. Such pain is therefore unreferred although it is poorly localized. Ross[38] in 1888 hypothesized the double nature of visceral pain and named the unreferred component "splanchnic pain." This category of pain is less well substantiated. It should be recognized, however, that gastrointestinal tract pain, although referred elsewhere than the point of stimulation, appears to come from much deeper within the body than does the referred parietal pain.

Referred Pain. The reference of pain from the central zone of the diaphragm, innervated by a somatic nerve, provides a clue to the nature of referred pain. So, too, does the common observation that pain arising in the teeth cannot be localized to the correct tooth, even though the sensory innervation of the teeth is somatic (trigeminal). Referred pain is therefore not a phenomenon associated exclusively with the viscera, and the reference of visceral pain is therefore not due to any unique properties of the visceral pain pathways. Lewis and Kellgren[30] induced pain in observers with experience of angina pectoris by injecting hypertonic saline into the first thoracic interspinous ligaments. The subjects recognized the similarity of the two types of pain. The common denominator of referred visceral pain and referred muscular pain is that they both originate deep to the skin and in a general sense are deep pain. Faultiness of localization perhaps represents the failure to evolve a topographically organized neural apparatus for localization. The faulty projection of deep pain to the surface is the result of (i) infrequency of deep pain, and (ii) inability to use vision to verify the source of stimulation. Thus, learning appears to be an important factor in referred pain.

Habit reference. Evidence that reference of sensation is a learned phenomenon can be found in the clinical observation that a pain may be referred not to its usual point of reference but to the site of a previous surgical operation, trauma or localized pathologic process. Experimentally this was demonstrated repeatedly in Jones' study[24] of gastrointestinal pain resulting from distension by balloons. Aberrant projections of pain, for example those falling to one side of the midline when the balloon was in the upper level of the gastrointestinal tract, were explicable as references to pre-existing surgical scars.

Habit reference had the status only of a clinical observation until recently, when it was suspected of being the cause of a bizarre pain phenomenon and was subjected to formal experimental proof by Reynolds and Hutchins.[22, 37] During high-altitude flying some individuals suffer severe pain localized to the teeth (aerodontalgia). After every possible dental cause for the pain had been excluded, it was discovered that the pain stimulus was the expansion of air trapped in the maxillary sinus. Some individuals referred this pain to the face; others referred it to the teeth. The latter group had a high incidence of traumatic dental work on the side of reference, suggesting habit reference of pain. To test this hypothesis, dental work was done without anesthesia on one group of young men and with anesthesia in another group. Two weeks later, the ostium of the maxillary sinus was pricked with a pin. Over 90 per cent of the no-anesthesia group referred this pain to the dental area where the work had been done. This response could still be elicited two months after the dental trauma. The anesthesia group did not refer the pain to the teeth.

Habit reference, secondary hyperalgesia and referred pain are subject to two explanations, one peripheral and the other psychologic. With the above experiments as an example, the first explanation is that the traumatized teeth were the source of a subthreshold discharge of pain impulses which was facilitated by impulses from the sinus. The other interpretation is, as the term "habit reference" implies, that a projection of pain is learned and that the pain impulses from the sinus, conducted in an overlapping pathway, were simply given the previously learned reference for impulses in that path.

Mechanism of Referred Pain. To account for the dermatomal reference of pain, MacKenzie[31] suggested that sensory impulses from the viscera were unable to pass directly to the brain, having no connection with the spinothalamic tract, but created an "irritable focus" in the segment at which they entered the spinal cord. Afferent impulses from the skin were thereby magnified, causing pain which was literally cutaneous pain. Stated in modern language, MacKenzie's theory of irritable focus amounts to the suggestion that visceral impulses facilitate somatic pain impulses normally coming from the skin in insufficient quantities to excite the spinothalamic tract fibers. Hyperalgesia and referred pain would be the consequence. Wiggers,[49] Hinsey and Phillips,[20] and others have stated the MacKenzie theory very clearly in modern physiologic terms. It can be called the *convergence–facilitation* theory to distinguish it from the convergence–projection theory.

Convergence–projection theory. Although facilitation may well be essential for hyperalgesia of dermatomal distribution, it is not essential for reference of pain. An adequate explanation of referred pain is that some visceral afferents converge with cutaneous pain afferents to end upon the *same* neuron at some point in the sensory pathway—spinal, thalamic, or cortical—and that the system of fibers is sufficiently organized topographically to provide the dermatomal reference. The first opportunity for this is in the spinothalamic tract. The resulting impulses, upon reaching the brain, are interpreted as having come from the skin, an interpretation which has been learned from previous experiences in which the same tract fiber was stimulated by cutaneous afferents. The same explanation

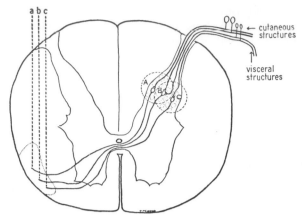

Fig. 13. Convergence–projection mechanism of referred visceral and somatic pain based upon Sherrington's neuron–pool concept. *A, B* and *C* represent a neuron pool consisting of all the spinothalamic tract fibers originating in one segment of spinal cord. *A* is field of neurons having connections only with afferent fibers from cutaneous sense organs. *B* is field of overlap constituted by neurons which receive impulses from *both* visceral and cutaneous afferents, and impulses in *B* will give rise to pain referred to skin. *C* are those neurons of pool which connect only with afferent fibers from visceral cavities, and give rise to unreferred or true splanchnic pain. Only one neuron in each category is represented; others are indicated by "ghost cells." *a, b* and *c* are fibers in spinothalamic tract having cell bodies in fields *A, B* and *C,* respectively.

serves equally well for referred parietal or diaphragmatic pain.

The pain fibers in the posterior roots outnumber the spinothalamic tract fibers, so that several pain fibers must converge upon one tract fiber. Therefore, it is likely that a share of the afferent pain fibers coming from the diaphragm converge with cutaneous pain fibers entering the same segment to end upon the spinothalamic tract neurons. According to the doctrine of specific nerve energies, impulses in a spinothalamic tract fiber are identical whatever their origin. On all previous occasions when these particular spinothalamic neurons have been activated, stimulation of the body surface, verified by other senses, was responsible. Thus, when impulses of visceral origin reach the cerebral cortex, the interpretation is made which experience has built up—that of a pain arising from cutaneous pain neurons.

Figure 13 illustrates the convergence–projection theory of referred pain applied to visceral sensation. The spinothalamic tract fibers originating at one segment of the spinal cord are regarded as a pool of neurons. The visceral pain afferents entering the posterior root of that segment come into synaptic relation with one group of cells, and the cutaneous pain afferents synapse with an overlapping field in the pool. Those spinothalamic tract neurons within the field of overlap, when stimulated by visceral afferents, give rise to pain referred to the cutaneous surface. In Figure 13, certain spinothalamic tract fibers are "private" to visceral afferent neurons. These fibers are responsible for "splanchnic" or unreferred visceral pain. Facilitation of cutaneous nerve impulses within the overlap probably accounts for hyperalgesia, but facilitation is not involved in referred pain. Thus is avoided the unphysiologic and unnecessary supposition that cutaneous pain afferents are perpetually discharging at an amount inadequate to discharge spinothalamic fibers unless facilitated.

Attempts to demonstrate facilitation within pain systems in man, by means of radiant heat, have failed. Unfortunately, pain fibers are too small to be studied easily by bioelectric methods, but in such studies on other somatosensory systems the evoked cortical response to peripheral stimulation has given little indication of facilitation in sensory systems.[1] One afferent volley tends to block another either by occlusion or by what resembles inhibition in reflex arcs. Clinical experience also teaches that the effect of a cutaneous pain or a strong stimulus (e.g., mustard plasters) is to reduce visceral pain, not facilitate it.

The crucial experiment to decide the role of facilitation versus simple convergence and projection would seem to be injection of procaine into the area to which the pain is projected. Such experiments have been carried out on man and animals for a variety of referred visceral and somatic pain, but with conflicting results. Unfortunately, no agreement has been reached, despite extensive investigations. It seems certain that visceral and somatic pain are referred after injection of procaine into the projection site or surgical deafferentation of it so that the convergence–projection mechanism is substantiated. Why in other situations the pain is alleviated is not clear. If, as the convergence–projection theory holds, the reference of pain is a psychologic phenomenon, several factors must be considered: (i) the subjective nature of the pain and its tendency to be reduced by any form of therapy, (ii) procaine injection does not produce a blankness, as does a visual field defect, but a feeling of numbness which may suppress the projection to the area, and (iii) the strength and persistence of the referred pain. In view of the conflicting nature of the evidence, perhaps it is best to accept both mechanisms as operative.

The only evidence that facilitation is a necessary feature of referred pain lies in the experiments of Weiss and Davis[44] and others, in which procaine injection into the skin over the area of reference ended the referred pain or caused it to migrate. However, studies by Carmichael, on anginal pain, and by Livingston, on diaphragmatic pain, have shown that procaine injection of an area of reference has no effect upon the reference. White et al.[47] denervated the thoracic wall by section of the intercostal nerves in dogs and observed that ischemia of the myocardium continued to produce pain; Wolff[53] also found that superficial anesthesia in most instances did not prevent the superficial reference of deep pain experimentally produced.

Rigidity and Deep Tenderness. This phenomenon is a special example of the sustained muscle contraction and resulting soreness which were discussed in connection with deep pain. Unlike referred pain, the rigidity which accompanies visceral disease is distributed regionally rather than segmentally. It appears to be a sustained reflex comparable to the flexion reflex of the limbs to nociceptive stimuli. Like referred pain, rigidity is typical of pain stimulation arising from the deep somatic tissues as well as that from diseased viscera, and is readily produced experimentally by hypertonic saline injections.

In fact, the rigidity of visceral disease is most marked when the body wall is involved (parietoskeletal reflex). Pain from some hollow organs is not accompanied by rigidity, whereas that from others is accompanied by a marked rigidity and a resulting deep tenderness that outlasts and outweighs the original pain.

McLellan and Goodell[32] described an experiment in which the ureter of a female patient was stimulated electrically near the kidney (Fig. 14). Pain with typical references anteriorly along the border of the rectus muscle at the level of the umbilicus was reported. This pain subsided quickly, but the muscles of the abdominal wall on the side of stimulation remained contracted, and, after about half an hour, the "side commenced to ache." This ache became severe and lasted six hours; the side was tender the next day. The course of this pain is shown in Figure 14. Similar experiments on the kidney pelvis yielded a similar result. The initial transient pain was referred to the back at the junction of the ribs and vertebral column, and the back muscles ached and became tender. If, in visceral disease, the source of pain continues, it is clear that the resulting pain may be a mixture of referred visceral pain and pain arising from sustained skeletal muscle contraction. Since the muscle ache and tenderness may be at a considerable distance from the site of the projected pain, rigidity and tenderness are an additional source of confusion in diagnosis.

Specific Applications. Although a detailed

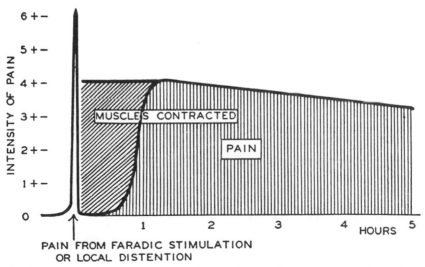

Fig. 14. Diagram to show sequence of sudden pain, muscle contraction and muscle ache from stimulation of ureter or kidney pelvis. (From McLellan and Goodell, *Res. Publ. Ass. nerv. ment. Dis.,* 1943, *23*:252–262.)

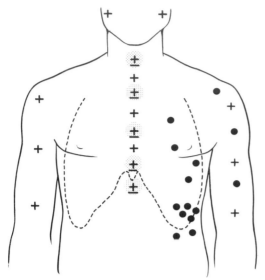

Fig. 15. Projection of pain and the diagnosis of coronary artery disease. The "false" pain indicated by black circles seems real to the patient but is "false" in leading to a diagnosis of coronary or other serious disease. The ±'s may be "false" in relation to coronary disease, but indicative of other serious organic disease. (From Macmillan, *N. Carolina med. J.*, 1952, *13*:9–11.)

consideration of pain characteristics of specific viscera is beyond the scope of a textbook of physiology, a few examples illustrating the mechanisms of visceral pain will be given.

Pains in the chest. As in Figure 15, these may be grouped as (i) due to angina pectoris or myocardial infarction, (ii) due to one of several disorders of the chest and abdomen, and (iii) "false" pains that have no diagnostic significance. The need to recognize (i) and (ii) is obvious. It is also extremely important to recognize the false pains, both in cardiac and other patients lest a cardiac neurosis be created.

Gastrointestinal pain from distension. Pain arising from the gastrointestinal tract has been investigated by Jones[24] in normal subjects (medical students), and by Ray and Neill[36] in patients during sympathectomy operations. Pain induced by inflation of a balloon at various levels in the upper end of the gastrointestinal tract (i) is usually anterior (but sometimes goes through to the back), (ii) is usually projected to the midline, and (iii) moves caudally as the stimulus is moved through the tract. As the position of the balloon moves through the esophagus, the point of projection moves with it (Fig. 16). Thus, esophageal sensation in this respect, as in others, is transitional between that typical of the exterior and that of the interior of the body. In contrast, the lower esophagus, the stomach and the duodenal cap all project to the region overlying the xiphoid (Fig. 17). The duodenal projections extend from the xiphoid to the umbilicus and are deep, resembling "a gas pain." The upper, middle and lower jejunum and the ileal projections are grouped around the umbilicus, and variations of several feet in the position of the balloon make no appreciable difference in the localization. The pain is well localized and sharp or cramplike. When the balloon is in the large bowel, the pain differs by being more diffusely localized and less intense; it is more often localized to one side of the midline and is always localized below the umbilicus, but with less correlation between locus of the balloon and locus of the projection. At three points, the hepatic and splenic flexures and the sigmoid, the loci of the balloon and of the projected sensation coincide. In part this correlates with the fixation of the colon and could be explained on the basis of unreferred somatic pain. However, Ray and Neill[36] found that these lateral projections are lost after sympathectomy.

Heart burn (pyrosis). This term describes a hot, burning, almost painful sensation deep to the sternum, popularly ascribed to regurgitation of acid gastric contents into the esophagus. However, such sensations are described when free gastric acidity is absent, and

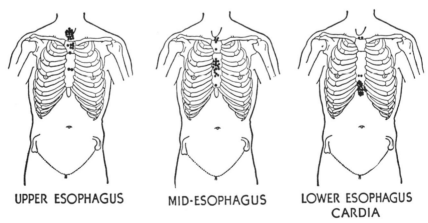

UPPER ESOPHAGUS   MID-ESOPHAGUS   LOWER ESOPHAGUS
CARDIA

Fig. 16. Reference of pain produced experimentally by distension of esophagus at various levels with balloon. (From Jones, *Digestive tract pain: diagnosis and treatment; experimental observations.* New York, Macmillan, 1938.)

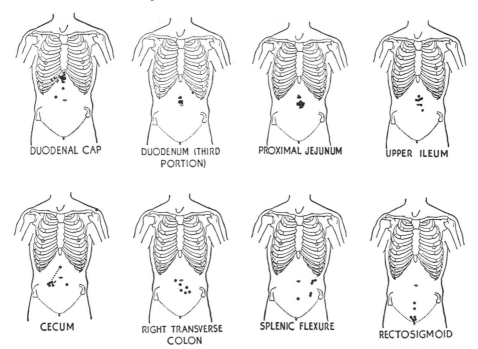

Fig. 17. Reference of pain produced experimentally by distension of small and large intestine at various levels. Note rapid downward progression of reference points as distending balloon progresses along duodenum and also that pain from jejunum and ileum are referred to about the same point. Note also shift of reference point from right center to left center combined with downward progression in passing from cecum to rectosigmoid. (Selected records from Jones, *Digestive tract pain: diagnosis and treatment; experimental observations.* New York, Macmillan, 1938.)

Jones[24] induced exactly the same burning sensation with mere inflation of a balloon inserted into the lower end of the esophagus. Actually, cold water or 0.1 normal NaOH was a more effective stimulus than 0.1 normal HCl. Often accompanying heart burn is what is popularly known as "acid regurgitation," in which a burning sensation seems to run up the esophagus with or without regurgitation of gastric contents into the mouth. X-ray observation shows that this sensation is accompanied by reverse esophageal peristalsis and that periods of heart burn are accompanied by constriction of the lower esophagus. Jones concluded that both phenomena result from abnormal neuromuscular activity and that the chemical constituency of any regurgitated fluid is of little importance.

Stomach pain. Pain from the stomach does not lend itself to study by the balloon technique. However, Wolf and Wolff[51] have studied the sensitivity of the gastric mucosa in a modern Alexis St. Martin, much as the sensitivity of skin has been studied. To mechanical and thermal stimulation, the gastric mucosa responded as does skin, but was not so sensitive. Nocuous stimuli such as pinching, electric shocks and strong chemicals did not arouse pain in normal mucosa, but did so if the mucosa was engorged or inflamed. Since the engorgement underlying such hypersensitivity could be produced by stress situations or psychologic probing, the experiments clearly illustrate a psychosomatic mech-

anism. Physiologically, this phenomenon seems to resemble primary cutaneous hyperalgesia, but whether secondary hyperalgesia is involved is not known.

Peptic ulcer pain. A variety of clinical and experimental facts, including the observations referred to in the previous paragraph, suggest that acidity is the immediate precipitating cause of pain in end-organs rendered excessively excitable by ulceration. Local vascular and inflammatory factors play a critical role. Mechanical factors such as hyperperistalsis are insufficient to evoke pain in the absence of acid, but play a subordinate role. The effect of surgical section of the vagus in ending pain is so immediate and dramatic some have thought that the vagus carries the pain impulses. However, direct evidence disproves such a theory, and the immediate relief must be interpreted to mean that the vagotomy immediately changes some factor in the equation of acid + local sensitivity = pain.

Appendicitis. The two stages in acute appendicitis illustrate two of the types of visceral pain described above. The first stage, consisting of pain localized diffusely to the midline at the epigastric level and not accompanied by muscular rigidity, is a classic example of unreferred visceral pain. The second stage, with pain much less diffuse, localized to the lower right quadrant and accompanied by rigidity and deep tenderness, illustrates referred parietal pain.

Gallbladder pain. Consistent with the studies of Ray and Neill,[36] gallbladder pain is localized to the right and above the umbilicus. It is a pain involving purely sympathetic innervation. Because the pain fibers from the gallbladder, pancreas, duodenum and stomach enter the spinal cord within a few thoracic segments, the references of pain are similar enough to make diagnosis difficult.

Pain Reaction versus Pain Perception. No discussion of the difficulties attending the interpretation of pain is complete without the recognition that different individuals evaluate the degree of pain quite differently. Chapman *et al.*,[13] using the Hardy–Wolff type of apparatus, measured the pain threshold of a normal and a psychoneurotic group of subjects. No clear difference was found in threshold. There seems little justification for the belief of psychoneurotics that they are "so sensitive to pain." When the test was conducted so that it measured the stimulus necessary to cause a reaction to pain— flinching, blinking or withdrawing—as opposed to mere detection of pain, there emerged a clear difference in the average threshold for reaction. On the average, the psychoneurotic group reacted more readily to pain. However, the amount of overlap was so great that it is perhaps more correct to say that *some* psychoneurotics react more to pain. Clearly, evaluation of pain at this level requires an understanding of the highest levels of cortical function. This subject will be discussed in the chapter on the cerebral association areas.

Pain as a Feeling State.[4, 8] The subject of pain extends considerably beyond pain as a sensation and the distortions of it seen in neurologic disease. In speaking of the "significance of pain" to the individual, one is dealing with emotion and the whole background of life experience which has contributed to giving pain emotional significance. Deflection of attention away from pain is a powerful factor in the end result of a painful stimulation. Whatever the agent used to control pain, it is necessary to examine whether it interferes mechanically and chemically with the pain pathways at some point, acts on some overt result of painful stimuli such as muscular contraction, or acts on the mechanisms of attention or emotion. Severing the connections of the prefrontal areas with the brain (prefrontal leukotomy) decreases the suffering from intractable pain but does not necessarily elevate the pain threshold or the subjective sensation of pain as nearly as that can be made out.

The lessened response to or evaluation of pain is described under a number of terms.

The unattentive, withdrawn element of the prefrontal leukotomy syndrome is a factor because when attention is focused on the source of painful stimuli, a sensation of pain and even suffering is reported accompanied by external signs of pain. The relief of pain by opiates and placebos thought to be opiates presents similar problems. The effectiveness of the placebo in about 35 per cent of subjects indicates that pain is elaborated in some way centrally where it is amenable to control by situational factors—in this case the belief in the supposed drug's effectiveness, the physician, etc. Morphine itself appears to relieve pain not by elevating the pain threshold or altering the subjective pain sensation. Much the same terms are used to describe the effect of morphine and of frontal leukotomy —an effect on anxiety or fear and upon attention by way of a "bemused state."

The concept that various agents and procedures and the make-up of the individual can alter the subjective response to pain without altering the pain sensation or its threshold seems well established. The study of the mechanism involved has only just begun. Clearly, evaluation of pain at the highest level requires an understanding of the highest levels of cortical function as well as the more primitive parts of the brain, which will be discussed in the next and subsequent chapters.

REFERENCES

1. AMASSIAN, V. E. *Res. Publ. Ass. nerv. ment. Dis.,* 1952, *30:* 371–402.
2. ARTHUR, R. P. and SHELLEY, W. B. *J. invest. Derm.,* 1955, *25:*341–346; and In *Pain and itch: nervous mechanisms,* Wolstenholme, G. E. W. and O'Connor, M., eds. Boston, Little, Brown and Co., 1959.
3. ASSOCIATION FOR RESEARCH IN NERVOUS AND MENTAL DISEASE. *Pain. Research Publications,* vol. 23. Baltimore, Williams & Wilkins, 1943.
4. BARBER, T. X. *Psychol. Bull.,* 1959, *56:*430–460.
5. BICKFORD, R. G. *Clin. Sci.,* 1938, *3:*377–386.
6. BISHOP, G. H. *J. Neurophysiol.,* 1943, *6:*361–382.
7. BISHOP, G. H. *J. invest. Derm.,* 1948, *11:*143–154.
8. BEECHER, H. K. *Pharmacol. Rev.,* 1957, *9:*59–209.
9. BONICA, J. J. *The management of pain.* Philadelphia, Lea & Febiger, 1953.
10. CANNON, B. *Amer. J. Physiol.,* 1933, *105:*366–372.
11. CAPPS, J. A., with collaboration of G. H. COLEMAN. *An experimental and clinical study of pain in the pleura, pericardium and peritoneum.* New York, Macmillan, 1932.
12. CHAPMAN, L. F., RAMOS, A. O., GOODELL, H. and WOLFF, H. G. *Arch. Neurol. (Chic.),* 1961, *4:*617–650.

13. CHAPMAN, W. P., FINESINGER, J. E., JONES, C. M. and COBB, S. *Arch. Neurol. (Chic.)*, 1947, *57:*321–331.

14. DORPAT, T. L. *Mechanisms of muscle pain.* M.D. Thesis, University of Washington, 1952.

15. ECHLIN, F. and PROPPER, N. *J. Physiol.,* 1937, *88:*388–400.

16. FEINDEL, W. H., WEDDELL, G. and SINCLAIR D. G. *J. Neurol. Psychiat.*, 1948, *11:*113–117.

17. GRIMSON, K. S., HESSER, F. H. and KITCHIN, W. W. *Surgery,* 1947, *22:*230–238.

18. HABGOOD, J. S. *J. Physiol.,* 1950, *111:*195–213.

19. HARDY, J. D., WOLFF, H. G. and GOODELL, H. *J. clin. Invest.,* 1950, *29:*115–140.

20. HINSEY, J. C. and PHILLIPS, R. A. *J. Neurophysiol.,* 1940, *3:*175–181.

21. HOLMES, T. H. and WOLFF, H. G. *Res. Publ. Ass. nerv. ment. Dis.,* 1950, *29:*750–772.

22. HUTCHINS, H. C. and REYNOLDS, O. E. *J. dent. Res.,* 1947, *26:*3–8.

23. INMAN, V. T. and SAUNDERS, J. B. DEC. M. *J. nerv. ment. Dis.,* 1944, *99:*660–667.

24. JONES, C. M. *Digestive tract pain: diagnosis and treatment; experimental observations.* New York, Macmillan, 1938.

25. KELLGREN, J. H. *Clin. Sci.,* 1938, *3:*175–190.

26. KINSELLA, V. J. *The mechanism of abdominal pain.* Sidney, Australasian Medical Publishing Co., 1948.

27. Klingon, G. H. and Jeffreys, W. H. *Neurology, (Minneap.),* 1958, *8:*272–276.

28. LEWIS, T. *Pain.* New York, Macmillan, 1942.

29. LEWIS, T. and HESS, W. *Clin. Sci.,* 1933, *1:*39–61.

30. LEWIS, T. and KELLGREN, J. H. *Clin. Sci.,* 1939, *4:*47–71.

31. MacKENZIE, J. *Brain,* 1893, *16:*321–354. See also his *Symptoms and their interpretation,* 2d ed. London, Shaw and Sons, 1912.

32. McLELLAN, A. M. and GOODELL, H. *Res. Publ. Ass. nerv. ment. Dis.,* 1943, *23:*252–262.

33. MOORE, R. M. *Surgery,* 1938, *3:*534–555.

34. MORLEY, J. *Abdominal pain.* New York, William Wood & Co., 1931.

35. PARK, S. R. and RODBARD, S. *Amer. J. Physiol.,* 1962, *203:*735–738.

36. RAY, B. S. and NEILL, C. L. *Ann. Surg.,* 1947, *126:*709–724.

37. REYNOLDS, O. E. and HUTCHINS, H. C. *Amer. J. Physiol.,* 1948, *152:*658–662.

38. ROSS, J. *Brain,* 1888, *10:*333–361.

39. ROTHMAN, S. *Res. Publ. Ass. nerv. ment. Dis.,* 1943, *23:*110–122.

40. SHELLEY, W. B. and ARTHUR, R. P. *Arch. Derm. (Chic.),* 1955, *72:*399–406.

41. SHELLEY, W. B. and ARTHUR, R. P. *Arch. Derm. (Chic.),* 1957, *76:*296–323.

42. SIMONS, D. J., DAY, E., GOODELL, H. and WOLFF, H. G. *Res. Publ. Ass. nerv. ment. Dis.,* 1943, *23:*228–244.

43. SINCLAIR, D. C., WEDDELL, G. and FEINDEL W. H. *Brain,* 1948, *71:*184–211.

44. WEISS, S. and DAVIS, D. *Amer. J. med. Sci.* 1928, *176:*517–536.

45. WHITE, J. C. *Res. Publ. Ass. nerv. ment. Dis.,* 1943, *23:*373–390.

46. WHITE, J. C., GARREY, W. E. and ATKINS, J. A. *Arch. Surg.,* 1933, *26:*765–786.

47. WHITE, J. C., SMITHWICK, R. H. and SIMEONE, F. A. *The autonomic nervous system; anatomy, physiology, and surgical application,* 3d ed. New York, Macmillan, 1952.

48. WHITE, J. C. and SWEET, W. H. *Pain. Its mechanisms and neurosurgical control.* Springfield, Ill., Charles C Thomas, 1955.

49. WIGGERS, C. J. Chap. 6 in LEVY, R. L., ed. *Diseases of the coronary arteries and cardiac pain.* New York, Macmillan, 1936.

50. WILLIAMS, A. F. *Thorax,* 1950, *5:*40–42.

51. WOLF, S. and WOLFF, H. G. *Human gastric function,* 2d ed. New York, Oxford University Press, 1947.

52. WOLFF, H. G. *Harvey Lect.,* 1944, *39:*39–95.

53. WOLFF, H. G. and WOLF, S. *Pain.* Springfield, Ill., Charles C Thomas, 1949.

54. ZOTTERMAN, Y. *J. Physiol.,* 1939, *95:*1–28.

CHAPTER 17

Taste, Olfaction and Visceral Sensation

By HARRY D. PATTON

TASTE[43, 56]

In the previous chapter, the pain aroused by noxious stimuli in visceral and deep structures was discussed. Scattered through the mesentery and within the walls and mucosa of the viscera are end-organs which mediate other sensations. The adequate stimulus for these receptors is usually either mechanical (distension or contraction) or chemical. The sense of taste falls into the latter category.

Four distinct gustatory submodalities are recognized: sweet, salt, bitter and sour or acid. The complex sensations aroused by mixed gustatory stimuli are a fusion of these four primary modalities along with various somatosensory and olfactory components. Application of pure solutions to various regions of the tongue reveals differences in sensitivity. The tip of the tongue is sensitive to all four modalities, but mostly to sweet and salt. The lateral margins of the tongue are most sensitive to sour or acid stimuli, but may also respond to salt. The basal portion of the tongue is sensitive to bitter stimuli.

The zonal distribution of sensitivity complicates determination of thresholds, because the threshold for a modality varies with the region of the tongue. For example, Kiesow reported the following thresholds (grams per cent) for quinine sulfate:

Base of tongue	0.00005%
Tip of tongue	0.00029%
Right edge of tongue	0.00020%
Left edge of tongue	0.00021%

Similar regional variations in threshold can be demonstrated for other pure stimuli.

Receptors. The taste buds are ovoid structures on the tongue, palate, anterior faucial pillars, pharynx and larynx. They are most numerous on the circumvallate and fungiform papillae of the tongue. The mid-dorsal region of the tongue lacks taste buds. Strangely, the larynx, particularly the laryngeal surface of the epiglottis and the medial and lateral surfaces of the arytenoids, is significantly populated with taste buds. Stimulation of these regions by solutions applied through a laryngoscope elicits taste sensations. Each bud is composed of a number of elongated receptor cells (about 10 μ in diameter) clustered together into a barrel-shaped structure about 50 μ in transverse diameter (Fig. 1, upper left). The apical tips of these cells project through the surface epithelium forming the gustatory pore; here sapid substances dissolved in the saliva come into contact with the membrane of the receptor cell. Electron micrographs reveal that the tips of the cells project through the pore as a number of filiform microvilli each 0.1 to 0.2 μ in diameter and 2 μ or more long (see Fig. 1, upper right). The space between the microvilli is filled with a dense homogeneous osmophilic material. The cytoplasm contains numerous mitochondria and large numbers of dense spherical granules.

The taste bud is innervated from its base. Here myelinated nerve fibers 1 to 6 μ in diameter approach the basement membrane, lose their myelin and form a plexus. The fibers of this plexus fall into two size groups: (i) 0.5 to 1.0 μ and (ii) less than 0.5 μ. Some of the latter measure only 50 millimicrons. The fibers of the plexus penetrate the basement membrane and occupy positions in invaginations of the receptor cell membrane, the relationship being similar to

that between axon and Schwann cell in the plexus (see lower half of Fig. 1). The larger fibers often lie between the boundaries of two receptor cells, forming intimate contact with both; smaller fibers are buried more deeply and have long mesaxons. The cytoplasm of both large and small fibers has numerous vesicles similar to those seen in presynaptic terminals; their significance is unknown.

The receptor cells appear to have a brief life cycle, degenerates being constantly replaced with new cells formed by mitotic division of adjacent epithelial cells. After injecting colchicine, which blocks mitotic division, Beidler[10] found numerous arrested mitotic figures in surrounding epithelium but none in the taste buds. After 8 to 10 hours the buds degenerated (presumably because they were not rejuvenated by addition of new receptor cells) and nerve responses to chemical stimulation of the tongue disappeared. In unpoisoned animals the chromosomal material of the dividing cells can be tagged with radioisotopically labeled thymidine, which can be detected radioautographically. After such an injection, the number of tagged cells in taste buds increases sharply, reaching a peak in about 100 hours, suggesting that the receptor cells are all of relatively recent origin. If this picture of rapid turnover is correct, it raises the perplexing question of how connections of nerve terminals and receptor cells are maintained.

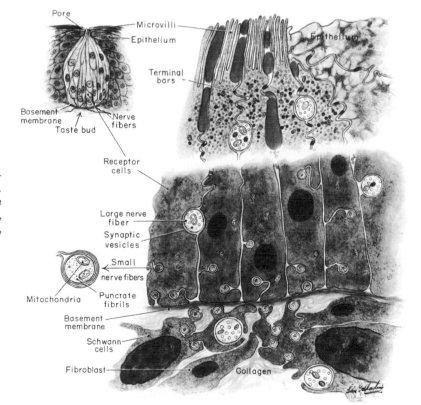

Fig. 1. Structure and innervation of the taste bud. (From de Lorenzo, In: *Olfaction and taste,* Y. Zotterman, ed., New York, The Macmillan Co., 1963.)

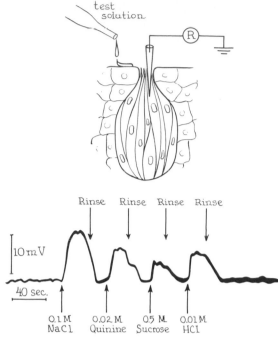

Fig. 2. Intracellularly recorded responses of taste receptor cells to gustatory stimuli. (After Kimura and Beidler, *J. cell. comp. Physiol.*, 1961, *58*:131–139.)

GENERATOR POTENTIALS. A microelectrode introduced through the gustatory pore may be positioned to record steady potentials of −50 to −95 mV. relative to an indifferent electrode on the neck muscles.[33, 53] The potential differences appear abruptly as the electrode is slowly advanced into the pore and disappear equally abruptly with further minute advance of the electrode. For these reasons, their occurrence is assumed to signal penetration of a receptor cell, and their magnitude to measure the transmembrane potential of the cell. Application of sapid substances to the surface of the tongue elicits a positive-going potential shift (Fig. 2) the magnitude of which varies with concentration of the stimulating solution (Fig. 3). The electrode records no all-or-nothing spikes; presumably the potential shifts are isolated graded generator potentials developed across the receptor cell membrane. How these generator potentials excite the nerve terminals nestled in the folds of the receptor cell membrane is not known, but a linkage between the two events is strongly suggested by the close correspondence between the amplitude-intensity curves of the receptor potential and of the integrated response of the nerve trunk (see below) supplying the tongue (Fig. 3).

Figure 2 shows that the same receptor cell responded to salty, sweet, bitter and sour test solutions although sensitivity was greatest for NaCl, which, in 0.1 molar solution, elicited a 10 mV. depolarization. Such promiscuous but "sensitivity-specific" behavior is commonly found and presents a serious difficulty for the long-cherished hypothesis that taste submodalities are mediated by separate specifically sensitive receptor cells.

Nerve Fiber Discharges. Taste-evoked conducted spikes can be recorded from single fibers teased from one of the nerve trunks supplying taste buds, usually the chorda tympani (see below). Figure 4 shows the response of such a fiber to application of varying concentrations of NaCl to the tongue. Generally such units, like other receptor units, signal increased intensity of stimulation by increased rate of firing and increased number of units firing. With prolonged stimulation the discharge adapts. Gustatory fibers, like the receptor cells which they supply, show only crudely quantitative selectivity in their responsiveness to solutions which give rise to markedly different taste sensations. For example, the NaCl-sensitive unit shown in Figure 4 also responded to HCl and to KCl.

A frequently used and convenient additional method of measuring the total neural response to gustatory stimulation is to record from the whole chorda tympani trunk using an integrating amplifier. Such amplifiers add together the asynchronous impulses in individual nerve fibers and give an approximate meas-

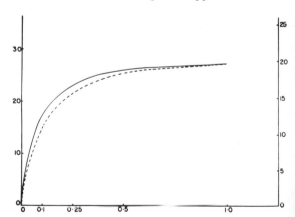

Fig. 3. Amplitude of receptor potential (solid line) and of integrated chorda tympani response (dashed line) to varying strengths of NaCl. *Abscissa,* concentration of NaCl; *ordinates,* amplitude of integrated response (right) and of receptor potential (left). Scales arranged so that asymptotes of two curves coincide. (From Kimura and Beidler, *J. cell. comp. Physiol.*, 1961, *58*:131–139.)

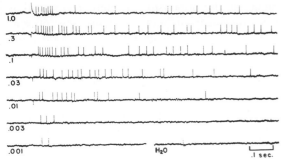

Fig. 4. Response of single afferent fiber in rat chorda tympani to NaCl applied to tongue. Numbers under records give molar concentration of solution. *Lower right record,* Control with water as stimulus. (From Pfaffmann, *J. Neurophysiol.,* 1955, *18:*429–440.)

ure of the magnitude of response of a population of units. Integrated records provided the data for construction of the dashed curve in Figure 3.

Neural Mechanism of Submodality Discrimination. The nonspecific sensitivity of receptor cells (and hence of the afferent fibers which serve them) to stimuli easily discriminated subjectively is puzzling. A single gustatory unit indiscriminately responsive to each of several substances cannot distinctively signal by its discharge which of these substances elicited the discharge. This is true even if the unit shows (as most do) some quantitative variation in sensitivity to various substances, because concentrations for each substance could still be found which would produce identical discharge rates. Pfaffman[43] suggests that the frequency pattern of the discharge of a *population* of receptors constitutes the basis for discrimination. Erickson,[24] using an ingenious combination of electrophysiologic and behavioral techniques, has tested this theory. In a number of single fibers teased from the chorda tympani he measured the discharge rate elicited by NH_4Cl, KCl and $NaCl$ solutions on the tongue. The correlation between sensitivities to NH_4Cl and KCl was $+0.83$; i.e., fibers which had high sensitivity to NH_4Cl tended to have high sensitivity to KCl. Sensitivities to $NaCl$, however, were poorly correlated with those to KCl (-0.09) or to NH_4Cl (-0.11). If the population discharge pattern determines submodality discrimination, it might therefore be predicted that animals would find the discrimination between NH_4Cl and KCl more difficult than the discrimination between either of these substances and $NaCl$. Behavioral tests showed this to be the case. Rats were trained to avoid drinking KCl by giving them a painful shock each time they sampled the solution. When animals so trained were presented a free choice to drink KCl, NH_4Cl or $NaCl$, they avoided not only KCl but also NH_4Cl, but their consumption of $NaCl$ solution was little altered.

Taste Pathways. At least two cranial nerves are involved in the transmission of taste impulses from the tongue. The taste buds of the posterior one-third of the tongue are innervated by the *glossopharyngeal nerve;* those from the anterior two-thirds by the chorda tympani branch of the *facial nerve*. Also, a few fibers in the vagus may supply the buds of the larynx and pharynx. The trigeminal nerve mediates general somatic sensation from the tongue, but apparently contains no gustatory afferents.

Taste fibers entering the glossopharyngeal nerve continue with it into the brain. The course of taste fibers leaving the tongue in the chorda tympani is complicated, apparently being subject to individual variation. Of the four known peripheral pathways for these fibers, only two need be described here. The first is a direct route via the chorda tympani until it joins the facial nerve and thence in this nerve to the brain. The second pathway is via the chorda tympani through its anastomoses with the otic ganglion. The taste fibers pass through this ganglion to the greater petrosal nerve and in it to the geniculate ganglion of the facial nerve. The former is the usual route, but the petrosal nerve may be important in a few people.

That taste fibers in both the facial and glossopharyngeal nerves are small may be inferred from the small amplitude and slow conduction of impulses aroused by gustatory stimulation. Zotterman[55] assigned taste fibers a diameter of less than 4 μ. In the "demotored" chorda tympani of the cat, 18 per cent of the fibers are unmyelinated (less than 1.5 μ), and myelinated afferents range from 1.5 to 6.0 μ.[26]

The afferent fibers of the VIIth, IXth and Xth nerves, after entering the medulla, form a well-defined common descending tract, the *tractus solitarius*. In this respect, taste fibers behave like the pain and temperature fibers of the trigeminal nerve, which descend in the neighboring spinal trigeminal tract (Fig. 5). Most of the taste and viscerosensory fibers terminate in the gray matter adjacent to the solitary tract, *nucleus tractus solitarius*.[45] The fibers of the three nerves terminate at different levels in the nucleus. Fibers from the facial and glossopharyngeal nerve terminate in the rostral part of the nucleus, only vagal fibers entering the caudal portion. Consequently, secondary taste neurons are concentrated in the rostral part of the nucleus.

The axons of the secondary neurons pursue a course up the brain stem in close relation to the medial lemniscus and the ventral secondary quintothalamic tract. The gustatory fibers relay in the most medial part of the nucleus ventralis posteromedialis (arcuate nucleus). Lesions of

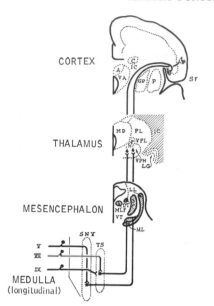

Fig. 5. Summary diagram, highly schematic, representing taste and somatosensory pathways from face. *A,* Anterior thalamic nucleus; *BC,* brachium conjunctivum; *C,* caudate nucleus; *CM,* n. centrum medianum; *DT,* dorsal secondary trigeminal tract; *GP,* globus pallidus; *IC,* internal capsule; *LG,* lateral geniculate body; *LL,* lateral lemniscus; *MD,* n. medialis dorsalis; *ML,* medial lemniscus; *MLF,* medial longitudinal fasciculus; *P,* putamen; *PL,* n. lateralis posterior; *SF,* sylvian fissure; *SNV,* spinal nucleus of 5th nerve; *TS,* nucleus of tractus solitarius; *VA,* n. ventralis anterior; *VPL,* n. ventralis posterolateralis; *VPM,* n. ventralis posteromedialis (arcuate nucleus); *VT,* ventral secondary trigeminal tract.

this nucleus in the monkey severely impair the animal's ability to discriminate between quinine solutions and water.[15, 41] Single units isolated in the medial arcuate nucleus are driven by gustatory stimulation of the tongue; these cells are distinct from more laterally situated cells which respond to thermal or mechanical stimuli to the tongue.[12, 14]

In the cortex the taste-receiving area lies in close association with the representation of other modalities from the tongue.[13, 14, 34, 39] In monkey and chimpanzee, taste deficits follow lesions which destroy the cortex buried in the sylvian fissure at the foot of the fissure of Rolando.[9, 40, 47] Benjamin[12] believes that the claustrum may be involved in taste perception.

Biologic Value of Taste.[44, 46] Superficially, taste appears to be an unimportant sensory modality. Richter,[46] however, has shown that taste plays a critical role in nutrition and in the maintenance of a constant internal environment for the organism. He demonstrated that rats suffering from dietary or endocrine deficiencies select foodstuffs or liquids containing the substances required to correct their deficiencies. For example, an adrenalectomized rat shows a marked appetite for saline and, if allowed to do so, will selectively drink sufficient sodium chloride not only to maintain life but to gain weight; adrenalectomized animals not offered saline die within a few days. Similarly, a parathyroidectomized animal displays an increased appetite for solutions containing calcium, and this appetite can be abolished by parathyroid implants. Vitamin-deficient rats will also eat selectively those foods containing the necessary vitamins. Taste provides the sensory cue by which these vitally important discriminative selections are made. Animals with their peripheral taste nerves sectioned are no longer capable of regulating their diets to correct deficiencies, but tend to eat and drink indiscriminately.

OLFACTION[36, 56]

The olfactory mucosa occupies an area of 2.5 sq. cm. in each nostril, including the upper third of the septum and the superior concha. Little of the air entering the nostrils in quiet respiration reaches the olfactory crypt. Rapidly diffusing molecules of volatile substances may, however, reach the mucosa, and sniffing creates currents which aid in carrying molecules upward into this secluded location.

Absolute olfactory thresholds vary considerably, depending on the methods of measurement, but agree in indicating very high sensitivity. For example, artificial musk can be detected at a concentration of only 0.00004 mg. per liter of air and mercaptan at 0.00000004 mg. per liter of air.

Relative thresholds can be measured more easily and yield consistent results. Although variations from person to person occur because of differences in the construction of the nasal passages,[23] ranges of normal values have been obtained, and repeated determinations on a man give constant values. In women, the individual results are also consistent, but acuity increases just before and during the menstrual period.

The first apparatus for testing olfaction in the human was designed by Zwaardemaker. It consists of two concentric tubes. The inner wall of the outer tube is porous so that it may be saturated with an odorous solution. The inner tube, graduated in arbitrary units of length termed *olfacties,* may be inserted into the outer tube to any depth. This controls the area of odorous material exposed. The tube is held to one nostril and the subject inhales through it. Unfortunately, this procedure does not control the force of inhalation, which can affect the threshold. To overcome this, Elsberg[23] designed an apparatus by which the odorous material is pumped into the nostril while the subject holds his breath. With this apparatus, the minimum identifiable odor (MIO), or threshold, is determined as the least quantity of air saturated with the olfactory substance which can be smelled when injected with uniform force.

These olfactory testing methods have some application in clinical neurology. In 74 per cent of patients with tumors in or around the frontal lobes, the MIO was found to be elevated.[23] No changes were found in patients with lesions below the tentorium. Through lack of sufficient postmortem verification of the lesions, such studies have failed to contribute much to the understanding of how the various parts of the olfactory system function.

Receptors. The olfactory mucosa is composed of two intermingled vertically oriented cell types: (i) the sustentacular cells and (ii) the receptor cells (Fig. 6). The former are columnar cells with filamentous processes (microvilli) abutting the nasal cavity. The receptor cells are bipolar neurons which serve both as receptors and ganglion cells. At their dendritic extremities they expand and present toward the nasal cavity 6 to 12 cilia. The expanded portion (called the olfactory rod) contains vacuoles and mitochondria as well as numerous vesicles resembling those seen in presynaptic terminals. At its basal extremity the receptor cell dwindles; its membrane is continuous with that of the axon from which it derives. Each axon gives rise to only one receptor cell.

The olfactory nerve fibers pass through the cribriform plate to enter the olfactory bulb. The individual axons, which average $0.2\ \mu$ in di-

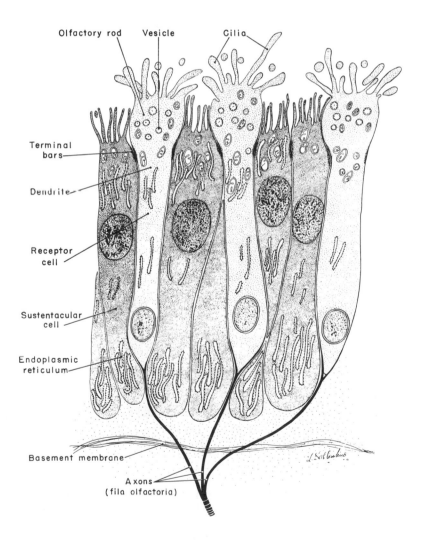

Fig. 6. Structure and innervation of the olfactory mucosa. (From de Lorenzo, In: *Olfaction and taste,* Y. Zotterman, ed., New York, The Macmillan Co., 1963.)

ameter, bear a unique relation to the Schwann sheath: each Schwann mesaxon surrounds not a single axon (cf. Fig. 10, Chap. 3) but a cluster of closely packed axons, the membranes of which are separated by spaces only 100 to 150 Å wide.[27, 56]

GENERATOR POTENTIALS.[35]   The small size of olfactory receptors precludes intracellular recording. An electrode placed on the surface of the olfactory mucosa records a slow negative potential (electro-olfactogram) when a jet of odorous air is directed over the mucosa (Fig. 7). The amplitude of the potential increases approximately logarithmically with increasing odor intensity. The potential persists after application of cocaine to the mucosa in doses sufficient to block impulse traffic in the olfactory nerve fibers. These similarities to unitary generator potentials (see Chap. 4) suggest that the electro-olfactogram reflects the local graded potential of a population of primary olfactory receptors under the electrode. Since the potential is a mass response, it provides little information about the excitatory process in individual receptor cells; nevertheless, as shown in Figure 7, different odorants elicit potentials of different configurations and durations.

RECEPTOR SPIKES.[30]   Spike activity of individual olfactory receptors may be recorded extracellularly with microelectrodes positioned in the olfactory mucosa (Fig. 8). A minute (0.2 ml.)

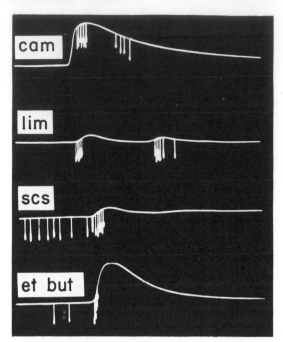

Fig. 8.   Electro-olfactogram and receptor spike discharges recorded during stimulation of frog olfactory mucosa with brief jets of odorous air. From above downward stimuli were: camphor, limonene (two puffs), carbon disulfide and ethyl butyrate. Sweep lengths 10 seconds. (From Gesteland *et al.* In: *Olfaction and taste,* Y. Zotterman, ed., New York, The Macmillan Co., 1963.)

puff of odorized air evokes bursts of spikes lasting for 1 to 4 seconds and reaching frequencies up to 20 per second. Increasing the volume of the jet increases both the amplitude of the electro-olfactogram and the number and frequency of spikes. Individual units are only crudely odor-selective; most show especially strong responses to one or more odorants and weaker responses to others (Fig. 8). Just how such receptors signal to the brain the many subjectively discriminable odor submodalities is not clear.

Olfactory Bulb and Central Olfactory Pathways.   The axons issuing from the olfactory receptors enter the cranial cavity through the cribriform plate of the ethmoid bone. On the ventral surface of the frontal lobes near the midline they enter the olfactory bulb. The bulb, like the retina, is a part of the brain proper. In lower animals it is prominent and possesses a cavity which communicates with the ventricular system of the brain. In man, the central cavity is obliterated by a mass of neuroglia. Next to the neuroglia is a deep layer of myelinated fibers passing from the bulb to the olfactory tract (Fig.

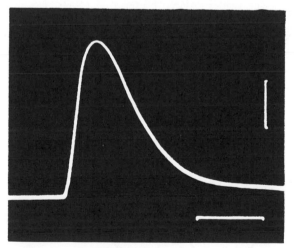

Fig. 7.   The electro-olfactogram recorded from surface of olfactory mucosa of frog. Stimulus was a brief jet of air containing butanol. Upward deflection signifies negativity of mucosal surface to distant electrode. Horizontal bar, 2 seconds; vertical bar, 1 mV. (From Ottoson In: *Olfaction and taste,* Y. Zotterman, ed., New York, The Macmillan Co., 1963.)

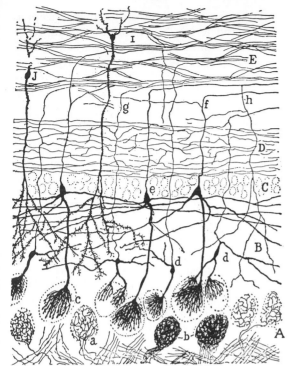

Fig. 9. Olfactory bulb of a kitten, Golgi stain. Surface of bulb is at bottom; core white matter at top. *A*, Layer of glomeruli; *B*, external plexiform layer; *C*, layer of mitral cells; *D*, internal plexiform layer; *E*, layer of granule cells and white matter; *I*, *J*, granule cells; *a*, *b*, glomerular terminals of primary olfactory fibers; *c*, glomerular terminal of mitral cell dendrite; *d*, tufted cells; *e*, mitral cell; *h*, recurrent collateral of mitral cell axon. (From Ramón y Cajal.)

9). Superficially there is a layer of unmyelinated fibers which are the terminations of the olfactory nerve. Situated between the two fiber layers is a mass of gray matter which contains three types of neurons, the tufted cells, the mitral cells and the granule cells. The tufted cells are the most superficial. The mitral cells form a compact layer just beneath them. The dendrites of both types of cells course toward the periphery of the bulb and break up into rounded, bushy terminals, the olfactory glomeruli, which form synapses with the primary olfactory fibers. The axons of the mitral and tufted cells join the deep myelinated fiber layer of the bulb to pass into the olfactory tract. The axons of the tufted cells probably leave the tract to reach the opposite olfactory bulb via the anterior commissure; they do not degenerate if the olfactory tract is severed. The mitral cells are thus the secondary olfactory neurons. The granule cells are most deeply situated and send short axons toward the surface of the bulb.

The olfactory tract courses caudally on the base of the frontal lobes. Both tract and bulb are derivatives of the brain, and the fibers of the tract are capped dorsally by gray matter continuous with the gray matter of the bulb; the tract is really a gyrus in which the gray matter has been greatly reduced. The site of termination of the tract fibers is not entirely settled. The most careful studies[19] indicate the following direct connections: (i) the opposite bulb (via the anterior commissure), (ii) the prepyriform area and parts of the amygdaloid complex, and (iii) the olfactory tubercle. Contrary to the usual statement, there appear to be no direct connections with either the hippocampus or the septal area.[17] Unlike all other sensory modalities, olfaction does not seem to have a thalamic representation.

Olfactory Discrimination. An amazing variety of odors can be distinguished even by man, in whom olfaction is much less acute than it is in lower animals. It is therefore interesting to inquire how the centrally transmitted message varies when the mucosa is excited by psychologically discriminable odorants. An estimated 26,000 receptors converge upon a single glomerulus. Also, each glomerulus receives axons from some 24 mitral cells and 68 tufted cells.[5] This extreme convergence and divergence allows for a complex variation of pattern in the centrally directed message.

Fine electrodes thrust into the central white matter of the bulb satisfactorily record spike activity of individual secondary units (axons of mitral and/or tufted cells).[3] In the anesthetized animal breathing odorous air, each inspiration is accompanied by a burst of activity in secondary axons; this ceases when charcoal-filtered air is substituted for odorous air. For each mitral unit isolated there is one odor which will stimulate it at a concentration too low to affect other units in touch with the electrode. The selective sensitivity is usually greatest for one substance, but chemically related substances may also be effective.[4]

Electrodes in different parts of the bulb record differential activity with different odorants.[2] In rabbits the anterior part of the bulb responds briskly to inhalation of substances with a fruity odor, e.g., amyl acetate, whereas a posteriorly situated electrode records little. The posterior part, however, responds readily when oily-smelling substances, e.g., benzene or pentane, are added to inspired air. Adrian[2] suggests that such spatial differences (as well as certain observable temporal differences) may constitute a basis for odor discrimination.

The spatial arrangement of the projection of the olfactory mucosa onto the bulb can be mapped because receptors whose axons are interrupted rapidly undergo retrograde degeneration.[20] By making discrete lesions of the bulb and mapping the areas of atrophy in the mucosa, one can map the spatial pattern of projection. Such studies first led to the conclusion that there is no topographic organization of the projection onto the bulb.[20] Subsequently, Le Gros Clark[18] repeated these experiments and found mucosal degeneration was not completely diffuse following discrete bulbar lesions, but tended to appear in patches, the boundaries of which were sometimes sharp. It is evident, however, that there is no point-to-point projection of mucosa onto the bulb in the sense that each local area of sensory epithelium is represented centrally in an orderly sequence of equivalent areas having the same spatial relationship. The reason for this is the plexiform distribution of the primary fibers after they reach the surface of the bulb. Normal material shows olfactory fibers randomly approaching and entering individual glomeruli from different directions.

VISCERAL SENSATION

Since the afferent fibers of the autonomic and

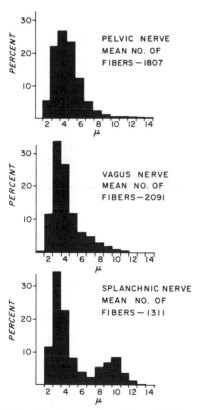

Fig. 10. Histogram of myelinated afferent fibers in "demotored" autonomic trunks supplying viscera. Abscissae show fiber diameters in μ; ordinates, percentage incidence of fibers at each diameter. (From Griffin, Griffin and Patton, unpublished studies.)

somatic nervous systems are similar except in course, the terms "sympathetic visceral afferents" and "parasympathetic visceral afferents" do not imply any functional peculiarity of these afferents as compared with somatic afferents (see Chap. 16). Actually, the sensory innervation of the visceral cavities is derived from both the autonomic and the somatic nervous system.

The number of visceral afferent fibers traversing somatic pathways cannot be estimated, but about 10,500 myelinated visceral afferents traverse autonomic pathways. To this should be added an uncounted but large number of unmyelinated (type C) visceral afferents reaching the spinal cord by both pathways. Figure 10 shows the size distribution of myelinated, visceral, autonomic afferents in the cat. The data were obtained by enumerating and measuring osmic acid-stained fibers remaining after section had caused degeneration of the efferent fibers. In all three nerves there are prominent peaks at 3 to 4 μ (A delta fibers). The splanchnic nerves show a second smaller peak at 10 μ (A alpha fibers). The vagal afferents shown are almost wholly derived from thoracic and cervical structures. Compound action potentials elicited by stimulating the vagus just above the diaphragm show only a C elevation, and sections of "demotored" supradiaphragmatic vagus show few or no myelinated afferents. Vagal afferents from abdominal viscera are thus nearly all unmyelinated.

Reflex Afferents. Not all of the visceral afferents are truly sensory. Many form reflex connections in the cord and bulb without projections to the higher sensory centers. Such fibers do not mediate conscious sensation. The origin of visceral afferents and the reflex and sensory functions which they subserve are shown diagrammatically in Figure 11. The afferent limbs of the reflex arcs controlling vital visceral phenomena—cardiac reflexes, aortic reflexes, Hering–Breuer reflex, micturition, etc.—are without exception found in *parasympathetic nerves.* True, stimulation of the central end of the splanchnic nerve will elevate blood pressure and initiate polysynaptic reflex discharges in adjacent ventral roots, but these appear to be pain reflexes. Gentle stimulation of the mesentery[29] or weak stimulation of the central end of the splanchnic nerve, although adequate to excite the large afferent fibers, does not elicit reflex discharge. This occurs only when stimuli are sufficiently strong to excite smaller A delta fibers.[7] The sympathetic afferent fibers, although abundant, are not essential to the reflex regulation of the visceral organs. Reflexes from parasympathetic afferents are regulatory reflexes operative under normal conditions of life, whereas the reflexes from sympathetic afferents occur in response to strong stimuli and in pathologic conditions. The contrast between sympathetic and parasympathetic motor function (Cannon) applies equally well to afferent function. The sympathetic afferents are "dispensable."

In this chapter, the visceral sensory afferents are discussed. Visceral reflex afferents are described in the chapters dealing with the organ systems which they serve.

Sensory Visceral Afferents and Their Central Pathways

Somatic and Sympathetic Afferents. Noxious stimulation (pinching, burning, application of hypertonic NaCl or acid) of the diaphragm sets up a shower of small centripetally conducted spike potentials in the phrenic nerve.[28] Light tactile stimulation is without effect. When the nerve is subdivided, individual spikes can be recorded and conduction velocities estimated from spike size and duration. Such studies indicate that the active fibers are of A delta or C size. Similar small spikes appear in the splanchnic nerve when the intestine is pinched.[29] Passage of strong peristaltic waves and spastic contractions of the intestinal wall induced by local application of acetylcholine also excite splanchnic A delta and C fibers. It thus appears that

visceral and cutaneous pain are conducted by similar fibers.

Light mechanical stimulation of the mesentery elicits in the splanchnic nerve large spikes with conduction velocities in the alpha range.[29] These fibers supply the pacinian corpuscles of the mesentery.[50] However, some of the large splanchnic afferents must end in other kinds of receptors, because there are more large splanchnic afferents than pacinian corpuscles.[7] The sensory function of mesenteric pacinian corpuscles is not entirely clear. They are rapidly adapting receptors and are exquisitely sensitive to mechanical distortion; the air vibration induced by the spoken voice is often sufficient to excite a brief shower of spikes.

Both A alpha and A delta groups project to the cerebral cortex and hence presumably subserve conscious sensation. Stimulation of the splanchnic nerve evokes typical surface-positive potentials in the contralateral postcentral gyrus.[6] The splanchnic receiving zone lies between and overlaps the areas for the arm and leg in the somatosensory cortex. A similar topographic projection of splanchnic impulses obtains in the lateral part of the posteroventral thalamic nucleus.[38] This accords with expectation in a topographically organized system. There appears to be no special cortical or thalamic area devoted to visceral as opposed to somatic sensation.

Weak stimuli liminal for A alpha fibers evoke a smooth cortical wave with a latency of 8 to 12 milli-

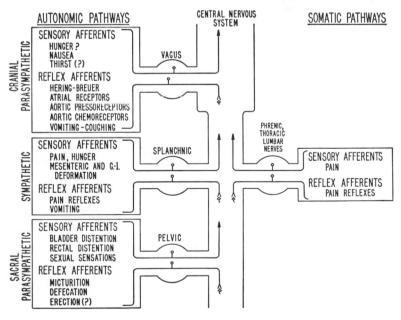

Fig. 11. Diagram showing origin and function of visceral afferent fibers.

seconds. Mechanical stimulation of the mesentery produces a similar response, although the latency may be slightly greater (15 milliseconds). Stronger shocks recruiting A delta fibers into the afferent volley produce a double wave, the second wave (latency about 20 milliseconds) being superimposed on the rising limb of the first. Thus, at least some of the impulses carried by A delta afferents reach the cortex. The spinal pathway for the large afferent fibers is via the dorsal columns; shocks strong enough to excite A delta fibers evoke electrical activity in the contralateral anterolateral column.[7]

Conduction of visceral afferent impulses to the cortex is conditioned by activity in somatic afferents. A shock to the splanchnic nerve which produces a maximal cortical response when delivered alone may produce little or no response if it is preceded by a shock to somatic afferents.[8] Blockage of conduction of splanchnic impulses may also occur with antecedent tactile stimulation of the skin. Blocking interaction is readily demonstrated at the thalamic level. It may explain the efficacy of cutaneous irritation (mustard poultices) in relieving visceral distress.

Vagus Nerve. The evidence for a specific cortical projection of vagal afferents is much less clear. Dell[22] recorded short-latency (8 to 10 milliseconds) cortical responses to vagal stimulation. The responsive cortical area was in the inferior part of the face somatosensory area. In the thalamus responses of 5 to 6 milliseconds latency were recorded in the midline nuclei medial to the face somatosensory relay nuclei. Other investigators have failed to record specific cortical responses to vagal stimulation.[48, 49]

In conscious humans, stimulation of the postcentral cortex within the sylvian fissure elicits sensations referred to the pharynx.[42] Nausea, "sinking sensations of the stomach," belching and vomiting may result when the island of Reil is stimulated. It is, however, quite possible that the primary effect is motor and that the sensations are secondary.

Most of the myelinated vagal afferents appear to subserve purely reflex functions.[37] Sensations aroused by irritation of the pharynx or the lining of the respiratory tree (the adequate stimulus for the gag and cough reflexes) may be subserved by myelinated afferents since these structures are clearly supplied with some of the larger afferent fibers of the vagus. However, we have seen that the abdominal viscera have few if any myelinated vagal afferents. Specific cortical projection of impulses traversing C fibers has never been clearly demonstrated by electrical recording methods. This may be due to the small size of potentials conducted in small fibers, or it may indicate that sensations mediated by C fibers are elaborated at subcortical levels.[48]

Pelvic Nerve. Stimulation of the central end of the pelvic nerve evokes small primary cortical responses in the most medial part of the leg somatosensory cortex to which tactile impulses from the sacral segments project. Whether these responses represent the neural substratum of bladder or genital sensation, however, is open to question; cortical stimulation in conscious patients produces neither micturition nor sensations referable to the bladder.[42] Similarly, electrical stimulation of cortex does not elicit sexual sensations, although contralateral noncrotic sensations projected to the genitalia occur when the postcentral gyrus is stimulated on the mesial surface of the hemisphere.

Erickson[25] reported the case of a female patient in whom a tumor arising from the falx and compressing the paracentral lobule produced seizures characterized by erotic sensations and intense desire for intercourse. The patient described the sensations as more intense on the side opposite the tumor. She was first diagnosed as a nymphomaniac, and an unsuccessful attempt was made to induce artificial menopause by ovarian irradiation. Subsequent discovery and removal of the tumor abolished the symptoms.

Summary. Two features are notable in the cortical projections of autonomic visceral afferents. First, despite their common origin in visceral structures, the three nerves have quite separate cortical receiving zones. This is because they enter the nervous system at different levels: sacral, thoracic, and bulbar. The orderly segmental pattern of afferent inflow is preserved in cortical localization which respects neither functional similarity nor anatomic propinquity of the organs represented.[48] Secondly, relatively small areas of cortex are devoted to the viscera. This corresponds to the poverty of spatial discrimination in visceral sensations as compared, for example, with cutaneous tactile sensation, vision, or audition, which have extensive cortical receiving zones. Precise spatial discrimination apparently requires large numbers of cortical cells.

ORGANIC SENSATIONS

In the previous chapter it was emphasized that visceral pain is chiefly mediated by afferent fibers traveling with sympathetic and somatic nerves. The remaining sensations from visceral organs (hunger, thirst, bladder fullness, sexual sensations, etc.) are termed "organic sensations." Organic sensations signal body needs and lead to behavior which satisfies those needs. They are mediated by both sympathetic and parasympathetic afferents.

Hunger. Hunger, defined generically as all those processes which lead to the ingestion of food, has at least three components: appetite, hunger sensations or pangs, and a third, unnamed, physiologic state or hunger-drive which leads to the ingestion of food.

APPETITE. The term "appetite" refers to a food preference which "arises from the experience of previous pleasures; a wishing, longing or yearning for something especially desirable" (Cannon). Associated with appetite are conditioned gastrointestinal reflexes. The sight, smell or taste of favored food elicits copious secretions of saliva and gastric juice, whereas similar presentation of food for which the subject has little liking is a much less potent stimulus. Since most obesity appears to result from strong appetites and their free indulgence, it often is primarily a psychologic problem. Although previous experience is most important in determining appetite, genetic factors obviously determine food preferences of different species; for example, lions do not eat tomatoes, nor do monkeys eat meat. Appetite as reflected by food preference patterns may also be altered by dietary or metabolic deficiencies, as discussed in the previous section on taste. The preference pattern is invariably of a type which combats or offsets the deficiency. The mechanism of such homeostatic changes of appetite is poorly understood.

HUNGER SENSATIONS. Although appetite may determine *what* we eat under situations of free choice, it does not determine *when* or *how much* we eat. In the human, frequency of eating is largely determined by social custom and by appetite. There is, however, a physiologic mechanism for signaling that it is time to eat—*hunger sensations*. These are described as "a very disagreeable ache or pang or sense of gnawing or pressure which is referred to the epigastrium." Hunger pangs recur periodically and with a fair degree of regularity. Prior to 1911, hunger sensation was considered to be a sensation of the depletion of bodily stores of foodstuffs in blood or tissues. Cannon discovered that hunger pangs

are sensations derived from contractions of the empty stomach.

Frequency and amplitude of hunger contractions are greatest in the empty stomach. They disappear promptly with ingestion of food and are temporarily stopped by sham chewing or swallowing, by smoking, by alcohol, or by tightening the belt. Strong emotional states also abolish them. Sleep, however, does not inhibit them. Restlessness and dreams are associated with their occurrence, as was proved by a simultaneous recording technique (Carlson). Newborn infants are restless before feeding time as though disturbed by unpleasant sensations, and random activity of rats interpretable as food seeking is associated with onset of hunger contractions. Recent observations suggest that hunger sensations do not cause the increased random activity, but that both are manifestations of some more deep-seated phenomenon. For example, lowering the blood sugar level by injection of insulin increases hunger contractions, spontaneous activity and food intake. In prolonged fasts hunger sensations disappear after the first few days, but the hunger contractions persist. This appears to be due to some central adaptive process.

Hunger contractions, both spontaneous and insulin-induced, are abolished by vagotomy.[51] It is thus difficult to test the time-honored hypothesis that the afferent path of hunger sensations is vagal. At least part of the impulses traverse sympathetic pathways. Grossman and Stein[31] stated that sympathectomy abolishes hunger sensations although the contractions persist. This is not surprising, since hunger pangs are disagreeable sensations allied to pain, which is, of course, mediated via sympathetic pathways.

HUNGER DRIVE. Although hunger contractions signal to the nervous system emptiness of the stomach (and possibly hypoglycemia), they are not essential for the maintenance of food intake sufficient to support caloric balance. Neither vagotomy (Bash, Morgan) nor gastrectomy (Tsang) seriously affects food intake, food seeking activity or weight maintenance. In vagotomized humans, insulin-induced hypoglycemia no longer elicits hunger contractions, but usually creates a desire for food.[31] Finally, cessation of hunger contractions (which occurs with the ingestion of a few mouthfuls of food) does not correlate with termination of eating. Rather, eating normally continues until sufficient calories have been ingested to maintain requirements. Mature rats fed diets diluted with cellulose or kaolin eat increased quantities and maintain constant caloric intake and weight.[1] Similarly, fat-fortified high caloric diets lead to decreased bulk intake until constant caloric intake is achieved.[*][52] Thus it must be concluded that *hunger as a physiologic state leading to ingestion of food and in amounts adjusted to energy expenditure is something different from hunger as a sensation.* Hunger as a drive is discussed in Chapters 11 and 25.

Thirst.[54] Thirst, like hunger, appears to consist of a sensory component and a physiologic state or drive. The sensory component is mediated by the glossopharyngeal and vagus nerves which signal the dryness of throat which accompanies dehydration. Salivary secretion, for example, decreases markedly with advancing dehydration; with water deficits of 8 per cent of the body weight (computed from weight loss during dehydration), salivary flow drops to near zero. The resulting dryness of the mucous membranes is sensed. This sensation can be abolished by anesthetizing the mucous membrane or by administering drugs which stimulate salivary flow.

The presence or absence of a sensation of oral and pharyngeal dryness does not, however, govern the frequency or amount of drinking. Neither section of the IXth and Xth nerves nor removal of the salivary glands affects water intake. Drugs (e.g., pilocarpine) which stimulate salivary secretion prevent oral dryness but do not alter the amount of water drunk by dehydrated humans. Obviously, then, there is a thirst drive or "urge to drink" which is relatively independent of the sensory component of thirst.

The mechanism of the thirst drive is entirely unknown, but experiments show that the intensity of the drive is directly related to the water deficit. A dehydrated dog, when offered water, at once drinks enough to replace its water deficit and bring the body fluid content to the threshold of diuresis. In other words, in a few moments all the water the body will hold is metered with some accuracy through the pharynx.[11] The same behavior is exhibited by dogs with an esophageal fistula which prevents ingested water from reaching the stomach; hence receptor activation in the stomach is not the cue to stop drinking. In fact, when enough water to replace the deficit is introduced into a

*Such readjustment of bulk intake to maintain constant caloric intake requires several days. Caloric balance is thus a relatively long-term regulation and does not account for the amount ingested in any one feeding period.

dehydrated dog's stomach through the distal end of the fistula, it still sham drinks that amount if water is offered immediately. If the interval between prewatering and presentation of water is 20 minutes or more, the dog does not drink. Two satisfactions thus appear to be involved, a temporary one produced by passage of an appropriate quantity of water through the throat, and a more lasting one following absorption and distribution of water from the stomach.

Dehydrated man is more deliberate in replacing water deficits than is the dog, rabbit or burro; within 30 minutes after breaking a water fast, man replaces only about 80 per cent of the water deficit. Nevertheless, dehydrated man has a strong urge to replace water deficits, and this urge is unaffected by drugs. Dehydration in both man and animals is accompanied by anorexia, but ingestion of moderate amounts of food does not alter the thirst drive. The diet of choice during water deprivation is carbohydrate, because its oxidation yields a mol of water for every mol metabolized, and because its other combustive product, CO_2, requires no water for excretion.

Nausea.[16] Nausea is an unpleasant sensation vaguely referred to the epigastrium and abdomen and often culminating in vomiting. However, vomiting does not always follow nausea, nor is nausea a necessary antecedent of vomiting. Vomiting produced by mechanical irritation of the pharynx and the "projectile vomiting" of children with tumors in or near the fourth ventricle may occur without nausea. In animals, the salivation, swallowing and rhythmic licking preceding vomiting are often taken as signs of nausea. With some emetic agents, e.g., cardiac glycosides, a conditioned vomiting response may be established, suggesting that such drugs cause true nausea as well as vomiting.

Stimulation of the vomiting center in the dorsolateral reticular formation of the medulla consistently produces vomiting in decerebrate cats.[16] The vomiting is projectile in nature, stimulus-bound (i.e., persists only during the stimulus), and can be repeatedly initiated. This is probably comparable to the projectile vomiting, often unassociated with nausea, that is seen with cerebellar tumors. Spontaneous nausea and vomiting occur in response to a wide variety of stimuli. Emetic drugs initiate nausea and vomiting either by central action alone or by combined peripheral and central action. Central action is not directly upon the vomiting center in the reticular formation, but upon a "chemoreceptor trigger zone" situated near the fasciculus solitarius and the area postrema, dorsal to the vomiting center.

Lesions of the trigger zone abolish vomiting induced by intravenous or oral apomorphine, whereas combined vagotomy and abdominal sympathectomy have no effect.[16] Trigger zone lesions do not prevent vomiting induced by orally administered copper sulfate, whereas combined vagotomy and abdominal sympathectomy greatly elevate the threshold and prolong the latency of emesis. The effectiveness of intravenous copper sulfate is not altered by peripheral denervation. Neither copper sulfate nor apomorphine causes vomiting when the vomiting center is selectively destroyed and the trigger zone is left intact. Thus, whereas apomorphine acts solely via the trigger zone, copper sulfate acts both peripherally and centrally.

The emetic effectiveness of digitalis glycosides is greatly reduced by destruction of the trigger zone, but large doses produce delayed vomiting even when the gut is denervated and the trigger zone ablated.

Impulses from the abdominal cavity which cause nausea and vomiting traverse both vagal and sympathetic pathways, although the former predominate. Copper sulfate, mustard, Escherichia coli peritonitis, staphylococcus enterotoxin and distension of the biliary tract elicit nausea and vomiting which are ameliorated by vagotomy but abolished only by combined vagotomy and abdominal sympathectomy. Vomiting which results from experimental intestinal distension (simulating intestinal obstruction) is abolished by sympathectomy, but anorexia (presumably indicating nausea) persists until the vagi are sectioned.

MOTION SICKNESS. The term "motion sickness" is a misnomer; continuous movement at uniform velocity in one direction does not induce nausea. Only when the speed or direction of motion is repeatedly varied does nausea occur; hence, the term "acceleration sickness" is more appropriate. The responsible receptors are in the vestibular apparatus; section of the VIIIth nerve or labyrinthectomy renders susceptible animals immune to acceleration. Also, nausea may be invoked by irrigating the ear with hot or cold solutions which stimulate vestibular receptors by inducing convection currents in the endolymph. Finally, nausea and vomiting commonly accompany the attacks of vertigo in acute labyrinthitis and Menière's disease.

When the provocative acceleration is linear, as in an elevator or a vehicle accelerating in a straight line, the responsible impulses arise largely from the saccular macula. Angular accelerations (spinning) stimulate principally the cristae of the semicircular canals, and the resultant nausea is accompanied by nystagmus. Many accelerations producing nausea have angular as well as linear components, e.g., in swings, ships, airplanes and automobiles, but linear components constitute the major share of the movement. Susceptibility to nausea from such motions is affected by the position of the head. For example, horizontal position reduces susceptibility to wave accelerations simulating the conditions in boats.

The belladonna alkaloids, the barbiturates and certain antihistaminic drugs are useful in combating acceleration sickness. All are central nervous system depressants and produce drowsiness. Whether their effectiveness is due solely to such general action or whether they have a specific action on the central neural apparatus of vomiting has not been settled.

REFERENCES

1. ADOLPH, E. F. *Amer. J. Physiol.,* 1947, *151:*110–125.
2. ADRIAN, E. D. *Brit. med. Bull.,* 1950, 6:330–332.
3. ADRIAN, E. D. *Année psychol.,* 1951, *50:*107–113.
4. ADRIAN, E. D. *Brit. med. J.,* 1954, *1:*287–290.
5. ALLISON, A. C. and WARWICK, R. T. T. *Brain,* 1949, *72:* 186–197.
6. AMASSIAN, V. E. *J. Neurophysiol.,* 1951, *14:*433–444.
7. AMASSIAN, V. E. *J. Neurophysiol.,* 1951, *14:*445–460.
8. AMASSIAN, V. E. *Res. Publ. Ass. nerv. ment. Dis.,* 1952, *30.* 371–402.
9. BAGSHAW, M. H. and PRIBRAM, K. H. *J. Neurophysiol.,* 1953, *16:*499–508.
10. BEIDLER, L. M. In *Olfaction and taste.* Y. Zotterman, ed. New York, The Macmillan Co., 1963.
11. BELLOWS, R. T. and VAN WAGENEN, W. P. *Amer. J. Physiol.,* 1939, *126:*13–19.
12. Benjamin, R. M. In *Olfaction and taste.* Y. Zotterman, ed. New York, The Macmillan Co., 1963.
13. BENJAMIN, R. M. and PFAFFMANN, C. *J. Neurophysiol.,* 1955, *18:*56–64.
14. BLOMQUIST, A. J., BENJAMIN, R. M., and EMMERS, R. *J. comp. Neurol.,* 1962, *118:*77–88.
15. BLUM, M., WALKER, A. E. and RUCH, T. C. *Yale J. Biol. Med.,* 1943, *16:*175–191.
16. BORISON, H. L. and WANG, S. C. *Pharmacol. Rev.,* 1953, *5:* 193–230.
17. BRODAL, A. *Brain,* 1947, *70:*179–222.
18. CLARK, W. E. Le Gros. *J. Neurol. Psychiat.,* 1951, *14:*1–10.
19. CLARK, W. E. Le Gros and MEYER, M. *Brain,* 1947, *70:* 304–328.
20. CLARK, W. E. Le Gros and WARWICK, R. T. T. *J. Neurol. Psychiat.,* 1946, *9:*101–111.
21. COHEN, M. J., LANDGREN, S., STRÖM, L. and ZOTTERMAN, Y. *Acta physiol. scand.,* 1957, *40* (Suppl. 135):1–50.
22. DELL, P. *J. Physiol. Path. gén.,* 1952, *44:*471–557.

23. Elsberg, C. A. In *Medical physics*. O. Glasser, ed. Chicago, Year Book Publishers, 1944.

24. Erickson, R. P. In *Olfaction and taste*. Y. Zotterman, ed. New York, The Macmillan Co., 1963.

25. Erickson, T. C. *Arch. Neurol. Psychiat. (Chic.)*, 1945, *53:* 226–231.

26. Foley, J. O. *Proc. Soc. exp. Biol. (N. Y.)*, 1945, *60:*262–267.

27. Gasser, H. S. *J. gen. Physiol.*, 1956, *39:*473–496.

28. Gernandt, B. *Acta physiol. scand.*, 1946, *12:*255–260.

29. Gernandt, B. and Zotterman, Y. *Acta physiol, scand.*, 1946, *12:*56–72.

30. Gesteland, R. C., Lettvin, J. Y., Pitts, W. H., and Rojas, A. In *Olfaction and taste*. Y. Zotterman, ed. New York, The Macmillan Co., 1963.

31. Grossman, M. I. and Stein, I. F., Jr. *J. appl. Physiol.*, 1948, *1:*263–269.

32. Kare, M. R. and Halpern, B. P., eds. *Physiological and behavioral aspects of taste*. Chicago, Univ. of Chicago Press, 1961.

33. Kimura, K. and Beidler, L. M. *J. cell. comp. Physiol*, 1961, *58:*131–139.

34. Landgren, S. Chap. 23 in *Sensory communication*. W. R. Rosenblith, ed. New York, John Wiley and Sons, 1961.

35. Ottoson, D. *Acta physiol. scand.*, 1956, *35* (Suppl. 122): 1–83.

36. Ottoson, D. *Pharmacol. Rev.*, 1963, *15:*1–42.

37. Paintal, A. S. *Ergebn. Physiol.*, 1963, *52:*74–156.

38. Patton, H. D. and Amassian, V. E. *Amer. J. Physiol.*, 1951, *167:*815–816.

39. Patton, H. D. and Amassian, V. E. *J. Neurophysiol.*, 1952, *15:*245–250.

40. Patton, H. D., Ruch, T. C. and Fulton, J. F. *Fed. Proc.*, 1946, *5:*79.

41. Patton, H. D., Ruch, T. C. and Walker, A. E. *J. Neurophysiol.*, 1944, *7:*171–184.

42. Penfield, W. and Rasmussen, T. *The cerebral cortex of man*. New York, The Macmillan Co., 1950.

43. Pfaffmann, C. Chap. 20 in *Handbook of physiology, Section 1: Neurophysiology*, vol. 1. J. Field, ed. Washington, D.C., American Physiological Society, 1959.

44. Pfaffmann, C. In *Olfaction and taste*. Y. Zotterman, ed. New York, The Macmillan Co., 1963.

45. Pfaffmann, C., Erickson, R. P., Frommer, G. P. and Halpern, B. P. Chap. 24 in *Sensory communication*. W. A. Rosenblith, ed. New York, John Wiley and Sons, 1961.

46. Richter, C. P. *Harvey Lect.*, 1943, *38:*63–103.

47. Ruch, T. C. and Patton, H. D. *Fed. Proc.*, 1946, *5:*89–90.

48. Ruch, T. C., Patton, H. D. and Amassian, V. E. *Res. Publ. Ass. nerv. ment. Dis.*, 1952, *30:*403–429.

49. Sachs, E., Jr., Brendler, S. J. and Fulton, J. F. *Brain*, 1949, *72:*227–240.

50. Sheehan, D. *J. Anat. (Lond.)*, 1932, *67.*233–249.

51. Stein, I. F., Jr. and Meyer, K. A. *Surg. Gynec. Obstet.*, 1948, *86:*473–479.

52. Strominger, J. L., Brobeck, J. R. and Cort, R. L. *Yale J. Biol., Med.*, 1953, *26:*55–74.

53. Tateda, H. and Beidler, L. M. *J. gen. Physiol.*, 1964, *47:* 479–486.

54. Wolf, A. V. *Thirst*. Springfield, Ill., Charles C Thomas, 1958.

55. Zotterman, Y. *Skand. Arch. Physiol.*, 1935, *72:*73–77.

56. Zotterman, Y., ed. *Olfaction and taste*. New York, The Macmillan Co., 1963.

CHAPTER 18

Audition and the Auditory Pathway

By ARNOLD L. TOWE

MECHANICAL PROPERTIES OF THE EXTERNAL AND MIDDLE EARS

The auditory system transmits information about pressure variations in the air to the central nervous system through a mechanism consisting of (i) the external and middle ears, (ii) the cochlea and (iii) the auditory nerve and pathways to various central neural structures. The first stage is an effective mechanical impedance-matching device which transmits pressure variations from the air to the cochlear fluid with little energy loss. The second stage is the site of excitation of nervous tissue, a process depending upon both an external and an internal energy source. Energy for the subsequent nerve conduction and synaptic transmission is supplied entirely by the metabolizing organism. For our purposes, schematic diagrams (Fig. 1*A, B*) suffice to portray the functional anatomy of the auditory mechanism; knowledge of the detailed anatomy of the middle and inner ear should be obtained from special works on anatomy and histology. The mechanical principles of energy transmission can be outlined without recourse to detailed anatomy. Figure 1*B* illustrates the sequence of events in the ear when a wave of compression reaches the ear. The tympanic membrane is displaced inward, deflecting the middle ear bones and thereby compressing the fluid of the cochlea. Inward movement of the stapes is accompanied by a downward deflection of the basilar membrane and outward movement of the membrane sealing the round window. The displacement of the basilar membrane is "measured" by the nervous tissue attached to it and signaled to the central nervous system.

Resonance. Longitudinal waves enter the external auditory meatus, where they lose their energy to the walls of the tube and the tympanic membrane. Some of this energy is reflected

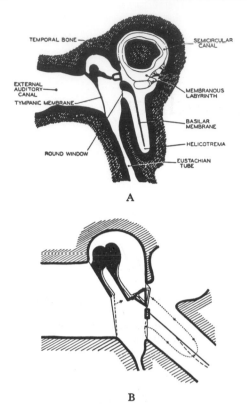

A

B

Fig. 1. *A,* Highly schematic diagram of middle and internal ear in which cochlea is shown as though uncoiled. Oval window (unlabeled) lies just above round window and opens into vestibule and scala vestibuli, which is separated from scala tympani by basilar membrane. (After Békésy. Redrawn for Stevens and Davis, *Hearing: its psychology and physiology,* John Wiley & Sons, Inc., 1938. Reprinted by permission.) *B,* Highly schematic diagram of auditory portions of middle and inner ear showing position of ossicles and various membranes at rest and following inward displacement of tympanic membrane (*shadow lines*) by a sound wave. Dotted lines and arrows represent path of sound waves. (Reprinted by permission from Stevens and Davis, *Hearing: its psychology and physiology,* New York, John Wiley & Sons, Inc., 1938.)

back to the air but some appears as motion of the membrane. The external meatus behaves as a closed tube, so that sound pressures are greater at the closed end than at the open end. A resonance curve may be constructed by plotting the pressure difference between the two ends against the applied frequency. The curve thus obtained is not sharply peaked but, largely as a result of the damping effect of the nonrigid tympanic membrane, is broad and rounded. The maximum increase in pressure occurs when the applied sound has a wave length four times the effective length of the external meatus

(about 12 decibels* at 3400 to 4000 cycles per second). The curve falls off on either side of the resonant frequency, being above 5 db over the interval from 2000 to 6000 cps.[65] The resonant frequency is nearly 3000 cps above the major speech frequency.

The tympanic membrane completely separates the air-filled external and middle ears. It is shaped like a shallow funnel with its apex, or umbo, somewhat below the center and directed inward. The handle of the malleus is directed downward and attaches to the umbo. Radial fibers radiate from the umbo, except in a pie-shaped wedge under the handle of the malleus, and circular fibers interfuse the membrane. This membrane acts like a pressure receiver, being insensitive to velocity changes but exceedingly sensitive to pressure changes. Its specific behavior varies with the applied frequency. At low frequencies the membrane vibrates like a rigid body about a horizontal axis at its upper edge. At frequencies exceeding 2400 cps the drum membrane vibrates in segments, the particular pattern depending upon the applied frequency. However, measurement of maximum membrane displacement shows that it approximates the amplitude of motion of the air molecules at nearly all frequencies. At the threshold of hearing, this ranges from 10^{-5} cm. for low frequencies to 10^{-9} cm. at 3000 cps.[66]

Impedance Matching. The unique problem solved by the middle ear is one of transferring sound energy from a gas to a liquid without significant loss.† This feat is accomplished by the drum membrane–ossicular chain system (Fig. 1*B* and Fig. 2), which amplifies the applied pressures by means of a lever arrangement and a "hydraulic press" action. Movements of the drum membrane are communicated to the tip of the malleus. The malleus and incus rotate as a unit about an axis through the short process of the incus and along the tympanic side of the

*The standard unit of sound intensity is the decibel (db), 1/10 bel. The bel is the logarithm of the ratio of the applied power or energy to some reference power or energy; measurement of the "absolute" energy level is difficult. The reference usually taken in auditory work is the power necessary for a 1000 cycle per second (cps) pure tone to be just audible; this is about 10^{-16} watts per cm.² Thus, $N_{db} = 10 \log_{10} P/P_o$, where P = applied power and $P_o = 10^{-16}$ watts per cm.²

†An air-water interface reflects about 99.9 per cent of the sound energy back to the air, a 30 db loss in transmission.

malleus. Because, when measured to this axis, the manubrium is a longer lever than the long process of the incus, the force appearing at the stapes is greater than that at the tympanic umbo by about 1.3 to 1.

The area of the drum membrane averages about 64 sq. mm., and the stapedial footplate measures about 3.2 sq. mm. If the two structures moved as simple pistons, the resulting pressure amplification could readily be estimated. However, neither structure behaves so simply. As mentioned above, the mode of vibration of the tympanum varies with frequency, the effective area being 60 to 75 per cent of the total. Because the annular ligament fixing the stapedial footplate into the oval window is narrowest at its posterior margin, the stapes rotates about a vertical axis near its posterior border.[5] Hence, the ratio of effective areas could vary from ear to ear between 13 to 1 and 16 to 1. Since the force delivered to the stapes is amplified by the lever action described above, the total pressure gain would range from 17 to 21 for the average ear. This gain, equivalent to about 25 db at the oval window, signifies a long step toward matching the impedance of the inner ear mechanism to the air. At all frequencies, however, some energy is reflected, and some is lost to frictional resistance. The energy flow through the system can be calculated when the impedance is known; at the threshold of hearing, the impedance is large for low frequencies and minimal around 1000 cps, increasing again at higher frequencies. This relationship means that the ear is most sensitive in the region of 1000 cps.

When the phase shifts of the reflected portion of a sound wave are measured,[60, 64] it becomes clear that the stiffness (elastic reactance) of the ear mechanism is large at low frequencies, whereas the mass of the system (mass reactance) predominates at high frequencies. Somewhere between 300 and 3000 cps these two reactances, which are 180° out of phase, just cancel, and the only limitation becomes the frictional losses. Thus, transmission losses are least in the region of 1000 to 2000 cps.

Overloading and Damping. Contraction of either or both of two small muscles in the middle ear, the *tensor tympani* and *stapedius*, will increase the stiffness of the middle ear mechanism, thereby decreasing the energy flow of low frequencies. The tensor tympani has a long tendon inserted onto the manubrium of the malleus; this tendon can pull at right angles to the plane of motion of the malleo-incudal system. The stapedius muscle inserts onto the neck of the stapes and likewise pulls at right angles to its main axis. This muscle thus tends to rotate the stapes out of the oval window, opposing the action of the tensor tympani, which indirectly forces the stapes into the oval window.

Reflex contraction of these muscles can be produced by (i) clicks, tones and noises, (ii) irritation of the external meatus, pinna or face and (iii) bodily movements, especially swallowing and yawning. This *acoustic reflex* begins in the stapedius muscle about 15 milliseconds after sound stimulation and a bit later in tensor tympani, although the latency varies markedly with sound intensity. To prolonged intense sound, the reflex contraction attains an initial maximum and then gradually lessens, falling to prestimulation tension in a half hour or more. The reflex is bilateral. Johannes Müller proposed that this reflex acts as a protective mechanism like blinking of the eyelids and constriction of the pupils; increasing tension in the system disturbs the impedance match for lower frequencies such that less energy (as great as 40 db loss) is transmitted to the inner ear mechanism. With the exception of explosive changes, which develop full effect before this reflex can come into play, the damping protects the system from being "shaken apart." However, this mechanism is more than a mere emergency device called forth under exceptional conditions; Carmel and Starr[16] have shown it to be a dynamic system almost constantly in operation. It comes into play during bodily movements and vocalization, and can readily be sensitized by prior auditory experience. Its failure in Bell's palsy and perhaps

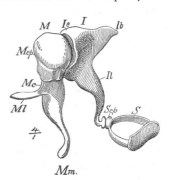

Fig. 2. Bones of middle ear in functional connection. *M,* Malleus; *Mcp,* head; *Mc,* neck; *Ml,* processus gracilis; *Mm,* manubrium; *I,* incus; *Ic,* body of incus; *Ib,* short process; *Il,* long process; *S,* stapes. (From Helmholtz, *Die Lehre von den Tonempfindung,* Braunschweig, F. Wieweg & Son, 1896.)

in acute myesthenia gravis may be the source of the frequent complaint of hyperacusis.

Static Pressure Matching. By connecting the middle ear cavity with the pharynx and thus with the exterior, the *eustachian tube* provides a means of adjusting the air pressure in the middle ear. In this way the pressures on the two sides of the tympanic membrane can be kept equal. Normally, the soft, slitlike pharyngeal orifice is closed; it is opened by the tensor palati muscle during swallowing, yawning and sneezing. Without thinking, man swallows whenever the sensations from the tympanic membrane warn him of inequality in the pressures upon its two sides. In upper respiratory infections, however, the auditory tube may be blocked by inflammation or collection of mucus. As the trapped air is partially absorbed, the tympanum is pushed inward; the resulting pressure sensations and impairment of hearing are quite discomforting.

In severe changes of atmospheric pressure, such as those encountered in flying,[3] the adjustment of air pressure within the middle ear can present serious problems. In ascent, with the ambient pressure decreasing, the excess pressure in the middle ear can force the eustachian tube open, even if it is not opened by swallowing. In descent, however, swallowing is the sole mechanism for equalizing pressure. If muscular action is absent, as may occur in sleeping passengers or in unconscious wounded who are transported by air, the tubes remain closed or are held closed by the higher pressure in the nasopharynx. Weak solutions of phenylephrine hydrochloride (Neo-Synephrine) or ephedrine are frequently sprayed into the nostrils to shrink the tissue around the eustachian orifice, thus aiding in pressure equalization. If negative pressures of 60 to 80 mm. Hg develop within the middle ear, pain is severe and deafness, tinnitus and vertigo supervene. At pressures of 80 to 90 mm. Hg, muscular contraction may not open the tube, and at negative pressures between 100 and 150 mm. Hg the eardrum may rupture. Such rupture is marked by the sensation of a loud explosive sound, piercing pain, nausea and even shock. Short of rupture, pressure differences may produce traumatic inflammation of the middle ear.[3] The eardrum is sometimes pierced with a fine needle to allow pressure equalization; small defects of the tympanum so produced quickly close and heal.

AUDITION

Before studying the inner ear mechanisms we should become familiar with some basic phenomena of hearing. We live in an auditory world rich in variety and complexity; but ours is not the only such world. Many insects which prowl unobtrusively about us carry on boisterously at frequencies too high for our ears to detect. The vocalizations of fish and cetaceans,* although at "our" frequencies, are reflected at the water surface. Bats utilize their "auditory radar" system almost entirely when flying and feeding; they emit short scanning runs from 100,000 down to 20,000 cps a dozen or more times each second while flying. Although primates are best described as "visual" animals, they possess a remarkable auditory capability. To analyze this capability, the physiologist uses quite simple kinds of auditory stimuli; to employ richer auditory stimuli has its analogy in studying the digestive physiology of a Dagwood sandwich.

Physical and Psychological Dimensions of Sound.[50] Sound waves are longitudinal; i.e., they depend upon molecular motion parallel to the direction of energy transmission. Alternate waves of condensation and rarefaction move through a medium with specifiable velocity according to the characteristics of the medium and independently of the intensity of the wave. The simplest sound wave, a sinusoid, can vary in amplitude, frequency and phase (provided some time referent is used). The perceived *pitch* of such a wave is largely determined by its frequency; the *loudness* of such a wave is determined both by its amplitude and by its frequency. Such simple waves are produced by tuning forks or electronic oscillators, but rarely occur in the natural environment. Most sound sources produce compound waves consisting of a fundamental frequency and overtones of various amplitudes and phase angles. The overtones bear a simple arithmetic relationship to the fundamental frequency (or first harmonic); a single string vibrates not only as a whole but also in halves, thirds, fourths, etc. It is the fundamental frequency, with its greater amplitude, that determines the pitch of the sound; however, overtones can also be heard with their own pitches. The relative amplitudes of the various harmonics yield a unique wave-form for each sound

*Some cetaceans emit sounds as high as 150,000 cps.

source, giving the sound its *timbre* or *quality*. It is this property of complex sound which enables us to distinguish between different musical instruments, human voices or other sound sources, even when they emit at equal fundamental frequency and intensity. No matter how complex, a wave-form is "musical" if its pattern is regularly repeated through several cycles; nonperiodic vibrations, which constitute the vast majority of sound waves emanating from the natural environment, are "noise." However, even noise has a crude sort of pitch, for some frequencies in the jumble have a greater amplitude than others. When many frequencies are represented about equally, as in the thermionic emission of a vacuum tube, the resulting sensation is termed "white noise" (by analogy to white light). In studying the ear, it is usually convenient to use sinusoidal waves or clicks of various forms.

Loudness.[51] That loudness depends upon both the amplitude and the frequency of a sinusoid is revealed in the audibility curve (Fig. 3). Loudness is a perceptual response to the *intensity* (or energy flux density) of a sound wave, which is proportional to the square of amplitude. The weakest intensity of any sinusoid which can just be heard depends strongly upon the frequency of the sinusoid. Figure 3 shows this dependency for the human ear; at each frequency, two threshold intensities can be found, one for hearing and one for feeling. Between these two extremes, loudness varies as the logarithm of intensity. At the threshold of audibility, measured under delicate experimental conditions, the effective pressures at the tympanum and the consequent movements of the tympanum are extremely minute. Displacements of the tympanum *less* than the dimensions of a hydrogen atom (10^{-8} cm.) are effective. Why pressure variations and vibrations of the blood vessels of the tympanum and cochlea do not produce distracting sounds is puzzling in view of this extreme sensitivity; such sources become audible only in anechoic chambers.

The striking feature of the audibility curve is the degree to which it depends upon frequency. Hearing is keenest in the 1000 to 4000 cps range, decreasing sharply for higher and lower frequencies. On the other hand, the threshold for feeling discomfort* is fairly constant at about

*Sound waves, when sufficiently intense, will stimulate somesthetic sense organs. The resulting sensations include touch, tickle, pressure and even pain.

10^{-3} watts per cm.[2] The fundamental and major overtones of the human voice are all at lower frequencies than the peak sensitivity of the ear. About 100 times greater sound energy is required to just hear middle C (256 cps†) than two octaves higher (1024 cps). The audibility curve is determined to a large extent by the energy losses in the middle and inner ear and to a small extent by the resonance properties of the external ear. The purely resistive losses occur in the range of the resonant frequency of the external meatus; thus, several factors combine to make the ear most sensitive in a range slightly above vocalization frequencies.

Audiometry. Because the auditory threshold varies so sharply with frequency, the rough-and-ready clinical methods of testing hearing—whispering and the ticking watch—merely sample hearing. A more comprehensive clinical index of hearing ability is found in the *audiogram,* which plots a patient's auditory threshold for several different frequencies relative to "normal." The normal or mean threshold value, determined for each frequency from measurements on a large number of "normal young adults," differs by 15 to 20 db from the "absolute" auditory threshold because the audiogram measure-

†Musical instruments are usually tuned to middle C at about 262 cps.

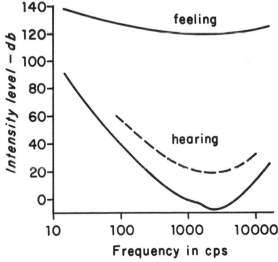

Fig. 3. Audibility curve in man, showing threshold under ideal conditions and under conditions in which audiometer tests are administered. Energy which excites tactual and pain receptors is about a million million times energy at threshold of hearing at 1000 cps. (After Licklider, Chap. 25 in *Handbook of experimental psychology,* S. S. Stevens, ed. New York, John Wiley & Sons, 1951.)

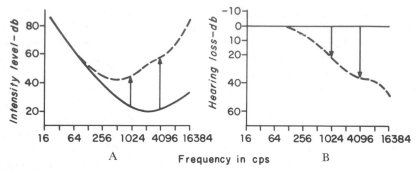

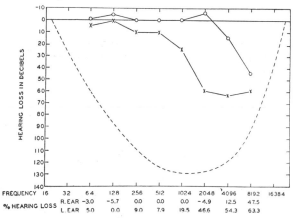

Fig. 4. Left graph shows threshold of hearing for audiometer curve (solid line) and audibility curve for aged person with high tone hearing loss (dashed line). Right graph shows same data plotted as *audiogram* with normalized audiometer curve; this form of plotting hearing loss relative to "normal" is convenient.

ments (dashed line in Fig. 3) are made in less than ideal conditions. Figure 4A shows a deviant audiogram for one patient in relation to the normal. It is apparent at 1024 cps that sound intensity must be raised 22 db above the normal value (an increase of about 160 times the energy) to be just audible to this patient. The standard *audiogram* plot of the same information about this patient is shown in Figure 4B; it is based on a normalized auditory threshold curve and hence displays more clearly the deviation of hearing loss from normal.

Fig. 5. Graphic representation of hearing ability (audiogram) of individual suffering from high-tone deafness. Circles indicate auditory sensitivity of right ear; crosses, that of left ear. Figures at bottom show calculation of per cent hearing loss, with broken line, the threshold of feeling, representing complete loss of hearing. For convenience, normal threshold of hearing is taken as zero (or reference point) on a decibel scale. In absolute physical units threshold energy varies considerably throughout audible range of frequencies. (Reprinted by permission from Stevens and Davis, *Hearing: its psychology and physiology,* New York, John Wiley & Sons, Inc., 1938.)

The audiometer consists of an electronic oscillator arranged to produce 10 to 12 different frequencies at octave intervals on one or both of a pair of earphones. Wearing the earphones in an otherwise quiet environment, the patient flashes a light whenever he hears a sound. The examiner steadily decreases the intensity of an intermittently sounded tone until the patient no longer signals its occurrence consistently. The sound intensity at this point is read from the intensity dial (calibrated in decibels above and below the normal for that frequency, but sometimes scaled in sensation units), and is entered on the audiogram. This fixes one point on the patient's audibility curve; the procedure is repeated for the remaining frequencies. Then the other ear is tested. In interpreting such curves, the following facts should be noted. Hearing loss may be stated either in terms of decibels loss or in terms of percentage loss of useful hearing. If at any point the patient's threshold coincides with the broken line of Figure 5, representing the threshold of feeling, the loss of hearing is complete. If the threshold falls halfway between the 0 line and the broken line, the loss in that ear is 50 per cent.

THE COCHLEA

The ear of man is a mechanoreceptor with a long phylogenetic history. The hydrozoan statocysts represent an "ear" in the most general sense. True hearing organs first appear with the chordotonal organs and scolophores of the arthropods and become progressively elaborated in the terrestrial vertebrates, reaching a pinnacle of development in the bats. Man does not possess such an elaborate pinna or the capability of directing it, and his directional sensitivity is of a lower order.

Structure. The manner in which the ear analyzes complex sound waves into component frequencies was originally deduced by Helmholtz from the structure of the inner ear. He was struck by the fact that the ear contains a very large number of neurosensory units arranged along a membrane interposed in the path of the sound wave. He viewed this membrane as a system of tuned elements that resonated so that a given unit would be the one most vigorously stimulated by sound waves of a given frequency. This arrangement would result in a different nerve fiber discharging more actively for each frequency within the audible range, and the discharge of this unit, transmitted over the auditory pathway, would be recognized by the cerebral cortex as a given pitch. Although significant advances have been made in the theory of auditory receptor excitation, Helmholtz set the basic philosophy that the functional anatomy and the physiology of the inner ear are inextricably bound together.

The auditory portion of the inner ear, like the middle ear, is housed in a system of cavities and tunnels known as the osseous labyrinth (Figs. 1 A and 6). The cochlear portion of the osseous labyrinth consists of a fluid-filled tube about three centimeters long that is coiled in a spiral about a central pillar (modiolus). Except for a small opening in the apical end (helicotrema), the tube is completely divided into two canals by a stout connective tissue membrane (basilar membrane) and a bony shelf (spiral lamina) extending from the modiolus. At the base of the tube, the cochlear partition consists mainly of spiral lamina, the basilar membrane being narrowest at this end. Farther up around the spiral the bony lamina becomes smaller and the basilar membrane widens until the helicotrema is reached at the apex. The latter opening serves to equalize slowly developing pressure differences between the two divisions of the cochlea.

Sound waves enter the part of the cochlea *above* the basilar membrane (*scala vestibuli*) by way of the oval window in the vestibule—hence its name (Fig. 1 B). The passageway below the basilar membrane (*scala tympani*) communicates with the middle ear by way of the round window, which is closed by the *secondary tympanic membrane*.

Within the osseous labyrinth lies the membranous labyrinth, a portion of which extends into the cochlea to contribute *Reissner's membrane*, the basilar membrane and the *organ of Corti* (thus forming the cochlear duct, or *scala media*). In a sense, the scala media occupies the lower third of the scala vestibuli; Reissner's membrane is so delicate that the two scalae probably function as a single tube in the transmission of sound. In fact, the term "scala vestibuli" is often loosely used to include the cochlear duct.

The membranous labyrinth, floating in the *perilymph* of the osseous labyrinth, contains a special fluid, the *endolymph*. Endolymph is similar to intracellular fluid in its ionic content but is rather low in protein.[48] The endolymph apparently does not occupy the tunnel of Corti or the space of Nuel (Fig. 6); its very high K^+ content should render the cochlear nerve fibers traversing these spaces inexcitable or unstable. The perilymph is similar to spinal fluid in having a high concentration of Na^+, but it has twice the concentration of protein.

Sensory epithelium of the cochlea. The fibers of the cochlear branch of the VIIIth nerve, which number 25,000 to 30,000 in man, arise in bipolar cell bodies lodged within the modiolus (*spiral nucleus*) and arborize around the sensory *hair cells* of the organ of Corti. These hair cells are in a position to be affected by sound waves and, in turn, generate nerve impulses in the fibers of the auditory nerve. The general arrangement and relations of these cells are indicated in Figure 6. The hair cells are divided by a supporting arch (rods of Corti) into a single row of *inner hair cells* and three or four rows of *outer hair cells*. Up to 120 stereociliar type hairs arise from the surface of each cell, project through the *reticular lamina* and make contact with the overlying *tectorial membrane*. While the cilia of the inner hair cells form a continuous double row running the length of the cochlea, those of the outer hair cells form a distinctive "long-horned W" pattern from two or three rows of cilia, with the "horns" pointing toward the spiral lamina.[22] In man, there are about the same number of hair cells as cochlear nerve fibers; however, this does not mean a one-to-one pattern of innervation. The 3- to 5-μ fibers of the cochlear nerve lose both their myelin and their Schwann sheaths as they emerge from the spiral lamina to radiate outward and arborize around the bases and sides of the hair cells. Two distribution pat-

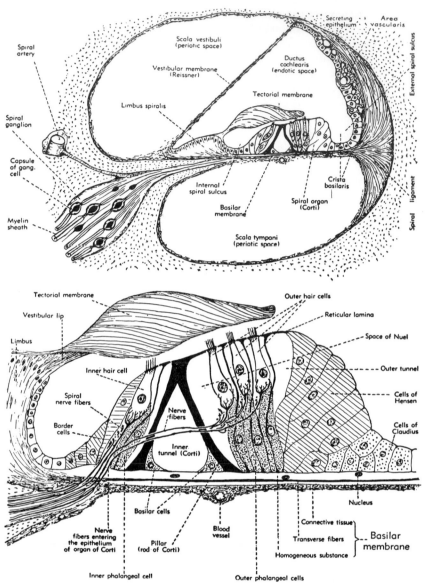

Fig. 6. *Upper,* Vertical section of human cochlea showing organ of Corti and adjacent structures. *Lower,* Organ of Corti and basilar membrane in greater magnification. (From Rasmussen, *Outlines of neuro-anatomy,* 3d ed., Dubuque, Ia., William C. Brown Co., 1943.)

terns are recognized. Each *radial fiber* makes contact with two or three hair cells, and each hair cell receives endings from two or three radial fibers.[24] Although radial fibers are distributed to most hair cells, they form the major innervation of the inner hair cells. Another group of fibers, the *spiral fibers,* turn sharply after emerging from the habenula perforata to form a small internal spiral bundle, a tunnel bundle and a large external spiral bundle. These fibers extend about a quarter of a turn through the organ of Corti, arborizing around *many* different hair

cells. Fernandez[24] believes that the internal spiral fibers are *efferent;* their cell bodies lie in the superior olivary complex of the opposite side of the brain stem.

The inner hair cells are histologically quite distinct from the outer hair cells. They excite radial fibers and receive an efferent supply from the internal spiral fibers. On the other hand, the outer hair cells, which possess a much denser array of nerve endings, excite largely external spiral fibers. Studies with the electron microscope have revealed several different types

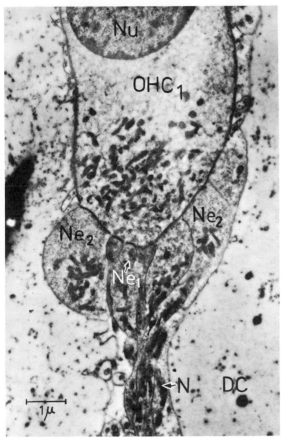

Fig. 7. Electron micrograph of outer hair cell of guinea pig (OHC₁), showing its nucleus (Nu) and the supporting cells of Deiter (DC). Two types of nerve endings, the small (Ne₁) and larger, vesicular (Ne₂), can be seen arising from the nerve fibers (N). (From Engström in *Neural mechanisms of the auditory and vestibular systems,* G. L. Rasmussen, and W. F. Windle, eds., Springfield, Ill., Charles C Thomas, 1960.)

of "synaptic" endings around each cell.[46, 47, 49] Chemical transmission between hair cell and nerve fiber is suggested by the marked accumulations of mitochondria and vesicles at the base of many hair cells, and similar thoughts are provoked by the structure of the "synaptic" membrane regions (Fig. 7). However, the functional significance of these various terminal structures is as yet only speculative.

Excitation in the Cochlea. The cochlea as a whole is a device whereby sound waves, transmitted through the fluid of the inner ear, are translated into nerve impulses. It is apparent from the arrangement of the cochlea that the vibration imparted to the basilar membrane by a pressure variation in the scala vestibuli is one

stage in this process. This is shown directly by the observation that excessive vibrations produced by loud sounds may dislodge the organ of Corti from the basilar membrane. Moreover, the segment of the basilar membrane undergoing the widest excursion shifts progressively with frequency.[51] As this shift occurs, different auditory fibers undergo maximal excitation. Because nerve impulses remain canalized as they pass through the fibers of the auditory system, ultimately each tone results in a peak of activity in some patch of auditory cortex.[2, 67] The doctrine of specific nerve energies (Chap. 14) holds that which patch of cortex is involved determines which pitch is experienced. This view of cochlear function is the "place theory" of hearing, somewhat irreverently known as the "pitch-is-which" theory. It differs from the "frequency" theory, which accords the pattern of firing in auditory fibers a more important role than which particular fibers are firing.[61]

Although theories regarding the manner in which the basilar membrane responds to different sound frequencies differ widely enough to require separate categories—resonance, traveling wave, standing wave, telephone—yet they have much in common. Békésy[11] has shown it possible to obtain results consistent with any of these theories merely by varying the amount of stiffness and the rate of change of stiffness with distance along the membrane. It is thus essential to know the physical properties of the cochlear partition. Helmholtz had been led by several histologic features to regard the basilar membrane and its burden of receptors and supporting elements as a series of tuned resonators. However, Békésy[6, 12] has shown that the membrane is under slight transverse tension; the most liberal calculations show that no resonance theory could account for more than four and one-half of the ten and one-half octaves available to the human ear.[64]

Several theories of cochlear mechanics invoke traveling waves like pressure pulse waves in blood vessels; the basilar membrane introduces enough elasticity into an otherwise rigid tube to justify the analogy. From measurements of the travel time for pulses along the membrane and from study of phase displacements at selected positions on the basilar membrane, Békésy[11] concluded that the basilar membrane indeed does support traveling waves. Such a conclusion

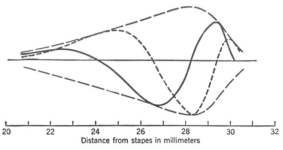

Fig. 8. Diagram illustrating traveling wave theory of basilar membrane movement. Solid and short dash lines represent same sound wave at two instants of time. Long dash line is described by connecting the peaks at successive instants of time. Scale at bottom represents distance along basilar membrane. (After Békésy, *J. acoust. Soc. Amer.*, 1947, *19*:452–460.)

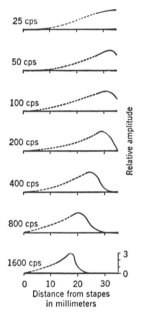

Fig. 9. Displacement amplitude along basilar membrane for different frequencies (constant amplitude) of stapes vibration. Solid lines were obtained by measurement, dotted lines by extrapolation from other observations. (From Békésy and Rosenblith, Chap. 27 in *Handbook of experimental psychology*, S. S. Stevens, ed., New York, John Wiley & Sons, Inc., 1951.)

does not preclude resonance altogether, but means that adjacent regions are strongly coupled and cannot resonate independently.

A positive pressure pulse at the oval window spreads instantaneously (20 μsec.) throughout the cochlea, bulging the secondary tympanic membrane. The relatively stiff regions near the base of the basilar membrane move downward toward the scala tympani in phase with the

stapes, while the more elastic apical regions lag significantly. Thus, the displacement of the membrane "moves" toward the apex. With sinusoidal driving pressures, the stiffer basal region "wags" the more apical regions, yielding a wave-form illustrated in Figure 8. The region of maximal displacement of the membrane, revealed by the envelope of the traveling wave, varies with the driving frequency (Fig. 9). Low frequencies displace the entire membrane in a whiplike manner while high frequencies damp out a short distance from the stapes. Thus, high tones are represented at the base of the cochlea and low tones throughout the cochlea but with maximal effectiveness near the apex.

Movements of the basilar membrane slide the tectorial membrane over the reticular lamina, thereby stressing the cilia of the underlying hair cells. By this mechanism, the force displacing the cochlear partition is greatly amplified at the cilia. A simple upward movement of the cochlear partition displaces the tectorial membrane toward the supporting cells of Hensen. Because of the relative tilts of the inner and outer hair cells, this radial displacement pulls on the cilia of the inner hair cells and pushes or bends the cilia of the outer hair cells. But the movements of the cochlear partition are not quite so simple (Fig. 10); the mean vector of the shearing force has both radial and longitudinal components which change in magnitude not only with the phase of the applied sinusoid but also according

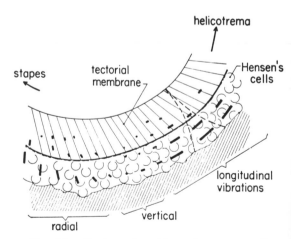

Fig. 10. Section of cochlear duct as seen from above through Reissner's membrane, showing distribution of radial and longitudinal vibrations along organ of Corti for stimulation with a tone. Maximal displacement of cochlear partition occurs along central zone of transition (vertical). (From Békésy, *J. acoust. Soc. Amer.*, 1953, *25*:770–785.)

to site on the basilar membrane relative to the applied frequency. Vertical movements predominate in the region of maximal membrane displacement (see envelope in Fig. 10). Longitudinal movements develop more distally, where the rate of change of displacement with distance along the membrane is greatest; radial movements predominate toward the stapes. We have come a long way from a simple system of tuned resonators.

Electrical activity of the cochlea. Accompanying the mechanical responses of the cochlear partition are several characteristic electrical changes. Even in the unstimulated condition, however, the cochlear duct maintains a potential some 80 mV. above ground.[8, 9] The electrical energy for this latter potential, the *endocochlear potential*, is supplied continuously by the *stria vascularis* that overlies the spiral ligament on the lateral aspect of the cochlear duct[19, 57] (Fig. 6). A small potential exists in the perilymph, grading from 3 mV. in the apical half of the scala vestibuli through ground potential halfway down the scala tympani to −2 mV. at the round window.[11] The cellular elements of the cochlea have typical intracellular potentials (−20 to −80 mV.). But the entire fluid-filled scala media and the tectorial membrane are about 80 mV. positive to the perilymph. Thus, the voltage drop across the reticular lamina, from endolymph to hair cells, can be as high as 180 mV. This voltage is highly dependent upon an adequate oxygen supply, but is not a consequence of the "intracellular" ionic composition of the endolymph. It can be increased or decreased through several millivolts by static displacements of the basilar membrane,[9, 55] especially by longitudinal displacement near the limbus.[7]

When a sinusoidal or a complex sound wave is applied to the eardrum, a potential which "faithfully mirrors" the applied wave-form can be recorded from the region of the ear. Because this *cochlear microphonic* (Fig. 11) was first recorded from the auditory nerve,[62, 63] it was initially mistaken for a series of auditory action potentials. Analysis soon showed that these voltage variations originate in the cochlea and spread decrementally along the nerve and throughout the tissue surrounding the cochlea. The cochlear microphonic appears with no apparent threshold and negligible latency. It increases linearly with increase in the pressure of the applied sound wave to a maximum of 2 mV. and decreases with further increase in sound pres-

sure. Unlike nerve action potentials, the cochlear microphonic is highly resistant to drugs, anesthesia, cold and fatigue. At death it drops rapidly to a low level, but it sustains this level for hours.

When recorded at the round window, the cochlear microphonic is nearly inverted from its configuration at the oval window. If a microelectrode is passed vertically through the organ of Corti during sound stimulation, the microphonic is seen to go through a 180° phase shift at the reticular lamina;[55] this coincides exactly with the 160 mV. drop in voltage from endolymph to hair cells. Radial displacements of the basilar membrane have been shown most efficacious in producing the microphonic,[7, 10] and it is well established that the outer hair cells are responsible for this potential change during such displacement.[10, 19] Thus, the behavior of the cochlear partition during sound stimulation determines the characteristics of the microphonic potential at each position along the membrane. The microphonic shows the increas-

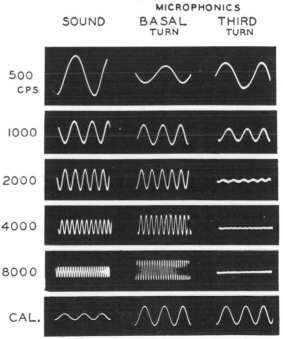

Fig. 11. Microphonic electrical records from base and from a point near apex of guinea pig cochlea in response to sound waves of various frequencies. Note that basal turn responds to all frequencies as demanded by traveling wave theory, and that amplitude of sound waves need not be altered greatly (10 db) to give equal responses. Note absence of response to high frequencies at third turn. (From Tasaki, *J. Neurophysiol.*, 1954, *17:* 97–122.)

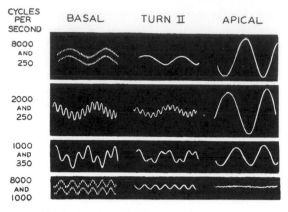

PAIRED ELECTRODES, SCALAE VESTIBULI AND TYMPANI, IN EACH TURN

Fig. 12. Simultaneous recordings of cochlear microphonic made at three sites along the cochlea of the guinea pig. When an 8000 cps and a 250 cps tone are sounded simultaneously, the 8000 cps tone appears only near the base, while the 250 cps tone affects the entire membrane, but the apex maximally. From the bottom trace, it can be seen that neither a 1000 cps nor the 8000 cps tone produces any microphonic at the apex. In the middle records, it is shown that complex microphonics appear everywhere except in the region where the lowest frequency has maximal effect. (From Tasaki, Davis and Legouix, *J. acoust. Soc. Amer.,* 1952, 24:502–519.)

ing latency and phase shift with distance from the stapes expected on the traveling wave hypothesis.[56] It is generated over the entire cochlear duct when low sound frequencies are used, but is restricted to the basal region when high frequencies are used (Figs. 11 and 12). This distribution has made it possible to check very simply the concept of *tonal localization in the cochlea* developed through a variety of ingenious and painstaking methods; the results are in essential agreement and are summarized in Figure 13. Because of its close relation to inner ear behavior, the cochlear microphonic has become a valuable tool in analyzing middle ear and inner ear function.

However the cochlear microphonic results from stimulation of outer hair cells, a different sort of response has recently been associated with stimulation of inner hair cells.[18, 19] Moderate to strong stimulation decreases the voltage difference between the cochlear duct and the vestibule, and this decrease is maintained as long as sound stimulation persists. It is therefore termed a *negative summating potential* (Fig. 14). Like the cochlear microphonic, it shows no threshold and negligible latency. Unlike the microphonic, it continues to increase in ampli-

tude with increasing sound pressure; its amplitude is proportional to the root mean square value of the applied sinusoid. The summating potential appears most prominently where the traveling waves reach their maximum amplitude on the cochlear partition and where they are steep and short. They are best produced by longitudinal displacement of the tectorial membrane over the medial part of the reticular lamina.[7, 10] Summating potentials may grow to 10 mV. or even greater, bringing the endocochlear potential down below 70 mV.; this is several times the maximum amplitude attained by the cochlear microphonic.

Békésy[9] has calculated that the mechanical energy of the sound wave cannot supply all the electrical energy of the microphonic potential. Maximum displacements of the basilar membrane at the threshold of hearing are of subatomic magnitude. In order to secure maximum energy transfer, a very good impedance match must be attained; the middle ear matches the air to the fluid-filled cochlea and translation of vertical displacement of the basilar membrane into a shearing force at the reticular lamina provides a second internal match. It is possible but

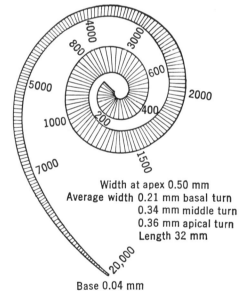

Width at apex 0.50 mm
Average width 0.21 mm basal turn
0.34 mm middle turn
0.36 mm apical turn
Length 32 mm

Base 0.04 mm

Fig. 13. Schematic diagram of human cochlear duct, showing areas of maximal displacement of the partition for pure tones of different frequencies. The 200 cps tone, although displacing the entire cochlear partition, has maximum effect near the apex. The 20,000 cps tone has maximum effect at the base, and damps out completely near the base. (From Stuhlman, *An introduction to biophysics,* New York, John Wiley & Sons, 1943.)

AP, CM AND SP FROM BASAL TURN

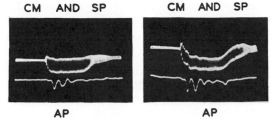

TONE BURST   7000 CPS   +10 DB

Fig. 14. Cochlear microphonic and summating potentials (upper) and simultaneously recorded auditory nerve action potential (lower) from basal turn of guinea pig cochlea in response to moderate (left) and 10 db stronger (right), 7000 cps tonal burst. Action potential shows successive, synchronized volleys of activity. (From Davis in *Neural mechanisms of the auditory and vestibular systems,* G. L. Rasmussen and W. F. Windle, eds., Springfield, Ill., Charles C Thomas, 1960.)

by no means proved that these shearing forces serve to "valve" the energy stored in the endocochlear potential for excitation of the auditory nerve terminals.

Auditory nerve action potentials. The foregoing discussion has shown that, both mechanically and electrically, the cochlea behaves as an acoustic analyzer. The analysis is coded in terms of all-or-none activity in single auditory nerve fibers and is transmitted to the central nervous system. Tasaki[54] recorded the response of single auditory nerve fibers to tonal "pips" of different frequencies and intensities, and found that at threshold a fiber is excited only by a narrow band of frequencies (Fig. 15). This band widens as the sound intensity is increased, expanding rapidly into lower frequencies (gradual cut-off) and almost not at all into higher frequencies (sharp cut-off). This pattern of responsiveness is precisely that expected on the traveling wave hypothesis; high frequencies affect a limited stretch of basilar membrane near the stapes, whereas low frequencies affect the entire membrane. A sufficiently intense low frequency sound excites a large number of auditory fibers ranging over half or more of the cochlear partition. For sinusoids below 1000 cps the individual spikes are synchronized with the sound wave. Excitation occurs when the cochlear duct goes negative, i.e., when the basilar membrane is displaced toward the tectorial membrane. Such a movement bends the cilia of the hair cells

toward the supporting cells of Hensen, exciting the fibers innervating the outer hair cells. The discharge pattern of the fibers innervating the inner hair cells, driven by the constant current of the negative summating potential (by bending cilia of inner hair cells toward the apex of the cochlea), is probably quite different but has not yet been recognized.

The whole nerve response, seen best following click stimulation (Figs. 16 and 19), seems to be dominated by the activity of fibers from the basal turns of the cochlea. It consists of two distinct components, N_1 and N_2, each about one millisecond in duration. The latency of the first component varies with the sound intensity (and frequency) from 1.0 to 2.3 milliseconds. Neither component grows linearly with increasing sound pressure; N_1, with the lower threshold, grows in such a way as to suggest the activity of two different sets of receptor elements with quite different thresholds. The nerve response is very sensitive to anoxia, cold and various drugs, and can be reduced or precluded by the activity of efferent inhibitory fibers (see below). The precise mechanism for excitation of the fibers whose activity makes up the whole nerve response is not known; electron microscopic studies and the latency to the action potential support a chemical mediator concept although current thinking still favors electrical excitation of the nerve terminals.

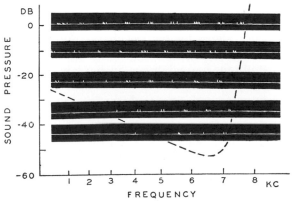

Fig. 15. Single auditory nerve responses to tone "pips" of different frequencies and intensities. Each strip of record shows a short burst of repetitive discharges in the single fiber in response to a tone which is increased in frequency between pips. Each strip of record represents a different sound level, lower record representing weakest intensity used. Dashed line encloses "response area" for this fiber. (From Tasaki, *J. Neurophysiol.,* 1954, *17*:97–122.)

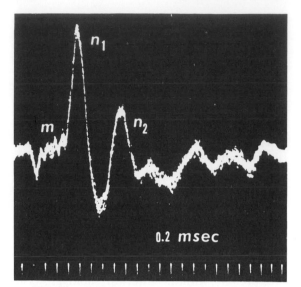

Fig. 16. Auditory nerve response in cat following 0.1 millisecond click stimulation. The cochlear microphonic (m) is evident at the beginning of N_1. Ten superimposed traces. (Courtesy D. Humphrey, University of Washington.)

After examining the mechanics of transmission and the consequent nerve fiber activity, we are still left with the two major theories—the place theory and the frequency theory. Volleys of all-or-none discharges follow in phase with an applied sinusoid up to 2000 cps—about three octaves above middle C and covering the entire range of speech frequencies. A frequency theory must handle pitch in terms of discharge frequency and handle loudness in other terms, such as number of active fibers. The place theory allows for the fact that a pure tone, if intense, will throw a long stretch of the basilar membrane into vibration. Such a vibration has a maximum at some region, and the nerve fibers leading from this region discharge at the highest rate. The place theory handles pitch in terms of which fibers are active and loudness in terms of both frequency of firing and number of fibers active.

Routes of Conduction.[61] Sound waves in the ear reach the organ of Corti by three routes, the first of which may be termed the *physiologic* or *ossicular route*. The vibrations are transmitted from the tympanum through the ossicular chain and oval window to the scala vestibuli and scala media, and thence through the organ of Corti and basilar membrane to the scala tympani and, finally, to the round window. This route has already been discussed at some length; the

important role of the round window is discussed below.

The second route of conduction through the middle ear may be termed the *air route*. This begins at the tympanum and passes via the air in the middle ear to the round window, scala tympani, etc. The air route is principally by way of the round window, because this window is covered by only a thin membrane, whereas the oval window is stoppered by the stapes, especially when the chain is ankylosed ("frozen"). But transmission through the round window is inefficient because it lacks the impedance matching device of the ossicular chain; most of the sound energy is reflected.

When the ossicular chain is broken, the air route conducts less well than might be expected from the acoustical matching value of the chain (30 db). The hearing loss from interruption of the chain varies between 30 db for low tones and 65 db for the middle range. Two factors are involved. One is that the tympanum, weighted by the interrupted ossicular chain, becomes an obstacle to sound transmission to the air of the middle ear. The second is that the sound waves transmitted through the round window and scala tympani push the basilar membrane upward during the phase of positive pressure while the same wave conducted by the now unhindered oval window and scala vestibuli pushes the membrane downward. If this interference is prevented experimentally by leading the sound through a tube to only one window, the hearing loss is 30 db. Fortunately, the sound paths are not equally long, and therefore the sound waves are not 180° out of phase. The cancellation is thus imperfect, and the net loss due to this factor is about 12 db.

More common than interruption is a fixation of the ossicular chain, resulting from adhesions in the wake of a middle ear infection or from a pathologic change in the temporal bone that seals the stapes into the oval window (otosclerosis). Understanding of the resulting deafness and its surgical relief hinge on an appreciation of the physiologic significance of the round window.

The function of the round window apparently is to provide "give" in the otherwise rigidly encased cochlea. Deformation rather than mere compression is required for stimulation of skin receptors and also of hair cells. For deformation to occur, the basilar membrane must actually move, no matter how slightly, and the membrane closing the round window must bulge to permit this. The volume displaced in hearing is of the order of 10^{-8} to 10^{-9} cm³.

In otosclerosis, hearing is severely impaired partly because the ossicular route of conduction is lost. Further, the air route of conduction to the round window cannot function to best advantage because "give" is lacking. Such "give" is successfully provided in Lempert's *fenestration* operation by drilling a small window into the horizontal semicircular canal, which is in continuity with the vestibule of the cochlea. A flap of skin is placed over this fistula, and hearing is significantly improved (usually within 20 to 30 db of normal) as long as the new passage remains patent.

The third route by which sound can be conducted to the inner ear is by means of bone conduction—the *osseous route.* Sound waves reach the inner ear through the bones of the skull; the middle ear is, as it were, "short-circuited or bypassed." Unlike the ossicular and air routes, bone conduction plays little, if any, part in hearing ordinary sounds because so much energy is lost in the passage of a sound wave from air to the bone of the head. However, if a tuning fork which is unheard when sounded in air is held with its base against the skull (better acoustical matching), it can be heard clearly. Bone conduction is important in distinguishing between types of deafness, and it is employed for one type of hearing aid. Conduction by this route must be ruled out in testing an ear with sounds louder than 50 to 60 db above the threshold for 1000 cps, for at this level bone-conducted sound may reach the normal ear. Ear plugs are, of course, useless, but hearing of bone-conducted sound can be eliminated by introducing a *masking* sound into the ear. Suitable adjustment of the intensity and phase of a sinusoid conducted via the *ossicular* route can completely cancel the perception of the same sinusoid via the *osseous* route.[4] Thus, the mechanism of excitation in bone conduction must be the same as that in air conduction, viz., fluid movements near the stapes. These movements develop because inertia prevents the stapes and cochlear fluid from following exactly the oscillations of the head bones, and the resulting differential movements deflect the basilar membrane and the secondary tympanic membrane.

Types of Deafness.[61] Deafness, including partial impairment of hearing, is classified into three main types according to where the block occurs. *Conduction deafness* is any interference

with the passage of sound waves through the external or middle ear. Common causes are collections of pus, exudates or wax; adhesions of the ossicles to the bony walls; thickening of the tympanum as a result of infection; and new growths of bone that bind the stapes. The Weber and Rinné diagnostic tests are based on the difference between the air-ossicular route and the bone route of conduction. Because it "bypasses" the middle ear, bone conduction is little affected when the air-ossicular route is impeded. The deafness is never total because some sound is conducted through the skull. Also, in these patients, audiograms tend to be "flat"; i.e., the loss is about equal for all frequencies. The patient, paradoxically, seems to hear best in noisy surroundings, because voices are raised and he is not disturbed by the lower intensity background noise—it is unheard. He tolerates hearing aids and is greatly benefited by them.

The second type of hearing impairment, once termed *perception deafness,* is now known as *nerve deafness.* The defect is not in the cortical process of sound perception but is caused by a degeneration of sensory cells of the inner ear, tumors of the auditory nerve, etc. Because the damage is in the portion of the hearing mechanism common to air and bone conduction (hair cells and auditory nerve), a failure of both routes is diagnostic. The hearing of high tones (4000 cps) is typically the most impaired (hence "high tone deafness"). This distorts the *timbre* of sounds, making it hard for the patient to discriminate sound sources and interfering with the perception of consonants. For some reason, as the intensity of a tone is increased, the perceived intensity (loudness) increases more rapidly than it does when hearing is normal. The loud sounds may be just as unpleasant as they are to the normal ear, making the patient intolerant of loud speech or hearing aids. Since this is the deafness of old age, the familiar phrase, "Don't shout, young man," is understandable. Nerve deafness may be temporary when caused by fatigue or partial trauma, as in exposure to prolonged loud sounds ("boilermaker's deafness"), or permanent when caused by degeneration through exposure to very intense sounds, senility, disease or toxic agents. The problem of acoustic trauma is one of growing medical and legal importance.

The third type of deafness, *central deafness,* is rare. It may result from interference with the pathway of nerve impulses to the cerebral cortex, but is more often a manifestation of aphasia (Chap. 23) or of a psychogenic disorder. Recent studies[26, 27] on suppression of auditory nerve discharge may have some bearing on these latter disorders.

PHYSIOLOGY OF THE CENTRAL AUDITORY PATHWAYS

Information about the state of the cochlear partition is continuously transmitted to the central nervous system via the VIIIth cranial nerve. The rather varied and complex peripheral ramifications of the bipolar cells in the spiral ganglion have already been discussed. The central axons of the bipolar cells enter the pons at its junction with the medulla, bifurcate and connect with both the ventral and the dorsal cochlear nuclei. In the nerve, the fibers from the base and apex twist like a rope, but do not

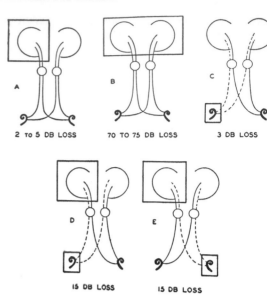

Fig. 18. Summary diagram of series of experiments demonstrating bilaterality of auditory pathway in dog. Number below each diagram is hearing loss in decibels, and a box around symbol for cerebral cortex or cochlea indicates destruction of it. Observe that in *D* hearing depends on *uncrossed* fibers of left lateral lemniscus, whereas in *E* hearing depends upon crossed fibers of right lateral lemniscus; hearing loss is equal in the two cases. (Experiments by Mettler *et al., Brain,* 1934, *57:*475–483; diagram after Stevens and Davis, *Hearing, its psychology and physiology,* New York, John Wiley & Sons, Inc., 1938.)

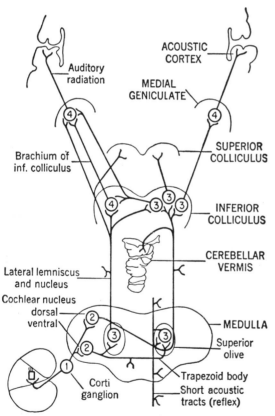

Fig. 17. Afferent acoustic pathways. Numbers in circles represent first, second, third and fourth neuron of chain. Drawing summarizes work of several investigations, mainly on cat. (From Davis, Chap. 28 in *Handbook of experimental psychology,* S. S. Stevens, ed., New York, John Wiley & Sons, Inc., 1951.)

intermingle randomly; synaptic terminals are so distributed that the cochlear nuclei become "uncoiled" reflections of the cochlea. The ventral cochlear nucleus of higher mammals developed from the more dorsally situated nucleus magnocellularis of the terrestrial amphibians and reptiles, while the newer dorsal cochlear nucleus finds its homologue in the nucleus angularis that developed in reptiles in close association with the magnocellular nucleus. These nuclei project to the more medially placed superior olivary complex, which appeared in the amphibians and developed rapidly in reptiles and birds. In the submammalian forms, fibers arising from the superior olivary complex, forming the lateral lemniscus, end chiefly in the mammalian homologue of the inferior colliculus. With the rapid encephalization in mammals, the system stretched out through the medial geniculate body of the thalamus to reach the cerebral cortex. This latter addition failed to develop crossing fibers; Figure 17 shows the extensive crossing fibers at lower levels. Action potentials can be recorded from both the ipsilateral and contralateral lateral lemnisci when one cochlea is stimulated.[34] From the size and timing of the activity, the ipsilateral fibers apparently equal the contralateral in number, and the same number of synapses is involved. Chow[17] has shown that the number of fibers progressively increases at each stage of the auditory system. For each fiber in the spiral ganglion, two issue from the cochlear nucleus, 14 issue from the medial geniculate and some 340 occur in the auditory cortex.

The bilaterality of the auditory system was well demonstrated physiologically in the ingenious experiments by Mettler *et al.*[35] (Fig. 18). After various components of the auditory pathway in dogs had been interrupted, the degree of hearing loss was determined by the conditioned reflex method. By removing one cerebral cortex in combination with one or the other cochlea, Mettler and his coworkers discovered that the "acoustic values" of the ipsilateral and contralateral pathways are equal. Nearly complete bilaterality of representation also characterizes the auditory system of man. Unilateral cortical lesions affect hearing only slightly, and, since both auditory areas are seldom attacked by the same pathologic process, deafness is rarely produced by cortical lesions.

In addition to the specific projection to the auditory cortex outlined above, a more diffuse route can be traced through the reticular formation. Although several major stages in this system are undefined, the ascending reticular system is clearly implicated by the observation that sounds continue to arouse decerebellate cats after the specific auditory system has been severed. It has even been possible to evoke a "normal" auditory primary evoked response in the cortex of the cat after complete transection of the brachium of the inferior colliculus.[28]

Centrifugal Auditory Pathway. Anatomically, it is known that a bundle of fibers originates in the superior olivary complex and terminates in the cochlea of the same side (about 20 per cent) and the opposite side (80 per cent). This pathway, called the bundle of Rasmussen or the bundle of Oort, consists only of about 500 fibers in the cat.[40] Nonetheless, it has a rather powerful influence on cochlear output. By applying electric shocks to this olivocochlear bundle of Rasmussen in the cat, Galambos[27] was able to alter the response of the auditory nerve to click stimuli (Fig. 19). When the muscles and ossicles of the middle ear were removed

and the animal was curarized, the suppression began 20 to 30 milliseconds after the first shock of the train of stimuli and continued as long as 500 milliseconds beyond stimulation. The outer hair cell response (cochlear microphonic) was unaltered during these maneuvers, but the auditory nerve response was suppressed (strong clicks) or totally abolished (weak clicks). It is evident that the central nervous system can modulate its input via this system; malfunction of the system could result in significant alteration from normal hearing.

Cochlear Nuclei.[25, 42] In the cat, each auditory nerve fiber which enters the brain stem, radial and spiral fiber alike, bifurcates to send one branch rostrally into the anterior part of the ventral cochlear nucleus and another branch caudally through the posterior part of the ventral cochlear nucleus and then dorsally into the overlying dorsal cochlear nucleus. Each fiber forms synaptic endings on a multitude of neurons. Fibers terminate in an orderly sequence such that those from the apex of the cochlea end first while those from the base of the cochlea penetrate farthest into the nuclei before bifurcating and terminating. Several different types of synaptic structures are recognized, but their functional significance is still unknown. These nuclei receive fibers from other regions of the brain stem as well as from the cochlea and display a complex and in some regions a laminar arrangement. The laminar dorsal cochlear nucleus projects into the tuber vermis of the cerebellum and into the contralateral inferior colliculus, while the ventral coch-

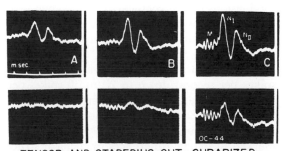

TENSOR AND STAPEDIUS CUT; CURARIZED; STAPES DISARTICULATED

Fig. 19. Suppression of auditory nerve response to click stimulation by shocks to olivocochlear bundle. *A*, Response to weak click totally abolished by 100/sec. shocks to medulla. *B, C*, Stronger clicks, showing incomplete suppression. *M*, Hair cell response. N_I and N_{II}, Auditory nerve response. (From Galambos, *J. Neurophysiol.*, 1956, *19:*424–437.)

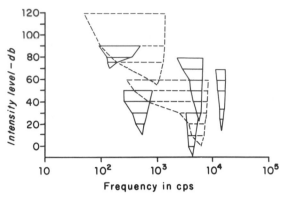

Fig. 20. Auditory response curves from cochlear nucleus of cat, showing both narrow (solid lines) and broad band (dashed lines) receptive areas. The "best frequencies" for each neuron are the lower "peaks" of the response curves. Note that most neurons respond to lower, but not higher, pure tones as the intensity level is increased. (After Rose *et al., Bull. Johns Hopk. Hosp.,* 1959, *104:*211–251.)

lear nucleus sends fibers to the superior olivary complex bilaterally.

Neurons in these nuclei behave much as the single auditory nerve fibers studied by Tasaki.[54] Rose *et al.*[42] found that at sufficiently weak stimulus intensities, only one frequency excited the neuron. As the intensity was increased, the range of excitatory frequencies increased toward the low frequencies but hardly at all to higher frequencies (Fig. 20). These frequency-intensity graphs define the *response area* or "receptive field" of a neuron, and the frequency at minimum or threshold intensity is termed the *best frequency* for the neuron. It is evident in Figure 20 that some neurons have wide and some narrow response areas; both types are found in all subdivisions of the cochlear nuclei. When prolonged tones were employed, the neurons responded with an initial high frequency of spike discharge and then a gradual decline in discharge rate to a steady, low value (from 200 spikes per second down to 20 to 30 spikes per second). Similar response properties have been found in the nucleus magnocellularis and nucleus angularis of the pigeon,[52] in spite of the marked histologic differences in cochlear structure (birds possess neither rods of Corti nor reticular lamina, and but a primordial tectorial membrane "improperly" located).

When a penetrating microelectrode traverses first the dorsal and then the ventral cochlear nuclei, the *best frequencies* of the neurons isolated along the way show an orderly sequence from high to low, with a sudden jump to high again

as the ventral nucleus is entered. Three such *tonotopic organizations* can be found in the cat, oriented from high frequencies dorsomedially to low frequencies ventrolaterally, one in the dorsal cochlear nucleus, one posteriorly in the ventral nucleus and another anteriorly in the same nucleus. This corresponds well with the orderly termination of auditory nerve fibers in these nuclei; a full tonal spectrum is found in each division. This is not simple duplication of representation, however. The dorsal division receives a heavy input from central brain stem structures and shows certain inhibitory phenomena not commonly seen in the ventral divisions. Evidently considerable "processing" of auditory information goes on at these primary auditory relays.

Superior Olivary Complex.[25]   The superior olive itself, its accessory nucleus, the pre-olivary nuclei, trapezoid body and the cells of origin of the olivocochlear bundle of Rasmussen constitute this complex. It receives fibers primarily from the ventral cochlear nucleus, some bilaterally and some unilaterally. Curiously, when the cochlear nuclei are destroyed on one side, terminal degeneration in the accessory superior olive is confined to the dendrites toward the lesion.[53] The complex gives rise to the lateral lemniscus, but also sends fibers into motor nuclei in the brain stem and the ubiquitous reticular formation. These nuclei have been regarded as supporting reflex functions but recently have assumed a more important place in the main stream to the cortex. Little is known of the physiology of this complex; trapezoid neurons show narrow response areas and may not be tonotopically arranged.[32]

Inferior Colliculus. A main or central nuclear mass overlaid by an external nucleus constitutes the main feature of this nucleus, although other subdivisions are recognized. Input fibers arrive directly from the contralateral dorsal cochlear nucleus and from both superior olivary nuclei; a large amount of "intercommunication" occurs within the various subdivisions of the nucleus and across the midline, and more input fibers arrive from rostral sites. Output fibers are sent not only to the medial geniculate body, but also to the superior colliculus and down into lower brain stem nuclei. However, the main body of the lateral lemniscus by-passes the inferior colliculus; the latter is probably more involved in auditory reflex activity than in perceptual analysis.

Response areas of the different neurons in the inferior colliculus are uniformly narrow.[32] A tonotopic organization has been found in these nuclei[43] which is inverted between the external nucleus and the central mass. Moving in a general dorsoventral direction, starting caudolaterally and moving toward the rostroventral aspect of the nuclear mass, one finds best frequencies arranged from high to low in the external nucleus and from low to high in the central mass. Rose *et al.*[43] found some neurons to behave like a portion of those in the dorsal cochlear nucleus—with increasing sound intensity, the number of spikes in the response first increases but then decreases, as though the higher sound intensities call into play some inhibitory mechanism. Similar observations have been made in the inferior colliculus of the bat.[30] Intracellular recordings have shown that active inhibitory effects do occur in this structure; Nelson and Erulkar[38] found both excitatory and inhibitory postsynaptic potentials, depending upon which ear was stimulated, upon whether clicks or tones were used, and upon the frequency and intensity of the tones. Continuous tones often produced slowly rising depolarizations; at the cessation of the tone, such depolarizations declined equally slowly.

Medial Geniculate Body.[25] The medial geniculate body consists of an apparently nonauditory superior lobe* and an inferior lobe, containing a medial magnocellular division and a lateral, crescent-shaped principal division. Large fibers from the lateral lemniscus and the brachium of the inferior colliculus enter the *principal nucleus* to arborize around many cells; thin fibers spread throughout the *magnocellular nucleus,* each fiber likewise ending on many cells. Corticogeniculate fibers end chiefly in the principal nucleus. The axons of the small, densely-packed neurons in the principal nucleus form the auditory radiation to the cerebral cortex. Thus, the pars principalis of the medial geniculate body constitutes the primary relay en route to the cerebral cortex; the pars magnocellularis is still largely an unknown.

Exploration of the medial geniculate region with microelectrodes has shown only the principal nucleus to be activated by sound stimulation.[41] Neurons in this nucleus have narrower response areas than elsewhere along the audi-

* The commissural fibers forming Gudden's tract interconnect the superior lobes and have no known auditory function.

tory pathway,[33] even though many wide response areas can also be found here. According to Katsuki and coworkers,[32, 33] the response areas of individual neurons become progressively narrower as one moves from the primary auditory nerve fibers through the cochlear nuclei, the superior olivary complex, inferior colliculus and finally to the medial geniculate. The initial response latency to clicks or tonal pips averages 12 milliseconds at the medial geniculate, no matter which ear is stimulated. In terms of threshold sound intensity, however, the contralateral ear is slightly favored.[29] Although a tonotopic organization within the pars principalis probably exists, it has not been clearly defined.

Primary Auditory Cortex. The *auditory cortical field* shows a variety of architectonic configurations (see Chap. 12). It consists of a central field surrounded by a band of tissue divisible into three sectors (Fig. 21). The central field, AI, receives direct projections from the pars principalis of the medial geniculate body; input to the surrounding sectors seems to be indirect, either through collaterals from the geniculocortical projection fibers or through other thalamic nuclei.[44] The specific projection fibers from the pars principalis end heavily in layer IV and to some extent in layer III, each fiber making contact with a large number of neurons. The nonspecific thalamic afferents and cortical association fibers end throughout the upper two-thirds of the cortex. Area AI consists of a very dense array of medium to small, more-or-less rounded polymorphic cells, in such profusion that the normal cortical lamination is blurred and layers II, III and IV seem to be "fused." This contrasts sharply with the bordering sectors, which show distinct lamination and an increasing pyramidalization; layer III possesses larger cells than layer II. The transition between sectors is gradual.

Neuron response properties. About two in every three neurons isolated with a microelectrode in the primary sector, AI, respond in some way to sound stimulation. Although stimulation of either ear is effective, cortical neurons show a 5 to 20 db higher threshold to ipsilateral stimulation than to contralateral stimulation. As at all other levels of the auditory pathway, two response patterns occur—either an initial burst of spikes with failure to continue, or a burst of spikes at onset of a tone followed by a rapid decline in firing frequency to a lower level that is

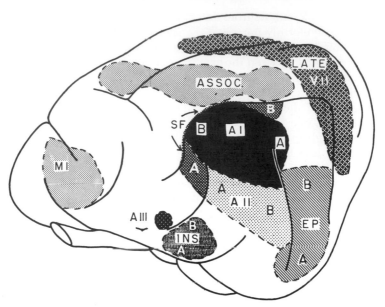

Fig. 21. Lateral view of left cerebral hemisphere of cat showing the four central areas of auditory cortex, with the cochlea represented anteroposteriorly from base (B) to apex (A) in AI and AII and from apex to base in the suprasylvian fringe area (SF). The posterior ectosylvian area (EP), like the insula (INS), displays the cochlea from apex to base in a more vertical arrangement. Auditory responses appear late in motor (MI) and associate cortex and very late in visual II. (From Woolsey in *Neural mechanisms of the auditory and vestibular systems,* G. L. Rasmussen and W. F. Windle, eds., Springfield, Ill., Charles C Thomas, 1960.)

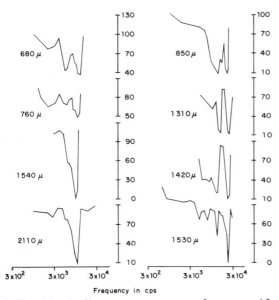

Fig. 22. Auditory response curves from area AI of the cat. Left series shows response curves for neurons recorded at successively lower depths in the cortex; note similarity in "best frequencies" and compound nature of curves. Right series, taken from penetration more posteriorly, shows higher "best frequencies." (After Hind, Chap. 14 in *Neural mechanisms of the auditory and vestibular systems.* G. L. Rasmussen and W. F. Windle, eds., Springfield, Ill., Charles C Thomas, 1960.)

maintained as long as the tone is sounded. The latter "sustained" response pattern characterizes neurons in the cochlear nuclei, but the "onset" pattern occurs with increasing frequency at successively higher levels and is the rule in auditory cortex. The response areas of cortical neurons are wider than in the medial geniculate body but not so wide as in the cochlear nucleus.[31, 33] They remain narrow from threshold intensity to about 60 db above threshold and then broaden sharply; often two or even three smaller "peaks" are evident (Fig. 22), especially when both ears are stimulated.[31]

Area AI is tonotopically organized; in subprimate forms, the best frequencies are arranged in a rostrocaudal direction from high to low (from base to apex of cochlea), but the reverse is true of primates. When the microelectrode penetrates down through the cortical layers, the best frequencies of the neurons isolated are about the same[31] (Fig. 22). However, even though a high degree of order is present at all levels of the auditory pathway, including the auditory cortex, the system also specializes in diversity. Occasionally wide deviations from the "normal" best frequency for a region occur. Response areas can be altered markedly in configuration by continuous background or "masking" tones, although the best frequency remains as such. The threshold intensity at the best frequency varies widely from one neuron to the next, being bounded near the audibility curve on the low side but ranging to 40 or even 60 db above that value. The entire auditory pathway specializes in inhibitory phenomena; neurons are excited by some frequencies and inhibited by others—or are inhibited by the same frequencies but at a different intensity. Thus, when a simple sinusoidal sound wave impinges on the ear, neurons at all sites in the auditory pathway respond in various degrees. Activity is canalized; it is maximal at a region in each auditory nucleus that is determined by the frequency of the sinusoid, and the magnitude of "maximal" is determined by the amplitude of the sinusoid. Around this region of maximal response, neuron activity rapidly falls off. Farther away, neurons are actively "turned off" or made unresponsive to particular tones. The response of the auditory pathway to simple sounds is thus highly canalized and consistent with the place theory of hearing.

Auditory areas. In 1942 Woolsey and Walzl[67] studied the *primary evoked response* (see Chap. 22) that is produced in the cortex of the cat by focal electrical stimulation along the edge of the osseous spiral lamina. They found two complete representations of the cochlea on the ectosylvian and sylvian gyri, one in the cortex heavily innervated by the medial geniculate body (called AI; see Fig. 21) and a second more laterally disposed (AII). The representations became evident when they observed that slight changes in the site of cochlear stimulation changed the point of maximal electrical activity on the auditory cortex. Stimulation near the base of the cochlea caused activity in the anterior part of AI, while stimulation at the apex caused activity posteriorly; intermediate cortical regions were activated by stimulation of intermediate cochlear regions. The order of representation of the cochlea was reversed in AII. Tunturi[58] soon verified the AI "map" by employing tonal stimuli (Fig. 23) and also identified a third auditory response area (AIII) sharing cortex with the second somatosensory area.[59] Two additional representations of the cochlea have been found, immediately adjacent to the primary auditory area, AI (Fig. 21). The place theory, which asked for only one representation of the cochlea in the cortex, finds itself with an embarrassing richness of tonotopic "maps."

At first it seemed that the auditory areas immediately adjacent to AI were brought into activity by fiber projections from AI,[1, 14] and such interconnections have been demonstrated.[21] But ablation of AI had no effect on tonal discrimination either in cat[36] or monkey;[23] complete bilateral destruction of all auditory areas seemed necessary to interfere permanently with the ability to distinguish small changes in frequency of a tone. These "fringe" areas have been shown to possess independent afferent projections.[21] Further, it appears that with different training methods,[15] animals can relearn frequency discriminations after ablation of all these cortical auditory areas. Nor does the cortex appear to play any role in discrimination in changes in intensity of a tone.[39] However, the ability to locate a sound in space is severely impaired following bilateral ablations of AI, AII and Ep but little affected if the ablation is unilateral.[37] Clinical evidence is in dispute on this point.

The function of AI may lie in some "higher" auditory activity. AII seems essential to pattern discrimination, whereas AI is not.[20] If tones A and B are used to make two tonal patterns, ABA and BAB, the transition between them is easily discriminable by a cat before operation. After removal of the three main auditory areas, pattern discrimination, unlike single frequency discrimination, is lost and cannot be relearned. Impairment in the understanding of speech is evident in cases of human temporal lobe dam-

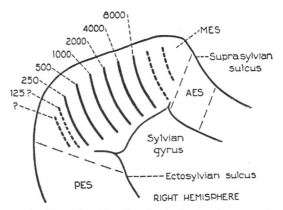

Fig. 23. Tonal localization in dog's primary auditory area. *AES*, Anterior ectosylvian area; *PES*, posterior ectosylvian area; *MES*, middle ectosylvian area. Bands indicate point at which strychnine spikes occurred with lowest intensity. Bands indicated by dashes were not determined experimentally. (After Tunturi from Bremer, *Some problems in neurophysiology*, London, Athlone Press, 1953.)

age,[13, 45] and quantification of the deficit shows that the ear contralateral to the lesion suffers more deficit. Patients with cortical damage often make mistakes in the perception of nasal sounds,[45] whereas patients with peripheral auditory damage less often show such a defect.

REFERENCES

1. Ades, H. W. *J. Neurophysiol.*, 1943, *6:*59–63.
2. Ades, H. W., Mettler, F. A. and Culler, E. A. *Amer. J. Physiol.*, 1939, *125:*15–23.
3. Armstrong, H. G. *Principles and practice of aviation medicine.* 3rd ed. Baltimore, Williams & Wilkins, 1952.
4. Békésy, G. von. *Ann. Physik.*, 1932, *13:*111–136.
5. Békésy, G. von. *Acta oto-laryng. (Stockh.)*, 1939, *27:*281–296.
6. Békésy, G. von. *J. acoust. Soc. Amer.*, 1948, *20:*227–241.
7. Békésy, G. von. *J. acoust. Soc. Amer.*, 1951, *23:*29–35.
8. Békésy, G. von. *J. acoust. Soc. Amer.*, 1951, *23:*576–582.
9. Békésy, G. von. *J. acoust. Soc Amer.*, 1952, *24:*72–76.
10. Békésy, G. von. *J. acoust. Soc. Amer.*, 1953, *25:*786–790.
11. Békésy, G. von. *Experiments in hearing*, N.Y., McGraw-Hill, 1960.
12. Békésy, G. von and Rosenblith, W. A. Chap. 27 in *Handbook of experimental psychology*, S. S. Stevens, ed. New York, John Wiley & Sons, 1951.
13. Bocca, E. *Laryngoscope (St. Louis)*, 1958, *68:*301–309.
14. Bremer, F. *Some problems in neurophysiology.* London, Athlone Press, 1953.
15. Butler, R. A., Diamond, I. T. and Neff, W. D. *J. Neurophysiol.*, 1957, *20:*108–120.
16. Carmel, P. W. and Starr, A. *J. Neurophysiol.*, 1963, *26:*598–616.
17. Chow, K. L. *J. comp. Neurol.*, 1951, *95:*159–175.
18. Davis, H., Deatherage, B. H., Eldredge, D. H. and Smith, C. A. *Amer. J. Physiol.*, 1958, *195:*251–261.
19. Davis, H., Deatherage, B. H., Rosenblut, B., Fernandez, C., Kimura, R. and Smith, C. A. *Laryngoscope (St. Louis)*, 1958, *68:*596–627.
20. Diamond, I. T. and Neff, W. D. *J. Neurophysiol.*, 1957, *20:*300–315.
21. Downman, C. B. B., Woolsey, C. N. and Lende, R. A. *Bull. Johns Hopk. Hosp.*, 1960, *106:*127–142.
22. Engström, H., Ades, H. W. and Hawkins, J. E., Jr. *J. acoust. Soc. Amer.*, 1962, *34:*1356–1363.
23. Evarts, E. V. *J. Neurophysiol.*, 1952, *15:*443–448.
24. Fernández, C. *Laryngoscope (St. Louis)*, 1951, *61:*1152–1172.
25. Galambos, R. *Physiol. Rev.*, 1954, *34:*497–528.
26. Galambos, R. *Ann. Otol. (St. Louis)*, 1956, *65:*1053–1059.
27. Galambos, R. *J. Neurophysiol.*, 1956, *19:*424–437.
28. Galambos, R., Myers, R. E. and Sheatz, G. C. *Amer. J. Physiol.*, 1961, *200:*23–28.
29. Galambos, R., Rose, J. E., Bromiley, R. B. and Hughes, J. R. *J. Neurophysiol.*, 1952, *15:*359–380.
30. Grinnel, A. D. *J. Physiol.*, 1963, *167:*38–66.
31. Hind, J. E. Chap. 14 in *Neural mechanisms of the auditory and vestibular systems*, G. L. Rasmussen and W. Windle, eds. Springfield, Ill., Charles C Thomas, 1960.
32. Katsuki, Y., Sumi, T., Uchiyama, H. and Watanabe, T. *J. Neurophysiol.*, 1958, *21:*569–588.
33. Katsuki, Y., Watanabe, T. and Maruyama, N. *J. Neurophysiol.*, 1959, *22:*343–359.
34. Kemp, E. H., Coppée, G. E. and Robinson, E. H. *Amer. J. Physiol.*, 1937, *120:*304–315.
35. Mettler, F. A., Finch, G., Girden, E. and Culler, E. *Brain*, 1934, *57:*475–483.
36. Meyer, D. R. and Woolsey, C. N. *J. Neurophysiol.*, 1952, *15:*149–162.
37. Neff, W. D., Fisher, J. F., Diamond, I. T. and Yela, M. *J. Neurophysiol.*, 1956, *19:*500–512.
38. Nelson, P. G. and Erulkar, S. D. *J. Neurophysiol.*, 1963, *26:*908–923.
39. Raab, D. H. and Ades, H. W. *Amer. J. Psychol.*, 1946, *59:*59–83.
40. Rasmussen, G. L. *J. comp. Neurol.*, 1946, *84:*141–219.
41. Rose, J. E. and Galambos, R. *J. Neurophysiol.*, 1952, *15:*343–357.
42. Rose, J. E., Galambos, R. and Hughes, J. R. *Bull. Johns Hopk. Hosp.*, 1959, *104:*211–251.
43. Rose, J. E., Greenwood, D. D., Goldberg, J. M. and Hind, J. E. *J. Neurophysiol.*, 1963, *26:*294–320.
44. Rose, J. E. and Woolsey, C. N. *J. comp. Neurol.*, 1949, *91:*441–466.
45. de Sa, G. *Laryngoscope (St. Louis)*, 1958, *68:*309–317.
46. Smith, C. A. *Ann. Otol. (St. Louis)*, 1961, *70:*504–527.
47. Smith, C. A. *Trans. Amer. otol. Soc.*, 1961, *48:*35–60.
48. Smith, C. A., Lowry, O. H. and Wu, M-L. *Laryngoscope (St. Louis)*, 1954, *64:*141–153.
49. Smith, C. A. and Sjöstrand, F. S. *J. Ultrastruct. Res.*, 1961, *5:*523–556.
50. Stevens, S. S. and Davis, H. *Hearing: its psychology and physiology.* New York, John Wiley & Sons, 1938.
51. Stevens, S. S., Davis, H. and Lurie, M. H. *J. gen. Psychol.*, 1935, *13:*297–315.
52. Stopp, P. E. and Whitfield, I. C. *J. Physiol.*, 1961, *158:*165–177.
53. Stotler, W. A. *J. comp. Neurol.*, 1953, *98:*401–431.
54. Tasaki, I. *J. Neurophysiol.*, 1954, *17:*97–122.
55. Tasaki, I., Davis, H. and Eldredge, D. H. *J. acoust. Soc. Amer.*, 1954, *26:*765–773.
56. Tasaki, I., Davis, H. and Legouix, J-P. *J. acoust. Soc. Amer.*, 1952, *24:*502–519.
57. Tasaki, I. and Spyropoulos, C. S. *J. Neurophysiol.*, 1959, *22:*149–155.
58. Tunturi, A. R. *Amer. J. Physiol.*, 1944, *141:*397–403.
59. Tunturi, A. *Amer. J. Physiol.*, 1945, *144:*389–394.
60. Waetzmann, E. *Akust. Z.*, 1938, *3:*1–6.
61. Wever, E. G. *Theory of hearing.* New York, John Wiley & Sons, 1949.
62. Wever, E. G. and Bray, C. W. *J. exp. Psychol.*, 1930, *13:*373–387.
63. Wever, E. G. and Bray, C. W. *Proc. nat. Acad. Sci. (Wash.)*, 1930, *16:*344–350.
64. Wever, E. G. and Lawrence, M. *Physiological acoustics.* Princeton, N.J., Princeton University Press, 1954.
65. Wiener, F. M. and Ross, D. A. *J. acoust. Soc. Amer.*, 1946, *18:*401–408.
66. Wilska, A. *Skand. Arch. Physiol.*, 1935, *72:*161–165.
67. Woolsey, C. N. and Walzi, E. M. *Bull. Johns Hopk. Hosp.*, 1942, *71:*315–344.

CHAPTER 19

The Eye as an Optical Instrument

By FRANK W. WEYMOUTH*

THE eye is the peripheral organ of vision. By means of its physical structure (Fig. 1), rays of light from external objects are focused upon the retina and there set up nerve impulses that are transmitted by the fibers of the optic nerve and the optic tract to the visual area in the cortex of the brain. Here is aroused the reaction we call seeing. In studying the physiology of vision we must first consider the eye as an optical instrument that is physically adapted to form an image on its retina and that is provided with certain physiologic regulatory mechanisms.

FORMATION OF AN IMAGE

The image on the retina is formed by virtue of the refractive surfaces of the cornea and the lens. The curved surfaces of these transparent bodies act substantially like a convex glass lens, and the physics of the formation of an image by such a lens is used to explain the refractive processes in the eye.

*Deceased. Chapter revised by Theodore C. Ruch.

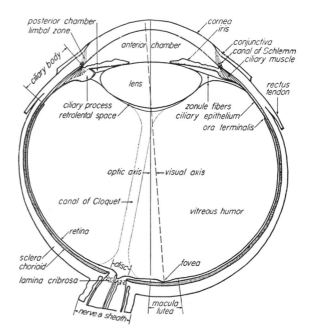

Fig. 1. Horizontal section of human eye. (From Walls, *The vertebrate eye.* Bloomfield Hills, Mich., Cranbrook Institute of Science, 1942.)

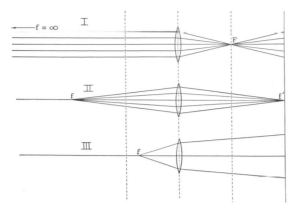

Fig. 2. Refraction of light by convex lens. *I*, Refraction of parallel rays; *II*, refraction of divergent rays; *III*, refraction of divergent rays from a luminous point nearer than principal focal distance. *F*, Principal focus; *f*, luminous point; *f'*, focused image of *f*.

Image Formation by a Convex Lens.

The most common artificial lens is a piece of glass with polished spherical surfaces surrounded by air. Such lenses are of two types, the converging lens with convex surfaces (thick in the middle) and the diverging lens with concave surfaces (thin in the middle). The *principal axis* of a lens with two spherical surfaces is a line passing through the centers of curvature that is therefore perpendicular to these surfaces where it pierces them. Real images that may be caught on a screen are formed only by convex (converging) lenses.

Light from a point on the principal axis so distant that the rays are parallel when they strike the lens will converge at a point, the *principal focus,* on the principal axis behind the lens (*F* in Fig. 2, I).* The distance between the principal focus and the lens is the *principal focal distance.* This distance, which is a measure of the refractive power or "strength" of the lens, depends upon the curvatures of the lens surfaces and the refractive index of the glass. Absolutely parallel rays emanate from an infinitely distant source of light; practically, however, objects not nearer than about 20 feet give rays which diverge so little that they may be considered to be parallel. On the other hand, if a luminous object is placed at *F* in Figure 2, the rays that pass through the lens will emerge as parallel rays. If

*In all such diagrams, the curvatures and thickness of the lens are greatly exaggerated. Statements concerning the course of rays are strictly true only for an ideally thin lens and for a small area about the principal axis.

a luminous point (*f* in Fig. 2, II) is placed in front of the lens at a distance greater than the principal focal distance but not far enough to give practically parallel rays, the cone of diverging rays from this source will focus at *f'*, which is farther away than the principal focus. Conversely, the rays from a luminous point at *f'* will be brought to a focus at *f.* Such points as *f* and *f'* are spoken of as *conjugate foci.* All luminous points within the limits specified have corresponding conjugate foci at which their images are formed by the lens. Lastly, if a luminous point is placed nearer to the lens than the principal focal distance, as at *f* in Figure 2, III, the cone of strongly divergent rays, although refracted, is still divergent after leaving the lens, and consequently is not focused and forms no real image of the point.

Any lens contains an *optical center,* or nodal point, on the principal axis; in Figure 3, *DE* is the principal axis, and *o* is the optical center. All other straight lines passing through the optical center, i.e., rays coincident with the principal axis or any secondary axis, are not bent in passing through the lens. Moreover, the conjugate focus of any luminous point not on the principal axis will lie somewhere upon the secondary axis drawn from this point through the optical center.

The exact position of the image of such a point can be determined by the construction illustrated in Figure 3, I. *A* represents a luminous point throwing a cone of rays upon the lens; the limiting rays of this cone are

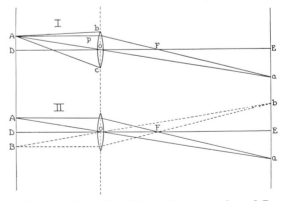

Fig. 3. Formation of image by convex lens. *I*, Relation of a point (*A*) to its image (*a*). *Ab* and *Ac* are limiting rays of cone of light reflected by *A*; *Ap*, ray parallel to optic or principal axis (*DE*) of lens; *F*, principal focus; *o*, optical center. *II*, Relation of luminous object and its image points. *A, B*, luminous points; *a, b*, images of points.

represented by *Ab* and *Ac*. Ray *Ap* is parallel to the principal axis and will therefore pass through the principal focus, *F*. If the focal distance is known, the line *Ap* can be extended, as indicated, to pass through *F* after leaving the lens. The point at which the prolongation of this line cuts the secondary axis, *Ao*, marks the conjugate focus of *A* and gives the position, *a*, at which all the rays are focused to form the image.

To calculate the position of the image of any object in front of the lens, the same method may be used, a construction being drawn to determine the images of two or more limiting points, as shown in Figure 3, II. If *AB* is an arrow in front of a lens, the image of *A* is formed at *a* on the secondary axis *Ao* and the image of *B* at *b* along the secondary axis *Bo*. The images of all the intervening points will, of course, lie between *a* and *b*, so that the entire image is that of an inverted arrow. This image may be caught on a screen at the distance indicated by a construction drawn to scale.

The principal focus of a convex lens in air may be determined experimentally, or it may be calculated from the formula

$$\frac{1}{F} = \frac{1}{f_1} + \frac{1}{f_2}$$

where F represents the principal focal distance, and f_1 and f_2 the conjugate focal distances for an object farther away than the principal focus. That is, if the distance between the object and the lens, f_1, is known, and the distance of its image, f_2, is determined experimentally, the principal focal distance of the lens, F, may be determined from the formula.

Image Formation by the Eye. Although the refractive surfaces of the eye act essentially like a convex lens, they are more complex. As indicated in Figure 4, the eye contains three refractive surfaces. The light is refracted at the anterior surface of the cornea, where the rays pass from the air into the denser medium of the cornea; at the anterior surface of the lens, where they again enter a denser medium; and at the posterior surface of the lens, where they enter the less dense vitreous humor. The relative refractive effects on these various surfaces depend upon the curvatures and the indices of refraction* of the various media of the eye and therefore differ.[6, 8]

$$\text{Index of refraction} = \frac{\text{velocity in air}}{\text{velocity in x}} = \frac{\text{sine i}}{\text{sine r}}$$

The following illustrate the data on the index of refraction:

*The index of refraction is the ratio of the velocity of light in air (or, more exactly, in vacuum) to the velocity of light in the substance considered; this index is commonly measured by the ratio between the sine of the angle of incidence and the sine of the angle of refraction.

air	= 1.000
water	= 1.333
aqueous and vitreous humors	= 1.336
crystalline lens (index of an equivalent thin lens)	= 1.413

Because the difference between the index of refraction of air and that of the cornea is greater than the difference between the indices for the lens and its surroundings, light is more strongly bent on entering the eye than in passing through the lens.

In a lens system like the eye, composed of media with different indices of refraction separated by surfaces of varying curvatures, it is possible, but laborious, to trace accurately the entire path of the light. However, the course of light rays through the eye can be followed with sufficient accuracy by means of a simplification, the *reduced eye*.[4] All refraction is presumed to occur at a single interface between air and the contents of the eye, here assumed to be homogeneous and to have the same index of refraction as water, 1.333. The interface (*c* in Fig. 5) corresponding to the surface of the cornea has a radius of 5 mm., and its center of curvature is the optical center or nodal point (*n*) of the system. The retina lies 15 mm. posterior to the nodal point and 20 mm. from the cornea; this is also the principal focal distance of the system, so that distant objects are focused on the retina of the reduced eye at rest. The anterior principal focus, i.e., the point at which rays parallel within the eye would converge on emerging, lies 15 mm. in front of the cornea. The anterior and posterior focal distances are different because the light travels in air outside the eye and in denser media inside the eye. If the interior focal distance, 20 mm., is divided by the index of refraction of the reduced eye, the result will equal the anterior focal distance, $20/1.333 = 15.0$.

As mentioned above, the surfaces and distances in the completely relaxed ideal eye are

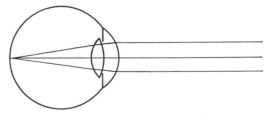

Fig. 4. Chief ocular interfaces at which light rays are refracted. Rays are refracted at air-cornea, aqueous-lens and lens-vitreous interfaces.

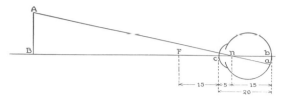

Fig. 5. Diagram of reduced eye with dimensions and construction required for location and size of retinal image. *AB*, Object; *ab*, image; *n*, nodal point; *F*, principal focus (anterior); *c*, corneal surface.

so related that the posterior focal point coincides with the retina and images of distant objects are focused on it. The formation of the image on the retina can therefore be shown by a construction like the one presented in Figure 5. Secondary axes are drawn from the limiting points of the object—*A* and *B*—through the nodal point. Where these axes meet, the retinal image of the object will be formed. That is, all the rays of light from *A* that penetrate the eye will be focused at *a*, and all those from *B* at *b*. The image on the retina will therefore be inverted and smaller than the object. The angle formed at the nodal point by the lines *An* and *Bn* (angle *AnB* or *anb*) is known as the *visual angle*; it varies inversely with the distance of the object from the eye.

Retinal Image and Spatial Perception. The apparent position of objects is related to the position of their retinal images, as produced by these physical processes. Stimulation of retinal point *a* in Figure 5 indicates an object at *A,* the point in the outside world from which light would normally come to focus on *a*. If point *a* is stimulated in some other manner, as by finger pressure on the eyeball producing a phosphene, the sensation is projected, i.e., appears to come from the direction of *A*. This relation occurs in the congenitally blind just as it does in persons who have "used" their retinas for years.[16]

It is clear that the relation of the direction in which an object is "seen" to the part of the retina stimulated is innate; it is present as soon as a child's behavior indicates a recognition of up and down, right and left. Salamanders in which an eye has been rotated through 180° during an early larval stage snap down for food held above the nose and never learn to correct this confusion. In man, when an abnormal position of an eye causes the stimulation of its retina to indicate an object position disagreeing with that indicated by other sources of information, including the other eye, the afferent impulses

from the divergent eye are, after a period of confusion, excluded from consciousness. The nonconforming eye is then said to be amblyopic and is, for certain purposes, blind. However, when the images in both eyes have been reversed by lenses, experimental subjects have, after some confusion, performed tasks in a manner indicating proper orientation in space. When the inverting lenses were then removed, a second period of disorientation followed. In man there seems to be a certain plasticity of brain function which is poorly understood, but which is clinically important in ambylopia.

Size of Retinal Image. The size of the retinal image may readily be calculated from the size of the actual object and its distance from the eye. As can be seen from Figure 5, the triangles *AnB* and *anb* are similar; consequently, we have the following equality of ratios:

$$\frac{AB}{ab} = \frac{An}{an}$$

or

$$\frac{\text{object size}}{\text{image size}} = \frac{\text{object distance from nodal point}}{\text{image distance from nodal point}}$$

Suppose it is desired to find the size of the retinal image of a tree 40 meters high at a distance of 2 km. Reducing all measurements to meters and substituting in the above equation, we have

$$\frac{40}{\text{image}} = \frac{2000}{0.015}$$

$$\text{image} = \frac{0.6}{2000} = 0.0003 \text{ m. or } 0.3 \text{ mm.}$$

The image of the tree is thus about the size of the fovea.

ACCOMMODATION

Accommodation of Eye for Objects at Different Distances. In the *emmetropic* or ideal refractive state, parallel rays from distant objects are brought to a focus on the retina when the eye is at rest. In other words, the structures are usually so correlated that the retina lies very near the second principal focus of the relaxed eye's combined refractive surfaces. When objects are brought closer to the eye, however, the rays proceeding from them become more and more divergent. Were the eye to remain unchanged, the rays would strike the retina before coming to a focus; in consequence, each luminous point in the object, instead of forming a point upon the retina, would form a circle, known as a *diffusion circle*. Thus, the retinal image as a whole would be blurred. Up to a certain point, the eye *accommodates* itself to focus rays from nearer objects so that blurring does not occur.

That a change in the curvature of the lens is the essential factor of accommodation for near objects is demonstrated by a simple and conclusive experiment utilizing the Purkinje images. The eye to be observed is relaxed, i.e., gazes into the distance. A lighted candle is held to one side and the observer takes a position on the other, where he can see the light of the candle reflected from the observed eye. With a little practice, and under the right conditions of illumination, the observer can see three images of the candle reflected from the eye as from a mirror. One image, the brightest, is reflected from the convex surface of the cornea (image *a*, Fig. 6 *A*). A second, larger and much dimmer, is reflected from the convex surface of the lens (image *b*); this image is larger and fainter because the reflecting surface is less curved. The third image (*c*) is inverted and is smaller and brighter than the second. This image is reflected from the posterior surface of the lens, which acts as a concave mirror in this instance. If the observed eye now gazes at a near object (Fig. 6 *B*), the first image (*a*) does not change at all, the third image (*c*) also remains practically the same, but the middle image (*b*) becomes smaller and approaches nearer to the first. This result can only mean that in the act of accommodation the anterior surface of the lens becomes more convex. In this way, its refractive power is increased and the more divergent rays from the near object are focused on the retina. Helmholtz demonstrated that the curvature of the posterior surface of the lens also increases slightly, but this change is so slight that the increased refractive power is referred chiefly to the change in the anterior surface. The means by which the change is effected was first satisfactorily explained by Helmholtz.

Fig. 6. Effect of accommodation on Purkinje images. *A*, eye at rest; *B*, eye accommodated for near objects; *a*, image reflected from air-cornea interface; *b*, from aqueous-lens interface; *c*, from lens-vitreous interface.

The structures involved (Fig. 7) and their action as envisioned by Helmholtz will be described briefly. The tiny *ciliary muscle* lies in a thickened anterior portion of the vascular layer, called the *ciliary body*, which lies as a collar between the anterior margin of the functional retina and the root of the iris surrounding the lens. Some of the smooth fibers making up the ciliary muscle take a radial course, originating in the sclera near the margin of the cornea and inserting in the chorioid* near the posterior margin of the ciliary body. Other fibers, tending to lie more central to these, have a circular course like that of the fibers of a sphincter muscle.

The lens is suspended by the *zonula,* which consists of delicate transparent membranes and fibers bridging between the ciliary body and the elastic capsule covering the lens. *When the ciliary muscle is relaxed, the zonula is under tension* and pulls

* The spelling *chorioid* is preferred to *choroid* as etymologically more correct and closer to the intended meaning, "resembling the chorion."

Fig. 7. Detail of anterior segment of human eye. Ciliary process has been distorted in cutting of section. Scleral roll is a narrow shelf of scleral tissue, on under side of which radial or meridional fibers of ciliary muscle originate. (After Bloom and Fawcett, *A textbook of histology,* Philadelphia, W. B. Saunders Co., 1962.)

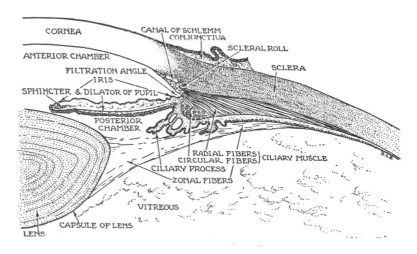

on the equator of the lens so that the lens is flattened. When the ciliary muscle contracts, it pulls the ciliary body toward the lens, relaxing the zonula. The tension which held the lens in its flattened shape having been reduced or abolished, the elasticity of the capsule, like the rubber of a toy balloon, tends to mold the plastic lens into a more convex form.

Although other theories have been proposed both before and since the time of Helmholtz, his view of the mechanism, with minor changes resulting from recent work,[8] is still the most adequate.

Other mammals accommodate in the same way as man, but not all vertebrates do. In most bony fish, for example, the mechanism is wholly different. The lens moves backward and toward the retina, thus focusing the eye for more distant objects.[2, 22]

Near and Far Points of Distinct Vision. When an object is brought closer and closer to the eye, a point is reached at which even the strongest contraction of the ciliary muscle will not result in a clear image of the object. The rays from it are so divergent that the refractive surfaces cannot bring them to a focus on the retina. Therefore, each luminous point makes a diffusion circle on the retina, and the whole image is indistinct. The nearest point at which an object can be distinctly seen, with full accommodation, is called the *near point*. The distance between the near point and the eye increases with age, slowly in early life, most rapidly in the early 40's, and very slowly after 50. The rate of this decline is shown in Figure 8. Recession of the near point is usually ascribed to

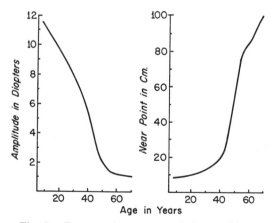

Fig. 8. Decrease in accommodation and increase in distance to near point of vision with age. (Based on data gathered by Duane[6] in over 4000 subjects.)

a progressive loss of the plasticity of the lens, so that, although contraction of the ciliary muscle reduces the tension of the zonula, the lens is less and less capable of being molded into a more convex form. The progressive loss starts as early in life as the near point can be satisfactorily measured; this process is one of many showing that senescence begins practically at birth. This decline in the power of accommodation is little noticed until it begins to interfere with reading, usually between the 40th and 50th years, when the condition is called *presbyopia* or old-sightedness (p. 408).

In the normal eye, parallel rays are brought to focus on the retina from infinity. If large enough, objects at distances greater than 20 feet are seen distinctly without accommodation— i.e., with the eye at rest. Practically, then, a distance of 6 meters (20 feet) is the *far point* of the normal eye.

Refractive Power and Amplitude of Accommodation. The refractive power of a lens is usually expressed in terms of its principal focal distance. A lens with a focal distance of 1 meter is taken as the unit and is designated as having a refractive power of 1 diopter, 1 D. Compared with this unit, the refractive power of lenses is expressed in terms of the reciprocal of their principal focal distances measured in meters; thus, a lens with a principal focal distance of 1/10 meter is a lens of 10 diopters (10 D.), and one with a focal distance of 5 meters is 1/5 diopter (0.2 D.).

The reduced eye at rest has a refractive power of 66 2/3 D. This value is the reciprocal of the focal distance in air when measured in meters (1/0.015 = 66 2/3 D.), or the reciprocal of the focal distance within the medium of the eye multiplied by the refractive index of that medium (1.333/0.020 = 66 2/3 D.). This power is somewhat greater than that—about 58 D.— derived from measurements of the eye. The cornea contributes about twice as much to this power as does the lens. Thus, the loss of the lens, as in cataract operations, does not lessen the refractive power as much as does the abolition of the action of the cornea occurring, for example, when the eye is opened under water.

In accommodation, greater curvature of the lens increases the total refractive power of the eye. Thus when a 20 year old emmetrope, with a near point of 1/10 meter, accommodates, the eye not only brings to a focus parallel rays (66-2/3 D.) but overcomes in addition the divergence of light from the near point (10 D.). It is as though the eye were left at rest, and a glass lens of 10 D. were placed before the cornea. The amplitude of accommodation may thus be expressed by the number of diopters added to the refractive power of the eye by the action of the ciliary muscle. Figure 8 shows the amplitudes of accommodation at various ages corresponding to the near points plotted in Figure 8. Both of these charts are derived from data collected by Duane.[5, 6]

OPTICAL DEFECTS AND ABNORMALITIES

Optical Defects of the Emmetropic Eye. As in other optical systems, spherical, chromatic and other aberrations are present in the eye, but they seldom appreciably affect vision. There are several reasons why these aberrations rarely distort the retinal image. First, the shape and structure of the cornea and the lens and the location of the iris near the nodal point reduce aberrations. In addition, several physiologic factors favor clear vision. The most severe distortions fall on the peripheral retina, where visual acuity is low and more distinct images cannot be appreciated; the important "finder" function of this part of the retina is not thereby impaired. Another factor is the lesser sensitivity of the retina to the wavelengths at the ends of the spectrum—the extreme reds and blues—where chromatic aberration is most marked. Thus, since scattered light and diffraction fringes are of low intensity, they tend to fall below the retinal threshold. For these reasons, what may be called the "physiologic image" is commonly better than the physical image.

Ametropia. As pointed out above, emmetropia is that refractive state of the eye in which, without accommodation, parallel rays focus on the sensitive layer of the retina, or in which the far point is infinitely distant; a person with such eyes is often called an "emmetrope." Any deviation from the condition of emmetropia is called *ametropia*. Obviously, emmetropia does not require any particular total refractive power or size of eye so long as there is a proper proportion between the axial length and the refractive powers of the cornea and lens.

Only recently have accurate measurements been available for a sufficient number of living eyes to permit analysis of the interrelations among the various optical elements.[10, 17] As with other human measurements, all values vary from person to person, the distribution for nearly all elements following a normal frequency curve. The deviations from emmetropia, as measured by the lens needed to bring parallel rays to focus in the resting eye, give a distribution more peaked than normal and with a scatter far less than would result from a chance association of the refractive elements. Correlations of the axial length, the refractive power of the cornea and the lens, and the other optical elements tend to reduce ametropia. In consequence, emmetropia is surprisingly common. Thus, if emmetropia is construed as embracing values from -0.5 to $+0.5$ D., about 25 per cent of young adults are emmetropic; if the range is expanded to include values between -1 and $+1$ D., about 65 per cent fall in this category.[14, 17]

At one time those biologic variations constituting ametropia excluded the afflicted from occupations requiring good vision. Now, most defects can be remedied by eyeglasses and are hardly noticed.

Ametropia may result from an unusually large or small value for any optical element, or from some combination of these elements not resulting in the compensatory correlations mentioned above. Analysis of Stenström's data[17] indicates that: (i) unusual values for the axial length are the most common cause of ametropia, (ii) about half as common is variation in the corneal refraction, and (iii) less important are separation of the cornea and lens or other optical elements. Ametropia of necessity falls into two types. In one, parallel rays come to a focus before reaching the retina; in the other, they reach the retina before coming to a focus. In the first, the axial length is relatively too long for the refractive power—this is called *myopia*.[9] In the second, the axial length is relatively too short—this is called *hyperopia* (hypermetropia). The frequency distribution of the refractive state in adults shows, as stated above, a crowding of cases toward emmetropia (the mean is about 0.5 D. hyperopic), with some extreme cases of myopia and hyperopia, so that the form of the curve is distinctly peaked.[3, 11, 14, 19, 20]

MYOPIA. During growth (from about six to 20 years, but particularly at puberty) in a small proportion of persons, the increase in length is relatively more rapid than the decrease in refractive power. As a result, they become myopic.

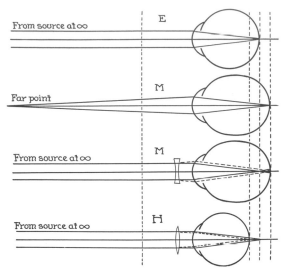

Fig. 9. Diagram of emmetropia (*E*) (reduced eye to scale), myopia (*M*), and hyperopia (*H*). Dotted lines in two lower diagrams show effect of proper correcting lenses.

In myopia, without accommodation, parallel rays of light come to a focus in the vitreous and diverge again to form diffusion circles on the retina. In any degree of myopia there is some point, nearer than that giving parallel rays, from which the light is sufficiently divergent to come to a focus on the retina of the unaccommodated eye; this is the myopic far point. The distance of this far point may be only a few centimeters, and all more distant objects will appear in some degree blurred—the more so the more distant they are. This condition is represented by diagram *M* in Figure 9. The obvious remedy is to use concave lenses for distant vision. By this means, the rays can be made divergent enough that the focus will be thrown accurately on the retina. Since the myopic eye at rest can focus rays of some degree of divergence, it can in full accommodation focus on very near objects; i.e., its near point is nearer than that of an emmetropic eye with equal amplitude of accommodation. This situation has led to the term "nearsightedness."

HYPEROPIA. This condition is represented in diagram *H* of Figure 9. In the eye at rest the retina is reached before the light has come to a focus, and each point source of light is represented by a diffusion circle. A converging lens of the proper strength will obviously bring light rays to the eye with that additional amount of convergence needed for their focus on the sensitive layers of the retina. The uncorrected hyper-

ope may see distant objects clearly only by use of his accommodation. Clear vision is accomplished at the expense of eyestrain arising from constant excessive accommodation without corresponding convergence of the two eyes. Further, since some accommodation is used to see even far objects, less is available for viewing near things. Consequently, the near point is more distant than it is in an emmetrope with equal amplitude of accommodation. The extra effort required for near work limits the amount of effective reading or other close work and leads to headaches or other evidences of eyestrain.

The term "farsightedness" for hyperopia is misleading. The "far" refers only to the excessive distance to the near point. The hyperope sees distant objects no better than does an emmetrope. In fact, when the farsighted person sees them as well, it is at the cost of some eyestrain.

PRESBYOPIA. A decline in the amplitude of accommodation is termed presbyopia and, as indicated earlier, is a consequence of aging. The near point of distinct vision recedes farther and farther from the eye until near work is difficult or impossible. Because his near point is initially more distant, the uncorrected hyperope will experience difficulty with near work earlier than will the emmetrope, and the myope will experience reading difficulty late in life, or perhaps never. A myope with a near point of 20 or 30 cm. can see near objects even if no accommodation remains; those people who can read fine print at 80 or 90 are, in all cases, myopes. All properly corrected eyes will become presbyopic at about the same time, at an age of approximately 45; after that age, an additional convex lens will be necessary for comfortable reading.

Astigmia or Astigmatism. In an ideal eye, the refractive surfaces of the cornea and lens would be spherical surfaces with equal curvatures along all meridians. In many eyes, however, the corneal surface is not spherical. In such a case there is a meridian of least curvature and a meridian of greatest curvature at a right angle to the first. Rays from a luminous point, refracted in passing through such a surface, will not form a point image; rays falling along the meridian of greatest curvature will tend to reach a focus before those falling along the meridian of least curvature do, and may already be diverging when the latter reach a focus.

The effect is illustrated by Figure 10, which represents the refraction of rays from a distant luminous point by a lens in which the curvature is greater along the vertical than along the horizontal meridian. The rays along the vertical meridian are brought to a focus (G) while those along the horizontal meridian are still converging. A screen placed at this point will reflect an image having the shape of a horizontal line (a–a'). The rays along the horizontal meridian are brought to a focus at B, but those from the vertical meridian, having passed through the focus at G, are by this time spread out vertically. A screen placed at this point will show the image as a vertical line (b–b'). In between, the image of the point may be elliptical or circular, as represented in the diagram.

Astigmia may be due to a toric cornea or to the decentering of the cornea or the lens. Such conditions, producing the image forms just described, are called *regular astigmia*. Regular astigmia may be corrected by a cylindrical lens or by a combination of spherical and cylindrical lenses of such strength and so placed that they equalize the refraction in the meridians of greatest and least curvature. Since in a markedly astigmatic eye the image of a point is an ellipse or line, the image of a line, which may be considered a series of points, will be a series of small image lines. If these image lines have the same direction as the entire image, this image will be dark and clear (except for a slight blurring at the ends); but if the image lines are transverse, the entire image will appear broad, gray and indistinct. Because of this, a chart like Figure 11 may be used to detect astigmia and to locate the axes of least and greatest curvature. If the lines appear to differ in clearness, astigmia is present, and the two axes at right angles correspond to the blackest and grayest sets of lines.

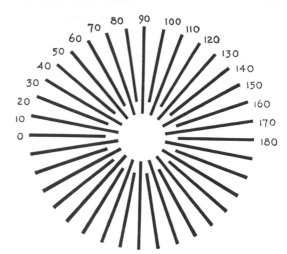

Fig. 11. Lancaster-Regan chart used to test for astigmia.

Related to astigmia is the characteristic image defect of rays about a central point when a point image might be expected. This defect is a result of the peculiar structure of the crystalline lens, since it is absent in aphakics (individuals whose lenses have been removed). The stars, which furnish accurate point sources of light, do not give rise to point images in the human eye, but rather to radiate figures, the exact form of which varies from eye to eye. The "star" form is thus not characteristic of the heavenly bodies but of our eyes.

OPTICAL EFFECTS OF OTHER FACTORS

Iris and Pupil. The iris has important optical and sensory functions, and, because its innervation is exposed to lesions in several locations, the size and reactions of the pupils are important diagnostically in a surprising variety of conditions. The iris, the colored portion of the eye, arises from the anterior surface of the ciliary body and lies between the cornea and the lens, being in contact with the latter. As seen through the cornea, the iris is slightly magnified. It is pierced by a central opening, the pupil. The stroma of the iris contains, besides the visible pigment, a rich network of blood vessels and black pigment on the interior surface. Because of the abundant pigment the iris is impervious to light and forms an excellent diaphragm. Between the layers mentioned lie the muscles of the iris, the larger and better developed sphinc-

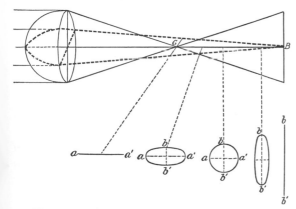

Fig. 10. Diagram of conoid of light emerging from an astigmatic lens. Lower figures represent cross sections of light at points indicated; note that image of distant point of light is never a point.

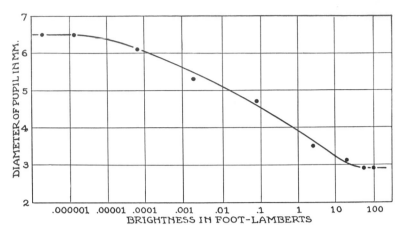

Fig. 12. Relation of pupil diameter to illumination. Data obtained by infrared photography. (From Wagman and Nathanson, *Proc. Soc. exp. Biol.* (*N. Y.*), 1942, *49*:466–470.)

ter near the pupillary margin and the smaller and less completely differentiated dilator near the posterior surface next to the pigment layer.

The iris exerts its principal effect in producing clear images. By constricting, it excludes the periphery of the lens, where spherical and chromatic aberration are greatest. The constriction also increases the depth of focus; i.e., the diffusion circles produced by cones of light from points just too near or too far to be in focus are reduced in area. Both these effects are greatest during near work. Constriction of the pupil occurs in conjunction with accommodation and convergence in near vision. The illumination must be adequate at such a time, since constriction reduces the amount of light falling on the retina, a factor which strongly affects the acuity of vision (see Chap. 20).

LIGHT REFLEX. An increase in light intensity causes the pupil to constrict, and a decrease in light intensity permits it to dilate. An increase of light in one eye leads to changes in the size of both pupils. The reaction of the pupil illuminated is called the *direct* light reflex and that of the opposite pupil the *consensual* light reflex. Over a considerable range of ordinarily encountered illumination, a person's pupils have a nearly constant average or habitual size. A slight increase in light intensity causes a slight constriction of the pupil, which then gradually dilates again as the retina adapts to the new higher level of illumination, and in a short time the pupil has resumed its habitual size.

When the new intensity is above this normal range, the change in pupillary size persists. This is illustrated by Figure 12, which shows the pupil diameter at illuminations over a range of a millionfold.[21] It will be seen that at both ends of this huge range of illumination, the pupil reaches a constant size representing its limit of dilation or constriction. These diameters are approximately 2.9 mm. and 6.5 mm.; there is, therefore, a fivefold change in area. Obviously, such a small change in area is utterly inadequate to compensate for the enormous range of experimental intensities or even for the smaller range of intensities met during daily variations in light. (This compensation is accomplished by retinal adaptation; see Chapter 20.) A fivefold alteration of area, however, helps the eye adjust to the sudden moderate changes in illumination to which it is constantly exposed. If the amount of light decreases, dilation of the pupil, although far less effective than retinal adaptation, is more prompt and gives, within 15 or 20 seconds, an appreciable improvement in the ability to see in dim light. If the amount of light increases, the still more rapid constriction of the pupil, in 3 or 4 seconds, shields the retina from light too intense for the existing level of sensitivity.

Intraocular Pressure. The position of the refracting surfaces relative to each other and to the retina must be maintained with great exactness. That minute variations in the axial length will cause ametropia is often not realized. When refraction was carefully measured in 1000 school children 12 years and older, 47 per cent showed ametropia of 0.50 or 0.25 D.[11] The change in axial length necessary to produce these degrees of ametropia is 0.187 mm. or less. Clearly if there is to be any constancy in refraction, even of an individual eye, the constancy of the size and shape of the globe must be assured.

The fixed distance of the refractive surfaces from the retina is maintained because the inelastic scleral envelope is under a constant intraocular pressure of 20 to 25 mm. Hg. This pressure results from a balance between the production and the escape of intraocular fluid. The volume of vitreous humor is relatively constant, although it may absorb or lose water to some extent. The chief changes occur in the aqueous humor.

The mechanism maintaining intraocular pressure is complex and, although much studied, is not completely agreed upon; the following appears to be the most satisfactory view. The aqueous consists of about 1 per cent solids, about one-eighth the solid content of the serum. All the constituents of the serum are found in the aqueous. The proteins are present in little more than traces, but the electrolytes appear in amounts about equal to those in the serum, the anions being clearly more abundant. According to some studies,[15] the total osmotic activity is above that of the blood. The material of the aqueous is derived from the blood —chiefly from that in the ciliary body, although to some extent from that in the iris—partly by secretion and partly by diffusion; and the aqueous escapes by leakage into the canal of Schlemm, nonselectively, at a rate of 5 or 6 ml. a day.[13] From the canal of Schlemm and the connecting canaliculi, the aqueous reaches the venous system through the aqueous and intrascleral veins.[1, 18] It is claimed that the hypertonicity results from secretion of the electrolytes. Interference with the outflow leads to a rise in the intraocular pressure which may damage the fibers of the optic nerve where they pass out of the globe (glaucoma).

Nutrition of the Lens and Cornea.   The eye contains the largest nonvascular mass in the body. No blood vessels are found in the cornea, the aqueous, the lens or the vitreous after the early fetal period of rapid growth; obviously, blood vessels would seriously interfere with the optical function of all these structures. None of these tissues has a high metabolic rate, the rates of the aqueous and vitreous being negligible; but interference with the oxygen supply of the cornea, for example, is promptly followed by loss of transparency.

Like other organs of epithelial origin, the lens continues to grow throughout life, and, even though its metabolic rate is low, must maintain an interchange with the blood. This exchange is carried on through the intraocular fluid which, as pointed out above, contains at least a trace of all the constituents of the blood.

The transparency of the cornea, so necessary to its optical function and impaired in so many pathologic conditions, has attracted much study. Histologically the stroma of the cornea is not strikingly different from that of the opaque white sclera. The corneal stroma, however, differs in its osmotic relations, since it is covered by closely investing semipermeable membranes, epithelium on the exterior and endothelium on the interior surface. The normal transparent cornea is markedly dehydrated. When excised and placed in water, the cornea swells to three or four times its normal thickness and becomes opaque. When placed in contact with a hypertonic solution, the uninjured surface of the cornea loses water rapidly enough to remain dehydrated and transparent. Under normal conditions, the water of the cornea is derived from the vascular margin. It slowly diffuses toward the center and is lost through both surfaces to the hypertonic tears and to the aqueous.[12] This slow circulation of fluid from the periphery together with the diffusion from the aqueous supplies the slight metabolic needs of the cornea. In addition, oxygen reaches it directly from the external air.

CHIEF INSTRUMENTS FOR EYE EXAMINATION

Among the instruments designed for study of the eye, three have proved outstandingly useful. The *ophthalmoscope* makes visible the interior of the eye and is of value to the internist or surgeon as well as specialists on the eye. The *retinoscope,* or skiascope, provides an objective and accurate method of determining the refraction of the eye. The *ophthalmometer,* designed to measure corneal curvature, has been a valuable source of data on optical constants, but its usefulness in modern practice is limited. Because ophthalmoscopic inspection of the eye is an important part of the general physical examination, this instrument will be described here briefly. Descriptions of the retinoscope and the ophthalmometer may be found in ophthalmologic manuals.

Ophthalmoscope.   Light entering the eye is largely absorbed by the black pigment of the retina and the chorioid. In leaving the eye, the part that is reflected, chiefly by the blood vessels, approximately retraces the path by which it entered. Merely holding a light near the eye does not, therefore, enable us to see into it, since to see this emerging light an observer must place his head where it blocks the entering light. If, however, the light could enter the observed eye as though it proceeded from the observer's own eye, then the returning rays might be utilized to give a view of the retina and its blood vessels, or the *fundus,* as it is called.

The principle of the ophthalmoscope is well repre-

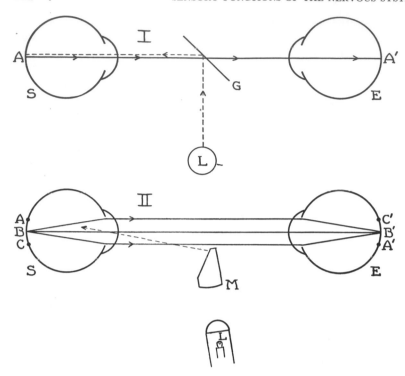

Fig. 13. Course of light in ophthalmoscope; *S,* eye of subject; *E,* eye of examiner. Entering light is indicated by dotted line; emerging light by solid line. *I,* Diagram of original model devised by Helmholtz; *L,* light; *G,* unsilvered glass; *A,* illuminated point in observed eye; *A',* image in examiner's eye. *II,* Diagram of ophthalmoscope with May prism; *L,* electric bulb in handle; *M,* May prism. *A, B* and *C,* three illuminated points in observed eye, here assumed to be emmetropic; *A', B'* and *C',* images in examiner's eye, also emmetropic.

sented by the original form, shown schematically in Figure 13, *I. S* represents the observed eye and *E* the eye of the examiner. Between these two eyes is placed a piece of glass inclined at an angle. Some rays from a source of light falling upon this glass are reflected to enter eye *S;* these rays then emerge from eye *S* along the same course, pass through the glass and enter eye *E.* The glass plate used by Helmholtz was soon replaced by a mirror, either one with a small hole in the center or one with a small area of silvering removed to permit the returning light to reach the examiner's eye. The source of light was later placed in the handle of the instrument, and at present light is thrown into the observed eye not by a mirror but by a prism of special form. This prism directs the light into the lower half of the pupil while the returning rays emerge through the upper half and reach the examiner's eye over the top of the prism (Fig. 13, *II*).

Irrespective of the manner in which the light reaches the fundus, this surface becomes a luminous object sending out rays of light. If eye *S* is emmetropic, any three objects on the retina, *A,B,C,* are at the principal focal distance, and the rays sent from each are in parallel bundles after emerging from the eye. These rays enter the examiner's eye as though they came from distant objects. If his eye is also emmetropic, or is made so by suitable glasses, these bundles of rays will be focused on his retina without an act of accommodation. In fact, in looking through the ophthalmoscope, he must gaze, not at the eye before him, but through the eye and into the distance, as it were, in order to relax his accommodation. In this way he will see the illuminated portion of the retina; the images of the objects seen will be inverted on his own retina and therefore will appear erect. If the observed eye is myopic, its

retina is farther back than the principal focus of its refracting surfaces; consequently the emerging rays converge and cannot be focused on the retina of the examiner's eye. By inserting a concave lens of proper power between his eye and the mirror, the examiner can render the rays parallel and thus bring out the image. Just the reverse happens if the observed eye is hyperopic. In such an eye the retina is nearer than the principal focal distance of the refractive surfaces; consequently the light emerges in bundles of diverging rays which cannot be brought to focus on the retina of the examiner unless he exerts his own power of accommodation or interposes a convex lens between his eye and the mirror.

The battery of lenses in the ophthalmoscope is valuable in estimating the degree to which objects lie above or below the general level of the fundus. For example, the head of the optic nerve normally occurs in a slight conical pit, the *physiological depression* or *cup* (Fig. 14). When intraocular pressure is greatly elevated, as in glaucoma, this depression may be transformed into an excavation. Conversely, in papilledema caused by increased intracranial pressure, the physiologic cup may be eliminated and the nerve head swollen. The difference in the power of the lenses required to bring the center of the optic disc into sharp focus as compared with that required for its margin may be recorded in diopters. Thus, the progress of cupping may be followed and the depth estimated from the fact that 3 D. correspond to about 1 mm. The usefulness of the ophthalmoscope is twofold. First, it renders conditions within the eye as visible as they would be in a superficial structure; second, the blood vessels of the retina are a sample of those in all parts of the body and reveal certain general circulatory conditions.

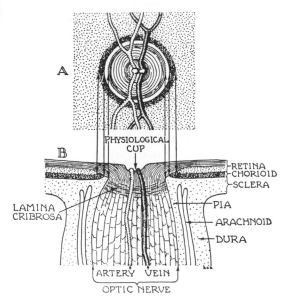

Fig. 14. Ophthalmoscopic appearance of optic disc (*A*) correlated with histologic section through it (*B*). Arrows indicate corresponding points on the two views. Pigmented ring is emphasized in *A* to show manner of its formation.

EXTERNAL MUSCLES OF THE EYE

The dioptric and neural mechanisms for accurate vision at the central portions of the retina are rendered more useful by a provision for training this area upon objects requiring close examination. The gaze can be transferred quickly from point to point or it can be fixed steadily on a single detail. Two kinds of movements are executed so that light from an object will always fall upon the fovea in each eye, making possible fusion of the images: (i) convergence-divergence movements occurring when the eyes are fixed upon near or far objects, and (ii) conjugate movements in which the eyes sweep from side to side, etc., in unison.

Eye Movements. Each eyeball is moved by six extrinsic, striated muscles which are innervated by three cranial nerves. By means of these muscles the eyeballs execute various movements best considered as *rotations* of the eyeball around various axes. These axes are: (i) the horizontal, which corresponds with the visual axis; (ii) the transverse; (iii) the vertical; and (iv) the oblique axes, which include all axes of rotation making oblique angles with the horizontal axis. Rotations around the oblique axes move the eyeballs obliquely upward or downward. The share of the individual eye muscles in producing rota-

tion of the eyeball around the various axes is shown in Figure 15, which indicates the paths traversed by the visual axis when each muscle separately moves the eyeball.

The eyes can be moved sufficiently to fix on objects within a circular area having a diameter equal to 100° of visual angle. Rotations to the left and right are approximately equal in extent, but vertical upward movements are more limited (40°) than vertical downward movements (60°). The range of eye movements is tested with a *tangent screen* and is an important diagnostic sign in neurology.

In *conjugate deviations* the eyes move in a way to keep the visual axes of the two eyes parallel or else to converge them upon a common point, the medial rectus of one eye acting with the lateral rectus of the other. In movements of convergence, the medial recti of the two eyes are associated. Normally, it is impossible to diverge the visual axes beyond the parallel. A movement of this kind would produce useless double vision (diplopia).

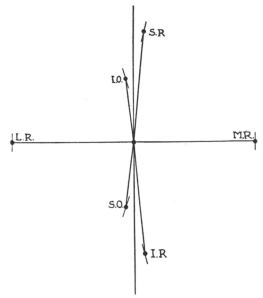

Fig. 15. Hering's diagram showing actions of individual eye muscles. Lines radiating from primary fixation point show path which visual axis would describe on screen placed in front of eyes when they are rotated by each muscle acting singly. Short line through terminus of each line represents tilt of eyes from vertical imparted by action of each eye muscle in executing each movement. Abbreviations are: *I.O.* and *S.O.,* inferior and superior oblique; *I.R.* and *S.R.,* inferior and superior recti; *L.R.* and *M.R.,* lateral and medial recti. (From Martin and Weymouth, *Elements of physiology.* Philadelphia, Lea & Febiger, 1928.)

The smooth intrinsic and striate extrinsic muscles of the eyeball and lids are controlled by a group of nuclei centered about the midbrain. These are closely interconnected to integrate the activities of the various muscles. Provision is made for the simultaneous activation of one muscle and inhibition of the motoneurons supplying its antagonist (reciprocal innervation). Provision is also made for associating the activities of two or more muscles. Even simple upward or downward movement requires unison contraction by two muscles. Reading requires simultaneous conjugate movements and a slight convergence. Transference of the gaze from a far to a near point involves the "fixation triad": (i) constriction of the pupil, (ii) accommodation of the lens, (iii) convergence. The strong linkage of these explains one form of "muscle strabismus" (see below).

Coordination of Eye Muscles—Strabismus. Useful binocular vision requires a beautifully balanced or coordinated action of the opposing muscles to move the eyeballs in absolute unison. The visual axes must unite upon the object or point looked at. In looking about or in reading, the individual readjusts his eyes continually to bring point after point at the junction of the visual axes. When he looks at a distant object, the visual axes should be parallel. If this balance does not exist, a condition designated as *heterophoria* is present.

In heterophoria a constant contraction of one or more muscles is required, even in far vision, to prevent diplopia. When the eye at rest tends to drift toward the temporal side because of the unbalanced pull of the lateral rectus, the condition is known as *exophoria*. If there is a tendency to drift to the nasal side, the condition is described as *esophoria*. A tendency to drift upward is *hyperphoria* and downward is *hypophoria*. A lack of resting balance of this kind may also make itself felt in near work, such as reading and sewing, since it will require an increasing activity of the muscle overbalanced by its antagonist. The resulting muscular strain causes much distress. When muscular effort no longer brings the visual axes to bear upon the same point, a condition of squint or *strabismus* (*exotropia, esotropia, hypotropia,* or *hypertropia*) exists. Since both eyes cannot fix, double vision would result were it not for suppression of the image; this, however, leads to a reduction of visual ability (see below) in the squinting eye.

Severe defects of long standing and those caused by actual muscle weakness may be remedied by surgical operations upon the muscles or by the use of proper prisms with bases adjusted to direct light upon the fovea. Recognition of the physiologic causes operative in a "functional" type of strabismus permits a more fundamental treatment. *Convergent concomitant strabismus* in which one eye turns inward is usually due to uncorrected hyperopia in early childhood. For a hyperope to focus on near objects, excessive accommodation is necessary. Because accommodation and convergence are closely linked in the midbrain region, this convergence is appropriate to the excessive accommodation and in excess of that required to converge on the object. Early correction of the hyperopia, forced use of the squinting eye, and orthoptic training in binocular vision often render operative treatment unnecessary.

REFERENCES

1. Ascher, K. W. *Amer. J. Ophthal.,* 1942, (3) *25*:31–38.
2. Beer, T. *Pflüg. Arch. ges. Physiol.,* 1894, *58*:523–650.
3. Brown, E. V. L. *Arch. Ophthal. (N. Y.),* 1942, n.s. *28*:845–850.
4. Donders, F. C. *On the anomalies of accommodation and refraction of the eye. With a preliminary essay on physiological dioptrics,* tr. by W. D. Moore. London, New Sydenham Society, 1864.
5. Duane, A. *Ophthalmoscope,* 1912, *10*:486–502.
6. Duane, A. *Amer. J. Ophthal.,* 1922, (3) *5*:865–877.
7. Duke-Elder, W. S. *Text-book of ophthalmology,* vol. 1. St. Louis, C. V. Mosby Co., 1939.
8. Fincham, E. P. *Brit. J. Ophthal.,* 1937, Suppl. *8*:5–80.
9. von Helmholtz, H. *Treatise on physiological optics,* J. P. C. Southall, ed. Rochester, N. Y., Optical Society of America, 1924–25.
10. Hirsch, M. J. and Weymouth, F. W. *Amer. J. Optom.,* 1947, *24*:601–608, and *Arch. Amer. Acad. Optom.,* 1947, Monogr. 39.
11. Kempf, G. A., Jarman, B. L. and Collins, S. D. *Publ. Hlth. Rep. (Wash.),* 1928, *43*:1713–1739.
12. Kinsey, V. E. and Cogan, D. G. *Arch. Ophthal. (N. Y.),* 1942, n.s. *28*:449–463.
13. Kinsey, V. E. and Grant, W. M. *Brit. J. Ophthal.,* 1944, *28*:355–361.
14. Kronfeld, P. C. and Devney, C. *v. Graefes Arch. Ophthal.,* 1931, *126*:487–501.
15. Roepke, R. R. and Hetherington, W. A. *Amer. J. Physiol.,* 1940, *130*:340–345.
16. Schlodtmann, W. *v. Graefes Arch. Ophthal.,* 1902, *54*:256–267.
17. Stenström, S. *Acta ophthal. (Kbh.),* 1946, Suppl. *26.*
18. Thomassen, T. L. and Bakken, K. *Acta ophthal. (Kbh.),* 1951, *29*:257–268.
19. Tron, E. *v. Graefes Arch. Ophthal.,* 1934, *132*:182–223.
20. Tron, E. J. In *Modern trends in ophthalmology,* F. Ridley and A. Sorsby, eds. New York, Paul B. Hoeber, Inc., 1940.
21. Wagman, I. H. and Nathanson, L. M. *Proc. Soc. exp. Biol. (N. Y.),* 1942, *49*:466–470.
22. Walls, G. L. *The vertebrate eye and its adaptive radiation.* Bloomfield Hills, Mich., Cranbrook Institute of Science, 1942.

CHAPTER 20

Vision

By THEODORE C. RUCH

In the previous chapter the eye was portrayed as an optical instrument focusing light rays from objects at various distances and regulating the amount of light falling upon the retina. However, the formation of a physical image on the retina is of no value unless that image is translated into a pattern of nerve impulses from which the cerebral cortex can reconstruct a reasonably accurate perception of the external world. In this perception, color, fineness of detail and sharpness of contour all play a part.

The eye contains not one but two end-organs, each specialized for quite different visual functions although closely knit anatomically. One system of receptors, the cones, is specialized to function in daylight when the surroundings are brightly illuminated. Objects are then seen clearly with much detail and many grades of color. The pupil constricts, sharpening the image. Visual acuity is at its best. The second system of receptors, the rods, is specialized for twilight and night vision. Then, low threshold is desirable. By a chemical process in the retina, the eye becomes many times more sensitive to light (dark adaptation) and dilation of the pupil admits more light to the eye. The human retina is extraordinarily able to use the slightest light energy afforded by the environment, nearly attaining the theoretical lower limit of sensitivity—sensitivity to 1 quantum of light. But specialization in one direction has meant loss of capacity in another. The apparatus for night vision does not record the color of objects or fine details and sharp boundaries.

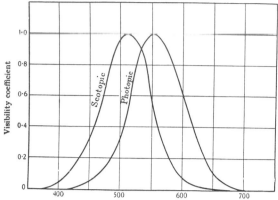

Fig. 1. Visibility or luminosity of a bright spectrum as seen by cones (photopic) and of a dim spectrum as seen by rods (scotopic). Ordinates are the reciprocal of the energy which is just visible for each wavelength of light (scotopic) or which matches a moderately bright standard light (photopic). Curves were adjusted to a common scale by making maximum of each curve equal to one. On an absolute scale of intensities, rod curve would fall far below that for cones, which are much less sensitive than rods. (From Rawdon-Smith, *Theories of sensation,* Cambridge, Cambridge University Press, 1938, after Hecht and Williams, *J. gen. Physiol.,* 1922, 5:1–34.)

Yet perception of objects as dark, indistinct masses makes the difference between blindness and visual orientation to the environment at night.

The retina itself is specialized into the fovea centralis for color and detail vision, and the periphery for light and dark vision. The fovea contains only cones, and in the periphery rods predominate. The neural pathways give further evidence of a double function. The "duplicity" theory is, then, the organizing principle to be used in describing vision. Originally, this theory referred only to the existence of two types of receptor cells, but it is now applied to the central mechanism of vision as well.

Visual Stimulus. The eye is sensitive to a narrow band of wavelengths, the visible spectrum (723 mμ to 397 mμ) lying between the long, infrared heat waves and the short, ultraviolet "chemical" waves. The wavelengths within this range are not equally effective in stimulating the retina. The wavelength influences the intensity of light necessary to elicit a sensation and also determines the hue or chroma. The curve which expresses that relation is the *visibility curve* (Fig. 1). Before any curve or other quantitative data can be under-

stood, the nature of the visual stimulus and the units in which it is measured must be defined.

In the audibility curve, the base line is frequency; in the visibility curve, it is wavelength, i.e., the inverse of frequency, since the speed of light is divided by frequency to obtain the wavelength. A wavelength is stated in Ångstrom units (1 Å = 1/10,000,000 mm.) or, more usually, in millimicrons (1 mμ = 1/1,000,000 mm.). The unit for the ordinate must express the intensity of the light. As in audition, the physical unit most useful is one with a psychologic reference. The basic unit is the *international candle,* which is the total luminous energy emitted in all directions by a standardized candle with a flame 1 inch high. To state the amount of light *falling upon* an object, the illumination (a more usual requirement), the distance between the object and the candle must be defined because the total energy becomes less per unit area as it spreads over a larger sphere. The *foot-candle* is the amount of light falling on a square foot of area placed 1 foot from the standard candle. But not all of the light is reflected by the surface and only reflected light can be seen. The *brightness* of an object, which is the amount of light reflected from it, is measured in *millilamberts.* This is the amount of light reflected by an ideal surface 1 foot square illuminated by 0.93 foot-candle. Since the size of the pupil of the eye affects the amount of light entering the eye, another unit, the *photon,* has been devised which takes this factor into account. Photons are the number of millilamberts × sq. mm. of pupil area. In experiments this is easily calculated because an artificial pupil—a screen with an aperture smaller than the pupil—is usually employed.

The visibility curve is affected by the distribution of energy among the different wavelengths of the particular light source employed—daylight, carbon lamp, etc.—but can be calculated for an equal energy spectrum. Also, light is filtered by the cornea, lens and vitreous body. When all physical factors are properly accounted for, the visibility curve becomes an index of the manner in which the retina utilizes light of different wavelengths. The visibility curve expresses one fundamental parameter of visual sensation, luminosity, whether aroused by colored or uncolored light.

Intensity Functions. The intensity of the physical stimulus must be distinguished from the intensity of the resulting visual experience. Although these two intensities are related causally, intervening photochemical and neural processes may considerably alter the correlation between the two. *Luminosity, brilliance* and *apparent brightness* always refer to the response; *brightness* is restricted to the intensity of the physical stimulus. Three main intensity functions are distinguished: the *absolute threshold,* the least that can be seen; the *difference threshold,* the least discriminable difference between two intensities; and the *critical flicker fusion frequency.*

The principal factors affecting the absolute threshold will be discussed in detail later, but may be enumerated as follows: (i) intensity of light, (ii) wavelength of light, (iii) size of illuminated area, (iv) duration of exposure, (v) state of the retina (dark adaptation, etc.), and (vi) the region of retina stimulated. Much the same factors influence the difference threshold, which is basically similar to the absolute threshold. The Weber fraction is not constant for brightness discrimination. The curve of $\Delta I/I$ rises sharply for weak and strong stimuli and is constant for the middle range of intensities only if small changes are ignored (by coarse plotting). The absolute threshold under the most favorable conditions appears to approach the theoretical minimum, the receptors being sensitive to 1 quantum of light according to the calculations of Hecht.[17]

As few as 54 quanta of light incident upon the cornea are perceptible. An estimated half of these are reflected or absorbed by the ocular media. Of the 27 quanta reaching the retina, perhaps only 5 are absorbed by the visual purple of the rods. These rods, spread over a retinal area containing an estimated 500 rods, are so few that at threshold a given rod must rarely receive more than 1 quantum of energy. According to Einstein's photochemical equivalence law, 1 quantum of energy will break down one molecule of visual purple. Thus, the evolution of the eye has progressed to the theoretical maximum of sensitivity. The threshold for a foveal cone is estimated to be no more than 5 to 7 quanta.

The *critical fusion frequency* (*c.f.f.*) *for flicker,* once determined by rotating a sectored disc in front of a light source at a speed controlled by the observer, is now determined by electronically controlled flashes. With low frequencies intermittent flashes of light are seen, but at a certain rate for each intensity the light seems steady—the critical fusion frequency. The higher the intensity of the light, the higher the c.f.f. For the middle range of intensities, c.f.f. = log I + k (Ferry-Porter law). When the light falls on the periphery of the retina, the duality of the visual mechanism produces a sharp inflection in the curve relating c.f.f. to log I (Fig. 2). For the fovea, the curve shows no inflection. The first

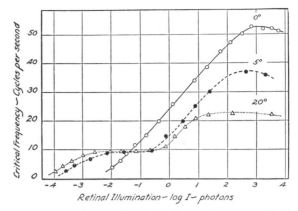

Fig. 2. Curves showing relation between critical fusion frequency (c.f.f.) and logarithm of intensity for three retinal locations: fovea, and 5° and 20° from fovea. (From Hecht and Verrijp, *J. gen. Physiol.,* 1933–34, *17:*251–268.)

part of the duplex curve is interpreted as a response of the rods and the second as a response of the cones.

PHOTOCHEMICAL BASIS OF VISION[10a]

Visual Purple—Rhodopsin. The change taking place in the rods and cones which translates physical energy, light, into nerve impulses involves a photochemical step, i.e., light waves set up chemical changes in rods or cones which, in turn, give rise to nerve impulses. The retinal rods contain a red pigment which is bleached by light (Boll, 1877), *visual purple* or *rhodopsin.* The cones probably contain another pigmented substance.

Solutions of visual purple are also bleached when exposed to light. Visual purple is, therefore, an unstable substance readily altered by light energy. That this photochemical property of rhodopsin accounts for the visibility curve was first suggested by Kühne (1878), who studied the effectiveness of different wavelengths in bleaching rhodopsin. According to Draper's law, the photochemical effect of a given wavelength is proportional to its absorption. The absorption spectrum of visual purple from the frog's retina has been accurately determined (Fig. 3). Moreover, a fair degree of success has been attained in superposing the absorption spectrum and the visibility curve of the human eye. The success of one such attempt is shown in Figure 4. The visibility curve for rod function appears, therefore, to be determined by the photochemical properties of rhodopsin. If so, rhodopsin must be the photochemical intermediary standing between the light stimulus and the optic nerve impulse.

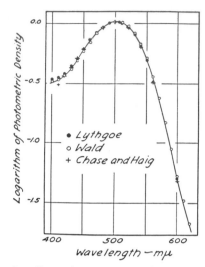

Fig. 3. Absorption spectrum of the visual purple from frog. Data obtained by three independent observers were made equal at 500 mμ. Ordinates show degree to which each wavelength is absorbed, with 0.0 representing maximal absorption. (From Hecht, *Amer. Scientist*, 1944, *32:*159–177.)

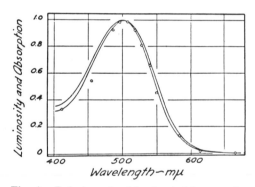

Fig. 4. Relation of subjective brightness of spectrum (luminosity, circles) to absorption curve of visual purple (frog). Visibility curve is corrected for transmissional losses, quantum effectiveness, etc., and therefore is not identical with that shown in Figure 1. Two solid lines give absorption spectrum calculated by assuming that 20 and 5 per cent of light are absorbed by visual purple. (From Hecht *et al., J. gen. Physiol.*, 1942, *25:*819–840.)

The same in vitro demonstration has not yet been made for cone pigment, although the intermediation of a rhodopsin-like photosensitive substance *iodopsin* (visual violet), is strongly suspected.[33] Others are inferred by stimulating curves and will be discussed under Color Vision.

Dark Adaptation. The retina possesses to a remarkable degree the ability to become sensitive to dim light* and thus to make maximum use of weak light reflected from objects. This is especially true of the periphery of the retina. When one passes from daylight into a dark room, vision is at first very imperfect, but it rapidly improves "as the eye becomes accustomed to the dark." This change is known as *dark adaptation.* Loss of the sensitivity attained through dark adaptation occurs upon re-exposure of the eyes to light and is called *light adaptation.*

A curve of dark adaptation is plotted by repeatedly determining the weakest flash of light which is visible. The rate of dark adaptation for rods is initially rapid, although not so rapid as the rate of light adaptation. Dark adaptation is about 60 per cent accomplished in the first five minutes and virtually completed in 20 minutes, after which the curve is asymptotic. A curve with this simple form is obtained by starting from levels of illumination too low to stimulate the cones and by observing with the peripheral portions of the retina where there are few cones. It is therefore the rod adaptation curve.

When both cones and rods are stimulated, the curve is made up of two curves (Fig. 5). First there is an initial rapid fall in threshold which tends to strike a plateau. After about seven minutes of darkness, a further drop occurs which is less rapid but is quantitatively much greater. Analysis shows that the curve

* The change from full sunlight to the least light perceptible at night is a change of approximately 10 billion to 1.

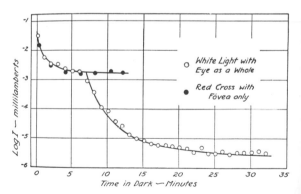

Fig. 5. Curve of dark adaptation obtained by plotting visual threshold against time spent in darkness. Initial limb of curve for whole eye (*circles*) is due to cones; lower portion is due to rods. To obtain complete curve for cones alone (*black dots*), stimulation of the more sensitive rods was avoided by employing red light and foveal fixation. (From Hecht, *A handbook of general experimental psychology,* C. Murchison, ed., Worcester, Clark University Press, 1934.)

before its breaking point is due to dark adaptation of the cones. Dark adaptation is therefore not a phenomenon peculiar to the rods. Cone adaptation is much more rapid than rod adaptation but produces less reduction of threshold.

Factors Influencing Dark Adaptation.

The extent and rapidity of dark adaptation are critical in many military and civilian activities including the viewing of the fluoroscopic screen and x-ray films. Several factors are involved.

AVOIDANCE OF LIGHT. The most effective means of securing dark adaptation is to prevent unnecessary exposure to light. Obvious as this is, it has often been overlooked.

Miles'[24] introduction of red goggles as an aid to the acquisition of dark adaptation illustrates effective application of physiology to a practical situation. A tedious 20 to 30 minute wait in a completely dark room evidently is avoided by wearing the goggles, which allow cone vision to continue while the rods are adapting to dark. As the visibility curve shows, wavelengths longer than 640 mμ stimulate the rods only very weakly. Thus, red goggles, by passing only longer wavelengths, prevent light adaptation of the rods.

Other factors influencing dark adaptation are:

PREADAPTATION ILLUMINATION. The more intense the illumination and the longer the time during which the eye is light-adapted, the longer the period necessary to attain complete dark adaptation.[19, 35] This phenomenon appears explicable on the basis of a slow and a fast resynthesis of rhodopsin (see p. 420).

NYCTALOPIA.* This is a rare organic and often hereditary abnormality in which rod function is seriously disturbed or, in extreme cases, absent. Dark adaptation is correspondingly reduced in extent and greatly slowed. The result is *night blindness*. Color vision is normal. There is no evidence that vitamin A therapy will affect the congenital form of nyctalopia.

VITAMIN A DEFICIENCY. Severe vitamin A deficiency experimentally induced interferes with the mechanism of dark adaptation, and irreversible changes can be produced. Dark adaptation of cones as well as of rods is affected. The measurement of dark adaptation has not proved useful in detecting vitamin A deficiencies in the degree present in the population.

ANOXIA AND METABOLIC FACTORS. McFarland and Evans[23] have shown that the visual threshold of the completely dark-adapted eye is elevated 2.5 times by anoxic anoxia resulting from exposure at 15,000 feet. Glucose neutralized the effects of anoxia and insulin intensified them. Hyperventilation at sea level relieved visual threshold[36] and CO_2 added to air doubled it. Such changes, although small in relation to the whole range of dark adaptation, are significant in night flying. Because these changes occur more rapidly than

* "Hemeralopia," the term for inability to see in bright light, is sometimes used instead of "nyctalopia."

photochemical changes, it is believed that the anoxic effects are exerted on the synaptic apparatus of the retina.

Curve of Light Adaptation. After a period of darkness, light of moderate intensity at first seems intense, dazzling and even painful, but after a few minutes the eye becomes less sensitive. In other words, the sensitivity gained by dark adaptation is lost when the eye is stimulated by light. Light adaptation is simply the absence of dark adaptation, and the expression is somewhat misleading. It is an active process, since the first intense stimulation results from bleaching of the rhodopsin accumulated during dark adaptation, resulting in intense visual stimulus. It takes much less time to lose dark adaptation than to acquire it. Light adaptation is largely completed in just a few minutes.

Mechanism of Rod Stimulation and Dark Adaptation.[17, 33]

Rhodopsin is the intermediary in the excitation of rods by light and changes in its concentration are believed to be the basis of dark adaptation. The simplest possible photochemical mechanism employing rhodopsin is as follows:

Light———→rhodopsin———→excitatory decomposition
                              product———→nerve impulse

During dark adaptation rhodopsin is regenerated. Until recently it seemed possible to account for the principal features of excitation and dark adaptation on the basis of a simple equation from photochemistry.[33] In brief, light was conceived of as breaking down photosensitive material (rhodopsin) at a rate dependent on the light intensity and the amount of photochemical substance present. It now seems that bleaching a small amount of rhodopsin causes the threshold to rise enormously; for the human eye, the bleaching of 0.006 per cent of the visual purple decreases the visual sensitivity 8.5 times, and a 0.6 per cent bleaching lowers the sensitivity an estimated 3300 times.[34] Nevertheless, bleaching and regeneration of rhodopsin follow the same time courses as light adaptation and dark adaptation (Fig. 6), and this is true of the faster adaptation of the cones.[28, 30] However, the concentration of rhodopsin is proportional to the *logarithm* of the sensitivity. Whether a neural factor must be introduced into the equation to gain quantitative agreement is still to be learned.

Photochemical Cycle of Retina. Using a

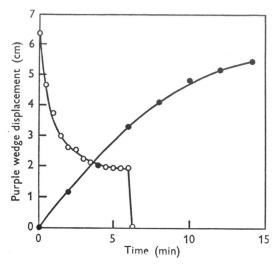

Fig. 6. Time course of bleaching (o) and subsequent regeneration (•) of rhodopsin in the human eye. Sudden drop at 6 minutes was caused by flash of very bright light. (From Campbell and Rushton, *J. Physiol.*, 1955, *130*:131–147.)

spectrographic technique to follow the changes in the photochemical substances, Wald[32, 33] established the broad outlines of the photochemistry of the visual cycle.* Three main reactions were observed (Fig. 7). The first is a rapid reaction:

$$\text{Rhodopsin} \underset{\text{dark}}{\overset{\text{light}}{\rightleftharpoons}} \text{Retinene} + \text{Protein.}$$

Visual purple, which has a high molecular weight (270,000), is a conjugated protein, i.e., a protein molecule united to a pigment group (*retinene*), and is related to the carotene compounds. Rhodopsin is stable unless exposed to light, when it bleaches owing to a dissociation into protein and retinene. In the dark it is reconstituted (Fig. 6). Because the rate and extent of decomposition depend on the intensity of light and the duration of exposure, this phase is believed to be the photochemical basis of light and dark adaptation. Retinene is reduced to vitamin A by the conjoint action of an enzyme (alcohol dehydrogenase) and the coenzyme DPN. Rushton and his colleagues[31] have been able to measure rhodopsin in the human retina. The changes in the density of rhodopsin in passing through the fovea and the optic nerve head into the peripheral retina conform to the known density of rods. Proceeding much more slowly

* Several intervening substances have been partially defined biochemically.

is a thermolabile reaction in which rhodopsin is re-formed with vitamin A as an intermediate step. Vitamin A from blood is also a source for restoring the retinal level of vitamin A and rhodopsin. These reactions therefore form the photochemical cycle, which may be divided into a photodynamic and a thermolabile phase. In Figure 7 the length of line connecting the substances indicates roughly the speed of the reaction.

The effect of preadaptation illumination on the rate of dark adaptation is explained by a "slow" and a "fast" synthesis of rhodopsin. If the completely dark-adapted retina, charged with rhodopsin, is light-adapted by a *short exposure to intense light*, much retinene and little vitamin A are produced. Therefore, subsequent dark adaptation is rapid because rhodopsin is re-formed by the "fast route" from retinene. Exposure to weaker adapting lights for a seven-minute period is followed by a slowed adaptation curve, because more retinene has gone to vitamin A and must be resynthesized by the slower route.

In addition to the visual functions which seem interpretable on the basis of photodynamic action there are certain processes which depend on the neural mechanisms of the retina.

Electrical Activity of Retina. Depending on the size and placement of the recording electrodes, four types of changes in potential are obtained from the retina: (i) a steady corneoretinal potential, (ii) phasic potentials produced by light (electroretinogram), (iii) unit responses from the level of the bipolar cells, and (iv) action potentials of ganglion cells and optic nerve

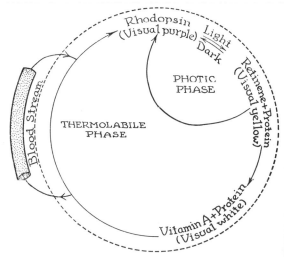

Fig. 7. Retinal photochemical cycle according to Wald. Length of arrows suggests speed of reaction.

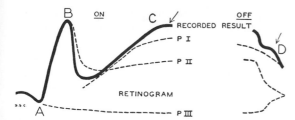

Fig. 8. Compound electric potential (heavy line) recorded from retina (electroretinogram, ERG) in response to stimulation by light. Upward deflections indicate electropositivity. *A, B, C, D,* are potential waves of ERG, and broken curves, *P I, P II, P III,* are one analysis (Granit) of compound potential into its components. (From Bartley, *Psychol. Rev.*, 1939, *46*:337–358.)

fibers. The steady potential recorded between the front and back of the eyeball is produced by the retina, probably across Bruch's membrane of the chorioid. In penetration experiments with ultramicroelectrodes, Brown and Wiesel[7] recorded a 30 to 60 mV. potential across the membrane with the chorioidal side negative. When recorded from the tissues about the eyes, the steady potential can be used to measure eye movements.

ELECTRORETINOGRAM (ERG). This is a complex of potential changes, shown in Figure 8 as recorded and as analyzed into components by Granit. The significance of the ERG is that it can be recorded for clinical purposes by electrodes applied to the cornea; otherwise it is a phenomenon to be explained rather than being explanatory. However, its components can now be interpreted more fully in light of recent experiments by Brown and Wiesel[7, 8] involving intraretinal or "depth" recording with ultramicroelectrodes.

The A wave, a small, sharp, downward cornea-negative wave, represents a photopic response. It is more marked in cone-rich retinae and in response to red light, which has little effect on rods; penetration experiments show it to be largest near Bruch's membrane. It has been demonstrated directly that the A wave probably comes from the outer segments of the receptors and is identical to Granit's P_{III} (see below). The C wave is also maximal near Bruch's membrane and probably originates in the cells of the pigment layer. It is abolished by iodate, which severely damages the pigment layer, while the A and B waves and the neural layers of the retina escape unimpaired.

The B wave waxes in the dark and wanes in

the light; it is strongest at intermediate retinal depths, centering on the outer plexiform layer. It is derived from activity in the inner nuclear or ganglionic layer and disappears when the retinal circulation is blocked. Penetration experiments show that Granit's P_{II} is made up of a B wave and a separate D.C. component; the latter starts abruptly, maintains a steady plateau during the stimulus period, and afterwards declines, at first abruptly and then more slowly.

THE RECEPTOR POTENTIALS. Brown and Watanabe[6] confirmed the deductions about the origin of the A wave. They recorded intraretinally from the pure cone fovea of the monkey, which lacks much of the nuclear layer and all of the ganglionic layer. In addition, they obtained records before and after pressing on the optic nerve head, which presumably leaves the retinal structure with a blood supply only from the choriocapillaries. With the B wave progressively eliminated by these procedures, as seen in Figure 9, the A wave emerges until it is seen as a sharply developing potential which holds steady (for seconds) and then rises abruptly

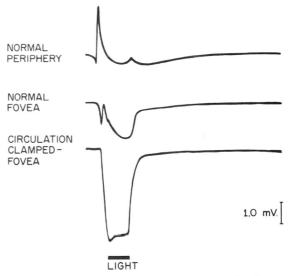

Fig. 9. The A wave of ERG isolated by depth recordings in the region of the receptor cells of the monkey. Note in top record, normal periphery, the small, positive downward potential and the large upward B deflection; in lower record of the fovea, clamping the retinal circulation reduces activity in ganglion and bipolar cells, eliminating the B wave, and allowing the A wave to emerge, presumably in nearly pure form. Stimulus duration applies to bottom record only. The records are arranged so that waves are in the same direction as in Figure 8. (After Brown and Watanabe, *Nature (Lond.)*, 1962, *193*:958–960.)

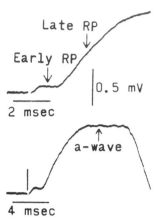

Fig. 10. Time course of the early and late RP (receptor potential), at slow sweep speed (below) and at more rapid sweep speed (above). The initial negative wave is lost in the shock artifact. Stimulus is shown by a break in the base line, marked by a vertical line in lower record. (From Brown and Murakami, *Nature* (*Lond.*), 1964, *201*:626–628.)

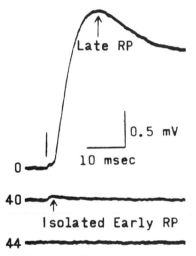

Fig. 11. Selective effect of anoxia on the late RP, isolating the early RP. Retinal circulation is clamped and respiratory movements are paralyzed. Artificial respiration was turned off before the upper record was taken (0 time). The second record was made 40 minutes later and the early RP is undiminished. At 44 minutes it disappears, proving that the potential is not due to light acting on the electrode. Vertical line gives time of stimulation. (From Brown and Murakami, *Nature* (*Lond.*), 1964, *201*:626–628.)

when the stimulation ceases. The A wave seen in the ERG is therefore the leading edge of this receptor potential; the remainder is obliterated by the rapidly rising B wave (see below). The A potential, with a latency of 1.7 milliseconds, is interpreted not as a generator potential but as a depolarization of the presynaptic terminals. With finer analysis of the A wave under precise conditions, by intraretinal recording Brown and Murakami[5] discovered a small negative-positive potential, termed *early RP* (latency 50 μsec.), as opposed to the balance of the A wave termed *late RP* (Fig. 10). The early RP is seen in pure form after a combined ischemic and respiratory anoxia (Fig. 11). It strongly resembles the microphonic potential of the cochlea and, like it, is linearly proportional to energy intensity. It has been identified in the ERG.[9a] A preliminary interpretation is that the early potential is triggered by the nearly instantaneous isomerization of rhodopsin. Wald holds this to be the chemical reaction that initiates visual excitation.

NEURAL BASIS OF RETINAL FUNCTION

Functional Anatomy of Retina.[25] The neural layers of the retina are three strata of densely packed cell bodies and two intervening synaptic layers consisting of intertwining dendritic and axonic brushes (Fig. 12). The retinal layer nearest the chorioid is made up of pigmented cells which probably produce and store photochemicals such as visual purple. The layer next to the pigment cells contains two kinds of neurons, one bearing a cone-shaped process and the other a rod-shaped process. The rods and cones, packed closely together, are the structures actually sensitive to light. The axons of the rod-bearing and cone-bearing neurons end upon the dendrites of the middle layer of bipolar cells, which in turn give axons to the dendrites of ganglion cells. The axons of the ganglion cells sweep to a point just slightly to the nasal side of the center of the retina. There they pierce the chorioid and sclera in the company of the blood vessels and make up the optic nerve. It is an instance of nature's lack of wisdom that light must pass through blood vessels, nerve fibers, and cell bodies to reach the rods and cones. The rod and cone neurons are the receptor cells. The bipolar and ganglion cells are, respectively, second and third order neurons; this makes them part of the brain. Like other parts of the brain, they form complex synaptic relations.

To study human and monkey retinas, Polyak employed the Golgi technique, which fully impregnates only occasional neurons so that the cell body, dendrites and axon of single neurons can be distinguished. The distinctness of the rod and cone systems is not maintained at the level of the bipolar cells. Many bipolar cells synapse with both rod and cone neurons, and this is not an occasional variation. The rod and cone systems are thus incompletely separated in their pathways to the brain. This finding obviously embarrasses the theory of specific receptors and private pathways for each phenomenon, but its exact significance is yet to be realized. Polyak recognized two types of bipolar cells. The most common type is variously termed the *diffuse, polysynaptic* or *rod and cone* bipolar cell because of its widely spread dendritic branches through which it receives impulses from a group, sometimes large, of rod and cone neurons. The bipolar cell termed the *individual, monosynaptic, cone* or *midget* bipolar cell connects only with cones, sometimes only one (fovea). The third order neurons also fall into two categories: (i) *diffuse* ganglion cells which connect with a great number of bipolar cells, and (ii) *monosynaptic* or *individual* ganglion cells which establish synaptic connections, by way of midget bipolar cells, with only one or two cones.

NEURAL BASIS OF AREAL INTERACTION. Thus, there are two systems of neurons in the retina. One, identified exclusively with cones, is highly canalized and spatially organized so that each cone in it has a private path in the optic nerve. The other system, one of mixed rods and cones, is marked by the convergence of many receptors on bipolar cells and of many bipolar cells upon ganglion cells. Convergence is, as pointed out in connection with spinal reflexes, the neural substrate for an interaction of streams of impulses that results in facilitation and inhibition phenomena. An arrangement of this sort, therefore, affords a basis for the receptors of a retinal region to interact at the bipolar and ganglion cell. Interaction is further provided for by a system of intraretinal association neurons. These include (i) *horizontal* cells, (ii) *centrifugal* bipolar cells, and (iii) possibly some of the *amacrine* cells. The horizontal cells are named for their axons, which run horizontally for long distances in the outer plexiform layer. They appear to connect various points of the layer of rod and cone neurons.

REGIONAL VARIATIONS OF RETINA.[25] By confining the stimulus to the fovea, cone function can be studied in isolation; by confining the stimulus to the extreme periphery, rod function almost free of cone activity can be studied. However, there are important differences between foveal and peripheral vision besides the ratio of cones to rods, e.g., the synaptic relationships.

The retina extends through roughly 180°. In the center of this hemisphere (in line with the visual axis) is a yellow pigmented area, the *macula lutea*, within

Fig. 12. Primate retina based on Golgi impregnation, showing principal cell types and their synaptic relations. Various cell types are: *c,* horizontal cells; *d, e, f,* diffuse or polysynaptic bipolar cells; *h,* individual cone (midget) bipolar cell; *i, l,* "amacrine cells"; *m, n, o, p, r, s,* ganglion cells, of which *s* is the individual or monosynaptic ganglion cell. (From Polyak, *The retina,* Chicago, University of Chicago Press, 1941.)

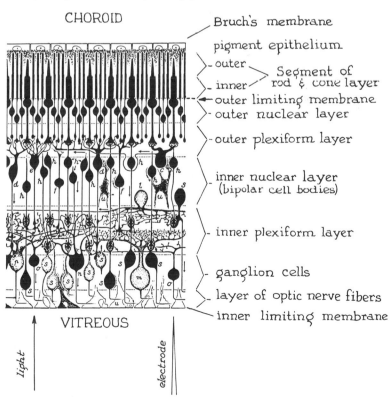

CHOROID

Bruch's membrane
pigment epithelium
outer
inner — Segment of rod & cone layer
outer limiting membrane
outer nuclear layer
outer plexiform layer
inner nuclear layer (bipolar cell bodies)
inner plexiform layer
ganglion cells
layer of optic nerve fibers
inner limiting membrane

VITREOUS

light

electrode

which is a round pitlike depression 1500 μ in diameter, the *fovea centralis,* which in turn encompasses a slighter depression containing the finest cones, the *foveola.* In man an area of 1200 μ, or 2° of arc, is rod-free, the rods appearing just within the margin of the fovea. It contains approximately 34,000 cones varying from 1 μ (12 to 15′) to 3.3 μ (40′) in diameter.

The fovea is specialized for detail vision in four ways: (i) the cones are more slender and densely packed, especially in the foveola; (ii) it is rod-free; (iii) blood vessels and nerve detour around it, and the cellular layers are deflected to the side, reducing the scattering of light; and (iv) the cones have a "private line" to the optic nerve.

In passing peripherally, two principal changes occur. The cone-to-rod ratio rapidly decreases in the first 5° of arc. A few cones (6 to 8 per 100 μ linear distance) occur even in the extreme periphery. Another difference is an increased convergence of receptor elements on single ganglion cells. The ideal ratio of one cone to one ganglion cell is probably approached in the fovea centralis. In the periphery (beyond 10° from the fovea), there are as many as 250 rods and cones per ganglion cell.

RETINAL SUMMATION AND INHIBITION

Summation Effects in Man.   When the objects are small the threshold for the human fovea

is inversely proportional to the area of the test object (Ricco's law). Such areal effects represent mutual facilitation between units occupying the field of stimulation, just as fibers within a nerve trunk facilitate one another synaptically.

Graham and Granit[12] used the flicker technique to show summation between retinal areas by throwing two illuminated half circles upon the retina and varying their separation. The two areal stimuli facilitated one another to a degree depending on their proximity. Under special conditions, one of which is foveal position, stimulation of one area reduces the sensitivity of the other—a form of inhibition.

Summative interactive phenomena are less pronounced in the fovea than in the periphery, where the degree of convergence and lateral connection is greater. Facilitation appears to be the mechanism by which the periphery of the retina attains a higher degree of sensitivity (higher c.f.f.) than the fovea,[10] even though the peripheral cones are less sensitive. When the test object has a very small area, the c.f.f. drops very sharply as the stimulus passes from central fixation to 3 to 5°. In fact, under these conditions, the c.f.f. is lower throughout the periphery than at the fovea, because use of a small area reduces the amount of intra-areal facilitation.

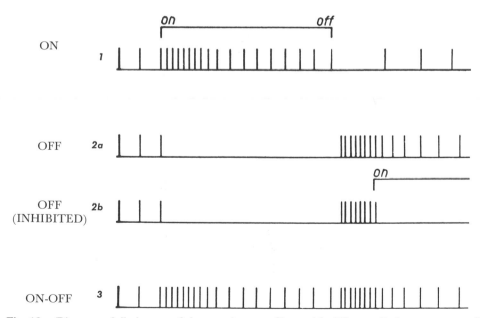

Fig. 13.   Diagram of discharges of three optic nerve fibers with different discharge patterns. Beginning and end of stimulus indicated by horizontal bar. In *2b* note inhibitory effect of light on discharge of "OFF" fiber, which otherwise would have fired as in trace *2a.* This diagram collects observations by Adrian and Mathews, Hartline and Granit. (From Granit, *Receptors and sensory perception,* New Haven, Yale University Press, 1955.)

But with large test patches permitting intra-areal summation, the peripheral sensitivity is greater than the foveal.

Thus, the retinal periphery has two means of increasing its ability to respond to weak stimuli: (i) photochemical reactions (rhodopsin) and (ii) summative neural mechanisms. Both are operative in dim light, but only the latter is operative in daylight. The second mechanism is probably also a factor in endowing the scattered rods of the extreme periphery with good perception of movement. Neural interactions of an inhibitory nature occur in the foveal regions and are significant to detail vision.

Ganglion Cell Responses. Recording singly from a number of ganglion cells reveals that optic nerve axons send three kinds of signals to the brain. Certain axons may respond to the onset of light—the "ON fibers." Others, if responding prior to the stimulus, cease to fire during it and resume firing when it ends—the so-called "OFF fibers." (This should be understood as "OFF fiber behavior"; it depends upon function, not some fixed mechanism.) A third type of fiber behavior is firing at the start and after the end of a stimulus—the "ON-OFF" fibers. These three types are shown in Figure 13, which illustrates the ways the receptor cells manipulate the ganglion cells. The slowing of the background spontaneous discharge after an "ON" response (record 1, Fig. 13) suggests a concealed inhibition of the ganglion cell which shows up sharply by a total inhibition of the "OFF" response by light (2b, Fig. 13). Such concealed inhibition is often seen in spinal reflexes. A purely inhibitory ganglionic response is seen when the stimulus is strong (Fig. 14). The inhibition continues after the cessation of the stimulus. With weaker stimuli the inhibition begins one discharge later, is less complete (slowing of discharge) and is followed by a definite OFF response. The strong stimulus (first and last record in Fig. 14) blocks the concealed excitation of the ganglion cell after, as well as during, the stimulus. A somewhat weaker inhibition of the ganglion cell allows the concealed excitatory influence to manifest itself after the stimulus ceases. The OFF response may therefore be likened to so-called postinhibitory rebound[11] in spinal reflexes. The OFF response is greater than the spontaneous discharge prior to stimulus because the stronger light has stimulated the excitatory as well as inhibitory receptors to the ganglion cell.

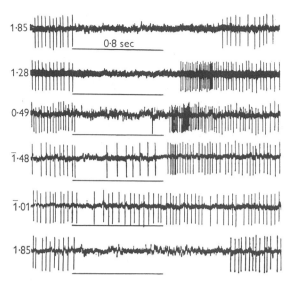

Fig. 14. Responses of a ganglion cell, showing lability of response to changes in light intensity. The response at stimulus strength 1.28 would be labeled OFF but at $\overline{1}.01$ would be labeled ON. (From Brown and Wiesel, *J. Physiol.*, 1959, *149*:537–562.)

Intracellular recording from ganglion cells by Brown and Wiesel[8] indicates that increased discharge frequencies are accompanied by depolarization of the cell membrane. Inhibition of impulses was linked with hyperpolarization, indicating a direct inhibition of ganglion cells rather than cessation of excitation.

Alternate but not exclusive explanations of the OFF effect can be made in terms of persisting membrane changes more deserving of the term "rebound." The OFF effect may be a mixture of persisting membrane phenomena and afterdischarge of a delay path.

Receptive Fields of Ganglion Cells. The receptive field of a retinal ganglion (or bipolar) cell is defined as that portion of the visual field from which the discharge of a given ganglion cell can be increased or decreased. These fields can be mapped out in the intact eye with the aid of penetrating electrodes, punctate light sources and direct observation of electrode positions.

In 1953, Kuffler discovered that the receptive field has an annular organization in which the center and periphery are mutually antagonistic. If the center increases discharge as in Figure 15, top, stimulation of the periphery causes discharge only when the light goes off. In another cell, the center of the receptive field may be inhibitory (Fig. 15, bottom), giving a response only when the discharge ceases, while the pe-

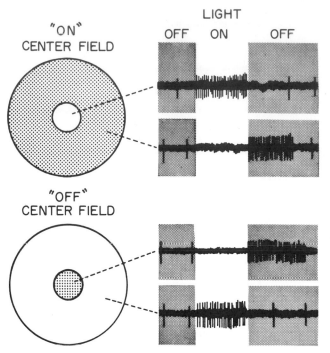

Fig. 15. The topographic organization of receptive fields of ganglion cells of the retina (left) and the ON and OFF discharge. Each dashed line could be viewed as an exploring spot of light in one of the many positions in the center or the peripheral zone of the receptive field, which would give a discharge from the ganglion cell as shown in the corresponding record. Note that in the upper diagram, where the center produces a discharge when the light is on, none is produced by stimulation of the peripheral zone until the light goes off. (Hubel, *Scientific American*, 1963, *209*:54–62.)

riphery gives an ON response during the discharge. From an ON center ganglion cell, Kuffler recorded a faster and faster discharge by increasing the size of a light spot (Ricco's law), indicating mutual facilitation between the receptors corresponding to the center of the receptive field. However, when the spot grew large enough to reach and encompass the periphery, the discharge was reduced in frequency and even eliminated. An annular ring of light of appropriate size is strongly inhibitory to an ON center ganglion cell. Figure 16 shows that in a similar experiment the receptive fields of cells in the inner nuclear layer resemble those of ganglion cells.

The size of the field varies with the state of dark adaptation and with the strength of stimu-

lus. As predicted by the greater convergence upon ganglion cells in the periphery than in the fovea, the receptive fields are correspondingly larger in the periphery. In the monkey, the arc of the receptive field ranges from 4 minutes to 2 degrees. Penetration experiments prove that small ganglion cells and cells in the inner nuclear layer have similarly round fields with concentric excitatory and inhibitory areas (Fig. 16). Since what are presumably bipolar cells exhibit hyperpolarization, part of the ganglion cell inhibition is indirect, i.e., shutting off of stimulation. That the concentric rings for a given ganglion cell must represent a mixture of receptors which are excitatory and inhibitory to the cell is required for the interpretation of OFF and ON effects given above. Such evidence has been

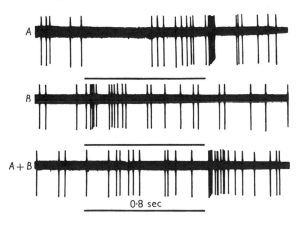

Fig. 16. Records from a cell in the inner nuclear layer of the retina demonstrating the mutual inhibitory relationship between the center (predominantly excitatory) and the periphery (predominantly inhibitory) of the receptor field of the retina. The stimulus pattern for each record is shown at the right. (From Brown and Wiesel, *J. Physiol.*, 1959, *149*:537–562.)

obtained from experiments on goldfish, which, unlike the cat, have color vision.

Goldfish eyes show OFF, ON, and ON-OFF ganglion receptive fields concentrically arranged which have the advantage that the OFF effect has a maximum spectral sensitivity at 650 mμ wavelength and the ON a maximum at 500 mμ. Figure 17 shows the result of traversing the receptive field with the OFF-650 mμ and the ON-500 mμ stimuli and determining the sensitivity at each point. There is a central zone of higher sensitivity yielding OFF response; the higher threshold ON responses are obtained from the central as well as the peripheral zone of the receptive field.

It is easy to see that a suprathreshold stimulus of intermediate wavelength (550 to 600 mμ) restricted to the center of the receptive field would produce more inhibition than excitation because the inhibitory units are more sensitive. No ON response would occur because of the stronger inhibition; it would be classed as an OFF-center field. In the periphery of the field the excitatory process is more strongly driven so that an ON effect occurs. Whether the discharge increases at the end of stimulation depends on what mixture of excitatory and inhibitory units are excited, which in turn depends on wavelength and position in the border between center and periphery.

The interaction of predominantly excitatory and inhibitory zones and the size and shape of receptive fields have a great importance to visual acuity and the perceptions of movement. This will be discussed in connection with visual pathways (Chap. 22).

VISUAL ACUITY AND DETAIL VISION[10a]

Biologically, visual acuity is the sharpness with which detail and contours are perceived and constitutes the basis for form or object vision. From the point of view of testing, it is often measured by finding the smallest distance by which two lines may be separated without appearing as a single line. This distance is the *minimum separable*. Visual acuity is thus the *resolving power* of the eye, i.e., its ability to resolve two lines, and is akin to the two-point threshold of the skin. Lines or contours of solid fields placed closer together than the minimum separable blur into one another and may, if sufficiently close, appear homogeneous. Thus, if visual acuity is low, the fine details of environment are blurred and the intricate patterns of detail and contour give way to structureless masses with fuzzy outlines. Tests of visual acuity are simply standardized and quantified means of sampling a basic physiologic function—detail vision. Visual acuity can also be expressed in terms of the *minimum visible,* the narrowest line or the finest thread that can be discriminated from a homogeneous background. Weymouth[38] has shown that the *minimal angle of resolution* (M.A.R.) is a better designation for many purposes than is the minimum separable.

Dioptric Factors. The minimum separable varies with many conditions which are of two main kinds—dioptric and stimulus factors. The first have to do with the physical formation of a sharply focused image on the retina (Chap. 19). Under this heading come: (i) the "normal" errors of dioptric mechanisms: spherical and chromatic aberration, diffraction by imperfections in the ocular media and scattering of light by reflection from the retina. (ii) Errors of refraction: myopia, hyperopia and astigmatism. (Detection of such errors is the main purpose for clinical tests of visual acuity. (iii) Pupillary

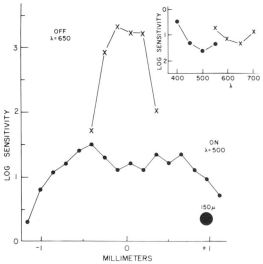

Fig. 17. Topographic organization of a "color-coded" ganglion cell receptive field. The curves are sensitivity profiles of an OFF center ganglion cell obtained by determining thresholds along a line cutting across the receptive field. Solid dots represent sensitivity of ON responses. The crosses designate a similar curve for a wavelength yielding response at terminations of the stimulus. Abscissae are retinal distance and the ordinates the reciprocal of threshold energy or sensitivity. Large dot is the stimulus size. (From Wagner, *et al., J. opt. Soc. Amer.,* 1963, *53*:66–70.)

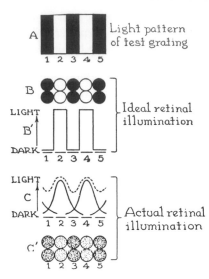

Fig. 18. Diagram illustrating hypothetical mechanism of detail vision or visual acuity. *A* is test grating; *B* and *C'* are receptors with intensity of the illumination represented by shading; *B'* and *C* are plots of intensity of illumination, with dotted line in *C* representing algebraic summation of two underlying curves. For further explanation, see text.

size: constriction increases visual acuity by minimizing factors (i) and (ii), although undue constriction hinders detail vision by increasing diffraction. (iv) The composition of the light: monochromatic light increases visual acuity by decreasing chromatic aberration. (v) Random variations of fixation: these occur even when control of eye muscles is normal and cause a slight shifting (30' of visual angle) of the image on the retina, thus blurring it.

Ratliff and Riggs[26] have recorded such movements by attaching a mirror to a contact lens. While the eyes are supposedly fixated no less than four types of movement are being made, varying from rapid movements (30 to 70 per sec.) averaging 17.5' of visual angle to slow drifts and rapid jerks averaging 5' of visual angle. Such movements have proved to be not a hindrance to vision but an actual necessity.[11] An optical stabilizing of the retinal image, counteracting movement, results not in more detailed vision but in an actual fading of the image. Consistently stabilizing the eye and moving the stimulus slightly has dramatic effects on the rate of discharge of a cortical neuron in the visual cortex.[25a] As indicated earlier, something appears to be gained by the introduction of variability into the system.

Stimulus Factors. With the printed page as the stimulus, there are four ways in which the stimulus can be altered to make its recognition more difficult.[22] The letters may be reduced uniformly in size; the ink may be bleached to the white of the background or the background may be darkened; the light falling on the page can be diminished; and, finally, the time allowed for observation can be shortened. The four factors influencing visual acuity are, then, size of detail, brightness contrast, illumination, and exposure time. All must be considered in attaining efficient vision in the school room or industry.

Retinal Grain. A third group of factors influencing visual acuity involves the anatomic and physiologic grain of the retina. Just as one factor in obtaining detail in photography is fineness of the grain in the film, so retinal grain is a factor in visual acuity. The dense packing together of exceedingly minute receptor elements is undoubtedly based upon the need for a finely grained receptive mechanism. The minimum separable, converted from seconds of visual angle to retinal distance and the diameter of a cone are of about the same order of magnitude. This suggests that two white lines on a black field could not be seen as two unless an unstimulated row of cones separated the stimulated ones ("ideal retinal illumination," Fig. 18). Yet we know this is not true. The eye distinguishes the lines even though optical imperfections and eye movements have caused the edges of the light bands to spread randomly over the intervening cones (diagrams *C* and *C'*, Fig. 18). If the lines are brought closer together, the curves representing the random distribution of light will be drawn together until the summated stimulus on the center cones equals that on the neighboring cones. So long as there is a discriminable difference in intensity of illumination between the shaded cone and its neighbors, a dark stria is visible. Visual acuity therefore resolves into the discrimination of a light-dark pattern. With these facts in mind, the retinal factors influencing visual acuity may be enumerated.

RETINAL REGION. Visual acuity is far from uniform over the entire retina. The fovea centralis is a region specialized for high visual acuity and is employed for accurate inspection of fine detail. The zone immediately surrounding the fovea possesses the next greatest capacity for detail vision, etc. The falling off in acuity in passing from fovea to periphery is quite abrupt (Fig. 19). With the foveal visual acuity taken as

1, the acuity at the edge of the macula (2.5°) has fallen to one-half; at 7.5° from the fovea it is one-fourth, and in the extreme periphery it is only one-fortieth. This curve, difficult to characterize, tends to become a straight line if plotted as the minimal angle of resolution, as in Figure 20;[38] at least two factors operate to produce this result. Extrafoveal cones are both larger in diameter and fewer per unit area, being "diluted" by rods. Secondly, more cones converge on a single ganglion cell in the periphery than in the central zones; as shown in Figure 21, visual acuity falls off more rapidly than intercone distance. On the other hand, the sep-

aration of ganglion cells in minutes of visual angle, plotted against degrees of eccentricity, forms a straight line. This confirms the deductions made from Figure 21.

Figure 20 also shows the marked difference between the visual acuities of the rod and cone mechanisms. With light below cone threshold, the fovea has the lowest visual acuity. In training for night vision, observers are taught to use the parafoveal regions of the retina. The acuity of rod vision increases throughout 10° owing to the increasing proportion of rods. Rod vision by night is inferior to cone vision by day within a 30° zone surrounding the fovea, not because the

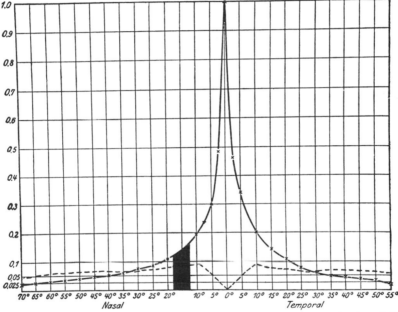

Fig. 19. Curve of relative acuity of vision in central and peripheral fields of retina. Solid line represents acuity of cone vision (light-adapted eye), and dotted line represents acuity of rod vision (approximate). Black area is the blind spot. (After Wertheim, *Z. Psychol.*, 1894, *7*:177–187.)

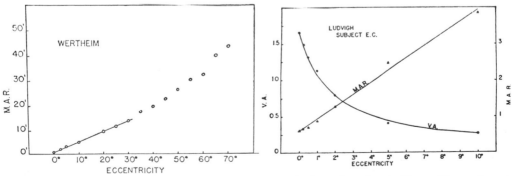

Fig. 20. *Left,* Graph showing approximation to straight line when data in Figure 19 are plotted as minimal angle of resolution. *Right,* Graph of data obtained by Ludvigh to show value of expressing visual acuity as minimal angle of resolution. (From Weymouth, *Amer. J. Ophthal.*, 1958, *46*:102–113.)

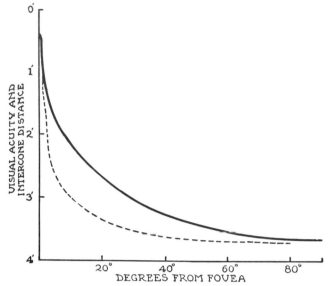

Fig. 21. Comparison of visual acuity and cone density for central and peripheral portions of retina. Dotted line shows visual acuity in minutes of visual angle. Note that the lower the curve the larger is the minimum separable. Heavy line shows cone gradient of retina in terms of intercone distance for periphery and cone width for rod-free areas, plotted on same ordinate as visual acuity. Failure of curves to correspond proves that factors other than density and diameter of cones determine minimum separable. (After Polyak, *The retina,* Chicago, University of Chicago Press, 1941.)

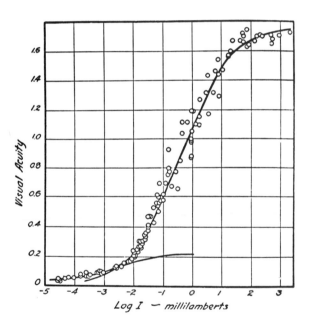

Fig. 22. Curves showing relation between visual acuity and level of illumination. Circles represent experimental determinations by König of visual acuity (reciprocal of minimum separable on ordinate) for a wide range of intensities of illumination (abscissa). Two solid lines, one for rods (lower) and one for cones (upper), show the success with which a normal probability integral can be fitted to data. According to Hecht's theory, curve represents number of receptor units whose threshold is attained by a given intensity of illumination, thresholds of receptors being distributed according to normal probability curve. (From Hecht, *A handbook of general experimental psychology,* C. Murchison, ed., Worcester, Clark University Press, 1934.)

rods are "diluted" by inactive cones but because many rods converge ultimately upon a single ganglion cell. This is a second indication that the number of "lines" available to carry information to the brain, as well as the anatomic grain of the receptor elements, is important.

FUNCTIONAL GRAIN AND CONTOUR VISION. Hecht explains the familiar effect of illumination on visual acuity in terms of "functional retinal grain." He assumes that cone thresholds are distributed according to a normal frequency curve like heights or weights of individuals. By integrating* such a curve, the S-shaped line in Figure 22 is obtained, and agreement of the theoretical curve and the experimental data justifies the assumption.

Figure 23 shows why dim lighting results in fuzzy, blurred contours. For convenience of illustration, Hecht's theory of cone thresholds is adopted. Circles represent the anatomic grain of the retina; the filled circles, the cones active at successively higher levels of illumination, A, B and C. The central vertical line demarcates a shadow cast upon the retina by a black object; the heavy line represents the boundary between lighted and shaded cones. A progressively sharper definition is obtained as more active cones are available to "draw" the contour, which is therefore sharpest at high illumination. (The same diagram also illustrates

---

*This can be done graphically by adding the low threshold cones to those of the next lowest threshold to get the second part on the curve, and so on for each class.

the difference in contour vision in peripheral [A], paracentral [B] and central [C] regions of the retina under conditions of bright illumination, the unfilled circles then being considered rods [inactive] and the filled circles cones.)

Clinical tests of visual acuity. Visual acuity is usually measured by the familiar chart on which the letters in each line are smaller than those in the previous line.

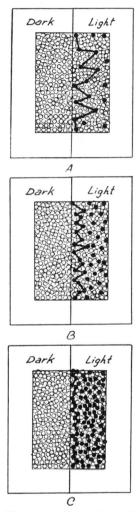

Fig. 23. Diagrams illustrating relation between level of illumination and perception of contours. *A, B, C* represent increasing levels of illumination of right-hand side of field, left-hand field being shielded by the shadow of an object. Filled circles represent active units and unfilled circles inactive units, rods and cones, retinal ganglion cells, or cells of striate cortex. Where many units are active, contour is quite sharply defined, but when few units are active contour is fuzzy. Same diagram serves to compare contour vision of peripheral (*A*), intermediate (*B*), and macular (*C*) regions of retina, with filled circles representing active cones, and unfilled circles inactive rods.

The chart is always viewed from the virtual far point of vision (6 m., or 20 ft.), so that accommodation is not needed. The number at the end of each row of type is the distance at which a whole letter of the size found on that line subtends an angle of 5′ on the retina, and each stroke of the letter subtends a visual angle of 1′. Snellen (1876), in making the chart, believed that the components of a letter should be separated by a distance equal to the minimum separable for the letter to be perceived by the normal eye. The situation is more complex than this. For example, the letters differ considerably in legibility; if B, the hardest letter to distinguish, is taken as 1, G and H are next hardest at 0.92, and L is the easiest at 0.71. However, the shortcomings of the test appear to compensate for one another, and the test serves its purpose very well. The chart must be well lighted; each eye is tested separately.

If at 20 feet the individual reads the letters of the line marked 20 feet, visual acuity is stated as 20/20 and is considered normal. If an individual can read only the line marked 100 (which a normal eye can read at 100 feet), his visual acuity is given as 20/100. Lines of test type smaller than the 20/20 line are provided and are rated 20/15, 20/13 and 20/10. Such ratings mean that the individual has better than normal acute vision and *do not mean that the individual is hyperopic.* As pointed out in the previous chapter, the hyperope does not see better than the emmetrope at a distance, but sees with less need for accommodation when objects are at a distance. To reduce the visual acuity to a fraction by saying that a person with 20/40 vision has 50 per cent normal visual acuity is like saying that a temperature of 80° is twice as hot as 40°. In some Snellen test charts the lines of type are labeled in terms of percentage of useful vision.

COLOR VISION[10a]

The sensations of color or hue resulting from the stimulation of the retina by the successive wavelengths of the visible spectrum and the *extraspectral* color, purple, form the *chromatic series.* It is paradoxical that the series of whites and grays—which in common parlance denotes a lack of color—is most conveniently considered a form of color vision, the *achromatic series.*

Achromatic and Chromatic Series. Objects reflecting to our eye all the visible rays of sunlight give us a white sensation. Black, on the contrary, is the sensation caused by withdrawal of light. In order to see black one must have a retina. In the region of the blind spot one sees not black but nothing. Thus, it is not improbable that black is a sensation connected with a definite retinal activity.

In the chromatic series many different colors (technically hues) may be detected—some observers record as many as 160. We generally give specific names only to those that represent quite distinct sensations. The limiting wavelengths (mμ) of the commonly named colors are: red, 723–647; orange, 647–585; yellow, 585–575; green, 575–492; blue, 492–455; indigo, 455–424; violet, 424–397.

Color saturation. The term "saturation" means the amount of color or freedom from dilution by white sensation. Pale or pastel shades is the nontechnical name for unsaturated colors. However, even monochromatic light does not produce a color experience entirely free from white sensation, since the monochromatic rays induce the retinal processes underlying white as well as those underlying its own special color (see below).

Laws of color vision. There are a number of laws which any theory of color vision must explain. Some of these are more in the province of psychology than physiology. We must, therefore, content ourselves with a brief statement of the main laws of color vision.

(i) *Color mixture or fusion.* When two or more wavelengths fall upon the same retinal area, the resulting sensation is often quite different from any aroused by the individual wavelengths. (ii) *Primary colors.* Color fusion experiments show that three wavelengths may be selected from the spectrum, one from the red end, one from the blue end, and one from the middle, whose combinations in different proportions will give a sensation of white, of any intermediate color shade, or of extraspectral purple (obtained by mixing the two ends of the spectrum). It is customary to designate these three wavelengths as primary colors.* (iii) *Complementary colors.* For any given color there is a complement which combines with it to produce white. Because the colors of the spectrum differ in saturation, widely differing intensities may be necessary. Colors that are closer together in the spectral series than the complementaries give on fusion some intermediate color. Thus, red and yellow, when fused, give orange. Colors farther apart than the distance between the complementaries give some shade of purple. (iv) *After-images.* After one stops looking at a color, he may continue to see it for a short time (positive after-image) or he may see its complementary color (negative after-image). This is a retinal phenomenon. (v) *Color contrasts.* If a piece of blue paper is laid upon a yellow paper, the color of each of them is heightened—color contrast.

Theories of Color Vision.

Many theories have been proposed to explain the facts of color vision. None of them is entirely successful. The oldest and simplest theory is that of Young and Helmholtz.

YOUNG-HELMHOLTZ THEORY. Proposed by Thomas Young[39] in 1801 and later modified by Helmholtz, this theory assumes three fundamen-

*There are many combinations of three wavelengths with which the spectrum can be matched.

tal color sensations—red, green and violet. Corresponding with these are three classes of cones containing three different photochemical substances. Decomposition of each of these substances stimulates different nerve fibers, and the impulses are conducted to different systems of nerve cells in the visual cortex. The theory, therefore, assumes specific nerve fibers and specific cortical cells, corresponding respectively to the red, green and violet photochemical substances.†

When these three cone types are equally excited, a sensation of white results. All other color sensations, including yellow, are compounded by combined stimulation of the three receptors in different proportions. It is assumed, furthermore, that each photochemical substance is acted upon to some degree by all of the visible rays of the spectrum, but that the rays of long wavelengths at the red end of the spectrum affect the red substance most strongly, etc.

The theory of Helmholtz accords with the doctrine of specific nerve energies, since each photochemical substance serves simply to excite a nerve fiber and the quality of the sensation aroused depends on the ending of this fiber in the brain.

Negative after-images are explained as follows: If we look fixedly at a green object, the corresponding photochemical substance is chiefly acted upon. When the same cones are subsequently exposed to white light, the red and violet substances, having been previously less acted upon, now respond in greater proportions to the white light, and the after-image takes a red-violet— that is, purple—color. Many objections have been raised to the Young-Helmholtz theory. It fails to explain some of the subjective phenomena of color vision in normal and "color-blind" persons, and why, in the periphery, yellow and, farther out, white or gray are perceived in otherwise color-blind zones. Finally, recent neurophysiologic and anatomic information suggests that the theory is oversimplified.

Photochemistry of Color Vision.

Cone pigment has proved more elusive than rod pigment. The high threshold for cones suggests that the pigment is less concentrated in cones than rods. Trichromatic theories of color vision require three pigments. A violet-sensitive substance—

†Helmholtz's hypothesis of zonal representation of color in the cerebral cortex has not proved justified. Le Gros Clark, however, has made the interesting suggestion that the three layers of the lateral geniculate body are related to the three receptors of the trichromatic theory.

iodopsin—was extracted from the chicken retinae by Wald in 1937 and since has been synthesized by adding an isomer of retinene to a preparation of the outer segments of rods and cones. The absorption spectrum of iodopsin fits reasonably well with the photopic sensitivity curve of the fowl when shifting of the curve by oil droplets in the eye of the fowl is taken into account.

By spectroscopic analysis of the retina *in vivo* and *in vitro*, its photochemical substances can be studied without chemical extraction. Rushton[28, 30] obtained the first direct spectral sensitivity evidence of cone pigments by an ophthalmoscopic procedure directed to the human fovea.

Brown and Wald[8a] made precise physical measurements of the spectral sensitivity of the receptor substances in the green and red range, finding maxima at 535 and 565 mμ respectively. The blue substance inferred from psychological experiments proved elusive. Recently, the tiny cones of the human and monkey retina were studied microspectroscopically *in vitro*.[23a] The existence of the blue receptor substance was unquestionably demonstrated. Further, because *single* cones were studied it was learned that each cone contains one specific photochemical substance, though the possibility that the red receptor may contain some green pigment could not be wholly ruled out. It seems safe to speak of blue and green receptors. Finally, Wald[34a] has been able to gain evidence for the blue pigment in man and to obtain good correlation between spectra determined psychologically and physically. Figure 24 shows the degree of fit, which is remarkable, since colored degradation products will distort the curve (green curve) as will any bleaching of some green pigment in determining the absorption spectrum of the red pigment.

The trichromatic theory of color vision (see below) is strongly supported by the proof that three pigments exist in the retina and, with one reservation, three color cones. How the discharges from these cells interact with others of

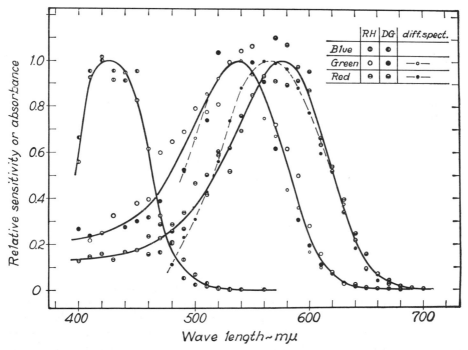

Fig. 24. Comparison of action spectra of color pigments of the human retina obtained by psychological methods (solid lines) with difference spectra obtained by physical methods (red and green only). Sensitivity spectra are adjusted to the same height. The curves for green and red would be of about the same height, but that for blue would be much less. (From Wald, *Science*, 1964, *145*:1007–1016.)

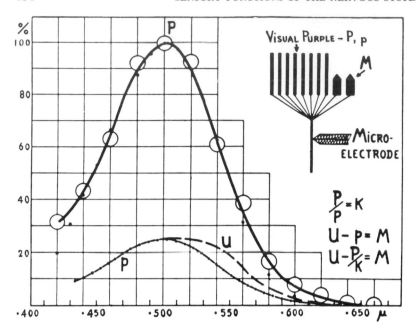

Fig. 25. Average sensitivity curve (large circles) of receptors connected with single ganglion cell of cat's retina when dark-adapted. Black dots are Lythgoe's curve for the absorption of light by visual purple. *U* is experimentally obtained curve from which curve *P* in appropriate magnitude (*p*) is subtracted to give sensitivity of specific color receptor. (From Granit, *J. Neurophysiol.,* 1945, *8*:195–210.)

their kind or of opposite kind is a question which must be answered at each stage of the visual system.

Responses to Color—Ganglion and Geniculate Cells. Granit's[15] pioneer studies of the spectral sensitivity of ganglion cells were carried out on cats, which, though not entirely color-blind, are nearly so. The monkey has color vision comparable to man's, but its ganglion cell spectra have not been determined. However, the cells of the geniculate body on which the ganglion cells end exhibit definite color specificity. Maxima were found at 580, 540, and 450 millimicra wavelengths, agreeing very well with the results of Marks, *et al.* for single monkey cones.[23a] It is of importance to color vision that in many cases cones of different spectral sensitivity converge on the same geniculate cell and are mutually inhibitory.

Specific Color Receptors. The spectral sensitivity of the ganglion cell can be determined by recording from it with microelectrodes while subjecting the eye to different wavelengths of light (Granit). The three curves corresponding to the three pigments indicated by color mixture experiments and by direct observation of bleaching are not found. All units studied exhibited sensitivity to a wide band of wavelengths. The curve of sensitivity obtained in the dark-adapted eye agreed closely with the absorption curve of visual purple (Fig. 25). Un-

der conditions of light adaptation, a curve resembling the photopic visibility curve was obtained. A structural basis for this is that both rods and cones converge through bipolar cells upon the same ganglion cell. The shift from the scotopic to the photopic curve presumably means that rods cease to function at the intensities that stimulate cones. Granit terms this response the *scotopic and photopic dominator response.* The conscious response is presumably achromatic.

In addition to these dominator responses, some units in the light-adapted eye respond to a *narrow* band of wavelengths, narrower than the spectral sensitivity of cone pigments known directly (iodopsin) or indirectly by ophthalmoscopic bleaching experiments. This is termed the modulator response; it may represent the activity of individual cones. The sensitivity curves tend to vary slightly, but cluster into three groups (Fig. 26): red-yellow (580 to 600 mμ), green (520 to 540 mμ), and blue (450 to 470 mμ). The visibility curve reconstructed from these curves agrees satisfactorily with that of the human eye. This direct evidence therefore indicates that Helmholtz's trireceptor theory may be true in the statistical sense that the cones fall into three groups within which the receptors of narrow band sensitivity have similar, though not identical, sensitivity. Apparently many ganglion cells discharge in response to several

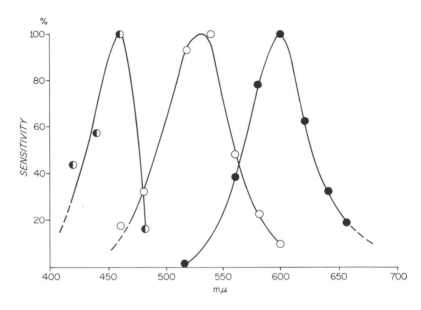

Fig. 26. Sensitivity curves for blue (*left*), green (*middle*), and red (*right*) color receptors. These were obtained by selective adaptation and by averaging curves of several individual receptors, which varied from average by amount indicated by upper contours. (From Granit, *J. Neurophysiol.,* 1945, *8:*195–210.)

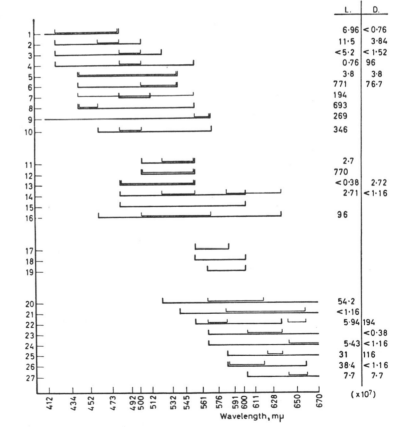

Fig. 27. Spectral sensitivity of 27 single cortical units. The wide bracket shows band of wavelengths eliciting responses at high intensities and narrow bracket at low intensities. (From Andersen, Buchman and Lennox-Buchtal, *Vision Res.,* 1962, *2:*295–307.)

receptors, each sensitive to a narrow band, which collectively give the ganglion cell a sensitivity (visibility) curve like that of the whole eye. Such units, which are numerous, probably give rise to a sensation of white. Other ganglion cells connected with single receptors serve color discrimination.

Spectral Sensitivity of Cortical Neurons. A single cortical neuron, like a retinal ganglion cell, can respond in two ways: broad band responders yielding a burst or train of impulses and narrow band responders yielding one or two impulses. Most frequently single cortical neurons responded to white light selectively or to many monochromatic lights distributed throughout the spectrum (Fig. 27). Most significantly, some could respond to a narrow spectral band when tested with diffuse flashes of monochromatic light. Near threshold a third of the units with restricted response were discharged by only one filter ($<$ 15 mμ). At high intensities the most selective unit found was responsive to a 30 mμ band; the more usual was to a 60 to 100μ band. Some units responsive only to blue, green, red and yellow wavelengths were found, but usually the sensitivity spread into the wavelengths for other colors. This selective spectral sensitivity is not fixed. In repeated trials the frequency most often responded to could shift from one band to another and back again without change in stimulus conditions. Under chloralose anesthesia a unit which has responded to a narrow band can irreversibly lose its selectivity and respond to all wavelengths and to white light. The narrowest effective band was smaller than that so far recorded from the lateral geniculate body, or for the modulator response of the retinal ganglion cell. The sharpening of the band sensitivity is probably a cortical function in which inhibition favored by diffuse illumination plays a part. A similar problem and explanation will be encountered in the study of visual acuity.

Clinical Correlations: Color Blindness and Anomalies. The discovery of color blindness (1794) is credited to the British chemist and physicist, John Dalton (of the gas law), who was himself "color-blind."

CLASSIFICATION OF COLOR BLINDNESS. The conventional classification of color blindness derives from the Young-Helmholtz theory of three specific receptors, color blindness being ascribed to an alteration in one of them. Defects in color

vision are no longer described in terms of red, green and violet blindness, because, for example, the individuals Helmholtz called red blind are actually red-green blind. They see the spectrum as yellow and blue (see p. 437). Instead are employed the more noncommittal categories suggested by von Kries: protanopia, deuteranopia and tritanopia, implying merely a defect in the first (*protos*), second (*deuteros*) or third (*tritos*) receptor. The suffixes -anomaly and -anopia distinguish color weakness and color blindness, respectively. The conventional classification is as follows:

I. TRICHROMATS

1. normal color vision
2. protanomaly
3. deuteranomaly

II. DICHROMATS

1. protanopia
2. deuteranopia
3. tritanopia

III. MONOCHROMATS

This classification, like the parent Young-Helmholtz theory, characterizes adequately the objective phenomena of color mixture in the color-blind and is not meant to describe the appearance of the spectrum. The normal and color-weak trichromats require three primary colors to match all colors in the spectrum, but they use the colors from the red and green parts of the spectrum in different proportions. In matching yellows by mixing red and green wavelengths, they employ quite different ratios; the protanomalous requires more of the red, and the deuteranomalous more of the green. Their defect may be slight or may be nearly as severe as in dichromatism.

Dichromats are so named because they can match the spectrum as they see it with only two primary colors, a red and a blue for the deuteranope and a green and a blue for the protanope. These two conditions are believed to be reduction systems representing the loss of one of the three Young-Helmholtz color receptors. Tritanopia is an extremely rare form of color blindness in which a wavelength from the long end and one from the middle of the spectrum suffice to duplicate the spectrum. The monochromat duplicates the spectrum with only one wavelength by adjusting its intensity. Apparently, only grades of light and dark are seen.

Luminosity of spectrum in color blindness.   To the

deuteranope-deuteranomalous the luminosity of the spectrum (visibility curve) is virtually normal; to the protanope-protanomalous it is distinctly abnormal, the spectrum being shortened. The longer (red) wavelengths are not even appreciated as light; it is as though they did not reach the retina. This explains why a protanope can confuse a red with a black and appear at a funeral wearing a red tie. The point at which the spectrum seems brightest is shifted from 552 mμ to approximately 540 mμ. No intermediate forms link the protanope to the normal (Fig. 28), and the visibility curves for protanopes and protanomalous are identical. The term *scoterythrous* has been suggested for this state. The visibility curve of the deuteranope shows no such abnormality; hence, it is a form of pure color blindness, whereas protanopia is a *color plus light* blindness.

Color confusions. The color-blind person is satisfied with the appearance of his visual world, rarely misnames a colored object or even a color, and is often tardy in discovering his abnormality. His deficiency is usually first noticed because he confuses certain colors, and tests of color vision depend on these confusions. The protanomalous and deuteranomalous find difficulty in distinguishing the red-green range, and the tritanomalous finds difficulty in distinguishing the blue-yellow range; the dichromat fails entirely.

Subjective phenomena.[17, 37] How does the spectrum appear to the color-blind? To the dichromat, protanope and deuteranope, the spectrum is divided into two halves by a band of gray in the neighborhood of 493 to 497 mμ (greenish blue), the so-called neutral point above which all wavelengths seem yellow and below which all wavelengths seem blue (Fig. 29). The colors gain in saturation in passing away from the neutral point. Dalton described the spectrum as follows: "My yellow comprehends the red, orange, yellow and green of others; and my blue and purple (dark blue?) coincide with theirs." The few cases of monocular color vision examined confirm this description of the spectrum. So, too, the color confusions of deuteranope and protanope are only subtly different. From the point of view of their subjective experiences, protanopes and deuteranopes both are red-green color-blind, but in slightly different ways. Protanopia is characterized by a shortening of the spectrum and a decreased luminosity of the longer (red) wavelengths.

An explanation of why the spectrum appears to be made up of yellow and blue, rather than green and blue and red and blue, is as follows: In protanopia the "red receptor" is supposed to have the same wavelength sensitivity as the "green receptor," but retains its central "red" reaction unaltered. Therefore, neither green nor red is ever separately experienced, their receptors being always excited together, resulting in a color mixture. The spectrum corresponding to the whole red and green range appears as yellow or orange,

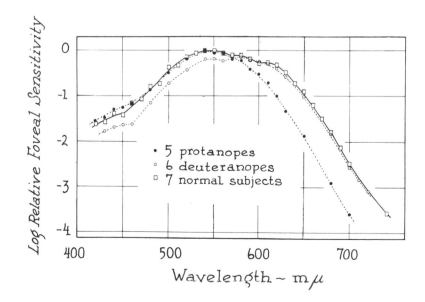

Fig. 28. Luminosity curves of color blind and normal subjects. Downward in the graph represents loss of sensitivity, the log of the reciprocal of threshold energy. (From Hsia and Graham, *Proc. nat. Acad. Sci.,* (*Wash.*), 1957, *43*:1011–1019.)

• 5 protanopes
○ 6 deuteranopes
□ 7 normal subjects

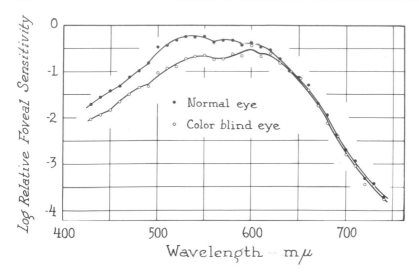

Fig. 29. Luminosity curves of the fovea in a unilaterally color blind (dichromatic) subject. Downward on the graph indicates less sensitivity in log units, which occurs in the blue-green region of the spectrum. (From Graham and Hsia, *Proc. nat. Acad. Sci. (Wash.)*, 1958, *44*: 46–59.)

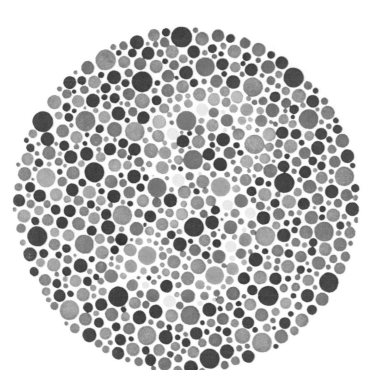

Fig. 30. Hidden-figure chart for detection of color blindness. Normal eye sees figure 5, color blind eye sees figure 2. (Copied by permission from Ishihara's *Series of plates designed as tests for color blindness*, Tokyo, Kanehara & Co., 1920.)

the hues resulting from mixing red and green wavelengths. Deuteranopia may consist of a change in the cone normally most sensitive to the green wavelength so that it has the same sensitivity as the red-sensitive cone.

Classified on the basis of etiology, color disability may be (i) *acquired* through a variety of retinal, cerebral, systemic and toxic disorders, including avitaminosis, or (ii) *congenital* because

of inherited lack of some mechanism vital to color vision. Red-green blindness and weakness are strongly sex-linked. According to one study it is present in some degree in 8 per cent of boys and 0.5 per cent of girls. It passes from father by way of a daughter to a grandson. The lesser incidence among females is presumably due to the necessity for the disability to be received from both parents if it is to be exhibited. Total color blindness seems to be inherited as a simple recessive trait. Difficulty with blue and yellow is usually acquired; too few individuals born with this form have been discovered to learn much of its genetics.

Tests of color blindness. For the purpose of explaining the principles involved, the simplest of the many tests for color vision is Holmgren's. A number of skeins of wool are used, and three standard colors are chosen: standard I, a pale, pure green skein, which must not incline toward yellow-green; standard II, a medium purple (magenta) skein; and standard III, a vivid scarlet skein. The subject is given skein I and is asked to select quickly from the pile of assorted colored skeins those that have approximately the same color. Those who are dichromatic will see the test skein as a gray with some yellow or blue shade and will select, therefore, not only the green skeins, but the grays or grayish-blue skeins. To ascertain whether the individual is a protanope or a deuteranope, standards II and III may then be employed.

With standard II (medium purple) the protanope will select, in addition to other purples, only blues or violets; the deuteranope will select as "confusion colors" only greens and grays.

With standard III (red) the protanope will select as confusion colors greens, grays or browns less luminous than the standard color, and the deuteranope will select greens, grays or browns of a greater brightness than the standard.

The second test of color vision in common use is the Ishihara or some other version of Stilling's (1876) pseudo-isochromatic charts. This test, familiarly known as the "hidden digit" test, consists of a book of plates containing digits made up of spots of color set in a field composed of spots of the confusion color (Fig. 30). Spots of several shades are used because the luminosity of certain hues is altered for color deviates. In constructing the original tests, Stilling was guided in choice of colors by a red-green blind painter and a blue-yellow blind school teacher. In the Ishihara test one number is seen by the normal eye and another by the color-weak eye. By appropriate choice of colors and chroma levels, the test can be made qualitatively and quantitatively diagnostic.

REFERENCES

1. ANDERSEN, V. O., BUCHMANN, M. B. and LENNOX-BUCH-THAL, M. A. *Vision Res.,* 1962, *2:*295–307.
2. BARLOW, H. B. *J. Physiol.,* 1953, *119:*58–68; 69–88.
3. BARLOW, H. B., FITZHUGH, R. and KUFFLER, S. W. *J. Physiol.,* 1957, *137:*338–354.
4. BRINDLEY, G. S. *Physiology of the retina and the visual pathway.* London, Edward Arnold, Ltd., 1960.
5. BROWN, K. T. and MURAKAMI, M. I. *Nature (Lond.),* 1964, *201:*626–628; *ibid.,* 1964, *204:*739–740.
6. BROWN, K. T. and WATANABE, K. *Nature (Lond.),* 1962, *193:*958–960.
7. BROWN, K. and WIESEL, T. N. *Amer. J. Ophthal.,* 1953, *46* (No. 3, Pt. 2): 91–98.
8. BROWN, K. and WIESEL, T. N. *J. Physiol.,* 1959, *149:*537–562.
8a. BROWN, P. K. and WALD, G. *Nature (Lond.),* 1963, *200:* 37–43.
9. CAMPBELL, F. W. and RUSHTON, W. A. H. *J. Physiol.,* 1955, *130:*131–147.
9a. CONE, R. A. *Nature (Lond.),* 1964, *204:*736–739.
10. CREED, R. S. and RUCH, T. C. *J. Physiol.,* 1932, *74:*407–423.
10a. DAVSON, H., ed. *The eye,* vol. 2, *The visual process.* New York, Academic Press, 1962.
11. DITCHBURN, R. W. and GINSBORG, B. L. *J. Physiol.,* 1939, *119:*1–17.
12. GRAHAM, C. H. and GRANIT, R. *Amer. J. Physiol.,* 1931, *98:* 664–673.
13. GRAHAM, C. H. and HSIA, Y. *Proc. nat. Acad. Sci. (Wash.),* 1958, *44:*46–49.
14. GRANIT, R. *J. Neurophysiol.,* 1945, *8:*195–210; also *Nature (Lond.),* 1943, *151:*11–14.
15. GRANIT, R. *Receptors and sensory reception.* New Haven, Yale University Press, 1955.
16. HARTLINE, H. K. and RATLIFF, F. *J. gen. Physiol.,* 1958, *41:*1049–1066.
17. HECHT, S. Pp. 704–828 in *A handbook of general experimental psychology,* C. MURCHISON, ed. Worcester, Clark University Press, 1934.
18. HECHT, S. *Amer. Scientist,* 1944, *32:*159–177; also pp. 1–21 in *Visual mechanisms,* H. KLÜVER, ed. Lancaster, Pa., Jaques Cattell Press, 1942.
19. HECHT, S., HAIG, C. and CHASE, A. M. *J. gen. Physiol.,* 1937, *20:*831–850.
20. HSIA, Y. and GRAHAM, C. H. *Proc. nat. Acad. Sci. (Wash.),* 1957, *43:*1011–1019.
20a. HUBEL, D. H. and WIESEL, T. N. *Physiologist,* 1964, *7:* 162.
21. KUFFLER, S. *J. Neurophysiol.,* 1953, *16:*37–68.
22. LUCKIESH, M. and MOSS, F. K. *The science of seeing.* New York, Van Nostrand Co., 1937.
23. McFARLAND, R. A. and EVANS, J. N. *Amer. J. Physiol.,* 1939, *127:*37 50.
23a. MARKS, W. B., DOBELLE, W. H. and MacNICHOL, E. F., *Science,* 1964, *143:*1181–1183.
24. MILES, W. R. *Fed. Proc.,* 1943, *2:*109–115.
25. POLYAK, S. L. *The retina.* Chicago, University of Chicago Press, 1941.
25a. PRITCHARD, R. M. Chap. 15 in *The oculomotor system,* M. B. Bender, ed. New York, Harper & Row, 1964.
26. RATLIFF, F. and RIGGS, L. A. *J. exp. Psychol.,* 1950, *40:*687–701.
27. RIGGS, L. A., RATLIFF, F., CORNSWEET, J. C. and CORNSWEET, T. N. *J. opt. Soc. Amer.,* 1953, *43:*495–501.
28. RUSHTON, W. A. H. *Nature (Lond.),* 1957, *179:*571–573.
29. RUSHTON, W. A. H., *Nature (Lond.).,* 1958, *182:*690–692.
30. RUSHTON, W. A. H. *Ann. N. Y. Acad. Sci.,* 1958, *74:*291–304.
31. RUSHTON, W. A. H., CAMPBELL, F. W., HIGGINS, W. A. and BRINDLEY, G. S. *Optica acta,* 1955, *1:*183–190.
32. WALD, G. *J. gen. Physiol.,* 1935, *19:*351–371.
33. WALD, G. Pp. 1658–1667 in *Medical physics,* O. GLASSER, ed. Chicago, Year Book Medical Publishers, 1944.
34. WALD, G. Chap. 28 in *Handbook of physiology, Section 1: Neurophysiology,* vol. 1, J. Field, H. W. Magoun and V. E. Hall, eds. Washington, D.C., American Physiological Society, 1959.

34a. WALD, G. *Science,* 1964, *145:*1007–1016.

35. WALD, G. and CLARK, A. B. *J. gen. Physiol.,* 1937, *21:*93–105.

36. WALD, G., HARPER, P. V., JR., GOODMAN, H. C. and KRIEGER, H. P. *J. gen. Physiol.,* 1942, *25:*891–903.

37. WALLS, G. L. *The vertebrate eye and its adaptive radiation.* Bloomfield Hills, Mich., Cranbrook Institute of Science, 1942.

38. WEYMOUTH, F. W. *Amer. J. Ophthal.,* 1958, *46:*102–113.

39. YOUNG, T. *Phil. Trans.,* 1801, *92:*12–48.

CHAPTER 21

Binocular Vision and Central Visual Pathways

By THEODORE C. RUCH

VISUAL FIELDS AND BINOCULAR VISION

Visual Fields—Perimetry. By the visual field of an eye is meant the entire extent of the external world which can be seen without a change in the fixation of the eye. Because of the lens, the visual field is inverted upon the retina, so that objects in the upper visual field fall upon the lower half of the retina and objects in the right half of the visual field fall upon the left half of the retina. The retina is sensitive out to the ora serrata and, if the eye protruded sufficiently from its orbit, its visual field projected upon a flat surface would be a circle, the center of which would correspond to the fovea centralis. However, the nose, eyebrows and cheek bones cut off a considerable part of this field, giving it an irregular outline. The normal field of vision (Fig. 1) is therefore of little interest, but testing of the visual fields is an important clinical maneuver, especially in cases of suspected brain tumor.

To outline the visual field it is only necessary to keep the eye fixed and then to move a small object inward along a meridian until it is seen, keeping it at the same distance from the eye. This is repeated for each meridian and the results are combined upon an appropriate chart. An instrument, the perimeter, facilitates this process and is also useful for charting the peripheral fields. For plotting the central region of the visual field in detail, use is made of a large piece of black velvet marked off in degrees of visual angle and viewed from a distance of 1 meter (Bjerrum screen).

The outer zone of the retina has no color sensitivity. In this region, as ordinarily tested with light at moderate levels of illumination, a colored object gives rise only to an achromatic sensation. In passing toward the fovea color sensitivity develops gradually, the blue colors being perceived first and the greens last. The color zones of the retina may be plotted by means of a perimeter. Ferree and Rand[8] state that the color blindness of the periphery of the retina is relative and not absolute. An important innovation in perimetry is the use of the blind spot to control fixation and to detect formation of a pseudofovea (see below). For use of color and flicker fusion frequency in plotting visual fields, see Teuber et al.[31]

Binocular Vision. When the two eyes are fixed upon a point straight ahead, each eye has its own visual field that may be charted by

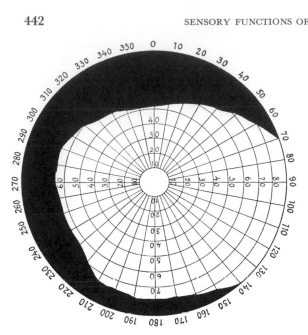

Fig. 1. Perimetric chart to show field of vision for *right* eye when eye looks straight ahead and does not move. Temporal field is to right, nasal to left of chart. Numbers along vertical and horizontal meridians are degrees of visual angle from center of fovea.

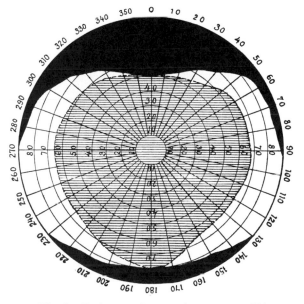

Fig. 2. Perimeter chart to show extent of binocular visual field. Shaded area is portion of visual field seen by both eyes; white areas at both sides are the monocular crescents seen only by extreme nasal portion of each retina.

means of the perimeter. But the two fields overlap for a considerable portion of their extent. This area of overlap constitutes the field of binocular vision (see Fig. 2). At both sides of this field is a region which can be seen by only one eye. It is known as the *monocular crescent,* or the *temporal half-moon.* Every point in the binocular field forms an image upon both retinas. Whether a given object is seen single or double depends upon whether its image does or does not fall upon corresponding points in the two retinas.

Corresponding points. Physiologically defined, corresponding points in the two retinas are those which, when simultaneously stimulated by the same luminous object, give a single sensation. Noncorresponding points are, of course, those which when so stimulated give two visual sensations. It is evident that the foveae form corresponding points or areas. When we look at any object, the visual axes of the two eyes converge upon and meet at the point looked at. If, while observing an object, one eyeball is gently pressed upon from the side, two images are seen, and they diverge farther and farther from each other as the pressure is increased. Experiment shows that portions of the retina symmetrically placed to the right side of the foveae correspond, and the same is true for the two left halves. The right half of the retina in one eye is noncorresponding to the left half of the other retina. Doubling of objects that do not fall on corresponding points is readily demonstrated for objects that lie either closer or farther away than the object looked at (physiologic diplopia). If one holds the two forefingers in the median plane, one close to the face and the other as far away as possible, the nearer finger is seen double when the eyes are fixed on the far one and vice versa. The reason for this is seen in Figure 3. In this same experiment, most people will find that closing one eye makes a finger appear out of line to one side, the right-hand finger being seen by the left eye and vice versa. If, when one eye is closed, the fingers stay lined up, the open eye is the dominant one. When both eyes are open this finger (image) out of line does not seem as clear as when only the heteronymous (opposite) is open. The image in this eye is partially suppressed.

Suppression of visual images. One of the images of an object falling upon noncorresponding points is usually ignored or suppressed. When failure to fix comes on suddenly, as in pressing

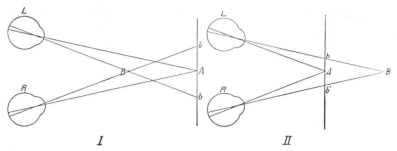

Fig. 3. Diagrams to show homonymous and heteronymous diplopia: In *I*, eyes are focused on *A*; images of *B* fall on noncorresponding points—that is, to different sides of foveae—and are seen double, being projected to plane of *A*, giving heteronymous diplopia. In *II*, eyes are focused on nearer point, *A*, and farther point, *B*, forms images on noncorresponding points and is seen double—homonymous diplopia—images being projected to focal plane *A*.

on one eyeball, double vision results. But in cases of long standing, the image from the abnormal eye is usually suppressed. The "suppressed" eye eventually shows a reduction or loss of visual ability, even blindness, when tested separately; this condition is called *amblyopia*.

Binocular rivalry. When the images of two dissimilar objects are thrown on corresponding parts of each retina, binocular rivalry ensues. If the image consists of vertical lines on one eye and horizontal lines on the other, only one field is seen at a time, first one, then the other; or the field is broken, vertical lines in part and horizontal lines in part. There is no genuine fusion in a continuous constant picture.

Judgments of solidity and depth.* Vision gives us knowledge not only of the surface area of objects, but also of their depth or solidity. The visual sensations upon which this conception is built are of several different kinds, partly monocular and partly binocular. If we close one eye and look at a bit of landscape or a solid object, we are conscious of the perspective, of the right relations of foreground and background. Nevertheless, it is true that with binocular vision the perception of depth and solidity are far more perfect. This is mainly because the slightly different views of an object given by the two eyes are subjectively combined to give the third dimension. This principle is illustrated by the stereoscope.

*Depth perception is measured with the Howard-Dolman apparatus. A short, upright rod is mounted 20 feet from the subject on a wire passing around a pulley. The two ends of the wire are manipulated by the subject until this rod and a stationary rod appear to be equidistant. The error is then measured and the average of repeated tests is made.

CENTRAL VISUAL PATHWAYS[24, 31]

Retina, Optic Nerve and Chiasm. The fibers composing the optic nerve originate in the ganglion cells of the inner layer of the retina. They converge to form the optic nerve and pierce the chorioid and scleral coats of the eyeball. Morphologically the point of convergence forms the optic nerve head, disc or papilla; physiologically it produces a *blind spot* in the visual field because only nerve fibers are present at that point. The nerve head lies 15° to the nasal side of the fovea centralis; because the lens reverses spatial relationships, the blind spot is 15° to the temporal side in the visual field.

Fibers from the macula lutea are numerous and form a distinct bundle running horizontally to the nerve head, the *maculopapillary bundle*. Fibers to the nasal side of the nerve head pursue a direct course like the spokes of a wheel. Since no fibers pass through the fovea, fibers from the temporal portion of the retina arch above or loop below the fovea centralis, forming a geometrically sharp "watershed" along a horizontal line drawn through the fovea to the temporal margin of the retina. In this fashion, the temporal retinal fibers (and some of the fibers of the nasal half) become separated into an upper and a lower quadrant by the interposition of the macular fibers,† an arrangement continued throughout the central visual pathways.

A vertical line drawn through the macula divides the retina into two hemimaculas and

† In discussion of the central visual pathways, the terms "macula" and "macular" do not always mean the region of the macula lutea. In clinical literature, these are almost synonyms for "central," and denote any central zone less than about 10° of visual angle.

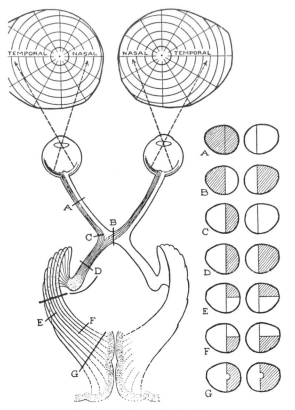

Fig. 4. Diagram of central visual pathways passing to left hemisphere. Shaded areas in inserts indicate visual field defects resulting from lesions at point indicated by corresponding letter on left-hand figure. For convenience, visual fields for two eyes are shown separated, but actually they superimpose so that vertical meridians coincide: *A,* complete blindness of left eye; *B,* bitemporal hemianopsia; *C,* unilateral nasal hemianopsia; *D,* right homonymous hemianopsia—interruption of either optic tract or geniculocalcarine projection; *E* and *F,* right upper and lower quadrant hemianopsias; *G,* right homonymous hemianopsia from a large lesion of occipital lobe. (From Homans, *A text-book of surgery,* 5th ed., Springfield, Ill., Charles C Thomas, 1941.)

hemiretinas. Fibers from the temporal hemiretina of the left eye continue through the *optic chiasm* and, without crossing, pass in the optic tract to the *lateral geniculate body* of the left side; those from the temporal side of the right eye enter the right optic tract (Fig. 4). Fibers from the nasal half of each retina decussate in the optic chiasm and enter the optic tract of the opposite cerebral hemisphere, where they join the uncrossed fibers from the temporal half of the other eye, thence to the lateral geniculate body. Thus, the termination for fibers from the nasal half of the retina is contralateral. Because of

this regrouping of fibers, lesions of the optic chiasm, or central to it, cause visual defects different from those induced by lesions of the retina or optic nerve.

The effects of lesions at various points in the visual system upon the visual fields of the two eyes are shown in Figure 4. It is also profitable to consider their effect on the field of vision when both eyes are open. From complete interruption of one optic nerve there is, on the same side as the lesion, a slight lateral narrowing of the field of vision when both eyes are open. This is due to loss of vision in one temporal half-moon (seen only by the extreme nasal portion of the ipsilateral retina). However, interruption of the visual pathway central to the chiasm on one side blocks impulses from *both* eyes, conveying impressions from one-half the binocular visual field plus one temporal half-moon. The result of such a lesion in, for example, the left hemisphere is a visual field defect known as *right lateral homonymous hemianopsia*—"half-blindness" because the blindness extends over a geometric half of the visual field; "homonymous" because the corresponding halves of the two retinas are blinded; "lateral" because nothing to one side is seen; and "right" because the disturbance is named for the side of the visual field defect, not for the side of the "retinal blindness." The lesion is always on the side opposite the visual field defect.

Occurring less commonly, an expanding tumor of the pituitary body, the stalk of which is located in the bay formed by the two optic tracts, may split the decussating fibers from the nasal half of each retina, producing a *bitemporal hemianopsia;* then only the nasal half of each visual field is seen. Similarly, a pathologic expansion of both internal carotid arteries lying in the angle formed by the optic nerve and tract of each side may interrupt the fibers from the two temporal hemiretinas, yielding a *binasal hemianopsia.* These are *heteronymous* because noncorresponding retinal fields of the two eyes are affected and little restriction is noticeable when both eyes are open.

Between the optic chiasm and the lateral geniculate bodies optic tract fibers, or collaterals from them, representing every portion of the hemiretinas, pass to the pretectal region lying just rostral to the superior colliculus. This group of fibers constitutes the afferent limb of the pupillary reflexes to light. These fibers were once believed to end in the superior colliculus, but now are known to end in the pretectal region.[19, 26] Hemianopsia *with* retention of the light reflex therefore characterizes lesions central to this regrouping. The "visual fibers" continue to the lateral geniculate body of the diencephalon, where they enter synaptic relations with the fourth order neurons, which continue on to the occipital lobe.

Lateral Geniculate Bodies and Geniculostriate Bundle. This nucleus is made up of six layers of cells separated by layers of fibers, giving the structure its conspicuous laminated appearance. Alternate layers of fibers are contributed by the hemiretinas of the two eyes.[4] Impulses from corresponding retinal points presumably first converge in the occipital cortex, which makes fusion a cortical function. In the monkey each optic nerve fiber breaks up into a spray of five or six branches, each branch ending by means of a *single* bouton related to the cell body (never the dendrites) of a neuron of the lateral geniculate body.[11] This is a remarkable instance of *divergence* and is the only known instance in which a cell is excited by single synapse stimulation.

By transneuronal[5] and Marchi[1] degeneration studies, the projection of the retina upon the lateral geniculate body has been established. Note in Figure 5 that the macular sector is interposed between sectors containing fibers from the upper and lower extramacular quadrants and that the lower retinal quadrant is lateral. Note also that, relative to its small retinal area, the macula is represented by a disproportionate amount of the nucleus. The oral-caudal relationship is the same as in the retina, i.e., the macular region is posterior to the periphery in both.

Fourth order neurons constituting the geniculostriate bundle, especially the inferior part, swing forward and around the ventricle of the temporal lobe before running posteriorly to the striate area of the occipital lobe. *Meyer's loop* or *detour*, so formed, accounts for the occurrence of visual field defects from lesions well forward in the temporal lobe (Cushing).

As the geniculostriate bundle enters the occipital pole, the macular fibers separate those from the upper and lower quadrants. Those representing the upper quadrant of the retina pass above the tip of the posterior horn and end in the superior lip of the calcarine fissure; those representing the lower retinal quadrant pass below the horn and end on the lower lip of the calcarine fissure. The macular fibers swing around the end of the ventricle and can be traced mainly to the posterior part of the calcarine fissure. The interposition of macular fibers between peripheral ones explains how a quadrant visual field defect having a sharp horizontal border can occur. An irregularly shaped pathologic process could produce a quadrant defect with a geometrically shaped horizontal boundary only if the fibers from the two quadrants were to some degree topographically separated as they are by intervening macular fibers.

Careful perimetry in cases of gunshot wounds has disclosed fields incompatible with the above arrangement of the visual radiation, e.g., sector-shaped field defects sometimes lying along the horizontal meridian.[29, 31] Also, quadrant defects having a sharp, straight, vertical border may fall short of or pass across the horizontal meridian. To explain these cases Spalding[29] has proposed that in the anterior portion of the geniculostriate bundle "the fibers subserving central vision are spread over the lateral aspect of the radiation, tending to congregate towards the intermediate point, whereas fibers subserving peripheral vision are spread out on the medial aspect, tending to congregate at the upper and lower margins." This is illustrated in Figure 6. Because of the exposed lateral posi-

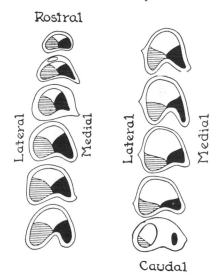

Rostral

Lateral   Medial   Lateral   Medial

Caudal

Fig. 5. Sections through left lateral geniculate body of monkey. Terminations of fibers from retina are indicated as follows: *hatched area*, lower peripheral quadrant; *white*, macula, upper and lower quadrants; *black*, upper peripheral quadrant. According to the work of Le Gros Clark and Penman, this diagram shows too much macula at rostral end and too much peripheral representation at caudal end. (After Brouwer and Zeeman, *Brain*, 1926, *49:*1–35.)

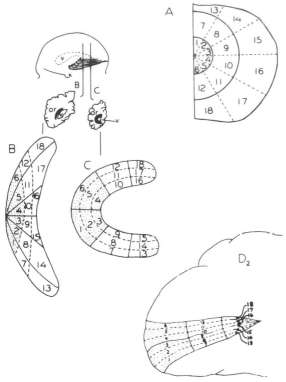

Fig. 6. Diagram of a hypothetical representation of the right homonymous visual field (*A*) and the corresponding fibers that serve this field in the anterior (*B*) and posterior (*C*) parts of the left optic radiation and along the lip (*D*) of the calcarine fissure. (After J. M. K. Spalding, from Teuber *et al., Visual field defects after penetrating missile wounds of the brain.* Cambridge, Mass., Harvard University Press, 1960.)

tions of the fibers representing the horizontal meridian, this sector of the retinal field would be, as is the case, most often affected.

Macular Sparing.[25] A hemianopsia which includes macular vision is rarely caused by lesions of the occipital lobe. More often, the vertical or median border of the blind area is not a straight line ("macular splitting") but is indented so that 3° to 5° of central vision are "spared." Noted by Forster,[9] who in 1867 introduced the perimeter for the study of neurologic patients, macular sparing has been an intriguing neurologic puzzle for nearly a century.

The macula may escape when ischemia damages the cortical receiving area, because the macular projection area receives a double blood supply; its fibers may therefore be relatively less affected. In patients with bilateral thrombosis of the posterior calcarine artery, macular vision is spared. Other times the macula may escape although peripheral vision is affected because the latter is represented by so few fibers that

functional loss caused by pressure or ischemia has a greater effect on it. Some patients deviate their eyes slightly and form a pseudofovea (Fig. 7). However, Teuber *et al.*[31] have demonstrated that the "blind spot" is found in its normal position in some cases so that true macular sparing must exist.

Macular sparing after extensive surgical resections of the occipital lobe cannot be accounted for by either of the first two factors mentioned above. Two explanations have been advanced: (i) that the macular region is bilaterally represented in the cerebral cortex, and (ii) that the macula is extensively localized throughout the striate area so that only rarely is the whole representation destroyed. This might be accomplished without intermixing of macular and peripheral representations if the macular field extends forward, as shown in Figure 9. This would make an absolute central scotoma difficult to explain. To the first there are serious objections.[10, 30] For example, electrical activity is detectable in the macular representation of the left occipital lobe only when light is flashed upon the left hemimaculas of the eyes. Electrical responses of both striate areas suggestive of bilateral representation have never been observed. However, interest in this possibility has revived because some degree of macular sparing occurs in lesions of the tract and geniculate bodies, suggesting that crossing might occur lower in the system. In this case how an occipital lesion could ever cause splitting becomes the puzzle. Studies by Glickstein *et al.*[11a] with the Nauta technique for staining small degenerating axons rather than myelin sheaths of large axons are revealing visual fibers crossing in the corpus callosum to Area 18. If they serve visual sensation, they would explain macular sparing from posterior lesions and splitting from more anterior ones.

There is some presumptive evidence for diffuse localization of the macula, since macular sparing occurs in some lesions of the optic radiations, but electrical studies do not bear out this theory. However, the macular region may be more extensively localized anteriorly than was suggested in the previous section. That the macula is heavily represented at the posterior end of the calcarine fissure has been firmly grounded anatomically by mapping the visual cortex in monkeys.[30] Yet lobectomies which fall short of destroying the whole extent of the calcarine fissure tend to spare the macula; whereas, if resection is carried out farther for-

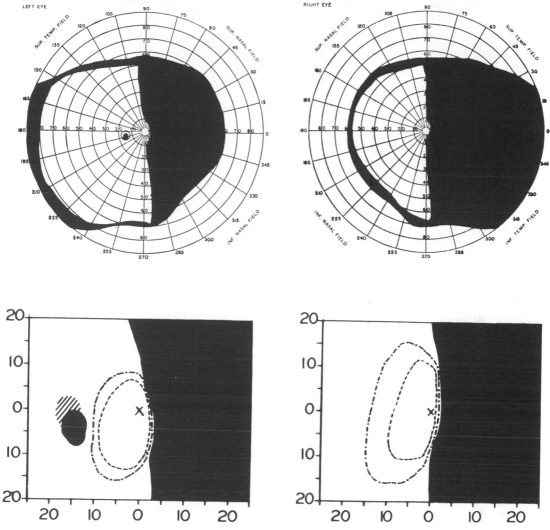

Fig. 7. Right homonymous "macular sparing" visual field defect presumably due to a shifting of fixation (pseudo-fovea). Note the indentation on the vertical boundary of the unseen portion of the visual field. In the lower half of the figure are plots of the central visual fields. The blind spot is displaced 4° to 5° downward and 2° to 3° to the right from the normal position (cross hatching). Dotted circles are color fields for green (inner) and red (outer) and are normally more nearly coincident. The ordinates and abscissae are in degrees from the center of the campimeter. (From Teuber *et al., Visual field defects after penetrating missile wounds of the brain.* Cambridge, Mass., Harvard University Press, 1960.)

ward to include the extreme anterior tip of the striate area, macular vision is not spared. It is almost necessary to suppose that the macular area extends farther forward than the representation of the peripheral retinal zones.

CORTICAL VISUAL AREAS

The cortical visual area in man is almost completely concealed from view in a longitudinal infolding on the mesial and cerebellar surfaces of the occipital lobe, the *calcarine* fissure. Cytoarchitecturally the region is characterized by a conspicuous line of Gennari visible to the naked eye without staining and often called the *striate area.* The cellular structure (Fig. 8) is the highly granular type associated elsewhere in the cerebral cortex with sensory function because of the great development of the outer and inner granular layers. The striate area, which is Area 17 in Brodmann's numeration, is surrounded by a concentric band, Area 18 or the *parastriate*

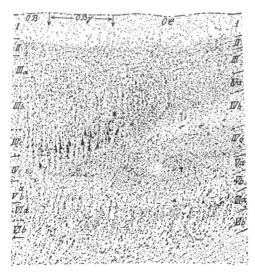

Fig. 8. Cytoarchitecture of transition zone (*asterisk*) between Area 17 (*right*) and Area 18 (*left*) of upper lip of calcarine fissure. On right (*striate area*) note that inner and outer layers of pyramidal cells are virtually absent. The almost clear area, *IVb,* corresponds to line of Gennari. Observe band of large pyramidal cells in layer *IIIc* of Area 18. Cell stain and 44× magnification. (From von Economo, *Zellaufbau der Grosshirnrinde des Menschen,* Berlin, J. Springer, 1927.)

cortex, and between them is an exceedingly abrupt transition in cytoarchitecture. A second more anterior concentric zone is the *peristriate* area, Brodmann's Area 19. The optic radiations terminate mainly in Area 17; some including crossing axons pass to Area 18.

Topographic Organization. Knowledge of the way fibers of the optic radiations terminate in the cerebral cortex aids in the diagnosis of damage to the occipital pole and permits deductions about function; clinical and anatomical studies have been followed by macro- and microelectrode recordings yielding greater detail and a greater wealth of functional interpretations.

As shown in Figure 9, the representation of the upper quadrant of the *retina* is on the upper lip of the calcarine fissure; that of the lower retinal quadrant is on the lower lip of the fissure. Thus lesions of the lower lip, for example, produce a defect in the upper quadrant of the visual field. Much evidence[13, 23] indicates that the anteroposterior dimension of the striate area corresponds to the periphery-macula (meridional) dimension of the retina. The rule is that the macula is posterior in the eye, and its representation is posterior in the lateral geniculate body and posterior in the occipital lobe. The

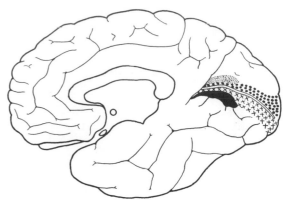

Fig. 9. Projection of retina upon calcarine fissure of man. Fine dots and black are, respectively, representation of upper and lower *peripheral* quadrants of retina; heavy dots and crosses are, respectively, representation of upper and lower quadrants of *macula.* Rostral extension of macular representation is hypothetical. (Modified from Brouwer, *Res. Publ. Ass. nerv. ment. Dis.,* 1934, *13:*529–534.)

periphery is most anterior at these three levels. As in the geniculate body, the area of cortex devoted to the macula is very large compared to the area for the periphery.

How this arrangement came about may be easily visualized as follows: Imagine the left hemiretinas of the two eyes superimposed with their foveae coinciding. They are then folded forward from top to bottom along the horizontal meridian and inserted into the calcarine fissure with the fold coming at the bottom of the fissure and the point (fovea) posterior. If the meridians are imagined as closing like the blades of a Japanese fan, it becomes clear that the periphery will be located anteriorly. But this fails to suggest that a larger cortical area is devoted to the fovea than to the periphery. The ribs at the handle end of the fan would have to be farther apart to have the relations that exist in the cortex. Note that the free edges of the infolded retinas are the two halves of the vertical meridian which are *vis à vis* to the vertical meridian of the right hemiretinas located in the opposite hemisphere. This explains why midline lesions affecting both occipital lobes may produce a confluent midline scotoma of the right and left visual fields.

If this arrangement is correct, it means that at the occipital lobe the macular fibers for the first time cease to lie interposed between the upper and lower peripheral quadrant fibers. Such a rearrangement is somewhat unlikely. It is possible that the macular fibers do not all pass to the posterior end of the calcarine fissure, but form a wedge, the point of which is directed forward, separating the upper and lower quadrants as shown in Figure 9. Some evidence demands that a portion of the macular fibers extend even farther forward than the peripheral fibers.

Congruence of Field Defects.[31] The more carefully visual fields are plotted, the clearer it becomes that homonymous visual fields have the same general shape but are not strictly identical or congruent. Such incongruence is manifest along the vertical border of an hemianopsia and along the margins of a scotoma. Minor incongruence from lesions in or near the geniculate bodies presents no problem, since the contributions from the two eyes do not fuse in the geniculate body; further, macular fibers may spread diffusely in the radiation and then reunite. However, visual fusion is supposed to involve convergence at the striate cortex level so that a scotoma should show a mathematical congruence, although it never does. Electrophysiologic evidence throws some light on this problem.

Functional Significance of Topographic Organization. What is the significance of the topographic organization of the occipital lobe? Is it simply an engineering convenience, or is it the neural basis for detail vision, vision of forms and patterns and visual localization? Is it possible to think that the pattern of light on the retina is translated into a pattern of impulses on the occipital cortex with each unit holding its topographic position relative to other units? That this is the case is suggested by the fact that minute injuries of the cortex produce contiguous areas of blindness of the visual field. That the retina is projected point-to-point on the cortex is confirmed anatomically within the limits of our techniques. Thus, Polyak[23] finds that a lesion of the occipital cortex 1 sq. mm. in extent causes a degeneration confined to a single band of cells in the geniculate body only four to five cells wide. Moreover, the extent of the striate cortex devoted to the fovea justifies belief that the fineness of grain in the occipital cortex is the basis for the high degree of visual acuity exhibited by the fovea.

Talbot and Marshall[22, 30] recorded the points of maximal electrical activity in the striate area of the monkey while systematically exploring the retina with a point of light. The foveal representation is situated at the anterior border of the striate area on the lateral surface of the occipital lobe not far from the ear (Fig. 10). This region becomes posterior when the striate area largely disappears from the free surface of the cortex in the chimpanzee and man as a result of an expansion of the parietal association area. Even in the monkey, only 8° of the periphery (little more than the macular area) is on the wide expanse of the free surface of the occipital cortex. The first 8° are arranged in concentric bands medial to the fovea. The portion of the striate area devoted to the hemifovea is 6 mm. in radius. Retinal distance and cortical distance compare

as follows: within the foveal representation, 1 mm. of cortex is devoted to only 2' of visual angle; whereas at the representation for 5° from the fovea, 18' of visual angle are crowded into 1 mm. Much greater ratios must obtain for the extreme peripheral regions of the retina. This is borne out when the buried as well as the exposed visual cortex of the baboon is mapped out from reconstructed results of many recordings from penetrating electrodes.[7] In moving from the foveal to the peripheral representation in the cortex (Fig. 11), it can be seen that cortex available for visual discrimination decreases rapidly, little being available to serve the periphery of the retina. The falling off is equal in all

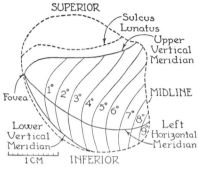

Fig. 10. Map showing projection of retina upon occipital lobe of monkey as charted by electrical methods. Left occipital lobe is shown as viewed from behind; foreshortening decreases apparent size of central representation. (Redrawn from Talbot and Marshall, *Amer. J. Ophthal.,* 1941, *24*:1255–1264.)

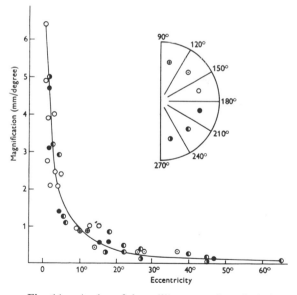

Fig. 11. A plot of the millimeters of cortical distance devoted to each degree of the visual field for central and peripheral areas (eccentricity), showing the rapidity of fall-off in magnification and that it is equal in all directions. The data for six radii have been grouped. (From Daniel and Whitteridge, *J. Physiol.,* 1961, *159*:203–221.)

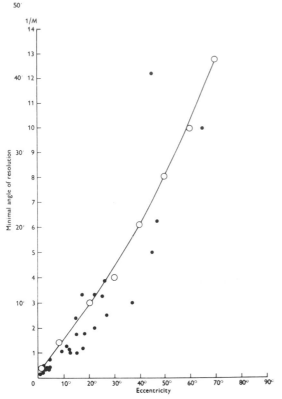

Fig. 12. The minimal angle of resolution in minutes for man (open circles) (from Weymouth's data) and the reciprocal of the degrees of visual field served by one millimeter of cortex (monkey) are both plotted against degrees of arc from the fovea. (Daniel and Whitteridge, *J. Physiol.*, 1961, *159*:203–221.)

meridians. The degrees of visual field served by a millimeter of cortex is called by Daniel and Whitteridge[7] the "magnification factor." At the fovea this magnification is more than 6, which, analogous to light magnification, is consistent with the fact that one sees finer detail in this region.

Figure 12 shows that the minimal angle of resolution (MAR) and the reciprocal of the amount of cortex devoted to each degree of visual field agree quite well throughout the retina. It appears to take an equal amount of cortex to do an equally fine discrimination whether in the periphery or in the fovea. For the monkey 67 μ of cortical distance, the width of about 5 cells in the densest part of layer IV, corresponds to the minimal angle of resolution measured at the fovea.[7]

Magnification of the retina on the striate cortex can be determined in yet another way. In the monkey the number of cells in the lateral geniculate body is approximately the same as the number of fibers in the optic nerve, on the order of 1,000,000. In the striate cortex the number of cells increases to more than 145,000,000. Talbot and Marshall calculate that a circular foveal area 1′ in diameter (5 μ, or the width of 2 foveal cones) is represented by a cortical region 100 times as wide (0.5 mm.) with an area 10,000 times as great.

With nerve cells spaced at 20 μ, the ratio between cone and cortical cell is 1:100.

In the physical transmission of light to the retina, the energy tends to spread over a wide region, and in neural transmission there is a further tendency for lateral spread of excitation; yet the cortical grain is finer than the retinal grain. As seen in Chapter 19, acuity is a question of discrimination of intensity differences between peaks and valleys of excitation, discriminations much less than cone width are theoretically possible because of the fine cortical grain. An offset in a line of only 2.5″ of visual angle (vernier acuity of "aligning power") is discriminable. Perhaps the fine cortical mosaic is used for such discriminations or for registering the slight differences in the images seen by the two eyes which form the basis of stereoscopic vision. On the other hand, the multiplicity of units may be significant for intensity discrimination, the number of active units being one way of reflecting intensity.

FUNCTIONAL ABILITIES OF SINGLE NEURONS

Cortical destruction, experimentally or pathologically produced, gives insight into the kinds of visual function in which given areas participate. The recordings of evoked potentials from a small area, but with many hundreds of cortical cells, reveals much information about the organization of the visual projection system. The recording by Hubel and Wiesel[13, 14, 15] from single cortical units, especially with respect to the organization of their receptive fields, has in recent years given insight into how the cerebral cortex analyzes the spatial aspects of a stimulus object.

Receptive Fields of Geniculate Neurons. The frog, which is adept at detecting and catching small insects, can apparently accomplish at the ganglion cell level some of the detection and rejection[22a] which in mammals requires the geniculate bodies and cerebral cortex.

Even in the monkey the geniculate bodies seem to accomplish little more than the retina.[14] Like the rods of the retina, some geniculate cells (Type III) have no color sensitivity.[17] Other cells (Type I) respond to white light and to monochromatic stimulation of the retina.[17] In both cases their receptive fields are round and, like the receptive field of ganglion cells, divided into a central field and a surrounding concentric ring, with mutual antagonism between the field and the ring.[14] (For some geniculate cells specific color cones acting antagonistically to one another are spread evenly throughout the receptive field.) Light falling on the periphery of a receptive field for a typical geniculate cell inhibits responses to the stimulation of the central zone and vice versa. The notable difference between geniculate and ganglion cells is the greater ability of the inhibitory surrounds of the geniculate cells to inhibit responses to stimulation of an excitatory center. This accounts for the initially puzzling fact that diffuse illumination of the retina produces very little activity or even none in many geniculate cells.

Simple Cortical Neurons.[13, 15] Although the receptive fields of many visual cortical neurons have the mutually antagonistic center and peripheral zone, the field is never round. The receptive field of a *simple* cortical neuron is often a long and narrow ellipse or oval, the division between center and periphery being a straight line; often the fields are not bilaterally symmetrical, the peripheral cells being massed on one side and few on the other side of the elongated slender center. This may be carried to the degree that the annular structure is replaced by an excitatory and inhibitory field lying side by

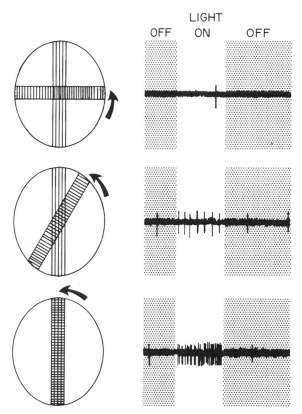

Fig. 14. Behavior of a line detector neuron of the striate area. At the left is shown the orientation of the horizontal illuminated slit in relation to the vertical elongated excitatory center of the receptive field and at the right the action potentials of the cortical neuron. The amount of cortical discharge depends on the mixture of excitation (center) and inhibition (periphery) discharge onto the cortical cell. (After Hubel, *Scientific American*, 1963, *209*:54–62.)

side (as *g* in Fig. 13). The division between center and periphery or between halves of an unsymmetrical field is always a straight line. The orientation of this axis varies from cell to cell and may be up, down, or in all intervening degrees of obliqueness (compare *a* with *c*, Fig. 13).

Even the symmetrical simple cell has potentialities for spatial discrimination, because the shape and spatial orientation of the stimulus are critical to the neuron's responsiveness. As in Figure 14, an elongated light patch may produce no discharge if it is at right angles to the axes of the receptive field, because it includes the inhibitory fringe. A thin slit of light or the edge of an object properly oriented may produce a massive discharge. This means that the retina is concerned with lines (and with the con-

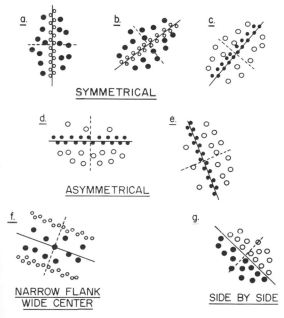

Fig. 13. Receptive field of single cortical neuron of the "simple" variety (filled circles are inhibitory and open circles excitatory). Continuous line represents the axis of the field and may be vertical, horizontal or oblique. Inhibitory and excitatory units may or may not be evenly distributed on each side of the axis, but the over-all contour of the receptive field is never round. (After Hubel and Wiesel, *J. Physiol.,* 1959, *148*:574–591.)

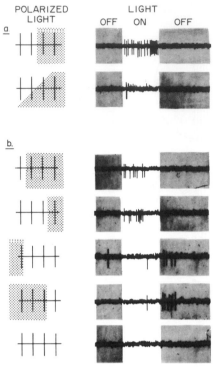

Fig. 15. The behavior of a "complex" cortical cell in the visual area to various illuminations of its large receptive field ($8 \times 16°$). The vertical and horizontal lines are used to suggest that simple cells with similarly oriented receptive fields are connected with the complex cell, the response of which is shown by the record at the right. The contour of the light patch is critical, since the cell is a detector of vertical lines. Note that in *a* there is a train of responses to the vertical contour but only one response to the sloping one. The first two records of *b* show the discharge of the same complex visual cell (shown in *a*) to a light patch occupying the left portion of the receptive field. Note that the cortical cell discharges wherever the edge falls in the receptive fields in contrast with simple cells which discharge only as the edge passes the line separating the inhibitory from the excitatory parts of the receptive field. When light occupies the right side of the field, the discharge occurs when the light is off, but again is about the same wherever the edge falls. When the whole field is illuminated, there is no response. (From Hubel and Wiesel, *J. Physiol.*, 1962, *160*:106–154.)

tours of objects*) and that the orientation of a stationary contour can be detected. Since cells having receptive fields with widely varying axial orientations are intermingled in a given cortical area, some cells will be maximally responding even though the orientation of the contour is shifting. While this could be interpreted by the

* Internal details of an object can be resolved into lines and contours. See Chapter 20.

brain as movement, bilateral asymmetry of single receptive fields seems to provide certain single cortical neurons with the ability to detect the direction of movement.

Cells having a thin inhibitory fringe on one side and a fat one on the other respond differently to a contour oriented to its axis, depending on the direction from which it approaches. When the edge of a light patch approaches from the side of the thin fringe, a strong discharge occurs; on approach from the other side, the inhibitory fringe suppresses the center and, in extreme cases, no discharge occurs. A *single* cortical cell with properly organized field and a properly oriented axis could provide the information for knowing the direction of an object's movement. The cerebral cortex probably never behaves in quite such a simple fashion. Nevertheless, the basic device—the structuring of the receptive field—is a simple way of analyzing the lines and contours of the external world into modal points of heightened neuronal activity.

Complex Cortical Neurons. The receptive fields of "complex cells" are homogeneous rather than separated into excitatory and inhibitory zones but are even more sensitive to the orientation of a straight line or contour than are simple cells.[15] In fact, a straight contour can be detected anywhere in the field. The response of a typical complex neuron might be excitatory if the stimulus occupies the left portion and inhibitory if it occupies the right (Fig. 15). However, complex neuron behavior differs from simple cell behavior (such as *g* in Fig. 13) in that the complex cell fires in some degree wherever the contour of the object impinges on the field rather than just at the border between inhibitory and excitatory fields.

Hubel and Wiesel[15] explain this behavior with a scheme involving a direct connection of the complex cell with simple striate area cells. They suggest that a complex cell is connected with several simple cells having the same excitatory and inhibitory field organization and axes with the same spatial orientation and distribution throughout the entire extent of the complex neuron's receptive field. This hypothesis is strengthened by the fact that simple cells having receptive fields in roughly the same retinal area and having the same inhibitory-excitatory field organization are arranged in surface-to-depth columns in the striate cortex. The arrangement greatly reduces the number of fibers needed to connect many simple cells with the complex cell and enable it to abstract a common property of contour orientation.

Because the retinal position of simple cells is

distributed over a certain small area, the complex cell could record the orientation, to some degree independently of position and hence of fine random eye movements.

Hypercomplex Cortical Neurons. About 5 to 10 per cent of the cells in Brodmann Area 18 and more than half of those in Area 19 are termed "hypercomplex."[16] As with complex cells, they respond especially well to borders of a stimulus object and, to stimulate effectively, the border must coincide with the axis of the receptive field of the unit. However, if this coincidence is too elongated, the unit's response may be inhibited. The receptive field of a hypercomplex cell seems to be broken up into activating and antagonistic fields, arranged end to end along an axis. The antagonistic field thus "stoppers" the response at one or both ends. Some hypercomplex cells appear to have two axes at right angles to each other so that a cross is an effective stimulus pattern. As in Area 17, cortical neurons with the same general receptive field orientation are found in the same cellular column. Hypercomplex cells are thought to receive axons from two complex cells (or groups of cells) whose fields lie end to end, one being inhibitory and one excitatory to the hypercomplex neuron. An inhibitory-excitatory-inhibitory arrangement of a field ("stoppered at both ends") would require three complex cells or groups of cells. An occasional hypercomplex cell with two axes of orientation could result from convergence on it of two hypercomplex cells, each with single axes and oriented 90° from one another. Hubel and Wiesel[16] point out the implications of these studies to perception somewhat as follows. In the striate area the complex cells respond well to the contours of forms. The border will activate those complex cells whose fields are (i) crossed by the boundary and (ii) oriented in the direction of the boundary. Hypercomplex cells would be especially sensitive to corners or curved contours since they would avoid the end antagonistic zone. Such studies hold promise for the eventual understanding of the neural basis of perception.

VISUAL FUNCTIONS OF STRIATE AREA

The role of the cerebral cortex in vision increases steadily throughout the phylogenetic series. The great visual acuity of birds and fish, which is legendary, is subserved entirely by subcortical structures. In the mammalian series, visual function becomes progressively corticalized or encephalized until, in primates, the superior colliculi serve largely reflex functions. A corollary of the increasing importance of the cortex is therefore that the cerebral cortex is essential for certain types of visual function, whereas other types can be carried on by subcortical structures.

In man, occipital lobectomy abolishes all types of visual discrimination—light from dark, lights of different intensities, colors and patterns (form), but in animals some visual ability is sustained by subcortical levels. Visual discrimination in animals is tested by establishing the habit of choosing between two differently illuminated alleys or stimulus objects in order to receive food. In rats, cats and dogs[21, 28] discrimination of light from dark, a rod function, survives complete removal of the striate areas. The ability to discriminate may be temporarily lost, but it seems to be merely the discriminatory habit which is upset because the discrimination itself is readily relearned. The fineness of discrimination is decreased, but not greatly so. In monkeys, the disturbance is more severe, but even these animals can relearn.

When discrimination between two bright lights or between patterns (form) is tested, functions involving cone vision, the opposite result is obtained. Such discriminations are not possible after destruction of the striate areas. Even in the rat, pattern vision is impossible and no amount of retraining restores the ability.

Much evidence indicates that the two categories of results reflect the duality of vision so obvious at the retina. The clinching evidence is based on the fact that monkeys exhibit rod and cone visibility curves similar to man's. After ablation of the occipital lobes, the monkey's visibility curve even at high illumination is that characteristic of rods.[19] The conclusion therefore is that rod vision is not corticalized to the same extent as cone vision, and that even in the monkey rod vision can be carried out at subcortical levels of the brain. However, pattern vision demands a topographically organized system of fibers consisting of multiple discrete units such as the foveal cones and their central connections provide.

Levels of Visual Function. Whether scotomata involve an all-or-nothing impairment of vision throws light on the function of the visual area. Teuber and his co-workers[31] have shown that in man scotomata should be interpreted in terms of levels of function. In the recovery from damage as opposed to destruction (and in passing from a stable scotoma to a normal part of the field) the defect is not equal for all visual functions. First to recover is a sensation of light without color, shape or direction. Awareness of movement returns early, but its direction or rate cannot be appreciated. When object vision returns the contours are fuzzy; and color is last to return. Appreciation of flicker is a sensitive test of cortical damage; areas bordering on a scotoma apparently normal in ordinary perimetry show a lowered cortical fusion frequency. In view of the supposed chemical nature of dark adaptation, it is surprising that the curve of dark adaptation falls slowly and never reaches normal low levels, nor does it show the cone-rod inflection (Chap. 20).

Areas 18 and 19.[3] These areas surrounding the striate area are strongly developed in the primates and are concerned with vision. Evidence indicates they are efferent as well as sensory. Stimulation of them induces eye movements (Chap. 12).

As is true of the somesthetic and auditory areas, there are a visual area II and a visual area III, each having some topographic organization.[16, 30] These areas coincide with cytoarchitectural Areas 18 and 19 respectively. The latency of the evoked responses in them, and their failure to survive ablation of Area 17, together with electrical and histologic evidence of connections of Area 17 with 18 and 19, qualify these areas as "association areas."[6, 16] However, the receipt of a thalamic projection system, as supported by anatomic[11a] and electrophysiologic evidence, makes them, like other so-called association areas (Chap. 23), difficult to identify electrophysiologically. The receptive fields of many single cells in Areas 18 and 19, like those in 17, respond to edges and lines, critically oriented in respect to the axis of the receptive field.[16] No simple cells are found outside visual area I. In Area 18, as noted previously, 5 to 10 per cent of the cells are hypercomplex, (the remainder are complex), while in Area 19 this increases to 58 per cent, indicating a higher level of sensory function. As brought out above, hypercomplex cells are superimposed on complex cells, giving meaning to the phrase "elaboration of input to visual area I" by the surrounding visual areas.

Several skilled investigators have sought by a wide variety of objective behavior techniques to discover disturbances of higher visual ability after destruction of this region. As we have seen, a great deal of higher visual function seems to be carried out by the primary receptive areas rather than by the intervention of association areas. Nevertheless, some brain activity of the highest levels involving visual function is performed by and carried out by association areas

sometimes at a considerable distance from the visual area. The subject, therefore, merges into the general problem of association area functions and will be discussed later (Chap. 23).

REFERENCES

1. BROUWER, B. and ZEEMAN, W. P. C. *Brain*, 1926, *49*:1–35.
2. CHOW, K.-L., BLUM, J. S., and BLUM, R. A. *J. comp. Neurol.*, 1950, *92*:227–239.
3. CHOW, K.-L. and HUTT, P. J. *Brain*, 1953, *76*:625–677.
4. CLARK, W. E. LE GROS. *Brit. J. Ophthal.*, 1932, *16*:264–284.
5. CLARK, W. E. LE GROS and PENMAN, G. G. *Proc. roy. Soc.*, 1934, *B114*:291–313.
6. COWEY, A. *J. Neurophysiol.*, 1964, *27*:366–393.
7. DANIEL, P. M. and WHITTERIDGE, D. *J. Physiol.*, 1961, *159*:203–221.
8. FERREE, C. E. and RAND, G. *Psychol. Rev.*, 1919, *26*:16–41, 150–163.
9. FORSTER, R. *Klin. Mbl. Augenheilk.*, 1867, *5*:293–294.
10. FOX, J. C., JR. and GERMAN, W. J. *Arch. Neurol. Psychiat. (Chic.)*, 1936, *35*:808–826.
11. GLEES, P. and CLARK, W. E. LE GROS. *J. Anat. (Lond.)*, 1941, *75*:295–308.
11a. GLICKSTEIN, M., MILLER, J. and RUCH, T. C. *Fed. Proc.*, 1964, *23*:209.
12. HOLMES, G. and LISTER, W. T. *Brain*, 1916, *39*:34–73.
13. HUBEL, D. H. and WIESEL, T. N. *J. Physiol.*, 1959, *148*:574–591.
14. HUBEL, D. H. and WIESEL, T. N. *J. Physiol.*, 1961, *155*:385–398.
15. HUBEL, D. H. and WIESEL, T. N. *J. Physiol.* 1962, *160*:106–154.
16. HUBEL, D. H. and WIESEL, T. N. *J. Neurophysiol.*, 1965, *28*:229–289.
17. HUBEL, D. H. and WIESEL, T. N. *Physiologist*, 1964, *7*: Fall meetings.
18. KLÜVER, H. *J. Psychol.*, 1941, *11*:23–45.
19. MAGOUN, H. W. and RANSON, S. W. *Arch. Ophthal. (Chic.)*, 1935, *13*:791–811, 862–874.
20. MALMO, R. B. *Psychol. Bull.*, 1940, *37*:497–498.
21. MARQUIS, D. G. *Res. Publ. Ass. nerv. ment. Dis.*, 1934, *13*: 558–592. See also: *Arch. Neurol. Psychiat. (Chic.)*, 1935, *33*:807–815.
22. MARSHALL, W. H. and TALBOT, S. A. Pp. 117–164 in KLÜVER, H., ed. *Visual mechanisms.* Lancaster, Pa., Jaques Cattell Press, 1942.
22a. MATURNA, H. R., LETTVIN, J. Y., McCULLOCH, W. S. and PITTS, W. H. *J. gen. Physiol.*, 1960, *43*:Supplement 129.
23. POLYAK, S. *Res. Publ. Ass. nerv. ment. Dis.*, 1934, *13*:535–557.
24. POLYAK, S. *The vertebrate visual system*, H. KLÜVER, ed. Chicago, University of Chicago Press, 1957.
25. PUTNAM, T. J. and LIEBMAN, S. *Arch. Ophthal. (Chic.)*, 1942, *28*:415–443.
26. RANSON, S. W. and MAGOUN, H. W. *Arch. Neurol. Psychiat. (Chic.)*, 1933, *30*:1193–1202.
27. RIDDOCH, G. *Brain*, 1935, *58*:376–382.
28. SMITH, K. U. *J. genet. Psychol.*, 1937, *51*:329–369.
29. SPALDING, J. M. K. *J. Neurol. Neurosurg. Psychiat.*, 1952, *15*:99–109; 169–183.
30. TALBOT, S. A. and MARSHALL, W. H. *Amer J. Ophthal.*, 1941, *24*:1255–1264.
31. TEUBER, H. L., BATTERSBY, W. S., and BENDER, M. B. *Visual field defects after penetrating missile wounds of the brain.* Cambridge, Mass., Harvard University Press, 1960.

CEREBRAL CORTEX IN GENERAL: NEURO-PHYSIOLOGY OF BEHAVIOR

CHAPTER 22

Electrophysiology of the Cerebral Cortex: Consciousness

By ARNOLD L. TOWE

THE cellular elements of the cerebral cortex, like all other cells, have distinctive electrical properties. The cortical tissue, which is a collection of innumerable neuronal and glial elements, shows both a continuous, rhythmic alternation of electrical potential and a variety of localized, larger voltage responses consequent to receptor activity. The former rhythm is called "spontaneous" because its origin is not known; the latter responses are called "evoked" because they are closely associated with sensory input. Knowledge of the mechanism whereby the evoked potentials occur should lead to an understanding of the origin and meaning of spontaneous activity in the brain.

CONTINUOUS ACTIVITY[13, 14, 18, 19]

Although the continuous waxing and waning of electrical potential in the brain was known some 50 years earlier, it remained for Hans Berger, in 1929, to announce that it could be recorded from the intact skull of man and to use it as an index of health and disease in the brain of man. Via leads placed on the human head, exceedingly small (up to 50 μV. peak-to-peak in normal adults), irregular potentials can be recorded from frontal, parietal, occipital and temporal regions. The record thus obtained (Fig. 1) is called an *electroencephalogram,* abbreviated EEG. Typical differences exist between any two regions, the pattern depending upon the "state of the system" and the manner of recording.*

* A *bipolar* recording shows the difference in potential between two active leads, and a *monopolar* recording shows the variation of potential at a single lead compared with a stable reference point. A good reference or indifferent lead is difficult to establish, so that "monopolar" recording is in some disrepute.

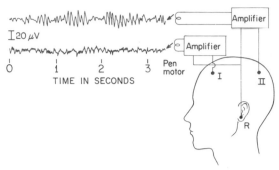

Fig. 1. Arrangement for recording EEG. The potential difference between frontal lead (*I*) and reference lead (*R*) shows low amplitude, fast activity of waking, relaxed human. Simultaneously, occipital lead (*II*) shows higher amplitude, slower activity.

Although the normal EEG consists of many different frequencies, one frequency predominates. This characteristic has proved more important than has amplitude of the wave and is used in naming the EEG pattern. If the dominant rhythm is between 8 and 14 per second, it is called an *alpha* rhythm; *beta* rhythms are those with frequencies of 14 to 60 per second; *theta* rhythms, 4 to 8 per second; and *delta* rhythms slower than 4 per second. Several other minor rhythms and "complexes" (e.g., spike and dome complex) are also recognized. In all these rhythms, the amplitude of the waves is inversely proportional to the typical frequency. By convention, high-frequency (short duration) waves are called "fast activity" and low-frequency (long duration) waves are called "slow activity."

State of the System. A whole constellation of factors affects the pattern of the EEG. At birth, the predominant rhythms are 0.5 to 2 per second and 20 to 50 per second; by 14 to 19 years, the adult pattern is fully developed. During childhood, the *theta* rhythms predominate; both the *delta* rhythms of infancy and the *theta* rhythms of childhood appear most clearly over the temporo-occipital regions of the brain. The precise EEG pattern that develops during maturation is typical of the individual and is stable, provided no disease or injury to the brain supervenes. Records from the frontal and parietal regions tend to show higher frequencies than records from the occipital region. However, during visual, attention-provoking stimulation, a fast rhythm of greatly reduced amplitude supersedes the normally preponderant *alpha* rhythm of the waking state; this phenomenon is called "alpha blocking" or "desynchronization."

When the sensory stimulus ceases to hold the individual's attention, the slower *alpha* rhythm reappears. The pattern of the EEG is also markedly altered when the blood or oxygen supply to the brain is altered. For example, slowing of the basic rhythm results when, in cerebral venous blood, O_2 saturation falls below 30 per cent, when blood sugar decreases to 35 mg. per ml., or when CO_2 level increases above 52 volumes per cent. On the other hand, fast activity predominates when CO_2 level decreases; forced overbreathing is used clinically to reveal certain latent abnormalities of the EEG.

A striking correspondence exists between the dominant frequency of the EEG and the apparent state of arousal of the individual (Fig. 2). In deep sleep, waves of 3 per second or less are seen; Bremer[5, 6] found a similar situation in the unanesthetized, isolated cerebrum produced by mesencephalic transection and concluded that sleep results from a functional deafferentation of the cerebral cortex. In moderately deep sleep, so-called "sleep spindles"—bursts of 10 to 12 per second activity—begin to appear. As sleep lightens, such bursts of activity appear at progressively shorter intervals, until the EEG is

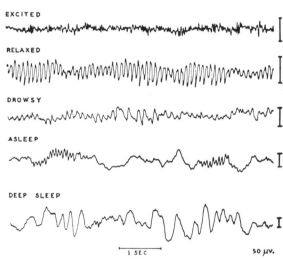

Fig. 2. Electroencephalographic records during excitement, relaxation and varying degrees of sleep. In fourth strip runs of 14/sec. rhythm, superimposed on slow waves, are termed "sleep spindles." Note that excitement is characterized by a rapid frequency and small amplitude and that varying degrees of sleep are marked by increasing irregularity and by appearance of "slow waves." (From Jasper, in Penfield and Erickson, *Epilepsy and cerebral localization*, Springfield, Ill., Charles C Thomas, 1941.)

gradually transformed into that typical of the waking state. Similar spindle activity is seen in an animal anesthetized with a barbiturate, the period between bursts being inversely related to the depth of anesthesia. As an individual goes from a drowsy to a relaxed to an excited state, the EEG progressively increases in frequency and decreases in amplitude. The behavioral change is called "arousal" and the electrical change is called "activation." These changes can be mimicked in an experimental animal by appropriate stimulation of the midbrain reticular formation.[26] Although activation of the EEG and behavioral arousal have been thought of as coeval, Feldman and Waller[11] have shown that this may not always be so. They produced EEG activation in cats made permanently somnolent by destruction of the posterior hypothalamus, and observed behavioral arousal in other cats with midbrain reticular lesions, lesions which rendered the EEG pattern of the cats "immobile" in slow activity or independent of the state of behavioral arousal. Nonetheless, EEG's do correlate with behavioral states in intact animals. *Theta* rhythms, 4 to 8 per second, develop during emotional stress and following withdrawal of pleasurable stimulation; they often appear in brain disease, especially in disease of thalamic structures. The slow *delta* rhythms not only dominate in deep sleep, but are often present in brain damage or disease, especially involving midline structures.

Focal damage to the cerebral cortex is localized electroencephalographically by the occurrence of irregular and abnormal activity (usually the slow activity mentioned above) in the neighborhood of the lesion or by the *reversal of phase* in records taken from opposite sides of the lesion with the reference lead over the lesion or acting as an indifferent lead. Asymmetry of the records from corresponding positions over the two hemispheres is very suggestive of focal damage. Epileptogenic lesions produce briefer waves, or "focal spike activity."

Epilepsy. The principal types of epilepsy cause distinctive electroencephalograms during the attack and brief, less pronounced, less characteristic abnormalities between attacks.[15] However, the latter are of major importance in diagnosis. Figure 3 shows the sequence of electrical events during an electroshock convulsion, which mimics the *grand mal* seizure of man. Fast activity is seen in the tonic period, and the clonic phase is marked by spike—slow-wave complexes, synchronous with the clonic jerks. The postseizure stupor is accompanied by high-voltage, slow, rolling waves which be-come very pronounced after repeated convulsions. *Petit mal* attacks consist of momentary lapses of responsiveness and consciousness without falling, often manifested to the observer only by a fixed stare. The EEG shows a doublet of a fast and a slow wave (spike and dome complex) repeated at the rate of about 3 per second. *Psychomotor epilepsy,* perhaps better called *epileptic automatisms,* usually originates in a focus in the temporal lobe. The attack takes the form of a stereotyped behavior pattern, sometimes an emotional outburst, of which the patient has no subsequent memory. In this, as in other instances of epilepsy arising from foci outside the sensory and motor areas, there is a strong element of "paralysis" rather than stimulation of function.

Physiologic Basis of the EEG. Several lines of evidence show that the EEG depends upon the electrical properties of cortical cells. Certain characteristics of the essential process can be surmised from the basic properties of individual cells. As shown in Chapter 2, the electrical space-constant of the cell body is so large that the cell body must behave nearly as a unit, i.e., shows no dipolar properties. On the other hand, the more distant and minute dendritic extensions of the soma, because of their high internal resistance, have space constants less than their own length and thus should be seen as dipoles by a distant electrode immersed in the same volume conductor. It is for this reason that many believe the EEG to result from the summation of dendritic activity, and especially of activity in any vertically oriented projections, which should be, on the average, closer to the surface electrode and show a greater solid angle. Recent evidence shows that the major part of the primary evoked response (see below) results from activity in neurons whose cell bodies occupy the upper third of the cortex.

Waves as seen in the EEG imply a nonrandom distribution of cellular activity. Synchrony and regular recurrence of cellular activity might be explained by reverberating activity in closed neuronal circuits or as a consequence of "spontaneous" rhythmic excitability changes in various neurons. A consideration of the environment in which a cortical cell is immersed leads to a qualitative understanding of the latter kind of explanation. If the extensive dendritic ramifications of a cortical neuron are influenced by the activity of adjacent neurons, whether ephaptically or by some more active process, then the entire cell membrane will be affected by the electrotonic spread of such changes. Consequently, in the absence of any disrupting input,

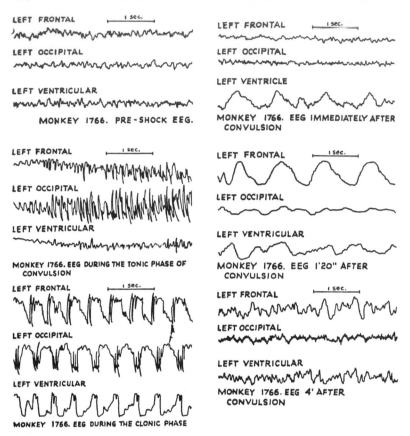

Fig. 3. Electroencephalographic records of successive stages of an electroshock convulsion in a monkey. One lead was taken from the lateral ventricles. Note especially the "slow waves" 1' 20" after the convulsion. These were associated with stupor which became more prolonged after repeated convulsions. (After Lennox *et al.*, *Electroenceph. clin. Neurophysiol.*, 1951, *3*:63–69.)

the excitability of cells in a local cluster would tend to vary as a unit. Likewise, the local cluster would synaptically activate other neurons in near synchrony with itself. This becomes a statistical process in which, eventually, the entire system might tend to fluctuate in excitability as a unit at some unique frequency. The process could be disrupted by an afferent input, but at the termination of such afferent domination, the system would again slowly establish its resting or "idling" condition. Andersen and Eccles[3] have proposed a different sort of mechanism dependent upon a prolonged, apparently recurrent, postsynaptic inhibition in primary thalamocortical projection fibers. This inhibition stops cell discharge for 100 msec.; no driving mechanism to discharge these neurons upon recovery to normal excitability has been proposed.

EVOKED CORTICAL POTENTIALS[7, 33]

In addition to the continuous electrical activity of the cerebral cortex, various discrete electrical changes can be produced by stimulation of sense organs or of some point along the ascending pathways to the cerebral cortex. Study of such potentials reveals that two systems of fibers connect the sense organs with the cerebral cortex, one proceeding directly through three or four neurons with a high degree of topographic organization and the other branching from the direct route at the medullary and midbrain level, passing via the reticular substance of the brain stem and diencephalon, and eventually terminating diffusely in the cerebral cortex. A separate component of the latter pathway diffuses at the thalamic level. The properties of these two systems are largely known from the potentials they induce in the cortex and the manner in which they initiate or modify rhythmic potential phenomena. These evoked potentials will be described before the pathways leading to their production are discussed.

Single Neuron Response. Two classes of potential change occur in the cerebral cortex following sense organ stimulation: (i) a very abrupt alteration lasting one or two milliseconds and (ii) a more slowly developing, much longer lasting voltage variation. The former change is associated with the electrical field in the immediate vicinity of an active cortical cell, and is usually called the "unit spike." Not until recently did techniques for prolonged, systematic observation of such unit activity in the cerebral cortex become available[4]; these extracellular unit spike recordings are now readily obtained and sample a much wider range of neurons than intracellular recordings in the same tissue. Microelectrodes less than 2 microns in tip diameter are usually used to avoid damaging the cell whose activity is being recorded. The patterns of activity of cortical neurons have been found to be highly complex, but one generalization is possible: *No facet of neuron response is invariant* (Fig. 4). Although their behavior is probabilistic, statistical studies show that real and systematic differences in discharge patterns do exist between neurons[4, 34]; differences in temporal patterns are believed to convey sensory information.

Cortical neurons are "discriminatory" in their behavior. In the somatosensory cortex, as we have seen, it is not uncommon for a neuron to respond to deflection of the hairs in an area of 1 square centimeter but to no other input—or to cutaneous touch in a larger area. The area of skin effective in discharging the neuron (the *receptive field*) is often ringed by a band of skin which, when stimulated, prevents the neuron from responding to any excitatory input for periods of 100 to 200 milliseconds (the "inhibitory surround"). The boundary between the excitatory field and the inhibitory surround is not sharp; it is a tenuous region where the excitatory process provoked by the stimulus and impinging on the neuron becomes too feeble to be detectable. Neurons responsive to stimulation distally (e.g., hand or foot) have smaller receptive fields than neurons responsive to more axial sites of stimulation; however, a few large receptive fields can be found distally on the limbs. One class of cortical neuron consistently shows very large receptive fields—even to the extent of crossing the midline into ipsilateral regions.[35] By contrast with those in primary sensory cortex, neurons in motor cortex and in association areas characteristically respond to a wide range of stimuli of various modalities.

Primary Evoked Response.[2]   When a large electrode is placed on the cortical surface, it is possible to record the second sort of potential change mentioned above. Stimulation of a sensory organ, a sensory nerve or a thalamic relay nucleus results in a very large (about 1 mV.),

diphasic potential (Fig. 5*A*, *B*) restricted to the sensory receiving areas of the cortex. As pointed out previously, such responses are used to map the projection of the body surface, retina or cochlea on the cortical sensory areas. This mapping is possible because the primary response results from synchronous activity in the direct, fast-conducting sensory pathways, which show a high degree of topographic organization. Since the primary response resulting from stimulation of a local site on the skin appears over a large extent of cortex, the mapping is accomplished by associating the site on the cortex yielding the *largest amplitude* primary response with the skin site stimulated.

The configuration of the primary response changes with the recording position; on the surface of the cortex it usually has an initial positive phase followed by a long-duration negative, phase, whereas deep in the cortex it is inverted (Fig. 5*D*). The level of "reversal" of the primary response is 0.2 to 0.3 mm. below the pial surface.

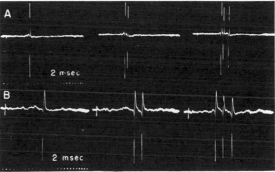

Fig. 4.   Extracellular spikes of two neurons (A, B) recorded from monkey postcentral gyrus, showing variation in initial spike latency and number of spikes per discharge when sampled at three different times. Positivity downward. (Towe and Amassian, *J. Neurophysiol.*, 1958, *21*:292–311.)

Although no single cortical structure can yet be designated as *the* source of the gross cortical potentials, it is evident that the external granular layers are intimately involved.[35] The major vertical component of current flow during the primary response occurs in these layers (0.2 to 0.8 mm. below the pial surface). The evoked primary response begins as activity ascends into the fine terminal ramifications of the thalamocortical afferent fibers and continues for 20 to 30 milliseconds. Single cortical neurons are active throughout the duration of the primary response, discharging either once or firing repetitively. Maximum spike discharge occurs

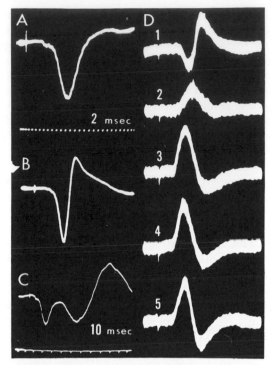

Fig. 5. Primary evoked discharge recorded from cat. *A,* Primary response recorded from cortical surface of somatosensory area I. *B,* Primary from somatosensory area II. *C,* Primary response and secondary discharge from area I. *D,* Superimposed microelectrode traces from surface (1) in 480 μ steps to 1920 μ (5), showing reversal of primary discharge and change in initial response latency with depth.

halfway through the primary response at the level of termination of thalamocortical afferent fibers (Fig. 6). The precise mode of spread of activity above and below the level of termination of the afferent fibers is unknown, but activity spreads upward from this level at 0.1 to 0.2 meters per second (apparently too slowly for conduction along apical dendrites or fine afferent fibers).

Repetitive Waves. In the lightly anesthetized animal, a short train of 8 to 12 per second positive waves sometimes follows the primary evoked response. These waves, initiated by the primary response volley in the thalamus, have been described as a thalamic afterdischarge (Adrian) and as a result of reverberating activity between thalamus and cortex (Chang). The findings of Andersen and Eccles mentioned above support Adrian's afterdischarge hypothesis. The repetitive waves are restricted to the same area of cortex as the primary evoked response.

Secondary Discharge.[12] In deep anesthesia, the primary evoked response is often followed by a second positive-negative potential (Fig. 5C) that appears throughout both hemispheres after a fairly uniform latency (30 to 80 milliseconds). This phenomenon does not depend upon spread of activity from the primary focus but appears to be mediated via the diffuse projection system described above. In the primary sensory receiving areas, the neurons that discharge during the primary evoked response do not respond during the secondary discharge; a different set of cortical neurons is involved.[33] Furthermore, the secondary discharge is not everywhere the same; the secondary associated with the visual primary response appears to be a different phenomenon from that found simultaneously in association cortex.[32] The secondary discharge is very closely related to the following two phenomena.

Spontaneous Cortical Bursts. Under moderate to deep anesthesia and in the absence of known sensory stimulation, a succession of waves with a frequency of 8 to 12 per second waxes and wanes over wide areas of both hemispheres in near synchrony. These surface-negative waves are strikingly like "sleep spindles" and the *alpha* rhythm (Fig. 7). This phenomenon is not truly an evoked potential, although similar burst activity can be produced by stimulation of the thalamic reticular system.[10] The presence of spontaneous cortical bursts precludes the appearance of the generalized sec-

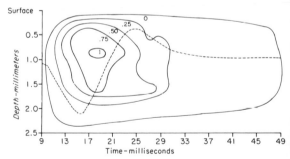

Fig. 6. Distribution of neuron response in time after contralateral forepaw stimulation and depth below the cortical surface in the "sensory-motor" cortex of the cat. The graph should be read like a contour map; it shows the density of neuron spike activity. Most spike discharge occurs 0.7 to 1.0 mm. deep in the cortex, 17 to 20 milliseconds after the forepaw stimulus. Dashed line shows the associated primary evoked response recorded from the surface. (After Towe, Patton and Kennedy, *Exp. Neurol.,* 1964, *10*:325–344.)

ondary discharge—apparently an "occlusive" process—without altering a primary evoked response. Such burst activity can be regarded as a manifestation, not a cause, of the periodic waxing and waning of excitability in the "idling" system, because most evoked responses are potentiated during burst activity and depressed during the interburst periods. Because burst activity can be recorded from the thalamus and can be produced in the cortex by stimulation of the thalamic reticular system, it has been thought that it originates in and is regulated by the thalamus, or that it reflects a thalamocortical reverberating system. However, Jasper[20] has demonstrated burst activity from isolated cortex and has found that spindle bursts may occur independently in the thalamus and cortex of intact animals. Despite their similarity, spontaneous cortical bursts and repetitive waves do not share the same neuronal elements; the former are produced via a diffuse thalamic projection system whereas the latter depend upon the "specific thalamic nuclei" for their production.

Recruiting Response. Repetitive shocks delivered to the intralaminar thalamic nuclei produce a series of diphasic (negative-positive) potentials in both hemispheres after a 15 to 60 millisecond delay. If 5 to 15 stimuli are delivered each second, the amplitude of the potentials builds up during the first few shocks (Fig. 7) and then proceeds to wax and wane at a frequency of 8 to 12 per second.[25] Not only are the shape and frequency of this response similar to those of spontaneous cortical bursts, but its distribution in the cortex is identical to that of burst activity. Discovery of this phenomenon[25] and an observation by Bremer, described later, initiated the physiologic analysis of the electroencephalogram.

Neural Basis of Recruiting Response and Spontaneous Cortical Bursts. Study of the cortical potentials resulting from stimulation of the thalamus has led to a new, functional classification of the thalamic nuclei. Because focal stimulation of the relay and association nuclei results in short-latency (1 to 5 milliseconds) localized activity in the cortex, these structures are considered "specific thalamic nuclei."

The name derives from the writings of Lorente de Nó, who described two types of thalamocortical afferents in Golgi preparations. The "specific" afferents come from relay nuclei and end with many synaptic terminals in layer IV, but have little lateral spread throughout the cortex. They thus form a point-to-point projection. The "nonspecific" thalamocortical afferents terminate less profusely but more widely, giving branches to more than one and perhaps many cytoarchitectural areas. Their origin in the thalamus is not known anatomically, and whether such afferents form the diffuse thalamocortical projection system is problematic.

Stimulation of other thalamic nuclei results in widespread, bilateral cortical activation of the recruiting type. Such nuclei are considered "nonspecific thalamic nuclei." They include the midline and intralaminar nuclei, including n. ventralis anterior and n. centrum medianum, and the more lateral reticular nucleus.[31] The reticular nucleus is continuous with the midbrain reticular substance through the zona incerta. Although stimulation of these thalamic nuclei sometimes has an effect on cortical electrical activity different from that of stimulation of the brainstem reticular system, the nuclei are collectively considered to be a continuation of the midbrain reticular substance.

Because the nonspecific thalamic nuclei did not appear to be sufficiently endowed with pro-

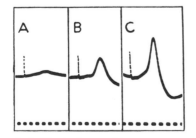 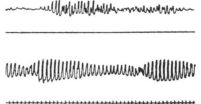

Fig. 7. *Left,* Cortical recruiting response to three successive shocks to intralaminar thalamic region. Initial vertical line is shock artefact. Negativity is upward. *Right,* A "spontaneous" 1–12/sec. burst (*upper record*) and a waxing and waning response (*lower record*) to continuously repeated shocks to intralaminar thalamic region. Bottom line is stimulus signal. (From Morison and Dempsey, *Amer. J. Physiol.,* 1942, *135*:281–292.)

jection fibers to the cortex, McLardy[24] proposed that their effect on cortical activity depends upon an intrathalamic diffusion system which activates specific thalamic relay and association nuclei. Starzl and Magoun[29] later concurred in this proposal. However, when Hanbery and Jasper[17] selectively destroyed the relay and association nuclei and then stimulated the centrum medianum or the n. ventralis anterior, recruiting potentials appeared in the cortex to which the relay nuclei project. Evidently these two nuclei, neither of which is known to project directly to the cerebral cortex, have their effect via the reticular nucleus. Rose[28] and Chow[9] have shown that the n. reticularis of the thalamus projects to the cortex in a systematic manner. The anteroposterior axis of the nucleus is represented mediolaterally on the cortex; the dorsoventral axis appears in a caudorostral arrangement. Hanbery and coworkers[16] have proposed that the thalamic reticular nucleus is the final outflow to the cortex of the reticular system.

The cortical neurons activated via the diffuse projection system are scattered widely throughout the cerebral mantle; in the primary sensory receiving areas they are not the same neurons activated during the primary evoked response. Specific thalamocortical afferent fibers break into dense terminal arborizations in layer IV, while the nonspecific afferents seem to be more widely distributed and to terminate more densely in the superficial layers. It is the cortical neurons discharged via the diffuse system that produce the continuous electrical activity of the brain known as the EEG.

ACTIVATION OF THE EEG; ALERTNESS AND SLEEP[23]

It is now evident that the EEG's of the waking and the sleeping animal are strikingly different and that afferent stimulation can transform the EEG into the "alerted" pattern. The latter phenomenon is termed *activation* or "desynchronization." Moruzzi and Magoun[26] discovered that stimulation of the reticular substance of the brain resulted in a phenomenon resembling activation (Fig. 8), and interpreted the effect as a desynchronization of cortical cellular activity. Bremer[5] had shown earlier that a waking pattern prevailed in the unanesthetized cat following a bulbospinal transection (*encéphale isolé*), but that the cortex falls into a kind of sleep after a mesencephalic transection that leaves the blood supply intact (*cerveau isolé*). The latter transection deprives the rostral part of the nervous system of the trigeminal and vestibular inputs that maintain the waking pattern in the *encéphale isolé* preparation.[27] Although it previously had been thought that the arrival of impulses over the direct sensory pathways (specific projection system) was responsible for the alerting of the cerebral cortex by a sensory stimulus, the analysis by Magoun and his coworkers[22, 30] showed otherwise. As illustrated in Figure 9, impulses carried in a system of fibers branching from the main sensory systems and traversing a slower, multisynaptic route through the reticular substance of the brain are actually responsible. This explains why a sensory stimulus evokes a potential in the somatosensory areas within 10 milliseconds,

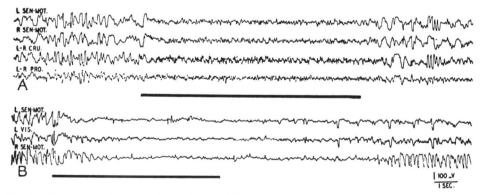

Fig. 8. Desynchronization of electrical activity of cortex by left bulboreticular stimulation during period marked by horizontal black line. *A* is from an "encéphale isolé" cat lightly anesthetized; *B* is from intact cat heavily anesthetized with chloralosane. Abbreviations at left give origin of activity: sensorimotor areas, gyrus cruciatus or proreus and visual area. (From Moruzzi and Magoun, *Electroenceph. clin. Neurophysiol.*, 1949, *1*:455–473.)

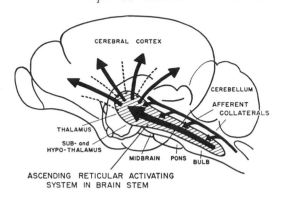

ASCENDING RETICULAR ACTIVATING
SYSTEM IN BRAIN STEM

Fig. 9. Sagittal section of cat brain showing neural basis of arousal response. (From Starzl *et al.*, *J. Neurophysiol.*, 1951, *14:*479–496.)

whereas the changes in the *alpha* rhythm associated with sensory stimulation appear only after 40 to 60 milliseconds.

Experimental sensory stimuli cause replacement of the highly synchronized, large-amplitude, long-lasting potentials of barbiturate-induced sleep by low-amplitude, fast activity, an event termed activation. It is clear that the arrival of nerve impulses at the cortex over the familiar sensory pathways does not "wake up" the cerebral cortex since a sensory stimulus will still cause the cortical activation response when these pathways are interrupted by a lesion placed laterally in the midbrain. The specific relay nuclei of the thalamus have been bypassed, and impulses are still reaching the cortex. Consistently, evoked potentials can be recorded in the reticular substance after sensory stimulation. Throughout the brain stem, collaterals given off by the somatosensory and auditory systems enter the central reticular substance (ventromedial reticular substance and tegmentum bordering the periaqueductal gray). Impulses ascend slowly and enter the dorsal hypothalamus, the subthalamus and the reticular and ventromedial part of the thalamus. They then pass on into the internal capsule and finally reach the cerebral cortex. On the other hand, the specific relay and association nuclei are not activated by midbrain reticular substance. Thus, cortical activation occurs after destruction of all but the basal part of the thalamus and the hypothalamus.

The similarity of cortical activation resulting from stimulation of the ascending reticular system and that accompanying "normal" waking can be seen by comparing Figures 2 and 8. The sleeplike state of the cortex in Bremer's *cerveau isolé* preparation was analyzed in the experiment shown in Figure 10. When the ascending afferent systems were interrupted in the midbrain, the animal was awake and the EEG corresponded. However, if the reticular activating system was interrupted by medially placed lesions, the animal was continuously somnolent and the EEG showed slow waves and spindles typical of sleep. Thus, despite the integrity of the long sensory and motor pathways, the animal was not "conscious" and did not move. A chronic state of somnolence can be produced without the accompanying EEG changes by bilateral destruction of the posterior hypothalamus without involvement of the midbrain reticular formation.[11] Thus, the diffuse "reticular activating system" is yet more diffuse, involving a separate system for behavioral arousal.

Fig. 10. Typical behavior and EEG records of cats with midbrain lesion sparing tegmentum (*A* and *A'*) and with lesion of tegmentum (*B* and *B'*). Cat *B* appeared continuously asleep or comatose during postoperative survival. (After Lindsley *et al.*, *Electroenceph. clin. Neurophysiol.*, 1950, *2:*483–498.)

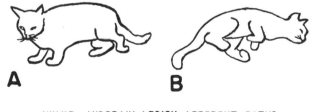

A   **B**

AWAKE : MIDBRAIN LESION AFFERENT PATHS

A'

CC-17 21ST PO. DAY

ASLEEP : LESION MIDBRAIN TEGMENTUM   100 μV

B'

CC-12 12TH PO DAY   1 SEC.

Such observations explain the akinetic states which occur clinically[8] and which can be produced experimentally by lesions in the region of the periaqueductal gray matter and posterior hypothalamus. If the EEG records shown in this chapter are studied, it will be seen that the EEG varies from the high-frequency response of the excited state through the slower activity of the relaxed state to the slow activity of sleep and the long, rolling waves of stupor following multiple electroshock convulsions.[21] Feldman and Waller[11] have demonstrated that this association between state of arousal and activation may not be causal. Adametz[1] has further shown that the severity of the behavioral deficit following bilateral lesions in the midbrain tegmentum depends not only on the size of the lesions but also on whether they are produced in one stage or successively in two or more stages. This shock factor, or *diaschisis,* is illustrated clinically by the paucity and late appearance of neurologic deficits in slowly developing lesions of the central nervous system as compared with the dramatic and debilitating deficits in acute injury or rapidly developing lesions.

REFERENCES

1. ADAMETZ, J. H. *J. Neurosurg.,* 1959, *16:*85–97.
2. ADRIAN, E. D. *J. Physiol. (Lond.),* 1941, *100:*159–191.
3. ANDERSEN, P. and ECCLES, J. C. *Nature,* 1962, *196:*645–647.
4. AMASSIAN, V. E. *Electroenceph. clin. Neurophysiol.,* 1953, *5:*415–438.
5. BREMER, F. *C. R. Soc. Biol. (Paris),* 1935, *118:*1235–1242.
6. BREMER, F. *Boll. Soc. ital. Biol. sper.,* 1938, *13:*271–290.
7. BREMER, F. *Some problems in neurophysiology.* London, Athlone Press, 1953.
8. CAIRNS, H. W. B. *Brain,* 1952, *75:*109–146.
9. CHOW, K. L. *J. comp. Neurol.,* 1952, *97:*37–59.
10. DEMPSEY, E. W. and MORISON, R. S. *Amer. J. Physiol.,* 1942, *135:*293–300.
11. FELDMAN, S. M. and WALLER, H. J. *Nature,* 1962, *196:*1320–1322.
12. FORBES, A. and MORISON, B. R. *J. Neurophysiol.,* 1939, *2:*112–128.
13. GIBBS, F. A. Pp. 361–370 in Glasser, O., ed., *Medical physics.* Chicago, Year Book Publishers, Inc., 1944.
14. GIBBS, F. A. and GIBBS, E. L. *Atlas of electroencephalography,* 2nd ed. Cambridge, Mass., privately printed, 1950 and 1952, 2 vols.
15. GIBBS, F. A., GIBBS, E. L. and LENNOX, W. G. *Arch. Neurol. Psychiat. (Chic.),* 1938, *39:*298–314.
16. HANBERY, J., AJMONE-MARSAN, C. and DILWORTH, M. *Electroenceph. clin. Neurophysiol.,* 1954, *6:*103–118.
17. HANBERY, J. and JASPER, H. *J. Neurophysiol.,* 1953, *16:*252–271.
18. HILL, D. and PARR, G., eds. *Electroencephalography, a symposium on its various aspects.* London, Macdonald, 1950.
19. JASPER, H. H. Chap. 14 in Penfield, W. and Erickson, T. C. *Epilepsy and cerebral localization.* Springfield, Ill., Charles C Thomas, 1941.
20. JASPER, H. H. *Electroenceph. clin. Neurophysiol.,* 1949, *1:*405–420.
21. LENNOX, M. A., RUCH, T. C. and BUTERMAN, B. *Electroenceph. clin. Neurophysiol.,* 1951, *3:*63–69.
22. MAGOUN, H. W. *Res. Publ. Ass. nerv. ment. Dis.,* 1952, *30:*480–492.
23. MAGOUN, H. W. *The waking brain.* Springfield, Ill., Charles C Thomas, 1958.
24. McLARDY, T. *Electroenceph. clin. Neurophysiol.,* 1951, *3:*183–188.
25. MORISON, R. S. and DEMPSEY, E. W. *Amer. J. Physiol.,* 1942, *135:*281–292.
26. MORUZZI, G. and MAGOUN, H. W. *Electroenceph. clin. Neurophysiol.,* 1949, *1:*455–473.
27. ROGER, A., ROSSI, G. F. and ZIRONDOI, A. *Electroenceph. clin. Neurophysiol.,* 1956, *8:*1–13.
28. ROSE, J. E. *Res. Publ. Ass. nerv. ment. Dis.,* 1952, *30:*454–479.
29. STARZL, T. E. and MAGOUN, H. W. *J. Neurophysiol.,* 1951, *14:*133–146.
30. STARZL, T. E., TAYLOR, C. W. and MAGOUN, H. W. *J. Neurophysiol.,* 1951, *14:*461–477.
31. STARZL, T. E. and WHITLOCK, D. G. *J. Neurophysiol.,* 1952, *15:*449–468.
32. TORRES, F. and WARNER, J. S. *Electroenceph. clin. Neurophysiol.,* 1962, *14:*654–663.
33. TOWE, A. L. *Confin. neurol. (Basel),* 1956, *16:*333–360.
34. TOWE, A. L. and AMASSIAN, V. E. *J. Neurophysiol.,* 1958, *21:*292–311.
35. TOWE, A. L., PATTON, H. D. and KENNEDY, T. T. *Exper. Neurol.,* 1964, *10:*325–344.

CHAPTER 23

The Homotypical Cortex—
The "Association Areas"

By THEODORE C. RUCH

THE classic primary sensory areas with their highly granular cortex and the classic motor areas with their agranular cortex constitute only a fraction of the cerebral mantle. Both are specializations of the basic cellular pattern. The intervening area, increasingly extensive in the mammalian and primate series, has all of the six cellular layers and therefore is called homotypical cortex. This term can be considered a synonym for, and preferable to, the conventional designation, "association areas." In the light of laboratory experimentation, it is not clear what the "association areas" associate. For example, the classic idea that they associate (connect) the primary sensory areas with the motor area in an immediate fashion is not established. The view of the homotypical cortex in which the primary motor and sensory areas are islands is more elusive and nebulous than the idea of "linkage" conveyed by the term "association area." The breakdown of the association concept resulted from several developments in the 1930's, namely (i) that the function of the prefrontal area is concerned with recent memory (Jacobsen[19]) and that ablation of it causes hyperactivity (Richter and Hines[43]), (ii) the motor and somatosensory areas are self-sufficient, each having both an afferent input and an efferent output, and therefore not completely dependent on association areas; (iii) areas of homotypical cortex proved to have a sensory function independent of the neighboring sensory cortex, e.g., the posterior parietal lobes (Areas 5 and 7) perform somatosensory discrimination independent of the input to the primary somatosensory area (Ruch[48]), a phenomenon especially well documented for the association areas surrounding the primary auditory areas (Chap. 18); (iv) all classic association areas, with the possible exception of the temporal lobe and a portion of the prefrontal lobe, receive a projection from the thalamus and, hence, are not dependent only upon impulses relayed from the primary sensory areas (Walker[55]), and (v) some association areas have direct descending projections to subcortical structures, e.g., to the hypothalamus and caudate nucleus.

Where the homotypical cortex borders on sensory and motor areas the cortex is transitional in structure. Three general association areas are recognized: (i) frontal (or prefrontal), (ii) anterior temporal, and (iii) parietotemporopreoccipital area. These cortical regions are phylogenetically more recent and become myelinated later in development than the primary sensory and motor areas.

Far from being a mere link between sensory and motor areas or an appendage to sensory areas where association occurs, the homotypical cortex has a rich and varied input, the full extent of which will not be known until the Nauta stain is fully exploited.

The whole prefrontal lobule systematically receives fibers from the large lateral (neothalamic) portion of nucleus medialis dorsalis of the thalamus.[56] The anterior cingulate gyrus (mesopallium) receives fibers from the hypothalamus by way of the mammillothalamic tract and the anterior thalamic nuclei. As pointed out in Chapter 15, the pulvinar, a large and recently developed thalamic nucleus, projects to the entire parietotemporo-preoccipital sector (except the insula and superior temporal gyrus) and the lateral surface of the temporal lobe. Nucleus lateralis posterior and n. lateralis dorsalis project to the parietal association cortex. In addition to these connections, the entire cerebral cortex, as mentioned in the previous chapter, receives fibers from n. reticularis of the thalamus.

PREFRONTAL AREAS[5, 57]

Connections. The "frontal association

area," also known as the prefrontal area or lobule, occupies the anterior pole of the frontal lobe. It extends fully upon the orbital surface of the frontal lobe and merges posteriorly with olfactory structures. On the dorsolateral surface of the hemisphere its posterior border is Area 8, which is transitional, both cytoarchitecturally and functionally. Because the "free" and orbital surfaces of the frontal lobe are projection areas of a single nucleus (n. medialis dorsalis, pars lateralis), this region is sometimes called the "orbitofrontal" cortex.[44] The orbital and lateral surfaces receive projections from cytoarchitecturally different parts of the dorsomedial nucleus (Fig. 1) and one area on the medial and most dorsal portions of the frontal lobule appears now to have no projection and may be truly "association" cortex.[2] The afferent input to the orbital surface from the amygdala, septal and tegmental regions via the magnocellularis zone of the dorsomedial nucleus has been identified. The input to the parvicellular portion of this nucleus and, hence, to the free surface of the frontal lobe remains in doubt.

Studies by Nauta[36] indicate three main streams of

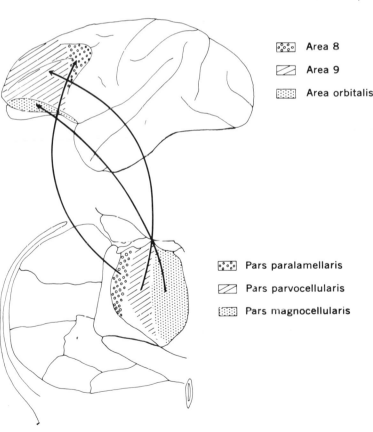

Area 8

Area 9

Area orbitalis

Pars paralamellaris

Pars parvocellularis

Pars magnocellularis

Fig. 1. Projections from zones of the nucleus medialis dorsalis to subregions within the frontal granular cortex. (From Akert, K, Chap. 18 in *The frontal granular cortex and behavior.* New York, McGraw-Hill Book Co., 1964.)

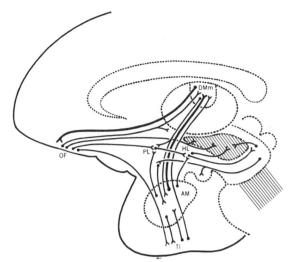

Fig. 2. Connections of the caudal part of the orbital surface of the frontal lobe (OF) with the dorsomedial nucleus (DMm) and with the amygdalar complex (AM) indirectly through the inferior surface of the temporal lobe (TI). The small round dot indicates the cell body, and the bifurcation at the other end symbolizes terminal arborization. Note that connections with the lateral preoptic and hypothalamic regions (PL, HL) link the system to the mesencephalic reticular formation. (From Nauta, *Brain*, 1962, *85*:505–520.)

efferent projection fibers from the prefrontal lobe, all of which connect with structures involved in emotional behavior or visceral control.

(i) From the lateral as well as the mesial surface, fibers join the cingulum and distribute terminals to the gyrus cinguli, gyrus fornicatus and, streaming ventrally, terminate as far forward as the presubicular region.

(ii) Fibers from the orbital surface and from the lateral surface inferior to the sulcus principalis pass through the large uncinate bundle to the temporal lobe, which is known to project to the amygdalar complex. Nauta[36] sees a three-way system of reciprocal connections between the orbital surface, the amygdala complex and the medial or magnocellularis part of the dorsomedial nucleus. For further details, especially, on the multiple efferent connections of this system with the hypothalamus, see Figure 2.

(iii) A subcortical stream originating widely in the frontal cortex mainly enters the internal capsule and connects, both directly and via collaterals, with the head of the caudate nucleus and the putamen. There are also direct connections with the hypothalamus, especially its lateral part, and with the intralaminar nuclei and reciprocal connections with the dorsomedial nucleus. Other important connections are with the subthalamic region and the rostral mesencephalic gray substance. When the orbitofrontal region is removed en masse, further details of its projection can be made out,[8] as shown in Figure 3.

The frontal pole appears to be the way the neocortex funnels impulses into the limbic system. Such connections arise from the lateral convexity of the frontal region as well as from the medial and orbital surface. Also efferent projections of the prefrontal cortex converge with those of the limbic forebrain (septum, an-

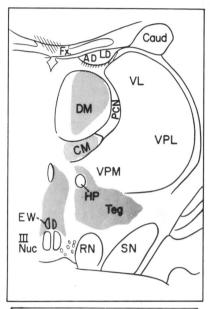

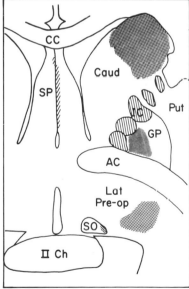

Fig. 3. Connections based on prefrontal lobectomy (sparing Area 8) showing more extensive subcortical areas with degenerating fibers and terminals than text description based on smaller lesions. Crosshatching, terminal fibers; oblique lines, fibers of passage; shading, both types of degeneration. The abbreviations are mnemonic. (From DeVito and Smith, *J. comp. Neurol.*, 1965, *123*:413–419.)

terior cingulate gyrus) to end in the hypothalamus and rostral mesencephalon.

Ablation — Hyperactivity.[22, 27, 38, 49] Reflexes, posture and discrete movement are not affected by ablation of the orbitofrontal cortex; nor can any definite impairment of general intelligence be measured. However, definite disturbances of *behavior* are produced. Unlike those of the language functions, the behavior disturbances are marked only when the frontal areas are damaged *bilaterally*. As recently as 1922, Bianchi described in purely mentalistic terms from "naked eye" observations the results of extirpating the orbitofrontal areas in animals. Since that time, definite, objectively demonstrable disturbances of behavior have been discovered, and methods have been devised for quantifying them.

In monkeys ablation of the entire orbitofrontal lobule or its subareas induces a state of hyperactivity manifested by incessant, stereotyped walking or pacing, much like that of certain zoo inhabitants (notably the carnivores). The pacing appears aimless. It is continued for hours, almost without pause, but ceases in darkness. In its extreme form it is almost maniacal. This hyperactivity, like that of certain problem children, is stopped by amphetamine and certain other cerebral excitants. It has been observed in cats, rats and monkeys, but not as yet in chimpanzees or man. The squirrel monkey appears not to develop hyperactivity after prefrontal lesions.[33] In *Macaca mulatta* monkeys it seems to appear sometime between one and two years of age. To some degree, the whole orbitofrontal cortex is concerned with the regulation of activity,[22] but bilateral lesions of posterior portions of the orbital surface (Area 13 of Brodmann) produce nearly maximal hyperactivity.[49] Livingston *et al.*[27] studied quantitatively the activity before and after lesions of Area 13 and estimated that activity increased eight to sixteen times following the lesion. The onset of hyperactivity is more rapid after lesions of Area 13; some prefrontal ablations sparing this region do not result in marked hyperactivity.

The enduring hyperactivity is usually preceded by a period of hypoactivity: apparent apathy, drooping of the head, sluggishness of movement, blankness of expression, and a tendency to sit staring into space and to ignore human presence. (This sequence of underactivity followed by overactivity—cf. flaccidity–spasticity—usually means that the ablated structures contain neurons of opposite influence on the function observed. This would lead to the prediction of a system originating in the prefrontal lobes which *facilitates* locomotor activity.) This state of hypoactivity, which may also be ascribed to diaschisis, lasts from several days to two or three weeks after operation. It gradually gives way to bouts of stereotyped pacing, which punctuate the periods of inactivity; these bouts of activity become progressively longer. Once established, the pacing persists indefinitely (Fig. 4). When hyperactivity is severe, random activities—the varied patterns of manipulations and posturings, the quick play of grimacing, and head and eye movements—give way to stereotyped walking.

Recent evidence suggests that the hyperactivity may result from an interruption of fibers passing to the hypothalamus, since, in rats, lesions in septal–preoptic regions[29] produce incessant running behavior reminiscent of that following stimulation of certain hypothalamic areas by implanted electrodes.[28] As will be discussed later, lesions in the head of the caudate nucleus of the monkey also produce a hyperactivity that is diminished by darkness; interestingly, these lesions need not be bilateral to produce their effect.[7]

Ablation — Delayed Response.[5, 19, 57] Responses to the temporally and spatially immediate environment constitute much of an animal's behavior. However, many responses, although called forth by the immediate situation, owe their direction to sensory information gained previously. Experimentally, this capacity is assessed by the delayed response test, which may take a variety of forms. In one form, a monkey or chimpanzee is allowed to view through bars a piece of food being deposited beneath one of two or more cups on a sliding tray. An opaque door is then lowered in front of the animal for a chosen interval. The tray is then pushed forward to the cage and the door is raised, permitting the animal to reach the cups. The animal is allowed to select one cup, the reward being obtained if the proper cup is selected. With training, a normal monkey makes successful choices after delays as long as 90 seconds between seeing the food and choosing among the cups. After bilateral orbitofrontal ablation, even delays as short as 5 seconds make successful response a matter of chance; the animal is at a complete loss in selecting the cup concealing the food. (In fact, only that fraction making up the banks and depths of *sulcus principalis* within the wings of the arcuate fissure, e.g., Figure 2, Chapter 12, need be ablated to produce nearly maximal deficit in delayed response.[35]) Neither unilateral frontal lobule ablation nor extirpation of other cortical areas has this effect. However, lesions in the caudate nucleus produce a similar deficit in delayed alternations (see below). No other part of the cerebral cortex can substitute for the orbitofrontal areas in this capacity, since the problem cannot be relearned. Nor is complete failure in the delayed response test due to a general impairment of intelligence or ability to learn. After frontal lobectomy, monkeys can retain or learn a visual discrimination quite as well as normal monkeys. A chimpanzee with a prefrontal lobectomy can successfully perform the "stick and platform" problem, which assesses the animal's ability to solve complex problems.[20]

A chimpanzee in a barred cage is confronted with a platform on which a piece of food and a stick or rake have been placed. The food is out of arm's reach but can be reached if the rake is used. After this task is mastered, a series of sticks is introduced, a short stick being used to secure a longer stick, etc., until one long enough to reach the food is obtained. An orbitofrontal lobectomized chimpanzee is able to grasp these relations and organize a serial response involving four sticks, but only if the whole problem is within its view

at one moment. If two platforms are used, the lobectomized animal fails totally when a stick from one platform must be carried to the other in order to secure the next longer stick, and it experiences great difficulty when only one stick is involved but the food is on the other platform.

A test similar to delayed response is that of *delayed alternation,* in which the animal learns to make alternate right and left turns and to remember which turn comes next, despite an enforced delay after each turn is completed. Even rats show definite deficiencies in this problem after bilateral injury to the frontal poles. Monkeys with similar lesions are deficient in *double alternation* problems in which the correct choices are RRLLRRLL.[25]

The inability to perform delayed response and delayed alternation may be operationally termed incapacity for "immediate memory," for, in fact, this is what the monkey fails to do—remember under which cup the reward lies. "Memory," when the right and wrong places change from trial to trial, differs from remembering a visual discrimination when a given intensity is always right or wrong, or remembering a motor skill like ice skating in which standing up or sitting down is right or wrong. The latter two types of remembering are not affected by prefrontal lesions. Several causes for failure

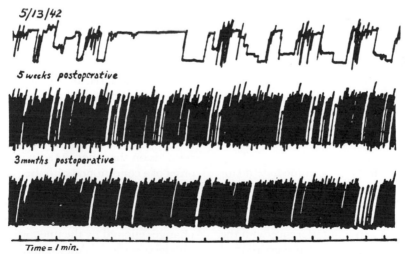

Fig. 4.   Activity records of monkeys before and after posterior orbital lesions. Freely movable bottom of oblong activity cage rests on pneumatic pad connected to tambour which records upon kymograph. Any movement toward or away from end resting on pad causes a pen excursion, height roughly reflecting extent of animal's movement. In top record, notice varied pattern of activity and frequency of small movements of a normal monkey indicated by small pen excursions. Second and third strips show hyperactivity induced by bilateral ablation of Area 13. Observe absence of pauses longer than a few seconds and that hyperactivity was undiminished three months after operation. (From Ruch and Shenkin, *J. Neurophysiol.,* 1943, *6:*349–360.)

CONDITIONED EMOTIONAL RESPONSE
Monkey #471 (Roxanne)

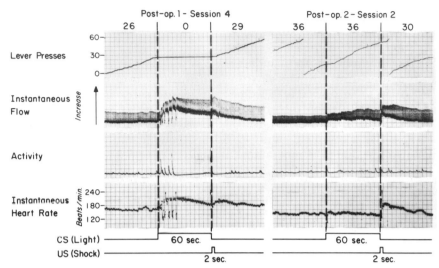

Fig. 5. The three panels of records on the left are (i) controls showing the resting state (ii) the effect of conditioned (light) and (iii) the unconditioned (shock) stimuli on lever pressing to receive food pellets and on instantaneous aortic blood flow, heart rate and general body activity, which is also reflected as an artifact in flow and rate records. The same records on the right were obtained after bilateral ablation of the frontal lobes anterior to Area 8 and a small lesion in the hypothalamus. (Unpublished records furnished by O. A. Smith, Jr. See also Stebbins and Smith, *Science,* 1964, *144:*881–883.)

of immediate memory have been suggested and tested. Also, factors mitigating the absolute nature of the loss may afford a clue to its mechanism. For example, emphasizing the correct cup or increasing motivation has been found to decrease the severity of the effect of prefrontal lesions on delayed response. They may simply make the task easier, and the impaired animals have more room for improvement than the normal, control animals. Many of these are general, i.e., effective on many of the deficits following neural lesions. It is the factors specific to delayed response which are analytical and will be mentioned.

The defect basic to "loss of immediate memory" may be one or several of the following: (i) failure to attend (as might be caused by hyperactivity), (ii) passive but rapid decay of the "stimulus set," (iii) active interference with the set, i.e., distractability, and (iv) preservation of sets from one trial to another. Indeed, reduction of external stimuli (and of activity) through elimination of light during the delay period, administration of sedative drugs, exposure of the correct object of two which are presented later, or "heightening attention to the stimulus" results in improved performance by lobecto-

mized monkeys. Clearly, the loss of this capacity to respond correctly after a delay is not absolute.

Ablation—Emotion. Clinical observations, visceral changes resulting from stimulation in animals (Chap. 26), and the anatomic connections of the prefrontal homotypical cortex to the hypothalamus and limbic system suggest that the frontal areas are concerned with emotion. This has been recently established[52] with the conditioned emotional response (CER) as documented by the heart rate and the instantaneous rate of blood flow in the aorta, on the one hand, and the rate of lever pressing to obtain small rewards on the other. As seen in Figure 5, at the onset of a conditioned stimulus, a light which has previously been associated with electric shock, lever-pressing ceases and flow and heart rate increase sharply—as much as or even more than changes elicited by the unconditioned stimulus, an electric shock. After combined lesion of the frontal lobes and of a critical area in the hypothalamus (neither lesion alone is effective), lever-pressing continues unaltered after the conditioned signal, and the circulatory responses are reduced to a small delayed rise in blood flow. That the brain mechanism of induced autonomic response is intact is shown by the persisting response to the electric shock (extreme right). The most likely interpretation is that the frontal areas in this case form a learned link between a light stimulus and the lower centers controlling vascular responses, a function shared by the hypothalamus.

Ablation—Neurosis.[20, 26, 31, 38] Certain experimental situations produce behavior in animals which strongly resembles neurotic behavior in man, although the identity of the two states is not yet proved. The classic experiment was conducted in Pavlov's laboratory in 1914 and involved the discrimination of a circle from an ellipse. A dog was "conditioned" to salivate when confronted with a circle, but not when an ellipse appeared. The ellipse was then made progressively more circular until the difference was no longer discriminable. Continued training failed to improve discrimination and, in fact, the habit deteriorated. The animal displayed neurotic behavior which Pavlov[38] described as follows:

"At the same time the whole behaviour of the animal underwent an abrupt change. The hitherto quiet dog began to squeal in its stand, kept wriggling about, tore off with its teeth the apparatus for mechanical stimulation of the skin, and bit through the tubes connecting the animal's room with the observer, a behaviour which never happened before. On being taken into the experimental room the dog now barked violently, which was also contrary to its usual custom; in short, it presented all the symptoms of a condition of acute neurosis."

Experimental neurosis is not merely a momentary emotional response. In sheep, the neurosis continues to affect behavior outside the experimental situation.[26] Twenty-four hour records of spontaneous activity or respiratory rhythm and of heartbeat yield evidence of an excited state that persists outside the experimental room. Paradoxically, birds seem susceptible to something like experimental neurosis despite their primordial cerebral cortex. Pigeons have been reported to display excessively agitated behavior or to become cataleptic for 5 to 30 minutes when confronted with "indiscriminable" visual figures in place of the readily discriminated training figures.[54]

Monkeys and chimpanzees working on difficult discrimination problems or problems near threshold tend to exhibit neurotic behavior like that of Pavlov's dogs. In a highly emotional chimpanzee unable to perform delayed reac-

tions successfully in preoperative tests, Jacobsen[20] observed the following behavior:

"This animal was extremely eager to work and apparently well motivated; but the subject was highly emotional and profoundly upset whenever she made an error. Violent temper tantrums after a mistake were not infrequent occurrences. She observed closely loading of the cup with food, and often whimpered softly as the cup was placed over the food. If the experimenter lowered or started to lower the *opaque door* to exclude the animal's view of the cups, she immediately flew into a temper tantrum, rolled on the floor, defecated and urinated. After a few such reactions during the training period, the animal would make no further responses to this test, although she responded eagerly if examined on different problems. Training on this situation was continued daily for three weeks. At the beginning, the animal had been eager to come to the experimental room, and when released from the living quarters ran to the transfer cage, opened the door and entered. But by the end of this period it was necessary to drag the animal from the living cage to the transfer cage, and in turn force her into the experimental cage. It was as complete an 'experimental neurosis' as those obtained by Pavlov's conditioned reflex procedures."

After bilateral lobectomy the animal's behavior changed profoundly. She now entered the experimental room and worked with alacrity. Mistakes and failures to obtain food caused no emotional manifestation although many more errors were made than before operation. "It was," in Jacobsen's words, "as if the animal had . . . placed its burdens on the Lord."

These observations by Jacobsen provided a rationale for "psychosurgical" operations upon the frontal areas. In 1935, Egas Moniz, a Portuguese neurologist, introduced an operation—frontal lobotomy—designed to interrupt most of the connections between the orbitofrontal area and the deeper portions of the brain without completely isolating it from the remainder of the cerebral cortex.* Certain neurotic symptoms of man, like those experimentally engendered in the chimpanzee, are altered by lobotomy. The effects of this procedure are most favorable in disorders characterized by emotional tension, e.g., anxiety neuroses, involutional depression and manic-depressive psychosis. This does not mean that the patient becomes incapable of displaying emotion; he may even be emotionally over-reactive. But, the force of the emotion or its connection with imagination and thought processes is reduced. Anxieties, thoughts or delusions which have distressed and incapacitated the patient may persist, but are remote and of no concern. Unfortunately, other matters, such as household

* For this work he shared the Nobel Prize with Hess in 1949.

duties, sexual proprieties or regard for the feelings of others, may also become of no concern to the patient.

Frontocaudate Relations. The caudate nucleus has long been associated with the control of voluntary movement (Chap. 13). Its anatomic position in the core of the frontal lobes, the newly established corticocaudate connections and some behavioral evidence suggest that the caudate nucleus (and perhaps other basal ganglia) are concerned with behavior functions as well as motor skills. On the anatomic level, Nauta[36] and DeVito and Smith[8] agree that terminal degeneration from prefrontal lesions occurs in the caudate nucleus as direct connections or by collateralization from fibers in the surrounding white matter. There is a strong possibility that fibers from the prefrontal cortex pass through the caudate nucleus since it shrinks greatly in size after prefrontal lesions and has a minutely punched-out appearance.[4] Obviously, prefrontal lesions, if deep posteriorly, may injure the caudate nucleus or its projection fibers, and, vice versa, a caudate lesion might affect the cortical projections passing beside and certainly any passing through the caudate nucleus.

Davis[7] has found that bilateral lesions of the caudate nucleus produce hyperactivity measured objectively; this hyperactivity ceases during darkness. The fact that *unilateral* lesions of the head of the caudate produce increased activity (circling) suggests that the increased walking may differ from that produced by prefrontal lesions and may be like that from lesions of Area 8.[21] Moreover, large, bilateral caudate lesions may not produce hyperactivity[9] and, in view of the anatomic relationships, negative evidence may outweigh positive evidence. Finally, the inhibitory influence of "caudate stimulation," consistent with a release of motor activity following ablation, may be caused by spread of current to fibers in the adjacent white matter, presumably coming from the prefrontal lobe (Chap. 13).

That the caudate nucleus is concerned with cognitive behavior is clearer. Bilateral lesions of the head of the caudate nucleus produce defects in delayed alternation[45] proportional to the size of the lesion;[47] similar deficits in delayed response are found.[3]

The caudate nucleus and other basal ganglia (globus pallidus) may also be involved in the third behavioral category, emotion, in which the prefrontal cortex has been implicated. The rate of extinction of a conditioned avoidance response in which a neutral stimulus is given significance by combining it with an "affective stimulus" and then withholding the affective stimulus is often considered to be indicative of neurosis and emotionality. A *decreased* rate of extinction indicates anxiety and fear. Lesions of the caudate nucleus, alone or in combination with frontal lesions, and lesions of the globus pallidus[24]—like lesions in areas more usually associated with emotion—increase the rate of extinction for some time after the operation. Thus, the basal ganglia may be concerned with the behavioral as well as the motor aspects of frontal lobe function, either as a relay station or as a detour in the pathways from the anterior and the more posterior motor areas of the frontal lobe.

FRONTAL LOBE FUNCTION IN MAN[10, 11, 32, 34, 53]

Damage of the orbitofrontal area in man produces a bewildering diversity of symptoms difficult to describe. These vary from patient to patient even though the lesions are closely similar. The manner of damage may be natural (trauma or tumor) or intentional (lobotomy, lobectomy, topectomy or gyrectomy).*

Whether the damage is bilateral is certainly important. Surgical cases provide the best evidence of the physiology of the orbitofrontal lobule in man, although the recent work of Weinstein and Teuber[58] on patients with penetrating wounds of the brain affords better information on the pre-injury status than is usually available. In both cases, evaluation of brain injury must take into account the possibility that, rather than the loss of frontal tissue being responsible for the symptoms, the scar causes abnormal neural discharge,[16] which in turn causes behavioral deficits and abnormalities. Postmortem study of the lesion is rare. In one extensively reported case, tumors were found at necropsy in many regions besides the original frontal one removed surgically. In fact, the prefrontal area's reputation for producing varied and inconsistent results may be based on the paradoxical reason that tumors may grow there with relatively few symptoms

---

* In lobotomy (or leukotomy) the fibers of the white matter of the prefrontal lobe are incised; in the other three operations, a lobule, cytoarchitectural area or gyrus, respectively, is removed.

to call attention to them, in contrast with more posterior tumors which quickly cause motor, somatosensory and visual disturbances.

Four factors contribute to the diversity of symptoms: (i) The symptoms have not been adequately reduced to objective description; (ii) different investigators studying single cases emphasize different symptoms prominent in their individual cases; (iii) except with penetrating wounds, the patients are usually psychiatrically abnormal before lobotomy and no control group with surgical damage elsewhere in the brain is available; and (iv) a control group having tumors or trauma in other regions was not studied. Teuber's[53] analysis of the pitfalls in frontal lobe studies is widely applicable to the clinical study of the brain. The following are some of the more frequently encountered disturbances.

Intelligence and Intellectual Functions.[34, 53] The prefrontal lobes, because of their prominence in man (and for very little other reason), were once considered the seat of the "intellectual" functions. However, loss of intelligence as tested by familiar mental tests is not conspicuous after orbitofrontal lobotomy;[16, 46] indeed, the most careful work comparing pre-injury scores on the Army General Classification Test with similar scores obtained ten years after destruction of the frontal lobes through penetrating wound injury has failed to show any intelligence deficit.[58, 59] In studies of lobotomy cases the greatest reliance should be placed on a comparison of test scores prior to the psychiatric disorder leading to the lobotomy. Rosvold and Mishkin[46] found both the immediate pre- and postlobotomy scores to be lower. Lobotomy has been observed to improve rather than hinder performance on intelligence tests,[10] probably by relieving the patients of anxiety. Thus, the frontal lobes are clearly not the traditional "seat of intelligence"—but they do contribute to intelligence, as do other parts of the cerebral cortex.

Recent attempts to find and to characterize cognitive defects due to frontal pole lesions have met with surprising difficulty. The more carefully sources of error in experimental design are eliminated and the more sophisticated the tests, the more elusive become the defects. Thus, if patients with posterior "association" area injury are included as a control for brain damage *per se,* they sometimes have more difficulty than the experimental group not only with verbal tests, as would be expected, but with nonverbal tests as well.

Many tests expected to present difficulty do not do so. Milner,[34] like many others, has found that one of the tasks most sensitive to prefrontal damage is a "sorting test." As shown in Figure

 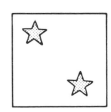 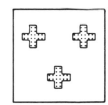 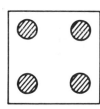

 Red
Green
Yellow
Blue

Fig. 6. Wisconsin Card Sorting Test. The response cards in the pack are placed by the patient in front of the appropriate cue cards according to whether the instruction for matching is color, number or form. The exposed card matches three of the four response cards. (Milner, Chap. 15 in *The frontal granular cortex and behavior,* Warren and Akert, eds., New York, McGraw-Hill Book Co., 1964.)

Fig. 7. A sample test field, used to test visual searching, contains 40 patterns (some repeated, so that there are 48 in all) distinguished by either shape or color or both. In each trial a duplicate of one of the patterns appears in the center of the screen (here a filled circle); the subject's task is to find the matching pattern in the periphery. (From Teuber, in *The frontal granular cortex and behavior.* Warren and Akert, eds. New York, McGraw-Hill Book Co., 1964.)

6, the patient sees four stimulus cards differing in color, form and number of geometric designs. The patient matches each card in his pack to one of the stimulus cards according to one cue, e.g., color, until ten consecutive responses are made and then that cue becomes wrong and another becomes right, etc., until all cues have been used.

Analysis shows that the errors of patients with dorsolateral frontal lesions, as opposed to those with lesions of posterior cortical areas, are perseverative, i.e., the patients tend to continue using a cue after it has ceased to be correct. A similar tendency has been detected in animal experiments and is a possible explanation of hyperactivity.

As with delayed response, the inability to shift response to meet changing environmental response is subject to more than one explanation, possibly to an inability to suppress an acquired response tendency or to a perseverative interference from previous sensory cues.

Teuber[53] found that posterior cortical lesions (traumatic) can produce as great or greater deficits than frontal lesions in tests of intelligence: sorting tests, problem-solving, and standard and specially designed tests of recent memory. Paradoxically, he found that patients with frontal lesions were relatively more affected by

tests involving perception, as in the "visual searching" test shown in Figure 7. Tests involving shifting of perceptions (or stabilization of perception when the body's position is shifted) were relatively more affected when the injury was frontal than when more posterior in the brain.

The challenge presented by the frontal (and the posterior) homotypical cortex is not only to discern a unitary defect and to characterize it verbally, e.g., in such terms as "inflexibility of behavior" and "perseveration," but also to analyze it in terms of its neural mechanisms.

Personality Changes. Since 1848, the date of the famous "crowbar" case of Phineas P. Gage, the relation of the frontal areas* to personality has been recognized. The nature of such changes is not the same in all cases of frontal lobe damage, but some form of personality alteration is usually reported.

Phineas P. Gage, an "efficient and capable" foreman, was injured on September 13, 1848, when a tamping iron was blown through the frontal region of his brain. He suffered the following change in personality, according to the physician, J. M. Harlow, who attended him. "He is fitful, irreverent, indulging at times in the grossest profanity (which was not previously his custom), manifesting but little deference to his fellows, impatient of restraint or advice when it conflicts with his desires, at times pertinaciously obstinate yet capricious and vacillating, devising many plans for future operation which are no sooner arranged than they are abandoned in turn for others appearing more feasible. ... His mind was radically changed, so that his friends and acquaintances said he was no longer Gage."†

The absence of consistency of purpose and behavior reported in this classic description is noted in many cases of damage to the orbitofrontal areas. The patients are highly distractable, turning from one activity to another according to the novelty of a fresh stimulation rather than to any plan. A lack of foresight, an inability to plan activity, and a failure to anticipate future events on the basis of past experience —all intellectual functions—contribute to a lack of continuity in behavior. The patient may not feel the ambitions, responsibilities and proprieties of his life circumstances and may be so

* In respect to localization, a crowbar leaves something to be desired; the lesions were probably frontal and if they were also hypothalamic, the fact that personality and emotionality is changed by brain damage has been before the laboratory scientist for more than a century.

†Harlow, *Boston med. surg. J.*, 1848, *39*:389.

altered that he seems a different and sometimes unacceptable person to his relatives and friends. A classic character change is *Witzelsucht,* a tendency toward frivolous and sometimes stupid and tedious joking, often at the expense of others. Some patients react with a light remark to situations of considerable gravity, and their ebullient spirits may conceal an emotional dulling. In other cases, unresponsiveness, inertia, apathy and masking of facies are characteristic, especially in the early postoperative period, and may alternate with restlessness. This calls to mind the sequence of events observed in the monkey after frontal lobectomy and after lesions of Area 13—apathy followed by an excess of activity—which in both instances is likely to be perseverative and stereotyped.

It is equally certain that the personality changes following extensive bilateral lobectomies may be slight and transitory, as in the case thoroughly studied by Hebb and Penfield.[16] More than 50 investigators from several disciplines applied a highly diversified battery of objective personality tests to a series of topectomy patients.[32] Although striking initial defects and some persisting ones were observed, no stable, characteristic pattern could be demonstrated. The results varied from individual to individual with similar lesions. It is as though the orbitofrontal lobes embody the emotional development and experience of each individual and their loss effects a change according to the original personality structure.

Lobectomy is becoming unpopular because the operation may deprive the patient of further psychiatric treatment, may alter the patient–family relationship, and produces an unfavorable admixture of desirable and undesirable effects. On the other hand, many patients have been relieved of intense suffering, saved from suicide or drug addiction and restored to something approaching a normal existence. In recent years, medication has tended to replace "psychosurgery."

TEMPORAL LOBES

Animal Experiments. Apart from the small area on the superior surface devoted to audition (Heschl's gyrus), the temporal lobe consists of a wide expanse of cerebral cortex receiving few thalamocortical projection fibers and having abundant reciprocal connections with other ho-

motypical areas. The temporal lobe intimately interconnects with auditory and visual association cortex, with the prefrontal cortex—especially the orbital gyrus—and with the limbic system. As a part of a band extending across the orbital, uncinate and cingulate gyri, the tip of the temporal lobe is involved in respiratory and vasomotor phenomena and perhaps emotion (Chap. 26).

The search for an association function in the homotypical cortex immediately adjacent to the striate area (Areas 18 and 19) has been unsuccessful.[1, 23] A search of the parietotemporo-preoccipital area was also substantially negative in respect to visual discrimination learning, though some difficulties with more elaborate somatosensory and visual learning were found. Quite surprisingly, the temporal lobe has proved to be concerned with the learning and memory of visual discriminations.[4]

A monkey, after bilateral lesions of the inferotemporal cortex (Area 21 of Brodmann), learns a visual discrimination habit more slowly than monkeys with lesions in any other part of the homotypical cortex. Moreover, if animals are first trained to criterion on a visual problem and then subjected to inferotemporal lesions, memory of the correct response is lost. The deficit caused by such temporal lesions is specific to that region and to visual problems, though the visual pathway (Meyer's loop) is not damaged. No other cortical lesions produce a comparable effect, and discriminations involving other sensory modalities are not affected by inferotemporal lesions. However, it has been learned more recently that the memory defect is not absolute. If the monkeys are trained sufficiently beyond a conventional criterion performance (90 per cent correct in a day's trials), the habit will survive the ablation.[6, 37] This raises an interesting problem as to what is the neural difference between a "just learned" and a "well learned" problem. Other examples of cortical areas which participate in learning but are widely removed from the receptive area involved in the test will be discussed in the next chapter.

Observations on Man. In the late nineteenth century, Hughlings Jackson recognized the relationship of the visual and auditory hallucinations of epileptic patients to irritating lesions in the temporal lobes—which also involved the sense of smell when a tumor encroached on nearby rhinencephalic structures.[18] Penfield[39] found that complex, well formed visual and auditory images corresponding to the past events in the individual's life are aroused by electrical stimulation of the temporal lobe surface during a brain operation. If, in Penfield's example, the patient hears music, it seems to be a specific rendition he had heard years before. He may see the orchestra or the singer, and he may re-experience the emotion aroused in him by the music long ago.

Such hallucinatory re-enactments or "flashbacks" occur at the normal tempo of life. They are elicited from the temporal lobe between the auditory and the visual sensory areas, and there is no overlap with the zone of cortex devoted to the ideational processes of speech.[39] Whereas these "evoked memories" have a clarity and tempo akin to normal memories, electrical stimulation of the temporal lobe in conscious patients paradoxically may alter the character of immediate conscious experience of what is going on at the time. As during temporal lobe epileptic discharge, the patient may feel "distant" or removed from the immediate situation. Events unfold at a slower tempo and seem absurd or fearful; they may seem strange or they may seem to have occurred before (*déjà vu* phenomenon). Occasionally the patient feels that he is far away in space and observing himself.

A syndrome of temporal lobe disease is widely recognized, the presenting symptoms varying with the locus of the lesion. With medially located tumors, "uncinate fits,'' attacks of unpleasant olfactory sensations, are frequent. Tinnitus, a slight decrease in auditory acuity and, occasionally, narrowing of the peripheral visual field opposite the lesion (involvement of adjacent visual radiation fibers) are evident. However, "dreamy states" characterize temporal lobe disease—brief or prolonged bouts of arrested consciousness, unaccompanied by convulsions, in which the individual passes off into a dream world of vivid visual and auditory hallucinations. He frequently shows some speech deficit and a poor sense of time and space. The clinical syndrome from irritative lesions obviously resembles the subjective responses to electrical stimulation of the temporal lobes.

AGNOSIA, APRAXIA, APHASIA

The loss of the memory of learned reactions,

sometimes referred to as intellectual functions, which results from cortical damage takes three principal forms—agnosia, apraxia and aphasia.

Agnosia. By this is meant loss of the ability to recognize common objects, i.e., to perceive the significance of sensory stimuli. Four forms of agnosia are distinguished: (i) *astereognosis* or tactual agnosia, the failure to recognize common objects by palpating them (see Chap. 14); (ii) *auditory agnosia* or *psychic deafness*, which merges into aphasia; (iii) *visual agnosia* or *psychic blindness*, the inability to appreciate the meaning of objects seen, of colors or of visual space in the absence of a primary visual defect; and (iv) *autotopognosis* (e.g., *finger agnosia*), failure to recognize the parts of the body, to differentiate right and left or, in general, to recognize the relationship of objects to the body.

Apraxia. In 1886, Hughlings Jackson described a selective disturbance of the higher levels of motor function known as apraxia. His patient could not stick out his tongue when asked to do so, but used it well in semiautomatic acts such as chewing and swallowing. There was no true paresis or paralysis. Thus, motor apraxia is characterized by an inability to perform voluntary movements in the absence of motor paralysis.

Both agnosia and apraxia are usually accompanied by some primary sensory or motor deficit, respectively, but not sufficient to explain the difficulties exhibited.

Aphasia.[15, 42, 60] The word "aphasia" means literally a loss of the power of speech, but the term as now used includes any marked interference with the ability either to use or to comprehend symbolic expressions of ideas by spoken or written words or by gestures, and any interference with the use of language in thinking. Formerly a sharp distinction was made between sensory and motor aphasia. By "motor aphasia" was meant the inability to speak in the absence of paralysis of the muscles of articulation; "sensory aphasia" was an inability to understand written, printed or spoken symbols of language in patients without defective vision or hearing. The aphasias are still so described, but later work indicates that the clean-cut separation formerly claimed rarely, if ever, exists in clinical cases; intermediate forms are far more numerous.

Motor or expressive aphasia. The first definite identification of the portion of the brain involved in motor aphasia seems to have been made in 1825 by Bouillaud, who attributed the defect to lesions of the frontal lobe. Then, in 1886, Marc Dax drew attention to the relationship between aphasia and lesions in the left cerebral hemisphere.

Broca made a more restricted localization— the posterior part of the third or inferior frontal convolution. This region is anterior to the lateral end of the precentral gyrus (region S in Fig. 8) and is known as Broca's area. It is now recognized that this localization is too limited and that defects in the power of speech also result from lesions of contiguous areas. Broca's region is not the cortical representation of the muscles of speech in the precentral gyrus but lies just anterior to it. (Broca's area has a characteristic cytoarchitecture, even in monkeys [Area 44 of Brodmann], and is possibly a development of the portion of Area 6 from which vocalization can be produced in monkeys by direct electrical stimulation.) As a result, aphasia occasionally occurs without voluntary paralysis of these muscles; also, the motor act of speech may sometimes be disturbed with relatively little influence on the symbolic aspect of speech.

Broca's area and adjacent regions apparently are necessary in forming the organized complex of appropriate sounds and words with which to name objects and to express concepts. Lesions affecting this area destroy more or less the ability to use spoken words appropriately. Motor aphasia may be exhibited in all degrees of completeness and in many curious varieties.

The individual may retain a limited number of words with which to express his whole range of ideas, as, for instance, in the case described by Broca in which the word "three" was made to serve for all numerical concepts. Or, only the last words spoken before a bursting cerebral vessel may survive. Thus, an English woman stricken while ordering boiled beef for luncheon had for expressing her whole range of ideas but one word—"horseradish." Automatic word series— e.g., the days of the week or counting—tend to survive, as does reactive speech demanded by a particular situation—for example, "hello" and "good-bye." When no words can be commanded for the expression of ideas (propositional speech), speech expressive of emotion— ejaculations or swearing—may persist. Usually associated with disturbance of speech is a loss of ability to write (agraphia), whether spontaneously, to dictation or from copy. Since writing involves a different set of muscles, it was natural to assume that a different cortical area is responsible for this form of expression, as in Figure 8. Although pure agraphia is rare, in some aphasics the expression of thoughts by writing is more definitely affected than is speech. When the difficulty is

in finding the word and writing it correctly, agraphia is considered comparable to aphasia; when the errors are in forming the letters, the disturbance is related to apraxia.

Sensory or receptive aphasia. In this form of aphasia, the individual suffers from an inability to *understand* spoken or written language. Classically, inability to understand spoken language (word deafness) has been attributed to lesions involving the superior and middle temporal convolutions contiguous to the cortical center for hearing (H, Fig. 8); loss of power to understand written or printed language (word blindness, alexia) is traced to lesions centered on the inferior portion of the posterior parietal lobule, the gyrus angularis, contiguous to the occipital visual area (V, Fig. 8). This separation is much too schematic. Weisenberg and McBride[60] found that some patients have greatest difficulty in comprehending spoken words; for others, the greatest difficulty is with written language; but many patients have equal trouble in both spheres. It is possible that cases of reputed word blindness or word deafness are in reality special manifestations of visual and auditory agnosia. Furthermore, Weisenberg and McBride found little evidence of pure sensory aphasia. Because of the associated expressive difficulties, they refer to this group as "predominantly receptive aphasia."

The foregoing descriptions of aphasia are strongly influenced by the "pure case" and are couched in abstract and nonquantitative termi-

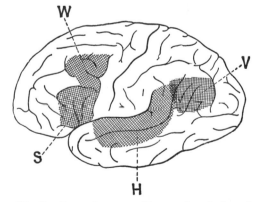

Fig. 8. Lateral aspect of human hemisphere indicating one view of localization of language areas; cortical area *V*, damage to which produces mainly word blindness; cortical area *H*, damage to which produces mainly word deafness; cortical area *S*, damage to which causes loss of articulate speech; cortical area *W*, damage to which particularly affects ability to write. (After Donaldson.)

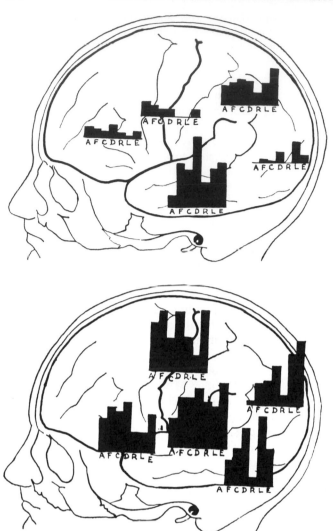

Fig. 9. A quantitative representation (average from a series of patients) of the disturbance of various aspects of language (abscissae of the histograms). The upper half of the figure represents lesions confined to one lobe, except for the cases represented by the histogram straddling the central fissure, i.e., lesions of the pre- and postcentral gyrus. In the lower half of the figure two lobes or lobules were damaged. The histogram beginning at the top represents lesions in the fronto-parietal, fronto-temporal, parieto-temporal, parieto-occipital and temporo-occipital. A, Articulatory disturbances. F, Difficulties in the fluency of speech. C, Disturbances of verbal comprehension. D, Disturbances of naming. R, Disturbances of repetition. L, Disturbances in reading. E, Disturbances of writing.

nology of faculty psychology; current attempts to classify speech difficulties have become more operational and quantitative even to the point of employing the techniques of the philologists, who can characterize Americanese, U-Talk or Swahili with the same notation.[42] Figure 9 represents a less ambitious attempt to describe quantitatively the disturbances of the various aspects of speech characteristic of lesions in the various lobes of the brain. In each case, seven aspects of speech are shown by a histogram mnemonically labeled (in French); each bar represents the degree of disturbance on the conventional, clinical, five-point scale, in which scaling units were carefully defined. Note that the temporal and, in lesser degree, the parietal lobe lesions cause a significantly greater disturbance than lesions in other lobes. When two or three lobes are damaged, the disturbance of

speech is greatly increased. The profile of the histogram indicating kind of disturbances varies when the lesion is in different lobes, the motor difficulties being *relatively* more prominent in anterior lesions and defects in the more sensory aspects of language being more prominent after the posterior lesions—so-called "sensory aphasia." These more quantitative studies bear out those of Weisenberg and McBride.[60]

Aphasia as an intellectual defect. Aphasics once labeled "expressive" or "receptive" are found, on close examination, to have disturbances of language as a symbolic function and disturbances of intellectual function in general.

Disturbance of the language mechanism at a high level is *amnesic aphasia*, which may exist in a relatively pure form. In this form of aphasia, which may appear with lesions anywhere in the dominant speech cortex, the articulation of words is normal and the understanding of language is not gravely affected. Nevertheless, the patient finds the naming of objects difficult and often searches for words while speaking. According to Schiller,[50] some difficulty in word finding is evident in all true aphasias. Temporal lobe aphasia presents, above the impairment of hearing, both difficulty of understanding and of memory for spoken language. According to Goldstein,[12] there are disturbances of an intellectual character—e.g., the inability to categorize, to sort miscellaneous collections of objects according to classes. These defects are supposed to result not from lesions affecting the speech areas, but from widespread although not severe cortical damage.

REFERENCES

1. ADES, H. W. and RAAB, D. H. *J. Neurophysiol.*, 1949, *12:* 101–108.
2. AKERT, K. Chap. 18 in WARREN and AKERT.[57]
3. BATTIG, K., ROSVOLD, H. E. and MISHKIN, M. *J. comp. physiol. Psychol.*, 1960, *53:*400–404.
4. BURANDT, D. C., FRENCH, G. M. and AKERT, K. *Confin. neurol. (Basel)*, 1961, *21:*289–306.
5. CHOW, K. L. and HUTT, P. J. *Brain*, 1953, *76:*625–677.
6. CHOW, K. L. and SURVIS, J. *Arch Neurol. Psychiat. (Chic.)*, 1958, *79:*640–646.
7. DAVIS, G. D. *Neurology*, 1958, *8:*135–139.
8. DeVITO, J. L. and SMITH, O. A., JR., *J. comp. Neurol.*, 1965, *123:*413–419.
9. DeVITO, J. L. and RUCH, T. C. Unpublished observations.
10. FREEMAN, W. and WATTS, J. W. *Psychosurgery in the treatment of mental disorders and intractable pain,* 2nd ed. Springfield, Ill., Charles C Thomas, 1950.
11. FULTON, J. F. *Functional localization in the frontal lobes and cerebellum.* Oxford, Clarendon Press, 1949.
12. GOLDSTEIN, K. *Language and language disturbances.* New York, Grune & Stratton, 1948.
13. GROSS, C. G. and WEISKRANTZ, L. *Exp. Neurol.*, 1962, *5:* 453–476.
14. GROSS, C. G. and WEISKRANTZ, L. Chap. 5 in WARREN and AKERT.[57]
15. HEAD, H. *Aphasia and kindred disorders of speech.* New York, Macmillan Company, 1926.
16. HEBB, D. O. and PENFIELD, W. *Arch. Neurol. Psychiat. (Chic.)*, 1940, *44:*421–438.
17. HÉCAEN, H. and ANGELERGUES, R. In: de Reuck and O'Connor.[42]
18. JACKSON, J. H. and BEEVOR, C. E. *Brain*, 1889, *12:*346–357.
19. JACOBSEN, C. F.. *Comp. Psychol. Monogr.*, 1936, *13*, no. 63:3–60.
20. JACOBSEN, C. F., WOLFE, J. B. and JACKSON, T. A. *J. nerv. ment. Dis.*, 1935, *82:*1–14.
21. KENNARD, M. A. and ECTORS, L. *J. Neurophysiol.*, 1938, *1:* 45–54.
22. KENNARD, M. A., SPENCER, S. and FOUNTAIN, G., JR. *J. Neurophysiol.*, 1941, *4:*512–524.
23. LASHLEY, K. S. *Genet. Psychol. Monogr.*, 1948, *37:*107–166.
24. LAURSEN, A. M. *Acta physiol. scand.*, 1963, *57:*81–89.
25. LEARY, R. W., HARLOW, H. F., SETTLAGE, P. H. and GREENWOOD, D. D. *J. comp. physiol. Psychol.*, 1952, *45:* 576–584.
26. LIDDELL, H. S. Chap. 26 in *Physiology of the nervous system,* 3rd ed., J. F. Fulton, ed. New York, Oxford University Press, 1949.
27. LIVINGSTON, R. B., FULTON, J. F., DELGADO, J. M. R., SACHS, E., JR., BRENDLER, S. J. and DAVIS, G. *Res. Publ. Ass. nerv. ment. Dis.*, 1948, *27:*405–420.
28. MAIRE, F. W. Unpublished observations.
29. MAIRE, F. W. and PATTON, H. D. *Amer. J. Physiol.*, 1954, *178:*315–320.
30. MALMO, R. B. *J. Neurophysiol.*, 1942, *5:*295–308.
31. MASSERMAN, J. H. *Behavior and neurosis; an experimental psychoanalytic approach to psychobiologic principles.* Chicago, University of Chicago Press, 1943.
32. METTLER, F. A., ed. *Selective partial ablation of the frontal cortex; a correlative study of its effects on human psychotic subjects.* New York, Paul B. Hoeber, Inc., 1949.
33. MILES, R. C. and BLOMQUIST, A. J. *J. Neurophysiol.*, 23: 471–484, 1960.
34. MILNER, B. Chap. 15 in WARREN and AKERT.[57]
35. MISHKIN, M. *J. Neurophysiol.*, *20:*615–622, 1957.
36. NAUTA, W. J. H. Chap. 19 in WARREN and AKERT.[57]
37. ORBACH, J. and FANTZ, R. T. *J. comp. physiol. Psychol.*, 1958, *51:*126–129.
38. PAVLOV, I. P. *Conditioned reflexes: an investigation of the physiological activity of the cerebral cortex.* London, Oxford University Press, 1927.
39. PENFIELD, W. and KRISTIANSEN, K. *Epileptic seizure patterns.* Springfield, Ill., Charles C Thomas, 1951.
40. PENFIELD, W. and PEROT, P. *Brain*, 1963, *86:*595–696.
41. PRIBRAM, H. B. and BARRY, J. *J. Neurophysiol.*, 1956, *19:* 99–106.
42. de REUCK, A. V. S. and O'CONNOR, M., eds. *Disorders of language.* Ciba Foundation Symposium. Boston, Little, Brown and Co., 1964.
43. RICHTER, C. P. and HINES, M. *Brain*, 1938, *61:*1–16.
44. ROSE, J. E. and WOOLSEY, C. N. *Res. Publ. Ass. nerv. ment. Dis.*, 1948, *27:*210–232.
45. ROSVOLD, H. E. and DELGADO, J. M. R. *J. comp. physiol. Psychol.*, 1956, *49:*365–372.
46. ROSVOLD, H. E. and MISHKIN, M. *Canad. J. Psychol*, 1950, *4:*122–126.
47. ROSVOLD, H. E., MISHKIN, M. and SZWARCBART, M. K. *J. comp. physiol. Psychol.*, 1958, *51:*437–444.
48. RUCH, T. C. *Res. Publ. Ass. nerv. ment. Dis.*, 1934, *15:* 289–330.
49. RUCH, T. C. and SHENKIN, H. A. *J. Neurophysiol.*, 1943, *6:*349–360.
50. SCHILLER, F. *J. Neurol. Psychiat. (Chic.)*, 1947, *10:*183–197.
51. SERAFETINIDES, E. A. and FALCONER, M. A. *Brain*, 1963, *86:*333–346.
52. STEBBINS, W. C. and SMITH, O. A., JR., *Science*, 1964, *144:* 881–883.
53. TEUBER, H.-L. Chap. 20 in WARREN and AKERT.[57]
54. TOWE, A. L. *J. comp. physiol. Psychol.*, 1954, *47:*283–287.
55. WALKER, A. E. *The primate thalamus.* Chicago, University of Chicago Press, 1938.
56. WALKER, A. E. *J. comp. Neurol.*, 1940, *73:*59–86.
57. WARREN, J. M. and AKERT, K., eds. *The frontal granular cortex and behavior.* New York, McGraw-Hill Book Co., 1964.
58. WEINSTEIN, S. and TEUBER, H.-L. *J. comp. physiol. Psychol.*, 1957, *50:*535–539.
59. WEINSTEIN, S. and TEUBER, H.-L. *Science*, 1957, *125:*1036–1037.
60. WEISENBERG, T. and McBRIDE, K. E. *Aphasia, a clinical and psychological study.* New York, Commonwealth Fund, 1935.

CHAPTER 24

Neurophysiology of Learning and Memory

By MITCHELL GLICKSTEIN

ONE of the most characteristic attributes of man and of higher animals is the ability to learn, to modify behavior as a result of experience. It is now a basic postulate, although it did not appear self-evident to the ancients, that all of the remarkable functions of learning and memory are mediated by the nervous system.

In broadest terms, learning is a kind of plasticity of the nervous system. The nervous system, especially in mammals, can store information, can modify response to stimuli, and can even recover functionally from irreversible structural damage. It is a common clinical observation that the initial severe impairment following trauma or vascular damage to the nervous system may improve with time, even to the point that initial deficits disappear entirely. Since residual brain damage is still present at the end of improvement, the mechanism of recovery is a central question allied to learning. How is the brain reorganized when an aphasic patient regains the power of speech? Our understanding of the mechanism of plasticity is very limited. There is, however, a body of knowledge gained from laboratory experiments that establishes something of the nature of the problem and provides suggestions about its ultimate solution.

It is useful to distinguish at the outset between two related aspects of the problem of neural mechanisms in learning and memory. One is the detailed molecular changes associated with these phenomena; the other is the neural organization as it relates to learning and memory. There must be some morphologic change in the nervous system which is identifiable with the process of learning. Several theories relating learning to structural changes at the synapse or chemical alterations within nerve cells have been proposed. At present, however, all such explanations are largely speculative; even if one or more of them should prove correct, an important problem would remain unsolved—the problem of total organization of the nervous system for learning and memory. How does an organism store and retrieve information? Are memory traces stored in single cells or groups of cells, or are they a property of the entire nervous system? Are memory traces singly or multiply represented?

The two problems—molecular basis of memory and brain organization for learning—are not identical, although they are closely interrelated. The interrelationship may be exemplified by an analogy to a computer. In most complex digital computing machines some part of the structure is devoted to a form of "memory store." Relays, magnetic cores, tapes, etc., are among the storage devices. But an understanding of the specific "memory" mechanism would not give complete insight into the role of memory elements in the function of the machine. In order to understand this role, much more knowledge of the coding of input to the memory store and the way the information is retrieved and used is needed. In the problem of brain function, an analogous distinction exists between detailed molecular or physical changes identifiable with learning and the total neural organization for processing, coding and storing sensory input.

The most puzzling feature of learning is the time scale. Neurophysiologists are accustomed to neural events which occur in milliseconds or, at most, seconds. In contrast, learned material and motor skills may be retained over many years. Hence, it seems likely that learning mechanisms differ qualitatively and quantitatively from simple reflexes.

Of the many experimental studies dealing with learning, most concern behavioral changes brought about by varying environmental conditions rather than underlying physiologic mechanisms. For example, studies have dealt with the effects of varying the time between learning trials on the speed of learning. In other experiments the effect of varying the amount and timing of rewards has been studied. Since such studies provide a basis of facts and techniques for physiologic analysis, some of them will be reviewed.

TYPES OF LEARNING

Behavioral studies of learning fall into two broad classes. The first is a type of learning situation in which the subject plays a relatively *passive* role in the training, as exemplified by Pavlovian conditioning and by habituation. In the second type of learning situation, the subject plays a relatively more active role, as in the experiments on the acquisition and retention of such behavior as bar pressing, maze learning and avoidance of painful stimuli.

Often some one type of learning situation is assumed to be the "simplest" or the "most general" type of learning. For example, Pavlovian conditioning, to be described below, has often been considered as *the* model for all learning. However, no model theory or experimental approach seems clearly to be the simplest or the most logical candidate for physiologic study.

Pavlovian Conditioning. Many of the early studies of learning in animals were conducted in the laboratory of I. P. Pavlov.[42] Accordingly, the technique he employed for study of the learning mechanism has been called *Pavlovian* or classical conditioning. In a typical experiment, a dog in a restraining harness was presented with a variety of stimuli and its responses, usually the secretion of saliva, were measured. Figure 1 shows the apparatus. Pavlov found that repeated presentation of a stimulus, which in itself elicited no salivation, e.g., a bell, called

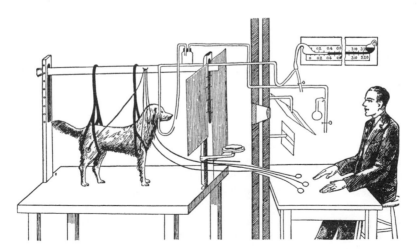

Fig. 1. Dog in apparatus used by Pavlov for establishing or experimenting upon conditioned responses. Observer is in separate room with three keys to manipulate. With one of the keys he controls injection of acid into mouth, resulting flow of saliva being indicated by scale (greatly enlarged) above his head. With other two keys he can stimulate mechanically skin of dog at two points, one on foreleg and one on hindleg. (After Pavlov, *Lectures on conditioned reflexes*, 1927.)

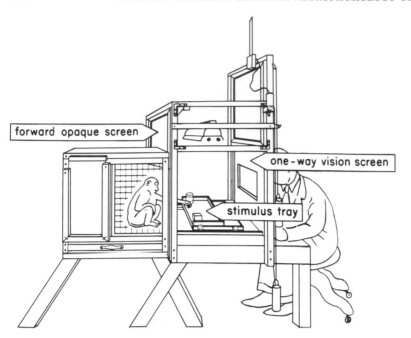

Fig. 2. Sketch showing Wisconsin General Test Apparatus suited to primates. The experimenter can present the monkey with a variety of discrimination tasks and remain unobserved during the training. (From Harlow and Bromer, *Psychol. Rec.*, 1938, 2:434–436.)

the *conditioned stimulus* (CS), when quickly followed by the presentation of a salivation-eliciting stimulus such as food or a weak acid, the *unconditioned stimulus,* brought about a striking behavioral change. Initially, the dog salivated only to the presentation of the unconditioned stimulus, e.g., food. In time, after a number of pairings of bell with food, a salivary response to the bell alone gradually developed. Pavlov termed this response to the bell a *conditioned reflex.*

Studies of conditioned reflexes have led to many important observations about the nature of the learning process. Pavlov found, for example, that conditioning would occur only if the conditioned stimulus preceded the unconditioned stimulus. If the bell was presented after the food, despite repeated trials, "backward conditioning" was never clearly established.

Pavlov also found that after a conditioned response was well established, repeated presentation of the conditioned stimulus (bell) alone elicited less and less salivation on successive presentations until finally the bell alone elicited no salivary response at all. This progressive decrease in the conditioned response to the conditioned stimulus presented alone Pavlov termed *extinction.* He suggested that extinction was not simply due to a passive "forgetting" of the conditioned response, but was an active process brought about by some "inhibitory" mechanism. Evidence for an inhibitory process

in extinction is that if the same animal is tested with the bell alone after a rest period, the conditioned response typically reappears. That is, there is spontaneous recovery of the conditioned reflex. After conditioning is established, a stimulus similar in some respect to the conditioned stimulus will also elicit a conditioned reflex. For example, if a bell with a different tone is now presented, it too will elicit salivation. This phenomenon Pavlov called *generalization.* He further found that with further training he could teach the animal to *discriminate* between reinforced (paired with food) and unreinforced (unpaired with food) stimuli.

In the original classical conditioning experiments, the interval between the onset of the conditioned stimulus and the unconditioned stimulus was brief; on the order of 1 to 5 seconds. In such cases, the conditioned response of a trained animal typically occurs almost immediately after the onset of the conditioned stimulus. If in such an animal the interval between presentation of conditioned and unconditioned stimuli is increased, the latency of the conditioned response gradually increases. Pavlov termed such responses *delayed reflexes.*

Habituation.   If an animal is subjected to an unfamiliar stimulus, it actively "attends" to the stimulus; e.g., the dog turns its head in the direction of a novel sound. Pavlov considered such a response to be general and innate in all men and animals and termed it the "investigatory" or

"What is it?" reflex. It is now more usually termed the "orienting reflex." If the stimulus is presented repeatedly, such orienting behavior gradually decreases until finally no detectable behavioral response is elicited. The decrement in behavioral response produced by repeated presentation of an unreinforced stimulus is called *habituation*. Since habituation typically occurs within a few trials and is observed in many species,[56] it has been used as an experimental model of neural plasticity.

Instrumental Conditioning. In Pavlovian conditioning, the animal is a passive participant in the experimental procedure, stimuli and food being presented to him in fixed order irrespective of his behavior. In *instrumental conditioning*, by contrast, the animal must make some response, which determines whether the conditioning is or is not *reinforced*. The apparatus is thus used as an instrument upon which the animal performs and the behavior is termed an *instrumental response*. One of the earliest studies of instrumental conditioning utilized the problem box of Thorndike.[55] A cat was placed inside a box with food outside. To reach the food the animal had to manipulate one or more catches on the door of the box. In successive trials the time necessary for the animal to emerge from the box and gain its reward became less and less. Thus, the animal was required to respond actively to be reinforced.

Since then a large number of problem boxes, mazes, and discrimination apparatuses have been developed and are classified as instrumental learning devices. One of these which has become widely used is the *Wisconsin General Test Apparatus* (WGTA) (Fig. 2). A monkey is placed in a testing cage in which is a tray containing one or more hollowed-out wells. These wells may be covered by blocks on which are painted or mounted distinctive patterns, colors, or objects. Animals learn to displace distinctive blocks to obtain a raisin or other reward. Such *discrimination learning* is useful in studies on cortical localization in learning and sensory function.

Another technique involves a specific instrumental response to escape from or avoid entirely a noxious stimulus. As an example of such *escape and avoidance conditioning*, an animal is placed in one part of a two-compartment box with a grid floor. At a specified time or after the onset of a distinctive stimulus, the grid floor of the starting compartment is electrified, delivering a mild shock to the animal's feet so that it must *escape* to the non-shock side of the box, which it does more and more promptly with successive trials. If this procedure is repeated often enough, the animal learns to leave the starting compartment immediately, *before* the onset of voltage in the grid floor. That is, he learns to *avoid* the noxious stimulus entirely.

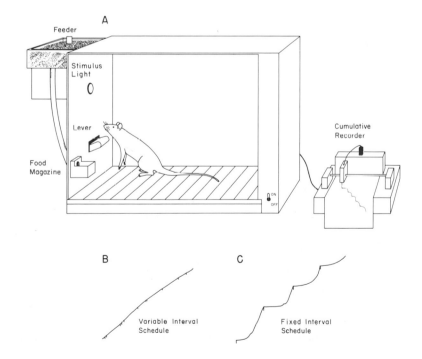

Fig. 3. *A,* Diagram of a typical "Skinner Box." Pressing the lever will lead to the delivery of a pellet in the food magazine below. Each lever press is registered by advancing the recorder pen upward on a slowly moving paper. *B* and *C,* Typical cumulative records of behavior during variable and fixed interval reinforcement. Downward deflections are reinforced responses.

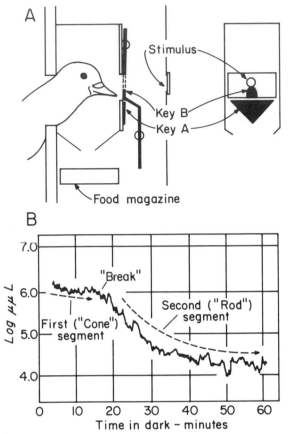

Fig. 4. *A,* Apparatus for determining visual thresholds in the pigeon. Side view left; pigeon's view at right. Use of two keys is explained in the text. *B,* Curve of dark adaptation in the pigeon, obtained by continuous recording of brightness threshold in a darkened chamber. (After Blough, *J. comp. physiol. Psychol.,* 1956, *49*:425–430.)

Skinner[47] has developed a sensitive, flexible and widely used apparatus for the study of instrumental responses (called *operant* responses by him) which automatically records the responses. An animal is put into a chamber containing a lever, which if depressed delivers a small pellet of food. The apparatus is arranged to permit cumulative recording of such lever-pressing responses. Once the lever-pressing response is well established, any desired modifications in the delivery of reinforcement may be instituted. For example, the animal may receive food for only every fifth lever press. Alternatively, it might be reinforced for a lever press only after a fixed or variable interval of time has elapsed. Each of these so-called *schedules of reinforcement* produces characteristic temporal distributions of behavioral response.[15] Figure 3

shows a typical Skinner Box and some characteristic cumulative records of lever pressing under varying schedules of reinforcement.

The Skinner Box can also be used for discrimination training. One way is by reinforcing the animal only in the presence of a specific stimulus. For example, pressing the lever might activate the feeder only when a lighted window over the lever is illuminated.

The Skinner Box is a versatile instrument. It may be modified to study a variety of species; the behavior required is not necessarily restricted to lever pressing, nor is food the only effective reinforcer. Pigeons, for example, are usually trained to peck a key in the Skinner Box. The apparatus may even be modified so that the response is instrumental for the avoidance of a mild shock. It is initially highly improbable that behavior such as lever pressing in the Skinner Box or cup displacement in the WGTA will occur on the part of an untrained animal. Therefore, attainment of the desired behavior is not usually left to chance. Rather, the behavior is gradually *shaped* by reinforcing successive approximations to the desired response. For example, a rat might first be reinforced whenever it was *near* the lever, then whenever it *touched* the lever, and finally only after it had *pressed* the lever. By skillful use of shaping, many behavioral responses can be rapidly trained.

Some of the experimental techniques employed in the study of learning have proved widely useful for other problems. By skillful use of reinforcement one may measure physiologic variables in experimental animals which in man are mediated by verbal report, e.g., sensory threshold. For example, Blough[1] trained pigeons in a box containing two keys so that they pecked at key A when a standard light was on and key B when the light was off. He then arranged a circuit, such that pecking on key A not only recorded the fact of pecking, but also lowered the illumination of the standard. Thus, the pigeon would now peck until the illumination had been reduced below its visible threshold. Then the pigeon pecked at key B. Key B recorded the fact of pecking and also *increased* the illumination. In this way, it was possible to establish a precise visual intensity threshold for the pigeon. The apparatus and one application are shown in Figure 4. Such behavioral data can be as precise as any obtainable from a human subject. By appropriate use of conditioning techniques, it has been possible to determine thresholds for several modalities of sensation and to measure in experimental animals such phenomena as reaction time[54] and to plot perimetric visual fields.[9]

In the preceding discussion of behavioral studies, the important concept of reinforcement has not been defined. The word is used in a rather different way in Pavlovian and instrumental learning. In Pavlovian conditioning reinforcement refers simply to the temporal pairing of conditioned and unconditioned stimuli. In instrumental learning, it is the prompt pairing of a *response* and some relevant stimulus consequence such as food. The stimulus consequence often is thought to produce satisfaction of a drive or need.

CENTRAL "CIRCUITS" IN LEARNING

Ablation and Stimulation. Many of the early investigators of the neural basis of learning attempted to determine the central point at which the learning process occurs, and in search of this point they followed the route which is taken by neural activity from the sensory input to the motor output in learned behavior. Like Pavlov's experiments, such a view of the learning process is obviously modeled after the concept of a reflex. It is not surprising, therefore, that many early investigators used Pavlovian conditioning as a basic tool in an attempt to learn at what point in the nervous system the learned connection between the conditioned stimulus and the unconditioned response takes place. Many studies have shown that Pavlov's own view of a reflex-like pathway within the cortex is far oversimplified. Lashley[31] found that retention of learned responses in rats is unaffected by deep cuts that section transcortical association fibers connecting visual and motor cortex. Moreover, Sperry has reported that extensive subpial crosshatching,[49] and transverse implantation of tantalum metal[51] or mica[50] within the cortex are without effect on learning or memory, skilled visual discrimination, or precisely patterned movements.

Loucks was one of the first to analyze classical conditioning neurophysiologically. He originated a technique for stimulation of neural centers and pathways with buried electrodes in un-

anesthetized animals.[35] * He used such stimulation in an effort to determine the neural structures essential for learning. He found that central stimulation could serve as the conditioned stimulus.[37] Thus, instead of using a peripheral sensory stimulus such as light or tone, he established that direct stimulation of a spinal afferent pathway or the cerebral sensory cortex may serve as a conditioned stimulus for salivation or leg flexion when appropriately paired with food or shock. In contrast, Loucks was unable to establish a conditioned response when central stimulation was applied to the motor side.[36] An electrode was placed in a cortical region which reliably elicited leg flexion in experimental animals. Despite hundreds of pairings of other (conditioned) stimuli with stimulation of such a cortical point, a response to the conditioned stimulus alone was never observed. The point of stimulation was below the point of connection of the conditioned stimulus and the unconditioned response. These studies seemed to indicate that the connection between a conditioned and unconditioned response occurs somewhere between the sensory and motor areas of the cortex. Several experiments, early and recent, suggest that this is not so.[31, 49]

Recently, many of these pioneering observations of Loucks have been repeated and extended. Doty *et al.*[11] were able to employ cortical stimulation as a CS (thus confirming Loucks), and have also reported conditioning established by using brain stimulation as the unconditioned stimulus. Resolution of these discrepant observations awaits further experimentation.

Electrical Recording. A number of recent studies have employed electrical recording of neural activity in chronic experimental animals in an attempt to gain further information on possible neural circuits involved in learning. One of the first such studies was reported by John and Killam.[28] They suggested that low frequency stimuli might serve as "tracers" for detecting those neural structures "processing" the conditioned stimulus. They reasoned that if electrical activity at the frequency of the "tracer" stimulus could be recorded from a given nucleus or tract at one phase of the learn-

*He buried the secondary of an induction coil and led wires from it to the brain. A primary coil was placed just over the secondary to induce a current in it. No electrodes are passed through and cemented to the skull.

ing process, this would constitute evidence that the structure was involved in the learning process at that time. They used a 10 per second flickering light as CS and recorded evoked 10 per second activity in many brain sites. If the CS were presented repeatedly without reinforcement (habituation) such activity was seen to drop out and in fact was recorded with difficulty even in the primary visual pathways themselves. When the 10 per second stimulus was now paired with painful foot shock in a double grill box (avoidance conditioning), activity recurred at the flash frequency in many (but not all) of the recording sites.

These studies give us a valuable introduction to the problem of the neural pathways of conditioning. Many of the techniques and principles described are new and there is still a good deal of contradiction and confusion in the literature. Thus, they have not as yet provided conclusive evidence as to a route from the conditioned stimulus to the unconditioned stimulus. The question of the locus or loci at which the conditioned and unconditioned stimuli interact is still an unsettled one.

Spinal and Subcortical Conditioning. Closely related to the problem of the neural circuits involved in conditioning is the question of the neural structures which might be capable of being conditioned. For example, studies have been directed at determining whether conditioning may occur in the spinal cord alone. If spinal conditioning were possible, one might hope to have a simpler preparation for the study of learning. Moreover, a demonstration of spinal conditioning bears upon the problem of neural plasticity: Is it a property of all groups of neurons? The weight of the evidence[16] suggests that spinal conditioning of adult mammals either does not occur or that it is, at best, a very crude type of response. On the other hand, experiments[10] have shown that the cerebral cortex is not necessary for establishment of learned responses. However, conditioning in a decorticate animal is slowly established and is crude in the sense that only a gross, widespread conditioned response is obtained after the cortex is ablated. We might infer from these studies that the cortex is a basic and important site of at least some learning processes. However, to conclude that the cortex is the only organ of learning would be wrong. Learning *may* occur in the absence of a cerebral cortex in the mammal, and is certainly exhibited by many nonmammalian forms with little true cerebral cortex. The pigeon, for example, is capable of rapidly learning extremely refined and difficult visual discriminations. Indeed, excellent discrimination learning has been clearly demonstrated in the octopus.

Evoked Potentials During Habituation. We have already given an example of chronic electrical recording from experimental animals used to study possible pathways in establishment of a conditioned response. A number of studies have been reported attempting to determine whether changes in such potentials might be associated with changes in the "significance" of the stimulus evoking them. Habituation has been described as a decrement in behavioral response associated with repeated presentation of an unreinforced stimulus. It is natural to wonder whether habituation is correlated with any observable changes of the evoked potential elicited by the habituated stimulus. Parallel with the development of behaviorally observed habituation there is a corresponding decrease in the amplitude or distribution of evoked potential recorded from the cortex.[17, 25, 39] Such changes have been seen in subcortical sensory relays as well. A decrement may even be seen in the "arousal" effects elicited by repeated stimulation of the brain stem reticular formation.[20]

If a habituated stimulus is paired with an unconditioned stimulus such as shock to the paw, a gradual increase in the amplitude of the potential evoked by the conditioned stimulus and a more widespread distribution are recorded. Obviously, then, neurophysiologic changes in evoked potentials may be associated with behavioral changes. However, although such observations may point the way to studies of neural events associated with learning, there are some cautions in interpreting such data at present. One problem of these studies is a lack of clarity in the meaning of the term *response*. The word is borrowed from behavioral experiments, in which it has a direct meaning: that which the animal *does*. In evoked potential studies the concept of response is often carried over and applied to an electrical event such as the amplitude of an evoked potential. Some authors tend to cloud the important distinction between such electrical "responses" and a behaviorally observed event. Since the precise mechanism of evoked potentials is itself still unclear, such research at present can serve only as a rather crude index of possible brain mechanisms in habituation and arousal.

THE LOCUS OF MEMORY STORAGE

The studies already presented concern neural circuits, minimal necessary amount of neural tissue, and electrical correlates of learning. The studies in the present section are largely concerned with the *locus* of memory storage. Typically, these studies have sought to establish whether memory is stored in any single brain locus or whether it is stored more diffusely. The questions have been asked: Are storage patterns different for motor as opposed to sensory learning? Is learning associated with one or another sensory input stored in any characteristic locus relative to the anatomic projections of that sense? Typically, these studies have used some form of instrumental learning as a basic tool. Animals have been trained to perform a response and the effects on that response of brain lesions has been tested.

Cortical Ablations. Many of these studies have their origin in the work of Lashley, a psychologist, whose life work spanned more than thirty years, during which he originated many of the ideas and experimental approaches currently employed in the study of the neural basis of learning and memory.[31, 33] Two major sequences of Lashley's experiments form the basis for many subsequent experiments. Their objective is not to study instrumental conditioning as such, but rather the perceptual or sensory reorganization involved in learning and memory. Instrumental conditioning has been employed to provide an *index* of such reorganization. Although Lashley's studies did not answer the problem of brain mechanisms in learning, they swept away oversimplified and speculative explanations; any final understanding will have to take account of his many observations on the nature of the "engram"—the name he used for the neural substrate of learning. In one of Lashley's first experiments rats were trained to select one of two passageways in a discrimination apparatus, the one leading to food being signaled by the presence or absence of a light. Lashley found that rats mastered this discrimination after complete destruction of striate cortex and, in fact, equaled the performance of their normal cage mates. However, if the brightness discrimination was learned prior to the lesion, the response was lost but could be reacquired in the same number of trials. Lashley found that if the optic tectum and pretectal regions were de-

stroyed as well, the brightness discrimination was permanently abolished. He concluded that in the absence of visual cortex, brightness learning was mediated by the tectum, but that the tectum did not participate in visual learning so long as the cortex was intact.

For his second series of experiments, Lashley devised a simple maze. He studied acquisition of maze running ability in rats which had been subjected to prior cortical lesions, and retention in rats which were trained as normals and *then* were operated upon. Cortical lesions made it relatively difficult for a naive animal to acquire the maze response or for a trained animal to reacquire it after lesion. Also, cortical lesions interfered with retention of a preoperatively learned maze response. Lashley looked carefully for the localization of this learning in one or another region of the cerebral cortex. He found that in no case was loss of the maze response associated specifically with damage to any single cortical structure, but was in every case a function simply of the *amount* of cortical tissue removed. Lashley's theoretical explanation of these experimental results was that the cortex has a nonspecific, "mass action" effect and that cortical lesions interfere with the acquisition and/or retention of the solution to a difficult problem independent of locus.

Lashley's conclusions were quickly criticized[26] because the learning of the maze habit is contingent on many sensory cues. Hence, it might be expected that no specific localization would be found for it. If the maze habit were partly learned on a visual and partly on a proprioceptive basis, learning would not be completely impaired by a lesion which affected only visual or proprioceptive function. Moreover, it is very difficult to disentangle the two effects of a lesion, namely, sensory loss and learning ability *per se*, and hence to evaluate whether the phenomenon of "mass action" truly exists.

Man and animals learn an amazing variety of motor skills. Lashley[30] asked whether the learned element of these skills is "localized" in the classical motor cortex. He trained monkeys to manipulate locks and hasps to obtain food, and then ablated large areas of cortex anterior to the central sulcus. While there was a great deal of postoperative paralysis, when the animals were somewhat recovered and presented with the problem boxes, they successfully and errorlessly performed the task that had been

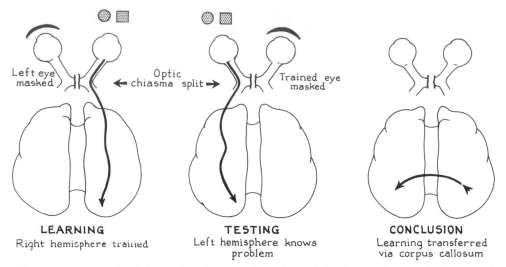

LEARNING
Right hemisphere trained

TESTING
Left hemisphere knows
problem

CONCLUSION
Learning transferred
via corpus callosum

Fig. 5. Diagram of training and testing procedures for studying interocular transfer in a cat after section of the optic chiasma. (After Myers, *J. comp. physiol. Psychol.*, 1955, *48*:470–473.)

learned preoperatively. Thus, the mechanisms of execution were affected but the "know-how" of the habit was not.

Many other studies have shown that learned motor responses are not *simply* localized within the brain. Lashley[31] found that rats with cerebellar lesions were so disturbed that they rolled instead of running a previously learned maze but with no decrease in accuracy of performance.

Chimpanzees with massive bilateral lesions of parietal cortex which caused severe initial inability to discriminate between weights showed not the slightest defect in the habit of alternately "hefting" the weights before selecting one—except that due to paralysis.[43]

In classical neurology, learning has been ascribed to the association cortex. For example, the visual impulses which project to striate cortex classically are thought to be stored in the immediately surrounding prestriate cortex Areas 18 and 19 of Brodmann). To test this, Lashley[32] made massive lesions of prestriate cortex in experimental animals, and found little or no decrement in learning or retention of visual patterns.

So far most of the evidence for engram localization has been negative. However, two phenomena reliably associated with damage to association cortex in primates were discussed in the previous chapter. One is Jacobsen's discovery[27] that lesions to the frontal lobes anterior to the arcuate sulcus resulted in an inability of a monkey or chimpanzee to perform a task re-

quiring memory of the position of an object during a period of forced delay (the so-called delayed response). While such frontal lesions appear to affect immediate memory in the monkey, paradoxically, they seem to be without a major effect on long-term memory (or the initial acquisition) of a discrimination habit. In contrast, as pointed out previously, such visual discrimination habits are lost after lesions of the inferior temporal Area 21 (Brodmann) of the monkey,[6] an association area. The effects of these lesions far removed from the visual areas are not attributable to mere sensory loss; no effect on the visual acuity of monkeys is found.[57] Recently studies of the mechanisms involved in these association cortex functions have suggested that they are mediated by cortico-cortical pathways. Chow[7] has shown that the inferotemporal cortex is functionally connected to striate cortex via cortico-cortical association fibers presumably relaying in prestriate cortex. An analysis of the pathways involved in delayed response performance suggests that the occipital cortex is probably in functional connection with frontal cortex via a cortico-cortical route.[22]

Interhemispheric Transfer of Learning. The localization of learned response can be studied free of possible damage to sensory areas or pathways in experiments involving section of the corpus callosum. This operation is not associated with any obvious changes in an animal's behavior or its sensory or motor capacity.[29] Similarly, intensive neurologic study of patients with surgical section of part or all of the corpus

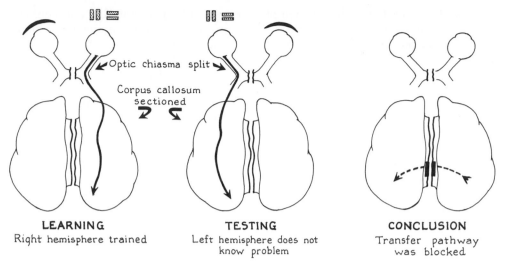

LEARNING
Right hemisphere trained

TESTING
Left hemisphere does not know problem

CONCLUSION
Transfer pathway was blocked

Fig. 6. Diagram of training and testing procedures for studying interocular transfer in a cat after section of the optic chiasma and corpus callosum. (After Myers, *Brain*, 1956, *79*:358–363.)

callosum revealed little effect on motor, sensory or intellectual functions.[2] The function of the corpus callosum was mysterious, although, retrospectively, there was a clue to this puzzle. Bykov,[5] in Pavlov's laboratory, found that if a normal dog is conditioned to salivate to tactile stimulation of a specific point on the body surface, stimulation of a contralateral point elicits the conditioned response. He then showed that section of the corpus callosum abolished such generalization. Moreover, he found that it was possible to establish independent conditioned responses in the two hemispheres after section of the corpus callosum. Bykov's experiments were largely ignored until recently when a series of experiments on the corpus callosum were inaugurated in Sperry's laboratory. In the first of these studies, Myers[40] sectioned the optic chiasm of cats in the midline so that impulses from the eyes would go only to the optic cortex of the same side. He then trained the cats to discriminate between two visual forms with one eye covered. He found that animals would reliably perform the problem when tested with the second eye (previously covered). Cats showed excellent interhemispheric transfer. Since the left eye projected only to the left hemisphere and the right eye only to the right hemisphere, something must have been transferred from the left to the right hemisphere. However, if the corpus callosum was sectioned as well as the optic chiasm, the two hemispheres appeared to function independently for learning and memory. Animals could be trained using one or the other eye, but

a problem learned with one eye and hemisphere while the other eye was masked would not transfer to the second eye and hemisphere. The animal gave no evidence of any benefit from the prior training. Figures 5 and 6 illustrate these experiments diagrammatically. Figure 7 shows learning curves for a learned visual discrimination from each eye in succession. As a matter of fact, Sperry *et al.*[52] have shown that opposite habits can be established easily in the two hemispheres of animals with chiasm and callosum sectioned. More recent studies have elaborated these findings.

The majority of somesthetic input is contra-

Fig. 7. Learning curves, left and right eye for cat, Gbb, which had been previously subjected to splitting of optic chiasma and corpus callosum. In this animal, learning proceeded at the same rate in each hemisphere. There was no evidence of the animal's having benefited from prior uniocular training when tested for transfer to the untrained eye. (After Sperry *et al., J. comp. physiol. Psychol.*, 1956, *49*:529–533.)

lateral; it would appear likely that section of corpus callosum alone would block interhemispheric transfer of responses to somesthetic stimuli. Callosum-sectioned cats trained to respond differentially to one of two tactile cues with one paw showed no transfer of this habit when tested with the second paw.[53] More recently, this absence of interhemispheric transfer in "split brain" animals has been shown for visual and tactile discrimination in the monkey.[12, 21]

However, some limitations on the role of the corpus callosum are indicated by the experiments of Meikle and Sechzer,[38] who trained cats which had undergone prior sections of the optic chiasm and corpus callosum to make a brightness discrimination with one eye. Such responses transferred to the second eye. Their results suggest that still other midline connections were able to function for the interhemispheric elaboration of learned response.

The role of the corpus callosum in interhemispheric transfer can be explained in two ways. The corpus callosum may either be used to establish an engram in the contralateral hemisphere as well as the originally trained hemisphere, or it simply might allow the second hemisphere to "read" the engrams of the first. To study this problem, Myers[41] first sectioned the optic chiasm of cats, trained them monocularly to discriminate a visual form and then ablated the visual cortex ipsilateral to the eye that had been trained. For simple visual problems, the second hemisphere exhibited good knowledge of the learned problem despite the cortical ablations, suggesting that for these simpler problems a dual trace or engram system had been established.

Such demonstrations of multiple engrams allows a re-evaluation of the results of some of Lashley's experiments. It is clear that the same engrams may be stored in more than one locus in the brain. Thus, the results obtained by Lashley might have been brought about by this very multiplicity of cortical representation. Multiple storage of memory might tend to give the appearance of a "mass action" or nonspecific nonlocalizable function of memory.

Cortical ablations are irreversible, making it difficult to describe the function of a cortical region by inference from the loss caused by ablation. To circumvent this difficulty, some have used spreading depression to produce a *reversible* functional decortication. Bures[3] observed that if spreading depression were initiated by application of 25 per cent KCl and confined to one hemisphere of the rat, memory for responses formed during the depression tended to be localized in the hemisphere which was active during the training. In effect, he showed that the formation of memory can be channeled by functionally ablating one of the two hemispheres during training.

MECHANISMS OF MEMORY

Temporary Memory Storage (Consolidation Hypothesis). Many of the foregoing studies have been concerned with how much an animal can learn and others with the process of acquisition of learning *per se*. Similarly, it is becoming clear that "engram formation" should be distinguished from "engram storage." It seems probable that there is a major difference in the way information is temporarily stored as it is being acquired and the way it is permanently stored in the brain. Such a "two-process" theory of memory acquisition and storage has been proposed by Hebb,[23] and his theoretical arguments have stimulated much of the research on a two-process theory of memory. In briefest terms, he suggested that initially (during a learning "trial" for example) an immediate "trace" is established which is evanescent and unstable. Moreover, this temporary trace "might cooperate with the structural change, and carry the memory until the growth change is made."[23]

The evidence for some such two-process mechanism comes from experimental studies with animals as well as clinical observation on *retrograde amnesia*. Following a severe blow to the head, electroconvulsive shock or some other such massive trauma,[44] memory for events just preceding the event is lost, hence "retrograde amnesia." Temporary memory traces seem more evanescent and more easily interfered with by severe cortical insults. Evidence of a "consolidation process" is exemplified by the work of Duncan,[13] who trained animals with one trial per day to leave the starting chamber of a two-compartment box immediately in order to avoid a mild shock. Seizures were induced electrically at varying times after each training trial, at intervals varying from a few seconds to several hours. The acquisition of the habit was disrupted regularly only in the animals experiencing seizures shortly after each training trial.

If the seizures were induced one or more hours later, acquisition of the learned response was not disturbed (Fig. 8). These data suggest that the temporary traces aroused in the situation were slowly being stored in permanent memory and that if a major brain insult, such as electroconvulsive shock (ECS), was inducd during the storage period, acquisition of the habit was retarded.

In Duncan's experiment,[13] disruption of consolidation was inferred from retardation of learning. However, if the ECS were painful and the animals were made afraid of the compartment into which they ran, this too might retard learning. Duncan attempted to rule out this possibility by comparing the effects of ECS with the effects of (painful) foot shock to animals in a control group. These animals showed some retardation of avoidance learning but not nearly so much as those given ECS.

Coons and Miller[8] suggested that fear may be a very important confounding variable in such experiments. They showed that, under suitable conditions with many (24) ECS administrations, the fear effect may completely mask any presumed disruption of consolidation. Thus, if disruption of consolidation with ECS was to be shown unequivocally, a better technique was needed. One-trial avoidance learning seems to be such a technique. In one-trial avoidance learning the subject first learns to respond (for

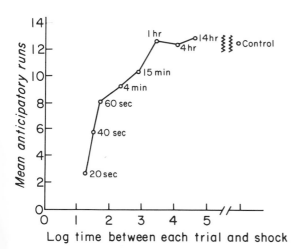

Fig. 8. Efficiency of learning in rats subjected to post-trial electroconvulsive seizures. The data suggest that some process ("consolidation") may be required for an event to be stored in permanent memory. These data also suggest that the consolidation mechanism is essentially complete after one hour. (From Duncan, *J. comp. physiol. Psychol.,* 1949, *42:*32–44.)

example, running down an alley toward a drinking spout) until a stable level of performance is reached. Next, a *single* intense foot shock is administered for making the response. The effect of this foot shock is to suppress the response completely. At predetermined times after the foot shock, ECS is given. The test is whether the animals given ECS will "forget" the foot shock and respond when tested the next day. There are several advantages of one-trial avoidance. First, the fear and disruption of consolidation effects are pitted against each other. If ECS is simply fear-producing, it is to be expected that this fear would simply add to that produced by the foot shock, to produce more pronounced avoidance learning. Another advantage is that disruption of consolidation can be shown after only one administration of ECS.

A one-trial avoidance experiment by Heriot and Coleman[24] produced a pronounced consolidation effect. King,[28a] also using one-trial avoidance, showed a consolidation effect that fully confirmed Duncan's interpretation.

Physical Basis of Memory. The most easily conceived theories of memory involve a physical change as the memory trace. Such theories have been of two sorts; one predicates some form of active electrical process, the other, a more permanent alteration in brain chemistry or synaptic structure.

Short-term memory. One of the suggestions that have been made for the memory trace is a reverberatory circuit in the brain: that memory is stored by closed chains of neurons reactivating one another.[4] Long-term memory traces are strongly resistant to deep anesthesia and disruptive effects such as electrically induced seizures. These data tend to discount such a reverberation process as the basis for all learning. However, the experiments supporting a consolidation hypothesis suggest that a reverberatory mechanism might account for some of the temporary retention prior to permanent storage.

Neural plasticity as learning models. Any time the nervous system behaves differently as a result of previous activity a kind of learning in the broadest sense has occurred. For example, the recovery from brain damage or transection of the spinal cord (Chap. 8) beyond that due to subsidence of edema, pressure or vascular deprivation is reminiscent of learning.

Many investigators have examined simple neural phenomena which might give some clue to the nature of learning mechanisms. One such phenomenon is so-called "mirror-focus epilepsy." Alumina cream applied to the surface of an animal's cortex may lead to abnormal electrical activity at that point and periodic epileptic convulsions. If the animal is examined several days later, a similar focus of disordered electrical activity may be identified in the contralateral hemisphere. This "mirror-focus" epilepsy takes several days to become established and is prevented by prior section of the corpus callosum. It has been suggested that the elaboration of such "mirror foci" might serve as a simple model for the plastic changes one observes in the nervous system.[39]

Another proposed model of neural plasticity is post-tetanic potentiation. As was stated in Chapter 6, rapid and prolonged stimulation of the presynaptic limb of a monosynaptic reflex arc causes a long-term hyperexcitability of that reflex (post-tetanic potentiation). Eccles and McIntyre[14] found that this post-tetanic potentiation may last as long as several hours in a chronically de-afferented preparation, and suggested that this phenomenon might serve as a model for synaptic plasticity in general and might be studied to gain insight into the structural basis of learning.

Another model of synaptic plasticity is Bechterew's nystagmus. If one vestibule of an animal is damaged a characteristic nystagmus is produced that disappears in time. Damage to the second vestibule produces a nystagmus opposite in direction from that of the first. Since a single stage *bilateral* operation produces no such effect, there must have been some dynamic recovery of functional equilibrium which was upset by the second operation. Such a recovery process is another example of neural plasticity.

Permanent Memory Storage. Several explanations of the permanent memory trace based on structural changes have also been proposed. For example, it has been suggested[23] that activation of a synapse might induce a dendritic growth or new formation of the axonic *boutons terminaux*, which would strengthen the connection between two neurons. Growth of posterior root axons has been established in the segments below a spinal transection (Chap. 8).

A more recent theory of learning is that it is somehow stored in large molecules within the central nervous system. The recent advances in genetics demonstrate that enormous amounts of information can be precisely coded by large molecules such as deoxyribonucleic acid (DNA) and ribonucleic acid (RNA). Thus, a molecular coding might also account for the large capacity of the nervous system for memory storage, as well as for its multiplicity of localization, though no plausible schema for translation of nerve impulses into molecular structure and vice versa has been forthcoming. Some authors[18] have argued that the glial cells are involved in such microcoding.

SUMMARY

In summing up the state of our knowledge of the all-important problem of learning, no general theory of learning or its mechanism can be advanced. Nevertheless, much progress has been made over the past 50 years in *techniques* for the study of learning. Techniques for the objective and quantitative study of behavior have been developed. Animals have been taught to perform well at tasks which were thought impossible in an earlier generation. Moreover, the need to distinguish between short-term and permanent memory in analysis of the learning process has been demonstrated. It is clear that permanent memory storage is not localized in any restricted region of the brain. However, the recent studies of interhemispheric transfer and of pathways mediating immediate memory and visual discrimination learning show the importance of cortico-cortical circuits for learning and memory. Moreover, the demonstration of multiple storage of memory traces explains some of the more perplexing aspects of Lashley's discoveries. Progress in our understanding of such storage may come from detailed study of a restricted neural pathway, which induces memory traces such as interhemispheric connections. It may be expected that a combining of experimental behavioral techniques with a careful regard for known anatomic and physiologic mechanisms will yield increasing information on the general problem of brain mechanisms in learning. Although the understanding of the mechanism of learning and neural plasticity is elusive, the prediction of Sherrington[46] in 1906 is still valid:

"New methods of promise seem to me those lately followed by Franz, Thorndyke [sic], Yerkes, and others. For instance, the influence of experimental lesions in skilled actions recently and individually, i.e., experimentally acquired. . . . by combining the methods of comparative psychology (e.g., the labyrinth test*) with the methods of experimental physiology, investigation may be expected ere long to furnish new data of importance toward the knowledge of movement as an outcome of the working of the brain."

* "Maze test."

REFERENCES

1. BLOUGH, D. S. *J. comp. physiol. Psychol.*, 1956, *49:*425–430.
2. BREMER, F., BRIHAYE, J. and ANDRE-BALISAUX, G. *Schweiz. Arch. Neurol. Psychiat.*, 1956, *78:*31–87.
3. BURES, J. In: *The central nervous system and behavior,* M. Brazier, ed. New York, Josiah Macy, Jr., Foundation, 1959.
4. BURNS, B. *The mammalian cerebral cortex.* London, Edward Arnold, 1958.
5. BYKOV, K. *Zbl. ges. Neurol. Psychiat.*, 1925, *39:*199.
6. CHOW, K. L. *J. comp. physiol. Psychol.*, 1952, *45:*109–118.
7. CHOW, K. L. In: *Brain mechanisms and learning,* J. Delafresnaye, ed., Springfield, Ill., Charles C Thomas, 1961.
8. COONS, E. E. and MILLER, N. E. *J. comp. physiol. Psychol.*, 1960, *53:*524–531.
9. COWEY, A. *Nature (Lond.)*, 1962, *193:*302.
10. CULLER, E. A. and METTLER, F. A. *J. comp. Psychol.*, 1934, *18:*291–303.
11. DOTY, R. W., RUTLEDGE, L. T., JR. and LARSEN, R. M. *J. Neurophysiol.*, 1956, *19:*401–415.
12. DOWNER, J. L. DE C. *Fed. Proc.*, 1958, *17:*37.
13. DUNCAN, C. P. *J. comp. physiol. Psychol.*, 1949, *42:*32–44.
14. ECCLES, J. C. and McINTYRE, A. K. *J. Physiol.*, 1953, *121:*492–516.
15. FERSTER, C. B. and SKINNER, B. F. *Schedules of reinforcement.* New York, Appleton-Century-Crofts, Inc., 1957.
16. FORBES, A. and MAHAN, C. *J. comp. physiol. Psychol.*, 1963, *56:*36–40.
17. GALAMBOS, R. In: *The central nervous system and behavior.* M. Brazier, ed. New York, Josiah Macy, Jr., Foundation, 1958.
18. GALAMBOS, R. *Proc. nat. Acad. Sci., (Wash.)*, 1961, *47:*129–136.
19. GLICKMAN, S. E. *Psychol. Bull.*, 1961, *58:*218–233.
20. GLICKMAN, S. E. and FELDMAN, S. M. *Electroenceph. clin. Neurophysiol.*, 1961, *13:*703–709.
21. GLICKSTEIN, M. and SPERRY, R. W. *J. comp. physiol. Psychol.*, 1960, *53:*322–327.
22. GLICKSTEIN, M., ARORA, H. A. and SPERRY, R. W. *J. comp. physiol. Psychol.*, 1963, *56:*11–18.
23. HEBB, D. O. *The organization of behavior.* New York, John Wiley & Sons, 1949.
24. HERIOT, J. T. and COLEMAN, P. D. *J. comp. physiol. Psychol.*, 1962, *55:*1082–1084.
25. HERNANDEZ-PEON, R. *Electroenceph. clin. Neurophysiol.*, 1960, Suppl. *13:*101–114.
26. HUNTER, W. S. *J. gen. Psychol.*, 1930, *3:*455–468.
27. JACOBSEN, C. F. *Comp. Psychol. Monogr.*, 1936, *13,* no. 63: 3–60.
28. JOHN, E. R. and KILLAM, K. F. *J. Pharmacol. exp. Ther.*, 1959, *125:*252–274.
28a. KING, R. A. *J. comp. physiol. Psychol.*, 1964 (in press).
29. KORANYI, A. V. *Pflüg. Arch. ges. Physiol.*, 1890, *47:*35–42.
30. LASHLEY, K. S. *Arch. Neurol. Psychiat. (Chic.)*, 1924, *12:* 249–276.
31. LASHLEY, K. S. In: *Physiological mechanisms in animal behavior.* Symposium of the Society for Experimental Biology. New York, Academic Press, 1950.
32. LASHLEY, K. S. *Genet. Psychol. Monogr.*, 1948, *37:*107–166.
33. LASHLEY, K. S. *Brain mechanisms and intelligence.* Chicago, University of Chicago Press, 1929 (Reprinted, New York, Dover Publications, 1963.)
34. LEUKEL, F. A. *J. comp. physiol. Psychol.*, 1957, *50:*300–306.
35. LOUCKS, R. B. *J. comp. Psychol.*, 1934, *18:*305–313.
36. LOUCKS, R. B. *J. Psychol.*, 1935, *1:*5–44.
37. LOUCKS, R. B. *J. comp. Psychol.*, 1938, *25:*315–332.
38. MEIKLE, T. H. and SECHZER, J. A. *Science*, 1960, *132:*734–735.
39. MORRELL, F. *Physiol. Rev.*, 1961, *41:*443–494.
40. MYERS, R. E. *Brain*, 1956, *79:*358–363.
41. MYERS, R. E. In: *Brain mechanisms and learning.* Springfield, Ill., Charles C Thomas, 1961.
42. PAVLOV, I. P. *Conditioned reflexes,* G. V. Anrep, tr. and ed. Oxford, Oxford University Press, 1927 (Reprinted, New York, Dover Publications, 1960.)
43. RUCH, T. C. *Res. Publ. Ass. nerv. ment. Dis.*, 1934, *15:*289–330.
44. RUSSELL, W. R. and NATHAN, P. W. *Brain*, 1946, *69:*280–300.
45. SHARPLESS, S. and JASPER, H. H. *Brain*, 1956, *79:*655–680.
46. SHERRINGTON, C. S. *The integrative action of the nervous system.* New Haven, Conn., Yale University Press, 1947.
47. SKINNER, B. F. *The behavior of organisms.* New York, Appleton-Century-Crofts, 1938.
48. SKINNER, B. F. *Amer. Scient.*, 1957, *45:*343–371.
49. SPERRY, R. W. *J. Neurophysiol.*, 1947, *10:*275–294.
50. SPERRY, R. W. and MINER, N. *J. comp. physiol. Psychol.*, 1955, *48:*463–469.
51. SPERRY, R. W., MINER, N. and MYERS, R. E. *J. comp. physiol. Psychol.*, 1955, *48:*50–58.
52. SPERRY, R. W., STAMM, J. S. and MINER, N. *J. comp. physiol. Psychol.*, 1956, *49:*529–533.
53. STAMM, J. S. and SPERRY, R. W. *J. comp. physiol. Psychol.*, 1957, *50:*138–143.
54. STEBBINS, W. C. and LANSON, R. N. *J. exp. Anal. Behav.*, 1961, *4:*149–155.
55. THORNDIKE, E. L. *Psychol. Monogr.*, 1898, *2:*No. 8.
56. THORPE, W. H. *Learning and instinct in animals.* London, Methuen, 1963.
57. WEISKRANTZ, L., MIHAILOVIC, L. and GROSS, C. G. *Science*, 1960, *131:*1443–1444.

CHAPTER 25

Physiologic Basis of Motivation

By ORVILLE A. SMITH, JR.

INTRODUCTION

BEHAVIOR is characterized by two phenomena —*plasticity*, or the ability to acquire new modes of responding, and *energetics,* or variability in the intensity of responding. The learning process accounts for the first and the process of motivation for the second. At one moment, an organism may act very rapidly and forcefully, while at another time it may act slowly and with little vigor or enthusiasm, or it may not act at all. The kinds of environmental variations which bring about the changes in the intensity of behavior may be quite diverse (e.g., water deprivation, intense illumination, pain, fatigue, etc.), but the commonality of their effects on behavior allows one to infer that a common physiologic process is being evoked. This process is called *motivation.*

The same variations which affect the intensity of behavior may also guide the organism's behavior so that one part of the environment is responded to in preference to other parts; e.g., the hungry rat eats avidly from a dish of food, ignoring a water cup; the same rat when thirsty drinks from the cup and ignores the food.

Motivation, then, has two major aspects, one concerned with the intensity or vigor of the behavior, which may be labeled the *drive* aspect, the other concerned with the guidance of the behavior, which may be labeled the *directional* aspect. The latter is so intimately related to the topics of learning and perception that for the purposes of this chapter it will be referred to but briefly.

Measurement of Drive. One method of measuring the drive aspect of motivation has been to observe the effect produced on a measurable facet of behavior by varying the intensity of a stimulus. The stimuli to be varied may be internal to the organism (e.g., the amount of food or water deprivation) or external (e.g., the strength of an electric current applied to the skin or the degree of illumination). The biologic effects of such stimuli have traditionally been assessed by measuring (i) gross motor activity, (ii) latency of a learned response, (iii) how much obstruction will prevent an animal from achieving a goal, (iv) allowing the animal a choice of two or more stimuli (preference method), (v) the force (or amplitude) of a response, and (vi) autonomic measures.

Figure 1 illustrates the simultaneous measurement of three variables as a function of the number of hours of food deprivation.

Relation between Motivation and Learning. The relationships between these variables are not simple. For one thing, measuring drive which is unaffected by learning is by itself difficult. In his *Principles of Behavior*, Clark L. Hull[36] attempted to formalize the determinants of behavior with the equation $S^ER = S^HRX D$; S^ER is the symbol for the reaction potential or what the organism actually does, S^HR the symbol for habit strength or the degree of learning in a specific stimulus situation, and D the symbol for drive or the organism's motivational status. The equation, of course, indicates that if either S^HR or D equals zero the organism does nothing; therefore the drive aspect uninfluenced by learning cannot be measured.* As a further complication, in a later revision, Hull[37] indicated his belief that other variables such as "stimulus intensity dynamism," reward magnitude and delay of reinforcement were also primary factors in the equation and also acted multiplicatively with S^HR and D. Also, a commonly used defining characteristic of a motivating stimulus is that it mediate new learning.

* Several autonomic measures show promise of reflecting motivational level independent of learned responses, especially skin conductance.

Learning and motivation are further interrelated by the factor of "acquired or secondary drive." Originally innocuous stimuli which have been associated with a situation inducing considerable motivation in an organism may themselves acquire an ability to increase motivation in that organism. These acquired drives are responsible for the major portion of human behavior, such as the drive for social position or money for its own sake.

Problems in Dealing with Motivation. A motivational state is usually inferred from a particular kind of behavior and is given a name. The name is generally chosen from the vocabulary developed from our own introspections. For example, when an organism drinks water the inference is that a state of "thirst" has energized it to drink. Having once applied this term, a person tends to assume that only one biologic mechanism is responsible for this state and the resultant behavior. Using drinking behavior and the motivational state of "thirst" implied from that behavior, let us examine possible reasons for the drinking behavior:

(i) Water deprivation. This is the usual physiologic situation that elicits drinking behavior. The neural mechanisms responsible for this behavior involve the hypothalamic osmoreceptors, which sense the high tonicity of the plasma (Chap. 11), and

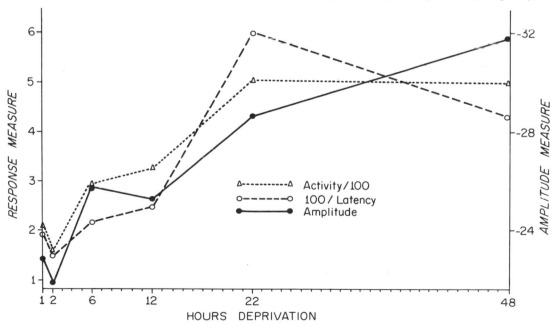

Fig. 1. Gross bodily activity, latency of response between a signal and pushing a panel to receive a food reward (left ordinate), and the amplitude of the panel pushing (right ordinate) as a function of number of hours of food deprivation.

the cells of the lateral hypothalamus, which are somehow necessary for drinking.[50]

(ii) Dry mouth drinking. Epstein[19] has shown that if the salivary glands are removed from rats that are fed only a dry food, they exhibit a peculiar behavior which involves taking a piece of food and immediately following this with a small drink of water. This occurs even if the rat is completely hydrated, probably because there must be some moisture in the mouth and throat for the animal to swallow the food.

(iii) Emotional drinking. If rats are placed in a cage in which they have previously been given a painful shock, they will drink more water than control animals never shocked in the cage.

(iv) Avoidance drinking. Animals can be trained readily to drink water to avoid receiving a painful stimulus. Very large quantities of water may be ingested through this procedure.

(v) Reinforcement schedule drinking. Falk[23] showed that putting rats on a variable interval reinforcement schedule* increased water intake threefold over normal.

In the last four examples, dehydration due to water deprivation clearly is not the stimulus for drinking behavior. Yet, if the drinking behavior is used as the defining characteristic of "thirst," all these situations are immediately assumed to have a common origin in the motivational state "thirst" and, therefore, a common physiologic mechanism. It is much more meaningful to speak of dehydration drinking, emotional drinking, dry mouth drinking, etc., because the relevant mechanism is specified.

Similarly, the biologic reasons for eating may be as varied as for drinking. Sexual activity is often a result of stressful situations or a means of asserting dominance as well as a function of deprivation of sexual activity or of the time of the estrous cycle.

Other problems in using motivation as a meaningful scientific concept have arisen because of (i) the large number of factors which can influence the intensity of behavior, (ii) the wide range of organisms (ameba to man) which are under consideration, and (iii) the great

---

* A procedure used in learning studies in which a reward is given to an animal on the basis of his responding after a variable time interval has elapsed (Chap. 24).

---

variety of related terms available, each of which generally involves a failure of precise definition. Thus, the scientific utility of the motivation concept has been hampered by the use of terms such as *desire, wish, want, need,* etc., all of which may acquire slightly differing connotations.

MECHANISMS ALTERING INTENSITY AND DIRECTION OF BEHAVIOR

A usually unstated and unproved but rather obvious assumption is that, when the behavior output of a normal animal changes in magnitude, the change must result from alterations of central nervous system activity. Such activity can be influenced in several ways: (i) by afferent input, (ii) by humoral mechanisms, or (iii) by intrinsic activity.

Afferent Input. This is broken down into two familiar categories (Chap. 14), exteroceptive and interoceptive stimuli.

Exteroceptive stimuli. It may be stated, in general, that any sensory input has drive properties if it is intense enough. Loud auditory stimuli, intense illumination and temperature extremes have all been used to motivate avoidance behavior in animals. Other sensory inputs may be motivating in a positive fashion. Prime examples of this may be seen in the work of Young[69] and, more recently, of Pfaffman[54] dealing with taste; the former author made clear the presence of strongly motivating taste preferences; the latter has demonstrated especially well the effects of various taste stimuli on activity of nerve cells in the classic taste pathway which correlate with the preferences.

There is some evidence that a certain degree of any afferent input is optimal for a particular organism at a particular time and that the organism will seek to avoid the extremes of that input; however, it is also true that some inputs are much more motivating than others and, judged from human experience, these have a strong affective (subjective pleasure or pain) component. Generally, these are the stimuli of major concern in the study of motivated behavior.

Studies of sensory deprivation[34] in man show that the lack of sensory input may be as disturbing as excessive input and that the human organism, at least, develops hallucinations or false sensory effects when sensory deprivation is protracted. Some believe that certain hospital situations involve sufficient sensory deprivation to produce psychiatric symptoms in patients. The fact that the central nervous system is not merely a passive receiver and transmitter of afferent information because sensory input may be altered by central neural mechanisms has been mentioned previously (Chap. 12). Stimulation of reticular formation,[27] the cerebral cortex,[38] and the medullary pyramids[1] has been shown to exert such an effect.

Hernandez-Peon[33] has demonstrated in the unanesthetized animal that changing the motivational status of an animal can alter the amplitude of an auditory evoked potential. The suggested utility of this phenomenon is the reduction of distracting sensory influences when a high degree of concentration or attention is required.

Interoceptive stimuli. Stimuli coming from within the body, especially the viscera, are a major source of motivational afferents. Visceral movement or stretching or changes in the diameter of blood vessels may provide afferent input signaling bodily conditions which require, among other adjustments, the initiation of complex behavior to relieve the conditions. However, because other than free nerve endings are few in viscera and because most of the afferent fibers are small and either thinly myelinated or unmyelinated and therefore difficult to study, little is known about the kind or quantity of information conveyed by them (Chap. 17). There is a definite indication that sensory information is carried by larger myelinated fibers from the viscera to cortical levels.[2]

Humoral Mechanisms. Another major route of influence on central nervous system activity is the penetration of blood-borne hormones, nutrients or metabolites through the blood–brain barrier to act directly upon particular nerve cells. The blood–brain barrier is effective largely on the basis of mechanical resistance to passage of relatively large molecules through the capillary wall or through the membranous end feet of the neuroglia which surround the capillaries. The site of the blood–brain barrier is discussed in Chapter 47.

Endocrine secretions. Certain endocrine secretions have been shown to influence directly the activity of specific areas of the central nervous system. For example, Dell[17] has shown the facilitatory effects of epinephrine upon the ascending reticular activating system (ARAS), and Sawyer[59] has shown that the sexual hor-

mones may lower the threshold of a response to electrical stimulation of the reticular formation.

Tonicity changes. Inasmuch as there is some exchange between blood plasma and the fluid surrounding the nerve cells, it is reasonable to expect that changes in the tonicity of the plasma may influence the excitability of certain nerve cells. Such an effect may be illustrated by infusing hypertonic saline into the carotid arteries or directly into the ventricles themselves. A strongly motivated drinking behavior will immediately appear.

Nutritive substances and products of metabolism. During normal metabolism certain constituents of the blood increase in concentration and others decrease; these changes are reflected across the blood–brain barrier and may result in altered neural activity. The glucose–insulin balance is an obvious example of this: A deficiency of glucose, due to an overabundance of insulin, may bring about severe behavioral changes or even violent seizures.

Although metabolites such as lactic acid have been suspected of having motivational effects as concomitants of fatigue, such a relationship has not been definitely established.

Blood temperature. Another potentially powerful blood-borne factor is the temperature of the blood itself. Obviously, this factor, along with skin temperature, should play a major role in elicitation of motivated behavior concerned with regulation of body temperature, such as seeking shelter, curling up, etc. In addition, blood temperature may well influence all neural activity in general, purely because of the dependence upon temperature of all chemical reactions, including those of neural metabolism. Essman *et al.*[22] have shown that hypothermia can prevent the learning of an escape response.

Intrinsic Neural Activity. Although afferent input and humoral effects are the most obvious means of altering central nervous activity and, consequently, the intensity of behavior, certain behavior changes are not immediately referable to these sources. When the source of the effect is obscure, the appeal is made to "intrinsic" factors, and if the behavior under consideration has a temporally linked rhythm, it is suggested that a "biologic clock" is operative. Many types of behavior and physiologic processes may show a temporally determined repetitiveness such as sleep, eating, sexual behavior in the female, activity, etc. Most of these can be linked to a rhythmic process going on either outside the organism or at least outside the central nervous system. These processes can then act upon the central nervous system via a humoral or afferent route. However, some changes can be shown to be independent, or partially so, from other cyclic events; the natural conclusion from this is that the central nervous system has "clock" propensities of its own which may determine changes in the absence of an external stimulus.[29]

In animals, synchronous cortical discharges which are "spontaneous" when all afferent inputs have been successfully removed[9] suggest the existence of intrinsic neural activity with which, in the normal animal, incoming sensory effects may interact.

In lower animals, it can be shown that the central nervous system has pre-existing connections which may be activated to bring about inflexible but intricate patterns of behavior called *instincts*. Tinbergen[68] has shown that these behavior patterns are specific to a particular species and are triggered or released only by a particular external stimulus sometimes acting effectively only when a particular physiologic state has been induced in the animal, e.g., during mating or nesting seasons. Observation gives the impression that this is strongly motivated behavior. This particular combination of intrinsic neural processes and connections elicited only by a specific stimulus is most easily observed in insects, fish and birds. In the mammal the same situation may hold but, if so, its effectiveness is soon suppressed by a more flexible nervous system and the resultant greater learning abilities.

INITIATION AND METERING OF MOTIVATED BEHAVIOR

Traditionally, investigators have tried to determine which *one* input is responsible for establishing the motivational state in the organism; often this input has been extended to include the mechanism for termination of the state as well. A classic example of this is the dry throat theory of thirst postulated by Cannon.[11] He assumed that sensory receptors in the throat were sensitive to dryness and that, when the organism became dehydrated, the amount of saliva produced in the mouth decreased, thus causing a dry throat. The animal then supposedly was

motivated to ingest water, which consequently moistened the receptors in the throat and brought about the cessation of drinking. Thus, the initiation and termination of the behavior were held to be controlled by a single mechanism. The inadequacy of this theory is clear from the observation that once an animal takes a single swallow of water, the receptors in the throat are as wet as they will ever be and yet drinking continues for a long period.

Research in motivation over the last 25 years has shown that, although there may be in general a major factor responsible for the initiation of a specific behavior, the behavior may be influenced by multiple factors affecting the central nervous system through many of the routes listed above. Also, it seems that if the dominant source of information is removed, another may be substituted which, after a short time, initiates and regulates the behavior appropriately. In the case of water intake, it can be shown that either gastric or oral factors may serve to "meter" water intake of a water-deprived animal. Several of the most common sources of physiologically based motivation will be reviewed with special reference to the stimuli which *initiate* the behavior and those which *meter* the behavior and eventually result in *satiation*.

Initiation of Food Intake. Since the time of Cannon and Washburn,[12] contractions of the stomach and duodenum have been considered critical to eliciting the sensation called "hunger" and subsequent eating behavior. These contractions are probably related to the well known hunger pangs but are not solely responsible for the initiation (much less the metering) of food intake inasmuch as this is adequate when sensory connections from the stomach have been removed. There is greater gastric motility when food is present in the stomach than when it is completely empty. Gastrectomized human patients still report feelings of hunger.

Mayer[47] has suggested a "glucostatic" theory, according to which blood glucose utilization by certain cells of the nervous system is the critical factor in initiating and controlling food intake (Chaps. 11 and 55). According to this theory, low glucose levels—hence, low glucose utilization—excite certain neural elements in the hypothalamus and bring about the sensation of hunger. This theory will not encompass all the experimental facts[26] and must be considered as one of a whole complex of factors.

"Metering" Food Intake (Satiation). The problem of "metering" food intake, or satiation, is a related, though different, problem. Taken in the temporal order of events, metering might occur in the mouth and throat as a function of the quantity and taste of materials passing through these areas. By means of esophogeal fistulas so that food is chewed and swallowed but never reaches the stomach (sham feeding), it has been shown that animals eventually do stop eating, but that the total food intake is much larger than it would have been if food had actually reached the stomach.[39] So, metering via oral–pharyngeal feedback does occur but is somewhat gross.

In contrast, Epstein and Teitelbaum,[21] using an ingenious oral–esophageal bypass, have demonstrated that the rat can regulate food and water intake perfectly without the modalities of taste, smell and tactile or proprioceptive information from the mouth, pharynx or esophagus. They conclude that postingestion factors are sufficient ". . . to control the onset of feeding, the size of individual meals and the total amount of food eaten during a single day and for longer periods of time up to more than a month."

In attempting to determine the exact postingestion factors responsible, Janowitz and Grossman[39] have emphasized the role of stomach distension. One of the appealing aspects of the distension hypothesis is the immediacy of the effect. Any hypothesis of satiation based on metabolic factors is faced with explaining why the cessation of eating occurs long before digestion or absorption can occur. For example, the "glucostatic" theory asserts that for satiety to occur the critical neural cells must have available a high blood glucose level and sufficient insulin to allow a high rate of glucose utilization by these cells. However, in most animals, eating is so rapid that there is no time for digestion and the production of glucose before eating stops. In animals that eat rapidly there is an accompanying sympathetic reaction (as shown by increased heart rate and blood pressure, Fig. 3, Chap. 35) which could lead to the immediate production of glucose by glycolysis in the liver. This would lead to immediate increases in insulin release by the pancreas, and the necessary humoral situation at the critical neurons would be established. This could also be the reason for the abolition of hunger by acute psychologic stress, which has a sympathetic component.

The fat depots of the body may also be in-volved in this regulation. Kennedy[40] has suggested that a metabolite in equilibrium with fat depots acts upon the hypothalamic centers to control their activity. Studies with parabiotic rats[35] in which one member is made hyperphagic and the other subsequently becomes very thin support this idea.

Mook[51] has assessed the relation between oral and postingestional determinants of intake by producing both esophageal and gastric fistulas in the same animals so that the same or different substances could be presented orally and intragastrically, simultaneously. He concluded that the postingestional effect is not substance-specific and that the critical factor may be a gastric osmoreceptor. If different substances of equal osmolarity are presented to the mouth and stomach, the animal proceeds to consume the substance presented to the mouth at the normal rate for that substance. However, if different substances of differing osmolarity are presented to the mouth and stomach, respectively, consumption of the substance presented to the mouth is determined by the osmolarity of the substance introduced into the stomach. He concludes that food intake is determined by positive and negative oral factors (largely taste) and by a postingestional osmotic mechanism, thereby substantiating earlier work.[55, 61, 64]

The relationships between body temperature and food intake have led Strominger and Brobeck[65] to propose that the "specific dynamic action" (SDA) of foodstuffs is also a factor in the regulation of food intake. This hypothesis suggests that the heat produced by SDA (Chap. 11) of various foods is sensed by the critical neurons in the hypothalamus and that this results in satiety and the cessation of eating.

Control of food intake is therefore highly complex and involves many regulating mechanisms. The interactions between these factors and motivated behavior are highlighted by the work of Miller and Kessen,[49] who showed that animals learn to perform a new response when food is injected directly into the stomach, thus satisfying metabolic needs, but that they learn much more rapidly when allowed to take the same food orally, thus involving both oral and postingestional factors.

The cells of the lateral hypothalamic nucleus and the ventromedial hypothalamic nucleus are assumed to be the excitatory and inhibitory neurons, respectively, for the initiation and metering of food intake (Chap. 11). Other neu-

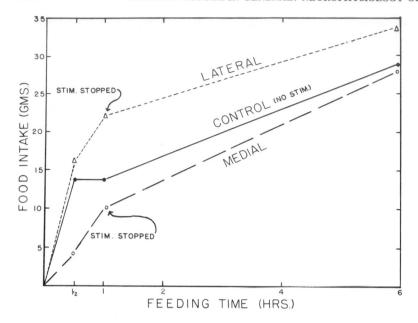

Fig. 2. Regulation of food intake by electrical stimulation of the lateral and medial hypothalamus in the same rat. The control record is the intake during a six-hour period averaged over three days. Stimulation of either the medial or lateral hypothalamus was carried out during the first hour of eating. At time 0 the rat had been deprived of food for 18 hours. (From Smith, in *Electrical stimulation of the brain.* D. E. Sheer, ed. Austin, University of Texas Press, 1961.)

ral areas have also been shown to influence food intake. Maire[57] has found that stimulation of the premammillary area and the anterior thalamic nucleus results in a precisely controlled food intake. The relation of these areas to the action of the hypothalamic control areas is obscure, but they may be linked together.

Eating as an index of motivation. It is tempting to infer the existence of a motivational state by observing consummatory behavior; e.g., an animal that is eating is therefore hungry and motivated to obtain and ingest food. The effects produced on food intake by appropriate ablation or stimulation (Fig. 2) of the hypothalamic control areas are so dramatic that they have been assumed to reflect changes in the organism's motivational state. However, Miller[48] and Teitelbaum[66] demonstrated that animals made hyperphagic by lesions of the ventromedial hypothalamus showed a *decreased* effort to obtain food despite the fact they consumed large quantities of food if given free access to it. While stimulation of this part of the hypothalamus reduces food intake,[62] as predicted from the effects of ablation, it also leads rats actively to avoid receiving such stimulation; therefore, the decreased food intake may be secondary to the noxiousness or upsetting effects of the stimulus.[42] On the contrary, however, lateral hypothalamic stimulation has qualified in all respects as increasing motivational state as well as food intake.[53] Maire has shown dramatically, if not quantitatively, that stimulus of the pre-

mammillary area induces truly motivated eating behavior (Fig. 3).

Recently, Baillie and Morrison[4] have questioned the assumption that the aphagia produced by lateral lesions has primarily a motivational basis. They suggest the effect to be primarily an inability to consume the food because their animals with lesions continued to press a lever for direct intragastric delivery of food while refusing both food and water orally.

Water Intake. Possible reasons for an animal's ingestion of water have already been mentioned. If we focus our attention on drinking elicited by water deprivation and ask the same questions that were asked about food intake, i.e., which stimuli initiate the behavior and which are responsible for the metering and eventual satiety effect, the following facts emerge:

The initiation of drinking results either from increased osmotic pressure of the plasma or from decreased extracellular volume.[23] The relationship between excretion and intake is important here, for both mechanisms act to keep the body in optimal water balance. There is little doubt that the supraoptic nuclei of the hypothalamus respond to changes in osmotic pressure by releasing antidiuretic hormone or a precursor to it, so that water excretion from the kidneys is retarded (Chap. 11). The effect of electrically activating these cells and the subsequent effect on drinking is shown in Figure 4. However, there seem to be other neural mechanisms which lead to the active and immediate intake of water. Andersson and McCann,[3] using goats, have shown that saline injection into, or electrical stimulation of, an area between the fornix and mammillothalamic tract leads to drinking. Figure 5 illustrates this effect from stimulating a similar locus in the rat. The lateral hypothalamic nucleus also plays a role in water intake.[50] Bilateral lesions of this region lead to a combined aphagia and adipsia,[68] providing a neurologic basis for the often observed positive relation between food and water intake.

A premammillary area close to that concerned with eating also causes drinking when stimulated (Maire[57]).

"Metering" is also carried out by an oral factor (Epstein[20]). Again, this type of metering with the consequent satiation occurs before any change in either tonicity or volume of the blood.

Sexual Behavior. Mating provides the prime example of behavior regulated by the production and subsequent action of an intrinsic biologic substance. The chemical substances concerned are testicular hormones in the male and ovarian hormones in the female. In lower mammals, if the sex glands are removed, sexual behavior ceases after a time, but the replacement of testosterone in the male and both estrogen and progesterone in the female reinstates appropriate sexual activity for these animals. Prepubertal male cats show male sexual behavior when given testosterone and female sex behavior patterns when stilbestrol is administered.[25] This reversibility does not hold in adult cats, however.

In rats, the initiation of mating behavior is due entirely to the availability of a sexually receptive female to a sexually mature male. Previous experience seems to play no role[7] and copulation is perfect without such experience. This example of innate behavior (an excellent example of "instinct") does not hold as specifically for other species.

The relation between the presence of one kind of hormone and the elicitation of a particular kind of sexual behavior does not apply rigidly. Young[70] prefers to emphasize the action of the hormone on the existing soma or substrate of all the tissues mediating sexual behavior, which implies that whatever behavior patterns are laid down by genetics or experience may be merely activated or brought into play by the presence of the hormone. Prenatally, the

hormones have an organizing function on subsequent mating behavior, particularly in the fe-

A. Before stimulus

B. Stimulus starts

C. Stimulus continues

D. Stimulus ends

Fig. 3. Male rat with electrodes implanted in the premammillary area placed in a cage containing a female rat in heat and food pellets scattered on the floor. *A,* The male begins sexual activity with female. *B,* Electric stimulation through implanted electrodes begins and the male promptly leaves the female and approaches food pellet. *C,* Stimulation continues, male rat eats food pellet. *D,* Stimulation ceases, male rat drops food and returns to female, sexual behavior is reinstated. (Furnished by F. W. Maire.)

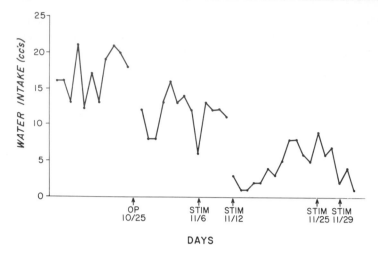

Fig. 4. Water intake following electrical stimulation of the supraoptic nuclei of a rat is decreased considerably. The effect is of long duration after the second (11/12) stimulation day. Control water intake is shown at the left before implantation of electrodes (OP 10/25). Effect is presumably secondary to increased water reabsorption in the kidneys due to extra output of antidiuretic hormone subsequent to stimulation.

male.[56] The experimental literature varies widely in affirming or denying the specificity of hormone to kind of behavior in the adult.

The initiation of sexual behavior is dependent not only upon the presence of the androgen in the male but also upon the action of the female hormones on the tissues of the female to produce the secondary sexual characteristics. In many cases it is the presence of these changes during estrus, such as the vivid red, swollen perineal region of monkeys, which acts as a trigger or releaser of sexual behavior in the male. This relationship is very important for species survival, for these changes occur concomitantly with ovulation and hence with fertility.*

There is a distinct change in phylogeny in the dependence of sexual behavior upon the hormones for its initiation. In birds and fish sex behavior is locked to seasonal variations and hormonal production, whereas in subhuman primates sexual behavior may occur at any time during the female cycle, but the greatest frequency is coincident with estrus and ovulation. Also, incompatibility can play a role at this level, certain individuals of both sexes showing preferences for certain sexual partners. In these animals the variety of sexual behavior also increases. In chimpanzees there have been reports of masturbation, homosexuality, rape, frigidity and prostitution.[6] In humans the increased role of psychological factors over hormonal action in determining sexual behavior can easily be documented. Many women past the menopause continue to have sexual desires, and castrated men sometimes continue to lead a normal sex life. In contrast, the castrated rat will not be aroused by a female in estrus until the appropriate sex hormone is injected. Kinsey et al.[41] have reported that the American female shows peaks of sexual desire just pre- and postmenstrually and actually an ebb in desire just at midcycle, when ovulation occurs. It has been suggested that this phylogenetic change in behavior, which is contrary to the biologic princi-

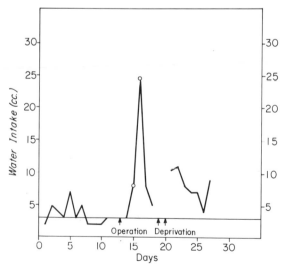

Fig. 5. Water intake produced by electrical stimulation of rostrodorsal hypothalamus of a rat. Open circles indicate days when short-term stimulation was carried out. The effect of two days' water deprivation is shown at right. This amount of deprivation does not produce water intake equivalent to stimulation of hypothalamus during the second period.

*In our primate quarters an exceptionally intelligent male monkey succeeded in picking the lock on his cage and the lock on the cage of a female in full estrus. The two animals were found free in the room the next morning, proving that "love laughs at locksmiths." Exactly 170 days later the female gave birth to an infant.

ple of species survival, is due to the effect of social factors, that is, the avoidance of excessive pregnancies, which seems to be able to overcome the basic biologic mechanisms.

In general, the initiation of sexual behavior shifts in phylogeny from a dependence on hormones to a greater dependence upon sensory factors, learning and the involvement of a more complex neural organization.

Satiation of sexual behavior is easily identifiable in the climax or orgasm. The sensory input from repeated mechanical stimulation of the glans penis in the male and the clitoris in the female acts on the central nervous system until an as yet undefinable neural process leads to ejaculation in the male and uterine and vaginal contractions in the female. In the young male particularly, psychological sexual stimuli may substitute for mechanical stimulation and ejaculation may occur in company with erotic dreams. One last facet that again illustrates the increasingly greater dependence of human sexual behavior upon psychological and experiential factors comes from medical reports of somatically male hermaphrodites who have been mistakenly raised as girls. These individuals acquire the mannerisms and characteristics of the female and prefer to be raised and considered as female.[70]

All levels of the nervous system contribute to the integration of sexual behavior. The spinal cord can integrate enough sexual mechanisms to produce penile erection and ejaculation. No complete pattern of sexual behavior is possible in animals with cord section, and paraplegics report a complete dissociation between their sexual feelings and the random priapisms which occur. With an intact brainstem, including most of the midbrain, some posturing involved in mating can be induced by stimulating the vagina. Again, no complete sexual behavior can be elicited.

Through its connections with the pituitary gland, the hypothalamus is critical for both the biologic fact of ovulation and the mechanism of estrus with its consequent mating behavior. These two facets of reproduction may be separated by differential lesions of the hypothalamus. Lesions of the anterior hypothalamic nucleus lead to anestrus (failure to come into estrus and mate) but do not interfere with ovulation. The fact that administration of additional female hormones to these animals does not reinstate estrus provides strong evidence that the hormones normally producing estrus are acting on this region of the hypothalamus and that this is a critical region in the organization of the somatic behavior involved in mating. Lesions placed between the ventromedial nucleus and the mammillary body result in atrophy of the ovaries and a failure of estrus, an effect probably upon the pituitary gonadotrophin. In contrast to the animals with anterior hypothalamic lesions, however, if estrogen replacement therapy is established, these animals demonstrate appropriate mating behavior.[60]

Other studies have shown that stimulation of the ventromedial nucleus produces ovulation.[32, 46] Male sexual behavior is also influenced by the action of the hypothalamus; stimulation of the tuberal region in the rat results in ejaculation, and stimulation of several areas of the septum and hypothalamus produces erections in squirrel monkeys.[45]

The cerebral cortex is relatively unimportant for mating behavior in most female mammals. In rats, removal of all the neocortex does not interfere with the estrus cycle, mating, pregnancy or delivery.[16] In the male rat however, the same lesions drastically impair sexual behavior.[5]

In contrast to neocortical removal, removal of rhinencephalic structures such as pyriform cortex and underlying amygdala may result in such extreme forms of hypersexuality that the appropriate sex object is not recognized and mating will be attempted with almost anything that moves (Chap. 26).

Temperature. The maintenance of body temperature is of such critical importance to survival of the organism that a very elaborate and accurate control system has evolved. This system involves changes at the autonomic level, not affecting the animal's gross behavior, and also at the somatic level, such as shivering, increased locomotion and the mediation of new learning. Hardy[28] has analyzed the system as having two sources of control: (i) *Automatic control* involves the two thermal capacities, core and peripheral tissues; three mechanisms, heat production (shivering and nonshivering thermogenesis), sweating and vasomotor activity; two detection systems, hypothalamic and cutaneous receptors; and an integrating system via autonomic central areas of the brain. (ii) *Servocontrol* involves behavioral adjustments such as altering amounts of clothing or shelter or in some other fashion using an external source to balance heat load or loss discrepancies.

Low ambient temperatures motivate rats to

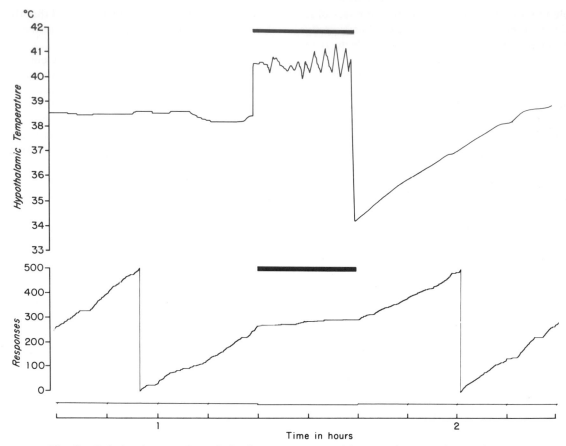

Fig. 6. Relation between hypothalamic temperature and bar-pressing to activate a heat lamp. Rats placed in a 0° C. environment learn to press a lever (cumulative record, lower line) to receive a 2-second exposure to a heat lamp. Hypothalamic temperature (upper line) shows that rat is receiving enough heat lamp warming to maintain a constant body temperature. When hypothalamus is heated (black bars on both records) the bar-pressing nearly stops and the failure to receive warmth from the heat lamp drops body temperature to 34.5° C. At the cessation of hypothalamic warming, the bar-pressing and consequent warming by the lamp are resumed and normal body temperature is again re-established. (Courtesy of H. J. Carlisle.)

press a bar which activates a mechanism to supply warm air[15] or turn on infrared heat lamps.[13] These observations provide the rationale for classifying the behavior involved in temperature maintenance as motivated behavior.

This behavior is initiated either by activation of temperature receptors in the skin or by change in the temperature of the blood. Normally, these two effects occur together, but it is not clear that these two sources of input work together to induce heat loss mechanisms in cases of overheating and heat conservation responses in cases of cooling. It has been suggested that the heat loss mechanisms are more directly controlled by blood temperature and heat conservation by peripheral receptor action.[8]

The critical role of the anterior hypothalamus in regulating heat loss mechanisms has been definitely established (Chap. 11) by ablation, stimulation and recording studies. These demonstrations have all been concerned with the automatic control source. Recently, two complementary studies demonstrated its role in the servocontrol source. Satinoff[58] succeeded in training rats to press a bar to turn on an infrared heat source when the hypothalamus was cooled, even when room temperature was normal. Carlisle[14] has achieved the complementary result of training animals in a cold chamber to press a bar for infrared exposure; when the anterior hypothalamus is heated, bar-pressing for the heat source ceases even though blood temperature has dropped precipitously (Fig.

6). These studies indicate that the anterior hypothalamus can override the effect of information coming in from the peripheral temperature receptors. The results also are tantamount to asking the animal whether he feels cold and receiving a "yes" or "no" answer.

BASIC HEDONIC DRIVES

Some behavior appears to be energized by stimuli which have no immediately identifiable strong survival value. Reference has already been made to the motivating properties of taste, and although taste preferences may be greatly affected by the learning process, the presence of inborn highly selective taste preferences in young infants is readily demonstrable.

In this same category falls the work of Harlow,[30] who has demonstrated a drive originating in the cutaneous modalities underlying the perception of texture. In studying the behavior of newborn monkeys, Harlow has shown that they prefer a terry cloth surrogate mother to one constructed of wire mesh. This preference continues in the face of feeding the infant only when it is on the wire mother and never feeding it in association with the terry cloth mother. The fact that the terry cloth is very similar to the natural mother's ventral surface, to which a baby monkey usually clings, may be irrelevant but probably is not.

Harlow[31] has also shown a strong "manipulation" or "curiosity" drive in which monkeys learn to operate complex puzzle boxes for no apparent reward. They will also learn complex tasks merely for the sake of viewing other monkeys.[10]

These behaviors may, in the long run, be extremely important in a teleologic sense, but the neural mechanisms underlying these actions, with the exception of the investigations of taste, have not been examined with neurophysiologic techniques.

Evidence which can be interpreted as delineating a neural apparatus for a hedonistic aspect of consummatory response will be discussed in the next chapter.

NEURAL SYSTEMS INVOLVED IN MOTIVATED BEHAVIOR

Manipulating different environmental and physiologic variables results in changes in behavior which have a common form. That is, food deprivation, water deprivation, sexual deprivation, temperature extremes, painful stimuli, particular tastes, visual stimulation, etc., will all mediate new learning, decrease the latency of response, increase activity and increase the amplitude of a response. It is reasonable to expect that, if all these varying stimulus situations have identical effects on behavior, there should be a common underlying neural system responsible for these effects.

One attempt to systematize the topic of motivation by postulating a common neurologic basis was that of Morgan,[52] who developed the concept of a "central motive state." He conceived of this "central motive state" as being the neural integrative activity "into which motivating factors pour and from which patterns of motivated behavior emerge." Although he stated that the central motive state is not specifically located in any particular part of the nervous system, he implicated the hypothalamus and other subcortical structures as being more important than other neural regions. Stellar,[63] in a direct development of this viewpoint, made the structures and the interrelationships much more specific by asserting that "the amount of motivated behavior is a direct function of the activity in certain excitatory centers of the hypothalamus," and that the amount of activity is determined by inputs from inhibitory hypothalamic centers, sensory stimuli, the internal environment and cortical and thalamic centers.

In a parallel development, Duffy[18] for many years has expounded the notion that it is profitable to arrange behavior on a continuum of intensity. This concept has received neurophysiologic support in the studies of the ascending reticular activating system (Chap. 20) and the integrative writings of Lindsley,[43] who believes that the "brain rhythm . . . changes constitute a kind of continuum, paralleled by behavioral changes, and both appear to be regulated by the ARAS . . . of the brain stem."

Although Lindsley presents evidence for a specific as well as this generalized functioning of the reticular system, depending on the kind of input, the very compelling experimental literature showing the complete patterns of highly specific motivated behavior which may be elicited from stimulating a restricted portion of the hypothalamus demands that the hypothalamus play an important role in the regulation of hunger, thirst and body temperature (and very probably sex and maternal behavior). These two systems probably work in conjunction to provide the major facets of motivated behavior, intensity and direction. Indeed, the experimental result demonstrating the importance of an "extrathalamic" cortical activation route passing through the "basal diencephalon"[44] (another term for the hypothalamus and subthalamus) may be very pertinent in this regard.

The problems of motivation merge into those of emotion, and in fact the two are difficult to distinguish. The discussion of sexual behavior could well appear in the chapter on emotion and the discussion there on intracranial self-stimulation is pertinent to the problem of the neural basis of motivation as well as emotion.

REFERENCES

1. ADKINS, R. J. *Corticofugal modulation of peripheral receptive fields of cells in the somatosensory cortex of cat.* Ph.D. dissertation, University of Washington, 1965.
2. AMASSIAN, V. E. *J. Neurophysiol.*, 1951, *14*:433–444.
3. ANDERSSON, B. and McCANN, S. M. *Acta. physiol. scand.*, 1955, *33*:333–346.
4. BAILLIE, P. and MORRISON, S. D. *J. Physiol.*, 1963, *165*: 227–245.
5. BEACH, F. A. *J. comp. Psychol.*, 1940, *29*:193–246.
6. BEACH, F. A. *Hormones and behavior.* New York, Paul B. Hoeber, Inc., 1948.
7. BEACH, F. A. *J. comp. physiol. Psychol.*, 1958, *51*:37–38.
8. BENZINGER, T. H., PRATT, A. W. and KITZINGER, C. *Proc. nat. Acad. Sci.* (Wash.), 1961, *47*:730–739.
9. BREMER, F. *Electroenceph. clin. Neurophysiol.*, 1949, *1*:177–193.
10. BUTLER, R. A. *J. comp. physiol. Psychol.*, 1953, *46*:95–98.
11. CANNON, W. B. *The wisdom of the body.* London, Kegan Paul, Trench, Trubner & Co., Ltd., 1932.
12. CANNON, W. B. and WASHBURN, A. L. *Amer. J. Physiol.*, 1912, *29*:441–454.
13. CARLISLE, H. J. *Behavioral temperature regulation in the rat and monkey.* Ph.D. dissertation, University of Washington, 1964.
14. CARLISLE, H. J. Personal communication.
15. CARLTON, P. L. and MARKS, R. A. *Science*, 1958, *128*:1344.
16. DAVIS, C. D. *Amer. J. Physiol.*, 1939, *127*:374–380.
17. DELL, P. Chap. 18 in *The reticular formation of the brain,* H. H. JASPER, ed. Boston, Little, Brown & Co., 1958.
18. DUFFY, E. *Activation and behavior.* New York, John Wiley & Sons, 1962.
19. EPSTEIN, A. N. Personal communication.
20. EPSTEIN, A. N. *Science*, 1960, *131*:497–498.
21. EPSTEIN, A. N. and TEITELBAUM, P. *J. comp. physiol. Psychol.*, 1962, *55*:753–759.
22. ESSMAN, W. B. and SUDAK, F. N. *J. appl. Physiol.*, 1942, *17*:113–116.
23. FALK, J. L. In: *Nebraska symposium on motivation,* M. R. JONES, ed. Lincoln, Neb., University of Nebraska Press, 1961.
24. GLICKMAN, S. E. *Canadian J. Psychol.*, 1958, *12*:45–51.
25. GREEN, J. D., CLEMENTE, C. D. and DE GROOT, J. *J. comp. Neurol.*, 1957, *108*:505–545.
26. GROSSMAN, M. I. *Ann. N.Y. Acad. Sci.*, 1955, *63*:76–91.
27. HAGBARTH, K. E. and KERR, D. I. B. *J. Neurophysiol.*, 1954, *17*:295–307.
28. HARDY, J. D. In: *The Harvey lectures,* Ser. XLIX. New York, Academic Press, 1955.
29. HARKER, J. E. *The physiology of diurnal rhythms.* Cambridge, Cambridge University Press, 1964.
30. HARLOW, H. F. *Sci. Amer.*, 1959, *200*:68–74.
31. HARLOW, H. F., HARLOW, M. K. and MEYER, D. R. *J. exp. Psychol.*, 1950, *40*:228–234.
32. HARRIS, G. W. *J. Physiol.*, 1948, *107*:418–429.
33. HERNANDEZ-PEON, R., SCHERRER, H. and JOUVET, M. *Science*, 1956, *123*:331–332.
34. HERON, W. In: *Sensory deprivation,* P. SOLOMON, ed. Cambridge, Harvard University Press, 1961.
35. HERVEY, G. R. *J. Physiol.*, 1959, *145*:336–352.
36. HULL, C. L. *Principles of behavior. An introduction to behavior theory.* New York, Appleton Century, 1943.
37. HULL, C. L. *Essentials of behavior.* New Haven, Conn., Yale University Press, 1951.
38. JABBUR, S. J. and TOWE, A. L. In: *Nervous inhibition,* E. FLOREY, ed. New York, Pergamon Press, 1961.
39. JANOWITZ, H. D. and GROSSMAN, M. I. *Amer. J. Physiol.*, 1949, *159*:143–148.
40. KENNEDY, G. C. *Proc. Roy. Soc.*, 1953, *140B*:578–596.
41. KINSEY, A. C., POMEROY, W. B., MARTIN C. E. and GEBHARD, P. H. *Sexual behavior in the human female.* Philadelphia, W. B. Saunders Co., 1953.
42. KRASNE, F. B. *Science*, 1962, *138*:822–823.
43. LINDSLEY, D. B. In: *Nebraska symposium on motivation.* Lincoln, Neb. University of Nebraska Press, 1957.
44. LINDSLEY, D. B., BOWDEN, J. W. and MAGOUN, H. W. *Electroenceph. clin. Neurophysiol.*, 1949, *1*:475–486.
45. MacLEAN, P. D., PLOOG, P. W. and ROBINSON, B. W. *Physiol. Rev.*, 1960, *40*(suppl. 4):105–112.
46. MARKEE, J. E., SAYER, C. H. and HOLLINSHEAD, W. H. *Endocrinology*, 1946, *38*:345–357.
47. MAYER, J. *Ann. N. Y. Acad. Sci.*, 1955, *63*:15–43.
48. MILLER, N. E., *Ann. N. Y. Acad. Sci.*, 1955, *63*:141–143.
49. MILLER, N. E. and KESSEN, M. I. *J. comp. physiol Psychol.*, 1952, *45*:555–564.
50. MONTEMURRO, D. G. and STEVENSON, J. A. F. *Canad. J. Biochem.*, 1957, *191*:248–254.
51. MOOK, D. G. *J. comp. physiol. Psychol.*, 1963, *56*:645–659.
52. MORGAN, C. T. *Physiological psychology.* New York, McGraw-Hill Book Co., 1943.
53. MORGANE, P. J. *Amer. J. Physiol.*, 1961, *201*:838–844.
54. PFAFFMAN, C. *Psychol. Rev.*, 1960, *67*:253–268.
55. PFAFFMAN, C. In: *Nebraska symposium on motivation.* Lincoln, Neb., University of Nebraska Press, 1961.
56. PHOENIX, C. H., GOY, R. W., GERALD, A. A. and YOUNG, W. C. *Endocrinology*, 1959, *65*:369–382.
57. RUCH, T. C., MAIRE, F. W. and PATTON, H. D. *Abst. Comm., Congr. int. Physiol.*, 1956, *20*:788–789.
58. SATINOFF, E. *Amer. J. Physiol.*, 1964, *206*:1389–1394.
59. SAWYER, C. H. In: *Reticular formation of the brain.* H. H. JASPER, ed. Boston, Little, Brown & Co., 1958.
60. SAWYER, C. H. and ROBISON, B. *J. clin. Endocrinol.*, 1956, *16*:914–915.
61. SMITH, M. and DUFFY, M. *J. comp. physiol. Psychol.*, 1957, *50*:601–608.
62. SMITH, O. A. Chap. 25 in *Electrical stimulation of the brain.* D. E. Sheer, ed. Austin, University of Texas Press, 1961.
63. STELLAR, E. *Psychol. Rev.*, 1954, *61*:5–22.
64. STELLAR, E., HYMAN, R. and SAMET, S. *J. comp. physiol. Psychol.*, 1954, *47*:220–226.

65. STROMINGER, J. L. and BROBECK, J. R. *Yale J. Biol. Med.,* 1953, *25:*383–390.

66. TEITELBAUM, P. *J. comp. physiol. Psychol.,* 1957, *50:*486–490.

67. TEITELBAUM, P. In: *Nebraska symposium on motivation.* M. R. JONES, ed. Lincoln, Neb., University of Nebraska Press, 1961.

68. TINBERGEN, N. *The study of instinct.* Oxford, Clarendon Press, 1951.

69. YOUNG, P. T. *Motivation of behavior.* New York. John Wiley & Sons, Inc., 1936.

70. YOUNG, W. C. Chap. 19 in *Sex and internal secretions,* vol. II. Baltimore, Williams & Wilkins Co., 1961.

CHAPTER 26

Neurophysiology of Emotion

By THEODORE C. RUCH

MOTIVATION or drive is a neural process which impels the organism to some action or goal, the attainment of which results in drive reduction. Less specifically, it is a state of alertness which increases the readiness to action. Emotion is often the end point of motivated behavior whether culminated or frustrated; bodily activity is then heightened, as primitively illustrated by fight, flight and sex behavior. Emotion may also be less manifest in action than in feeling; e.g., homesickness, in fact, may be expressed by retardation of activity, a slumping posture and a facial expression of sadness. Although emotion is a protean, multifaceted form of behavior which is difficult to define, an interesting definition has been provided by a neuropathologist, Vonderahe:[62]

"Emotion is a way of feeling and a way of acting. It may be defined as a tendency of an organism toward or away from an object, accompanied by notable bodily alteration. There is an element of motivation—an impulsion to action and an element of alertness, a hyperawareness or vividness of mental processes. There is of course the opposite, a depression of movement."

We can see from this definition that emotion has four aspects:

(i) *Cognition.* A situation must be perceived, related to past experiences and evaluated before emotion occurs. This evaluation mainly reflects past experience and the cultural influences of the family, society, etc., and often occurs not in a conscious, deliberative way but sometimes occurs with great suddenness and, according to many, on a "subconscious" level. Cognitive factors determine to what "fighting words," to what flag, to what development of the gluteal region man responds. They also determine what emotion in kind and degree is appropriate to a given situation. These complex evaluations are ascribed to the neocortex of the brain. However, there is evidence (see Chap. 23) that the prefrontal lobe is necessary for conditioned emotional responses of the cardiovascular system in simple conditioned avoidance situations.[55] Finally, not all emotion flows along a motivation→ stimulus→consummatory reaction. Much emotion or "frustration" occurs from blocking this flow. The cognitive aspect of emotion is mainly in the provenance of psychology, but some ways of evoking emotion in animals are simple enough to permit physiologic analysis.

(ii) *Expression.* Emotion is expressed outwardly in the form of somatic and autonomic activities—facial expression, lacrimation, vocalization, hair standing erect, flushing or paling, laughter, fighting or flight. Emotions are also "expressed" internally in the form of visceral and vascular changes executed by the sympathetic and parasympathetic nervous systems (Chaps. 10 and 11). Another kind of emotional expression is muscle tension, which, as we have seen (Chap. 16), causes discomfort and pain. Even if the obvious expression of emotion is suppressed as "inappropriate" in our society, the internal expressions may well occur or possibly be intensified. These especially are considered by some to be the cause of psychosomatic illness.

(iii) *Experience* is the subjective aspect of emotion that one feels when "emotional." On an introspective basis, psychologists once divided emotions into two categories by *affect:* those which are *pleasant* and those which are *unpleasant*. These feelings are conscious experiences and, therefore, are difficult to study quantitatively and objectively. Moreover, as was seen earlier in the discussion of sensation, there is evidence that the expressive and experiential aspects of emotion are dissociable by various lesions of the nervous system; this dissociation can be demonstrated in both animals and human patients. Despite these difficulties, some insight can be gained into what is presumptively the affective aspect of emotion even in animals.

(iv) *Excitement.* It is a matter of common knowledge that when we experience certain emotions we look and feel excited and our friends say, "Now, don't get excited" (which makes us more excited). As the above definition suggests, our mental processes may be excessively vivid. Conversely, sluggish and dull mental processes are commonly experienced during some emotions. The subjective side of excitement, like its affect, would seem impossible to study. However, as seen in the discussion of the ascending reticular systems, there seem to be reliable objective signs of alertness and excitement (electroencephalographic patterns) which can be used in animal experiments.

Emotion will be discussed in terms of the preceding categories, the first section dealing with what can be studied objectively and the second with what can be inferred about subjective events from objective study. The excitement parameter is discussed last. Although the hypothalamus and rhinencephalon are discussed separately here, they do not function separately. The chapter is centered on neural mechanisms to the neglect of a large and important body of psychophysiologic studies relating autonomic and somatic responses to stimulus situations calculated to arouse emotion. The patterning of emotional response will be discussed briefly.

EXPRESSION OF EMOTION[30]

Studies in which refined instrumentation, standardization of stimuli and quantitation are used indicate that, in man, emotional reactions to given situations certainly do not involve exclusively either sympathetic or parasympathetic discharge, an idea going back to Cannon (Lacey *et al.*; see Knapp[30]). In fact, correlation coefficients between specific autonomic reactions in individuals responding to the same situation tend to be low. The responses during psychiatric interview and therapy become complicated when more than one response is recorded.[31] Another finding in recent laboratory work is the suprisingly great autonomic response to cognitive functions; e.g., cardiac acceleration while the subject is doing mental arithmetic is as great as during a "cold pressor test" (immersion of the foot in ice water at 4° C.).[30]

In considering the neural basis of emotion we must keep in mind all of the factors just discussed. The expression and the experience of emotion are the main concern of this chapter, and their interrelations are far from obvious. While we would say that we run away because we are afraid, whether this or the reverse is the actual sequence has been debated since 1890, when William James and Lange independently suggested that emotional states (e.g., fear) result from rather than cause overt manifestations of emotion. Emotional experience and expression are not inseparably linked. Certain neurologic patients (pseudobulbar palsy) exhibit involuntary bouts of laughing and crying without experiencing emotion; conversely, patients with other lesions (parkinsonism) may experience emotion while remaining completely impassive and expressionless.[22]

Hypothalamus and Emotion. The visceral, vascular and glandular changes resulting from activity of the autonomic nervous system are elicited by stimulation at many levels of the central nervous system. These changes have already been discussed in their relation to the control of bodily processes.

They can also be profitably examined as contributors to the bodily manifestation of emotion. In 1890, Goltz described a dog whose cerebral cortex he had removed. Were externally expressed emotion executed by the cortical motor areas, none would have been seen in this decorticate dog. However, not only did it manifest reactions recognized as rage, but these were aroused by inconsequential stimuli. Thus, the apparatus for this kind of emotion was released from inhibitory control exerted by the cerebral cortex. On the other hand, Sherrington noted that the acute decerebrate animal is nearly, if not entirely, without emotional expression.* This finding narrowed the locus for the execution of a full angry display to the basal ganglia, diencephalon and anterior midbrain. Karplus and Kreidl in 1914 discovered that stimulating the hypothalamic portion of the diencephalon resulted in a variety of visceral responses.

In 1928, Bard made transections which localized the neural mechanism of rage chiefly to the diencephalon. By longitudinal sections removing the thalamus he narrowed the localization to the hypothalamus. The excitement or dynamic aspect of emotion is pointed up by the fact that the retention of a relatively few cubic millimeters of hypothalamic tissue makes the difference between a preparation which is an emotional vegetable and one which at a slight touch, or even "spontaneously," will go into a paroxysm of activity—struggling, baring of the claws, spitting, pupillary dilation, erection of hair and a variety of internal visceral responses. Whether this response is, in fact, "sham rage" (Bard) and a "pseudoaffective state" (Sherrington) will be discussed later.

It is important that these experiments should not be generalized to encompass emotional displays other than rage; it is still not known where all emotional activities are managed. However, basic sexual behavior appears to be integrated in the diencephalon. When given estrogens, a decorticate female cat displays normal feline estrous behavior, which Bard divides into (i) courtship activity (playful rubbing and rolling, vocalizing, estrous crouching, and treading with hind legs) and (ii) the after-reaction (frantic rubbing, licking, squirming, and rolling following vaginal stimulation). As with rage, the chronic high mesencephalic decerebrate cat shows only fragments of this behavior, the induced activity falling short of the full pattern of estrous behavior exhibited by normal and decorticate cats.

The neural mechanisms for the basic elements of sexual behavior and rage are localized

in the hypothalamus. It must be remembered that the principle of "levels of function" applies in this field, and many other neural structures are also involved.

DETAILED LOCALIZATION OF EMOTIONAL ACTIVITY IN HYPOTHALAMUS. Although the hypothalamus is a small structure, it contains the apparatus for several kinds of emotional behavior as well as a variety of feeding, drinking and satiety centers.

Focal stimulation and localized lesions have demarcated a restricted hypothalamic region concerned with emotional display. Lesions of the ventromedial nuclei of the hypothalamus induce rage and savageness in animals, which make well-directed attacks toward the experimenter.[60] Focal stimulation of unanesthetized, unrestrained animals through implanted electrodes with their tips in the hypothalamus† is highly valuable in more precise localization of the hypothalamic subcortical areas concerned with emotion.[19] The same point can be stimulated in successive animals with different strengths and durations of stimulation, and the exact point of stimulation can be determined histologically. Two types of behavioral (defensive) responses are obtained: (i) a fight or rage-like pattern (growling and hissing, flattening of the ears, piloerection and other sympathetic responses) and (ii) a flight or fearlike pattern (pupillary dilation, darting of eyes to and fro, turning of head from side to side as though searching for a pathway of escape, and finally flight). These are patterns, not fragments, of behavior involving somatic and visceral responses of the body as a whole. They are directed toward the experimenter or a weak point in a cage, respectively. They look like the way a cat responds to natural stimulus objects, e.g., a barking dog. In addition, visceral and other acts, such as micturition, defecation, salivation, retching and sniffing, can be elicited by stimulation of regions rather widely distributed through the hypothalamus.

According to the Zurich physiologists,[19, 21] the defense reaction is focused in the dorsal part of the midthalamus surrounding the descending column of the fornix; it extends forward into the preoptic and ventral septal area and caudally into the posterior hypothalamus and expands in the central gray matter of the mid-

---

* In a cat with a *chronic* section at the level of the midbrain, high threshold fragmentary expressions of anger can be elicited.[4] These responses indicate some participation of midbrain centers in emotional expression, but fall short of the integrated rage behavior seen in cats with transections above the hypothalamus.

† W. R. Hess of Zurich, Switzerland shared the Nobel Prize for introducing (1927) and prosecuting such studies of emotion.

brain. It is thus a narrow lamina 1 to 1.5 mm. in thickness running the whole length and slightly beyond the hypothalamus. Hunsperger[21] places flight reactions externally and fright reactions centrally in this lamina. According to Nakao,[40] loci for the two types of responses are found in the same concentric lamina, but flight mechanisms are manifest after stimulation of regions more rostral than those serving aggressive reactions. Similar reactions are obtained by stimulating the amygdalar region of the rhinencephalon.

Regardless of the details of localization, there are indications that an area beginning in the telencephalon, extending entirely through the hypothalamus and into the midbrain, instigates flight and aggressive motor behavior with accompanying autonomic manifestations; many other points in the hypothalamus, the hippo-campus and the cerebral cortex that have been explored do not give rise to these emotional responses. Further, a system of fibers involving the ventromedial nucleus appears to restrain emotional behavior, since rage and savageness occur in exaggerated form when these nuclei alone are destroyed.[55]

Limbic System; Rhinencephalon.[6, 7, 24, 49] A medial complex of cortex, subcortical nuclei and the tracts which connect them with the hypothalamus and other structures is known anatomically as the "rhinencephalon," literally "nose brain" (Fig. 1). It received this name because the olfactory tract enters it. However, the "nose brain" is well developed in animals having few or no olfactory receptors. According to electrophysiologic studies, only a fraction of the rhinencephalon is activated by olfactory stimuli. Ablation and stimulation studies indicate that

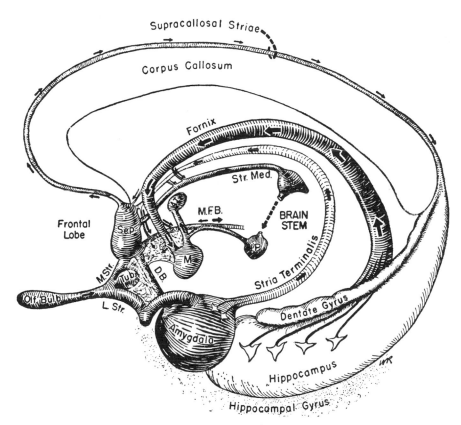

Fig. 1. Schematic representation of relationship of main subcortical structures and connections of rhinencephalon, drawn as though all of them could be seen from medial aspect of right hemisphere. For diagrammatic purposes some connections have been given an arbitrary course. Abbreviations: *A.T.,* anterior thalamic nucleus; *D.B.,* diagonal band of Broca; *H.,* habenula (part of epithalamus); *I.P.,* interpeduncular nucleus; *L.Str.,* lateral olfactory stria; *M.,* mammillary body (part of posterior hypothalamus); *M.F.B.,* medial forebrain bundle; *M.Str.,* medial olfactory stria; *Olf. Bulb,* olfactory bulb; *Sep.,* region of septal nuclei; *Str. Med.,* stria medullaris; *Tub.,* olfactory tubercle (head of caudate immediately underneath). (After Krieg; from MacLean, *Psychosom. Med.,* 1949, *11:*338–353.)

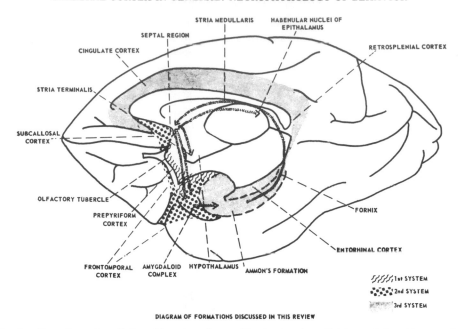

Fig. 2. Drawing of medial and basal surfaces of brain showing divisions of the rhinencephalon. Note smallness of first system, which has direct connections with olfactory bulb. Second system is defined as structures connected with the first system but not the bulb. Third system includes hippocampus and other structures of Ammon's cortex and juxtallocortex in entorrhinal (inferior), retrosplenial (posterior) and cingulate (superior and anterior) regions. Most of discussion in text pertains to the second system. (From Pribram and Kruger, *Ann. N. Y. Acad. Sci.,* 1954, *58:*109–138.)

the nonolfactory portions of the rhinencephalon are concerned with emotional life. MacLean,[36] to avoid the olfactory implications of "rhinencephalon," has popularized the terms "limbic lobe" and "limbic system." First used by Broca to describe this area, "limbic" means border. The cerebral hemispheres arise as a tremendous outgrowth from the diencephalon. The hilus or neck of this growth forms a concentric ring of cerebral cortex which, in a sense, is a *border* of the great neocortical vesicle.

The major part of the limbic system is composed of two rings of limbic cortex and associated subcortical nuclei. The inner ring of three-layered cortex includes part of the hippocampal formation and is phylogenetically the most primitive, being generally referred to as the "archipallium" or "allocortex." This area includes structures with olfactory connections (the olfactory tubercle, the prepyriform cortex, the periamygdaloid cortex, the corticomedial nuclei of the amygdala) and certain structures and areas which are connected with the thalamus and hypothalamus, mainly the entorrhinal area and the hippocampus. The next ring is designated "juxtallocortex," "mesopallium" or "transitional" cortex; it is homotypical six-

layered cortex. In its structure and phylogenetic history it is intermediate between the archipallium and the surrounding "neopallium" or "neocortex," from which it is separated by the cingulate sulcus. This outer ring consists of the cingulate gyrus and, anteriorly, the orbitoinsulotemporal cortex and, posteriorly, the presubiculum. Two important subcortical masses, the septal nuclei and the basolateral amygdalar nuclei, are associated with mesopallium. (Note in Figure 2 that Pribram and Kruger classify some of the mesopallium with their second system and some with the third.) The efferent projections from the mesopallium pass to subcortical centers, largely by way of the striatum. The fornix is the main efferent projection for the archipallium, which sends fibers to the septal region, the hypothalamus and the midbrain. The neuroanatomy of the rhinencephalon or limbic system is too complex to permit detailed description. Figures 1 and 2 represent it and some of its connections in a highly simplified fashion.

MESOPALLIUM. As pointed out in Chapter 12, the neopallium subserves some visceral functions, the responsible foci appearing to be discrete, specialized and generally associated with motor or sensory areas. Thus salivation is initiated from points ventral to the face area, pupillary dilation and lacrimation from the frontal eye fields, and limb vasoconstrictor responses by points in the arm and leg areas. We have also seen that stimulation of mesopallium results in autonomic responses. That stimulation of its orbital portion causes changes in respiration and visceral function was discovered in 1894 and again noted in 1940,[3] but not until 1949 was it learned that much of the mesopallium gives rise to respiratory, vascular and visceral changes when electrically excited. Kaada and his associates[25] have shown (Fig. 3) that such results are obtained by stimulating the whole stretch of cortex running from the anterior cingulate gyrus across the posterior orbital surface to the insula, the temporal pole, the pyriform cortex, the periamygdaloid and the posterior hippocampal cortex. As with hypothalamic stimulation, a wide variety of visceral responses to limbic stimulation have been obtained in both animals and man, but in general these responses are of lesser magnitude than are those induced by hypothalamic stimulation.

Many limbic areas affect the same visceral structure, and stimulation of the same point in the limbic lobe will cause several kinds of visceral or vascular responses. In fact, the various segments of the limbic cortex appear to be closely interrelated but only poorly connected with the neopallium. By applying strychnine to

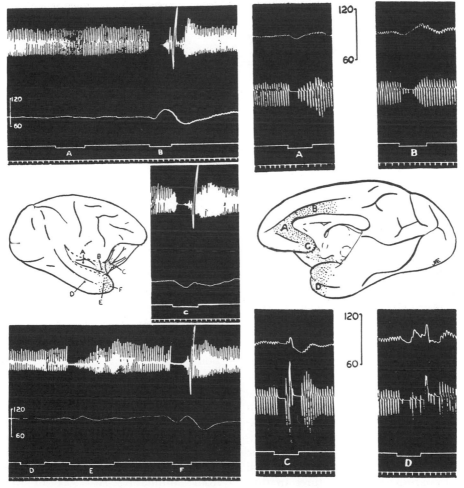

Fig. 3. Responses to stimulation of limbic cortex. *Left,* Respiratory (*upper record*) and blood pressure response (*lower record*) resulting from electrical stimulation of points designated on brain map. Insula, containing points *A* and *B,* is visualized by separation of temporal and frontoparietal operculum. Respiratory movements recorded through tracheal cannula. Stroke upward indicates expiration. *Right,* Same for mesial surface except that blood pressure is now the upper record. (From Kaada et al., *J. Neurophysiol.,* 1949, *12:*347–356.)

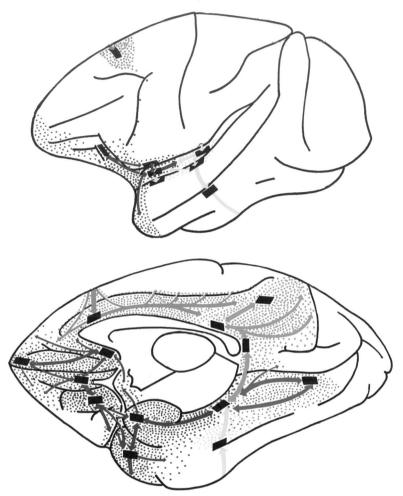

Fig. 4. Schematic representation of lateral (*top*) and mediobasal (*bottom*) surfaces of macaque brain showing segments of phylogenetically old and new cortex which appear related on basis of strychninization studies. Black rectangles indicate areas to which strychnine was applied. Respective colors indicate reciprocally connected areas. Note overlapping of shading at fringes. Extent of firing into neopallium is not shown. (Based on experiments by MacLean and Pribram; from Fulton, *Frontal lobotomy and affective behavior; a neurophysiological analysis.* New York, W. W. Norton and Company, 1951.)

various limbic areas and searching the limbic lobe for strychnine spikes, the interconnections between limbic areas shown in Figure 4 were identified. The interconnectedness of the limbic system is shown by the fact that stimulation in it produces prolonged repetitive afterdischarges, detectable electroencephalographically,[17] which spread readily throughout the limbic system and only to related structures such as the hypothalamus. These structures are thus identified as closely associated with the limbic system. However, the boundaries between mesopallium and neocortex should not be drawn too sharply because the supplementary motor area (Chap. 12) is half in each.

The responses of limbic structures to stimulation may mean that they serve as a regulatory system for visceral and vascular function superimposed upon the hypothalamus. On the other hand, the responses may mean that the limbic lobe is concerned with emotion. An involvement in emotional expression is suggested by the kind of somatic muscular response resulting from stimulation of these areas, e.g., vocalization from stimulating Area 24 in the anterior cingulate gyrus.

SUBCORTICAL LIMBIC STRUCTURES. The participation of the limbic system in emotion is especially clear when the subcortical limbic structures, e.g., the septal and amygdalar nuclei, are stimulated or ablated. The amygdalar nuclei lying beneath the pyriform cortex seem to be peculiarly important. The amygdala is a complex of nuclei with connections with the olfactory bulb and the temporal neocortex. The amygdala also projects to the septal region and the hypothalamus via the stria terminalis. The septal nuclei, rhinencephalic structures lying along the midline just beneath the anterior genu of the corpus callosum, are widely connected with structures known to be concerned with emotion and motivation—the preoptic region, the hypothalamus, the hippocampus, the brain stem tegmentum and the habenulae.

Stimulation experiments. Stimulation experiments by Gastaut[14] in France and MacLean[34, 37] in America focused attention on the amygdalar and periamygdalar region. Stimulation of these structures through implanted electrodes in unanesthetized cats and monkeys elicited responses clearly related to "eating" and the upper end of the gastrointestinal tract—sniffing, licking, biting, chewing, chop-licking,

gagging and retching (Fig. 5). (Somewhat inconsistently, hyperphagia following amygdalar lesions has been reported.[16]) A second category of responses were respiratory and autonomic responses elicited from the mesopallium directly. A third group of responses were classified as components of defense—attack, retraction of ears, growling and hissing, and protrusion of claws.

The defense responses elicited from the amygdala are similar to those from the hypothalamus and midbrain, but aggressive responses may be more easily obtained from the amygdala. All agree that the amygdala exerts its effects by way of the hypothalamus and midbrain, but the pathway is in question. Fernandez de Molina and Hunsperger[13] picture a hierarchy of centers, i.e., the amygdala, connecting by the circuitous stria terminalis with the hypothalamus, which in turn connects with the midbrain central gray matter. Hilton and Zbrozyna[20] contend that interruption of the stria terminalis does not block the effect of

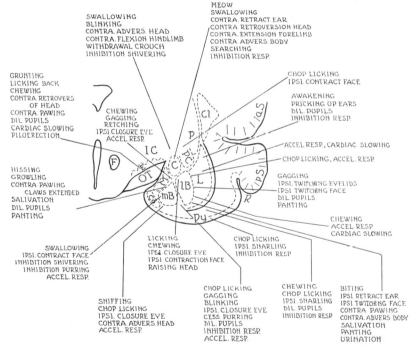

Fig. 5. Cross section through midregion of amygdala showing types of oral, facial and other behavior resulting from stimulation. Note the divisions of the amygdala and its relationship to other brain structures. Abbreviations: *LB* and *mB,* lateral and medial parts of basal nucleus of amygdala; *L,* lateral nucleus; *C,* central nucleus of amygdala; *F,* fornix; *OT,* optic tract; *Py,* pyriform cortex; *R,* rhinal fissure; *Cl,* claustrum; *P,* pulvinar; *IC,* internal capsule; *Co,* cortical nucleus of amygdala; *E,* entopeduncular nucleus; *M,* medial nucleus of amygdala; *PC,* putamen-central amygdaloid complex; *aS,* anterior sylvian gyrus; *pS,* posterior sylvian gyrus. (From MacLean and Delgado, *Electroenceph. clin. Neurophysiol.,* 1953, 5:91–100.)

amygdala stimulation permanently; they provide evidence for a narrow band of fibers connecting the amygdala more directly to the hypothalamus along its entire length. Nauta[41-43] has described a ventral amygdalo-fugal pathway in the same location as the narrow band of points yielding the defense reaction.

When amygdala stimulation was played against stimulation of a hypothalamic point proved to elicit aggressive behavior, the effect was sometimes facilitative, but more often it suppressed attack.[11] The two effects were obtained from different amygdalar loci. The suppressive effect especially supports the thesis that the amygdala is "upstream" to the hypothalamus in organizing emotional behavior.

Ablation of septal region. Lesions of this anterior, medial limbic region reduce responses in a "fear" or "anxiety" situation.[8] To establish an anxiety-producing stimulus, a clicking noise lasting three minutes was followed immediately by a painful shock to the feet. After a few such presentations the clicking noise alone caused an anxiety response—crouching, micturition and defecation. To obtain an objective measure of this conditioned fear or anxiety, rats were trained to depress a lever in order to secure a drop of water. The animals were rewarded only once in 60 seconds so that the rate of lever-pressing would remain high. The degree to which the clicking noise interfered with the lever pressing was taken as a measure of anxiety. In unoperated control rats, conditioned anxiety completely inhibited bar-pressing for water. After lesions of the septal region, the effect of the clicking noise on lever-pressing was much less pronounced.

Other methods supplied evidence of increases in other emotional behavior after such lesions. Following the operation, the rats were placed in a group cage. On emerging from anesthesia they were soon engaged in a free-for-all. Tame rats which had been petted freely with bare hands could now be handled only with gloves; they repeatedly attacked a bar of steel placed in front of them. Such attacks are not like sham rage but are extremely skillful and well directed. It can be concluded that the animals have become more excited and more savage, that they are less fearful and anxious.

Amygdalar ablations. In 1937, Klüver and Bucy[28, 29] produced bizarre behavioral disturbances (visual agnosia, exploration by smelling, compulsive exploratory behavior) in monkeys following bilateral temporal lobectomy which destroyed important limbic structures. Some of these behavior changes have already been described. Noted, too, were profound changes in emotional behavior in the direction of passivity or unresponsiveness. Objects which normally excite fear or wariness—a snake, a stranger, a cat or a dog—were approached without hesitation and without the vocalization and facial behavior which denote fear in the monkey. By contrast, other types of emotional behavior, especially sexual activity, were intensified and were aroused by an unusual diversity of objects. The monkeys manifested sexual behavior toward the opposite sex, the same sex, and themselves in a degree far beyond that seen in normal male monkeys. Also manifest was excessive oral behavior—biting and sucking of various parts of the body or inanimate objects.

In 1937 Papez[48] reached the conclusion from neuroanatomic considerations that the rhinencephalic structures were linked to the hypothalamic, thalamic and limbic cortical structures to form a neural mechanism of emotion. The impact of these two papers was postponed by World War II, but these pioneering studies probing the neural basis of emotion have since been widely extended in a number of laboratories throughout the world.

Of the limbic structures destroyed in Klüver and Bucy's operation, it is the amygdalar nuclei and overlying pyriform cortex whose loss produces the emotional changes. Ablation restricted to the limbic areas involved in Klüver and Bucy's experiments produces the emotional but not the cognitive part (e.g., psychic blindness) of the syndrome exhibited by their monkeys (but see below). Many investigators have reported fragments of the Klüver–Bucy syndrome resulting from lobectomy in animals[58] and even in man;[57] the most dramatic demonstration has been that by Schreiner and Kling.[52-54] After removal of the amygdalar nuclei and the overlying rhinencephalic cortex, cats and monkeys became exceedingly docile. The agouti and lynx, two animals selected for their savage natures, similarly became docile for a period of weeks following amygdalectomy. In recent confirmatory experiments indifference to a live mouse and absence of agressive behavior was demonstrated in nine cats with complete amygdalar lesions.[56]

Operated cats and monkeys clearly demonstrated hypersexuality, which they exhibited toward either sex without discrimination or toward animals of a different species, such as the hen. The sexual activity diminished after castration but was not caused by an increased production of testosterone. These results were confirmed, and the area concerned with sexual behavior has been delimited.[16] Hypersexuality follows lesions restricted to the pyriform cortex (Fig. 6) overlying the basal amygdalar nucleus but not lesions confined to the nucleus.

While a certain amount of placidity or calmness may follow many brain operations, that following amygdalectomy is specific. It is interesting that a placid amygdalectomized animal is made savage and rageful by lesions of the ventromedial nucleus of the hypothalamus.[52]

Conversely, rats made savage by septal lesions have been made placid by amygdalectomy.[26]

Some investigators have been unable to confirm these findings; others not only have observed the same disorders but have obtained them by producing fractional lesions of the amygdalar nuclei or the overlying cortex. This variation is perhaps not surprising when dealing with a behavior which is complex and difficult to quantify and study objectively, on the one hand,* and with an exceedingly complex neural structure on the other. Somewhat the

* For example, Rosvold *et al.*[51] have shown that an amygdalectomized baboon which was aggressive in a cage situation was submissive in a group hierarchy situation.

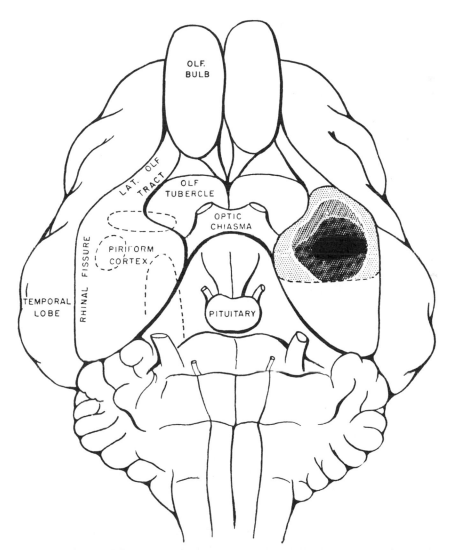

Fig. 6. Ventral aspect of cat brain showing surface projection of areas where destruction caused specific behavior problem. On right is concentric stipple circle showing quartile incidence of involvement in animals exhibiting hypersexuality. (From Green *et al., J. comp. Neurol.,* 1957, *108*:505–545.)

same difficulties were encountered in early studies of the hypothalamus, and these were resolved by the discovery that the hypothalamus contains pairs of oppositely acting centers. The same may be true of the limbic lobe.

The sorting out of symptoms in the Klüver–Bucy syndrome into limbic and neocortical has been unduly influenced by the demonstration of cognitive learning functions in the nearby inferotemporal region. The unconscious assumption that the behavioral changes of emotional significance are ascribable solely to the limbic structures is not sustained. Akert et al.[2] removed the neocortex of the temporal lobe contiguous across the rhinal fissure with the limbic cortex (see Fig. 6) with slight damage to it or the underlying nuclei. Some oral tendencies were exhibited transiently; fear of snakes, brooms, nets and hoses was absent for a month after operation, when reaction to these objects progressively returned. Akert et al. point out that a less severe and permanent effect on fearfulness is consistent with anatomic connection of the temporal cortex with the amygdala and other rhinencephalic structures. Such projections provide one means by which the amygdala is connected with the receptive and cognitive apparatus of the cerebral cortex.

ARCHIPALLIUM. Despite the anatomically well established connections of the hippocampal formation with the hypothalamus via the fornix and with the anterior cingulate gyrus (Area 24) via the mammillary bodies and the anterior thalamic nuclei, the emotional significance of these connections, hypothesized by Papez[48] and others[33] has not been clearly established experimentally. Although rather intangible changes in emotionality have been described as following lesions of Area 24 and other areas of the mesopallium, interference with this system is not accompanied by gross changes in emotional behavior like those following interference with the subcortical limbic nuclei. In one of the few studies[15] in which the hippocampal formations have been selectively but nearly completely ablated, changes in emotional behavior were confined to one element of the Klüver–Bucy syndrome—tameness and fearlessness. Monkeys and cats were nonreactive to the snake and dog test, respectively. The decrease in aggressiveness was only partial. Hypersexuality was not observed and the animals were possibly hyposexual. Oral tendencies were not observed. It is now clear that the hippocampal formation

does not execute any gross form of emotional behavior.

Quite possibly Papez's system serves the cognitive and other subjective aspects of emotion. There is, in fact, some evidence that the hippocampal formation is concerned with the subjective or inner aspect of emotion. We are left with the original deduction from anatomy that it is part of a system by which the limbic and neocortical functions are related to one another in a manner too subtle for present methods of analysis.

AFFECTIVE ASPECTS OF EMOTION

Sherrington, recognizing the dangers of inferring subjective experiences from motor behavior, spoke of "pseudoaffective" reflexes in the decerebrate cat. Cannon, in turn, cautiously spoke of "sham rage" in the decorticate or high decerebrate animal, implying that only the external and not the subjective manifestations of rage occurred. The groundwork for what may seem paradoxical—an objective attack on a subjective phenomenon—was laid by Loucks from 1934 to 1938, when he applied the buried-electrode technique to the analysis of the neural basis of conditioned reflexes.

Since Pavlov, it has been known that if a "neutral" stimulus (the conditioned stimulus) producing no visible reaction, or a reaction unrelated to the conditioned response, is presented at the proper time interval with or before a stimulus which causes a given reaction (the unconditioned stimulus and response, respectively), the conditioned stimulus subsequently presented alone will produce the same reaction (conditioned response). By stimulating at various points along the pathway of the *unconditioned* reflex (foot withdrawal from electric grid) from sense organ to muscle, Loucks and others found that stimulation of sense organs, posterior root or columns of the spinal cord, and thalamus can serve as an unconditioned stimulus; stimulation of the motor cortex, the anterior root, or the muscle, though producing a response, cannot serve as an unconditioned stimulus. In other words, a stimulus on the afferent side of the reflex is effective as an unconditioned stimulus; a stimulus on the efferent side is ineffective. It is also known that conditioning is exceedingly difficult and may be impossible if a neutral stimulus produces the unconditioned response, e.g., light→pupillary constriction or tendon tap →knee jerk. Going one step farther, one can restate this issue in terms of affect. The reflexes which serve well are those produced by unconditioned stimuli which a man would call pleasant or unpleasant—for example, an electric shock, or food or acid placed in the mouth.

Role of Hypothalamus in Affect. Masserman[39] applied the same type of analysis to the emotional display elicited by hypothalamic stimulation. He asked: Is the hypothalamus simply a motor structure organizing the external expression of emotion, or is it "upstream" on the afferent side? If hypothalamic stimulation can serve as an *un*conditioned reflex stimulus, then, following Loucks' analysis, the hypothalamus is upstream. Masserman established a series of criteria which have proved very useful in determining whether an emotional manifestation resulting from a central lesion or stimulus is a pseudoaffective or sham emotion. These criteria are: (i) Is the aggressive activity directed toward any specific object? (ii) Does the display inhibit and replace other activity? (iii) Does the display outlast the stimulus as does emotional excitement in intact animals? (iv) Does the animal become conditioned against the environment (the experimental box)? (v) Will brain stimulation serve as an unconditioned reflex in formal conditioning experiments? He answered these questions negatively for hypothalamic stimulation. Subsequent investigators have uniformly answered the same questions positively, and the reason for the discrepancy is not known.

Masserman's criteria have been widely used by others in working out the neurophysiology of emotion and motivation. Nakao,[40] like others, observed that the emotional display is not blind and undirected. When it is ragelike, it can be directed toward the experimenter or toward an innocent feline bystander; if the display is fearlike, attempts to escape are directed toward a weak point in the cage. Both Nakao and Delgado *et al.*[9] have found that hypothalamic stimulation giving rise to hissing, baring of teeth, biting, scratching, attempts to escape, etc., serve very well as unconditioned stimuli. Moreover, it is possible to show how the animal "interprets" the hypothalamic stimulation. Nakao placed an animal with electrodes implanted in its hypothalamus in a box with an electrified grid floor. He then taught the animal to turn off a shock to the feet by manipulating a paddle. The first time a hypothalamic shock is delivered, some

animals immediately turn off the shock. Delgado *et al.*[9] have shown further that the hypothalamic shock can motivate learning *de novo* and can act as a punishment strong enough to inhibit an animal's approaching food.

How well a hypothalamic stimulation in cats will serve as an unconditioned stimulus for a conditioned avoidance response depends on whether a flight or a rage type of reaction is elicited. When a flight reaction resulted, paddle pushing motivated by food stimulation was transferred to the hypothalamic stimulation immediately, whereas transfer did not occur when the stimulus produced fight reactions.[40]

Other subcortical regions give rise to emotional reactions which can be used as unconditioned stimuli.[10] Many of these regions are on the classic pain pathways. Others, like the hypothalamus and the medial nucleus of the amygdala (see below), are not. Electrical stimulation of the amygdala in man yields subjective reports of fear and rage.[18]

It should not be thought that the hypothalamus working alone is capable of initiating directed emotional behavior. The cerebral cortex is necessary for this. The emotional behavior of Goltz's decorticate dog or that resulting from hypothalamic stimulation in decorticate cats is not directed. It is quite possible that the hypothalamus discharges upward to the cerebral cortex, which directs the attack. Nor can it be assumed that the hypothalamus is the site of the affective experience, or whatever cerebral process is necessary for a stimulus to serve as an unconditioned stimulus. The hypothalamus may discharge to a thalamic or other area essential to affect. Additional investigation is necessary to work out these relations, but it is clear that the hypothalamus is more than an efferent structure downstream in the apparatus for emotional behavior. Further evidence of this is obtained from self-stimulation experiments (see below).

Self-stimulation. As pointed out in Chapter 25, if electrodes are implanted in the brain and the switch* which closes a stimulating circuit is arranged so that it can be manipulated by the animal, the affects of stimulation can be deduced from the animal's behavior. With the electrode tip in certain places in the animal's brain and the bar where the animal can close it

*The switch is usually activated by a bar or lever inserted into the testing box, so the laboratory jargon has become "bar-pressing" or "lever-pressing."

accidentally, in a few trials he will have learned the connection between the bar and the shock and will thereafter shun the bar. Quite otherwise, when the electrodes are in some other parts of the brain, the animal will stimulate itself repeatedly, as often as 5000 times per hour—more than once a second.[47] If permitted, this behavior will be continued to the point of exhaustion. In hour-long tests continued for a month no sign of satiation developed.[46] Shocks in still other areas are indifferent, i.e., the animal neither seeks nor avoids stimulation. That forms of behavior other than bar pressing can be motivated by self-stimulation has been proved in a variety of ways. A rat can be trained to run a maze for a brain shock as a reward, or will cross an electrified grid in order to receive a brain shock. In a Skinner box, a rat may press a bar more rapidly for a brain shock than for food.[6]

The rate of bar-pressing is used to measure the efficacy of given electrode positions. Self-stimulation results when the tip of the electrode is at any point in a rather wide extent of the brain. The neocortex, however, is a quite indifferent locus. The most effective regions are in the hypothalamus and the limbic system. The posterior hypothalamus just anterior to the mammillary bodies yields very high rates, perhaps the highest; the anterior hypothalamus yields much lower rates. The active points extend caudally into the midbrain tegmentum and rostrally into the preoptic region, the septal region and the median forebrain bundle. Other parts of the limbic system produce bar-pressing, but at low rates.

If mentalistic interpretations are permitted, drives and emotions can be divided into pleasant and unpleasant ones. Self-stimulation may indicate some pleasurable affect or some satisfaction resulting from the brain stimulus, although this is a point of view contested by many. Another approach to analysis of the phenomenon of self-stimulation is to establish a state of anxiety and discover either its effect on self-stimulation or the effects of self-stimulation on the anxiety. As in his experiments on ablation of the septal region, Brady[7] established two operant conditioned responses in a Skinner box, pressing the lever for water and for a brain shock. A clicking noise had previously been given anxiety-producing qualities by linking it with a shock to the feet. The clicking sound alone was then sufficient to elicit an anxiety response and to inhibit

bar-pressing for water. If self-stimulation in the median forebrain bundle was substituted for the water reward, bar-pressing was not suppressed by the conditioned anxiety, i.e., the clicking noise. Analysis shows that this persistence of bar-pressing is not due simply to self-stimulation being a more powerful reward. It may be "peace" rather than "joy" that is obtained by self-stimulation.

The difficulties besetting interpretation of self-stimulation experiments are somewhat analogous to those encountered in considering ablation experiments. With certain electrode placements, Roberts[50] found that stimulation would motivate some kinds of learning but not others. He suggested that the stimulation was rewarding at the onset but quickly became punishing, supposedly by summation within an aversive system simultaneously stimulated.[4] The apparent preference for short bouts of stimulation seems to be due to movements resulting from the stimulation, which release the bar. In two-bar experiments, one closing the circuit through the brain and the other opening it, preferred durations of stimulation increased tenfold.[59] The latter seconds of the stimulation were clearly not aversive.

Such discrepancies and other considerations have led to the development of a preference technique in which the rat receives brain stimulation or avoids it by walking from one compartment of a box to the other. The compartment yielding brain stimulation is randomly changed every minute so that repeated choices are made. The time spent in each chamber and the stimulus condition are recorded. This apparatus has the great advantage of determining the amount of aversive response. In bar-pressing, certain negative loci of brain shock may simply cause the rat to shun the bar, an unquantitative "yes—no" response.

By the preference method the most strongly aversive tegmental area coincides with the modern description of the pain tracts, namely, the dorsal portion of the central gray area and the dorsomedial tegmentum, especially the deeper layers of the superior colliculus or the nucleus of the posterior commissure. In contrast with the slow development of positive behavior to posterior hypothalamic stimulation, behavioral aversive responses developed within the first two 20-minute periods.

In one experiment the rat in the active compartment received hypothalamic and tegmental shocks alternating every 0.1 second. The interpolation of tegmental shocks, though strongly aversive when delivered alone, had relatively slight effects on rate of acquisition and level of positive responses from hypothalamic stimulation.

One large unknown in all self-stimulation experiments is whether the positive and negative reactions are central or secondary to the sensory return from visceral and vascular effects of the stimulus. It is profitless to deduce "pleasant" or "unpleasant" experience from approach or escape behavior insofar as laboratory experiments are concerned. Nevertheless, from a clinical point of view there is no denying the value of discovering where unpleasant experience is elaborated, especially if this proves to be a circumscribed area subject to surgical destruction. The practical consequences of learning the neural localization of pleasant feelings have yet to be contemplated.

EXCITEMENT

The importance of the excitement or dynamic aspects of emotion is clear since we often categorize psychiatric patients as manic or depressed. Whether in animals the overt signs of overactivity reflect a conscious state of excitement is not certain, but a parallelism can be assumed. The external manifestations of excitement can be increased or reduced by neural lesions. Thus while acting unopposed by more cephalad levels, as after a high decerebration, the posterior hypothalamus causes sham rage. Destruction of the posterior hypothalamus in otherwise intact animals results in somnolence, drowsiness, cataplexy, general stolidity and inactivity. The posterior hypothalamus is therefore a way station in the *descending* system producing emotional display and in the *ascending* reticular systems producing alertness and wakefulness (Chap. 22). Somewhat more anteriorly, destruction of the ventromedial nucleus produces hyperactivity as well as savageness. Maire and Patton[38] have demarcated the levels at which lesions produce general bodily hyperactivity, namely, the preoptic and anterior hypothalamic areas. Some anterior lesions produce hyperactivity combined with fatal pulmonary edema. This combination is a familiar sequel to mania.

Lindsley[32] has proposed an activation theory of emotion, perhaps better considered as the activation aspect of emotion. According to this theory, a discharge of hypothalamic nuclei downward, which produces the external aspect of emotions, is accompanied by a discharge upward which produces the subjective alertness or excitement typical of emotion. As we have seen in Chapter 22, this theory is well substantiated.[33] It is perhaps not too much to hope that underactivity of such a system will eventually be identified as causing the flatness of emotion in the schizophrenic and the obtunding of mental processes and depression of postural and motor activities in the depressed patient.

REFERENCES

1. ABRAHAMS, V. C., HILTON, S. M. and MALCOLM, J. L. *J. Physiol.*, 1962, *164:*1–16.
2. AKERT, K., GRUESEN, R. A., WOOLSEY, C. N. and MEYER, D. R. *Brain*, 1961, *84:*480–498.
3. BAILEY, P. and SWEET, W. H. *J. Neurophysiol.*, 1940, *3:* 276–281.
4. BARD, P. and MACHT, M. D. In: *Ciba Foundation symposium on the neurological basis of behavior*, G. E. W. WOLSTENHOLME and C. M. O'CONNOR, eds. Boston, Little, Brown and Co., 1958.
5. BOWER, G. H. and MILLER, N. E. *J. comp. physiol. Psychol.*, 1958, *51:*669–674.
6. BRADY, J. V. In: *Biological and biochemical bases of behavior*, H. F. HARLOW and C. N. WOOLSEY, eds. Madison, University of Wisconsin Press, 1958.
7. BRADY, J. V. In: *Reticular formation of the brain, Henry Ford Hospital International Symposium*, H. H. JASPER, L. D. PROCTOR, R. S. KNIGHTON, W. C. NOSHAY and R. T. COSTELLO, eds. Boston, Little, Brown and Co., 1958.
8. BRADY, J. V. and NAUTA, W. J. H. *J. comp. physiol. Psychol.*, 1953, *46:*339–346.
9. DELGADO, J. M. R., ROBERTS, W. W. and MILLER, N. E. *Amer. J. Physiol.*, 1954, *179:*587–593.
10. DELGADO, J. M. R., ROSVOLD, H. E. and LOONEY, E. *J. comp. physiol. Psychol.*, 1956, *49:*373–380.
11. EGGER, M. D. and FLYNN, J. P. *J. Neurophysiol.*, 1963, *26:* 705–720.
12. FERNANDEZ DE MOLINA, A. and HUNSPERGER, R. W. *J. Physiol.*, 1959, *145:*251–265.
13. FERNANDEZ DE MOLINA, A. and HUNSPERGER, R. W. *J. Physiol.*, 1962, *160:*200–213.
14. GASTAUT, H., NAQUET, R., VIGOUROUX, R. and CORRIOL, J. *Rev. neurol.*, 1952, *86:*319–327.
15. GOL, A., KELLAWAY, P., SHAPIRO, M. and HURST, C. M. *Neurology (Minneap.)*, 1963, *13:*1031–1041.
16. GREEN, J. D., CLEMENTE, C. D. and DE GROOT, J. *J. comp. Neurol.*, 1957, *108:*505–545.
17. GREEN, J. D. and SHIMAMOTO, T. *Arch. Neurol. Psychiat. (Chic.)*, 1953, *70:*687–702.
18. HEATH, R. G., MONROE, R. R. and MICKLE, W. A. *Amer. J. Psychiat.*, 1955, *111:*862–863.
19. HESS, W. R. and BRUGGER, M. *Helv. physiol. Acta*, 1943, *1:*33–52.
20. HILTON, S. M. and ZBROZYNA, A. W. *J. Physiol.*, 1963, *165:*160–173.
21. HUNSPERGER, R. W. *Helv. physiol. Acta*, 1956, *14:*70–92.

22. IRONSIDE, R. *Brain,* 1956, *79:*589–609.
23. JASPER, H. H., PROCTOR, L. D., KNIGHTON, R. S., NOSHAY, W. C. and COSTELLO, R. T., eds. *Reticular formation of the brain, Henry Ford Hospital International Symposium.* Boston, Little, Brown and Co., 1958.
24. KAADA, B. R. *Acta physiol. scand.,* 1951, *24*(Suppl. 83):1–285.
25. KAADA, B. R., PRIBRAM, K. H. and EPSTEIN, J. A. *J. Neurophysiol.,* 1949, *12:*347–356.
26. KING, F. A. and MEYER P. M. *Science,* 1958, *128:*655–656.
27. KLÜVER, H. *J.-Lancet,* 1952, *72:*567–577.
28. KLÜVER, H. and BUCY, P. C. *J. Psychol.,* 1938, *5:*33–54.
29. KLÜVER, H. and BUCY, P. C. *Arch. Neurol. Psychiat. (Chic.),* 1939, *42:*979–1000.
30. KNAPP, P., ed. *Expression of the emotions in man.* New York, International Universities Press, 1963.
31. LACEY, J. I. In: *Research in psychotherapy.* Washington, D.C., American Psychological Assoc., 1959.
32. LINDSLEY, D. B. Chap. 14 in *Handbook of experimental psychology,* S. S. STEVENS, ed. New York, John Wiley and Sons, 1951.
33. MACLEAN, P. D. *Psychosom. Med.,* 1949, *11:*338–353.
34. MACLEAN, P. D. *Electroenceph. clin. Neurophysiol.,* 1952, *4:*407–418.
35. MACLEAN, P. D. *Psychosom. Med.,* 1955, *17:*355–366.
36. MACLEAN, P. D. *J. nerv. ment. Dis.,* 1958, *127:*1–11.
37. MACLEAN, P. D. and DELGADO, J. M. R. *Electroenceph. clin. Neurophysiol.,* 1953, *5.*91–100.
38. MAIRE, F. W. and PATTON, H. D. *Amer. J. Physiol.,* 1956, *184:*345–350.
39. MASSERMAN, J. H. *Psychosom. Med.,* 1941, *3:*3–25.
40. NAKAO, H. *Amer. J. Physiol.,* 1958, *194:*411–418.
41. NAUTA, W. J. H. *J. Anat. (Lond.),* 1961, *95:*515–531.
42. NAUTA, W. J. H. *Brain,* 1962, *85.*505–520.
43. NAUTA, W. J. H. Chap. 19 in *The frontal granular cortex and behavior.* J. M. WARREN and K. AKERT, eds. New York, McGraw-Hill Book Co., 1964.
44. OLDS, J. *J. comp. physiol. Psychol.,* 1956, *49:*281–285.
45. OLDS, J. *J. comp. physiol. Psychol.,* 1958, *51:*675–678.
46. OLDS, J. *Physiol. Rev.,* 1962, *42:*554 604.
47. OLDS, J. and MILNER, P. *J. comp. physiol. Psychol.,* 1954, *47:*419–427.
48. PAPEZ, J. W. *Arch. Neurol. Psychiat. (Chic.),* 1937, *38:*725–743.
49. PRIBRAM, K. H. and KRUGER, L. *Ann. N. Y. Acad. Sci.,* 1954, *58:*109–138.
50. ROBERTS, W. W. *J. comp. physiol. Psychol.,* 1958, *51:*391–399; *idem,* 400–407.
51. ROSVOLD, H. E., MIRSKY, A. F. and PRIBRAM, K. H. *J. comp. physiol. Psychol.,* 1954, *47:*173–178.
52. SCHREINER, L. and KLING, A. *J. Neurophysiol.,* 1953, *16:*643–659.
53. SCHREINER, L. and KLING, A. *Arch. Neurol. Psychiat. (Chic.),* 1954, *72:*180–186.
54. SCHREINER, L. and KLING, A. *Amer. J. Physiol.,* 1956, *184:*486–490.
55. SMITH, O. A., JR. and NATHAN, M. A. *Physiologist,* 1964, *7:*259.
56. SUMMERS, T. B. and KAELBER, W. W. *Amer. J. Physiol.,* 1962, *203:*1117–1119.
57. TERZIAN, H. and ORE, G. D. *Neurology,* 1955, *5:*373–380.
58. THOMSON, A. F. and WALTER, E. A. *Folia psychiat. neurol. et neurochir. neerl.,* 1950, Brower Memorial Volume, 444–452.
59. VALENSTEIN, E. E. *Psychol. Rev.,* 1964, *71:*415–437.
60. VALENSTEIN, E. E. *J. comp. physiol. Psychol.,* In press.
61. VALENSTEIN, E. S. and VALENSTEIN, T. *Science,* 1964, *145:*1456–1458.
62. VONDERAHE, A. R. *New Scholasticism,* 1944, *18:*76–95.
63. WHEATLEY, M. D. *Arch. Neurol. Psychiat. (Chic.),* 1944, *52:*296–316.
64. WOOD, C. D., SCHOTTELIUS, B., FROST, L. L. and BALDWIN, M. *Neurology,* 1958, *8:*477–480.

BIOPHYSICAL PRINCIPLES OF THE CIRCULATION

CHAPTER 27

Hemodynamics and the Physics of the Circulation

By ALAN C. BURTON

WHY HEMODYNAMICS?

THE heart is a pump, and blood is a fluid forced by the arterial pressure through the blood vessels. Thus, an understanding of the circulation must be based on knowledge of the physical laws governing the behavior of fluids at rest and in motion. Poiseuille,* a French physician (1799–1869), wanted to know the relation between the "force of the heart" and the "amount of the circulation," so he investigated the steady flow of water in rigid tubes. His pioneer work,

accurate to three or four figures, laid the foundation of the science of rheology, the study of the flow of viscous fluids. While he is honored in every physics textbook, he was as much a physiologist as a physicist.

It is true that in applying these physical laws to the circulation in the living animal we must deal with many complications. Blood is not like water; it is a complex heterogeneous fluid with some abnormal properties of viscosity. The blood vessels are not rigid tubes but are distensible, so that their size depends on the blood pressure within them as well as upon the contraction of the smooth muscle in the vessel walls.

---

* Pronounced not as "poise-eel" but as "pwaz-œ-ye."

Also, the flow is not steady but pulsatile in most parts of the vascular bed. These complexities must not deter us from resting the whole structure of our thinking in hemodynamics upon fundamental physics, even if we cannot yet hope to reach the goal of completely understanding the dynamics of the circulation.

FLUIDS

A fluid is a substance that cannot *permanently* withstand even the slightest *shearing force,* i.e., a force which tends to change the shape of the substance and to cause one layer of it to slide over an adjacent layer (like the blades of a pair of shears). Gases as well as liquids are fluids; gases, however, differ from liquids in their low resistance to changes in volume but not in resistance to changes in shape; i.e., gases are compressible, whereas liquids are almost completely incompressible.

Unlike fluids, solids can resist changes (i.e., deformations) in both shape and volume by virtue of their *elasticity*, which is measured by the magnitude of the resisting force that they develop to a standard deformation. Since the walls of the blood vessels have many properties of solids as well as some properties of liquids, in hemodynamics we must deal with elasticity as well as with *viscosity,* which may be regarded as a kind of fugitive or transitory elasticity.

PRESSURE IN FLUIDS; HYDROSTATICS

Pascal (1623–1662), a French philosopher and mathematician, gave us the laws of fluids at rest, i.e., hydrostatics. He recognized the importance of *fluid pressure,* the force per unit area (dynes per sq. cm.) exerted by the fluid on any plane at right angles to this plane. His three laws are:

(i) *Fluid pressure is equal in all directions.* The plane over which we estimate the force may lie in any direction, and the fluid "pushes" sideways, upward or downward on any barrier at a given point with the same pressure. This law must have been difficult to understand in Pascal's day. Now that we have the concept provided by the kinetic theory of gases and liquids, with molecules moving rapidly in all directions at random, this first law is easy to grasp. The pressure results from the bombardment by molecules in their thermal agitation of any plane barrier placed in the fluid.

(ii) *Pressures at points lying in the same horizontal plane in a fluid are equal.* The free surface of the fluid is a special case; there the pressures are everywhere atmospheric. This property follows from the definition of a fluid, for if the pressures were not equal, there would be shear forces which would cause movement of fluid until the pressures became equal.

(iii) *The pressure increases with depth under the free surface.* In a fluid at rest under gravity, pressure increases uniformly with the depth. The increase is equal to $\rho g h$ dynes per sq. cm., where ρ is the density of the fluid (grams per ml.), g is the acceleration of gravity (980 cm. per sec. per sec.), and h is the depth (cm.). (Proof of this equation appears in elementary textbooks of physics.) This law underlies the use of the U-tube and the reservoir type of manometer (Chap. 30) in which the pressure is measured as the difference in the levels of two columns of water, saline or mercury supported by the pressure. This type of manometer provides the only practical way of measuring *absolute* pressures, and all other manometers, such as electromanometers, are calibrated by comparison with a fluid-column manometer. The absolute pressure, in dynes per square centimeter, is obtained by means of the above formula. For example, if a mercury column with the density of 13.6 is used, the pressure corresponding to 1 mm. Hg is:

$$\rho g h = 13.6 \times 980 \times 0.1$$
$$= 1{,}333 \text{ dynes per sq. cm.} \tag{1}$$

Alternatively we might use a column of water or physiologic saline (density 1.04) in the manometer. The pressure corresponding to 1 cm. of saline is:

$$\rho g h = 1.04 \times 980 \times 1$$
$$= 1{,}019 \text{ dynes per sq. cm.}$$

To transform a value from millimeters of mercury to centimeters of saline we must multiply by the fraction 13.6/1.04, so that 1 mm. Hg pressure = 13.1 mm. = 1.31 cm. of saline pressure.

The density of blood is about 1.055, and a pressure of 1 mm. Hg corresponds to the pressure of 12.9 cm. of blood. The pressure in the arteries at heart level is pulsatile with a mean value of about 100 mm. Hg. This pressure will support a column of blood 100 × 13.6/1.05 mm. or 129 cm. high, as the Reverend Stephen Hales found in his famous experiment in which he cannulated the carotid artery of a horse with a long vertical tube (described in his book *Haemostaticks** in 1733).

The important point is that the hydrostatic factor, $\rho g h$, applies to the vascular system, as it must. As we shall see later, the resistance to flow in the large arteries (and veins) is very small; therefore, the flow of blood introduces only very small pressure drops in these vessels. If the body is horizontal, the mean arterial pressures in the brain and feet are approximately the same (Fig. 1*A*). When the body is erect, however, the hydrostatic factor reduces the arterial pressure in the brain and increases that in the feet (Fig. 1*B*).

The factor $\rho g h$ is considerable. Suppose that the artery in the head is 50 cm. above the heart level: the mean pressure there is now not 100 mm. Hg but 100 − 500/13, or only about 62 mm. Hg. Similarly, the arterial pressure in the feet (130 cm. below the heart) may be 100 + 1300/13, or 200 mm. Hg. It is obvious that very active cardiovascular reflexes are required to deal with the changes in pressure in the distensible vessels.

One interesting direct application of this principle is to aviation physiology in connection with accelerations experienced in high-speed aircraft in acrobatics (Fig. 1*C*). At the bottom of a "loop," the centripetal acceleration may amount to many times *g*. At that instant, the blood effectively has a density correspondingly greater than normal; in other words, we add the centripetal acceleration, toward the feet in this case, instead of *g* in the formula $\rho g h$. Suppose that this acceleration is twice gravity (usually written as 2 *g*). The factor $\rho g h$ to the head arteries is now 3 × 500/13, or 114 mm. Hg. Subtracting this value from the mean pressure of 100 mm. Hg at the heart results in a pressure actually less than atmospheric pressure in the cerebral arteries; i.e., there is no pressure to keep the arteries open so that they can pass the necessary blood to the brain. On this basis we would predict that the limit of human tolerance to acceleration ("positive *g*") without *blackout* resulting from brain anoxia must be close to 3 *g*. Actually, the tolerance of fit young pilots is not much greater, although cardiovascular reflexes can raise the blood pressure during the maneuver to pro-

*This book did not enjoy the popularity of his next publication (1734) entitled *Friendly Admonition to the Drinkers of Brandy, etc.*, which ran through six editions.

duce a slightly greater tolerance, and the tissue pressure in the brain (C.S.F. pressure) may change.

If the acceleration force is opposite to that of gravity (this occurs at the start of a power dive) and exactly equal in magnitude, we may have the condition of "weightlessness," of great interest in space medicine since it occurs in the "free motion" of a space satellite. In this condition the *g* of the hydrostatic factor is effectively zero, and pressures in the circulatory system will be independent of the posture and presumably the same as when the man lies in a horizontal plane. Serious effects of weightlessness on the circulation are not to be expected. When the opposite acceleration force exceeds the force of gravity, the blood pressure in the brain is above normal. Congestion with blood in the retina results in a visual disturbance known as *red-out*.

The same hydrostatic factor applies to the venous system, although it is modified by the action of the valves in the peripheral dependent veins. If a vein in the foot is cannulated and connected to a long vertical tube of saline, the top of the saline will rise approximately to the level of the heart when the subject is standing absolutely motionless. However, as soon as the leg muscles are contracted rhythmically, the blood in the veins is massaged upward through the valves and cannot return (the "muscle pump"). The venous pressure in the foot then falls markedly. The high venous pressure in the dependent vessels during motionless standing or sitting will increase the capillary pressure and lead to a

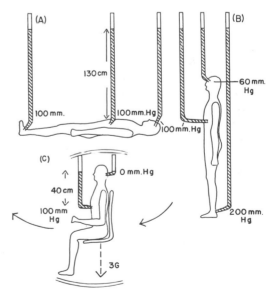

Fig. 1. Hydrostatic factor $\rho g h$ in operation on arterial blood pressure of man: *A*, supine; *B*, erect; and *C*, under acceleration of 3 *g* directed toward feet. Cannulae inserted into aorta and arteries of brain and foot would support columns of blood to heights shown.

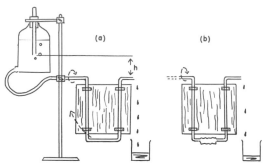

Fig. 2. Simple apparatus to demonstrate principle of syphon as it operates (*a*) in system of nondistensible tubes and (*b*) where vessels are distensible.

shift of fluid from the blood stream to the tissues (dependent edema). Who has not discovered that his feet were so swollen that he could not put on his shoes after motionless sleep in a sitting position on a train or plane? Again, very active vasomotor reflexes are required to counteract the effects of the hydrostatic factor on the venous and capillary pressures when the erect posture is assumed.

When arterial blood pressures are measured in the arm or leg or elsewhere in a patient not on a horizontal plane, they *must be corrected to heart level* for comparison with standards which are based on values correct at heart level. This correction is made by subtracting the factor ρgh if the site of measurement is below the heart, or by adding this factor if the site is above. An approximate value in millimeters of mercury is obtained by dividing the difference in level, in centimeters, by 13 (i.e., 13.6/1.055). The clinical indirect measurement of blood pressure is usually made on the forearm of a seated subject. In this case the level is close enough to that of the heart to require no correction.

Application of the Syphon. Archimedes (287–212 B.C.) discovered the principle of the *syphon*. This principle is that the flow of a fluid from point A to point B depends on the difference between the pressures or levels at these points, and not at all upon the levels of the pipe between them, provided that the fluid column is not broken.

Figure 2 shows a simple demonstration of how this principle applies during changes in posture. In *a*, the water from the reservoir flows through a U of rigid glass tubing. The rate of flow shown by the drops emerging is not altered at all, even temporarily, if the plane of the U-tube is swung from horizontal to vertical below or above the bottle, since the pressure head of ρgh is unchanged. If the blood vessels were rigid (in-

distensible), changing the posture from lying to standing would have no effect at all on the circulation. However, the vessels, especially the veins, are very distensible; therefore, when a man stands up the dependent veins tend to dilate passively. To imitate this condition, a segment of distensible rubber tubing is inserted in the U-tube (Fig. 2*b*). Now when the U is turned from the horizontal to the vertical plane, there is a transient stoppage of flow as the water entering the rubber tube fills its increased volume (resulting from the increased pressure) instead of flowing on. However, as soon as the steady state is reached and the rubber tube is full, the flow is resumed at the original rate.

Thus temporarily, and *temporarily only*, the blood entering the dependent veins will remain in them to fill the increased volume there, rather than flowing on to the heart. However, once the veins are full under the increased pressure (due to ρgh) the venous return will be restored. There is, of course, a persistent effect on the circulation because the blood volume has shifted to fill the dependent vessels. This shift may cause circulatory collapse (fainting) if the "muscle pump" does not relieve the condition. However, this persistent effect does not depend on the venous return being "uphill." In fact, owing to the applicability of the principle of the syphon, it is a "howler" in fundamental physics to state that the venous return to the heart is made more difficult in the erect posture because such a return is uphill.

FLUIDS IN MOTION (HYDRODYNAMICS); VISCOSITY

A key word in the definition of fluids given at the beginning of this chapter is "permanently," for all fluids can resist a shearing force temporarily. Their resistance to shear depends on the rate of change of deformation (i.e., rate of shear), not upon the amount of deformation or shear that has occurred. Thus shear deformation can be slowed by fluids but cannot be permanently prevented. This property of fluids, the ability to slow changes in their shape, is called *viscosity*. Blood is a fluid with a considerable viscosity. The best description of what we mean by "viscosity" is still that given by Sir Isaac Newton, who said it is "*a lack of slipperiness between adjacent layers of fluid.*"

Figure 3 attempts to illustrate the fact that in a viscous fluid in motion, adjacent layers or laminae slide over each other with different velocities, given by the *velocity gradient*, which is also

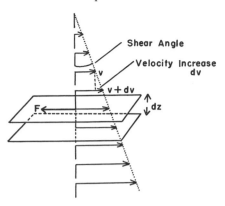

Vel. Gradient = Rate of Shear = $\frac{dv}{dz}$

Fig. 3. Diagram of velocity gradient in a flowing viscous fluid and tangential force (F) between laminae. (After Edser, *General physics.* London, Macmillan, 1926.)

the rate of shear. Then, because there is a "lack of slipperiness" between adjacent layers, the slower layer or lamina tends to retard the faster one, and vice versa. This effect results in a *tangential force* (F in Fig. 3) on the interface between the two layers. Newton made the simplest assumption possible, that the tangential force per unit area, i.e., the shear stress, is proportional to the rate of shear.

$$\text{Tangential Force/Area} = \eta \times dv/dz \quad (2)$$

where η is the coefficient of viscosity in poise and dv/dz is the velocity gradient (which is the same as the "rate of shear"), z being the direction at right angles to the stream. The unit, the poise, is of course named in honor of Poiseuille. In words we may define the absolute viscosity, η, as the tangential force per unit area (dynes per sq. cm.) when the velocity gradient is unity, i.e., 1 cm. per second per cm. Viscosity therefore has the dimensions of mass over the product of length times time ($M \cdot L^{-1} \cdot T^{-1}$).

By a fortunate accident, the viscosity of water at about room temperature, i.e., at 20.2° C., is 0.010000 poise (at 37° C. it is 0.0069 poise). It is thus convenient to use the *centipoise* (0.01 poise) as a practical unit, and to remember that water at room temperature has a viscosity of about 1 centipoise. The viscosity of blood is considerably greater than that of water—three or four times as great for the normal hematocrit value of 50 per cent, mainly because red cells are present. (Details of the viscosity of blood are

given in a later section.) A fluid which obeys Newton's equation is said to be "Newtonian." Water and most simple fluids are quite accurately Newtonian. Blood is only approximately so, and is said to have an "anomalous" viscosity, i.e., non-Newtonian.

Flow of a Viscous Fluid in a Tube; Poiseuille's Law. It is sometimes erroneously said that force is required to move blood through the blood vessels because there is "friction between the blood and the walls of the vessels." This statement is completely incorrect. There is a cohesive force between liquids and the solids which they wet, partially or completely. This force prevents movement of the layer of fluid immediately at the wall. Thus an infinitely thin layer of blood in contact with the wall of the blood vessels has a zero velocity of flow. The next layer, a little closer to the axis, has a small velocity; the layer inside the second has a greater velocity; and so on until the axis is reached. There the velocity is maximal. Thus the resistance to flow of blood in the circulation results from the inner friction—the viscosity—of the blood, not at all from friction with the wall. Even the roughness of the wall plays very little part, except at high rates of flow greater than those usually found in the normal circulation. (At these very high rates the flow is quite different from the streamline flow we are describing and becomes turbulent.)

Figure 4 shows how the velocity of an element of fluid in a tube depends on the distance from the axis. The driving force that causes flow through the tube from cross section A to cross section B is a difference of pressure (force per unit area) from A to B. Pressure in a fluid acts at right angles to any cross section and must be the same at all points in a given cross section; if this were not so, there would be a component of flow at right angles to the axis of the tube. This situation is not present in streamline flow in a

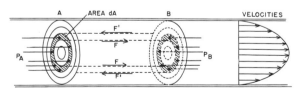

Fig. 4. Diagram of flow of viscous fluid through a tube in concentric cylindrical laminae, showing parabolic distribution of velocities. Pressure force ($P_A - P_B$)dA is balanced by difference between shear forces, F and F'. F' is greater than F because velocity gradient is increased closer to wall.

straight line. In such flow each lamina of fluid, here a coaxial cylinder, slips over adjacent laminae without any movement from one lamina to another.

Consider the equilibrium of one of the annular cylindrical laminae of fluid in Figure 4. At A the cylinder is being pushed by a force $P_A \times dA$ (force = pressure × cross-sectional area) and at B by a force $P_B \times dA$ exerted in the opposite direction. The net force is $(P_A - P_B) \times dA$.

If the flow is steady, i.e., if there is no acceleration or deceleration, Newton's first two laws of motion tell us that the net force must be zero; there must be an opposite force balancing the force $(P_A - P_B)dA$. This balancing force is provided by the tangential forces due to the viscosity of the adjacent layers and described by Newton's equation given above. This viscous force depends on the velocity gradient at each of the two interfaces. By this line of reasoning, Hagen used the methods of calculus to determine the velocity gradient, and therefore the velocities across the tube, for a fluid that has normal viscosity—one which obeys Newton's equation. The calculation is very easy and is given in elementary textbooks of physics. The results are:

(i) The velocity profile (Fig. 4) is a parabola with the maximum flow on the axis of the tube. The velocity at any radius (r) from the axis is given by:

$$V_r = V_m \left(1 - \frac{r^2}{R^2}\right) \qquad (3)$$

where V_m is the maximum velocity along the axis and R is the radius of the tube. The velocity at the wall (r = R) is zero. The value of V_m in terms of the viscosity coefficient and the pressure gradient (ΔP) down the tube, i.e., the drop of pressure per unit length of tube, is:

$$V_m = \frac{\Delta P \cdot R^2}{4\eta}$$

where R is the radius of the tube.

(ii) The velocity gradient, in contrast, is greatest at the wall and zero on the axis. Most of the viscous force is therefore near the wall, where the gradient of velocity is highest. *The fluid near the wall is much more important in determining the total viscous resistance than is that near the axis.*

Hagen proceeded to calculate the total flow of fluid by adding up (integrating) the contribution to flow of each concentric annular space (Fig. 4). The result is the famous Poiseuille–Hagen formula for the flow, F.

$$F = (P_A - P_B) \times \left(\frac{\pi}{8}\right) \times \left(\frac{1}{\eta}\right) \times \left(\frac{R^4}{1}\right) \quad (4)$$

If P_A and P_B are in c.g.s. units (dynes per sq. cm.), if η is in poises, and if the dimensions of the tube, its radius (R) and length (l), are in centimeters, the flow (F) will be in milliliters per second.

Poiseuille's formula has been written above in four terms to make obvious how simple it is to remember and understand. Most of it is common sense. We would expect the flow to be proportional to the driving force, the pressure difference $(P_A - P_B)$ across the ends of the tube. There follows a numerical term $(\pi/8)$. The π is there because we are dealing with a cylindrical tube; the 8 arose in the process of Hagen's integration. The next term $(1/\eta)$ is the viscosity term. Again, we would expect the flow to be inverse to the viscosity, since the more viscous the fluid the harder it will be to push it through the tube. Finally we have the geometrical term (R^4/l) depending on the dimensions of the tube. Here we would expect the length to be the denominator. The only unexpected feature is that the radius of the tube appears to the fourth power; we might have expected the cross-sectional area to be the factor concerned and the radius to be squared (R^2).

The dependence on the fourth power of the radius has a most important physiologic consequence. The distribution of the blood to different parts of the body is controlled mainly by means of special bands of smooth muscle in the walls of the arterioles. By the contraction of this smooth muscle under the influence of the nerves or circulating hormones, the blood vessel constricts, i.e., the radius of its lumen is decreased. Other things (the driving pressure and the viscosity) being equal, a decrease to half the radius will actually decrease the flow to a sixteenth of the original value. A decrease of only 19 per cent in radius will halve the flow. There is thus an exquisitely sensitive and effective control of the flow by the arterioles.

Viscosity of Blood. *Dependence on hematocrit value.* The viscosity of blood measured in the usual viscometer* very greatly increases as the percentage of the volume of whole blood occupied by erythrocytes (hematocrit value) in-

*Usually an instrument which measures the volume of fluid that flows per unit time at a given driving pressure through a tube of known dimensions.

creases (Fig. 5, *upper curve*).[25] The curve rises more and more steeply, as does an exponential curve; indeed, when the hematocrit value exceeds 60 per cent, blood can hardly be regarded as a fluid any longer. The discoid cells are then tightly packed, and flow must involve their deformation. The accelerated rate of increase in viscosity as the hematocrit value increases is probably a very serious factor in polycythemia (excess of erythrocytes in blood), increasing the work the heart must perform to maintain the circulation. Conversely, during chronic anemia when the hematocrit value is abnormally low, the reduced viscosity may also embarrass the circulation and the heart. Thus, in anemia, if the arterial blood pressure is maintained at normal values (important cardiovascular reflexes tend to ensure this), the total blood flow through the peripheral tissues will be abnormally great and, consequently, cardiac output will be increased.

Dependence on temperature; relative viscosity. Decrease of temperature greatly increases the viscosity of blood, as it does of all aqueous fluids. The viscosity is about two and one-half times as great at 0° C. as at 37° C. The relative change with temperature is very nearly the same as that in water.[2] Thus the *relative viscosity* of blood, which is defined as the ratio of the viscosity of blood at any temperature to the viscosity of water at the same temperature, is practically constant. The increase in viscosity of the blood in the extremities exposed to cold must be an important factor in reducing the circulation of these parts, as in frostbite or "immersion foot."

Viscosity of blood in very small tubes; Fahraeus–Lindqvist effect. Viscosity is usually measured by using a length of narrow-bore glass tubing as a viscometer and employing Poiseuille's formula to calculate the absolute viscosity; or the relative viscosity may be determined by comparing the flow of water and the test fluid under the same pressure gradient. This comparison was used by Whittaker and Winton[25] to obtain the upper curves of Figure 5. When they compared the rates at which water and blood flowed through the isolated hindlimb of a dog (*lower curve*, Fig. 5), the relative viscosity appeared to be only about half as great for each hematocrit value. The difference between the curves lies in the diameters of the tubes employed as viscometers. The glass tube used by Whittaker and Winton was about 1 mm. in diameter, but the diameter of the arterioles, which offer the

greater resistance, is less than 0.1 mm. Fahraeus and Lindqvist[9] found that with water the size of the tube did not alter the calculated viscosity, but that with blood this value *fell* markedly if the diameter of the tube was less than 1 mm. (Fig. 6). On the basis of their curve, the resistance vessels of the leg of the dog in Whittaker and Winton's experiments had an equivalent diameter of 55 μ, which would correspond to the diameter of arterioles.

There has been much confusion regarding the reason for the Fahraeus–Lindqvist phenomenon. It was thought to have something to do with the axial accumulation of cells (p. 530). It turns out that the phenomenon could be explained as what is called a *sigma effect*, by which Dix and Scott-Blair[8] explained similar phenomena in colloidal suspensions. Suppose the vessel is so narrow that there is room for only five red cells abreast; we cannot integrate for a series of infinitely thin laminae in deriving Poiseuille's formula. Instead we should sum (sigma is the Greek symbol used by mathematics for a sum of terms) the five terms. This means that the total flow should depend on the sum of the cubes of the natural numbers ($1^3 + 2^3 + 3^3 + 4^3 + 5^3 = 225$)* instead of the integral of r^3 (corresponding to $r^4/4 = 5^4/4 = 156$). On this basis, the effective viscosity in a tube of radius R (R)

*The sum of the cubes of the natural numbers from 1 to n is equal to $\dfrac{n^2(n+1)^2}{4}$.

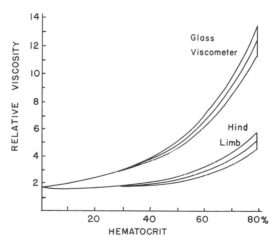

Fig. 5. Relative viscosity of blood versus hematocrit value. *Upper curve,* Values obtained with glass viscometer with a capillary tube radius of 1 mm. *Lower curve,* Values with vessels of dog's hindleg as viscometer. Standard deviation shown on each side of the curves. (From Whittaker and Winton, *J. Physiol.*, 1933, *78:* 339–369.)

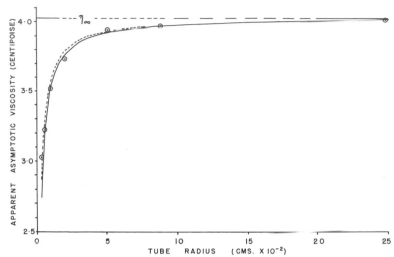

Fig. 6. Fahraeus–Lindqvist effect of size of tube on viscosity (normal hematocrit). Values calculated on sigma theory for red cell diameters of 6.0 µ (*solid line*) and 6.6 µ (*dotted line*). (Data from Kumin; calculations from Haynes, *The rheology of blood.* Ph.D. Thesis, University of Western Ontario, 1957.)

is related to that in a tube of infinite radius (η_∞) by the formula[1]

$$\eta_R = \eta_\infty / (1 + d/R)^2 \qquad (5)$$

where d is the diameter of the particle and R is the radius of the tube. Figure 6 (*broken line curve*) shows how well the experimental curve for blood can be fitted by this formula if the value chosen for d is 6 µ, which is the diameter of the ox erythrocytes used. The sigma effect is a very satisfactory explanation of the Fahraeus–Lindqvist phenomenon for blood of normal hematocrit, though not so plausible for results with lower hematocrit. The physiologic result is that the work by the heart to force blood through the narrow small vessels of the circulation is less than would be required if the flow there were in laminae of infinitesimal thickness. Axial accumulation (see below) may also play a part.

Dependence of viscosity of blood on rate of flow; anomalous viscosity. A complicated fluid such as blood could hardly be expected to be Newto-

nian in its viscosity. The proteins of the plasma are not spherical and will be oriented as the rate of flow increases; therefore, viscosity will change. Blood has been said to have the properties of a plastic fluid, which shows no flow at all until the shearing force exceeds a critical value. However, the work of Bingham,[2] after whom plastic fluids are called "Bingham bodies," has shown that neither plasma nor blood is to be thought of as plastic. The effects of the orientation of the plasma proteins and of the discoid red cells by streaming have been demonstrated, but this takes place at such exceedingly low velocities of flow as to be of no physiologic importance at normal rates.

Plasma (measured in glass viscometers) has a relative viscosity of about 1.8 owing to its content of proteins, and this viscosity is quite accurately Newtonian. The addition of the red cells, however, definitely makes the viscosity of blood anomalous, although the consequences of this condition in hemodynamics probably have been greatly overemphasized. The anomaly is almost entirely due to the redistribution of red cells in the stream when the blood is caused to flow. Breaking up of rouleaux formations by low shear rates is also a factor.

Axial accumulation of red cells. It has long been known—even since Poiseuille's day—that the red cells in flowing blood tend to accumulate in the axis of the blood vessel and to leave a zone near the wall that is relatively free from cells ("plasma skimming"). This situation can be clearly seen in motion pictures of the circulation in small vessels. The physiologic consequences of axial accumulation may be very important; for instance, small side branches of a blood ves-

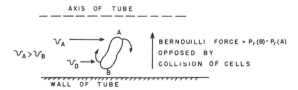

Fig. 7. Diagram of force causing axial accumulation of red cells in a flowing stream. Cells rotate continuously in a velocity gradient. This rotation leads to a difference in side pressure between *A* and *B* (Bernouilli effect). This effect is eventually balanced by collisions between cells as they accumulate near axis.

sel may draw off blood containing a proportional volume of blood cells considerably less than that for the whole circulation. It is well known that the hematocrit value for blood samples drawn from the capillaries (by needle prick of the skin) is about 25 per cent less than that for whole body blood from the same patient.[10] Plasma skimming may play an important role in the function of the kidney.[15]

In the attempts to explain the established fact of axial accumulation there has been great confusion and controversy. Bayliss,[1] in a review, stated that there are no known physical forces to move the cells toward the axis. More extensive reading of the literature of hydrodynamics (which depends on advanced mathematics) and Starkey's work[21, 22, 23] have elucidated the matter. A particle, even if spherical, in a stream where there is a velocity gradient across the tube will rotate in a complicated way (the Magnus effect). As a result, the path of the particle will be modified by a *Bernouilli force* (like that on a spinning tennis ball), which will cause the particle to swerve (Fig. 7). Moreover, Starkey has demonstrated that a stream of colloidal particles introduced near the wall of a tube carrying a streamline flow is deflected toward the axis. Müller,[13] using a large model in which rubber disks in flowing glycerine solutions imitated red cells, found that the disks, which rotate continuously as predicted, are obviously accumulated at the axis when the rate of flow is increased. A relatively disk-poor zone is left near the wall.

It is easy to see in which direction the effective viscosity will be affected by axial accumulation. The hematocrit value of laminae near the wall of a blood vessel will be reduced; the value at the "core" will be increased. Since the velocity gradient is so much larger near the wall than at the core, the effect of the reduction in viscosity at the periphery greatly outweighs the effect of the increase in viscosity near the axis. As a consequence, the effective viscosity of blood is less than it would be if no axial accumulation took place.

Axial accumulation will also change the velocity profile from the parabolic curve of a Newtonian fluid to one that is flatter at the axis. The alteration is not great, however (Fig. 8). The solution of the difficult problem of measuring the concentration of cells across the tube was made possible by a recently discovered method[12] of deducing the velocity gradient

across the stream from the shape of the pressure-flow curve in a rigid tube. This method is applicable even when the fluid is non-Newtonian.

However, the point at issue has been whether the effective viscosity of blood depends upon the velocity with which it flows. The faster it flows, the greater the force causing axial accumulation. Theoretically, then, the viscosity would depend upon the rate of flow (be reduced for higher rates of flow), and in the Poiseuille equation for flow η would not be a constant but a function of flow. In these circumstances the pressure-flow curves, even in rigid glass tubes, would not be straight but would curve up toward the flow axis (i.e., there would be more flow than expected at high driving pressures). It was thought that this factor of anomalous viscosity might explain the marked nonlinearity of pressure-flow curves of blood in certain vascular beds.

More complete investigation of the pressure-flow curves of blood in glass tubes with different diameters, and the interpretation of these curves by Haynes,[12] have shown that *in the physiologic range of blood flow, blood behaves as if it were a Newtonian fluid.* Axial accumulation occurs, but reaches a saturation value at a very low velocity of flow; i.e., further speeding up of the flow does not accomplish any appreciably greater axial accumulation. This accounts for

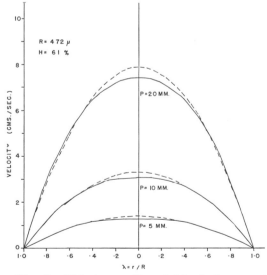

Fig. 8. Velocity profile of blood (hematocrit value, 61 per cent) flowing in a tube (radius 472 μ) at three different values of pressure gradient (*P*). Broken line is parabola that would apply if there were no axial accumulation. (From Haynes, *The rheology of blood.* Ph.D. thesis, University of Western Ontario, 1957.)

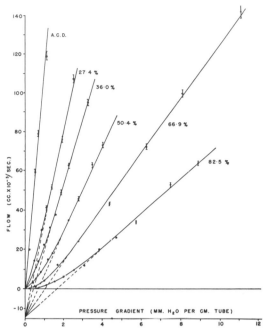

Fig. 9. Empirical flow-pressure curves for suspensions of red cells with different hematocrit values in acid-citrate-dextrose solution in a glass tube with radius of 185 μ; data from Haynes. All curves soon become straight lines with curious property of pointing to common nodal point (*broken lines*). Vertical lines about points represent standard deviations of the means.

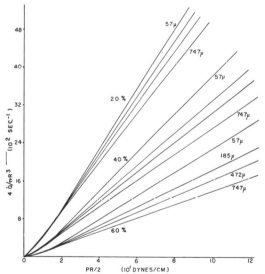

Fig. 10. Rheologic plot bringing together results with glass tubes of different radii (*ordinate*) and at various velocities of flow and hematocrit values. *Abscissa,* Pressure times radius of tube divided by 2. Separation in bundle for each hematocrit value results from Fahraeus–Lindqvist effect. Curves would be straight lines for Newtonian fluids. It is seen that when PR/2 is greater than 20 dynes per cm., the non-Newtonian blood acts as a Newtonian fluid would.

the pressure-flow curves in glass tubes (Fig. 9) being straight lines except near their origin. The saturation value is reached when the quantity pR/2 (where p is the pressure gradient per unit length of tube and R the radius of the tube) exceeds a critical value of about 20 (Fig. 10). (The quantity pR/2 is an important rheologic parameter equal to the tangential stress at the wall.) Since the normal average physiologic velocities of flow and the diameters of the various blood vessels—the aorta, arteries, arterioles, capillaries and veins—are known, pR/2 can be estimated for each. It turns out that the lowest value is 60, which is found in the veins. The lowest value for the arterioles—where anomalous viscosity would have the greatest effect since these vessels offer the major part of the total resistance to flow—is about 200. These are well above the critical point (pR/2 = 20) below which blood behaves in a non-Newtonian fashion.

Thus we can conclude that, while axial accumulation takes place and constitutes an important difference between still and flowing blood, in normal physiology we deal nearly always with blood in which axial accumulation is complete. We may thus consider the viscosity as Newtonian within the physiologic range of flow.

Summary. To summarize the discussion of the viscosity of blood, we must consider the following:

(i) The great dependence on the percentage volume of red cells (the hematocrit value).

(ii) The dependence on the size of the tube, the Fahraeus-Lindqvist effect, which has a simple explanation as a sigma effect. It is of importance in the vascular bed, where the resistance vessels are very small.

(iii) The dependence on velocity of flow, complicated by axial accumulation of cells, a factor which does not play a significant role in the physiologic range of blood flow. In this range the effective viscosity in the blood vessels is a constant, like that of a Newtonian fluid, although this constant is less than it would be if there were no axial accumulation.

STREAMLINE FLOW AND TURBULENCE

When Poiseuille's experiments on fluids flowing through rigid tubes are plotted for very high rates of flow, the curves relating the driving pressure and the resulting flow show a point of inflection (Fig. 11). The first part of the relation is linear, as predictable from Poiseuille's law; but, when a *critical velocity* of flow is reached, the slope of the curve changes, and thereafter the velocity does not increase with driving pressure as much as before. An English engineer, Osborne Reynolds,[16] in 1883 showed that at this point of transition the flow changes from streamline, where each lamina slips over adjacent laminae and there is no mixing or interchange of fluid between laminae, to *turbulent flow*. During turbulence, the tube is filled with eddies or whirlpools that are generated and break off from the stream in a rhythmic manner (Fig. 11). In streamline flow a dye injected from a small needle into a given lamina will remain in that lamina and will not mix with the rest of the stream.* In turbulence, the dye immediately appears throughout the tube. In streamline flow, the energy produced by the driving pressure is dissipated against the viscosity of the fluid; in turbulent flow the driving energy is used largely to create the kinetic energy of the eddies, and a new law replaces Poiseuille's law. The resistance to flow now depends on the density of the fluid rather than on its viscosity (since kinetic energy $= \frac{1}{2} \rho V^2$).

Osborne Reynolds showed that the critical velocity at which turbulence appears depends on the viscosity of the fluid, its density and the radius of the cylindrical tube by the relation

$$V_C = \frac{K\eta}{\rho R} \qquad (6)$$

where V_C is the critical velocity (in cm. per sec.), η is the viscosity (in poises), ρ the density (in grams per ml.), and R is the radius of the tube (in cm.). K is a constant called *Reynold's number*. It is close to 1000 for many fluids including blood.[7] However, this is for a long straight tube of uniform diameter. The critical Reynolds number is much less than 1000 in curved tubes and where there is a narrowing (stenosis).

The velocity of the blood stream is greatest in the aorta at the height of systole (ejection of blood from the heart). Let us see if the critical velocity is reached here. When the values $\eta = .04$ poise for blood, $\rho = 1$ and R = 1 cm. for the aorta are placed in equation 5, the critical

velocity is $(1000 \times 0.04)/(1 \times 1) = 40$ cm. per second. Now, for a man at rest, the cardiac output (i.e., the rate of volume flow in the aorta) is about 5 liters per minute, or 83 ml. per second. The human aorta has a cross-sectional area of about 3 sq. cm., so the *mean* velocity throughout the cardiac cycle is about 30 cm. per second (83/4), less than the critical value for turbulence. The velocity during the *ejection period* at the start of systole, however, will exceed the critical velocity. In heavy exercise, when the cardiac output may be four or five times the resting value, there will be turbulence in the aorta during a longer portion of systole. Nowhere else in the normal circulation, except near the heart valves when their opening and closing create sudden high local velocities of flow, will there be turbulence.

Sounds of the Circulation.   Understanding that turbulence depends on a critical velocity of flow is extremely important in connection with the *sounds* in the circulation. Streamline flow is necessarily silent. Nothing about it is vibratory or pulsatile; the laminae of fluid just slip quietly over each other. Turbulence, in contrast, is oscillatory, pulsatile or vibratory; the eddies of turbulence throb and vibrate. Thus noise is created. This is the explanation of the *heart sounds*. They are associated with turbulence in the blood when the valves open or close. It is a matter of controversy whether the sounds heard are generated mostly by the eddies in the blood itself or by vibration of the walls of the vessels or the leaflets of the valves. In any case, the

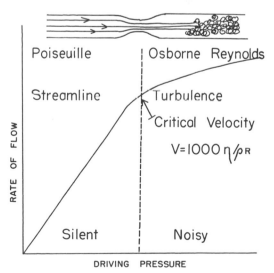

Fig. 11. Change in type of flow from streamline to turbulent at the critical velocity.

---

* This makes it very difficult to obtain a really representative *mixed* sample of venous blood in studies of cardiac output (Chap. 33).

existence of a sound depends on the reaching of a critical velocity of flow.

When abnormal sounds (murmurs) are heard in the circulation, an abnormally high velocity exceeding the critical velocity has been reached somewhere. In arteriovenous aneurysm, a direct "shunt" between an artery and a vein has been created by trauma or congenital malformation. Blood rushing through this shunt may greatly exceed the critical velocity, and the vibration, called a "thrill," can be felt over the shunt. Another abnormality which may lead to turbulence is the narrowing of a cardiac valve, as in mitral stenosis. The blood flowing through the valve from atrium to ventricle would normally not be turbulent, but when the orifice is narrowed the flow may become so. The systolic murmurs heard in children during heavy exercise are due to the very greatly increased cardiac output and may be quite innocent. The medical student will do well to remember the advice of the doggerel verse:

> Streamline flow is silent.
>   Remember that, my boys,
> But when the flow is turbulent
>   There's sure to be a noise.
> So when your stethoscope picks up
>   A bruit, murmur, sigh,
> Remember that it's turbulence
>   And you must figure why.

Korotkow's sounds, heard during the indirect measurement of blood pressure (Chap. 34), are an example of the creation of turbulence by the method of measurement. A cuff is wrapped around the upper arm, and the bell of a stethoscope is applied over the brachial artery at the elbow below the edge of the cuff. It is important to realize that if the cuff is not inflated, nothing can be heard from the artery, since the flow in it is streamline. When the cuff is inflated to a pressure above the systolic pressure, the artery is closed by compression and again nothing is heard. As the pressure is allowed to fall below systolic pressure, the artery opens, briefly and slightly, at the height of systole. The jet of blood passing through this narrowed opening exceeds the critical velocity; turbulence results, and a tapping sound signals the event (the systolic criterion). As the pressure in the bag falls below diastolic pressure, the artery will remain open enough throughout the cardiac cycle that the critical velocity for turbulence is no longer reached. All sounds will then cease (the point of "disappearance of sound"). If it is realized

that this disappearance of sound corresponds to the velocity falling below the critical value, an event which logically has nothing to do with the diastolic pressure, the mistake will not be made of relying on this point as a criterion for diastolic pressure.[18] (In a normal subject at rest the point of disappearance may accidentally correspond with the true criterion, muffling of the sound— but only accidentally.) Compression of an artery by finger pressure over the superficial tissues will often cause sufficient turbulence beyond the pressure point to allow sounds to be heard with a stethoscope.

In contrast, there is good logic to support a relation between diastolic pressure and the "muffling" of the sound, i.e., a change in its nature, which precedes its disappearance. If the pressure in the cuff is still above the diastolic pressure, there will be a period in each cardiac cycle at the end of diastole during which the artery is closed by the cuff pressure. The sound is thus interrupted by a brief period of silence between cycles and becomes "staccato." As soon as the cuff pressure falls below the diastolic pressure, the artery presumably will remain open throughout the cardiac cycle, and the periodic interruption of the sounds will disappear. The sounds then become continuous instead of staccato. Comparison of arterial pressures measured by direct catheterization and manometers with those obtained by the indirect cuff method[18] has verified this theoretical prediction that muffling rather than disappearance of sound is the best criterion of diastolic pressure.

KINETIC ENERGY OF FLOW; SIDE AND END PRESSURES

A fluid in motion possesses kinetic energy. Reckoned per unit volume (milliliter) of fluid, kinetic energy is very easily calculated as ½ × density × velocity squared. If the velocity is in centimeters per second, this calculation will give the kinetic energy in ergs per cubic centimeter, which is the same as dynes per square centimeter. Thus the value for kinetic energy has the dimensions of a pressure.

The kinetic energy in a fluid is created from the potential energy, which is the pressure. The principle of Bernouilli, enunciated by this great mathematician in 1726, states that where the velocity of a fluid is greatest, the lateral pressure against the walls is least. A simple demonstration of this is shown in Figure 12. The velocity of the fluid in a tube is greatly increased in the narrow portion, where the cross-sectional area is reduced and where the level of the fluid in the vertical tube (lateral or side pressure) is reduced.

Physiologists, in recording the arterial blood pressure of an animal during an acute experiment, usually sacrifice an artery by cutting across it and tying into it a straight cannula connected to a manometer (Fig. 20, Chap. 34). The velocity of blood flow is thus eliminated in the cannula and the kinetic energy of flow is reconverted into pressure. This is an *end pressure.* Alternatively, a T-cannula can be inserted in the artery so that the arterial flow continues and the pressure is measured from the side tube of the T. In this arrangement, the pressure is a *side* or *lateral pressure,* and it will be less than the end pressure in the same artery by an amount equivalent to the kinetic energy of flow, since Bernouilli's principle states that the total energy, i.e., pressure energy plus kinetic energy, must remain a constant.

It is easy to estimate the importance of the kinetic energy factor in the normal circulation. The mean velocity in the aorta for a resting cardiac output (5 liters per minute) is about 20 cm. per second. The kinetic energy per milliliter of blood will then be $\frac{1}{2} \times 20^2$, or 200 ergs per ml., or dynes per sq. cm. For the usual pulse curve of velocity, the mean kinetic energy (the time mean based on the square of the velocity, rather than on the velocity itself as was the mean above) may then be twice this value, i.e., 400 dynes per sq. cm. Since 1330 dynes per sq. cm. equals a pressure of 1 mm. Hg (Equation 1), this is a very small value indeed, being only about 0.3 mm. Hg for the mean difference between the side pressure and the end pressure in the aorta. However, in the ejection period of systole, the velocity may be three times the mean, and the kinetic energy will be nine times as great, i.e., about 3 mm. Hg. This value agrees with the experimentally measured difference between the pressure in the left ventricle (where there is no appreciable kinetic energy) and that at the same instant in the aorta (where kinetic energy is present and must have been created at the expense of pressure).

It is concluded, then, that in the "resting" subject the kinetic energy factor in the total work of the heart (the difference between the side and end pressures in the aorta) is not very great (3 per cent). However, during heavy exer-

cise, when the cardiac output may be five times the resting level and the velocity in the aorta correspondingly greater, the kinetic energy factor would be 25 times (5^2) this value, i.e., as great as 75 mm. Hg. In these circumstances the kinetic energy created becomes an important part of the total work of the heart, possibly as much as 30 per cent.

In arteries other than the aorta, and in the smaller vessels, the velocity of flow is much less and the kinetic energy factor is completely negligible in normal physiology. For example, the velocity in the capillaries is of the order of 1 mm. per second. The kinetic energy of capillary flow is then $\frac{1}{2} \times 1 \times 0.1^2$ dynes per sq. cm., which is equivalent to about .000004 mm. Hg, and certainly of no significance at all.

In diseased arteries, however, Bernouilli's principle and the difference between the side and end pressures may become very important. If an atherosclerotic plaque narrows the lumen of, say, a coronary artery (stenosis), the velocity of flow will correspondingly increase through the narrowed portion. The velocity of flow in a main coronary artery is such that the kinetic energy is equivalent to only 0.1 mm. Hg pressure. If, however, the diameter of the lumen is only one-fifth of normal, the cross-sectional area will be 25 times smaller; and if the total resistance to flow in the coronary circuit is still not seriously increased, the velocity of flow will be increased 25 times. Since kinetic energy depends on the square of the velocity, this energy will be increased by a factor of 25^2, or 625 times. Thus the kinetic energy of flow through the

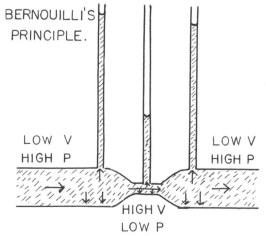

Fig. 12. Principle of Bernouilli. Velocity (V) is increased in narrow portion of tube, and de pressure (P) is correspondingly reduced.

stenotic vessel will amount to 62.5 mm. Hg, and the side pressure will be 62.5 mm. less than the end pressure.

The side pressure available to resist further stenosis is greatly reduced, in accordance with Bernouilli's principle, as the lumen narrows. Thus there is an instability in arteries so that narrowing of their lumina tends to persist. If the cross-sectional area is reduced sufficiently, the side pressure may be reduced below zero (atmospheric pressure), as in the laboratory "filter pump," so there is nothing to prevent complete closure of the lumen. However, closure will reduce the flow to zero. The side pressure will then rise to equal the end pressure, and the vessel will open once more.

This sequence of events is the basis of *flutter* in a distensible tube through which a fluid is driven rapidly. Flutter is the basis of the noise produced in all reed instruments, such as the oboe, and in instruments depending on vibrations of the lips, for example, the bugle. The most familiar demonstration of the principle of Bernouilli is perhaps the "sucking in" of the shower curtains when the water is fully turned on.

Summary. The kinetic energy of the flow of blood is not of great importance in the work of the heart with a "resting" cardiac output, except at the height of systole. Kinetic energy becomes important when the cardiac output and work are increased by heavy exercise. The importance of the kinetic energy of blood is slight in normal distributing arteries and quite negligible in smaller vessels. However, kinetic energy becomes exceedingly important when local narrowing of arteries occurs, as in atherosclerosis, since it tends to make such narrowing persist by lowering the side pressure.

PRESSURE-FLOW RELATIONS IN VASCULAR BEDS; DISTENSIBILITY OF BLOOD VESSELS

The Poiseuille–Hagen law (Equation 4) for flow of a Newtonian fluid through rigid tubes predicts that flow is proportional to the driving pressure. Accordingly a plot of flow versus driving pressure is linear. If the geometric factor is reduced (radius decreased or length increased), the slope of the straight line on the graph is correspondingly less. Because of this linearity, it is convenient to define *resistance to flow* as the ratio of the driving force to the flow

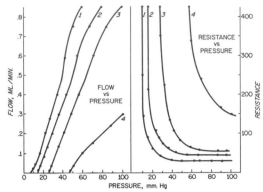

Fig. 13. Flow-pressure curves in rabbit ear (*left*) and resistance-pressure curves deduced from them (*right*). For a Newtonian fluid in rigid tubes, flow-pressure curves would be straight lines through origin and resistance-pressure curves horizontal lines. Curves *1* to *4* represent increasing vasomotor tone produced by electrical stimulation of sympathetic nerves at increasing frequencies from 0.5 to 20 impulses per second.

that results. Thus from Poiseuille's equation comes:

$$\text{Res} = \frac{P_A - P_B}{F} = \left(\frac{8}{\pi}\right) \times \eta \times \left(\frac{L}{R^4}\right) \quad (7)$$

For Newtonian fluids in rigid tubes the resistance is constant at a given temperature because the viscosity factor in the equation is independent of the pressure or the rate of flow. Likewise, in rigid tubes the geometric factor is independent of pressure or flow.

When we turn to actual flow-pressure curves, experimentally determined in an isolated vascular bed, they often are very far from linear. For example, Girling[11] (Fig. 13) measured the flow-pressure curves in the ears and legs of rabbits when their sympathetic vasoconstrictor nerves were stimulated electrically at different frequencies to cause different degrees of constriction of the arterioles. At zero level of stimulation, the vessels were dilated, and the flow-pressure relation was almost a straight line; when the constriction was moderate, the curves were sigmoid. When the constriction was very great, the flow fell rapidly as pressure was reduced and became zero, even though there was still a considerable driving pressure. This point at which there is no flow has been called the *zero flow pressure* or the *critical closing pressure,* the latter term being used because at this point the small vessels have closed completely (i.e., the resistance is infinite).

A feature of the curves is that at sufficiently high pressures, considerably greater than the critical closing pressure, the flow tends to become proportional to the driving pressure; i.e., the resistance reaches a constant value (Fig. 13). All the data on flow-pressure curves obtained by various investigators yield relations between resistance to flow and pressure similar to those shown in Figure 13, although for reasons which need not be given the resistance often does not become infinite.

Reasons for Shape of Actual Flow-Pressure Curves in Vascular Beds. There has been much controversy over the explanation of the peculiar shape of the flow-pressure curves for vascular beds. Some have attributed it entirely to the anomalous, non-Newtonian, viscous behavior of blood; others entirely to the fact that blood vessels are distensible, causing the geometric factor of Poiseuille's law (R^4/L) to change with the pressure. It is important to note that it is not primarily the driving pressure (arterial pressure minus venous pressure) that determines the size of the distensible vessels but rather the *transmural pressure,* the difference between the intravascular pressure in a given vessel and the pressure outside its wall (tissue pressure, etc.). It now appears quite certain[3] that, although anomalous viscosity of blood plays a role at very low rates of flow, the factor of overwhelming importance is the distensibility of the blood vessels. Two facts attest to this:

(i) If the anomalous viscosity of blood were responsible, blood flow in rigid tubes should show similar nonlinear curves. In fact, the nonlinearity is very slight and only at very low flows (Fig. 9); there is no trace of zero flow or critical closing pressure in these circumstances.

(ii) Again, if anomalous viscosity were responsible, we would expect the flow-pressure curves for vascular beds perfused with Ringer's solution (which is a Newtonian fluid) to be linear. In fact, the shapes of the curves for blood and saline are very similar to Figure 13, although the absolute viscosity of Ringer's solution is much less and flows are greater.

The zero flow pressure cannot be attributed to "slip," as seen with some plastic fluids, since blood exhibits no sign of such behavior. The explanation, not only of the critical closing pressure but also of the peculiar shape of the curves, is to be found in an analysis of the *equilibrium of the forces acting on the walls of the distensible blood vessels.*

Equilibrium of the Blood Vessel Wall. The key to this analysis,[3] and to an understanding of tension and pressure in hollow organs in general, is the *Law of Laplace.** The distinction and relations between pressure and tension are often poorly understood, and the words are used interchangeably. In some instances, as in bladder physiology, this habit has greatly retarded the advance of knowledge.

The law of Laplace will be familiar as applying to soap bubbles. In a curved membrane like the cylindrical wall of a blood vessel, the tension (T) can be thought of as the dynes per centimeter of the length of an imaginary slit in the membrane. The pressure inside the membrane must exceed the pressure outside by an amount that depends on this tension and on the shape of the membrane. The shape is characterized for each point on the membrane by two *principal radii of curvature,* R_1 and R_2, in centimeters. The law of Laplace is that this difference of pressure (P), which is best called the *transmural pressure,* is given by the equation:

$$P = T(1/R_1 + 1/R_2) \qquad (8)$$

For a cylindrical membrane, as in blood vessels, one radius of curvature (that is in the longitudinal plane) is infinite and the other is the radius of the cylinder; the formula thus becomes (see Fig. 14):

$$P = T/R \qquad (9)$$

For a sphere, $R_1 = R_2$ and $P = 2T/R$ (*cf.* the formula used for soap bubbles). Equation 9 enables us to calculate the total tension in the walls of different categories of blood vessels from the physiologic mean values of the pressures in them and their histologically determined radii (Table 17).

The tension varies from 200,000 dynes per cm. (about 200 grams per cm.) for the aorta to only 14 dynes per cm. (14 mg. per cm.) for the capillaries. We see that the very thin-walled capillary is able to withstand the capillary blood pressure because its radius of curvature is so very small. (A single layer of facial tissue paper will withstand about 50 grams per cm. before tearing, 3000 times as great a force as the capillary is called upon to withstand.) As the radius increases from capillaries to veins, the total

---

* This law was first stated by the Marquis de Laplace, French mathematician and physicist, in his *Mécanique céleste* about 1820.

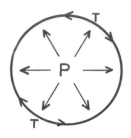

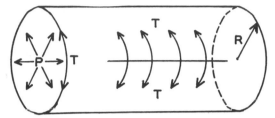

Fig. 14. Diagram of forces operating in equilibrium of wall of cylindrical vessel. Tension (T) is in dynes per cm. of length of vessel, pressure (P) in dynes per sq. cm., and radius (R) in cm.

tension in the wall increases, even though the blood pressure is reduced. This explains the presence and amount of elastic tissue in the walls of the various vessels. This elastic tissue maintains, without any expenditure of energy, a tension in the wall to balance the distending force of the blood pressure. The contraction of the smooth muscle of the wall, to control the flow, requires a continuous expenditure of energy.

The law of Laplace enables us to transform data on the distensibility of blood vessels into

tension-length diagrams for the wall (Fig. 15). For arteries and veins, and for arterioles as deduced from resistance-pressure curves, such elastic diagrams of all blood vessels have a common feature, which was noted long ago by Roy.[19] *As the wall is stretched it resists, not proportionately to each stretch but more and more strongly at each additional stretch.* This feature is absent in such simple elastic systems as a rubber band or a steel wire. These obey Hooke's law; i.e., they give a straight line in the tension-length diagram until, at high degrees of stretch, they yield and the curve is downward, not upward as in Figure 15*B*.

The peculiar elastic behavior of blood vessels has been shown to result from the combination of elastin and collagen fibers in the wall. The elastin fibers are brought into action by a very slight stretching of the wall, and the much less extensible collagen fibers do not reach their unstretched length until the vessel is considerably distended.[4, 17] The collagen fibers form a protective limiting "jacket." A similar structure of rubber with a canvas jacket is used in garden hose.

Figure 16 shows how, from such a tension-length diagram for the wall of a blood vessel, we can predict the size of the lumen for different transmural pressures when only elastic tension is present. The value for the size must be at the intersection (A) of the straight line representing the Laplacian law (T = PR) and a curve for the elastic tension of the typical shape for blood vessels. If the pressure is reduced, the Laplacian line has a reduced slope and the point of inter-

TABLE 17. *Application to Blood Vessels of Pressure–Curvature–Tension Relation ($T = PR$)*

TYPE OF VESSEL	MEAN INTERNAL PRESSURE (mm. Hg)	(dynes per sq. cm.)	RADIUS (R)	TENSION (T) IN WALL (dynes per cm.)	AMOUNT OF ELASTIC TISSUE
Aorta and large arteries	100	1.3×10^5	1.3 cm. or less	170,000	Very elastic, two coats
Small distributing arteries	90	1.2×10^5	0.5 cm.	60,000	Much elastic tissue but more muscular
Arterioles	60	8×10^4	0.15 mm. $-62\,\mu$	1200–500	Thin elastic intima only
Capillaries	30	4×10^4	$4\,\mu$	16	None
Venules	20	2.6×10^4	$10\,\mu$	26	None except in largest
Veins	15	2×10^4	$200\,\mu$ or more	400	Elastic fibers reappear
Vena cava	10	1.3×10^4	1.6 cm.	21,000	Very elastic, fibers increasing in size

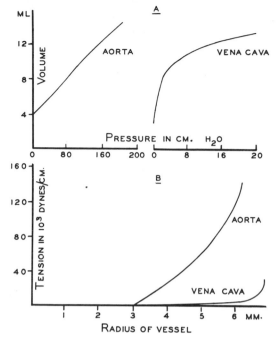

Fig. 15. *A*, Volume-pressure curves for human aorta and vena cava (after Green). *B*, Tension-length diagram derived from curves in *A* by use of law of Laplace.

section moves to a smaller radius, corresponding to point *D*. Thus the equilibrium, under *pressure* and *elastic tension alone*, is completely stable. If the vessel should increase in radius from *A* to *B*, the elastic tension would exceed that required for equilibrium of external and internal pressure and would return the radius to its original value. Similarly, if the vessel grew smaller, the forces would return it to equilibrium.

We now suppose that the contraction of the smooth muscle in the wall has added an *active tension* to the elastic tension produced by the stretch (Fig. 17) and that, as a result, the radius of the vessel has decreased (R_1 to R_2). The total tension BR_2 must be given by the Laplacian line for this new radius. The elastic tension has decreased to CR_2. The active tension must then have been equal to the remainder (*BC*). Thus we can see how much active tension is required to reduce the radius of the vessel by different amounts. Inspection of the diagram and a little thought will lead to the conclusion that a certain active tension is required to reduce the vessel to near the unstretched condition (*DE*) and, paradoxically, that no more (actually even less) is required to reduce the radius to zero and

cause a complete closure of the vessel, unless new forces prevent this.

Thus there is a fundamental instability in the equilibrium of a cylindrical blood vessel in which the smooth muscle supplies an active tension, i.e., a tension which persists even though the elastic fibers are no longer stretched. Elastic fibers have the important function of making possible a limited stability, but when the vessel wall is unstretched, complete instability appears once more. Blood vessels such as the glomus bodies of arteriovenous anastomoses, which are without elastic tissue, and other structures which have very little, such as the sphincters of the gastrointestinal tract, must be unstable. Typically, such structures are either open or closed and cannot maintain an intermediate size of lumen. The elastic tissue in the

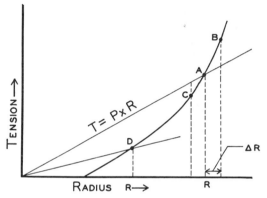

Fig. 16. Diagram to show that radius of a vessel under a given transmural pressure can be deduced from tension-length diagram. (From Burton, *Amer. J. Physiol.*, 1951, *164*:319–329.)

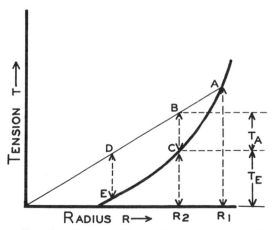

Fig. 17. Same as Figure 16 with active tension from contraction of smooth muscle added. (From Burton, *Amer. J. Physiol.*, 1951, *164*:319–329.)

wall of a blood vessel is necessary for the stability of its equilibrium under vasomotor tone.

Such reasoning led to an explanation of *critical closing pressure*. For a given degree of vasomotor tone, produced by vasomotor nerves or by pressor drugs, the arterioles in some vascular beds close if their transmural pressure falls below a critical value. Experimentally, critical closing pressures in vascular beds have been found to vary from a minimum of a few millimeters of mercury to a maximum which, in "spasm" of the blood vessels, may greatly exceed the available blood pressure.[6, 10, 14] The same physical analysis, based on the typical shape (Fig. 15) of the tension-length diagram for blood vessel walls, can explain the variety of shapes of flow-pressure curves found in vascular beds. Only a very small degree of distensibility of the resistance vessels (i.e., the arterioles and capillaries) is required to explain the marked nonlinearity of these curves.

There is no doubt regarding the existence of this fundamental limitation of the stability of cylindrical blood vessels under vasomotor tone. Many factors may obscure "critical closure" in vascular beds. While many arterioles may close completely if the transmural pressure is sufficiently reduced, as long as some channels remain open the total blood flow will not be reduced to zero. In many vascular beds, like those in muscle, local mechanisms (reactive hyperemia) lead to vasodilatation if the supply of blood and oxygen is reduced, so that the tendency to close is reduced or absent as the pressure is lowered. Enzymes in the walls of vessels (e.g., amine oxidase) destroy some physiologic pressor agents like norepinephrine. As the flow is reduced, destruction catches up with the supply of the hormone and, again, critical closure will not be achieved. It is astonishing that, in spite of all these factors, actual zero flow pressures have been found in several vascular beds. The importance of the theory lies in its explanation of the rapid rise of resistance if the blood pressure is reduced, so that flow-pressure curves are very nonlinear. A consequence is, as Girling[11] pointed out, that the maintenance of the normal levels of blood pressure is given a new importance. For example, a given degree of vasomotor tone, i.e., a certain number of nerve impulses per minute in sympathetic vasoconstrictor nerves has a much more drastic effect in reducing peripheral blood flow when the blood pressure is low (as in hypotensive shock) than when it is normal.

The Two "Hemodynamic Pressures." In summary, it should be emphasized that *in hemodynamics there are two important pressures*. The first is the *driving pressure*, the difference between the arterial and venous pressures across any part of a vascular bed. The driving pressure primarily governs flow. The second is the *transmural pressure*, particularly of those vessels that supply the major resistance to flow, such as the arterioles. Since the vessels are distensible, the transmural pressure will affect the geometric factor in Poiseuille's law and change the resistance to flow.

Thus, strictly speaking, we cannot think of a single relation between flow and pressure in any vascular bed, but must recognize a whole family of such curves according to the level of the transmural pressures. For instance, if the arterial and venous pressures are raised equally so that their difference (the driving pressure) is the same, the flow will increase because the raised transmural pressure will, owing to the stretching of elastic tissue, "passively" increase the lumina of the small vessels. Similarly if, as is usual in perfusion experiments or in the body, the arterial pressure is increased while the venous pressure remains constant, the transmural pressure in the arterioles, which will be approximately halfway between that in the artery and that in the veins, will be altered. The nonlinear nature of the flow-pressure curves we obtain is mainly due to this change in the transmural pressure (and hence the size) of the arterioles as the arterial pressure is altered.

USE OF RESISTANCE TO FLOW

The several complications have made physiologists reluctant to use the concept of resistance to flow to its full advantage. However, once it is recognized that, universally, the distensibility of the vessels always results in a passive decrease in resistance when transmural pressure rises, and vice versa, interpretation of changes in resistance is usually possible. Suppose that measurements of the driving pressure and flow in, say, a limb show increased resistance. Is this increase indicative of active vasoconstriction (an increase in vasomotor tone), or is the mechanism passive (a result of the distensibility of the vessels)? Usually in such cases (as with a pressor drug) the pressure has either risen or remained constant. An increase in transmural pressure would "passively" tend to increase the luminal diameter of the vessels and so decrease the resistance. The actual increase in resistance must have been, therefore, "active" vasoconstriction. If, however, the pressure has fallen, an interpretation could not be made without detailed knowledge of the curve of resistance versus transmural pressure for that particular vascular bed (e.g., as in Fig. 13). More often than not, there is no uncertainty in the interpretation.

LAPLACE'S LAW AND THE HEART

In 1892, Woods,[26] a throat surgeon of the Dublin Children's Hospital, demonstrated that the law of Laplace applied to the heart: that the pressure produced in the ventricles depends not only on the tension developed by the cardiac ventricular muscle in contraction, but also on the size and shape of the heart (i.e., the principal radii of curvature). It is now realized that the load on the heart, which governs its requirement for oxygen, depends mainly on the tension that must be developed in the ventricular muscle and the time this tension is maintained,[5] and very little upon the external work of pumping by the heart. Thus if the heart is dilated, as in heart failure, the heart muscle is at a mechanical disadvantage. If the diameter of the heart is doubled, the radii of curvature are doubled, and the tension per unit length of ventricular wall must be twice as great to produce the same systolic blood pressure (Fig. 18). In effect, the total tension of the muscle is quadrupled. Thus *any increase in the size of the heart increases the load of the heart*. Similarly *increases in heart rate* increase the tension-time integral of the heart muscle, since the time of each contraction is not correspondingly shortened and the speeding up is at the expense of diastole. Also, *increases in blood pressure* impose a great load on the heart since, by the law of Laplace, the tension required is proportional to the pressure. Thus the classic law of Laplace is very important in cardiac management, for it predicts that excitement, which raises the heart rate and blood pressure, may impose a much greater strain on the heart than does mild exercise. A round of golf may be far less dangerous to a cardiac patient than an angry argument with his wife.

External work and efficiency of the heart. Work done is force times distance moved. For a fluid propelled by pressure, this formula becomes pressure times volume moved. As the pressure in the ventricle changes greatly throughout the ejection period of the cardiac cycle, we must integrate. The work done is $\int P_v \cdot dO$, the integral of the pressure with respect to the output. This integral

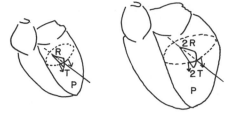

$$P = T(1/R_1 + 1/R_2)$$

RADII OF CURVATURE	X2
TENSION. DYNES/CM.	X2
'CIRCUMFERENCE'. CM.	X2
FORCE PER FIBER. DYNES TO PRODUCE THE SAME P.	X4

Fig. 18. Application of law of Laplace to heart showing that, if linear dimensions of heart are doubled, ventricular muscle must produce a tension four times greater to secure same systolic pressure. (From Burton, *Amer. Heart J.*, 1957, *54*:801–810.)

can be evaluated directly if we have a plot of ventricular pressure versus ventricular volume, as Rushmer determines these.[20] However, physiologists more often use the aortic pressure (P_A) than the ventricular pressure (P_v). In this case the kinetic energy factor, $\dfrac{PV^2}{2}$, must be added; i.e., work $= \int \left(P_A + \dfrac{PV^2}{2} \right) dO$. It has become the practice to use a mean pressure times the output instead of the true integral, but the mean should be a mean with respect to the output, not the usual mean with respect to time. Such approximate calculation of the work of the heart can be very inaccurate, and since the external work has little physiologic importance in the total load on the heart, they would seem hardly worth the effort.

The mechanical efficiency of the heart is defined as the external work done divided by the total energy exchange, which is the sum of the external work and the tension-time integral. Measurements of the efficiency of the heart in heart-lung preparations have shown that it is very low, usually less than 10 per cent. This reflects the fact that of the two terms the tension-time integral is by far the greater. For the same reason, the efficiency increases markedly as the amount of external work is increased.

REFERENCES

1. Bayliss, L. E. Chap. 6 in *Deformation and flow in biological systems*, A. Frey-Wyssling, ed. Amsterdam, North Holland Publishing Co., 1952.
2. Bingham, E. G. and Roepke, R. R. *J. gen. Physiol.*, 1944, *28*:79–83.

3. BURTON, A. C. *Amer. J. Physiol.*, 1951, *164*:319–329.

4. BURTON, A. C. *Physiol. Rev.*, 1954, *34*:619–642.

5. BURTON, A. C. *Amer. Heart J.*, 1957, *54*:801–810.

6. BURTON, A. C. and YAMADA, S. I. *J. appl. Physiol.*, 1951, *4*: 329–339.

7. COULTER, N. A., JR. and PAPPENHEIMER, J. R. *Amer. J. Physiol.*, 1949, *159*:401–408.

8. DIX, F. J. and SCOTT-BLAIR, G. W. *J. appl. Physiol.*, 1940, *11*:574–581.

9. FAHRAEUS, R. and LINDQVIST, T. *Amer. J. Physiol.*, 1931, *96*:562–568.

10. GIBSON, J. C., SELIGMAN, A. M., PEACOCK, W. C., AUB, J. C., FINE, J. and EVANS, R. D. *J. clin. Invest.*, 1946, *25*: 848–857.

11. GIRLING, F. *Amer. J. Physiol.*, 1952, *170*:131–135.

12. HAYNES, R. H. *The rheology of blood.* Ph.D. Thesis, University of Western Ontario, 1957. See also, HAYNES, R. H. and BURTON, A. C. *Proc. 1st nat. Biophys. Conf.*, 1959, p. 452; *Amer. J. Physiol.*, 1959, *197*:943–950.

13. MÜLLER, A. *Arch. Kreislaufforsch.*, 1941, *8*:245–282.

14. NICHOL, J., GIRLING, F., CLAXTON, E. B. and BURTON, A. C. *Amer. J. Physiol.*, 1951, *164*:330–344.

15. PAPPENHEIMER, J. R. and KINTER, W. B. *Amer. J. Physiol.*, 1956, *185*:377–390.

16. REYNOLDS, O. *Phil. Trans.*, 1883, *174*:935–982.

17. ROACH, M. R. and BURTON, A. C. *Canad. J. Biochem. Physiol.*, 1957, *35*:681–690.

18. ROBERTS, L. N., SMILEY, J. R. and MANNING, G. W. *Circulation*, 1953, *8*:232–242.

19. ROY, C. S. *J. Physiol.*, 1880–1882, *3*:125–159.

20. RUSHMER, R. F. *Cardiac diagnosis, a physiologic approach.* Philadelphia, W. B. Saunders Co., 1955.

21. STARKEY, T. V. *Brit. J. appl. Phys.*, 1955, *6*:34–37.

22. STARKEY, T. V. *Brit. J. appl. Phys.*, 1956, *7*:52–55.

23. STARKEY, T. V. *Brit. J. appl. Phys.*, 1956, *7*:448–449.

24. THOMA, R. *Abderhalden's Handb. biol. Arbeitsmeth.*, Abt. 5, 1928, *4*(2):1103–1258.

25. WHITTAKER, S. R. F. and WINTON, F. R. *J. Physiol.*, 1933, *78*:339–369.

26. WOODS, R. H. *J. Anat. (Lond.)*, 1892, *26*:362–370.

CIRCULATION OF BLOOD AND LYMPH

CHAPTER 28

General Characteristics of the Cardiovascular System

By ROBERT F. RUSHMER

THE energy expenditures involved in vital functions are derived from chemical reactions which require a continuous movement of metabolic substrate into the cells and a discharge of toxic waste products away from the cells. Living cells maintain an equilibrium with their environment by the process of diffusion—the movement of solutes from regions of high concentration into contiguous regions of lower concentration. As a cell utilizes oxygen the concentration of this specific substance is diminished within the cell. The concentration of oxygen diminishes below that of the immediate environment and oxygen moves from the extracellular fluid into the cell and a concentration gradient is established. The rate of movement of oxygen is determined by the mobility of oxygen in the medium and by the slope of the concentration gradient. The steepness of the concentration gradient is determined by the difference in concentration and the distance over which this gradient is distributed. Each of the metabolic fuels moves toward the cell at a rate determined by its own concentration gradient. The metabolic waste products attain greatest concentration within the cell and move outward away from the cell along concentration gradients.

The Nature of Diffusion. As a mechanism for local delivery of materials to and from cells, diffusion can be visualized in terms of a random walk. Consider a drunkard standing in the center of a level field. He starts off in a particular direction and after taking each step he changes his direction of motion in a random manner. The most probable distance from the starting point can be predicted statistically as the product of the mean step-length (L) and the square root of the number of steps, $N:(D = L \sqrt{N})$. In the case cited the most probable position of the drunkard after 100 steps will be at a distance of

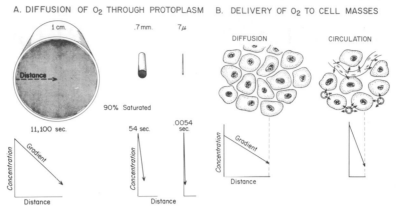

Fig. 1. *A,* Diffusion of oxygen through protoplasm occurs extremely rapidly over small distances and much more slowly over long distances. For example, a cylinder of protoplasm 1 cm. in diameter plunged into an atmosphere of pure oxygen would become 90 per cent saturated with oxygen in 11,100 seconds (about 3 hours). In contrast, a cylinder of the same sort of protoplasm only 7 microns in diameter would become 90 per cent saturated in 0.0054 second because of the very steep concentration gradient.

B, Cell masses packed together tend to have shallow concentration gradients so that diffusion to the center is slow. Capillaries interspersed between cells bring blood with high concentrations of oxygen and metabolic materials into close proximity to the individual cells, steepen the concentration gradients and facilitate delivery of materials to cells by more rapid diffusion.

10 steps from his starting point. If several drunkards begin to disperse from a group and obey the same rules (random change in direction after each step), they will occupy positions at different distances from the starting point, but the average distance will be 10 steps from the starting point after 100 steps. Diffusion in a liquid is a random walk of many different particles in three dimensions. For example, if a drop containing a high concentration of colored molecules is introduced into a small volume of stationary liquid, the molecules gradually become dispersed by a process of diffusion throughout the liquid. All the molecules in the liquid are in motion because of its thermal agitation. Molecules of water are closely packed such that the free path-length of motion is only about one hundred millionth of an inch. Traveling at about 0.1 mile per second each molecule collides and changes direction 1,000,000,000,-000 times per second. The average distance traveled during the first second is only 0.01 inch as given by the product of the path length times the square root of the number of collisions. In three hours, the average dye molecule will have traveled about 100 times farther (about 1 inch). Over distances as large as an inch diffusion is a very slow process. However, over very short distances, diffusion occurs extremely rapidly.

Consider a cylinder 1 cm. in diameter composed of material equivalent to the protoplasm in a nerve but devoid of oxygen throughout (Fig. 1*A*). If this cylinder were suddenly placed in an environment of 100 per cent oxygen, the protoplasm would become 90 per cent saturated in about 3 hours (11,100 seconds). In contrast, a cylinder of protoplasm only 7μ in diameter would become 90 per cent saturated in only about .0054 second.[3] As the distance of diffusion from the periphery of the cell to its center becomes very small the concentration gradients become very steep, and diffusion occurs with extreme rapidity.

As cells become grouped together into larger and more complex masses, the distance of diffusion becomes so large that the innermost cells cannot survive by simple diffusion and the necessity for circulatory systems arise (Fig. 1*B*). The basic function of the mammalian circulatory system is to bring blood into close proximity to each living cell, thus providing rapid delivery of oxygen and metabolic fuels along steep concentration gradients to the cells (Fig. 1*B*). At the same time waste products are propelled toward the blood by steep concentration gradients in the opposite direction. To achieve this kind of rapid diffusion to cells which are actively metabolizing requires a very large number of very small channels in the immediate vicinity of each group of cells. Cells with modest metabolic requirements can be spaced at considerable distances from the flowing streams of blood and still survive (i.e., in connective tissue). Cells with very high demands for oxygen and metabolic fuel must be very near a stream of flowing blood, and in some tissues a blood capillary is immediately adjacent to each cell (e.g., in skeletal muscle and in the heart). In skeletal muscle, each capillary serves a volume of tissue only about 12 times the volume of blood within the capillary. Under these conditions, the concentration gradients are very steep and the diffusion rates are adequate so long as the blood flows rapidly through the capillaries. However, if the blood flow is slow in relation to the rate of metabolism, the concentration gradients become flattened, diffusion rates slow and the tissues become deficient in oxygen. Some tissues are seriously affected by cessation of blood flow for very short periods. For example, interruption of blood flow to the brain leads to unconsciousness in about 7 seconds.

These considerations dictate that the circulatory system in man must be organized to provide rather steady and uninterrupted flow of blood in the immediate vicinity of highly specialized cells in the body. In tissues with widely varying levels of activity the blood flow rate

must be adjusted in relation to functional requirements of the cells. These requirements can be achieved by a very large number of tiny tubes with thin walls.

Functional Consequences of Vascular Arborization. Blood pumped by each ventricle of the heart enters a single major outflow channel and is distributed to millions of capillaries in the immediate vicinity of all body cells. This type of distribution is achieved through a diffuse arborization of branching arteries.[2] The significance of this arborization is more evident in a schematic presentation[6] in which vessels of corresponding caliber are arranged in vertical array as illustrated in Figure 2. The cross-sectional area of each pair of branches is larger than the area of the parent vessel. Total cross-sectional area increases gradually through the first few branches. The number of branches increases tremendously in the terminal arteries and capillaries; the total cross-section area of the very smallest vessels becomes very large. For example, the estimated total cross-sectional area of the arterioles is some 125 times that of the aorta. Correspondingly, the cross-sectional areas of the capillaries and venules are in the range of 500 to 600 times that of the aorta. Since the quantity of blood flowing through the aorta per minute is precisely the same as the quantity

THE RELATION BETWEEN CROSS-SECTIONAL AREA AND THE VELOCITY OF FLOW IN THE SYSTEMIC CIRCULATION

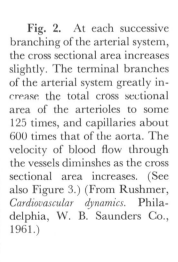

Fig. 2. At each successive branching of the arterial system, the cross sectional area increases slightly. The terminal branches of the arterial system greatly increase the total cross sectional area of the arterioles to some 125 times, and capillaries about 600 times that of the aorta. The velocity of blood flow through the vessels diminishes as the cross sectional area increases. (See also Figure 3.) (From Rushmer, *Cardiovascular dynamics.* Philadelphia, W. B. Saunders Co., 1961.)

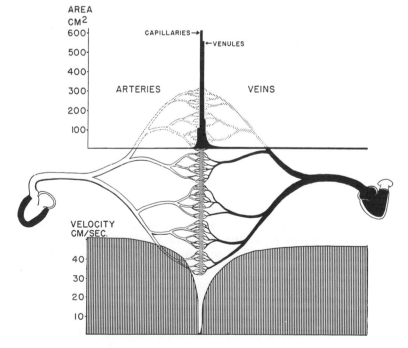

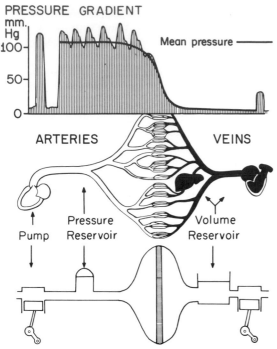

PRESSURE GRADIENT

Fig. 3. Each successive contraction of the heart ejects blood into the arterial system and maintains a mean arterial pressure in the range of 90 to 100 mm. Hg. Because the cardiac ejection is intermittent, the pressure fluctuates above and below this mean level. In the terminal branches of the arterial system, the hydraulic resistance is very great. The steep drop in pressure represents the large amount of potential energy dissipated as heat due to friction as the blood flows through these tiny channels. In a hydraulic system, the pump corresponds to the heart, a decompression chamber is represented by the elasticity of the arterial walls, the capillary networks correspond to an exchanger, and the reservoir corresponds to the variable capacity venous system.

flowing through all the capillaries, the blood flows very slowly through the capillaries. Just as a rushing stream of water confined within narrow banks slows as it enters a broad pool, so the velocity of blood flow through the capillaries becomes very slow (i.e., about 0.07 mm. per second). Since the capillaries are very short, this slow velocity of flow provides time for rapid exchange of substances between blood and tissues.

Pressure Gradients in the Systemic Circulation. The heart functions to convert chemical energy into mechanical energy in the form of pressure and flow of blood. Each successive ventricular contraction produces an elevation of pressure and ejection of blood into the arterial system (Fig. 3). Between ventricular contrac-

tions, the pressure in the arterial system declines as blood leaves the arterial system. During ventricular contraction (systole) the arterial pressure rises to about 120 mm. Hg and at the end diastole this pressure declines to about 80 mm. Hg. The pressure in the arteries normally fluctuates above and below a mean pressure of about 90 mm. Hg. In this way, the distensible arterial system serves as a pressure reservoir, preserving a pressure head during the intervals when the ventricles are filling and damping the fluctuations in pressure and flow which stem from the intermittent character of cardiac contraction.

The energy imparted to the blood by the contracting myocardium is dissipated as heat due to friction within the blood as it flows through the vascular arborization. The rate at which the energy is dissipated by internal friction is indicated by the pressure drop between two points along a vascular channel. The factors which affect the pressure drop during laminar flow of a homogeneous, viscous fluid along straight, rigid tubes of constant caliber are expressed by the Poiseuille-Hagen law (Chap. 27). Solving this equation for pressure gradient gives the following expression:

$$P_a - P_b = \frac{8n\, 1\, F}{\pi R^4}$$

Since the pressure drop in the vascular system is due to pulsatile flow of a nonhomogeneous fluid through tapered, distensible and branching tubes, the equation is not directly applicable. However, the length of the channels and the viscosity of the blood do not change much from moment to moment. The caliber of the major arterial trunks is very large in relation to the flow velocities encountered. Thus, the drop in mean pressure from the aortic valves to the bifurcation of the aorta is only about 1 mm. Hg, a drop which is thoroughly obscured by the fluctuating pressures in the system.[5] In other words, a mean driving pressure of only about 1 mm. Hg is sufficient to drive the total flow of blood along the full length of the aorta. The pressure drop from the aorta to the radial artery at the wrist with the arm at rest is only about 2 mm. Hg.

Sites of Controlled Resistance. With progressive branching of the terminal arteries, the caliber of each successive set of branches is reduced and the hydraulic resistance (inversely proportional to the fourth power of the radius) increases tremendously in the very small branches just upstream from the capillaries. As the blood flows through these very small branches, the frictional resistance is so great that the pressure drops precipitously (i.e., 30 to 50 mm. Hg in only a few millimeters of travel). This process can be visualized in terms of the pressure required to force water through a small glass capillary. Small changes in caliber of these small vessels have a profound effect on the rate of energy loss as friction, so that minor degrees of dilation or constriction of these vessels can increase or decrease blood flow through the capillary networks downstream. These are the fundamental principles by which the distribution of blood flow through various capillary networks in the body is controlled by adjustments in caliber of the terminal muscular arteries and arterioles in the circulation (see Chap. 31).

Capillary Exchange. The distance factor of diffusion is so critical that little or no transfer occurs across the thick wall of arteries. The wall-thickness of the arteries tends to diminish progressively as their caliber becomes smaller with each branching. In the terminal arteries and arterioles the vascular walls are composed only of an endothelial lining enclosed within one, two or three layers of smooth muscle cells and a thin connective tissue sheath. Even these thin walls serve as an effective barrier to the transport by diffusion of materials to and from the tissue cells. Virtually all of the exchange between blood and tissue cells occurs across the capillary walls, which consist of only a single layer of endothelial cells about 1 micron in thickness externally supported by basement membranes and variable numbers of extravascular cells (i.e., pericytes) (see Chap. 32). Thus, the very steep concentration gradients required for rapid diffusion between blood and cells are achieved over the very thin barriers of the capillary endothelial walls.

Capillary structure and function pose at least two questions which immediately attract attention: (i) By what mechanisms can thin-walled capillaries support high internal pressures? (ii) What keeps the water in the blood from pouring through capillary walls? The pressure within capillaries normally ranges up to 35 mm. Hg when they are positioned at or near heart level. In the erect position, the pressure in long hydrostatic columns of blood from heart to heels is equivalent to about 90 mm. Hg, so the capil-

lary pressure must exceed this value (see Fig. 7, Chap. 27). If one questions how a single layer of endothelial cells about 1 micron thick can withstand an internal distending pressure of more than 100 mm. Hg without bursting, he will find an answer in the very small caliber of these vessels.[5] In Chapter 27, the Law of Laplace was expressed in terms of the formula $P = T/R$, where P is pressure in a hollow cylinder, T is wall tension and R is the radius of the tube. In tubes of very small caliber, very high pressures can be supported by extremely slight wall tension.

The properties of capillaries which permit rapid diffusion of substances across the walls should also permit rapid loss of water under the pressures within the capillaries. The importance of the effective osmotic pressures of plasma proteins in retaining water within the capillary lumen will be considered in Chapter 32. Under many conditions, fluids of the blood escape from the capillaries into the spaces between tissue cells. Such fluid is returned to the blood stream by way of the lymphatic system (see Chap. 32).

Venous Volume Reservoirs. The veins serve as conduits by which blood is returned from the capillary networks to the heart. The caliber of the veins increases rapidly as the venules unite to form small veins, which in turn join to form larger and larger venous channels. As in the arterial system, the pressure gradients required to propel blood along the venous channels are very shallow—particularly in the veins of larger caliber (Fig. 3). Most of the pressure energy imparted by the heart is dissipated as the blood passes through the microcirculation so that the veins are essentially a low pressure system except when they are dependent and must support long hydrostatic columns.

The total blood volume is subject to change under many different conditions. Any sustained imbalance between intake and output of body fluids as occurs with diarrhea, excessive sweating, large fluid intake, hemorrhage, etc., may theoretically alter blood volume. The changes in total blood volume are accommodated primarily within the veins of the systemic and pulmonary vascular systems. The distribution of blood is also variable (i.e., during a change in position from supine to standing). The veins above heart level tend to become partially emptied while those below heart level tend to be distended by the hydrostatic columns. Dur-

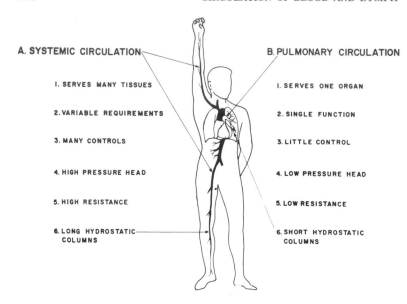

A. SYSTEMIC CIRCULATION

1. SERVES MANY TISSUES

2. VARIABLE REQUIREMENTS

3. MANY CONTROLS

4. HIGH PRESSURE HEAD

5. HIGH RESISTANCE

6. LONG HYDROSTATIC COLUMNS

B. PULMONARY CIRCULATION

1. SERVES ONE ORGAN

2. SINGLE FUNCTION

3. LITTLE CONTROL

4. LOW PRESSURE HEAD

5. LOW RESISTANCE

6. SHORT HYDROSTATIC COLUMNS

Fig. 4. The systemic circulation differs from the pulmonary circulation in a number of distinctive characteristics. These differences may be related to the differences in the functions, organization and environment of the two vascular beds.

ing all these adjustments, the pressure at the outlet from the systemic and pulmonary veins must be maintained above some minimal value to provide for filling of the right and left ventricular chambers. Changes in the capacity of venous reservoirs in various parts of the body are essential features of cardiovascular regulation, although very little is known about this control system.

Characteristics of the Systemic Circulation. The systemic circulation encompasses the vascular beds receiving blood flow, pumped by the left ventricle and distributed through branches of the aorta (Fig. 4). The vascular beds included in this category serve the nervous system, myocardium, gastrointestinal tract, genitourinary tract, musculoskeletal system, endocrine system, and even the proximal airways of the lung by way of the bronchial arteries. The functional properties of the systemic circulation are related to the fact that it serves a widely diversified group of tissues differing in function and in levels of activity. For example, the total blood flow through the brain varies little and is not influenced to any large extent by the level or intensity of mental or nervous activity. Blood flow through the skin is greatly influenced by external temperatures, by emotional factors and many other conditions. The metabolic requirements of skeletal muscles are increased several fold in the transition from rest to exertion and these changes must be supported by appropriate alterations of blood flow. The large blood flow through the kidneys is exorbitant in

relation to the oxygen requirements but apparently is necessary for the excretory function of the kidneys. Gastrointestinal activity and blood flow vary in relation to digestive processes. Adequate perfusion of the vascular beds of these different tissues requires adjustment of the distribution of blood flow among the various networks and also the capacity for changing the total flow through the system by altering the output of the heart. The distribution of blood in individual beds is regulated by variations of resistance in response to local chemical action and to neural (or vasomotor) action. The output of the heart is also regulated by local mechanical and chemical factors and by neural control mechanisms. Thus, changes in blood flow adapt to meet the requirements of active tissues without compromising function of vital tissues such as the brain, heart and kidneys.

The systemic circulation maintains steep pressure gradients from arteries to veins, a condition which implies a high mean systemic arterial pressure and a high level of hydraulic resistance to the flow of blood through the micro-circulation. The high resistance and high pressure have important functional connotations. First, systemic arterial pressure represents a store of potential energy, immediately available to propel blood through open vascular channels. This pressure head permits rapid shifts in blood flow from one vascular bed to another as the caliber of the small vessels (i.e., arterioles) alters. For example, sudden dilation of the arterioles in skeletal muscles is immediately followed by greatly increased flow through these beds.

The extension of the systemic circulation to the tips of the extremities creates long columns of fluid which may be horizontally oriented at one time and vertically positioned at others. Under the influence of gravity, the hydrostatic columns above the heart tend to diminish the driving pressure developed by the left ventricle (i.e., in the upraised arm). For example, the pressure at the root of the aorta required to elevate blood against gravity to the tips of the upstretched fingers is in the order of 50 to 60 mm. Hg, leaving only 60 to 70 mm. Hg pressure to force blood through the arterioles, capillaries and venules.

Thus, the systemic circulation can be characterized as a highly controlled, high-pressure, high-resistance system serving a wide variety of tissues dispersed over long distances from the heart (Fig. 4).

Characteristics of the Pulmonary Circulation. Since the systemic circulation is in series with pulmonary circulation, the quantity of blood passing through the lungs must precisely equal the quantity passing through the remainder of the body. The pulmonary circulation differs from the systemic circulation in many important respects.

The pulmonary circulation is distributed only to the lungs. Since pulmonary tissue is the same in the various lobes and segments, no purpose is served normally by shifting blood flow from one region of functioning lung tissue to another. In contrast with the systemic circulation, the pulmonary vascular bed has extremely slight capacity for control.

The muscular terminal branches of the pulmonary arterial system divide into a very extensive network of capillary vessels in the walls of the air sacs. Vessels which correspond to arterioles in the systemic circulation are not found in the transition from terminal arteries to capillaries in the lungs. Since there is little or no control over flow distribution in the lungs and the hydrostatic columns of blood are very limited, the pressure gradient from pulmonary arteries to pulmonary veins is much less steep than in the systemic circulation. Under normal conditions, right ventricular contraction elevates pressure in the pulmonary artery to about 25 mm. Hg. At the end of the cycle, the pulmonary arterial pressure reaches a low point

(diastolic pressure) around 8 mm. Hg. The mean pulmonary arterial pressure is only about 13 mm. Hg, as compared to a mean systemic arterial pressure of about 90 mm. Hg. Thus, the pulmonary vasculature is a low-pressure system offering slight hydraulic resistance. Increased flow through the lungs occurs with little or no increase in driving pressure, suggesting that the vessels of the lungs distend passively in response to increased outflow from the right ventricle.

The pulmonary capillary surface area is estimated to be about the same as the alveolar surface area: about 70 to 80 square meters.[4] The diffusion distance between capillary blood and alveolar air is very short in the lungs, measuring from 0.36 to 3.5 μ.[7] Electron micrographs reveal three distinct layers separating blood and air: capillary endothelium, basement membrane and alveolar epithelial cells.

Comparison of Right and Left Ventricles. The right ventricle ejects blood at relatively low pressure into the low resistance pulmonary circuit. In contrast, the left ventricle ejects the same quantity of blood into a high-pressure, high-resistance systemic circuit. The normal left ventricle is architecturally arranged to serve as an effective high-pressure pump. It has thick walls containing a heavy cuff of circumferentially oriented fibers in the form of a cylinder which compress blood in the chamber like the clenching of a fist. In contrast, the right ventricle is a crescentic shaped cleft between two broad surfaces, contracting like a bellows to pump large volumes under low pressure. The manner in which these dissimilar chambers contract synchronously and in a coordinated manner is described in the next chapter.

REFERENCES

1. BURTON, A. C. *Amer. J. Physiol.*, 1951, *164*:319–329.
2. GREEN, H. D. In *Medical physics*, vol. 1, O. GLASSER, ed. Chicago, Year Book Medical Publishers, Inc., 1944.
3. HILL, A. V. *Proc. roy. Soc.* 1928, *104B*:39–96.
4. LIEBOW, A. A. In *Ciba Foundation symposium on pulmonary structure and function*, A. V. S. DE REUCK and M. O'CONNOR, eds. Boston, Little, Brown and Co., 1962.
5. McDONALD, D. A. and TAYLOR, M. G. The hydrodynamics of the arterial circulation. In *Progress in biophysics and biophysical chemistry*, vol. 9, J. A. V. BUTTER and B. KATZ, eds. London, Pergamon Press, 1959.
6. RUSHMER, R. F. *Cardiovascular dynamics*, 2nd ed. Philadelphia, W. B. Saunders Co., 1961.
7. SCHULZ, H. In *Ciba Foundation symposium on pulmonary structure and function*, A. V. S. DE REUCK and M. O'CONNOR, eds. Boston, Little, Brown and Co., 1962.

CHAPTER 29

Mechanical Events of the Cardiac Cycle

By ALLEN M. SCHER

As stated elsewhere in this text, survival of large multicellular organisms depends on the constant replenishment of the extracellular fluid with materials rich in oxygen and metabolic substrate and on the removal of metabolic wastes. Although this process depends on the exchange of materials across the walls of capillaries the basic energy is supplied by the pumping action of the heart. In many types of circulatory distress the ultimate cause of incapacity or death is the lack of transfer of material across capillaries; in a high percentage of such cases the deficiency is not in the capillaries but in the performance of the heart, which may be impaired by a large variety of causes. Thus during the most routine physical examination, the physician spends a large percentage of time investigating the function of the heart. Before the advent of certain newer diagnostic procedures, he depended to a large extent on information supplied by his own sense organs. Even now, the careful physician examines the veins for signs of enlargement and high venous pressure. Placing his stethoscope in many places over the thorax, he carefully examines the chest for abnormal impact which may be imparted to it by the heart. Such examination supplements the use of newer diagnostic tools. At times specialized laboratory tests are suggested to the physician by information gained from such examination.

In interpreting the information which he receives from his own sense organs and newer measuring devices, the physician must have a reference; i.e., he must know whether or not a particular sign or symptom is within the normal range. In addition, the scientific physician should know what sequence of physiologic phenomena produces the information he receives and should have some understanding of what types of physiologic derangements lead to abnormal events. For such an examination of the cardiovascular system, it is essential that the physician know the normal sequence of mechanical and electrical events which take place in the cardiac chambers.

Functional Anatomy. In many properties cardiac muscle is intermediate between striated and smooth muscle. This intermediacy is both structural and functional. Cardiac muscle is cross-striated like skeletal muscle but, like smooth muscle, it is involuntary, i.e., is not under the control of the will. Functionally, if not anatomically, cardiac muscle appears to be a syncytium like smooth muscle. That is, the units of the muscle are functionally interconnected, so that, once electrical depolarization is initiated in some unit, it continues through all units of the syncytium (see Chap. 30). This aspect of cardiac function will be discussed in the next chapter. Striated muscle is able to develop a large amount of tension in a short time, but will fatigue; in contrast, smooth muscle contracts slowly but is capable of exerting moderate amounts of tension for long periods of time. In this respect, cardiac muscle is closer to skeletal muscle, because the heart can contract rapidly, although not as rapidly as skeletal muscle. Like smooth muscle, cardiac muscle is almost continuously in rhythmic action. The heart is composed of a large number of separate muscle bundles which can be separated only with difficulty. The individual bundles have been named, but in the adult heart they have merged to such an extent as to be virtually indistinguishable.[9]

The fibrous skeleton of the heart may be considered as a supporting framework which includes the valves and to which the muscle masses are attached.[11] The fibrous skeleton separates the atria and ventricles and surrounds the tricuspid and mitral valve orifices, the atria and ventricles being attached about these openings. The fibrous skeleton also surrounds the smaller aortic and pulmonary valve orifices. The two atria and the two ventricles, as well as the aorta and the pulmonary artery, thus insert into the fibrous skeleton. Figure 1 indicates this general structure.

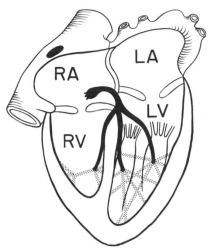

Fig. 1.   Diagrammatic view of heart showing cavities of both ventricles and atria. *Upper left,* Superior and inferior venae cavae may be seen entering right atrium. Black ellipse in this area indicates general region of sino-atrial node. Atrioventricular node is indicated above tricuspid valve cusps in interatrial septum. Right bundle passes down into right ventricle; the two branches of left bundle pass into left ventricle. Numerous Purkinje branches cross ventricular cavity on both sides.

In addition to the general myocardial muscle mass we must note the conduction system of the heart (Fig. 2). It consists of the *sino-atrial* (sino-auricular) node, which is the mammalian analog of the sinus venosus, the A-V node, the common bundle, the right and left bundles and the ventricular Purkinje* fibers. The sino-atrial node (S-A node), or the node of Keith and Flack, is the pacemaker of the mammalian

* Named for its discoverer Johannes Evangelista Purkinje (1787), a Bohemian physiologist. Pronounced "pur-kin'-je."

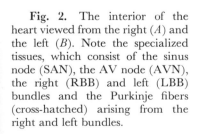

Fig. 2.   The interior of the heart viewed from the right (*A*) and the left (*B*). Note the specialized tissues, which consist of the sinus node (SAN), the AV node (AVN), the right (RBB) and left (LBB) bundles and the Purkinje fibers (cross-hatched) arising from the right and left bundles.

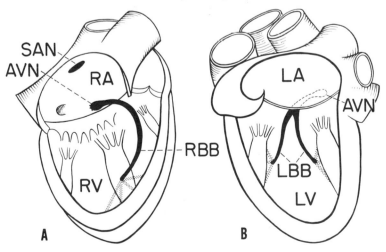

heart. A section of Keith and Flack's description of this node follows:

"Our search for a well-differentiated system of fibres within the sinus, which might serve as a basis for the inception of the cardiac rhythm, has led us to attach importance to this peculiar musculature surrounding the artery at the sino-auricular junction. In the human heart, the fibers are striated, fusiform, with well-marked elongated nuclei, plexiform in arrangement, and embedded in densely packed connective tissue—in fact, of closely similar structure to the Knoten (A-V node). The amount of this musculature varies, depending upon how much of the sinus has remained of the primitive type; but in the neighborhood of the taenia terminalis there is always some of this primitive tissue found. Macroscopically, the fibers resemble those of the a.-v. bundle in being paler than the surrounding musculature, i.e., in being of the white variety. . . ."[4]

The tissue of the S-A node consists of small, closely interlaced cells interspersed with connective tissue. The region is easily recognized microscopically with low magnification.

In the region of the interatrial septum, near the coronary sinus, there is a second mass of specialized conduction tissue, the atrioventricular node (A-V node), or node of Tawara. The A-V node, as indicated, closely resembles the S-A node. The A-V node gives rise to the common bundle, which passes through the fibrous skeleton. The A-V node and the Purkinje tissue constitute a bridge for electrical conduction of the impulse from the atria to the ventricles.

The so-called Purkinje tissue, a system of specialized muscle fibers, begins at the common bundle and continues through the right and left bundle. Its network of branching fibers covers much of the endocardium. Purkinje tissue has anatomic and electrical characteristics somewhat different from those of ordinary myocardium. In general, the fibers of the common bundle and the right and left bundles are larger, have clearer cytoplasm, and contain more glycogen (indicated by glycogen-specific stains). These fibers conduct more rapidly than ordinary cardiac muscle, and in some species, particularly the ungulates, are surrounded by a substantial connective tissue sheath; in ungulates, the Purkinje tissue penetrates the walls of the ventricles. This tissue, like the rest of the myocardium, is functionally syncytial. Electrically, the differences are less marked, the intracellular action potential differing somewhat from that of ordinary myocardial fibers.

Electrical Precursors of Mechanical Activity.

The sequence of contraction and relaxation of cardiac muscles results from the cyclic electrical depolarization and repolarization of the membranes of the cardiac muscle units. The normal sequence of electrical events in single muscle cells has been discussed previously (see Chap. 4), and the electrical events within the entire cardiac mass will be discussed in detail in the next chapter. It is necessary, however, to summarize briefly the sequence of electrical changes in the heart as an introduction to the consideration of cardiac mechanical events.

CARDIAC PACEMAKER. Certain tissues of the heart have the ability to act as a pacemaker, i.e., to depolarize spontaneously. Localization of the cardiac pacemaker cells in cold-blooded animals was anticipated in some very early experiments performed by Harvey in 1628. He found that isolated small bits of cardiac tissue continued to beat rhythmically and that pieces of atrium had a higher inherent rate than did pieces of ventricular muscle. Several other kinds of experimental evidence can be produced.

In the elementary physiology laboratory, it is a common experiment to place and temporarily tighten ligatures in the frog heart (i) between the sinus venosus and the atria and (ii) between the atria and the ventricles. These are known as Stannius' ligatures. After either ligation, the pre-ligature heart rate is maintained only above the ligature, since the pacemaker is in the sinus venosus. In the mammalian heart, the S-A node is the pacemaker. Warming or cooling the pacemaker in the heart of a cold-blooded or a warm-blooded animal will change the rate of the entire heart, whereas warm or cool applications placed on regions which cannot function as pacemakers will not. Similar results are obtained with drugs, such as epinephrine or acetylcholine, which increase or slow the heart rate. At times, if a warm rod or an accelerator drug is applied to a tissue which is not acting as the pacemaker but which *can* function as a pacemaker, the entire heart may accelerate. This technique thus demonstrates potential as well as actual pacemaker sites.

The pacemaker at any instant is that portion of the heart with the highest rate. Techniques for electrical mapping of pacemaker sites have been suggested by Lewis.[7] Recently, intracellular recording has been used to find pacemaker cells, which indeed have unique characteristics (see Chap. 30, Fig. 9).[13] Study of the embryonic development of the chick heart shows that pacemaker activity begins in the precursor of ventricular muscle and moves, first to the atrial muscle and then to the sinus venosus.

SPREAD OF ACTIVITY. Once electrical activity is initiated in the atrial pacemaker, the activity spreads through both atrial walls and through the interatrial septum. The wave of excitation spreads in all directions concentrically from the S-A node at a rate slightly less than 1 meter per second. The spread of depolarization through the entire human atrium requires about 80 milliseconds. This spread produces an electrical event which may be recorded at the body surface, called the "P wave" of the body surface electrocardiogram (Fig. 1, Chap. 30). The electrically excited state in the atrium continues for approximately 150 milliseconds. Atrial repolarization occurs during the depolarization of the ventricles.

The sole muscular connection between the atrium and the ventricle consists of the A-V node, the common bundle and the right and left conducting bundles. The velocity of conduction in the A-V node is very low (about 0.1 meter per second). The conduction velocity in the bundles is about 2 meters per second. In the body surface electrocardiogram, there is a period between the end of the excitation of the atrium and the beginning of the excitation of the ventricles when no potential changes are recorded. After the electrical wave has traveled down the right and left bundles, it rapidly traverses the Purkinje fibers, which are widely distributed to the endocardium on both sides. Consequently, excitation is distributed quite synchronously to most of the mural and septal endocardium. The velocity of conduction along the endocardium is about 1 meter per second.

The electrical wave then travels through the ventricular muscle, generally from endocardium to epicardium at about 0.3 meter per second. Ventricular excitation produces an electrical potential at the body surface, the "QRS complex" (Fig. 1, Chap. 30). In man, about 80 milliseconds are required for all the ventricular muscle to become electrically excited. During the period when the ventricles are depolarizing, the atria are repolarizing, i.e., returning to the resting state. The ventricular cells remain depolarized for about 300 milliseconds, the range being from slightly above 200 milliseconds to slightly below 500 milliseconds. In the electro-cardiogram, the "T wave" signals ventricular repolarization.

Summarizing these electrical events, we have a wave of depolarization moving through the atrial myocardium, producing the P wave. The repolarization of the atrium occurs while the ventricles are depolarizing. The ventricular myocardium starts to depolarize about 80 milliseconds after the end of atrial depolarization and remains in a depolarized state for about 300 milliseconds before returning to the resting state. Ventricular depolarization produces the QRS complex, and ventricular repolarization produces the T wave. The chemical link between the electrical and mechanical events in muscle has not been elucidated, but cardiac cells begin to contract about 10 milliseconds after they become depolarized and remain in the contracted state while they remain depolarized. After a variable period of electrical inactivity, this process is repeated. The recurring electrical events lead to a rhythmic contraction of the cardiac muscle which pumps the blood.

Mechanical Characteristics of the Heart. Let us now consider the mechanical characteristics of the system in which these events take place and the techniques used to record them. The atria may be likened to a single, irregularly shaped, thin-walled cone split into two chambers by the interatrial septum. The chambers have little ability and opportunity to do work. The right atrium produces a pressure differential of 5 to 6 mm. Hg as it contracts; the left atrium, a differential of 7 to 8 mm. Hg.

The right ventricle, which pumps blood returned from the systemic circulation into the pulmonary artery, is a crescent-shaped chamber which sits atop the free wall of the interventricular septum. This ventricle appears suited to the accommodation and ejection of large and variable amounts of blood with minimal myocardial shortening. The shape does not appear suited to the development of high pressures. Right *intraventricular* systolic pressure is about 25 mm. Hg*;

---

* In discussion of pressures in the cardiovascular system, the values given are the pressure in excess of atmospheric pressure. Systolic pressure is the highest pressure produced by contraction. If used without qualification "systolic pressure" refers to the peak pressure in the aorta. Diastolic pressure is the lowest pressure reached during ventricular relaxation. At times the terms "electrical systole" and "electrical diastole" are used loosely to designate the period of the cardiac action potential and the period between action potentials, respectively.

diastolic pressure is nearly the same as atmospheric pressure. The shape of the left ventricle may be compared to a cylinder with a small cone at the end. This ventricle is in effect a pressure pump[11] (that is, it tends to eject a constant stroke volume against pressures which vary widely), and its function is to pump oxygenated blood, returned from the lungs, into the aorta. Left ventricular systolic pressure is approximately 120 mm. Hg.

The right heart can easily adapt to changes in stroke volume, the left to demands for increased pressure. The atrium and ventricle on each side are separated by valves which move in response to pressure-induced flow changes. If the pressure in the atria is higher than that in the ventricles, the atrioventricular (A-V) valves will open and blood will enter the ventricles. Conversely, if the ventricular pressure is higher, backflow will tend to occur and the valves will close. The aortic and pulmonary valves function in a similar manner. If, for instance, the pressure in the aorta is higher than that in the left ventricle, the aortic valves will be closed; if ventricular pressure is higher, the valves will open and blood will flow from the ventricle into the aorta.

Some of the blood ejected into the aorta and pulmonary artery during systole distends the elastic walls of these vessels, storing potential energy. This stored potential energy is released during diastole. The aortic and pulmonary arterial pressures rise to a peak during the contraction of the ventricle, but the pressures in either the greater or lesser circulation do not fall to zero between beats. Peak systolic pressure is normally about 120 mm. Hg in the aorta and 25 mm. Hg in the pulmonary artery. The diastolic pressure in the aorta is about 80 mm. Hg; that in the pulmonary artery is about 7 mm. Hg. The intraventricular diastolic pressure, though, falls to nearly zero.

Measurements. The events of the cardiac cycle consist of a number of physical changes. The electrocardiogram has been considered briefly and will be discussed further in the next chapter. The mechanical contraction which results from activation of the cardiac muscle produces cyclic pressure changes in the chambers of the heart, in the aorta and in the veins. These pressure changes were recorded in experimental animals during the last four decades by Wiggers and his coworkers.[14] Recently, some of the measurements have been repeated in humans and in intact dogs with essentially similar results.[2] A discussion of pressure recording techniques is presented in Chapter 34.

In the classic studies, the combined volume of two ventricles was recorded by placing both of them in a glass container which was closed by a rubber ring around the atrioventricular groove. The container was connected to a recording tambour, i.e., a rubber diaphragm which moved a pen or mirror. This system could be used only on experimental animals with opened chests. Recently designed transducers[11] permit the estimation of ventricular volume from measurements of ventricular diameter or circumference. Further, as indicated in Chapter 34, it is now possible to measure stroke volume in animals in either short-term or long-term experiments with flowmeters of either the electromagnetic or ultramicrosonic type.

EVENTS OF THE CARDIAC CYCLE

Because electrical events precede mechanical events, let us draw the conventional electrocardiogram and then try to deduce what mechanical changes take place during the various phases of the cycle. We are here concerned with changes in a number of variables through a single cardiac cycle. The events will be described vertically—that is, we will describe the changes in all variables in one phase of the cycle, then discuss the next portion of the cycle, etc. In this discussion, too, the attempt will be made to discuss first that mechanical change which is of primary importance in each phase.

It is a general rule that where two chambers are directly interconnected, the pressure pulses will be identical with a small pressure gradient in the direction of flow. When the chambers are separated by closed valves, there may be a mechanical effect of one on the other. The phases of contraction and relaxation are named in a fashion which describes the activity of the ventricle. Figure 3 shows the events of the cardiac cycle; the vertical lines mark the beginning of the successive phases.

Diastasis (Fig. 3). As drawn, the cycle begins at the end of diastole. The pressure in the aorta is falling, owing to the "runoff" of blood into the peripheral vessels. Volume and pressure in the atria and ventricles are rising slightly since the venous pressure exceeds the pressure within the chambers. The atrioventricular valves have long been open. No potentials are recorded in the electrocardiogram, and no sounds are heard stethoscopically. The diastolic period extending from the end of the rapid filling phase in one cycle to the atrial contraction in the next cycle is known as the period of *diastasis*. Diastasis is of variable duration and de-

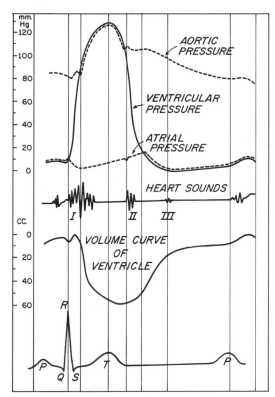

Fig. 3. Events of the cardiac cycle. This diagram consists of the five labeled curves plus the electrocardiogram (lowest curve). The various phases of the cardiac cycle are separated by the vertical lines. Detailed description in accompanying text. (After Wiggers, *Circulatory Dynamics*. New York, Grune and Stratton, 1952.)

pends on the heart rate. The P wave of the electrocardiogram occurs at the end of this phase.

Atrial Contraction. Slightly after the beginning of the P wave (during the diastolic period) the atria commence their contraction. This contraction leads to a surprisingly slight rise in the intra-atrial pressure (the pressure change is about 5 mm. Hg). With atrial contraction, the ventricular volume and pressure increase slightly owing to the atrial ejection of blood (ventricular pressure increases by about 3 mm. Hg). The major portion of ventricular filling occurs during the period of diastasis (see discussion below of period of rapid filling). Atrial contraction has generally been considered as a relatively trivial contributor to the filling of the ventricles. It now appears that, if the heart rate is slow enough so that there is a true period of diastasis, atrial contraction produces a rise in ventricular pressure and the A-V valves often

close because of atrial ejection, so that this rise in pressure is maintained. If the heart rate is rapid, which is the case in many acute experiments on animals, ventricular pressure records show no clear atrial component.[3] It has been estimated that the atria contribute 20 per cent or less to ventricular filling. During this time, the pressure in the aorta continues to decrease as blood flows into the arterioles. A very faint atrial vibration, not normally perceived as a sound, occurs at this time. The ventricles begin to depolarize during this period, as shown by the beginning of the QRS complex. The atrial pressure wave lasts about 0.1 second.

Ventricular Isometric (Isovolumetric) Contraction. The next event is the onset of ventricular contraction. It begins shortly after the onset of the ventricular electrocardiographic complex (QRS). The first period of ventricular contraction is called the "isometric phase." At the beginning of ventricular contraction, the A-V valves may be open or closed. If they are open, as the interventricular pressure rises and exceeds the atrial pressure, the valves close. The aortic and pulmonary valves are, of course, also closed. Since fluid is incompressible, this is by definition an "isovolumetric" or "isometric" phase of contraction; i.e., the volume of blood in the ventricles is constant.

At the beginning of ventricular contraction, aortic pressure is about 80 mm. Hg, pulmonary pressure is about 7 mm. Hg, and ventricular pressure is only slightly above atmospheric pressure. The ventricles change dimensions as the muscle fibers contract, but no blood is ejected into the arteries and none flows retrograde into the atria once the valves close. Pressures in the arteries and the atria are thus not directly affected even though ventricular pressure rises steeply; both pressure and muscle fiber length change. During this phase, several investigators[11, 14] have observed a slight increase in *apparent* ventricular volume despite the fact that both inflow and outflow valves are closed. When the diameter or circumference of the ventricle is measured during this period, a change in shape is observed in the record. This change probably results from contraction of portions of the myocardium near the endocardium, possibly the trabeculae carnae or parts of the papillary muscles or both.[10]

RAPID EJECTION. When the pressure in the left ventricle first exceeds the pressure in the aorta, the aortic valves open. Since there is now

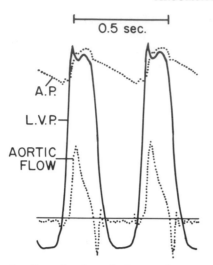

Fig. 4. Records of aortic flow and pressure and ventricular pressure. (From Spencer.[12]) Note that ventricular pressure exceeds aortic pressure only during the earliest phase of ejection. The flow curve shows an initial period of very rapid ejection followed by a slower return to zero flow.

a large orifice between the aorta and the ventricle, the two form virtually a single chamber; pressure curves measured in the two regions follow one another closely. Blood flows rapidly from the ventricle into the aorta. During this period of maximal ejection, the ventricular volume decreases sharply. Since the original description of the events of the cardiac cycle by Wiggers and co-workers, aortic flow records have been made in a number of laboratories. It appears from these records, as particularly well described by Spencer, that the ventricular volume curve recorded with a cardiometer (Fig. 4) does not accurately represent ejection (or flow). In the original figures the peak of ventricular and aortic pressure was believed to indicate the end of rapid ejection. Flow was apparently assumed to reach its maximal velocity as pressure reached its peak. Newer evidence from aortic flowmeters shows that flow reaches its peak velocity in about 0.10 second, whereas pressure reaches its maximum in about 0.18 second. The flow curve is very asymmetrical, with rapid initial ejection followed by a slower return to zero. By the time pressure reaches its peak, flow may have declined to two-thirds or one-half of its maximal value. Atrial pressure even falls below venous pressure, and the atria begin filling at this time. At the end of the period of maximal ejection, the beginning of ventricular repolarization is signaled by the onset of the T wave.

As indicated, the period of increasing rate of flow (i.e., positively accelerating flow) is short. Although flow from ventricle to aorta continues, the velocity decreases. Rate of change of velocity is negative. Spencer has pointed out that, while the flow velocity is decreasing, the aortic pressure is slightly *higher* than the ventricular pressure.[12] On the average, ventricular pressure exceeds aortic pressure only during the initial 45 per cent of the ejection phase. The simple "ohmic" equation, relating pressure to flow and resistance, is $\Delta P = \dot{Q}R$, where Q indicates volume and $\dot{Q}$ is the instantaneous rate of flow. All pressure drops in this relationship are frictional. For a more exact description, an additional term is required involving the inertiance (L) of the blood:

$$\Delta P = \dot{Q}R + (\rho l/A)(d\dot{Q}/dt)$$

The term $(\rho l/A)$ is the inertiance, L; in this term, ρ is the density of the blood, A the area of the segment, and l its length; $d\dot{Q}/dt$ is the instantaneous rate of change of flow.

Using Spencer's data (Fig. 4), let us assume no $\dot{Q}R$ pressure fall: after reaching its peak, the flow rate falls from about 9000 cm.[3] per second to zero in about 0.25 second. The acceleration (negative) is thus $-36,000/60 = -600$ cm.[3] per second per second. If we assume an area of 4.0 cm.[2] and a density of 1, with l = 4 cm., the inertiance term has the value of $\dfrac{1 \times 4 \times 600}{4} =$ -600 dynes per cm.[2] $= 600/980$ cm. $H_2O =$ about -0.5 mm. Hg. Aortic pressure thus can exceed ventricular pressure by about 0.5 mm. Hg. Spencer's measurements indicate that an inertiance term is present but not large during aortic ejection. If l is increased (i.e., if pressure differences are recorded over longer distances), the amount by which aortic pressure exceeds ventricular pressure will be higher.

DECREASED EJECTION. Following the initial period of rapid ejection, the rate of outflow from the ventricle decreases markedly and there is a period of reduced ejection. The ventricular volume curve starts to level off, and then ventricular and aortic pressures begin to fall. Decreased ejection results because the fibers have reached a shorter length, are contracting isotonically, and can no longer contract forcefully. The ventricles appear to exert their maximal effort during the initial phase of ejection. It is also possible that there is some influence of the end of depolarization. The venous pressure continues to be greater than atrial pressure; the atria continue to fill. Electrically this period is marked by the major deflection of the T wave; i.e., ventricular repolarization becomes complete.

Phase of Isometric (Isovolumetric) Relaxation (Fig. 5). When the ventricular ejection per unit time falls to zero, the left ventricular pressure falls below the pressures in the aorta and pulmonary artery. The aortic and pulmonary artery valves therefore close. The ventricular pressure continues to fall rapidly as the ventricles relax. The A-V valves remain closed while the ventricular pressure exceeds atrial pressure. This is the period of isometric relaxation. Because the valves at both ends of the ventricles are closed, the amount of fluid contained in the ventricles obviously cannot change except for small amounts of blood flowing into the right heart from coronary veins. The term "isovolumetric relaxation" seems appropriate here.

Phase of Rapid Ventricular Filling. The isometric relaxation phase ends when the ventricular pressure falls below pressure in the atria; the A-V valves then open, and a phase of rapid ventricular filling begins. It should be noted that, during all of this period, flow of blood from the aorta to the peripheral arteries continues and the aortic pressure falls slowly. It has recently been claimed that ventricular diastolic suction contributes to the ventricular filling.[1] Apparently the ventricle is able to do work filling itself with blood, i.e., the fact that the ventricle is empty but relaxed makes the atrioventricular pressure difference greater than the difference between the atrial and intrathoracic pressures. If "suction" is important in the normal heart, it is during this period of rapid filling.

The phase of rapid inflow is followed by a variable phase of diastasis during which filling is much less rapid. Filling is limited, too, because the ventricle has come close to a maximum diastolic size, which, for a given cycle length is determined by the atrial pressure (although it may be changed by nervous, hormonal and other factors). This period of diastasis ends the cycle and is terminated by atrial systole, which begins the next cycle. The durations of the various phases in seconds, taken from Wiggers, are as follows:[14]

	MAN	DOG
Isometric contraction	.05	.05
Maximum ejection	.09	.12
Reduced ejection	.13	.10
Total systole	.27	.27
Protodiastole*	.04	.02
Isometric relaxation	.08	.05
Rapid inflow	.11	.06
Diastasis	.19	.29
Atrial systole	.11	.11
Total diastole	.53	.53

* The protodiastolic period, which has not been discussed, is the period after the ventricles cease to eject and before the aortic valves close. It is here included in the period of isometric relaxation.

Pressure changes in the human heart have been recorded during cardiac surgery.[2] In gen-

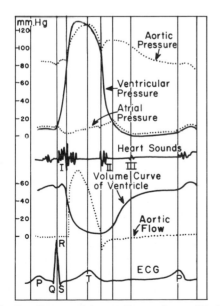

Fig. 5. Events of the cardiac cycle modified from Figure 3 to show (1) actual relationship between aortic and ventricular pressures and (2) aortic flow velocity.

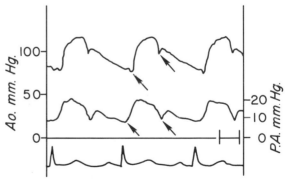

Fig. 6. Aortic (upper curve) and pulmonary arterial (lower curve) pressures in the human. Electrocardiogram below. Comparison of first arrows on upper and lower curves shows that pulmonary pressure rises first and that pulmonary valves open before aortic valves. Second arrows indicate valve closure, which is later on the right. (After Braunwald *et al., Circulation Res.,* 1956, *4:*100–107.)

eral the results are similar to those previously described. Right atrial contraction precedes left atrial contraction by about 20 milliseconds. Right ventricular ejection also begins slightly earlier than does ejection from the left (Fig. 6). Further, mitral valve closure follows tricuspid closure and the pulmonic valves open before and close after the aortic valves. In general, therefore, when the two ventricles have equal output, there will be a higher mean flow rate on the left (Mean Rate × Time = Stroke Output, which is the same on both sides).

HEART SOUNDS

The mechanical events that take place during the cardiac cycle produce sounds which may be heard at the body surface. The sound-producing events include oscillations of the blood, movements of the heart wall and the valves, and turbulence of blood flow. These sounds may be heard by placing the ear on the chest wall or by using a stethoscope, or they may be recorded by placing a microphone against the chest wall and connecting it to a proper recording system. The various sounds are heard with differing intensities at various locations on the body surface. In certain experimental procedures, microphones or catheters connected to microphones have been placed within the chambers of the heart.

We shall first consider the mechanism of production of each of the sounds and its relationship to the events of the cardiac cycle. We shall also consider the location on the body surface at which each sound may be heard most clearly and the effects on the perceived vibrations of the type of instrument used to listen to them. For further details, the reviews of McKusick[8] and Lewis[6] should be consulted.

Causes of Specific Heart Sounds. From the graph of the events of the cardiac cycle, it is obvious that during diastole blood is flowing smoothly from the atrium into the ventricle and from the aorta into the peripheral vascular beds. This smooth flow of blood produces no audible vibrations.

FIRST HEART SOUND. The first heart sound occurs at the termination of atrial contraction and the onset of contractions of the ventricles. Before ventricular contraction, the A-V valves (mitral and tricuspid) are open and, as ventricular pressure rises, blood moves toward the atrium. As indicated above, the contraction of the atria may also move blood into the ventricle and may play a part in initial (or tricuspid?) valve closure. The atria may thus contribute to this source. As a result of this movement, the atrioventricular valves close. The initial movement of the blood, the closure of the valves, and the resulting abrupt cessation of movement of blood into the atrium produce sounds which are part of the *physiologic first sound*. It is probable that vibration of the taut valves and of the atrial and ventricular walls contribute to this sound.

Valve closure is generally considered the major contributor to the first sound;[5] however, the continued increase in ventricular pressure moves blood within the great vessels, and the distention of these vessels by the increased pressure may produce vibrations which are part of the first heart sound. Thus the great vessels, the valves, the blood and the ventricular walls may all be vibrating interdependently. A further component of the first sound may result from turbulence in the flow of blood through the arteries (Chap. 27); if this component becomes clearly perceptible at the body surface, it is referred to as a *murmur*.

Although several components of the first sound have been described, it must be remembered that, with each perceived sound, several structures generally move. It would be presumptuous at this time to attempt to identify components of the perceived sound with movement of specific structures. In many normal persons, the mitral and tricuspid valves apparently close slightly asynchronously. If the asynchrony of valve closure is marked, a *split first sound* will be heard. A stethoscope especially adapted for the perception of high frequency sounds can often detect the asynchrony, or it can be accentuated with phonocardiographic recording devices.

If the P-R interval is long (0.2 second or more), and if ventricular contraction is therefore delayed, the valve leaflets will have moved close together before ventricular contraction occurs. In this case, the valves will not travel far to close, and the first sound will be unusually faint. If the P-R interval is short (25 to 75 milliseconds in the dog), valve closure will be abrupt and the first sound will be loud. If the atrial pressure on either side is abnormally high, the valve leaflets may remain widely open and then close abruptly during ventricular contraction. The first sound will be abnormally loud in this

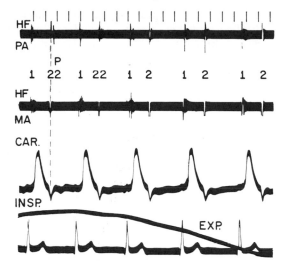

Fig. 7. Phonocardiograms correlated with carotid pulse, respiration and electrocardiogram. Phonocardiograms were obtained with a high frequency recording phonocardiograph from pulmonary (*PA*) and mitral (*MA*) areas. Below heart sounds is indirect carotid pulse recorded with a device which is sensitive to changes in pressure but not to absolute pressure. Below this are indicated the phases of respiration and conventional lead II ECG. Note that first sound is always simultaneous with upstroke of carotid pulse.

Second sound in pulmonary area has two components during inspiration but only one during expiration. During inspiration first component is synchronous with downward notch in carotid pulse. This dicrotic notch is synchronous with closure of aortic valves. Second component of second sound is perceived in pulmonary but not in mitral area and occurs after closure of aortic valves. These observations indicate that second component is of pulmonary origin. As recorded in mitral area, second sound correlates only with aortic valve closure; in pulmonary area, closure of pulmonary as well as aortic valves is indicated and resultant sounds may be fused or separate. Time intervals are 40 milliseconds. (After Leatham, *Lancet,* 1958, 2:703–708.)

case. Increase in thickness of a valve by growth of connective tissue will also increase the sound intensity.

SECOND HEART SOUND. Once the flow of blood from the ventricle into the aorta has been established and the valves are open, no sounds will be heard until the onset of the relaxation phases, unless the blood flows turbulently. When the ventricular pressure falls below the aortic (or pulmonary arterial) pressure, the tendency for backflow to occur will close the aortic and pulmonary valves. The sequence of events includes a slight backflow of blood toward the ventricles and rapid cessation of the movement

as the valves close. This recoil initiates movements of the ventricular chambers and of the stretched valve cusps. As with the first sound, various components of the perceived sound have been considered to be produced by movements of specific structures. Also, valve movement is generally considered of prime importance.[5] When highly sensitive electronic recorders are used, low frequency vibrations are seen which are considered to be produced by movements of the aortic walls and by the opening of the mitral and tricuspid valves. If the pressure in the pulmonary artery or aorta is abnormally high, the closure of the valves may be exceptionally rapid and the sounds may be very loud.

As previously stated, right ventricular systole terminates after left ventricular systole. Consequently, it is possible for the right and left ventricular components of the second sound to be separated or split. This splitting is more marked in inspiration and, usually, during right bundle branch block; it is possibly due to increased right ventricular filling. In the instance of the respiratory variation, filling is increased during inspiration because the transmural pressure is then greater. Contributions made by the left ventricle to the second sound are considered to be greater than those of the right ventricle. Figure 7 shows normal first and second sounds. Figure 8 shows relations of the sounds to aortic, ventricular and atrial pressures and also shows

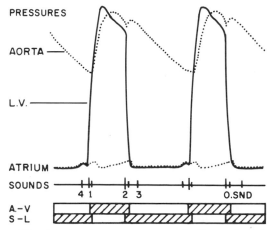

Fig. 8. Aortic pressure, ventricular and atrial pressures plotted above; sounds and valve movements below. Cross-hatched areas indicate that valves are closed. Note times when both valves are closed. (After McKusick *et al.,* Chap. 21 in *Handbook of Physiology, Section 2: Circulation,* vol. 1. Washington, D.C., American Physiological Society, 1962.)

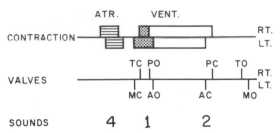

Fig. 9. Order of mechanical contraction, valve movement and sounds for right and left cardiac chambers. Isometric ventricular contraction shown by dots. Valves referred to are tricuspid (T), mitral (M), pulmonary (P) and aortic (A). Opening is shown by O, closing by C. Numbers below show sounds 4, 1 and 2. (After Braunwald *et al.*, *Circulation Res.*, 1956, *4*:100–107, and McKusick *et al.*, Chap. 21 in *Handbook of Physiology, Section 2: Circulation*, vol. 1. Washington, D.C., American Physiological Society, 1962.)

the opening and closing of atrioventricular and semilunar valves. Figure 9 shows a comparison of events in the left and right heart—atrial and ventricular contraction, tricuspid initial and aortic valve opening and closing and the sounds.

THIRD HEART SOUND. The third and fourth heart sounds are known as "diastolic" sounds, in contrast to the first and second or "systolic" sounds. Their origin is less perfectly understood. As the ventricles relax, their internal pressure drops below the pressure in the atrium. The atrioventricular valves will then open, and blood will move into the relaxed ventricular chambers. This movement has a rapid initial phase; then the period of diastasis or slow filling occurs. Movement of blood into the ventricle produces vibrations of the chamber walls at about the time that the rapid filling phase terminates.

ATRIAL SOUND; FOURTH HEART SOUND. The first mechanical event of the cardiac cycle, the contraction of the atrium, moves blood through the partially open atrioventricular valves into the well distended ventricles. This movement gives rise to a vibration of low frequency and amplitude preceding the first heart sound. These sounds possibly originate in movements of blood back and forth from atrium to ventricle and in vibrations of the atrial wall, the distended ventricular wall and the A-V valves. The third and fourth sounds are generally inaudible.

AUDIBILITY OF HEART SOUNDS. Lewis and coworkers[6] have devised a procedure for intracardiac phonocardiography in man. In the

right heart—the region which they studied —the first and third heart sounds were loudest in the right ventricle. The second sound was loudest in the pulmonary artery; the fourth was loudest in the right atrium. These results are compatible with the concepts of the origins of the sounds given above and indicate that movement of the blood within the chambers is probably necessary for transmission of the heart sounds.

When one uses a stethoscope, only two distinct sounds are normally heard. The first heart sound is of lower pitch, more booming and longer. Its frequency content is apparently between 30 and 100 cycles, whereas the second heart sound contains higher frequencies. (Remarks about the frequency of these sounds are misleading unless one specifies where and how they are recorded.) The third sound, when present, is not loud; the atrial sound is rarely heard unless some form of amplification is used. The first heart sound has a duration of between 50 and 100 milliseconds. The second sound lasts from 25 to 50 milliseconds.

The heart sounds have their maximum intensities at different locations; these depend on the site of origin of the sound and on the way in which the fluids of the body conduct the sound to the surface (Fig. 10). When valvular defects produce murmurs and turbulence, it is usually

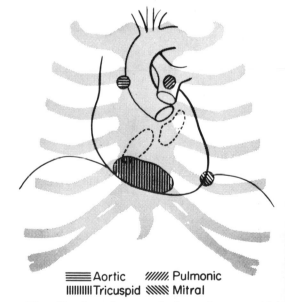

≡ Aortic   ▨ Pulmonic
‖‖‖ Tricuspid   ▧ Mitral

Fig. 10. Locations on body surface at which sounds from particular valve regions are best perceived.

possible to identify the defective valve from the location of the sound. The pulmonary valve produces sounds in the pulmonary area at the third (and second) left intercostal space in the left parasternal line. The aortic valve produces sounds which are of maximum intensity at the right of the sternum in the second right intercostal space. The sounds of the tricuspid valve are loudest at the right sternal border in the fourth intercostal space; those from the mitral valve are heard best near the apex of the heart. It should be noted that the sounds from the pulmonary and tricuspid valves tend to be of maximal amplitude near the underlying valvular positions. However, the sounds from the aortic and mitral valves are not heard best over the valve rings, probably because the sounds are transmitted more successfully through a liquid medium than directly through the lungs. That the first and second sounds are generally audible in all four valvular areas indicates that valvular vibrations alone are not important in sound production. The physician usually moves his stethoscope from one area to another, noting where the sounds are loudest and picking out components from each valve in seeking to assess the sound.

Characteristics of Systems Used in Detecting the Heart Sounds. Sound involves a wavelike motion in which energy is imparted from particle to particle in a homogeneous or inhomogeneous medium without any net movement of the medium. Within the thorax, this medium of transmission is liquid or, in the case of the lungs, liquid and air. When sound reaches the body surface, it causes that surface to move, and this movement may be perceived by the physician placing his ear directly in contact with the thorax. In such a situation, he will perceive the sound through the gas, solids and liquid of his outer, middle and inner ear. The sensation which he receives may not at all represent the actual events at the surface of the thorax because, as will be recalled from our study of the audibility curve, the auditory system cannot perceive sounds below 20 cycles per second. Even where it can perceive low-frequency sounds, the auditory system is not linear—i.e., the perceived intensity of sound at different frequencies is not proportional to the actual intensity of the vibrations (Chap. 18). Heart sounds are generally between 20 and 200 cycles per second. In this range, low frequency sounds are

minimized by the nonlinearity of the ear. The stethoscope is commonly employed as a convenience in listening to heart sounds; it does not amplify sound but actually distorts it, changing its characteristics and generally accentuating the nonlinearity of the auditory system. In this respect, it is important that various types of stethoscope have different effects on sounds and that for certain purposes one type may be better than another. For example, a stethoscope of the diaphragm type selectively attenuates the low frequencies, whereas the bell type attenuates the high frequencies.

PHONOCARDIOGRAPHY. Phonocardiography is the technique of directly recording the heart sounds so that a visual record is obtained. Such records supplement auscultation, i.e., the use of the stethoscope to hear the heart sounds. The technique has not been widely accepted. A large number of variations on the basic technique have been described. The major problem with respect to phonocardiography concerns the differences between behavior of the ear and the responses of the conventional microphones, amplifiers and recorders—both optical and direct—which have been used. As mentioned above, the perception by the ear of vibrations in the audible range (20 to 1500 cycles) is nonlinear. To date, the microphones available for phonocardiography have been either linear in their response or nonlinear in a manner different from the nonlinearity of the ear. The physician who wishes to see a phonocardiogram which accurately represents the perception of the sound will be disappointed if the phonocardiographic system is one which faithfully reproduces the sounds. Since identification of strange sound patterns and their correlation with diagnostically valuable patterns obtained by auscultation are difficult, attempts have been made to modify the responses of electronic systems to duplicate the auditory responses. A discussion of such techniques can be found in McKusick, et al.[8]

Abnormalities. SPLITTING OF HEART SOUNDS. In a number of circumstances a dissociation of the component vibrations of a sound takes place, dividing it into separate parts, each of which is heard or recorded as a separate entity. As far as the first sound is concerned, this may be a purely physiologic event, and frequently can be recorded as an exaggerated separation of the two major components, the isometric

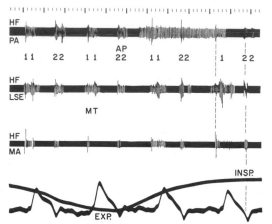

Fig. 11. Splitting of first and second sounds sometimes occurs in complete right bundle branch block. Closure of tricuspid valve (*T*) [seen in second record taken at left sternal edge (*LSE*)] and of pulmonary valve (*P*) (seen in upper record from pulmonary region) are both delayed, although mitral and aortic valve closures, indicated by *M* and *A*, are at approximately the normal time. Delayed tricuspid component of first sound at lower left sternal edge is not altered by respiration, but splitting of second sound in record from pulmonary area is greater during inspiration, because closure of pulmonary valve is delayed owing to increased filling during inspiration. First component of split second sound is synchronous with dicrotic notch in carotid tracing (there is some delay in carotid recording system). Pulmonary nature of second component is indicated by its great intensity at pulmonary area. (From Leatham, *Pediat. Clin. N. Amer.*, 1958, pp. 839–870.)

phase and the ejection phase components; this may often occur at the end of expiration (Fig. 7).

Splitting of the second sound proceeds from an entirely different cause, namely, asynchronous closure of the aortic and pulmonary valves, so that the sound is, in fact, reduplicated. The phenomenon occurs occasionally in normal subjects, but is understandably more frequent during right bundle branch block when the interval between right and left ventricular contraction is abnormally prolonged (Fig. 11). The second sound associated with some ventricular extrasystole (i.e., beats which originate in abnormal sites and during which more time than normal is required for ventricular depolarization) may also be split for the same reason. In left bundle branch block the natural asynchrony may be masked.

OPENING SNAP OF MITRAL VALVES. In mitral stenosis (pathologic narrowing of the mitral ori-

fice) a third sound is heard, and, when it is recorded phonocardiographically, it is found to be coincident in time with the opening of the A-V valves. It represents an abnormal intensification of a component of the normal second heart sound, which, because of attenuation in the stethoscope-ear combination is not normally heard (Fig. 12).

GALLOP RHYTHMS. When a loud third sound is heard in a rapidly beating heart, the resulting triple rhythm has a cadence resembling the sound of a galloping horse. The loud third sound can be shown phonocardiographically to represent (i) an intensified third sound (rapid filling gallop), (ii) an intensified atrial sound (presystolic or atrial gallop), or (iii) a combination of the third heart sound and the atrial sound, when the rapid filling phase and atrial systole occur more or less simultaneously (summation gallop). Such gallop rhythms are heard most frequently in cases of serious cardiac disease, and it is presumed that the abnormal intensification of the third or the atrial sound is related in some way to an altered ventricular response to rapid filling or atrial systole. A systolic gallop may occasionally be heard when there is marked splitting of the first heart sound.

MURMURS. When fluid flows slowly through a smooth tube of uniform diameter, no sound may be heard through a stethoscope placed on the tube. If, however, the velocity of flow is greatly increased or the viscosity of the fluid reduced, flow is no longer smooth but becomes turbulent; i.e., eddy currents are set up, and these produce vibrations which may be audible. The velocity at which turbulence begins is greatly diminished by annular expansions or

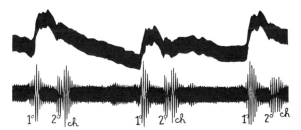

Fig. 12. Opening snap of mitral valve in mitral stenosis. Snap (*ch*) represents an increase to an audible stage of vibrations normally present but inaudible. *Above:* Central arterial pulse. *Below:* Phonocardiogram. (From Orias and Braun-Menéndez, *The heart sounds in normal and pathological conditions,* 1st ed. London, Oxford University Press, 1939.)

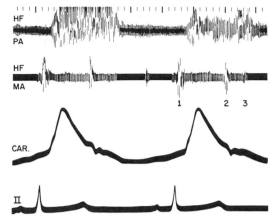

Fig. 13. In patent ductus arteriosus blood flows continuously from the high pressure aorta to the low pressure pulmonary artery. Resultant murmur is loud, often increases in intensity late in systole, and differs in its characteristics from murmurs which result from regurgitation. (From Leatham, *Pediat. Clin. N. Amer.,* 1958, pp. 839–870.)

constrictions of the tube or inequalities of its surface. These factors therefore favor the development of murmurs.

In the normal heart with altered diameters at the orifices and the presence of valves as impediments to streamlined flow, the critical velocities for turbulent flow are not quite attained in average circumstances. In strenuous muscular exercise and in other conditions in which cardiac output is increased and the velocity of flow augmented, systolic murmurs may appear in normal hearts. Increased velocity of blood flow during the ejection phase, with resulting turbulence, is probably also responsible for the systolic murmurs that may appear in anemia and in thyrotoxicosis. The murmurs of a patent ductus arteriosus (Fig. 13), the hum over arteriovenous aneurysms, the Korotkow sounds (sounds heard during auscultatory determination of blood pressure) and Duroziez' sign (systolic and diastolic murmurs heard over the femoral artery in aortic incompetence and modified by the degree of pressure exerted by the stethoscope) are other examples of sounds produced by turbulence at constrictions in smooth tubes.

Abnormal narrowing of an orifice such as occurs in mitral or aortic stenosis will both increase flow velocity and lower the velocity at which turbulence occurs. These effects account in the main for the murmurs heard in these con-

ditions, although the roughening of the walls of the orifice by scarring and partial destruction of the valves undoubtedly also contribute in some measure. In mitral stenosis the murmurs will be diastolic, occupying typically the periods of rapid filling and atrial systole, although the murmur may be continuous throughout diastole owing to overlapping of the two phases. The typical murmur of aortic stenosis occurs in systole during the phase of ejection.

It is understandable that in the presence of valvular incompetence in addition to stenosis, murmurs may be heard during systole in mitral valvular disease and during diastole in aortic valvular disease, due in part to the regurgitation of blood through the narrow orifice (Fig. 14). Another mechanism may also contribute to the murmur heard in these circumstances; the regurgitated column of blood may set up vibrations in structures upon which it may impinge and thus produce sounds not related to turbulent flow. In mitral incompetence, the atrium itself may be set in vibration by the blood forced back during ventricular systole, causing a "collision" murmur; the regurgitation of blood against the anterior mitral valve leaflet in aortic

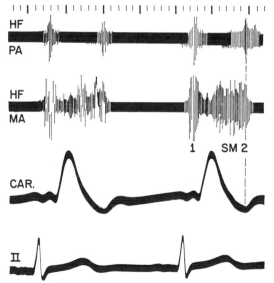

Fig. 14. Heart sounds in a mild case of mitral regurgitation. The murmur, as seen in mitral area, extends throughout systole, although its intensity diminishes during rising phase of carotid pulse. Note relative absence of this murmur in pulmonary region and tendency for murmur to blend with and virtually obscure second sound. (From Leatham, *Pediat. Clin. N. Amer.,* 1958, pp. 839–870.)

incompetence is thought to give rise to the pre-systolic murmur of "relative" mitral stenosis, the "Austin Flint murmur."

Abnormal heart sounds will be discussed more fully in Chapter 37.

REFERENCES

1. BLOOM, W. L. and FERRIS, E. B. *Proc. Soc. exp. Biol.* (*N.Y.*), 1956, *98:*451–454.
2. BRAUNWALD, E., FISHMAN, A. P. and COURNAND, A. *Circulation Res.,* 1956, *4:*100–107.
3. BROCKMAN, S. K. *Amer. J. Physiol.,* 1963, *204:*597–603.
4. KEITH, A. and FLACK, M. *J. Anat.* (*Lond.*), 1907, *41:*172–189.
5. LEATHAM, A. *Lancet,* 1958, *2:*703–708, 757–766.
6. LEWIS, D. H. Chap. 22 in *Handbook of Physiology, Section 2: Circulation,* vol. 1, P. Dow and W. F. Hamilton, eds., Washington, D. C., American Physiological Society, 1962.
7. LEWIS, T. *The mechanism and graphic registration of the heart beat,* 3rd ed., London, Shaw and Sons, Ltd., 1925.
8. McKUSICK, V. A., TALBOT, S. A., WEBB, G. N. and BATTERSBY, E. J. Chap. 21 in *Handbook of Physiology, Section 2: Circulation,* vol. 1, P. Dow and W. F. Hamilton, eds., Washington, D. C., American Physiological Society, 1962.
9. ROBB, J. S. *Med. Wom. J.,* 1934, *41:*143–152.
10. RUSHMER, R. F. *Amer. J. Physiol.,* 1956, *184:*188–194.
11. RUSHMER, R. F. *Cardiac diagnosis,* Philadelphia, W. B. Saunders Co., 1955.
12. SPENCER, M. P. and GREISS, F. C. *Circulation Res.,* 1962, *10:*274–279.
13. WEIDMANN, S. *Electrophysiologie der Herzmuskelfaser,* Bern, Hans Huber, 1956.
14. WIGGERS, C. J. *Circulatory dynamics,* New York, Grune and Stratton, 1952.

CHAPTER 30

Electrical Correlates of the Cardiac Cycle

By ALLEN M. SCHER

INTRODUCTION

At about the turn of the twentieth century Willem Einthoven,[16, 17] a Dutch physician, designed and constructed a galvanometer which made it possible routinely to record voltages produced at the body surface by electrical activity of the heart. A record of these voltage changes in time is referred to as an electrocardiogram. From Einthoven's time until the late 1940's, electrocardiography developed as a useful, but at times empirical, clinical tool; the gross relationships between the electrocardiogram and the electrical activity of the heart were elucidated, and some foundations of scientific electrocardiography were established by Lewis and co-workers[26, 27, 28] in England and by Wilson and co-workers[56, 57, 58] in the United States, among others. Over the years, recording techniques also improved. Einthoven's original galvanometer, which required photographic processing of records, was ultimately replaced by recording systems that could produce records instantaneously. Although not always as rapid in frequency response as the photographic galvanometer, these devices proved to be excellent for electrocardiographic recording.

P, QRS, T. The normal electrocardiogram

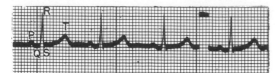

Fig. 1. Normal lead II electrocardiogram. Initial, low, rounded deflection about 1 mm. high and 2 mm. long is the P wave. Second deflection, about 1 mm. wide and 10 mm. high shows a rapid rise and fall and is called the QRS complex. Third, peaked deflection, about 3.5 mm. high and 6 mm. long is the T wave. Here sequence is repeated three times. Standardization at right, 1 mV. Small black vertical lines are 40 milliseconds apart; larger lines (five spaces) are 200 milliseconds apart; heaviest lines are 1 second apart. (From Winsor, ed., *Electrocardiographic test book.* New York, American Heart Association, 1956.)

for a single heart beat consists of three main complexes which, as indicated in the last chapter, are designated the P, QRS and T waves. If electrodes are connected to the right arm and left leg of a normal adult and the difference in potential between these extremities is recorded in the fashion described later in this chapter, curves of voltage-in-time like those appearing in Figure 1 will result. The initial upright, low, rounded deflection is called the *P wave.* It results from the depolarization of atrial muscle. The second deflection, called the *QRS complex,* is produced by depolarization of the ventricular myocardium. The final deflection, the *T wave,* results from the return of the ventricular muscle to the polarized or resting state. At times, the T wave is followed by a small *U wave* which seems, like the T wave, to be produced by ventricular repolarization. These potentials result *only* from *electrical* changes within the heart.

An understanding of the shape of any electrocardiographic complex—and thus of the origin of the normal (or abnormal) electrocardiogram—depends on three types of information. (i) What electrical changes take place in single cells as they pass from the resting to the depolarized (or active) state and then return to the resting state? (ii) How do cells in a conducting medium produce potentials at recording electrodes within, or at, the boundaries of that medium? Analysis of current flow in such volume conductors should encompass conductors of the shape and conductivity of the human torso. (iii) What are successive positions of the boundary between resting and active cells during depolarization and repolarization of the

heart? This means that we must know the exact pathway of depolarization and of repolarization of the muscular mass surrounding the cardiac chambers.

Although early analysis in the fields of electricity and magnetism developed much information about the second factor (volume conduction), little was known about the first (cellular activity) and third (pathway of activity). Hence our understanding of the electrocardiographic complex was severely limited. However, during the last decade our knowledge of these two factors has substantially increased, and the outlook is now much improved for a more complete quantitative understanding of the normal (or abnormal) electrocardiogram. These advances in knowledge have resulted from studies along the following lines:

In 1946 Graham and Gerard[22] described a hollow glass ultramicroelectrode so small (about 1 μ in diameter) that it could be inserted into a single cell. Ling and Gerard[29] utilized this electrode to record the potentials in muscle cells, and this marked the beginning of a study of electrochemical events within excitable cells. The ultramicroelectrode and other techniques which permit the same type of measurement have been used to study many types of excitable cells. About 1950 a number of laboratories[14, 15, 44, 45, 49, 50] began gathering information about the sequence of excitation of the atrial and ventricular musculature. They utilized small, usually multiterminal, metal *extracellular* electrodes which were inserted into the myocardium to record the time of activity at many sites. In the early 1950's there appeared to be substantial promise of furthering our understanding of electrochemical events within the cardiac cells and of conduction within the heart, and through these two of furthering our knowledge of the origin of the electrocardiogram. Substantial progress in these areas has indeed been made between 1950 and the present.

The term "cardiac electrophysiology" has been used to describe a large area of research extending from the study of electrochemical events in single cells up to the clinical use of the electrocardiogram. Between these two extremes are several other areas of study, particularly the study of pacemaker activity, of conduction from cell to cell, of the pathway of cardiac excitation and of the action of ions and hormones on cardiac cells. In this chapter we will attempt to cover the physiology of cardiac cells, normal cardiac conduction and the origin of the normal electrocardiogram. We will then discuss some abnormalities of conduction and newer recording methods.

Electrochemical Events in Cardiac Cells. In Chapter 2 the ionic changes associated with the activity of nerve cells were considered in detail. The resting nerve was found to be electrically polarized because of the action of the "sodium pump." Positive charges are lined up against the outer cell membrane and negative charges against the inner membrane. In nerve the underlying mechanism of depolarization is a brief increase in permeability of the membrane to sodium; this change is voltage-dependent. It leads to a net influx of sodium ions which are driven into the cell by the membrane potential and by the high outside concentration of sodium. The two changes are linked, increased sodium permeability leading to a decrease in membrane potential, and a decrease in membrane potential leading to an increase in sodium permeability. During the initial rapid phase of depolarization the membrane potential approaches the sodium equilibrium potential. The increased permeability to sodium is transient, the permeability returning to near resting values in about a millisecond. The change in potential during the action potential increases the permeability to potassium ions. This, combined with the decrease in sodium permeability, tends to return the membrane potential to the resting level. In nerve these phenomena produce an action potential about 1 millisecond in duration. Cardiac muscle is obviously different, at least quantitatively, since the action potential has a much longer duration, often up to 300 milliseconds in mammalian cells (and even longer in cold-blooded animals). Unlike nerve and skeletal muscle, which repolarize almost immediately, cardiac muscle cells remain depolarized during a long "plateau" period before repolarization takes place. The Hodgkin-Huxley equations (Chap. 2), which appear to account for the action potential of the nerve, would therefore have to be modified to account for an action potential of such a long duration. Of course, the mechanisms elucidated for nerve by Hodgkin and Huxley might not be applicable to cardiac muscle, particularly during the plateau period and thereafter. That is, some mechanism other than those prevalent in nerve might operate during the terminal portion of the action potential. This possibility, which is difficult to test, has become a subject of serious disagreement among a small number of experts who are studying the electrochemical events in cardiac cells. A discussion of this question will not be included in this chapter, but the interested reader is referred to articles by Noble,[32] Woodbury[59] and Johnson.[25] At this writing, it appears that the initial phase of depolarization in ordinary myocardial cells involves mechanisms similar to those during the initial depolarization of nerve and that the events after the initial phase of depolarization are different in nerve and in cardiac muscle. During this plateau phase, the cardiac muscle membrane has a largely time-dependent (rather than voltage-dependent) permeability to potassium.[25, 59]

Cell-to-Cell Conduction in Cardiac Muscle. Since the earliest studies of cardiac muscle, it has been known that electrical or mechanical stimulation at a point within a mass of heart muscle usually leads to depolarization of the entire muscle mass. For instance, if a point in the atrium is stimulated, a wave of depolarization travels away from this point to depolarize the entire atrium. Generally, this wave passes through the atrioventricular conducting system into the ventricles. Atrioventricular conduction may, however, be impaired if the specialized conduction tissue is not functioning normally. Similarly, when a ventricular point is stimulated, a wave of depolarization passes through the entire ventricle (retrograde conduction from ventricle to atrium does not always follow stimulation within the ventricle). Conduction thus seems to be syncytial, i.e., large masses of myocardium behave like a network of interconnected fibers or like a single cell, and when a wave of depolarization is started at any place, it proceeds throughout most of the network or "cell."

Light microscopy reveals no serious anatomic objection to this network analogy, and early representations of the microscopic structure of cardiac muscle usually showed adjacent cells connected by small "bridges" of myocardium. Electron micrographs, however, reveal that the myocardium is anatomically divided into units by "cellular" membranes (Fig. 2).[48] The intercalated discs which are perpendicular to the long axes of the fibers appear to be transverse continuations of the longitudinal cell membranes. The cells thus are completely bounded by membrane and there are no bridges. These

Fig. 2. Reconstruction by Sjostrand of submicroscopic anatomy of cardiac muscle. Long narrow structures running from left to right in anterior aspect are myofibrils. Vertical and horizontal double membranes divide the mass of muscle into "units" in these planes. Cutaway section shows continuation of these vertical and horizontal membranes into the intercalated disks, the many tonguelike processes which extend from left to right. These discs form a boundary between "domains" of muscle and constitute justification for discarding the term "syncytial" insofar as anatomy is concerned. Insofar as conduction is concerned, however, the cardiac mass does seem to be syncytial or ephaptic.

findings seem to eliminate the anatomic basis for syncytial conduction. However, this apparent conflict between anatomic and physiologic findings has recently been resolved through studies by Woodbury and Crill[60] and by Deleze and Weidmann.[12] In the former, current was directed into a single cell of the right atrium of the rat through a single intracellular electrode, and the spread of this current was mapped with a second intracellular electrode. These studies revealed that the intercalated disc, although anatomically indistinguishable from the longitudinal cellular membrane, has markedly different electrical properties. The resistance of the intercalated disc is less than 5 ohm-cm.² compared with 2000 ohm-cm.² for the longitudinal membrane. This difference is such that, although the longitudinal membrane constitutes a high resistance barrier to electrical current flow, current can flow easily through the intercalated discs to adjacent cells. In a different approach, Deleze and Weidmann studied the

movement of potassium from one portion of the cardiac muscle mass to another and calculated a similar figure for intercalated disc resistance. The low resistance pathway discovered in these studies insures that current generated as a cell depolarizes will be more than sufficient to depolarize contiguous cells. It thus appears that the heart, although anatomically divided into units, is functionally a syncytium, with the obvious exceptions of the regions of specialized cells. Chapter 5 includes a discussion of cell-to-cell current flow in cardiac muscle.

Volume Conduction. As discussed in Chapter 3, the instantaneous potential produced at a point in a homogeneous and infinite volume conductor by a boundary between active and resting cells is a function of (i) the number of charges per unit area across the boundary, (ii) the solid angle subtended by the boundary at the point, and (iii) the resistivity of the medium. This is shown in the formula:

$$\mathcal{E}_p = K_1 K_2\, \Omega\, \phi$$

in which $\mathcal{E}_p$ denotes the potential at a point, K_1 is a constant for tissue resistivity, K_2 a geometric constant, Ω the solid angle subtended at the point by the boundary, and ϕ is a voltage proportional to the charge density per unit solid angle across the boundary; ϕ is normally constant and is equal to 120 mV. (overshoot minus resting potential) where the solid angle is 4π steradians.

To understand why a potential of a certain magnitude exists at a particular point on the body surface at some instant during the electrocardiogram (i.e., to apply this formula), we must know the position and geometry of the boundary at that instant, the dipole moment (number of charges multiplied by distance between poles) per unit area across the boundary, and the corrections necessary to compensate for the shape and resistivity of the torso (Fig. 3). Rush, Abildskov and McFee[39] found specific resistivity for blood and lung to be 160 ohm-cm. and 2000 ohm-cm. respectively. Heart muscle averaged 400 ohm-cm. but is anisotropic, i.e., resistance has one value along one axis of the tissue and another in a perpendicular direction. These measurements indicate that tissue resistance will have to be taken into account when a quantitative model of the electrocardiogram is developed.

A cell or aggregation of cells in the resting

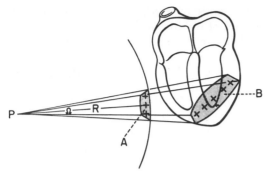

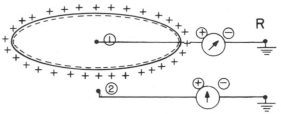

Fig. 3. Hypothetical boundary between active and resting muscle within heart. Potential at point *P* is a function of the dipole moment per unit area across this boundary and of the solid angle subtended at *P* by the boundary. *A* is the projection of *B* on sphere of radius *R*. Solid angle is A/R. *B* is boundary between resting and active tissue.

Fig. 4. The resting cell is polarized; i.e., there are charges distributed evenly around its membrane, negative charges on the inside and positive charges on the outside. If we record the potential between electrode *1*, inside the cell, and an external ground reference electrode at *R*, the potential inside will be negative. However, an electrode outside the cell, as at *2*, is equally influenced by the positive and negative charges from the resting cell and therefore records no potential.

state or otherwise uniformly polarized or depolarized can give rise to no potential at an external recording electrode (Fig. 4). This is also shown by Figure 17 in Chapter 3. But if a cell is partially depolarized, an electrode which faces the *resting* portion of the cell will record a positive potential (Fig. 17 in Chap. 3) This would occur (Fig. 18 in Chap. 3) if a wave of depolarization were moving from left to right or if the cell were repolarizing from right to left (Fig. 4).

An alternative to the "solid angle" analysis of potentials in a volume conductor is to consider an active cell or aggregation of cells as a "dipole." A dipole consists of equal numbers of positive and negative charges separated by an infinitesimal distance. The potential at a point in an infinite homogeneous medium produced by such a dipole is proportional to the dipole moment (number of charges per pole multiplied by the distance between the poles), and to the cosine of the angle between the recording point and midpoint of the line joining the two poles, and inversely proportional to the square of the distance between the recording point and the dipole:

$$\varepsilon = \frac{m \cos \theta}{r^2}.$$

In practice, the dipole concept is applied semiquantitatively or qualitatively. An aggregation of charges such as a boundary in the heart is approximated by a single arrow with its head pointing in the direction of the positive charges. The boundary between resting and active cells is thus approximated by a single arrow (Fig. 5).

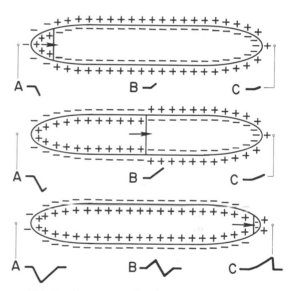

Fig. 5. As a wave of activity moves from the left-hand side to the right-hand side of the cell, as shown, the potentials recorded at *A*, *B*, and *C* are as indicated. Note that initially the electrode at *A* views the negative side of the depolarized section on the left-hand side of the cell and also views the negative (inside) portion of the resting portion of the cell (on the right). This process continues, so that *A* records only a negative potential as the cell goes from the resting to the depolarized state. The electrode at *B* is initially closest to the positive charges across the resting portion of the membrane at the right and to the positive charges across the depolarized portion of the membrane at the left. It thus records an initial positive potential. However, when the electrode passes it, it records a negative potential. The electrode at *C* at the right-hand side of the cell records only positive (approaching) activity as the cell depolarizes.

If such an arrow is drawn for an instant during the period of depolarization, the head will point in the direction of the movement of the wave front. In some recent electrocardiographic techniques, the entire heart has been considered as a single dipolar generator. These techniques will be considered later in this chapter.

Anatomic Features. We shall here consider the specialized tissues of the heart and the configurations of the atria and ventricles. The specialized tissue of the heart consists of the sinus node and the atrioventricular conduction system. The sinus node, as indicated previously (Chap. 29), lies at the junction of the superior vena cava with the right atrium and is the site of origin of impulses within the heart. The atrioventricular conduction system, which conveys impulses from the atria to the ventricles, is composed of the AV node, the common bundle and the right and left bundles. The AV node lies in the interatrial septum just above the tricuspid valve. It gives rise to the common bundle, which passes into the basal interventricular septum, giving rise to the right and left bundles. These course along the septum toward the apex, the right bundle as a single strand, the left usually dividing into two or more strands. The bundles terminate in the middle regions of the septum and give rise to numerous strands of Purkinje tissue that cover much of the ventricular endocardium in the dog and man and penetrate widely into the ventricular myocardial mass in ungulates. (Purkinje fibers can be observed grossly in the ungulates and less clearly in dog and man.) There is still some disagreement regarding the extent to which Purkinje fibers penetrate the canine or human myocardium.[15] The sinus node and each of the constituents of the atrioventricular conduction system differ somewhat in their histologic appearance from the cells of the ordinary atrial and ventricular myocardium.[54]

The atrial walls can be considered as two triangular sections of a sphere, curved to join superiorly to the interatrial septum and superiorly, posteriorly and anteriorly to each other. Inferiorly, the walls and septum join the fibrous ring to which are attached the corresponding ventricular structures.

The following structural details are important in considering ventricular electrical activity (see also Chap. 29): (i) The right bundle merges with the ventricular musculature near the right anterior papillary muscle, where it divides to send strands of Purkinje fibers to the endocardium of the free wall from this location. (ii) The left bundle usually splits into anterior and posterior divisions, which run, respectively, toward the anterior and posterior papillary muscles on the left and give rise to numerous false tendons (Purkinje strands) that cross the left cavity and merge with ordinary myocardium near the endocardium. (iii) The right wall is normally thin, generally no more than 3 or 4 mm. thick; the left wall is up to 15 mm. thick. (In infants the two ventricular walls are about equally thick.) (iv) The endocardial Purkinje network is more widespread in the central and apical portions of the wall and septum bilaterally. This network is sparse or nonexistent in the basal septum.

EXCITATION OF THE HEART

The direct knowledge of the pathway of cardiac excitation has been obtained primarily from animal experiments, mostly on dogs. Although the various components of the canine electrocardiogram last about one-half as long as do those of the human cycle, results obtained in dogs are considered applicable to man. This extrapolation can be justified by several facts: (i) Human and canine hearts are anatomically similar, both grossly and histologically. (ii) Electrocardiograms of similar shape can be recorded from both hearts.[50, 56] (iii) Electrocardiographic abnormalities in humans affect the electrocardiographic complexes in a fashion which is in accord with plots of excitation in animals.[1, 5, 24] A small amount of direct evidence indicates that the pathways of excitation are similar.[50, 56]

The Cardiac Pacemaker; Excitation of Atrium. As indicated previously (Chaps. 5 and 29), one property of cardiac tissue is automaticity—the ability to beat rhythmically without external stimuli. The cells with the most rapid inherent rhythm are called "pacemaker cells." In cold-blooded animals, pacemaker activity seems to be possible for all parts of the heart, but in intact warm-blooded animals, pacemaker activity is normally confined to the S-A node and the AV node (Fig. 6). Other parts of the Purkinje system may normally generate impulses, but whether this is always true of mammalian tissue is not certain. However, it is clear that with even minor departures from normal physiology, extrasystolic (i.e., abnormal) beats may originate at both atrial and ventricular sites. The pacemaker with the highest inherent rhythm dominates the heart rate, and impulses conducted from it depolarize slower pacemakers faster than they can generate impulses. Normally, the dominant pacemaker is the S-A node. The AV node is the pacemaker with the second highest inherent rate; if the S-A node fails or is abnormally slowed, the AV node usually determines the heart rate.

The process by which the S-A and AV nodes generate impulses is not entirely clear. According to Trautwein and Kassebaum,[53] these cells differ from ordinary myocardium in being more permeable to sodium when at rest. Because of a decrease in potassium conductance, the pacemaker cells gradually depolarize to threshold at the end of each cycle.

Electrical activity in the atrium commences in the S-A node and spreads in a pattern like that produced by dropping a stone into still water. The elliptical shape of the area of initial depolarization probably results from nearly simultaneous pacemaker activity at many points in the S-A node. Plots of atrial excitation by Lewis and co-workers,[27] by Puech,[37] and by Paes de Carvalho and co-workers[34] agree closely (Figs. 7 and 8). From the region of the S-A node the wave of atrial depolarization proceeds at a velocity of slightly less than 1 meter per second toward the borders of the two atria and of the interatrial septum. The right atrium, being nearer the sinus node, is normally excited before the left. No specialized pathway for atrial excitation has been discovered to date, although

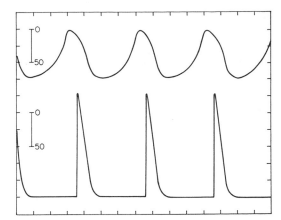

Fig. 6. *Upper trace,* Potentials recorded by ultramicroelectrode in the pacemaker region. *Lower trace,* Potentials recorded by second ultramicroelectrode in normal atrial tissue. Note diastolic prepotential of smaller amplitude in record from pacemaker; also, notice differences in shapes of potentials in rabbit. (After West *et al., J. Pharmacol.,* 1956, *117*:245–252.)

some evidence has been presented for an atrial conduction system.[50] If we consider the shape of the atrium and its position in the body, we may think of normal atrial excitation as consisting of three divergent waves moving inferiorly from the S-A node toward the atrial borders. Initially the direction of activity is to the right and anteriorly; later activity is directed leftward and posteriorly.

Passage of the Impulse through the AV Node. The period from the beginning of the P wave to the beginning of the QRS complex is referred to as the P-R interval. It usually has a duration of 0.12 to 0.2 second (average 0.16 second) in man and 0.08 second in the dog. The

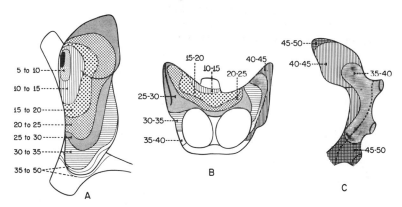

Fig. 7. Pathway and mode of atrial activation. *A,* Right atrium and right atrial appendage viewed from right. Activity begins in sinus node (*black*) and progresses toward borders of atrium. *B,* Activation of atria viewed from anterior aspect. *C,* Activation of left atrium and appendage. Shading shows areas activated within each 5 millisecond period. Duration of P wave was 50 milliseconds. (After Puech. *L'activité électrique auriculaire.* Paris, Masson et Cie, 1916.)

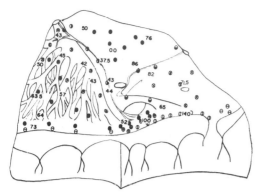

Fig. 8. A view from the interior of the rabbit's right atrium. Trabeculated area is at the left. Numbers indicate the instant of activity in milliseconds after depolarization of the sinus node. Note that activity spreads approximately radially from the sinus node, which is in the upper central region of the figure. The shapes of action potentials recorded are indicated by the various symbols in the figure. Note the region of the common bundle along the atrioventricular margin on the right (circle with vertical line). Immediately upstream from this (circle with cross) are cells from an intermediate region along the AV conduction pathway, which the experimenters termed nodobundle cells. Above these (black circle with horizontal white line) are cells which the researchers considered to be the first link in the AV transmission system and which they termed atrial-nodal cells. Note further that these atrial-nodal cells extend from the trabecular region into the AV nodal region. (From Paes de Carvalho, De Mello and Hoffman, *Amer. J. Physiol.*, 1959, *196*:483.)

potentials generated by the AV node and the Purkinje fibers are far too small to influence electrodes at the body surface or to be recorded by extracellular electrodes that are farther than a few millimeters from these tissues. Recently, however, it has become possible to record potentials from the cells in and near the AV node with both intracellular and extracellular electrodes.

The atrial musculature in the region near the AV node is depolarized when atrial depolarization is about two-thirds complete (Fig. 8). Records made with intracellular electrodes by Cranefield and Hoffman[10] indicate that a large part of the time between atrial firing and firing of the common bundle is consumed while the electrical wave passes through cells in the AV nodal region. The cells in this region differ in electrical characteristics from either atrial or bundle cells, resembling instead cells of the sinus node (Fig. 9). AV nodal cells have a diastolic prepotential, a slower rate of initial

depolarization than other cardiac cells and a smaller action potential. Recently, Paes de Carvalho and Langan[33] have further shown that these cells may be chemically different from ordinary myocardial cells.

An extracellular electrode in the AV nodal region of a dog[44] records no clear potentials for 5 to 15 milliseconds after the depolarization of the SA node (Fig. 10). Then in unipolar records the upper AV node displays a negative-going potential which develops slowly (over 10 to 15 milliseconds), remains at its maximal negative value for some time, and returns more rapidly toward zero. The potential in the center of the node is positive-negative, and that at the lower end of the node is positive and is terminated by a negative-going common bundle potential.

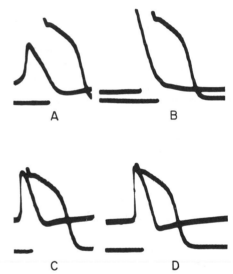

Fig. 9. Intracellular records from sinus node, atrial muscle, A-V nodal region and common bundle. For timing purposes, large potential which has lowest base line is repeated and is taken near common bundle. *A,* Smaller potential which begins earlier is from sinus nodal region. It shows a diastolic prepotential and slow rate of depolarization with lack of overshoot. *B,* Earlier potential, which has a resting potential slightly lower than that of common bundle and which depolarizes to about the same extent, is from ordinary atrial muscle. Atrial potential occurs somewhat later than potential from sinus node. *C,* Earlier potential, from upper A-V node, shows a smaller amplitude and a small diastolic prepotential after rapid repolarization. *D,* A similar potential with a diastolic prepotential is seen occurring somewhat later and closer in time to the depolarization of the common bundle. This potential is from the mid A-V node. (From Hoffman *et al., Circulation Res.,* 1959, *7*:11–18.)

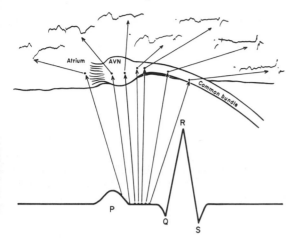

Fig. 10. Potentials recorded extracellularly at seven sites near A-V nodal and common bundle region. Potential at far left is recorded from atrial muscle upstream from A-V node. As can be seen, it occurs during downstroke of P wave. Second potential from left is from head or upper end of A-V node. It shows an atrial potential followed by a large negative-going A-V nodal potential. Third potential from left is recorded in middle of A-V node. It shows a positive-negative atrial potential followed by a rapid negative-going common bundle potential. Farther downstream, common bundle potentials show more positivity, becoming positive-negative at the far right. As can be seen, a large part of interval between end of P wave and beginning of QRS complex is occupied by events in the A-V nodal region. (From Scher *et al., Circulation Res.,* 1959, 7:54–61.)

These potentials are found only within the AV node. Their shapes are similar, but not identical, to those recorded from a propagated wave in a muscle strip (see Chap. 5), and we may conclude that conduction *within* the AV node qualitatively resembles conduction elsewhere in the heart and involves no chemical transmission like that found at the myoneural junction or at the central synapses. If the atrium is stimulated at a very rapid rate, conduction time between atrium and ventricle gradually increases, and then complete block occurs. During much of this period of prolonged conduction (first degree block), the AV nodal potential occurs later than normal (Fig. 11), but its configuration is not altered. This indicates that the block is between the atrium and the AV node, and it appears that cells immediately above the node are the most susceptible to AV block; i.e., the impulse reaches this region, but conduction is slowed or at times does not proceed into the AV node proper or into the ventricular Purkinje system.

Because of this susceptibility to incomplete and complete block, the region of the AV node can be said to have the lowest safety factor found in the atrioventricular conduction system. The region lying immediately upstream from the AV node is composed of very fine muscle fibers interspersed with connective tissue. The slow conduction velocity (0.05 meter per second) and the low safety factor here may result from some property of the muscle fibers (their small size and their particular ionic permeabilities) or from their geometric relation to the AV node or both.

Within the AV node the conduction velocity (about 0.1 meter per second) is somewhat faster

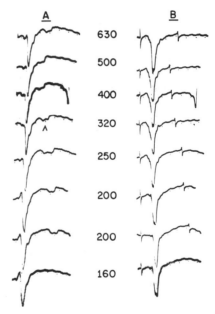

Fig. 11. Effects of changing frequency of atrial stimulation on potentials recorded from AV node and common bundle. In column A a large negative potential due to depolarization of the atria is followed by a smaller negative potential (marked by arrow in fourth record from the top), produced by electrical activity of the AV node. In column B, recorded from a different site, the atrial potential is followed by a much more rapid negative-going potential produced by the depolarization of the common bundle. As the interval between stimuli decreases progressively from 600 to 160 per second, the nodal potential at first occurs closer in time to the atrial potential, but with progressively shorter intervals, it occurs progressively later, but without changing shape, which indicates that the slowing of conduction ("block") is above the node. At an interstimulus interval of 160 milliseconds, the AV nodal potential no longer appears, and the common bundle is not depolarized (complete block). (From Scher *et al., Circulation Res.,* 1959, 7:54.)

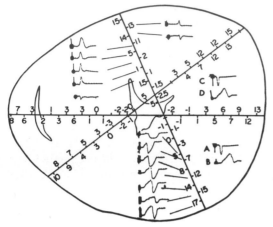

Fig. 12. Cross-section of dog's heart near its apex showing potentials recorded at various sites. Unipolar records appear below horizontal line and bipolar records above. Unipolar records near cavity show mostly a negative (downward) potential; those near surface of heart show a positive potential followed by a negative potential. Bipolar records are generally upright, indicating that wave of activity moves from inside out in posterior left wall. Instant of activity at a point is indicated by peak of bipolar record. Numbers indicate time of local activity as measured from the bipolar records.

Instant of local activity can be *approximated* by finding an inflection point in unipolar record. Such an inflection point marks time when over-all activity shifts from approaching to receding. Time reference potential *A* and electrocardiogram *B* were taken simultaneously with unipolar records; *C* and *D* were simultaneous with bipolar records. Last points to be activated in wall are near epicardium; first points near endocardium. Latest point in section shown is in center of septum along horizontal electrode. (From Scher and Young, *Circulation Res.*, 1956, 4:461–469.)

than in the region immediately above the node. Once the AV node is excited, the impulse passes to the Purkinje fibers of the common bundle and the right and left bundles, and thence to the ventricles. First-degree conduction block (slowing of conduction) *within* the node is rare and occurs during rapid stimulation only when severe block already exists in the region upstream from the node. The conduction velocity in the Purkinje fibers of the bundles is much higher, up to 2.0 meters per second, and reflects their large size. The conduction system is syncytial and responds in an all-or-none fashion to atrial activation, as demonstrated by Weidmann[55] and confirmed in studies with extracellular electrodes. Potentials recorded from the conducting bundles under all conditions always have the same configuration during forward, i.e., atrioventricular, conduction.[44]

Ventricular Activation. As in the atrium, the direct determination of ventricular excitation pathways has been limited largely to animal experiments. Ventricular activation has been plotted in detail only in the dog, although some limited studies have been conducted on the rhesus monkey and on man,[13] but much evidence suggests that data obtained from the canine heart are applicable to the human. When applied to humans, figures for the time of activity in the dog should be multiplied by about 2.5 since ventricular depolarization in the dog requires only 35 milliseconds compared to about 80 milliseconds in the human.

Some classic experiments concerning ventricular activation were performed by Lewis and Rothschild in 1915.[28] They noted that the time required for the impulse to travel from a point of stimulation on the ventricular surface to another surface point was not altered if the epicardial muscle between these points was cut. They concluded that the impulse travels slowly from the point of stimulation to the endocardium, moves rapidly over the endocardial surface, and then travels slowly from the inside to the outside at the recording point. They further deduced that the endocardial Purkinje network conducts more rapidly than mural myocardium and that the impulse normally travels outward in the wall. They calculated propagation velocities for endocardial and mural depolarization that agree well with those directly measured. Finally, they plotted the times of arrival of activation waves over the ventricular surface.

Although the pathway of excitation within the walls could not be determined from Lewis' plots, a deductive approximation of this pathway has been made.[21] Ventricular depolarization in the dog has been plotted with extracellular electrode assemblies consisting of several recording terminals along a central shaft.[15, 45, 49]

A 15-terminal electrode assembly is used in conjunction with multichannel oscilloscope recording apparatus.[45] The terminals are usually placed 1 mm. apart along a central shaft. If this electrode is inserted perpendicular to the ventricular wall, activity in the entire thickness of muscle can be recorded without moving the electrode. Two types of records are taken. In one, the potential difference is recorded between each terminal and an "indifferent" (i.e., distant) point, usually at the body surface (Fig. 12). In such a "unipolar" record, the potential is positive if the net sum of all electrical activity within the heart is approaching the recording point. If the activity is receding from that point, the potential is negative. Thus, the shapes of the potentials can indicate the movement of the boundaries between resting and active muscle. In the other type of record, termed "bipolar," the voltage difference between two adjacent terminals on the electrode is recorded. Such a record is not influenced by activity at a distance, but accurately indicates the instant of activity between the two terminals (Fig. 13). The multichannel recording technique makes it possible to determine the time of activity at many points—as many as 900 in a single experiment—by inserting a large number of electrodes at different locations in the ventricles. The time of activity is determined with reference to some fixed point in the ventricles, and it is then possible to construct a map which indicates in three dimensions the pathway followed by the wave of depolarization (Fig. 14).

The spread of activity in a coronal section of a dog heart illustrates some salient features of the process. Although the section shown in Figure 13 did not contain the first and last points activated in the ventricles, it can be seen that the general direction of excitation in the right and left walls is from within out. It can also be seen that the process is not entirely uniform; the direction of activation may reverse, particularly in the regions near the endocardium and under the papillary muscles and trabeculations. The major portion of the septum is excited by waves

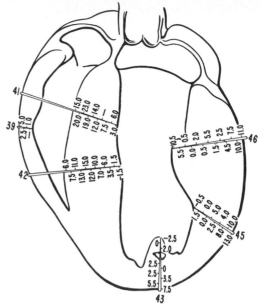

Fig. 13. Coronal section of dog's heart showing time of activation at many points along six electrodes. In wall, activity generally moves from inside out. There are, however, several reversals of directions. Under papillary muscle along electrode 46, wave of activity moved toward endocardium and toward epicardium. Septum is excited by waves moving centrally from both septal surfaces. Latest points activated are in middle of basal septum.

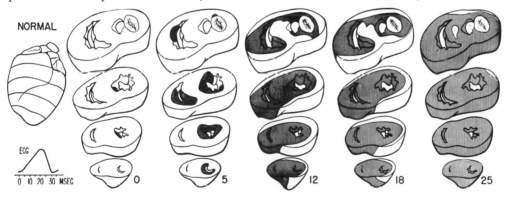

Fig. 14. Pathway of normal ventricular excitation in dog as discerned by noting extent of depolarization at 0, 5, 12, 18 and 25 milliseconds after beginning of QRS complex. Small drawing of heart indicates positions of planes in which records were taken. Lead II electrocardiogram is labeled to indicate total duration of electrical activity.

At 0 millisecond, small amount of muscle bordering left cavity is active. Apparently this volume of muscle is too small to give a deflection in peripheral electrocardiogram at this amplification. At 5 milliseconds after beginning of QRS, an incomplete and irregular cone of activity surrounds left cavity, mostly on septal aspect, and a smaller cone surrounds right cavity. By 12 milliseconds after beginning of QRS, these two cones have united in lower three sections and have joined slightly in upper section. Heart now contains a cone of depolarized muscle within an incomplete cone of muscle which is still in resting state. Notice breakthrough of electrical activity anteriorly on right. This leaves activity in posterior and leftward portion of ventricles unopposed. This pattern of excitation continues during next 6 milliseconds. Picture at 18 milliseconds is generally unchanged, although amount of muscle depolarized is, of course, larger; fraction of posterior and left portions in resting state has become smaller. At 25 milliseconds after beginning of QRS complex, only a small amount of muscle in posterior and lateral portion of left wall and of basal septum remains to be excited.

moving toward its center from both endocardial surfaces; however, the activation of the basal septum is predominantly from the left.

The average velocity of conduction through the ventricular muscle is about 0.3 meter per second. Calculation of this velocity requires use of a three-dimensional plot of activity and measurement of the time and distance between two successive positions of the wavefront. If velocity is calculated in a direction other than that followed by the activating wave, the value obtained is too high. The velocity of the activation wave on the endocardial surface appears to be several meters per second, but this is an apparent velocity resulting from the activation of many points on the endocardium nearly simultaneously. If endocardial velocity is ascertained by stimulating an endocardial point and recording the resultant spread of activity, the velocity is about 1 meter per second.[43] These general aspects of ventricular excitation are widely accepted, although disagreement remains concerning the extent to which direction reverses in the left wall and concerning the excitation of the septum.[2, 15, 30]

ACTIVATION OF MURAL MYOCARDIUM. The manner in which activity spreads near the endocardium is difficult to establish. Some investigators claim that the inner and outer portions of the wall are excited "simultaneously."[36] However, the general movement in the walls is from within out, although there are reversals of direction near the endocardium. In the right wall, activity always moves from the inside to the outside.

SEPTAL ACTIVATION. In spite of the disagreement concerning septal activation, a number of investigators have reached similar conclusions, which are stated as follows:[2, 13, 43, 45] The Purkinje fibers on the left give off numerous branches to the endocardium of the middle and apical septum. On the right, the Purkinje fibers have less extensive terminations. Consequently, as the QRS complex begins a sizeable amount of septal tissue is excited on the left and there is a smaller excitation wave on the right. On both sides of the septum, activity proceeds toward the center of the septum with a preponderance of left-to-right activity. Sodi-Pallares and co-workers[30, 49] at one time postulated a barrier to conduction in the central septum, but this has not been confirmed. In the basal septum there is little Purkinje tissue; this region is excited very late in QRS and mainly from left to right.

DETAILS OF VENTRICULAR ACTIVATION (Fig. 14).[43, 45] Since, as stated above, septal activity is at first primarily left to right, ventricular activity likewise usually begins earlier on the left and proceeds toward the right. On the right the earliest activity occurs at the septal termination of the right bundle in the region of the anterior papillary muscle of the right ventricle. Even when activity does not begin earlier on the left, more tissue on that side is activated early in ventricular depolarization. The smaller and usually later activity on the right is directed from right to left. The resultant of these opposing forces is directed to the right.

Immediately after the regions near the septal terminations of the bundles are activated, the impulse spreads very rapidly over a large portion of the endocardium near the apex of the heart and in the central region on both sides. This rapid activation is possible because the conduction system ramifies extensively along the endocardium on both sides. We may liken the intraventricular conduction to a tree, with the impulses starting near the trunk. Although the speed of propagation is only 1 meter per second, the impulse reaches the peripheral branches and excites the subendocardial myocardium at many places almost simultaneously. Within a short period, most of the central and apical endocardium on both sides is activated, and the impulse can then proceed in only one general direction, from endocardium to epicardium.

In the dog, the rapid excitation of the endocardium produces, on both sides, incomplete cones of depolarized muscle which extend through both walls and the septum. At 5 milliseconds, as at 10, after the beginning of the QRS complex, these cones are growing by movement of the advancing wave outward in the walls and toward the center of the septum. Electrocardiographically, a consequence of the double invasion of the septum is that the septal forces tend to cancel one another. At 12 milliseconds after the start of the QRS, the cones have united in the septum and have broken through to the surface of the thinner right ventricle. As a consequence of the breakthrough to the anterior right epicardial surface, there is no longer a boundary between active and resting tissue in this region, and the boundary on the left and posterior parts of the heart is now unopposed. At 18 milliseconds after QRS has begun, invasion of the left and right central ventricular surface is complete. At this time, a thin slice of tissue extending from base to apex in the lateral and posterior left wall remains in the resting state, as does a portion of the basal septum. At the end of 25 milliseconds, a small region in the posterior left wall and another in the basal septum remain unexcited. Activity in these regions, directed from apex to base, continues until the end of the QRS complex. A search for the regions which are depolarized last indicated that these lie in the basal septum bordering the atrium.

Atrial and Ventricular Repolarization. From the duration of the action potential, it is apparent that repolarization of the atrium in the dog and man normally occurs during the depolarization of the ventricles. There is an isoelectric period between the end of atrial depolarization and the beginning of ventricular repolarization during the plateau of the intracellular action potential. During this time, portions of the atrioventricular conduction system are depolarizing. Repolarization of the atrium probably progresses in a direction similar to that followed by atrial depolarization.

However, the wave of repolarization, as reflected in the electrocardiogram, tends to move oppositely to the wave of depolarization. The duration of the action potential in ventricular cells is such as to indicate that repolarization occurs during the T wave of the electrocardiogram. Both atrial and ventricular depolarization will be considered in greater detail later in the chapter.

ORIGIN OF THE ELECTROCARDIOGRAM

Electrocardiographic Recording Apparatus and Conventions. APPARATUS. Einthoven's string galvanometer,[16, 17] which made electrocardiographic recording possible, has been supplanted by the direct-writing galvanometer employing vacuum tube or transistor amplifiers. In this device, the small voltages at the body surface are amplified to produce currents that can drive a large galvanometer, which in turn moves a hot stylus across heat-sensitive paper (Fig. 15).

The usual amplifier has a "push-pull" or balanced input to make it relatively insensitive to the alternating currents that may be picked up in any location near conventional wiring. Alternating current is picked up either through a capacitive coupling between a lead-in to the amplifier and a wire which carries AC,

or because alternating magnetic fields cut across the electrocardiographic recording leads. The alternating current is, however, picked up nearly equally by both input leads of the push-pull circuit. Since the amplifier measures the differences in potential between these leads, the alternating current in the leads will tend to cancel.

Electrocardiographic amplifiers are also condenser-coupled. That is, each lead is interrupted by a condenser (Fig. 15). Condenser coupling has two purposes: (i) Maintained differences in voltage, i.e., "direct currents," at the two recording leads do not pass condensers. Such voltages may be produced by electrolytic processes (identical to those in batteries) involving the electrodes, electrode paste, perspiration, etc. These effects are generally much larger than the electrocardiographic voltage, and, since they will usually change in time, much rebalancing would be necessary were they not eliminated. (ii) Condenser coupling also makes it easier to construct a drift-free amplifier because the amplifier may be condenser-coupled between stages. This feature minimizes changes in vacuum tube performance attributable to temperature, aging, etc. Condenser coupling for electrocardiographic recording has a time constant of 3 seconds; i.e., if a constant voltage is applied between the two input terminals, the pen will return about two-thirds of the way to its zero position in 3 seconds (Fig. 16). This time constant

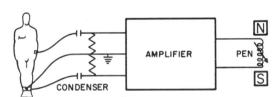

Fig. 15. Conventional electronic amplifier-pen recorder. Voltages recorded from left arm and leg of patient lead to input tubes of amplifier through a resistance-condenser input. There is also a ground connection, and input is "balanced." Output of amplifier is sufficient to drive a large galvanometer, which moves a recording stylus across a paper. In this way, a record is instantaneously available.

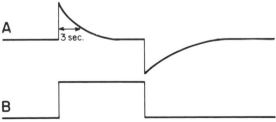

Fig. 16. When a square wave input (*B*) is applied to the input of a conventional electrocardiographic recorder, the response will be as shown in *A*. Because of input condensers, the amplifier does not respond to a maintained ("D.C.") input. The 3-second time constant is sufficiently long that electrocardiographic potential changes are faithfully recorded.

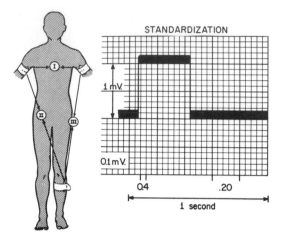

Fig. 17. Electrocardiographic limb lead connections and conventions for sensitivity and paper speed. Conventionally, 1 mV. equals 1 cm. vertically; 1 mm. horizontally equals 40 milliseconds. Over-all horizontal speed is 25 mm. per second. Conventional bipolar limb leads, designated *I, II* and *III*, are recorded as indicated by the Roman numerals.

makes it possible to record the slower components of the ECG and does not affect the rapid components. The European standard is 2 seconds.

CONVENTIONS. Electrocardiographic convention specifies that 1 mV. input to the amplifier shall produce a 1 cm. deflection of the pen. Recording paper is moved at 25 mm. per second. The conventional bipolar limb leads, designated leads I, II and III, record differences between the right arm, left arm and left leg (Fig. 17). We can think of the extremities merely as lead wires connected to the body; i.e., the potentials are not altered if the electrodes are moved along the extremities; for convenience the wrists and ankles are used as recording points. Electrocardiographic electrodes are fabricated of corrosion-resistant metal. They are coated with a film of conducting paste and are applied lightly but firmly to the body with rubber straps. It is important that the electrical contact with the body be good, and for this purpose the paste may be rubbed into the skin. The right leg is used as a ground connection. The amplifier is connected to these leads as indicated. In lead I, positivity of the left arm (or negativity of the right arm) produces an upward deflection. In leads II and III, positivity of the leg or negativity of the appropriate upper extremity produces an upward deflection. These conventions were originally established by Einthoven, who arranged them so that the

major deflection in each lead would be upright in a normal subject.

In the present technique for recording limb and precordial "unipolar" leads,[4] the negative terminal of the amplifier (the one which will produce an upward pen deflection if its potential is negative) is connected, through a resistive network (Fig. 18), to all three extremities. This arrangement constitutes Wilson's "central terminal." The positive electrode is designated the "exploring electrode"; it is connected to the limb electrodes individually and moved through several precordial positions, designated V_1 through V_6 (Fig. 19). The purpose of the unipolar leads is to record predominantly the potential at the point where the exploring electrode is placed. Wilson's central terminal is considered to be approximately a "zero terminal"; that is, it approximates the potential at some point which, because of its symmetry with respect to the voltages produced by the heart or

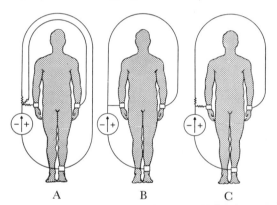

Fig. 18. Various types of connection used in electrocardiographic recording of unipolar leads.

A, Recording of unipolar leads according to convention established by Wilson. All three extremities are connected by a resistive network; resistors are usually 5000 ohms or larger. This network is connected to negative terminal of amplifier. Exploring or positive electrode is either connected to each extremity (for unipolar limb lead recording) or placed at precordial positions shown in Figure 19.

B, Modified unipolar *limb* lead recording system devised by Goldberger. Potential at one limb electrode, connected to positive terminal of amplifier, is recorded against potential of other two, connected together *without* resistors.

C, Form of unipolar limb recording devised by Wilson wherein potential at one extremity is compared with potentials at other two connected *with* resistors. System shown in *C* has been generally replaced by system shown in *B* for unipolar limb lead recording. System shown in *A* is used for recording of unipolar *chest* leads.

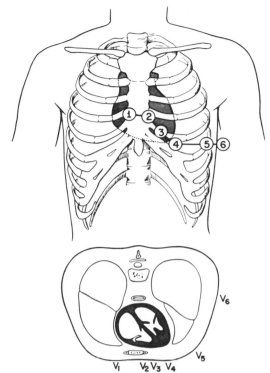

Fig. 19. Positions of unipolar precordial (chest) leads as routinely recorded in electrocardiography. V_1 is immediately to right of sternum at fourth intercostal space. V_2 is just to left of sternum in fourth intercostal space. V_4, in fifth intercostal space, is in midclavicular line. V_3 is between V_2 and V_4. V_5 is in fifth intercostal space in anterior axillary line. V_6, in fifth intercostal space, is at midaxillary line. The two portions of figure indicate vertical and horizontal positions of these leads.

because of its great distance from the heart, is not influenced by the voltages produced by the heart. The idea that a true zero potential can be found on the body surface is theoretically unsound and has been criticized;[20] practically, however, the Wilson terminal, or a modified version thereof, seems to be adequate.[56]

The unipolar limb leads are designated VR, VL and VF. The letter R indicates that the exploring electrode is connected to the right arm, L to the left arm, and F to the left foot. The V indicates that the Wilson terminal is the reference. Potentials so recorded may be slightly smaller than desirable, and for this reason a system of augmented unipolar extremity leads, originally described by Goldberger and designated as aVR, aVL, etc., is more commonly used. In this system the potential difference is recorded between one extremity and the other

two, both of which are connected directly to each other (Fig. 18). Goldberger's leads are wired into most electrocardiographic recorders.

HEART POSITION. The shape of an electrocardiographic complex recorded at the body surface is determined by the pattern of activation within the heart and the position of the heart and of the recording electrode. In discussing the origin of *human* electrocardiographic complexes, we shall transpose patterns of cardiac activity measured in animals, primarily the dog, to the human heart as it lies in the human thorax. The dog heart lies vertically in the chest, with its major axis parallel to the long axis of the chest. The human heart lies quite differently. The right chambers tend to be anteriorly placed, the left posteriorly. The interatrial and interventricular septa are nearly parallel to the anterior chest wall, etc. (Fig. 19). These factors will be considered in the discussion of electrocardiographic complexes which follows.

Origin of the P Wave. The two atrial chambers can be considered as equivalent to three roughly parallel sheets of muscle, lying in the chest in the position shown in Figure 20. We can think of normal atrial excitation as consisting of three waves moving inferiorly and to the left from the sinus node. Initially the wave moves anteriorly as the right atrium is depolarized earlier. During the latter half of atrial depolarization, there is activity moving posteriorly in the left atrium. A plane can be imagined drawn through the middle of the atrial mass and extending from the left shoulder down to the level of the sixth interspace beneath the right axilla. Along this plane the potentials due to

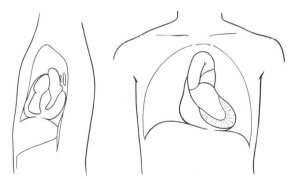

Fig. 20. Position of heart with respect to body surface in man. Right ventricle is anterior and left ventricle is posterior when viewed from left side. When viewed from front, left ventricle is tilted to left and upward.

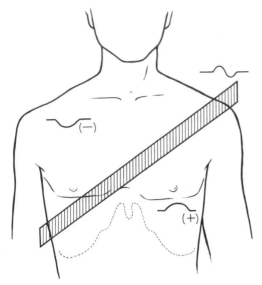

Fig. 21. Diagrams of shapes of P waves which would be recorded at various places at body surface. Since general direction of atrial activation is from right arm toward left leg, electrodes on upper part of body will see a negative potential during atrial activation; those on the lower part will see a positive potential. There will be a plane, as indicated on drawing, where an electrode would record both positive and negative activity.

atrial excitation would be initially positive, then negative (Fig. 21). This would be the "zero line" (equal positive and negative potentials) for atrial depolarization. A recording electrode placed above this, when paired with the Wilson central terminal, would record a predominantly negative potential. All of the normal precordial leads are positive during atrial depolarization. Lead VR, the unipolar right arm lead, shows a negative P wave, as do certain esophageal leads which are at times recorded, particularly to diagnose atrial abnormalities. The P wave, in general, has a smooth and rounded contour with little notching or peaking and has an average duration of 90 milliseconds in man and an amplitude of less than 0.25 mV.

THE SILENT PERIOD. As mentioned previously, the initial phase of depolarization in cardiac cells is followed by a plateau, during which the membrane potential changes little. During this period of "electrical systole," all cells are in nearly the same electrical state, and virtually no current flows from one region to another. Consequently, no changes of potential are seen in extracellular leads until the rapid phase of repolarization terminates electrical systole and produces the repolarization complex. There is

thus a period between the end of the P wave and the beginning of the QRS complex when the normal electrocardiogram shows a flat baseline. During this period, cells of the AV conduction system are depolarizing, but the number of cells is so small that they produce no potentials in electrocardiographic leads. Electrocardiographic results of repolarization of the atria will be discussed later.

Ventricular Activation and the QRS Complex. In man, the right ventricle lies anteriorly and the left posteriorly. The septum is tilted slightly forward apically, and the base-to-apex axis of the ventricle is often nearly parallel to the diaphragm (Fig. 20). The human ventricular electrocardiogram can be closely approximated if we transpose the dog's activation pattern to the human thorax and take into account the differences in QRS duration.

As indicated, the initial phase of ventricular activity is usually directed from left to right in the septum and results from earlier or greater initial left-to-right activity or both. This activity, transposed to the human heart (Fig. 22), would produce a wave directed to the right, toward the head (since the left side of the septum lies caudally) and slightly anteriorly. This wave will produce an initial negative deflection in leads I, II and III, which accounts for the Q wave. For the leads on the precordium, the pic-

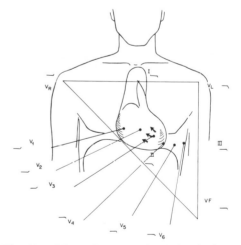

Fig. 22. Mean direction of activity during earliest portion of QRS transposed from canine to human heart. First activity goes from left to right in septum. Because of position of septum in human chest, this results in negative deflection in all bipolar limb leads, positive deflection in VR and in leads on right side of precordium (V_1 through V_4), and negative deflection in V_5, V_6, VL and VF.

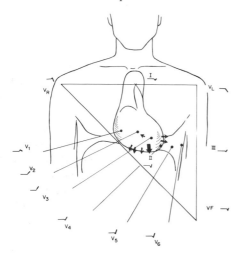

Fig. 23. When about one-quarter of QRS interval has passed, activity is proceeding from left to right in septum, and activity from inside out in wall has begun. Total activity is such that potentials are near zero in all limb leads, both bipolar and unipolar, and in V_1 and V_6. Other leads on chest are positive because activity proceeds toward the apex and free left wall.

ture is also clear. The leads on the right side of the chest (V_1 and V_2) face the positive side of wavefront and record an upward deflection, while those on the far left (V_5 and V_6) record a negative deflection.

Immediately after invasion of the septum begins (Fig. 23), rapid conduction through the Purkinje system results in an irregular pattern of inside-out spread in the walls; the transition from the first phase of activity to this second and major phase of ventricular activity is smooth. Within the septum, left-to-right activity predominates slightly. Arrows drawn perpendicular to the advancing wavefront depict the instantaneous vector of depolarization. At 12 milliseconds after the beginning of QRS in man (by extrapolation from the dog), the average direction of these arrows indicates a pattern of activity directed slightly forward to the right and from base to apex. Such a pattern will result in negative deflections in leads II and III and little or no deflection in lead I, which may be either positive or negative at this time. The potentials in the leads on the anterior chest surface will differ slightly from those occurring during the earlier phase, since the leads on the right will now "see"* both approaching (left to right) and receding (base to apex) activity. The ap-

*What is meant by an electrode "seeing" is explained in Chapter 3.

proaching activity will be in the right wall and on the left septal surface, the receding activity in the left wall and on the right septal surface. At this time, there may be little or no potential in these leads and a positive deflection in V_3.

At about 35 to 40 milliseconds after the onset of QRS (Fig. 24), union of the two separate masses of activated tissue has produced strong forces directed posteriorly, to the left and inferiorly. The breakthrough of activity to the anterior right wall has greatly reduced the left-to-right component, and over-all activity is directed apically, posteriorly and to the left. The major source of potentials is in the apical, lateral and anterior left wall. Some opposing inside-out activity persists in the basal right wall. At this time, positive deflections will appear in all standard limb leads, and the leads on the left side of the chest will "see" approaching activity. The continuation of this pattern results in the eventual disappearance of the wavefront anteriorly, on the right, and in the central and apical portions of the heart; i.e., all of the myocardium in these regions has fully depolarized. Overlying precordial leads will therefore record negative potentials.

The over-all pattern of activity immediately following the above, i.e., about midway through QRS, is a continuation of the movement toward the thin slice of lateral posterior left ventricle which remains in the resting state and a smaller

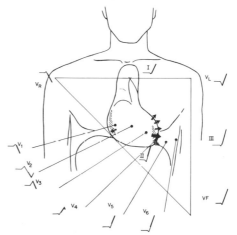

Fig. 24. At about middle of QRS interval, breakthrough of activity to anterior right ventricle has left forces moving to left posteriorly relatively unopposed. The result is a negative deflection in lead VR and positive deflections in all other limb leads. The leads on far right of chest (V_1 and V_2) now see negative activity; potential at V_3 is near zero, and potentials at V_4, and V_5 and V_6 are positive.

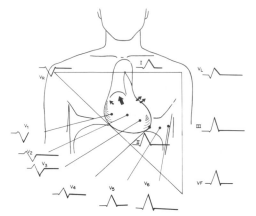

Fig. 25. During terminal portion of QRS complex, activity is directed to left and posteriorly in basal left ventricle and basally in upper septum. This condition results in potentials which are small in all leads. Deflection in VR is positive, deflections in all other limb leads are negative. Potentials are now returned to zero from negative peak in V_1 and V_2 and from positive peak in V_4, V_5 and V_6. This activity results in slight negative potentials in V_3, V_4, V_5 and V_6.

movement toward the basal septum. Depolarization reaches the apex of the heart on the right, but some muscle in the apical region of the left ventricle remains to be depolarized. The net result is a wave moving posteriorly, leftward and slightly toward the apex. Again, the limb leads will be positive. The chest leads except V_5 and V_6 (on the far left) will, however, show negativity.

Finally, after depolarization of the apical regions is complete (60 milliseconds after the onset of QRS), i.e., for the last quarter of the QRS complex, a wave moves toward the base of the left ventricle, particularly posteriorly and from apex to base in the septum. This wave is relatively ineffective in causing potentials in lead I, although leads II and III should show a negative potential; the potentials in the chest leads will be small but generally negative (Fig. 25).

In Figure 14 it can be seen that the process exhibits a great amount of symmetry around the longitudinal axis of the heart. At various instants, activity is proceeding in opposite directions in the lateral walls or in the septum or in both. This symmetry of depolarization leads to "cancellation" of much of the cardiac electrical activity as recorded from the body surface. It has been estimated that the recorded potentials are 5 to 10 per cent of what might be expected if there were no cancellation.[42] Any condition which alters the sequence of ventricular depolarization in a manner to reduce this cancellation will, of course, produce an increase in the magnitude of the potentials recorded in one or more leads. This is true of bundle branch block and of many types of infarction, and also of cases in which the impulse arises in abnormal sites.

To summarize, we may divide ventricular activation into three phases, remembering that they succeed one another smoothly and are not separate. The first of these phases is from left to right and anteriorly in the septum. The second, consisting of inside-out activity in the wall plus double invasion of the septum, produces very strong forces directed from base to apex, somewhat posteriorly and to the left. The final phase is the activity—directed from apex to base, leftward and posteriorly—resulting from activation of the basal posterior left wall and the basal septum. Duration of QRS is about 80 milliseconds. Voltages are of the order of 1 mV. but vary with the recording lead. A normal 12-lead electrocardiogram is shown in Figure 26.

Repolarization of Atria and Ventricles. As previously noted, the passage of a wave of depolarization along the cell can be likened to the passage of electrical negativity along the outer surface of the cell membrane. In nerve, depolarization is virtually instantaneously followed by repolarization which tends to make any recorded potential a mixture of the two effects (Fig. 20 in Chap. 3). Because of the long duration of the action potential in cardiac muscle, depolarization and repolarization are almost always separated in time and produce their effects quite separately. Repolarization can be likened to passage of a wave of positivity along the cell membrane. Thus, we would expect that, if cardiac muscle cells had symmetrical boundaries during depolarization and repolarization, and if a depolarizing wave moving along a cell were followed a few hundred milliseconds later by a repolarizing wave, the potential produced by repolarization would have electrical polarity opposite that produced by depolarization. The pathways of atrial and ventricular repolarization have not been successfully traced in mammalian hearts because the injury potentials produced by extracellular electrodes obscure the potentials caused by repolarization. Intracellular electrodes cannot be used for this purpose either since, although they work effectively with surface cells, they cannot easily give information about the repolarization of deeper myocardial cells. Furthermore, repolarization potentials are changed by almost any type of experimental intervention (opening the chest, etc.). Therefore, to get any hint of the direction of normal repolarization, we must use whatever information is available; most of this information, particularly in humans, comes from the body surface electrocardiogram.

THE Ta WAVE. Atrial repolarization in the dog and in man normally occurs during the depolarization of the ventricles, and the repolarization potential is concealed by the much larger potentials of the ventricles. There is thus an isoelectric period between the end of atrial depolarization and the beginning of ventricular depolarization, although, as has been discussed, portions of the atrioventricular (AV) conduction system are depolarizing during this time. Infrequently, the ventricular potentials do not conceal the atrial repolarization potential (referred to as the Ta wave), and it may be seen as a very small mirror image of the P wave. Thus, it is probable, although there is no direct evidence to support this contention, that repolariz-

ation of the atrium progresses in a direction similar to that followed by depolarization. The small size of the repolarization complex reflects the fact that, during repolarization, activity in some portions of the atrium cancels activity of other portions. Also, the repolarization deflection occurs during the terminal (most rapid) phase of cellular repolarization, and during this phase the total voltage change is much less than that during depolarization.

THE T WAVE. In most electrocardiographic leads in *man,* the T wave has the same electrical polarity as the QRS complex, i.e., is usually upright when the QRS complex is upright and vice versa. This indicates that repolarization does not follow the same pathway as depolarization, and indeed that the pathways tend to be opposite. It is important in this connection to consider whether repolarization is electrically propagated, as is depolarization. In studies with the intracellular electrode by Cranefield and Hoffman[11] and by Weidmann,[55] repolarization of a fiber could be induced by appropriate stim-

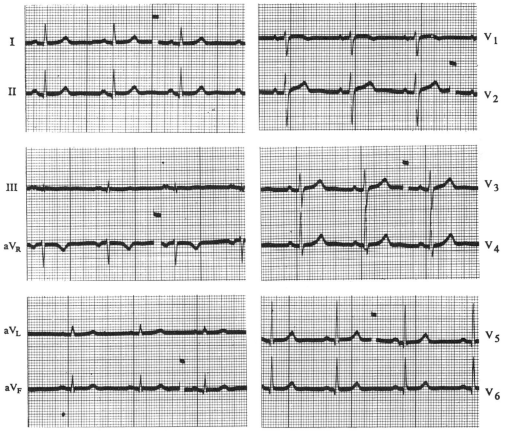

Fig. 26. A normal 12 lead electrocardiogram. (From Winsor, ed., *Electrocardiographic test book.* New York, American Heart Association, 1956.)

ulation (i.e., by stimuli causing the *inside* of the fiber to become negative) and could propagate through a fiber. In cardiac tissue in low calcium solutions, induced repolarization may propagate through several fibers. Calculations of the density of current flow indicate that the current flowing during repolarization is less than 1 per cent of that flowing during depolarization. Such a small current probably cannot initiate a propagated wave.

If repolarization is not propagated, we may wonder why the configuration of the T wave is consistent under normal conditions. Several factors have been thought to control the sequence of repolarization; among them are temperature and pressure. According to one theory, the pressure differential within the walls favors initiation of repolarization in the outer layers, and repolarization occurs later near the endocardium.[28] Potentials within the right and left cavities of the human heart are negative during repolarization. Sodi-Pallares[49] interpreted these findings as indicating that the T wave normally results from spread of repolarization from the outside to the inside of the left wall. He believed further that electrical forces from other portions of the ventricles cancel one another and that the right wall and the septum are electrically silent during repolarization, i.e., have no clear-cut direction of repolarization but repolarize at random. Available data do not allow complete acceptance of any theory concerning ventricular repolarization, although the normal "pathway" of repolarization is apparently independent of, although statistically generally opposite to, the pathway of depolarization (note the T waves in Figure 26).

ABNORMALITIES OF THE ELECTROCARDIOGRAM

Arrhythmias. The term "arrhythmia" refers to a disturbance of the heart rate, the cardiac rhythm, and the sequence in which the chambers are excited. The arrhythmias have two main causes: disorders of impulse formation and disorders of conduction. In the first of these, the impulse may be generated in the normal site (the S-A node) but at an abnormal rate, or some other portion of the myocardium may function as pacemaker. Origination of the heart beat in the AV node is abnormal, even though this tissue normally has the ability to generate

impulses. Arrhythmias also may result from pacemaker activity in the branches of the conduction system or even within unspecialized tissues—sites which do not normally generate impulses.

SINUS RHYTHM. The term *normal sinus rhythm* indicates that the pacemaker is within the S-A node and that the heart rate is constant and within normal limits. In the condition called *sinus arrhythmia* (Fig. 27), common in children and young adults, the heart rate changes phasically during the respiratory cycle. Sinus arrhythmia is not pathologic and is most commonly seen when the person is resting; it may disappear when the heart rate increases. The electrocardiographic complexes will, of course, have a normal configuration in the normal heart.

In certain disorders, the impulse originates in the sinus node, but at a rate below or above the normal range. In *sinus bradycardia* (Fig. 28) the rate at which the S-A node is producing impulses is subnormal; the heart rate is below 60 beats per minute but rarely below 40 beats per minute. Conversely, the heart rate is more than 100 beats per minute in *sinus tachycardia* (Fig. 29) because the sinus node is producing impulses at an accelerated rate. Aside from the change in rate, the electrocardiographic complex is nor-

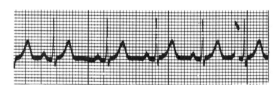

Fig. 27. Sinus arrhythmia; lead II of a child. Intervals between successive QRS complexes from left to right are 17, 15, 15 and 13 mm., or 680, 600, 600 and 520 milliseconds respectively. Heart rates calculated on this basis would be 88, 100, 100 and 115 beats per minute. (From Winsor, ed., *Electrocardiographic test book.* New York, American Heart Association, 1956.)

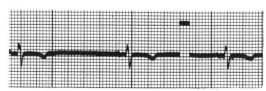

Fig. 28. Sinus bradycardia; lead III in an athlete. Interval between QRS complexes is 1400 milliseconds (34 msec. × 40 msec. per mm.). Also shows some sinus arrhythmia. Heart rate is 43 beats per minute. (From Winsor, ed., *Electrocardiographic test book.* New York, American Heart Association, 1956.)

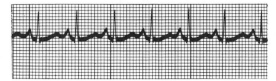

Fig. 29. Sinus tachycardia in a 13-year-old child (lead II). Heart rate is 130 per minute; pacemaker is in sinus node, since each QRS complex is preceded by a P wave at a normal interval. In children of this age, heart rate should not exceed 109 beats per minute. S-T segments are considered to be normal in view of rapid rate. (From Winsor, ed., *Electrocardiographic test book.* New York, American Heart Association, 1956.)

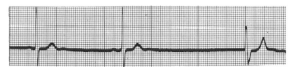

Fig. 30. Sinus arrest induced by pressure in carotid sinus in a normal subject (lead V_3). Two normal beats at a slow rate (33 beats per minute, interval 1.8 seconds) followed by a ventricular premature contraction not preceded by a P wave (vagal escape). (From Winsor, ed., *Electrocardiographic test book.* New York, American Heart Association, 1956.)

mal in either of these conditions, and these definitions are somewhat arbitrary. In infants, the normal resting pulse rate is frequently 120 beats per minute or more. When the rate exceeds 160 beats per minute, the condition is usually *atrial tachycardia,* in which case the pacemaker is atrial tissue. In paroxysmal atrial tachycardia the reversion to sinus rhythm is abrupt, and during the paroxysm the rhythm is very regular. Paroxysmal tachycardia of sinus origin is rare; the pacemaker is usually an atrial focus outside the sinus node. As will be discussed, this condition can produce AV block. The condition is at times controlled by pressure on the carotid sinus or on the eyeballs, procedures activating receptors which can reflexly decrease the heart rate. Ventricular tachycardia will be discussed below. Atrial flutter and fibrillation, two disorders in which the atrial rate is higher than that seen during tachycardia, will also be discussed later.

Sinus arrest (Fig. 30) is a rare condition in which the sinus node does not initiate impulses. It usually results from treatment of heart disease with drugs. Often, the P waves occur less and less frequently and then disappear.

A final disorder which may be mentioned is called *wandering pacemaker.* In this condition there are minor changes in the shape of the P wave and changes in the P-R interval, yet the heart rate is not greatly disturbed. It is thought that this condition arises from movement of the pacemaker.

ATRIOVENTRICULAR NODAL RHYTHM. As indicated previously, the AV node has the second highest rhythmicity of the specialized cardiac tissues. Thus, if activity of the sinus node becomes depressed, or if the rhythmicity of the AV node is increased, the latter may take over the task of initiating impulses and become the cardiac pacemaker. Conduction will progress normally to the ventricular myocardium and often, but less frequently, will also move in a retrograde direction to the atrium.

From direct measurement of conduction along the AV conduction system, it can be seen that the P wave occurs *during* the QRS complex when an impulse originating in the AV node is conducted normally to the ventricle and also backward into the atrium. If the impulse originates in the upper part of the AV node, the P wave should occur immediately before the QRS complex. In either instance, the P wave in most leads should be inverted, since the general direction of atrial activation is the reverse of normal. In the clinical literature, the terms "upper," "middle" and "lower" AV nodal rhythm are used, the last describing the situation in which the P wave occurs relatively late with respect to the QRS complex. However, it can be seen from Figure 10 that, if ventricular conduction is normal, the P wave should not occur after the QRS complex unless retrograde conduction is definitely slower than forward conduction. It is possible that certain disorders ascribed to pacemaker activity of the AV node actually arise from pacemaker activity of the common bundle. As long as ventricular conduction is normal, the QRS complex itself is normal.

EXTRASYSTOLES. All cardiac tissue seems to be capable of generating impulses. Slight injury, anoxia, mechanical trauma or friction apparently can increase this tendency, so that a nonspecialized part of the myocardium may become, either continuously or sporadically, a pacemaker for the heart. Such beats are referred to as "ectopic." Abnormal impulses may be formed in the atrium outside the sinus node (atrial premature beats), in the AV node (nodal premature beats), in the conducting bundles, or in the ventricular musculature (ventricular ectopic beats). A second class of extrasystoles

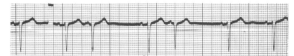

Fig. 31. Two atrial premature contractions (lead V_1). First two complete complexes are followed by a premature beat, which is followed by a compensatory pause. Fourth complex is followed by a second premature contraction. Fifth beat is again delayed by a compensatory pause; last complex is at a normal interval. Two premature complexes bear a fixed relationship to preceding beats. (From Winsor, ed., *Electrocardiographic test book*. New York, American Heart Association, 1956.)

arises in the sinus node as an interpolated premature beat.

Atrial premature contractions (Fig. 31). Alteration in the site of the atrial pacemaker may result from failure of the sinus node to function normally or from increased excitability of some other locus. If the atrial pacemaker is not within the S-A node, an abnormal P wave will result, but it usually will be followed by normal QRS and T complexes. Should the pacemaker be appreciably closer to or farther from the AV node than the sinus node, the P-R interval will also be prolonged or shortened. The duration of the P-R interval will be prolonged if an atrial extrasystole arrives at the AV node during the relatively refractory period of the latter. As has been indicated, the AV node has a low safety factor and cannot conduct impulses which arrive at a high frequency. If the atrial extrasystole arrives during the absolutely refractory period of the AV node, the abnormal P wave is not followed by a QRS complex.

Nodal premature beats. Although the AV node at times acts as the pacemaker for the heart or for the ventricles, extrasystoles seldom arise within the AV node.

Ventricular extrasystoles (Fig. 32). An irritable focus within the ventricle may cause regular or irregular ventricular extrasystoles. When the ectopic beat originates within the Purkinje system, the ventricular complex may be normal (origin of beat within the common bundle) or abnormal (origin of beat below the origin of the common bundle). When a beat originates in the ventricular myocardium, the QRS complex will be abnormal in shape and duration. In fact, the origin of an extrasystole can often be deduced from the shape of the QRS complexes recorded from the body surface. For example, if during the extrasystole all chest leads show a marked increase in positivity, the beat must originate in the posterior portion of the heart.

In general, the QRS complex will be prolonged, since conduction over the Purkinje system is not following the normal path. If the analogy between the Purkinje system and a tree is recalled, it will be seen that an impulse originating near a peripheral branch of the tree must be conducted along that branch until it intercepts the normal conduction pathway near the trunk. Even though the ectopic impulse is conducted along the endocardium at normal Purkinje velocity, about 1 meter per second, the time required for depolarization of the ventricles will be increased. With prolongation of the interval between the beginning and the end of ventricular depolarization, those regions which depolarize first tend to repolarize first, and the direction of the T wave will often be opposite that of the QRS complex.

At times, a ventricular extrasystole arises from a single focus which, for unknown reasons, discharges rhythmically to produce a wave with a fixed shape and often with a constant relationship to the normal QRS complex. Such a beat is referred to as a *coupled beat*. It may occur after every normal beat or, often, after every third, fourth, or fifth normal beat. The resulting rhythm is referred to as bigeminy, trigeminy, etc. When an ectopic beat originates below the AV node, the atria will often beat independently, since the safety factor for retrograde conduction is lower than that for forward conduction. An ectopic beat may be conducted in a retrograde direction and may depolarize either the AV node or, if conducted to the atria, the sinus node. If the S-A node is thus depolarized, it cannot generate a normal impulse until repolarized. Consequently, the interval between the extrasystole and the next normal sinus beat will be abnormally long, and the ventricles will fill to a degree greater than normal. The stroke

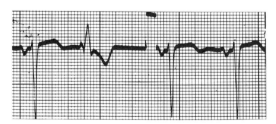

Fig. 32. Second complex is followed by a ventricular premature beat. Note absence of P wave before this QRS complex, abnormal shape of QRS, altered polarity of T wave. (From Winsor, ed., *Electrocardiographic test book*. New York, American Heart Association, 1956.)

TABLE 1. *Upper Limits of the Normal P-R Interval**

HEART RATE	BELOW 70	71–90	91–110	111–130	ABOVE 130
Large adults	0.21	0.20	0.19	0.18	0.17
Small adults	0.20	0.19	0.18	0.17	0.16
Children, ages 14 to 17	0.19	0.18	0.17	0.16	0.15
Children, ages 7 to 13	0.18	0.17	0.16	0.15	0.14
Children, ages 1½ to 6	0.17	0.165	0.155	0.145	0.135
Children, ages 0 to 1½	0.16	0.15	0.145	0.135	0.125

*From Ashman, R. and Hull, E.: *Essentials of electrocardiography.* 2nd ed. New York, The Macmillan Co., 1945.

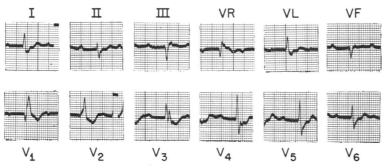

Fig. 36. First degree A-V block in a heart with several other abnormalities. P-R interval, measuring 320 milliseconds, is very much prolonged; at this heart rate, upper normal limit is 200 milliseconds. That this is first degree A-V block is indicated by QRS complex following every P wave. It should be noted further that there are negative S-T segment shifts in leads V_1, V_2, and V_3. Late activity coming toward right in these leads suggests right bundle branch block. This subject shows a first degree A-V block and a right bundle branch block. (From Winsor, ed., *Electrocardiographic test book.* New York, American Heart Association, 1956.)

perimental animals by stimulation of the atrium at progressively increasing rates. An increase in the heart rate of a normal person results in a *decrease* in P-R interval (over the range of 70 to 130 beats per minute, [Table 1]) as long as the heart rate is not faster than 2 beats per second. This response of normal man and experimental animals is attributable to unknown alterations in the physiologic condition of the cells as the heart rate increases. Thus, it would seem that first degree block occurring in man at lower heart rates follows depression of the AV node by anoxia or some similar factor which makes it impossible for the node to conduct at a normal velocity, even though impulses are arriving at a normal frequency. (In some otherwise normal individuals, AV block is present from birth.) When, as in paroxysmal tachycardia, impulses arrive at the AV node at an abnormally high rate, the node may be unable to conduct normally. First degree block or a more serious block may then be seen.

In *second degree block* (Fig. 37), atrial excitation does not always lead to ventricular excitation; i.e., some P waves are not followed by QRS complexes. This condition is an extension of that seen in first degree block and is observed in the dog when the heart rate is artificially raised above 5 beats per second. When only alternate P waves are followed by a ventricular complex, the condition is referred to as 2:1 block.

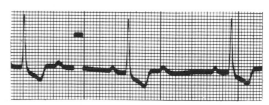

Fig. 37. Two-to-one A-V block. In lead II, record shows three QRS complexes and four P waves; second and fourth P waves are not followed by QRS complexes. Other two P waves are followed by QRS complexes at about a normal interval. Disease is suggested, although by no means proved, by inverted T wave. (From Winsor, ed., *Electrocardiographic test book.* New York, American Heart Association, 1956.)

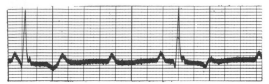

Fig. 38. Complete A-V block. Atria and ventricles are beating independently. Atrial rate is 90 beats per minute; ventricular rate is 29 beats per minute. Atrial pacemaker appears to be in sinus node, and, although it cannot be seen from this record, ventricular pacemaker appears to be near base of ventricles. (This rate is somewhat slower than would be expected were pacemaker in A-V node, and tracings are somewhat prolonged—a finding also indicating that ventricular pacemaker is probably not in A-V node.) (From Winsor, ed., *Electrocardiographic test book*. New York, American Heart Association, 1956.)

Other ratios commonly seen are 3:1, 3:2, 4:1, etc.

In second degree AV block, a *Wenckebach phenomenon* may also occur. In this condition the sinus node generates impulses at a constant rate, but the P-R interval grows progressively longer during several beats until there is an atrial complex which is not followed by a ventricular complex. The next atrial complex is followed by a QRS complex and there is a short P-R interval; the interval again grows progressively longer, and the phenomenon is repeated. In experimental animals, the Wenckebach phenomenon can be duplicated with high-frequency stimula-

tion at a rate almost sufficient to cause 2:1 AV block. Although the exact mechanism is not known, it would appear that the cells between the atrial and the AV node are functional but close to failure. Consequently, with each successive beat, AV conduction is slower until, finally, it is completely blocked. When complete block occurs, the cells have a long time in which to recover, so the beat after complete AV block has a short P-R interval.

Third degree or complete AV block (Fig. 38) is a condition in which the AV node is entirely unable to conduct impulses. A pacemaker within the AV node or in the ventricle controls the ventricular beat, which is independent of and slower than the atrial beat.

Bundle branch block. Bundle branch block results from failure of transmission in either the right or left conduction bundles or in their terminal ramifications. The usual cause is probably myocardial damage from infarction or fibrosis from long-standing cardiac disease, although right bundle branch block may occur in normal young persons. The term "complete bundle branch block" is an arbitrary designation for beats originating in the AV node but having a QRS duration of over 120 milliseconds in man. The pattern of ventricular excitation in complete left bundle branch block in the dog is shown in Figure 39; Figure 40 indicates the changes resulting from right bundle branch

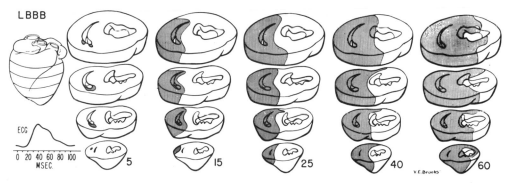

Fig. 39. Ventricular depolarization after left bundle branch block. This figure should be compared with Figure 14, which shows a normal depolarization pattern. Shaded area represents portion of myocardium depolarized up to particular instant indicated at bottom of column, and this is compared with lead II electrocardiogram. Note that activity begins around right cavity, proceeds gradually across septum as depolarization of right free wall is completed, and has reached approximately center of septum at 25 milliseconds after beginning of QRS. Activity continues across septum through 40 milliseconds, and, even at 60 milliseconds after beginning of QRS, lateral left ventricle is not completely excited. Note that both septal activation and activation of left wall are altered by bundle branch block. Increased time required to excite septum and left wall accounts for prolongation of depolarization in complete left bundle branch blocks. This figure, like Figure 14, represents activity in the dog heart, in which the duration of QRS is 40 milliseconds or less. (Becker *et al.*, *Amer. Heart J.* 1958, *55*:547–556.)

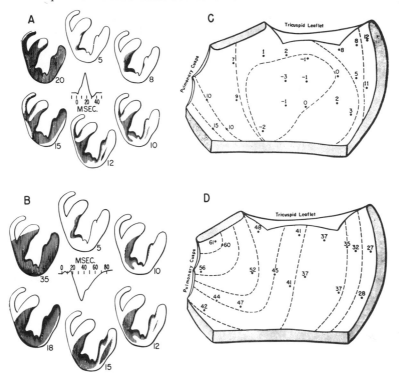

Fig. 40. Pattern of ventricular depolarization before and after right bundle branch block. *A* and *B*, Sagittal sections through right and left ventricles showing pathway as measured by nine multipolar insertions. Small figures show position in heart of depolarization wave at various stages of depolarization, *A*, Normal depolarization; normal lead II QRS is shown at center. *B*, Pattern of ventricular depolarization during right bundle branch block (same insertion as in *A*). Lead II QRS is typical of canine right bundle branch block.

C and *D*, Pattern of activation of right mural endocardium as viewed from inside right cavity. Shaded areas indicate junction of right wall and septum. Numbers indicate time of depolarization in milliseconds after onset of QRS. Dotted lines approximate wavefront position at 5 millisecond intervals. *C*, Normal depolarization. *D*, Pattern of activation after right bundle branch block. (From Erickson *et al., Circulation Res.,* 1957, 5:5–10.)

block. As might be expected, after the main bundle is interrupted, the normal double envelopment of the septum is replaced by one-way activation from the unblocked side, and activation of the free wall begins at the sites first reached by spread of depolarization across the septum. The wave of excitation utilizes the endocardial Purkinje fibers and travels across the endocardium on the blocked side at about 1 meter per second.[5, 18]

Prolongation of the QRS complex in bundle branch block results both from the longer time required to activate the septum and from the longer time required to activate the blocked free wall. The change in the activation of the free wall during right bundle branch block in the dog is shown in Figure 40. Normally, it requires about 18 milliseconds to activate the right

mural endocardium, and a large central area is activated within a few milliseconds by the branching Purkinje system. After block, the impulse reaches the wall at the inferior and posterior junctions of the wall and the septum and spreads anteriorly and superiorly. The smooth progression of the wave is altered as it breaks through the septum superiorly. The total time required to activate the right free wall after block is 35 milliseconds.[18] Similar changes in mural activation are seen in left bundle branch block.

In the dog, complete right bundle branch block doubles the duration of QRS; complete left bundle branch block increases it two and one-half times. Comparable durations of the QRS in man would be 160 and 200 milliseconds for complete right and complete left block,

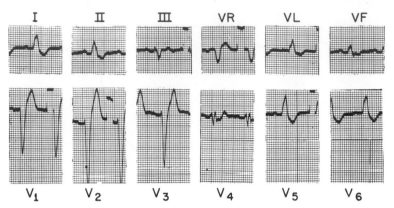

respectively. A clinical diagnosis of complete block is based on far less prolongation of the QRS complex, i.e., 120 milliseconds or more. In complete right bundle branch block we would expect that the right wall would be the last portion of the heart to be activated, a situation which would produce late positive deflections in V_1 and V_2 and aVR. Grant[23] believed that these conditions are met only rarely in clinical examinations and concluded that truly complete right bundle branch block is extremely rare. Complete left bundle branch block (Fig. 41) is more common and is accompanied by clear signs of right-to-left activation of the septum and left ventricle. In bundle branch block, as in ventricular ectopic beats, those portions of the ventricular myocardium which depolarize first tend to repolarize first and, similarly, the last areas to fire are the last to recover. Consequently, the T wave tends to become a mirror image of the QRS complex; leads in which the QRS is upright show a downward T wave, etc.

In conditions clinically described as incomplete bundle branch block, the QRS lasts up to 120 milliseconds. The mechanism of such prolongation is not at all clear. Possibly damage to fine strands of the Purkinje network (arborization block) or even frank myocardial damage might lead to such lengthening of the QRS.

MYOCARDIAL INJURY; ISCHEMIA AND INFARCTION. *Phase I.* If a region of myocardium is partially deprived of oxygen, the first change observed electrocardiographically is an alteration of the T wave. Apparently the region of ischemia cannot repolarize normally. Possibly the ischemic region remains depolarized while adjacent regions have returned to the resting state. An overlying electrode will therefore record a negative T wave that is usually larger than normal. A similar change in the T wave is seen during recovery from an infarction. It should be noted that the T wave is a most labile portion of the electrocardiogram and less reliable for diagnostic purposes than other portions of the ventricular complex. Changes similar to those resulting from ischemia arise also from benign causes. If the entire heart is uniformly deprived of oxygen, T wave changes may be widespread.

Phase II. When a blood vessel supplying the ventricular myocardium is completely occluded by a thrombus or deposition of atheromatous plaques in the vessel wall, and when no collateral circulation exists, the cells previously supplied by this vessel will be completely deprived of oxygen. A complicated series of events will ensue, *all* of them causing the same change in the relationship between the S-T and T-Q segments (Fig. 42).

The first change which takes place is a shortening of the intracellular action potential. This occurs a few seconds after the tying of a ligature in an experimental animal, as has been demonstrated by several investigators.[40, 52] When the action potential is shortened, the injured cells depolarize normally but repolarize more rapidly than do adjacent normal cells. For this reason, during the period of repolarization, i.e., during the S-T segment of the electrocardiogram, current flows from the injured cells to the adjacent normal cells (since, by definition, current flow is from positive to negative). This flow then leads to a change in the S-T segment, which becomes elevated in unipolar leads facing the area of the infarct. This elevation is a primary change in the S-T segment; it is transient, however, and recovery from this phase occurs within a few minutes. While this change is still in effect (and during the period of recovery), a second change takes place: a decrease in the resting potential of the injured cells. Since the resting potential of the injured cells is now lower than that of the adjacent uninjured cells, current flows from the normal cells into the injured ones during electrical diastole. (This current is frequently referred to as the "current of injury.") This condition produces a depression of the T-Q segment of the electrocardiogram in unipolar electrodes facing the area of injury. At first this depression adds to the true S-T segment shift mentioned previously, but it continues after the initial change disappears.

The input capacitors of the electrocardiographic recorder prevent its use to discriminate between a shift in the T-Q segment and a shift in the S-T segment. In the clinical literature, both of these changes are referred to as "S-T segment elevation" in electrodes facing the injury. (Electrodes facing the rear of the injury record the opposite changes.) At present, there seems to be no need to discriminate among these various causes of "S-T segment elevation" during acute and chronic occlusion of the vessels, and such discrimination would present overwhelming technical problems.

A later change, beginning about 30 minutes after occlusion of a vessel, has been described by Durrer.[14] At this time, some cells in or near the "infarcted" region fail to depolarize normally. The injured cells depolarize much later than they normally would. A unipolar electrode fac-

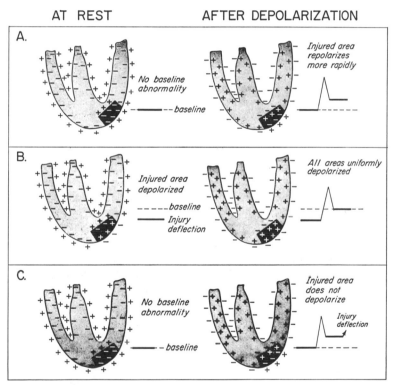

AT REST **AFTER DEPOLARIZATION**

Fig. 42. Several possible modes of production of S-T segment changes. In *A*, heart is shown as uniformly depolarized, i.e., there are negative charges on outside and positive charges on inside of all the membrane—except for muscle, which is in repolarized state (positive charges on outside of membrane), near epicardial surface. Electrode on right will view positive charges; that at left will view negative charges. This "injury current" occurs *after* QRS complex, and resultant potential is a change of S-T segment.

B, Myocardium is uniformly polarized, i.e., at rest, except for a region in center which is injured. Owing to flow of current into this region from adjoining regions, baseline is depressed at rest. This is truly a T-Q segment change, and is commonly considered cause of S-T segment changes. Heart is uniformly depolarized, but depolarizing wave cannot move into a portion of muscle. Wave stays fixed at this location, so that there is an S-T segment shift. In this instance, however, depolarization does not become completed. Changes shown in *A* and *B* have been found during acute infarction; change shown in *C* has not.

ing the area of injury thus sees approaching (positive) activity immediately after the QRS complex. Again, this change produces a true S-T segment elevation, but it has not been demonstrated that conduction time is equal to the S-T interval (200 milliseconds). It is likely that this change and the second change, which is a true T-Q depression, exist together during the period of chronic injury in patients, although there is no direct evidence at present.

Phase III. After the initial phases of ischemia and injury have disappeared, the S-T segment and T wave may return to normal. The diagnosis of such chronic infarcts is a difficult problem for the practitioner and may be important in determining whether a patient should be treated or should limit his activity. The major problem exists with regard to the QRS complex. In many cases, a sizable portion of the myocardium will have been replaced by scar tissue which is, of course, electrically silent. If the conduction system has not been impaired by the infarction, the duration of the QRS complex may be normal; but if a large amount of myocardium is missing, the complex will be changed, i.e., it will lack the potentials previously contributed by the infarcted region. An electrode which faces the infarcted region and which previously recorded approaching (positive) activity from that region will record less positivity than normal, or it may record a negative deflection. If the area of infarction is in a part of the heart which is normally depolarized early, this increased negativity may either produce an initial negative deflection or increase the magnitude of a negative deflection which would normally occur in the lead facing the region. An initial negative deflection is referred to as a Q wave, and an *abnormal Q wave* is the most common diagnostic sign of chronic infarction. Q waves are not abnormal *per se:* the abnormality is frequently definable only in terms of magnitude or duration of the wave in a particular lead. Some portions of the body surface normally show Q waves. Although this sign is useful, if it is the sole criterion of infarction, a diagnosis obviously can be made only when the infarction lies in regions which are depolarized early in QRS. Several recent textbooks of electrocardiography have described successful techniques for the detection of an infarction which affects the later portions of the QRS complex.

Some large infarcts may damage the conduction system, thus causing a prolongation of the QRS complex. It may be important to differentiate such prolongation from that seen in bundle branch block, since the latter may be present and innocuous in an otherwise healthy heart. The value of a control electrocardiogram taken before any reason exists to suspect myocardial damage should be apparent.

It is interesting that, during the period after infarction, a fixed relationship between changes in the S-T segment and T wave is often observed: those leads which show elevated S-T segments show a negative T wave. Although the mechanism has not been directly determined, a possible explanation is available by extrapolation from the observations of Durrer[14] and Conrad and co-workers.[9] Since depolarization is delayed in some cells in the infarcted region, might not these cells also repolarize late? Late depolarization would elevate the S-T segment and late repolarization would cause a negative T wave over the region. That is, the wave of repolarization would approach a lead over the infarction so slowly as to give a large negative deflection. (Remember that approaching repolarization produces a negative potential.)

ANALYSIS OF THE ELECTROCARDIOGRAM

The foregoing discussion is intended as a physiologic consideration and not as an account of electrocardiography. Indeed, a perusal of a complete electrocardiographic textbook will show that only a small fraction of the usual topics have been considered here; and the interpretation of clinical electrocardiograms obviously requires both much more familiarity with pathologic changes and much practical experience. Nevertheless, we shall briefly list here a sequence of procedures to be used in the evaluation of the electrocardiogram. This procedure will probably be sufficient only for the diagnosis of the common arrhythmias which have been listed in this chapter and at times will indicate that other electrocardiographic abnormalities exist, although the exact nature of the lesion may not be apparent.

The conventional electrocardiogram contains the tracings from three unipolar limb leads, the three bipolar limb leads and the six unipolar chest leads. The first procedure is to make sure that these tracings are technically above reproach and to make sure that all the leads have been recorded. At this time the standardization record should be examined to see whether a deflection of exactly 1 cm. has been produced by 1 mV. standardization. Each time that the standardization is repeated this accuracy should be checked again. Of course, if the amplitude of the standardization is slightly less or more than 1 cm., a correction is easily applied. Rarely, with damaged electronic components, the standardization may exhibit gross overshoot or slurring; if these occur, they are a sign that the instrument is in need of repair. Each electrocardiographic lead recorded should contain several beats. The tracing for each lead should have a baseline that does not drift up and down too widely, and there should be no artifact caused by loose electrodes, 60 cycle interference or muscle tremor.

Second, the cardiac rate should be determined by noting the interval between successive beats. At standard speed each millimeter of the electrocardiographic record equals 40 milliseconds; 25 mm. equal 1 second. Computation of the heart rate is thus quite simple. Electrocardiographic textbooks contain tables which enable one to measure the interval in millimeters and read off the rate directly; calibrated rulers are also available. The ventricular and atrial rates must be determined separately if the chambers depolarized independently. It should be noted whether the rate is regular or irregular; if it is irregular, the number of beats within 10, 20 or 30 seconds must be noted to determine the number of beats per minute. The irregularity may itself be significant. It should next be noted whether the relationships of the P, QRS and T waves are constant or variable. The P-R interval (from the beginning of the P wave to the beginning of QRS) should be measured to see if it is normal, longer than normal, or irregular. Changes in P-R interval result from abnormal activity of the conduction system. The duration of QRS and the Q-T interval (from the beginning of QRS to the end of the T wave) should also be measured. Changes in QRS duration occur in bundle branch block, after infarction, and during extrasystolic beats. The Q-T interval is altered by abnormal concentration of ions which can occur for a variety of reasons. Since these parameters are related to rate and age, tables must be consulted for normal limits.

The next step is to examine the complexes to see whether their shapes and durations are normal. We have previously considered conditions in which the P wave might have an abnormal shape. Several conditions are listed among the arrhythmias in which the QRS complex would be definitely abnormal in shape or prolonged or both. Electrocardiographic diagnosis of ventricular infarction, as can be seen above, rests on alterations in the T wave, the S-T segment or the T wave and the QRS complex or combinations of such alterations. It is common practice to determine the electrical axis of the heart (see below), since much diagnosis of electrocardiographic abnormality depends on this determination.

The above procedures should enable even the beginning student to detect many arrhythmias; however, it should be borne in mind that bundle branch block, particularly, cannot be diagnosed by analysis of a single tracing. Neither can the origin of many extrasystoles be adequately determined in this way. In cases of myocardial infarction, the problem is more complicated, and, although the example given perhaps may seem clear to the student, there are many types of infarcts and there is no substitute for experience in diagnosis.

Calculation of the Electrical Axis. At any instant during QRS, the electromotive force developed by the ventricles can be considered to have an average magnitude and direction closely related to the ventricular activation process. To plot accurately such a "vector" in the plane of the limb leads, we need two simultaneous recordings. In practice, a mean vector for all of the QRS complex is plotted according to a procedure developed by Einthoven. For this purpose, it is assumed that (i) the extremities form an equilateral triangle in the frontal plane, (ii) the heart lies at the center of this triangle, (iii) the mean polarity of a lead (i.e., the net area or mean voltage multiplied by time) can be determined from the difference between the positive and negative peaks of the QRS complex, and (iv) the body is a homogeneous conductor.

These assumptions contain certain inaccuracies; nevertheless, the electrical axis has empirical usefulness. The algebraic sum of the positive and negative peaks in a lead is measured in millimeters and is plotted along the proper side of the triangle, as shown in Figure 43. A perpendicular is then drawn at the termination of this line. The procedure is repeated for a second lead. The line joining the center of the triangle and the intersection of the two perpendiculars is the mean electrical axis. In most normal persons the axis falls between 0° and +90°. If the mean electrical axis lies at an angle greater than +90°, there is said to be *right axis deviation*. If the axis falls in the negative portion of the circle, *left axis deviation* is present. Again, a table of normal and abnormal values should be consulted in borderline cases. A procedure for determining the mean electrical axis by inspection from a *hexaxial* reference system involving unipolar and bipolar limb leads is also often used.[23] Changes in electrical axis often indicate hypertrophy of one or both chambers or abnormal heart position or both. They also occur after infarction.

Vectorcardiography. Much of our present understanding of electrocardiographic recording stems from the pioneering work of Dr. F. N. Wilson and his associates.[56, 57, 58] Wilson and co-workers developed our present system of recording unipolar chest leads.[58] He also pioneered in the recording of *vectorcardiograms,* which are at present widely considered as a type of recording which may partially supplant conventional scalar recordings. A vectorial recording plots voltage in one lead (on one axis)

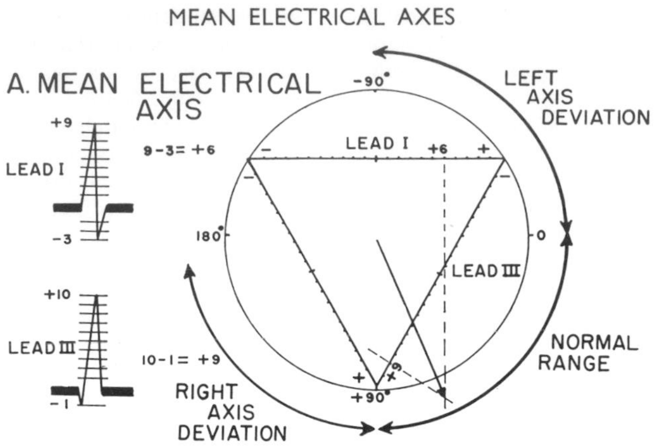

MEAN ELECTRICAL AXES

Fig. 43. *A,* The mean electrical axis is computed from two of the three standard limb leads (e.g., leads I and III). The sum of the downward deflections is subtracted from the sum of the upward deflections. For example, the vertical height of the R wave above the baseline is measured in millimeters (+9 mm. in lead I). The total amplitude of the downward deflections (−3 mm. in lead I) is added algebraically to the height of the R wave (+9) and leaves a net value of +6. At a point 6 units toward the plus sign on the lead I line of the triangle, a perpendicular is erected. The net amplitude of upward and downward deflections in lead III is +9 (+10 − 1). A perpendicular erected 9 units toward the plus sign on lead III is extended to intersect the perpendicular from lead I. An arrow drawn from the center of the triangle to the intersection of these two perpendicular lines is the *mean electrical axis.* (From Rushmer, *Cardiovascular dynamics.* Philadelphia, W. B. Saunders Co., 1961.)

against voltage in a second lead (on a second recording axis). Conventional scalar recordings show changes in one lead as a function of time. The major competition between these systems concerns the recording of the QRS complex.

To emphasize the difference between these recording methods, we may regard the conventional scalar recordings as based on the theory that ventricular depolarization produces some purely "local" potentials on the body surface; that is, each chest lead records in part the unique activity of the immediately underlying myocardium, and adjacent chest leads do *not* merely record different views of the same phenomenon.

Vectorcardiography, on the other hand, is based on the assumption that the heart is electrically so distant from the body surface that the potentials on that surface (or at least the important potentials on the body surface) can be considered to arise from a single fixed-location dipole within the chest. We may consider such a dipole to be a special case of the more general condition when three, and only three, independent current generators are connected to the body. If three such generators deliver voltage to the body, the potential at a given point on the body surface will be a linear function of the instantaneous current of each of these generators.

In the case of the cardiac dipole, its X, Y and Z components can each be considered a single instantaneous current generator, and the voltage at a particular body surface point can be considered the resultant of the instantaneous current in the X, Y and Z directions. Actually, at present, no basis exists for differentiating between the dipolar and the more general three-function system. In either case, vectorcardiography is based on the assumption that the voltages recorded on the body surface are indistinguishable from those which would be produced by a dipole within the thorax. Further, the vectorcardiographic technique involves the assumption that all the (important) information that can possibly be derived about ventricular depolarization is contained in three leads which can be recorded from four or more body surface recording points. (Note that a lead in such a case might be recorded from an array of more than two electrodes.) Recording more than three independent leads may add no new information.

Schmitt [47] and Frank [20] have devised widely used lead placement systems for vectorcardiography. They have further presented evidence that a dipolar interpretation of cardiac electrical activity gives most of the information derived from our present scalar recording techniques. A study of electrocardiographic techniques through factor analysis has indicated that most of the "information" on the body surface can be ascribed to three internal generators. It has, however, been clearly shown by Taccardi[51] that the body surface potential distribution is at times not compatible with what would be expected from a dipolar generator in a homogeneous conductor. Other objections have been voiced by Brody and co-workers[6] and by Evans et al.[19] A search continues, particularly by Brody, for recording systems which will bring some of this nondipolar information to light.

Vectorcardiographic display employs a cathode ray oscilloscope. A single such record is taken by connecting one electrocardiographic lead to the horizontal amplifier of the oscilloscope and another lead to the vertical amplifiers. The leads used are selected to show the anterior-posterior, head-to-foot and left-to-right components of the heart's electrical activity. There are many competing schemes for making the connections to the body surface. Figure 44 shows the pathway of ventricular activity and resultant scalar potentials on the chest in the horizontal plane (front-to-back and left-to-right leads). Figure 45 shows a similar vectorial "loop" on a cathode ray tube from an anterior-posterior and a left-to-right lead.

Grant[23] has devised a system of electrocardiographic interpretation in which vectorial arrows are constructed by using the conventional twelve-lead scalar electrocardiogram. Diagnosis in this system depends on the relationship of the arrows.

Unfortunately, even if the three-function or vectorcardiographic approach is accepted, the

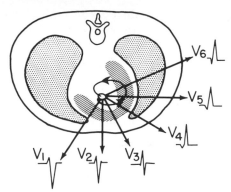

Fig. 44. A representation of a horizontal cross-section through the chest, showing the locations of the lungs and heart. The figure in the center indicates the sequential directions of the wave of ventricular depolarization within the ventricle. Note the arrows. Initial direction in this is anteriorly and to the right. In the middle of QRS there is a large lateral, posterior, leftward direction of activity, and finally a direction of activity toward the base of the heart, equivalent to the terminal activity in the septum. Outside the thoracic outline are shown the potentials which would be recorded from this "vectorial" representation of activity on the chest surface. It can be seen that the V leads are merely representations of this summed activity.

next step is not clear. The vectorcardiographic recording is in some respects more difficult technically than the recording of scalar leads. The fact that only three factors (i.e., three independent voltage changes in time) are involved in ventricular depolarization does not necessarily indicate that these should be recorded vectorially. It is thus possible that recording of three scalar leads will be the method of choice at some future date. The vectorcardiographers themselves do not agree on the recording system to

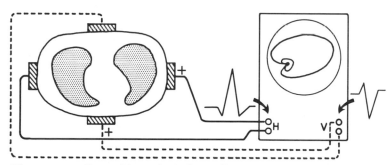

Fig. 45. The vectorcardiographic method of recording a tracing in the horizontal plane employs two sets of electrodes, one recording left-to-right potential differences, the other recording anterior-posterior potential differences. On the right of the figure are shown the potentials that would be recorded on each of these two leads, and on the oscilloscope face is shown a loop which would be described by the potentials shown. Vectorcardiograms can be "constructed" from scalar leads or can be recorded in this fashion with a cathode ray oscillograph.

be used. At present, there are several systems of vectorcardiographic recording, each having its proponents. Certainly the vast majority of clinical electrocardiograms consist of scalar leads exclusively, although an increasing number of cardiologists utilize the principles of vector analysis to interpret them and attempt to relate the information to normal depolarization pathways. Whether any future system of recording will increase the usefulness of electrocardiography remains to be seen.

Computer Analysis of the Electrocardiogram and Vectorcardiogram.[7, 35] The high-speed digital computer is being widely examined as a tool for both the researcher and the diagnostician. Computers have been used in electrocardiographic studies in a number of ways, including attempts to duplicate the analysis that might be made by a competent physician and attempts to discover new diagnostic data. Computer programs exist which rapidly produce the measurements (heart rate, duration of intervals and complexes, electrical axis, etc.) routinely made by the physician. Other computer programs indicate the probability of a particular cardiac abnormality.

REFERENCES

1. ABILDSKOV, J .A., WILKINSON, R. S., VINCENT, W. A. and COHEN, W. *Amer. J. Cardiol.*, 1961, *8*:485–492.
2. AMER, N. S., STUCKEY, J. H., HOFFMAN, B. F., CAPPELLETTI, R. R. and DOMINGO, R. T. *Amer. Heart J.*, 1960, *59*:224–237.
3. ANGELAKOS, E. T. and SHEPHERD, G. M. *Circulation Res.*, 1957, *5*:657–658.
4. BAYLEY, R. H. *Ann. N. Y. Acad. Sci.*, 1957, *65*:1110–1126.
5. BECKER, R. A., SCHER, A. M. and ERICKSON, R. V. *Amer. Heart J.*, 1958, *55*:547–556.
6. BRODY, D. A., BRADSHAW, J. C. and EVANS, J. W. *IRE Trans. Biomed. Electronics*, 1961, *BME8*:139–143.
7. CACERES, C. A. *Arch. intern. Med.*, 1963, *111*:196–202.
8. CARMELIET, E. and LACQUET, L. *Arch. int. Physiol.*, 1958, *66*:1–21.
9. CONRAD, L. L., CUDDY, T. E. and BAYLEY, R. H. *Circulation Res.*, 1959, *7*:555–563.
10. CRANEFIELD, P. F. and HOFFMAN, B. F. *Circulation Res.*, 1959, *7*:11–18.
11. CRANEFIELD, P. F. and HOFFMAN, B. F. *J. gen. Physiol.*, 1958, *41*:633 649.
12. DELEZE, J. and WEIDMANN, S. In: *Electrophysiology of the heart*, B. Taccardi, ed. New York, Pergamon Press, 1965.
13. DURRER, D. In: *Electrophysiology of the heart*, B. Taccardi, ed. New York, Pergamon Press, 1965.
14. DURRER, D., V. LIER, A. A. W., V. DAM, R. TH., JONKMAN, E. and DAVID, G. *Res. Comm., Congr. mond. Cardiol.*, 1958, *3*:355–356.
15. DURRER, D. and VAN DER TWEEL, L. H. *Ann. N. Y. Acad. Sci.*, 1957, *65*:779–802.
16. EINTHOVEN, W. *Ann. Phys.*, 1903, *12*:1059–1071.
17. EINTHOVEN, W. *Arch. int. Physiol.*, 1906, *4*:132–164.
18. ERICKSON, R. V., SCHER, A. M. and BECKER, R. A. *Circulation Res.*, 1957, *5*:5–10.
19. EVANS, J. W., ERB, B. D. and BRODY, D. A. *Amer. Heart J.*, 1961, *61*:615–621.
20. FRANK, E. *Ann. N. Y. Acad. Sci.*, 1957, *65*:980–1002.
21. GARDBERG, M. and ASHMAN, R. *Arch. intern. Med.*, 1943, *72*:210–230.
22. GRAHAM, J. and GERARD, R. W. *J. cell. comp. Physiol.*, 1946, *28*:99–117.
23. GRANT, R. P. *Clinical electrocardiography.* New York, McGraw Hill Book Co., 1957.
24. JACOBSON, E. D., RUSH, S., ZINBERG, S. and ABILDSKOV, J. A. *Amer. Heart J.*, 1959, *58*:863–872.
25. JOHNSON, E. A. In: *Proceedings, International Union of the Physiological Sciences,* vol. 1, part 1, New York, Excerpta Medica Foundation, 1962.
26. LEWIS, T. *The mechanism and graphic registration of the heart beat.* London, Shaw and Sons, 1925.
27. LEWIS, T., MEAKINS, J. and WHITE, P. D. *Phil. Trans.*, 1914, *B205*:375–420.
28. LEWIS, T. and ROTHSCHILD, M. A. *Phil. Trans.*, 1915, *B206*:181–226.
29. LING, G. and GERARD, R. W. *J. cell. comp. Physiol.*, 1949, *34*:383–396.
30. MEDRANO, G. A., BISTENI, A., BRANCATO, R. W., PILEGGI, F. and SODI-PALLARES, D. *Ann. N. Y. Acad. Sci.*, 1957, *65*:804–817.
31. MINES, G. R. *J. Physiol.*, 1913, *46*:349–383.
32. NOBLE, D. In: *Proceedings, International Union of Physiological Sciences,* vol. 1, part 1, New York, Excerpta Medica Foundation, 1962.
33. PAES DE CARVALHO, A. and LANGAN, W. B. *Amer. J. Physiol.*, 1963, *205*:375–381.
34. PAES DE CARVALHO, A., DE MELLO, W. C. and HOFFMAN, B. F. *Amer. J. Physiol.*, 1959, *196*:483–488.
35. PIPBERGER, H. V. *Circulation Res.*, 1962, *11*:555–562.
36. PRINZMETAL, M., SHAW, C. McK., JR., MAXWELL, M. H., FLAMM, E. J., GOLDMAN, A., KIMURA, N., RAKITA, L., BORDUAS, J. L., ROTHMAN, S. and KENNAMER, R. *Amer. J. Med.*, 1954, *16*:469.
37. PUECH, P. *L'activité électrique auriculaire.* Paris, Masson et Cie, 1916.
38. ROSENBLUETH, A. and GARCIA-RAMOS, J. *Amer. Heart J.*, 1947, *33*:677–684.
39. RUSH, S., ABILDSKOV, J. A. and McFEE, R. *Circulation Res.*, 1963, *12*:40–50.
40. SAMSON, W. E. and SCHER, A. M. *Circulation Res.*, 1960, *8*:780–787.
41. SANO, T. and SCHER, A. M. *Circulation Res.*, 1964, *14*:117–125.
42. SCHAEFER, H. *Ann. N. Y. Acad. Sci.*, 1957, *65*:743–766.
43. SCHER, A. M. In: *Handbook of Physiology, Section 2: Circulation,* vol. 1, J. Field, ed. Washington, D. C., American Physiological Society, 1962.
44. SCHER, A. M., RODRIGUEZ, M. I., LIIKANE, J. and YOUNG, A. C. *Circulation Res.*, 1959, *7*:54–61.
45. SCHER, A. M. and YOUNG, A. C. *Ann. N. Y. Acad. Sci.*, 1957, *65*:768–778.
46. SCHERF, D. and SCHOTT, A. *Extrasystoles and allied arrhythmias.* New York, Grune & Stratton, 1953.
47. SCHMITT, O. H. *Ann. N. Y. Acad. Sci.*, 1957, *65*:1092–1109.
48. SJOSTRAND, F. S., ANDERSSON-CEDERGREN, E. and DEWEY, M. M. *J. Ultrastruct. Res.*, 1958, *1*:271–286.

49. SODI-PALLARES, D. *New bases of electrocardiography.* St. Louis, C. V. Mosby Co., 1956.

50. SODI-PALLARES, D., BRANCATO, R. W., PILEGGI, F., MEDRANO, G. A., BISTENI, A. and BARBATO, E. *Amer. Heart J.,* 1957, *54:*498–510.

51. TACCARDI, B. *Circulation Res.,* 1963, *12:*341–352.

52. TRAUTWEIN, W. and DUDEL, J. *Pflüg. Arch. ges. Physiol.,* 1956, *263:*23–32.

53. TRAUTWEIN, W. and KASSEBAUM, D. G. *J. gen. Physiol.,* 1961, *45:*317–330.

54. TRUEX, R. C. In: *Electrophysiology of the heart,* B. Taccardi, ed. New York, Pergamon Press, 1965.

55. WEIDMANN, S. *Electrophysiologie der Herzmuskelfaser.* Bern, Hans Huber, 1956.

56. WILSON, F. N., JOHNSTON, F. D., ROSENBAUM, F. F., ERLANGER, H., KOSMANN, C. E., HECHT, H. H., COTRIM, N., MENEZES DE OLIVEIRA, R., SCARSI, R. and BARKER, P. S. *Amer. Heart J.,* 1944, *27:*19–85.

57. WILSON, F. N., MACLEOD, A. G. and BARKER, P. S. *Proc. Soc. exp. Biol. (N. Y.),* 1932, *29:*1006–1010.

58. WILSON, F. N., ROSENBAUM, F. F. and JOHNSTON, F. D. *Advances intern. Med.,* 1947, *2:*1–63.

59. WOODBURY, J. W. In: *Proceedings, International Union of Physiological Sciences,* vol. 1, part 1. New York, Excerpta Medica Foundation, 1962.

60. WOODBURY, J. W. and CRILL, W. E. In: *Nervous Inhibition,* E. Florey, ed. New York, Pergamon Press, 1961.

CHAPTER 31

The Arterial System: Arteries and Arterioles

By ROBERT F. RUSHMER

COMPONENTS OF THE SYSTEMIC ARTERIAL SYSTEM

The systemic arterial system is composed of a central complex of elastic arteries (aorta and its major branches), muscular arteries, and peripheral sites of controlled resistance. The large elastic arteries are distinguished from the muscular distributing arteries by the large quantity of connective tissue in their walls. Elastic fibers are organized in repeating systems of concentric layers. Smooth muscle cells in elastic arteries are not fusiform but exhibit multiple extensions or arms which attach to the elastic framework between the lamellae of elastin.[17] Collagenous fibers are profusely distributed throughout the media, particularly adjacent to elastic lamellae.

In the few muscular arteries which have been studied with the electron microscope, the media was composed of multiple laminae of smooth muscle with elastin fibers interposed in concentric layers.[16] Elastic arteries contain large numbers of smooth muscle cells in the media and the muscular arteries contain elastic fibers between the layers of smooth muscle. Thus, the functional distinction between the two types of arteries may not be as great as the names imply. Because changes in the dimensions of those large arteries probably do not play any significant role in regulating distribution of blood flow to the various tissues, distribution of blood flow is most directly influenced by the pressure head in the arterial system and the caliber of terminal arteries at the sites of controlled resistance upstream from the capillary networks. The major sites of controlled resistance consist of the terminal arterial branches, arterioles and precapillary sphincters. The terminal branches of the arterial system are short and profuse. The caliber of individual terminal branches tapers over very short distances, but the total cross sectional area of this portion of the vascular bed increases precipitously.

The terminal arterial branches, the arterioles, metarterioles and precapillary sphincters are encircled by smooth muscle cells, believed to be innervated by autonomic fibers and are also affected by autonomic hormones or by locally produced chemical agents. The small caliber vessels with their smooth muscle investments constitute the principal sites of controlled resistance. Dilation or constriction of these vessels regulates the blood flow from the arterial system into the capillary networks which they serve. The anatomic arrangement of the microcirculatory beds is illustrated in Figure 5. Vasomotor control of arterioles and metarterioles influences blood flow distribution among the capillary networks; the precapillary sphincters control the amount and direction of flow within the capillary networks.

BASIC FUNCTIONS OF THE SYSTEMIC ARTERIAL SYSTEM

The systemic arteries are a highly branched system of distensible tubes which subserve four distinct functions: (i) conduits, (ii) dampers of oscillations, (iii) pressure reservoir and (iv) flow regulating valves.

Arterial Conduits. An efficient conduit conveys fluid with minimal loss of energy due to friction. Such loss of energy as fluid flows along a tube is indicated by the drop in pressure per unit length. Waste of energy in flowing liquids is greatly increased by turbulence, the

cause of noise in water pipes. The arterial system is remarkably free of turbulence; normally turbulence occurs only at the roots of the aorta and pulmonary artery. Elsewhere in the arterial system, the flow is normally nonturbulent and silent, despite its pulsatile character. The efficiency of the arterial conduits is indicated by the fact that the total cardiac output (some 5 liters per minute) is propelled the full length of the aorta by a pressure drop in the range of 1 to 2 mm. Hg.[13] Similarly the pressure drop between the axillary artery and the radial artery is only about 2 mm. Hg. These pressure gradients are so gradual that they can barely be measured in the presence of the arterial pressure oscillations occurring with every cardiac cycle (Fig. 1).

Damping of Pressure Oscillations. At the onset of each ventricular systole blood in the ventricles is rapidly accelerated and discharged into the ascending thoracic aorta. The long columns of blood in the arterial system cannot be abruptly accelerated so that the initial increment of blood leaving the ventricles is stored in the elastic arch of the thoracic aorta. To accommodate this outrush of blood, the first portion of the aorta is distended, and the wall tension of this proximal segment is increased above that in the adjacent section of aortic wall. A pulse of distension and pressure rapidly progresses down the entire length of the arterial tree. By placing his fingertips over any peripheral artery, a physician can feel the pulse wave which follows each cardiac contraction by an

ARTERIAL FUNCTIONS

Fig. 1. Four functions of the systemic arterial system are represented schematically. The conduit function refers to the vascular channels along which blood flows towards the periphery with minimal frictional loss of pressure head. The combination of distensible walls and high outflow resistance accounts for the pressure reservoir function which also allows damping of oscillations in pressure and flow. The sites of controlled hydraulic resistance in the peripheral vascular beds control the distribution of blood flow to the various tissues and organs.

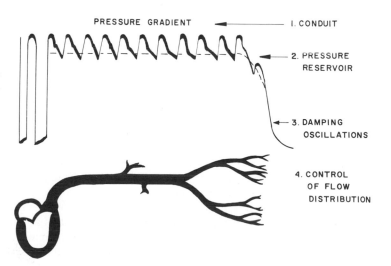

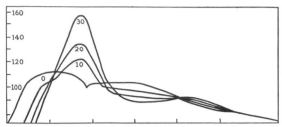

Fig. 2. As it moves along the arteries, the arterial pulse wave becomes distorted. These changes can be seen in the superimposed records above taken from the root of the aorta and from sites 10, 20 and 30 cm. downward from the root. Characteristically, there are a delay in upstroke, due to transmission time, and a more rapid rise of pressure to a higher and sharper peak, followed by oscillations in pressure.

interval dependent upon the transmission velocity of the pulse along the arteries. In the aorta, the pulse wave travels at a rate of about 5 meters per second. This is much faster than the mean rate of blood flow along the aorta (less than 100 cm. per second). In the branching arterial system, the walls become stiffer, i.e., less distensible, as their caliber is reduced with successive branches. For this reason, the transmission velocity of the pulse increases in the smaller arteries to values as high as 10 or 15 meters per second. In the very smallest arterial branches the wall stiffness, and therefore the pulse velocity, is even greater.

The shape of the arterial pulse wave changes progressively as it travels peripherally (Fig. 2). The reason for this change is controversial. One of the most common explanations is based on the concept that the pulse wave is reflected from branch points back toward the aortic arch to set up pressure oscillations. In an elastic tube a traveling pressure wave is reflected to some extent wherever there is discontinuity in the system (i.e., points of branching, local obstructions or sharp bends). If the tube is completely blocked, reflection of pulse wave energy is complete and is 180° out of phase.[13] If a pressure wave travels with increasing velocity toward the periphery and reflects back from regions where many branches occur over a short distance, the oncoming pressure wave is distorted, attaining a higher peak pressure and wider fluctuations following the peak (see Fig. 2). At the root of the aorta, the initial upstroke of pressure is extremely rapid; during the remainder of systole the pressure wave is rounded or dome-shaped. The end of systole is clearly marked by

a sharp dicrotic notch accompanying closure of semilunar valves. During the diastolic run-off the pressure declines almost linearly. In the femoral artery, the rising wave front ascends to a peak of pressure which is considerably higher than the maximum pressure in the aorta (Fig. 2). The pressure descends rapidly, and during the run-off period there is an additional wave called the dicrotic wave. By measuring the pressure pulse contour at various points along the arterial system, Hamilton and Dow[9] demonstrated that the pressure pulse increases in amplitude gradually from the aortic arch to the femoral artery, although the mean pressure remains remarkably constant. Each new pulse of pressure travels down the arterial system and its wave form is distorted by the fluctuations of the pressure reflected up and down the large arteries. This "standing wave" theory of the arterial pulse distortion has been criticized.[13] In the first place, the concept of the standing wave depends on reflected pressure waves of substantial magnitude from the peripheral arterial system. Peterson and Shepard[20] found that large pressure waves experimentally created in a femoral artery were scarcely detectable at the root of the aorta. Moreover, a pressure pulse set up in the aortic arch appeared lower in the arterial system without obvious distortion attributable to discrete reflections.[19] On the other hand, the amplitude of the pulse wave is too great to be completely damped out so that reflected waves must occur to some extent. By virtue of the law of Laplace and the stiffness of vascular smooth muscle, the smallest arteries, in spite of their very thin walls, have elastic moduli of the same order as that of the aorta.[28] The arterial pulse wave is frequently recorded in the terminal arterial branches (see Fig. 3), reflecting the fact that the thin walls of these small vessels act like very stiff tubes in accordance with the law of Laplace. The very great hydraulic resistance at the arterioles and precapillary sphincters tends to damp out the arterial pressure oscillations before the blood reaches the capillary networks except in the presence of very wide vasodilation. In this way, fluctuating pressure and flow in the arterial system are converted into relatively steady pressure and flow in the capillary networks.

Warner[27] simultaneously recorded pressure pulses at the root of the aorta and in a peripheral artery (i.e., femoral or radial artery). He then constructed an electronic analog representing the mechanical characteristics of the arteries between the two points of measurement. By adjusting coefficients in this analog computer he was able to arrive at settings which electronically transformed the central aortic pulse to a wave form closely resembling that in the peripheral artery. Thus, the electronic analog served as a model of the transfer function of the arterial system between the measuring points. For example, the pressure wave distortion along a 15 cm. segment of thoracic aorta, in an open-chest dog, was satisfactorily reproduced by the computer when it was "fed" with a value of 4.4 cycles per second for the resonant frequency and 0.28 for the ratio of damping to critical damping.

In addition to distortion of the wave form re-

sulting from reflected waves from a wide variety of peripheral points, changes in the pulse wave form can be visualized in terms of its frequency content. Any pressure pulse can be considered as the sum of a number of sinusoidal wave forms varying in amplitude and phase, as illustrated in Figure 4A. A wave so constituted is distorted during transmission for two reasons. First, the transmission velocity of the high frequencies is faster than that of the low frequencies. Under these circumstances, the more rapidly traveling high frequency waves could theoretically produce increased peaking of the pressure pulse and corresponding deformation of the remainder of the pulse. Second, high frequencies are damped more effectively than low frequencies so that the relative amplitude of the constituent

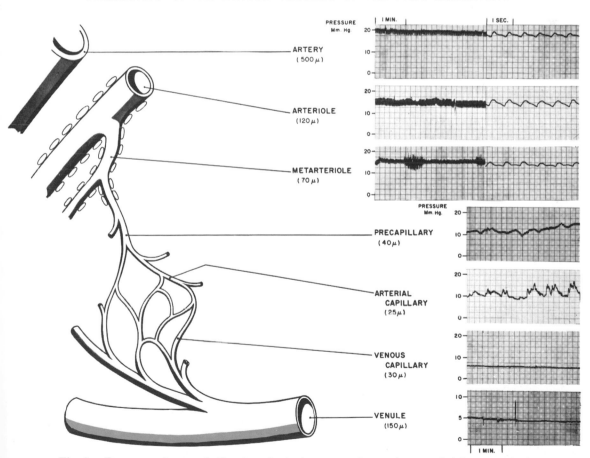

PRESSURES IN THE MINUTE VESSELS OF THE FROG MESENTERY

Fig. 3. Pressure pulses much like those in the larger arteries can be recorded from terminal arterial branches down to and including metarterioles, particularly if vasoconstriction exists downstream. This phenomenon indicates a high degree of stiffness in these vessels. Pressure fluctuations in the arterial end of the capillary are often associated with changes in flow. The pressure in the venules and venous ends of the capillaries remains stable except in severe vasodilation. (After Wiederhielm *et al., Amer. J. Physiol.,* 1964, *207:*173–176.)

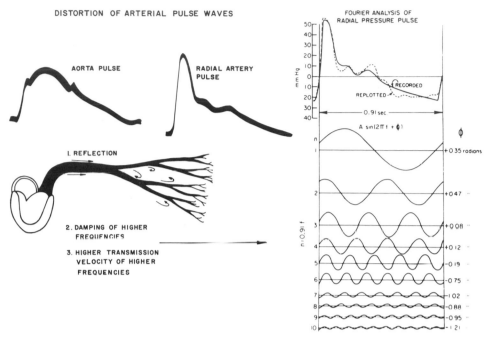

Fig. 4. The distortion of the arterial pressure pulse (see Fig. 1) can be ascribed to several mechanisms. Pressure waves reflecting from branching points and sites of narrowing may reach higher peaks. As shown on the right, the arterial pressure pulse is composed of many frequencies. The arterial walls may selectively damp the higher frequency components. Moreover, higher frequencies may have higher transmission velocities.

frequencies varies with transmission distance. In view of the controversial nature of this topic, it seems appropriate to regard the distortion of the wave form as the result of several factors including reflected waves combined with increased transmission velocities of high frequencies and greater damping of these components, as indicated in Figure 4.

Distortion of the pulse wave form has more than purely academic interest. A physician must expect to record a higher systolic pressure, a greater pulse pressure and a slightly lowered diastolic pressure in peripheral arteries than in the central aorta. With improved techniques for recording pressures within the arterial system, the amplitude of arterial pulses is being increasingly explored as a clue in the diagnosis of cardiovascular disease. For example, an obstruction between the aorta and some peripheral artery alters the form of the pressure pulse recorded distal to the narrowing (i.e., in coarctation of the aorta).

Arterial Pressure Reservoir. Blood is ejected by the left ventricle into the aorta intermittently during each successive systolic inter-val. During diastole, the aortic valves are closed and the aortic pressure declines progressively as blood leaves the arterial system through the terminal branches. Although the diastolic run-off normally lasts about twice as long as the systolic inflow, the arterial pressure does not approach zero. Instead, the next systolic ejection normally occurs before the pressure has declined much more than one-third of the way from the peak systolic pressure. A pulse pressure fluctuation of about 20 mm. Hg on either side of a mean pressure of about 90 mm. Hg is attained by an equilibrium between stroke volume, heart rate and peripheral resistance. Under these conditions, a pressure head for perfusion of blood through the microcirculation is maintained within the arterial system. Since the pressure gradients along the arterial trunks are quite small, this pressure head is well maintained out to the smaller arterial branches. It serves to drive blood to the head and to the extremities when they are elevated above the head or to drive blood through sites of controlled peripheral resistance into capillary networks. Thus, the systemic arterial pressure reservoir provides a pressure head to accelerate promptly the flow of blood through vascular beds dilated in response to peripheral vascular controls.

Sites of Controlled Resistance and Flow Regulation in Vascular Beds. A large portion of the drop in systemic arterial pressure occurs in the arterioles and precapillary sphincters (Fig. 5). The organization and control of the capillary networks, according to the classification of Zweifach,[29] includes sites of controlled resistance of several types. For example, the terminal arteries and arterioles are enclosed within a continuous investment of smooth muscle which tends to regulate flow into the networks. Metarterioles have an incomplete investment of smooth muscle. Metarterioles are continuous with channels having more or less continuous blood flow, although the rate of flow may vary with changes in caliber of the arterioles and metarterioles. These vessels are termed thoroughfare channels since the blood flow through them is rarely interrupted (Fig. 5). Branching from the thoroughfare channels (also called a-v capillaries) are the networks of

true capillaries, which consist of endothelial tubes without a smooth muscle investment. The exchange between blood and tissues takes place in the true capillaries, through which both the amount and direction of blood flow are adjusted by variations in the caliber at their points of origin from the thoroughfare channel. The opening into each true capillary is guarded by a cuff of smooth muscle (the precapillary sphincter) which tends to regulate the flow of blood into the capillary it serves. At intervals of 30 seconds to 2 minutes, some of the precapillary sphincters open up while others close down to produce a continuously changing pattern of blood flow, rate and direction through the individual capillary segments. The phasic diameter changes of sites of controlled resistance are termed *vasomotion*. Its importance in the capillary exchange is considered in the next chapter.

The concept of total peripheral resistance includes the impedance offered by terminal arteries, arterioles, precapillary sphincters, capillaries and veins. The functional relations of arterioles, precapillary sphincters and veins to the function of capillary networks are considered in subsequent chapters. The major control over regional blood flow distribution is exerted by control of the caliber of terminal arteries, arterioles and precapillary sphincters.

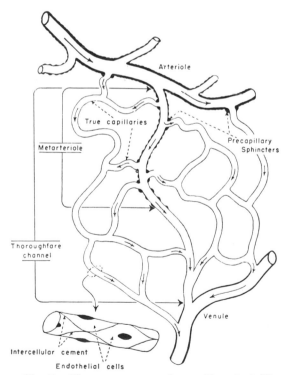

Fig. 5. The components of a capillary bed. The sites of smooth muscle which control the caliber of the channels are indicated for the arteriole, metarteriole and precapillary sphincters by the heavier wall thickness.

MECHANISMS OF VASOCONSTRICTION

Constriction of blood vessels is achieved by contraction of smooth muscle in the walls. The active tension exerted by the smooth muscle cells tends to reduce the caliber of the vessels. In Chapter 27 Burton described his concept that, in accordance with the law of Laplace, the tension required to sustain the transmural pressure diminishes with reduction in caliber, so that at a critical pressure the vessel is in an unstable state, being either widely open or completely closed. The concept of a critical closing pressure is based on the assumption that the vascular walls can be considered extremely thin in relation to the radius of the vessel lumen. Under these conditions, smooth muscle tension would not be dissipated in deforming the structural elements of the arterial wall. The familiar histologic pictures of vascular walls depict vessels which are partially constricted during the process of fixation. Mesenteric arteries (about 1 mm.

Small Artery   Terminal Artery

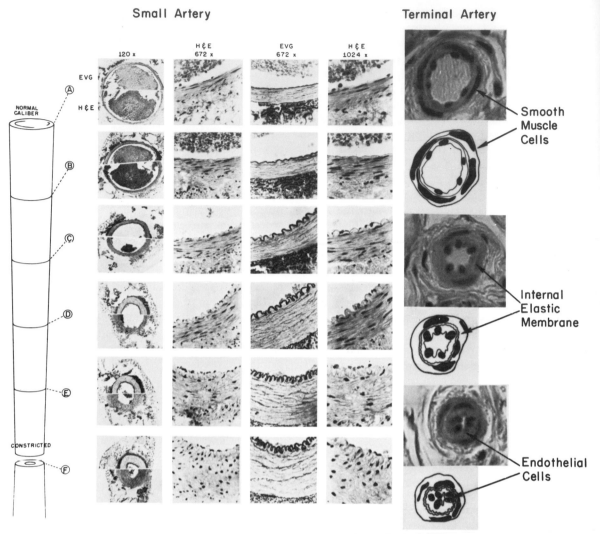

Fig. 6. *Left,* the wall of a small artery (about 1 mm. outside diameter) is very thin in the dilated state (upper figure) and the components are stretched out circumferentially. As the artery constricts, the wall thickens and the components become rounded and deformed. Such vessels do not become occluded at maximal constriction. (From Van Citters, Wagner and Rushmer, *Circulation Res.,* 1962, *10*:668–675.) *Right,* Terminal branches may become occluded by the endothelial cells, which have become rounded, tending to serve as a plastic plug.

outside diameter), quick frozen under conditions otherwise as normal as possible, show a very thin wall. Van Citters *et al.*[26] produced a localized constriction in such arteries and obtained serial sections to determine the changes in wall structure accompanying vasoconstriction (Fig. 6). In the dilated state, the endothelial cells and nuclei are flattened and dispersed widely over the internal surface of the vessel. The internal elastic membrane is a smooth circle without convolutions or wrinkles, the smooth muscle cells are highly elongated, and the nuclei are much longer than their girth. The wall thickness was only about 1/30 of the radius.

Maximum constriction reduced the lumen to about 25 per cent of the control diameter. The wall to lumen ratio was about 1:2 and the lumen was never completely obliterated. The endothelial nuclei were rounded and perched on top of the folds of a highly convoluted internal elastic membrane. The smooth muscle cells were severely distorted and the nuclei were rounded. The walls of constricted arteries amply demonstrate the degree of internal structural distortion which accompanies vasoconstriction. A substantial portion of the smooth muscle tension must be dissipated in producing the deformation of wall structure so the critical closing pressure concept must be adjusted to account for the wall thickness and wall distortion.

Arteries with diameters averaging about 1 mm. never completely close even after administration of concentrated solutions of powerful vasoconstrictor drugs. Apparently the tension developed by the smooth muscle reaches equilibrium with the tensions in the walls of the vessels resulting from the extreme distortion of the structural elements, as illustrated in Figure 6.

The smallest arteries and arterioles become completely occluded through the plugging effect of the endothelial cells. When a vessel is dilated, the endothelial cells are distributed as a thin layer over the internal surface of the vessel. During constriction, the reduced caliber of the vessel is accompanied by a rounding of the endothelial nuclei and a bunching up of endothelial protoplasm (Fig. 6, right column). As the vessel approaches maximal contraction, the endothelial cells become progressively rounded to form a cellular plug which fills in the lumen, much as one might plug a tube with wax.

CONTROL OF PERIPHERAL BLOOD FLOW DISTRIBUTION

The systemic arterial pressure serves as a pressure head to propel blood through the terminal branches of the arterial system into the capillary networks. Variations in the caliber of the terminal arteries regulate the quantity of blood flowing into various portions of tissues and organs. Adjustments in the caliber of the arterioles and precapillary sphincters regulate the quantity of blood entering the capillary networks and individual capillary channels. Constriction of these sites of peripheral resistance is considered in terms of three groups of mechanisms (i) autonomic nerves, (ii) circulating hormones and (iii) local vasoactive chemicals.

Neural Control of the Peripheral Blood Flow. The general principles of autonomic regulation and the anatomic organization of the sympathetic outflow to the heart and peripheral vessels are described in Chapter 10. Although some tissues and organs receive dual innervation from both the sympathetic and parasympathetic divisions of the autonomic nervous system, vascular smooth muscle is generally supplied by fibers derived solely from the sympathetic nervous system. In certain specialized tissues and organs (e.g., skeletal muscle) increased activity of some of the sympathetic nerve fibers leads to a dilation at the sites of controlled resistance. In certain glandular structures, increased activity of the secretory cells is induced by increased discharge along the parasympathetic nerves. Stimulation of the motor nerves to the glands is followed by extreme dilation of the blood vessels within the glands. These three types of vasomotor control will be considered individually.

Sympathetic vasoconstriction. By far the most widespread and functionally important vasomotor control is exerted through the constrictor fibers of the sympathetic nervous system. Nerve cell bodies in the intermediolateral cell column of the thoracic division of the spinal cord give off axons that pass through the ventral roots to synapse either in the ganglia of the sympathetic chain or in accessory ganglia. The postganglionic axons follow the segmental nerves, branching to form perivascular plexuses.

In most tissues, the action of the sympathetic nerve fibers is to induce vasoconstriction of the sort illustrated in Figure 6. Since the degree of vasoconstriction is related to the number of nerve impulses arriving at the nerve ending per unit time, the caliber of the various sites of controlled resistance can be diminished by more intensive sympathetic discharge. Inhibition of the sympathetic discharge can induce vasodilation because relaxation of the smooth muscle permits vascular distension by the intraluminal pressure. In this way a wide range of control can be exerted merely by changes in the number of nerve impulses traversing the sympathetic nerve fibers. Sympathetic nerve fibers transmit impulses to the peripheral vessels at rates varying between 1 and 10 per second. Vasomotor nerve trunks are rarely completely inactive and the smooth muscle they supply is usually in a state of partial contraction which varies with the frequency of nerve discharge. Such a picture leads to a concept of vascular "tone," which refers to a variable degree of tension maintained by the smooth muscle fibers.[6, 12] The degree of vascular tone maintained in various tissues is frequently estimated by computing the hydraulic resistance through a particular vascular bed and then cutting the autonomic nerve supply. The extent to which the blood flow increases and the resistance falls indicates the degree of vasoconstriction maintained by the autonomic nerves to the organ.

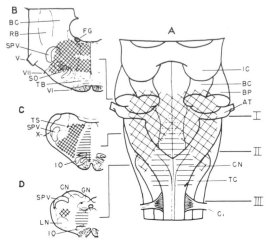

Fig. 7. Location of "pressor" (*diagonal cross hatch*) and "depressor" (*horizontal hatch*) centers in medulla of cat. *A*, Diagram of brain stem; *B, C* and *D,* cross sections of brain stem at levels I, II and III in *A. AT,* Auditory tubercle; *BC,* brachium conjunctiva; *BP,* brachium ponti; C_1, first cervical nerve; *CN,* cuneate nucleus; *FG,* facial genu; *GN,* gracile nucleus; *IC,* inferior colliculus; *IO,* inferior olivary nucleus; *LN,* lateral reticular nucleus; *RB,* restiform body; *SO,* superior olivary nucleus; *SPV,* spinal trigeminal tract; *TB,* trapezoid body; *TC,* tuberculum cinereum; *TS,* tractus solitarius; *V, VI, VII, X,* corresponding cranial nerves; *I, II, III,* levels of transection. (From Alexander, *J. Neurophysiol.*, 1946, 9:205–217.)

The role of sympathetic vasomotor nerves differs greatly in various tissues. For example, sympathetic constrictor fibers appear to exert little or no influence on blood flow through the brain and heart, but they completely dominate the caliber of certain cutaneous vessels (arteriovenous shunts) which are of great importance in control of heat exchange. Other tissues display levels of sympathetic control between these two extremes.

Pathways for sympathetic constrictor control. The discharge of sympathetic vasoconstrictor preganglionic fibers is influenced by a variety of afferent inputs.[18] For example, afferent nerve impulses entering the cord may directly or indirectly affect the sympathetic discharge by spinal reflex mechanisms. Warming of the skin may affect blood flow through internal organs. Stimulation of pain fibers may produce constriction in the skin vessels. Such effects may be observed when the spinal cord is severed in the cervical region, indicating that higher neural centers are not involved.

Visceral afferent fibers from many different

sites which enter the medulla oblongata greatly influence the vasomotor sympathetic discharge. The vagus (X) and glossopharyngeal (IX) cranial nerves contain fibers carrying impulses from the distortion receptors in the walls of carotid sinus and aortic arch. Discharge of these receptors reflects changes in arterial pressure and is of great importance in regulation of the systemic arterial pressure. Blood pressure regulation is described in detail in Chapter 34. Stimulation of various sites in the medulla produces profound increases (pressor responses) or decreases (depressor responses) of blood pressure and changes in peripheral flow distribution (Fig. 7). Such sites are termed vasomotor centers even though there is no anatomic evidence for clearly defined bulbar nuclei subserving vasomotor control. Similarly, stimulation in the hypothalamus and in many other parts of the brain has powerful effects on vasomotor control.[18, 23] In general, stimulation of any area which may induce muscular contraction may produce changes in peripheral flow.[22] Since the various tissues and organs have different functions with different requirements for blood flow, the mechanisms of vascular control must be considered for each tissue individually.

Sympathetic vasodilator fibers. The existence of sympathetic vasodilator fibers is not readily demonstrated. Stimulation of a nerve containing both vasoconstrictor and vasodilator fibers tends to produce over-all vasoconstriction. Reflex inhibition of vasoconstrictor neurons may produce vasodilation which may be mistakenly ascribed to activation of vasodilator neurons. The blood flow through resting skeletal muscle is increased two to three times after block of the tonic vasoconstrictor discharge.[6] However, this is not the maximal possible flow because intense muscular work may increase blood flow by another four- or fivefold. This means that complete elimination of vasoconstrictor influence does not cause maximal vasodilation and that some other mechanism must operate to produce the maximal blood flow observed during exercise. Evidence for the existence of sympathetic vasodilator fibers is based on several lines of investigation.[3, 7, 25] Sympathetic vasoconstrictor endings can be blocked selectively by pharmacologic agents. Also, they are believed to degenerate more rapidly following nerve section and to be more susceptible to cold than vasodilator fibers. These techniques have been employed to depress or eliminate selectively vaso-constrictor effects so that vasodilator influences can be disclosed by stimulating nerves containing both types of fibers.

Although sympathetic vasodilator fibers to skeletal muscle have been the focus of attention in recent years, similar fibers have been reported to innervate blood vessels of certain areas of the skin of the face and the mucous membranes of the mouth and nostrils. In the dog, sympathetic vasodilator fibers have been postulated to run from the stellate ganglion to the coronary arteries, providing increased blood supply to the myocardium during muscular exercise. This mechanism has not been definitely established. Sympathetic vasodilator fibers to the abdominal viscera have also been suggested. However, the evidence for the existence of sympathetic vasodilator fibers is best in skeletal muscle. A mechanism by which the blood supply to muscles is automatically increased by action of the central nervous system at the onset of exercise or before is most attractive as an explanation for the cardiovascular adjustments that occur in a runner at the starting line of a race.

The sympathetic vasodilator system is activated by nerve fibers that descend from the brain. Electrical stimulation of selected sites in the motor cortex, hypothalamus and medulla oblongata have been reported to elicit vasodilation in skeletal muscle. Indeed, stimulation of specific sites in the diencephalon at the base of the brain has been shown to induce in alert animals changes in the distribution of blood flow similar to those which occur during exertion in the same animals.[21] In this case, the blood flow to the hind quarters is greatly increased while flow to the kidney and intestine is somewhat diminished.

Parasympathetic vasodilator mechanism. Stimulation of the nerves to certain glandular structures is accompanied by greatly increased secretion of the gland and by profuse blood flow within the gland. For example, stimulation of the chorda tympani induces profuse secretion of saliva and extreme vasodilation of the salivary gland. Such observations in the past led to the conclusion that the parasympathetic nerve impulses were capable of inducing vasodilation in glandular structures. More recently, Hilton and Lewis[10] presented evidence that actively secreting glandular cells release into the interstitial spaces an enzyme (bradykinin) which acts on

tissue proteins to split off a polypeptide with vasodilator properties. Evidence is being accumulated that a similar mechanism is applicable to skin and perhaps to the gastrointestinal tract. This type of control should be distinguished from the direct action of autonomic nerves because of the differences in the chemical transmitter substances.

Chemical transmitter substances at autonomic nerve endings. Sympathetic nerve fibers influence effector cells by releasing transmitter substances. Sympathetic vasoconstrictor terminals are believed to release norepinephrine, a catechol amine which induces contraction of vascular smooth muscle, although its potency varies rather markedly in different vascular beds. The transmitter substance released from parasympathetic nerve endings is apparently acetylcholine, which has a very powerful vasodilator effect on vascular smooth muscle. However, the vasodilator effects of parasympathetic stimulation to glands is currently attributed to the release of bradykinin rather than to the direct action of acetylcholine. The vasodilator action of acetylcholine can be blocked by the administration of atropine. The sympathetic vasodilator fibers are also blocked by the administration of atropine. This and other evidence suggests that the transmitter substance for the sympathetic vasodilator nerves in skeletal muscle is acetylcholine. This is not the only example of cholinergic sympathetic fibers; the sweat glands are also activated by acetylcholine and blocked by atropine (see Chap. 10).

Vasomotor Effects of Circulating Hormones. The transmitter hormones released at nerve endings have powerful effects on vascular smooth muscle. They also have potent effects when injected intravenously. However, this fact does not necessarily assure a functionally important role of circulating neurohumors in circulatory control. For example, intravenous administration of acetylcholine produces a powerful vasodilation but large doses are required to produce even transient effects because the blood has a high content of choline esterase, an enzyme that rapidly inactivates acetylcholine. The vasoconstrictor agent norepinephrine is destroyed more gradually by monoamine oxidase and has a longer-lasting action. Norepinephrine is secreted at sympathetic nerve endings and also by the adrenal medulla, which functions like a specialized sympathetic ganglion secreting catecholamines into the blood stream (see Chap. 10). Norepinephrine constitutes only about 20 per cent of the total adrenal secretion, the remainder being in the chemically related form of l-epinephrine. The responses to these two catechol amines are decidedly different in the various vascular beds. For example, epinephrine is a more potent vasoconstrictor than norepinephrine in skin, but they have about equal potency in mucous membranes. In skeletal muscle, norepinephrine produces constriction and epinephrine produces vasodilation. Although there is a wealth of experimental observations on the action of these substances when injected intravenously, it is now believed that circulating humors have very limited importance in cardiovascular control. For example, Folkow[6] pointed out that the cutaneous shunts are so sensitive to circulating catechol amines that they respond to even minute concentrations by increased tone. Actually, the resting normal organism does not even have the low blood levels required to affect constriction of the cutaneous shunts.[12] The effects of catechol amines from the adrenal gland appear to be relatively insignificant compared with the direct control by constrictor nerves.[4]

Local Chemical Control of Peripheral Blood Flow. If the blood flow through an extremity is arrested by an occluding cuff or tourniquet for five to ten minutes, release of the occlusion is promptly followed by flushing of the skin, increased warmth and often by tingling or throbbing. These signs of increased blood flow through a part which has been temporarily deprived of blood flow is termed "reactive hyperemia." Reactive hyperemia is usually attributed to reduction in oxygen and accumulation of vasodilator materials in the ischemic tissues. The increased flow is commonly regarded as a mechanism for repaying a blood flow "debt" incurred during the time that tissues were metabolizing without normal blood flow. The magnitude of reactive hyperemia depends upon the temperature,[15] and its duration is related to the duration of arrested blood flow. These observations indicate that hyperemia may be related to metabolic activity. The concept that deficient circulation through tissues results in the accumulation of vasodilator materials among the "metabolites" is an extremely attractive hypothesis since it suggests that local control of blood flow through capillary networks is automatically linked to the metabolic activity of the

tissue. However, in controlled experiments the "flow debt" is not accurately repaid by hyperemia. No specific agent or substance has been established as the cause of vasodilation under conditions of deficient blood flow. Although low oxygen in the tissues may cause smooth muscle fibers to relax, Anrep and von Saalfeld[2] concluded from carefully controlled experiments that low oxygen tensions are probably not a major direct factor in inactive hyperemia. Matthes[14] changed the arterial oxygen saturation of finger blood in three groups of subjects by having them breathe different oxygen mixtures. Although the arterial oxygen saturation was 100 per cent, 96 per cent and 70 per cent, respectively, at the onset of vascular occlusion of the finger and dropped after ten minutes in the ischemic finger to 80 per cent, 55 per cent and 45 per cent, respectively, the magnitude and duration of reactive hyperemia was approximately equal in the three groups.

Effects of pH, CO_2 and metabolites. The fact that increased energy release by cells tends to be accompanied by the production of acid metabolites has led to the widely accepted notion that decreased pH or accumulation of CO_2 and other metabolic products may serve as vasodilators responsible for increased blood flow during increased activity. Fleisch and Sibul[5] investigated the vasoactive properties of a large number of organic acids which are intermediaries in carbohydrate metabolism. Free acids (i.e., lactic acid, acetic acid) produce some vasodilation while their sodium salts have little effect on the blood flow through perfused hind limbs of cats. Thus the vasodilation induced by organic acids is presumed to be due to changes in pH rather than a direct response to the specific anion. Kester, Richardson and Green[11] found that alterations in pH either above or below 7.4 produced vasodilation in hind limbs. Alkaline buffers produced vasoconstriction in skin, whereas muscle displayed vasodilation when hydrogen ion concentration was either decreased or increased. To produce substantial changes in blood flow required rather extreme changes in pH (outside physiologic ranges). Even drastic changes in pH fail to produce changes in blood flow comparable to that seen during reactive hyperemia in extremities. For example, the largest change in muscle blood flow observed by Fleisch and Sibul[5] amounted to 140 per cent as contrasted with increases of 400 to 1000 per cent commonly seen during reactive hyperemia. Although changes in pH may play some role in local vascular adjustments, other mechanisms must also be invoked to explain the total response.

Although perfusion fluids saturated with CO_2 have vasodilator properties, these are usually attributed to the changes in pH. Immersing the hands in carbonic acid produces a flushing although the increased flow is slight relative to the change in color, indicating a change in blood content of the skin. Carbon dioxide does not appear to be a strong candidate for a key role in local chemical control.

Of a variety of metabolic intermediaries, most have been found to be relatively inactive with the possible exception of acetate, citrate, the amines and bile acids. No one of these substances appears to play a dominant role in local vascular control although combinations of them may be more effective than individual species.

Certain of the high energy phosphates have profound vasodilator effects. For example, adenosinetriphosphate (ATP) and adenosinediphosphate (ADP) have powerful vasodilator effects and are closely related to metabolic energy release. However, ADP and adenosine have considerably less vasodilator activity than ATP. Unless the cell membrane permeability to ATP is very limited at rest and ADP is released from cells during activity or insufficient oxygen, this mechanism would not function properly to explain increased blood flow when energy output is increased.

Histamine is a powerful vasodilator; it ranks second among the most effective known vasodilator agents. Histamine content of venous blood after occlusion of blood flow is not consistently elevated and the injection of antihistamines does not consistently modify reactive hyperemia. Thus the role of this substance is far from clearly established.

In summary, many different chemical substances have been studied as possible agents responsible for reactive hyperemia or for vasodilation accompanying increased metabolism. Although some of these chemical agents have vasodilator properties, no specific metabolic product has been demonstrated to play a significant functional role. To avoid cloaking our ignorance with an attractive name or concept, it is preferable to continue to explore the "unidentified vasodilator substances."

VASCULAR CONTROL IN SPECIFIC TISSUES

A variety of different neural, hormonal and chemical mechanisms are generally ascribed roles in the adjustments of peripheral blood flow. The caliber of vascular channels at any moment apparently represents a balance of these interacting factors. Smooth muscle cells enclosing peripheral blood vessels appear similar in all tissues but the vascular networks vary remarkably in their responsiveness to the individual mechanisms described above. For this reason, generalizations about vasomotor control are likely to be misleading. The factors involved in circulatory control should be considered for each tissue or organ individually. A review by Green and Kepchar[8] and a comprehensive review edited by Abramson[1] are valuable reference sources for recent data and current concepts of peripheral vascular control. An exhaustive survey of control mechanisms of all the tissues of the body is not appropriate here. Instead, some representative examples are chosen to illustrate variations in function and control of vascular beds in selected tissues.

Skin. The skin serves as a protective covering and as a site for heat exchange in the regulation of body temperature. Neither of these functions involves large or varying requirements for energy conversion or oxygen consumption. Thus, the flow of blood through cutaneous vessels is adjusted not primarily to the requirement of skin for oxygen (approximately 0.8 ml. per minute per 100 grams tissue) but rather to the functional requirement of the body for dissipation or conservation of heat. For example, resting subjects may have finger skin blood flows in the range of 15 to 50 ml. per minute per 100 grams of tissue. A large portion of this high flow is through arteriovenous shunts which bypass the cutaneous capillaries and perfuse extensive venular plexuses from which heat is conducted to the outside. These plexuses also function on occasion as a store of blood which may be released into the circulation. This reservoir function is also independent of the nutritive requirements of the skin.

Cutaneous blood flow depends primarily upon variations in tonic sympathetic vasoconstrictor discharge. Although this discharge is varied through spinal, medullary and hypothalamic reflexes, blushing from embarrassment

SKIN VASCULATURE

A. VASOCONSTRICTOR MECHANISMS

  1. Neural

    (a). Sympathetic n.

  2. Hormonal

    (a). L–Epinephrine

    (b). Norepinephrine

B. VASODILATOR MECHANISMS

  1. Neural

    (a). Axon reflex

  2. Hormonal

    (a). Bradykinin (glands)

    (b). Acetyl choline

  3. Local chemical

    (a). Unidentified metabolites

    (b). $\uparrow CO_2 \downarrow O_2$

    (c). Histamine

  4. Radiation

    (a). X–Ray

    (b). Ultraviolet

    (c). Infrared

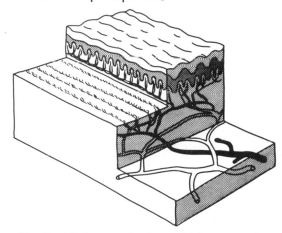

Fig. 8. Various mechanisms which may produce vasoconstriction or vasodilation in the vascular bed in skin.

and blanching from fear suggest cortical influences. Norepinephrine and l-epinephrine in the smallest to the largest effective doses invariably produce cutaneous vasoconstriction; skin vasculature appears to be somewhat more sensitive to the action of these substances than are most other vascular beds. Intra-arterial injection of acetylcholine produces mild dilation, but there is no definitive evidence that parasympathetic or any other cholinergic fibers participate in normal control. Evidence has been presented that nerve impulses initiated in cutaneous receptors may progress toward the spinal cord and also antidromically along branches of the same afferent fiber to reach adjacent blood vessels. This so-called axon reflex has been ascribed a role in the production of hyperemia of the skin subjected to irritants. This concept is based on indirect evidence and has not been irrevocably established. It is widely accepted and difficult to disprove.

Cutaneous reactive hyperemia occurs promptly and prominently after temporary occlusion of the arterial blood supply in man. In contrast, temporary arterial occlusion of blood flow to the dog's paw produces little or no reactive hyperemia. Temperature control in the dog is effected by mechanisms which are different from those of man. Recognizing the existence of such species differences is important in evaluating experimental data.

Various forms of radiation (infrared, ultraviolet, x-ray) increase cutaneous blood flow. In addition, trauma to the skin produces increased blood flow, presumably due to the release of histamine or some related chemical. There is no evidence that histamine or related chemicals have any normal control function.

From this description it is obvious that the skin is equipped with a very large and diverse group of mechanisms which can influence blood flow. Most of these have some functional role in regulating the distribution of blood flow. Situated on the surface of the body, the skin blood flow is commonly affected by factors such as radiation and trauma which are not so likely to affect the deeper structures.

Skeletal Muscle. Blood flow through skeletal muscle is regulated in relation to muscle oxygen requirements, which vary widely between rest and vigorous exercise. For example, blood flow through resting muscles is of the order of 0.1 to 0.3 ml. per gram per minute; in exercise flow increases 20 to 30 times. Histologic examination of muscle samples obtained at rest and immediately after exercise reveals a tremendous increase in the number and diameter of open capillaries. Although skin blood flow can increase by about the same amount, much of the increased flow is through arteriovenous shunts. In contrast, the increased flow in skeletal muscle passes through thoroughfare channels and capillary networks since arteriovenous shunts are rarely found in this tissue. Regulation of muscle blood flow is attained by a combination of neural and local chemical mechanisms (Fig. 9).

Stimulation of sympathetic fibers serving muscle vascular beds produces vasoconstriction. The vasoconstrictor fibers supplying muscle beds appear to participate in vascular influxes important in maintaining systemic arterial blood pressure (see Chap. 34). Stimulation of deep nerve trunks after the constrictor fibers have been blocked may produce a pronounced vasodilation through the action of cholinergic sympathetic vasodilator fibers (see above). A substantial body of evidence indicates that increased blood flow through skeletal muscle can be initiated by higher levels of the central nervous system via pathways which have been traced from motor cortex down through the medulla with or without synapses to the spinal cord. This sympathetic vasodilator system appears capable of initiating increased blood flow through skeletal muscle even in anticipation of exercise or during fainting reactions when no accumulation of local chemical vasodilators should have occurred. Although it is possible that the sympathetic vasodilator fibers may increase blood flow principally through the thoroughfare channels, such an increase can provide a volume of blood which may, with the accumulation of local vasodilator materials, be

SKELETAL MUSCLE

A. VASOCONSTRICTOR MECHANISMS

1. Neural

    (a). Sympathetic constrictor n.

2. Hormonal

    (a). Norepinephrine

B. VASODILATOR MECHANISMS

1. Neural

    (a). Sympathetic vasodilator n.

2. Hormonal

    (a). L-Epinephrine

    (b). Acetyl choline

3. Local chemical

    (a). Unidentified metabolites

    (b). ATP, ADP

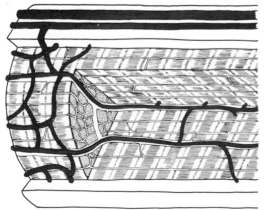

Fig. 9. Blood flow through vascular beds in skeletal muscle is affected by a wide variety of neural, hormonal and chemical factors and, thus, is extremely variable. Note that sympathetic nerves contain fibers which can constrict and others which can dilate the vasculature of this specialized tissue.

rapidly shunted through the true capillary networks.

Circulating autonomic hormones produce rather confusing responses in muscle vascular beds. For example, norepinephrine tends to produce vasoconstriction whereas l-epinephrine tends to produce vasodilation, but these responses vary with dosage levels and fluctuations between vasoconstriction and vasodilation may be observed. Injections of acetylcholine tend to produce vasodilation. Responses to intravenously injected epinephrine have been described in terms of five potential mechanisms by Green and Kepchar:[8] (i) vasoconstrictor response to relatively large doses due to stimulation of the so-called α receptor, which is more prominent in man than in dogs, (ii) direct effects on another group of receptor sites in the vascular bed (the β receptors), which induce direct vascular vasodilation, (iii) reflex inhibition of sympathetic vasoconstrictor "tone," (iv) release of vasodilator substances of unknown source and character and (v) central activation of the sympathetic vasodilator system from which acetylcholine is released at the nerve endings to activate the so-called γ receptors. With these many possibilities, the exact action of circulating autonomic hormones is difficult to determine. However, there is reason to believe that circulating hormones play minor or insignificant roles in normal regulation of muscle blood flow. The major factors are believed to be the balance of neural and local vasodilator effects.

The concept that muscular activity releases acid vasodilators is attractive because such a mechanism would automatically adjust blood flow to the widely varying requirements of muscle. Reactive hyperemia following temporary arrest of the circulation to skeletal muscle is increased in proportion to the "blood flow debt" and is greater when the limb is warmed. This and other evidence lend support to the concept of local control, but the specific vasodilator material or combination of substances responsible has not been identified.

Contraction of skeletal muscle mechanically affects muscle blood flow. The contracting muscle fibers apparently exert external pressure on the vasculature, extruding blood from the capillaries and veins and impeding inflow from the arteries. Thus, during contraction, outflow is accelerated and inflow is impeded. When relaxation occurs, blood surges through the arteries

into the emptied vascular channels and inflow is accelerated while outflow is temporarily retarded. Although the muscle serves as a pump capable of propelling venous blood past an occluding cuff inflated to 90 mm. Hg,[3] the net effect of muscular contraction may be an increased impedance to blood flow. Blood flow through a relaxed extremity may be somewhat higher immediately after strenuous alternating muscular contraction than it was during the exercise.

Coronary Blood Flow. The coronary blood flow has many features in common with that through skeletal muscle. However, control of coronary vessels is obscured by the fact that the myocardium is the source of the energy to propel the blood so that any change in ventricular function tends to influence the coronary vessels which supply it. The nature of coronary flow regulation is treated extensively in Chapter 36.

Kidney. The excretory function of the kidney is based on the filtration of large quantities of fluid in the glomeruli and selective reabsorption of most of the water and essential solutes as the filtrate passes through the tubules. The functional significance of the vascular structures in the kidney are considered in Chapter 44. The blood flow through the kidneys is approximately one-fifth of the total cardiac output. Approximately a liter of blood pours through these two small organs each minute. The enormous blood flow is unrelated to the oxygen requirements of the kidney parenchyma; the oxygen extraction is only about 1 to 2 ml. from each 100 ml. of blood.

Sympathetic nerves to the kidney are predominately constrictor and are capable of reducing total renal blood flow to approximately zero (Fig. 10). Such profound renal vasoconstriction tends to occur in response to startle or fright rather than during exercise of moderate degree.[21] Severe exercise undoubtedly involves profound reduction in renal flow, effectively diverting this proportion of the cardiac output from the kidney to active skeletal muscles.

Circulating l-epinephrine and norepinephrine produce intense vasoconstriction and reduced renal blood flow in spite of the elevated systemic arterial pressure which these substances tend to produce. Local metabolites probably have no functionally significant role in normal renal flow regulation although reactive hyperemia can be produced by brief occlusion of the renal artery. Other vasoconstrictor mechanisms such as the renin-angiotensin system produce diminished renal blood flow and have generated considerable interest as possible factors in the production of abnormally high systemic arterial pressure (hypertension).

Splanchnic Vascular Bed.   The blood vascular system of the intestines is profusely supplied with sympathetic vasoconstrictor fibers which exercise an extremely important role in the control of systemic arterial blood pressure. When systemic arterial pressure falls because of blood loss or of vasodilation of other vascular beds, the blood flow through the splanchnic viscera is attenuated by reflex vasoconstriction. The digestive function of the gastrointestinal tract is held in abeyance for the protection of the total organism. Circulating autonomic hormones (l-epinephrine and norepinephrine) produce vasoconstriction. Reactive hyperemia can be produced in the intestine, indicating an effectiveness of metabolic vasodilator substances. However, the sympathetic vasoconstrictor fibers are the dominant mechanism for regulating blood flow through the intestines.

Brain.   The central nervous system has a remarkably constant oxygen consumption. Although the cerebral vascular system appears to be served by sympathetic nerve fibers, there is little evidence that these exercise any important regulatory control of cerebral blood flow. In general, transient changes in systemic arterial pressure are accompanied by corresponding changes in cerebral blood flow. Changes in blood flow reflecting changes in perfusion pressure suggest limited vascular control. Although the total cerebral blood flow varies little, Sokoloff[24] has demonstrated that active regions of the brain may have increased blood flow (e.g., visual cortex) without demonstrable changes in total cerebral blood flow.

Increased CO_2 (i.e., by inhaling gas mixtures with increased CO_2) is accompanied by increased cerebral blood flow, presumably by direct action of this substance on the cerebral vasculature. Conversely, hyperventilation with diminished arterial CO_2 content apparently results in cerebral vasoconstriction. On the other hand, changes in oxygen content in the arterial blood appear to have no influence on cerebral blood flow.

In general, the cerebral blood flow appears to be remarkably constant and exhibits little evidence of control. The complicated control mechanisms which maintain arterial pressure

relatively constant at the base of the brain (carotid sinus region) also tend to assure sufficient cerebral perfusion pressure. In contrast with other vascular beds, the cerebral vasculature seems unresponsive to the wide variety of mechanisms which might influence the caliber of these vessels.

Lungs.   The pulmonary vascular bed occupies a unique position in parallel with the systemic circulation by serving a single organ with a well-defined function. Although the quantity of blood passing through the lungs each minute is the same as that passing through the systemic circulation, the differences in these circulations are profound. The pulmonary vascular system is remarkably unresponsive to the usual vascular control mechanisms. For example, sympathetic nerve stimulation and the administration of epinephrine and other vasoconstrictor agents have insignificant effects on pulmonary vascular resistance. During exercise pulmonary blood flow may increase two- or threefold without any measurable increase in the very small pressure gradient from pulmonary artery to pulmonary vein. This phe-

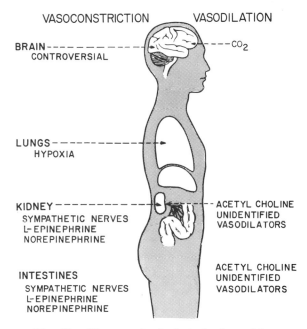

Fig. 10.   The vascular beds in brain and lungs are remarkably unreactive, responding only slightly and equivocally to neural and hormonal influences. These beds are affected by carbon dioxide and by reduced oxygen in brain and lungs respectively. In the kidneys and intestines, the vascular beds are affected by several mechanisms, some of which are still unidentified.

nomenon is commonly attributed to a passive vasodilation of the pulmonary vessels to accommodate the increased flow with a corresponding reduction in vascular resistance. The mechanism of this adaptation is not known. There is some evidence that diminished oxygen tension in the blood or alveoli may reduce local pulmonary blood flow (presumably to local vasoconstriction). This mechanism is believed to account for observations that collapse of pulmonary tissue (atelectasis) is accompanied by diversion of blood from the functionless area. In general, the lungs may be regarded as essentially unresponsive to the wide array of vascular control mechanisms and as participating in no active manner in the peripheral vascular regulation.

REFERENCES

1. ABRAMSON, D. I., ed. *Blood vessels and lymphatics.* New York, Academic Press, 1962.
2. ANREP, G. V. and VON SAALFELD, E. *J. Physiol.,* 1935, *85:* 375–399.
3. BARCROFT, H. and SWAN, H. J. C. *Sympathetic control of human blood vessels.* London, Edward Arnold Ltd., 1953.
4. CELANDER, O. *Acta physiol. scand.,* 1954, *32:*Suppl. 116.
5. FLEISCH, A. and SIBUL, I. *Pflüg Arch. ges. Physiol.,* 1933, *231:* 787–804.
6. FOLKOW, B. In: *Blood vessels and lymphatics,* D. I. Abramson, ed. New York, Academic Press, 1962.
7. FOLKOW, B. *Physiol. Rev.,* 1955, *35:*629–663.
8. GREEN, H. D. and KEPCHAR, J. H. *Physiol. Rev.,* 1959, *39:* 617–686.
9. HAMILTON, W. F. and DOW, P. *Amer. J. Physiol.,* 1939, *125:*48–59.
10. HILTON, S. M. and LEWIS, G. P. *J. Physiol.,* 1956, *134:*471–483.
11. KESTER, N. C., RICHARDSON, A. W. and GREEN, H. D. *Amer. J. Physiol.,* 1952, *169:*678–687.
12. LÖFVING, B. and MELLANDER, S. *Acta physiol. scand.,* 1956, *37:*134–141.
13. MCDONALD, D. A. and TAYLOR, M. G. *Progr. Biophys.,* 1959, *9:*107–173.
14. MATTHES, K. *Kreislaufuntersuchungen am Menschen mit fortlaufend registrierende Methoden.* Stuttgart, Georg Thieme Verlag, 1951.
15. PATTERSON, G. C. and WHELAN, R. F. *Clin. Sci.,* 1955, *14:* 197–211.
16. PEASE, D. C. and MOLINARI, S. *J. Ultrastruct. Res.,* 1960, *3:* 447–568.
17. PEASE, D. C. and PAULE, W. J. *J. Ultrastruct. Res.,* 1960, *3:*469–483.
18. PEISS, C. N. In: *Blood vessels and lymphatics,* D. I. Abramson, ed. New York, Academic Press, 1962.
19. PETERSON, L. H. *Circulation Res.,* 1954, *2:*127–139.
20. PETERSON, L. H. and SHEPARD, R. B. *Surg. Clin. N. Amer.,* 1955, *35:*1613–1628.
21. RUSHMER, R. F., FRANKLIN, D. L., VAN CITTERS, R. L. and SMITH, O. A. *Circulation Res.,* 1961, *9:*675–687.
22. RUSHMER, R. F. and SMITH, O. A. *Physiol. Rev.,* 1959, *39:* 41–68.
23. SMITH, O. A. Chap. 3 in *Nervous control of the heart,* W. C. Randall, ed. Baltimore, Williams and Wilkins Co., 1965.
24. SOKOLOFF, L. In: *New research techniques in neuroanatomy,* W. F. Windle, ed. Springfield, Ill., Charles C Thomas, 1957.
25. UVNÄS, B. *Physiol. Rev.,* 1960, *40*(Suppl. 4):69–80.
26. VAN CITTERS, R. L., WAGNER, B. M. and RUSHMER, R. F. *Circulation Res.,* 1962, *10:*668–675.
27. WARNER, H. R. *Circulation Res.,* 1957, *5:*79–84.
28. WIEDERHIELM, C. A., WOODBURY, J. W., KIRK, S. E. and RUSHMER, R. F. *Amer. J. Physiol.,* 1964, *207:*173–176.
29. ZWEIFACH, B. W. *Sci. Amer.,* 1959, *200:*54–60.

CHAPTER 32

The Capillaries, Veins and Lymphatics

By HUBERT R. CATCHPOLE

CAPILLARIES

AT the present time, many aspects of capillary anatomy and physiology are under intensive scrutiny, partly because of new investigations into the histochemistry and ultrastructure of these vessels which have led to a re-examination of physiologic teaching regarding the capillary circulation and partly because of a conviction that concepts limited to the vessel alone are inadequate to explain the manifold physiologic events and pathologic disturbances that occur in blood-tissue exchanges.

The functions of the cardiovascular system are integrated and directed toward the maintenance of the constant composition and temperature of the tissue environment. Capillaries form the ultimate subdivision of the blood vascular system. The primary action of the heart, distributing arteries and arterioles, collecting venules and veins, is to conduct blood to and from the capillaries. These minute vessels, 10 to 20 microns in diameter or less, are the locus of exchange of oxygen, carbon dioxide, water, ions, nutrients, metabolites and humoral products between blood and tissues. Forming a dense network between arterioles and venules, capillaries are usually in close relation with parenchymatous cells. Besides the capillaries proper, various precapillary arterioles and postcapillary venules may, because of their intrinsic permeability, be included in the physiologic category of capillaries.

The term "microcirculation" is applied to the whole system of minute vessels 100 microns or less in diameter and therefore just below the limit of naked eye resolution. The greater part of the total circulating blood is at all times contained within the microcirculation. Capillaries are included in this system, of which they form the ultimate subdivision.

Capillary density varies greatly in different organs and tissues. Thus the thyroid gland is richly vascular, the cornea very sparsely so, and epiphyseal cartilage and the lens lack a capillary supply. In the latter tissues it must be surmised that other routes provide for the supply of essential nutrients and the removal of waste products. Under normal conditions—for example, in resting glands and muscles—a certain proportion of the capillaries may be collapsed and individual vessels may show periodic opening and closing. Intense tissue activity is always signalized by patency of its entire capillary system and by an increase in its blood flow. These increases are mediated by local hormonal and neural controls which will be examined in subsequent sections. Changes in the composition of the blood, representing additions and withdrawals as it passes through the capillary circulation, are restored in the lungs and the kidneys.

CIRCULATION THROUGH THE CAPILLARIES

The classic observations on the capillary circulation were made on such external structures as the web of the frog's foot. Also, the tongue or mesentery of the frog and the food pouch of the hamster were exteriorized and spread out as thin membranes in a moist chamber. The tissues were transilluminated and examined under moderate ($\times$ 200 or more) powers of the dissecting microscope. Studies of this kind will always be associated with the name of August Krogh[27] who pioneered modern capillary physiology. Other basic study methods of capillary distribution and flow are (i) transillumination of organs and tissues *in situ* using the fused quartz rod which conducts light by internal reflection around turns and bends, (ii) the "window" technique in which a glass and mica chamber is permanently mounted in the rabbit ear; tissue invades the chamber and its circulation may be

studied over days or weeks, (iii) observation of the bulbal conjunctival vessels in man with a stereobinocular microscope under special illumination.

The exact patterns of the arteriovenous pathways form an integral part of the special anatomy and physiology of tissues. While differences associated with the structural organization of tissues exist, the basic pattern is the same.

The smaller arterioles terminate, by a quite rapid transition in structure, in the capillaries. The dense muscular and fibrous walls disappear, leaving only delicate endothelial tubes. These arise by abrupt branching from a parent arteriole, often at angles up to 90°, and they reunite to form polygonal nets or anastomoses of variable form and density which empty into the venular channels (Fig. 1). The principal variation which has been described in this pattern is the presence in some circulations, e.g., the mesentery of the dog and rat, of more direct arteriovenous channels with distinct muscular coats in the proximal part, in which blood flow is continuous. These "through channels" also give rise to true capillary offshoots. At the point of branching of capillaries from arterioles or through channels, there are collections of smooth muscle cells functioning as precapillary

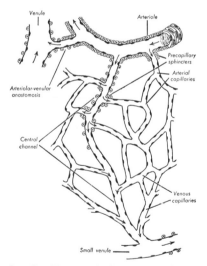

Fig. 1. Capillary bed, diagrammatic. Arrows indicate direction of blood flow. Muscle cells (highly diagrammatic) shown surrounding arteriole, less densely around venule and scattered along the proximal part of a through channel. They are present at the point of origin of the true capillaries. An arteriovenous (A-V) anastomosis, or by-pass is also shown. (From Copenhaver in: Bailey's *Textbook of histology*, 15th ed. Baltimore, Williams and Wilkins Co., 1964.)

sphincters. These are the terminal points of neuromuscular control of capillary flow.

The length of capillaries is somewhat indeterminate. Defined as the shortest path from arteriole to venule, capillaries measure from 0.4 to 0.7 mm. (400 to 700 microns) and the meshes of the capillary network may range from 100 to 200 microns up to several hundred microns across. Capillary diameter varies from 15 to 20 microns down to 5 microns or less, so that the smallest vessels are commensurate in size with the cells that pass through them. By use of the techniques described combined with microcinematography, vivid impressions of the capillary circulation and its moment to moment variations have been provided. Previously closed capillaries are observed to admit a flow of blood cells, while active capillaries may abruptly close. These changes are attributed to relaxation or constriction of the precapillary sphincters. Flow in a capillary may be suddenly reversed in direction, since many alternative paths exist. After injecting India ink into the circulation, Krogh counted five capillaries per square millimeter in resting muscle and 190 per square millimeter after stimulation. It was estimated that only 1/20th to 1/50th of the total capillary bed of muscle is open in the resting state. At the other extreme, in the brain the number of open capillaries tends to remain constant at all times.

In the narrowest capillaries there can of course be no swiftly moving axial stream such as is seen in arterioles. Microscopic observation gives the illusion of rapid movement in capillaries but it must be remembered that speed is also magnified. The speed of red cells in mesenteric capillaries varies from 0.8 to 2.0 mm. per second, by no means an impetuous rate. Cells may appear to be squeezing through the smallest capillaries and are temporarily deformed in the process. In free flow through capillaries, cells assume very characteristic "parachute" or "thimble-like" shapes, with a convex front and a concave back aspect.[23] These effects are part of the complex rheology of blood flow through the fine conduits of the microcirculation and are attributed in part to drag effects at the capillary wall, in part to the elastic properties of red cells.

Cell Aggregation.[32] If red cells form rouleaux or aggregations *in vivo*, flow through the smaller vessels will be greatly impaired. "Sludging" of red cells has been described in injury and infection and during such procedures as use of the extracorporeal heart pump (open heart operations). It is ascribed to interaction of cells with those plasma proteins involved in the normal clotting mechanism. The observed effects are flow stasis and pooling of cells within the microvasculature, leading to an apparent anemia. Cell aggregation may be reversed by the intravenous administration of low molecular weight dextrans (mol. wt. 40,000 to 70,000), which are thought to reduce the electrostatic bonding forces between the cells. Dextrans also increase the total fluid volume within the circulation, presumably through osmotic action. A spectacular instance of natural interference with capillary blood flow is seen in sickle cell anemia. The sickling effect is most pronounced in areas of low oxygen tension and the affected cells, by reason of their interlocking shapes and high rigidity, readily plug capillary and post-capillary vessels.[44]

In man the total extent of the capillary wall in muscle alone has been placed at 6000 square meters,[27] and it is believed that the whole of this enormous area is available for gaseous exchange. A very high percentage of this figure represents the flattened cytoplasm of endothelial cells which make up the capillary wall. The remainder consists of the cellular junctions which, on the basis of a rough calculation from present electron micrographs, may represent at most 2 or 3 square meters.

Capillary Blood Flow, Density and Surface.[8] The blood supply of a given organ or tissue depends on the richness of its capillary supply and on the proportion of open capillaries. For a complete quantitative description, it would be necessary to know the proportion of total capillary surface to unit tissue volume. An approximation can be made in several ways. If an animal is injected with India ink and the tissues obtained are instantaneously frozen in liquid nitrogen and dried *in vacuo*, a histologic estimate of capillary density can be made. In the alveoli of the lung, the capillary network is dense and the meshes are only a few times the diameter of the capillary itself. A closely similar situation obtains in intestinal villi. Other methods depend on the enumeration of red cells per tissue unit. Table 1 summarizes data on blood flow and Table 2 gives some of the limited data on surface–volume relations. Tissues with poor blood supply include fat, bone marrow and resting muscle; active skeletal muscle, heart muscle

TABLE 1. *Blood Flow in Tissues and Organs*

TISSUE OR ORGAN	ANIMAL	BLOOD FLOW (ml. per 1000 grams per minute)
Thyroid	Man; mouse	4000; 3240
Kidney	Man; dog; rabbit	3400; 3300; 3200
Brain	Monkey	850 (range 600–1000)
	Man	650 (range 460–1040)
Spinal cord (white)	Cat	140
Heart	Dog	500–750
Muscle (dilated)	Dog	110–580
Fat	Man	12–15

(After Catchpole and Gersh, *Physiol. Rev.,* 1947, *27*:360–397.)

TABLE 2. *Capillary Surface of Tissues in Relation to Total Tissue Volume (S/V)*

TISSUE		ANIMAL	s/v (cm.$^{-1}$)	
			Total (open plus closed capillaries)	Open capillaries
Fat	Fat-rich	Rat	51.9	23.5
	Fat-poor	Rat	222.2	64.1
Muscle		Rabbit	150–513	
		Dog	494	
		Guinea pig		186–507
		Mouse		486–923
Cardiac muscle		Man	1184	

(After Catchpole and Gersh, *Physiol. Rev.,* 1947, *27*:360–397.)

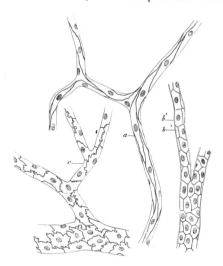

and brain have a moderate supply and kidney and thyroid a very rich supply. The white matter of the brain is something under one-half as richly vascularized as the gray. Lying outside this general classification are organs like the spleen with its intermittent blood flow and the liver, which has a dual blood supply.

Physiologically and pathologically these values are of great significance (i) during activity of a tissue or organ when the circulation must adjust to increased metabolic demands; (ii) during decompression when gases may be trapped and released in a poorly vascularized tissue (aeroembolism); (iii) in all forms of metastatic embolism, e.g., by blood clots, fat or tumor cells.

FINE STRUCTURE OF CAPILLARIES

The capillaries are minute tubes composed of flattened endothelial cells closely apposed or interdigitated. This much was known to the older histologists, as a picture taken from a text of 1871 shows (Fig. 2). Each endothelial cell contains a single nucleus and these cells tend to be disposed rather regularly in the capillary

Fig. 2. Woodcuts of various capillaries with intercellular junctions stained with silver nitrate. *a,* Mesentery of Leuciscus (chub), a narrow capillary with spindle shaped cells; *b,* capillary from pecten of the bird's eye, with polygonal cells; *c,* capillary from snail stomach with irregularly edged cells. (From Stricker, *Handbuch der Lehre von der Gewebe,* vol. 1, Leipzig, W. Engelmann, 1871.)

structure. The cells are so flattened that in the light microscope only the nuclei show up distinctly in cross section. The cell junctions were recognized early by their strong direct staining with silver nitrate.

By the early 1940's capillary structure could be described as follows:[9, 10] The capillary wall is composed of endothelial cells with an intercellular cement between them, believed to be a calcium proteinate secreted by the cells. On the inner wall of the capillary is a thin, noncellular endocapillary layer of some protein supposedly derived from the blood plasma. External to the capillary is a pericapillary distribution of connective tissue fibrils staining positively with silver (argyrophilic). A capillary basement membrane was dismissed as unlikely by Krogh. The capillary environment was viewed as a "space" occupied by tissue fluid and fibrillar material. Thus the capillary wall separated two essentially fluid compartments. Minute pores in the capillary wall, probably restricted to the cell junctions, were held to be the route of fluid and material exchange.[40]

A modern view of the capillary must take account of (i) chemical and histochemical studies of the extracellular, extravascular connective tissue, which is composed of fibrillar elements and a gel-like ground substance with which "tissue fluid" is intimately associated; (ii) electron microscope and other studies of the capillary endothelium and its surrounding structures, including a basement membrane. The older concept is replaced by one of a highly organized sheet of endothelial cells in contact with blood on the one side and with a complex colloidal matrix on the other (Fig. 3). Both are significant in determining blood-tissue exchange.

Electron micrographs of thin sections of capillaries from muscle, for example, show endothelial cells with a bulging nucleus and attenuated cytoplasm (Fig. 4). The cells have an ultrastructure delineated by the fixing and staining agent used, which is commonly osmium tetroxide. Features seen are a rather irregular nucleus with one or more nucleoli, a small Golgi complex and a pair of centrioles, rather few mitochondria and a sparse endoplasmic reticulum with scattered ribonucleoprotein granules.

Fig. 3. Diagram of relations of connective tissue ground substance (*light stipple*) to cells, fibers and a blood vessel. The heavier stipple represents basement membrane of epithelium, muscle and endothelium of a small blood vessel (capillary). (After Gersh and Catchpole, *Perspect. Biol. Med.*, 1960, *3*:282–319.)

Fig. 4. Diagram of an endothelial cell in cross section of capillary wall. Impression drawn from electron micrograph of a cutaneous capillary. (Courtesy of Dr. H. H. Friederici.)

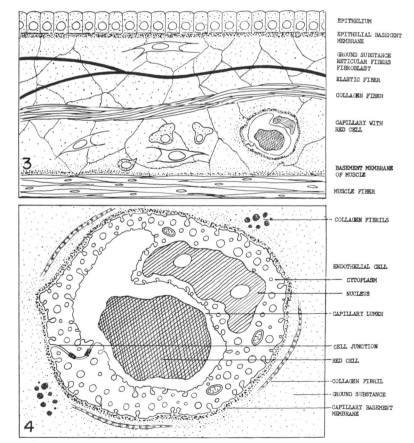

Small vesicles 600 to 1000 Å in diameter are seen at both cell borders (*caveolae intracellulares*) and within the cell (*pinocytotic vesicles*). Filaments some 50 to 100 Å wide have been described in the cytoplasm and may represent contractile elements.[14]

The junction between the cells is much narrower than once believed and is seen as a tortuous space 90 to 150 Å wide, moderately dense in appearance. Cell margins may overlap by 0.5 to 1.0 micron and may be provided with peculiar marginal flaps of unknown function. Denser areas at the cell junctions are not likely to be *desmosomes*, which are exceedingly rare in mammalian vessels. Once called *attachment bands,* they are now reinterpreted as "tight junctions"[13] according to the "unit membrane" view of the cell junction. According to Robertson, the unit membrane is a three-layered sheet about 75 Å thick.[42] The middle, least dense layer is lipoidal, whereas the other layers facing the cell cytoplasm and extracellular environment, respectively, are protein or mucopolysaccharide, appearing dark in electron micrographs. Normally in any tissue, a space of 50 to 100 Å exists between the outer (extracellular-facing) layers of the unit membranes. However, at the tight junctions, this space vanishes and the outer layers of the unit membranes fuse; this line of fusion is continuous over long distances and may be thought of as a "gasket" between cells. Indeed, Farquhar and Palade[13] show that these junctions are sufficiently sealed that little hemoglobin in the lumen of renal tubules can diffuse between the epithelial cells of the tubules and into the extracellular tissue matrix. The tight junction then appears to be an important barrier between capillary endothelial cells, and while the hemoglobin experiment shows that the tight junction is relatively impermeable to molecules the size of hemoglobin (65 Å), it is uncertain whether the junction would permit diffusion of smaller molecules. Tight junctions, like desmosomes, serve to hold cells together.

Electron micrographs show a loose, fluffy endocapillary layer of protein or acid mucoprotein, irregular in thickness and reaching in places several hundred Ångstroms.[31]

Surrounding the entire base of the endothelial cells of certain capillaries is a basement membrane 500 to 600 Å in width, commonly described as an electron-dense, homogeneous layer. It corresponds in position, therefore, with the basement membrane described in light microscopic studies following special staining. With improved staining a "felt-work" of fibrils 50 to 100 Å thick is seen in the basement membrane. They are imbedded in an electron-dense matrix. Peripheral to the basement membrane, bundles of collagen fibrils in profusion are present, cut in all planes, and showing the characteristic 640 Å periodicity. The ground substance seen in light microscopic sections is poorly visualized in the electron microscope, possibly for various technical reasons.

In the older descriptions of capillaries, cells with long cytoplasmic processes disposed along the outside wall of the endothelial tube were prominently featured. These were the Rouget cells, believed to be homologues of smooth muscle cells and responsible for capillary contraction. They are present in the nictitating membrane of the frog's eye. In the mammal, at least, contractile cells of this nature are not now believed to be present. Cells (pericytes) adjacent to the endothelium are seen in electron micrographs. They may be fibroblasts engaged in secretion of pericapillary fibers and ground substance.[24]

The Capillary Environment. The capillary exists in relationship with a complex environment, the extravascular connective tissue. Viewed in the light microscope the connective tissue, after appropriate staining (e.g., the use of periodic acid leukofuchsin for the demonstration of protein–carbohydrate compounds), is seen to be composed of fibers which course through a ground substance (Fig. 3). Fibers are classified on the basis of morphologic and chemical criteria as collagen, reticular and elastic fibers. Collagen and reticulin are chemically closely related proteins and show a similar periodicity of 640 Å at high resolution. The ground substance is nonfibrillar, optically homogeneous, and stains pink or red with periodic acid leukofuchsin. The capillary basement membrane stains as a dense line with this reagent and may represent a condensation of components of the ground substance.

The ground substance comprises a heterogeneous group of materials, some arising by local synthesis in fibroblasts and other cells, some derived from the blood (Table 3). Certain components, particularly those of the mucopolysaccharide group, have been isolated and characterized in the past twenty years.[38] These probably exist in the tissues in close association with proteins, as a consequence of their strongly acidic, negatively charged character. The tissue mucoproteins are probably responsible for the periodic acid leukofuchsin histochemical reaction and are also acidic materials. Both these categories of substances bind cations. Of the other proteins, soluble collagen no doubt arises locally, and there is present a wide spectrum of proteins which have diffused from the blood. Noncolloidal substances and water are mainly of blood origin, with the exception of metabolites of local origin.

The kinds and amounts of the various macromolecular components vary in different connective tissues and undoubtedly contribute strongly to their specific differences. Thus the matrix of cartilage, containing large amounts of chondroitin sulfate, is quite rigid; that of umbilical cord, with considerable hyaluronic acid, is rubbery or gelatinous; that of the vitreous body is a gel which almost collapses under its own weight. In all these tissues, water and colloidal components are organized as stronger or weaker gels which are in part responsible for the variation in physical properties. The strongly acidic nature of many of the macromolecules confers ion-binding and ion-selective properties. All these features must be reflected in a varying relationship with the capillary and with capillary exchange.[20, 21]

By freeze-dry fixation, special staining and viewing in the electron microscope, the amorphous-appearing ground substance of muscle has been resolved at a submicroscopic level into a structure consisting of fluid-filled vacuoles 600 to 1200 Å in diameter (the "water-rich" phase) surrounded by denser walls (the "colloid-rich" phase). When ferrocyanide is injected intravenously into mice, it localizes first in the water-rich vacuoles and can be demonstrated there, under strictly controlled conditions, by the Prussian blue reaction.[11] These two phases are thought to exist in equilibrium, somewhat as in a stable foam. A change in the relative proportions of the two phases, initiated by many different stimuli, is thought to be the basis of reversible changes in the physical character of the ground substance.

Special Capillary Adaptations. In the capillaries of all endocrine glands, thyroid, parathyroid, adrenal cortex, pancreatic islets, pituitary gland, and in the gastric and intestinal mucosa, the thickness of the endothelial cytoplasm may be so reduced as to give *fenestrations* 300 to 500 Å in diameter, closed only by a membrane or *diaphragm* less thick than the cell membrane elsewhere. These fenestrations form a mosaic pattern.

In the kidney glomerulus, similar fenestrations but lacking diaphragms abut on a very thick and prominent basement membrane

TABLE 3. *Summary of Major Constituents of Ground Substance of Connective Tissues*

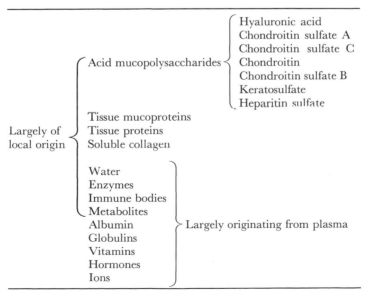

(After Gersh and Catchpole, *Perspect. Biol. Med.*, 1960, *3*:282–319.)

measuring 2800 ± 600 Å in thickness in the adult man. The glomerulus shows a further capillary modification in that its surface is closely invested by epithelial cells closely applied to the basement membrane by means of "foot processes."

In the central nervous system, vascular basement membranes are similarly invested by glial cells; here, however, fenestrations are absent.

In spleen, liver, bone marrow and lymphoid organs the characteristic channel between arteriole and vein is the sinusoid. Sinusoids have irregular, tortuous walls up to 40μ in diameter, lined with cells generally ascribed to the reticuloendothelial system and showing phagocytic properties. Liver sinusoids are lined in part by endothelium, in part by phagocytic Kupffer cells. Blood flow in these channels is sluggish. Cell junctions do not stain with silver and may show gaps between adjacent cells up to 5μ. Sinusoids lack a definite basement membrane and are invested with a dense network of reticular fibrils.

A classification of capillaries has been suggested on the basis of three criteria: (i) the presence or absence of a complete basement membrane, (ii) the presence or absence of fenestrations in cells, or of gaps between them, (iii) the presence or absence of a complete layer of pericytes outside the basement membrane.[3] The classification may have physiologic significance in relation to the ease or difficulty of passage of materials through the various investments, and so through the capillary as a whole. However, the physiologic correlates of these anatomic features are at present inferential. To be a complete physiologic system, the thickness of the basement membrane and the characteristics of the ground substance should be taken into account. All these are essential to an understanding of vessel-connective tissue relationships in any given locus.

EXCHANGES IN THE CAPILLARIES

Blood moves through the capillaries, delivering oxygen and nutrients to the tissues and receiving metabolic products from them; there is an incessant interchange of water, electrolytes and dissolved substances. In this exchange two simultaneous processes are recognized: filtration and diffusion. Filtration implies a bulk passage of water and dissolved substances across the capillary wall by reason of a hydrostatic pressure difference on either side—much like the passage of a solution through a filter paper. If the membrane is such that colloidal material is retained, the process is one of ultrafiltration. By diffusion is meant the passage of a substance across the membrane because of a concentration difference, or more strictly, because of a difference in chemical potential which drives the material from a region of high to one of low chemical potential.

Thus a given dye, for example, may diffuse from blood plasma into a lipid phase (fat) where its concentration is actually higher than in blood. It "moves up a concentration gradient." This is because its standard chemical potential is high in blood and low in fat. This rather trivial instance may have an important application in biology where the various cellular and tissue phases may be expected to be different from the blood plasma.

Diffusion of a solute may occur if the hydrostatic pressure difference on either side of the membrane is zero, or even in an opposed direction. It represents the kinetic tendency of a substance to mix as widely as possible.

The rapid exchange of water and electrolytes between blood and tissues has been most vividly illustrated and measured by the use of labeled normal physiologic constituents of the blood, where extraneous effects on the circulation would be considered negligible. Labeled water (deuterium oxide, D_2O; tritiated water, H_2^3O) leaves the circulation in a matter of seconds or minutes and is entirely equilibrated with the total body water in 4 or 5 minutes with a half-life of about $2\frac{1}{2}$ minutes. This is true also of C^{14}-labeled urea and tritiated thymidine. Some 90 per cent of labeled potassium K^{42} disappears from the rabbit's circulation in 1 minute, a faster rate than either water or sodium, probably indicating that the potassium is being delivered specifically to intracellular locations. On the other hand, larger molecules remain in the vessels much longer. Thus, I^{131}-labeled plasma proteins take several hours to mix with extravascular proteins. The restriction on the movement of molecules of this order of magnitude, i.e., 50,000 or above, although by no means absolute, is sufficient for the plasma proteins to display a measurable osmotic pressure. This osmotic pressure, together with the ambient hydrostatic pressure relations, provides the basis for the Starling hypothesis, which describes filtration in the capillaries.

The Starling Hypothesis.[43] Fluid movement through the capillary wall represents the resultant of two forces, hydrostatic and osmotic, within and without the capillary.

The effective hydrostatic pressure, P, driving fluid out is

$$P = P_i - P_o$$

(i = inside capillary, o = outside capillary).

The effective osmotic pressure π bringing fluid in is

$$\pi = \pi_i - \pi_o$$

The total outward force, $P - \pi$, is given by

$$P - \pi = (P_i - P_o) - (\pi_i - \pi_o)$$

Validation of the Starling hypothesis required the assessment of each of these quantities.

Osmotic Relationships. The osmotic pressure of the blood is that of the colloidal plasma protein constituents, since it is assumed that smaller molecules diffuse readily and exert no osmotic pressure in the capillary. Starling's osmometer was a small glass bell closed at its mouth with a piece of peritoneal membrane soaked in 10 per cent gelatine and provided with a vertical tube. When bell and membrane were immersed in protein-free saline or in serum ultrafiltrate, osmotic flow began and at equilibrium was measured by the height of water in the tube. These physiologic measurements were of great importance because they opened up a way for the first time to measure the molecular weight of proteins (since $\pi = RTc$, where c = moles per liter, R the gas constant and T the absolute temperature) (Table 4). Starling's 1899 value of the osmotic pressure of human serum was 25 mm. Hg; the value stands today. For frogs and turtles, serum osmotic pressures are much lower, 5 to 10 mm. Hg. Protein solutions at high concentrations show a disproportionate increase in osmotic pressure. This has physiologic implications: A large fluid loss from plasma is countered by a greater than expected increase in the osmotic restoring force. Similarly, in the kidney glomerulus, where the plasma fraction filtered may be as great as 45 per cent, the increased osmotic pressure may (i) limit the filtration rate and (ii) assist transcapillary tubular reabsorption.

Osmotic relations outside the vessels are harder to assess, since the extravascular environment is a colloidal matrix which is partly soluble and partly insoluble. The osmotic pressure of the largest soluble aggregates will be low and that of the insoluble ones nil. The extravascular region is not inert and local changes in molecular aggregation or disaggregation may decrease or increase the number of molecular species. There is also a flux of plasma protein through this region estimated to represent 0.7 to 2.1 grams per 100 ml. The normal protein content of lymph is 3 to 4 grams per 100 ml. The figure of 5 mm. Hg osmotic pressure usually assigned to the extravascular region is thus fraught with some uncertainty. If accepted, it leaves an osmotic balance of some 20 mm. Hg in favor of reabsorption.

Capillary Pressure. The pumping action of the heart is converted by the elasticity of the larger vessels to a rather constant force by the

TABLE 4. *Osmotic Pressures of Serum and Certain Blood Proteins*

	PROTEIN CONCENTRATION	TOTAL PER CENT PROTEIN	MOLECULAR WEIGHT	OSMOTIC PRESSURE	REF.
	grams/100 ml.			mm. Hg.	
Human serum	7.56	100		41	Starling 1896*
Human serum	7.56	100		25	Starling 1899
Albumin	3.6	51	69,000	16.4	
Gamma globulins	0.7	11	156,000	0.9	
Other globulin fractions	1.79			2.8	
Total	6.0	87		ca. 20	
Unidentified	1.0			5	

* Bacterial degradation of protein may have caused an increase in the true value.

(After Landis and Pappenheimer in *Handbook of physiology, Section 2: Circulation*, vol. 2, Dow and Hamilton, eds. Washington, D.C., American Physiological Society, 1963.)

TABLE 5. *Blood Osmotic Pressures and Capillary Hydrostatic Pressures in Different Tissues and Species*

TISSUE	SPECIES	CAPILLARY PRESSURE (P_i)			OSMOTIC PRESSURE π_i
		Arteriolar End	Summit of Loop	Venous End	
		mm. Hg	mm. Hg	mm. Hg	mm. Hg
Mesentery	Frog	10.6		7.4	5–10
Mesentery	Rat	22.1		12.5	16–21
Skin	Man	32(av.)	24(av.)	15(av.)	21–29(av. 25)
Kidney	Rat	60–65 (Glomerular)		14–18 (Post-glomerular)	
Lung	Man	11–21 (av. 16) (Pulm. art.)		7–15 (av. 6) (Pulm. cap.)	

(After Landis and Pappenheimer in *Handbook of physiology, Section 2: Circulation,* vol. 2, Dow and Hamilton, eds. Washington, D.C., American Physiological Society, 1963.)

time the arterioles are reached. Measurement of actual capillary pressures was the work of Landis while a medical student.[29] The minute vessels of the web of the frog's foot were cannulated by the aid of a micromanipulator with micropipettes of 5 μ tip diameter, under microscopic visualization. Measurements were later extended to capillaries of other tissues including those of man (Table 5). In man, capillary pressure at the arterial end is 32 mm. Hg and at the venous end 15 mm. Hg (skin capillaries). At the summit of the capillary loop in the nail bed the pressure is 24 mm. Hg. There are strong regional variations in capillary pressure which must be taken into account in the special physiology of organs. Thus, in the kidney the glomerular capillary pressure is high and promotes the high rate of filtration characteristic of the organ. In the lung capillary pressures tend to be low and, together with osmotic forces, favor reabsorption of fluid from the alveolar spaces.

Extracapillary (Tissue) Pressure. Tissues show a natural resilience or resistance to pressure. Also, when fluid is injected into them they first resist the inflow; then a "breaking point" is reached after which injection is easier. Edematous tissue is well known to leak fluid when cut. Pressures are measured by inserting a microneedle attached to a manometer. The most acceptable measurements are obtained when the instrument is balanced so that fluid neither enters nor leaves the tissue (Table 6). Usually rather small positive pressures are registered, e.g., not above 6.5 mm. Hg in the subcutaneous tissue of man and usually less. Tissue pressures are highly sensitive to venous and lymphatic

TABLE 6. *Tissue Pressures*

TISSUE	SPECIES	TISSUE PRESSURE (P_o) mm. Mg
Hand, subcutaneous	Man	0.6–2.2
Forearm "	"	0.8–2.9
Leg "	"	4.1–6.5
Eyelid "	"	1.2–3.0
Cutaneous	"	1.8–4.9
Muscle (gastrocnemius, soleus, biceps)	"	0.7–8.9
Kidney	Rat, rabbit, guinea pig	10

(After Landis and Pappenheimer in *Handbook of physiology, Section 2: Circulation,* vol. 2, Dow and Hamilton, eds. Washington, D.C., American Physiological Society, 1963.)

congestion and to muscular contraction. Regional differences are exemplified by the eyelid, which readily accumulates fluid even at low pressures, and by the pretibial area, where pressures are high. In the kidney an increase in renal vein pressure or in ureteral pressure causes an increase in peritubular interstitial pressure.

A summary of capillary and tissue forces (Table 7) justifies the application of the Starling hypothesis. There is available, at the arterial end of the capillary, a hydrostatic force of 37 mm. Hg or better to filter fluid and a counter osmotic force of 25 to 35 mm. favoring reabsorption, leaving a balance of 2 to 12 mm. Hg. In some tissues, e.g., the kidney, the force favoring filtration is much greater. At the venous end of the capillary the force favoring filtration is 20 mm. Hg and reabsorption 25 to 35 mm. Hg, with a comfortable margin of 5 to 15 mm. Hg favoring re-entry of fluid into the vessel.

Capillary Diffusion, Permeability and Transport.[29] In the capillary there is a flow and ebb of water and solutes between blood and tissues related to the all-important hydrostatic forces bringing blood to the tissues. Superimposed upon this is an incessant process of diffusion involving gases, water, ions, un-ionized crystalloidal solutes and larger molecular species including colloids. Capillary permeability to these is judged by certain observed effects. Molecules up to a molecular weight of some 5000 appear to pass readily. Beyond this there are restrictions on the rate of passage of molecules. However, labeled albumin with a molecular weight of 70,000 disappears steadily from plasma and appears in lymph at the rate of 0.1 per cent of the total circulating plasma protein per minute. This amounts to passage through the capillary in 24 hours of a total equal to the mass of protein in the circulating blood. At the other end of the scale, a volume of water equaling 66 per cent of the blood volume is exchanged between the blood and the extravascular water per minute.[17] Questions of diffusion across the capillary wall have traditionally concerned the site of diffusion and the nature of the "porous membrane."

The atmospheric gases O_2 and N_2, the noble gases and carbon dioxide are all to some extent water-soluble and to a considerable degree oil-soluble. Thus, theoretically, they can pass readily through the lipid plasma membrane of cells, and therefore the whole endothelial surface of the capillary wall, including cells and cell junctions, would be available for gaseous exchange. For the same reasons the lipid-soluble anesthetic gases have ready access to tissues across the entire capillary wall.

There is considerable reluctance to concede a cellular route for the diffusion of water, ions and other solutes, including large molecules, based on two assumptions: (i) that the endothelial cell is relatively impermeable to them, and (ii) that such a flow would disturb cellular homeostasis of the endothelium. As dogmas, both of these assumptions must be questioned. A steady state transcellular flux of water and small molecules, at least, is entirely consistent with homeostasis. As to (i), the enormous cell area involved might well compensate for any deficiency in permeability to water and solutes.

Nevertheless, diffusion of water and its solutes has usually been placed at the cell junctions. Based on an analysis of diffusion rates of molecules of different sizes, Pappenheimer[40] postulated an intercellular membrane furnished

TABLE 7. *Summary of Capillary Hydrostatic and Osmotic Forces in Man (Starling's Hypothesis)*

DIRECTION	FORCE	ARTERIOLAR END mm. Hg	VENOUS END mm. Hg
Out of capillary	Blood pressure	32	15
	Tissue osmotic pressure	5+	5+
	Total	37+	20+
Into capillary	Tissue pressure	0–10	0–10
	Plasma osmotic pressure	25	25
	Total	25–35	25–35
Balance favoring filtration at arterial end		12–2	
Balance favoring reabsorption at venous end			5–15

with pores 35 to 40 Å in diameter, with a density of 10^9 pores per sq. mm. A porous element comprising as little as 0.2 per cent of the total capillary surface was estimated to be sufficient to provide the observed diffusion rates.

Several considerations have thrown doubt on this physical model of a part of the capillary wall. Such a capillary membrane would not differ greatly from a collodion or cellophane membrane of fixed porosity. However, the structure of the cellular junction as presently accepted does not favor the existence of diffusion tubes or fixed pores. A calculation already referred to indicates that the interendothelial areas represent only 0.03 per cent of the total surface. Pores have not been visualized in tissue sections examined at such resolution in the electron microscope that they should be readily seen. The basement membrane has gradually assumed more importance as the "continuous membrane" or "ultimate barrier" in the average capillary, distasteful though the latter expression is, inasmuch as the function of capillaries is to let materials through. It is suggested by Luft[31] that the diaphragm is a selective filter of small pore size.

A thermodynamic analysis was made by Kedem and Katchalski[25] of the permeability of biologic membranes to nonelectrolytes. Essentially, they attempted to combine the concepts of filtration and diffusion into a unified equation of exchange, recognizing that these are not independent processes. Movement of water and solutes through pores involves the following molecular interactions: water-solute, water-pore and solute-pore; the relative magnitude of each of these depends on pore size. Apart from the exact nature of the pores, these derivations also make the implicit assumption that cells and tissues obey ideal solution laws, and that deviations may be corrected by the use of activity coefficients. They do not consider those nonideal properties of living matter which are not amenable to such a treatment.

There are alternatives to the concept of a membrane with fixed pores. Doubt has already been expressed whether cell junctions provide a functional barrier, and the filtration role of the basement membrane has been suggested. Basement membrane and ground substance regions are occupied by proteins, mucoproteins and mucopolysaccharides organized as polymers and forming a three-dimensional lattice.

This may act as a molecular sieve through the interstices of which water and other molecules move with greater or less freedom. Since the components of this structure possess fixed charges, an element of selectivity may enter, and some materials may be bound. In such a molecular lattice, it is possible to imagine even very large molecules ultimately making their way through, which would conform to experience.

The suggestion has been made that certain submicroscopic structures described in the cytoplasm vesicles and at the luminal and basal borders of endothelial cells (pits) may be concerned in active transport of materials across cells. These vesicles apparently take up fluid and solutes at either border, mimicking, on a micro scale, the process of *pinocytosis* described by Warren Lewis in 1931 for protozoal cells (amebae). Alternatively, it is proposed that endothelial cells take up material at one border and discharge it at the other (*cytopempsis*). There is increasing evidence that such a process plays little or no role in capillary exchanges. Vesicles have been implicated in the passage of particles above 120 Ångstroms, as has the occasional failure of the cells to come together where three cells join.[31]

CAPILLARY REACTIONS

Capillary endothelial cells possess the attribute of irritability and have an inherent but restricted ability to change their form. This reactivity may be associated with the presence of organized fibrils in the cytoplasm. Whether or not the capillary as a whole is independently contractile has been debated. In the mammal it is presently agreed (i) that vessels recognized as capillaries lack contractile pericapillary cells or nerve fibrils, and (ii) that a few innervated smooth muscle cells may be grouped at the precapillary junction with the arteriole, where they may function as a sphincter. It is unlikely that such a sphincter system could act cooperatively to control any large area of capillary supply because of the richness of by-passes and anastomoses. Arterioles well supplied with neuromuscular elements are believed to register their principal effects on blood supply by way of the capillary circulation. In this way blood is shunted to the muscles or to and from the splanchnic areas. In general, constriction of the arterioles causes pressure to fall in the capillaries supplied by them while dilatation causes an increase in capillary pressure. Any increase in venous pressure causes an increase in capillary pressure, and at the same time causes diminished reabsorption of fluid.

Humoral Factors. Interest has for many years centered on humoral factors as being dominant in producing readjustments of different elements of the microcirculation.

VASODILATOR SUBSTANCES. Histamine is the most potent capillary dilator; its action is independent of innervation and occurs directly on a contractile cellular mechanism. Local injection of histamine produces an effect so close to the triple response (see below) that Lewis[30] postulated an H-substance in that reaction.

Arterioles are constricted by histamine in rodents but dilated in dog, monkey and man. There is usually a fall in blood pressure in man, due to capillary dilatation. With large doses the vessels show increased permeability with loss of fluid, plasma proteins and red cells from the vessel. The basis of this is not known; histamine, an organic cation, is well known to bind to body proteins and it is possible that the capillary environment is also affected, permitting freer passage of large molecules. It is also possible that retraction of cells may expose larger areas of basement membrane to free diffusion from the blood vessels.

Carbon dioxide and anoxia. The word "anoxia" carries a heavy burden of implications which makes it difficult to attribute any given effect to decreased oxygen tension *per se*. Carbon dioxide appears to have a local vasodilator effect independently of its action on local pH. The conclusion seems justified, originally drawn by Gaskell in 1877 and by Roy and Graham-Brown in 1879, that "There is a local mechanism independent of centers in the medulla and spinal cord, by which the degree of dilatation of the vessels (capillaries) is varied in accordance with the requirements of the tissue." Nowadays this would be recognized as a feed-back device. Lactic acid liberation is traditionally associated with muscular activity and may be a factor in capillary dilatation during exercise.

VASOCONSTRICTOR SUBSTANCES. Epinephrine and norepinephrine constrict the arterioles and capillaries of skin and mucosa and produce the effect of "turning white with anger or fright." On the other hand, vessels of the mus-

cles are dilated, allowing the choices of "fight or flight" in these circumstances.[6]

AGENTS AFFECTING VASCULAR PERMEABILITY. It appears unlikely that in the ordinary course of events there are wide changes in permeability in the vessels of a given organ or tissue. Special adaptations already provide a range of behavior in individual circulations. The capillaries of skin and muscle are considered "normally" permeable, those of the mesentery highly permeable, and brain capillaries relatively impermeable to molecules of high molecular weight.

If the capillary wall is regarded as a membrane with fixed pores, an increase in permeability would indicate that in some way these pores had become enlarged. The weaknesses of this concept have already been considered. An amplified view of capillary permeability would include the properties of the intercellular ground substance and basement membrane colloids whose total behavior controls the extravascular distribution of water and solutes. Objective measurement of capillary permeability employs a colloidal dye such as Evans blue which combines reversibly with albumin and is normally restricted to vascular channels. In areas of increased permeability Evans blue escapes from the vessels and stains the local area. Studies have shown that the dye localizes initially in the ground substance, probably as a result of dye binding to altered ground substance components.

Histamine increases the permeability of capillaries. Histamine is a normal component of tissues and certain cells, existing in all probability in a form bound to cellular and extracellular protein, from which it is liberated by various stimuli. Among the "histamine liberators" are the organic compound 48/80 and such drugs as curare, morphine and atropine. Another organic amine, 5-hydroxytryptamine (serotonin), found in mast cells and blood platelets, gives the same response as histamine when injected intradermally.

Kinins (polypeptides). In 1936 Menkin[37] isolated from inflammatory exudates a polypeptide, leukotaxin, which greatly stimulated the migration of leukocytes from capillaries. Subsequently a variety of substances of protein or polypeptide nature were derived from plasma protein digests (kinin or bradykinin, "globulin factor," etc.) and were shown to influence capillary permeability. Likewise a heterogeneous group of nucleotides and nucleosides derived from nucleoprotein breakdown may contribute effects on vessels. These substances are in all probability liberated in inflammatory reactions; their role in normal capillary homeostasis is unknown.

Spreading factors. Duran-Reynals[12] demonstrated the presence of factors, subsequently shown to be enzymes, in testis, snake venom and certain bacteria which promoted the spread of India ink particles when simultaneously injected into skin. The spreading factors have as their substrate hyaluronic acid and chondroitin sulfate, which are known components of the ground substance matrix. Their action is to depolymerize the mucopolysaccharides, thereby reducing their viscosity and the tenacity of the ground substance gel, and so permitting particles to diffuse more readily. Vascular permeability in the region is likewise increased and Evans blue escapes from the local circulation. Hyaluronidase, a purified enzyme of the spreading factor, produces a transient edema when given intravenously.

The Triple Response. A series of astute observations made on the skin and its underlying vascular bed have become classic as the basis for understanding capillary reactions in normal and pathologic (inflammatory) states. The "triple response" of Thomas Lewis[30] can readily be elicited on the skin in front of the forearm.

When the forearm is stroked lightly with a blunt instrument a line of pallor appears in about 15 to 20 seconds along the path of the instrument. The pallor increases in intensity for about 30 to 60 seconds, then fades gradually (3 to 5 minutes). This "white reaction" is due to capillary contraction following direct stimulation, and at the height of the pallor the capillaries will remain closed against a pressure of at least 100 mm. Hg. Presumably the effect is at the precapillary sphincters.

If the instrument is drawn across the skin more firmly, a red instead of white line appears after a shorter latent period (3 to 15 seconds) and may last for several minutes up to half an hour. This "red reaction" depends for duration and intensity on the degree of stimulus provided and is due to capillary dilatation. It occurs with full intensity when the circulation to the skin is obstructed by means of a tourniquet and when all nerves to the area are cut and have degenerated. The reaction is therefore an active process,

not dependent on blood pressure in the arterioles nor on neural stimulation.

With a stronger or repeated stimulus, a bright red flush or flare spreads outward from the border of the red line, usually within 15 to 30 seconds after the first appearance of the red reaction. The "red flare" reaction does not occur if the circulation is obstructed and therefore depends on arteriolar dilatation. It occurs if the nerves to the skin are simply cut but not after they have degenerated. It is therefore mediated by a local axon reflex.

With a still more intense stimulus the local red reaction becomes paler and begins to rise above the surrounding skin surface. This local edema or wheal formation reflects the escape of a protein-rich plasma exudate from injured capillaries. The sequence of red reaction, flare and wheal formation is called the "triple response." It was explained on the basis of a substance released from cells following trauma or injury and called H-substance. Its effects are the same as those given by a local injection of histamine: capillary dilatation by a direct effect on endothelial cells; arteriolar dilatation through an axon reflex; wheal formation (edema) through increase in capillary permeability. H-substance is now generally identified with histamine and the term is historical. Although the reactions of the triple response are most easily observed in skin, they may be elicited on the surface of viscera also: liver, kidney and spleen. With unusually sensitive skins, words may be "written" which persist as distinct wheals for half an hour or more (dermatographism).

Passage of Cells (Diapedesis). The vascular membrane is relatively impermeable to large molecules, and it has always been rather puzzling to reconcile its structure with the passage of the enormously larger whole cell. It appears that the essentially colloidal nature of vascular junctions, basement membrane and ground substance adequately explain cell migration. Electron microscope studies have illustrated leukocytes, lymphocytes, monocytes and erythrocytes passing between endothelial cells.[18] The process is said to occur principally in venules rather than in capillaries proper. While diapedesis is probably common at all times in the capillaries of the mesentery and in sinusoids, the process occurs far more frequently in areas of inflammation. The dynamics of the reaction are obscure; there may be increased stickiness of the endothelium to which the leukocytes first adhere and then pass through the gel-like material at the cell junctions by active ameboid movements. Nonmotile cells may cross in the wake of active ones. The point of crossing "reseals" without a trace. Basement membranes are crossed, and the ground substance is entered in the same way.

RELATION OF CAPILLARIES TO PHYSIOLOGIC AND PATHOLOGIC STATES

Under normal conditions, capillary exchanges in tissues are determined by two sets of factors. The special distribution of capillaries permits more or less blood to be brought to the tissue through nervous and humoral stimuli. Passage of substances from the capillary, generally described by the term "permeability," is the resultant of changes in the capillary wall and in contiguous structures. Here the principal mechanisms are humoral.

The following may be mentioned as indices of alteration in the perivascular structures: increased deposition of vital dyes such as Evans blue and increased histochemical staining with the periodic acid leukofuchsin reagent; increased solubility of colloidal components; increased water uptake; change in physical properties toward a less aggregated physical state.

Among the many situations in which some or all of the above changes can be demonstrated are: tissue injury and inflammation; tissue growth; hormone actions on tissues; antigen-antibody reactions *in vivo;* various vitamin deficiencies (e.g., scurvy or vitamin C deficiency); malignant tumors. Illustrative of these, hormone actions and inflammation will be briefly considered.

Hormone Action. Tissue responses to hormones seem invariably to involve vascular reactions which may appear at an early stage. Increase in the blood supply to the organ is conspicuous in the action of estrogens on the uterus, of gonadotropins on the ovary and testis, of androgens on the cock's comb and generally as the response of a tissue to its specific hormone.[21, 41] Increase in blood supply may be in part through the opening up of existing capillary channels, but for the greater part it would appear to represent growth of new capillaries. These reactions occur concomitantly with increase in size of the organ and with cell multi-

plication and spatial remodeling of the organ or tissue.

Inflammation. Inflammation is a basic response of tissues to injury. It follows a stereotyped course dominated initially by vascular reactions as already described for the triple response, and is independent of all except local innervation. Early events observed following the infliction of a superficial wound, for example, are fragmentation of epithelial and vascular basement membranes in the area, increased uptake of vital dye, increased stainability, and water uptake. The disaggregation of structures surrounding the blood vessels may contribute to the observed leakage of blood proteins including fibrinogen. In the relatively less dense matrix it is reasonable to suppose that cell migration may be assisted and intensified. This would include diapedesis of cells from the capillaries, re-epithelialization by lateral movement of epithelial cells at the surface, and budding of endothelial cell channels to produce granulation tissue, which is a feature of early healing wounds.

Edema. A knowledge of lymphatics is needed to understand this important pathophysiologic phenomenon. Edema will be discussed later.

VEINS

VENOUS BLOOD FLOW

As the blood leaves the capillaries it enters the veins, a system of converging vessels serving both as a conduit and as a low pressure reservoir of large and variable capacity. From this reservoir the blood is fed to the right heart.

The walls of the veins are suited to this storage function at low pressure. They are thin, elastic and, except for the portal system, sparsely clothed with muscle fibers. The thin, flaccid walls of an empty vein are flattened and approximated, but they yield to very small increments of internal pressure. A rise of a few millimeters of water may increase the capacity of the lumen threefold; a rise of 130 mm. H_2O may increase the capacity about sixfold. Beyond this level the increment of increase in capacity per unit rise in pressure falls off rapidly. The variations in capacity resulting from low pressure fluctuations are opposed by the muscular elements in the walls; these elements respond to nervous, hormonal and chemical stimuli. The

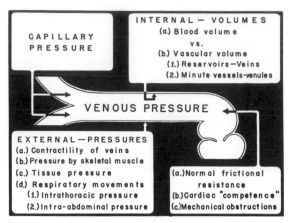

Fig. 5. Schematic representation of factors concerned in maintenance of venous pressure. (After Landis and Hortenstein, *Physiol. Rev.*, 1950, *30*:1–32.)

force developed by the smooth muscle is very limited. Except possibly for those regions in which the hydrostatic forces are pronounced, the resistance offered to changes in venous caliber is small, because the capacity of the right ventricle apparently increases passively with very small increments of pressure. The increased return to that cavity, resulting from the decrease in the capacity of the venous reservoir, is transferred to the pulmonary circulation by an increase in the stroke volume and rate in those conditions in which the Starling law of the heart operates (Chap. 33). Thus the changing capacity of the principal components of the venous reservoir—the portal system with its appendage, the spleen, and the venous plexus in the skin—serves to regulate the cardiac output by controlling the volume of blood that reaches the right heart per unit of time.

When the systemic system is in equilibrium, blood is returned to the right heart from the venous reservoir at the same rate at which it enters from the capillaries, and the volume of blood in each segment of the vascular net—the aorta, the arteries, the capillaries and the veins—is relatively constant.

A rise in the capacity of the capillary bed through an increase in the number of patent capillaries in an active tissue is most probably balanced by a decrease in the capacity of the venous reservoir. Conversely a decrease in the capacity of the capillary segment of the systemic circuit can be balanced by an increase in the volume of blood held in the veins. That is to say, the veins play an important role in regulating the distribution of the blood and act re-

ciprocally with the arteries and the capillaries. Although the measurements required to validate this probability have not been made, the relative distensibility of arterial and venous trees can be adduced as evidence: When the heart of an adult pumps 80 ml. into the aorta, the aortic pressure rises 40 mm. Hg. The usual blood loss during a blood donation (500 ml.) obviously could not be taken from the aorta, especially since the blood donor's arterial pressure does not fall appreciably.

In man at rest, whether recumbent, sitting or standing, the blood from the venules is returned to the right side of the heart by the pressure head in the arterial reservoir, although the pressure gradient between venules and right atrium and the flow can be modified by a number of accessory factors, i.e., action of the muscles of respiration, elasticity of the lungs, the force of gravity, the action of skeletal and visceral muscles, the valves of the veins, and, finally, the action of the right heart (see Fig. 5). In the recumbent subject, as relaxed as possible, the pressure is of the order of 80 to 245 mm. H_2O (average about 150 mm. H_2O, or 11 mm. Hg) in the venous ends of the capillaries and 5 mm. H_2O in the great veins at their entrance to the right atrium. This pressure gradient is adequate to promote the flow of blood back to the heart, but can be steepened (i) by arteriolar dilatation and increased pressure in the venous capillaries and venules, and (ii) by an increase in the rate at which the right heart transfers the blood from the great veins into the pulmonary system; cardioacceleration serves to reduce the pressure in the great veins.

This pressure gradient between the venous capillaries and the right atrium is somewhat larger than the absolute difference from the barometric pressure due to the negative intrathoracic pressure. In the natural state, the pressure in the thorax at any instant is less than atmospheric by about 80 to 120 mm. H_2O in quiet expiration and inspiration, respectively, and by 400 to 640 mm. H_2O during deepest inspiration. That is to say, the pressure gradient established by the heart between the venous capillaries and the right atrium (150 − 5, or 145 mm. H_2O) is further increased in the recumbent, relaxed person to about 225 mm. H_2O (145 + 80) through the recoil of the elastic tissue of the lungs.

The pressure on the intrathoracic veins can be further diminished or increased voluntarily and reflexly when the respiratory and abdominal muscles act to alter the capacity of the thorax with the glottis closed, as during the expiratory effort in lifting a heavy weight or straining at stool. Accordingly, the intrathoracic pressure rises, the negative pressure due to elastic recoil of the lungs is offset, the heart decreases in size, and the venous return is impaired. Conversely, a normal inspiratory effort or one made with the glottis closed increases the venous return via the superior vena cava by further decreasing the intrathoracic pressure. This effect on the venous return from the inferior vena cava is variable, however, for accessory factors—increased intra-abdominal pressure, narrowing of the caval opening in the diaphragm—that tend to offset the reduction in intrathoracic pressure come into play. (See Franklin[19] for a detailed discussion of these factors.)

Thus far, only the principal factors influencing the venous return in recumbent and relaxed individuals have been discussed. Consider now the manner in which the venous return is affected when the individual stands up. In a system of tubes with rigid walls and filled with fluid, pressure is everywhere the same when the system is horizontal. When the system is placed vertically, it remains filled with fluid throughout, but the pressure is greater in the bottom than in the top by an amount equal to the length of the vertical column of fluid multiplied by its density. When an elastic distensible system of tubes, similarly filled, is shifted from the horizontal to the vertical position, the fluid accumulates in the dependent parts—other factors remaining the same—under the influence of the hydrostatic and atmospheric pressures.

The vascular bed is such a system of elastic tubes. Accordingly, when a person moves from a recumbent to a vertical position, blood tends to accumulate in the dependent and most distensible portions, i.e., the veins and the capillaries. Thus the return of blood from the regions below the atrium, although promoted by the force of ventricular contraction and the negative pressure in the thorax as in the recumbent position, is opposed by the force of gravity. Hence one might expect the pressure in the venous capillaries of any dependent part to equal the weight of a column of blood of the same length as the vertical distance between the venous point and the level of the atrium or, in the case of the arm, the level of the subclavian vein.

Observations on the capillary pressures in the hand at the level of the clavicle demonstrate that this expectation is fulfilled[7, 29] (see Fig. 6). As the hand is lowered below the reference point —the clavicle—the pressure in the capillaries increases regularly with the increase in vertical distance, although the pressure tends to be somewhat less than expected at the lowest level. The constancy of the capillary pressure in the hand at levels above the right atrium (approximately 7 cm. below the clavicle) appears to be due to the negative pressure in the chest and the flaccidity of the veins. As the hand is raised and the blood momentarily flows more rapidly toward the heart, the veins begin to collapse and in doing so increase their resistance to blood flow. The flaccid veins yield to the slightest external pressure; as a consequence, the negative

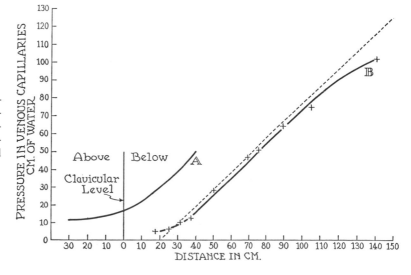

Fig. 6. Graph illustrating variation in pressure in venous capillaries of (*A*) hand, (*B*) foot, measured at positions relative to clavicle. (Based on data of Landis[28] and of Carrier and Rehberg.[7])

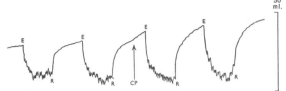

Fig. 7. Recorded changes in volume of calf of leg illustrating action of muscle pump during rhythmic exercise. Decrease in volume is signaled by downward movement of writing point. At *E,* calf muscles contracted once per second for 10 seconds. *R,* 10 seconds rest. At *CP,* cuff above knee inflated to 90 mm. Hg until end of record. (From Barcroft and Swan, *Sympathetic control of human blood vessels,* London, E. Arnold & Co., 1953.)

pressure which would develop in a rigid tube raised above the level of its entrance into the chest is offset by the increase in the functional resistance of the veins, since they flatten more and more as the hand is raised.

Similarly, the pressure on the blood in the veins of the dorsum of the foot of a man at rest is equal to the pressure exerted by a column of blood extending from the vein to the level of the right atrium (Fig. 6). This pressure is of the order of 90 mm. Hg or 115 cm. of blood. During exercise—walking—the pressure is reduced to about 22 mm. Hg (range 11 to 31) by the action of the so-called muscle pump. Each venous segment, guarded at its ends by valves or the capillary resistance, is pressed upon by the contracting muscle, driving the blood toward the heart and filling the adjacent headward segments. As the muscles relax their pressure, the venous valves prevent regurgitation, and the empty venous segments are filled from the periphery as a result of the propelling force of the left ventricle. The action of the pump is readily demonstrated by means of the plethysmograph arranged to measure calf volume. Figure 7 shows a record of the changes in calf volume during alternate periods of rest and exercise. With exercise, the calf volume is decreased as the blood accumulated during the rest period is pumped out of the veins toward the heart. The record further illustrates the pressure developed by the "muscle pump." At *CP* a cuff above the knee was inflated to 90 mm. Hg, yet the pump reduced the volume of blood in the calf veins against that resistance; blood was forced out under the cuff. A similar pumplike action is said to be exercised on the blood in the splanchnic bed by the rhythmic contractions of

the stomach and the intestine. A detailed discussion of the physiology of the veins is presented by Alexander,[1,2] who discusses venous distensibility, capacitance, and alterations thereof. The veins change their pressure–volume relationship if adrenergic drugs are administered. There also must be changes in the amount of blood stored in the veins in postural adaptation, blood loss, and possibly in other situations in which arteriolar resistance changes. Whether such alterations are produced by active nervous control seems debatable or, at least, not clearly demonstrated. Further reference to this matter is found in Chapter 34.

MEASUREMENT OF VENOUS PRESSURE

The simplest clinical method for the estimation of the pressure in the right atrium in the resting subject is that of Gaertner. The arm is allowed to hang by the side until the veins fill with blood; then it is slowly raised until the veins in the back of the hand just begin to collapse. The height above the heart level at which this collapse occurs indicates the venous pressure in millimeters of blood in the right atrium, since the arm vein is essentially a manometer tube ending in the right atrium. ("Heart level" for the recumbent subject is midway between the dorsal aspect of the thorax and the xiphoid process; when one is sitting up, the reference level is a plane passing horizontally through the fourth intercostal space at its junction with the sternum.) Another convenient index of the venous pressure at the right atrium of a recumbent person with his head raised on a pillow is the height above the clavicle to which the external jugular vein is visibly distended.

The pressures in peripheral veins can be measured with a small glass chamber sealed to the skin overlying a vein and connected to a pressure bulb and a water manometer. The pressure in the air-tight chamber is raised until the vein collapses; the pressure registered by the water manometer then equals the venous pressure. More satisfactory results can be obtained by inserting a hypodermic needle, connected to a water manometer, directly into the vein. An apparatus such as a phlebomanometer (Fig. 8) can then be used to measure the pressure in various superficial veins, both large and small. In this phlebomanometer[4] a very sensitive aneroid barometer is used to measure the pressure. A rubber tube leads to a glass adapter which holds the hypodermic needle, and the tube also communicates with a small pressure chamber in which the pressure can be varied by turning a screw. The pressure in the chamber is reduced to draw a little sodium cit-

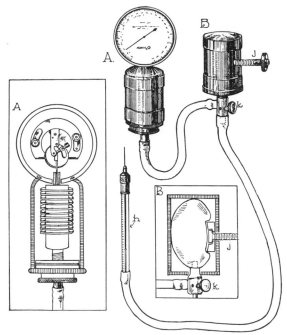

Fig. 8. Diagram of phlebomanometer: *A*, aneroid manometer; *B*, pressure chamber with screw, *j*, for varying pressure; *k*, needle valve; *h*, glass adapter holding hypodermic needle. (Through courtesy of Dr. G. E. Burch, School of Medicine, Tulane University.)

rate solution into the needle to form a meniscus in a glass adapter. When the needle is inserted into the vein, the pressure causes blood to enter the needle and move the meniscus farther along the glass adapter. The pressure in the chamber is increased until the meniscus assumes its original position; the pressure as registered on the barometer measures the venous pressure.

To eliminate the gravitational difference, venous pressure usually is measured with the subject reclining. The result is corrected to the heart level by determining the vertical distance between the point of measurement and the level of the heart. This distance is added to or subtracted from the venous pressure as measured in centimeters of water.

Measurements of venous pressure in man in a basal condition, i.e., after he has been lying down for at least 15 minutes, demonstrate con-siderable variations in different individuals. The pressure in the median basilic vein, for example, varies between 40 and 100 mm. H_2O after correction for differences from the reference plane of the heart. Conditions under which the blood flow is increased cause only a temporary rise in venous pressure, for the heart normally meets the greater demand by increasing its rate and stroke volume. These increases enable the heart to transfer a greater amount of blood from the venous to the arterial side of the circulation per unit time. A sustained elevation of the pressure in the roots of the great veins clearly points to a myocardial insufficiency. Venous pressure changes in heart failure are discussed elsewhere in this text (Chap. 38).

VENOUS PULSE

Usually the arterial pulse wave disappears in the arterioles, although as a result of arteriolar dilatation it may spread through the capillaries and appear in the veins. The term *venous pulse*, however, is generally applied to a quite different phenomenon—a pulse observed in the large veins (jugular) near the heart. This pulse results not from a pressure transmitted through the capillaries but from positive and negative pressure changes occurring in the heart or neighboring arteries and transmitted to the great veins. The records are usually taken from the external or internal jugular vein, where the venous pulse is quite large. In certain pathologic conditions it is also plainly discernible at greater distances from the heart and may even cause a noticeable pulsation of the liver ("liver pulse"). The curve of the venous pulse is a means of determining the contraction rate of the atria, just as the arterial pulse curve permits counting of ventricular contractions. For this reason venous pulse records are important in the interpretation of various irregularities of the heart beat.

Tracings of the typical venous pulse in the jugular veins show three positive main waves, labeled *a*, *c* and

Fig. 9. Upper tracing records pulse of jugular vein; lower tracing is from carotid artery. (After Best and Taylor, *The physiological basis of medical practice*, 1st ed., Baltimore, W. Wood & Co., 1937.)

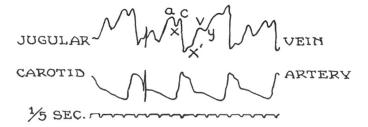

v in the same manner as the waves in the atrial pressure curve are labeled, and three negative waves, x, x' and y (Fig. 9). Many tracings, however, are far from typical. Frequently successive waves are merged together, and subsidiary waves sometimes appear. In disease it may be impossible to identify the waves unless one has a simultaneous record of the arterial pulse from which he can determine the beginning of ventricular systole.

In the venous pulse the positive wave immediately preceding ventricular contraction is the a wave caused by atrial contraction. Following this is the first negative wave, x, which marks the beginning of atrial relaxation. Next comes the positive c wave, resulting primarily from a rise in atrial pressure synchronous with ventricular contraction; transmission of the pulse from the neighboring carotid artery may also contribute to the c wave. It is followed by the negative wave, x', which is attributed to the shortening of the ventricle from base to apex so that the septum is drawn down and the atrioventricular valves are closed. The next wave is the positive v wave, which reflects the rise in atrial pressure as the chamber is filled. The last negative wave, y, reflects the fall in atrial pressure when the atrioventricular valves open and the blood is emptied into the ventricle. The y wave passes into the positive a wave, and the cycle is repeated.

LYMPHATICS

The extracellular region, supplied with water and dissolved substances through the walls of the capillary network, is drained by a network of lymphatics. This system compares in extent and distribution with the capillary system (Fig. 10). It begins as a series of closed tubes which unite to form lymphatic plexuses. These converge to become small and finally large lymphatic vessels and lymphatic trunks. In development and essential structure lymphatics are modified veins, lined by an endothelium derived from veins, and they invade the body as do the blood vessels. Some tissues appear to lack lymphatics, e.g., bone marrow, lung alveoli, cartilage, epithelium, fetal placenta, splenic pulp and probably the central nervous system.[46] However, small lymphatics are notoriously hard to recognize in tissue sections. Lymphatics are abundant in dermis and periosteum and in the submucosa of the genitourinary, respiratory and gastrointestinal tracts. The larger lymphatic channels are interrupted by lymph nodes widely distributed throughout the body but concentrated in groups throughout the prevertebral region, the mesentery and the connective tissue of axilla and groin. Generally several afferent lymph vessels converge on the capsule of a node.

Inside the node they immediately break up into numerous sinuses lined by lymphoid cells. The sinuses pervade the node and reunite into one or more efferent lymph channels carrying lymph from the node. Ultimately all lymphatics converge to two main trunks, the thoracic and the right lymphatic ducts, which empty into the junctions of the subclavian and internal jugular veins on the left and right sides, respectively, to return the entire lymphatic drainage to the blood system. The thoracic duct is the main channel for both lower extremities, the pelvis, abdominal cavity and left thorax, pleura, head and neck and upper extremity. The right lymphatic serves the right head and neck, thorax and upper extremity. It should be noted that the lymphatic system is entirely separate from the cavities of the mesoderm such as the peritoneal cavity, bursae, etc.

The ultimate lymphatic capillaries are thin-walled tubular structures perhaps double the diameter of the finest blood capillaries (e.g., 10 to 40 μ) but irregular in form, sometimes constricted, sometimes bulging, and anastomosing freely. They form a closed system and their terminal branches end blindly with rounded or swollen ends. They may lie in close proximity to blood vessels but are independent of them.

FINE STRUCTURE OF LYMPHATICS

The walls of lymph vessels are composed of endothelial cells which are somewhat larger and thinner than those of blood capillaries but otherwise resemble them closely in appearance and in ultrastructure. Intracellular vesicles (caveolae) in lymphatic endothelium are said to be less numerous than in capillaries; there are no fenestrations in the cytoplasm and the cell margins are not so closely apposed or interlocked as in capillaries. In lymphatics of the diaphragm there appear to be actual gaps between cells (filled possibly with a water-containing gel of some kind). The basement membrane of lymphatics is tenuous and may be imperfect or absent. The main perilymphatic investment is therefore one of fibers, fibrils and ground substance of the connective tissue. Lymph channels larger than 100 to 200 μ progressively acquire heavier coats of interlaced elastic and collagen fibers and smooth muscle bundles held within a ground substance. The larger lymphatics are provided with delicate paired valves pointing in the direction of lymph flow, which arise as

TABLE 8. *Composition of Lymph and Plasma*

SUBSTANCE	UNIT	SOURCE OF LYMPH	ANIMAL	PLASMA		LYMPH	
Na	mEq. per liter	Thoracic duct	Man	127.0		127.0	
K	mEq. per liter	Thoracic duct	Man	5.0		4.7	
Ca	mEq. per liter	Thoracic duct	Man	5.0		4.2	
Cl	mEq. per liter	Thoracic duct	Man	96.0		98.0	
CO_2	ml. per 100 ml.	Cervical duct	Dog	56.8		58.8	
Glucose	mg. per 100 ml.	Thoracic duct	Man	123.0		124.0	
NPN	mg. per 100 ml.	Thoracic duct	Dog	27.2		27.0	
				a*	b*	a*	b*
Total protein	grams per 100 ml.	Thoracic duct	Dog	7.08	7.00	4.89	2.80–3.60
Albumin	grams per 100 ml.	Thoracic duct	Dog	2.86	3.50	2.34	1.64–2.45
Globulin	grams per 100 ml.	Thoracic duct	Dog	4.16	2.50	2.56	1.16–1.15

* a and b show, respectively, two groups of findings.

(From Yoffey and Courtice, *Lymphatics, lymph and lymphoid tissue.* Cambridge, Mass., Harvard University Press, 1956.)

folds of the innermost layers and are composed of endothelium and connective tissue. Directly above each pair of valves the vessel may show prominent layers of smooth muscle cells; contraction of these would serve to propel the lymph centrally.

COMPOSITION AND ORIGIN OF LYMPH

Ordinarily, the volume of lymph represents the difference between the volume of fluid which leaves the capillaries at their arterial end and the volume reabsorbed at the venous end. Lymph balances the vascular fluid exchange in a tissue or part. In man about 2 to 4 liters of lymph leave the tissues and are returned to the circulation daily. Lymph represents therefore only a small fraction of the total flux of fluid across the capillaries, estimated to be equal to 70 per cent of the blood volume per minute. Yet this flow stabilizes the over-all volume of a tissue and, if blocked, leads promptly to swelling and edema. In a fasting animal lymph is a transparent liquid usually slightly yellowish in color, because of the presence of red cells. Shortly after a meal it appears milky from the presence of minute globules of fat, and if the intestines are examined the lymphatics are seen as fine white lines passing from mucosa to mesentery. Accordingly, these lymphatics are called lacteals; their content in the aggregate is known as chyle. On reaching the blood, the fat globules are discharged as chylomicrons having a diameter of 1 micron or less.

A comparison of lymph and blood plasma (Table 8) shows the close similarity of all con-

stituents with the exception of protein, which in lymph is variably one-half the plasma value. Nevertheless, all plasma proteins are present in lymph, indicating that the capillary wall is only relatively impermeable to the blood proteins, even those of the largest molecular size such as fibrinogen. Lymph clots on standing and presumably possesses the same clotting factors as does blood. Lymph shows regional differences in protein content, that from liver being high (6.6 per cent) and from skin low (2 per cent); these values are presumably related to local differences in capillary permeability and to total flux of materials.

Lymph may be expected to contain a representative fraction of substances, almost too

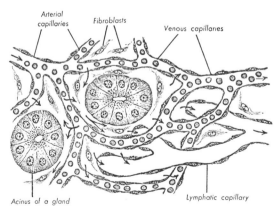

Fig. 10. Lymphatic capillaries of a gland in relation to arterial and venous capillaries. Arrows show direction of fluid flow. (From Copenhaver, in: Bailey's *Textbook of histology*, 15th ed. Baltimore, Williams and Wilkins Co., 1964.)

numerous to mention, derived from cell metabolism and cell secretion, including enzymes, hormones and metabolites. It represents fluid and solutes gathered from the blood, from cells and from tissue occupying the whole area through which these fluids are diffusing, namely the extravascular connective tissue. The lymph thus represents "extracellular fluid" in its broadest sense. If the connective tissue is accepted as a colloidal matrix consisting of partly soluble and partly insoluble components in equilibrium both with the blood and with tissue cells, then a flux of solvent will carry soluble materials into the lymph. However, a study of the lymph for such components as soluble collagen, hyaluronic acid, tissue mucoproteins, etc., does not appear to have been made. In addition to solutes, lymph contains particulate matter escaping from the capillaries. Bacteria, blood cells and their breakdown products are "scavenged" by lymphatics and may be phagocytized wholly or in part in the lymph nodes. In its passage through the lymph nodes, lymph acquires an important population of cells. Peripheral lymph contains a total of a few hundred white cells per cu. mm., and the thoracic duct lymph may contain 8,000 to 12,000 cells, which are mostly lymphocytes. Lymph from specialized areas, e.g., from postnodal lacteals, may contain an average of 40,000 white cells per cu. mm., representing, as will be shown later, largely recirculated cells.

LYMPHATIC PRESSURES AND FLOW

Pressures in the peripheral lymphatic vessels are low; values of around 1 mm. Hg are usually quoted. This may be compared with mean tissue pressures of up to 10 mm. Hg (Table 6). Somewhat higher pressures of 4 to 11 mm. Hg were reported for the lymphatic pressure at the ankle in the dog, comparable to mean pressures at the venous end of capillaries. Pressure in the thoracic duct is 15 mm. Hg. The osmotic pressure relationships of lymphatics are by no means clear. It would appear that the protein content of lymph, if as high as 4 to 5 per cent, should exhibit some 14 to 18 mm. Hg pressure as against a tissue osmotic pressure of 5 mm. Hg. Not all of this pressure may be exerted across the rather leaky lymphatic wall. There has been some discussion of why these very thin vessels do not simply collapse; possibly they are anchored in the connective tissue matrix by fine reticular filaments, although histologically these are not strikingly evident. Lymph actively moves in the amphibia, where beating lymph "hearts" propel it forward. In the mammal, movement of lymph is active and readily perceived. Hudack and McMaster[24a] injected dye in the human forearm at rest and found it 15 cm. from the point of injection in 5 minutes. The capacity of lymphatics to pick up dyes is used in lymphangiography (see below). Fluid motion in the lymphatic system, as in small veins, appears to be assisted by compression, massaging and tonic activity of surrounding tissues while valves prevent backflow. Larger vessels have a neuromuscular supply, and spontaneous contractions of lymphatics have been observed in the bat, rat and guinea pig but not in the cat, dog or man. Thus, descriptions of the mechanisms of lymph movement are largely reduced to enumeration of special situations in which motion may be considered to aid flow either intermittently or continuously, such as in muscular contraction, heart beat, peristalsis or contraction of intestinal villi. The injection of pilocarpine, muscarine or pituitrin, which increases the contraction of smooth muscle, greatly increases the flow of lymph from the intestines.

Lymph flow is also increased by any procedure or agent which augments the rate of filtration from the capillary, e.g., raising the venous pressure. Obstruction of the venae cavae above the point of entry of the hepatic veins greatly increases flow in the thoracic duct because of increased pressure in hepatic capillaries. Similarly, ligation of the portal vein causes increased pressure in the intestinal capillaries and greatly increased intestinal lymph flow. A generalized increase in arterial pressure has little effect, as would be expected, but a decrease leads to diminution or stoppage of lymph flow.

It was previously believed that both muscular activity and glandular secretion (e.g., submaxillary gland, pancreas, kidney) gave rise to an over-all increased lymph flow, but the classic experiments are now disputed or have been shown to be inconclusive.

Lymphogogues. About one hundred years ago Heidenhain and others noticed that extracts of leech heads, crayfish muscle and strawberries as well as histamine, peptone and other proteins increased the rate of flow and the amount of solid constituents of thoracic lymph in the dog. These "lymphogogues of the first class" actually exert their effect on capillary permeability, and the lymph flow is the result of increased filtration. Leech heads contain, among other components, the enzyme hyaluronidase, and crustaceans are rich in histamine, features which may be of significance in the reactions.

Other materials affecting lymph flow are Heidenhain's "lymphogogues of the second class" such as hypertonic sodium chloride and hypertonic glucose (50 per cent). When injected intravenously they promptly leave the capillary bed and by osmotic withdrawal of water from parenchymal cells produce lymph flow.

PERMEABILITY OF LYMPHATICS

Proteins which leave the capillary circulation enter the lymph vessels. Despite the relative difficulty with which proteins of the size of serum albumin leave the capillaries, about 50 per cent or more of the total body protein is circulated daily in this way. Once within the lymphatic vessel protein moves centrally into vessels with thicker and thicker investments from which escape becomes progressively less likely. In a characteristic experiment, I^{131} albumin or dextran (molecular weight 51,200) was infused into a leg lymphatic of a dog at the rate of 0.5 ml. per minute for a total time of 50 minutes. After a time lag of 10 minutes, the first sign of labeled albumin appeared in the cannulated thoracic duct; then the radio activity counts rose rapidly to a plateau. When infusion was discontinued 50 minutes after the start of the experiment, the level of labeled protein in thoracic lymph fell to zero by 150 minutes. Meanwhile, the maximum plasma concentration reached was less than 0.1 per cent of the maximum lymph level, indicating that little of the infused material left the lymphatic system other than by the thoracic duct.[36]

The permeability of the lymphatic wall resembles that of the capillary in its basic features and therefore in its basic problems. The external investments of the lymphatic are less well organized than those in the capillary; however, as in the capillary it may be supposed that the relationship of the lymph vessel is to the total environment. An explicit system of "pores" with diameters in the Ångström range seems not to have been proposed for lymphatics. However, openings or potential openings up to 22.5 μ have been suggested as passages for various particles from the peritoneum to the diaphragmatic lymphatics.

Alternatively, as for the capillaries, we may suppose that exchanges in the lymph vessel occur in a three-dimensional polymer lattice through which water, salts and dissolved crystalloids move with ease. Larger molecules move with more or less restraint, but presumably with less interference than in the basement membrane of blood capillaries. In lymph vessels, the intercellular junctions are wider than in capillaries and the basement membrane is incomplete or missing. It has been suggested, as for the capillary, that exchanges of water and solutes, proteins and chylomicrons take place through cell junctions rather than through cell cytoplasm, and that large particles and cells also use this route. For water and small molecules, at least, the same criticism of this assumption holds for the lymphatic as for the capillary. Presumably the entire endothelial cell surface is available for gaseous diffusion.

The microvesicles as devices for transport do not lack the support of some investigators. Endothelial cells of lymph vessels do not appear to possess the extensive submicroscopic structure usually associated with active secretion. In general, the effects of known physicochemical forces should be exhausted before unknown "biologic" processes are postulated to explain material distribution in either lymphatics or capillaries.

LYMPHOID TISSUE

The lymph nodes are flattened, rounded bodies 1 to 25 mm. in diameter consisting of a capsule of dense collagenous fibers from which radiate branching trabeculae that provide a framework for the organ. Between the trabeculae is a finer network of reticular fibrils and perhaps a ground substance. This framework supports the cellular stroma of the node, namely primitive reticular cells and fixed macrophages, which form the walls of the lymphatic sinuses through which the lymph is flowing. By mitotic division, primitive reticulocytes may produce either lymphocytes of different sizes (principally small lymphocytes, however) or plasma cells. Lymphocytes lie free in the lymphatic sinuses and gradually enter the blood stream, whereas plasma cells, now considered to be the main antibody-producing cells, remain *in situ*.

In addition to the lymph nodes, considerable lymphatic tissue is also present in the spleen and thymus gland. A small amount exists in bone marrow, and variable amounts occur as nests in the respiratory and genitourinary tracts and in the alimentary tract (tonsil, Peyer's patches). In the latter, lymphatic tissue cells are related primarily to blood capillaries and sinuses rather than to lymphatic vessels. Lymphoid tissue constitutes about 1 per cent of the total body weight.

Function of Lymph Nodes. The lymph node can effectively arrest small particles reaching it through the lymph stream. This filtering function was recognized in 1860 by the pathologist Virchow. On reaching the node, lymph flow is slowed down in the numerous sinusoidal channels. Particulates may be trapped in the tortuosities of the channels and phagocytized by macrophages attached to the sinus walls. The shape of the particle or bacterium is of significance here. After injection of bacteria into the afferent lymph channel and enumeration in the efferent lymph, 20 per cent of the rounded spores and vegetative cells of *Bacillus subtilis* passed through the node, whereas the chainlike vegetative cells of *Bacillus anthracis* were practically 100 per cent retained.[45]

Pyogenic organisms of sufficient virulence may be retained but not destroyed by the node. In this event they multiply and cause swollen, inflamed nodes. Living tumor cells similarly may lodge and proliferate to form metastases within lymph nodes.

Lymphocytes. The lymph node is the main source of the lymphocyte. The lymphocyte count in the peripheral lymph is low, but at some point large numbers of cells are added, either by the nodes or through massive recirculation, so that in the dog some 5×10^9 lymphocytes enter the blood daily from the thoracic duct alone, which extrapolated to a 70 kg. man gives a total of 3.5×10^{10} cells daily. Drainage from a thoracic duct fistula in the rat results in a precipitous fall in the number of lymphocytes, which can be restored by the infusion intravenously of compatible lymphocytes.[22] Further, intravenous infusion of cells labeled with P^{32} or deuterated thymidine produced a prompt appearance of labeled cells in the thoracic duct, equal to 80 per cent of the cells injected. These experiments point to the certainty of lymphocyte recirculation, and in fact the number of

newly formed cells represents only a small fraction of the total output of the thoracic duct.

FUNCTION OF LYMPHOCYTES. Lymph nodes have long been associated with antibody formation. McMaster and Hudack[34] showed that the lymph node draining a mouse's ear injected with antigen had a higher antibody content than one from a control ear. Also, lymph node cells taken from an immunized animal continued to form antibody when transferred to tissue culture or other suitable host.

Destruction of lymphoid tissue by whole body irradiation or cortisone treatment abolishes immune reactions and leads to a state of immunologic tolerance. Extirpation of the thymus gland at birth achieves the same end by removing the primary production site of lymphocytes. Similarly, chronic drainage of lymphocytes from a lymphatic duct fistula leads to loss of weight of all lymph nodes and to abolition of the primary response to an antigen such as tetanus toxoid or sheep erythrocytes. However, it is important to note that if animals are first permitted to give a primary reaction to antigen and then are depleted of lymphocytes, they still give the characteristic strong reaction to a second dose of antigen.

The following sequence of events has accordingly been postulated.[33] (i) Antigen produces a primary antibody response by direct interaction with lymphocytes in lymph nodes, or following phagocytosis by the numerous macrophages in the lymph node. (ii) These "prepared" lymphocytes enter the circulation and are scattered far and wide into other lymph nodes, where they become domiciled. They divide to produce a population of cells including plasma cells, having the same sensitivity as the "prepared" cells; depletion of lymphocytes leaves these cells relatively undisturbed. (iii) A second injection of antigen increases the rate at which the plasma cells are formed. Plasma cells are believed to be the principal source of antibody.[5, 35, 39]

LYMPHANGIOGRAPHY

Delineation of the lymphatic vessels and nodes is of importance for the detection of tumor metastases. Recent studies have also added to our understanding of the basic physiology of the system.[26] A diffusible dye (patent blue V) is injected locally into the dermis of the ankle or wrist, where it is rapidly picked up by lymph vessels and serves to outline the local flow. Under direct microscopic control, a lymph channel so visualized is cannulated with a needle of the finest bore. The needle is connected to a power-driven syringe attached to a reservoir of radiopaque material (diodone, ethiodol). Over several hours, this material is driven throughout the lymphatic system and is visualized finally with x-rays.

RELATION OF LYMPHATICS TO PHYSIOLOGIC AND PATHOLOGIC STATES

Edema. Normally the volume of a tissue remains constant. Swelling or edema is essentially a symptom of circulatory and tissue changes of diverse etiology which it is convenient to treat as a problem involving both blood vascular and lymphatic systems. The site of fluid accumulation is primarily the extracellular connective tissue, although parenchymal cells may participate in the reaction.

Fluids and electrolytes are held in the ground substance of connective tissue in some form of heterogeneous colloidal gel, in which the water content may vary from 65 per cent to well over 90 per cent. This water is not ordinarily microscopically visible, but forms a part of the colloidal structure. It is not "bound" in the chemical sense of strong covalent bonds, but is associated with colloid by electrostatic bonds (van der Waal's forces). Some of the ground substance colloids are recognized as hydrophilic materials, e.g., hyaluronic acid. Only in some pathologic states does water separate to form macroscopic accumulations.

It is a familiar fact that the feet swell during long journeys in the sitting position. The condition is attributed to venous stasis in the absence of a massaging action of muscles; walking rapidly relieves the condition, which is a mild reversible edema. At the other end of the spectrum are the grotesque swellings of elephantiasis. The lymph vessels become infested with the microfilariae of *Wuchereria bancrofti,* and ultimately vessels and nodes are blocked with the adult worms (5 to 8 cm. long). This produces a chronic but local edema accompanied by tissue proliferation. Local edemas tend to show redistribution of existing fluids, whereas systemic conditions such as the edemas of circulatory failure and starvation may show a generalized increase in body fluids. Systemic edemas may be accompanied by (or may be caused by) endocrine, circulatory and renal modifications.

Among the factors involved in edema are vasomotion, vascular pressures and tissue pressures, vascular and tissue osmotic relationships, lymphatic and lymph node drainage, and capillary permeability. These possibilities substantially comprise the subject matter of the present chapter. Specific examples of edema associated with each will be considered.

VASOMOTION. The dependent edemas mentioned above result from impaired venous return which increases venous pressure (Starling's P terms). Venous swelling, particularly in the superficial veins of the lower extremities, results from such causes as lax tissue support, valvular incompetence and obstruction. The resulting increased filtration from the capillaries may lead to edema. The condition is exacerbated by standing and is relieved by elevation of the limb or by tight bandaging to increase tissue pressure.

VASCULAR HEMODYNAMICS AND TISSUE PRESSURE. The classic situation is the edema of chronic heart failure. An increased circulating volume of blood from whatever cause results in increased venous hydrostatic pressure and decreased fluid reabsorption. The submucosa of the skin may appear grossly thickened and translucent. Pitting of the skin at a point of pressure indicates free fluid in the tissues. Fluid accumulates in body cavities (hydrothorax, ascites).

Low or lax pressure of tissues in the presence of normal vascular pressures may cause edemas which are cosmetically annoying but relatively benign, as in "bags under the eyes."

BLOOD AND TISSUE OSMOTIC PRESSURES. Lowering of the plasma proteins (in particular, albumin) occurs in the nephrotic syndrome (loss of protein in the urine), liver cirrhosis (failure of synthesis) and chronic starvation. There is reduced water retention (Starling's π factors) and edema when the plasma protein levels fall below critical values. In the all too familiar "prison camp" edemas, severe dietary imbalances, besides limitation of food *per se,* may contribute to the syndrome.

The colloidal osmotic pressure of tissues represents a more speculative factor in edema. It was proposed many years ago by Schade and by Fischer[16] that increasing the *p*H of tissue colloids increases their water-holding capacity. In a somewhat different form, this idea of colloid modification is basic to theories which invoke changes in connective tissue components to explain edema. Closely related to colloid deposition are the tissue swellings of the "sex skin" of macaque monkeys and baboons.[47] Both the regular estrus cycle and estrogens induce hyaluronic acid secretion and water retention in the perineal skin of these primates. No obvious changes in hemodynamics or in blood osmotic pressure seem to be involved.

A failure in secretion of thyroid hormone produces myxedema, with the accumulation of hyaluronic acid-containing mucins in the skin.

In these conditions hydrophilic colloids are increased. In other situations, a breakdown of existing colloidal aggregates, increasing the number of colloidal particles, should also cause an increase in water uptake. This appears to be the case when the symphysis pubis of the guinea pig is caused to "relax" with estrogen and relaxin. The net result is a softening and increased flexibility of the symphysis.

LYMPHATIC DRAINAGE. Mechanical blocking of lymph vessels is easy to visualize as a factor in edema. Following removal of lymph nodes, as for example in radical mastectomy, lymphedema develops if the area is left without adequate lymphatic drainage.

CAPILLARY PERMEABILITY. An acute increase in capillary permeability produces edema if the drainage capacity of the lymphatics is swamped. The local wheal of the triple response is of this nature and normally soon vanishes. Histamine and other vasoactive materials also produce such a response. Allergic edemas resulting from a local antigen–antibody reaction are usually attributed to histamine liberation.

A series of toxic chemical substances (thiourea, alloxan, methylsalicylate) affect capillaries by direct poisoning of endothelial cells. Their effects are most noticeable in the lung. Toxic effects, also manifested principally in the lung after direct inhalation, are produced by chlorine and phosgene gases and by the volatile liquid chloropicrin. The vesicant or blistering agents, mustard gas (dichlorethylsulfide) and lewisite (chlorvinyldichlorarsine), affect skin and mucous membranes on contact, and the lachrymators or tear gases affect the eyes and respiratory passages. Vascular poisoning seems to be the common action of all these agents, which produce local or systemic edemas of varying severity.

REFERENCES

1. ALEXANDER, R. S. *Fed. Proc.,* 1952, *11*:738–749.
2. ALEXANDER, R. S. Chap. 31 in *Handbook of physiology, Section 2: Circulation,* Vol. 2, P. Dow and W. F. Hamilton, eds. Washington, D.C., American Physiological Society, 1963.
3. BENNETT, H. S., LUFT, J. H. and HAMPTON, J. C. *Amer. J. Physiol.,* 1960, *196*:381–390.
4. BURCH, G. E. and WINSOR, T. *J. Amer. med. Ass.,* 1943, *123*:91–92.
5. BURNET, F. M. *The clonal selection theory of acquired immunity.* Nashville, Tenn., Vanderbilt University Press, 1959.
6. CANNON, W. B. *The wisdom of the body.* London, Kegan Paul & Co., 1932.
7. CARRIER, E. B. and REHBERG, P. B. *Skand. Arch. Physiol.,* 1923, *44*:20–31.
8. CATCHPOLE, H. R. and GERSH, I. *Physiol. Rev.,* 1947, *27*: 360–397.
9. CHAMBERS, R. and ZWEIFACH, B. W. *Amer. J. Anat.,* 1944, *75*:173–205.
10. CHAMBERS, R. and ZWEIFACH, B. W. *Physiol. Rev.,* 1947, *27*:436–463.
11. CHASE, W. H. *Arch. Path. (Chic.),* 1959, *67*:525–532.
12. DURAN-REYNALS, F. *Bact. Rev.,* 1942, *6*:197–252.
13. FARQUHAR, M. G. and PALADE, G. E. *J. Cell Biology,* 1963, *17*:375–412.
14. FAWCETT, D. W. In: *The microcirculation.* S. R. M. Reynolds and B. W. Zweifach, eds. Baltimore, Williams & Wilkins Co., 1958.
15. FAWCETT, D. W. In: *The peripheral blood vessels,* J. L. Orbison and D. E. Smith, eds. Baltimore, Williams & Wilkins Co., 1963.
16. FISCHER, M. H. and HOOKER, M. O. *The lyophilic colloid.* Springfield, Ill., Charles C Thomas, 1933.
17. FLEXNER, L. B., GELLHORN, A. and MERRELL, M. *J. biol. Chem.,* 1942, *144*:35–40.
18. FLOREY, H. Chap. 3 in *General pathology,* Philadelphia. W. B. Saunders Co., 1962.
19. FRANKLIN, K. J. *A monograph on veins.* Springfield, Ill., Charles C Thomas, 1937.
20. GERSH, I. and CATCHPOLE, H. R. *Amer. J. Anat.,* 1949, *85*: 457–522.
21. GERSH, I. and CATCHPOLE, H. R. *Perspect. Biol. Med.,* 1960, *3*:282–319.
22. GOWANS, J. L. *J. Physiol.,* 1959, *146*:54–69.
23. GUEST, M. M., BOND, T. P., COOPER, R. G. and DERRICK, J. R. *Science,* 1963, *142*:1319–1321.
24. HAN, S. S. and AVERY, J. K. *Anat. Rec.,* 1963, *145*:549–572.
24a. HUDACK, S. S. and McMASTER, P. D. *J. exp. Med.,* 1933, *57*:751–774.
25. KEDEM, O. and KATCHALSKI, A. *Biochim. biophys. Acta,* 1958, *27*:229–246.
26. KINMONTH, J. B. *Clin. Sci.,* 1952, *11*:13–20.
27. KROGH, A. *The anatomy and physiology of capillaries.* London, Oxford University Press, 1922.
28. LANDIS, E. M. *Heart,* 1930, *15*:209–228.
29. LANDIS, E. M. and PAPPENHEIMER, J. R. Chap. 29 in *Handbook of Physiology, Section 2: Circulation,* Vol. 2, P. Dow and W. F. Hamilton, eds. Washington, D.C., American Physiological Society, 1963.
30. LEWIS, T. Chap. 5 in *The blood vessels of the human skin and their responses.* London, Shaw & Sons, Ltd., 1927.
31. LUFT, J. H. Chap. 3 in *The inflammatory process.* L. Grant, B. W. Zweifach and R. T. McCloskey, eds. New York, Academic Press, 1965.

32. LUTZ, B. R. *Physiol. Rev.,* 1951, *31:*107–130.

33. McGREGOR, D. D. and GOWANS, J. L. *J. exp. Med.,* 1963, *117:*303–320.

34. McMASTER, P. D. and HUDACK, S. S. *J. exp. Med.,* 1935, *61:*783–805.

35. MÄKELÄ, O. and NOSSAL, G. J. V. *J. exp. Med.,* 1962, *115:* 231–244.

36. MAYERSON, H. S. Chap. 30 in *Handbook of Physiology, Section 2: Circulation,* Vol. 2, P. Dow and W. F. Hamilton, eds. Washington, D.C., American Physiological Society, 1963.

37. MENKIN, V. *Dynamics of inflammation,* New York, The Macmillan Co., 1940.

38. MEYER, K., HOFFMAN, P. and LINKER, A. In: *Connective tissue symposium,* R. E. Tunbridge, ed. Oxford, Blackwell Scientific Publications, 1957.

39. NOSSAL, G. J. V. and MÄKELÄ, O. *J. exp. Med.,* 1962, *115:* 209–230.

40. PAPPENHEIMER, J. R. *Physiol. Rev.,* 1953, *33:*387–423.

41. PEREZ-TAMAYO, R. *Mechanisms of disease.* Philadelphia, W. B. Saunders Co., 1961.

42. ROBERTSON, J. D. *Progr. Biophys.,* 1960, *10:*343.

43. STARLING, E. H. *J. Physiol.,* 1896, *19:*312–326.

44. WELLS, R. E., Jr., *New Engl. J. Med.,* 1964, *270:*832–839; *idem,* 889–893.

45. WIDDICOMBE, J. G., HUGHES, R. and May, A. J. *Brit. J. exp. Path.,* 1955, *36:*473–478.

46. YOFFEY, J. M. and COURTICE, F. C. *Lymphatics, lymph and lymphoid tissue.* Cambridge, Mass., Harvard University Press, 1956.

47. ZUCKERMAN, S., VAN WAGENEN, G. and GARDINER, R. H., *Proc. zool. Soc. (Lond.),* 1938, *108:*385.

CHAPTER 33

Control of Cardiac Output

By ROBERT F. RUSHMER

THE tissues and organs of the body subserve a wide variety of functions calling for adjustments in the quantity of blood flowing through the vascular networks in response to changes in functional demand. For example, blood flow through the skeletal muscle increases during physical exertion, flow through cutaneous networks increases during dissipation of heat, flow through mesenteric vessels increases during digestion of food. Although some of these changing requirements can be met by changing distribution of blood flow, most cardiovascular adjustments involve changes in the total blood flow through the circulation: the cardiac output.

The term *cardiac output* indicates the quantity of blood ejected each minute by either the right or the left ventricle, not the combined output of both ventricles. This definition is based on the concept that the systemic and pulmonary circulations are connected in series so that the blood passes in sequence through one circuit and then through the other. In general, the amounts of blood flow through pulmonary and systemic vascular beds are regarded as precisely equal so that the output of right and left ventricles should be identical. This picture is correct except for that portion of bronchial arterial flow that drains into the pulmonary veins and back to the left ventricle. The mean cardiac output in milliliters per minute can be divided by the heart rate to give the quantity of blood ejected per stroke: the *stroke volume.*

Control of cardiac output can best be visualized in terms of the various factors which influence the quantity of blood pumped by the heart each minute (Fig. 1). As in any mechanical pump, the volume of fluid ejected per stroke multiplied by the number of strokes per minute gives the output of the pump per minute (cardiac output). The heart rate is determined by the frequency with which waves of excitation are generated in the sino-atrial node in the right atrium (see Chap. 30). Pacemaker activity of the sino-atrial node is under the influence of sympathetic and parasympathetic nerves.

Most reciprocating mechanical pumps have a fixed stroke volume represented by the excursion of the piston within the cylinder. The stroke volume of the ventricles represents the difference between the volume of blood contained within the ventricles at the end of diastole minus the quantity of blood remaining in the ventricles at the end of systolic ejection (Fig. 1). If the diastolic volume increases, the stroke volume also generally increases. The diastolic volume is determined by at least three factors: (i) the filling pressure, which represents the pressure difference between the inside and the outside of the ventricular chambers during the diastolic inter-

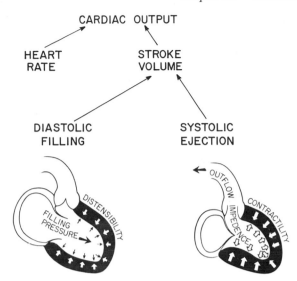

Fig. 1. The cardiac output stroke volume multiplied by the number of strokes per minute (heart rate). The stroke volume represents the difference between the ventricular volume at the end of diastole and at the end of systole. The ventricles are not necessarily maximally filled at the end of diastole nor completely emptied at the end of systole. For this reason, the stroke volume must be considered in terms of factors which influence diastolic volume (i.e., filling pressure and distensibility) and which affect systolic volume (i.e., contractility and outflow impedance). (From Rushmer, *Cardiovascular dynamics*. Philadelphia, W. B. Saunders, Co., 1961.)

val, (ii) the resistance of the ventricular walls to distension (distensibility), (iii) the variable amount of blood injected into the ventricular chambers by the contraction of the atrium immediately preceding the ventricular systole. At fast heart rates, the filling time becomes an important factor in determining diastolic volume.

The increase in stroke volume which results from greater diastolic distension depends on the length-tension relationship of myocardial fibers. In contrast, increased stroke volume achieved by action of the sympathetic nervous system on the ventricular myocardium generally involves more complete systolic emptying of the ventricles. Since cardiac output is regulated through variations in heart rate, diastolic volume and systolic volume, the mechanisms of cardiac control will be considered in terms of these three major categories.

CONTROL OF HEART RATE

Normally, the heart rate is established by the periodic discharge of excitatory impulses generated in the sino-atrial (S-A) node. The pacemaker activity of the S-A node is discussed in Chapter 30. The heart rate is continuously under the influence of a balance established between the slowing effects of discharges along parasympathetic nerves and the accelerating effects of the sympathetic nerves distributed to the pacemaker cells. If both the vagus and sym-

HEART RATE
A. AUTONOMIC BALANCE IN HEART RATE CONTROL

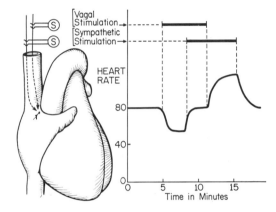

B. STROKE VOLUME DURING ARTIFICIAL TACHYCARDIA

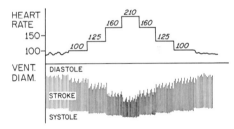

Fig. 2. *A,* The heart rate is determined by the inherent rate at which the sinoatrial node discharges impulses as affected by the balance between the slowing effect of vagus nerve impulses and the speeding effect of sympathetic nerve impulses arriving in the vicinity of the pacemaker cells. Electrical stimulation of the vagus nerve produces slowing of the heart rate; stimulation of the sympathetic nerves produces acceleration as shown.

B, Acceleration of the heart rate usually produces an increase in cardiac output, but not always. For example, artificially induced tachycardia produces a progressive reduction in ventricular diameter and also in stroke volume such that cardiac output may remain unchanged over a wide range in heart rates. (From Rushmer, *Cardiovascular dynamics*. Philadelphia, W. B. Saunders Co., 1961.)

pathetic nerves to the heart are cut, the heart rate increases. For this reason it is generally believed that the vagal effects predominate at rest. Changes in heart rate during normal activity involve adjustment in the balance between the effects of the two sets of autonomic nerves. For example, during exercise, the heart rate accelerates because of simultaneous increase in sympathetic discharge and reduced discharge along vagal nerve fibers to the sino-atrial node.

In a mechanical pump with a fixed stroke volume, the output of the pump per unit time can be adjusted merely by varying the repetition rate of successive cycles. In contrast, the output of the heart may be little affected by an increase in heart rate. For example, if the heart rate is increased in a stepwise manner by stimulating the S-A node at varying frequencies, each increment of increased heart rate is accompanied by a reduction of stroke volume which may balance the increase in heart rate so exactly that the output of the heart remains relatively constant over variations in heart rate ranging from 70 per minute to 150 per minute. This phenomenon is schematically illustrated in Figure 2; with each increase in heart rate the stroke volume was reduced even as the diastolic and systolic dimensions diminished. Thus, a fast heart rate alone may not necessarily increase cardiac output. For this reason, it is necessary to consider mechanisms by which the stroke volume can be sustained or increased in the presence of an accelerated heart rate.

CONTROL OF STROKE VOLUME

Since the heart contains a pacemaker and conduction system which function automatically, the organ continues to pump even after isolation from the body. As early as 1884 Howell and Donaldson[8] studied isolated mammalian hearts and found that the stroke volume and cardiac output increased when the rate of inflow into the heart was increased. The capacity of the isolated heart for altering its stroke volume may reasonably be regarded as an intrinsic control mechanism due to the contractile properties of the muscle. When the heart is *in situ,* autonomic nerves and autonomic hormones in the blood also produce changes in the output of the ventricles. Neural and hormonal control of the heart is exerted by alterations in the contractile characteristics of the muscles and can be

considered as an extrinsic mechanism for control.

Intrinsic Control: the Length–Tension Relationship. Myocardium is a striated muscle exhibiting many of the properties of skeletal muscle (see Chap. 5). For example, relaxed myocardium displays a static length–tension relationship very much like that illustrated for skeletal muscle in Figure 12, Chapter 5. Progressive increase in the resting length of a myocardial strip produces a gradual increase in tension over a range up to 200 per cent of the unstretched length. In other words, the increase in tension with each increment of increased length becomes progressively larger as the degree of stretch increases. Otto Frank[5, 6] demonstrated that myocardial fibers induced to contract at various resting lengths display a contractile tension superimposed on the resting tension attained at each specific length. The magnitude of the contractile tension (total tension minus resting tension) increases with stretch up to a peak and then diminishes (see Chap. 5, Fig. 12).

In 1914 Starling and his associates[23] studied the intrinsic control of the heart using the well known heart–lung preparation illustrated in Figure 3A. A large branch of the aorta was cannulated with a large-bore tube which led to a controlled resistance. This resistance consisted of a collapsible tube which was compressed by external pressure to maintain the pressure upstream (arterial pressure) at any desired level. This artificial resistance served as a substitute for the total hydraulic resistance offered by the entire systemic circulation. The blood flowing through the resistance was collected in a reservoir from which it drained into the right atrium. The inflow into the right ventricle could be adjusted at will by elevating the venous reservoir to modify the volume flow through the circuit. The outflow resistance from the left ventricle could be varied by adjusting the controlled resistance. The heart–lung preparation permitted continuous recording of the arterial pressure in the artificial extracardiac circuit. The venous filling pressure was registered at the entrance to the right ventricle. The combined volume of right and left ventricles was recorded by means of a cardiometer. Starling and his associates noted that when the systemic arterial pressure was artificially elevated by a compression of the controlled arterial resistance, both the diastolic and systolic volumes of the combined ventricular chambers were substantially increased without a change in stroke volume. In this way the increased energy release required of the contracting ventricle was attained through an increase in the degree of diastolic distension such that the stroke volume was maintained in the face of an increased outflow resistance. On the other hand, if the arterial pressure was maintained constant and the cardiac output was increased by elevating the inflow reservoir, the increased filling pressure caused increased diastolic distension of the ventricular chambers. The results of these studies could be summarized most simply by stating that the response of the ventricular chambers to an increase in either pressure load or volume load was met by a greater degree of diastolic distension of the ventricular walls. Since an increase in the volume of the ventricles must be accompanied by an increase in the length of the individual muscle fibers, Starling enunciated the principle that the heart performs in the same general manner as the skeletal muscle, namely, "that the mechanical energy set free on passage from the resting to the contracted state depends upon the length of the muscle fibers." Using the length–tension relationship of myocardium (Fig. 3*B*) reported by Frank,[5, 6] a concept was derived by which the relationship between end-diastolic volume and the energy released by the contracting ventricles could be visualized. If the ventricles function at a volume less than that indicated by the dotted line, an increase in end-diastolic volume would be accompanied by an increase in the tension developed by the myocardium and the energy released by the myocardium. Using such a concept, it was postulated that during the transition to a higher cardiac output, the diastolic volume was progressively increased with each successive cycle. The stroke volume would correspondingly increase and level off at a plateau representing a new outflow rate. Through such a mechanism the cardiac output could theoretically be increased with no increase in heart rate. An increase in stroke volume accompanied by a tachycardia could increase the total cardiac output to an even greater extent. This attractive concept was termed "Starling's law of the heart" and the mechanism was regarded as the

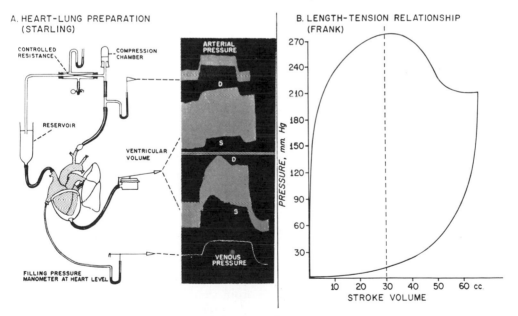

Fig. 3. *A*, The ventricles in the heart-lung preparation respond to an increased work load (either higher arterial pressure or increased inflow) by greater diastolic distention. These observations suggest that the energy released by the myocardium was determined by the length of the myocardial fibers (end-diastolic volume).

B, The length-tension diagram derived from frog myocardium by Otto Frank was used to illustrate Starling's concept that greater contractile tension developed as the myocardium was progressively stretched within limits. The pressure and volume scales represent Starling's estimate of values for man. (From Rushmer, *Cardiovascular dynamics.* Philadelphia, W. B. Saunders Co., 1961.)

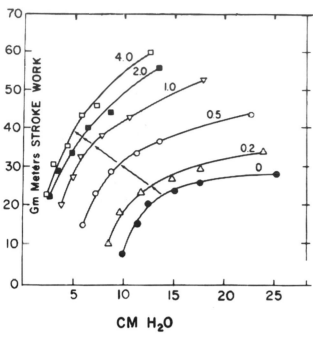

Fig. 4. A family of "Starling curves" can be drawn by plotting the stroke work of the ventricles against filling pressure as it is varied by infusion of blood into the vascular system. Stimulation of sympathetic nerves to the heart at frequencies noted above each curve displaces the curve upward and to the left. This is interpreted as an increase in the "vigor of contraction." (From Sarnoff and Mitchell, *Handbook of Physiology, Circulation: Section 2,* vol. 1. Washington, D.C., American Physiological Society, 1962.)

dominant control of stroke volume in both health and disease. This short-sighted view has required modification and this "law" is more appropriately called the Frank-Starling mechanism.

Extrinsic Control: Variations in Ventricular Contractility. No one seriously questions that under constant experimental conditions isometrically contracting myocardium displays a length–tension relationship of the sort illustrated in Figure 3*B*. These properties are regularly observed in isolated strips of myocardium, in the heart–lung preparation and in exposed hearts of anesthetized animals. However, direct and quantitative measurements of various cardiovascular adaptations in normal human subjects and active healthy animals have demonstrated that the length–tension relationship may not be the dominant mechanism for cardiovascular adjustment.

Deviations in ventricular performance from the responses predicted from the Starling mechanism have been attributed to alterations in contractile properties of the myocardium or its "contractility" (see Fig. 4). One mechanism for illustrating the deviation of ventricular performance from that predicted solely on the basis of the Frank–Starling mechanism has been proposed by Sarnoff and his associates.[19] By artificially increasing the effective filling pressure

of the ventricle and measuring the energy output of the ventricle in terms of stroke work, a curve was plotted which constituted a single "Starling curve." By inducing alterations in the characteristic of the ventricular contraction by norepinephrine, nerve reflex mechanisms, or impaired coronary flow, a family of curves could be produced to demonstrate that the work performed by the contracting ventricular muscle varied at the same end-diastolic ventricular pressure.

Although a family of "Starling curves" illustrates that the performance of the ventricles at a particular degree of diastolic distension may be varied by external factors, functional significance of these changes can be more fully appreciated by considering some other experimental preparation. For example, the length–tension relationship of myocardium illustrated in Figure 3 is based on experiments in which the contracting myocardium was prevented from shortening. However, a muscle which is not permitted to shorten can perform no external work and can pump no blood. When myocardial fibers are permitted to shorten, contractile tension diminishes.[10] The drop in contractile tension during shortening suggests a high viscosity within the muscle fibers tending to oppose any rapid change in length. If myocardial fibers are studied during isotonic contraction when the fibers are permitted to shorten while moving a constant weight or load, the contractile properties are no longer described by the simple length–tension relation. For example, Sonnenblick[21] studied the isotonic contraction of isolated papillary muscles as illustrated schematically in Figure 5. When the muscle was induced to contract, a weight was elevated by a lever. By simultaneous measurement of the length of the papillary muscle and the tension being developed when the load was lifted, a series of curves was recorded. When the papillary muscle elevated a very small load the shortening began after a very brief latency. The initial velocity of shortening (I.V.) was extremely rapid. The degree of shortening was great and the duration of shortening was long. If the load being elevated by the same papillary muscle was materially increased, the papillary muscle developed much higher tension before shortening began, the initial velocity of contraction (I.V.) was much slower, and the degree of shortening was smaller (Fig. 5). The graphic relationship between velocity of shortening and load (Fig. 5*B*) is comparable to a similar plot obtained from skeletal muscle (see Chap. 5, Fig. 14).

The normal cardiac cycle of the intact heart begins with a period of almost isometric contraction during which all of the cardiac valves are closed (see Chap. 29). During the ejection period, the myocardial fibers shorten while ventricular pressure is maintained fairly constant. The contraction during ejection is almost isotonic. Finally, systole is terminated by a period during which relaxation occurs more or less isometrically. For this reason, it is not possible to predict the exact nature of the contraction of the intact ventricle from myocardial samples contracting either isometrically (Fig. 3*B*) or isotonically (Fig. 5). The dynamic properties of left ventricular contraction can be illustrated by continuous measurements of critical variables such as aortic pressure, aortic flow velocity, acceleration of the blood through the aortic

valve and the pressure developed within the left ventricle (Fig. 6). If a continuously recording flowmeter is installed at the root of the aorta, a very characteristic wave-form is consistently recorded under "normal" conditions. The rate of blood flow out of the left ventricle into the aorta rapidly attains a peak in early systole. This means that the blood leaving the heart is accelerated rapidly.[22] Acceleration of the flow is indicated by the slope of the upstroke on the aortic flow rate curve (Fig. 6). Since the outflow of blood from the ventricles indicates the net shortening of the myocardial fibers comprising that chamber, aortic flow rate is an indicator of the net rate of myocardial shortening. Aortic flow curves demonstrate that the initial rate of shortening is extremely rapid initially, but during the later portions of systole the rate shortening tends to diminish. During the latter part of systole, the flow velocity gradually diminishes towards zero, and at the end of systole the flow tends to reverse in a retrograde surge. This characteristic is consistent with observations on myocardial strips (Fig. 5).

The driving force for outflow velocity is a left ventricular pressure which also tends to be elevated extremely rapidly during the isovolumic period of ventricular contraction. The maximal rate of change of pressure (dP/dt) occurs during the midportion of the upstroke of the ventricular pressure curve. The forward driving force propelling the blood into the aorta is determined by the difference in pressure between the left ventricle and the root of the aorta. The fact that aortic flow velocity reaches a peak early in systole and then declines has important functional implications. This phenomenon can occur only if the pressure difference between the left ventricle and the aorta is extremely high at the onset of systole while the outflow rate is accelerating. After peak flow velocity has been reached, a deceleration of the blood in the aorta signifies that the pressure gradient has been reversed. In other words, the pressure in the ventricle must be lower than the pressure in the

Fig. 5. Isolated papillary muscles, contracting isotonically, begin to shorten after they have developed sufficient tension to elevate the load. The rate of shortening is greatest at the onset. The rate of shortening is diminished with an increasing load. (After Sonnenblick, *Amer. J. Physiol.,* 1962, *202:* 931–939.)

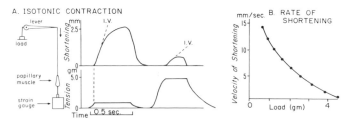

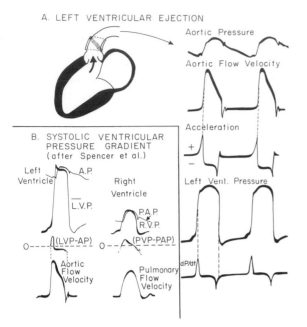

Fig. 6. *A,* The characteristics of left ventricular ejection are illustrated in terms of aortic pressure, aortic flow, acceleration of blood through the aortic root, left ventricular pressure and the rate of rise and rate of fall of ventricular pressure.

B, Left ventricular pressure exceeds aortic pressure by a substantial amount at the onset of ejection when the blood is being rapidly accelerated out of the aorta. The rapid development of peak outflow rate means that momentum is rapidly imparted to the blood leaving the ventricle. During the latter part of ventricular systole, this momentum acts to carry the blood along the aorta. The outflow velocity slows and the pressure gradient reverses so that aortic pressure actually slightly exceeds ventricular pressure during the later portions of systole.[14, 22] (From Rushmer, *Circulation,* 1964, *29:*268–283; by permission of the American Heart Association, Inc.)

aorta when blood flow out of the ventricle is decelerating. This reversal of the pressure gradient has been directly measured in both the left ventricle and in the right ventricle by Spencer and his associates,[22] as indicated in Figure 6B. These observations indicate that the ventricle does not contract like a fist squeezing on an orange but rather like a piston being struck with a mallet. In the latter case momentum is rapidly imparted to the fluid. The momentum of this moving blood tends to carry it forward after the impact of the mallet has terminated.

The Ventricles as Impulse Generators. The peak outflow rate of blood results from the force (F) applied by the contracting ventricular myocardium and the time (t) over which this force acts. This relationship (F ∫ dt) is a very well

established physical quantity termed *impulse* (I), which is very closely related to momentum (mv). Thus, the product of the force and the time the force acts is impulse and impulse is the gain or loss of momentum. The ventricles act as impulse generators, as evidenced by the rapid acceleration of blood to peak outflow rates in the first portion of systole.[14] Since the characteristics of each ventricular ejection are established during the initial ventricular ejection period, the nature of the *initial ventricular impulse* is extremely important for evaluating the performance of the ventricular chambers. The initial ventricular impulse can be estimated from the magnitude of the peak flow velocity, and the rate at which this velocity is attained (acceleration). The acceleration of blood can be estimated from the upslope of the aortic flow rate curve or by differentiating this curve to register peak acceleration (Fig. 6). The rate of increase of ventricular pressure and the magnitude of the pressure difference between ventricle and aorta during early systole are both related to the magnitude of the initial ventricular impulse.

Since the initial ventricular impulse was found to be diminished under experimental conditions designed to simulate clinical disease states including acute coronary occlusion, exsanguination hypotension, premature contractions, general anesthesia with certain agents, and ventricular arrythmias, the nature of the ventricular impulse may have importance in evaluating the status of the heart.[13] In contrast, sympathetic stimulation augments the initial ventricular impulse. The importance of these phenomena relates to the fact that extrinsic mechanisms of ventricular control influence most decisively the initial acceleration of the blood and the peak flow velocity. Stimulation of sympathetic nerves distributed to the ventricular myocardium causes more rapid acceleration of the blood, very markedly higher peak flow velocity and reduced duration of the ejection period.

CHANGES IN VENTRICULAR CONTRACTILITY

Changes in ventricular performance which are not predictable on the basis of the Starling mechanism are frequently attributed to alterations in "contractility." The term contractility has been employed to indicate a wide variety of meanings[14] including alterations in the "vigor of contraction," the "inotropic" effects of catecholamines, the degree of ventricular emptying, the "force" of contraction, the rate of systolic ejection, and the changes in slope of ventricular function curves. In general, the concept of contractility has been derived from observations of the effects of neural control mechanisms as they affect ventricular function. Clearly, the term "contractility" covers a wide variety of phenomena and may not be subject to a single unique definition.

The characteristics of ventricular performance, illustrated in Figure 6*A*, are altered by the sympathetic stimulation, neural reflexes, or spontaneous adjustments in cardiac performance such as exercise.[12] For example, the peak ventricular pressure attains a higher than normal level both during exercise and during stimulation of sympathetic nerves to the heart. The upslope of the ventricular pressure recording is steeper, indicating that the rate of pressure elevation is faster. The rate of pressure decline is also steeper near the end of systole (Fig. 7). The peak outflow rate tends to be increased very markedly, but the duration of systole is shortened. In other words, the stroke volume may be increased slightly but the peak rate of ventricular outflow is considerably higher than during the control period. The rate at which ventricular muscle converts chemical energy into external work (power) is also greatly increased although the work per stroke is only slightly augmented. The absolute change in ventricular diameter is about the same, although both diastolic and systolic dimensions tend to be smaller. However, the rate of change of diameter is considerably accelerated. The duration of systole is curtailed and the heart rate is greatly increased. In Figure 7 the quantities are illustrated in one column and the rates of change of these same quantities are illustrated in the second column. The rate of change of pressure, rate of ventricular outflow, rate of ventricular work, rate of change of diameter and heart rate are all greatly increased, whereas the absolute increase in ventricular pressure, stroke volume, stroke work and ventricular diameter are only slightly altered and the duration of systole is actually reduced. One can, then, summarize contractility as a change in ventricular performance which causes the ventricles to function much faster although the total quantity of the change during each stroke may not be so greatly increased. The increased rate of ejection provides a mechanism by which the stroke volume can be maintained or increased in the face of an accelerated heart rate. Since the discharge of sympathetic nerves to the heart has the function of increasing heart rate and speeding up the contractile process in the myocardium, the shortening of systolic interval has the effect of lengthening the filling period (diastole) for any given heart rate. In this way the sympathetic nerves produce a kind of integrated response in the ventricles by simul-

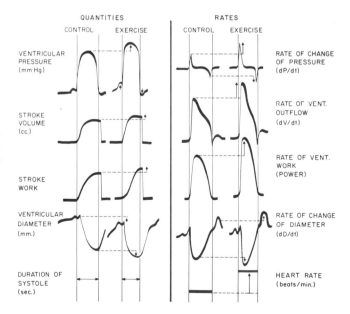

Fig. 7. Stimulation of sympathetic nerves to the heart affects ventricular performance primarily by causing it to function at more rapid rates. Ventricular pressure, stroke volume, stroke work increase slightly while ventricular diameter and duration of systole are reduced. In contrast, the rate of change of ventricular pressure, the rate of ventricular outflow, the rate of ventricular work, the rate of change of diameter and the heart rate all increase markedly. (From Rushmer, *Handbook of Physiology, Circulation: Section 2*, vol. 1. Washington, D.C., American Physiological Society, 1962.)

taneous effect on the pacemaker, conduction system and contractile mechanism.

VENTRICULAR ADAPTATION DURING SPONTANEOUS ACTIVITY

When the performance of the heart is studied under experimental conditions in which the investigator induces the responses, an assumption is implied that the procedure employed to produce the change has some correspondence with mechanisms actually utilized under normal conditions.[18] When an increase in cardiac output is induced in the heart–lung preparation by elevating the venous reservoir, an increase in stroke volume and stroke work accompanying greater ventricular distension is consistently observed (Fig. 8A). For many years, increasing stroke volume was believed to be attained by this mechanism during exercise, but this is now recognized as being incorrect (vide infra). Studies of spontaneous cardiovascular adaptations in both men and dogs have revealed evidence that the length–tension relationship (Frank–Starling mechanism) can be clearly demonstrated under some circumstances whereas neural control mechanisms appear to dominate in others. This statement is not meant to imply that either mechanism inexplicably disappears. On the contrary, one mechanism may dominate while the other is obscured.

Postural Adaptation. When either dogs or human subjects are fully relaxed in the supine position, the heart functions at or near its maximal size, as evidenced by direct measurements of ventricular dimensions in dogs[15] and x-ray measurements in man.[11, 20] During the rapid filling period the ventricular dimensions rapidly increase to reach a plateau which is sustained until the next systolic ejection. Further distension of the ventricles was not obtained in dogs even when the filling pressure was increased 15 or 20 mm. Hg by intravenous infusions of blood.[17] The heart rate is slow (70 to 90 beats per minute) and the stroke volume is very great in relation to its maximum. Any change from this condition produces a reduction in both the diastolic dimensions and in the stroke volume.[11, 15, 20] For example, a loud noise, standing up or even lifting the head to look around is sufficient to produce a prompt reduction in diastolic dimensions, stroke work, peak outflow rate and acceleration of blood. Conversely,

spontaneous reclining is accompanied by an increase in diastolic dimensions and stroke volume, as illustrated in Figure 8B. This response is clearly consistent with the Frank–Starling mechanism, although its functional utility is not immediately obvious.

Changes in Heart Rate. In a healthy, resting dog or man, the heart rate is not only relatively slow but also tends to be somewhat irregular. With each respiratory excursion, the heart rate accelerates and decelerates (sinus arrhythmia, see Chap. 30). These spontaneous changes in cycle length are accompanied by corresponding changes in the duration of the diastolic interval. As a general rule, such changes in heart rate are accompanied by variations in diastolic dimensions and in stroke volume. For example, as the heart rate slows, diastolic interval is prolonged, diastolic ventricular dimensions tend to increase and the stroke volume is greater. A somewhat exaggerated example of this phenomenon is illustrated in Figure 8C. Such changes in heart rate may be regarded as phasic changes in the number of impulses arriving at the pacemaker over the vagus nerve. When changes in cardiac response result from bombardment by the sympathetic nerves to the heart, tachycardia is accompanied by the other characteristic changes in ventricular performance to maintain stroke volume and to sustain the diastolic filling interval through reduced systolic duration (see Figs. 7, 8).

Cardiac Response during Exertion. When the ventricular adaptation does not conform to predictions from the Frank–Starling mechanism, the adaptations are commonly attributed to changes in "contractility" as indicated in Figure 8D. The important changes in ventricular performance can now be described in accepted engineering terms with appropriate definitions and units as illustrated in Figure 8 (right hand column).

Ventricular adjustment in response to exercise on a treadmill at 3 miles per hour on a 12 per cent grade was characterized by changes in performance of the sort illustrated in Figure 8. In other words, the heart rate was considerably accelerated and the duration of systole was shortened. Left ventricular systolic pressure was higher and the rate of change of systolic ventricular pressure was greatly augmented. The aortic outflow rate was considerably increased and the stroke volume was increased to a lesser extent. The cardiac output, which is a product of the stroke volume and the heart rate, was greatly augmented primarily by tachycardia. The acceleration was increased to a lesser degree. The changes in ventricular performance during exertion (Fig. 8) are closely related to the changes induced by increased sympathetic discharge to the heart or to the direct effects of cathechol amines (Fig. 7). They represent the mechanisms by which control over the heart is exerted by way of the central nervous system.

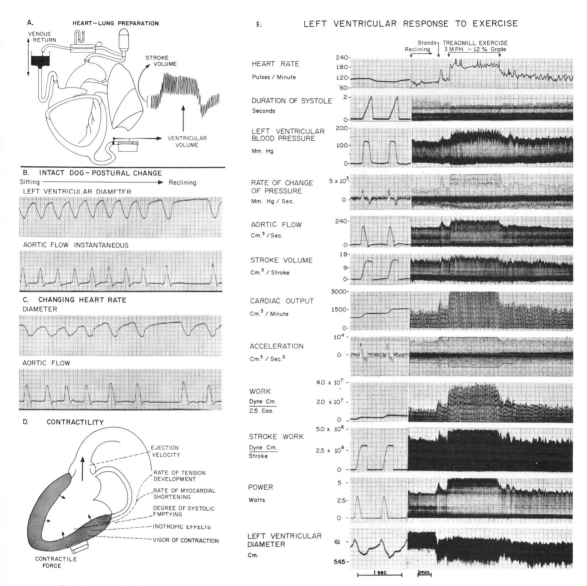

Fig. 8. *A,* In the heart-lung preparation, the ventricle responds to an increase in either volume load or pressure load by diastolic distension and increased energy release (Frank-Starling mechanism).

B, In intact dogs, the Frank-Starling mechanism is readily demonstrable in the increase in energy release associated with increased diastolic distension as the animal reclines.

C, This mechanism also occurs during spontaneous changes in heart rate (i.e., sinus arrhythmia) which represent variations in vagal discharge.

D, Changes in ventricular performance which do not conform to the Frank-Starling mechanism are commonly attributed to changes in "contractility," a term which has so many connotations that it is relatively meaningless.

E, The ventricular responses to exercise by healthy active dogs correspond to the changes induced by sympathetic stimulation as illustrated in Figure 7. (From Rushmer *et al., Circulation,* 1963, *17:*118–141.)

NEURAL CONTROL OVER
CARDIAC PERFORMANCE

Sympathetic nerves to the heart are distributed to the entire atrial and ventricular myocardium and are concentrated in the regions of the sino-atrial node and atrioventricular node. The sympathetic cardiac nerves can be traced back to the stellate ganglion and upper sympathetic ganglia and further back to the intermediolateral cell columns in the thoracic cord. The sympathetic outflow is influenced by a very large number of neural pathways representing local spinal reflexes, medullary reflexes and higher centers of control in the central nervous system. Electrical stimulation has demonstrated that nerve elements having powerful effects on cardiac function are diffusely distributed throughout the medullary region. These poorly defined regions have been traditionally called cardioaccelerator centers or cardioexcitatory centers, where stimulation produces tachycardia, increased cardiac output, increased systolic ventricular pressure, etc. Nearby is the motor nucleus of the vagus nerve from which branches are distributed to the sino-atrial node, atrial musculature and atrioventricular node. However, the vagus nerves have little or no effect on the mechanical performance of the ventricular myocardium. Stimulation of the motor nucleus of the vagus nerve and certain surrounding areas produces slowing of the heart, so these regions have been called cardioinhibitory centers. Reciprocal innervation of the cardioregulatory centers provides a mechanism by which excitation of one set of fibers is accompanied by inhibition of the others. The origin, course and distribution of the autonomic nerves is presented in more detail in Chapter 10.

Higher levels of the central nervous system have powerful effects on cardiovascular function as is evidenced by common experiences like blushing, fainting at the sight of blood, the pounding in the chest accompanying fear or the increased heart rate in anticipation of exertion. Stimulation of many different sites on the cortex of the brain and within its substance produces profound changes in cardiovascular adaptations.[16]

Neural control of the cardiovascular system is much too complicated to be treated in any detail here. Instead it seems desirable to describe two different types of neural controls as

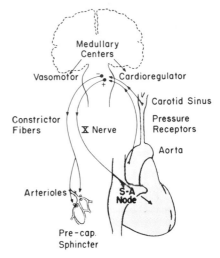

A. ARTERIAL PRESSURE REGULATION

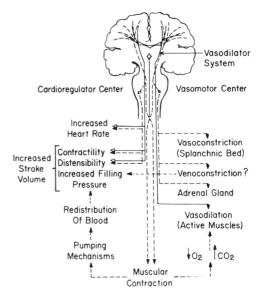

B. INITIATION OF EXERCISE RESPONSE

Fig. 9. *A,* Regulation of arterial pressure involves pressoreceptors responding to pressure in the carotid sinus and aortic arch. The impulses play upon the medullary centers of cardiovascular control, which in turn adjust peripheral vascular resistance and cardiac output to compensate for changes in arterial pressure.

B, Cardiovascular adjustments to exertion are apparently initiated by higher centers of nervous system, acting through autonomic pathways directly to produce vasodilatation in skeletal muscles, vasoconstriction in inactive tissues, tachycardia and increased myocardial contractility and distensibility. These changes would be augmented by peripheral factors such as metabolites, muscular and respiratory pumping action, etc.

examples of the way in which neural regulation may be expressed (Fig. 9).

Servocontrol of Systemic Arterial Pressure. The systemic arterial pressure tends to be maintained within a fairly narrow range by the action of a servocontrol loop consisting of recep-tors in the carotid sinus and aortic arch which have a discharge frequency related to both the mean arterial pressure and the rate of change of arterial pressure (Fig. 9*A*). Nervous discharges from these receptors travel over the glossopha-ryngeal and vagus nerves to the medulla where

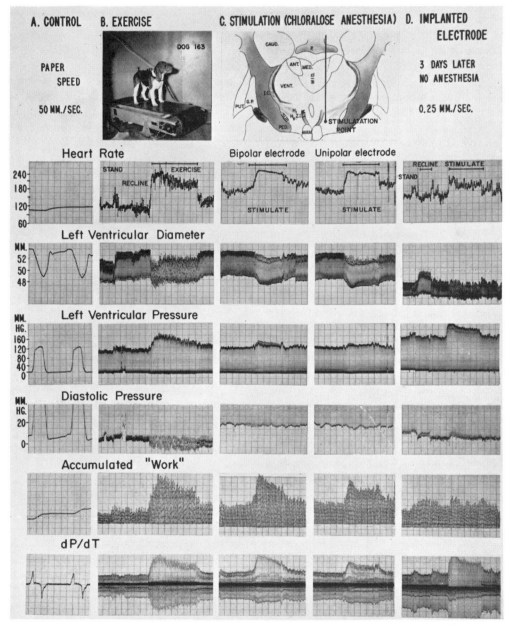

Fig. 10. *A,* Control records on a dog taken at paper speed of 50 mm. per second. *B,* Left ven-tricular response to running on a treadmill at 3 m.p.h. at a 5 per cent grade. *C,* Later the same day, dog was anesthetized, and a highly localized stimulus near the H_2 field of Forel produced a marked ventricular response. The electrode was sealed in place. *D,* Three days later, the hypothalamic region was stimulated through implanted electrode. Left ventricular response accurately mimicked that previously seen during exercise, but was not accompanied by movement of the animal. (From Rushmer and Smith, *Physiol. Rev.,* 1959, *39:*41–68.)

they impinge upon the cardioregulatory and vasomotor areas. From these sites, nervous impulses travel to the heart and to the peripheral vascular system to compensate for a change in systemic arterial pressure. In response to reduced systemic arterial pressure, cardiac output is increased and peripheral vessels constrict to restore promptly systemic arterial pressure to normal levels. Reflex loops of this sort tend to maintain function within a narrow range in response to changes induced from other causes. The mechanisms for control of systemic arterial pressure are described in detail in Chapter 34.

Initiation of Cardiovascular Adaptation to Exertion. Servocontrol loops tend to provide a static kind of control, maintaining a level of function within some range. In contrast, many mechanisms tend to induce changes in performace. For example, intense muscular exercise requires a prompt increase in blood flow through the contracting skeletal muscle to meet their metabolic requirements (Fig. 9B). Cardiovascular adaptation actually may anticipate the exercise, indicating that these adjustments may be initiated by higher levels of the central nervous system without the intervention of control loops. For example, a runner at the starting line of a race may be aware of increased heart rate, increased pounding in his chest, deeper breathing. The cause of such adaptations may be explored by stimulating discretely localized areas within the brain. For example, electrical stimulation of a site at the base of the brain no larger than 1 mm. in diameter can produce many of the changes commonly associated with exercise, as illustrated in Figure 10. Here the cardiac response to treadmill exercise was recorded in terms of changes in heart rate, left ventricular diameter, left ventricular pressure and some other derived variables. Stimulation of the small region in the H_2 fields of Forel produced the responses shown in Figure 10C under chloralose anesthesia. The electrode was implanted in this position and three days later, stimulation of the same point was accomplished after the animal had recovered from the anesthesia. The response was remarkably similar to the original exercise response (Fig. 10D). Extensions of this type of study have demonstrated that stimulation at or near this site can initiate a full blown integrated response affecting several different systems. For example, the pacemaker region is excited to produce tachycardia. The conduction system of the heart conducts a little more rapidly

so that the ventricles are excited more nearly synchronously. The ventricular myocardium develops tension more quickly and contracts more rapidly. The control over the peripheral vascular system is adjusted to open up blood vessels in the muscles of the extremities. (See sympathetic vasodilator system, Chap. 31.) Respiratory activity is enhanced with deeper and faster breathing and in some instances alternating movements of the extremities are induced even in animals under anesthesia. Thus, neuroanatomic pathways exist which have the capacity for producing fully integrated cardiovascular-pulmonary-somatic responses containing most of the components of the normal exercise response. On this basis, it seems reasonable to assume that the brain is capable of initiating complex integrated reactions by mechanisms of the sort illustrated in Figure 9B. Responses with specific patterns may be manifest spontaneously under conditions such as startle reactions, fear, anticipation of exertion, or embarrassment.

CARDIOVASCULAR RESERVE

In recumbent animals, the diastolic dimensions of the heart and the stroke change in dimensions were about as large as were observed under any circumstance (Fig. 11). When an animal stood up spontaneously the diastolic dimensions and stroke change in dimensions both diminished promptly to much lower levels. Under these conditions, an increase in stroke volume can result from greater diastolic distension or more complete systolic ejection (Fig. 11). However, during moderate exercise, the diastolic dimensions and stroke change in dimensions were changed only slightly if at all.

These observations led to a survey of the literature to collect data on the changes in stroke volume in normal human subjects during various levels of exercise. Values from ten such studies were plotted against the measured oxygen consumption to indicate the severity of the exercise (Fig. 12). The absolute values for stroke volume showed little increase (i.e., 20 per cent) over a very wide range of oxygen consumption up to levels approaching the maximum exercise that can be sustained for only a few minutes.

Since the stroke volume did not increase progressively from mild to severe exercise, the increase in oxygen delivery must be attributed to other factors. The heart rate increased progressively with greater work loads until it reached a maximum of about 180 beats per minute (Fig. 12*B*). This level of heart rate is generally regarded as about the maximum effective rate, beyond which further acceleration causes reduced stroke volume and no net gain in cardiac output. Any increase in cardiac output above that which occurs with a heart rate of 180 beats per minute must be accomplished by greater stroke volume. It is seen that at the extreme degrees of exertion, some increase in stroke volume may be detected, although the scatter of the data is increased by technical difficulties. The extraction of oxygen from the blood also increases progressively and fails to plateau even at the maximum levels of exercise. The oxygen content of venous blood from the exercising extremities tends to be driven to a minimum level (ranging around 4 to 5 ml. per 100 ml. blood).

Blood leaving actively contracting muscles is almost completely devoid of oxygen but the blood flow through skin remains high because of the requirements for heat dissipation. In veins draining inactive tissues, the oxygen is also thoroughly extracted when the exercise is severe. This means that compensatory vasoconstriction in inactive tissues slows the blood flow to the point that oxygen extraction is nearly as complete in areas like the intestines as it is in the extremities.

If the cardiovascular reserve is defined in terms of the amount of increase in oxygen delivery which can be attained above the resting level, the arteriovenous oxygen difference (oxygen extraction), heart rate and stroke volume all contribute but not to the same degree at any particular level of exercise. In the original report of these findings,[16] emphasis was placed on the constancy for the stroke volume over the

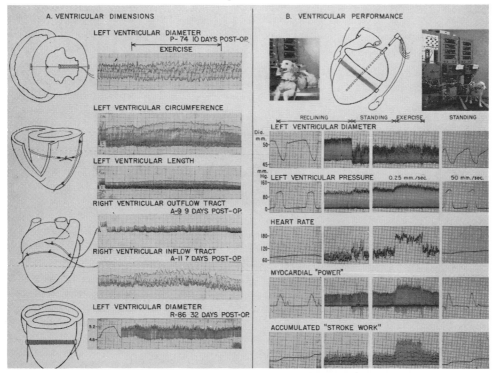

Fig. 11. *A,* The ventricular response to exertion by intact dogs involves very little change in the several ventricular dimensions which were measured directly. A slight increase in systolic excursion was produced by increased diastolic distention, more complete systolic ejection, or both.

B, In resting recumbent dogs, the left ventricular dimensions are maximal; they diminish when the animal stands. Exercise results in slight changes in dimensions, increased systolic ventricular pressure, little change in mean ventricular diastolic pressure, pronounced tachycardia, increased power output by the myocardium, and greater work per stroke and work per unit time. (Fom Rushmer and Smith, *Physiol. Rev.,* 1959, *39:*41–68.)

very wide range of exercise illustrated in Figure 12. This new report conflicted directly with a large body of opinion and data to the effect that stroke volume does in fact increase with exercise. Much of the subsequent controversy was assuaged when it was pointed out that the control values for stroke volume in Figure 12 included data from both erect and supine subjects.[1, 15, 24] Thus, the stroke volume over a wide range of exercise in the supine position increased slightly or not at all over the control values obtained in recumbent subjects.[24] The stroke volume, during quiet standing, is lower (by 20 to 40 per cent in humans) than in the recumbent position. Any exertion undertaken in the erect position produces a prompt increase in stroke volume to a level which remains about the same over a very wide range of exertion. For example, Wang et al.[24] showed that the slightest possible leg exercise (marking time by alternately lifting feet off the floor) in erect subjects promptly produced an increase in stroke volume almost comparable to that attained during moderate exercise on a moving belt. The stroke volume increased only slightly from minimal exercise to moderate exercise. Chapman et al.[1] also presented data which demonstrated values for stroke volume which also conformed to the same pattern; a marked reduction in stroke volume from recumbent controls to quiet standing, a marked increased in stroke volume to about the same levels as the recumbent control during mild and moderate exercise and a further increase in stroke volume during maximal exercise. The data are clear that stroke volume increases slightly or not at all over a wide range of exercise from marking time to rather severe exercise. Stroke volume is definitely increased

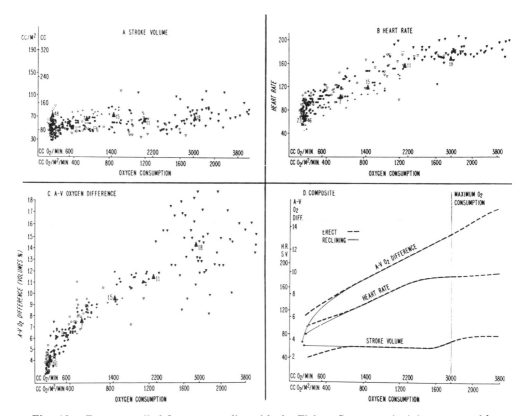

Fig. 12. Data compiled from ten studies with the Fick or Stewart principle on normal human subjects. *A,* Stroke volume tends to remain at approximately the recumbent control level during exertion sufficient to increase total oxygen consumption more than tenfold. *B,* Heart rate increases progressively with greater physical exertion until rate is about 180 beats per minute; it then levels off. *C,* Oxygen extraction from the blood, indicated by arteriovenous oxygen differences, appears to increase with exertion until oxygen consumption has attained maximal values. *D,* Control values in erect subjects are characterized by smaller stroke volume, faster heart rate and higher arteriovenous oxygen difference than those in recumbent subjects. During exertion, stroke volume increases somewhat above erect control values.

during the transition from quiet standing to any level of exercise and also perhaps at the very highest levels of exertion that can be endured. Stroke volume also increases by about the same amount during the transition from quiet standing to the supine position. These adjustments are undoubtedly caused by different mechanisms, the former predominantly by sympathetic control and the latter by the Frank–Starling mechanism.

Confusion is sometimes injected into the relative role of the components of cardiovascular control by quoting the values for stroke volume and heart rate at the extremes of exercise as evidence for the importance of increased stroke volume. The range of exertion over which the stroke volume is remarkably constant includes the levels of exercise which are encountered by virtually all persons during virtually all times at work and play, except for athletes and manual laborers doing heavy work. For example, Ford and Hellerstein[3] measured oxygen consumption in representative workers at three companies manufacturing various products including electric motors, automobile and airplane parts, bearings and nonferrous metal products. Their average rate of energy expenditure during the work shift was two calories per minute, a level which is difficult to distinguish from resting levels. The maximum levels of oxygen consumption rarely exceeded twice the resting rate. These subjects were regarded as representative of at least one-third of the working population of a large industrial city. In contrast, men working in steel mills were found to attain energy expenditures ranging from 2 to 5 calories per minute, which is the maximum which can be sustained for an extended period.[4] These values are much lower than the maximal values in Figure 12A. In these subjects, the periods of heavy work are alternated by periods of rest. In this modern day, the average man is seldom called upon to exercise to his maximum capacity.

The contribution of increasing stroke volume to the cardiovascular reserve is greatly increased by any condition which restrains or prevents a progressive acceleration of the heart in relation to the exertion. For example, administration of atropine to dogs produces acceleration of the heart during the control period and during exertion. Under these conditions, the cardiac output increases to about the same extent as normal by a substantial increase in stroke volume.[9] Warner and Toronto[25] controlled the heart rate

in dogs with heart block both at rest and during exercise. They also demonstrated that with the heart rate constant, the stroke volume increased to attain approximately normal cardiac output. Such experiments indicate the potential contribution of stroke volume to increasing cardiac output. They do not indicate what actually happens nor the control mechanisms which cause the normal response to exercise.

REFERENCES

1. CHAPMAN, C. B., FISHER, J. N. and SPROULE, B. J. *J. clin. Invest.*, 1960, *39*:1208–1213.
2. COURNAND, A., RILEY, R. L., BREED, E. S., BALDWIN, E. deF. and RICHARDS, D. W., Jr. *J. clin. Invest.*, 1945, *24*:106–116.
3. FORD, A. B. and HELLERSTEIN, H. K. *Circulation*, 1958, *18*:823–832.
4. FORD, A. B., HELLERSTEIN, H. K. and TURRELL, D. J. *Circulation*, 1959, *20*:537–548.
5. FRANK, O. *Z. Biol.*, 1895, *14*:370–437.
6. FRANK, O. *Amer. Heart J.*, 1959, *58*:282–317; *idem*, 467–478.
7. HAMILTON, W. F. and REMINGTON, J. W. *Amer. J. Physiol.*, 1947, *148*:35–39.
8. HOWELL, W. H. and DONALDSON, F., JR. *Phil. Trans.*, 1884, *B175*:139–160.
9. KECK, E. W., ALLWOOD, M. J., MARSHALL, R. J. and SHEPHERD, J. T. *Circulation Res.*, 1961, *9*:566–570.
10. LUNDIN, G. *Acta physiol. scand.*, 1944, *7* (Suppl. 20):1–86.
11. MUSSHOFF, V. K. and REINDELL, H. *Dtsch. med. Wschr.*, 1956, *81*:1001–1008.
12. RUSHMER, R. F. Chap. 16 in *Handbook of Physiology, Section 2, Circulation*, Vol. 1, W. F. Hamilton and P. Dow, eds. Washington, D. C., American Physiological Society, 1962.
13. RUSHMER, R. F. *Circulation*, 1964, *29*:268–283.
14. RUSHMER, R. F. In: *Proceedings, symposium on pulsatile flow*, E. O. Attinger, ed. New York, McGraw-Hill Book Company, 1964.
15. RUSHMER, R. F. *Circulation*, 1959, *20*:897–905.
16. RUSHMER, R. F. and SMITH, O. A., JR. *Physiol. Rev.*, 1959, *39*:41–68.
17. RUSHMER, R. F., SMITH, O. A., JR. and FRANKLIN, D. L. *Circulation Res.*, 1959, *7*:605–627.
18. RUSHMER, R. F., VAN CITTERS, R. L. and FRANKLIN, D. L. *Circulation*, 1963, *17*:118–141.
19. SARNOFF, S. J. and MITCHELL, J. H. The control of the function of the heart. Chap. 15 in *Handbook of Physiology, Section 2, Circulation*, Vol. 1, W. F. Hamilton and P. Dow, eds. Washington, D. C., American Physiological Society, 1962.
20. SJOSTRAND, T. *Minn. Med.*, 1954, *37*:10–15.
21. SONNENBLICK, E. H. *Amer. J. Physiol.*, 1962, *202*:931–939.
22. SPENCER, M. P. and GREISS, F. C. *Circulation Res.*, 1962, *10*:274–279.
23. STARLING, E. H. *The Linacre lecture on the law of the heart, given at Cambridge, 1915.* London, Longmans, Green, 1918.
24. WANG, Y., MARSHALL, R. J. and SHEPHERD, J. T. *J. clin. Invest.*, 1960, *39*:1051–1061.
25. WARNER, H. R. and TORONTO, A. F. *Circulation Res.*, 1960, *8*:549–552.

CHAPTER 34

Control of Arterial Blood Pressure: Measurement of Pressure and Flow

By ALLEN M. SCHER

INTRODUCTION

HUMAN arterial blood pressure (and insofar as we know, blood pressure in other mammals) stays within narrow limits over a wide variety of bodily postures and states. Indeed, under normal conditions only massive changes in bodily activity cause a substantial alteration in the arterial blood pressure. The mean blood pressure rises in exercise, and this appears to be partly an adjustment to increased energy expenditure. With substantial blood loss, the blood pressure can fall, but here the compensatory mechanisms, which operate to maintain the normal pressure and which are described in this chapter, are functioning maximally. The necessity for blood pressure control can be teleologically considered to be related to the maintenance of a constant internal environment and to the maintenance of various higher functions of the organism. The first of these is necessary for simple cellular survival, the second for the complex nervous activities in higher animals. Concerning the first, it was pointed out during the discussion of motor functions of the nervous system that vertebrate organisms tend to—in fact, are forced for survival to—maintain a relatively constant internal environment. This requires control of the composition of the extracellular fluid. For the physiologist, Claude Bernard's picture of the regulated *milieu interne*[8] or Cannon's *homeostasis*[14] conceptualize this control of extracellular fluid composition. The importance of pressure regulation here is that, when the pressure is maintained, the blood circulates adequately and the plasma is continually transported to the extracellular space after oxygenation in the lungs, addition of metabolites in the gastrointestinal organs, and removal of metabolic end products in the kidney. Diffusion from the extracellular space to this constantly replenished plasma (as discussed in Chap. 45) maintains the proper environment for the cells. Fluid transfer from the vascular system to the extracellular space through filtration also depends, in part, on the maintenance of adequate arterial blood pressure. This is of importance in certain special cases, i.e., the formation of urine, cerebrospinal fluid, etc.

The importance of the maintenance of blood pressure for the continued function of higher organisms is seen in the fact that a certain level of pressure is necessary to maintain an adequate blood supply to the brain, to the heart, etc. As previously noted, these most essential organs have little vasoconstrictor potential. Even if sympathetic "tone" is increased throughout the body, with a rise in arterial pressure, the brain and heart will have a nearly normal vascular resistance. They thus have a certain priority or protection insofar as perfusion with blood is concerned.

This textbook has already featured limited discussions of regulation through feedback control and of the stretch reflex as it functions to maintain the upright posture (Chap. 7). The most important known reflexes involving the circulatory system are those which function to control the arterial blood pressure. The blood pressure is altered by reflexes initiated by receptors (pressoreceptors) which are sensitive to *pressure* (or to a function of pressure). Blood pressure is also strongly influenced by receptors (chemoreceptors) which are sensitive to the chemical composition of the blood. These two classes of reflexes are the major subjects of this chapter, which also includes details of a variety of mechanisms of a local or central nature and other regulatory systems which can change the blood pressure.

THE PRESSORECEPTOR REFLEXES

A diagram of the anatomic units concerned in blood pressure regulation is presented in Figure 1. Receptors are located in two general sites. Those which are most discretely localized, the carotid sinus receptors, are at the bifurcation of the carotid artery in the neck. Another group of receptors, referred to collectively as the aortic

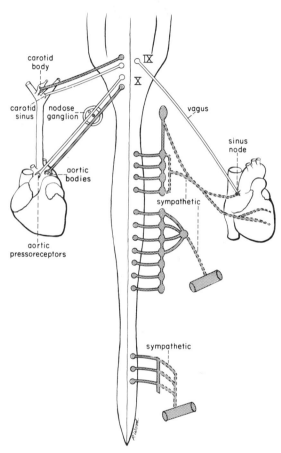

Fig. 1. The medullary blood pressure control system. Sensory elements are shown on the left of the figure. The pressure receptors are the carotid sinus pressoreceptors and the receptors of the aortic arch. Chemoreceptors are the carotid and aortic bodies. The aortic receptors give rise to afferent nerve fibers in the vagus nerve (and depressor nerve). The carotid receptors send impulses to the central nervous system via the nerve of Hering, which joins the glossopharyngeal trunk.

Effectors are shown on the right. The vagus nerve alters the heart rate through its effect on the sinoatrial node. Sympathetic fibers alter heart rate and strength of cardiac contraction. They run to the sinoatrial node (pacemaker) and to the ventricular musculature. Sympathetic fibers also alter pressure by their widespread innervation of the arterioles.

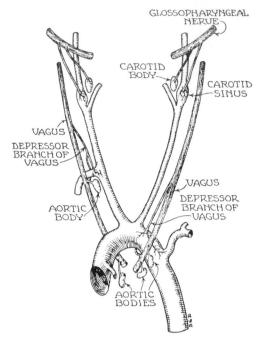

Fig. 2. Diagram illustrating position and nerve supply of carotid sinuses and aortic arch, together with carotid and aortic bodies.

receptors, are found in the general region of the arch of the aorta and the origin of the subclavian arteries (Fig. 2). There are apparently receptors scattered along the blood vessels between these two sites.[35] Detailed anatomic and physiologic characteristics of these receptors will be presented later, but their major characteristic is that they change their rate of firing with changes in the arterial blood pressure; i.e., the higher the pressure, the greater the firing rate, and the lower the pressure, the smaller the number of impulses sent to the nervous system per unit time. Impulses generated by the receptors in the carotid sinus travel along the nerve of Hering (or carotid sinus nerve), which joins the glossopharyngeal nerve. Afferent impulses from the receptors in the region of the aortic arch travel in sensory fibers accompanying the vagus nerve. At normal arterial pressure some receptors are active. As the pressure rises, these receptors produce impulses more frequently, and other receptors begin to fire. This increase in the number of active receptors and in the frequency of depolarization of individual receptors continues with further increase in pressure. Conversely, if the pressure decreases, the frequency of impulses from each receptor decreases, and some receptors cease to be active.

The afferent nerve fibers from the receptors enter the brain stem with the glossopharyngeal and vagus nerves and travel to the medulla oblongata, entering the vasomotor center or cardiac center or both. Here, through one or more synaptic connections, the impulses from the pressoreceptors can alter the discharge in the appropriate motor nerves. These motor nerves are from the sympathetic nervous system and from the vagal branches of the parasympathetic nervous system. The reflex connections are such that when the pressure rises (and the frequency of impulses in the pressoreceptor nerves increases), activity decreases in the sympathetic nervous system and increases in the vagal fibers.

Tonic activity normally is present in both the sympathetic and parasympathetic outflow from the brain stem. In the case of the sympathetic nervous system, a decreased activity in the fibers running to the heart, which might reflexly arise from increased arterial pressure, tends to decrease the heart rate. Further a decreased tonic activity in fibers to peripheral blood vessels allows the caliber of the vessels to increase, thereby decreasing the peripheral resistance. A further effect of decreased sympathetic activity to the heart is a decline in the vigor of cardiac contraction (Chap. 33). The increase in vagal firing occasioned by an increase in arterial blood pressure reduces the heart rate, synergistically with the decreased sympathetic activity. When arterial blood pressure falls, activity is decreased in the afferent fibers which run from the pressoreceptors to the brain stem. This leads to a reflex increase in sympathetic motor activity and a decrease in vagal motor activity. The increased sympathetic activity tends to increase the heart rate, the strength of cardiac contraction, and the degree of constriction of the peripheral blood vessels. The decrease in vagal activity increases the heart rate.

The qualitative description of the reflexes is as follows: When the pressoreceptor impulses increase, vagal discharge to the heart increases reflexly, slowing the heart. Concomitantly, sympathetic firing to the heart and blood vessels decreases. Decreased sympathetic discharge to the heart also leads to a decrease in the strength of ventricular contraction. The decreased discharge to the vasoconstrictor nerve fibers allows the arterial pressure to fall. Thus, the blood pressure tends to remain at a normal level.

The existence of the carotid sinus reflex was

classically demonstrated by Heymans.[34] He ingeniously arranged two dogs so that the carotid arteries of one, the recipient (including his carotid receptors), were perfused by a second dog, the donor. Blood was returned to the donor from the recipient's jugular vein. The nervous connections between the recipient's head and the rest of its circulatory system were intact. When the blood pressure of the donor animal was raised through drugs or otherwise, the pressure in the recipient's carotid arteries also increased (Fig. 3). This produced a reflex fall in the systemic blood pressure of the recipient. The carotid receptors of the recipient were exposed

to the increased pressure, and it is accepted that only these receptors could have produced this reflex change in the recipient's blood pressure. The nervous connections to the recipient's effector organs were, of course, intact. A schematic diagram of the control system is seen in Figure 4. Treatments of various aspects of blood pressure control in terms of engineering control theory have started to appear recently.[4, 16, 30, 38, 50, 58]

Fragmentary pieces of evidence indicated the existence of the blood pressure control reflexes long before they were clearly elucidated. In 1866 de Cyon and Ludwig[18] noted that stimulation of the aortic nerve in

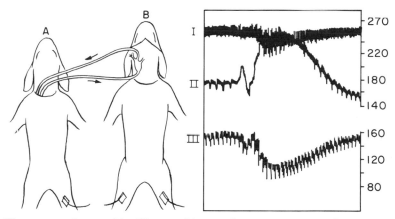

Fig. 3. The preparation used by Heymans[34] to study pressoreceptor reflexes. A recipient dog (*B*) is arranged so that its carotid arteries are perfused by the donor dog (*A*). Blood is returned to the donor from the recipient's jugular vein. In this experiment, the blood pressure of the donor animal (*II*) was raised by an injection of epinephrine. This, of course, raised the pressure in the carotid arteries of the recipient. This led to a marked fall in pressure (*III*) in the major portion of the recipient's circulation, which was perfused normally. The recipient's heart rate also fell (*I*).

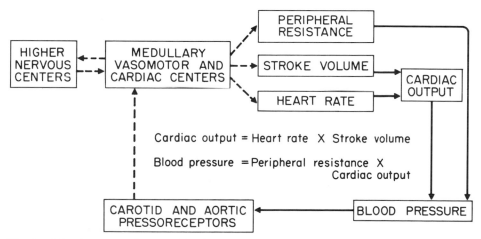

Fig. 4. Blood pressure is sensed by the pressoreceptors, which send impulses to the medulla. The medullary centers send impulses to motor fibers of the sympathetic and parasympathetic nervous system. When pressure at the receptor rises or falls, it is reflexly corrected by an alteration of heart rate, stroke volume and peripheral resistance. Dotted lines indicate nervous connections.

the rabbit produced a reflex fall in heart rate and in blood pressure. This nerve, commonly called the depressor nerve, is separate in rabbits (and in some cats) and runs parallel to the vagal trunk. It appears to contain, largely or exclusively, fibers from the aortic pressoreceptors.

In 1925 Hering noted that mechanical stimulation of the carotid sinus in a patient produced a reflex bradycardia.[33] This effect was due, of course, to increased firing of the receptors initiated by the mechanical stimulation. Hering later stimulated the nerves from the receptors in animals, with results similar to those reported by Ludwig and de Cyon. Because of technical difficulties in duplicating Hering's experiments, there followed a long period of time when the reflexes were a subject for controversy. In 1929 Heymans[34] performed the ingenious series of experiments previously cited, ending the confusion over these reflexes. His work led to a Nobel Prize in 1938.

Characteristics of Pressorceptors and Pressoreceptor Reflexes.

The carotid sinus can be grossly observed as a dilatation of the internal carotid artery at its origin. This region has rich sensory innervation from the sinus nerve, and the wall of the vessel appears to be extremely thin.[15, 35] The aortic arch receptors cannot be grossly observed but can be seen in histologic section.

The pressoreceptors, on histologic examination, appear to be the terminal ramifications of undifferentiated nerve fibers which branch extensively in the adventitia and media of the carotid sinus and aortic arch regions (Fig. 5). The exact details of their connection to adjacent structures are not clear; i.e., we do not know whether they are "in series" with or parallel to

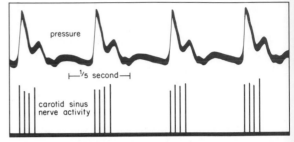

Fig. 6. Blood pressure above; impulses in the carotid sinus nerve below. Impulses occur during the rise in pressure early in each beat. (After Bronk and Stella, *Amer. J. Physiol.*, 1935, *110*:708–714.)

the muscle fibers of the vessel wall. However, when the vessel increases in diameter because of increased blood pressure, the receptors are stretched. It is through this deformation of the wall and of the fine nerve terminations that the receptors transform pressure into nerve impulses. They are not, therefore, truly pressoreceptors but are indicators of length or deformation of a nerve termination within a vessel segment. De Castro[15] found about 700 myelinated fibers in the carotid sinus nerve of the cat. Most of these were smaller than 5μ in diameter. Paintal[44] measured a conduction velocity of 12 to 53 meters per second in the aortic depressor nerve of the rabbit. This agrees well with the measured fiber diameter.

The functional characteristics of the pressoreceptors have been studied by several investigators.[13, 23, 39] The carotid sinus receptors are better adapted to these studies because the carotid sinus nerve contains only sensory (pressoreceptor and chemoreceptor) fibers and because the carotid bifurcation can be isolated and the pressure therein controlled. In general, the sinus nerve is carefully dissected, and a few fibers or single fibers are carefully teased out of the main nerve trunk. These fine fibers are laid on electrodes connected to an amplifier and recording oscillograph. The response to normal blood pressure changes can then be observed (Fig. 6). If responses to other pressure waves are to be studied, the carotid sinus is at times converted to a closed sinus; that is, the major branches of the internal and external carotid arteries are tied. Careful surgical technique is required to avoid damage to the sinus nerve. The pressure in the carotid sinus can then be altered, using various types of hydraulic systems. The receptor response can, for convenience, be divided into two main portions. The first of

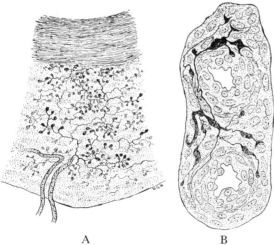

A   B

Fig. 5. Diagram showing characteristics of afferent endings in (*A*) carotid sinus and (*B*) carotid body. (After de Castro.)

these is the static response, i.e., the response when the rate of change of pressure is zero. The second is a response to phasic pressure changes.

Static response (Fig. 7). The static response of the receptors was studied by Bronk and Stella[13] and by Landgren.[39] They subjected the carotid sinus to varying mean blood pressure levels and recorded impulses in the sensory nerve. Below a certain threshold pressure, the receptor does not fire. This threshold is variable but seems to be as low as 30 mm. Hg for some fibers.[39] At the threshold pressure the receptor begins to fire but fires at very low frequency. As the mean pressure at the receptor is raised past the threshold, the firing rate increases roughly in proportion to the increase in pressure. Eventually, the firing rate reaches a maximum for a particular fiber, usually about 10 impulses per second. This rate is reached at 180 to 220 mm. Hg. It must be borne in mind, however, that the receptor region contains fibers of various sizes and pressure thresholds. Landgren[39] compared the responses of large and small nerve fibers from the receptor and found that the small nerve fibers, which are difficult to isolate and from which it is difficult to record, have approximately the same characteristics as the larger fibers, more commonly examined experimentally. Bronk and Stella[13] changed static pressures at the receptor but did not eliminate pulsatile pressure changes. Landgren controlled the pressure more completely. However, the results are similar.

Phasic response. The second portion of the receptor response concerns phasic changes in pressure. Such changes in pressure are, of course, normally imposed on the receptor by the beating of the heart. In experiments on the presso-

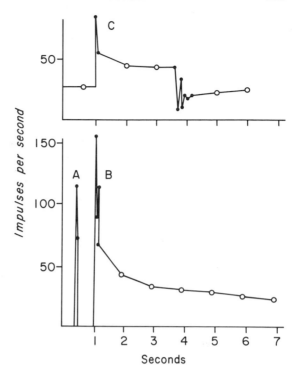

Fig. 8. Effects of changing pressure levels on the discharge from pressoreceptors. In *A* the pressure was changed from 40 to 60 mm. Hg. Note that the receptor fires only for a short period of time. In *B* the pressure was raised from 60 to 80 mm. Hg. The firing rate increases markedly and then is constant at about 25 impulses per second. In *C* the pressure was raised from 100 to 120 and then lowered again. Note "overshoot" and "undershoot."

receptors, phasic inputs are often generated by external hydraulic systems. Such studies have been conducted by Landgren[39] and by Green (see Heymans and Neil[35]). With phasic inputs, the receptors fire most rapidly when the pressure is increasing and when the rate of change of pressure is greatest. When the rate of change of pressure becomes negative, i.e., when pressure is falling, the receptor often ceases to fire, even when the pressure is above the threshold. These responses are clearly seen when square waves or sine waves are imposed on the receptors (see Figs. 7 and 8). The receptor is thus not only a mean pressure level sensing device, but is also, like other mechanoreceptors, sensitive to the rate of change of pressure (Chap. 7).

Receptor equation. From the work cited above, the simplest receptor equation seems to be the following:

$$F_0 + K_3\, dF_0/dt = K_1\,(P_I - P_T) + K_2\, dP_I/dt$$

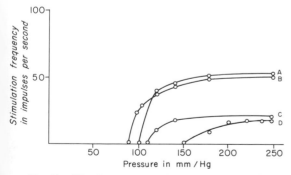

Fig. 7. The frequency of firing versus mean pressure for several pressoreceptors. Receptors have a threshold, then increase firing rate with mean pressure until a maximal firing rate is achieved. (After Landgren, *Acta physiol. scand.*, 1952, *26*:1–34.)

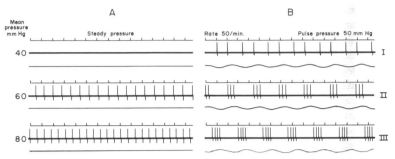

Fig. 9. On the left, the response of a single fiber of the common carotid nerve to various maintained pressure levels. Note that at 40 mm. Hg the nerve does not fire. In the records on the right, mean input pressure is the same as on the left, but sinusoidal pressure variations are also imposed on the receptor. At 40 mm. Hg the nerve is now active; at higher frequencies the firing occurs mostly when the pressure is increasing. (After Green in *Reflexogenic areas of the cardiovascular system,* Heymans and Neil, eds. London, J. & A. Churchill, Ltd., 1958.)

where F_O is the receptor frequency, P_I the arterial pressure, P_T the threshold pressure, and dF_O/dt and dP_I/dt the derivatives of frequency and pressure, respectively. That this receptor equation is justified is seen most clearly when square waves of pressure are applied to the receptor. Here the response to a step increase in pressure is initially a marked increase in firing ("overshoot"), followed by a gradual fall to a new firing frequency higher than that seen at the original pressure (Fig. 8). The necessity for the term in dP_I/dt is seen in the initial overshoot. The necessity for the dF_O/dt term is seen in the fact that the rate of firing continues to change after the input has become stationary. At a mean pressure just below threshold, the receptor will not fire; however, if pulsations are added to the pressure *without* changing the mean level, the receptor will fire during the positive-going portion of these pulsations. The receptor thus fires although the mean level has not changed (Fig. 9). This nonlinear receptor property apparently accounts for a type of "rectification" seen in the carotid sinus reflex (see below). The receptor equation above is possibly oversimplified, since the receptor may have a very different quantitative response to a positive rate of increase of pressure than to the same rate of change of pressure when the pressure is going in a negative direction. (If true, this means that we need more terms in our equation.) This question cannot be resolved until the receptor has been more carefully studied.

Several investigators have claimed that the sensitivity of the receptor can be reflexly set. According to this view, the sympathetic fibers which terminate near the receptor discharge, changing the diameter of the vessel or the sensitivity of the receptor, so that the firing is different at a given pressure than it would be without sympathetic activity. There is some disagreement concerning the existence of this reflex alteration in receptor sensitivity.

Medullary Vasomotor and Cardiac Control Regions. Impulses from the carotid and aortic receptors travel in the ninth and tenth nerves to a region of the medulla oblongata where the major integration of cardiovascular responses takes place. The importance of this region has been investigated by three methods: (i) progressive brain stem sectioning, (ii) electrical stimulation of the brain stem, and (iii) recording of electrical activity of the region's nervous structures. If the brain stem is sectioned transversely at the level of the upper pons[3] (Fig. 10), the blood pressure is well maintained, as are the basic blood pressure-controlling reflexes. When the brain stem is sectioned below the upper pons, the pressure falls, and this fall is greater the more caudal the section. Finally, when the brain stem is sectioned at the first cervical segment, pressure is markedly reduced and reflexes cannot be elicited from the pressoreceptors.

Stimulation experiments have been conducted by Ranson and Billingsley[47] and by Alexander,[3] Landgren,[40] Uvnäs,[55] and others. The results indicate that the blood pressure can be altered by stimulation in a region extending from the middle of the pons to the obex. Stimulation of certain regions of the lateral reticular formation in the rostral two-thirds of the medulla increases blood pressure (a "pressor" response). This region is therefore referred to as the "pressor" center. Stimulation of a more central and caudal "depressor center" produces a fall in blood pressure (Fig. 11). These regions overlap to some extent in the anteroposterior direction and laterally. As indicated below, there is substantial evidence that the pressor center is normally "tonically" active, i.e., that it constantly discharges impulses to the preganglionic vasoconstrictor neurons of the periphery; these tonic impulses tend to maintain some degree of constriction in the blood vessels and to increase the heart rate. That the depressor center is also tonically active is indicated by the existence of a tonic vagal discharge to the heart. (Vagotomy leads to an increase in heart rate.)

Section of the brain stem is, of course, a gross alteration of structure, interrupting many tracts concerned with other functions than those being directly examined. Stimulation of local medullary regions produces clearer results, but these are difficult to evaluate since one cannot assume that punctate stimulation bears a real relationship to what normally takes place. The

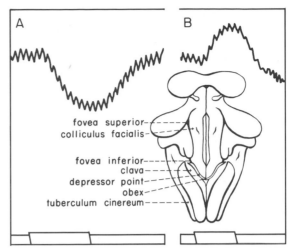

Fig. 11. A view from below of the brain stem in the region of the floor of the fourth ventricle. Curve *A* shows the results of electrical stimulation in the region of the area postrema lateral to the obex ("depressor point" in the drawing). Curve *B* shows results of stimulation near the fovea inferior, which is a "pressor point." (After Ranson and Billingsley, *Amer. J. Physiol.*, 1941, *134*:359–383.)

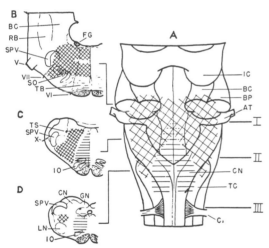

Fig. 10. Location of "pressor" (diagonal cross hatch) and "depressor" (horizontal hatch) centers in medulla of cat. *A*, Diagram of brain stem; *B, C* and *D*, cross sections of brain stem at levels I, II and III in *A. AT*, Auditory tubercle; *BC*, brachium conjunctiva; *BP*, brachium ponti; *C$_1$*, first cervical nerve; *CN*, cuneate nucleus; *FG*, facial genu; *GN*, gracile nucleus; *IC*, inferior colliculus; *IO*, inferior olivary nucleus; *LN*, lateral reticular nucleus; *RB*, restiform body; *SO*, superior olivary nucleus; *SPV*, spinal trigeminal tract; *TB*, trapezoid body; *TC*, tuberculum cinereum; *TS*, tractus solitarius; *V, VI, VII, X*, corresponding cranial nerves; *I, II, III*, levels of transection. (From Alexander, *J. Neurophysiol.*, 1946, *9*:205–217.)

sectioning and stimulation experiments both indicate that control of cardiovascular functions is widely distributed in the medullary region rather than discretely localized.

Better understanding of the blood pressure control system would be achieved if the system could be separated into functional units for which "input" could validly and accurately be related to "output." An apparently ideal technique for acquiring this information would be the recording of impulses from each nervous structure. This technique has been valiantly applied to the study of "cardiovascular" neurons in the central nervous system, but the number of such neurons discovered in many attempts is small.

Neurons have been found which fire in synchrony with the arterial blood pressure (Fig. 12); some fire when the arterial pressure is increasing, others later in the cycle. Since we know the characteristics of the receptor so well, we would hope to advance our understanding by recording impulses from cells which are one or more synapses removed from the afferent fiber. Some fibers of this sort have been studied,[31] but the present data do not permit more than a qualitative statement of the function of the medullary centers. Many neurons which change firing level when circulatory reflexes are engendered do not show a cardiovascular rhythm.[51] Efferent discharge has been recorded only in the sympathetic fibers, where firing has been found to be synchronous with the heart beat in some studies and synchronous with respiration in others (particularly studies of splanchnic nerve discharge).[12, 21, 28]

The exact nature of the input-output relationship across the nervous system must be anticipated from future experiments.

Centers. As indicated above, the medullary regions are often referred to as centers, and the following names have been used: vasomotor center, cardiac center, vasoconstrictor center, vasodilator center, cardio-accelerator center, and cardio-inhibitory center. These names suggest the existence of a specific organization in the medulla, perhaps like a telephone switchboard with separate controls for each function. Apparently, the medullary regions have many connections to the "input" and "output" cells of the blood pressure control system and to interneurons, but the specificity of the organization seems doubtful. Connections occur in this region between cells concerned with cardiovascular regulation and those concerned with other forms of autonomic regulation and with respiration. Also,[43] the neurons which descend from the higher centers and which influence the cardiovascular system synapse here with those cells concerned with basic autonomic regulation. The higher centers, including the hypothalamus and the cortex, apparently contribute to regulation of the circulatory system through their effects on the medullary neurons.[46, 57] These facts justify the use of the term "center" but should

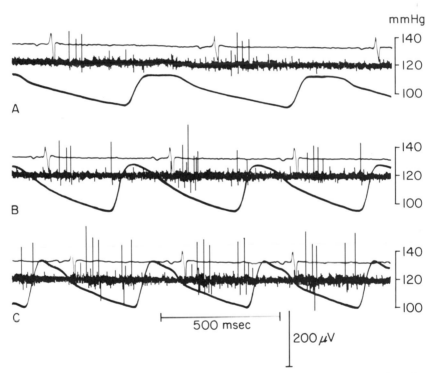

Fig. 12. Records of one type of nerve impulse recorded in the rhombencephalon of the cat associated with cardiovascular events. *A*, A control record obtained from the electrocardiogram (top curve), an electrode in the medulla (second curve), and the femoral arterial pressure (lower curve). In this control record, several nerve impulses can be seen in synchrony with the heart beat, approximately during the T wave of the electrocardiogram and halfway between the peak of systole and the end of diastole.

During *B* and *C*, an infusion of epinephrine was given. The firing of the neurons seen in the control record is augmented sporadically as the arterial pressure rises, and a second "group" of nerve impulses is seen later in diastole. This second group might arise from atrial activity or from the increased pressure. All of the impulses seem to be recorded from nerve fibers one or more synapses removed from the receptors. (After Hellner and von Baumgarten, *Pflüg. Arch. ges Physiol.,* 1961, *273:* 223–234.)

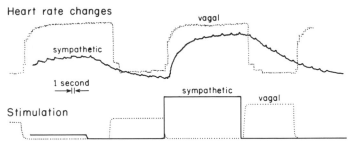

Fig. 13. The lower record shows the duration of stimulation of the sympathetic (solid line) and parasympathetic (dotted line) fibers to the heart. The curves above show the effects on heart rate of the two types of stimulation. The curves have been superimposed to facilitate comparison. Note that the cardiac slowing in response to vagal stimulation, accomplished very rapidly—less than 1 second —is required for the response to be virtually complete. The "off" response when vagal stimulation ceases is slightly slower. In contrast, the heart rate increase in response to sympathetic stimulation may not be fully complete in 20 seconds, and the slowing of the rate when sympathetic stimulation ceases is even slower. (After Warner and Cox, *J. appl. Physiol.*, 1962, *17*:349–355.)

not be taken to indicate a specific localized type of control. As will be discussed later, the medullary regions are sensitive to certain metabolites, and the intensity of the tonic discharge to the periphery is modified by changes in the concentrations of these metabolites, as well as by impulses from the pressor afferents and from the other receptors which influence blood pressure. Further, peripheral chemoreceptor afferents act to modify the activity of the medullary centers.

Motor Responses. The vagal fibers originate in the dorsal motor nucleus of the vagus and descend in the vagal trunk to ganglia in the cardiac plexus, and possibly in the atrial wall. The most important distribution of these endings is to the sino-atrial node and to the AV node. Sympathetic outflow (described in detail in Chap. 10) originates in the intermediolateral column of T1–5 and passes through the ventral roots to the postganglionic neurons in the upper thoracic and cervical ganglia. The cardiac nerves originate here and run to the cardiac plexus and then to the heart, most importantly to the sinus node and to the ventricular myocardium. As previously mentioned, there is an extensive sympathetic innervation of the blood vessels in most of the organs perfused by the systemic circulation.

We cannot at present separate the characteristics of the neuroeffector junction from those of the effectors; i.e., we must lump the characteristics in our description. The effectors have been evaluated partly by observing the entire reflex and partly by stimulating the motor nerves and observing the results. The most quantitative

studies of the cardiovascular innervation are those of Wang and Borison[56] and of Warner and Cox (Fig. 13).[58] The sympathetic effects on resistance have been studied by Scher and Young.[52] Parasympathetic innervation of the heart acts rapidly. Comparisons of sympathetic and parasympathetic effects by Wang and Borison indicate that heart rate can be altered within the interval of one heart beat, and a change may be complete within three or four heart beats (i.e., in about as many seconds). Effects of the sympathetic motor nerves on the blood vessels and on the heart are much slower, and a complete response to a change in motor nerve activity may require twenty seconds. The control of heart rate by the vagus is rapid and can provide virtually instantaneous regulation, but the slow response of the heart and blood vessels to sympathetic activation makes it appear that these cannot function when extremely rapid adaptation must occur.[54, 56]

A DESCRIPTION OF THE INTEGRATED REFLEX

We can at this time improve somewhat upon our earlier account of the reflex. A simple technique which gives important information has been utilized by Koch,[38] Scher and Young,[52] and others. It consists of controlling the pressure in the carotid arteries (and thus on the receptors) through a hydraulic system and noting the effects on systemic pressure as pressure at the receptor is changed. Only the pressure in the carotid sinuses is controlled in these experiments

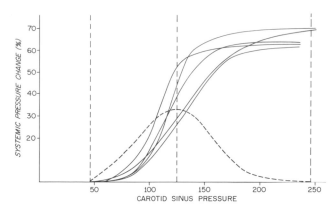

Fig. 14. Changes in systemic pressure resulting from changes in carotid sinus pressure in the dog. Solid lines show systemic pressure changes plotted as percentage of the resting pressure. Dotted line is the slope of one of the solid curves and can be considered a "gain" curve. (After Koch, *Die Reflektorische selbsteuerung des Kreislaufes.* Leipzig, D. Steinkopff, 1931.)

since the pressure in the aortic arch is virtually impossible to control. To eliminate the reflex effects of changing pressure levels at the aortic receptors, the vagi are cut, permitting the carotid sinus receptors to be studied separately. If the aortic arch receptors are functioning, change in frequency of impulses from them tends to correct any change in systemic pressure caused by alteration of the carotid sinus pressure. Motor effects of the vagus nerve on the heart are eliminated in experiments of this sort. With a low pressure (50 mm. Hg) at the receptor, the

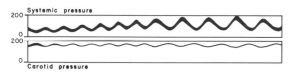

Fig. 15. Bottom curve shows a sinusoidal pressure change imposed on the carotid sinus receptors. At the left of the figure, the frequency of this sine wave is 1/50 cycle per second, and at the right, 1/100 cycle per second. The upper curve shows the systemic pressure response to this carotid change. Note that the response is larger at the slower frequency. Note also that the mean systemic pressure is higher when the input frequency is lower. (After Scher and Young, *Circulation Res.,* 1963, *12*:152–162.)

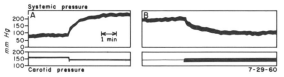

Fig. 16. Lower curve shows pressure change imposed on the carotid sinus receptors. At left, the pressure at the receptors fell 15 mm. Hg, and the systemic pressure rose about 75 mm. Hg. On the right, pressure oscillations at 10 cycles per second are imposed on the receptor without changing the mean pressure. The systemic pressure falls.

systemic pressure is high. As the pressure in the receptor is raised a fixed amount, systemic pressure at first falls slightly because of vasodilation. At a somewhat higher pressure (120 mm. Hg) the response to a similar increase in pressure is much greater, but at very high pressures (180 to 220 mm. Hg) the response again decreases. The curve showing the relationship of carotid pressure to systemic pressure is sigmoidal in shape (Fig. 14). The ratio of change in systemic pressure to change in carotid pressure can be considered an "amplification factor." It is equal to the slope of the carotid versus systemic pressure curve. The amplification is not constant but is peaked at some input pressure level. Koch found the greatest sensitivity of the reflex response near the animal's "normal" pressure. Scher and Young[52] found a maximal amplification factor of 10 to 15 in some cats.

If the receptor is subjected to sudden steps of pressure, the systemic pressure changes in a direction opposite to the imposed change, often overshoots, and then returns to a new level. The overshoot is similar to that described previously for the receptor but has a slower time course. If the pressure at the receptor changes sinusoidally and the systemic pressure response is monitored, systemic pressure change is in phase with the carotid pressure only at low frequencies (0.01 cycle per second); at higher frequencies (0.4 cycle per second) the systemic pressure lags the carotid pressure. The systemic response is larger at the lower frequencies (Fig. 15).

A third characteristic of the response can be seen when phasic pressures are imposed on the receptor, while the mean pressure at the receptor does not change (Fig. 16). In this case, systemic blood pressure reflexly decreases to an extent depending on the frequency and amplitude of the phasic inputs to the receptor (i.e., the greater the frequency and amplitude, the greater the decrease in blood pressure). This feature can be loosely referred to as "rectification"; i.e., a varying pressure at the receptor appears as a change in *mean* systemic pressure.

We have so far described three reflex properties: (i) a varying effectiveness or amplification with mean pressure, (ii) a slow response with overshoot to steps and a lagging response to sine waves, and (iii) rectification. These properties are described for a preparation which has mainly vasomotor responses, but substantial evidence indicates that heart rate responses are qualitatively similar.

The first characteristic of the reflex, the change in sensitivity with mean input pressure level, appears to result from the thresholds and sensitivities of the many receptors in the carotid sinus. The overshoot, when steps of pressure are applied at the receptor, appears to result from the sensitivity of the receptor to rate of change of pressure. The reflex response of the blood pressure to steps and sine waves of pressure at the carotid sinus appears to be due to the slow response of the neuroeffector junction or of the smooth muscle itself or both. The rectification in the reflex response appears to be a reflection of the receptor properties; i.e., the receptors rectify through their threshold and their response to rate of change of pressure (see earlier description of receptor). Possibly, the central nervous response also contributes to these properties of the reflex.

In the above experiments, of necessity, the vagal response has been eliminated. The vagus,[56, 58] through its effect on heart rate, has the ability to make rapid corrections in blood pressure, whereas the sympathetic controls to the heart and blood vessels are relatively slow. Rapid postural changes or other rapid stresses are probably initially compensated by vagal motor responses—notably, change in heart rate —and sympathetic effects on heart rate and blood pressure occur later. These responses differ somewhat in various species, sympathetic control being more prominent in the cat and vagal control in the dog.

Generalized Equation for the Carotid Sinus Reflex.[52] As an approximation to the static reflex response, the curve of "gain" versus input pressure can be considered to have the form of a power function, symmetrical about the point of maximal gain. The resulting equation is:

$$\Delta P_O = -[G_M + K_7 (P_I - P_M)^n] (\Delta P_I) \quad (1)$$

where ΔP_O and ΔP_I are changes in output and input pressure respectively, G_M is maximal gain, P_M is the input pressure at which gain is maximal, and n is an even number. Heart rate responses are described by a similar equation.

Transient responses. Equation 1 must be supplemented when dP_I/dt is not zero.

Square and sine waves. When the input pressure change is a square wave, 2 to 4.5 seconds elapse before any response; the output pressure then changes slowly, taking up to 100 seconds to reach a new level. In many experiments, the time constant is as long, but the output pressure shows an early overshoot and then slowly attains the new level.

The fact that the output pressure slowly reaches a new level requires that the output side of the equation contain a term one derivative higher than any term on the input side. If there are no derivative terms on the input side (no overshoot), the output is a function of the input and the derivative of the output. With overshoot the output is further responding to the rate of change of input. The terminal period is again a slow movement to the final pressure. A linear approximation is

$$K_2 (dP_O/dt) + K_3 (d^2P_O/dt^2) = K_1 (dP_I/dt) \quad (t - t_0) \quad (2)$$

where dP_O/dt is rate of change of output pressure, d^2P_O/dt^2 is second derivative of output pressure, dP_I/dt is rate of change of input pressure, and $(t - t_0)$ shows a time delay. The sine wave data are consistent with equation 2.

The vagal heart rate responses to square or sine waves imposed on the carotid sinus when the vagus is intact can be described if the corresponding rate terms are substituted for the output pressure terms in equation 2; the constants and time constants will differ. Equation 2 accounts for only the transient or phasic responses to transient or phasic inputs and must be used with equations 1 and 3 (below); 1 and 3 must make equation 2 inaccurate to some degree.

Effects of phasic input on mean pressure. As phasic inputs are imposed, with the mean input pressure held constant, the mean pressure falls. As the frequency or amplitude of these phasic inputs increases, the pressure falls farther. This frequency-dependent rectification requires an additional equation:

$$\overline{\Delta P_O} = -G_R (P_I + dP_I/dt - K)$$
$$\frac{[Sgn (P_I + dP_I/dt - K) + 1]}{2} \quad (3)$$

where $\overline{\Delta P_O}$ is the change in mean output pressure due to phasic inputs, G_R is an amplification factor for rectification, and Sgn (signum) is a function having a value of $+1$ when positive and -1 when negative. This form of equation also appears to describe mean heart rate changes with phasic inputs.

The effectiveness of any reflex control depends in major part on the sensitivity or "gain." This is, in general, the ratio of a change in output to a change in input and, in the equation above, is specified for an "open-loop" system, i.e., a system in which the receptor can be separately controlled, and the reflex effect of the control can be monitored. The effectiveness of control in a normally functioning system, referred to as a "closed-loop" system, is related to this open-loop gain by the equation

$$G_C = G_O/(1 + G_O)$$

where G_C is a closed-loop gain and G_O an open-loop gain. It is assumed in the above equation that the receptor or measuring device is exposed to the entire change made by the control system. If a system has an open-loop gain of 1.0, the closed-loop gain is 0.5. In such a system, any disturbance of the measured variable will be only one-half corrected. For the blood pressure system, some outside influence which would, if uncontrolled, change the blood pressure by approximately 100 mm. Hg would, when opposed by a regulatory system with open-loop gain of 1.0, change the pressure by 50 mm. Hg. This would not be a very efficient control system. In the literature, the maximal amplification of the carotid sinus reflex appears to be very low, usually about 1.0. This finding probably reflects the fact that no search for higher amplification was made, that the input pressure changes used were very large, and it may also show the effects of anesthesia. In the experiments of Scher and Young,[52] some cats had a high open-loop gain, up to 15, and dogs a gain up to 8. Although this is far below what an engineer would build into a control system, the gain of 15 indicates that any external factor which tends to alter the blood pressure will be more than 90 per cent corrected, and the reflex thus appears to be quite powerful.

CHEMORECEPTOR REFLEXES

Although chemoreceptor reflexes have their major effect on respiration and are extensively discussed later (Chap. 42), several important effects on the cardiovascular system will be considered here. The chemoreceptors—called the carotid and aortic bodies—are found near the carotid and aortic pressoreceptors, but they are separate and should not be confused with the pressoreceptors. The carotid body, sometimes visible as a small reddish ball of tissue, lies between the external and internal carotid arteries a few millimeters ventral to the carotid sinus. It is supplied with blood from the occipital and ascending pharyngeal arteries. Venous drainage is via the internal jugular vein. Fibers from the carotid body join the carotid sinus nerve, which merges with the glossopharyngeal trunk. The aortic bodies are found in two main sites: (i) scattered around the aortic arch, particularly between the root of the aorta and the origin of the left subclavian artery on the curvature of the aortic arch, and (ii) at the root of the right subclavian artery. They are not easily visible, but lie close to the large vessels. Carotid and aortic chemoreceptors are similar histologically and probably physiologically (see Figs. 1, 2 and 5). They consist of epithelioid cells surrounded by a large network of sinusoidal blood vessels. The nerves from the chemoreceptors travel with the corresponding pressoreceptor nerves, i.e., with the carotid sinus nerve from the carotid body and with the vagus from the aortic body. The blood supply of the receptors appears to be extremely large per gram of tissue, although the receptors are very small. The blood flow of the carotid body, which weighs about 2 mg., has been estimated at 2000 ml. per minute per 100 grams of tissue. This should be compared with a flow for the kidney of 400 ml. per minute per 100 grams; the kidney is the most favored among the larger organs of the systemic circulation with respect to blood flow per gram of tissue. The physiology of the chemoreceptors is studied in much the same fashion as that of the pressoreceptors.[4, 35] The carotid body is commonly studied because of the ease of separating out the important sensory nerve fibers. In such studies the vessels of the carotid region are isolated for perfusion with fluids of various composition, and the firing of the nerve fibers is recorded (Fig. 17). In general, when a few fibers are isolated, both baroreceptor and chemoreceptor firing are seen at the same time. Chemoreceptor fibers are between 2 to 5 μ in diameter.[44] Conduction velocities are 7 to 12 meters per second. In general, recording is more difficult from chemoreceptor fibers than from pressoreceptor fibers, probably because of the smaller size of the former. Recording impulse activity in apparently pure chemoreceptor preparations, von Euler et al.[24] found that chemoreceptor fibers in cats, anesthetized with chloralose but breathing normal room air, had slight tonic activity. The chemoreceptors responded to a 4 per cent fall in blood oxygen saturation—i.e., from 100 to 96 per cent (Fig. 17). Changes in carbon dioxide concentrations caused the chemoreceptors to fire even when the alveolar CO_2 tension was below normal (30 mm. Hg). The firing was greatly increased by anoxia or by increased carbon dioxide or decreased pH (for gases the partial pressure of the dissolved gas, rather than the gas content is important, of course). There

is some question as to the importance of regulation by the chemoreceptors under normal conditions;[24, 35, 51] the arterial concentrations of gases at the carotid and aortic sites do not appear to change significantly, except in fairly severe anoxia, hemorrhage, hypercapnia, etc. Whether or not the chemoreceptors are constantly responding over the normal range of blood gas concentration, they certainly do function in severe stress. *Increased* firing of the chemoreceptors has cardiovascular effects similar in some respects to the effects of *decreased* arterial pressure; i.e., increased chemoreceptor firing increases peripheral resistance. When the oxygen in arterial blood is decreased or the carbon dioxide is increased, there is ordinarily a reflex tachycardia. Although this response seems appropriate, it apparently is *not* due to increased firing of the peripheral chemoreceptors. Indeed, Bernthal *et al.*[9] have shown that hypoxia or hypercapnia of the receptors alone—i.e., and not of the medullary regions—produces a bradycardia. The tachycardia, resulting from generalized hypoxia or hypercapnia, is probably due to an effect of altered blood gases on the medullary centers (*vide infra*). Further, as postulated by Daly and Scott,[20] the tachycardia may be secondary to hyperpnea produced by the gases.

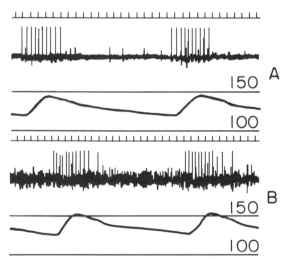

Fig. 17. Upper record, time marks at 50 cycles per second; middle record, firing of carotid sinus nerve; lower record, arterial blood pressure. *A*, Animal breathing air. A burst of impulses from a pressoreceptor fiber is seen during each systolic rise in arterial pressure, and a few nerve impulses are seen between these bursts. *B*, Animal breathing 10 per cent oxygen in nitrogen. Note the greatly increased chemoreceptor activity seen as an increase in baseline firing between the bursts of activity of the pressoreceptor fibers.

CHEMORECEPTOR EFFECTS FROM THE MEDULLARY CENTERS

As far as we know, the chemoreceptor fibers run to the same medullary regions as the pressoreceptors. The medullary centers are sensitive to changes in the tension of O_2 and CO_2 in the perfusing blood. The effects are most prominent in regulation of respiration, but cardiovascular effects are also noted. The effects of systemic anoxia or hypercapnia are similar to those from decreased stimulation of the baroreceptors. Gernandt and co-workers[28] feel that the sensitivity is primarily to CO_2 since effects on splanchnic nerve discharge of increasing or decreasing oxygen in cerebral perfusion fluid (but not effects of CO_2) can be eliminated by buffer nerve section. Anoxia alone appears to depress the vasomotor center; i.e., with a fall in oxygen or an increase in CO_2, there are an increased peripheral resistance, increased heart rate, and possibly an increase in strength of cardiac contraction.

OTHER REFLEXES

Spinal Vasomotor Effects. Sectioning the cord is followed initially by a period of spinal shock in which the blood pressure is extremely low; after this period, some vasomotor tone returns in blood vessels below the section. In addition, there is some evidence of reflex activity,[1, 22] including limited cutaneous vasoconstriction in man from stimulation of pain fibers. Some reciprocal vasomotor activity also crosses the cord; i.e., warming one extremity in monkeys (see Chap. 11) below a spinal section leads to a vasoconstriction of the opposite extremity, while a vasodilatation occurs in the warmed extremity. Loven found in 1866 that stimulating the central end of a cut sensory or motor nerve to an extremity caused respectively a vasodilatation or a vasoconstriction in that extremity.

The Axon Reflex. The axon reflex apparently does not require participation of spinal vasomotor neurons or of higher centers. For instance, stimulation of an afferent fiber running from the skin can result in a dilatation of nearby blood vessels. This reflex is considered to arise because afferent fibers from cutaneous mechanoreceptors may run to ganglia which give off collateral nerves to blood vessels. The axon reflex may be important in the response to inflammation, and the spinal reflexes may operate in respone to pain or in the regulation of cutaneous blood flow, but the contribution of these reflexes to cardiovascular regulation is not yet quantitated; indeed, they have been referred to as pseudoreflexes.[36]

The Bainbridge Reflex; the McDowall Reflex. In 1915 Bainbridge found that cardiac acceleration was induced by a rise in venous pressure, produced by intravenous infusion of saline or blood.[6] Section of the sympathetic fibers to the heart reduced this response, as did atropinization (which causes a chemical motor vagotomy). Bilateral vagotomy, however, prevented the response. Bainbridge concluded that the increased heart rate was due to stimulation of receptors in the great veins and possibly in the right atrium. As part of the common game of transatlantic oneupmanship, it may be said that this reflex has been elicited only in England. Indeed, several investigators have since been unable to reproduce it, despite intense effort. Possibly related to this proposed reflex are the passive effects on heart rate of stretching the atrium and great veins. Many pharmacologic and physiologic studies have shown that strips of excised atrial muscle must be stretched slightly to make them beat spontaneously. The apparent loss of the supposed reflex response[6] following vagotomy in Bainbridge's experiments might

have resulted from the fact that vagotomy leads to an increase in heart rate. McDowall[42] in 1924 proposed a reflex quite opposite in its general effects to the Bainbridge reflex. After sectioning the vagi in cats which had been subjected to severe hemorrhage, McDowall observed a decrease in systemic blood pressure. He proposed that, prior to vagotomy, atrial receptors stimulated by a fall of atrial pressure had prevented a fall of systemic blood pressure. He felt that the atrial receptors induced a vasoconstriction. Vagotomy, he felt, abolished the afferent impulses from the atria. Although the proposed effector organs are different, the effect of this reflex would be opposite to that proposed in the Bainbridge reflex.

Other Pressoreceptors. Pressoreceptors are found along the pulmonary artery. The afferent fibers travel in the vagus nerve. The effects appear to be similar to those of the systemic pressoreceptors, but, again, their real importance is not yet fully understood.

Cardiac Receptors. Receptors in the walls of the atria and ventricles send their sensory fibers into the brain stem with the vagus nerve. In experiments of Aviado *et al.*[5] increased pressure in the isolated right atrium caused a reflex brachycardia and hypotension. Again, the effect has not been quantitated, and it is not known how these receptors interact with the carotid and aortic receptors. Electrical recording from the vagus nerve indicates that some receptors discharge during atrial systole, and others fire when the venous pressure rises because of ventricular contraction. Receptors in the left atrium appear to be involved with the regulation of total body fluid volume.[32] They are considered to regulate the release of the antidiuretic hormone of the pituitary gland. Some evidence indicates that increased pressure in the left ventricle causes reflex bradycardia and vasodilatation.[5, 19] Ventricular receptors can be stimulated by drugs of the veratrine family. Also, the pacinian corpuscles of the mesentery have been observed to fire in synchrony with the heart beat. These last groups of receptors have not been shown to have an importance in circulatory regulation.

Motor Effects Involving the Veins. Like most other blood vessels, the veins have a smooth muscle layer in their wall. This layer has been considered indirect evidence that they can reflexly change their caliber. Such a change in caliber is believed to cause substantial shifts of blood from arterial to venous beds and thereby to play an important role in circulatory regulation. There is some evidence that veno-

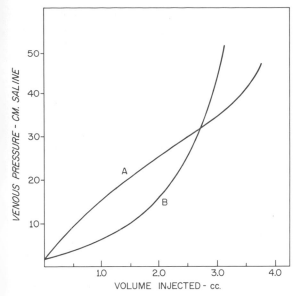

Fig. 18. Volume–pressure relationship of veins in an isolated intestinal loop. Curve *A* was taken when the mean arterial pressure was raised to 310 mm. Hg by vagal stimulation. Curve *B* is a control taken at mean arterial pressure of 82 mm. Hg. Curve *A* is considered to show venoconstriction. (After Alexander, *Circulation Res.,* 1954, *2:*405–409.)

constriction can occur,[2] although negative results have also been seen.[11] It has also been claimed that, since the veins contain such a large portion of the total blood volume (two-thirds if the lungs are included), they can easily change the arterial pressure if slight venoconstriction moves blood into the arterial side of the circulation. The most definitive support for this view comes from Alexander[2] (Fig. 18), who observed that changes in carotid pressure led to changes in the pressure-volume relationship of the veins. Most supporters of venous regulation presume that, if the veins did constrict and change their capacity, the filling pressure of the ventricles would be increased, resulting in greater cardiac pumping through the Starling mechanism and a *rise* in systemic arterial pressure. Active participation of the veins in circulatory control is difficult to prove because of the lack of measurable changes in venous pressure.

Sympathetic Vasodilator Fibers. Blood vessels of skeletal muscle are innervated by adrenergic sympathetic fibers which respond in an expected fashion to baroreceptor activity. In addition, a cholinergic sympathetic vasodilator innervation of muscle blood vessels has been described, particularly by Barcroft and co-

workers[7] In Barcroft's experiments, sympathetic vasodilator fibers were shown to be active when fainting was caused by passive tilting in human subjects (Fig. 19). Many other attempts have been made to find the physiologic importance of these reflexes. In certain studies, sympathetic vasodilator fibers appeared active during severe fright.[10] However, the writer shares the opinion of Uvnäs regarding sympathetic vasodilation: "We know virtually nothing of its functional significance."[55]

Respiratory–Circulatory Interrelationship. In 1847 de Cyon and Ludwig[18] described changes in heart rate associated with respiration. This condition, referred to as sinus arrhythmia, is most common in children and young adults. Angelone and Coulter[4] have recently shown that the phase relationship between respiration and heart rate changes with respiratory frequency. Several mechanisms might be responsible for the arrhythmia: (i) There may be a direct effect of the respiratory center on the cardiovascular centers in the medulla, (ii) Discharge of lung afferent nerves, which are concerned with respiratory regulation, may alter the activity of the respiratory center and therefore contribute to the above effect, both of these leading to an increase in heart rate during in-

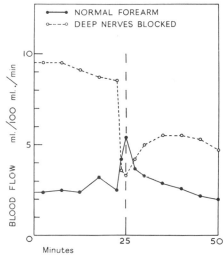

Fig. 19. Changes in blood flow during induced posthemorrhagic fainting. The solid curve shows the increase in blood flow in normal forearms. The dotted curve shows the decrease in flow in "chemically sympathectomized" forearms. The fact that the normal forearms show greater flow than the blocked forearms is considered to show active sympathetic vasodilation. (From Barcroft and Swann, *Sympathetic control of human blood vessels.* London, Edward Arnold, 1952.)

spiration. Possible indirect effects are: (i) The increase in movement of blood into the thorax during inspiration may increase the discharge of some cardiovascular receptors and reflexly alter the heart rate. (ii) Increased ventricular filling, according to the Starling mechanism, may result in an increase in stroke volume, raising the pressure and activating the arterial pressoreceptors.

The change in heart rate during sinus arrhythmia leads to small but significant changes in blood pressure. Recently, Clynes[16] developed a mathematical model in which respiration is related to sinus arrhythmia. He produced a set of differential equations which quite adequately describe the sinus arrhythmia as a function of respiratory frequency and amplitude. He believes the arrhythmia is initiated by stretch receptors within the muscles of the thorax, a view which seems incompatible with the large amount of available literature.

Reactions During Hemorrhage; Shock. The effects of hemorrhage on the heart can be likened to depriving a pump of the fluid to be pumped. Obviously, with complete loss of circulating blood volume the heart cannot function as a pump. Insufficiency of fluid for normal pumping is apparent fairly early in hemorrhage (stroke volume falls). Interestingly, gradual hemorrhage may not decrease systemic blood pressure.[49] However, as stated, the stroke volume is decreased, and the heart rate does not increase sufficiently to compensate for the decreased stroke volume; i.e., the cardiac output is decreased. If the pressure is maintained, peripheral resistance must increase. Concerning the carotid and aortic reflexes, we have seen that the receptors are sensitive not only to mean pressure but also to the rate of change of pressure. A decrease in the pressure pulse, as occurs in hemorrhage, is thus interpreted as a lower mean pressure; i.e., the receptors send fewer impulses to the central nervous system. In this condition we would expect a reflex vasoconstriction. This explanation is hypothetical, however, and evidence is insufficient to implicate pressoreceptor or other reflexes. Another hypothesis postulates that venoconstriction is a compensatory mechanism in hemorrhage. The term "venoconstriction" can be extended to include not only constriction of the veins, but also a release of blood from the liver, spleen, lungs and any other hypothetical blood depots. Again, direct evidence is lacking.

With severe hemorrhage, blood flow to the brain may be insufficient. Here the chemoreceptor reflexes, involving both the sino-aortic receptors and the medullary centers, may be activated by changes in the tissue concentrations of O_2, CO_2 or H^+. These reflexes are so potent that they can often raise the pressure after the sino-aortic receptors have exerted their maximal effect.[50] Also, with a fall in capillary pressure due to vasoconstriction, the balance of fluid transfer across the capillary is so changed that fluid moves from the extracellular space back into the blood vessels, replacing some of the blood loss.

Neurogenic and Renal Hypertension. If afferent nerves from both aortic and carotid receptors are sectioned in experimental animals, the arterial blood pressure rises, usually to a mean level of 180 to 300 mm. Hg. This procedure is not easy to accomplish since, as stated above, vagotomy leads to death from noncirculatory causes. However, the rise in pressure from denervation has been clearly demonstrated in several studies.[38] This maneuver produces a vasoconstriction similar to that expected if the pressoreceptors are exposed to pressures near zero, indicating that no strong reflexes are controlling the blood pressure. High blood pressure in humans does not often appear to be caused by decreased sensitivity of the carotid sinus receptors. The most important form of high blood pressure in humans, referred to as "essential hypertension," is of unknown origin. This condition is operationally defined as a blood pressure greater than 135/90 (120/80 is "normal") although other levels are used at times. Since "normal" blood pressure changes with age, the clinical presence of disease is diagnosed at different pressures for different age groups. In essential hypertension, the systolic, diastolic and mean blood pressures are all elevated. In the early stages this condition is classified as benign. Here blood pressure fluctuates widely without much evidence of arteriosclerosis or other abnormalities. After a time the pressure remains high, does not return to normal, and cannot be controlled by sedatives. Because of the high blood pressure, the heart hypertrophies, and blood vessel walls become thickened, decreasing the size of the vessel lumina. The composition and volume of the urine also change because of the higher pressure.

Malignant hypertension is far more serious, with blood pressures as high as 260/150.

Changes are much more severe and may even include necrosis of the blood vessels (commonly seen in the retina as papilledema) and, at times, renal failure. This condition, if prolonged sufficiently, leads to death from heart failure, hemorrhage, vascular thrombosis or renal failure.

These conditions appear quite different from neurogenic hypertension, in which the heart rate is high and there is little sign of reflex response to carotid sinus pressure changes. In essential hypertension, at least in the benign stage, there is a reflex response to pressure changes in the carotid artery.

Renal Hypertension. In 1934 Goldblatt[29] demonstrated that chronic partial occlusion of one renal artery can produce a maintained high blood pressure. Hypertension occurs more surely and rapidly and is more severe if the second kidney is removed. There are several techniques for producing hypertension by manipulation of the kidney or its blood supply. This type of hypertension is not neurogenic since it can be caused by altering the circulation to a kidney transplanted into the neck or to a denervated kidney. Present theory relates this hypertension to a series of chemical changes. The ischemic kidney produces a substance known as renin, which acts on a pseudoglobulin of the blood to produce a pressure substance known as angiotonin. Angiotonin, also called hypertensin, appears to be a potent vasoconstrictor. Hypertension in the human is at times clearly of renal origin and can be cured by removal of a diseased kidney or of a kidney with inadequate blood supply. Whether or not essential hypertension is of renal origin has been a subject of continued controversy.[29, 54]

Edematous Hypertension. If total body fluid is accidentally allowed to increase, through dialysis (artificial kidney) or other means, hypertension ensues. This finding, initially important in the discussion of the origin of renal hypertension, is now especially important when patients with chronic renal failure are treated by periodic dialysis. Although no direct evidence exists, it appears that increased peripheral resistance in this condition may be due to (i) edema of the arterioles, causing the lumina to become smaller and the resistance to increase, or (ii) edema of the pressoreceptors, which lose their ability to respond to the blood pressure, particularly to the pulsatile component of the normal blood pressure. Suggestions relating

these effects to hypertension have been made by Peterson[45] and Tobian.[54]

The role of the carotid and aortic pressoreceptors in hypertension remains to be elucidated. The questions may be stated as follows: (i) Are the ordinary pressoreceptor reflexes inactive during hypertension—i.e., is the level of pressure regulation reset? (ii) If that question is answered negatively, how can hypertension develop if the pressoreceptor reflexes are active? The studies by McCubbin *et al.*[41] of experimental renal hypertension in the dog indicates that sensitivity of the pressoreceptors may be decreased, but this remains a subject, nevertheless, for future study. It should be borne in mind, however, that the existence of a regulatory mechanism cannot be established merely by looking at the regulated phenomenon. (If a person falls to the ground when he is hit by a safe dropped from a high building, this does not prove that he did not have stretch reflexes to maintain his posture.) Apparent failure of regulation may be due to deficiency of a regulatory mechanism or, even if reflex mechanisms are intact, an "input" or "perturbation" may be so exceedingly powerful that it cannot be reflexly corrected.

Changes During Exercise. During exercise the arterial pressure and pulse rate are generally higher than at rest, while, as indicated in Chapter 33, stroke volume appears to be relatively unaffected. Probably because of the increase in locally produced metabolites, there is extensive vasodilatation in exercising muscle. This appears to be compensated for by the increase in heart rate with a maintained stroke volume and by a vasoconstriction in other vascular beds. The cardiovascular response to exercise cannot be satisfactorily explained at present. The same situation exists with respect to the respiratory response to exercise; i.e., there is no adequate explanation for the increased respiratory minute volume during exercise since the changes in levels of the regulating gases cannot account for the observed respiratory changes. The cardiovascular responses in exercise have been related to muscular pumping, which increases the venous pressure and thus the return of blood to the heart. This has been hypothesized to increase the stroke volume. However, stroke volume in exercise does not appear to increase greatly, and the venous pressure does not appear to rise. Important nervous influences probably descend from higher centers to the hypothalamus and thence to the medullary regions, causing an increased sympathetic discharge to the periphery during exercise (Chap. 35). Certainly, emotional cardiovascular responses are often seen which would appear similar. The fact that the blood pressure rises above normal during exercise should not be taken as an indication that the baroreceptor reflexes are not functioning. In fact, they might be functioning maximally during the exercise response, or if discharge from some higher center is changed, thereby effectively changing the "level setting" of the baroreceptors, they might be keeping pressure at a new elevated level.

MEASURES OF PRESSURE AND FLOW

The first known measurement of blood pressure was made in 1733 by the Rev. Stephen Hales, who connected the carotid artery of a horse to a vertical glass tube 9 feet in length, utilizing the trachea of the goose as a flexible connection. Hales found that blood rose to a mean height of 8 feet above the ventricle. In many laboratories the mercury manometer

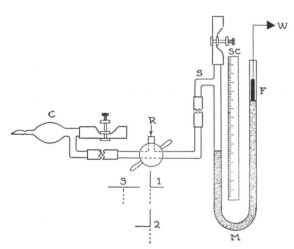

Fig. 20. Recording mercury manometer and its connections. *M,* Manometer with float (*F*) and writing point (*W*). Levels of mercury are read off scale (*SC*). *S,* Side tube of manometer, connected by rubber tubing to three-way stopcock at *R*. *R,* Reservoir of citrate solution, about 6 feet above level of manometer. Three positions of stopcock are shown: *1,* for raising pressure in manometer; *2,* for flushing out cannula; and *3,* for recording. *C,* Cannula, connected to stopcock with rubber tubing.

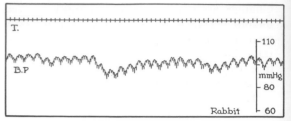

Fig. 21. Typical blood pressure record obtained with mercury manometer. *T,* Time scale; vertical lines are 1 second apart. *B.P.,* Recorded pressure; actual arterial pressure is distance from baseline—line of zero pressure—to trace, multiplied by two. Values for this experiment are given at right. Three influences on blood pressure are indicated. Brief notches, effects of heart beat; longer peaks, effects of respiration; prolonged gradual waves, effects of vasomotor changes. The relative heights of peaks caused by heartbeat and respiration are the reverse of actual relative increases in pressure; owing to inertia, mercury cannot follow completely rapid changes during systole.

(Fig. 20) is used to measure pressure in conjunction with the kymograph. In this manometer the blood pressure supports a column of mercury which, because of its high density, does not need to be as high as the column of blood in Hales' experiments (1 mm. Hg = 13 mm. H_2O). A difficulty with the mercury manometer is the inertia of the mercury, which makes this technique useful only for recording nonpulsatile pressures (Fig. 21). In the 1930's, following the work of Wiggers, excellent optical membrane manometers came into use for a time. In the best of these instruments, designed by Hamilton, a stiff metal membrane was exposed to the pressure through hollow tubing. A mirror attached to the membrane deflected with changes in pressure, and the movements of the mirror were optically amplified onto photographic paper. All of these devices have been generally replaced by electronic manometers of several types in recent years.[43] In these electronic manometers, change in pressure moves a diaphragm. Movement of the diaphragm is amplified in one of several ways: (i) the diaphragm may stretch strain-sensitive wires (strain gauge manometer) (Fig. 22); (ii) the diaphragm may be one plate of a condenser and the change in capacitance can be converted to an electrical signal; (iii) the diaphragm may be the movable "slug" in a differential transformer or variable reluctance gauge. All of these devices have more than adequate characteristics for blood pressure measurement, although the use of long, fine tubes between any of them and the pressure-recording site may lead to some damping of the pressure.

Indirect Method of Measuring Arterial Blood Pressure in Man. It is not routinely possible to insert a cannula into human blood vessels, as must be done with the manometers mentioned previously for animal work. The conventional blood pressure cuff, known as the Riva-Rocci cuff, is not as accurate as the newer methods used in animals but gives adequate indication of the pressure. Undoubtedly, a person reading this chapter will have had his blood pressure taken by this procedure. A cuff containing an inflatable balloon is placed snugly but not tightly around the upper arm. The cuff is rapidly inflated with air by means of a bulb to a level well above the systolic pressure, as indicated by a mercury manometer or by an aneroid gauge. A stethoscope is held over the brachial artery at the elbow. The physician then

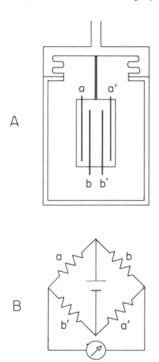

Fig. 22. Representation of a resistance wire pressure transducer. *A*, Four strain-sensitive wires are connected to a diaphragm so that movement of the diaphragm stretches two of them (*a*, *a′*) and compresses the other two (*b*, *b′*). The diaphragm is exposed through tubes to the pressure to be measured. *B*, The strain-sensitive wires are arranged so that the compressed and stretched elements form alternate legs of a bridge circuit.

allows the cuff pressure to fall slowly by opening a small valve on the inflating bulb. When the pressure is above systolic pressure, no sound is heard through the stethoscope. As the pressure falls, however, sounds are heard which are in phase with the heart beat. The level at which sounds first occur is considered the systolic pressure level. As the pressure falls lower, the sounds become louder and then begin to fade, become muffled, and finally disappear. The pressure at which the sounds begin to fade is generally taken as an indication of the diastolic pressure. When compared with direct techniques, this method does not determine diastolic pressure as accurately as the systolic pressure. Clearly, when the pressure is above the systolic pressure, no sound can be heard since no blood passes the cuff. When the cuff is deflated to just below the systolic pressure, sounds will be heard because blood vessels beneath the cuff open at each systolic peak, and the blood vessels below the cuff dilate with the peak pressure. Further opening of the cuff leads to a greater transmission of each pulse, and when the cuff falls to the diastolic pressure level, the blood vessel is continually open to the circulatory system so that the sound loses its abrupt characteristic and becomes muffled.

Measurements of Flow. In animal experiments, flow has been measured by various techniques.[37] Older techniques which can still be used to advantage involve direct measurement of flow into a beaker or into a stromuhr which permits return of the blood to the circulatory system manually or semiautomatically. Another device similar to the stromuhr is the bubble flowmeter: A bubble is injected into a long length of fine tubing (which may be straight or curved), and the time the bubble takes to traverse the tubing is used as a measure of flow; i.e., if the volume of the tube is known, flow = volume/time. The bubble is removed at the distal end of the tube. Differential pressure manometers have also been used, usually with orifice flowmeters in which fluid passes through a small orifice and the pressure drop across this orifice is measured. One problem with these devices is the tendency of blood to clot. With a fine orifice, a clot may form in a critical part of the flow "head," changing the calibration; this cannot be prevented by careful use of anticoagulants. These instruments are often not linear. An instrument considerably used in the 1930's

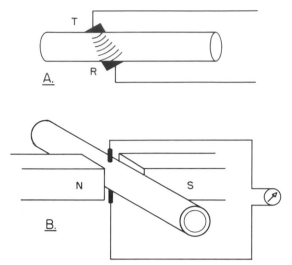

Fig. 23. *A,* In the ultrasonic flowmeter, transducer crystals (*T*) are used to set up sound waves. These are received at *R*. Flow of blood in the tube changes the sound velocity, and this velocity change is detected electronically as a flow signal. *B,* In the electromagnetic flowmeter a magnetic field is set up perpendicular to the direction of flow in a blood vessel. Electrodes, perpendicular to the field and to the flow, pick up currents generated by movements of the conductor (blood) in the field.

was the thermostromuhr; here the ability of a flowing stream to remove heat from a heated wire was used as an indication of flow.

Two newer flowmeters, which permit short-term or long-term measurement of flow in experimental animals, are the ultrasonic flowmeter and the electromagnetic flowmeter (Fig. 23). The ultrasonic flowmeter measures the change in sound velocity produced by the blood flow. The sound travels faster in the direction of blood flow and slower in the reverse direction. The electromagnetic flowmeter is based on the fact that if a conductor (blood) is moved in a magnetic field a voltage is generated perpendicular to the conductor and to the field. In electromagnetic flowmeter heads, a magnetic field is generated perpendicular to the direction of flow in a vessel, and electrodes perpendicular to the flow and to the field pick up a voltage proportional to flow.

Measurement and Estimation of Cardiac Output in Man.[17] The flowmeters available for stroke volume measurement in animals can be used in humans only rarely and temporarily at surgery. Nevertheless, procedures are available which permit accurate and useful determination of cardiac output in man, several of

which stem from suggestions made about 1870 by A. Fick. The so-called Fick principle, disarming in its simplicity, is merely a restatement of the law of conservation of mass. An example seems the easiest method of explanation. Suppose 1 mg. of a detectable dye is added to the arterial stream near the heart each minute. If there is adequate mixing and the final concentration of the dye is 0.1 mg. per liter, each minute's injectate is diluted in 10 liters and the flow is 10 liters per minute. If dye were present in the arterial stream before injection, we still could have calculated flow by using the *difference in concentration*. We can represent this procedure in a formula:

Flow =
$$\frac{\text{amount of substance added per unit time}}{\text{concentration difference produced by this addition}}$$

In the most straightforward use of the Fick principle to measure cardiac output, the blood flow through the lungs is calculated. The oxygen added to the blood as it passes through the lungs in a unit of time can be acurately measured with a spirometer which records oxygen consumption (Chap. 39). The difference in concentration of oxygen as it passes through the lungs can also be determined by measuring oxygen content of blood in the right heart (or pulmonary artery) and in the systemic arteries.

$$F = \frac{\dot{Q}_0}{A_0 - V_0}$$

where $\dot{Q}_0$ is oxygen consumption per unit time and A_0 and V_0 are arterial and venous concentrations of oxygen respectively.

In practice, obtaining a *venous* sample requires that a catheter be threaded into the right heart or pulmonary artery from a peripheral vein, usually the antecubital vein of the arm. The arterial sample may be taken from any systemic artery. The determination of oxygen consumption per unit time requires measurement over a relatively long period, about 15 minutes. The withdrawal of the appropriate blood samples usually requires a competent surgeon. In 1929, Forssmann catheterized his own heart several times,[26] and in the 1940's, Cournand, Richards and co-workers[17] reported the use of catheterization to measure human cardiac output.

There are also a number of less demanding and less exact "respiratory" techniques which are indirect attempts to acquire the same information (indirect Fick procedure, acetylene technique, nitrous oxide technique). Variations of the direct Fick procedure are also used to measure flow in a number of vascular beds.

Dye dilution procedure. A more widely used application of the Fick procedure involves the injection of a foreign dye into the circulatory system and determination of its downstream concentration after mixing is complete. If such an injection is made into the right heart and the concentration of dye in the arterial blood is measured continuously for a time after injection, a curve of dye concentration-in-time like that shown in Figure 24 can be drawn.[27] Note that the first appearance of the dye is delayed, and then the concentration at the monitoring site rises rapidly for a time and commences to fall. Shortly after the decrease in concentration begins, there is a secondary rise in the dye concentration due to recirculation. In calculating the cardiac output from such a curve, the descending limb of the concentration curve is extrapolated to zero concentration, usually by assuming that the fall-off in concentration follows an exponential time course. This assumption is easily realized by plotting the concentration against time on semilogarithmic paper. To calculate the flow, we need to know the amount injected, the time it takes this amount to pass the monitoring point, and the mean concentration during that time. The time required to pass the monitoring point is the time between the initial appearance of the dye and the intersection of the extrapolated curve with the time axis. Mean concentration during the passage of the dye (the equivalent of arteriovenous difference in the direct Fick procedure) can be determined from a linear curve of concentration in time, again assuming an exponential fall-off.

There are many variations of the procedure. Isotopes, radioactive indicators, or substances which differ in temperature or conductivity from blood can be used instead of dye. In the case of radioactive substances, changes in concentration can be sensed by placing a radiation detector on the surface of the chest. In addition, catheterization can give valuable information (presence or absence of shunts, volume of the mixing bed, etc.) about the state of the cardiovascular system.

The pulse wave as an indicator of stroke volume. If the aorta were a closed distensible bag of known elastic properties, the amount ejected

into the bag could be determined from the pressure change at ejection. Since the arterial pressure is relatively easy to measure, and since the cardiac output is such an important variable, much study has been devoted to the exact relationship between aortic (and other) pressure waves and the stroke volume. Like the x-ray and ballistocardiographic techniques, procedures based on pressure pulse, which are seemingly most suitable for short-term measurements, are poorly adapted to measurement of the actual stroke volume.

Ballistocardiography. With each heart beat the contents of the ventricles are suddenly accelerated toward the aorta and pulmonary artery. Ejection of the blood from the heart imparts to the body an acceleration in the opposite direction, which can be measured in several ways. A record of the movements of the body—a ballistocardiogram—shows several peaks; the details vary with the recording system. Many attempts have been made to use the ballistocardiogram to measure stroke volume. Changes in the ballistocardiographic curves can possibly be used to estimate changes in stroke volume, but the procedure gives no indication of the absolute value of stroke volume.

X-ray cardiometry. At one time, changes in the volume of the heart during each stroke were used as indices of stroke volume. More recently, this approach has been improved considerably

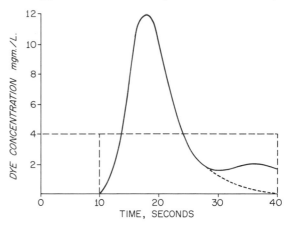

Fig. 24. An idealized indicator dilution curve. It is assumed that the zero concentration time (40 seconds) was determined by using a semilogarithmic plot. If 10 mg. of the dye is injected and the passage time is 30 seconds, the "amount per minute" is 20 mg. The mean concentration (horizontal dotted line) is 4 mg. per liter, and the flow is 20/4 or 5 liters per minute. (From Fox and Wood in *Medical Physics,* Glasser, ed. Chicago, Year Book Medical Publishers, 1960.)

by mixing radiopaque materials with the blood and then using roentgenography to measure the changes in the silhouette of the left ventricular chamber. Ideally, two x-ray exposures are made in order to achieve three-dimensional visualization. These techniques are most valid to date in showing beat-to-beat changes, but their usefulness for exact measurement remains to be determined.

Other techniques which measure flow. Flow can be estimated by the change in color of certain organs. Blanching is considered to indicate vasoconstriction and flushing to indicate vasodilatation; these, in turn, are considered to indicate increase and decrease in flow. Obviously, color indicates only blood content in those layers which can be seen. Certain estimations utilizing this procedure have undoubtedly been correct; others may have been incorrect. The volume of an organ can also be estimated by completely enclosing it in a device called a plethysmograph. The plethysmograph is adaptable to animal experiments and to human subjects. In using this device, the changes in volume of the organ are often considered equivalent to changes in blood flow. Volume changes, like changes in color of an organ, do not necessarily indicate flow although they may at times be proper indices. A modification of the plethysmograph which has been extensively used in humans is the venous occlusion plethysmograph. A finger or limb is enclosed in the plethysmograph, and a cuff is placed central to the plethysmograph. When a measurement is to be made, the pressure in the cuff is raised above venous pressure, blocking venous outflow from the tissue. Its volume therefore rises as arterial inflow continues. This initial volume change is recorded, and the initial slope of the volume change is used as an indication of the rate of flow. This technique has also been used for clinical studies.

REFERENCES

1. ALEXANDER, R. S. *Amer. J. Physiol.,* 1945, *143:*698–708.
2. ALEXANDER, R. S. *Circulation Res.,* 1954, *2:*405–409.
3. ALEXANDER, R. S. *J. Neurophysiol.,* 1946, *9:*205–217.
4. ANGELONE, A. and COULTER, N. A., JR., *J. appl. Physiol.,* 1964, *19:*479–482.
5. AVIADO, D. M., JR., LI, T. H., KALOW, W., SCHMIDT, C. F., TURNBULL, G. L., PESKIN, G. W., HESS, M. E. and WEISS, A. J. *Amer. J. Physiol.,* 1951, *165:*261–277.
6. BAINBRIDGE, F. A. *J. Physiol.,* 1915, *50:*65–84.
7. BARCROFT, H. and SWANN, H. J. C. *Sympathetic control of human blood vessels.* London, Edward Arnold, Ltd., 1953.
8. BERNARD, C. *De la physiologie générale.* Paris, Hachette et Cie., 1872.
9. BERNTHAL, T., GREENE, W., JR. and REVZIN, A. M. *Proc. Soc. exp. biol.,* 1951, *76:*121–124.
10. BLAIR, D. A., GLOVER, W. E., GREENFIELD, A. D. M. and RODDIE, I. C. *J. Physiol.,* 1959, *148:*633–647.
11. BLAIR, D. A., GLOVER, W. E., GREENFIELD, A. D. M. and RODDIE, I. C. *J. Physiol.,* 1959, *149:*614–625.
12. BRONK, D. W., FERGUSON, L. K., MARGARIA, R. and SOLANDT, D. Y. *Amer. J. Physiol.,* 1936, *117:*237–249.
13. BRONK, D. W. and STELLA, G. *Amer. J. Physiol.,* 1935, *110:*708–714.
14. CANNON, W. B. *The wisdom of the body.* London, Kegan, Paul & Co., 1932.
15. DE CASTRO, F. *Acta physiol. scand.,* 1951, *22:*14–43.
16. CLYNES, M. *Science,* 1960, *131:*300–302.
17. COURNAND, A., RILEY, R. L., BREED, E. S., BALDWIN, E. DE F. and RICHARDS, D. W. *J. clin. Invest.,* 1945, *24:*106–116.
18. DE CYON, E. and LUDWIG, C. *Ber. sächs Ges. Wissench.,* 1866, *18:*307.
19. DALY, I. DE B. and VERNEY, E. B. *J. Physiol.,* 1927, *62:*330–340.
20. DALY, M. DE B. and SCOTT, M. J. *J. Physiol.,* 1958, *144:*148–166. See also *J. Physiol.,* 1962, *162:*555–573.
21. DONTAS, A. S. *Circulation Res.,* 1955, *3:*363–373.
22. DOWNMAN, C. B. B. and McSWINEY, B. A. *J. Physiol.,* 1946–7, *105:*80–94.
23. EAD, H. W., GREEN, J. H. and NEIL, E. *J. Physiol.,* 1952, *118:*509–519.
24. VON EULER, U. S., LILJESTRAND, G. and ZOTTERMAN, Y. *Skand. Arch. Physiol.,* 1939, *83:*132–152.
25. FOLKOW, B. and UVNÄS, B. *Acta physiol. scand.,* 1948, *15:*365–388.
26. FORSSMANN, W. *Klin. Wschr.,* 1929, *8:*2085–2087.
27. FOX, I. J. and WOOD, E. H. *Medical physics,* vol. 3, O. Glasser, ed. Chicago, Year Book Medical Publishers, 1960.
28. GERNANDT, B. E., LILJESTRAND, G. and ZOTTERMAN, Y. *Acta physiol. scand.,* 1946, *11:*230–247.
29. GOLDBLATT, H. *The renal origins of hypertension.* Springfield, Ill., Charles C Thomas, 1948.
30. GRODINS, F. S. *Control theory and biological systems.* New York, Columbia University Press, 1963.
31. HELLNER, K. and VON BAUMGARTEN, R. *Pflüg. Arch. ges Physiol.,* 1961, *273:*223–234.
32. HENRY, J. P., GAUER, O. H. and REEVES, J. L. *Circulation Res.,* 1956, *4:*85–90.
33. HERING, H. E. *Die Karotissinus reflexe auf Herz und Gefässe.* Leipzig, D. Steinkopff, 1927.
34. HEYMANS, C. *Le sinus carotidien.* London, H. K. Lewis, 1929.
35. HEYMANS, C. and NEIL, E. *Reflexogenic areas of the cardiovascular system.* London, J. & A. Churchill, Ltd., 1958.
36. HILLARP, N. A. Chap. 38 in *Handbook of physiology, Section 1: Neurophysiology,* Vol. 2, J. Field, ed. Washington, D. C., American Physiological Society, 1960.
37. JOCHIM, K. E. *J. appl. Physiol.,* 1962, *17:*378–380.
38. KOCH, E. *Die Reflektorische selbsteuerung des Kreislaufes.* Leipzig, D. Steinkopff, 1931.
39. LANDGREN, S. *Acta physiol. scand.,* 1952, *26:*1–34.
40. LINDGREN, P. and UVNÄS, B. *Amer. J. Physiol.,* 1954, *176:*68–76.
41. McCUBBIN, J. W., GREEN, J. H. and PAGE, I. H. *Circulation Res.,* 1956, *4:*205–210.

42. McDowall, R. J. S. *J. Physiol.,* 1924, *59:*41–47.
43. Noble, F. W. *Electrical methods of blood pressure recording.* Springfield, Ill., Charles C Thomas, 1953.
44. Paintal, A. S. *J. Physiol.,* 1953, *121:*182–190.
45. Peterson, L. H. *Circulation Res.,* 1963, *12:*585–594.
46. Pitts, R. F., Larrabee, M. G. and Bronk, D. W. *Amer. J. Physiol.,* 1941, *134:*359–383.
47. Ranson, S. W. and Billingsley, P. R. *Amer. J. Physiol.,* 1916, *41:*85–90.
48. Rushmer, R. F. *Cardiovascular dynamics.* Philadelphia, W. B. Saunders Co., 1961.
49. Rushmer, R. F., Van Citters, R. L. and Franklin, D. *Circulation,* 1962, *26:*445–459.
50. Sagawa, K., Taylor, A. E. and Guyton, A. C. *Amer. J. Physiol.,* 1961, *201:*1164–1172.
51. Salmoiraghi, G. C. *J. Neurophysiol.,* 1962, *25:*182–197.
52. Scher, A. M. and Young, A. C. *Circulation Res.,* 1963, *12:*152–162.
53. Schmidt, C. F. and Comroe, J. H., Jr., *Physiol. Rev.,* 1940, *20:*115–157.
54. Tobian, L. *Physiol. Rev.,* 1960, *40:*280–312.
55. Uvnäs, B. Chap. 54 in *Handbook of physiology, Section 1: Neurophysiology,* Vol. 2, H. W. Magoun, ed. Washington, D. C., American Physiological Society, 1960.
56. Wang, S. C. and Borison, H. L. *Amer. J. Physiol.,* 1947, *150:*712–728.
57. Wang, S. C. and Ranson, S. W. *J. comp. Neurol.,* 1939, *71:*457–472.
58. Warner, H. R. and Cox, A. *J. appl. Physiol.,* 1962, *17:*349–355.

CHAPTER 35

Cardiovascular Integration by the Central Nervous System

By ORVILLE A. SMITH, JR.

INTRODUCTION

CORTICAL ORIGINS OF CIRCULATORY CONTROL
    Neocortex
    Limbic cortex

SUBCORTICAL INTEGRATION AREAS

BRAINSTEM CARDIOVASCULAR PATH-WAYS

MEDULLARY INTEGRATION

SPINAL CORD INTEGRATION

THE central nervous system is involved in cardiovascular regulation in many ways: (i) The cerebral cortex provides the sensory discriminative functions and the interneuronal relationships necessary for the conditioning or learning of circulatory responses. It also provides direct regulatory activity, some of which may be related to control of emotional behavior imputed to the limbic system. (ii) The subcortical areas probably provide integration of cardiovascular functions with somatic behavior of an alimentary, sexual, emotional and motor nature. (iii) The lower brainstem exerts its control mainly by receiving afferent input of cardiovascular reflexes and interacting these inputs with the descending influences from the higher levels of the central nervous system; it also gives rise to an important output—the vagus nerve. The spinal cord gives rise to the remainder of the major efferents of the cardiovascular system. The spinal reflexes are fed by both somatic and visceral afferents and are mostly intersegmental arcs leading to widespread discharge of spinal efferents.

Pathologic conditions may arise as a result of malfunctioning at any of these levels.

CORTICAL ORIGINS OF CIRCULATORY CONTROL

The cardiovascular response to a painful electric shock comprises increased heart rate, increased arterial blood pressure and increased blood flow to the striated musculature. If a previously innocuous signal, e.g., a light flash, is repeatedly presented just before the electric shock, eventually the light flash will produce the same cardiovascular response as the shock. This response is not a secondary consequence of respiratory activity or gross bodily movements which might cause similar cardiovascular changes but rather results from conditioning or learning and is an example of the highest level of neural control over the cardiovascular system.[6] The cerebral cortex is essential for all except the most rudimentary learning in higher mammals, providing both the fine sensory discriminative function and the anatomic structure required for the learning process. In this case the process of learning allows an external stimulus to gain control over a system which cannot be brought under voluntary control. Conditional cardiovascular responses demonstrate all the principles of learning (Chap. 24) including extinction, stimulus generalization, spontaneous recovery, etc. They differ from some learned responses in being slow to extinguish and in having a broad gradient of generalization. Slow extinction rate means that when the electric shock is omitted following the light, the circulatory response to light alone persists for many trials, dying away only slowly. A broad gradient of stimulus generalization implies that once the conditional response to light is established, many stimuli other than light will also produce the cardiovascular response. By extending these laboratory observations to everyday life, we may infer that situations associated with emotionally laden stimuli may continuously produce extensive and long lasting autonomic effects. These effects are manifested in a system lacking voluntary control and therefore the response cannot be prevented or avoided. For this reason, the learned cardiovascular response is a prime suspect in cardiovascular pathology and may be a main culprit in hypertension and even coronary heart disease.

Certain areas of the cerebral cortex have a direct autonomic function,[11] as demonstrated by electrical stimulation and by ablation. Even though such a direct control effect from the cortex is not a requisite for the possibility of establishing a conditional cardiovascular response —that is, the cortex could be responsible for the occurrence of learning and a subcortical connection for the cardiac effect—one immediately suspects these areas as being critical for the elaboration of such a process.

Neocortex. Hoff *et al.*[10] found that stimulation of the sigmoid gyrus of cats caused renal ischemia severe enough to produce necrosis. Eliasson *et al.*[5] have concluded that the sympathetic vasodilator system supplying the vessels in skeletal muscle has its cortical origins in the sigmoid gyrus. The area just anterior to the precentral motor cortex of monkeys is also reactive.[8] Because in both cat and monkey the effective cortical areas are contiguous to the classic motor areas, the observed circulatory response may be related to those which normally accompany somatic movements. The decreased temperature noted in affected limbs of cortical hemiplegics may reflect interference with this control.[3]

Limbic Cortex. Stimulation studies reveal both "pressor" and "depressor" sites in the rostral cingulate gyrus (Area 24).[12] "Depressor" responses seem to result from inhibition of sympathetic discharge. In trained monkeys removal of Area 24 disrupts the form of a conditional cardiovascular response by increasing the basal heart rate level and reversing the direction of the arterial pressure response. Taylor[25] interpreted these results as being due to the loss of a tonic sympathetic constrictor effect which leads to a drop in pressure followed by a reflex tachycardia.

The frontal association areas have been im-

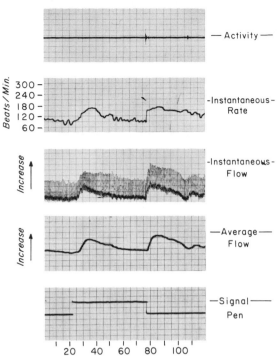

Fig. 1. Conditional response of heart rate and of terminal aortic blood flow of a monkey occurring at the onset of a signal light (upward deflection of signal pen) and the unconditional response to a peripheral electric shock (simultaneous with downward deflection of signal pen). Forty-fifth trial is shown. (From Smith, in *Effect of anesthetics on the circulation,* Price and Cohen, eds. Springfield, Ill., Charles C Thomas, 1964.)

plicated in autonomic activity.[21] Figure 2 illustrates that a combination of prefrontal lobotomy and anterior hypothalamic lesions eliminates a conditioned circulatory response.[24] The ablation may affect primarily the basic learning processes because unlearned circulatory responses still occur.

Other parts of the cortex, including the tips of temporal lobes and insula[11] yield cardiac effects on electrical stimulation. All of these structures are part of the limbic system, which suggests that the effects are a part of emotional behavior (see Chap. 26).

SUBCORTICAL INTEGRATION AREAS

The subcortical regions affecting the circulation have direct anatomic connections with those cortical areas concerned with cardiovascular function.[4]

The preoptic region of the hypothalamus has several disparate cardiovascular functions. MacLean[13] demonstrated that stimulation above and below the anterior commissure as well as in other brainstem areas results in penile erection, a vascular phenomenon. With preoptic lesions, Maire and Patton[14] produced a fatal pulmonary edema which resulted from massive shifts of blood from the systemic into the pulmonary circuits. Also, the muscle vasodilator system originating in cortex relays in the preoptic region.[5]

Immediately posterior to the preoptic region lies the region of the anterior hypothalamus critical for the maintenance of body temperature. Here local heating produces peripheral vasodilation and activates other heat loss mechanisms.[1]

The middle and posterior hypothalamic areas and the subthalamus, when stimulated

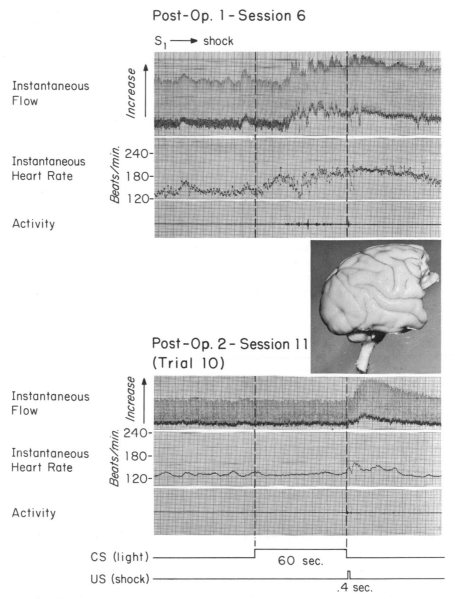

Fig. 2. Conditional cardiovascular response in animals with hypothalamic lesions before and after ablation of tissue anterior to pre-motor area. At top left (between dashed vertical lines) is shown the conditional response to a light always followed by shock. At bottom, after cortical lesion, the complete lack of response to the light is shown, whereas the response to shock is still present.

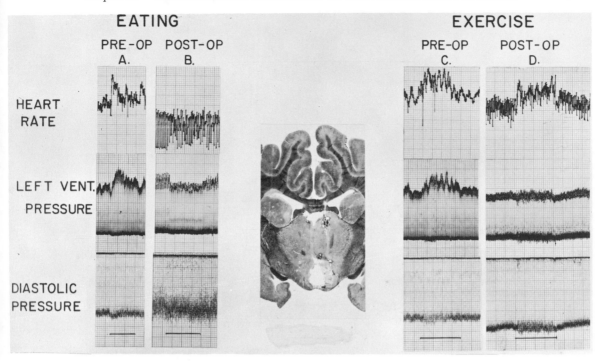

Fig. 3. Cardiovascular responses to eating and exercise before and after removal of the periventricular gray matter of the hypothalamus. The postoperative response to eating is disrupted both in heart rate and ventricular pressure while only the pressure is affected during the exercise response. (From Smith *et al., Physiol. Rev.,* 1960, *40* [Suppl. 4]:136–141.)

electrically, alter cardiovascular parameters. All combinations of variation of heart rate, arterial pressure, heart diameter,[23] contractility[16] and flow[19] can be elicited by stimulating various portions of the hypothalamus. Also these areas are involved in epinephrine and norepinephrine secretion from the adrenal medulla.[6] Experimental lesions of the hypothalamus and subthalamus can alter the circulatory responses which normally accompany given types of behavior. Figure 3 shows that the cardiovascular response to eating and to treadmill exercise may be disrupted by bilateral hypothalamic lesions. Such results suggest that cardiovascular adjustments associated with these modes of behavior depend on the central nervous system and that the adjustments are not, as was once believed, merely secondary to changes in venous return, local metabolic conditions, etc.[20] The hypothalamus integrates both somatic and autonomic components of various behavioral patterns—eating, drinking, sex, temperature regulation and emotional reactions.

The failure of some patients with Wernicke's encephalopathy to regulate arterial pressure may be due to the hypothalamic and periventricular lesions associated with the disease.

BRAINSTEM CARDIOVASCULAR PATHWAYS

There is no evidence for critical integrative cardiovascular centers between the diencephalon and the medulla oblongata. This is in contrast with the control of respiration and micturition (Chaps. 41 and 51). Responses elicited by stimulating the midbrain and pons are probably due to excitation of fiber tracts. There are multiple descending paths which have circulatory efferent function,[22] including a very important midline path below the medial longitudinal fasciculus ending in the ventromedial medulla and dorsomedial inferior olive, a path through the reticular formation, a bundle accompanying the medial lemniscus and a fine fiber system in the periventricular gray matter. The terminations of these paths in the reticular nuclei, the periventricular gray, the inferior olive and in thoracic regions of the cord are important be-

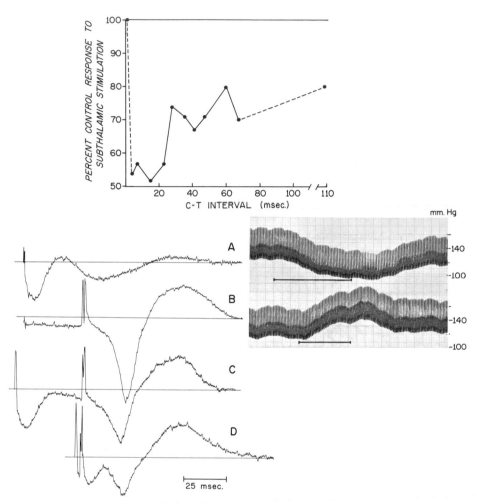

Fig. 4. The reduction in amplitude of the medullary response to subthalamic stimulation (expressed as percentage of the control response shown in B) preceded by a conditioning shock to the sinus (Hering's) nerve. Stimulation and recording positions are ipsilateral. All traces of evoked potentials represent the sum of 60 individual responses recorded by the Computer of Average Transients. The recording electrode was situated in the medial reticular formation, just dorsal to the inferior olive.

A, Left: Medullary response to single shock stimulation of the carotid sinus nerve. Right: Blood pressure response to stimulation of the sinus nerve of vagotomized cat.

B, Left: Medullary response to single shock stimulation of the subthalamic region. Recorded at same point as A above. Right: Blood pressure response to stimulation of the subthalamus at a frequency of 10 per second for 12 seconds.

C, Interaction at 40 millisecond conditioning-testing interval showing reduction in the amplitude of the medullary response to subthalamic stimulation when preceded by a shock to the sinus nerve 40 milliseconds earlier.

D, Interaction at 4 millisecond conditioning-testing interval showing a more marked reduction in the response to subthalamic stimulation occurring when the sinus nerve is stimulated 4 milliseconds prior to subthalamic stimulation.

The graph above indicates the percentage reduction of the response as a function of several C-T intervals. (Courtesy of D. Humphrey.)

cause it is at these sites that synaptic interaction, particularly with incoming cardiovascular afferents, probably occur. These interactions eventually result in the final output to the effector organs.

MEDULLARY INTEGRATION

The medulla oblongata receives the pressure and chemoreceptor afferents. Chapter 34 contains a complete description of these reflexes and the associated medullary vasomotor "centers." It is at this brainstem level that interaction between these afferents and the descending influences from higher levels probably occur. Pitts *et al.*[18] showed an interaction effect between the hypothalamus and baroreceptor reflex by measuring single unit discharge in the inferior cardiac nerve. Figure 4 shows an interaction recorded within the medulla.

Manning[15] and Peiss[17] have attacked the notion of an all-important vasomotor center in the medulla and believe that the higher levels of the nervous system may equally well serve as integrative and control areas. If the vasomotor center of the medulla were the main input to the preganglionic neurons supplying the outflow to the circulatory system, it would be expected that a large number of direct inputs from the medulla to the intermediate cell columns could be demonstrated. Actually, anatomic analysis shows that much of the direct input to these cells comes from hypothalamic sites. The connections both from hypothalamus and from medulla are to the intermediomedial cells, not to the intermediolateral cells.[22] The inputs to the intermediolateral cells have not yet been demonstrated.

Baker[2] has shown that in all poliomyelitis patients dying of circulatory failure the midline pathways just dorsal to the inferior olive mentioned above were involved.

SPINAL CORD INTEGRATION

In the spinal animal most of the descending pathways effecting tonic vasomotor control have been removed. The arterial pressure first falls to a relatively low level and then recovers (Chap. 8). This level is maintained largely by the afferents, both somatic and visceral, which impinge upon the spinal cord. The spinal animal responds with increased heart rate and pressure to peripheral nerve stimulation.[21a] In spinal paraplegics, Whitteridge[26] showed that bladder distension produces arterial hypertension and that emptying of the bladder leads to an immediate return to a basal level. The extent of this effect is directly dependent upon the level of section;[9] therefore, the reflex must be intersegmental.

REFERENCES

1. ADAMS, T. *J. appl. Physiol.*, 1963, *18:*772–777.
2. BAKER, A. B., MATZKE, H. A. and BROWN, J. R. *Arch. Neurol. Psychiat.* (*Chic.*), 1950, *63:*257–281.
3. BUCY, P. C. *Arch Neurol. Psychiat.* (*Chic.*), 1935, *33:*30–52.
4. DE VITO, J. L. and SMITH, O. A. *J. comp. Neurol.*, 1965, *123:*413–419.
5. ELIASSON, S., LINDGREN, P. and UVNÄS, B. *Acta physiol. scand.*, 1952, *27:*18–37.
6. FOLKOW, B. and VON EULER, U. S. *Circulation Res.*, 1954, *2:*191–195.
7. GANTT, W. H. *Physiol. Rev.*, 1960, *40* (Suppl. 4):266–291.
8. GREEN, H. D. and HOFF, E. C. *Amer. J. Physiol.*, 1937, *118:*641–658.
9. GUTTMANN, L. and WHITTERIDGE, D. *Brain*, 1947, *70:* 361–404.
10. HOFF, E. C., KELL, J. F., JR., HASTINGS, N., SHOLES, D. M. and GRAY, E. H. *J. Neurophysiol.*, 1951, *14:*317–332.
11. KAADA, B. R. *Acta physiol. scand.*, 1951, *24* (Suppl. 83): 1–285.
12. LÖFVING, B. *Acta physiol. scand.*, 1961, *53:* Suppl. 184.
13. MACLEAN, P. D., PLOOG, D. W. and ROBINSON, B. W. *Physiol. Rev.*, 1960, *40*(Suppl. 4):105–112.
14. MAIRE, F. W. and PATTON, H. D. *Amer. J. Physiol.*, 1956, *184:*351–355.
15. MANNING, J. W. Chap. 2 in *Nervous control of the heart*, W. C. Randall, ed. Baltimore, Williams & Wilkins, 1964.
16. MANNING, J. W. and PEISS, C. N. *Amer. J. Physiol.*, 1960, *198:*366–370.
17. PEISS, C. N. Chap. 6 in *Nervous control of the heart*, W. C. Randall, ed. Baltimore, Williams & Wilkins, 1964.
18. PITTS, R. F., LARRABEE, M. G. and BRONK, D. W. *Amer. J. Physiol.*, 1941, *134:*359–383.
19. RUSHMER, R. F., FRANKLIN, D. L., VAN CITTERS, R. L. and SMITH, O. A. *Circulation Res.*, 1961, *9:*675–687.
20. RUSHMER, R. F., SMITH, O. A. and LASHER, E. P. *Physiol. Rev.*, 1960, *40*(Suppl. 4):27–34.
21. SACHS, E., JR., BRENDLER, S. J. and FULTON, J. F. *Brain*, 1949, *72:*227–240.
21a. SHERRINGTON, C. S. Pp. 236–269 in *The integrative action of the nervous system.* New Haven, Yale University Press, 1947.
22. SMITH, O. A. Chap. 3 in *Nervous control of the heart*, W. C. Randall, ed. Baltimore, Williams & Wilkins, 1964.
23. SMITH, O. A., JABBUR, S. J., RUSHMER, R. F. and LASHER, E. P. *Physiol. Rev.*, 1960, *40*(Suppl. 4):136–141.
24. SMITH, O. A. and NATHAN, M. A. *Physiologist*, 1964, *7:*259.
25. TAYLOR, E. M. *The effect of anterior cingulate lesions on conditional cardiovascular responses in primates.* Ph.D. dissertation, University of Washington, 1964.
26. WHITTERIDGE, D. *Physiol. Rev.*, 1960, *40*(Suppl. 4):198–200.

CHAPTER 36

The Coronary Circulation: Metabolism and Nutrition of the Heart; Coronary Disease

By ROBERT L. VAN CITTERS

ANATOMY

Arteries. The myocardial blood supply is delivered through the first two branches of the aorta, the coronary arteries. The coronary ostia are located at the root of the aorta in the sinuses of Valsalva above the reflection of the aortic valve leaflets. The right coronary artery passes through the coronary sulcus at the base of the right ventricle to reach the posterior intraventricular groove on the diaphragmatic surface of the heart. The left coronary artery is short, dividing within a few millimeters of its origin into an anterior descending branch, which passes down the anterior intraventricular groove, and a circumflex branch, which courses in the coronary sulcus around the base of the left ventricle and terminates as the posterior descending branch. These major coronary arteries run on the epicardial surface near the base of the ventricles, and their branches descend toward the apex, subdividing into finer ramifications that penetrate the myocardium (Fig. 1).

In some species, e.g., dogs, the right and left coronary arteries supply their corresponding ventricles, but in man the pattern is more variable, depending largely upon the distribution of septal branches. In about 30 per cent of human hearts the coronary distribution is balanced, the right and left ventricles being supplied by their respective arteries. In these cases, the anterior ventricular septum is supplied by the left artery and the posterior septum by the right. In about 50 per cent of human hearts, the right coronary artery is preponderant and is distributed to the entire posterior septal area and part of the posterior left ventricle as well as the right ventricle. In the other 20 per cent, the left coronary artery supplies not only the left ventricle but also, through its circumflex branch, the posterior septum and portions of the right ventricle.[27] Contrary to earlier beliefs, recent analysis indicates that coronary artery pattern is poorly correlated with incidence or severity of artery disease.[24]

The sino-atrial node and atrioventricular

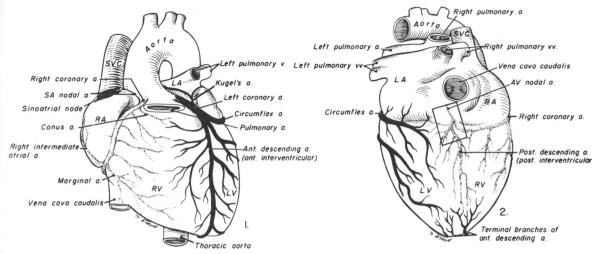

Fig. 1. Distribution of coronary arteries as they most commonly occur in man. *1*, Anterior surface of the heart. *2*, Posterior surface of the heart. (From Truex, in *Coronary heart disease*, Likoff and Moyer, eds. New York, Grune & Stratton, 1963.)

node are usually supplied by discrete branches of the right coronary artery. The branch to the S-A node arises near the origin and that to the AV node arises from where the artery turns on the posterior surface of the heart to descend toward the base[16] (see Fig. 1).

Capillaries. Smaller arteries branch perpendicularly from the major epicardial coronary vessels to penetrate the walls of the myocardium and arborize to supply the entire thickness. The ultimate ramifications are fine capillaries about 12 μ in diameter which form a meshwork paralleling the individual muscle fibers. In human hearts there is about one capillary for each muscle fiber. This ratio remains constant from adolescence to advanced age (Fig. 2). In cardiac hypertrophy the capillary/fiber ratio remains unchanged but the fiber diameters increase so that each capillary must supply a larger volume of tissue[30] (Fig. 3).

Two kinds of direct communication between coronary arteries and the cavities of the heart have been described. Small connections between arteriolar twigs and the heart chambers have been termed arterioluminal vessels. More numerous, however, are the arteriosinusoidal vessels, which originate from coronary arterioles and break up into irregular, large (50 to 250 μ) endothelial sinuses that empty directly into a cardiac chamber.

Veins. The architecture of the heart's venous drainage is conventional; capillaries are drained by venules, which coalesce into larger veins roughly paralleling the major arteries (Fig. 4). The veins terminate in the coronary sinus, which empties into the right atrium near the orifice of the inferior vena cava. A variable number of smaller veins, the anterior cardiac veins, arise over the surface of the right ventricle and empty independently into the right atrium.

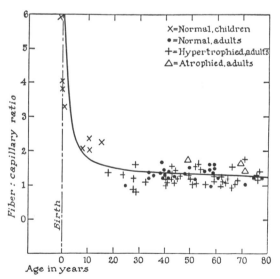

Fig. 2. Fiber:capillary ratio in human hearts. The number of capillaries per fiber is highest at birth and declines rapidly during early development. By young adulthood the fiber:capillary ratio is about 1:1, and remains essentially constant thereafter. No significant variations were observed in fiber:capillary ratios of hypertrophied or atrophied hearts. (From Roberts and Wearn, *Amer. Heart J.*, 1941, *21*:617–633.)

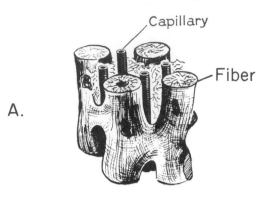

A.

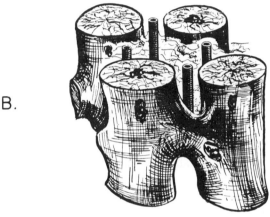

B.

Fig. 3. Relationship of myocardial capillaries and muscle fibers in normal and hypertrophied hearts. *A,* In the normal adult heart there is about one capillary per muscle fiber. *B,* In hypertrophied hearts the number of capillaries remains the same but the mass of individual muscle fiber is greatly increased. (After Wearn, *Harvey Lect.,* 1940, *35*:243–270.)

The thebesian veins are vessels that arise from capillaries and small veins and empty directly into either ventricle. Probably little blood is returned to the heart directly through any of the accessory channels (arterioluminar, arteriosinusoidal, thebesian), nor is there evidence of retrograde flow from the cavity through these channels.

Lymphatics. The cardiac lymphatic system comprises subendocardial, myocardial and subepicardial lymph plexuses; the latter can be easily observed grossly on the surface. The principal lymphatic trunk draining the heart passes under the arch of the aorta into the tracheobronchial lymph nodes. The volume of the lymphatic compartment is small.[22]

Collaterals and Anastomoses. Much of the controversy surrounding the role of cardiac col-

lateral and anastomotic circulation is due to variations in experimental technique. Intercoronary collateral channels may be demonstrated in normal hearts by perfusion of the coronary system with tracer solutions. Recovery of tracers from other portions of the coronary arterial system signifies collateral pathways but gives no indication of their size nor of their significance. Size of intercoronary anastomoses is estimated by injecting suspended particles of known graded dimensions; particles 40 μ in diameter pass anastomotic channels in less than 10 per cent of normal human hearts.[23, 32] In dogs, when a major coronary vessel is abruptly occluded, retrograde flow through collateral passages rarely exceeds a few milliliters per minute, only a small fraction of the vessel's normal flow. Acute coronary artery ligation in the normal dog heart, or sudden coronary occlusion in normal human hearts is followed by death of the tissue supplied by the occluded vessel. On this basis coronary arteries are functionally regarded as end arteries, supplying the full thickness of the myocardium and providing virtually the sole source of capillary blood to their region of distribution.

In contrast, functionally important collateral vessels are often formed in diseased hearts. Channels 40 to 350 μ in diameter may be demonstrated in nearly 100 per cent of human hearts with occlusive coronary disease, fibrosis of the

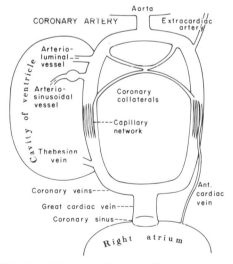

Fig. 4. Schematic diagram of vascular pathways in the myocardium. The great bulk of myocardial blood flows from coronary arteries through the capillary network into cardiac veins. Functional significance of the several alternate channels has not been established.

myocardium and infarction.[23, 32] In animals, functional collateral channels may be readily developed experimentally by procedures which cause myocardial hypoxia. In dogs, for example, the lumen of a major coronary artery may be progressively narrowed over several weeks, until the vessel is completely occluded, without causing myocardial infarction. Retrograde flow through such gradually obstructed vessels approaches normal coronary flow, and O_2 and CO_2 concentrations are normal. Intercoronary collateral channels may thus provide some protection against gradually developing coronary disease. Functionally significant collaterals develop following prolonged anemia, valvular disease, cardiac hypertrophy and diseases associated with coronary artery narrowing. Collateral channels also exist between coronary arteries and various vessels of the pericardium, mediastinum and diaphragm. These probably have little functional significance.

Various surgical procedures, based on the heart's ability to form collateral coronary circulation, have been devised to offset the effects of occlusive coronary artery disease. In some of these procedures, intercoronary anastomoses are used; in others, blood from extracardiac arteries is routed into coronary vessels.

CORONARY FLOW

Methods of Measurement. Coronary blood flow can be measured in human subjects only by indirect approaches such as the N_2O method or more recently developed techniques based on measuring externally the myocardial clearance of radioactive tracer substances. These methods, which have limited accuracy, can be used only during basal conditions and yield mean values rather than instantaneous flows. Most of our present knowledge of coronary flow is derived from experimental animals, primarily dogs; but even in experimental animals it is technically impossible to measure accurately blood flow rates within the myocardium itself, and most coronary flow measurements simply sample flow through a major epicardial coronary artery or vein. Only recently have methods been developed which enable flow to be measured under relatively physiologic conditions or in unanesthetized ambulatory animals, and even these techniques require surgical intervention for placement of flow-sensing devices.

Early studies of coronary flow depended on direct measurement, e.g., with beaker and stopwatch, of coronary sinus drainage in isolated hearts. Various adaptations of this method are still used for short-term experiments. Several kinds of flow-sensing devices based on fluid mechanical effects have been employed. These instruments, such as the Pitot tube, Venturi tube, orifice meter, rotameter and bubble flowmeter, must be inserted into the cut coronary vessel, and their use is thus limited to short-term experiments.[11] Better data are obtained from miniature instruments surgically implanted to sample flow through unopened coronary vessels; following recovery from surgery the animal can be studied during spontaneous activity, exercise, administration of drugs, etc. Gregg has employed electromagnetic flowmeters in this manner and has measured accurately fractional and total coronary flow in healthy dogs.[17] His studies have altered several well established concepts of the regulation of coronary flow. Very recently Franklin devised a miniature flowmeter with which it has been possible to continuously telemeter coronary blood flow from totally unrestrained animals.[4]

Phasic Flow in the Coronary System. Throughout the cardiac cycle, coronary arterial blood flow undergoes characteristic phasic variations which reflect the instantaneous balance between the driving force of the perfusion pressure in the coronary arteries and the impedance to blood flow (Fig. 5). In the proximal coronary arteries the perfusion pressure is about the same as that in the root of the aorta, but in more distal branches the pressure head drops because of progressive reduction of vessel caliber. Hydraulic impedance in the coronary circuit is both intravascular, because of vasomotor effects of smooth muscle in the walls of coronary arteries, and extravascular, because of the influence of the muscle mass surrounding the penetrating branches. Ventricular intramuscular pressure has not been measured accurately, but during systole it is highest near the endocardial surface, progressively decreasing outward. During early ventricular contraction, intramuscular pressure in the deepest part of the left ventricular wall probably exceeds intravascular pressure, collapsing smaller arteries, capillaries and veins. At this instant, left coronary artery flow transiently drops to zero. With the onset of ejection, left coronary flow again increases, so that the myocardium actually receives a significant amount of blood during systole. The peak left coronary flow rate occurs early in diastole, and

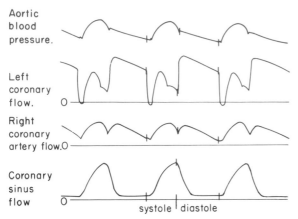

Fig. 5. Schematic representation of phasic flow in the coronary vascular bed, with aortic blood pressure as a reference tracing. Left coronary flow is maximal at the onset of diastole and gradually falls off throughout the balance of the diastolic interval. With the onset of systole, flow abruptly falls to zero, or may even be temporarily reversed. Net forward flow during systole is approximately 25 per cent of that during diastole. The right coronary artery flow pattern resembles the contour of the aortic pressure pulse; because extravascular compression by the right ventricle is small, flow does not approach zero. Myocardial compression augments emptying of coronary veins during systole; phasic flow through the coronary sinus is thus accentuated during this period. (After Gregg, Chap. 23 in *Circulation, Encyclopedia of cardiology,* vol. 1, Luisada, ed. New York, McGraw-Hill-Blackiston, 1959.)

throughout the balance of the diastolic interval flow declines only gradually. At rest the systolic component of left coronary artery flow is usually less than 25 per cent of that received during diastole.[10] Right ventricular pressure is much lower than left, and intramural tensions, even during systole, never become great enough to cause coronary shutdown. The pattern of flow in the right coronary artery resembles the contour of the aortic pressure pulse. Coronary sinus outflow increases sharply during isometric contraction, rising to its maximum during the protodiastolic phase, before gradually falling off to nearly zero at the end of diastole. This pattern suggests that venous blood is massaged out of the ventricular wall by ventricular contraction.

Distribution of Flow. The distribution of coronary blood flow in human hearts is not known. However, the turnover rate and tissue uptake of radioactive tracer substances is highest in the left ventricle and is progressively less in the right ventricle, left atrium and right atrium.[21] According to direct measurements in dogs, only about 15 per cent of the total coronary inflow enters the right coronary; the re-

maining 85 per cent is via the left. Of the latter, about half flows through the circumflex artery and about one-fourth through the descendens; most of the remainder is distributed via the septal artery. The total left coronary inflow in dogs averages about 75 ml. per 100 grams left ventricle per minute; approximately the same figure has been obtained indirectly in humans. In a given dog 80 to 90 per cent of the left coronary inflow may be recovered in the coronary sinus, whereas 90 per cent of right coronary flow drains via anterior cardiac veins. These percentages remain reasonably constant during changes in right and left ventricular pressures, administration of epinephrine and ventricular fibrillation.[22, 25] The mean coronary transit time, i.e., time required for blood to traverse the circuit from coronary ostium to coronary sinus, is about eight seconds in humans and six seconds in dogs.

The overlap in the distribution and drainage pattern is of practical importance when studying blood flow and metabolism of the heart. Right ventricular metabolism has not been studied precisely because the anterior cardiac veins have multiple exits into the right atrium, and much of the blood which they carry drains from adjacent myocardial territories. In contrast, the coronary sinus is a single easily accessible channel, and its outflow contains a more nearly representative sample of left ventricular flow and metabolism. For this reason left ventricular metabolism has been studied extensively both in dogs and, more recently, in man. In the latter instances, conclusions must be accepted with reservation, since in man data are not available to confirm the distribution of coronary artery flow or sources of coronary sinus flow.

Regulation of Flow. The heart extracts a greater percentage of available oxygen from the arterial blood than does any other organ. In man the arterial oxygen content is about 20 volumes per cent and coronary sinus blood contains about 5 volumes per cent oxygen; thus even at rest or under basal conditions the heart extracts about 75 per cent of the oxygen available. Heart muscle has little capacity for either storing oxygen or contracting an oxygen debt. The high degree of extraction of oxygen even when at rest and the inability to store oxygen or to develop oxygen debt suggest that requirements for additional oxygen must be met by increased coronary blood flow. The coronary flow rate is, indeed, labile, varying widely in response to numerous mechanical, neural and chemical influences.

Physical factors. Aortic blood pressure, the driving force for coronary perfusion, is a major factor in flow regulation. In general, mean coronary flow increases with rising blood pressure and decreases with falling blood pressure, but the extent of these changes varies among different experimental preparations and there is no fixed relationship between changes in pressure and the observed changes in flow. In open-chest dogs with the heart *in situ* the resistance of the coronary bed varies as the perfusion pressure is altered; this suggests that coronary arteries may be capable of autoregulation of blood flow[27] (see also Chap. 44). Clamping the aorta greatly increases both blood pressure and coronary flow. Experimentally induced increases in intraventricular pressure independent of changes in aortic pressure increase coronary flow in spite of augmented intraventricular compression. This response pattern is not affected by denervation. During hypotension due to hemorrhagic shock the coronary vascular resistance decreases while that in other beds increases, and the coronary blood flow is diminished proportionately less than flow in other beds.[9]

The mechanical work output of the heart and its determinants, cardiac output and blood pressure, all correlate closely with coronary flow. However, the coronary flow rate is higher in response to elevated blood pressure than to an increase in cardiac output, even though the calculated mechanical work is identical. High correlations exist between each of these factors and the oxygen consumption of the heart. These functionally important relationships may reflect the action of an intrinsic vasodilator mechanism which operates in response to metabolic requirements rather than mechanical factors.

When the heart rate is increased, diastole is shortened to a greater extent than systole, so that the time spent in diastole during each heart beat or per unit of time may be less than that in systole. Since peak coronary flow occurs during diastole, one might anticipate a reduction in coronary flow during tachycardia. Measurements indicate that tachycardia is accompanied by some degree of coronary vasodilation, probably incident to increased oxygen requirement. Limited studies in man indicate that coronary flow is increased during naturally occurring tachycardia.[3] During spontaneous excitement or sympathetic nerve stimulation in dogs, both the heart rate and flow per beat increase (Fig. 6). With mild exercise the increase in flow per

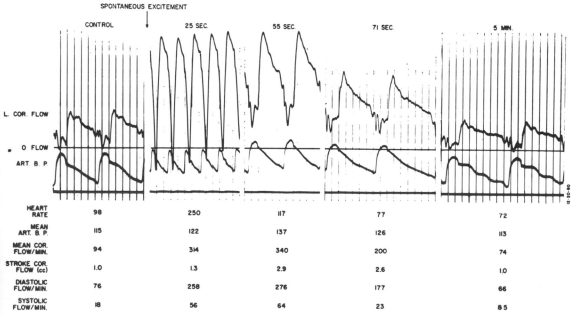

Fig. 6. Changes in coronary blood flow and aortic blood pressure in a dog during tachycardia induced by spontaneous excitement. Coronary flow increased threefold as the heart rate changed from 98 to 250 beats per minute. Flow per stroke was increased during both systole and diastole. Later, when the blood pressure was elevated, stroke coronary flow was greatly increased. (From Gregg and Fisher, Chap. 44 in *Handbook of physiology, Section 2: Circulation*, vol. 2, Hamilton, ed. Washington, D.C., American Physiological Society, 1963.)

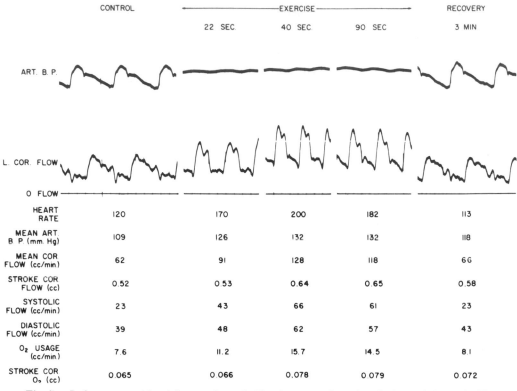

Fig. 7. Left coronary blood flow and aortic blood pressure in a dog during mild treadmill exercise. The total coronary flow increased proportionately with the heart rate, but neither flow per stroke nor flow during either systole or diastole were appreciably altered. This suggests that during mild exercise coronary flow is limited by heart rate. (From Gregg, *Circulation*, 1963, *27*:1128–1137; by permission of the American Heart Association, Inc.)

beat is small. During moderate exercise in which the heart rate increased to three times the resting level, coronary flow also tripled, so that stroke flow remained essentially constant (Fig. 7). On this basis, coronary flow appears to be limited by heart rate.[10, 18]

Neural control. The nerve supply of the heart includes vagal, sympathetic and dorsal root fibers, all of which are freely intermingled in the several cardiac plexuses located near the base of the heart. Thus, the identity of individual fibers at this level is obscure, and parasympathetic fibers cannot be distinguished from sympathetic fibers. The major coronary vessels are supplied by right and left coronary nerve plexuses, which adhere to the adventitia of the vessels in their proximal segments. Smaller penetrating coronary vessels are accompanied by finer nerve filaments. Similar filaments accompany arterioluminal vessels, but none has been described for arteriosinusoidal or thebesian channels. Electron micrographs of human myocardium indicate the presence of many nerve axons in the vicinity of the capillaries[19] (Fig. 8).

Some fibers may be afferent, since receptor-like structures in the coronary vessel walls have been described. But specific receptor activity in coronary smooth muscle has not been demonstrated.

The role of nerves in regulating coronary blood flow is difficult to assess. Both sympathetic and parasympathetic fibers innervate the atrial conduction system of the heart; sympathetic fibers also reach the ventricles. Stimulation of sympathetic nerves supplying the heart, whether in isolated hearts, open-chest preparations, anesthetized or healthy animals, increases coronary blood flow[6] (Fig. 9). It is hard to determine the extent to which these coronary flow changes represent direct vasomotor action, since sympathetic stimulation also influences heart rate, blood pressure and myocardial oxygen consumption. The fact that a flow increase may occur in healthy animals without an accompanying blood pressure elevation is evidence for active dilation of coronary vessels. The role of parasympathetic fibers is more obscure. Studies of heart-lung preparations led to the belief that parasympathetic impulses constrict the coro-

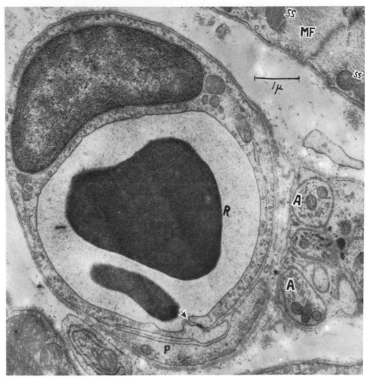

Fig. 8. Electron micrograph depicting close association of nerve axons and capillary elements in the myocardium. The section is through a protocapillary consisting of a single endothelial cell and containing two red blood cells (*R*); adjacent are cross-sectioned proto-axons (*A*) surrounded by Schwann's sheath. In either corner are myofibrils (*MF*) with sarcosomes (*SS*). Mag. 22000×. (Courtesy of Dr. Bruno Kisch.)

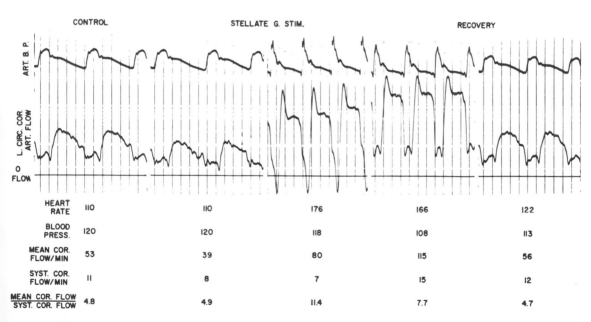

Fig. 9. Left coronary blood flow and aortic blood pressure in a dog during stimulation of the stellate ganglion. Initially coronary flow was slightly diminished without any change in rate or blood pressure. Seconds later, when tachycardia occurred, both mean coronary flow and diastolic flow increased while systolic flow was reduced. Still later coronary flow increased greatly throughout the cardiac cycle. Note the transient appearance of backflow in the coronary artery. (From Gregg, Chap. 44 in *Handbook of physiology, Section 2: Circulation,* vol. 2, Hamilton, ed. Washington D.C., American Physiological Society, 1963.)

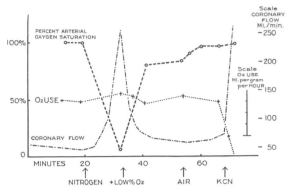

Fig. 10. Graph showing great increase in coronary blood flow in heart–lung preparation when ventilated with nitrogen or when KCN was administered. Oxygen consumption remains constant. (From Hilton and Eichholtz, *J. Physiol.*, 1924, *59*:413–425.)

reduced following acetylcholine administration or vagal stimulation, but only when the blood pressure is diminished. In fact, no direct evidence exists for neurally mediated coronary vasoconstriction.

There is widespread belief that the coronary vessels are subject to reflex control. Decreased coronary flow has been reported in response to pain, distension of a hollow viscus, stimulation of afferent nerves and experimental neurosis. In spite of the possible significance of such observations, no direct evidence indicates that any such flow changes are due to coronary vasomotor reflexes. In many experiments the metabolic, humoral or mechanical effects of such stimuli were capable of influencing coronary flow and were inadequately controlled. It has long been believed also that injury to a coronary artery, as by occlusion, leads to reflex vasospasm of adjacent vessels, but direct attempts to demonstrate noxious intercoronary reflexes have had only equivocal results.[12, 31]

nary vessels, but vasoconstrictor activity is not observed following vagal stimulation in open-chest or intact animals. Coronary flow may be

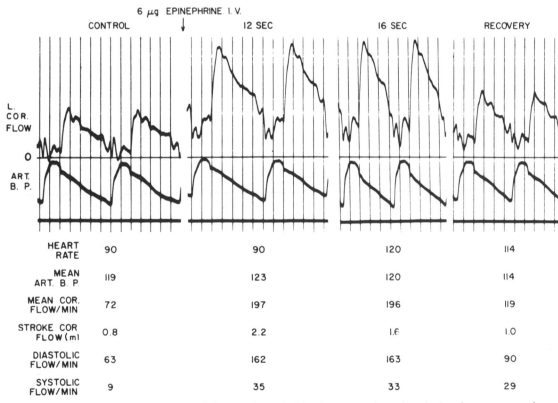

	HEART RATE	MEAN ART. B. P.	MEAN COR. FLOW/MIN	STROKE COR FLOW (ml)	DIASTOLIC FLOW/MIN	SYSTOLIC FLOW/MIN

Fig. 11. Left coronary blood flow and aortic blood pressure in a dog during intravenous administration of epinephrine. Following infusion of epinephrine there was nearly a threefold increase in coronary flow. The heart rate changed very little, and blood pressure remained constant, but there was a great increase in stroke flow, during both systole and diastole. (From Gregg, Chap. 44 in *Handbook of physiology, Section 2: Circulation*, vol. 2, Hamilton, ed. Washington D.C. American Physiological Society, 1963.)

Chemical control. Coronary flow is greatly increased in normal humans by procedures which render the myocardium hypoxic[13] (Fig. 10). In heart-lung preparations, reducing the arterial O_2 content or blocking O_2 utilization with cyanide increases coronary flow as much as 500 per cent. Similar results are obtained in isolated hearts, fibrillating hearts, anesthetized animals and intact animals.[8, 14] Decreasing the arterial oxygen saturation by only 5 per cent causes detectable increase of coronary flow. The increased flow during anoxemia occurs simultaneously in both right and left coronary arteries, during both systole and diastole, and is not abolished by denervation of the heart. Moreover, the flow increase occurs before, and hence is independent of, any changes in blood pressure, heart rate or work. It thus appears that myocardial hypoxia either directly or indirectly leads to coronary vasodilation. However, the mechanism by which this occurs is not known.

In heart-lung preparations, increased CO_2 tension moderately increases coronary flow but is much less effective in intact subjects. Increased pH also increases coronary flow but the change is small and of doubtful significance.

A number of naturally occurring chemical agents alter coronary flow. Epinephrine, and to a lesser extent norepinephrine, increases flow but it is difficult to determine to what extent the change is due to coronary dilation rather than to changes in cardiac function (Fig. 11). Acetylcholine also increases flow but its mechanism of action is masked by the effect of the drug on the heart. There is no positive evidence that it acts as a coronary vasoconstrictor in intact animals. In nonphysiologic doses, Pitressin causes prolonged vasoconstriction accompanied by electrocardiographic evidence of myocardial ischemia. Serotonin (5-hydroxytryptamine) is a powerful coronary vasodilator and is capable of increasing oxygen supply to the myocardium without increasing cardiovascular work.

Clinically, many drugs are employed as presumed coronary vasodilators in attempts to augment coronary blood flow in patients suffering from coronary heart disease. The most commonly used drug is nitroglycerin. The effectiveness of nitroglycerin results from its vasodilator action on the peripheral circulation, which greatly reduces cardiac work, as well as from its coronary vasodilator action.

CARDIAC METABOLISM

Methods of Study. The data basic to cardiac metabolism are the coronary flow and the coronary arteriovenous differences of oxygen and of metabolites such as glucose, lactate, fatty acids, etc. In early studies these data were obtained by cannulating the coronary sinus in isolated hearts and by measuring the concentrations of O_2 and metabolites in sinus blood and in arterial blood. The more recently developed technique of cardiac catheterization permits studies of intact animals and of healthy or diseased humans. In this procedure, a catheter is advanced through a superficial vein into the coronary sinus. Blood samples withdrawn through this catheter and simultaneously drawn arterial samples are analyzed for their content of oxygen and metabolites. Total coronary blood flow is also measured simultaneously, e.g., by the N_2O method; the rate of extraction of a given substance may then be calculated by multiplying coronary flow by the AV difference. It should be remembered that coronary AV differences reflect only over-all extraction and give little information concerning intermediary products or metabolic transformations, exchanges, storage and transport in heart muscle.

Foodstuffs.[1] Carbohydrate metabolism accounts for about 35 per cent of the energy supply of the human heart. Carbohydrates utilized by the human heart include glucose, pyruvate and lactate; fructose is probably not metabolized. The relative myocardial consumption of glucose and lactate varies in relation to their arterial concentrations. When arterial concentrations are in the normal range, approximately equal amounts of each are used. Pyruvate extraction is small.

About 60 per cent of the energy expended by the human heart is derived from catabolism of fatty acids. Of the total lipids extracted, free fatty acids represent slightly less than half, the balance being esterified. Myocardial uptake of fatty acids is greatly increased when the fatty acid level of the blood is increased. Apparently all of the individual free fatty acids may be extracted by the heart, but the rates of uptake and turnover vary significantly.

Metabolism of ketone bodies and amino acids may account for about 5 per cent of the total cardiac oxygen consumption. Utilization of these substances depends somewhat on their arterial concentration and also on the concentrations of other energy sources.

The myocardial extraction of various substrates is normal in human patients with congestive heart failure; utilization of metabolites is not significantly affected by administration of digitalis or its derivatives. In diabetic patients myocardial carbohydrate utilization is reduced, fatty acids and to a lesser extent ketone bodies supplying most of the energy requirement.

Metabolic Pathways. The energy expended by the heart is derived mainly from aerobic degradation of foodstuffs to CO_2 and H_2O; under normal conditions anaerobic metabolism accounts for less than 1 per cent of the total energy liberation. During hypoxia anaerobic metabolism may approach 10 per cent of the total.[15] Under completely anaerobic conditions energy liberation is inadequate to sustain ventricular contraction.

The structure and composition of the myocardium are adapted to facilitate rapid diffusion of oxygen; the capillary cross-sectional area is large in relation to that of the muscle fiber, and the muscle tissue is rich in myoglobin, oxidative enzymes and cytochromes. The site of energy production is the mitochondria and the basic process is one of oxidative phosphorylation in which energy is conserved in the form of the high energy compound ATP (Fig. 12). Substrates for energy production, derived from car-

bohydrates, fats and amino acids, follow a final common pathway in the citric acid cycle.[7]

Oxygen Consumption. Under basal conditions the human heart consumes about 9 ml. of oxygen per 100 grams of heart per minute. However, oxygen consumption is variable, depending primarily on heart rate and cardiac work. The empty arrested heart uses about 2 ml. O_2 per 100 grams per minute (Fig. 13); this amount of oxygen is required to maintain basic cellular processes independent of contraction. In the empty beating heart, with no pressure or volume load, the additional energy cost of contraction is about 1 ml. O_2 per 100 beats, while during ventricular fibrillation cardiac oxygen consumption is about 5 ml. per 100 grams per minute.[29]

In normal hearts the major determinant of O_2 consumption is the work output. This relationship, however, is not a direct proportion, since oxygen requirement is relatively higher at low work levels than at moderate or higher levels. Moreover, the kind of work performed is important; work expended in moving a volume of blood requires less oxygen than the identical physical quantity of work expended in overcoming pressure.

As in other organs, the oxygen consumption of the heart may be reduced by lowering its temperature (Fig. 14). The Q_{10} for heart tissue is 2.2; i.e., for each 10° C. decrease in temperature the ratio of reaction velocities and, hence, the

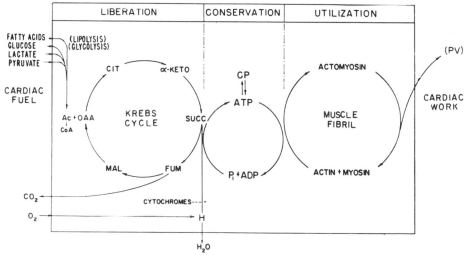

Fig. 12. Diagrammatic representation of the metabolic pathways involved in conversion of energy in foodstuffs to cardiac work. Substrates available to the cardiac muscle cell follow a final common pathway in the citric acid (Krebs) cycle. Energy is conserved in the form of the high energy compound ATP, and is converted to useful cardiac work and frictional losses by the shortening action which takes place in myofibrils. (From Olson, *Ann. N. Y. Acad. Sci.*, 1959, *72*:466–479.)

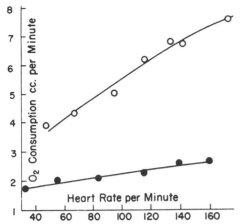

Fig. 13. Effect of heart rate on cardiac oxygen consumption in an isolated heart performing no external work (solid circles) and during a constant work load (open circles). The empty arrested heart required less than 2 ml. O_2 per min. When beating empty, it consumed an additional 1 ml. O_2 per 100 beats per minute. When the same heart was driven at increasing rates while performing a constant work load, the oxygen consumption curve had a steeper slope. A significant oxygen saving occurred in the working heart when it functioned at slower heart rates. (From Van Citters, *et al.*, *Amer. J. Physiol.*, 1957, *191*:433–445.)

O_2 consumption are diminished by a factor of 2.2. The lowered resting cardiac O_2 consumption during hypothermia reflects slower heart rate, decreased cardiac work and depressed resting metabolism. Hypothermic hearts require less oxygen than normothermic hearts to perform a given quantity of work.[26] The thermal sensitivity of tissue metabolism is the basis for using total body cooling during some types of surgery. For example, lowering the body temperature by 10° to 15° C. so reduces O_2 consumption of the heart and brain that the circulation can safely be arrested long enough to repair congenital heart defects.

Work. Mechanically the heart is a pump. With each cardiac contraction blood in the ventricular cavity is expelled into the aorta under pressure. Mechanical work is the product of force and distance:

$$W = FD$$

The hemodynamic equivalent of this expression is

$$W = \int P dV$$

where dV represents the change of ventricular volume and P the hydrostatic equivalent of the ventricular blood pressure. Because measure-

ments of the instantaneous changes in pressure and volume are seldom available, left ventricular work is more commonly estimated as the product of the mean aortic pressure and the cardiac output. In this case, calculation of total work must include a kinetic term, $MV^2/2g$, where M represents the mass of blood, V the velocity imparted, and g a gravitational constant. This term takes into account the kinetic energy expended in imparting velocity to the blood. Although this often neglected component is usually less than 10 per cent of the total energy expenditure at rest, it may, in instances of very high cardiac outputs or in calculations of right ventricular work, represent a significant percentage of the total energy liberated. The work output of the heart is properly expressed in dyne-centimeters per second or Newton-meters but is more commonly calculated in terms of kilogram-meters (KgM). The human left ventricle under basal conditions performs about 5 KgM of work per 100 grams per minute; this corresponds to a power output of about 1 watt.

Efficiency. The mechanical efficiency of the heart is calculated, as in a conventional ma-

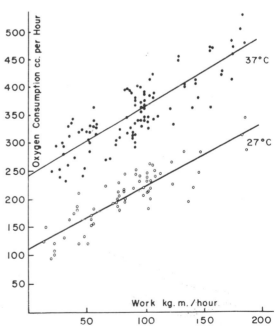

Fig. 14. Relationships between cardiac work and cardiac oxygen consumption at 37° centigrade (closed circles) and at 27° centigrade (open circles). Over a wide range of output loads, hypothermic hearts consumed significantly less oxygen than the same hearts at 37° centigrade and equal work performance. (From Reissmann *et al.*, *J. appl. Physiol.*, 1956, *9*:427–430.)

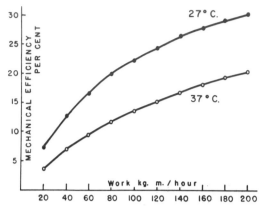

Fig. 15. Comparison of the mechanical efficiency of hearts at 37° centigrade (open circles) and 27° centigrade (closed circles) at various work levels. Within limits, the efficiency of the heart is higher at greater work loads. At any given work level the mechanical efficiency of the hypothermic heart is higher than that of the same heart at 37° centigrade. (From Reissmann *et al., J. appl. Physiol.*, 1956, 9:427–430.)

chine, by comparing its useful work output with the energy content of the fuel consumed. Cardiac energy requirements may be deduced from measurements of the oxygen consumption: In familiar equivalents the complete combustion of 1 ml. of oxygen releases the caloric equivalent of 2.07 KgM of work. Thus in human hearts under basal conditions an oxygen consumption of about 10 ml. per 100 grams per minute represents the work equivalent of about 20 KgM. On the basis of a resting work output of 5 KgM per 100 grams per minute, the efficiency of the left ventricle is about 5/20 or 25 per cent. About 20 per cent of the oxygen consumed by the heart is used for maintenance of basic cell processes quite independent of cardiac contraction. While obviously necessary, this idling consumption does not contribute to the performance of pressure-volume work. In addition, active shortening of muscle fibers is an exothermic process in which heat is generated by friction between myofibrils, chemical reactions, viscous effects, etc. About 50 per cent of the total oxygen consumption of the heart is expended in the production of heat and thus is not available for performance of useful work. When the actual pressure-volume work output of the heart is compared with the work equivalent of the total oxygen requirement the mechanical efficiency is usually found to be less than 25 per cent. This figure is comparable with that of many industrial machines. In general, the efficiency paral-

lels oxygen consumption in that, within limits, greater loads are handled with higher efficiency. Volume loads are handled with greater efficiency than pressure loads. The efficiency of the heart in hypothermia is higher than at normal temperatures (Fig. 15). The mechanical efficiency of human hearts in cases of congestive heart failure is reduced.[5]

INORGANIC IONS

A detailed discussion of the role of inorganic ions in the biophysics of the cell membrane was presented in Chapter 1. Abnormalities of electrolyte concentration which manifest themselves as disturbances in depolarization and repolarization of the cell membrane give rise to characteristic electrocardiographic and hemodynamic disturbances in intact animals or human patients.[20]

Sodium. Because of the action of the sodium pump in producing ionic gradients across the cell membrane, the normal serum sodium concentration of about 140 mg. per liter may be varied somewhat with little effect on cardiac function. Increases up to 200 mg. per liter in dogs produce only minor EKG changes, and gross hemodynamic alterations seldom occur, so that the cause of death in hypernatremia is usually extracardiac. However, when the serum sodium is abnormally lowered myocardial cells are unable to depolarize, and signs of profound cardiovascular collapse may develop, such as decreased blood pressure and cardiac output, and weak, rapid pulse.

Potassium. A decrease in the serum potassium concentration raises the resting potential of cardiac muscle so that depolarization is more difficult. Conversely an abnormally high serum potassium interferes with repolarization. The effects of alterations in potassium concentration are manifest in electrocardiographic abnormalities; hemodynamic alterations appear principally because of conduction disturbances (Fig. 16). In hyperkalemia progressively elevated T waves are first observed, after which conduction is progressively blocked, initially in the atrium, later at the AV node. Terminally, ventricular conduction is blocked and cardiac arrest occurs. The entire spectrum of electrocardiographic and cardiac changes due to hyperkalemia are often observed in patients with acute renal failure in whom the serum potassium level tends to rise progressively. The accompanying electrocardiographic changes are often used as an index for treatment by hemodialysis.

Calcium. Alterations of serum calcium concentration produce characteristic EKG changes but rarely cause significant functional disturbance of the heart unless very high concentrations are reached. Progressive increases in the serum calcium concentration are reflected in shortening of the ST segment and may be attended by bradycardia. When calcium concentrations exceed 15 mEq. per liter, tachycardia, ectopic beats and ventricular fibrillation may occur. Moderately elevated serum calcium concentrations occur in a variety of disease states, but increases sufficient to jeopardize cardiac function are more often seen after improper intravenous injection of calcium salts. Injected rapidly, the usual therapeutic dose can temporarily raise plasma concentrations to levels capable of inducing a fatal arrhythmia—an explanation which may account for sudden death during calcium therapy.

Magnesium. Magnesium is plentiful in food and the daily dietary requirement is low; consequently, magnesium depletion is unlikely except in patients chronically maintained on magnesium-free intravenous solutions. In the few such cases which have been reported, disturbances in other organ systems overshadowed the cardiovascular complications. The PR interval lengthens when serum magnesium con-

centration exceeds 10 mEq. per liter; at very high concentrations cardiac arrest occurs.

CORONARY DISEASE

The coronary arteries alone carry metabolic requirements to the pump which generates driving force for the circulation. Disease conditions which alter the ability of the coronary arteries to perform this vital function lead to disturbances in the performance of the pump. Coronary arteries are subject to the same diseases as other arteries; basically these diseases are significant in proportion to the impediment they impose upon the ability or capacity for carrying blood. The net effects of coronary disease relate to limitations imposed on coronary blood flow, and more particularly, to the consequent restrictions on delivery of oxygen to the myocardium.

Myocardial Ischemia. The *sine qua non* of coronary artery disease is myocardial ischemia, which is manifested whenever coronary blood flow is compromised. In humans, myocardial ischemia usually results from coronary artery disease *per se,* but it may also be precipitated by reduction in the oxygen-carrying capacity of the blood, as in anemia, or by deficiencies in arterial oxygen saturation, as in some forms of chronic pulmonary disease. Ischemia also occurs in diseases in which there is marked hypertrophy of ventricular muscle fibers, because the ratio of capillary area to fiber area is diminished. During advanced stages of valvular insufficiency, ischemia may develop because of the greatly increased work of the heart; in aortic insufficiency this is compounded by very low coronary perfusion pressures during diastole. Arterial hypotension of any cause may significantly reduce coronary blood flow owing to the diminished perfusion pressure. In hypertensive cardiovascular disease, myocardial ischemia may result from multiple factors; the work load is increased, and progressive muscular hypertrophy occurs. In addition, hypertension is often associated with development of coronary atherosclerosis.

Atherosclerosis. The most common cause of myocardial ischemia is impairment of coronary blood flow due to mechanical obstruction within the coronary artery. Occasionally this is due to coronary manifestations of more diffuse systemic diseases, such as periarteritis, sclero-

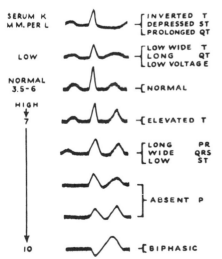

Fig. 16. Effect of serum potassium level on the configuration of the electrocardiogram. (From Darrow, *New Engl. J. Med.*, 1950, *242*:1014–1018.)

derma or syphilis. However, by far the most common cause of coronary obstruction is atherosclerosis. Once regarded as a degenerative disease attendant to aging, this condition is now recognized as a metabolic disease. Although the prime incidence of symptomatic atherosclerotic coronary disease is in men past the age of 40, atherosclerosis of coronary vessels is present in all age groups.

The lesion begins with lipid deposits which cause a thickening of the vascular intima. Typically, these deposits are round and elevated above the vascular surface. Later these lipid accumulations coalesce, become infiltrated with cholesterol, and become covered with hyaline-like connective tissue, thus forming a characteristic lesion, the atherosclerotic plaque. Associated fibroelastic changes also develop in the blood vessel walls. The disease not only encroaches progressively on the vascular lumen but also limits the capability of the vessels to dilate. The hydraulic consequences are predictable: the resistance to flow is increased, the perfusion pressure is lowered, and the blood flow is reduced. In addition, the velocity of blood flow above the lesion is reduced, which is believed to increase the possibility of thrombus formation. Atherosclerotic plaques may also be elevated by mural hemorrhages, or may become dislodged and completely obstruct the vessel farther downstream. Atherosclerosis, then, may gradually limit blood flow through coronary vessels or may precipitate an acute episode in which flow through a vessel is suddenly blocked.

Angina Pectoris. The most common manifestation of inadequate coronary flow is angina pectoris, a clinical syndrome marked by anterior chest pain which usually develops during exertion or excitement and which characteristically radiates to the neck and arms. Clinically, it is assumed that this painful sensation is triggered by ischemia of the myocardium and is referred to the chest wall. Although this assumption is logical, it is difficult to outline the mechanism and pathways involved. Pain fibers from the heart reach the upper four thoracic spinal nerves via sympathetic rami communicantes and enter the spinal cord over posterior roots, but the CNS pathways mediating cardiac pain are unknown.

Typically, angina is relieved by rest or by nitroglycerine. Rest reduces the work level of the heart; the relief afforded by nitroglycerine probably results from its vasodilator effect on coronary arteries as well as its effect on reducing cardiac work. Sometimes angina may be relieved by eliminating predisposing factors such as anemia, hyperthyroidism, etc. In rare instances of intractable angina, the pain pathways may be interrupted by posterior rhizotomy.

The role of coronary spasm in provoking angina is not clearly established. Clinical experience strongly suggests that vasomotor effects on the coronary circulation may be induced by pain, emotion, exposure to cold, etc., but no critical experiment has been performed in which secondary cardiac effects such as increased work, blood pressure and heart rate have been excluded, nor has the pathway for such vasomotor effects been demonstrated. Spasm of coronary vessels is probably not capable of producing angina pectoris in otherwise normal hearts; the hearts of patients who have suffered from angina quite routinely show evidence of myocardial disease.[2]

Coronary Occlusion. Sudden occlusion of a major coronary vessel is followed by development of acute myocardial infarction. Electrocardiographic changes may be detected within a minute (see Chap. 30). Cardiac arrhythmias are common; in some instances, ventricular ectopic foci develop. Ventricular fibrillation is a leading cause of death during the period immediately following the onset of occlusion. An ominous condition termed cardiogenic shock may also develop about this time. The condition is marked by drastically lowered blood pressure, weak, rapid pulse and other signs of clinical shock. This hypodynamic state is probably primarily due to death of heart muscle, but peripheral vasomotor responses undoubtedly contribute to circulatory collapse. During the first few days after myocardial infarction, oxidative enzymes escape from degenerating muscle cells into the serum. Consequently, their serum level is greatly elevated; serial measurements of certain of these enzymes, e.g., glutamic-oxalacetic transaminase, are of diagnostic and prognostic value. In about 10 per cent of the cases rupture of the infarcted myocardium may take place, usually between the fourth and tenth days. However, in most instances, the infarcted area is replaced by fibrous noncontractile connective tissue. Rarely, the replacement tissue is unable to sustain intraventricular blood pressure so that a progressive ventricular aneurysm develops.

The over-all mortality rate during the first month after acute myocardial infarction is about 25 per cent. Mortality is greater in the presence of other diseases which add to the load imposed upon the heart, e.g., hypertensive cardiovascular disease, diabetes, thyrotoxicosis, etc. In survivors, morbidity is determined largely by the extent of cardiac damage. The remaining viable myocardium may be sufficient to enable the patient to maintain a nearly normal exercise capacity. Coronary blood supply in these instances is augmented by development of functional intercoronary anastomoses. In other patients, however, the capacity of remaining patent coronary vessels may be limited by extension of the atherosclerotic process so that the blood supply to the remaining viable myocardium is inadequate. In these patients the work capacity is often seriously limited, the anginal syndrome is common, and the prognosis is grave.

REFERENCES

1. BING, R. J. *Amer. J. Med.*, 1961, *30*:679–691.
2. BLUMGART, H. L., ZOLL, P. M. and WESSLER, S. *Trans. Ass. Amer. Physicians,* 1950, *63*:262–267.
3. ECKENHOFF, J. E., HAFKENSHIEL, J. H., HARMEL, M. H., GOODALE, W. T., LUBIN, M., BING, R. J. and KETY, S. S. *Amer. J. Physiol.*, 1948, *152*:356–364.
4. FRANKLIN, D. L., WATSON, N. W., and VAN CITTERS, R. L. *Nature,* 1964, *203*:528–530.
5. GORLIN, R. *J. Amer. med. Ass.*, 1962, *179*:441–449.
6. GRANATA, L., HUVOS, A. and GREGG, D. E. *Physiologist,* 1961, *4*:42.
7. GREEN, D. E. and GOLDBERGER, R. F. *Amer. J. Med.*, 1961, *30*:666–678.
8. GREEN, H. D. and WEGRIA, R. *Amer. J. Physiol.*, 1942, *135*:271–280.
9. GREGG, D. E. In: *Shock, pathogenesis and therapy*, K. D. Bock, ed. Berlin, Springer-Verlag, 1961.
10. GREGG, D. E. *Circulation*, 1963, *27*:1128–1137.
11. GREGG, D. E. *The coronary circulation in health and disease.* Philadelphia, Lea & Febiger, 1950.
12. GUZMAN, S. V., SWENSON, E. and JONES, M. *Circulation Res.*, 1962, *10*:739–752.
13. HELLEMS, H. K., ORD, J. W., TALMERS, F. N. and CHRISTENSEN, R. C. *Circulation*, 1957, *16*:893.
14. HILTON, R. and EICHOLTZ, F. *J. Physiol.*, 1925, *59*:413–425.
15. HUCKABEE, W. E. *Amer. J. Physiol.*, 1961, *200*:1169–1176.
16. JAMES, T. N. and BURCH, G. E. *Circulation*, 1958, *17*:391–396.
17. KHOURI, E. M. and GREGG, D. E. *J. appl. Physiol.*, 1963, *18*:224–227.
18. KHOURI, E. M., GREGG, D. E., HALL, R. J. and RAYFORD, C. R. *Physiologist*, 1960, *3*:93.
19. KISCH, B. *Electron microscopy of the cardiovascular system.* Springfield, Ill., Charles C Thomas, 1960.
20. LEPESCHKIN, E. *Bibl. cardiol. (Basel)*, 1959, *9*:189–212.
21. LEVY, M. N. and DEOLIVEIRA, J. M. *Circulation Res.*, 1961, *9*:96–98.
22. PERLMUTTER, H. I. In: *Coronary heart disease*, Likoff, W. and Moyer, J. H., eds., New York, Grune & Stratton, 1963.
23. PITT, B. *Circulation*, 1959, *20*:816–822.
24. PITT, B., ZOLL, P. M., BLUMGART, H. L. and FREIMAN, D. G. *Circulation*, 1963, *28*:35–41.
25. RAYFORD, C. R., KHOURI, E. M., LEWIS, F. B. and GREGG, D. E. *J. appl. Physiol.*, 1959, *14*:817–822.
26. REISSMANN, K. R. and VAN CITTERS, R. L. *J. appl. Physiol.*, 1956, *9*:427–430.
27. ROSS, J., JR., MOSHER, P. W. and SHAW, R. F. *Circulation*, 1961, *24*:1025.
28. SCHLESINGER, M. J. *Amer. Heart J.*, 1938, *15*:528–568.
29. VAN CITTERS, R. L., RUTH, W. E. and REISSMANN, K. R. *Amer. J. Physiol.*, 1957, *191*:443–445.
30. WEARN, J. T. *Harvey Lect.*, 1940, *35*:243–270.
31. WEST, J. W., KOBAYASHI, T. and ANDERSON, F. S. *Circulation Res.*, 1962, *10*:722–738.
32. ZOLL, P. M., WESSLER, S. and SCHLESINGER, M. J. *Circulation*, 1951, *4*:797–815.

CHAPTER 37

Congenital Cardiac Disease; Acquired Valvular Disease

By ROBERT L. VAN CITTERS

CONGENITAL CARDIAC DISEASE

THE cardiovascular system is the first to reach a functional state in the human embryo. In early stages the respiratory, excretory and nutritional functions of the embryo are carried out by simple diffusion, but by about three weeks the embryo has attained such size that this means of transport is inadequate. The early development of a functional cardiovascular system provides a transport mechanism which enables the fetus to carry out these vital processes across the placenta. The first cells from which the cardiovascular system ultimately develops are apparent in the late presomite embryo (1 mm.) about three weeks after fertilization. Between the third and seventh weeks the heart develops rapidly from these few primitive cells into a complex organ with valves and appropriate septal divisions enabling it to function as two separate pumps. Following this initial period of development no major structural changes occur until immediately after birth, when additional adaptations take place to permit the system to function independently of the placental circulation. Structural imperfections may arise in the car-

diovascular system either during the early period of rapid development or during the period of postnatal adjustment. These imperfections may be the result of retardation or arrest of normal development, or of aberrant growth of otherwise normal structures. Such cardiovascular malformations are collectively referred to as congenital cardiac disease.

Until recently, recognition and classification of various congenital cardiac diseases were largely of academic interest because no therapeutic measures were available to alter their course. Recently both diagnostic and therapeutic techniques have been greatly improved; at present, physicians understand the anatomic and physiologic nature of most congenital cardiac lesions and can correct many malformations. Some of the more complex malformations for which no therapy now exists will almost certainly be curable one day. Recognition and evaluation of congenital malformations of the heart therefore now has practical significance.

Embryology of the Heart.[10, 14, 22] Understanding congenital cardiac disease requires an understanding of the major stages in the embryonic development of the heart. The primitive cells from which the heart is formed proliferate and fuse to form a simple straight tube, the cardiac tube, by about the twenty-third day. During the next several days the tube elongates greatly, but because it is attached at either end, this lengthening bends it, first into a U, and ultimately into an exaggerated S. Differential expansion accompanied by regional narrowings demarcates the tube by the thirty-fifth day into a primitive atrium, ventricle and truncus arteriosus or outflow tract. At about the fortieth day septa develop and the irregularly convoluted tube begins to be partitioned into a four-chambered heart with two separate outflow tracts (Fig. 1).

A ridge, the septum primum, in the dorsal aspect of the common atrial chamber marks the beginning of its subdivision into right and left compartments (Fig. 2*A*). This ridge extends toward the ventricles, gradually dividing the atrium into two chambers connected by a small opening, the foramen primum (Fig. 2*B*). Before the foramen primum closes, a second opening, the foramen secundum, develops high in the septum primum. Here a second structure, the septum secundum, develops in the right atrium and extends down over the foramen primum, imperfectly closing the foramen secundum (Fig. 3). The region of the septum secundum adjacent to the foramen secundum is termed the foramen ovale. Eventually the septum primum and septum secundum are fused, but at the foramen ovale the septum primum persists as a flaplike structure, acting as a flutter valve to permit flow from right to left atrium. A patent foramen ovale is characteristic of the fetal circulation (Fig. 4). In postnatal life the foramen ovale is usually closed, but it remains patent to probes in about 20 per cent of hearts. Usually such patency of the foramen ovale is benign. In contrast, incomplete closure of the foramen secundum is a clinically important malformation.

Growth of endocardial cushions from the dorsal and ventral aspects of the atrioventricular groove and growth of a muscular septum from the interventricular groove toward the base of the heart mark the beginning of subdivision of the common ventricular chamber. The endocardial cushion tissue also grows into the inferior aspect of the atrial chamber to meet the atrial septum and form its lowermost portion (Fig. 5). Defects in endocardial cushion growth result in various malformations of the atrioventricular canal, e.g., defects in the lower atrial septum ("ostium primum"), ventricular septal defects, cleft septal leaflets of the mitral or tricuspid valves, or combinations of these.

Simultaneously the truncus arteriosus divides into the pulmonary artery and aorta. Paired ridges in the bifurcation of the truncus extend spirally downward toward the ventricle. These ridges enlarge and fuse in the center of the trun-

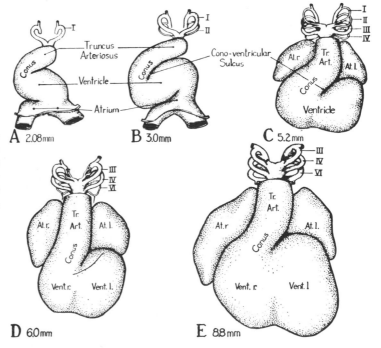

Fig. 1. Elongation and convolution of the cardiac tube in human embryonic hearts. Differential expansion and regional narrowing occur simultaneously to demarcate the tube into its major chambers. (From Kramer, *Amer. J. Anat.*, 1942, *71*:343–370.)

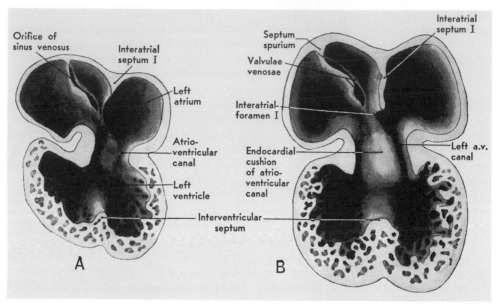

Fig. 2.   Interior views of partitioning of the human heart.   *A,* 5th week of development. The septum primum marks the beginning of division of the common atrium into 2 chambers.   *B,* 6th week of development. The two atria are connected by the foramen primum. Endocardial cushions are fusing to divide the A-V canal, and there is growth of the ventricular septum. (From Patten, *Human Embryology,* 2nd ed. New York, McGraw Hill Book Co., 1953, by permission.)

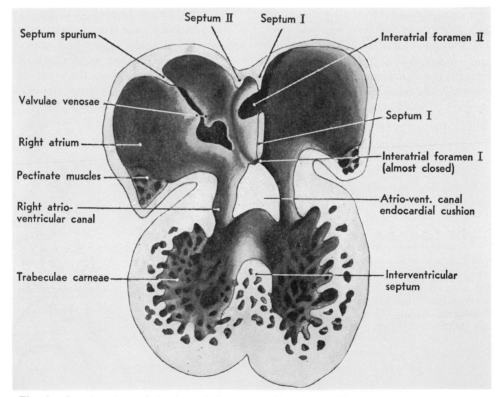

Fig. 3.   Interior view of the 7-week human embryo heart. The foramen primum is nearly obliterated, but a new interatrial communication, the foramen secundum, has developed. The septum secundum is developing on the right atrial aspect of the septum primum. Meanwhile, division of the A-V canal occurs through fusion of the endocardial cushions, and the muscular portion of the ventricular septum continues to grow. (From Patten, *Human embryology,* 2nd ed. New York, McGraw Hill Book Co., 1953, by permission.)

cus to form a continuous partition which ultimately joins the oncoming ventricular septum. The spiral of the truncus septum rotates through 180 degrees, and when it meets the ventricular septum, establishes a communication between the right ventricle and pulmonary trunk on the one hand, and left ventricle and aorta on the other (Fig. 6). The ventricular septum is finally closed by conjunction of the atrioventricular cushions, the ventricular septum and the spiral septum of the truncus, which forms a sheet of connective tissue called the membranous portion of the septum. Anatomic malformations in this region give rise to several forms of congenital heart disease; imperfect closure of the membranous portion of the ventricular septum is the most common kind of ventricular septal defect. Variations in the development of the truncal septum give rise to abnormalities in the outflow tracts of the ventricles.

During subdivision of the cardiac tube, pads of endothelial tissue grow out into the lumen at the juncture of the truncus with the ventricle; these later develop into the semilunar valve cusps. At about the same time, endothelial flaps proliferate at the atrioventricular junction to form the embryonic atrioventricular valves (see Fig. 6). The most common valvular malformation is stenosis due to fusion of the valve cusps, but valvular atresia (absence of valve cusps) also occurs. Atrial or ventricular septal defects may involve the valve ring, causing combined septal and valvular lesions.

Prior to the sixth week the truncus arteriosus connects both ventricles with the dorsal aorta through six pairs of aortic arches. With septation of the truncus the sixth arch joins the right ventricle and ultimately forms the pulmonary artery. A portion of the fourth arch persists as the aortic arch. Remnants of other arches become major thoracic and cervical arteries. A remnant of the sixth arch, the ductus arteriosus, normally persists during fetal life and serves as a communication between the pulmonary artery and aorta. The significance of the ductus arteriosus is discussed under the next heading.

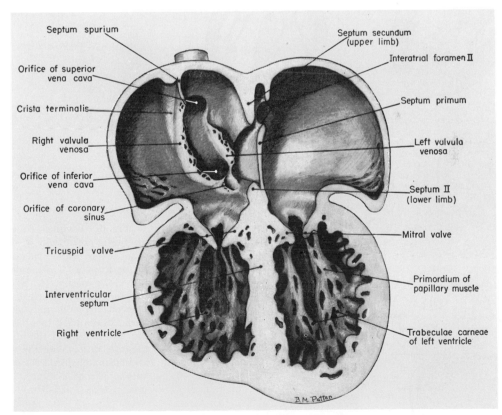

Fig. 4. Internal view of human heart during late fetal life. Partitioning and septation are complete and the pathway of fetal circulation is established. Most of the flow from the inferior vena cava streams across the foramen ovale to enter the left atrium. (From Patten, *Foundations of embryology*. 2nd ed. New York, McGraw Hill Book Co., 1964.)

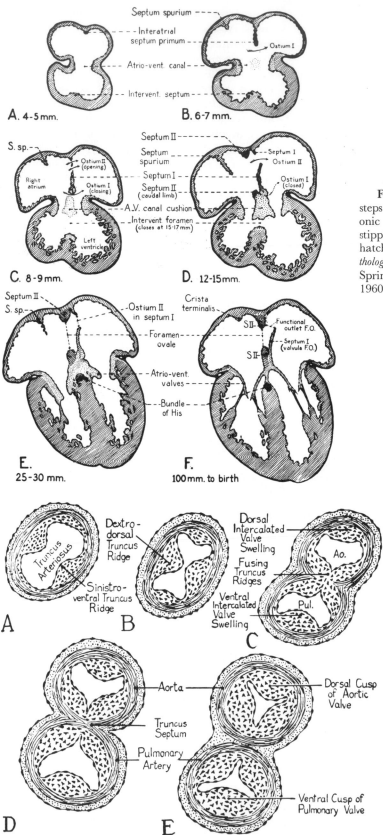

Fig. 5. Growth of cardiac septa and steps in partitioning of the human embryonic heart. Endocardial cushion tissue is stippled, muscle tissue is diagonally hatched. (From Patten, Chap. 2 in *Pathology of the heart*, 2nd ed. Gould, ed. Springfield, Ill., Charles C Thomas, 1960.)

Fig. 6. Division of the truncus arteriosus and origin of the semilunar valves. Paired ridges develop in the truncus (*A, B*), enlarge and fuse in the midline (*C*), and form a partition (*D, E*) which divides the truncus into pulmonary artery and aorta. Endothelial tissue grows out into the lumina at the junction of these structures with the ventricles and ultimately forms the semilunar valves. (From Kramer, *Amer. J. Anat.,* 1942, *71*:343–370.)

Fetal Circulation.[5, 23] By the eighth fetal week partitioning of the heart and great vessels is complete and the cardiovascular system attains a form and structure which persist until after delivery. During the intrauterine period the circulatory system is adapted to carry out respiration, excretion and nutrition by placental exchange. Hemodynamic measurements in human embryos are lacking. Present information is derived mostly from studies on other mammals, e.g., fetal lambs.

About 60 per cent of the fetal cardiac output is delivered to the placenta, where respiratory exchange occurs. The oxygen saturation of the blood returning to the fetus via the umbilical vein is about 80 per cent. Ultimately this blood enters the inferior vena cava, where it mixes with blood which has perfused the caudal half of the fetus; this blood represents about 15 per cent of the cardiac output and its oxygen saturation is only about 30 per cent. Venous blood from the cephalic portion of the fetus, which represents another 15 per cent of the cardiac output, returns via the superior vena cava and is also about 30 per cent saturated. The remaining 10 per cent of the cardiac output perfuses the pulmonary circuit and returns to the heart via pulmonary veins.

Most of the inflow from the inferior vena cava is shunted directly from right atrium to left through the foramen ovale; blood returning from the head via the superior vena cava is largely directed from the right atrium into the right ventricle.[11, 16] There is little mixing as these two streams pass through the right atrium, so that most of the oxygenated blood is transferred to the left side of the heart (see Fig. 4).[7] In lambs, for example, about 80 per cent of the inferior vena caval inflow passes through the foramen ovale. In the left atrium this blood mixes with a small amount of unsaturated blood returning from the lungs via the pulmonary veins. The oxygen saturation of mixed left ventricular blood is about 60 per cent.

The fetal left ventricle pumps about 60 per cent of the total cardiac output. Slightly less than one-third of this perfuses the cephalic portion of the fetus and the balance enters the descending aorta. Of the 40 per cent pumped by the right ventricle, only about one-third enters the pulmonary circuit, which in the fetus has a high resistance; the remainder passes through the ductus arteriosus into the descending aorta. The fetal circulation thus assures preferential delivery of oxygenated blood into the ascending aorta and its cephalic branches, while blood which is delivered via the descending aorta to the placenta and caudal half of the fetus contains relatively less oxygen.[5]

Postnatal Changes in the Circulation. In the newborn, ligation of the umbilical vein interrupts the placental source of oxygen and respiratory function must be assumed by the infant's own lungs. Inflation of the lungs reduces the resistance of the pulmonary circuit and pulmonary blood flow increases correspondingly. At the same time, functional closure of the ductus arteriosus begins. Functional closure takes place almost immediately, within minutes after birth, but complete anatomic closure may require weeks to months.[1, 16] Although several neural, mechanical and hormonal theories have been postulated,[23] the mechanism of obliteration of the ductus has not been conclusively demonstrated. With closure of the ductus arteriosus and increased pulmonary flow, left atrial inflow rises and left atrial pressure for the first time exceeds that in the right atrium. The flaplike valvula over the foramen ovale, which heretofore has permitted flow from right atrium to left atrium, is now forced in the opposite direction and effectively closes the opening. Closure of the valvula functionally completes the internal partitioning of the heart; permanent sealing of this foramen often requires many months.

Pathologic Physiology of Congenital Cardiac Disease. Congenital circulatory malformations may occur as single isolated entities or as combinations of several defects so that many kinds of congenital heart disease are possible. However, these anomalies tend to follow patterns; a dozen relatively easily recognizable forms comprise over 90 per cent of the cases. Congenital cardiac lesions are differentiated according to the disturbance they create in normal cardiovascular physiology: (i) obstruction to blood flow and (ii) shunts, i.e., flow of blood through abnormal pathways. In the simplest anomalies these disturbances appear singly and for the most part the physiologic consequences are straightforward. Combinations of shunts and obstructions present more difficult problems. In any case, an understanding of the physiologic implications of these two disturbances is required.

Obstruction to blood flow. Obstructive cardiovascular malformations may involve either the vessels or the structures within the heart itself. The most common obstructive lesions within the heart affect the valves or the tissues immediately proximal to the valves. In the latter instance, muscular hypertrophy and fibrosis of the ventricular outflow tract narrows the channel. Obstructive disease of the valve itself (stenosis) usually results from fusion of valve cusps along their commissures with resultant reduction of the valve orifice. Such a stenosed valve often resembles a membranous dome with a very tiny aperture, usually eccentrically located. The orifice may be completely lacking; such a malformation, called atresia of the valve, is always associated with one or more additional defects. Obstruction to flow through the major vessels is usually due to regional narrowing of the lumen. In the systemic circulation this is most common in the descending aorta near the ligamentum arteriosum, where a short segment of the vessel may be constricted so that its lumen is but a few millimeters in diameter. Obstruction in the pulmonary circuit commonly involves terminal radicles in the pulmonary vascular tree; the significance of this is discussed in a separate section.

When blood flow is obstructed, the hydraulic resistance is increased, so that a greater pressure is required to force blood past this region. The immediate hemodynamic consequence of an obstructive lesion is an increase in the pressure in the chamber or vessel immediately proximal to the obstruction. Most congenital cardiac lesions impede flow out of one of the ventricles, resulting in right or left ventricular hypertension. The affected ventricle responds to sustained pressure loads with progressive hypertrophy. This compensatory adjustment may initially be adequate, but any cardiac chamber which works against an abnormally high resistance necessarily functions closer to the limit of its reserve capacity and, therefore, under conditions of stress, is subject to failure. The right ventricle is especially vulnerable to pressure loads and often fails to cope with a long-term progressively obstructive lesion.

Obstructive lesions can be located by sampling the blood pressure proximal and distal to the suspected site; in the presence of a significant obstruction a gradient of pressure exists across the lesion; i.e., the pressure is higher above an obstruction than below it (see Fig. 15). Obstructions may be detected by a variety of other procedures. Ventricular hypertrophy is recognizable from the characteristic electrocardiographic changes (Fig. 10) or from radiographic visualization (Fig. 14). Blood flowing through a constricted channel attains a higher velocity, which tends to produce turbulence (see Chap. 27). Irregular variations in lumen size further interrupt the pattern of streamline flow. Such turbulence produces audible vibrations known as murmurs, which provide clues as to the nature of the underlying lesion.

The vascular lumen immediately distal to a localized obstruction is for unknown reasons often dilated. Such post-stenotic dilatation can often be detected radiographically.

Shunts. In shunts, blood flows through abnormal pathways. The requirements for shunting are an open or potentially open communication between vascular compartments and a pressure differential across the communication. The most common congenital defects are due to abnormal communications between the two atria, between the ventricles, or between major vessels. Such communications usually represent persistence of some embryonic stage of cardiovascular development.

The direction of blood flow through a shunt is determined by the pressure gradient across the opening; the quantity of flow depends on both the pressure differential and the size of the opening. Normally, pressure is higher in the systemic circulation than in the pulmonary circulation. Thus a direct communication between the two atria or between the ventricles results in a left-to-right shunt. In these instances pulmonary blood flow exceeds systemic flow and the right ventricle pumps more blood than the left. In left-to-right shunts due to communication between the pulmonary artery and aorta, the left ventricle pumps the greater volume.

Left-to-right shunts engorge the pulmonary vessels; pulmonary flow may exceed systemic flow by three to four times. The normal pulmonary circuit can accommodate great increases in flow with no great increase in pulmonary vascular pressure. However, in congenital cardiac disease the pulmonary vascular resistance is often increased and the pulmonary arterial pressure becomes progressively elevated. If the pressure in the pulmonary circuit exceeds that in the systemic, the direction of shunting may reverse, resulting in admixture of unsaturated venous blood from the right heart with the saturated arterial blood in the systemic circulation. The hallmark of a right-to-left shunt is systemic arterial unsaturation. It is important to realize that the oxygen saturation of the blood leaving the lungs is normal and that the decrease in P_{O_2} in the systemic blood is due to the admixture of unsaturated venous blood, not to diminished pulmonary blood flow.

Peripheral unsaturation is manifest as cyanosis, a bluish discoloration of the nail beds, lips and mucous membranes, due to the reduced oxygen tension in the superficial capillaries. Cyanosis becomes evident when the concentration of unsaturated hemoglobin in arterial blood reaches about 5 grams per 100 ml. Patients with marked anemia and a right-to-left shunt may not show cyanosis; those with polycythemia display it more readily. Cyanosis in a patient with congenital cardiac disease implies a right-to-left shunt and an obstruction in the pulmonary circulation.

Chronic arterial desaturation often results in compensatory increase of the red blood cell count and hemoglobin content. Although such polycythemia increases the oxygen-carrying capacity of the blood, it also causes an increased blood viscosity and a greater tendency to vascular thrombosis. Such patients are therefore susceptible to cerebral vascular accidents ("strokes"). Some patients with cyanotic congenital cardiac disease have low platelet counts and low fibrinogen levels, which may cause hemostatic problems during surgical repair of their defects.

Patients with right-to-left shunts often have marked enlargement of the terminal phalanges (hypertrophic pulmonary osteoarthropathy or clubbed fingers). The underlying mechanism of this disorder is not known; it also occurs in other pulmonary diseases without peripheral desaturation or polycythemia.

Some patients with congenital cardiac disease are often more comfortable in the squatting posture.[17] Various physiologic explanations have been offered, but the underlying basis for the symptomatic relief obtained through squatting is unknown.

Pulmonary hypertension.[6] In the fetal and neonatal period the pulmonary vessels are thick-walled with narrow lumina and vascular resistance is relatively high. Normally these structural characteristics regress, and the pulmonary vessels ultimately become thin-walled and compliant.[3] The normal adult pulmonary arterial pressure is about 25/10 mm. Hg. Increases in pulmonary flow, such as occur during exercise, are normally accommodated without significant pressure rise.

With congenital left to right shunts, pulmonary flow may be increased by three or four times, but even so the pulmonary arterial pressure may not exceed 40 mm. Hg. With prolonged exposure to such flow rates, the pulmonary resistance may increase and irreversible structural changes may develop in the smaller arteries. However, high flow rates are not always associated with increased pulmonary resistance. Pulmonary hypertension occurs in about 5 per cent of patients with atrial septal defects, in about 10 per cent of patients with endocardial cushion defects, and in 25 per cent of patients with ventricular septal defects. Since pulmonary blood flow is elevated in all of these conditions, other factors must be involved. Persistence of the fetal pattern is regarded as one factor.

Pulmonary hypertension ultimately leads to right ventricular hypertrophy and dilation of the pulmonary artery. Pulmonary hypertension is often progressive and pulmonary pressure may eventually equal or exceed systemic pressure, resulting in reversal of the direction of shunting. Auscultatory signs of pulmonary hypertension include accentuation of the pulmonary component of the second heart sound, progressive splitting of the second heart sound and a systolic murmur.

Methods for Study of Congenital Cardiac Disease. Physical signs and symptoms offer valuable clues to the nature of cardiovascular malformations, but accurate diagnosis usually requires in addition precise physiologic measurements. Much of our present knowledge of both normal and abnormal cardiovascular physiology is derived from cardiac catheterization.[28] In this procedure, a sampling tube is introduced into the heart for measuring blood pressures, withdrawing blood samples or injecting tracer materials. The cardiac catheter is a long, hollow, flexible tube which is introduced into a superficial vein, usually the antecubital or femoral, and is passed under fluoroscopic guidance into the right heart. An experienced operator can readily guide the tip of the catheter through the vena cava, right atrium and right ventricle into the pulmonary artery (Fig. 7). At each location the pressure is measured and blood samples are withdrawn for oxygen tension determinations. Abnormally high pressures signify flow obstruction; a sig-

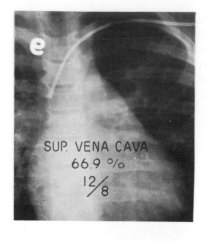

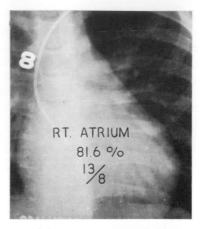

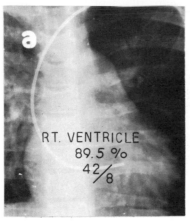

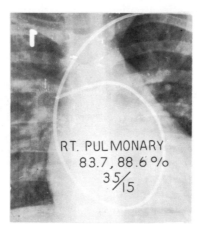

Fig. 7. Serial thoracic roentgenograms as a cardiac catheter is passed through the right heart. Measurements of blood pressure and oxygen content in each location are indicated. *Upper left,* The catheter was introduced into a superficial vein of the left arm and is shown as its tip enters the superior vena cava. *Upper right,* The tip of the catheter has entered the right atrium. *Lower left,* The catheter tip has passed through the tricuspid valve to enter the right ventricle. *Lower right,* The catheter tip now lies in the right pulmonary artery. Note that the oxygen content of blood in the right atrium is significantly higher than that in the vena cava; the anatomic diagnosis of atrial septal defect was confirmed at surgery. (Courtesy of Dr. Melvin M. Figley.)

nificant pressure gradient between two sites, e.g., right ventricle and pulmonary artery, may reveal the site of an obstruction. A sharp increase in the blood oxygen content in samples from successive cardiac chambers, e.g., right atrium or right ventricle, is strong evidence for a left-to-right shunt in that chamber. Sometimes the catheter can be passed through an abnormal communication; this constitutes direct evidence of a defect, but caution and judgment must be exercised in diagnosing the anatomic site. Failure to pass the catheter through a suspected defect has little diagnostic significance. The left heart is usually catheterized by retrograde passage through a peripheral artery and the aorta into the ventricle, but it may also be reached by needle puncture through the chest or a bronchus. This procedure is performed less frequently than right heart catheterization but is often of value in study of both acquired and congenital heart lesions (Fig. 8).

The course of the blood as it passes through the heart and great vessels may be traced radiographically after injection of radiopaque tracers either through a peripheral vein or through a carefully positioned cardiac catheter. The passage of radiopaque materials may be observed on a fluoroscope screen, but is usually recorded by accurately timed serial x-ray films (angiography) or high speed x-ray motion pictures (cineangiography). Such films often show clearly flow through abnormal communications and, in addition, show the size and configuration of cardiac structures.

Shunts and their direction of flow may also be detected—and estimates of the quantity of blood flowing through them may be made—by injection of tracer substances such as colored dye or radioactive materials into the venous system while their concentration in a peripheral artery is sampled.[18] The normal concentration-time curve of such injected material is altered in the presence of a shunt. With a left-to-right shunt some of the injected material is recirculated through the lungs so that the amount which reaches a peripheral arterial sampling site is less, and the slope of the concentration-time curve is more gradual. With a right-to-left shunt some of the dye reaches the arterial sampling site early; the dye curve shows an early peak immediately preceding the normal curve (Fig. 9). The site of a right-to-left shunt may be determined by making successive injections as the catheter is advanced; injections made distal to the site of the shunt result in normal curves. Shunts may also be localized by using two catheters, one for injection and a second for sampling. Foreign gases have recently been used as indicator substances; these permit bloodless left atrial "injection" since the inspired gases are equilibrated with blood in the lungs, and bloodless right heart "sampling" since the expired gases are also equilibrated with the blood. Mathematical treatment of dye dilution data permits estimation of volume flow through shunts.

Roentgenographic examination of the heart gives details of its size and configuration and

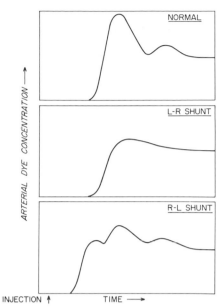

Fig. 9. Idealized representation of the arterial time-concentration curve of dye injected into a major vein. When an indicator substance is rapidly injected into the vein of a normal person, it traverses the heart and arrives at the sampling site some seconds later as a bolus so that a characteristic time-concentration curve is inscribed. If a right to left shunt is present, some of the dye passes directly to the left heart without passing through the lungs; as a result, the curve has an early deflection ("early arrival time") and a second peak indicating arrival of the balance of the substance, which followed the normal route. With left to right shunts some of the indicator substance recirculates through the defect; the maximum deflection is reduced and disappearance is delayed.

often provides data pointing to a specific malformation. Fluoroscopy is particularly valuable in a study of lung vascularity; in left-to-right shunts the pulmonary vessels are engorged with blood and rhythmic pulsation of these vessels may be seen near the hilum.

Right ventricular hypertrophy is especially common in congenital heart disease and is detected electrocardiographically.[25] Phonocardiography usually provides little more information than is already available to the well-trained observer with a stethoscope.

Common Forms of Congenital Cardiac Disease. The list of congenital circulatory abnormalities is too extensive to be treated in detail here. Instead, examples of some of the common varieties are described to illustrate the underlying disorders in cardiovascular physiology. Details are available in several standard references.[12, 13, 21]

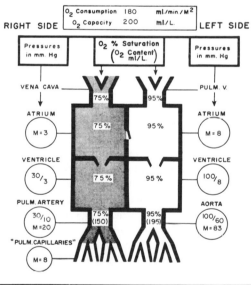

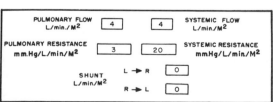

Fig. 8. Diagrammatic representation of circulatory dynamics with pressures and oxygen values determined by cardiac catheterization in a normal subject. (From Nadas, *Pediatric cardiology,* 2nd ed. Philadelphia, W. B. Saunders Co., 1963.)

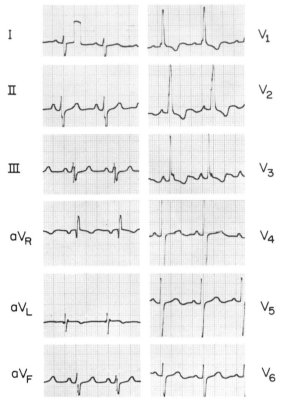

I

II

III

aV_R

aV_L

aV_F

V₁

V₂

V₃

V₄

V₅

V₆

Fig. 10. Electrocardiogram of a patient with an atrial septal defect, ostium primum type. Compare this with a normal ECG (Chap. 30). The abnormal pattern of depolarization shown here commonly occurs with right ventricular hypertrophy. (Courtesy of Dr. John Blackmon.)

Atrial septal defect. This is the most common congenital cardiac lesion. It has already been mentioned that in about 20 per cent of normal persons the flap of septum secundum which overlies the foramen ovale fails to seal in postpartum life. Although patency of the foramen ovale may be demonstrated in these cases by means of a probe, the flap continues to function as a one-way valve as long as atrial pressures are normal.

The fundamental hemodynamic consequences of an uncomplicated atrial septal defect are those of a left-to-right shunt. Flow is from left to right because throughout the entire cardiac cycle pressure is higher in the left atrium than in the right. Volume of flow through the defect depends upon its caliber. The resistance across a small defect (less than 1 sq. cm.) is high, so that the atrial pressure gradient remains normal (mean pressure in left atrium, 8 mm. Hg, in right atrium, 4 mm. Hg) and the amount of

blood shunted is small. With large defects the two atria effectively become a single chamber, a circumstance which favors right ventricular filling owing to the relative ease with which this chamber is distended in comparison with the left ventricle. Thus, pulmonary venous blood as well as caval blood preferentially enters the right ventricle, and right ventricular output exceeds left output. Recirculation may result in pulmonary volume flows exceeding 16 liters per minute while flow through the systemic circuit remains nearly normal. The right atrium, ventricle and pulmonary artery respond to this severe volume load by dilatation. Long-standing large left-to-right shunts often lead to obstructive pulmonary arteriolar lesions, progressive pulmonary hypertension and right ventricular hypertrophy. Pulmonary resistance may eventually exceed that in the aorta, causing reversal of flow through the shunt. This event is signaled by development of typical signs and symptoms of peripheral desaturation. Atrial septal defects may be complicated by associated deformities of the endocardial cushions, which lead to incompetence of mitral or tricuspid valves.

Atrial septal defects are readily detected by physical examination and special laboratory procedures. Because of the increased volume load, the right side of the heart is dilated, as can be demonstrated roentgenographically; in particular, the pulmonary artery is much enlarged. Auscultation typically reveals a systolic murmur over the pulmonary artery. This murmur is due to the increased volume and velocity of blood in the pulmonary artery rather than to flow through the atrial defect. Right ventricular hypertrophy is indicated electrocardiographically (Fig. 10) by right axis deviation and signs of incomplete right bundle branch block (see Chap. 30). Admixture of pulmonary and systemic blood may be demonstrated by measuring the oxygen content of blood samples removed via a cardiac catheter. The oxygen content of right atrial blood is usually increased by at least 2 volumes per cent over that of caval blood (Fig. 11). This finding of itself is only presumptive evidence for an atrial septal defect, since similar values may be found in another type of congenital defect in which one or more pulmonary veins empty into the right atrium. More definitive evidence for an atrial defect may be obtained from indicator dilution studies.

Patients with small atrial septal defects have a normal life expectancy, but there is a signifi-

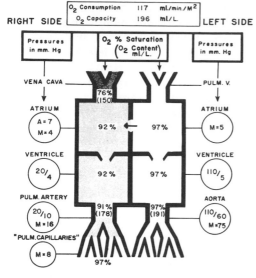

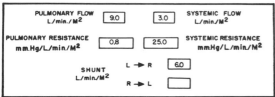

Fig. 11. Cardiac catheter data in a child with an atrial septal defect. Oxygenated blood is shunted from the left atrium to the right through the defect, causing an abnormal step-up in the oxygen content of blood between the superior vena cava and the right atrium. Compare with normal (Fig. 8). (From Nadas, *Pediatric cardiology,* 2nd ed. Philadelphia, W. B. Saunders Co., 1963.)

cant mortality among untreated patients with defects greater than 1 to 2 sq. cm. mostly from complications such as bacterial endocarditis, associated valvular disease or, ultimately, from right ventricular failure. The condition is readily amenable to surgical therapy. Mortality is low and the cure rate is high.

Ventricular septal defect. Ventricular septal defects usually occur in the membranous rather than in the muscular portion of the septum. Most are small and functionally unimportant. Defects of 0.5 to 2 sq. cm. permit significant left-to-right shunting. Large defects essentially convert the heart into a three-chambered organ.

The physiologic consequences of a ventricular septal defect are determined by its size and by the resistance to flow in pulmonary and systemic circuits. With small defects no significant shunting occurs because the hydraulic impedance across the defect is high. Nevertheless, the small amount of blood which is shunted attains

a high velocity and gives rise to the harsh pansystolic murmur typical of this disorder. In patients with larger defects the normal wide disparity between right and left ventricular pressure gives rise to a left-to-right shunt (Fig. 12). If the resistance of the pulmonary circuit is normal and the pulmonary vasculature is very compliant, there is no increase in pulmonary pressure. However, signs of left-to-right shunting are present: a systolic flow murmur, increased vascularity of lung fields, right ventricular hypertrophy, increased oxygen content of right ventricular blood, and delayed concentration-time curves for indicator substances.

Patients with ventricular septal defects frequently develop progressive obstructive pulmonary vascular disease with consequent progressive pulmonary hypertension. As pulmonary arterial pressure approaches aortic pressure, blood flow through the shunt decreases, and at this time roentgenograms of the lungs may ap-

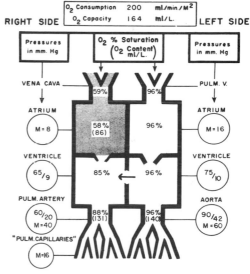

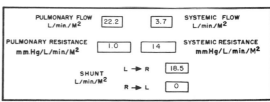

Fig. 12. Cardiac catheterization data from a patient with a large ventricular septal defect. The left to right shunt at the ventricular level causes a step-up in the oxygen content of blood between right atrium and ventricle. Pulmonary flow greatly exceeds systemic flow, and in this patient, there is pulmonary hypertension. (From Nadas, *Pediatric cardiology,* 2nd ed. Philadelphia, W. B. Saunders Co., 1963.)

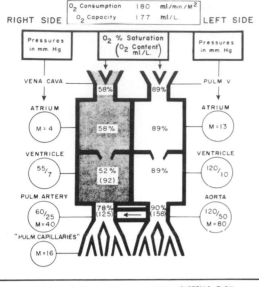

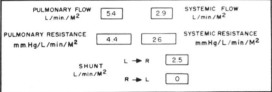

Fig. 13. Schematic diagram of the circulation and cardiac catheter findings in a patient with a patent ductus arteriosus. Blood is shunted from the aorta to the pulmonary artery; the oxygen content of blood in the pulmonary artery is thus higher than that in the right ventricle. This patient also has pulmonary hypertension. Pulse pressure in the aorta is wide and left atrial pressure is elevated. (From Nadas, *Pediatric cardiology,* 2nd ed. Philadelphia, W. B. Saunders Co., 1963.)

pear normal although the silhouette of the main pulmonary artery remains enlarged. Progressive increase in the right ventricular pressure is associated with electrocardiographic signs of hypertrophy of this chamber. The systolic murmur which is present during left-to-right shunting decreases in intensity, but there is a corresponding increase in the intensity of the pulmonic component of the second heart sound, a reflection of increased pressure in that circuit. Sometimes pulmonary vascular resistance exceeds that in the systemic circuit and shunt direction is reversed. The classic manifestations of right-to-left shunt then become apparent: peripheral arterial desaturation, cyanosis, polycythemia and clubbing of digits. Direction of flow through the shunt may be confirmed by angiocardiography, or inferred from concentration-time curves of injected tracer materials.

Surgical closure of uncomplicated ventricular septal defects is commonplace and involves little risk. When pulmonary hypertension is present, along with right-to-left shunting, surgical closure is hazardous because after the defect is closed, the right ventricle must pump the entire cardiac output through the greatly increased pulmonary arteriolar resistance with no assistance from the left ventricle.

Patent ductus arteriosus. During fetal life communication between the pulmonary trunk and aorta is maintained via the ductus arteriosus. Shortly after birth this structure undergoes functional closure, and during the ensuing weeks anatomic closure takes place, so that it becomes a solid connection, the ligamentum arteriosum. Failure of the ductus to close results in a shunt between the systemic and pulmonary circulations (Fig. 13). Flow through a patent ductus may be several liters per minute but seldom approaches that through a large septal defect, mostly because of the small diameter of the ductus, which gives it a significant hydraulic resistance.

In the absence of pulmonary hypertension, flow through a patent ductus is from aorta to pulmonary trunks, i.e., a left-to-right shunt. Because the site of shunting is distal to the pulmonary vessels, excess flow is pumped by the left atrium and ventricle with no additional load to the right ventricle. Since the aortic pressure is significantly higher than the pulmonary pressure throughout the cardiac cycle, blood flows through the shunt during both diastole and systole. This gives rise to a continuous cardiac murmur most intense during systole, called a "machinery murmur." Evidence of increased flow through the pulmonary vessels and enlargement of the left atrium may be detected radiographically. If the patent ductus is large, the diastolic run-off through the shunt may be great enough to depress the diastolic blood pressure, thus effectively widening the pulse pressure. Ligation of an uncomplicated patent ductus arteriosus involves little surgical risk and results in complete cure.

Some patients with patent ductus arteriosus ultimately develop progressive pulmonary hypertension. As a consequence, left-to-right shunting may be reduced or eventually reversed. In the latter instance, unsaturated blood from the pulmonary artery enters the aorta, but because of the anatomic site of the shunt the peripheral manifestations of arterial desaturation

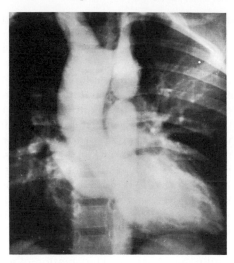

Fig. 14. Angiogram showing coarctation of the aorta. Radiopaque material was injected into the aorta and angiograms obtained during left heart opacification. The constricted segment of the descending aorta is clearly defined. (Courtesy of Dr. Melvin M. Figley.)

are more pronounced in the lower half of the body. The existence of patent ductus arteriosus with reversal of flow may be confirmed by comparing the oxygen content of samples of blood from the brachial and femoral arteries. Ligation of the ductus in such cases is usually fatal; apparently the right ventricle is incapable of sustaining circulation through the high resistance in the pulmonary circuit.

Coarctation of the aorta. This is an obstructive congenital malformation in which the lumen of the aorta is abruptly narrowed over a portion of its length (Fig. 14). In its most common form, the diameter of the aorta is reduced to a few millimeters at a point near the origin of the ligamentum arteriosum. Other less common forms exist in which the lumen is reduced immediately below the region of the ductus, which remains patent. Rarely, long segments of the aorta are completely obliterated.

The physiologic consequences of aortic coarctation are the result of flow obstruction. The cardiac output is usually normal, but greater driving pressure must be generated by the left ventricle to force blood through or around the constricted region. Blood pressure is therefore elevated in those vessels which originate proximal to the coarctation, while pressure in vessels below the lesion is significantly lowered and pulsations are diminished (Fig. 15). The disparity in blood pressure in the upper and lower

extremities and absence of palpable pulsation in the lower extremity are two of the distinguishing features of this malformation. Blood which passes through the coarctation reaches a high velocity, and the turbulence which is created typically gives rise to a systolic murmur. Immediately distal to the obstruction, the aorta is usually bulbously dilated. This post-stenotic dilatation is frequently apparent on chest roentgenograms. Collateral vessels usually develop to carry blood around the aortic coarctation. The major contributing vessels are the subclavians, but intercostal, internal mammary and epigastric arteries are also involved. All of these vessels are large and tortuous. The inferior margins of the ribs of patients with coarctation are frequently irregularly eroded, presumably by the tortuous pulsating intercostal arteries. This "notching of ribs" is readily detectable on routine thoracic roentgenograms.

Severe coarctation may lead to cardiac decompensation and death in infancy. In young persons with less severe coarctation, left ventricular hypertrophy may develop, but overt symptoms are usually lacking and the condition is often discovered incidentally during routine physical examination. Because of cerebral hypertension, young adults with this disease are prone to cerebral vascular accidents ("strokes"). Other causes of demise include development and rupture of aortic aneurysm, bacterial endocarditis or, eventually, left heart failure. For these reasons coarctation of the aorta, even when completely asymptomatic, should be remedied surgically. The operative risk is low.

Pulmonary stenosis; tetralogy of Fallot. Pulmonary stenosis may involve either the pulmonary valve itself or, less frequently, the subvalvular (infundibular) region. In the former instance,

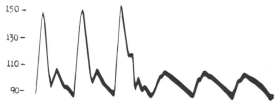

Fig. 15. Aortic blood pressure above and below the constricted region in a patient with coarctation of the aorta. This continuous recording was made as a cardiac catheter was withdrawn through the coarctation. There is a gradient of 40 mm. Hg across the narrowed zone. (Redrawn from catheterization data obtained by Dr. John Blackmon.)

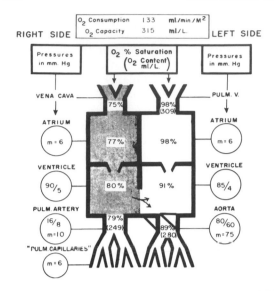

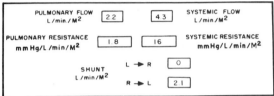

Fig. 16. Scheme of the circulation and cardiac catheterization data in a patient with the tetralogy of Fallot. There is a sharp pressure gradient across the pulmonary valve. Since pressure in the right ventricle is higher than in the left, flow through the ventricular septal defect is from right to left, and there is desaturation of blood in the left ventricle and systemic arteries. (From Nadas, *Pediatric cardiology,* 2nd ed. Philadelphia, W. B. Saunders Co., 1963.)

the valve cusps are fused and the orifice is but a tiny aperture. With infundibular stenosis, fibrous and muscular tissues restrict the size of the outflow tract. Either kind of stenosis causes right ventricular hypertension, but because of the pressure drop across the obstruction, the pulmonary vascular pressure is not elevated. Right ventricular hypertrophy and post-stenotic dilatation of the pulmonary artery ultimately occur. Isolated pulmonary stenosis does not produce cyanosis since the systemic blood is normally oxygenated and no shunting is involved.

Pulmonary stenosis is often associated with other congenital defects; infundibular pulmonary stenosis, which seldom occurs as an isolated anomaly, is often combined with a ventricular septal defect. This combination is the important part of the pathologic syndrome known as the tetralogy of Fallot. As originally described, this condition consisted of four abnormalities: pul-

monary stenosis, ventricular septal defect, an "overriding aorta" in which the aortic orifice lies over the interventricular septum, and right ventricular hypertrophy. Of these, the first two constitute the dynamic lesion. Typically, the septal defect is large and pulmonary stenosis is severe. Consequently, resistance to flow through the pulmonary circuit is very high, and during ventricular contraction unsaturated blood is shunted from right to left across the septal defect (Fig. 16). Only a fraction of the venous blood enters the pulmonary trunk. Signs of peripheral desaturation appear early but patients often survive into adult life. Surgical treatment involves creation of an artificial ductus arteriosus by anastomosis of the subclavian artery with the pulmonary artery, or by creation of a communication between the aorta and pulmonary

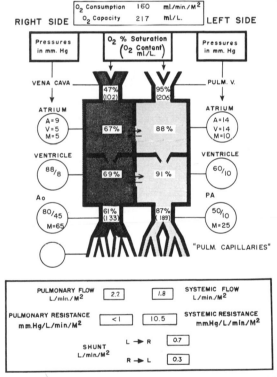

Fig. 17. Schematic diagram of the circulation and cardiac catheterization data in a patient with one type of transposition of the great vessels. Patients with this malformation must necessarily have an abnormal communication between right and left hearts; as a result, there is always a step-up in the oxygen content of blood distal to the vena cava. This patient has both atrial and ventricular septal defects. Note also the grossly distorted pressures. (From Nadas, *Pediatric cardiology,* 2nd ed. Philadelphia, W. B. Saunders Co., 1963.)

artery. These procedures are designed to increase pulmonary blood flow by supplementing it with systemic arterial blood.

Transposition of the great vessels. The pulmonary artery and aorta are formed by subdivision of the truncus arteriosus. The septum which divides the truncus arteriosus normally describes a spiral as it descends to meet the membranous portion of the ventricular septum. Failure of the truncal septum to undergo rotation results in transposition of these vessels so that the aorta originates from the right ventricle and the pulmonary artery from the left. When this occurs the heart is converted into two separate circulations with no intercommunication, a circumstance which is incompatible with survival. Patients with transposition of the great vessels therefore survive only if some abnormal communication exists between the atria, the ventricles, or the great vessels (Fig. 17). If there is only one such communication, blood must flow intermittently in either direction. Survival is thus more likely if the communication is large, and even more so if there are communications which increase the opportunity for mixing of pulmonary and aortic flows. Since the only opportunity for saturated blood to enter the systemic circulation is via an intermittent shunt, patients with transposition have severe desaturation of their arterial blood. Intense cyanosis from birth is thus a cardinal manifestation. Other manifestations of this disorder are related to the associated shunts. Most patients with this malformation die in infancy. Surgical correction is aimed at correcting the transposition, usually by transplantation of the venous inputs rather than the outflow vessels.

ACQUIRED VALVULAR DISEASE

Cardiac valves permit free flow of blood during one portion of the cardiac cycle and prevent retrograde flow during the balance of the cycle (Figs. 18, 19). The hydraulic resistance of a normal open cardiac valve is nearly zero, and the transvalvular pressure drop is scarcely perceptible. Closed cardiac valves easily tolerate pressure gradients of several hundred mm. Hg without permitting backflow. Valvular disease causes deformation, destruction and immobilization of valve structures. These lesions may result in impedance of free flow through normally open valves (stenosis) or in retrograde flow past

imperfectly closed valves (insufficiency). Disease of the aortic, mitral and tricuspid valves is usually acquired rather than congenital.

Aortic Valvular Stenosis.[9, 27] Aortic valvular stenosis is usually due to rheumatic fever, or less commonly it may be congenital. The defect begins with formation of adhesions between the valve cusps. The process originates near the commissures and extends to involve the free edges of the cusps, gradually reducing the orifice. Later the valve becomes progressively immobilized by scarring and calcification. Significant stenosis occurs when the cross-sectional area of the orifice is reduced to about 1 square centimeter. Severely scarred aortic valves usually leak during diastole; however, backflow is limited by the small size of the orifice and by the reduced pressure in the aorta.

The serious consequences of aortic stenosis are due to obstruction. A very small pressure gradient is adequate to move fluid along a cylinder; across a stenosed valve the same volume flow can be maintained only if the driving pressure increases. Increase in driving pressure is a poor adjustment because it exerts only a first power effect on flow, whereas resistance increases as the fourth power of the luminal reduction. The long-term effect of chronic aortic stenosis is left ventricular hypertrophy. This compensatory mechanism enables the ventricle to develop greater tension and to sustain the cardiac output by developing greater pressure. Most of the energy liberated by the ventricle is dissipated against the obstruction to blood flow. Thus, although the work performed by the ventricle is abnormally great, the useful work is quite small and ventricular efficiency is low. In severe aortic stenosis, coronary flow is compromised. Coronary blood flow depends upon the balance between the coronary perfusion pressure and the coronary vascular resistance. With aortic stenosis the pressure at the coronary ostia is reduced and intraventricular tension is elevated. Coronary flow is further curtailed because of prolongation of isovolumic contraction and ejection. Also, in ventricular hypertrophy the size of muscle fibers increases without an increase in the number of nutrient capillaries (see Fig. 2, Chap. 36). Thus, the average diffusion distance is greatly increased. All of these factors lead to myocardial ischemia.

The auscultatory signs of this disease precede the development of symptoms. A standard finding in aortic stenosis is a harsh systolic murmur,

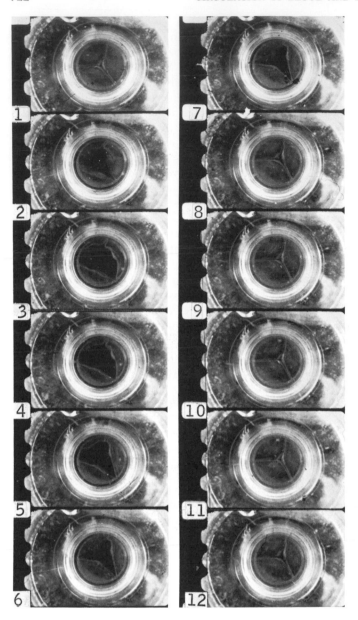

Fig. 18. Motion of normal human aortic valve leaflets during one cardiac cycle. The sequence is numbered serially. The view is from the aortic side of the valve and was photographed during studies with a pulse duplicator. Note especially that the aortic valve does not open fully, its cusp margins forming a triangular orifice. (From Davila, Chap. 1 in *Prosthetic valves for cardiac surgery,* Merendino, ed. Springfield, Ill., Charles C Thomas, 1961.)

loudest over the aortic valve area and transmitted up into the neck vessels. The murmur is due to turbulence created by the high-velocity jet of blood streaming through the narrowed valve orifice. The vibrations are often transmitted to the chest wall with such intensity that they may be felt manually (palpable thrill). Recorded phonocardiographically, the murmur of aortic stenosis typically has a diamond-shaped envelope because the vibrations are maximum during midsystole, when the flow is highest. Because the stiffened valve cusps do not close completely in diastole, the aortic component of the second heart sound is diminished. If the valve

cusps are fixed, regurgitation may occur during diastole.

The aortic pressure pulse is characteristically altered in aortic stenosis. The obstruction damps the pulse wave and delays its rise time. Because a longer time is required to force blood past the obstruction, the ejection period is prolonged. Experienced physicians can readily recognize these changes by palpating the radial artery, but they are better demonstrated by direct recording with a high frequency manometer and oscillograph. The hemodynamic significance of the lesion may be evaluated by measuring the gradient of pressure across the valve by means

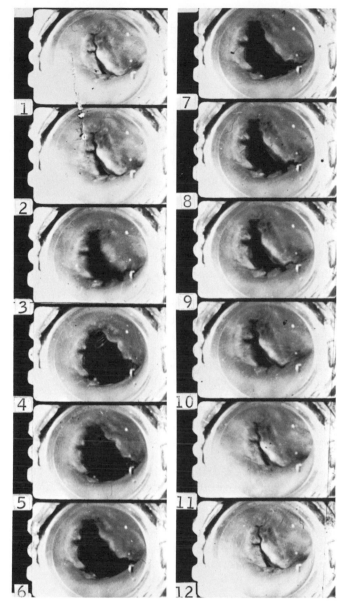

Fig. 19. Motion of normal human mitral valve during one cardiac cycle. The frames are numbered serially. This sequence was photographed from the atrial side of the valve as it was activated by a pulse duplicator. (From Davila, Chap. 1 in *Prosthetic valves for cardiac surgery,* Merendino, ed. Springfield, Ill., Charles C Thomas, 1961.)

of a cardiac catheter (Fig. 20). Other techniques for evaluating aortic stenosis include cineangiography, radiography and electrocardiography.

Patients with aortic stenosis are subject to episodes of syncope, especially during sudden exertion. Syncope results when a great proportion of the cardiac output is diverted into dilated skeletal muscle beds and the left ventricle fails to maintain aortic pressure adequate for cerebral perfusion. Chest pain during exertion is common; this is due to myocardial ischemia, caused by the disparity between cardiac work and available coronary flow (Chap. 36). For the same reason, myocardial infarction may

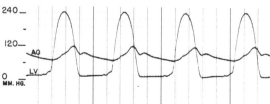

Fig. 20. Simultaneous recordings of aortic and left ventricular blood pressure in a case of aortic stenosis. There is a pressure gradient of over 120 mm. Hg across the valve; pressure rises slowly in the aorta and reaches its peak near end systole. Compare this tracing with normal (Fig. 5*b*, Chap. 33). (From catheterization data obtained by Dr. John Blackmon.)

occur even in the absence of coronary artery disease. Both chest pain and syncopal episodes are ominous signs which may precede sudden death. Aortic stenosis is treated by repair of the damaged valve or by replacement with a prosthetic valve.

Aortic Insufficiency.[9, 26] The flow of blood through normal aortic valves is unidirectional, from ventricle to aorta. Disease, e.g., rheumatic fever, may so deform the valve that it fails to form an effective seal or may dilate the aortic valve ring so that otherwise normal cusps are unable to join in closure. In either instance retrograde flow from the aorta back into the ventricle occurs. The maximum reflux occurs during early diastole when aortic pressure is highest and ventricular pressure is nearly zero. Because of regurgitation, aortic pressure drops quickly and is abnormally low at the end of diastole. This in turn greatly reduces resistance to the succeeding systolic ejection so that the period of isovolumic contraction is shortened and ventricular emptying is very rapid. Since the output includes both blood regurgitated into the ventricle and that added from the atrium during diastole, the stroke volume is greatly increased. Consequently, the aortic pressure rises steeply to high levels only to decline to abnormally low levels during diastole, when regurgitation recurs (Fig. 21). The pulse pressure is therefore widened and the radial pulse takes on the quality of a shock wave. The abnormal quality of the pulse is accentuated if the patient's hand is held above the head, for then the arteries may collapse during diastole. If a stethoscope is placed over a peripheral artery and gentle pressure is gradually applied, two distinct murmurs may be heard. This is Durozier's sign, which

was once attributed to movement of blood to and fro through the underlying vessel. More likely, the first portion of the murmur is due to the initial steep wave front, which strikes the indented vessel and forces a quantity of blood to pass under the stethoscope at a high velocity. At the same time, proximal to the indented segment, pressure rises and the wall dilates. With collapse of the initial wave front the proximal distended segment recoils and a second wave front with corresponding flow and murmur passes through. A double murmur is not heard unless a dicrotic notch is present in the pressure pulse. If additional pressure is applied with the stethoscope until the underlying vessel barely collapses, a single sound is heard (the pistol shot sound of Traube). This procedure and the resulting sound are analogous to the Phase I Korotkoff sound.

During diastole when arterial blood pressure and flow drop markedly, capillary flow halts so that peripheral tissues appear blanched. The steep pulse waves during systole are transmitted to the capillaries, where sudden filling is visible as flushing. Such pulsation of the capillary flow, called Quincke's pulse, is best observed in the nail beds, where it is accentuated by gentle pressure.

Reflux of blood into the ventricle during diastole causes a high-frequency murmur of low intensity which is usually heard along the left sternal border. Since most reflux occurs in early diastole, this murmur begins immediately with the second heart sound and decreases in intensity along with the falling aortic pressure (decrescendo murmur). In some patients a late diastolic murmur of lower frequency may also be heard near the apex. This murmur (the Austin Flint murmur) is attributed to the regurgitant jet of blood which rushes in through the insufficient aortic valve and strikes the anterior mitral valve leaflet, displacing it into the incoming stream of blood from the atrium.

Slowly developing aortic insufficiency may be asymptomatic for a long time. It has been estimated that reflux of as much as 25 per cent of the stroke volume may take place without symptoms. With severe aortic insufficiency 50 per cent of the stroke volume may flow back into the ventricle. Peak backward flow rates may approach 100 ml. per second. In response to chronically increased stroke volumes, dilation of the left ventricle occurs. This may represent a compensatory response to the volume load, since

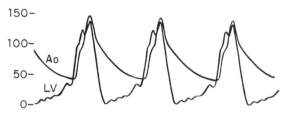

Fig. 21. Aortic and left ventricular pressures in a patient with aortic insufficiency. The aortic pressure pulse rises steeply and falls abruptly to an abnormally low level during diastole. Pulse pressure is widened. Note that left ventricular end diastolic pressure is elevated. (Reproduced from recordings provided by Dr. John Blackmon.)

in a dilated ventricle less shortening is required to expel a unit of volume. However, because of the increased ventricular diameter greater tension must be developed in the walls. This ultimately leads to ventricular hypertrophy. In patients with slowly developing aortic insufficiency these compensatory changes enable the ventricles to maintain adequate forward flow, but rapidly developing insufficiency, such as occurs with bacterial endocarditis or trauma, results in relentless progression of left ventricular failure. Replacement of the valve with a prosthesis offers promise of cure.

Mitral Stenosis.[8] Mitral valvular stenosis nearly always results from rheumatic heart disease. In addition to thickening, scarring and immobilization of the valve leaflets, the rheumatic process may also shorten and deform the chordae tendinae. The end result is a narrowing of the channel between the left atrium and ventricle. The normal mitral orifice is so large that even with large flow rates there is no measurable gradient of pressure between left atrium and left ventricle during diastole. When the orifice is reduced to about 1.5 sq. cm., ventricular filling is impeded and cardiac output is limited. The peak left atrial pressure rises and the left atrium enlarges. The elevated atrial pressure causes increased pulmonary capillary pressure, which, if it exceeds oncotic pressure, causes transudation of fluid into the alveoli. This reduces vital capacity and maximum breathing capacity and the patient is short of breath. During stress or physical exertion acute pulmonary edema may develop. With prolonged pulmonary congestion and elevated capillary pressure, the media of pulmonary vessels thickens and pulmonary vascular resistance increases. Right ventricular hypertrophy may in turn be severe enough to cause pulmonary valvular incompetence and tricuspid insufficiency. Eventually right ventricular failure ensues, with development of elevated venous pressure, hepatomegaly, ascites and edema. Very commonly patients alternate between the stage of pulmonary congestion and that of right ventricular failure.

Mitral stenosis produces distinctive changes in heart sounds. Normally ventricular filling begins after isometric relaxation and proceeds without auscultatory signs. In mitral stenosis left ventricular filling is prolonged and its onset is signaled by a short snapping sound about 80 milliseconds after the second heart sound. The sound, called the "opening snap," is probably caused by vibrations as the stiffened mitral leaflets are retracted. Turbulence created as blood flows through the restricted irregular mitral orifice causes a characteristic low-frequency diastolic murmur. Ventricular filling is rapid in early diastole and gradually wanes, but may be slightly accentuated by atrial contraction. Accordingly, the murmur is typically decrescendo with accentuation in late systole. When pulmonary hypertension is present, the second heart sound is commonly split and the pulmonary component is accentuated.

Confirmation of mitral valve disease may be obtained by cardiac catheterization. A special procedure involves recording the "pulmonary wedge pressure."[11, 15] A catheter is passed through the right heart into a small branch of the pulmonary artery and is advanced until its tip becomes wedged in a small radicle (Fig. 22). A manometer connected to the catheter thus measures pressure across the low-resistance pulmonary capillaries and the pulmonary veins to the left atrium. The wedge pressure approximately measures mean pressure in the left atrium; the recorded wave form is delayed left atrial pressure contour damped by transmission across the pulmonary capillaries. More precise information may be obtained by catheterization of the left heart.[2]

Hemoptysis in mitral stenosis is related to the unique anatomy of the bronchial circulation. The bronchial arteries arise from the systemic circulation and their capillaries nourish the bronchial walls, but their venous drainage is into pulmonary veins. With elevated left atrial and pulmonary venous pressure, these capillaries become sufficiently engorged and congested to rupture into the bronchial lumen.

Enlargement of the left atrium, prominence

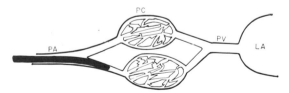

Fig. 22. Schematic representation of the pulmonary wedge pressure (*PA*, pulmonary artery; *PC*, pulmonary capillary; *PV*, pulmonary vein; *LA*, left atrium). A cardiac catheter passed through the right heart is wedged in a terminal pulmonary artery. The recorded pressure closely approximates the pulmonary capillary pressure and follows changes in the left atrial pressure, but is not influenced by changes in pulmonary artery pressure.

 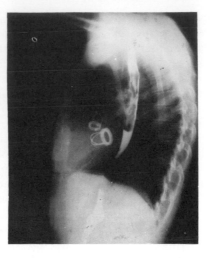

Fig. 23. *Left,* A prosthetic heart valve used for replacement of diseased aortic and mitral valves. The device is inserted into the valve ring; movement of the caged ball substitutes for action of valve cusps. *Right,* Lateral chest x-ray of a patient in whom both aortic and mitral valves have been replaced with prosthetic devices such as are shown on the left. (Courtesy of Dr. Albert Starr.)

of the pulmonary trunks and right ventricular hypertrophy may be detected by radiographic studies. Linear densities in the lung fields, the B lines of Kerley, interpreted as signs of pulmonary venous obstruction, may represent dilated lymphatic vessels. Electrocardiographic signs of mitral stenosis include broad, notched P waves, which may be biphasic (P mitrale). These changes are thought to be related to left atrial enlargement. Other ECG findings include signs of right ventricular hypertrophy or of atrial fibrillation, which is common in mitral stenosis.

Surgical treatment of mitral stenosis is directed at the valvular obstruction. Plastic procedures afford some benefit and are carried out with minimal mortality. Newer methods seek to replace diseased valves with prosthetic valves (Fig. 23). None of these has yet approached the efficiency and durability of normal heart valves, but remarkable advances have been made. Relief of valve obstruction is not necessarily followed by immediate reduction in pulmonary artery pressure. In time the pressure may gradually regress, but it seldom returns to normal, probably because of irreversible structural changes in the pulmonary vessels.

Mitral Insufficiency.[4, 24] Mitral insufficiency refers to imperfect closure of the mitral valve during ventricular systole. It is usually caused by rheumatic heart disease, which may stiffen and distort the valve leaflets or may dilate the valve ring. In mitral insufficiency there are two pathways out of the left ventricle during systole: forward flow into the aorta and backward flow across the mitral valve into the left atrium. Since aortic pressure is much higher than atrial pressure, a small valvular defect can result in

large reflux into the atrium. The forward flow of blood into the atrium during diastole combined with that regurgitated during systole provides a greatly increased atrial stroke volume. So long as the atrial and ventricular diastolic filling pressures are normal, the cardiac output remains adequate and symptoms do not develop. With progressive valvular disease, to and fro movement of blood increases sharply while effective left ventricular stroke output declines. Because of the large volume load, the left ventricle may ultimately approach the limit of its reserve; left ventricular end diastolic pressure is elevated and both atrium and ventricle dilate and hypertrophy. In long-standing disease elevation of left atrial pressure may be transmitted to the pulmonary circulation with ultimate development of obstructive pulmonary vascular diseases, right ventricular hypertension and eventual right heart failure.

With mitral insufficiency the pathway from left ventricle to left atrium remains open at the onset of systole (Fig. 24). Since the aortic valve does not open until after the isovolumic contraction, the characteristic murmur of mitral regurgitation begins before ejection and usually lasts throughout systole (pansystolic murmur). Because of rigidity of the valve leaflets, the intensity of the first heart sound may be diminished or, in some instances, may be replaced by the murmur.

Left atrial pressure recorded by left heart catheterization is elevated throughout systole, reaching a peak in late ejection. At this same time the contour of the ventricular pressure curve is deformed because of maximal regurgitant flow (Fig. 25). Regurgitation may be visualized by cineangiographic techniques, and estimates of the amount may be calculated from dye dilution data.

In mild mitral insufficiency the cardiac output may be normal and the disease may exist for many years without symptoms. When the effective forward stroke volume becomes limited, patients develop shortness of breath on

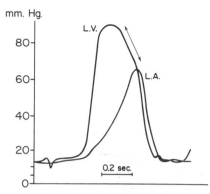

Fig. 25. Left atrial and left ventricular blood pressures in a human patient with mitral valvular insufficiency. (After Ross, Braunwald and Morrow, *Amer. J. Cardiol.,* 1958, 2:11–23.)

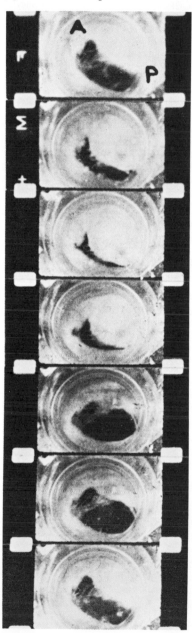

Fig. 24. Motion picture frames of an incompetent mitral valve during one cardiac cycle. Frames 1, 2 and 3 (from top) represent ventricular systole. The incompetent orifice was largest during early systole. (From Davila, *Amer. J. Cardiol.,* 1958, 2:135–158.)

exertion; cardiac decompensation often supervenes rapidly. Treatment is aimed at repair or replacement of the mitral valve.

Combined Valvular Disease.   Most patients with rheumatic mitral valve disease suffer from both stenosis and insufficiency. Usually, however, one or the other dominates. This is apparent from consideration of ventricular filling: Severe mitral insufficiency requires excess ventricular filling, whereas severe mitral stenosis greatly limits ventricular filling. It is important to define the dominant defect since this influences treatment.[19]

Tricuspid Stenosis.   Stenosis of the tricuspid valve occasionally occurs as an isolated entity but usually it is overshadowed by other accompanying valvular lesions. Consequently, tricuspid stenosis is frequently overlooked and its contribution to the total clinical syndrome may not be apparent until after the other valvular defects are corrected. The basic pathologic process is again rheumatic fever, which by scarring the valve obstructs flow between right atrium and right ventricle. Right atrial pressure is greatly elevated, and the pressure is transmitted back into the systemic veins, which subsequently become distended. Ascites and edema occur, and the right atrium is greatly enlarged. Typically there is a diastolic murmur which may be accentuated by inspiration. Venous pulse records show an accentuated A wave ("giant A wave"), which probably reflects the vigorous contraction of the hypertrophied right atrium, but the finding is not distinctive. A history of long-standing ascites and edema without shortness of breath or other pulmonary signs and symptoms suggests tricuspid stenosis. Proof lies in right heart catheterization and demonstration of a gradient of pressure across the valve during diastole.[20]

Tricuspid Insufficiency.   Tricuspid regurgitation probably develops in most patients with progressive cardiac decompensation usually because dilation of the right ventricle spreads the valve ring, not because of disease of the leaflets themselves. The cardinal features are related to the effect of right ventricular systole on the relatively unprotected right atrium and venous system: The right atrium is enlarged, and systolic pulsation may be recorded from the neck veins or felt over the liver.

REFERENCES

1. BARCLAY, A. E., BARCROFT, J., BARRON, D. H. and FRANKLIN, K. J. *Brit. J. Radiol.,* 1939, *12*NS: 505–517.
2. BRAUNWALD, E., MOSCOVITZ, H. L., AMRAM, S. S., LASSER, R. P., SAPIN, S. O., HIMMELSTEIN, O., RAVITCH, M. M. and GORDON, A. J. *Circulation,* 1955, *12*:69–81.
3. CIVIN, W. H. and EDWARDS, J. E. *Arch. Path.,* 1951, *51:* 192–200.
4. DAVILA, J. C. *Amer. J. Cardiol.,* 1958, *2:*135–158.
5. DAWES, G. S., MOTT, J. C., WIDDICOMBE, J. G. and WYATT, D. G. *J. Physiol.,* 1953, *121*:141–162.
6. EDWARDS, J. E. *Circulation,* 1957, *15*:164–196.
7. EVERETT, N. B. and JOHNSON, R. J. *Amer. J. Physiol.,* 1950, *162*:147–152.
8. GORLIN, R., HAYNES, F. W., GOODALE, W. T., SAWYER, C. G., DOW, J. W. and DEXTER, L. *Amer. Heart J.,* 1951, *41:*30–45.
9. GORLIN, R., MCMILLAN, I. K. R., MEDD, W. E.,

10. HAMILTON, W. J., BOYD, J. D. and MOSSMAN, H. W. Chap. 9 in *Human embryology,* 3rd ed. Baltimore, Williams & Wilkins Co., 1962.
11. HELLEMS, H. K., HAYNES, F. W. and DEXTER, L. *J. appl. Physiol.,* 1949, *2*:24–29.
12. KANJUH, V. I. and EDWARDS, J. E. *Pediat. Clin. N. Amer.,* 1964, *11*:55–185.
13. KJELLBERG, S. R. *Diagnosis of congenital heart disease,* 2nd ed. Chicago, Year Book Medical Publishers, 1959.
14. KRAMER, T. *Amer. J. Anat.,* 1942, *71.*343–370.
15. LAGERLOF, H. and WERKO, L. *Scand. J. clin. lab. Invest.,* 1949, *1:*147–161.
16. LIND, J. and WEGELIUS, C. *Cold Spr. Harb. Symp. quant. Biol.,* 1954, *19:*109–125.
17. LURIE, P. R. *Amer. J. Med.,* 1953, *15:*297–306.
18. MARSHALL, H. W., HELMHOLZ, H. F., JR. and WOOD, E. H. Chap. 14 in *Handbook of physiology. Section 2; Circulation,* vol. I, W. F. HAMILTON, ed., Washington D.C., American Physiological Society, 1962.
19. MARSHALL, H. W., WOODWARD, E., JR. and WOOD, E. H. *Amer. J. Cardiol.,* 1958, *2:*24–60.
20. MCCORD, M. C., SWAN, H. and BLOUNT, S. G., JR. *Amer. Heart J.,* 1954, *48:*405–415.
21. NADAS, A. S. *Pediatric cardiology.* Philadelphia, W. B. Saunders Co., 1963.
22. PATTEN, B. M. *Human embryology,* 2nd ed. New York, Blakiston, 1953.
23. REYNOLDS, S. R. M. Chap. 2 in *Cardiology,* A. A. LUISADA, ed. New York, McGraw-Hill Book Co., 1959.
24. ROSS, J., BRAUNWALD, E. and MORROW, A. G. *Amer. J. Cardiol.,* 1958, *2:*11–23.
25. SODI PALLARES, D. *New bases of electrocardiography,* R. M. CALDER, Tr. St. Louis, Mosby, 1956.
26. WIGGERS, C. J. *Circulatory dynamics.* New York, Grune & Stratton, 1952.
27. WOOD, P. *Amer. J. Cardiol.,* 1958, *1:*552–571.
28. ZIMMERMAN, H. A. *Intravascular catheterization.* Springfield, Ill., Charles C Thomas, 1959.

MATTHEWS, M. B. and DALY, R., *Amer. J. Med.,* 1955, *18:*855–870.

CHAPTER 38

Congestive Heart Failure

By ROBERT L. VAN CITTERS

DEFINITION AND COURSE

ETIOLOGY

RENAL FACTORS

HEMODYNAMIC ALTERATIONS

MANIFESTATIONS OF HEART FAILURE
    Right heart failure
    Left heart failure

DEFINITION AND COURSE

THE natural history of most cardiac diseases is gradual progression toward a state in which the heart is unable to maintain an output adequate for body requirements. When this occurs the heart is said to be failing. When manifestations include hypervolemia and elevated pressure in the venous beds of either right or left heart the patient is said to be in congestive heart failure. This term, widely used by physicians to designate a common, easily recognized clinical syndrome, is often difficult to define on the basis of its hemodynamic abnormalities.

The basic defect in congestive heart failure is incompetence of cardiac muscle fibers; as a result, the heart is unable to pump enough blood to meet metabolic demands. Whenever cardiac output is less than the requirements symptoms of cardiac failure appear. These usually occur initially during muscular exercise since exertion places greatest demands on the circulation, but with progressive deterioration of the cardiac reserve (Chap. 33) symptoms occur with less and less activity and eventually may occur even at rest. At this stage the cardiac output is barely adequate to sustain basal metabolic requirements. Blood flow to all tissues is chronically reduced, circulation time is prolonged, and the extraction of oxygen is more nearly complete so that the arteriovenous oxygen difference is widened. As a result, the function of organs other than the heart is affected. In fact, clinical evidence of disturbed renal function usually overshadows the cardiac findings.

ETIOLOGY

Cardiac failure results from a variety of diseases which impose a chronic overload on heart muscle or act to weaken heart muscle. Common causes of heart failure from overloading include hypertension, acquired valvular disease and congenital cardiac malformations. Diseases which cause sustained elevation in cardiac output, e.g., thyrotoxicosis, may also result in congestive heart failure through overloading. Common diseases which weaken cardiac muscle include rheumatic fever, atherosclerosis of coronary vessels and myocardial infarction; less commonly, heart action may be weakened by drugs or toxins, or the myocardium may be infiltrated by other noncardiac diseases.

The metabolic pathways available to failing hearts are identical to those available to normal hearts (see Fig. 12, Chap. 36). In failing dog and human hearts the myocardial uptake of substrates is normal, and there is no apparent alteration in oxidative metabolism. The defect in congestive heart failure thus lies in utilization of energy.[6] Failing hearts require more energy to accomplish a given work load than normal hearts; hence, their efficiency is lower. For example, the hearts of a group of patients in failure were all less than 15 per cent efficient, while those of a control group were all more than 25 per cent efficient. Further, the cardiac efficiency of the control group increased during exercise while that of the failure group did not.[9]

Olson and Piatnek found that myosin from normal dog hearts had a molecular weight of 225,000 whereas that from dogs in congestive heart failure exceeded 750,000. Actomyosin formed from this abnormal myosin aggregate has subnormal contractile properties. It has therefore been suggested that the defect in congestive heart failure lies in the contractile mechanism.[12]

RENAL FACTORS

Disturbances in renal function occur very early in the course of congestive heart failure, often well before outward cardiac manifestations. The basic renal defect is failure to excrete sodium; water retention occurs secondary to sodium retention (Chap. 45). Patients with cardiac failure thus develop a positive balance of both sodium and water.

Sodium retention occurs initially as the result of increased tubular reabsorption (Chap. 44). This has been shown in experiments with dogs given unilateral infusions of hypertonic saline via the renal artery; although glomerular filtration was normal, sodium excretion did not rise in dogs with chronic congestive heart failure as it did in healthy animals. However, sodium excretion was then greatly increased by administration of a diuretic drug which depressed tubular reabsorption.[1] Excessive tubular reabsorption of sodium in congestive heart failure is due at least in part to aldosterone (Chaps. 44 and 45). Both dogs and man in congestive heart failure have elevated blood levels of this hormone. Unilateral renal artery infusion of aldosterone results in sodium retention; this salt-retaining effect is facilitated by elevated venous pressure.[7]

Sodium retention is also due to reduced renal sodium secretion. This is primarily related to diminished renal blood flow and correspondingly smaller renal plasma flow and glomerular filtration rate (Chap. 44). Since the arterial blood pressure is usually normal, reduced renal flow is evidence of renal vasoconstriction. Unilateral renal infusion of Dibenzyline, an adrenergic blocking agent (Chap. 31), increases both renal blood flow and sodium excretion in dogs with congestive heart failure, but has no such effect in normal animals. Increased sympathetic activity indicated by this observation occurs early in the disease and increases with its progression.[2]

Because of sodium and water retention, circulating blood volume and interstitial fluid volume are both increased. Plasma volume is usually increased 10 to 20 per cent and the red cell mass may also be increased. The expanded blood volume is distributed to the most easily distended portion of the circulation, the veins (Chap. 32). Increased venous volume and peripheral vasoconstriction, which commonly occurs and may include the veins, are responsible for elevated venous pressure in both systemic and pulmonary circuits. The combination of increased blood volume and increased venous pressure is ultimately responsible for most of the clinical manifestations of congestive heart failure.

HEMODYNAMIC ALTERATIONS

Hemodynamic findings in patients with congestive heart failure are variable and none is diagnostic. Typically there is a tachycardia at rest, and often a gallop rhythm may be heard—three audible heart sounds with each cardiac cycle, following each other in rapid succession so that they resemble the sound of a galloping horse. The extra sound may be either an exaggerated third heart sound which immediately follows the second, or intensification of the fourth (atrial) heart sound just preceding the first; the prognosis may be bad in either case. Systolic murmurs heard over the heart may be due to valve ring dilatation related to general cardiac enlargement.

The failing heart is usually enlarged; inability to empty completely during systole and elevated end-diastolic filling pressure may both contribute to cardiac dilatation, while sustained cardiac loads usually cause some degree of hypertrophy. Heart size per se is also a factor in the altered hemodynamics of failure; large hearts require relatively less shortening to eject a given volume of blood, but require a greater wall tension to generate a given pressure (Chap. 33).

Further, since the oxygen cost of developing wall tension is high, the efficiency of large hearts is decreased.

Both systemic venous pressure and pulmonary capillary pressure are usually elevated, while systemic arterial blood pressure is usually normal. Left ventricular end-diastolic pressure is nearly always elevated. Although this finding is usually regarded as especially significant, it is not pathognomonic of congestive failure since similar elevations may occur in hypertrophied nonfailing hearts or in some noncardiac diseases.[3] Further, end-diastolic pressures are not always elevated in all patients in heart failure. Cardiac output, measured by the Fick method, is usually normal or low at rest. When patients with advanced failure exercise, ventricular end-diastolic pressure increases but cardiac output does not.[8, 11] Disparity between the outputs of the two ventricles during failure has often been postulated[4] but never recorded.

MANIFESTATIONS OF HEART FAILURE

Right Heart Failure. The right ventricle is an efficient volume pump capable of handling large cardiac outputs (as, for example, those of congenital cardiac shunts) for many years without evidence of failure. However, the right ventricle cannot bear up under sustained pressure load. Right ventricular failure most frequently develops after the left heart has failed; other common causes of right ventricular failure are disorders associated with pulmonary vascular hypertension, e.g., congenital cardiac disorders, mitral stenosis and primary pulmonary diseases.

The most obvious manifestations of right heart failure are those of increased systemic venous pressure. Venous pressure normally averages 8 to 16 cm. H_2O; in congestive heart failure it is usually well in excess of 16 cm. H_2O. Normal venous pressure is inadequate to distend veins located more than a few centimeters above heart level; distension of the jugular vein is often an early indication of the increased venous pressures which occur with expanding blood volume and may be obvious well before other manifestations of congestive failure occur.

Enlargement of the venous reservoirs, principally the liver and spleen, characteristically occurs in right heart failure. As a result, the liver is swollen and tender because of engorgement of the hepatic sinusoids with blood, and jaundice due to obstruction of bile ducts frequently occurs. Long-term hepatic congestion results in connective tissue proliferation and development of cirrhotic changes ("cardiac cirrhosis"). Liver function tests are abnormal during both the early period of hepatic congestion and the later period of scarring.

In right heart failure there is an increase in hydrostatic pressure at the venous end of the systemic capillaries. When capillary filtration pressure exceeds oncotic pressure, transudation of fluid occurs. This accumulation of interstitial fluid—edema—tends to collect in dependent areas, such as the extremities of ambulatory individuals or the sacral region of bed-ridden cardiac patients.

Left Heart Failure.[5, 10] Failure of the left ventricle most commonly follows hypertensive cardiovascular disease, aortic valve disease or inadequate nutrition of the myocardium due to coronary artery disease. The symptoms of left heart failure are those of pulmonary engorgement. The blood volume of the pulmonary circuit is greatly expanded and pulmonary venous pressure is elevated well above the normal value of about 8 mm. Hg. Elevation of left ventricular end-diastolic pressure, which commonly occurs in congestive failure, is transmitted to the pulmonary capillaries. When hydrostatic pressure in the pulmonary capillaries exceeds oncotic pressure, transudation into the alveoli occurs. This is the mechanism of pulmonary edema. It has been postulated that the volume of blood in the pulmonary circuit may be further augmented by sustained imbalance between the output of right and left ventricles, i.e., the failing left ventricle pumps less than the right, and the difference accumulates in the pulmonary bed. No means of measurement exists to test this hypothesis. Undefined central nervous system factors may contribute to pulmonary congestion: frank pulmonary edema has been produced by isolated hypothalamic lesions (Chap. 11), embolization of cerebral vessels, and cisternal injection of certain materials.

One of the earliest symptoms of left heart failure is "shortness of breath," or dyspnea. Dyspnea is related to pulmonary congestion, but the mechanism is not clear, since pO_2, pCO_2 and pH of the blood are usually normal. Some patients are unable to lie down without becoming acutely short of breath, and others may be awakened from sound sleep by a sudden onset of dyspnea. Both of these conditions result from redistribution of blood into the pulmonary circuit which occurs when the subject assumes a supine position. Such patients may be relatively comfortable only in a sitting posture. Occasionally pulmonary congestion is accompanied by bronchiolar spasm; this combination of events is termed "cardiac asthma." Patients with long-standing pulmonary congestion usually develop chronic vascular and parenchymal fibrosis of the lungs. This ultimately leads to pulmonary hypertension and right heart failure.

Fluid tends to collect in the body cavities of patients with combined right and left heart failure. Surprisingly, the amount does not correlate with the severity of the peripheral edema. The fluid which collects in the abdominal cavity (*ascites*) or thorax (*hydrothorax*) usually contains about 5 per cent plasma protein, as contrasted to about 0.5 per cent in edema fluid.

The efficacy of treatment of congestive heart failure greatly exceeds knowledge of its pathologic physiology. In chronic congestive heart failure, therapeutic measures include reducing the work load of the heart by limiting exertion, improving cardiac function by administering cardiac glycosides, reducing the blood volume by restricting sodium intake, and by using drugs such as diuretics. Acute pulmonary edema due to left heart failure is treated with oxygen, morphine and short-acting cardiac glycosides. An additional commonly used measure is that of applying venous occlusion tourniquets to the extremities; the rationale is to trap a portion of the expanded blood volume in peripheral veins, thus relieving pulmonary congestion.

REFERENCES

1. BARGER, A. C. *Circulation,* 1960, *21:*124–128.
2. BARGER, A. C., MULDOWNEY, F. P. and LIEBOWITZ, M. R. *Circulation,* 1959, *20:*273–285.
3. BRAUNWALD, E. and ROSS, J. *Amer. J. Med.,* 1963, *34:*147–150.
4. BURCH, G. E. and RAY, C. T. *Amer. Heart J.,* 1951, *41:*918–946.
5. CECIL, R. L. and LOEB, R. F., eds. *A textbook of medicine.* 11th ed. Philadelphia, W. B. Saunders Co., 1963.
6. DANFORTH, W. H., BALLARD, F. B., KAKO, K., CHOUDHURY, J. D. and BING, R. J. *Circulation,* 1960, *21:*112–123.
7. DAVIS, J. O. *Amer. J. Med.,* 1960, *29:*486–507.
8. EICHNA, L. W. *Circulation,* 1960, *22:*864–886.
9. GORLIN, R. *J. Amer. med. Ass.,* 1962, *179:*441–449.
10. HARRISON, T. R., ed. *Principles of internal medicine.* 4th ed. New York, McGraw-Hill Book Co., 1962.
11. KATZ, L. N., FEINBERG, H. and SHAFFER, A. B. *Circulation,* 1960, *21:*95–111.
12. OLSON, R. E. *J. chron. Dis.,* 1959, *9:*442–464.

SECTION VIII

RESPIRATION

CHAPTER 39

Anatomy and Physics of Respiration

By J. HILDEBRANDT and A. C. YOUNG

WITH the exception of certain microorganisms and a few parasites, plants and animals generally require free access to molecular oxygen to maintain their metabolic processes. In lower animals this oxygen supply is conveyed to metabolizing tissues in various ways: (i) direct diffusion (protozoa, bacteria), (ii) exchange through the skin (eels and hibernating frogs), (iii) gills (most larger aquatic animals), and (iv) air tubes (tracheae) which conduct air directly to the tissues (insects). In mammals, a more specialized mechanism is at work in which O_2 is collected by the blood during its passage through the capillaries of the lungs and distributed to the tissues by the flow of blood throughout the body.* The present chapter is

*In man, about 2 per cent of the O_2 consumed at rest is absorbed through the skin. Transdermal CO_2 exchange is somewhat greater because of the high solubility of CO_2.

concerned with the basic mechanical properties of this highly developed chest–lung system.

Abnormalities of these properties are characteristic of a number of diseases of the respiratory system. For example, breathing difficulties of varying degree are present in pulmonary emphysema, pleural and pulmonary fibrosis, hyaline membrane disease, cardiac disease and asthma. The aim in this chapter is mainly to describe the normal physical properties of the respiratory system, secondly to account for the changes that occur in certain diseases of the lungs and chest, and thirdly to provide guidelines for rational therapy of these diseases.

ANATOMIC RELATIONSHIPS

Movements of the Thoracic Cage. The lungs may be described as elastic multichambered bags suspended in the pleural cavities and connected with the exterior through the airways (Fig. 1). Air is drawn through these

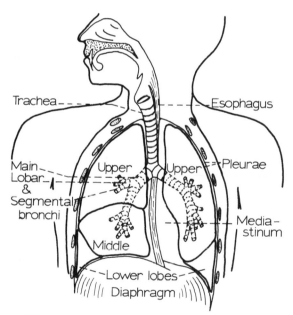

Fig. 1. The thoracic cavity is divided by the mediastinum into 2 major chambers which contain the right and left lungs. The right lung has 3 lobes (upper, middle and lower) separated into a total of 10 segments, and is supplied with air via 3 lobar bronchi which branch to form 10 segmental bronchi. The left lung is divided into 2 lobes (upper and lower) comprising 9 segments. Whenever intrathoracic or intra-abdominal pressure is to be increased, as in coughing, defecation, etc., the vestibular folds in the larynx "close the glottis."

tubes and into the gas-exchanging area as a result of the contraction of the diaphragm and certain thoracic respiratory muscles which enlarges the cavities occupied by the lungs. For example, contraction of the diaphragm increases the vertical dimension of the thorax by flattening the arched dome and displacing the abdominal contents downward. Thoracic inspiratory muscles increase the anteroposterior diameter of the thorax by moving the sternum up and forward ("pump-handle" movement). They also increase the transverse diameter of the chest by pulling the arched ribs up and laterally ("bucket-handle" movement). The consequence of these movements is an increase in the volume of the thorax, and, as a result of the expansible lungs, which, in turn, leads to an influx of air through the airways. In quiet respiration, expiration is passive and results from the elastic recoil of the lungs following relaxation of the inspiratory muscles. In more vigorous breathing, as in exercise, expiration is accelerated by contraction of expiratory muscles in the chest and abdomen, thus actively collapsing the thoracic cage and thereby expelling air.

Descent of the diaphragm appears to account for the larger part of the inspired volume. During quiet breathing (roughly 12 breaths per minute and 500 ml. per breath), the midthoracic chest circumference increases only 1.2 cm., while the diaphragm descends 1.5 cm.[96] Even in maximal respiration, only about half of the ventilation is due to lifting and expansion of the rib cage. Persons with bilateral diaphragmatic paralysis have about one-half the normal vital capacity in the erect position and about one-third normal in the supine position.[64] Following extensive paralysis (e.g., in poliomyelitis) adequate resting ventilation can often be maintained with the neck and shoulder muscles alone.

The role of various muscles attached to the thorax is revealed by electromyography. Simultaneous recordings of air movement and of a muscle's electrical activity enable the investigator to determine the relative strength of the contraction and its timing with respect to the respiratory cycle. In Table 1 are summarized data collected from normal subjects.[17, 90]

Airways and the Anatomic Dead Space. Air is brought to body temperature and saturated with water vapor (47 mm. Hg) as it passes through the highly branched airway system

TABLE 1. *The Respiratory Muscles That Are Active during Inspiration and Expiration at Various Minute Volumes (MV).*

	QUIET BREATHING OR MILD ACTIVITY (MV $<$ 50 L./min.)	MODERATE TO SEVERE EXERCISE (MV $>$ 50 L./min.)	VITAL CAPACITY (MAXIMAL BREATH)
Inspiration	Diaphragm (always) Internal intercostals of the parasternal region Scaleni (sometimes)	Diaphragm, external intercostals, scaleni, sternomastoids, vertebral extensors	All inspiratory muscles, plus anterolateral abdominals, adductors of the larynx
Expiration	Completely passive, except during early part of expiration, when some inspiratory contraction persists	Transverse and oblique abdominals; internal intercostals	Mainly abdominals, scaleni, sacrospinalis, internal intercostals Transversus thoracis

before reaching the respiratory surface of the lungs. The trachea bifurcates into two main bronchi that further divide within the lungs into lobar and segmental bronchi, which, in turn, branch repeatedly into pairs of smaller tubes, or bronchioles. In all, there are about 16 generations of conducting airways. The last few are noncartilaginous and are called *terminal bronchioles.*

A comprehensive study of pulmonary morphometrics has been published by Weibel.[98] Taking the trachea as the zeroth generation with a cross-sectional area of 2.54 cm.[2], he finds that the total cross-sectional area of the airways initially decreases to 2.0 cm.[2] at the third generation, then increases steadily by a factor of approximately 7/5 per generation to 180 cm.[2] at the sixteenth. These changes in area become important in determining the distribution of flow-resistive pressure drops which are to be discussed in a later section.

Up to and including the terminal bronchioles, the air passages are lined with cuboidal or columnar epithelium. No appreciable gas exchange occurs in this portion of the respiratory tree, and accordingly, the volume of this portion is termed the *anatomic dead space.* The dead space at end-expiration is roughly 150 ml. This space is lined with ciliated and mucus-secreting cells whose role in clearing the airways of deposited dust and aerosols is enormously important.

Throughout the tracheobronchial tree are found smooth muscle cells innervated by parasympathetic (vagal) and sympathetic fibers. Stimuli such as certain drugs and irritants, in-

creased CO_2 and decreased O_2, and deflation of the lung cause these bronchial muscles to contract.[100] In asthma, an increased resistance to the flow of air results from excessive active airway constriction.

The Respiratory Unit and the Air–Blood Barrier. The terminal bronchioles usually subdivide into three generations of *respiratory bronchioles,* which, like all gas-exchanging surfaces in the lung, are lined with thin squamous epithelium. Each respiratory bronchiole widens and divides into elongated thin-walled chambers, the *alveolar ducts,* which usually consist of a number of pouches or *alveolar sacs.* Ducts and sacs are thought to comprise the last four generations of the airway system. Finally, the sacs are partitioned by numerous interalveolar septa into small cavities called *alveoli.* To achieve intimate contact between gas and blood, the interalveolar septa are invested with a rich capillary network. All structures peripheral to a cartilaginous bronchiole form a lobule, while structures peripheral to a terminal bronchiole form an *acinus* (Fig. 2).

At birth, a child's lungs contain about 30 million alveoli, which proliferate rapidly during the first few postnatal years. The alveoli number 250 to 350 million by the age of eight.[41] Thereafter, lung growth proceeds solely by enlargement of existing spaces. The area of the alveolar surface in the adult lung totals 50 to 100 square meters, depending, of course, on the degree of inflation. In man, alveolar diameters range from 150 to 300 μ.[41, 61, 98] During the breathing cycle, the volumes of the alveolar ducts and alveoli apparently increase and decrease in equal proportions.[89] Airway dimensions also fluctuate, altering the dead space in proportion to total lung volume. The total capillary surface area (tissue–blood interface) is estimated to be about 90 m.[2], roughly the same as the air–tissue interface.[98]

During inspiration fresh air is moved by mass flow only as far as the mouth of the alveolus. Further movement of O_2 and CO_2 occurs in a fraction of a second by gaseous *diffusion*.[82] Diffusion of dissolved gases across the alveolocapillary barrier is also the mechanism for gas exchange between alveolar air and capillary blood. This barrier (Fig. 3)—normally about 0.4 μ thick, as revealed by electron microscopy—consists of a layer of flattened alveolar epithelial cells and a single capillary endothelial layer separated by basement membranes. The inner air-exposed surface of the alveolar membrane appears to be covered with a thin (100 to 200 Å) noncellular film[20] or *surface active lining*. (This lining will be discussed later.) Some investigators believe that a fine fluid layer, presumably produced as a transudate by alveolar epithelial cells, also is present at the surface,[28, 62, 91] and that the thickness of this layer and that of the interstitial space increases in pulmonary edema[88] and in hyaline membrane disease.[25]

Although gaseous diffusion through liquids is generally about ten thousand times slower than diffusion through other gases, the exquisitely

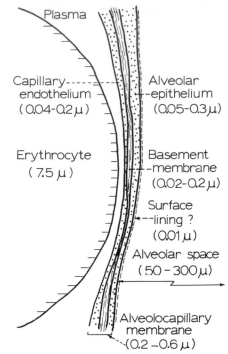

Fig. 3. The fine structure of the alveolocapillary membrane. From the relative dimensions it is apparent that the principal diffusion barrier is not the membrane, but rather the plasma and red cell itself.

thin tissue barrier presents no appreciable hindrance to alveolocapillary gas exchange. Even in disturbances such as chronic pulmonary congestion in which membranes are several times thicker than normal, incomplete oxygenation due to diffusion abnormalities alone is rarely observed.

PHYSICAL RELATIONSHIPS

Pressure and Volume.* Because of the elasticity of lung tissue, its properties are most easily compared with those of a balloon. With this analogy, a plot of lung volume against distending pressure should provide an accurate description of lung characteristics. However, the measurement of lung properties in the open chest, as first performed by Hutchinson,[55] results in an oversimplification when applied to lungs in the closed chest. The problem may

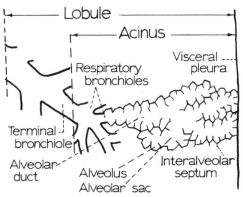

Fig. 2. The mammalian respiratory unit (diagrammatic). The terminal bronchiole gives rise to 10 to 20 respiratory bronchioles, each of which widens into alveolar ducts with many hundreds of alveoli. The alveolar duct often has several major partitions, the so-called alveolar sacs. Interalveolar septa are shown extending into the sacs; the irregular small spaces thus formed are the alveoli.

* The authors, whenever possible, have used the symbols contained in the *Handbook of Physiology, Section 3, Respiration*, vol. 1, W. O. Fenn and H. Rahn, eds. Washington, D.C., American Physiological Society, 1964.

be illustrated in the following way: Suppose a round balloon, R (Fig. 4*A*), when inflated *alone* has the p–v relationship shown by Figure 4*B*. However, when R is placed inside a long balloon (L, Fig. 4*C*) and the two are inflated *together*, neither balloon, obviously, is free to assume its natural *shape,* and each generates a new p–v curve (Fig. 4*D*). Experimental separation of the net curve (R + L) into its component curves is difficult. Furthermore, the lungs, consisting of a spongy plastic material with viscoelastic properties, do not act like a perfect fluid in which pressure applied at one point is transmitted equally to all other points.[57] Therefore, the study of physical characteristics might best begin with the p–v relations for the *combined* lung–chest system, since these are the only ones directly measurable in the intact human.

Definition of Lung Volumes and Capacities. For convenience, a description of lung–chest mechanics should first include a definition of certain volumetric parameters in common usage; the actual methods of measurement will be treated later. The four *lung volumes* and the four *lung capacities* are shown in Figure 5. The volumes are nonoverlapping; however each capacity includes more than one volume.

The volume of air inspired during any respiratory cycle is termed the *tidal volume.* The additional volume of air that could be inspired by maximal effort from the end-inspiratory level is the *inspiratory reserve volume,* and the volume that could be forcibly expelled from the end-expiratory level is the *expiratory reserve volume.* Tidal volume is therefore variable and during exercise may increase by encroaching on both the inspiratory and expiratory reserve volumes. The volume of air remaining in the lungs after

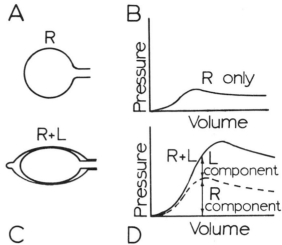

Fig. 4. Model to illustrate the effect of enclosing the lungs within the thorax. *A,* When a round balloon (R) is inflated, the resulting pressure as a function of volume might be as shown in *B.* If, as in *C,* the round balloon is placed inside an elongated balloon (L) and both balloons are inflated, the two together will assume a shape intermediate between those of the balloons blown up separately. *D,* The pressure–volume curve for the inner balloon (R), which represents the lungs, is altered when the shape of the balloon is distorted. When mutual distortion occurs, resolving the total pressure (R + L) into its two components is difficult to achieve with precision.

maximal voluntary expiration is called the *residual volume.*

The *functional residual capacity* is the volume of gas remaining in the chest at the *resting* end-expiratory level; the maximal volume of gas which can be inspired from this resting level is the *inspiratory capacity. Vital capacity* is the maximal volume that can be voluntarily expelled

Fig. 5. Lung volumes and capacities. In normal subjects the resting tidal volume is only about 1/10 of the total lung capacity. (After *Fed. Proc.,* 1950, 9:602–605.)

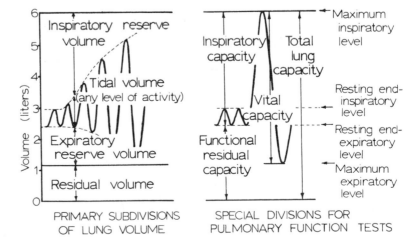

PRIMARY SUBDIVISIONS OF LUNG VOLUME

SPECIAL DIVISIONS FOR PULMONARY FUNCTION TESTS

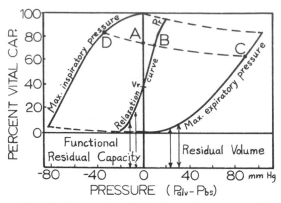

Fig. 6. Properties of the lung–chest system. The relaxation curve represents the passive inflation curve of the lung and chest together. The pressure axis refers to the pressure in the alveoli (Palv) relative to the pressure on the body surface (Pbs), which is usually atmospheric. Thus, while the muscles are relaxed, $Pr = Palv - Pbs$. Whenever Pbs can be taken as zero, then $Pr = Palv$. The maximum inspiratory and maximum expiratory pressure curves are derived during maximal muscular effort against a manometer in the mouth at a series of lung volumes while the nose is clamped and the glottis is open. The dashed lines represent sections of hyperbolas from the equation for an ideal gas, $(P - P_{H_2O}) V = nRT$, where n represents the number of mols of dry gas. Notice that whereas FRC is normally equal to Vr, it could equal any point on the relaxation curve when pressure is applied at the mouth. RV should be interpreted similarly. (After Rahn *et al.*, *Amer. J. Physiol.*, 1946, *146*:161–178.)

from the lungs following a maximal inspiration (inspiratory reserve volume plus tidal volume plus expiratory reserve volume). Finally, the sum of all four volumes is the *total lung capacity*.

Physical Properties of the Lung–Chest System. With the double-balloon analogy in mind, the *passive* volume–pressure relationship of a normal subject can now be examined. This relationship, illustrated in Figure 6, can be investigated by either of two methods: (i) The subject inspires air from a calibrated spirometer to a certain lung volume (e.g., point A, Fig. 6). With a nose clip in place, he then relaxes with open glottis against a manometer placed in his mouth. As he relaxes the pressure increases to point B and the gas in his lungs becomes slightly compressed (V decreases). This point represents the pressure required to hold the lungs and chest at the corresponding volume. The maneuver is repeated at several lung volumes in the vital capacity range to obtain the middle curve, or relaxation curve, of Figure 6. The relaxation pressure becomes negative at vol-

umes less than V_r, the usual functional residual capacity, because the tendency for the chest wall to *spring out* at lower volumes is greater than the tendency for the lung to collapse. (ii) Alternatively, the subject relaxes or is curarized and his mouth is connected to a pressure *source*. Volumes are measured at each of a number of pressures and a relaxation pressure curve is thus generated directly. (The same results are obtained if *negative* pressures are applied by a tank enclosing the body from the neck down, e.g., the Drinker respirator.)

The relaxation pressure curve indicates the passive elastic properties of the lung–chest system in the somewhat artificial situation of relaxed respiratory muscles and airway closed by the manometer. However, these pressures are the same as those which the contracting respiratory muscles *would* have to develop on the chest cage in order to maintain a certain volume *if* the airways were open. Hence, the relaxation pressure curve gives a measure of pressures required for respiration at any lung volume.

The two additional curves in Figure 6 represent the *maximum expiratory pressure* and the *maximum inspiratory pressure*. These are determined when the subject, after relaxing to reach point B, forcibly tries to exhale. With maximum expiratory effort the manometer reaches a point, C, that represents the maximum expiratory pressure, and with maximum inspiratory effort, a point, D, which is the maximum inspiratory pressure. The horizontal difference between the relaxation curve and the maximum expiratory curve represents the pressure developed by the expiratory muscles. The maximum expiratory pressure is therefore a common test for respiratory muscle weakness. Healthy subjects can attain pressures up to 250 to 300 cm. H_2O.[32]

During normal breathing, the air pressure in the *alveoli* (Palv) at both end-inspiration and end-expiration is equal to zero (atmospheric pressure). During the period that gas is flowing into the lungs, Palv is slightly negative and during expiration slightly positive. The middle loop of Figure 7 illustrates these pressure changes. Since expiration is passive* in quiet breathing, the lung–chest volume at end-expiration reaches the point V_r, where the relaxation curve crosses the zero pressure line.

*Expiratory muscles are inactive, although some inspiratory activity usually persists at the beginning of expiration. See Table 1.

A topic frequently of interest is pressure breathing. Positive pressure breathing is often used therapeutically (resuscitation, relief of obstructive airway disease, etc.); negative pressures are encountered under water (snorkel breathing). In Figure 7 pressure breathing curves have been superimposed on the relaxation curve. When a subject breathes from a tank which contains air under pressure ($+20$ cm. H_2O, for example), his lung volume alternates between the ends of the right-hand loop. Since neither of these points is on the relaxation curve, muscular activity must continue throughout the whole respiratory cycle. The vertical difference between this loop and the relaxation curve at $+20$ cm. H_2O represents the volume change due to the reflex contraction of the *expiratory* muscles at *end-inspiration*. At this particular pressure, breathing is accomplished entirely by the expiratory muscles (since the loop is completely *below* the relaxation curve). When the mouth pressure is negative (left loop) the *inspiratory* muscles never completely relax. Apparently, the stretch reflexes of the thorax always tend to bring the FRC back toward normal. The extent to which the pressure breathing curve deviates from the relaxation curve is variable.[57a] In many subjects, the curves are nearly coincident for moderate pressures (± 15 cm. H_2O), although it seems certain that a substantial deviation is always present at higher positive and negative pressures.

Physical Properties of the Lung. Although difficult for the reasons previously mentioned, an analysis of the passive properties of the lung-chest system is desirable in terms of its two components, the lungs and the chest wall. A convenient starting point is provided by the study of the mechanical properties of excised lung, or of the lung in the open chest. Later, methods for obtaining approximate estimates of lung properties in the closed chest will be described.

VOLUME–PRESSURE HYSTERESIS. The earliest quantitative account of lung elasticity was published by Carson in 1820.[19] He determined one point on a volume–pressure (v–p) graph, finding that, with a pressure of about 10 inches of water, dog lungs could be expanded to fill the opened thoracic cavity. (From this, he correctly deduced the active role of the diaphragm in inspiration and the passive nature of expiration.) The *functional* relationship between pressure and volume, however, was not published until Hutchinson's work on the excised human

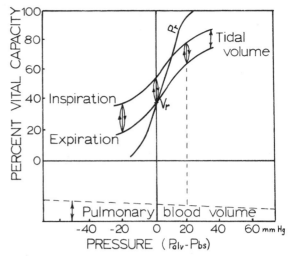

Fig. 7. Tidal breathing at atmospheric pressure (Pbs = 0) is shown by the center loop. V_r is the lung volume when the applied pressure is zero and the muscles are relaxed. Whenever the applied pressure is positive, e.g., 20 cm. H_2O, complete relaxation of the *expiratory* muscles does not occur at any phase of the respiratory cycle (right hand loop), whereas the *inspiratory* muscles are continuously active when a negative pressure is applied at the mouth (left loop). Reflex muscular activity accounts for the difference between the actual end-expiratory volumes and the volumes predicted by the relaxation curve. (After Rahn *et al.*, *Amer. J. Physiol.*, 1946, *146*:161–178.)

lung in 1849.[55] From measurements of volume at four different pressures, Hutchinson obtained values from which an approximately linear volume–pressure curve could be obtained. Later, Van der Brugh[93] published several deflation curves which were far from linear. Because of "unaccountable peculiarities" during inflation, he obtained reproducible results only by deflating the lungs from a fixed volume. It might be instructive to note in retrospect that in their efforts to endow the lungs with "perfect elasticity," many investigators were forced to ignore exactly half their data. Surprisingly, only within the last 12 to 15 years has a thorough attempt been made to describe and clarify the v–p curves of the lung.[1, 8, 23, 65, 78, 80]

If the chest is opened and the collapsed lungs are slowly filled and emptied (two or more minutes per cycle), a hysteresis loop* (solid line in Fig. 8*A*) will be generated. However, if the lungs are not allowed to collapse completely after a

---

* A system which fails to follow identical paths upon application and withdrawal of a forcing agent exhibits *hysteresis*, a phenomenon which the earlier investigators were reluctant to accept.

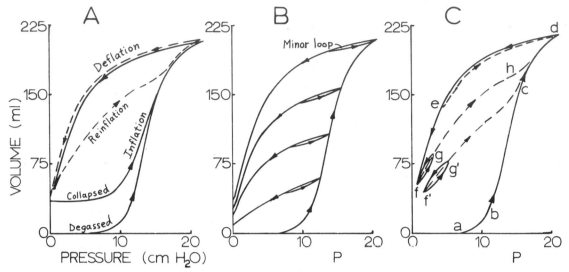

Fig. 8. Hysteresis loops of normal excised cat lung.

A, The degassed lung requires a high opening pressure of 8 to 12 cm. H_2O before inflation begins; thereafter small pressure increases produce large volume changes. At the start of deflation, pressure drops rapidly to quite low values. When the applied pressure has returned to zero, some of the gas remains trapped in the lung. If the lung is only partially deflated, reinflation occurs at lower pressures and the area of the loop is much less (dashed line). The area of any hysteresis loop represents the energy lost as heat during that cycle.

B, Deflation curves. The minor loops are drawn in a region where the lung appears to be quite stiff; that is, the compliance (dV/dP) is low.

C, Reinflation curves from volumes greater than the collapsed volume. Hysteresis is minimal when the lung is reinflated from a point such as *e,* but increases from points such as *f* at smaller volumes. On a fixed stroke pump a minor loop, *fg,* drifts slowly to *f'g'* as atelectasis and surfactant changes occur. The lung is returned to a low pressure and high compliance state by a full inflation or deep breath.

full inflation and are instead reinflated from FRC or from residual volume, the volume–pressure curve follows a different path in which hysteresis is much less evident (dashed line, Fig. 8*A*). The contradictory results of the earlier work can now be understood: the deflators worked on one part of the curves, and the inflators on the other. After complete degassing the hysteresis loop is even more pronounced.

The lung may be collapsed from any point on the inflation curve to yield a family of deflation curves, as indicated in Figure 8*B. Small* cyclic volume changes anywhere on these curves generate thin, almost elliptical loops. (In other words, the distinctly *nonlinear* v–p function is almost linear in a *small region.*) Since lung volume of the intact animal can vary only within the range of the vital capacity, the lung is normally prevented from collapsing completely. Thus, attention can be restricted to those values which fall between the residual volume and total lung capacity (points *f* and *d,* respectively, of Fig. 8*C*). Hysteresis is minimal

when the lung is deflated only to about half its maximum volume (approximately to functional residual capacity). During deflation, the *static compliance,* defined as the slope dv/dp, of the static v–p curve, reaches a maximum in the midvolume range. In this region a small change in pressure causes a large change in volume, and the energy cost of breathing is least.

The processes generating these complex v–p curves are not completely understood, but the evidence at present implicates at least four factors—alveolar recruitment, tissue elasticity, area-dependent alveolar surface tension and stress relaxation. The last factor—stress relaxation—results from the viscoelastic behavior of lung tissues and of lung lining.

ALVEOLAR RECRUITMENT. Microscopic examination of the pleural surface during inflation and deflation reveals that the alveoli do not behave uniformly. When air is pumped into a collapsed lung, inflation takes place regionally, so that certain segments or lobules of the lung become involved before others. Initially, only the larger alveoli are expanded in each region. As inflation proceeds, progressive recruitment of smaller alveoli continues up to volumes approaching total lung capacity.[79] During deflation the opened alveoli at first shrink simultaneously and proportionately until about one-fourth maximum volume is reached, at which time some of the smaller alveoli may begin to collapse.

Alveolar recruitment partially explains the hysteresis of the lung v–p curve: During inflation, pressures of about 8 to 12 cm. H_2O must be attained before volume begins to increase (point *a*, Fig. 8*C*) because the smaller airways and alveoli are held closed by surface adhesive forces. Further small increases in pressure open most of the remaining airways and alveoli, and lung volume increases sharply as the rate of alveolar recruitment becomes maximal (point *b*). At high lung volumes (from point *c* to point *d*) the slope of the v–p curve diminishes because the rate of recruitment is low and tissue fibers are now being stretched near their elastic limit.

As the lung is deflated (*d* to *e*), the alveoli initially decrease in size uniformly. With further deflation (*e* to *f*) some of the smaller units may collapse because the pressure is insufficient to hold them open and volume begins to drop more rapidly. On reinflation (*f* to *g*) only those units still open at point *f* are expanded, but at point *h* the pressure has again risen high enough to reopen the smaller units. At this pressure a change in slope or "knee" presumably marks the onset of recruitment.[8] (As will be shown later, it is likely that surface tension hysteresis also plays an important role in producing the open loop.)

Conditions during which alveolar closure (atelectasis) is especially noticeable include the following: maintaining an animal on a fixed-stroke respiratory pump for an hour or more,[5, 67] anesthetizing and artificially ventilating a patient at a fixed tidal volume,[7, 9, 42] or strapping the chest for a prolonged period to limit inspiration.[18] Under these conditions, as alveolar closure takes place the minor loop (*fg*) in Figure 8*C* shifts to the right and downward (toward *f'g'*). Progressive atelectasis is due in part to slow changes in the lung lining material producing alveolar instability[28] (see below) and in part to isolation of small lung regions by mucous plugs in the bronchioles and subsequent absorption of the trapped gas. The collapse of lung regions is readily visible during open-chest surgery and

results in incomplete oxygenation of arterial blood.[4, 87] Thus, as a preventive measure, the anesthetist periodically re-expands the lung (path *f'g'cdef*) to open collapsed areas. In normal respiration an occasional deep breath or sigh after prolonged shallow breathing returns the lung to its low-pressure, highly compliant nonatelectatic state.[45]

ALVEOLAR MECHANICS. The phenomenon of alveolar recruitment and the hysteresis of the lung v–p curve indicate that some kind of force hinders the opening of collapsed alveoli. Since the interior of the alveolus is moist, this force quite naturally is ascribed to surface tension at the air–liquid interface.

Surface tension. When the lower edge of a thin wettable plate, suspended from a force-measuring device or transducer, is dipped into a dish of water (Fig. 9), the water "creeps up" the sides of the plate and pulls downward with a certain force. The force is proportional to the length of the plate as shown by the equation, $F = \gamma L = 2\gamma l$, in which F is the force (dynes), L is the total length of the water–plate boundary (cm.), l is the length of the plate, and γ is the force per unit length (dynes per cm.) along the boundary. The proportionality constant, γ, is called the *surface tension* at the water–air interface and measures about 72 dynes per cm. A plasma–air interface has a γ of 40 to 50 dynes per cm., and detergent solutions in air about 25 to 45 dynes per cm.

Surface tension is important in lung v–p relationships for two reasons: (i) it is responsible for the high opening pressures of collapsed al-

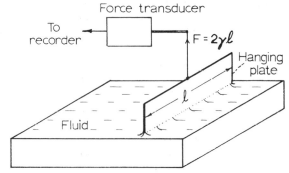

Fig. 9. The hanging plate method of measuring surface tension. A thin clean platinum plate dipping into the liquid is suspended from a force transducer or balance. The surface tension is directly proportional to the recorded force. (Changes in buoyant force on the plate are negligible.) This method has the advantage that the surface is never broken, thus permitting continuous measurement.

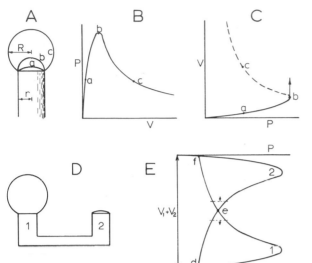

Fig. 10. Bubble properties.

A, The radius of curvature of a bubble blown on the end of a tube decreases to a minimum at *b,* then increases slowly (*c*).

B, Bubble pressure as a function of volume has been calculated from r and Laplace's law, $P = 2\left(\dfrac{2\gamma}{R}\right)$. (The factor 2 arises because a bubble in air has 2 surfaces—inside and outside.)

C, When pressure is the controlled (independent) variable, the bubble is stable up to point *b.* A slight increase in pressure above this point bursts the bubble.

D, Two bubbles, 1 and 2, are connected in parallel. The smaller promptly empties into the larger until the radii of curvature of the two are equal—i.e., until the pressures are equal.

E, In the 2-bubble system, the total volume is represented by $V_1 + V_2$. Curves 1 and 2 represent the v–p curves for the respective bubbles. If the pressure in bubble 1 is initially greater than in 2, the system will come to rest at point *d*—i.e., most of the volume is in 2, and 1 is almost collapsed. If the greater pressure is in bubble 2, the system will come to rest at point *f.*

veoli and (ii) it is partly responsible for the retractive force of expanded alveoli. The latter role might be more easily understood by thinking of the moist alveolar interior as if it were a bubble.

If a soap film covering the end of a tube is blown to form a bubble (Fig. 10*A*), the film's radius of curvature first decreases until the bubble is hemispherical in shape (*b*) and then increases (*c*). Because of surface tension a soap bubble behaves like a double elastic film in which both the inner and outer surfaces obey Laplace's law: $P = 2\gamma/R$. Consequently, the pressure, P, across the bubble wall first rises to a maximum when the radius of curvature is a

minimum and then falls once more (Fig. 10*B*). Here volume is the independent variable and the system is always *stable*—i.e., the equation, $P = f(V)$, represents a single-valued function (for each V only a single P exists). If, however, pressure is the independent variable, as in Figure 10*C,* the bubble is stable with respect to pressure only up to point *b;* beyond this point it is unstable—i.e., there is *no* V corresponding to a greater P, and so the bubble bursts. Even if one drops the pressure after passing point *b,* e.g. to *C,* the bubble still bursts, for here dv/dp is negative and the system proceeds to a lower energy state spontaneously.

If two bubbles of unequal size are connected together (Fig. 10*D*), the bubble having the smaller radius of curvature (and therefore the higher pressure) empties into the larger. The parallel system comes to rest at either of two stable equilibrium points—*d* or *f* of Fig. 10*E*—moving away from the unstable equilibrium point *e.* The problem of keeping parallel bubbles open is critical in the lung, where millions of alveoli exist side by side. If these alveoli were inflated like bubbles on tubes in the simple model, then the lung *ought* to be an unstable structure with only the large alveoli open. The fact that this is *not* so implies that other factors are involved.

Tissue elasticity. In addition to the retractive forces arising from the surface tension in the alveolar lining, the elastic tissue recoil of the alveolar wall must also be considered. This component of the total lung retractive force was first differentiated from the lung surface tension by von Neergaard.[94] By filling the degassed lung with an isosmotic fluid, he abolished the surface–air interface; thus, the pressure needed to fill the lung with fluid resulted from tissue elastic forces only* (Fig. 11*A*).

In Figure 11*B* a tissue elastic curve similar to that obtained from fluid-filled lungs is plotted along with the v–p curve for a single bubble. The pathway *afbecd* (dotted line) represents the sum of the pressures of these two curves. The stable portions of this curve are those where dv/dp is positive (but less than infinity). Thus, as the pressure in the bubble is increased, volume follows this summed curve to *b,* but unlike the unenclosed bubble in Figure 10*C,* it does not

*The surface elastic pressure component at any given volume may be determined approximately by subtracting the pressures of the fluid-filled lung from the pressures of the air-filled lung.

burst. It merely pops open with an almost immediate increase of volume to point *c*. Point *b* marks the *critical opening pressure*. (As already mentioned, "popping" alveoli are easily seen on the surface of lungs inflated from the collapsed state.)

Further increase of pressure carries the volume to point *d*. As pressure is diminished volume decreases along *dce*. At *e*—the *critical closing pressure*—a further decrease in pressure results in an abrupt volume decrease to *f* and thence to *a*. This theoretical curve displays hysteresis reminiscent of that obtained from the lung. However, it differs from normal lung by closing at a relatively high pressure and thus resembles more closely the curves obtained from the lungs of infants with the respiratory distress syndrome. In this condition, alveoli collapse with each expiration, inspiration is labored, and gas exchange with blood is poor. The interalveolar septa frequently become thickened and glassy (hyaline) within a few hours after birth.[51] Unlike the normal deflation curve, the curve for unstable atelectatic lungs (Fig. 11*A*) is shifted to the right, indicating that the lung collapses even at fairly high pressures. Following the bubble analogy one might suspect that either surface tension or tissue stiffness or both have

increased. Since the v–p curves of fluid-filled atelectatic lungs are similar to those of normal lungs, it appears that some disturbance relating to *surface tension* takes place early in the respiratory distress syndrome.[5] Later, with hyaline membrane formation and fibrin deposition, the tissue properties also change.

Although the simple tissue-enclosed bubble model accounts fairly well for the properties of the abnormal lung, it fails to explain how the alveoli of *normal* lungs are kept open at exceedingly low pressures. This happy property of normal lung is a consequence of the lining of alveoli—the lung "surfactant."

The lung lining layer. The pressure inside a small soap bubble is greater than that outside by the amount $\frac{4\gamma}{R}$ dynes per sq. cm. As a result, the contained gas tends to diffuse out through the wall and the bubble soon shrinks to nothing. Bubbles of lung edema fluid, on the other hand, are extremely durable, lasting many hours. Pattle[74] in England deduced from the stability of the edema bubble that its internal pressure must be exceedingly low and therefore its surface tension proportionately small. His calculations indicated a value of only about 0.05 dyne per cm. for the surface tension of lung edema bubbles.

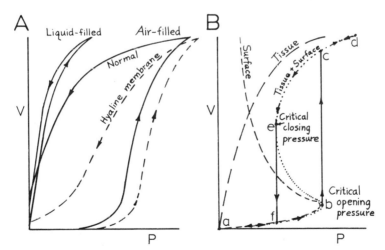

Fig. 11. *A*, Normal, hyaline and liquid-filled lungs. The curve for the normal air-filled lung shown here is the same as that shown in Figure 8. The lung from an infant who had hyaline membrane disease is unstable—i.e., it collapses at pressure of less than 5 cm. H₂O. *Fluid*-filled lungs, whether normal or unstable, are nearly alike: inflation pressures are low, hysteresis is negligible, and emptying is complete. The difference between normal and unstable lungs must therefore exist principally in the surface properties.

B, Here a tissue component is added to the surface component of the bubble illustrated in Figure 10. The net v–p curve is now given by the dotted line *afbecd*. After reaching *b* such a bubble "pops" open to *c*; when deflated it suddenly collapses from *e* to *f*. It is prevented from bursting by the presence of the limiting tissue sheath.

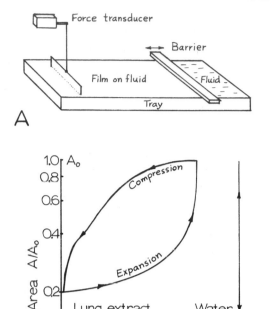

Fig. 12. Surface tension as a function of film area.

A, The surface balance consists of a tray filled to the top with fluid, a film of the material to be studied spread on the surface, a barrier to compress the film, and a hanging plate for continuously recording surface tension.

B, Lung extracts from healthy mammals show extensive hysteresis and a minimum tension of 0 to 5 dynes per cm. For comparison, the surface tension of water is shown to be constant at about 70 dynes per cm.

Since such a low surface tension in a single-phase liquid was unthinkable, Pattle reached the logical conclusion that the bubbles from the lung were lined by a thin, insoluble, possibly monomolecular, compressible *film.* Methods for studying surface films were available and an American physiologist, J. A. Clements, quickly picked up the bubble and ran.

In his approach, Clements[24] used an apparatus called a surface balance (Fig. 12*A*) designed to measure the surface tension of a fluid film as a function of its area. In this technique the material to be examined is spread on the surface of a fluid-filled Teflon tray and a movable barrier compresses or expands the film, thereby mimicking the changes in alveolar surface area produced during deep breathing. A hanging plate measures the surface tension.

By spreading small quantities of saline lung washes or minced lung extracts on the fluid filling the tray, Clements found that as the barrier was moved along the solution to about one-fourth of its initial area, the surface tension *fell* to very low values—e.g., 5 to 10 dynes per cm. in extracts from healthy lungs (Fig. 12*B*). On expansion a different curve was generated—i.e., the film displayed hysteresis. Surface tension rapidly increased toward that of plasma (40 to 50 dynes per cm.) but, upon reaching this value, remained fairly constant. Clements also concluded, from the fact that the surface tension depended on area, that some kind of insoluble film was present in the lungs.

When the area, A, of the film was decreased from its initial area, A_0, to no less than half A_0, the hysteresis loop was not as evident.[11] Within this range the film behaved more elastically. The change in lung volume corresponding to a change in surface area of one-half can be calculated as follows: If the volume were proportional to area raised to the $\frac{3}{2}$ power,* or $V = KA^{3/2}$, then when $A/A_0 = \frac{1}{2}$, the ratio of volumes would be as follows: $\frac{V}{V_0} = \left(\frac{A}{A_0}\right)^{3/2} = \left(\frac{1}{2}\right)^{3/2} \simeq \frac{1}{3}$. This means that if the film in the *lung* behaved like the film on the *tray,* the volume of the lung could be reduced to about ⅓ without significant volume–pressure hysteresis. Experimental data are fairly consistent with this deduction (Fig. 8*C*).

The physical events accounting for the hysteretic behavior of the film are not clear. It appears most likely that compression wrinkles the film and attractive forces between adjacent wrinkles hinder re-expansion. When stretched, the film breaks and the measured tension becomes that of the fluid subphase. Alternatively, compression may force some of the film into solution so that re-expansion of the attenuated film beyond its elastic limit leads to rupture. Over some ranges, lung volume could change without an increase in area of the air–tissue interface, e.g., by unfolding and flattening rather than by stretching alveolar corrugations.[98]

Alveolar stability. In the theoretical model shown in Figure 11*B*, surface tension was assumed to be constant. The finding that surface

---

*This relationship holds for any body of constant *shape.* The shape factor, K, has a value of about 4.8 for lung geometry and is fairly insensitive to slight variations in shape.[98]

tension of alveolar lining material depends on area will now be taken into account. As mentioned above, when the film is stretched, γ rises rapidly to about 50 dynes per cm. and remains virtually constant on further expansion (Fig. 12*B*). Consequently, the bubble pops open much as described earlier. But, during deflation the surface tension *falls,* and the pathway determined by the sum of surface tension and tissue elasticity varies accordingly. When γ drops to 30 dynes per cm., for example, the v–p point must lie on a *new* summed curve that describes a film in which γ = 30 dynes per cm. (point 2, Fig. 13*A*). As the bubble continues to deflate, the summed curve eventually proceeds through a point (3, Fig. 13*A*) where γ equals 10 dynes per cm. and so on. If, for this example, γ is assumed to fall only to 10, deflation follows the solid curve shown in Figure 13*A*. The significant feature now is the greatly extended range of stability: the bubble does not pop shut until

reaching very low values of pressure and volume. Since dv/dp is positive over a wider range, it can be verified, by the graphic method used in Figure 10*E,* that the volumes of two or more such bubbles in parallel can stably decrease to nearly zero before collapse begins. In this way a variable surface tension adequately accounts for the striking fall in pressure seen in normal deflation curves (Fig. 11*A*).

To demonstrate the effect of a surface lining not having a variable surface tension, Clements *et al.*[26] flushed lungs with a nonhysteretic detergent (γ = 30) and then determined a v–p curve with air (Fig. 13*B*). The opening pressure was somewhat lower than that in normal lungs, and the loop showed far less hysteresis. The alveoli were unstable on deflation and collapsed at relatively high pressures.

In *summary,* among the factors responsible for the major features of the static v–p curve are alveolar recruitment, tissue elasticity, and vari-

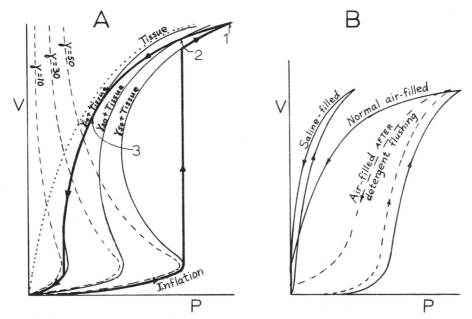

Fig. 13. *A,* The effect of a surface film, similar to that of Figure 12*B,* on the v–p curve of the model alveolus. The inflation curve is not significantly different from the one shown in Figure 11*B*. If, however, as deflation proceeds the surface tension drops rapidly from 50 to 10 dynes per cm. (or often less), the path on the v–p plane therefore joins the γ_{10} + Tissue line after partial deflation. This has the net result that pressure in the alveolus falls rapidly to low values, and the alveoli may be deflated to small volumes before collapse.

B, Air, detergent and saline filling. The curve of the *saline*-filled lung represents the elastic recoil of the lung *tissue* alone. In the curve of normal *air*-filled lung, both *tissue* and *surface* forces are acting. However, when a lung is flushed with a detergent solution and then refilled with air the surface lining material is modified. Instead of the area-dependent surface tension obtained from lung surfactant, the γ of a detergent such as Tween 20 is nearly constant at about 30 dynes per cm. As a result, alveoli collapse at high pressures and the v–p curve more closely resembles that of the hyaline lung (Fig. 11).

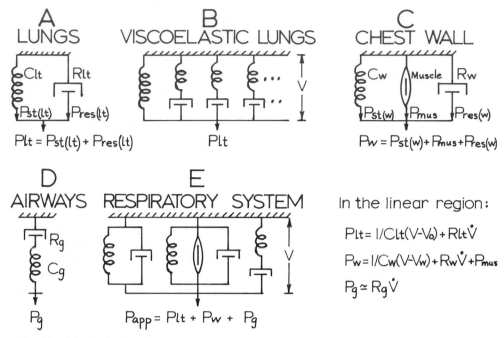

Fig. 14. Mechanical analogs.

A, Conventional model of lung tissue consisting of a pure elastic element with compliance, Clt, and a parallel tissue resistive element, Rlt. The applied pressure therefore has two components: elastic and tissue resistive; thus $Plt \equiv Palv - Ppl = Pst\ (lt) + Pres\ (lt)$.

B, A more complete model having properties like viscoelastic materials. It reduces to *A* for any single frequency. The spring–dashpot combinations have a range of time constants, from a fraction of a second to hundreds of seconds. Animal tissues and other materials such as polymers generally require a representation at least as complex as this.

C, The equivalent model of the chest wall and diaphragm consists of an elastic element and a resistive element, plus an active element developing pressures (Pmus) due to forces exerted by the respiratory muscles.

D, To a first approximation the airways may also be represented by a simple mechanical analog. When measured at alveolar pressure (Palv), the volume of gas in the lung is V, but measured at mouth pressure (Pao) it is $Vg = \dfrac{Palv - 47}{Pao - 47}$ V. The compliance of this amount of gas is Cg. The airway resistance (Rg) is assumed to be a constant.

E, This simplified composite model of the thorax includes elements to represent lung, chest and airways. Papp is the external applied pressure (if any) between the mouth and the chest surface. Inertial effects have been neglected. Since no unbalanced pressures can be present, the equation $Papp = Pg + Plt + Pw$ must always hold. All the (linear) static and dynamic properties discussed in this chapter can be treated as special cases of this more general model.

able surface tension. (A fourth factor, stress relaxation—involved in lung dynamics (Fig. 14) —is beyond the scope of the present account.) Alveolar recruitment is the progressive involvement of increasing numbers of alveoli during the inflation of a collapsed or partially collapsed lung; tissue elasticity limits alveolar sizes, preventing units from bursting when they "pop" open; and variable surface tension enables stable deflation to a low pressure and a high compliance.

Composition and origin of the lining layer. Pattle[74] presented evidence that the material lining the lung edema bubbles was an insoluble protein layer only a few molecules in thickness and that it originated from the lining of the alveoli. Subsequent work[58, 75] established that this lining layer is a lipoprotein complex. The lipid fraction is principally phospholipid, lecithin being the most prevalent. If exposed to air, the material loses its activity in three to four hours, suggesting that it must be continuously replenished in the alveoli.[27] The substance is chemically and structurally similar to cellular membranes, suggesting that it could be sloughed-off alveolar epithelial cell membranes or possibly a separate membrane entirely.[68]

The ability to form a normal alveolar film appears suddenly during fetal development— e.g., on the eighteenth day in the mouse, which has a gestation period of 19 days,[12] and around the seventh month in the human fetus.

Clinically important is the fact that a deficiency of lung surfactant can be induced in normal lungs by several procedures: by prolonged cardiopulmonary by-pass (humans and dogs), by temporary pulmonary artery occlusion (dogs), by bilateral vagotomy (guinea pigs)[92] or by asphyxia, the premature fetus being particularly susceptible.[70]

DYNAMIC PROPERTIES OF THE LUNG. To avoid the difficult problem of *rate-dependence,* all changes in the preceding discussion, whether of volume or of area, were treated as if they happened *slowly.* Because of frictional and inertial properties, the pressure needed to inflate a viscoelastic bag such as the lung depends upon the *rate* of volume change and upon the *volume acceleration.* The effect of the latter is usually negligible, leaving only elastic and viscous elements. The arrangement of these elements to represent lung properties (Fig. 14*A*) can be approached by regarding lung tissue and surface film together as a single elastic element (a spring) with *compliance,* Clt, and resting or trapped volume, V_o. The lung's small internal frictional resistance or "lung tissue resistance," Rlt, is represented by a dashpot (such as the device used in Sherrington's "fall table"). In the linear range the equation that describes the motion of the spring is: $Pst(lt) = \frac{1}{Clt}(V-V_o)$, where Pst(lt) is the static elastic pressure necessary to distend lung tissue, and the motion of the dashpot is described by: $Pres(lt) = Rlt\dot{V}$, where $\dot{V}$ is the rate of change of volume.* Taking the two elements together, the total pressure difference from alveolus to intrapleural space is: $Palv - Ppl \equiv Plt = Pst(lt) + Pres(lt) = \frac{1}{Clt}$ $(V-V_o) + Rlt\dot{V}$. Recent studies provide evidence that Clt and Rlt are not actually constants, but rather fall off slightly as respiratory rate increases.[53] The complex *viscoelastic* system represented by Figure 14*B* has most of the required properties and is applicable over limited

ranges of stretching to other tissues of the body such as blood vessels, bladder, muscle, etc., all of which also exhibit stress relaxation.**

Intrapleural, Esophageal and Lobar Pressure. A description of the normal functioning lung *in situ* is desirable in terms of v–p curves similar to those obtained from excised lungs. However, obtaining such a description involves a number of problems, some of which have already been mentioned. Most of the problems arise because of the differences in shape between the lungs and the chest. Thus, expansion of the thorax is accompanied by changes in its shape, thereby producing nonuniform forces on the surface of the lungs. Throughout the resting tidal volume range, discrepancies in the shape of the lungs and chest are small, but at volume extremes distortion is a significant factor.

In the closed chest system, the lung distending pressure, Plt, is the difference between the *alveolar* pressure, Palv, and the *intrapleural pressure,* Ppl, the latter being the pressure within the *intrapleural space:* Plt = Palv − Ppl. The pressure relationships are diagrammed in Figure 15. When the airways are *open* and *no flow* is taking place, Palv = 0, and so Plt = −Ppl. Since in this case, Plt is due to the static elastic pressure developed by lung tissue (Pres being zero), then Plt = Pst(lt) + Pres(lt) = Pst(lt) = −Ppl.

It should be emphasized that "pressure" really means *pressure difference;* in this chapter all pressures unless otherwise specified are taken relative to the pressure on the outside of the chest, usually atmospheric. For example, the statement, Palv = +10 cm. H_2O, means that alveolar pressure is 10 cm. H_2O greater than the pressure on the outside of the chest.

In actual fact, it is incorrect to speak of Ppl, the "pressure" in the intrapleural "space." Pressure, a scalar quantity, exists only in a homogeneous gas or liquid phase. The visceral and parietal pleurae adhere via a mucous film. In such a film, forces, shears and stresses arise which in general are vector and tensor quantities. To measure Ppl at a given point, one must *create* a homogeneous fluid phase by introducing, between the pleural layers, a drop of liquid or a small bubble of air at the end of a needle. Nevertheless, for convenience, the term intrapleural pressure is used even though it is not a pressure and varies to some extent from point to point over the lung surface.

Direct measurement of Ppl is inconvenient

---

* By Hooke's law, the change in length (x-x₀) of a spring with resting length x_o is proportional to the applied force (F): $Fst = K(x-x_o)$, where K is the spring constant. By analogy, a balloon with elastic constant 1/C is described approximately by: $Pst = (1/C)(V-V_o)$. From Newton's law of viscous flow, viscous drag in a fluid medium can be shown to be proportional to velocity of movement ($\dot{x}$): $F_\mu = \mu\dot{x}$ (μ is the frictional coefficient). Again by analogy, $Pres = R\dot{V}$.

** Stress relaxation is defined as the gradual reduction in stress (force) which follows a sudden change in strain (displacement). The resultant stress plotted against log (t) is frequently linear over several decades of time (t).

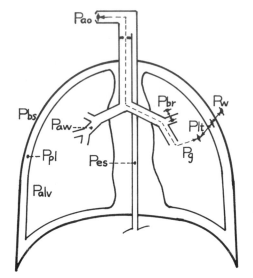

Fig. 15. Pressures pertinent to analysis of respiratory function. Pressures which are measured relative to an arbitrary reference, usually atmospheric pressure, include the following: pressure at the airway opening, Pao; alveolar pressure, Palv; esophageal pressure, Pes; airway pressure, Paw; pressure at the body surface, Pbs; and pleural pressure, Ppl. Pes is generally taken to be equal to Ppl. The lung transmural pressure, Plt, represents the pressure difference between the alveoli and the intrapleural space: Plt = Palv − Ppl. The difference between Pao and Palv is the gas flow pressure drop, Pg. The difference between Paw and Palv is the bronchial transmural pressure drop, Pbr. The trans-chest wall pressure, Pw, is the pressure difference from intrapleural space to chest surface: Pw = Ppl − Pbs. Whenever the airway is *open* and flow ($\dot{V}$) is zero, then Palv = 0, so that Plt = Pst (lt) = − Ppl = − Pes. With the airway *closed* and the muscles *relaxed,* Pw = Pst (w) = Ppl = + Pes (taking Pbs as zero).

because it entails puncturing the chest wall with a large blunt needle. Luciani[60] in 1878 and Rosenthal[85] in 1880 estimated intrathoracic pressure changes by measuring pressures in the lower esophagus through an open-ended tube. Where it passes through the intrapleural space, the esophagus is subjected to a distending force or "negative intrapleural pressure." A water-filled tube or an air-filled balloon inside the esophagus in this region will become distended, thus reflecting surrounding pressure changes. For some years the method was regarded with suspicion because of several inaccuracies. For example, the esophageal wall is muscular and therefore does not transmit pressures faithfully; indeed, peristaltic waves often generate spurious pressures. Furthermore, the pressures measured

depend greatly on the position of the tube or balloon in the esophagus. Recently, however, esophageal pressure measurement has returned to common usage largely because the limitations have been explored[16, 35] and the techniques have been improved.*

A latex balloon 1 cm. in diameter and 5 to 10 cm. in length and containing 0.5 to 1.0 ml. of air is attached to a flexible narrow tube leading to a manometer or pressure transducer. The gas in the balloon tends to accumulate at the point where the surrounding pressure is *least,* and so one records the most negative pressure appearing along its length. Directly measured intrapleural pressures compare well with esophageal pressure (Pes) for small tidal volumes, except at the apex and base of the lung.[44] For larger tidal volumes, esophageal pressures change less than intrapleural pressures ($\Delta Pes < \Delta Ppl$) throughout the lung.[21] Esophageal balloons are commercially available but can be fabricated more cheaply from split condoms.

A third way to measure intrapleural pressure changes is to use one of the natural balloons already located *in* the thorax—a lobe or a part of lobe. A catheter connected to a manometer is fed into a bronchus until it seals by wedging,[39] or until it can be sealed by an inflatable balloon surrounding the tube.[22] Since no air can enter or leave the blocked lobe, changes in intrathoracic pressure are accurately recorded from this lobe. Recent studies show that $\Delta P_{lower\ lobe}$ is greater than $\Delta P_{upper\ lobe}$, which in turn is greater than ΔP_{es}. These findings reflect the *plastic* properties of the lung and the *shape* discrepancy between lung and expanding chest.[57]

Physical Properties of the Chest Wall. Elastic chest properties are described by the relationship between static chest volume and the *relaxed* trans-chest wall pressure (Pst(w)). Since the chest wall contains contractile elements, measurements of passive elastic chest compliance can be made only when these muscles are *completely* inactive. Intrapleural pressure (Ppl) is equal to trans-chest wall pressure (Pw) at *all* times (since Pw ≡ Ppl − Pbs, and if Pbs = 0, then Pw = Ppl). However, since Pw may include components due to friction (Pres(w)) and muscular activity (Pmus), as well as to elasticity (Pst(w)), it is clear that Pst(w) = Ppl only when $\dot{V}$ = 0 and when Pmus = 0. The chest

---

* Besides, swallowing a balloon is (for some) easier and safer than withstanding an intercostal puncture. With a liberal supply of ice water, dedicated people are able to swallow and even to hold down a balloon with only slight flushing, sweating, eye-watering, gagging, choking, coughing and occasional vomiting.

compliance curve therefore can be derived from esophageal pressure, Pes $\simeq$ Ppl, while the subject relaxes against a closed glottis at a series of lung volumes or against another manometer which is simultaneously recording Palv for the lung–chest relaxation pressure (Fig. 16*A*). Thus Pes (or Ppl) can represent two very different quantities, depending on the experimental conditions. When the muscles are *relaxed* and the airway is *closed*, Pes = Pst(w) and data can be obtained for the v–p curve of the *chest*. However, when the muscles *hold* the chest at any given volume and the airway is *open*, then Pes = −Pst(lt) and data can be obtained for the v–p curve of the *lung*.*

The resting volume (Vw) of the thoracic cavity is considerably higher than FRC, averaging about 0.6 VC. Mechanically, the lung–chest system at rest can be represented by two springs with different resting lengths (Fig. 16*B*). The implication is that in the intact state the lungs, by elastic recoil, are continually "sucking in" the chest wall and diaphragm since the combined resting length of the springs is intermediate between the individual resting lengths. For this reason, whenever $\dot{V} = 0$ and the airways are open, the intrapleural pressure is *negative* with respect to pressure at the mouth.

The chest wall, like other tissues, undoubtedly has hysteretic properties but in the closed chest these are difficult to separate experimentally from the hysteresis of the lung. The common practice is to measure a *mean* relaxation curve and a *mean* lung deflation curve (using esophageal pressures) and then to subtract the lung curve from the relaxation curve to obtain a *mean* chest v–p curve.

Figure 14*C* shows a simplified mechanical analog of the chest wall similar to that of the lung. An element representing the muscles has, however, been added. The pressure developed by the muscles (Pmus) is positive during expiration and negative during inspiration. Thus the total pressure across the chest wall, Pw ≡ Ppl − Pbs, has three components: (i) Pmus, a pressure due to forces exerted by the muscles; (ii) Pst(w), due to the passive elastic properties of the chest, and equal to $\left(\dfrac{1}{Cw}\right)(V - Vw)$ in the linear range; (iii) Pres(w) due to tissue resistance and equal to $Rw\dot{V}$. Thus, Pw = Pmus + (1/Cw)(V − Vw) + $Rw\dot{V}$.

*Obviously, since Pst(lt) + Pst(w) = Pr (the relaxation pressure), the chest v–p curve may also be obtained indirectly by subtracting the lung v–p curve from the total relaxation curve of Figure 16*A*.

In Figure 14*D* is shown an analog of the airway system. Rg represents the gas flow resistance of the airways and Cg the compliance of the gas in the lung. Usually Cg is small compared to other compliances in the system, and can be neglected, so that Pg $\simeq$ Rg$\dot{V}$.

All the above elements may now be combined into a simple model of the respiratory system (Fig. 14*E*). This model is applicable to all situations in which volume excursions are not too large, e.g., less than 2 liters and in which flow rates are not too high, e.g., less than 50 liters per minute in normal subjects.

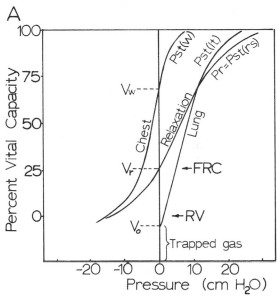

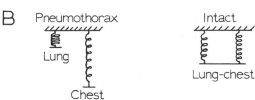

Fig. 16. The elastic components of the relaxation curve (Pr).

A, At any given volume, the sum of the static lung tissue elastic pressure (Pst (lt)) and the passive chest wall recoil pressure (Pst (w)) is equal to the relaxation pressure, i.e., the total static pressure of the respiratory system, Pst (rs). (Hysteresis has been ignored.) At a volume corresponding to FRC the tendency of the chest wall to expand is exactly balanced by the lung retractive force, so that Pr = 0. When air is admitted into the intrapleural space, the chest expands from FRC to its own resting volume (Vw), and the lung collapses to Vo.

B, The lungs and the chest may be represented (statically) by springs of different lengths. When combined, their length is intermediate between the original lengths.

ABSORPTION OF TRAPPED GAS AND FLUID FROM BODY SPACES

Since there is normally a "*negative* pressure" in the intrapleural space, one might ask why this "space" does not fill with air or fluid. Actually the opposite occurs; an induced pneumothorax or hydrothorax disappears over a period of hours or days.

Gas absorption from an intrapleural or other closed space in the body is accounted for as follows: When atmospheric pressure is 760 mm. Hg, the total pressure on gases trapped in the intrapleural space would be about 755 mm. Hg (i.e., Ppl = −5 mm. Hg), and the sum of the partial pressures of O_2, N_2, CO_2 and H_2O in the three regions of interest might be as shown in Table 2. As O_2 is extracted from arterial blood by the tissues, the blood P_{O_2} drops sharply, because extraction occurs over the *flat* part of the sigmoid O_2–IIb dissociation curve (see next chapter). However, P_{CO_2} does *not* rise an equivalent amount because addition of CO_2 occurs on the *steep* part of its dissociation curve. This is the key to the process which enables gas absorption. P_{N_2} remains unchanged, and P_{H_2O} is, of course, constant. As a result the total pressure of the gases in venous blood is only about 706 mm. Hg. In the trapped gas, P_{O_2} and P_{CO_2} almost equilibrate with surrounding tissues and venous blood. P_{H_2O} is fixed, and P_{N_2} makes up the remainder. Consequently, a diffusion gradient is set up for molecular nitrogen. As N_2 diffuses into the venous blood and is carried to the lungs, P_{N_2} in the space falls; therefore P_{O_2} and P_{CO_2} rise because the sum of all partial pressures must always be 755 mm. Hg. This rise in P_{O_2} and P_{CO_2} sets up a diffusion gradient for CO_2 and O_2, etc., and the process continues until all the gas disappears.

In the case of fluid resorption, it will be remembered that effective plasma protein osmotic pressure, or plasma oncotic pressure, is 25 to 30 mm. Hg. As long as Ppl is less than 25 to 30 mm. Hg the net driving force on the fluid is directed toward the blood. Abnormal stiffness of the lung (which leads to more nega-

tive Ppl), or increased permeability of the capillary walls and pleura to plasma proteins, would naturally tend to reverse the flow and produce *pleural* effusion. A similar argument applies to the etiology of *pulmonary* edema. Whenever the hydrostatic drive from capillaries to alveoli exceeds the osmotic drive in the reverse direction, accumulation of fluid in the interstitial tissues and alveolar spaces may be expected. The hydrostatic drive is heightened by increased pulmonary capillary pressure and by increased alveolar surface tension, while the reverse osmotic drive is lowered by protein leakage through the capillary wall. Blocked lymphatic drainage would enhance the edematous effects.

As Burns[13] has pointed out, once the pneumothorax or hydrothorax disappears, the negative *pressures* also disappear, and the visceral and parietal pleurae are held together by intermolecular *forces.* For example, West[99] long ago measured an attractive force of 3600 mm. Hg per sq. cm. between two mucosal sheets. The argument about reabsorption of trapped gas from body cavities is often misleadingly given as an "explanation" of the fact that the lung remains expanded in the normal chest.

AIRWAY RESISTANCE

Normally we are unconscious of the forces which move air into and out of the lungs; air movement becomes a problem only during severe exercise or illness. Disorders such as asthma, emphysema, bronchitis, croup, pneumonia, etc., are characterized by moderate to severe increases in resistance due to partial obstruction of airways.

The resistance to gas flow (Rg) within an airway is defined as the pressure difference between the ends of the airway, Pg, divided by the volume flow: $Rg = Pg/\dot{V}$. Poiseuille's law states that for laminar flow in straight tubes, Rg is a function of the tube dimensions and of the viscosity of the gas.

Flow in a branching distensible system where turbulence may exist is too complex for theoretical analysis. A practical way of avoiding the innumerable pitfalls of pure theory was suggested by Rohrer.[84] He proposed that the pressure drop, Pg, could be described adequately by two terms: $K_1\dot{V} + K_2(\dot{V})^2$. The first term was due mainly to laminar flow; the second term arose largely from nonuniform geometry resulting in turbulent flow at higher velocities. The factors K_1 and K_2 are proportionality constants for each particular system, obtained by fitting the equation to the experimental data. From this equation one sees that Rg for a given

TABLE 2.   *Partial Pressures of Body Gases**

	ARTERIAL	VENOUS	TRAPPED GAS
N_2	573	573	620
O_2	100	40	38
CO_2	40	46	50
H_2O	47	47	47
Total	760	706	755

*Partial pressures in arterial blood, in venous blood, and in gas in a pneumothorax some time after trapping. The large arteriovenous drop in P_{O_2}, without a corresponding increase in P_{CO_2}, lowers the total gas tension of venous blood. Trapped gases then move into venous blood in the direction of their diffusion gradients.

airway is not constant, but a function of $\dot{V}$: Rg $= Pg/\dot{V} = K_1 + K_2\dot{V}$. However, K_2 is sufficiently small so that the second term is insignificant during normal breathing. More extensive discussions of pressure–flow relationships may be found in books on hydrodynamics.

Determining airway resistance is not as simple as the equation $Rg = Pg/\dot{V}$ might suggest. Although flow can be satisfactorily measured by a variety of modern flow meters or pneumotachometers, a difficulty arises in evaluating $Pg \equiv Pao - Palv$ which requires that the pressure be measured at the *inner* end of the airway (in the alveoli) as well as at the mouth (airway opening). Several methods for estimating the alveolar pressure indirectly have been devised.[40, 66, 95]

The total airway resistance of about 3.3 cm. H_2O per liter per second has been partitioned into a series of smaller resistances, each representing a section of the air-conducting system. For example, the nasal passages alone account for about 50 per cent of Rg, the remaining upper airways for another 20 per cent, and the lower airways (bronchi and bronchioles) for the remainder. Even though *each* small bronchiole has a high resistance to flow, the number of bronchioles in parallel is so large that their *total* resistance is actually much lower than that of airways higher up. Turbulence which occurs in the trachea and larynx at even moderate velocities never occurs in the small bronchioles.*

Implicit in Rohrer's formulation of the pressure-flow equation is the assumption that airway dimensions are constant. We now know that airway size depends on the degree of lung inflation and, as Einthoven[43] predicted, on the flow-dependent pressure difference across the bronchial walls. Thus, it would seem that calculations of resistance should involve at least three variables: pressure, volume and flow, or P, V, $\dot{V}$. A model of the lung and airways which may be helpful in visualizing the complex relations of these three variables is shown in Figure 17. One may view the lung parenchyma as elastic tissue stretched between the visceral pleura and the airways.[15] During *inspiration*, while the lung volume is increasing, the augmented tension in the lung tissue (the springs in the model, Fig.

*Turbulence arises in long, straight, round tubes whenever the dimensionless quantity, Reynold's number (Re), is greater than about 2000; $Re = 2rv\rho/\eta$ (r = radius of the airway, v = linear velocity, ρ = fluid density, η = viscosity). When the tubular geometry is irregular, turbulence begins at much lower values of Re.

17) enlarges the intrapulmonary airways.** Meanwhile, Ppl is becoming more negative, distending the *extra*pulmonary airways—the trachea and primary bronchi. Because of the pressure drop along the bronchial tree due to air flow, the transbronchial pressure (Pbr) is positive as well: $Pbr \equiv Paw - Palv$ (Paw is the pressure inside the airway). Thus Pbr acts to enlarge the *intra*pulmonary airways. Consequently, the rate of inspiration is not limited; the faster the piston moves, the larger the airways become and the higher the flow rates.

During expiration, however, as the piston is forced to the right Ppl rises, often becoming quite positive. This pressure is applied directly to the lower trachea and primary bronchi and compresses them. Within the lung, since gas is now flowing from alveoli to the airways, Palv becomes greater than Paw causing compression of the intrapulmonary airways as well. Furthermore, as the lung volume diminishes, the tissue tension on the airways decreases, reducing airway dimensions even further. As a consequence of these "negative feedback" mechanisms, the rate of expiration *is* self-limiting. In fact, expiratory flow rates have even been shown to *decrease* with excessive expiratory effort. The most striking example of this "check-valve mechanism"[36] is seen in emphysema: the harder the patient blows, the more his airways collapse and the

**Since the bronchi of all mammals are enclosed in connective tissue sleeves (peribronchium), the larger intrapulmonary airways are protected against overdistension. The bronchioles have no surrounding sheath.

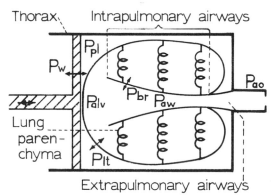

Fig. 17. Shown in this mechanical model of the respiratory system are factors that influence tracheobronchial dimensions. The airways are represented by a semiflaccid tube leading into an elastic "lung." The lung parenchyma is stretched between pleura and airways. Three factors determine bronchial size: (i) bronchial compliance, (ii) lung volume, which affects the parenchymal tension on the bronchi, and (iii) the transbronchial gas pressure. (After Fry and Hyatt, *Amer. J. Med.*, 1960, *29*:672–689.)

less is his expiratory flow rate.* His inspiratory flow rates may be much nearer normal. Patients with severe emphysema and asthma find partial relief by unconsciously maintaining a high FRC to distend the airways, by inspiring rapidly to allow more time for slow expiration, and by pursing the lips or narrowing the glottis to limit the flow rate and reduce airway collapse. In asthma, the heightened bronchomotor tone acts as an equivalent pressure on the airways, and the effect on expiration is similar to that seen in emphysema.[77]

DISTRIBUTION OF INSPIRED GAS IN THE LUNG

The discussion thus far has treated the properties of the *whole* lung without regard to the properties of its lobes, segments or lobules. There is reason to believe that in a complex structure such as the lung all subdivisions may *not* have the same properties, particularly in diseased lungs.[63] One result of this nonuniformity is *unequal distribution*** of gas on inspiration and *unequal emptying* of lung units on expiration. Desaturation may then arise because blood flowing through poorly ventilated regions is not fully oxygenated. Nonuniform distribution may arise from any of the following conditions: (i) unequal compliances leading to different degrees of volume change in various lung regions, (ii) unequal airway resistance to various parts of the lung,[72] or (iii) unequal forces on the lung surface—e.g., descent of the diaphragm preferentially inflating the lower lobes. Since blood flow (perfusion) is also greatest in the lower lobes (the resting pulmonary arterial pressure is almost insufficient to elevate blood to the apices), the ventilation-to-perfusion ratio is partially compensated.[10] Nonuniform ratios of ventilation to perfusion are, however, particularly prevalent in obstructive airway disease and also occur in pulmonary fibrosis, pneumonitis and pulmonary edema. *Ventilation–perfusion abnormalities are the most common cause of hypoxia and hypercapnia in clinical medicine.*[73]

---

* The reasons why airway collapse is facilitated in these lungs are discussed in a later section on Emphysema.
** Equal distribution occurs whenever $\dot{V}_{A_I}/V_0$ is the same for every region; $\dot{V}_{A_I}$ is the inspiratory alveolar ventilation of the region and V_0 its resting volume. In other words, with equal distribution the volume changes of all regions must be in the same *proportion* throughout the inspiratory phase.

TESTS OF PULMONARY MECHANICAL FUNCTION

Tests of pulmonary function may be grouped into four classes: measurements of flow, volume, compliance and nonuniform distribution. The first three require only a knowledge of volume and pressure, or of flow and pressure, as functions of time. However, the fourth, nonuniform distribution of gas in the lung, must be determined by methods involving blood gas and alveolar gas analyses.

Flow Measurements. (a) *Maximum voluntary ventilation (MVV):* The subject is asked to breathe as hard as he can voluntarily from a spirometer for 15 seconds. The spirometer has a mechanical summing device which adds each inspired tidal volume to the previous ones so that the total ventilation may be read directly. Normal values are roughly 120 to 200 liters per minute. MVV is distinguished from MBC (maximum breathing capacity), which is the maximum volume of gas that *can* be breathed per minute, e.g., when stimulated by high CO_2 or exercise.

(b) *Forced expiratory volume (FEV_t), or timed vital capacity:* The subject inspires to total lung capacity, TLC, then exhales as rapidly as possible while a spirometer records both his vital capacity and the volume expired in timed intervals. A normal person can exhale about 68 per cent of his VC in the first 0.5 second, 77 per cent in 0.75 second, 84 per cent in 1.0 second, 94 per cent in 2.0 seconds, and 97 per cent in 3.0 seconds.[49,69] This is a commonly used test in pulmonary function laboratories.

(c) *Maximum expiratory flow (MEF):* The highest flow rate during a maximal forced expiration can be recorded with a Wright Peak Flow Meter.[101] Healthy subjects reach peaks of 350 to 500 liters per minute. The Puffmeter,[50] a damped flow meter, measures the flow that can be maintained over a very short period of time, rather than the instantaneous peak. Both tests correlate well with MVV and can be made with relatively inexpensive equipment. They are therefore extremely useful office tests.

(d) *Walking ventilation index (WVI):* The ratio of the ventilation per minute while the subject walks on the level at two miles per hour for a four-minute period to the MVV is usually less than 0.35; in cases of severe dyspnea, it exceeds 0.55.[97]

(e) *Maximal midexpiratory flow (MMF):* The slope in the midvolume range of a recording from a conventional spirometer gives the flow rate, $\dot{V}$, at midexpiration. The flow rate at this point has been found to be a more sensitive indicator of obstructive impairment than FEV_t, MVV, or the measurement of the VC.[59]

Volume Measurements. Three of the four lung volumes can be measured with any simple spirometer. The residual volume, however, must be determined by indirect methods such as plethysmography, gas dilution or N_2 washout.[31]

Plethysmography has the virtue of detecting gas trapped in nonventilated regions of the residual volume as well as air in the ventilated regions. In this procedure, the subject is enclosed in an air-tight box, and his mouth is connected to a pressure transducer so that no flow can take place. When he makes an expiratory effort the *dry* fraction of the gas in his lung is compressed isothermally according to Boyle's law: $(P-P_{H_2O}) \times V$ = Constant.* Letting the subscripts i and f refer to initial and final values, respectively, one may write $(P_i - 47) \times V_i = (P_f - 47) \times V_f$. Since $P_f = P_i + \Delta P$ and $V_f = V_i - \Delta V$, the right side may be written as $(P_i + \Delta P - 47)(V_i - \Delta V)$, and one can then solve for V_i: $V_i = \Delta V \left(\dfrac{P_i + \Delta P - 47}{\Delta P} \right)$. The plethysmograph measures the change in lung volume (ΔV) during compression; P_i is the initial pressure (atmospheric); and ΔP is the change in alveolar pressure after compression. For convenience, the FRC might be chosen for the initial volume, V_i. Then RV = FRC − ERV, where ERV is measured from the resting end-expiratory level.

Dilution methods are based on the simple principle that the number of *mols* of a gas is unchanged when the gas is expanded. By rebreathing, a certain quantity of a relatively insoluble gas such as helium (He) in a bellows or spirometer is mixed with the air already in the lung; in other words, the He in the bellows expands into a larger total volume. The computation proceeds as follows: $C_iV_i = C_fV_f = C_f(V_i + V_L)$, or $V_L = V_i \left(\dfrac{C_i - C_f}{C_f} \right)$. Here C_i and V_i refer to initial He concentration and volume in the bellows, respectively; C_f and V_f are the final concentration and volume in the bellows–lung system; V_L, the desired volume, is FRC if the rebreathing is begun at resting end tidal expiration. Normal values are shown in Figure 5.

Compliance Measurements. (a) *"Static" lung compliance (Clt):* Measurement of the slope of the lung v–p curve in the tidal volume range

*Notice that only the *dry* fractions are used in the computation because saturated water vapor condenses when compressed, thus altering the *amount* of water in the gas phase. Boyle's law does *not* hold where condensation and evaporation can occur!

(as described earlier) requires only an esophageal balloon, a water manometer, and a spirometer. Normal compliances in adults average 0.18 to 0.27 liters per cm. H_2O. This quantity is more accurately called "quasi-static" compliance, because static values are usually not obtainable. In men over age 60, Clt is about 25 per cent greater than in younger men; very little change occurs in women.[29]

(b) *Static chest wall compliance (Cw):* As described earlier, Cw is the slope of the Pes versus V curve, obtained while the respiratory muscles are relaxed. It usually has approximately the same value as Clt.

(c) *Specific compliance:* To compare individuals of different sizes, the values of Clt and Cw must be standardized. As an example, mouse lungs having a compliance of 0.0001 liter per cm. H_2O are not 2000 times as "stiff" as human lung. In practice, therefore, the static compliance divided by a characteristic lung volume (e.g., FRC, VC or TLC) yields a "compliance per unit volume" or "specific" compliance.

(d) *Dynamic compliance (C_{dyn}):* The "static" compliance is ideally determined at zero frequency, meaning, in effect, that Pes has equilibrated before a reading is taken. Thus, if Pes has become *approximately* constant when the manometer is read, a "quasi-static" compliance is obtained. However, if the subject is breathing regularly at a fixed frequency, the measurement must be called the "dynamic" compliance at that frequency.

Although the data are easily obtained, the interpretation of C_{dyn} is highly complex and still controversial. Measurement is conveniently made by plotting (Pao-Pes) on the X-axis versus V on the Y-axis with either an XY recorder or an oscilloscope. Figure 18*A* shows three such dynamic v–p loops made at the same tidal volume but at three different frequencies. Loop *a* was made from a very slowly executed respiratory cycle (this curve is identical to the minor v–p loops of Figure 8). To generate loop *b* the subject breathed at a moderately rapid rate. Care should be taken to distinguish this *apparent* hysteresis loop from the lung hysteresis already detailed. The dynamic loop of Figure 18 arises almost entirely from gas flow-resistive pressure drop. In other words, in addition to the lung elastic pressure, Pst(lt), the chest must exert a pressure, Pg + Pres(lt) = Pres, to move gas and to overcome lung tissue resistance (Fig. 18*B*). On expiration Pres changes sign and is, in this case, subtracted from Pst(lt). Obviously Pres is zero at those two instants of the respiratory cycle when $\dot{V}$ is zero (the maxima and minima of V). Consequently the slope of the line joining these two points is

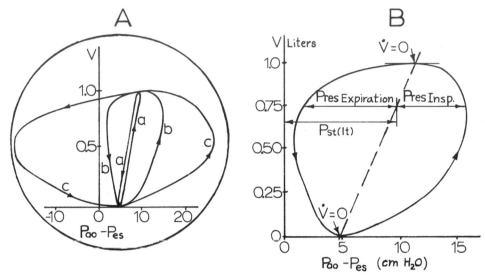

Fig. 18. Analysis of dynamic v–p loops of the lung.

A, These oscilloscopic tracings were made by simultaneously recording tidal volume from a spirometer on the vertical axis and transpulmonary pressure (Pao–Pes) on the horizontal axis at three breathing rates: (a) very slow breathing, about 3 breaths per minute, (b) moderately rapid breathing, about 40 breaths per minute, (c) near maximal breathing rate. In (a) the flow resistive pressure is negligible.

B, A line joining the two points at which $\dot{V} = 0$ gives the dynamic elastic v–p curve of the lung. Pst (lt) is due to the elastic lung retractive force while Pres is due mainly to gas flow resistive and partly to tissue resistive forces.

the dynamic compliance of the lung at that particular frequency. Loop *c* (Fig. 18*A*) illustrates the shape of the dynamic v–p loop obtained during maximal breathing frequencies. In elderly men[29] and in emphysematous patients, C_{dyn} clearly decreases as breathing frequency is increased, whereas in younger, healthy individuals it may remain more nearly constant.[37, 72] A fall in compliance as respiratory rate rises could be due to the lung's viscoelasticity[53] (Fig. 14*B*) or to unequal time constants (RC) in different lung regions,[72] or to both.

Tests of Nonuniform Distribution. (a) *Blood gases:* Whenever low O_2 and high CO_2 concentrations are found in arterial blood, the patient is usually suffering from either hypoventilation or ventilation–perfusion abnormalities. Hypoventilation may be ruled out if the measured minute ventilation is normal (6 to 8 liters per minute).

(b) *Nitrogen washout:* When a patient with poorly ventilated lung areas is given pure oxygen, the N_2 in the hypoventilated portions is more slowly washed out than in other areas. After breathing O_2 for seven minutes, the patient with normal lungs has only 2.5 per cent N_2 in forced expired (reserve) air, whereas the value may approach 20 per cent in persons with poor

mixing.[33] Uniform distribution is considered to be present when a plot of log $\overline{F_{E_{N_2}}}$ (mean fraction of N_2 in expired air) against number of breaths is linear.[46]

(c) *Nitrogen index:* Following a single breath of pure O_2, the nitrogen concentration in the succeeding expiration is continuously recorded. The increase in N_2 between the point at which the first 750 ml. have been exhaled and the point at which the next 500 ml. have been exhaled should not be greater than 1.5 per cent.[30] It should be noted that *uneven emptying* must accompany *unequal distribution* if a progressive increase in P_{N_2} is to be found, namely, that $V_{A_E}(t)/V_0$ is not the same in all regions. Consequently, the distribution abnormality itself is always underestimated. P_{CO_2} may show a similar late rise at the end of a forced expiration. If the *end-tidal* to *end-expiratory reserve* P_{CO_2} difference is greater than 5 mm. Hg, one can suspect uneven ventilation–perfusion ratios accompanying uneven emptying.[3]

(d) *Anatomic localization:* This may be made by bronchospirometry, lobar spirometry or small catheter studies of gas samples taken from segmental and subsegmental bronchi. Relatively

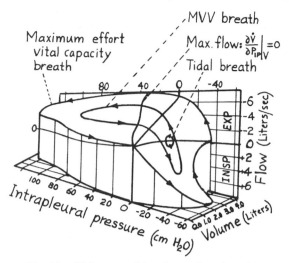

Fig. 19. If flow, considered as a function of intrapleural pressure and lung volume, is plotted on one of three perpendicular axes, a surface is obtained which describes the flow characteristics of a lung. Shown here are the data from a normal lung. Expiration is limited by airway collapse as indicated by the fact that the surface dips back down toward the PV plane for large positive pleural pressures. The intersection of the surface with the PV plane is the static PV curve of the lung, and the intersection with the VV̇ plane is the passive expiration curve. (After Fry and Hyatt, *Amer. J. Med.*, 1960, *29*:672–689.)

unventilated regions have a high N_2 content after a period of O_2 breathing.

A Unified Approach to Lung Mechanics. Only three variables (P, V and V̇) are necessary for an approximate description of lung characteristics. To illustrate the relationship between these variables, a unified approach based on the model shown in Figure 17 has been proposed by Fry and Hyatt.[48] Regarding V̇ as a function only of Ppl and V, they plotted these three variables on perpendicular axes to obtain a three-dimensional surface descriptive of each lung and airway system (Fig. 19). (For simplicity they neglect time-dependent properties.) The figure illustrates the remarks made in the section on Airway Resistance. During inspiration (+ V̇) the surface dips sharply toward high flows at even moderate pressures. However, due to airway collapse, flow reaches a *maximum* during expiration (− V̇) and at high pressures remains constant or falls slightly. The effect of lung volume on maximum flow rate is clearly seen, the surface sloping upward along the volume axis. The striking alterations in the P-V̇ relationship in the emphysematous patient have already been described. In this individual, the surface rises only slightly above the P-V̇ plane; that is, his expiratory flow is small and limited. For the student of

mechanics, a more complete discussion is offered by the original papers.[47, 48, 56]

WORK OF BREATHING

An attempt to calculate the work done by the respiratory muscles is certain to encounter nearly insurmountable difficulties. In one sense it is correct to say simply that the work done by a muscle as it lifts a weight is the external force exerted (F) times the distance moved (x), or ∫ Fdx. Yet, from the amount of work performed on the surroundings, we have no information about the dissipation of energy due to active antagonists, nor of the additional energy required by the muscle while holding a fixed length or even lowering the weight. Physiologists have been forced to define the work of breathing as consisting only of the measurable external work performed during part or all of the cycle.

Two mechanical elements in the respiratory system are dissipative: the tissue resistance and the gas flow resistance. Although both are nonlinear, they may be lumped for convenience into a single linear dashpot, R (Fig. 20*A*). Two *non*-dissipative elements in the mechanical analogue are the lung–chest elastance, 1/C, and inertance, I, related to the weight of the tissues. Inertance is normally neglected since it is significant only at frequencies in excess of 150 breaths per minute. The equation describing the motion of the system is, then: $P = \dfrac{1}{C} V + R\dot{V}$.

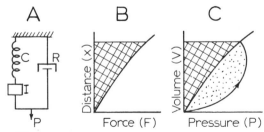

Fig. 20. *A,* Simplified mechanical analogue of the respiratory system. The elastance, resistance and inertance are represented by three pure elements, C, R and I, respectively. Inertance can be neglected except at very high volume accelerations.

B, The work of stretching a spring is the shaded area to the left of the force–elongation curve.

C, Similarly, the work of inflating a balloon is the shaded area to the left of the V–P curve. The stippled area represents the work done in overcoming inspiratory flow resistance.

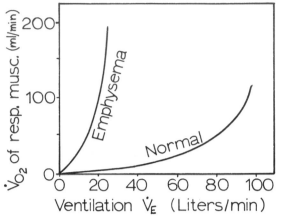

Fig. 21. These curves were obtained from one normal subject and one patient with emphysema. Ventilation was increased by added dead space (rebreathing). The patient with emphysema had a greater O_2 cost of breathing at resting levels of ventilation, but more striking was the rate of rise of $\dot{V}_{O_2}$ as ventilation was increased. (After Campbell *et al.*, *J. appl. Physiol.*, 1957, *11*:303–308.)

Because expiration, except in moderate or severe exercise, is almost entirely passive, work is expended mainly on inspiration (by extending the spring and dashpot). The frictional energy loss appears as heat, while the energy put into the spring is stored. Since this stored energy is not returnable to the muscles,* it is used to bring the system back to its resting volume; in other words, it is assumed to be dissipated in the dashpot during expiration.

The work (W) of stretching a spring may be computed as follows: $W = \int F dx$, represented by the cross-hatched area of Figure 20*B*. A simple development of this equation leads to a method for finding the work of inflating a balloon: $W = \int F dx = \int (F/A) \cdot A dx = \int P dV$ (A is the surface area). This is the cross-hatched region shown on the V-P curve in Figure 20*C*. When friction is present, the total applied pressure equals the sum of static pressure (Pst) and resistive pressure (Pres): $P = Pst + Pres$; thus $W = \int P dV = \int (Pst + Pres) dV = \int Pst dV + \int Pres dV$. The latter term is represented by the stippled area of Figure 20*C*; the sum is approximately the external work done for each breath. Whenever expiration is not passive, another term must be computed for this part of the cycle as well.

Otis *et al.*[71] have approximated the flow by a sinusoidal function to permit an analytic instead of a

*When an active muscle is stretched by an external force, it does not convert mechanical energy into chemical energy; it merely degrades chemical energy at a *lower rate*. Work done on an active muscle has been called *negative work*.

graphic integration. They were able to compute the energy required to maintain a certain alveolar ventilation for various respiratory rates. A graph of *computed power* versus *respiratory rate* for a fixed ventilation shows a power minimum at some frequency. Interestingly, it appears that most animals have adjusted their resting respiratory rates to fall somewhere near this minimum.[2, 34]

The work of breathing may be studied in a different way—i.e., by measuring the energy put *into* the respiratory system rather than the external work done *by* the system. Oxygen consumption is a measure of energy input since for every liter of O_2 consumed an average of 4.825 calories is produced. If a subject ventilates at a series of minute volumes ($\dot{V}_E$), from resting $\dot{V}_E$ up to MVV, it may be assumed that the respiratory muscles account for the additional O_2 consumption above the basal rate (Fig. 21). From this figure the plight of the emphysematous patient is quite apparent. By increasing his ventilation he may consume *more* O_2 in the respiratory muscles than can be provided by this additional ventilation, and consequently, the arterial oxygen tension falls. Normally, the limiting factor in exercise is likely to be the cardiac output.

A comparison of the external work with the caloric input yields a ratio which has been called "efficiency." Because of the difficulties mentioned, the values of efficiency so derived range rather widely, from 3 to 25 per cent.

INFLUENCE OF LUNG MECHANICAL PROPERTIES ON PULMONARY CIRCULATION

It is fairly easy to understand that alterations in the pulmonary vascular resistance would arise from changes in vasomotor tone or from obstruction to flow caused by embolism, thrombosis, chronic obstructive emphysema, fibrosis or metastatic carcinoma. However the influences of transpulmonary pressure, degree of lung inflation, and several other mechanical factors are more subtle and therefore should be explained in greater detail.

The heart and its large conducting vessels are suspended in the mediastinum and, like the esophagus, are subjected to distending forces due to the retraction of the lungs. These forces, as Donders recognized in 1853,[38] have a "sucking" effect on all structures opening into the thoracic cavity, thus facilitating venous return and slightly encumbering arterial flow out of the thorax. Significant alterations in intrathoracic pres-

Fig. 22. *A,* Schematic representation of the "waterfall" hypothesis. The collapsible segment is sometimes called a "Starling resistor." Flow is independent of pulmonary venous pressure, Ppv, except when Ppv > Palv. When either Palv or Ppv are equal to pulmonary arterial pressure, Ppa, flow ceases. (All pressures here are referred to pleural pressure, Ppl.)

B, Plot of flow through the cat's pulmonary vascular system at increasing levels of inflation (Palv) when the arterial pressure is held constant at 12.3 cm. above the base of the lung, and the venous reservoir is below the base of the lung. (After Riley, *Ciba symposium on pulmonary structure and function,* 1962.)

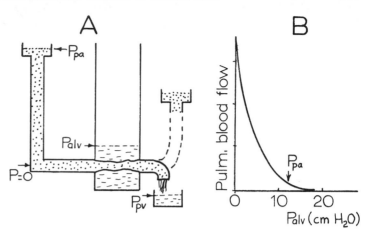

sures occur whenever the chest is opened; this should be kept in mind if physiologic deductions about the closed-chest situation are to be made from open-chest experiments regarding cardiovascular or pulmonary function. Open-chest conditions are simulated in an intact subject by inspiring to about 0.6 VC and then relaxing against a closed airway so that Ppl is zero.

As Burton and Yamada have pointed out,[14] studies of flow through collapsible blood vessels must take into account both the resistive pressure difference between the ends of the vessel (P_R) and the transmural pressure (TMP). This latter pressure (or more accurately, *effective transmural force*) determines the luminal size of a given vessel. The concept of TMP may be applied to the lung by grouping the pulmonary vessels into two broad categories: large and small.[54] The lung parenchyma is considered to be like an elastic mesh stretched from the visceral pleura to the major blood vessels, as well as to the airways. A force on this mesh such as results during inflation of the lungs, tends therefore to distend not only the airways but the larger blood vessels also.* The small vessels (principally gas-exchanging in function) are located *within* the interalveolar septa and consequently are *not* enlarged by tissue or surface forces. In fact, they are flattened or "squeezed" by a rise in alveolar pressure (Palv).

A simple model which may help to clarify the effect of Palv on small vessels is shown in Figure 22*A*.[54, 76, 83] The pulmonary arterial pressure, P_{pa}, is represented by the height of the first reservoir. The thin-walled, collapsible capillaries pass through a chamber whose pressure is Palv, and empty via a "waterfall" into the venous reservoir. Several points are immediately obvious: (i) a rise in Palv constricts the small vessels, acting as a "sluice gate";[6] (ii) moving the venous reservoir up or down has *no* effect on flow from the "waterfall," *except* when P_{pv} becomes positive (as in mitral stenosis); (iii) *either* a rise in P_{pa} *or* a positive P_{pv} enlarges partially compressed vessels; (iv) blood flow therefore normally depends on (P_{pa} – Palv), *not* on (P_{pa} – P_{pv}), except in

*This applies particularly to the venous side. The arteries are less distensible because of a connective tissue sheath similar to that enveloping bronchi.

abnormal cases in which there is "back pressure" from the pulmonary vein. The effects of lung inflation on blood flow are shown in Figure 22*B*. For a fixed P_{pa}, blood flow drops to nearly zero when Palv = P_{pa}. Thus, to minimize the work load on the right heart, it is desirable to keep the "sluice" pressure, Palv, as low as possible.

ALTERATIONS OF MECHANICAL PARAMETERS IN DISEASE

Respiratory problems are becoming increasingly important; 10 to 15 per cent of the American population over age 40 present readily detectable evidence of pulmonary disorders. A complete clinical account of the changes in mechanical function occurring in respiratory diseases can be found in such books as Gordon's *Clinical Cardiopulmonary Physiology.* In this chapter five common disorders have been selected to illustrate changes in lung mechanical properties in disease.

Asthma. Bronchospastic respiratory diseases are differentiable from nonspastic obstructive airway diseases by the former's positive response to bronchodilators. However, a considerable proportion of the airway resistance in asthma is due to the presence of edema fluid and mucus in the smaller bronchioles. In common with other obstructive diseases, the higher airway resistance in asthma hinders expiration and the mean lung volume rises; fortunately, this tends to enlarge the airways and to aid expiration by increasing the elastic recoil of the thorax. Lung compliance is generally not greatly affected by constriction of the airways. Treatment is aimed either at controlling an allergy— such as might result from an inhalant (pollen,

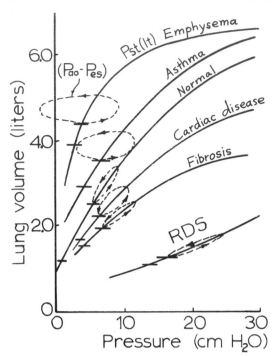

Fig. 23. Static and dynamic lung v–p curves illustrate the effects of certain diseases on lung compliance, lung volumes and airway resistance. The upper horizontal bar on each v–p curve represents a typical value for the functional residual capacity, and the lower bar the residual volume.

Augmented airway resistance is the predominant feature in asthma and emphysema (obstructive diseases), while decreased compliance is most obvious in pulmonary fibrosis and respiratory distress syndrome (restrictive diseases). Cardiac patients show some changes in both characteristics.

dust, etc.) or food (wheat, milk, etc.)—or at relaxing the smooth muscle with bronchodilators such as epinephrine whenever the primary cause of the constriction is unknown.

Emphysema. Emphysema has been defined as "a condition of the lung characterized by increase beyond the normal in the size of air spaces distal to the terminal bronchiole either from dilatation or from destruction of their walls" (Ciba Foundation Guest Symposium, *Thorax,* 1959, *14*:236). The compliance of emphysematous lungs is increased and the airways are more susceptible to collapse, probably for several reasons: (i) Inflammation may produce mucosal congestion and sputum which with bronchospasm results in increased airway resistance and consequent airway constriction due to the higher transbronchial pressure. (ii) Destructive changes in the walls of the bronchioles

or loss of lung parenchyma supporting the bronchioles increases airway and lung compliance. Collapse of the trachea and bronchi is in many instances even more important than bronchiolar obstruction.[52, 81, 86] The compensating mechanisms appearing in emphysema and asthma have already been mentioned in the section on Airway Resistance.

It is clear from Figure 23 that in actual fact a single value for compliance cannot be quoted since C_L, for these lungs in particular, depends on the volume at which the measurement is made.

Fibrosis. Thickening of the pulmonary membranes results in decreased compliance and a decreased diffusing capacity without consistent increases in airway resistance. The patient's outstanding symptom is exertional dyspnea—i.e., a subjective feeling of shortness of breath during exercise.

Respiratory Distress Syndrome (RDS). RDS accounts for approximately 30,000 deaths annually in the U.S. Premature infants are particularly susceptible. Usually within hours after birth such babies develop severe breathing difficulty as evidenced by marked inspiratory effort, sternal retraction, grunting expiration, and hypoxia or cyanosis. Blood shunt increases from the normal 3 per cent to 10 to 80 per cent. Mortality is highest on the first or second day; thereafter chances for survival improve sharply. Postmortem examination of the lungs reveals a dark liver-like appearance, widespread atelectasis and alveolar instability evidenced by lung collapse at fairly high pressures (5 cm. H_2O) and very little gas trapping. After several hours of respiratory difficulty, the infant's lungs show thickened glassy (hyaline) membranes in the gas-exchanging portions, hence the name "hyaline membrane disease." The surface tension of lung extracts made from atelectatic lungs generally does not fall below 20 dynes per cm. as compared to 5 dynes per cm. for normal lungs.

It has been suggested[51] that prior to birth an unknown form of stress affects the fetus, in some way reducing the activity of lung surfactant. The deficiency corrects itself after the second day, making the disease self-limited. Meanwhile high surface tension promotes transudation from blood and fibrin deposition in the lung membranes. An RDS almost identical with hyaline membrane disease appears in patients who have undergone cardiopulmonary bypass for prolonged periods. Loss of surfactant activity is also assumed to be the precipitating factor. A recent report[21a] indicates that perinatal stress (hypoxemia, acidemia, hypothermia, hypovolemia) may actually bring about *pulmonary vasoconstriction,* thereby causing a ductus arteriosus shunt. The surfactant deficiency then follows secondarily. Rational therapy, therefore, should be directed at correcting the vasoconstriction as well as relieving the above stresses.

Cardiac Disease. The first symptom of cardiac disease occurring downstream from the lungs is frequently dyspnea. The mechanism is not clear, although back-pressure from the left heart and consequent overdistension of the lungs with blood is known to occur. This leads to some loss of both lung volume and compliance and sometimes to decreased diffusing capacity from thickening of the alveolo-capillary membrane.

REFERENCES

1. Agostoni, E. and Taglietti, A. *Arch. Fisiol.,* 1957, *57:* 230–242.
2. Agostoni, E., Thimm, F. F., and Fenn, W. O. *J. appl. Physiol.,* 1959, *14:*679–683.
3. Anderson, W. H. *Dis. Chest,* 1963, *44:*478–484.
4. Anthonisen, N. R. *Amer. J. Physiol.,* 1964, *207:*235–238.
5. Avery, M. E. *Pediatrics,* 1962, *30:*324–330.
6. Banister, J. and Torrance, R. W. *Quart. J. exp. Physiol.,* 1960, *45:*352–367.
7. Bendixen, H. H., Hedley-Whyte, J. and Laver, M. B. *New Engl. J. Med.,* 1963, *269:*991–996.
8. Bernstein, L. *J. Physiol.,* 1957, *138:*473–487.
9. Bernstein, L., Phillips, H. H. and Paddock, R. B. *Physiologist,* 1963, *6:*139.
10. Bouhuys, A. and Lundin, G. *Physiol. Rev.,* 1959, *39:*731–750.
11. Brown, E. S., Johnson, R. P. and Clements, J. A. *J. appl. Physiol.,* 1959, *14:*717–720.
12. Buckingham, S. and Avery, M. E. *Nature (Lond.),* 1963, *193:*688–689.
13. Burns, D. *J. Physiol.,* 1940, *98:*26P.
14. Burton, A. C. and Yamada, S. *J. appl. Physiol.,* 1951, *4:*329–339.
15. Butler, J., Caro, C. G., Alcala, R. and DuBois, A. B. *J. clin. Invest.,* 1960, *39:*584–591.
16. Buytendijk, H. J. *Oesophagusdruck en longelasticiteit. Dissertatie, University of Groningen,* Oppenheim N. V. Electrische Drukkerij, 1949.
17. Campbell, E. J. M. *The respiratory muscles and the mechanics of breathing.* Chicago, Year Book Publishers, 1958.
18. Caro, C. G., Butler, J. and DuBois, A. B. *J. clin. Invest.,* 1960, *39:*573–583.
19. Carson, J. *Phil. Trans.,* 1820, *B110:*29–44.
20. Chase, W. H. *Exp. Cell. Res.,* 1959, *18:*15–28.
21. Cherniack, R. M., Farhi, L. E., Armstrong, B. W. and Proctor, D. F. *J. appl. Physiol.,* 1955, *8:*203–211.
21a. Chu, J., Clements, J. A., Cotton, E., Klaus, M. H., Sweet, A. Y., Thomas, M. A. and Tooley, W. H. *Pediatrics,* 1965, *35:*733–742.
22. Clark, E. R., Jr., Martin, C. J. and Politoff, S. *Dis. Chest,* 1958, *34:*150–153.
23. Clements, J. A. *Amer. J. Physiol.,* 1956, *187:*592.
24. Clements, J. A. *Proc. Soc. exp. Biol. (N.Y.),* 1957, *95:*170–172.
25. Clements, J. A. *Arch. environm. Hlth,* 1961, *2:*280–283.
26. Clements, J. A., Hustead, R. F., Johnson, R. P. and Gribetz, I. *J. appl. Physiol.,* 1961, *16:*444–450.
27. Clements, J. A. In: *Proceedings, International Union of Physiological Sciences,* vol. 11. New York, Excerpta Medica Foundation, 1962.
28. Clements, J. A., Tierney, D. F. and Trahan, H. J. *Physiologist,* 1963, *6:*159.
29. Cohn, J. E. and Donoso, H. D. *J. clin. Invest.,* 1963, *42:* 1406–1410.
30. Comroe, J. H., Jr. and Fowler, W. S. *Amer. J. Med.,* 1951, *10:*408–413.
31. Comroe, J. H., Jr., Forster, R. E., DuBois, A. B., Briscoe, W. A. and Carlsen, E. *The Lung,* Chicago, Year Book Publishers, 1962.
32. Cook, C. D., Mead, J. and Orzalesi, M. M. *J. appl. Physiol.,* 1964, *19:*1016–1022.
33. Cournand, A., Baldwin, E. de F., Darling, R. C. and Richards, D. W., Jr. *J. clin. Invest.,* 1941, *20:*681–689.
34. Crosfill, M. L. and Widdicombe, J. G. *J. Physiol.,* 1961, *158:*1–14.
35. Daly, W. J. and Bondurant, S. *J. appl. Physiol.,* 1963, *18:*513–518.
36. Dayman, H. *J. clin. Invest.,* 1951, *30:*1175–1190.
37. Defares, J. G. and Donleben, P. G. *J. appl. Physiol.,* 1960, *15:*166–169.
38. Donders, F. C. *Z. Rationale Medizin,* 1853, *3:*287–319.
39. DuBois, A. B. and Ross, B. B. *Proc. Soc. exp. Biol. (N.Y.),* 1951, *78:*546–549.
40. DuBois, A. B., Botelho, S. and Comroe, J. H., Jr. *J. clin. Invest.,* 1954, *33:*929.
41. Dunnill, M. S. *Thorax,* 1962, *17:*329–333.
42. Egbert, L. D., Laver, M. B. and Bendixen, H. H. *Anesthesiology,* 1963, *24:*57–60.
43. Einthoven, W. *Pflüg. Arch. ges Physiol.,* 1892, *51:*367–445.
44. Farhi, L., Otis, A. B. and Proctor, D. F. *J. appl. Physiol.,* 1957, *10:*15–18.
45. Ferris, B. G., Jr. and Pollard, D. S. *J. clin. Invest.,* 1960, *39:*143–149.
46. Fowler, W. S., Cornish, E. R. and Kety, S. S. *J. clin. Invest.,* 1952, *31:*40–50.
47. Fry, D. L. *Phys. in Med. Biol.,* 1958, *3:*174–194.
48. Fry, D. L. and Hyatt, R. E. *Amer. J. Med.,* 1960, *29:* 672–689.
49. Gaensler, E. A. *Amer. Rev. Tuberc.,* 1951, *64:*256–278.
50. Goldsmith, J. R. *Amer. Rev. Tuberc.,* 1958, *78:*180–190.
51. Gruenwald, P. *Acta Paediatrica,* 1964, *53:*470–477.
52. Herzog, H. *Bronches,* 1961, *11:*77–81.
53. Hildebrandt, J. Dynamic mechanical properties of excised cat lung determined without gas flow. In preparation.
54. Howell, J. B. L., Permutt, S., Proctor, D. F. and Riley, R. L. *J. appl. Physiol.,* 1961, *16:*71–76.
55. Hutchinson, J. In: *The Cyclopaedia of Anatomy and Physiology,* 1849–1852, R. B. Todd, ed., Vol. *4,* Part II.
56. Hyatt, R. E., Schilder, D. P. and Fry, D. L. *J. appl. Physiol.,* 1958, *13:*331–336.
57. Ishikawa, K., Martin, C. J. and Young, A. C. *J. appl. Physiol.,* 1964, *19:*823–826.
57a. Johnson, L. F., Jr. and Mead, J. *J. appl. Physiol.,* 1963, *18:*505–508.

58. KLAUS, M. H., CLEMENTS, J. A. and HAVEL, R. J. *Proc. Nat. Acad. Sci. (Wash.)*, 1961, *47*:1858–1859.
59. LEUALLEN, E. C. and FOWLER, W. S. *Amer. Rev. Tuberc.*, 1955, *72*:783–800.
60. LUCIANI, L. *Arch. Sci. med.*, 1878, *2*:177.
61. MACKLIN, C. C. and HARTROFT, W. S. *Report to the Canadian subcommittee on physiological aspects of chemical warfare.* June, 1943.
62. MACKLIN, C. C. *Lancet*, 1954, *266*:1099–1104.
63. MARTIN, C. J. and YOUNG, A. C. *J. appl. Physiol.*, 1957, *11*:371–376.
64. McCREDIE, M., LOVEJOY, F. W., JR. and KALTREIDER, N. L. *Thorax*, 1962, *17*:213–217.
65. McILROY, M. B. *Thorax*, 1952, *7*:285–290.
66. McILROY, M. B., MEAD, J., SELVERSTONE, N. J. and RADFORD, E. P., JR. *J. appl. Physiol.*, 1955, *7*:485–490.
67. MEAD, J. and COLLIER, C. *J. appl. Physiol.*, 1959, *14*:669–678.
68. MENDENHALL, R. M. and SUN, C. N. *Nature (Lond.)*, 1964, *201*:713–714.
69. MILLER, W. F., JOHNSON, R. L., JR. and WU, N. *J. appl. Physiol.*, 1959, *14*:157–163.
70. ORZALESI, M. M., COOK, C. D., CRAIG, J. M., HOLLISTER, D. J., JACOBSON, H. N., KIKKAWA, Y., MOTOYAMA, E. K. and REYNOLDS, E. O. R. *Physiologist*, 1963, *6*:248.
71. OTIS, A. B., FENN, W. O. and RAHN, H. *J. appl. Physiol.*, 1950, *2*:592–607.
72. OTIS, A. B., McKERROW, C. B., BARTLETT, R. A., MEAD, J., McILROY, M. B., SELVERSTONE, N. J. and RADFORD, E. P. *J. appl. Physiol.*, 1956, *8*:427–443.
73. PACE, W. R., JR., and MARTIN, C. J. *Northw. Med. (Seattle)*, 1963, *62*:30–34.
74. PATTLE, R. E. *Nature (Lond.)*, 1955, *175*:1125–1126.
75. PATTLE, R. E. and THOMAS, L. C. *Nature (Lond.)*, 1961, *189*:844.
76. PERMUTT, S., BROMBERGER-BARNEA, B. and BANE, H. N. *Medicina Thoracalis*, 1962, *19*:239–260.
77. PRIDE, N. B., PERMUTT, S. and RILEY, R. L. *Physiologist*, 1963, *6*:257.
78. RADFORD, E. P., JR., LEFCOE, N. M. and MEAD, J. *Fed. Proc.*, 1954, *13*:114–115.
79. RADFORD, E. P., JR. *Arch. Environm. Hlth*, 1963, *6*:128–133.
80. RADFORD, E. P., JR. In: *Tissue Elasticity*, J. W. Remington, ed. Washington, D.C., American Physiological Society, 1957.
81. RAINER, W. G., HUTCHINSON, D., NEWBY, J. P., HAMSTRA, R. and DURRANCE, J. *J. thorac. cardiovasc. Surg.*, 1963, *46*:559–567.
82. RAUWERDA, P. E. *Unequal ventilation of different parts of the lung and the determination of cardiac output.* Thesis, University of Groningen, Groningen, the Netherlands, 1946.
83. RILEY, R. L. In: *Ciba Symposium on Pulmonary Structure and Function*, A.V.S. DeReuck and M. O'Connor, eds. Boston, Little, Brown & Co., 1962.
84. ROHRER, F. *Arch. ges. Physiol.*, 1915, *162*:225–300.
85. ROSENTHAL, I. *Arch. Physiol.* DuBois-Reymond (Suppl. Ed.), 1880.
86. ROSENZWEIG, D. Y. and FILLEY, G. F. *Amer. Rev. resp. Dis.*, 1963, *88*:6–13.
87. STARK, D. C. and SMITH, H. *Brit. J. Anaesth.*, 1960, *32*:460–465.
88. STAUB, N. C., NAGANO, H., PEARCE, M. L., SAGAWA, Y. and NAKAMURA, T. *Physiologist*, 1963, *6*:280.
89. STOREY, W. F. and STAUB, N. C. *J. appl. Physiol.*, 1962, *17*:391–397.
90. TAYLOR, A. *J. Physiol.*, 1960, *151*:390–402.
91. TERRY, R. J. *Anat. Rec.*, 1926, *32*:223–224.
92. TOOLEY, W., GARDNER, R., THUNG, N. and FINLEY, T. *Fed. Proc.*, 1961, *20*:428.
93. VAN DER BRUGH, J. P. *Arch. ges. Physiol.*, 1900, *82*:591–602.
94. VON NEERGAARD, K. *Z. ges. exp. Med.*, 1929, *66*:373–394.
95. VUILLEUMIER, P. *Z. klin. Med.*, 1944, *143*:698.
96. WADE, O. L. *J. Physiol.*, 1954, *124*:193–212.
97. WARRING, F. C., JR. *Amer. Rev. Tuberc.*, 1945, *51*:432–454.
98. WEIBEL, E. R. *Morphometry of the human lung.* Berlin, Springer, 1963.
99. WEST, S. *Brit. Med. J.*, 1887, *2*:393–400.
100. WIDDICOMBE, J. G. *Physiol. Rev.*, 1963, *43*:1–37.
101. WRIGHT, B. M. and McKERROW, C. B. *Brit. Med. J.*, 1959, *2*(2):1041–1047.

CHAPTER 40

Gas Exchange and Transportation*

By RICHARD L. RILEY

PROPERTIES OF GASES AND LIQUIDS

THE behavior of the respiratory gases in the body cannot be understood unless the student is thoroughly familiar with the simple properties of gases and liquids. The following paragraphs

*Including material prepared for the 17th edition by L. F. Nims and for the 18th edition by L. D. Carlson.

present an elementary view of the kinetic concept of fluids. Fluids are composed of particles (molecules) in incessant motion. The molecules continually collide with each other and with the containing vessel, and the pressure exerted by a fluid is simply the summated impacts of the molecules on a confining wall. Diffusion in a mixture of substances is also a consequence of this motion, for the continual movement of the

761

individual particles will more or less rapidly equalize local differences in concentration produced when the mixture is made. In the gas state the individual particles are so far apart that their attraction for each other is negligibly small. A gas, because of the incessant motion of its individual particles, will completely fill all of the available volume. Gases therefore can exert only pressure. In the liquid state the molecules still have freedom of motion, but they are so close together that they are subject to strong intermolecular attractive forces. Liquids have a volume independent of the container.

The behavior of gases can be summarized by simple laws and principles. *Boyle's law* states that the pressure of a gas is inversely proportional to its volume, temperature remaining constant. This law is explained by the kinetic theory, for decreasing the volume of a gas increases the number of particles per unit volume and increases the number of impacts upon the walls of the container. *Charles' law* states that the pressure of a gas is directly proportional to its absolute temperature, volume remaining constant. This law is also explained by the kinetic theory, for increasing the temperature of a gas increases the velocity of the molecular motions and the force of the summated impacts. *Avogadro's principle* states that different gases which have the same volume at the same temperature and pressure contain an equal number of molecules, and is the basis of the volumetric method of determining the composition of gaseous mixtures. This principle, together with the laws of Boyle and Charles, can be combined in a simple mathematical expression, the *ideal gas law,*

$$PV = nRT$$

In this expression, P is the pressure exerted by the gas, V is the volume of the gas, n is the number of mols of the gas, T is the absolute temperature ($0°$ C. $= 273°$ A), and R is a constant whose value depends upon the units in which the variables are expressed. When the pressure is expressed in atmospheres, the volume in liters, and the temperature in degrees absolute, R has the value of 0.082 liter atmospheres per mol per degree. Real gases deviate slightly from this ideal expression, but the deviations are so small at ordinary temperatures that the gas law in the form given can be used with confidence to calculate the compositions or the pressures of the respiratory gases.

Partial Pressures. Each gas in a mixture of gases behaves as if it alone occupied the total volume and exerts a pressure, its partial pressure,* independently of the other gases present (*Dalton's law* of partial pressure). The sum of the partial pressures of the individual gases is equal to the total pressure. The partial pressure of a gas in a mixture is easily calculated from the composition of the mixture. Dalton's law in conjunction with the ideal gas law allows one to state that the partial pressure of a gas in a mixture is equal to the product of the mol fraction and the total pressure. The partial pressures of oxygen, nitrogen and carbon dioxide in dry air in millimeters of mercury when the total pressure is one atmosphere (760 mm. Hg) are therefore: $O_2 = 0.21 \times 760$, or 160 mm. Hg; $N_2 = 0.79 \times 760$, or 600 mm. Hg; $CO_2 = 0.0004 \times 760$, or 0.30 mm. Hg. In physiology it is customary to speak of the compositions of gases in terms of volumes per cent. Avogadro's principle makes it evident that volumes per cent and mols per cent are numerically equal for gas mixtures.

Vapor Pressures. The air of the lungs contains water vapor in addition to the other gases present. The water vapor obeys Dalton's law and exerts a pressure independently of the other gases present. Gases in contact with water receive water molecules by evaporation until the number of molecules leaving the liquid phase is equal to the number of molecules returning from the gas phase. Since the number leaving the liquid phase is proportional to the temperature of the liquid, the partial pressure of water in the gas phase is also proportional to the temperature. The temperature of the air in the lungs is $37°$ C., and the air of the lungs is thought to be in equilibrium with respect to water so that the partial pressure of water in the alveolar air is 47 mm. Hg. The composition of respired air is usually expressed as though it were dry, and to calculate the partial pressures from the composition it is necessary to subtract the partial pressure of water vapor from the total pressure before determining the partial pressures of other gases. For example, 5.6 per cent of a sample of dry alveolar air was CO_2. The partial pressure of CO_2 in the alveolar air at atmospheric pressure was $0.056 \times (760 - 47)$, or 40 mm. Hg.

*By convention, partial pressure is denoted by "P" followed by the chemical symbol for the gas, as P_{O_2}, P_{CO_2}, etc.

Solubility and Partial Pressures of Gases in Liquids. The quantity of gas physically dissolved in a liquid at constant temperature is directly proportional to the partial pressure of the gas in the gas phase (*Henry's law* of solubility of gases). At equilibrium the number of gas molecules leaving the liquid per unit time is equal to the number entering the liquid, and any change in the partial pressure of the gas produces a corresponding change in the equilibrium. The gas in the liquid phase also has a partial pressure, and under equilibrium conditions the partial pressures of the gas in the gas phase and in the liquid phase are said to be equal. To determine the partial pressure of a gas in a liquid it is necessary to determine the composition and pressures of the gas in an equilibrated gas phase.

The amount of gas dissolved in physical solution must be carefully distinguished from the pressure of the gas in solution. At the partial pressures equivalent to those found in the alveoli, blood contains 0.25 ml. of O_2, 2.69 ml. of CO_2 and 1.04 ml. of N_2 in physical solution per 100 ml. of blood.* The amounts of O_2 and CO_2 present in circulating blood are of course much greater than the amounts of the gases that are physically dissolved because the blood carries O_2 and CO_2 largely in chemical combination. The chemically combined gas does not contribute to partial pressure of the physically dissolved gas.

Determination of the amounts of O_2 and CO_2 in a particular blood sample is a procedure involving a high degree of chemical skill and has been well described in laboratory textbooks.[36] The gases from a sample of blood are extracted completely and in a condition for quantitative analysis by some form of a vacuum pump and then reabsorbed one by one in suitable chemical reagents. The volume, temperature and pressure are noted at each stage of the analysis, and the number of mols of each gas can then be calculated by substitution of the known quantities into the perfect gas equation. To determine the partial pressures of the gases in the blood, the blood is equilibrated with a volume of gas so small that no essential changes take place in the blood as equilibrium is approached. Chem-

*These volumes are expressed as the volumes that would be occupied by the dissolved gas if it were released, dried and measured at 0° C. and at a pressure of 760 mm. Hg, i.e., STPD (standard temperature and pressure, dry).

ical analysis of the gas phase will then allow a calculation of the partial pressures of the fluid phase. A method for measuring P_{O_2} in the tissues and blood of living animals depends on the fact that dissolved O_2 will react electrochemically at the cathode of an electrolysis cell and give rise to a current which is, under standardized conditions, proportional to the amount of O_2 present.[12]

PROPERTIES OF RESPIRED AIR

Composition. The constituents of atmospheric air important to human respiration are O_2, N_2 and H_2O. The rare gases (argon, krypton, etc.) have not been shown to be biologically significant, and in physiologic gas analysis their quantities or concentrations are determined and included with the values reported for N_2. With respect to O_2, N_2 and CO_2, the air we breathe has a remarkably uniform composition. Samples of dry air taken at many sites, from sea level to the highest attainable altitudes, have contained these constituents in the same proportions. Man does not have a method of storing significant amounts of O_2, but is dependent upon a continuous gas exchange with the air surrounding him.

The essential facts of external respiration are to be found in a knowledge of the compositions of inspired, expired and alveolar air. Respired air loses O_2 and gains CO_2; conversely, the blood absorbs O_2 and loses CO_2 according to the body needs. The composition of the expired air varies, of course, with the depth and frequency of breathing movements and during any one breath, but the respiratory mechanisms are so controlled (Chaps. 41 and 42) that the alveolar air is maintained with but slight changes in its composition despite wide fluctuations in the demands for O_2. The normal composition of respiratory gases is shown in Table 1.

The amount of O_2 absorbed is somewhat greater than the amount of CO_2 given off. This apparent discrepancy is explained by the general fact that O_2 is used to oxidize not only the carbon but also the hydrogen of ingested food; consequently, although most of the O_2 is eliminated in the expired air as CO_2, some is excreted as H_2O. The ratio of the amount of CO_2 expired to the amount of O_2 absorbed is called the *respiratory exchange ratio* (R). Knowledge of the R is helpful in interpreting data on O_2 consump-

TABLE 1. *Composition of Dry Inspired, Expired and Alveolar Air in Man at Rest, at Sea Level, in Mols Per Cent or Volumes Per Cent*

	N_2 MOLS %	O_2 MOLS %	CO_2 MOLS %
Inspired air	79.02	20.94	0.04
Expired air	79.2	16.3	4.5
Alveolar air	80.4	14.0	5.6

tion[13] and is necessary if the caloric value of a given amount of consumed O_2 is to be estimated (Chap. 53).*

Physiologic Significance of Nitrogen. The difference in concentration of N_2 in inspired and expired air recorded in Table 1 is not brought about by production of gaseous N_2 in the body, but is a reflection of the inequality in the amounts of O_2 and CO_2 exchanged. No known metabolic reaction of the human body involves molecular N_2. In ordinary circumstances, N_2 is merely a diluent of the O_2 in the air breathed.

Decompression sickness. The N_2 in the body is in simple physical solution and exists in all the tissues and the blood at a pressure equal to its average partial pressure in the alveolar air. The solubility of N_2 is greatest in fat. Caisson workers and deep-sea divers, of necessity, breathe air under greatly increased pressure, and the amount of N_2 dissolved in their tissues at equilibrium increases in direct proportion to the increased partial pressure of this gas in their alveolar air. When these workers return to normal pressure, their tissues are supersaturated with N_2. If they are too rapidly decompressed, this gas is released from solution as small bubbles, which are distributed in many tissues and in the blood stream.[24, 25] By mechanical distension of the tissues and by formation of aero-emboli, these gas bubbles can produce a variety of clinical symptoms,[28] manifest chiefly by pain and collectively termed *decompression sickness,* or "the bends." The aviator who flies above 25,000 feet may also experience decompression sickness, for his tissues are supersaturated with N_2 at the prevailing low pressures. Decompression sickness can be avoided by means of slow decompression or by elimination of a large part of the N_2 from the body before ascent.[21] Under atmospheric pressure the average man has about 1.5 liters of N_2 dissolved in his body tissues.[5, 6]

Temperature. Expired air is warmed to the body temperature, or nearly, and is saturated with water vapor. Since inhaled air is usually much cooler than the body and is far from being saturated with water vapor, the act of breathing evidently entails a considerable loss of body heat. Breathing is, in fact, one means by which body temperature can be regulated, although this is a subsidiary means in man. In the dog, on the other hand, panting is a very important aid to the control of body temperature. Heat is lost in respiration not only by warming of the air in the air passages, but also by evaporation of water in them. The conversion of water from its liquid to its gaseous form is attended by the absorption of heat; the lungs account for about 10 per cent of the heat exchange of the body (see Chap. 54).

INTERACTION OF GAS AND BLOOD

Blood can absorb more O_2 and CO_2 than can be carried in physical solution. Hemoglobin (HHb)† has the chemical property of combining reversibly with both O_2 and CO_2. If the blood contained no HHb, a circulating blood volume 75 times larger than the normal would be needed to satisfy the requirements for O_2. The combination of HHb with O_2, HHb + O_2 $\rightleftharpoons$ $HHbO_2$ (oxyhemoglobin), is regulated by the P_{O_2}. In the lungs, at a partial pressure of 100 mm. Hg, the reaction is 97 per cent complete. In the tissues, 60 per cent of the O_2 in the blood is released at a pressure greater than 20 mm. Hg.

Blood contains somewhat less than 15 grams of HHb per 100 ml. Each gram of HHb can combine with 1.36 ml. of O_2 so that fully oxygenated blood contains 20 ml. of O_2 per 100 ml. of blood (the O_2 capacity of the blood). Since HHb does not become completely saturated with O_2 until the P_{O_2} is 150 mm. Hg, arterial blood leaving the lungs is only 98 per cent saturated. The amount of O_2 per 100 ml. of blood in a particular sample is designated as the O_2 content of the blood.

Oxygen Dissociation Curve. When samples of blood are equilibrated with air containing O_2 at various partial pressures, the amount of O_2 in the blood is not directly proportional to the partial pressures. A plot of the observed O_2 content of each sample against the partial pressures of O_2 is distinctly S-shaped (Fig. 1). The dissociation curve of dilute purified $HHbO_2$ is hyperbolic. This is the expected result if O_2 com-

---

*In a steady state, R reflects accurately the mean gas exchange of the tissues (RQ).

†"HHb" is used to denote nonionized hemoglobin and also the fact that hemoglobin acts as an acid.

bines with HHb according to the reaction $HHb + O_2 \rightleftharpoons HHbO_2$. Studies of purified HHb solutions have shown that the oxygenation reaction of HHb is affected by the CO_2 content, the acidity, the ionic concentration, and the temperature of the medium in which the HHb is dissolved. The concentration of HHb itself is not without effect. Concentrated solutions of purified $HHbO_2$ give a distinctly S-shaped curve, but the S-shaped dissociation of whole blood most likely results from a summation of the various factors enumerated, the more important being the salt composition of blood and the highly concentrated form of HHb in the interior of the erythrocyte.

The shape of the O_2 dissociation curve of blood is of definite physiologic significance. That the curve is flat above a pressure of 80 mm. Hg insures a practically constant composition of arterial blood despite wide variations in the alveolar O_2 pressure. The steep portion between 20 and 60 mm. Hg insures delivery of a large amount of the blood O_2 to the tissues with a reasonable head of pressure.

Effect of temperature on O_2 dissociation curve (Fig. 2C). An increase in temperature will shift the

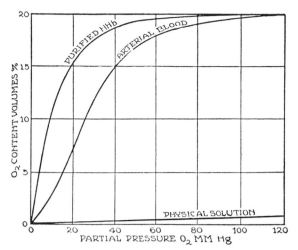

Fig. 1. O_2 contents of arterial blood and plasma (physical solution) and a dilute solution of purified HHb at various partial pressures of O_2. Note difference in shape of absorption curves of purified HHb and arterial blood and small amount of O_2 carried in physical solution. (After Barcroft.)

O_2 dissociation curve to the right. Less O_2 is held by the HHb at a given P_{O_2}. The temperature effect is of some aid in the release of O_2 to the tissues, for the temperature is somewhat

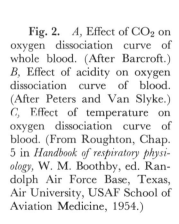

Fig. 2. *A*, Effect of CO_2 on oxygen dissociation curve of whole blood. (After Barcroft.) *B*, Effect of acidity on oxygen dissociation curve of blood. (After Peters and Van Slyke.) *C*, Effect of temperature on oxygen dissociation curve of blood. (From Roughton, Chap. 5 in *Handbook of respiratory physiology*, W. M. Boothby, ed. Randolph Air Force Base, Texas, Air University, USAF School of Aviation Medicine, 1954.)

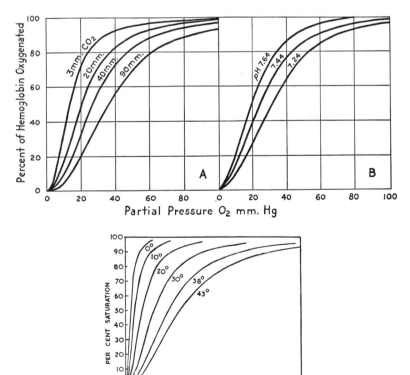

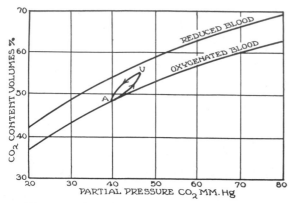

Fig. 3. CO_2 titration curve of whole blood. Note that oxygenated blood contains less CO_2 at a given pressure of CO_2 than reduced blood. Blood goes through a cycle, as indicated by A (arterial blood) and V (venous blood), in the capillaries of tissues and lungs. (After Peters and Van Slyke.)

higher in the vicinity of actively metabolizing cells than near resting tissues, and somewhat more O_2 is given up. It should be remembered that all tissues are not at 37° C. The temperature of the hand or foot may drop to 10° C. or lower, with a consequent temperature gradient along the arm or leg. Less O_2 will be given up for an equal tissue O_2 pressure. This effect of temperature on the release of O_2 is an important consideration in the extremities exposed to low temperatures, since the hemoglobin dissociation curve then resembles the myoglobin dissociation curve.

Effect of CO_2 and pH on O_2 dissociation curve. An increase in either the CO_2 pressure or the acidity of blood will also favor the dissociation of the acid $HHbO_2$ (Fig. 2A and B). The effect of CO_2 is particularly important physiologically, since the production of CO_2 by the tissues automatically favors the transfer of O_2. In fact, the amount of O_2 (or CO_2) the blood will hold is inversely related to the P_{CO_2} (or P_{O_2}) in the blood. The action of CO_2 in releasing O_2 from the blood is twofold. CO_2 increases the acidity of blood (lowers the *p*H) and forms carbamino compounds ($HHbCO_2$) with the hemoglobin. $HHbCO_2$ has much less affinity for O_2 than HHb has.[44] These reactions result in a lowering of the amount of O_2 which the blood will hold at a given O_2 pressure and therefore more O_2 is made available to the tissues.

Condition of CO_2 in Blood. The blood contains little CO_2 in physical solution; the major portion is carried in chemical combination. The forms of combined CO_2 now recognized

are carbonic acid (H_2CO_3) and bicarbonate ion (HCO_3^-), present in both cells and plasma, and carbamino hemoglobin ($HHbCO_2$). All the forms of CO_2 are in chemical equilibrium with one another. A further complication is that the red cell is relatively impermeable to cations; at equilibrium the concentration of HCO_3^- in the cell differs from that in the plasma. A CO_2 dissociation curve for whole blood can be obtained in the same way as one is obtained for O_2. Blood is equilibrated with gases containing CO_2 at various partial pressures, and the CO_2 content of the equilibrated blood is determined by blood gas analysis. The form of the CO_2 absorption curves for oxygenated and reduced blood is given in Figure 3. These curves demonstrate that the dissociation of CO_2 is affected by P_{O_2} in a fashion similar to that in which the O_2 dissociation curve is affected by CO_2 pressure. The absorption of O_2 aids in the unloading of CO_2 in the lungs, and the absorption of CO_2 aids in the unloading of O_2 in the tissues.

In a vacuum a $NaHCO_3$ solution gives off only half of its CO_2. $2NaHCO_3 \rightleftharpoons Na_2CO_3 + CO_2 + H_2O$. Plasma behaves like a simple bicarbonate solution. More of its bicarbonate is extracted in a vacuum, however, because acid phosphates and other weak acids which aid in driving off its CO_2 are present. Whole blood, on the other hand, will release most of its CO_2 in a vacuum. The difference in behavior between whole blood and plasma or bicarbonate solutions is due to the acid properties of hemoglobin. Both HHb and $HHbO_2$ can furnish sufficient H^+ to carry the reaction $H^+ + HCO_3^- \rightleftharpoons H_2CO_3 \rightleftharpoons H_2O + CO_2$ to completion. $HHbO_2$ is a stronger acid than HHb. In the lungs, the following series of reversible chemical reactions take place as O_2 enters the blood:

$$O_2 + HHb \rightleftharpoons HHbO_2 \rightleftharpoons HbO_2^- + H^+$$
$$H^+ + HCO_3^- \rightleftharpoons H_2CO_3 \rightleftharpoons H_2O + CO_2$$

The $HHbO_2$ releases H^+ to combine with HCO_3^-. Since the reactions are reversible, an increase of either O_2 or CO_2 in the blood will, in accordance with the law of mass action, drive the reaction in the appropriate direction. The actual titration curves of $HHbO_2$ and HHb with $NaOH$ are given in Figure 4. From this figure it is apparent that the oxygenation of HHb can furnish 0.7 mol of H^+ per mol of O_2 absorbed to combine with HCO_3^-.

$HHbCO_2$. Approximately one-fifth of the total CO_2 in the blood is carried[51] as $HHbCO_2$ in which, as first suggested by Henriques,[27] the CO_2 is combined directly with amino groups of the HHb molecules,

$$HHbNH_2 + CO_2 \rightleftharpoons HHbNHCOOH$$

Other protein molecules in the blood besides the HHb molecules can probably carry CO_2 in the same manner. The product formed by the combination of CO_2 with HHb is physiologically the more important of the carbamino compounds because it enters into a reversible reaction with O_2,

$$O_2 + HHbCO_2 \rightleftharpoons HHbO_2 + CO_2$$

This is an important reaction in the respiratory exchange, since it provides a rapid method[44] by which CO_2 can be taken up or released without marked changes in pH.

Velocity of the Reactions. The complex series of chemical reactions occurring in the blood as it gains or loses O_2 and CO_2 is apparently completed while the blood is passing through the capillaries (0.7 sec.). Roughton[44] and others have investigated the velocities of the various reactions and found that all but one are rapid enough to accomplish this end. The single exception is the reaction which comprises the hydration of CO_2 ($H_2O + CO_2 \xrightarrow{slow} H_2CO_3$). In a search for an explanation of the apparent speed with which this reaction is accomplished in the body, an enzyme, carbonic anhydrase, was discovered. This enzyme is not present in the plasma, but is found, like hemoglobin, in the red cells. Carbonic anhydrase speeds up the hydration of CO_2 and the dehydration of H_2CO_3 so that these reactions are also completed by the time the blood has left the capillaries.

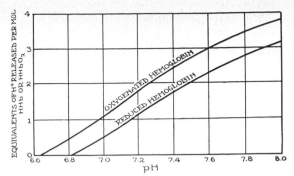

Fig. 4. Acid-base titration curves of oxygenated and reduced HHb. As O_2 is released from HbO_2, the weaker base Hb^- can combine with H^+ to form HHb. For each mol of O_2 given up to tissues, 0.7 mol of H^+ from the ionization of H_2CO_3 can be neutralized by the Hb without change in pH (isohydric cycle). (After Peters and Van Slyke.)

GAS EXCHANGE IN THE TISSUES

The chemical reactions that take place in the blood, as O_2 is delivered to the tissues can now be summarized. Figure 5 contains in outline form the important steps in this sequence of events. The series of reactions is reversed in the lungs. CO_2, being continually produced in the tissue cells, exists there at the highest partial pressures. CO_2 diffuses from the cells, through the interstitial fluid and the capillary walls, and into the plasma. Some of the CO_2 reacts slowly with H_2O in the plasma to form H_2CO_3 which in turn ionizes and liberates H^+. A considerable part of the H^+ immediately combines

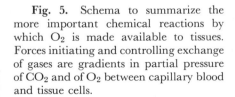

Fig. 5. Schema to summarize the more important chemical reactions by which O_2 is made available to tissues. Forces initiating and controlling exchange of gases are gradients in partial pressure of CO_2 and of O_2 between capillary blood and tissue cells.

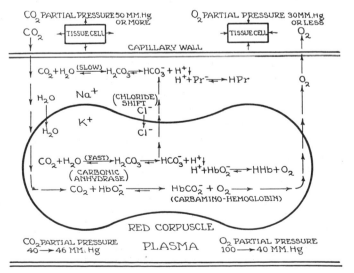

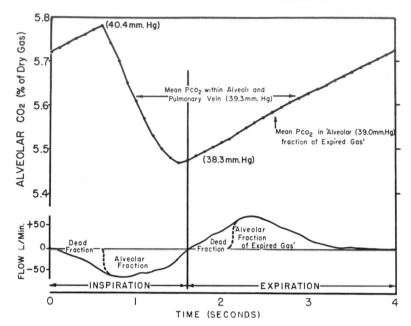

Fig. 6. Fluctuations in alveolar P_{CO_2} computed for a normal respiratory cycle. There is a damping effect owing to variation of blood flow and capacity of tissue for CO_2. The best time for an expired sample of mean alveolar gas for CO_2 determination is shortly after midexpiration. If most of the alveolar gas expired comes out early in expiration, the CO_2 therein will have a lower tension than that of mean arterial blood. (From DuBois *et al.*, *J. appl. Physiol.*, 1952, *4*:535–548.)

with the plasma proteins which tend to buffer the plasma. The major portion of the CO_2 diffuses into the red corpuscles, where it can carry out two reactions. The CO_2 can combine with water exactly as it did in the plasma; however, the reaction is rapid, since here it is catalyzed by carbonic anhydrase. The H^+ that is eventually released is taken up by HbO_2^- to form HHb and O_2, and the resultant O_2 diffuses out of the cell to supply the largest fraction of the O_2 gained by the tissues from the blood. This series of chemical reactions in the erythrocyte has been termed the *isohydric* cycle because the uptake of CO_2 and the release of O_2 is accomplished without the production of an excess of H^+. The buffering power of HbO_2^- allows a large amount of CO_2 to be absorbed and O_2 to be released without marked change in acidity. The excess HCO_3^- diffuses out of the cell into the plasma. This diffusion, if uncompensated, would leave an excess of positive ions in the cell. To keep the positive and negative ions in balance, Cl^- ions simultaneously move into the cell. The balance cannot be restored by movement of K^+ ions because the red cell membranes are relatively impermeable to positive ions. This exchange, called the *chloride shift*, serves the useful purpose of allowing a great deal of HCO_3^- to be carried in the plasma. Some of the CO_2 combines with the various forms of HHb, the most important reaction being with HbO_2, for this combination releases O_2 without involving a change in pH. The interrelations of O_2 and CO_2

in the red cell are only an example of the general mutual dependence of O_2 and CO_2 during the whole process of O_2 utilization.

Supply of O_2 to the Tissues. The tissues absorb what O_2 they need from the blood and leave the rest. The amount absorbed per unit time is a function of the blood flow through the tissue and the pressure of O_2 in the tissue.

The *coefficient of O_2 utilization* is defined as the arteriovenous difference in O_2 concentration divided by the concentration of O_2 in the arterial blood. The brain has a coefficient of $6.7/19.6 = 34$ per cent. Active muscle can remove all O_2 from the blood and thus have a coefficient of O_2 utilization approaching 100 per cent. When the activity of tissues and their need for O_2 increase, additional O_2 can be supplied only from an increased flow of blood through the tissues, since the O_2 content of the blood cannot be increased. The pressure gradient between the capillaries and the active cells increases both because the blood supply has increased and because the cells are using O_2 at a faster rate. The venous blood returning from these cells contains less O_2 than normal, and the coefficient of O_2 utilization is increased. The threefold or greater increase in blood perfusion rate plus the threefold or greater increase in the coefficient of O_2 utilization can mean a ninefold or greater increase in the rate at which O_2 is supplied to vigorously active tissues.

Respiration and Acid-Base Balance. The body has many defenses against an alteration of its acid-base balance (see Chap. 46). We have seen how O_2 and CO_2 are carried and exchanged in the blood without much change in pH. The blood becomes only slightly more acid as it passes through the tissues.

The body as a whole is buffered by a physiologic mechanism.[26] Respiration is so controlled that the partial pressure of CO_2 in the arterial blood normally does not deviate greatly from 40 mm. Hg. If the CO_2 production in the body rises slightly, ventilation increases and the elimination of CO_2 is rapidly adjusted to maintain constant pH. In a sense, respiration represents the first line of defense of the body against acid-base changes.

Summary. The events in one respiratory cycle (one breath) may be visualized with the aid of Figure 6. At the end of expiration, the air in the respiratory passages is that expelled last from the alveoli. During the interval before inspiration, O_2 continues to be removed and CO_2 to be added in the alveoli at rates determined by the blood flow and the partial pressures. On inspiration, the first gas to enter the alveoli comes from the respiratory passages (dead space) and is followed by inspired gas, diluting the gas already present by mixing with it. The size of the alveoli is such that diffusion is not a limiting factor.

PULMONARY GAS EXCHANGE

The lung is an organ in which gas and blood are brought very close together on either side of a membrane of large surface area to facilitate the exchange of gases by diffusion. In this way the demands of the body for uptake of oxygen and output of carbon dioxide are satisfied with less than a second of exposure time between an individual red blood cell and the alveolar gas. The lungs are the servant and not the master of the body's requirements for gas exchange. They do not determine the amount of gas exchange which they subserve; on the average, they facilitate the entry of O_2 into the blood and the exit of CO_2 from the blood in amounts which are determined by the metabolism of the body.

The efficiency of gas exchange can be assessed by the amount by which P_{O_2} decreases at each stage in the process of transfer from ambient air to blood (the lower the drop, the more efficient the lung), and by the amount by which P_{CO_2} decreases in being transferred from blood

to ambient air. There is normally a loss of about 50 mm. Hg in P_{O_2} between the ambient air and the alveoli, and there is a loss of at least 5 mm. Hg more between the alveolar gas and the arterial blood. When the lungs are damaged by disease the partial pressure difference between ambient air and blood may be much greater. Because of this, the P_{O_2} of the blood may be so low that the arterial blood is unsaturated with oxygen, causing cyanosis. Nevertheless, in a steady state the amount of O_2 transferred by the lungs must satisfy the requirements of the tissues for O_2. Since the P_{O_2} of the ambient air is fixed and the rate of O_2 transfer cannot be compromised, the P_{O_2} of the arterial blood falls to the level at which there is an adequate P_{O_2} difference to transfer the requisite amount of O_2 across the lungs. The price which the lungs exact for transferring O_2 is paid in the currency of P_{O_2}. The analysis of gas exchange involves a detailed accounting of transfer expense in terms of P_{O_2} and P_{CO_2}.

Symbols

General variables

V	volume
$\dot{V}$	a gas volume per unit time
$\dot{Q}$	volume flow of blood per unit time
P	a gas pressure, or partial pressure
F	fractional concentration in dry gas phase
C	concentration of gas in blood
S	O_2 saturation of blood
R	exchange ratio (CO_2 output divided by O_2 uptake)
T	transfer factor
D	diffusing capacity
f	frequency of breathing (lower case to avoid confusion with fractional concentration)

Symbols used to modify the above

I	inspired gas
E	expired gas
A	alveolar gas
D	dead space gas
S	shunt blood
M	membrane
B	barometric
L	lung
a	arterial blood
c	capillary blood
v	venous blood
p	plasma
ac	alveolar component
e	effective

The chemical symbols, O_2, CO_2, N_2, H_2O, etc., are also used as modifying subscripts.

A horizontal line over a symbol indicates a mean value.

O_2 Uptake and CO_2 Output of the Body. The amount of O_2 taken up by the body per unit of time is the difference between the amount of O_2 taken into the lungs in inspiration and the amount given out in expiration. In order to determine the amount going in or out, the total volumes in which the O_2 is contained must be multiplied by the fractional concentrations of O_2 to give ml. of O_2. These volumes of O_2 are usually corrected to standard conditions (0 degrees C., 760 mm. Hg, and dry: STPD) so that each ml. corresponds to a given number of O_2 molecules. In the form of an equation:

$$
\begin{aligned}
O_2 \text{ intake (STPD)} &= \text{amount taken in} - \text{amount given out} \\
\dot{V}_{O_2} &= \dot{V}_I F_{I_{O_2}} - \dot{V}_E F_{E_{O_2}}
\end{aligned}
\tag{1}
$$

Determination of the CO_2 output of the body involves similar considerations but the net transfer of CO_2 is in the reverse direction. Hence:

$$
\begin{aligned}
CO_2 \text{ output (STPD)} &= \text{amount given out} - \text{amount taken in} \\
\dot{V}_{CO_2} &= \dot{V}_E F_{E_{CO_2}} - \dot{V}_I F_{I_{CO_2}} \qquad \tag{2} \\
\dot{V}_{CO_2} &= \dot{V}_E F_{E_{CO_2}} \qquad \text{when } F_{I_{CO_2}} = 0. \tag{3}
\end{aligned}
$$

To apply these equations in determining gas exchange it would be necessary to know, (i) the volume of gas inspired and the volume of gas expired per unit time; and, (ii) the fractional concentrations of CO_2 and O_2 in the inspired and expired gas. In practice it would be cumbersome to measure inspired as well as expired volume, and unless these measurements were made with extreme accuracy, the calculated CO_2/O_2 exchange ratio would be in error. Accordingly, the following nitrogen relationships are used to calculate the volume of gas inhaled when only the volume exhaled is measured. They are based upon the fact that there is no net exchange of N_2 across the lungs.

$$
\dot{V}_{N_2} = \dot{V}_I F_{I_{N_2}} - \dot{V}_E F_{E_{N_2}} = 0 \tag{4}
$$

$$
\dot{V}_I F_{I_{N_2}} = \dot{V}_E F_{E_{N_2}} \tag{5}
$$

$$
\dot{V}_I = \dot{V}_E \frac{F_{E_{N_2}}}{F_{I_{N_2}}} \tag{6}
$$

Substituting (6) in (1):

$$
\dot{V}_{O_2} = \dot{V}_E \frac{F_{E_{N_2}}}{F_{I_{N_2}}} \times F_{I_{O_2}} - \dot{V}_E F_{E_{O_2}} \tag{7}
$$

$$
\dot{V}_{O_2} = \dot{V}_E \left(F_{I_{O_2}} \frac{F_{E_{N_2}}}{F_{I_{N_2}}} - F_{E_{O_2}} \right) \tag{8}
$$

Thus, to determine by these equations $\dot{V}_{CO_2}$ and $\dot{V}_{O_2}$, one must know, (i) the volume of expired gas per minute and (ii) the fractional concentra-

tions of O_2, CO_2 and N_2 in inspired and expired gas.

Respiratory Exchange Ratio. The respiratory exchange ratio, R, is the ratio of CO_2 output to O_2 intake.

$$
R = \frac{\dot{V}_{CO_2}}{\dot{V}_{O_2}} \tag{9}
$$

From (3) and (8)

$$
R = \frac{F_{E_{CO_2}}}{F_{I_{O_2}} \dfrac{F_{E_{N_2}}}{F_{I_{N_2}}} - F_{E_{O_2}}} \qquad F_{I_{CO_2}} = 0 \tag{10}
$$

An expression relating the alveolar component of the expired gas to R can be similarly developed:

$$
R = \frac{F_{E_{CO_2}}^{ac}}{F_{I_{O_2}} \dfrac{F_{E_{N_2}}^{ac}}{F_{I_{N_2}}} - F_{E_{O_2}}^{ac}} \tag{10a}
$$

[See also equations (56) and (57).]

Relationships between Dead Space, Alveolar and Expired Gas. The alveoli, in which gas exchange takes place, are reached only after the inspired air passes through airways in which gas exchange is negligible. These airways, which include the upper respiratory tract and the tracheobronchial tree, constitute the dead space (commonly called the anatomical dead space).

During a single expiration the first air to leave the mouth or nose is from the dead space and its composition (aside from the H_2O vapor) is virtually the same as that of inspired air. When the inspired air has been washed out of the dead space, the alveolar component of the expired gas follows. The volume expired in a single breath (V_E) is thus made up of an alveolar component (V_E^{ac}) and a dead space component (V_E^D).

$$V_E = V_E^{ac} + V_E^D \tag{11}$$

To calculate V_E^D, the Bohr equation is used. It is derived as follows:

Total CO_2 in expired gas	=	CO_2 in alveolar component of expired gas	+	CO_2 in dead space component of expired gas	
$V_E\,F_{ECO_2}$	=	$V_E^{ac}F_{ECO_2}^{ac}$	+	$V_E^D\,F_{ICO_2}$	(12)
$V_E\,F_{ECO_2}$	=	$V_E^{ac}F_{ECO_2}^{ac}$		when $F_{ICO_2} = 0$.	(13)

Since from (11) $V_E^{ac} = V_E - V_E^D$, substitution in equations (12) and (13) and rearrangement yields:

$$V_E^D = \left[\frac{F_{ECO_2}^{ac} - F_{ECO_2}}{F_{ECO_2}^{ac} - F_{ICO_2}}\right] V_E \tag{14}$$

$$= \left[\frac{F_{ECO_2}^{ac} - F_{ECO_2}}{F_{ECO_2}^{ac}}\right] V_E \tag{15}$$

when $F_{ICO_2} = 0$. Equations (14) and (15) are equally valid when expressed in terms of partial pressure (P) instead of fractional concentration (F). Since $F_{CO_2} = \dfrac{P_{CO_2}}{P_B - P_{H_2O}}$ substitution in equation (15) yields:

$$V_E^D = \left[\frac{P_{ECO_2}^{ac} - P_{ECO_2}}{P_{ECO_2}^{ac}}\right] V_E \tag{16}$$

Equation (14) can also be expressed in terms of P_{O_2}. In this case the order of the terms within the bracket is reversed for convenience.

$$V_E^D = \left[\frac{P_{EO_2} - P_{EO_2}^{ac}}{P_{IO_2} - P_{EO_2}^{ac}}\right] V_E \tag{17}$$

Relationships between Venous, Alveolar-Capillary and Arterial Blood. The arterial blood, like the expired gas, is a mixture. It is made up predominantly of blood from the alveolar capillaries, called the alveolar component of the arterial blood. To this is added a small amount of venous blood from the bronchial vessels and blood from pulmonary arteriovenous shunts, if any are present. Together, these contributions of poorly saturated blood comprise the venous admixture or shunt component of the arterial blood. Hence:

$$\dot{Q}_a = \dot{Q}_a^{ac} + \dot{Q}_a^s \tag{18}$$

where $\dot{Q}_a$ = total arterial blood flow or cardiac output; $\dot{Q}_a^{ac}$ = alveolar component of the arterial blood flow; and $\dot{Q}_a^s$ = shunt component of arterial flow.

The equation for $\dot{Q}_a^s$ is derived in a manner which is analogous to the derivation of the Bohr equation. It is based on the fact that the total amount of O_2 entering the arteries is made up of an alveolar component and a shunt component.

Total O_2 entering arteries per unit time	=	O_2 in alveolar component of arterial blood	+	O_2 in shunt component of arterial blood	
$\dot{Q}_a\,C_{aO_2}$	=	$\dot{Q}_a^{ac}\,C_{aO_2}^{ac}$	+	$\dot{Q}_a^s\,C_{vO_2}$	(19)

Since, from (18), $\dot{Q}_a^{ac} = \dot{Q}_a - \dot{Q}_a^s$, substitution in (19) and rearrangement gives:

$$\dot{Q}_a^s = \left[\frac{C_{aO_2}^{ac} - C_{aO_2}}{C_{aO_2}^{ac} - C_{vO_2}}\right] \dot{Q}_a \tag{20}$$

Equation (20) can also be expressed in terms of O_2 saturation of the blood. Since $C_{O_2} = S_{O_2} \times O_2$ capacity, substitution in equation (20) yields:

$$\dot{Q}_a^s = \left[\frac{S_{aO_2}^{ac} - S_{aO_2}}{S_{aO_2}^{ac} - S_{vO_2}}\right] \dot{Q}_a \tag{21}$$

The equation can also be expressed in terms of CO_2 content. In this case the order of the terms within the bracket is for convenience reversed.

$$\dot{Q}_a^s = \left[\frac{C_{aCO_2} - C_{aCO_2}^{ac}}{C_{vCO_2} - C_{aCO_2}^{ac}}\right] \dot{Q}_a \tag{22}$$

A Model for Analysis of Ventilation–Perfusion Relationships. Assume that a lung may be divided into three functional parts: one which is ventilated but not perfused with blood, a second which is evenly ventilated and perfused, and a third which is perfused but not ventilated. All gas exchange takes place in the second part because only here do blood and gas come into close contact. The second compartment is called the "effective" compartment. The gas expired from this compartment has "effective" partial pressures ($P^e_{E_{CO_2}}$ and $P^e_{E_{O_2}}$)

which, when perfect equilibrium is reached between blood and gas, are the same as the partial pressures in the blood contributed to the arteries from this compartment ($P^e_{a_{CO_2}}$ and $P^e_{a_{O_2}}$).

The Alveolar–Arterial P_{O_2} Difference: the "A–a Gradient." To some people the "A–a gradient" means $P^{ac}_{E_{O_2}} - P_{a_{O_2}}$ and to others it means $P^e_{E_{O_2}} - P_{a_{O_2}}$. Similar confusion exists with respect to P_{CO_2} differences. The following diagram shows the tension differences to be used when specific mechanisms affecting gas exchange are to be analyzed.

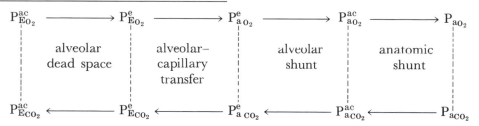

At high levels of O_2, $P^{ac}_{E_{O_2}} - P_{a_{O_2}}$ includes significant P_{O_2} differences attributable to alveolar dead space and to alveolar or anatomic shunt but no appreciable P_{O_2} difference related to alveolar–capillary transfer. At low levels of O_2 the effect of shunts is reduced but the A–a gradient is affected, in addition, by alveolar–capillary O_2 transfer.[9] Usually $P_{a_{CO_2}} - P^{ac}_{E_{CO_2}}$ is principally affected by alveolar dead space alone.[30, 49] It is never affected by alveolar–capillary transfer. In the presence of large shunts, whether alveolar or anatomic, a significant part of the total P_{CO_2} difference can be due to the shunt effect.

A detailed consideration of the effects of alveolar dead space, alveolar shunt and anatomic shunt on the A–a gradient follows after consideration of gas transfer from alveoli to capillaries.

Alveolar–Capillary Transfer Factor for O_2.[11] In the transfer of O_2 from the alveolus to the red blood cell and the transfer of CO_2 in the opposite direction, the gases must move across several layers of tissue which have now been identified by electron microscopy. O_2 must diffuse across the alveolar membrane, across interstitial fluid within the alveolar wall, across the capillary membrane, across the plasma within the capillary, and finally across the red cell wall and into the red blood cell where loose chemical combination with hemoglobin takes place. Further subdivision of layers is possible, but the respiratory physiologist is primarily

interested in the net resistance to the diffusion of gases which these structures as a whole interpose.

The quantity of O_2 transferred from alveolus to red blood cell depends on the mean P_{O_2} difference between the alveolus and the capillary blood, $P_{A_{O_2}} - \overline{P_{c_{O_2}}}$. The factor by which $P_{A_{O_2}} - \overline{P_{c_{O_2}}}$ must be multiplied to give the rate at which O_2 is transferred is called the transfer factor, T[11] (also called the diffusing capacity, D).

For any individual alveolus, i,

$$(\dot{V}_{O_2})_i = (T_{O_2})_i (P_{A_{O_2}} - \overline{P_{c_{O_2}}})_i \text{ and} \quad (23)$$
$$(T_{O_2})_i = \frac{(\dot{V}_{O_2})_i}{(P_{A_{O_2}} - \overline{P_{c_{O_2}}})_i} \quad (24)$$

where $(\dot{V}_{O_2})_i = O_2$ transferred, in ml. per min., in alveolus, i; $(P_{A_{O_2}} - \overline{P_{c_{O_2}}})_i$ = mean P_{O_2} difference between alveolar gas and capillary blood, in mm. Hg, in alveolus, i; and $(T_{O_2})_i$ = transfer factor, in ml. per min. per mm. Hg P_{O_2} difference, in alveolus, i.

The calculation of T_{O_2} for the entire lung ($T_{L_{O_2}}$) involves the use of values for the P_{O_2} of alveolar gas and end-capillary blood which represent the entire lung. Ideally these values should lead to a calculated value of $T_{L_{O_2}}$ which is equal to the sum of the individual values of $(T_{O_2})_i$ for all alveoli which are transferring O_2. The proper choice of alveolar and end-capillary values is a complicated matter because of difficulties created both by variations in ventilation–

perfusion ratio and by variations in diffusion characteristics in different parts of the lung. In terms of the three-compartment lung, the use of alveolar gas and end-capillary blood from the effective compartment ($P_{E_{O_2}}^e$ and $P_{a_{O_2}}^e$) provides a means of standardization with respect to ventilation–perfusion ratio since the effective values are the ones which would exist if the ventilation–perfusion ratio were constant in all gas-exchanging alveoli. Although the effective values may not provide perfect standardization with respect to variations in diffusion characteristics, they are theoretically better than any other available values. For the rest of this discussion, therefore, $T_{L_{O_2}}$ will be defined as

$$T_{L_{O_2}} = \frac{\dot{V}_{O_2}}{P_{E_{O_2}}^e - \overline{P_{c_{O_2}}^e}} \qquad (25)$$

where $P_{E_{O_2}}^e$ = effective alveolar P_{O_2} (contributed to the expired gas), and $\overline{P_{c_{O_2}}^e}$ = mean capillary P_{O_2} in the effective compartment.

The mean P_{O_2} difference ($P_{E_{O_2}}^e - \overline{P_{c_{O_2}}^e}$) is that P_{O_2} difference which, if present along the entire length of the capillary, would permit the existing rate of O_2 transfer to continue unchanged. Figure 7 shows the relationships between mean capillary P_{O_2} ($\overline{P_{c_{O_2}}^e}$) and the instantaneous values of $P_{c_{O_2}}$ along the course of the capillary, during air breathing at sea level and during low O_2 breathing.[9] For purposes of illustration, the mean P_{O_2} difference is approximately twice as big as it normally is in a resting person. Such a value would only occur in disease or during exercise.

In Figure 7A the P_{O_2} difference at the beginning of the capillary is 60 mm. Hg (100 − 40), and this is associated with rapid transfer of O_2 and rapid rise in $P_{c_{O_2}}$. The small P_{O_2} difference ($P_{E_{O_2}}^e - P_{a_{O_2}}^e$) at the venous end of the capillary (which contains oxygenated blood) indicates that transfer has almost ceased. Since, according to Fick's law of diffusion, the instantaneous P_{O_2} difference is proportional to the instantaneous rate of O_2 transfer, the area between $P_{E_{O_2}}^e$ and $P_{c_{O_2}}$ (product of rate × time) is proportional to the amount of O_2 transferred. The mean capillary P_{O_2} is the value, which if it existed along the entire length of the capillary, would not change the amount of gas exchange. Therefore, the area bounded by the horizontal lines $P_{E_{O_2}}^e$ and $\overline{P_{c_{O_2}}^e}$ must be the same as the area between $P_{E_{O_2}}^e$ and the curve of $P_{c_{O_2}}$ vs. time. The cross-hatched area shows the amount by which actual O_2 transfer exceeds the mean rate in the proximal part of the capillary and the equal amount by which it falls below the mean rate in the distal part.

In Figure 7B the corresponding relationships are shown under conditions of low O_2 breathing. The initial P_{O_2} difference is 30 mm. Hg (instead of 60) and the final P_{O_2} difference is 20 (instead of 1.5). The mean P_{O_2} difference of 23.5 mm. Hg is the same as during air breathing because of the assumption that neither the rate of O_2 transfer nor the characteristics of the

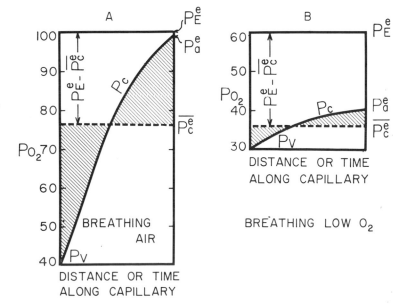

Fig. 7. Moment-to-moment changes in P_{O_2} along the course of the alveolar capillary during (*A*) air breathing at sea level and (*B*) low O_2 breathing. The mean alveolar-capillary P_{O_2} difference is the same in both cases. The end-capillary gradient ($P_{E_{O_2}}^e - P_{a_{O_2}}^e$) is small during air breathing and large during low O_2 breathing.

alveolar membrane have changed. The reason for the striking change in the curve of P_{CO_2} vs. time, in Figure 7B as compared to 7A, is the difference in the slope of the O_2 dissociation curve in the range which is applicable. Between $P_{O_2} = 30$ and $P_{O_2} = 40$ the dissociation curve is almost at its steepest, while in the upper part of the range between 40 and 100 the curve is very flat (Fig. 1). If the dissociation curve were vertical in the applicable range, the curve of P_{CO_2} vs. time would be a horizontal line superimposed on $\overline{P^e_{CO_2}}$ since $P^e_{E_{O_2}} - P_{CO_2}$ would be constant throughout. The closer the actual dissociation curve approaches the vertical, the flatter the curve of P_{CO_2} vs. time and the larger the end-capillary P_{O_2} difference becomes.

In calculating the mean alveolar–capillary P_{O_2} difference, $P^e_{E_{O_2}} - \overline{P^e_{CO_2}}$, it is necessary to know the effective alveolar P_{O_2}, the P_{O_2} at both ends of the alveolar capillary, and the shape of the physiologic O_2 dissociation curve for the intervening range. With this information and the knowledge that the rate of O_2 transfer is proportional to the partial pressure difference, one can apply graphic or other equivalent techniques for arriving at $P^e_{E_{O_2}} - \overline{P^e_{CO_2}}$. In this determination the P_{O_2} difference at the end of the capillary, $P^e_{E_{O_2}} - P^e_{a_{O_2}}$, is of critical importance. The smaller the end-capillary P_{O_2} difference, the greater is the error in estimating $P^e_{E_{O_2}} - \overline{P^e_{CO_2}}$. It is thus important to arrange the experimental conditions so that the P_{O_2} difference at the end of the capillary is of maximal size. This is accomplished by having $P^e_{a_{O_2}}$ close to 40 mm. Hg, a value which is not so low as to be hazardous yet low enough to involve the steep portion of the O_2 dissociation curve and hence cause $P^e_{E_{O_2}} - P^e_{a_{O_2}}$ to be as large as possible.[33] When the mean alveolar–capillary transfer gradient, $P^e_{E_{O_2}} - \overline{P^e_{CO_2}}$, is known, the transfer factor, $T_{L_{O_2}}$, is readily calculated from equation (25).

Alveolar–Capillary Transfer Factor for CO. Carbon monoxide (CO) has special properties which make it an extremely convenient gas with which to assess alveolar–capillary transfer characteristics. Up to the point where CO enters the red blood cell its behavior is much like that of O_2. Its mixing and diffusion in the gas medium is similar to that of O_2 and it is therefore distributed throughout the lung in a comparable manner. It diffuses in the fluid medium of the alveolar wall at a rate about 80 per cent of that of O_2. When CO reaches the red blood cell,

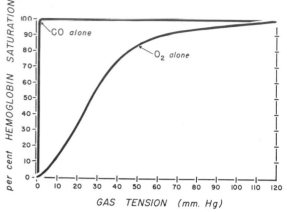

Fig. 8. Dissociation curves for HbO_2 and $HbCO$. Dissociation curves are plotted on the same scale. Maximal saturation of hemoglobin with O_2 is not reached until the P_{O_2} is greater than 120 mm. Hg; with CO, however, maximal saturation is attained with a P_{CO} of less than 1 mm. Hg. (From Comroe et al., The lung, Chicago, Year Book Publishers, 1955.)

however, its behavior differs sharply from that of O_2 because its affinity for hemoglobin is approximately 210 times as great as that of O_2. Thus, in the presence of CO alone, the blood takes up 210 times as much CO per unit of partial pressure. In spite of this huge difference in affinity for hemoglobin, CO, like O_2, forms a reversible combination with hemoglobin and, when the P_{CO} scale is expanded 210 times, the shape of the CO dissociation curve is similar to that of the O_2 dissociation curve. On the other hand, when the CO dissociation curve is plotted on the same scale as the O_2 dissociation curve, the CO curve is practically vertical until full saturation is reached (Fig. 8).

In the discussion of alveolar–capillary O_2 transfer, it was pointed out that if the dissociation curve were vertical, the end-capillary gradient and the mean gradient would be the same. In the case of CO this happy circumstance exists, and the estimation of mean capillary P_{CO} involves none of the difficulties which are present in the case of O_2. Furthermore, since CO is not normally present in the blood in significant quantities (in nonsmokers), the mean capillary P_{CO} can ordinarily be considered zero. When this is so, the mean alveolar–capillary transfer gradient, $P_{A_{CO}} - \overline{P_{c_{CO}}}$, becomes simply $P_{A_{CO}} - 0$, and the transfer coefficient is:

$$T_{L_{CO}} = \frac{\dot{V}_{CO}}{P_{A_{CO}}} \tag{26}$$

Marie Krogh was the first person to publish a method for evaluating alveolar–capillary transfer which took advantage of the unique properties of CO.[31] According to her method, a very small amount of CO is inhaled and the amount of CO taken up by the blood is estimated from the amount lost by the alveolar gas during a few seconds of breathholding. When a logarithmic rate of decrease of alveolar P_{CO} during the period of breathholding is assumed, the following expression for the CO transfer factor evolves:

$$T_{L_{CO}} = \frac{V_A \, 60}{713 \, t} \ln \frac{F^{ac}_{E_{CO_0}}}{F^{ac}_{E_{CO}}} \qquad (27)$$

where V_A = alveolar volume; t = time in seconds; $\ln$ = Naperian logarithm; $F^{ac}_{E_{CO_0}}$ = fractional concentration of CO in the alveolar component of the expired gas at time 0; and $F^{ac}_{E_{CO}}$ = fractional concentration of CO in the alveolar component at time t. Alveolar P_{CO} is referred to as the P_{CO} of the alveolar component of the expired gas because it is obtained by analysis of an expired sample. In evaluating alveolar–capillary transfer in patients with uneven distribution of gas and blood in the alveoli and uneven diffusion characteristics, the determination of the proper value for mean alveolar P_{CO} is a troublesome feature. This was true with Krogh's original method and remains true with the numerous modifications which have since been devised.[4, 16, 17, 18, 32]

Membrane Diffusing Capacity, Alveolar–Capillary Blood Volume and Rate of Reaction between CO and Hemoglobin. The total P_{CO} difference between the alveolar gas and the red blood cell in the alveolar capillary ($P^{ac}_{E_{CO}} - \overline{P_{c_{CO}}}$) is made up of two components: the P_{CO} difference between the alveolar gas and the

plasma of the capillary blood ($P^{ac}_{E_{CO}} - \overline{P_{p_{CO}}}$), and the P_{CO} difference between the plasma and the inside of the red blood cell ($\overline{P_{p_{CO}}} - \overline{P_{c_{CO}}}$). ($P^{ac}_{E_{CO}} - \overline{P_{p_{CO}}}$) is related to the membrane diffusing capacity, $D_{M_{CO}}$, and ($\overline{P_{p_{CO}}} - \overline{P_{c_{CO}}}$) is related primarily to the rate of reaction between CO and hemoglobin. To date, this subdivision of the total transfer gradient has been possible only in the case of CO. The following relationships will therefore be described in terms of CO, but there is no reason to doubt that the principles also apply to O_2.

Since the rate at which CO is transferred from alveolar gas to red blood cell ($\dot{V}_{CO}$) must be the same as the rate at which it crosses the alveolar membrane and must also be the same as the rate at which it combines with hemoglobin, the following relationships hold:

$$\dot{V}_{CO} = T_{L_{CO}} (P^{ac}_{E_{CO}} - \overline{P_{c_{CO}}}) \qquad (28)$$
$$\dot{V}_{CO} = D_{M_{CO}} (P^{ac}_{E_{CO}} - \overline{P_{p_{CO}}}) \qquad (29)$$
$$\dot{V}_{CO} = \theta V_c (\overline{P_{p_{CO}}} - \overline{P_{c_{CO}}}) \qquad (30)$$

where θ = reaction velocity between CO and hemoglobin in ml. CO per ml. blood per minute per mm. Hg P_{CO} difference between plasma and inside of red blood cell; and V_c = ml. blood in the alveolar capillaries. The units of θV_c are the same as those of $T_{L_{CO}}$ and $D_{M_{CO}}$.

Equations (28), (29) and (30) can be rearranged as follows:

$$\frac{\dot{V}_{CO}}{T_{L_{CO}}} = (P^{ac}_{E_{CO}} - \overline{P_{c_{CO}}}) \qquad (31)$$

$$\frac{\dot{V}_{CO}}{D_{M_{CO}}} = (P^{ac}_{E_{CO}} - \overline{P_{p_{CO}}}) \qquad (32)$$

$$\frac{\dot{V}_{CO}}{\theta V_c} = (\overline{P_{p_{CO}}} - \overline{P_{c_{CO}}}) \qquad (33)$$

Since

$$(P^{ac}_{E_{CO}} - \overline{P_{c_{CO}}}) = (P^{ac}_{E_{CO}} - \overline{P_{p_{CO}}}) + (\overline{P_{p_{CO}}} - \overline{P_{c_{CO}}}), \qquad (34)$$

$$\frac{\dot{V}_{CO}}{T_{L_{CO}}} = \frac{\dot{V}_{CO}}{D_{M_{CO}}} + \frac{\dot{V}_{CO}}{\theta V_c}, \text{ and} \qquad (35)$$

$$\frac{1}{T_{L_{CO}}} = \frac{1}{D_{M_{CO}}} + \frac{1}{\theta V_c} \qquad (36)$$

In vitro studies have shown that the rate of reaction between CO and hemoglobin is affected by the amount of O_2 which is present.[45, 46] This is because CO and O_2 compete for the available hemoglobin. The reaction rate, θ, is faster when

the O_2 concentration is low. When *in vivo* studies of the transfer factor, $T_{L_{CO}}$, are made at high and low levels of O_2, $T_{L_{CO}}$ is also found to vary inversely with the level of O_2.[19] Since it is unlikely that the diffusional characteristics of the

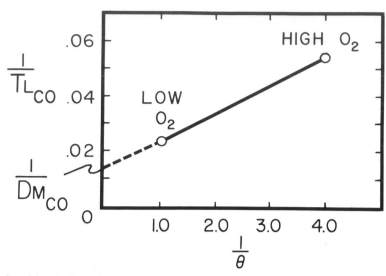

Fig. 9. Graphic solution of equation (36) for V_c and D_{Mco}. In the form $y = [a] \times + [b]$, equation (36) becomes $\dfrac{1}{T_{Lco}} = \left[\dfrac{1}{V_c}\right]\dfrac{1}{\Theta} + \left[\dfrac{1}{D_{Mco}}\right]$. $\dfrac{1}{V_c} = a$ and $\dfrac{1}{D_{Mco}} = b$. $\dfrac{1}{V_c} =$ slope of line connecting $\dfrac{1}{T_{Lco}}$ values obtained during high and low O_2 breathing. $\dfrac{1}{V_c} = \dfrac{.054 - .014}{4 - 0} = .01$; $V_c = 100$ ml. $\dfrac{1}{D_{Mco}} =$ zero intercept $\left[\dfrac{1}{T_{Lco}}$ when $\dfrac{1}{\Theta} = 0\right]$. $\dfrac{1}{D_{Mco}} = .014$; $D_{Mco} = 71$ ml. CO per minute per mm. Hg difference in P_{CO} across the membrane.

alveolar membrane or the volume of blood in the pulmonary capillaries are greatly affected by the level of O_2, the observed changes in the transfer factor are attributed to changes in the rate of reaction between CO and hemoglobin.

By using the *in vivo* data for T_{Lco} and the *in vitro* data for θ, values for T_{Lco} and θ can be introduced into equation (36) for conditions of high and low O_2. This yields two statements of the equation with two unknowns, D_{Mco} and V_c, which are assumed to remain constant at the two O_2 levels. A solution is therefore possible and is shown in graphic form in Figure 9. Studies of this sort suggest that the reaction between CO and hemoglobin constitutes a significant part of the total resistance to the transfer of CO between alveolus and red blood cells, and that the membrane diffusing capacity, D_{Mco}, is considerably larger than the transfer factor. The reaction velocity between O_2 and hemoglobin has not yet been thoroughly studied, but present evidence suggests that the rate of alveolar–capillary transfer of O_2 may also be limited to a significant degree by the rate of reaction between O_2 and hemoglobin.[47]

DETAILED ANALYSIS OF THE THREE-COMPARTMENT MODEL

Ventilation of the "effective" compartment. In terms of the three-compartment model, the gas expired in a single breath is a more complicated mixture than that indicated in equation (11). The alveolar component of the expired gas is itself a mixture of gas from the effective compartment and from the compartment which is ventilated but unperfused. Hence, the expired volume is made up as follows:

$$V_E = V_E^e + V_E^{D^{alv}} + V_E^{D^{anat}} \qquad (37)$$

where $V_E^{D^{alv}}$ = volume of "alveolar dead space" gas contributed to the expired volume from the unperfused compartment; and $V_E^{D^{anat}}$ = volume of the "anatomic dead space." When the volumes on the right side of equation (37) are multiplied by the respiratory rate in breaths per minute (f), the total minute volume derived from each source is shown.

$$\dot{V}_E = fV_E^e + fV_E^{D^{alv}} + fV_E^{D^{anat}} = \\ \dot{V}_E^e + \dot{V}_E^{D^{alv}} + \dot{V}_E^{D^{anat}} \qquad (38)$$

Since all alveolar–capillary gas exchange takes place in the effective compartment:

$$\dot{V}_{CO_2} = \dot{V}_E^e \, F_{ECO_2}^e \qquad (39)$$

where $F_{ECO_2}^e$ is the fractional concentration of CO_2 in the contribution to the expired gas from the effective compartment.*

Since $F_{CO_2} = \dfrac{P_{CO_2}}{P_B - P_{H_2O}}$

$$\dot{V}_{CO_2} = \dot{V}_E^e \, \dfrac{P_{ECO_2}^e}{(P_B - P_{H_2O})} \qquad (40)$$

When numerical values are introduced for P_B and P_{H_2O} and when a factor is introduced to take account of the usual practice of expressing $\dot{V}_{CO_2}$ in ml. per min. (STPD) and ventilation in liters per minute (BTPS), equation (40) becomes, when rearranged:

$$P_{ECO_2}^e = \dfrac{\dot{V}_{CO_2}}{\dot{V}_E^e} \, 0.864 \qquad (41)$$

Thus, when $\dot{V}_{CO_2}$ is constant, $P_{ECO_2}^e$ is inversely proportional to $\dot{V}_E^e$. If ventilation of the effective compartment doubles, the P_{CO_2} of the gas leaving the effective compartment is halved. The P_{CO_2} value of the arterial blood is correspondingly reduced. The P_{CO_2} in the tissues is determined both by ventilation and by the blood flow to the tissues.

Dead space: anatomic and alveolar. In the model, the first lung compartment is ventilated but not perfused. No CO_2 is added by the blood to the gas in these alveoli and the P_{CO_2} of the gas leaving the compartment in expiration is assumed to be zero (see footnote, below). When, during expiration, this gas is mixed with alveolar gas from the effective compartment, the mixed gas, which is the alveolar component of the expired gas, has a lower CO_2 and a larger volume than the gas from the effective compartment alone. Hence:

$$\dot{V}_E^{ac} F_{ECO_2}^{ac} = \dot{V}_E^e \, F_{ECO_2}^e = \dot{V}_{CO_2} \qquad (42)$$

The amount of dead space which is taken into account obviously affects the calculated value for dead space and for the ratio of dead space to total expired volume. To calculate this ratio for anatomic dead space, rearrangements of equations (16) and (17) are used:

$$\dfrac{V_E^{D_{anat}}}{V_E} = \dfrac{P_{ECO_2}^{ac} - P_{ECO_2}}{P_{ECO_2}^{ac}} = \dfrac{P_{EO_2} - P_{EO_2}^{ac}}{P_{IO_2} - P_{EO_2}^{ac}} \qquad (43)$$

*Even though all gas exchange with the blood takes place in the effective compartment, some of the alveolar component of the expired gas is inhaled from the anatomic dead space into the unperfused compartment at the beginning of each breath. Thus, the expired gas contains a small amount of CO_2 from the unperfused compartment.[30] We shall neglect this small contribution from the alveolar dead space and assume that all the CO_2 in the expired gas comes from the effective compartment.

The volume contributed to the expired gas by both the anatomic dead space and the alveolar dead space divided by the total expired volume is:

$$\dfrac{V_E^{D_{anat+alv}}}{V_E} = \dfrac{P_{ECO_2}^e - P_{ECO_2}}{P_{ECO_2}^e} =$$

$$\dfrac{P_{EO_2} - P_{EO_2}^e}{P_{IO_2} - P_{EO_2}^e} \qquad (44)$$

The ratio of the expired volume of alveolar dead space gas ($V_E^{D_{alv}}$) to the total alveolar component of the expired gas (V_E^{ac}) is calculated as follows (see footnote, left-hand column):

$$\dfrac{V_E^{D_{alv}}}{V_E^{ac}} = \dfrac{P_{ECO_2}^e - P_{ECO_2}^{ac}}{P_{ECO_2}^e} = \dfrac{P_{EO_2}^{ac} - P_{EO_2}^e}{P_{IO_2} - P_{EO_2}^e} \qquad (45)$$

If, in all parts of the lung that are ventilated, ventilation is distributed in proportion to the amount of lung tissue, then, in terms of the three-compartment lung:

$$\dfrac{\text{compartment 1}}{\text{compartment 1 + compartment 2}} =$$

$$\dfrac{V_E^{D_{alv}}}{V_E^{D_{alv}} + V_E^e} \qquad (46)$$

Since $V_E^{D_{alv}} + V_E^e = V_E^{ac}$, equation (45) is an expression of this ratio in terms of gas tensions.

Venous admixture or shunt: anatomic and alveolar. Blood leaving the perfused but unventilated compartment of the lung has the same composition that it had on entering the alveoli, namely, that of mixed venous blood. It therefore contributes to venous admixture or shunt. In a manner analogous to the subdivision of the dead space, the total shunt can be subdivided into anatomic shunt ($\dot{Q}_a^{s_{anat}}$) and alveolar shunt ($\dot{Q}_a^{s_{alv}}$).

To calculate the ratio of anatomic shunt to total arterial flow, the following rearrangements of equations (21) and (22) are used:

$$\dfrac{\dot{Q}_a^{s_{anat}}}{\dot{Q}_a} - \dfrac{C_{aCO_2} - C_{aCO_2}^{ac}}{C_{vCO_2} - C_{aCO_2}^{ac}} = \dfrac{S_{aO_2}^{ac} - S_{aO_2}}{S_{aO_2}^{ac} - S_{vO_2}} \qquad (47)$$

The amount contributed to the arterial blood by both the anatomic and the alveolar shunt divided by the total arterial flow is:

$$\dfrac{\dot{Q}_a^{s_{anat+alv}}}{\dot{Q}_a} = \dfrac{C_{aCO_2} - C_{aCO_2}^e}{C_{vCO_2} - C_{aCO_2}^e} = \dfrac{S_{aO_2}^e - S_{aO_2}}{S_{aO_2}^e - S_{vO_2}} \qquad (48)$$

where C_a^e and S_a^e refer to the arterial contribution from the effective compartment.

The ratio of the alveolar shunt ($\dot{Q}_a^{s_{alv}}$) to the total alveolar component of the arterial blood flow ($\dot{Q}_a^{alv}$) is the following:

$$\frac{\dot{Q}_a^{s\,alv}}{\dot{Q}_a^{alv}} = \frac{C_{aCO_2}^{alv} - C_{aCO_2}^{e}}{C_{vCO_2} - C_{aCO_2}^{e}} = \frac{S_{aO_2}^{e} - S_{aO_2}^{alv}}{S_{aO_2}^{e} - S_{vO_2}} \quad (49)$$

If, in all parts of the lung that are perfused, blood flow is distributed in proportion to the amount of lung tissue, then, in terms of the three-compartment lung:

$$\frac{\text{compartment 3}}{\text{compartment 3 + compartment 2}} =$$

$$\frac{\dot{Q}_a^{s\,alv}}{\dot{Q}_a^{s\,alv} + \dot{Q}^e} \quad (50)$$

Since $\dot{Q}_a^{s\,alv} + \dot{Q}_a^{e} = \dot{Q}_a^{ac}$, equation (49) is an expression of this ratio in terms of blood gas contents and saturations.

One can thus calculate the relative sizes of the three compartments subject to the assumptions implicit in equations (46) and (50).

The three-compartment model provides a "representation" of ventilation–perfusion relationships. For example, suppose that equation (46) yields the value 0.50 for the ratio of volume of the first compartment to the volume of the first and second compartments and that equation (50) yields the value 0.25 for the ratio of the third compartment to that of second and third compartments. Then the relative volumes of first, second and third compartments are in the ratio of 3:3:1. This example, used purely for purposes of illustration, is extremely abnormal since the effective compartment, in which all gas exchange takes place, is only 43 per cent (3/7) of the total lung. Such findings may occur during chest surgery.[35] Normally the unventilated compartment is less than 3 per cent and the unperfused compartment is also small in the horizontal posture. At rest in the upright position the unperfused compartment may increase because of failure of perfusion of the apices. The unperfused compartment is eliminated in exercise in association with the increased blood flow.

Critique of the three-compartment model. The division of the lung into three compartments representing the extremes of the relationships between ventilation and perfusion is helpful conceptually and convenient for practical reasons. The values for gas and blood leaving the effective compartment can be determined precisely, as will be shown, and they are the values which would exist if ventilation–perfusion relationships were perfectly even in all parts of the lung in which gas exchange takes place. Furthermore, uneven ventilation–perfusion relationships have an effect upon the O_2 and CO_2 in the gas and blood leaving the lung which can be simulated exactly by adding inspired air to the gas leaving the effective compartment or by adding mixed venous blood to the blood leaving the effective compartment. Hence the assumption of complete nonventilation and complete nonperfusion in certain parts of the lung creates a model which is equivalent in terms of gas exchange to the real lung. The simple model is capable of simulating the most complicated intrapulmonary relationships.

Data Required for Analysis of Ventilation–Perfusion Relationships. The values on the right sides of equations (45) and (49) must be known in order to quantitate the three-compartment model. Determination of the effective values is of key importance and will be discussed in a separate section. The expired gas and arterial blood values are determined by sampling and analysis. Because of the flatness of the O_2 dissociation curve at P_{O_2} values above 70 mm. Hg, C_{aO_2} can be determined by first determining P_{aO_2} and then converting to C_{aO_2} by reference to an O_2 dissociation curve. The direct determination of C_{vO_2} requires placement of a catheter in the pulmonary artery in order to obtain a sample of mixed venous blood. In practice, the composition of mixed venous blood can usually be estimated with sufficient accuracy from existing knowledge of arteriovenous differences. The P_{CO_2} of the alveolar component of the expired gas can be approximated by analysis of end-tidal samples, either following collection by special techniques[39] or by instantaneous analysis with an infrared CO_2 meter. $P_{ECO_2}^{ac}$ can also be back-calculated from equation (29) if anatomic dead space is determined by an independent method.[20, 50] The composition of the alveolar component of the arterial blood (equation 49) ordinarily is not known. Equation (48) can be used instead if anatomic shunt is minimal.

Respiratory Gases in the Gas and Blood Leaving the Effective Compartment: Theory. The effective values, which would exist in all gas-exchanging alveoli if the ventilation–perfusion ratio were constant, can be calculated by virtue of the fact that in a given steady state there is only one alveolar gas composition which is compatible with the CO_2/O_2 exchange ratio of the body. There may be a wide variety of ventilation–perfusion ratios in different parts of the lung, but for each different ventilation–perfusion ratio there is a different CO_2/O_2 exchange ratio and a different alveolar gas composition.[37, 38, 40] Only one of these, corresponding to the CO_2/O_2 exchange ratio of the body and hence of the lung as a whole, could exist homogeneously throughout all gas-exchanging alveoli. This, by definition, is the "effective" alveolar gas composition,[41] or more specifically, the composition of the gas leaving the alveoli of the effective compartment in expiration.

Determination of the effective values requires knowledge of the way in which alveolar gas and blood values are affected by different CO_2/O_2 exchange ratios. Equations must therefore be derived which describe these relationships.

The alveolar equation. The alveolar equation is a modified form of the equation for the CO_2/O_2 exchange ratio (R), which has already been presented (equation 10). Its usefulness depends upon expressing R in terms of the concentrations of CO_2 and O_2 in the inspired air and in the alveolar component of the expired gas. The following steps describe the conversion of equation (10) into this form.

The N_2 terms can be eliminated from equation (10) by substituting the following equalities:

$$F_{IN_2} = 1 - F_{IO_2} \qquad \text{when } F_{ICO_2} = 0 \quad (51)$$

$$F_{EN_2} = 1 - F_{EO_2} - F_{ECO_2} \qquad\qquad (52)$$

This substitution yields:

Total CO_2 or O_2 in expired gas	=	CO_2 or O_2 in alveolar component of expired gas	+	CO_2 or O_2 in anatomic dead space component of expired gas
$\dot{V}_E F_{ECO_2} = \dot{V}_E^{ac} F_{ECO_2}^{ac}$				$+\ 0 \qquad\qquad\qquad (54)$
$\dot{V}_E F_{EO_2} = \dot{V}_E^{ac} F_{EO_2}^{ac}$				$+\ (\dot{V}_E - \dot{V}_E^{ac})\, F_{IO_2} \quad (55)$

When equations (54) and (55) are solved for F_{ECO_2} and F_{EO_2} and these expressions are substituted in (53), the following equation results:

$$R = \frac{F_{ECO_2}^{ac}(1 - F_{IO_2})}{F_{IO_2}(1 - F_{ECO_2}^{ac}) - F_{EO_2}^{ac}} \qquad (56)$$

Since $P_x = F_x (P_B - P_{H_2O})$, where x = any gas species, multiplying both numerator and denominator of (56) by $(P_B - P_{H_2O})$ yields:

$$R = \frac{P_{ECO_2}^{ac}(1 - F_{IO_2})}{P_{IO_2}(1 - F_{ECO_2}^{ac}) - P_{EO_2}^{ac}} \qquad (57)$$

This is one form of the alveolar equation.[15]

Equation (57) can be rearranged in order to get it in a more convenient form for graphic representation using P_{O_2} and P_{CO_2} as coordinates:

$$P_{EO_2}^{ac} = -\left[F_{IO_2} + \frac{1 - F_{IO_2}}{R}\right] P_{ECO_2}^{ac} + [P_{IO_2}] \quad (58)$$

For any constant values of R, F_{IO_2} and P_{IO_2}, a linear relationship exists between $P_{ECO_2}^{ac}$ and $P_{EO_2}^{ac}$, the inverse of the slope being represented by the constant value in the first bracket and the zero intercept ($P_{EO_2}^{ac}$ when $P_{ECO_2}^{ac} = 0$) being represented by the value in the second bracket. Since the slope, but not the intercept, varies with R, the graphic representation of equation

$$R = \frac{F_{ECO_2}(1 - F_{IO_2})}{F_{IO_2}(1 - F_{ECO_2}) - F_{EO_2}} \qquad (53)$$

The expired values in (53) can be converted to values representing the alveolar component of the expired gas:

(58) is a family of straight lines originating at the inspired air point (Fig. 10). Each line passes through all compatible values for $P_{EO_2}^{ac}$ and $P_{ECO_2}^{ac}$ for the specified value of R.

The complexity of the alveolar equation arises from the factor introduced to take account of the slight difference in volume between inspired and expired gas. If this factor is omitted, the following simple form of the equation results:

$$R = \frac{P_{ECO_2}^{ac} - P_{ICO_2}}{P_{IO_2} - P_{EO_2}^{ac}} \qquad (59)$$

This approximation of the true relationships is adequate for many purposes. It shows that the ratio between CO_2 output and O_2 intake is approximately equal to the ratio of the respective partial pressure differences between inspired gas and the alveolar component of the expired gas.

When solved for $P_{EO_2}^{ac}$, equation (59) becomes:

$$P_{EO_2}^{ac} = P_{IO_2} - \frac{P_{ECO_2}^{ac}}{R}, \qquad \text{when } P_{ICO_2} = 0. \quad (60)$$

Equation for R in terms of blood gases. The difference between the amount of gas in the mixed venous blood entering the alveoli and in the capillary blood leaving the alveoli is the amount exchanged. Hence:

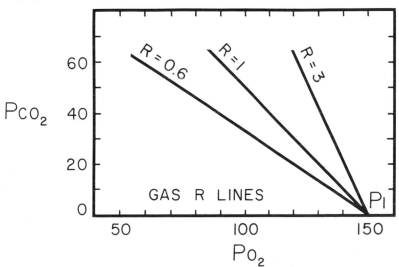

Fig. 10. Gas R lines plotted from equation (58). Isopleths radiating from the inspired air point define all possible values of $P_{EO_2}^{ac}$ and $P_{ECO_2}^{ac}$ at the stated value of R.

$$\text{CO}_2 \text{ output} = \text{CO}_2 \text{ entering alveoli} - \text{CO}_2 \text{ leaving alveoli}$$

$$\dot{V}_{CO_2} = \dot{Q}_a^{ac} C_{vCO_2} - \dot{Q}_a^{ac} C_{aCO_2}^{ac} = \dot{Q}_a^{ac} (C_{vCO_2} - C_{aCO_2}^{ac}) \quad (61)$$

$$\text{O}_2 \text{ intake} = \text{O}_2 \text{ leaving alveoli} - \text{O}_2 \text{ entering alveoli}$$

$$\dot{V}_{O_2} = \dot{Q}_a^{ac} C_{aO_2}^{ac} - \dot{Q}_a^{ac} C_{vO_2} = \dot{Q}_a^{ac} (C_{aO_2}^{ac} - C_{vO_2}) \quad (62)$$

$$R = \frac{\dot{V}_{CO_2}}{\dot{V}_{O_2}} = \frac{C_{vCO_2} - C_{aCO_2}^{ac}}{C_{aO_2}^{ac} - C_{vO_2}} \quad (63)$$

If equation (63) is plotted using C_{CO_2} and C_{O_2} as coordinates and if the mixed venous point (C_{vCO_2} and C_{vO_2}) and R are held constant, the equation describes a straight line whose slope is determined by R.

$$C_{aCO_2}^{ac} = -[R] C_{aO_2}^{ac} + [C_{vCO_2} + C_{vO_2} R] \quad (64)$$

When different values of R are used, a family of straight lines originating at the mixed venous point is generated (Fig. 11). Each line passes through all possible values for C_a^{ac} and $C_{aCO_2}^{ac}$ for the specified value of R. These lines are called "blood R lines" to distinguish them from the "gas R lines" shown in Figure 10.

Equation (64) cannot be easily expressed in terms of partial pressures because in blood the partial pressures of the respiratory gases are not linearly related to their concentrations. O_2 and CO_2 are not dissolved in blood according to Henry's law but are carried for the most part in chemical combination. The respective dissociation curves describe the curvilinear relationships which exist between partial pressure and concentration. In Figure 12 the blood R lines of Figure 11 have been plotted in terms of partial pressure by taking successive points along each blood R line, reading off the corresponding P_{O_2} and P_{CO_2} values from O_2 and CO_2 dissociation curves, and replotting.

Simultaneous solution of gas and blood equations for R. The R lines in Figures 10 and 12 define all possible

values of P_{O_2} and P_{CO_2} in the gas and blood leaving the alveoli (P_E^{ac} and P_a^{ac}) which are compatible with the stated value of R. When the blood and gas R lines which represent the whole body CO_2/O_2 exchange ratio in the person under study are plotted in the same way, there is only one point at which the two lines intersect (Fig. 13). This point of intersection identifies the only values of P_{O_2} and P_{CO_2} which could exist homogeneously throughout all gas-exchanging parts of the lung in both the gas and blood leaving the alveoli. They are therefore the effective values ($P_{E CO_2}^e$, $P_{E O_2}^e$, $P_{a CO_2}^e$, $P_{a O_2}^e$), provided no diffusion gradient exists between the gas and blood leaving the alveoli.

Although only the effective values can exist homogeneously throughout the lung, innumerable different alveolar values can exist locally in different parts of the lung as a result of variations in ventilation–perfusion ratio.[1, 54] Each ventilation–perfusion ratio is associated with a different value of R, and in alveoli having a given R, the composition of the gas and blood is determined by the intersection of the appropriate gas and blood R lines. In Figure 14, the three different gas and blood R lines shown in Figures 10 and 12 are plotted and their points of intersection are connected. The resulting curve, which extends from the inspired air point to the mixed venous blood point, is called the distribution curve.[14, 37, 40, 41] It passes through all possible values for alveolar gas and end-capillary blood which can exist, in the absence of an end-capillary diffusion gradient, in a lung in which the inspired and mixed venous values are as indicated. Alveolar dead space and alveolar shunt are represented at the extremes of the distribution curve, where ventilation–perfusion ratios equal zero and infinity.

No matter how widely scattered along the distribution curve individual alveolar values may be, the alveolar component of the expired gas and arterial blood must be consistent with the gas exchange of the entire lung and hence must lie on the gas and blood R lines for the lung as a whole. In contrast to the effective values, the alveolar components do not lie at the intersection of the gas and blood R lines for the lung as a whole, and they therefore do not lie on the distribution curve even though they represent a mixture of many small contributions each of which does lie on the distribution curve. Because the alveolar component of the expired gas is weighted in proportion to alveolar ventilation and the alveolar component of the arterial blood is weighted in proportion to alveolar perfusion, the two alveolar components are not equal to each other. In fact, as shown in Figure 13, P_E^{ac} is displaced along the gas R line from P_E^e toward P_I, and P_a^{ac} is displaced along the blood R line from P_a^e toward P_v.

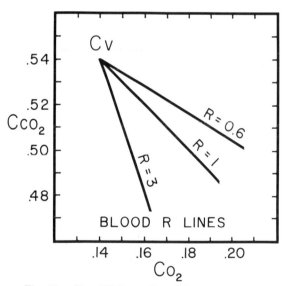

Fig. 11. Blood R lines plotted from equation (64). Isopleths radiating from the mixed venous blood point define all possible values of $C_{aO_2}^{ac}$ and $C_{aCO_2}^{ac}$ at the stated value of R.

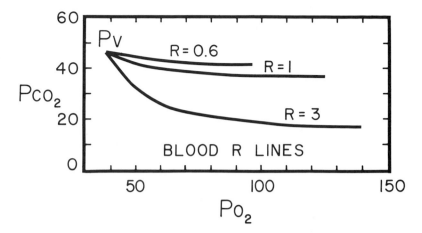

Fig. 12. Blood R lines plotted in terms of partial pressure. The conversion from blood gas content to partial pressure is made by taking successive points along the blood R lines of Figure 11, reading off the corresponding P_{O_2} and P_{CO_2} values from O_2 and CO_2 dissociation curves, and replotting.

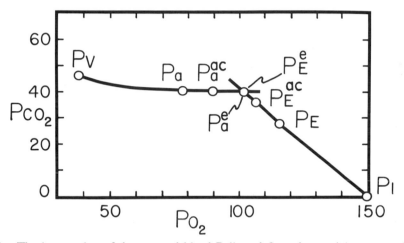

Fig. 13. The intersection of the gas and blood R lines defines the partial pressures in the gas (P_E^e) and blood (P_a^e) leaving the effective compartment during air breathing at sea level. Variations in ventilation–perfusion ratio cause displacement of the alveolar component of the expired gas (P_E^{ac}) away from P_E^e and displacement of the alveolar component of the arterial blood (P_a^{ac}) away from P_a^e. The same displacements can be caused by alveolar dead space and alveolar shunt.

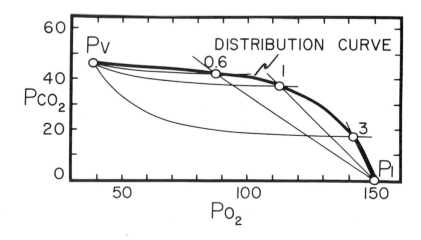

Fig. 14. Blood and gas R lines plotted on the same graph in terms of partial pressure. Points of intersection of blood and gas R lines of equal value are connected to form the "distribution curve."

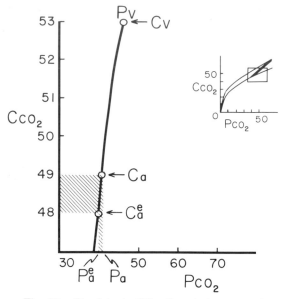

$$P_{a_{O_2}}^e = P_{E_{O_2}}^e \cdot \frac{\dot{Q}_a^{s^{anat+alv}}}{\dot{Q}_a} \text{ is now calculated from equa-}$$

tion (48). Using this value for total shunt, an approximate value for $C_{a_{CO_2}}^e$ is back-calculated from (48). When converted to $P_{a_{CO_2}}^e$, this value is used in equation (65) in the same way that $P_{a_{CO_2}}$ was used originally. This process can be repeated until true values for $P_{E_{O_2}}^e$ and $P_{E_{CO_2}}^e$ are obtained. In practice it is often possible to use $P_{a_{CO_2}}$ as an adequate estimate of $P_{E_{CO_2}}^e$,[43] but it should be emphasized that $P_{a_{CO_2}}$ is never exactly equal to $P_{E_{CO_2}}^e$ in the presence of venous admixture and that the correct value of $P_{E_{CO_2}}^e$ is always calculable, even when it differs from $P_{a_{CO_2}}$ by several mm. Hg.

When a low O_2 mixture is breathed (or when a person goes to high altitude where the P_{O_2} of the air is low), the O_2 tensions in the alveolar gas and in the blood leaving the alveolar capillaries may not reach equilibrium. Under these circumstances the effective alveolar values are not defined by the point of intersection of the blood and gas R lines (Fig. 16). Both $P_{E_{O_2}}^e$ and $P_{a_{O_2}}^e$ remain on their respective gas and blood R lines for the lung as a whole but they are separated from each other by the amount of the end-capillary diffusion gradient. The effective values continue to be the values that would exist if the ventilation–perfusion ratio were constant in all gas-exchanging parts of the lung, and $P_{E_{O_2}}^e$ is calculated as described above. $P_{a_{O_2}}^e$, which differs from $P_{E_{O_2}}^e$ by the amount of the end-capillary diffusion gradient, is calculated from equation (48) (in terms of $S_{a_{O_2}}^e$) using the shunt ratio $\frac{\dot{Q}_a^{s^{anat+alv}}}{\dot{Q}_a}$ determined in a separate study in which the P_{O_2} is high enough to eliminate an end-capillary diffusion gradient (usually room air at sea level).[42]

The Alveolar Component of the Expired Gas and the Arterial Blood. Classically the composition of alveolar gas has been estimated by direct sampling techniques. Since all such samples of necessity contain a mixture of gas from the unperfused compartment and from the effective compartment, they are samples of the alveolar component of the expired gas, according to the nomenclature adopted in this chapter.

The Haldane–Priestley method involves the giving of a sudden forced expiration through a long tube.[23] The last air to leave the mouth comes from deep in the lungs and is therefore alveolar gas. The forced expiration must be begun from the normal inspiratory or expiratory point in order not to alter the alveolar gas before it is expelled. A trained normal subject can give a representative sample of the alveolar component of the expired gas in this way and many important advances in respiratory physiology have been made on the basis of information so obtained. Automatic devices have also been made for trapping the last gas to leave the mouth during a series of normal expirations.[39] This end-tidal sampling technique eliminates the need for the subject to perform any unusual respiratory maneuver. When combined with rapid analysis of the end-tidal samples, a record of the changes in alveolar gas composition over a period of time can be obtained.

Fig. 15. Physiologic CO_2 dissociation curve (enlargement of heavy curve in inset). The curve is so steep that mixing 1 part venous blood (C_v) with 4 parts blood from the effective compartment (C_a^e)—a venous admixture of 20 per cent by equation (48)—causes a P_{CO_2} difference between P_a and P_a^e of only 1 mm. Hg (40 to 39 mm. Hg).

Determination of Respiratory Gases in the Gas and Blood Leaving the Effective Compartment. Although the effective values could be determined graphically as in Figure 13, this method would not be applicable in the presence of an end-capillary diffusion gradient. It is customary, therefore, to take advantage of the fact that arterial P_{CO_2} approximates effective alveolar P_{CO_2} (Fig. 13). This relationship exists because neither of the two factors which can cause a considerable P_{O_2} difference between alveolar gas and arterial blood creates a comparable P_{CO_2} difference. The two factors are venous admixture (shunt) and diffusion. Venous admixture (when not too great) causes only a small P_{CO_2} difference between the alveoli and the arterial blood because the physiologic CO_2 dissociation curve is very steep, indicating a small partial pressure change per unit change in content (Fig. 15). With respect to diffusion, CO_2 passes across the alveolar membrane much more freely than O_2 so that the diffusion gradient remaining at the end of the alveolar capillary is negligible ($P_{a_{CO_2}}^e - P_{E_{CO_2}}^e$). Since $P_{a_{CO_2}}$ approximates $P_{E_{CO_2}}^e$, the P_{O_2} point on the gas R line at a P_{CO_2} equal to $P_{a_{CO_2}}$ must approximate $P_{E_{O_2}}^e$. This value is calculated using $P_{a_{CO_2}}$ in place of $P_{E_{CO_2}}^{ac}$ in the following rearrangement of equation (58):

$$P_{E_{O_2}}^e = P_{I_{O_2}} + \frac{P_{a_{CO_2}} F_{I_{O_2}} (1-R)}{R} - \frac{P_{a_{CO_2}}}{R} \quad (65)$$

From this approximate value of $P_{E_{O_2}}^e$, $S_{a_{O_2}}^e$ is determined from an O_2 dissociation curve, assuming that

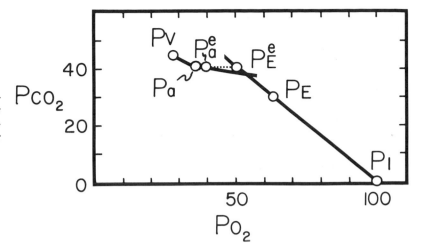

Fig. 16. Graphic representation of P_E^e and P_a^e during low O_2 breathing. Broken line identifies alveolar-capillary transfer gradient ($P_{E_{O_2}}^e - P_{a_{O_2}}^e$).

This has proved to be a powerful research tool, particularly for studying transients such as occur when the subject is suddenly switched to a different inspired gas mixture or a different state of activity. Instantaneous analysis of end-tidal P_{CO_2} is a help to the anesthetist in estimating the adequacy of alveolar ventilation but may be misleading in the presence of shallow breathing, large alveolar dead space, or large right-to-left shunts. Under such circumstances the arterial P_{CO_2} may be elevated in spite of a normal end-tidal value.

The alveolar component of the arterial blood cannot be determined directly, but, in the absence of significant right-to-left anatomic shunts, it can ordinarily be assumed that $P_{a_{O_2}}^{ac}$ is close to $P_{a_{O_2}}$.

CLINICAL CORRELATIONS

Whenever the cells of the body are forced to function at an abnormally low P_{O_2}, they are said to be suffering from *anoxia* (or, more precisely, *hypoxia*). If the P_{O_2} of the blood is abnormally low, the condition is called *anoxemia* (or, more precisely, *hypoxemia*). Cellular metabolism is not greatly reduced until the P_{O_2} approaches zero. Hence, as a rule, the low oxygen indicated by the term *hypoxia* refers to the P_{O_2} at which the cells operate, not the amount of oxygen which they consume. Histotoxic anoxia is an exception to the rule, for the reasons discussed below.

It is possible to differentiate four general types of anoxia. Delineation of these types is based on the physiologic factors described above and provides a rational classification of the clinical anoxias.* (i) *Stagnant anoxia* arises when the flow of blood through a tissue is reduced. (ii) *Anoxic anoxia* results from interference with the exchange of O_2 across the lungs or some preceding step in respiration. (iii) *Anemic anoxia* follows reduction of the O_2 carrying capacity of the blood. (iv) *Histotoxic anoxia*, occurs when the tissue cells cannot use efficiently the O_2 available to them. Figure 17 illustrates how a knowledge of the O_2 content and the percentage saturation of arterial and venous blood makes it

* The first three forms were originally described by Barcroft,[2] the fourth by Peters and Van Slyke.[36]

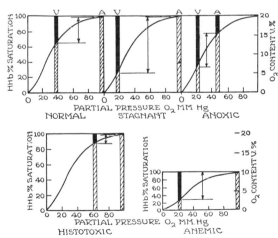

Fig. 17. Composition of arterial (*A*) and venous (*V*) blood found in various types of anoxia and their relation to O_2 absorption curve of hemoglobin. Hatched areas indicate amount of $HHbO_2$ present in blood. Amount of O_2 removed from blood as it passes through tissues is expressed as difference in O_2 content of arterial and venous blood. (After Means.)

possible to distinguish the various types of anoxia. The O_2 content of the arterial blood is normal in stagnant and histotoxic anoxia, and is reduced in anoxic and anemic anoxia. The venous blood contains less O_2 than normal if the anoxia is stagnant, anoxic or anemic; in histotoxic anoxia the O_2 content of the venous blood is above normal.

Stagnant anoxia.   When the blood flow is reduced, stagnant anoxia develops. The reduction in flow may occur locally as a result of interference with the peripheral circulation, as in arterial spasm, Raynaud's disease, embolism and other diseases of the blood vessels. Reduced flow may also occur generally, as it does in shock, cardiac insufficiency and vasomotor collapse. During certain maneuvers of an airplane, an aviator may experience short periods of stagnant anoxia in his retinas and brain, resulting in a loss of vision followed by unconsciousness—"blacking out." The heart cannot pump blood against the high centrifugal forces developed during rapid turns, and the brain is deprived of blood. Occlusion of the blood supply to the brain leads to unconsciousness within six seconds (syncope or fainting). The O_2 content of the arterial blood is normal in stagnant anoxia, but the percentage saturation of the venous blood is low. The blood flows through the tissues more slowly than usual, and more O_2 per unit volume of blood is removed by the tissues.

Anoxic anoxia.   Reduction of the P_{O_2} in the arterial blood causes anoxic anoxia. Its effects are general, and it may be produced by any condition reducing the amount of O_2 available for formation of oxyhemoglobin or interfering with the transfer of O_2 from air to blood in the lungs. Anoxic anoxia is encountered in pneumonia, drowning and paralysis of the respiratory muscles; it also results from breathing gases deficient in O_2. The threat of anoxic anoxia limits the altitudes men can attain by climbing or air travel. Paul Bert[7] demonstrated in 1870 that the deleterious effects of reduced barometric pressures are actually effects of the lowered P_{O_2}. Modern high altitude flights in airplanes would be impossible without equipment supplying O_2 at partial pressures approximating 150 mm. Hg. Anoxic anoxia is indicated by a low percentage saturation of arterial blood with O_2. The P_{O_2} of venous blood is also lowered because the tissues extract their needs from the low oxygen content of the arterial blood.

Anemic anoxia.   If the O_2 carrying capacity of the blood is reduced, the result is anemic anoxia. This capacity may decrease because there is insufficient HHb in the blood or because some HHb has been modified so that it can no longer transport O_2. The effects are general. A primary loss of HHb occurs in anemia and after hemorrhage. Nitrites, chlorates and many other substances can change HHb into methemoglobin, a modification of HHb which cannot combine reversibly with O_2. Carbon monoxide produces anemic anoxia by blocking the reactive groups of HHb with which O_2 combines. During anemic anoxia the O_2 content of the arterial blood is reduced and that of the venous blood is correspondingly reduced to supply the needed amounts of O_2.

Histotoxic anoxia.   When the tissue cells are unable to utilize O_2, histotoxic anoxia ensues. Alcohol, narcotics and such poisons as cyanide interfere with the ability of the cells to use the O_2 available to them, even though the P_{O_2} is entirely normal. In histotoxic anoxia, the venous O_2 saturation is higher than normal. The blood passing through the tissue does not lose its O_2, since the oxidative system of the cells cannot accept it. The anoxia produced may be either general or local, the site depending upon the distribution of the disturbing substances.

Effects of Oxygen Lack.   In general, the symptoms associated with anoxia depend more upon the rapidity with which the anoxic state develops, and upon the degree of anoxia reached, than upon the type of anoxia present. This relation is understandable, since the signs and symptoms are the expression of the malfunction of the anoxic cells; the type of anoxia becomes important only when treatment is considered. The small differences that do exist between the types of anoxia (except for histotoxic anoxia) are explained by the differences in the partial pressures at which a given amount of O_2 can be delivered. In histotoxic anoxia the consequences of selectively blocking a particular chemical reaction in the oxidative chain can differ greatly from the effects of failing to provide adequate O_2 for the final steps. The symptoms of acute, rapidly developing anoxia are like those of alcoholic intoxication, which is a form of histotoxic anoxia; the symptoms of chronic anoxia, on the other hand, are like fatigue.[2] All cells and tissues in the body are affected in some degree by anoxia.[53]

Fulminating anoxia.   The O_2 content of blood falls rapidly when atmospheres deficient in O_2

are breathed, when cardiac arrest occurs or when the breathing movements cease. Aviators at high altitudes who suddenly lose their O_2 supply, miners who walk into pockets of methane or of N_2 and CO_2, and patients who breathe nitrous oxide undiluted with O_2 can collapse and become unconscious in a minute or less. Death may follow in a very short time unless proper treatment is immediately given. Recovery is equally rapid if the O_2 supply of the tissues is restored promptly, and is quite complete if the anoxic state has been of short duration. While the anoxic state is developing, the individual can become unconscious without ever being aware that he is in any danger; and he may, on being restored to a conscious state, deny the lapse of consciousness. During the induction of the anoxic state the respiratory and the cardiovascular systems can be greatly stimulated. Hyperpnea, tachycardia and an elevated blood pressure may occur. As the anoxic state becomes profound, the respiration slows, becomes gasping and finally ceases. The blood pressure falls, and eventually the heart fails, usually a short time after the last breath has been taken.

Acute anoxia. If the anoxia develops more slowly, a variety of symptoms are produced. The symptoms of a mild anoxia, whether produced by alcohol, carbon monoxide or an ascent to high altitudes, are indicative of malfunction of the central nervous system. At first there is a feeling of well-being, a feeling of increased satisfaction and power. As the anoxia becomes progressively greater, a period characterized by unstable emotions and loss of judgment supervenes. The individual loses his critical capacity and is unaware of or cannot properly evaluate his deficiencies. Muscular incoordination, deterioration of vision and memory loss may be pronounced. Fixity of ideas may be predominant and the individual will persist in doing foolish things even at extreme hazard to his own welfare. He may be unable to accomplish a simple procedure that will insure his safety. Hyperpnea may be pronounced, or a feeling of lassitude and extreme weakness may set in. Nausea and vomiting frequently occur and the individual may suddenly collapse. Unconsciousness is often preceded by profound convulsions or may set in with cardiac syncope. The changes produced in respiration, in the heart rate and in the blood pressure are extremely variable, but a not uncommon finding is an increased ventilation and heart rate and an elevated blood pressure.

Chronic anoxia. If the anoxia develops so slowly that the compensating mechanisms of the body keep pace, the anoxia may be symptomless, or relatively so. Such anoxia is produced by living at high altitudes or by a leaky gas fixture. The main effect is a loss of physiologic reserve resulting in a limitation of the individual's physical activities. Such a person is easily fatigued, and as the chronic anoxia becomes more profound, he may become listless and constantly suffer from a feeling of extreme tiredness. Slight exertion will produce air hunger and dyspnea. Dwellers at high altitudes, even though acclimatized, may suffer at times from "mountain sickness." The symptoms are headache, weakness, nausea, loss of appetite and, occasionally, stupor and coma. Rapid deterioration may set in without warning, and unless the chronic anoxia is relieved the individual may die in a cardiac crisis.

In adapting to the low inspired P_{O_2} associated with high altitude, the body achieves maximal tissue P_{O_2} by bringing the level of tissue P_{O_2} as close as possible to the inspired level, i.e., by reducing the P_{O_2} difference between inspired air and tissues.[3] The inspired-alveolar P_{O_2} difference is minimized by increasing ventilation in relation to O_2 uptake.[52] This adaptation raises alveolar, and hence arterial, P_{O_2}. Increase in cardiac output and in the concentration of hemoglobin in the blood[48] minimizes the arteriovenous P_{O_2} difference and hence raises tissue P_{O_2}. These adaptations simultaneously reduce the P_{CO_2} in the alveolar gas, arterial blood and tissues, causing respiratory alkalosis. The H^+ concentration is slowly restored toward normal by renal excretion of base. These mechanisms of acclimatization minimize the loss of physiologic reserve at high altitude.

Cyanosis. In "cyanosis," the skin or mucous membranes appear bluish, and the color disappears if blood is pressed from the superficial capillaries. Cyanosis occurs only if these *capillaries contain more than 5 grams of HHb (unsaturated hemoglobin) per 100 ml. of blood.* The abnormal color appears because reduced HHb is purplish, whereas $HHbO_2$ is bright red; the color of the skin depends upon the absolute amount of reduced HHb. Cyanosis may be a prominent feature of anoxias other than histotoxic anoxia and some forms of anemic anoxia. In histotoxic anoxia, the HHb is, of course, properly oxygenated, and the blood is bright red. In anemia, less than 5 grams of HHb per 100 ml. of blood may be present.

The clinical appearance of cyanosis is dependent upon the state of the capillaries, the pigmentation and the thickness of the patient's skin. Since these factors vary from individual to individual, cyanosis is a poor indicator of the degree of anoxia. In the presence of polycythemia, or after adaptation to high altitudes, cyanosis is much increased and may appear when anoxia is relatively slight. In the anoxia produced by carbon monoxide, cyanosis does not occur, since the HHbCO compound is a bright cherry red. Methemoglobin is dark and, when present in large amounts, leads to appreciable cyanosis.

Cyanosis also occurs in normal individuals who develop anoxic or stagnant anoxia. In the first instance, arterial blood does not become fully saturated in the lung; in the second, the blood is abnormally deoxygenated in the tissues. In addition to respiratory causes, intermixture of arterial and venous blood, as in congenital heart defects, may result in cyanosis (see Chap. 37).

Hyperpnea. All of the manifestations of anoxia cannot be ascribed to O_2 lack. A prominent feature of acute anoxic anoxia is hyperpnea with an attendant loss of CO_2. When exposed to lowered barometric pressure, an animal increases its ventilation; CO_2 is washed out and the blood and tissues rapidly become alkaline.[8] If the degree of anoxia is not too great (O_2 saturation of arterial blood above 60 per cent), the change in acid-base balance is typical of a respiratory alkalosis, the uncompensated loss of CO_2 (see Chap. 46). Mosso[34] was among the first to recognize that a loss of CO_2 occurs and to insist upon the importance of *acapnia* in the production of the symptoms of acute anoxic anoxia. In many patients, the sequence of signs and symptoms during the development of anoxic anoxia is similar to the sequence brought on by voluntary hyperventilation of normal air.[29]

Hyperventilation syndrome. Certain persons appear to react to sensory stimulation or to life stresses by a hyperpnea which is not caused by anoxia. This response may be manifested by disturbances of cerebral function like those resulting from anoxia, by tetany, or even by unconsciousness and convulsions, especially in epileptic patients.

Therapeutic Use of Oxygen. When O_2 transfer across the lungs is impeded, as in pneumonia or pulmonary edema, dramatic relief can be provided by having the patient breathe an atmosphere enriched with O_2. The increased P_{O_2} in the alveolar air increases the rate at which O_2 diffuses through the air spaces and the alveolar membranes of the lungs, and the blood leaves the lungs with a greater load of O_2. If, however, the arterial blood is already fully saturated when it leaves the lung, little benefit is derived from breathing O_2 under an increased partial pressure, because only the small amount that can be carried as a result of the increased physical solubility is added to the blood.

The extensive use of O_2 to treat carbon monoxide anoxia is predicated upon a different principle. Increasing the P_{O_2} in the arterial blood aids in the dissociation of HHbCO, and the carbon monoxide is more easily eliminated. The objective in the treatment of carbon monoxide anoxia is to restore the O_2 carrying capacity of the blood as quickly as possible.

Some care must be taken in administering O_2. Comfortable masks and oxygen tents have been developed in which the atmosphere the patient breathes is easily controlled. It is common practice to maintain the O_2 concentration in the tent above 50 per cent or more, providing a partial pressure of 300 to 400 mm. Hg. In patients with respiratory acidosis such high levels of P_{O_2} may cause extreme hypoventilation, leading to coma.

O_2 toxicity. Paul Bert[7] was the first to observe that O_2 at high partial pressures is not tolerated well by warm-blooded animals. When exposed to a P_{O_2} of three atmospheres or more, such animals show signs of profound disturbance of the central nervous system. They may collapse and die in violent convulsions. If O_2 at a partial pressure of one atmosphere is breathed for a long time, edema of the lungs may ensue, with the paradoxical result that the animal dies of anoxia. These effects limit the therapeutic use of O_2, for, even though it is theoretically possible to increase the P_{O_2} to such an extent that the metabolic demands of the tissues could be met by the physically dissolved O_2, the tissues would die. A high P_{O_2} apparently blocks the oxidative chains of reactions by actually destroying some important enzymes.[51]

REFERENCES

1. Ball, W. C., Steward, P. B., Newsham, L. G. S. and Bates, D. V. *J. clin. Invest.*, 1962, *41*:519–531.
2. Barcroft, J. *Lancet*, 1920, *99*:485–489.

3. BARCROFT, J. *The respiratory function of the blood. Part I. Lessons from high altitude.* Cambridge, Cambridge University Press, 1925.

4. BATES, D. V. *Clin. Sci.,* 1952, *11:*21–32.

5. BEHNKE, A. R. *Harvey Lect.,* 1942, *37:*198–226.

6. BEHNKE, A. R., THOMSON, R. M. and SHAW, L. A. *Amer. J. Physiol.,* 1936, *114:*137–146.

7. BERT, P. *Researches in experimental physiology.* Hitchcock, M. A. and Hitchcock, F. A. (trans.). Columbus, Ohio, College Book Co., 1943.

8. CLARKE, R. W., MARSHALL, C. and NIMS, L. F. *Amer. J. Physiol.,* 1944, *142:*483–486.

9. COMROE, J. H., JR., FORSTER, R. E., DuBOIS, A. B., BRISCOE, W. A. and CARLSEN, E. *The Lung: clinical physiology and pulmonary function tests.* Chicago, Year Book Publishers, Inc., 1955.

10. CONSOLAZIO, C. F., JOHNSON, R. E. and MAREK, E. *Metabolic methods.* St. Louis, C. V. Mosby Co., 1951.

11. COTES, J. E. *Lancet,* 1963, *2:*843.

12. DAVIES, P. W. and BRINK, F., JR. *Rev. sci. Instrum.,* 1942, *13:*524–533.

13. DuBOIS, E. F. *Basal metabolism in health and disease.* Philadelphia, Lea & Febiger, 1936.

14. FARHI, L. E. and RAHN, H. *J. appl. Physiol.,* 1955, *7:*699–703.

15. FENN, W. O., RAHN, H. and OTIS, A. B. *Amer. J. Physiol.,* 1946, *146:*637–653.

16. FILLEY, G. F., MacINTOSH, D. J. and WRIGHT, G. W. *J. clin. Invest.,* 1954, *33:*530–539.

17. FORSTER, R. E. *Physiol. Rev.,* 1957, *37:*391–452.

18. FORSTER, R. E., FOWLER, W. S., BATES, D. V. and VAN LINGEN, B. *J. clin. Invest.,* 1955, *33:*1135–1145.

19. FORSTER, R. E., ROUGHTON, F. J. W., BRISCOE, W. A. and KREUZER, F. *J. appl. Physiol.,* 1957, *11:*277–289.

20. FOWLER, W. S. *Amer. J. Physiol.,* 1948, *154:*405–416.

21. FULTON, J. F., ed. *Decompression sickness.* Philadelphia, W. B. Saunders Co., 1951.

22. HALDANE, J. S. *Brit. med. J.,* 1919, *2:*65–71.

23. HALDANE, J. S. and PRIESTLEY, J. G. *Respiration.* London, Oxford University Press, 1935.

24. HARVEY, E. N., BARNES, D. K., McELROY, W. D., WHITELEY, A. H., PEASE, D. C. and COOPER, K. W. *J. cell. comp. Physiol.,* 1944, *24:*1–22.

25. HARVEY, E. N., WHITELEY, A. H., McELROY, W. D., PEASE, D. C. and BARNES, D. K. *J. cell. comp. Physiol.,* 1944, *24:*23–34.

26. HENDERSON, Y. *Physiol. Rev.,* 1925, *5:*131–160.

27. HENRIQUES, O. M. *Biochem. Z.,* 1928, *200:*10–17.

28. HILL, L. *Caisson sickness and the physiology of work in compressed air.* London, Edward Arnold, 1912.

29. HINSHAW, H. C., RUSHMER, R. F. and BOOTHBY, W. M. *J. Aviat. Med.,* 1943, *14:*100–104.

30. JULIAN, D. G., TRAVIS, D. M., ROBIN, E. D. and CRUMP, C. H. *J. appl. Physiol.,* 1960, *15:*87–91.

31. KROGH, M. *J. Physiol.,* 1915, *49:*271–300.

32. LEWIS, B. M., LIN, T.-H., NOE, F. E. and HAYFORD-WELSING, E. J. *J. clin. Invest.,* 1959, *38:*2073–2086.

33. LILIENTHAL, J. L., RILEY, R. L., PROEMMEL, D. D. and FRANKE, R. E. *Amer. J. Physiol.,* 1946, *147:*199–216.

34. MOSSO, A. and MARRO, G. *Arch. ital. Biol.,* 1903, *39:*387–394.

35. PERMUTT, S., VIRTUE, R. W. and BANE, H. N. (to be published).

36. PETERS, J. P. and VAN SLYKE, D. D. *Quantitative clinical chemistry.* Baltimore, Williams & Wilkins Co., 1931.

37. RAHN, H. *Amer. J. Physiol.,* 1949, *158:*21–30.

38. RAHN, H. and FENN, W. O. *A graphical analysis of the respiratory gas exchange: The O_2-CO_2 diagram.* Washington, D.C., American Physiological Society, 1955.

39. RAHN, H., MOHNEY, J., OTIS, A. B. and FENN, W. O. *J. Aviat. Med.,* 1946, *17:*173–179.

40. RILEY, R. L. and COURNAND, A. *J. appl. Physiol.,* 1949, *1:*825–847.

41. RILEY, R. L. and COURNAND, A. *J. appl. Physiol.,* 1951, *4:*77–101.

42. RILEY, R. L., COURNAND, A. and DONALD, K. W. *J. appl. Physiol.,* 1951, *4:*102–120.

43. ROSSIER, P. H. and BUHLMANN, A. *Physiol. Rev.,* 1955, *35:*860–876.

44. ROUGHTON, F. J. W. *Physiol. Rev.,* 1935, *15:*241–296.

45. ROUGHTON, F. J. W., *Amer. J. Physiol.,* 1945, *143:*609–620.

46. ROUGHTON, F. J. W., FORSTER, R. E. and CANDER, L. *J. appl. Physiol.,* 1957, *11:*269–276.

47. ROUGHTON, F. J. W. and FORSTER, R. E. *J. appl. Physiol.,* 1957, *11:*290–302.

48. SCHNEIDER, E. C. and HAVENS, L. C. *Amer. J. Physiol.,* 1915, *36:*380–397.

49. SEVERINGHAUS, J. W. and STUPFEL, M. *J. appl. Physiol.,* 1957, *10:*335–348.

50. SHEPARD, R. H., CAMPBELL, E. J. M., MARTIN, H. B. and ENNS, T. *J. appl. Physiol.,* 1957, *11:*241–244.

51. STADIE, W. C. and O'BRIEN, H. *J. biol. Chem.,* 1937, *117:*439–470.

52. TALBOTT, J. H. and DILL, D. B. *Amer. J. med. Sci.,* 1936, *192:*626–639.

53. VAN LIERE, E. J. *Anoxia, its effects on the body.* Chicago, University of Chicago Press, 1942.

54. WEST, J. B., DOLLERY, C. T. and HUGH-JONES, P. *J. clin. Invest.,* 1961, *40:*1–12.

Neural Control of Respiration

By ALLAN C. YOUNG

THE main functions of the respiratory system are to provide O_2, eliminate CO_2 and maintain a constant pH of the blood, but this system participates in many other functions. The chest, lungs and upper respiratory tract provide controlled movement of air for sniffing, coughing, sneezing and vomiting; for such expressions of emotion as laughing and sobbing; and for a variety of highly skilled voluntary movements such as speaking, singing and blowing a wind instrument. It is interesting that, as Campbell[8] has emphasized, both the relative and total extent to which various muscle groups are active may be very different in voluntary and involuntary breathing movements.

PERIPHERAL NEURAL MECHANISMS

Efferent Discharge. The phrenic nerves, originating in C2, C3 and C4, provide the innervation for the diaphragm. The intercostal muscles receive their innervation from T1-6 via the intercostal nerves; the abdominal muscles receive theirs from L1 and T7-12. The scaleni are innervated from C4-8, and the innervation of the sternomastoids is derived from C2 and the spinal accessory nerve. It is reasonable to speculate that the respiratory act is integrated in the brain stem rather than in the spinal cord, because so many segmental levels are involved in the innervation of respiratory muscle.

The periodic respiratory enlargement and contraction of the thoracic space are superimposed upon an underlying postural tone. Tidal exhalations do not leave the thorax in full expiration, but in a state of partial inspiration, which is not far from the midposition of the thorax. This state is maintained by a tetanus in a smaller or larger proportion of the inspiratory motor units, each unit firing at rather slow rates (5 to 20 impulses per second). The diaphragm as well as the intercostal muscles is involved.[6, 17, 18] Undoubtedly the source of this activity is in general postural, and it represents participation of the inspiratory mechanism in the maintenance of the upright posture. There is, however, a definite respiratory component, inasmuch as the degree of inspiratory tone is regulated, via the carotid and aortic bodies, by the O_2 and CO_2 content of the blood.[15]

The expiratory muscles also exhibit a basic tonic activity, since certain of them, like the inspiratory muscles, oppose by contraction the force of gravity and participate therefore in the maintenance of upright posture. Thus the muscles of the abdomen, while functioning in respiration as expiratory muscles, are also im-

Fig. 1. Discharge from single motor unit of external intercoastal muscle. Unit fired continuously throughout inspiration and expiration, but rate increased during inspiration. Middle line is pneumograph (inspiration up) and lower line is graph of impulse frequency. (From Bronk and Ferguson, *Amer. J. Physiol.,* 1935, *110*:700–707.)

portant postural muscles serving to retain the abdominal contents.

The act of inspiration begins against a background of tonic innervation of both inspiratory and expiratory muscles. Simultaneously two events centrally coordinated occur: (i) Those units supplying inspiratory muscles which are in tonic contraction increase their rate of firing (Fig. 1), and (ii) the tonic firing of expiratory units is reciprocally inhibited. As the size of the thorax increases and the diaphragm descends, the expiratory apparatus gives way in equal degree to accommodate for this movement. In addition, as inspiration proceeds, new units are added, or "recruited," so that the inspiratory act gains force as it proceeds (Fig. 2). The firing of individual units accelerates in rate, resulting in a progressive increment in the strength of contraction of each unit. By increase in the number of active units, and by augmentation in the strength of each unit's contraction through its increasing rate of discharge, inspiration grows to a peak determined by the various factors that control the depth of respiration. The whole accelerating tempo is then abruptly terminated. Other inspiratory units cease firing more slowly.[8] Units participating in the maintenance of inspiratory tone return to their former slow steady tetanus, which is maintained throughout expiration. The tonic expiratory discharge recommences.

In normal quiet breathing, this is at times the whole of the respiratory act, but often some traces of active expiration develop, reciprocating with inspiration (Fig. 3).

Virtually nothing is known of the size and

numbers of the motor units of the respiratory system. Much more is known about the rates of discharge in single phrenic and intercostal motor units, which have been studied repeatedly. Basically the rates are slow, particularly at the onset of inspiration, at the end of expiration and during the tonic phases, and may amount to no more than five to ten discharges per second. Accelerating as respiration progresses, the rates reach the neighborhood of 30 to 40 impulses per second at the end of normal inspiration. Even with an extreme respiratory drive producing a maximum hyperpnea, rates above 100 per second are rarely seen; this rate is close to the upper limit of motoneuron

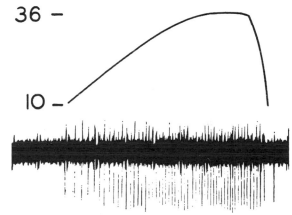

Fig. 2. Characteristic slowly augmenting inspiratory discharge of single motor fiber of phrenic nerve of dog. This record was obtained during complete motor paralysis produced by intravenous injection of curare. Vagus nerves are sectioned. Frequency of firing is plotted on ordinates above original electrogram. (From Gesell *et al., Amer. J. Physiol.,* 1940, *128*:629–634.)

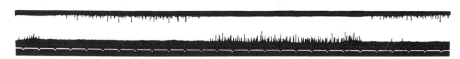

Fig. 3. Simultaneous records of motor nerve impulses to internal intercostal muscle (*upper record*) in expiration, and to external intercostal muscle (*lower record*) in inspiration; vagi and carotid sinus nerves cut; animal completely immobilized with curare. *Bottom line,* time—0.2 second intervals. (From Bronk and Ferguson, *Amer. J. Physiol.,* 1935, *110*:700–707.)

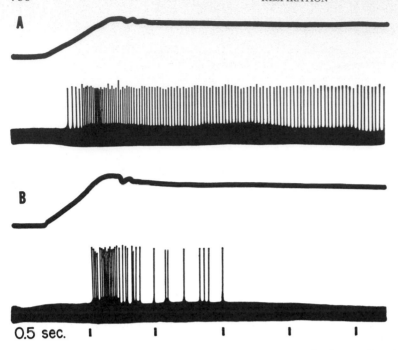

Fig. 4. Responses of two types of afferent vagal fibers to inflation of lungs (chest wall removed). Upper trace in both records, intratracheal pressure; respiration pump stopped in expiration just before start of both records. Fibers responding as shown in *A* adapt slowly. Fibers responding as shown in *B* adapt rapidly. (After Knowlton and Larrabee, *Amer. J. Physiol.,* 1946, *117*:100–114.)

discharge to skeletal muscle in normal circumstances.

Afferent Pathways.   The respiratory system is affected by stimuli, especially noxious stimuli, from many parts of the body; it is also affected to some extent by proprioceptors of the limb and possibly by other muscles. These proprioceptors may be of some importance in the control of breathing (Chap. 42). The afferent nerve fibers which are most effective in controlling and modifying respiration are contained in the glossopharyngeal (IXth) and vagus (Xth) nerves. These nerves carry impulses from the carotid and aortic bodies or glomera (Chap. 10), which contain chemoreceptors responsive to increased pCO_2 and lowered pO_2 in the arterial blood.[11, 12] The Xth nerve carries impulses from many types of receptor, but mainly from (i) chemoreceptors of the aortic glomus, (ii) stretch receptors in the large veins,[2] (iii) nociceptors subserving the cough reflex, and (iv) stretch receptors[16] located in the lungs—the most important type insofar as respiration is concerned.

Receptors which fire when the lungs are inflated were first studied by Adrian.[1] Two types are distinguished on the basis of threshold and rate of adaptation (Fig. 4).[22, 23] Slowly adapting receptors fire with relatively slight degrees of lung distension and reflexly decrease activity of phrenic motoneurons. Rapidly adapting receptors respond only to forcible distension of

the lungs, i.e., lung volumes exceeding eupneic tidal volumes, and elicit a brief increase in phrenic motoneuron discharge. Widdicombe[51] localized these receptors in the tracheobronchial tree and believed they are identical with the mechanoreceptors of the cough reflex. Lung stretch receptors are supplied by the larger vagal afferents having conduction velocities ranging from 14 to 59 m. per second. Deflation of the lungs elicits a marked increase in phrenic motoneuron discharge.[23] Knowlton and Larrabee[22] noted that inflation-sensitive receptors often fired also on lung deflation. However, Paintal[33] has identified units which respond to deflation but not to inflation. It is likely that these receptors are responsible for the increased inspiratory discharge when the lungs are deflated.

HERING-BREUER REFLEXES.   In 1865, Hering and Breuer[16] discovered that the stretch receptors detect inflation and deflation of the lungs and that the afferent discharge into the brain stem alters the respiratory cycle. Their findings were elaborated by Head in 1880. These investigators found that inflation of the lungs tends to terminate inspiration and that collapse of the lungs tends to initiate it. (The inflation-terminating receptor is the slowly adapting one mentioned above.) It was natural to conclude that these reflexes provide a self-regulatory mechanism or, in modern language, a regulatory feedback. The inspiratory-terminating reflex is supposedly operative in the range of eupneic breathing. However, the end organs for the inspiration excitatory reflex respond only to extreme deflation (either passive or active) or in deep respiration. Recent studies described below raise the possibility that these afferents do not control respiration cycle by cycle but rather provide a background of respiratory drive.

Cough reflex.[50, 51] Coughing results from mechanical or chemical irritation of endings in the respiratory passages. Discharge in mechanoreceptors elicited by introducing a tube into the trachea inhibits phrenic motoneuron discharge and causes expiratory efforts and bronchiolar constriction. Mechanoreceptors may also be excited by abrupt volume changes in the isolated tracheobronchial system. The receptive zone most sensitive to mechanical stimuli is the inner surface of the larynx. The tracheal bifurcation and the lower half of the trachea are also sensitive, but the main bronchi are relatively insensitive.

Chemically induced coughing follows inhalation of sulfur dioxide. This gas is effective when introduced through an endobronchial catheter so that the gas comes into contact with only the lungs and smaller bronchi. A weaker cough is produced by perfusing sulfur dioxide through the isolated tracheobronchial system. The individuality of the mechanosensitive and chemosensitive cough reflex afferents has been established by single unit recording. The former adapt rapidly to volume changes and are found in greatest concentration near the larynx and carina. They respond readily to mechanical stimulation or inhalation of powders, but are relatively insensitive to sulfur dioxide. The chemosensitive receptors adapt more slowly to volume changes, are widely distributed in the tracheobronchial system, and respond readily to sulfur dioxide. Both mechanically and chemically induced coughing are decreased by vagotomy, but both vagotomy and sympathectomy are required to abolish the reflex.

CENTRAL NEURAL MECHANISMS

As has been mentioned above, respiration is affected by a wide variety of afferent stimuli, is subject to voluntary control, and takes part in a variety of emotional expressions. It is not too surprising, then, to find that respiratory responses follow electrical stimulation of several levels of the central nervous system and several regions of the cerebral cortex.

Cerebral Cortex. Spencer[40] was the first to call attention to respiratory responses to stimulation of the presylvian area. Two general areas within this region have been mapped. (i) An *accelerator area* lies on the anterior sigmoid gyrus and immediately adjacent cortex of the medial surface of the hemisphere in the dog and cat; a comparable area in the monkey lies just rostral to the superior precentral gyrus. Portions of this area are rostral to the motor representation of the face, tongue, glottis, etc.; and stimulation of them gives rise to rhythmic licking, chewing and swallowing movements with salivation. Croaking, grunting and other forms of vocalization occur. (ii) An *inhibitory area* definable in the dog and cat is relatively large, including the gyrus compositus anterior and most of the cortex of the sylvian and ectosylvian gyri; in the cat the gyrus proreus is also included. In the monkey an inhibitory field is located just caudal to the lower end of the inferior precentral sulcus. Mastication is also obtained by stimulating this area. A second area producing acceleration of respiration coincides closely with motor area 2. Respiratory movements appear therefore to be localized in both cortical representations of the body musculature.

More recently, attention has been focused upon the respiratory effects of stimulating the *limbic* area of the cortex, i.e., the region forming the hilus of the hemispheres and embracing the medial and orbital surfaces of the frontal lobe (Chap. 26). Mapping of responsive zones reveals that the cortex of the posterior orbital surface, the cingulate gyrus, the tip of the temporal pole, the anterior temporal operculum and the anterior insula form a continuous strip of cortex giving rise to respiratory responses. The larger part of the "insular-orbital" area is inhibitory, as is the larger part of the cingulate gyrus. These findings have been confirmed in man by stimulation at the time of operation for prefrontal leukotomy.

Since alteration of autonomic activity may also be elicited by stimulation of the same general regions, they appear to subserve the autonomic and respiratory correlates of certain types of behavior. The close association with the olfactory area naturally recalls that sniffing and breathing are necessary for olfaction, and the nearness of the respiratory area on the convexity of the cortex to Broca's area suggests the integration of speech and breathing at a cortical level. The association of masticatory and swallowing movements with respiratory change on stimulation of area 6 points to a cortical integration of the various components of food-taking. If, as has been suggested, the orbital and other limbic

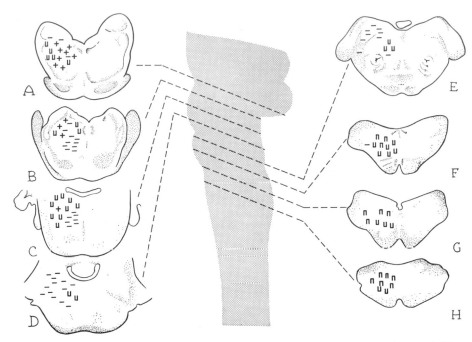

U = Inspiratory spasm   Π = Active expiration   − = Expiratory standstill
+ = Expiratory acceleration

Fig. 5. Summary diagram showing the types of respiratory responses elicited by stimulating brain stem at various levels between the isthmus of the pons (*A*) and 2 mm. caudal to the obex (*H*). (After Ngai and Wang, *Amer. J. Physiol.*, 1957, *190*:343–349.)

areas are concerned with emotional behavior, it is logical that breathing, which is a component of emotional expression, should be altered by stimulation of these areas.

According to conventional neurology, one would expect to find respiratory representation in cortical area 4, the motor area from which the pyramidal tracts arise, because respiration is subject to voluntary acceleration or inhibition. This does not appear to be so. Although the trunk and thoracic musculature is represented in this area, there is no evidence of coordinated employment of these muscles in acts suggestive of respiration when their cortical representation is stimulated, and pyramidal section in the cat does not influence the respiratory responses to cortical stimulation. It might therefore be concluded that respiration does not have a pyramidal control and that the voluntary regulation of respiration is mediated by extrapyramidal pathways.

Pons and Medulla. ELECTRICAL STIMULATION. The respiratory responses to stimulation of the pons and medulla are greater and more discrete than are the responses to cortical stimulation. When specific small regions are stimulated, the patterns of breathing change in a manner dependent upon the site of the stimulus. Changes in rate, inspiratory apnea (apneusis),

apnea at normal end expiration, and expiratory apnea are elicited by stimulation in different pontine and medullary areas.[32] Figure 5 shows the more or less discrete localization of the regions from which each of these effects may be produced. Earlier, less detailed work[7, 35] had yielded essentially similar results except for the localization of the regions causing expiratory apnea. It should be noted that stimulation of one side of the pons and medulla affects equally the respiratory muscles on both sides of the body. This finding, together with evidence from lesions,[37, 38] indicates extensive cross connections between the two sides of the brain stem and/or descent of impulses from one-half of the pons and medulla to musculature on both sides of the body.

SECTION AND ABLATION. The results of transection at various levels in the pons and medulla (Fig. 6) are quite different when the vagi are intact and when they are sectioned.

Transection with vagi intact. In an animal with the standard midcollicular decerebration, breathing is essentially indistinguishable from that in the intact animal. Thus, the influences of the cortical areas on respiration discussed above and of the temperature regulation centers in the hypothalamus (see Chap. 11) are not necessary for normal respiration. Transections in the pons do not markedly affect the pattern of breathing, although the rate is usually slowed. Transection in the rostral medulla,* however, may lead to marked changes in the breathing pattern,[4, 5, 19, 20, 49] which may be eupneic but is usually of a gasping type and may resemble Biot's breathing (brief periods of rapid breathing followed by pauses in expiration). Transection below a plane 2 mm. caudal to the rostral border of the medulla causes cessation of respiration.

Transection after section of vagi. When the above series of sections is made in an animal with both vagi cut or blocked, the effect of the pontine transections is very different.[4, 5, 19, 20, 24-28, 34-36, 41, 42] Although transection at the rostral border of the pons again produces little

---

*The medullopontine junction is defined here (after Wang) as a plane running from the acoustic stria dorsally to the caudal border of the trapezoid body on the ventral surface.

effect, transection slightly below this level causes dramatic changes. Initially rhythmic respiration gives way to sustained inspiration, or apneusis, which may last for minutes. This inspiratory spasm is usually followed by *apneustic* breathing. In this type of breathing, the inspiratory effort is strong and sustained, lasting for seconds or even minutes, and expiration consists only of a brief relaxation of the sustained inspiration. More caudal transections in the pons usually decrease the duration of the inspiratory phase and increase the duration of the expiratory phase. The effect on the inspiratory phase is the greater, so the net result is an increase in the mean respiratory rate. Thus the more caudal the lesion, the more nearly normal the rate and the duration of the inspiratory and expiratory phases.

The results of transection through the rostral medulla are not appreciably different when the vagi are cut and when the vagi are intact, even though the Xth cranial nerve enters the medulla below the level of section.

Respiratory centers. As a result of experiments

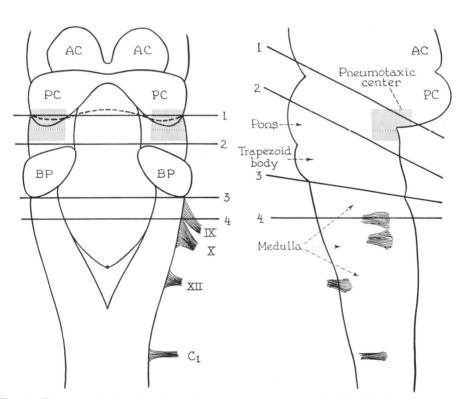

Fig. 6. Diagram showing location of pneumotaxic center and critical levels of transection. *1,* Lower midbrain section; *2,* high pontine section; *3,* section at medullopontine junction as defined by Wang *et al.; 4,* section 2 mm. caudal to rostral border. *AC,* Anterior colliculus; *PC,* posterior colliculus; *BP,* brachium pontis. (After Wang *et al., Amer. J. Physiol.,* 1957, *190*:333–342.)

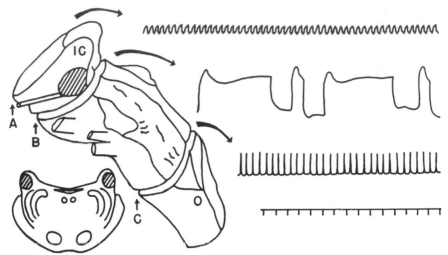

Fig. 7. Diagram showing respiratory patterns of vagotomized cats after brain stem lesions. *A,* Midcollicular transection results in rhythmic breathing resembling normal pattern. *B,* Transection caudal to inferior colliculi results in hypertonic breathing pattern (apneustic breathing). Same pattern can be obtained by bilateral lesions of hatched area. Lower left diagram shows a cross section through critical hatched area ("pneumotaxic" center or area). *C,* Transection 3 to 5 mm. above obex results in atonic breathing pattern (gasping). *IC,* Inferior colliculus; *O,* obex. Time in 10 second intervals. (From Tang, *Amer. J. Physiol.,* 1953, *172*:645–652.)

depending on transection and other surgical techniques, a series of centers (actually sub-centers) have been defined. The region in the anterior pons, destruction of which in combination with vagotomy leads to apneusis and apneustic respiration, is called the *pneumotaxic center.* From the transection experiments described above, this center clearly lies in the extreme rostral pons. Tang[45] has shown that bilateral ablation of a few cubic millimeters in the dorsolateral tegmentum of the pons leads to apneusis followed by apneustic breathing (Fig. 7). Unilateral lesions are ineffective. Subsequent workers[49] have found that somewhat larger bilateral lesions, placed slightly more medially, will also cause apneusis. All workers agree that midline lesions are ineffective. These differences in localization are very slight, a matter of 1 or 2 mm., and may be only apparent owing to damage beyond the visible sites of the lesions; or it may be necessary to remove only a portion of each pneumotaxic center to produce apneusis.

The *apneustic center* is defined as those regions of the caudal two-thirds of the pons which, subsequent to section of the vagi and ablation of the pneumotaxic center, *support* apneusis and apneustic breathing. This center, as its name implies, provides an inspiratory drive. As more and more of it is eliminated, the inspiratory phase becomes shorter and shorter, or less

apneustic. The apneustic center has not been localized to any particular pontine structure but apparently is part of the reticular facilitatory area.

The *medullary respiratory center* is often in error called simply "the respiratory center." Its exact localization and whether it is divided into an inspiratory and an expiratory center are matters of continuing investigation (see below).

ELECTRICAL RECORDING. The techniques of stimulation and ablation have certain limitations. With ablation it is difficult to know the exact limits of the destruction of nervous tissue; the question whether the effects are those of destruction of the cell bodies or of interruption of nerve pathways passing through the area is also a problem. With electrical stimulation, it is difficult to know whether the elements being stimulated are a "center" or fibers passing to or issuing from it; with unipolar electrodes, the spread of current is an additional problem. Also, it is not possible to know to what degree the response is abnormal, owing to the nearly synchronous volleys excited by electrical stimulation.

By recording with microelectrodes, one can determine the activity of cells or fibers subjected to only minimal damage (Chap. 1). The respiratory system is particularly suitable for study by this technique, since the firing of at least some cells involved in respiratory movements is periodic at the respiratory rate. However, considerable care is required to minimize the false periodic firing which is related to brain movements induced by breathing and which may cause the electrode to move with respect to the neurons. This source of confusion was not always recognized in early experiments. The criterion most useful in eliminating such an artifact is the constancy of spike amplitude during the respiratory cycle.

Electrical activity of the pons. Whether periodically firing cells exist in the pons has been a subject of controversy. However, at least in the decerebrate cat, it seems that there are pontine cells which fire trains of impulses with the same

periodicity as respiration, although usually not in phase with either inspiration or expiration.[10, 44] Periodic firing in the pneumotaxic center isolated from incoming impulses has not been found,[9] and therefore this center does not seem to be the site of the rhythmic neural activity responsible for the respiratory rhythm in the absence of the vagus.

Electrical activity of the medulla. The electrical activity related to respiration recorded from the medulla of decerebrate animals is more striking than that recorded from the pons.[13] Although a few active units may be found in other places, most of the activity is confined to the region near the level of the obex.[1, 14, 30, 48] As shown in Figure 8, potentials believed to be from cell

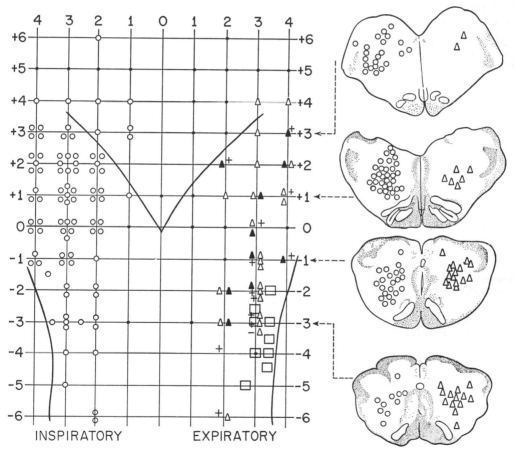

Fig. 8. Points in medulla and cervical cord of cat which are active during respiration.

Left, Points plotted along stereotaxic coordinates, in millimeters, rostral (+) and caudal (−) to obex; although separated here for clarity, inspiratory and expiratory points are present on both sides of midline. ○, Inspiratory points; ▲, early expiratory points; △, late expiratory; + expiratory of undefined timing; □, sites of activity appearing to be from fibers. (After Haber *et al., Amer. J. Physiol.,* 1957, *190*:350–355, and Nelson, *J. Neurophysiol.,* 1959, *22*:590–598.)

Right, Sections at levels indicated by arrows to stereotaxic grid. ○, Inspiratory points; △, expiratory points. (After Haber *et al., Amer. J. Physiol.,* 1957, *190*:350–355.)

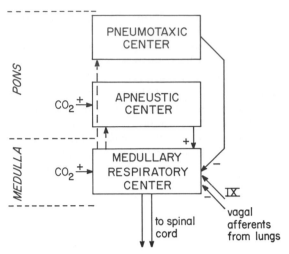

Fig. 9. Schematic diagram of the central respiratory centers showing possible interconnections and the points at which CO_2 and impulses from the lungs impinge; + augmentative and − inhibitory to inspiratory discharge.

bodies which fire during inspiration are recorded for the most part slightly rostral to the obex, whereas potentials from cell bodies firing during expiration tend to occur slightly caudal to the obex. These neurons are not afferents of vagal origin, since the activity persists when the vagal inputs are blocked. As will be seen by comparing Figures 8 and 6, the extent and location of the areas yielding electrical activity differ distinctly from those of areas yielding respiratory responses to stimulation. Impulses periodic with respiration which disappear when the vagi are blocked are also found in the medulla. These impulses are recorded mainly in the same general region as the inspiratory neurons, i.e., somewhat rostral to the obex. This activity appears to originate in the region of the tractus solitarius. Periodic neuronal activity has also been recorded in the isolated medulla. This activity presumably reflects the inherent rhythmic ability of the medullary respiratory center.

Activity of fibers from the inspiratory and expiratory cells has been traced from the medulla to the level of the second cervical segment.[28] The information from ablation, stimulation and recording can be incorporated in a schematic organization, as shown in Figure 9.

GENESIS OF THE RESPIRATORY RHYTHM

The experiments described above establish that the medullary portion of the respiratory center is capable of rhythmic activity which roughly resembles normal respiration. Section of the vagus nerve has little effect on this rhythm, which, in fact, endures in the absence of any neural input whatsoever (isolated medullary center). The initiation and maintenance of a rhythm can therefore be centrogenic; a model employing only two neurons will be described later.

Just above the medullary level is the apneustic center, which acts in conjunction with the medullary centers but which can exert an inspiratory drive that obscures rhythmic medullary activity in the absence of higher pontine centers and the vagal input. If the vagi are intact, rhythmic breathing is maintained. It may be inferred that the vagi operate through this apneustic center, although they enter the medulla farther down. As we shall see, at least two interpretations of the relation between the vagi and the apneustic center are possible: (i) At each breath the vagal impulses periodic with inspiration inhibit the inspiratory drive of the apneustic center; and (ii) the vagal impulses balance the inspiratory drive of the apneustic center at the medullary respiratory center, and the periodic nature of the vagal input is of secondary importance.

That the effect of vagal impulses is not solely a function of a waxing and waning of their bombardment of the respiratory centers is shown by the following experiment. Apneusis following anterior pontine section may be interrupted and a normal type of rhythmic respiration reinstated by steady stimulation of the vagus.[21, 46] This is done most physiologically by holding the lungs distended in the apparatus shown in Figure 10, thus evoking a continuous discharge from the stretch receptors in the lungs. Pressure measurements in the oil bath surrounding the animal reveal periodic respiratory efforts which are reasonably normal in rate and nature. When this vagal discharge is terminated by holding the lung at the end expiratory position, apneusis ensues. In passing it may be noted that chemical respiratory drives are also involved as a continuous and antagonistic respiratory drive. The amount of vagal discharge necessary to interrupt apneusis is determined by the pCO_2 of the blood; the higher the pCO_2, the greater the continuous vagal discharge necessary to reinstate rhythmic respiration.

The pneumotaxic center, like the vagus, opposes the apneustic center, since, in the absence of vagal input, the pneumotaxic center maintains the normal respiration of the decerebrate preparation. The ability of this center to promote rhythmic respiration is therefore clearly not due to periodic vagal impulses. Lumsden,[24, 25] as his choice of the term "pneumotaxic center" indicates, ascribed the rhythmicity of breathing to this pontine area. Pitts *et al.*[34-36] went further and ascribed respiratory rhythm to a breath-by-breath discharge of the pneumotaxic center. This was visualized as follows. As the "inspiratory center" discharged caudally to the respiratory muscles, it also discharged rostrally to the pneumotaxic center, which in turn discharged caudally to curb the inspiratory center discharge. Even within the reticular substance it is difficult to account for the time lapse in this hypothetical circuit. Moreover, Hoff and Breckenridge[4, 5, 19, 20] showed that the respiratory rhythm could be maintained by the medullary respiratory center separated from both the vagi and the pneumotaxic center.

Increasingly, the tendency is to think that respiratory rhythm is derived from the interplay of descending impulses and from the interaction between neurons. This view can be explained on two levels: (i) by appeal to simple analogy and (ii) by appeal to a knowledge of the factors which make for oscillation in electronic or other control systems.* An oversimplified model of a system which has some of the properties of

* Analogies to the respiratory system can be found in spinal reflex action, although the neural levels are different.[38] The divided spinal cord tends to yield alternate flexion and extension (stepping), and a favorable condition for bilateral stepping is the concurrent and equal stimulation of homologous nerves on both sides of the body. When the spinal cord is connected with the brain stem, oscillatory phenomena disappear and the system is biased toward extension (decerebrate rigidity). When still higher levels (upper midbrain and hypothalamus) are included in the system, flexor and extensor reflex excitability are again more nearly balanced, and oscillating phenomena occur (e.g., effective walking occurs). The principles derived from a study of control systems have applicability beyond the respiratory system, and these applications are just commencing to be realized.

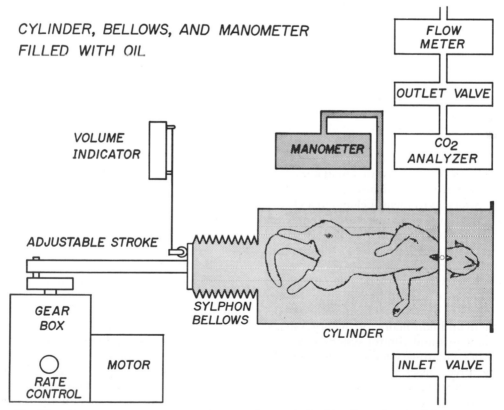

Fig. 10.   An apparatus to measure pressure–volume relationships (impedance) of the respiratory system. (From A. C. Young, unpublished experiments.)

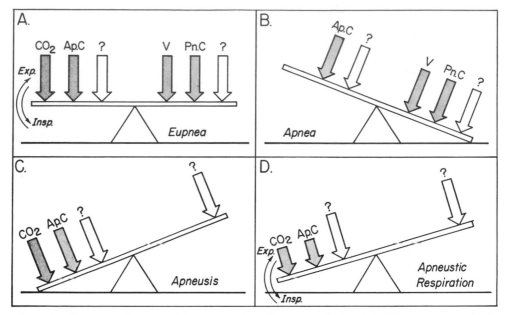

Fig. 11. Summary diagram of the summation of neural and chemical influences on respiration. *Ap.C* and *Pn.C,* Apneustic and pneumotaxic centers, respectively; *V,* vagal afferent impulses from the lungs. Forces to left of fulcrum tend to cause inspiration and those to right tend to inhibit respiration. Balance is the condition for oscillation (rhythmic breathing).

the respiratory system is the familiar seesaw. Figure 11 illustrates this. As long as the "forces" exerted on the two ends of the seesaw are approximately balanced, a minimum amount of energy will keep the system oscillating. When, however, the "force" on one side is appreciably greater than that on the other, the amount of energy required to keep the system oscillating will be increased. Either the resulting movement will stop, or the swings will be centered at the heavy end.

Respiration Viewed as an Oscillatory System. The central neural mechanism controlling respiratory movements belongs to a class of systems, including many mechanical and electrical systems, capable of oscillation. It is helpful in understanding the respiratory system to consider rather generally the properties of a system which lead to a rhythmic output, i.e., to oscillation. Since neural systems must be mechanistic, there *must* be a broad similarity between them and non-neural oscillatory systems. Mathematicians and control systems engineers conceive of oscillating systems as falling into the following three classes.[29, 43, 47]

TYPE I. LINEAR SYSTEMS. Consider a system with an input and an output. The system could be of any reasonable type—electrical, mechanical, chemical—or it could be a mixture of types.

For example, the input could be mols of O_2 used per minute in an electrochemical reaction, and the output could be amperes of current flowing as a result of the chemical reaction. The system might be one in which the input and the output were of the same type, like the input and output voltage in an amplifier; or, the number of impulses per second in an afferent neural volley could be the input and the number of impulses per second in the resulting efferent discharge the output. If, in any of these systems, the output is directly proportional to the input, that system is called "linear." A large number of physical and chemical systems are linear or nearly so, and their properties have been very thoroughly studied and applied. For our purpose, a few properties of linear systems will be considered.

(i) Sinusoidal inputs always lead to sinusoidal outputs. In general, the outputs are not the same shape as the inputs for other shapes of waves.

(ii) To make an oscillator of a linear system it is necessary to "connect" the output (i.e., feed it back) to the input. The conditions for oscillation are: (a) the phase shift from input to output must be exactly zero or exactly an integral number of cycles and (b) the output must be greater than the input. If there is a frequency at which these conditions can be met, the system will oscillate with the sinusoidal wave at this frequency. Oscillators of this type are in wide general use.

(iii) If the response of a linear system is known for all frequencies of the input, the properties of the system are completely known, and the output for any form of input can be calculated.

TYPE II. NEARLY LINEAR SYSTEMS. The theory of linear systems may be extended to account for the properties of systems which are nearly linear. In these, the output may contain frequencies which are harmonics of the input signal; however, such harmonics become negligible as the input and output amplitudes of the system are reduced. An example of this kind of system is the standard phonograph amplifier.

TYPE III. NONLINEAR SYSTEMS. A third type of system is currently being studied extensively by mathematicians and engineers. It is "nonlinear" because its output is not proportional to its input. Systems of this third type may have properties which cannot be approximated by linear and nearly linear systems. In general, nonlinear systems do not produce sinusoidal waves when used as oscillators, and the oscillations do not become sinusoidal as amplitude is reduced. Nonlinear systems may also produce subharmonics or fractional-order subharmonics; that is, if an input is of a particular frequency, the output may be at a frequency of one-third, one-half, two-thirds, etc., of the input frequency. Further, the properties of nonlinear systems cannot be completely determined from knowledge of their response to any one kind of input. There is no unique general method of studying these systems; each must be approached with a variety of analytic and experimental techniques. Some nonlinear systems do have properties which cannot be obtained in linear or nearly linear systems with the same number of elements. Nonlinear systems are used in counting and scaling circuits, in sweep circuits in oscilloscopes and television sets, and in pulse generators and coincidence counters.

System Analysis of Breathing. In the above terms, the type of system involved in the neural control of breathing can be determined with experimental techniques already familiar (Fig. 10). The volume of the lungs may be controlled in any desired manner in order to control vagal input to the respiratory centers in the brain stem. The output may be measured as changes in the pressure produced in the oil tank by the respiratory muscles. Alternatively, nerve impulses in the phrenic nerves can be recorded electrically. With the input from the vagus held constant, the chemical input may be controlled by varying the CO_2 level in the blood. Neural drive and chemical effects can thus be measured separately or in combination.

When the animal is rendered apneic by hyperventilation, the output drops to zero, and the system does not oscillate until the CO_2 concentration increases. The pressure changes produced during recovery from apnea are shown in Figure 12. It is clear that the output is not sinusoidal even at the lowest amplitudes, and it thus appears that the respiratory system is nonlinear. A further check is obtained when the lung volume is changed sinusoidally and the resulting pressure output is recorded. The output, depending on the input frequency, may be either harmonically or subharmonically related to the input frequency; Figure 12 shows an example that is subharmonically related. We may therefore conclude that the respiratory system is nonlinear, having at least two nonoscillating positions, apnea and apneusis, and an oscillatory range between these limits in which normal eupneic breathing occurs.

NONLINEAR NEURAL MODEL. A possible neural model of a system which would oscillate is shown in Figure 13. This model is much oversimplified in that it shows only two neurons; the actual system would be composed of many connected neurons. The neurons in Figure 13 must have three properties. The first is similar to adapta-

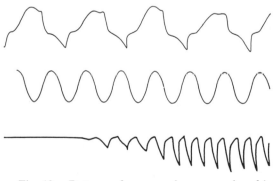

Fig. 12. Patterns of pressure changes produced in oil bath (see Fig. 10) by inspiratory activity of respiratory muscles. *Top,* Changes during imposed lung volume. *Center,* Sine wave for comparison with pressure curve above; note that it does not become sinusoidal even at low amplitude. (From A. C. Young, unpublished experiments.) *Bottom,* changes during recovery from apnea while lung volume was fixed.

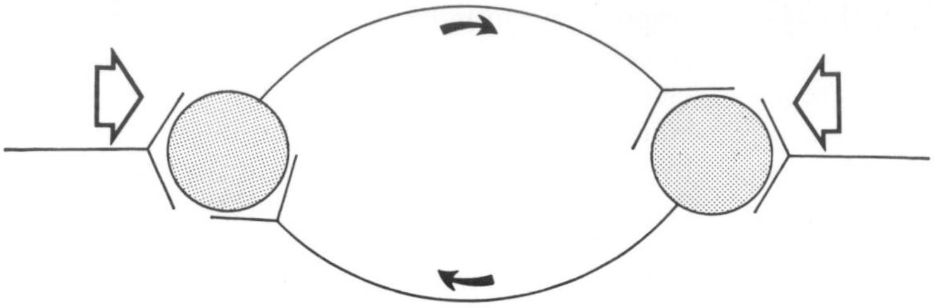

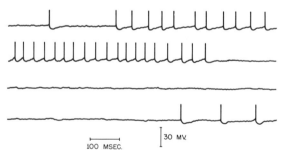

Fig. 13. Diagram of a simple two-neuron, oscillatory system giving properties described in text.

tion in sense organs. Thus, with a continuous bombardment by afferent impulses, the number of impulses from the neurons must at first be high and then gradually decline. Second, the number of efferent impulses per second at first must be actually higher than the number in the afferent volley (gain greater than unity). The third essential property is that at least one of the neurons must have a nonlinear relation between its output frequency and the frequency of the input to it. Both the first and second properties—"adaptation" and a gain greater than one—have been observed in interneurons in the spinal cord. The third condition is commonly encountered in the nervous system. When neurons with these properties are connected as shown in Figure 13, the system will give bursts of impulses, the interval of the bursts being determined by the "time constant" of the adaptation-like process and, to some extent, by the nonlinear properties of the cells. This situation can be simulated by an electric analogue and is, in fact, the well known multivibrator.

In such a system, if additional afferents synapse with the cells, a sufficiently strong continuous discharge will stop the oscillation of the system, in which case one of the cells will discharge continuously while the other cell is nearly quiescent. In the analogue, the corresponding effect is observable if the individual tubes in the multivibrator are biased with an impressed voltage. In general, systems of this nature have two or more stable positions and an intervening region of continuous oscillation. They also have the general properties listed in the discussion of nonlinear systems. These oscillating pairs of neurons could be in the medullary respiratory area and conform to the cells that fire during inspiration and expiration.

A more complete model would, of course, have to take into account interconnections between individual pairs of cells. Such interconnections are required to lock the oscillator together in order to gain a synchronous discharge like that occurring in breathing. The more complete model would also have to take into account additional interconnections between the neurons via pathways in the pons (apneustic

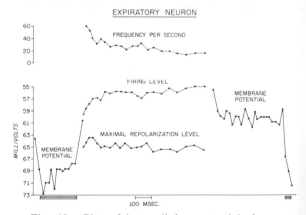

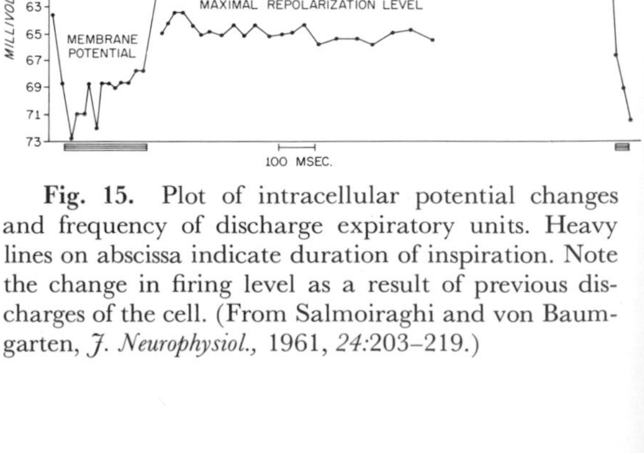

Fig. 14. Potential changes from inspiratory neuron during one respiratory cycle. Anesthetized, decerebellate, midcollicularly decerebrate cat. Bilateral pneumothorax. Positive pressure respiration with 100 per cent oxygen. Pressure foot on brain stem. In each set of records, upper trace: diaphragmatic motor units; lower trace: intracellular potentials. 2.8 M. KCl-filled micropipette. Continuous record from top to bottom. Membrane potential at beginning of record: 49.5 mV. Records retouched. Note the synaptic potentials which lead to firing of the cells. (From Salmoiraghi and von Baumgarten, *J. Neurophysiol.*, 1961, *24*:203–219.)

Fig. 15. Plot of intracellular potential changes and frequency of discharge expiratory units. Heavy lines on abscissa indicate duration of inspiration. Note the change in firing level as a result of previous discharges of the cell. (From Salmoiraghi and von Baumgarten, *J. Neurophysiol.*, 1961, *24*:203–219.)

and pneumotaxic center). These centers may act primarily as biases; there is evidence to the contrary, however, since electrical activity corresponding to the respiration has been recorded.[10, 44]

One critical test for the hypothesis that the periodicity of the respiratory center is due to the interconnection of reciprocally connected groups of neurons should be the presence of EPSP's and IPSP's causing the firing of these cells. Such intercellular potentials would not, of course, be present in the firing of cells such as those of the sino-atrial node (see Chap. 30). Von Baumgarten and Salmoiraghi recently have been successful in obtaining such records from cells of the medullary inspiratory and expiratory centers. The number of successful records is small (seven inspiratory cells and one expiratory cell).[36a] The presence of synaptic potentials which directly cause the firing of the neurons is shown in Figures 14 and 15.

Even more convincing is the result of antidromic stimulation of the descending respiratory pathways in the cord. Von Baumgarten and Nakayama have conclusively shown the existence of such axon collaterals from some cells of the medullary respiratory centers.[3a] These collaterals were shown to have reciprocal connections to the inspiratory and expiratory neurons; i.e., stimulation of the descending expiratory pathways caused facilitation of the expiratory neurons and inhibition of the inspiratory neurons. The excitability of these neurons was also shown to vary with their "spontaneous" firing during the respiratory cycle, being greater during periods of high activity.

The firing of the respiratory motor nerves does not follow exactly the firing of the cells in the respiratory center but is further modified by interconnections at the spinal levels. The presence of relatively large numbers of cells at the spinal level which fire synchronously with respiration, but are not motor cells, has recently been shown by Nelson.[31]

In relatively complex systems of this nature it is not usually possible to speak of the oscillation as resulting from connections between specific elements, but it may be a property of the interconnections of the relatively large number of cells. For this reason it is rather dangerous to think of the rhythmicity of such a system as residing in a particular region of the brain stem merely because this part is capable of oscillation

when isolated from other parts. It is possible that a large number of other groups of cells would also oscillate if they could be isolated surgically.

REFERENCES

1. ADRIAN, E. D. *J. Physiol.*, 1933, *79:*322–358.
2. AVIADO, D. M., JR., LI, T. H., KALOW, W., SCHMIDT, C. F., TURNBULL, G. L., PESKIN, G. W., HESS, M. E. and WEISS, A. J. *Amer. J. Physiol.*, 1951, *165:*261–277.
3. VON BAUMGARTEN, R. and KANZOW, E. *Arch. ital. Biol.*, 1958, *96:*361–373.
3a. VON BAUMGARTEN, R. and NAKAYAMA, S. *Pflügers Arch. ges. Physiol.*, 1964, *281:*245–258.
4. BRECKENRIDGE, C. G. and HOFF, H. E. *Amer. J. Physiol.*, 1950, *160:*385–394.
5. BRECKENRIDGE, C. G., HOFF, H. E. and SMITH, H. T. *Amer. J. Physiol.*, 1950, *162:*74–79.
6. BRONK, D. W. and FERGUSON, L. K. *Amer. J. Physiol.*, 1935, *110:*700–707.
7. BROOKHART, J. M. *Amer. J. Physiol.*, 1940, *129:*709–723.
8. CAMPBELL, E. J. M. *The respiratory muscles and the mechanics of breathing.* Chicago, Year Book Medical Publishers, Inc., 1958.
9. COHEN, M. I. *Amer. J. Physiol.*, 1959, *195:*23-27.
10. COHEN, M. K. and WANG, S. C. *J. Neurophysiol.*, 1959, *22:*33–50.
11. COMROE, J. H. *Amer. J. Physiol.*, 1939, *127:*176–191.
12. COMROE, J. H. and SCHMIDT, C. F. *Amer. J. Physiol.*, 1938, *121:*75–97.
13. GESELL, R., BRICKER, J. and MAGEE, C. *Amer. J. Physiol.*, 1936, *117:*423–452.
14. HABER, E., KOHN, K., NGAI, S. H., HOLODAY, D. A. and WANG, S. C. *Amer. J. Physiol.*, 1957, *190:*350–355.
15. HARRIS, A. S. *Amer. J. Physiol.*, 1945, *143:*140–147.
16. HERING, E. and BREUER, J. *S. B. Akad. wiss. Wien*, 1868, *57:*672–677; *58:*909.
17. HESS, W. R. *Pflügers Arch. ges. Physiol.*, 1936, *237:*24–39.
18. HESS, W. R. and WYSS, O. A. M. *Pflügers Arch. ges. Physiol.*, 1936, *237:*761–770.
19. HOFF, H. E. and BRECKENRIDGE, C. G. *Amer. J. Physiol.*, 1949, *158:*157–172.
20. HOFF, H. E., BRECKENRIDGE, C. G. and CUNNINGHAM, J. E. *Amer. J. Physiol.*, 1950, *160:*485–489.
21. KERR, D. I. B., DUNLOP, C. W., BEST, E. D. and MULLNER, J. A. *Amer. J. Physiol.*, 1954, *176:*508–512.
22. KNOWLTON, G. C. and LARRABEE, M. G. *Amer. J. Physiol.*, 1946, *147:*100–114.
23. LARRABEE, M. G. and KNOWLTON, G. C. *Amer. J. Physiol.*, 1946, *147:*90–99.
24. LUMSDEN, T. *J. Physiol.*, 1923, *57:*153–160.
25. LUMSDEN, T. *J. Physiol.*, 1923, *57:*354–367.
26. MARCKWALD, M. *Z. Biol.*, 1887, *23:*149–283.
27. MARCKWALD, M. *The movements of respiration and their innervation in the rabbit.* Trans. by HAIG, T. A., London, Blackie & Son, 1888.
28. MARCKWALD, M. and KRONECKER, H. *Arch. Anat. Physiol. wiss. Med.*, 1880, 441–446.
29. MINORSKY, N. *Introduction to non-linear mechanics.* Ann Arbor, Mich., J. W. Edwards, 1947.
30. NELSON, J. R. *J. Neurophysiol.* 1959, *22:*590–598.
31. NELSON, J. R. Personal communication.
32. NGAI, S. H. and WANG, S. C. *Amer. J. Physiol.*, 1957, *190:*343–349.

33. PAINTAL, A. S. *J. Physiol.*, 1953, *121*:341–359.

34. PITTS, R. F., MAGOUN, H. W. and RANSON, S. W. *Amer. J. Physiol.*, 1939, *126*:673–688.

35. PITTS, R. F., MAGOUN, H. W. and RANSON, S. W. *Amer. J. Physiol.*, 1939, *126*:689–701.

36. PITTS, R. F., MAGOUN, H. W. and RANSON, S. W. *Amer. J. Physiol.*, 1939, *127*:654–670.

36a. SALMOIRAGHI, G. C. and VON BAUMGARTEN, R. *J. Neurophysiol.*, 1961, *24*:203–219.

37. SCHIFF, J. M. *Lehrbuch der Physiologie des Menschen.* Lahr, Schaufenburg, 1858–59.

38. SCHIFF, J. M. MORITZ SCHIFF's *Gesammelte Beitrage zur Physiologie.* Lausanne, B. Benda, 1894, 4 vols. (see vol. 1).

39. SHERRINGTON, C. S. *J. Physiol.*, 1913, *47*:196–214.

40. SPENCER, W. G. *Phil. Trans.*, 1894, *B185*:609–657.

41. STELLA, G. *J. Physiol.*, 1938, *93*:263–275.

42. STELLA, G. *J. Physiol.*, 1939, *95*:365–372.

43. STOKER, J. J. *Nonlinear vibrations in mechanical and electrical systems.* New York, Interscience Publishers, 1950.

44. TAKAGI, K. and NAKAYAMA, T. *Science*, 1958, *128*:1206.

45. TANG, P. C. *Amer. J. Physiol.*, 1953, *172*:645–652.

46. TANG, P. C. and YOUNG, A. C. *Fed. Proc.*, 1956, *15*:184.

47. TRUXAL, J. G. *Automatic feedback control system synthesis.* New York, McGraw-Hill, 1955.

48. WALDRING, S. and DIRKEN, M. N. J. *J. Neurophysiol.*, 1951, *14*:227–242.

49. WANG, S. C., NGAI, S. H. and FRUMIN, M. J. *Amer. J. Physiol.*, 1957, *190*:333–342.

50. WIDDICOMBE, J. G. *J. Physiol.*, 1954, *123*:55–70.

51. WIDDICOMBE, J. G. *J. Physiol.*, 1954, *123*:71–104.

CHAPTER 42

The Chemical Regulation of Ventilation

By THOMAS F. HORNBEIN

VENTILATION, the movement of air into and out of the lungs, serves the function of carrying oxygen to and removing carbon dioxide from the blood. In contrast to the circulation this homeostatic role may be transiently subjugated to other functions such as coughing, sighing, yawning and talking. The stimuli influencing ventilation may be classified as nonspecific (wakefulness, pain and emotional responses), mechanical (the lung stretch and deflation reflexes) and chemical. The physiologic chemical stimuli increasing ventilation are hypoxia (decreased P_{O_2}), carbon dioxide (P_{CO_2}) and hydrogen ion concentration ([H+]). This chapter describes the manner in which these three chemical factors modify ventilation to provide adequate tissue oxygenation and a relatively constant body pH. Several recent reviews detail this facet of ventilatory control.[6, 19, 25, 37]

In 1892, J. S. Haldane and Lorraine Smith reported on studies in which a person was "allowed to remain in a closed chamber until the air became very impure."[16] As carbon dioxide accumulated in the chamber and oxygen content fell, ventilation increased markedly. Repeating the experiment with a carbon dioxide absorber in the chamber, they observed that breathing was unaffected until the oxygen content of the air had dropped from 21 per cent to below 15.5 per cent. They concluded that "excessive hyperpnea" in the first situation was "due almost entirely to excessive carbonic acid and not to deficiency of oxygen," though a sufficient fall in oxygen content "may also cause some hyperpnea." The essence of these simple and exceedingly significant studies is shown in Figure 1.

In 1911 Hans Winterstein proposed his "reaction theory" of ventilatory control.[46] This theory, which has been progressively modernized with the accumulation of new knowledge,[48] states that increase in [H+] within or near specific receptor cells is the unique stimulus to ventilation. By combining with water, CO_2 forms carbonic acid and thus H+. The greater effect of CO_2 on breathing than that of fixed acids would be explained by the observation that gases can diffuse rapidly through cell membranes, which are relatively impermeable to ions. Thus, blood-borne CO_2 should penetrate easily to a chemically sensitive receptor in the brain, altering [H+] locally while fixed acids might be confined largely to the blood. According to this theory the effects of hypoxia result

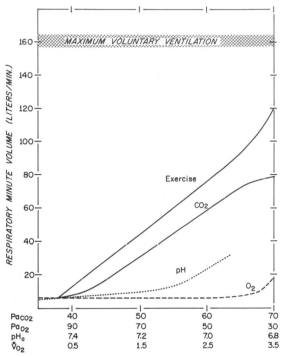

Pa$_{CO_2}$	40	50	60	70
Pa$_{O_2}$	90	70	50	30
pH$_a$	7.4	7.2	7.0	6.8
V̇$_{O_2}$	0.5	1.5	2.5	3.5

Fig. 1. Acute ventilatory response to chemical stimuli in a 70 kg. male. The abscissae for arterial P$_{CO_2}$, P$_{O_2}$ pH and oxygen consumption (V̇$_{O_2}$) are associated *respectively* with the curves labeled CO_2, O_2, pH and Exercise. Responses are compared to the maximum ventilation which the subject can attain transiently by voluntary effort. The curves represent responses of normal man with intact compensatory readjustments. Thus, the curves for hypoxia and metabolic pH changes show the response obtained as increasing ventilation yields a falling P$_{CO_2}$.

from accumulation of acid products of anerobic metabolism. The attractiveness of such a unitary concept of ventilatory control is obvious.

The reaction, or H$^+$, theory required its first revision in 1927 when peripheral chemoreceptors responsive to hypoxia were first discovered.[18] These aortic and carotid chemoreceptors were found to respond to P$_{CO_2}$ and [H$^+$] as well, but they appeared to be uniquely responsible for the ventilatory response to low P$_{O_2}$, since hypoxia depressed rather than increased ventilation after denervation of these structures. Even in the absence of peripheral chemoreceptors, P$_{CO_2}$ and [H$^+$] stimulate ventilation. The exact location of central chemosensitive areas is not completely delineated but recent work suggests the existence of a receptor which is responsive to changes in cerebrospinal fluid.

This chapter deals first with current knowl-

edge concerning structure and function of the peripheral and central chemosensitive areas. Ventilatory responses to P$_{O_2}$, P$_{CO_2}$, [H$^+$] and exercise will then be described. Since much investigation of the interaction between chemical stimuli in blood and cerebrospinal fluid (csf) is presently directed toward evaluation of the H$^+$ theory, we shall examine P$_{CO_2}$-[H$^+$] effects on ventilation for their compatibility with the theory. Present knowledge does not permit the inclusion of P$_{O_2}$ into such a framework. Gaps in the knowledge needed to support the H$^+$ theory will be apparent. Nevertheless it pro-

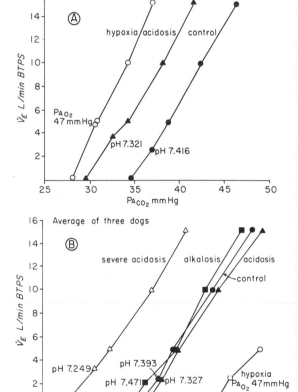

Fig. 2. CO_2 response curves in resting, unanesthetized dogs. *A,* With intact peripheral chemoreceptors. *B,* In chronically chemoreceptor-denervated dogs. The normal curve, obtained at sea level, is shifted to the right following denervation. Denervation profoundly alters the response to acute hypoxia and appears to eliminate the effect of mild metabolic acidosis. More marked acidosis stimulates ventilation in the absence of the peripheral chemoreceptors. (From Mitchell *et al.*, *Physiologist,* 1964, *7:*208; and personal communication.)

vides a reasonably simple approach to understanding chemical regulation of ventilation.

THE PERIPHERAL CHEMORECEPTORS

The extreme vascularity and rich innervation of the carotid body prompted De Castro[8] in 1926 to suggest that this structure might sense the chemical composition of blood. A year later, C. and J. F. Heymans[17] observed an increase in ventilation when the isolated aortic arch of a dog was perfused with blood from a donor animal breathing a gas low in oxygen. In 1930, C. Heymans, Bouckaert and Dautrebande[18] unveiled the exact physiologic role of the carotid body as predicted by De Castro four years before. For this work, C. Heymans received the Nobel Prize in 1938.

The importance of the carotid and aortic bodies to normal ventilation has been the subject of considerable debate. Some investigators felt that these structures had no significant role in control of normal breathing at sea level, that they served only an emergency function in response to severe hypoxia.[2] Supporting this view is the fact that section of the nerves from the peripheral chemoreceptors causes little change in normal ventilation or in the response to inspired carbon dioxide,[13] while lack of oxygen leads to respiratory depression rather than to stimulation (Fig. 2). Recent evidence suggests that peripheral chemoreceptors play a definite though unobtrusive role in the regulation of normal sea level ventilation.

Anatomy. The carotid body is a tiny nodule (about 5 mm. long in man) composed of large epithelioid "glomus" or glandlike cells within a network of connecting or sustentacular cells. The body lies just above the carotid sinus, affixed to the ascending pharyngeal or occipital artery, deriving its blood supply from one or two tiny branches of these vessels (Fig. 3). Venous blood drains into the internal jugular vein. The carotid nerve (nerve of Hering) containing afferent fibers from the carotid sinus and carotid body joins the glosso-pharyngeal nerve. Electron micrographs reveal that nerve fibers terminate near the sustentacular cells without penetrating into the epithelioid or glomus cells.[43] Histologically similar tissue has been found at several sites about the aortic arch and subclavian arteries.[3] Afferent fibers supplying the aortic bodies are carried in the vagus nerve or in a separate thin branch, the depressor nerve, which accompanies the vagus. The anatomic and physiologic characteristics of the aortic bodies have not been so clearly delineated as those of the carotid body. Though the relative participation of the carotid and aortic chemore-

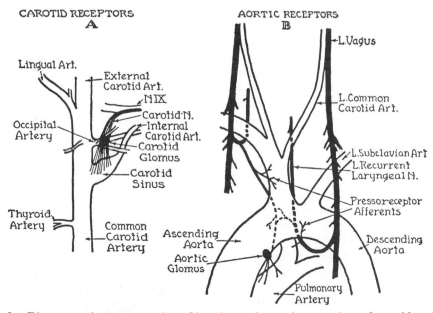

Fig. 3. Diagrammatic representation of location and neural connections of carotid and aortic chemoreceptors and pressoreceptors (dog). (From Comroe, *Amer. J. Physiol.*, 1939, *127*:176; and Comroe and Schmidt, *Amer. J. Physiol.*, 1938, *121*:75.)

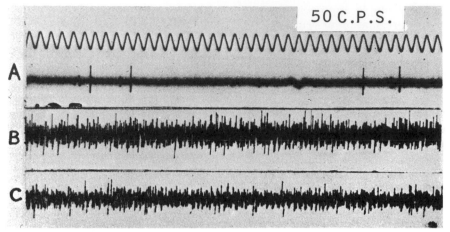

Fig. 1. Action potentials in a nerve twig from the carotid body of a cat artificially ventilated with room air. *A*, Control mean blood pressure is 150 mm. Hg. One pressoreceptor fiber is present. Chemoreceptor impulses are absent. *B*, After hemorrhage (50 ml.) mean blood pressure of 55 mm. Hg results in heavy chemoreceptor "impulse traffic." *C*, Immediately after the cervical sympathetic trunk is cut, chemoreceptor impulses are reduced. Blood pressure is unchanged at 55 mm. Hg. (From Floyd and Neil, *Arch. int. Pharmacodyn.*, 1952, *91*:230.)

ceptors in circulatory and ventilatory regulation appears to differ, the entire ventilatory contribution from both sites will be treated in the subsequent discussion as though from a single source, the peripheral chemoreceptors.

Blood Flow. With a rather intricate preparation, Daly and co-workers[7] estimated blood flow and metabolism of the cat's carotid body. The flow was found to be 2000 ml. per 100 grams per minute, a value nearly forty times that of brain. It could not be determined how much of this exceedingly high flow passed through the normal aortic–sinusoid–venous pathway as compared to that which bypassed chemosensitive tissue through arterial-venous shunts. Only when flow was diminished by lowering the blood pressure could an arterial-venous oxygen difference be detected. Under these conditions, oxygen consumption was calculated to be 9 ml. per 100 grams per minute, a very high metabolism compared to other organs, but small in comparison to total blood flow.

Stimuli. The carotid bodies respond to decreases in arterial P_{O_2} and flow and to increases in arterial P_{CO_2}, arterial $[H^+]$ and temperature.

Flow sensitivity. Carotid body blood flow is so high that the arterial-venous oxygen difference is immeasurable, suggesting that P_{O_2} and P_{CO_2}, rather than contents of arterial blood, reflect the true stimuli to the carotid body. Indeed, perfusion of the carotid body with Ringer–Locke solution equilibrated at normal gas tensions produces no ventilatory response, although, in the absence of hemoglobin, oxygen content of the perfusate is low.[2] Similarly, up to 70 per cent of blood hemoglobin can be bound with carbon monoxide without increasing electrical activity in the carotid nerve,[12] an observation which supports the importance of arterial P_{O_2} rather than oxygen content as the chemoreceptor stimulus. However, when perfusion is decreased, arterial gas tensions no longer correlate with carotid body response. Landgren and Neil[29] observed profound chemoreceptor discharge in cats rendered hypotensive by hemorrhage although arterial P_{O_2}, P_{CO_2} and $[H^+]$ were unchanged (Fig. 4). They suggested that this activity resulted from a lower P_{O_2}, a greater P_{CO_2} and an accumulation of acid metabolites within the glomus cells. Cervical sympathectomy decreased the activity, indicating that the diminished carotid body blood flow may have been due partly to active vasoconstriction. Conceivably, increased sympathetic activity from other causes, such as exercise, might contribute similarly to ventilation.

Temperature. Although Witzleb[49] found carotid body activity to be related directly to body temperature, he did not attempt to maintain blood gas tensions and *p*H constant. Thus, it is uncertain whether temperature or secondary alteration in arterial P_{O_2}, P_{CO_2} and *p*H was responsible.

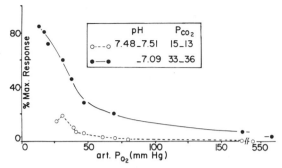

	pH	P_{CO_2}
o---o	7.48_7.51	15_13
•—•	_7.09	33_36

Fig. 5. Integrated neural discharge (expressed as percentage of maximum asphyxic activity) from the cat's carotid body in response to changing P_{aO_2} at two levels of arterial P_{CO_2}–pH achieved by altering ventilation. (From Hornbein and Roos, *J. appl. Physiol.*, 1963, *18*:580–584.)

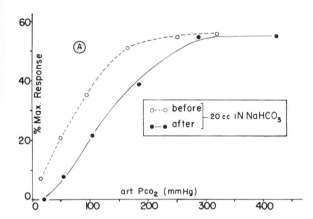

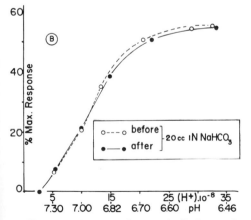

Fig. 6. Integrated neural discharge (expressed as percentage of maximum asphyxic activity) from the cat's carotid body in response to stepwise alterations in inspired P_{CO_2}. *A*, Response is related to arterial P_{CO_2}. *B*, Response is related to arterial [H+]. Addition of fixed base (20 ml. 1 N $NaHCO_3$) alters the steady state response for a given P_{aCO_2} (*A*), but not for a given [H+]$_a$ (*B*). (From Hornbein and Roos, *J. appl. Physiol.*, 1963, *18*:580–584.)

P_{O_2}, P_{CO_2}, [H+]. The carotid nerve of an anesthetized cat with normal arterial P_{O_2} has a low level of tonic activity (Fig. 5).[20] As the arterial P_{O_2} falls, the activity increases greatly. Significantly, combined hypoxia and hypercapnia produce more than a simple additive effect on chemoreceptor activity.[20] This interaction may account in part for the increased ventilatory sensitivity to carbon dioxide observed in subjects acutely exposed to lowered oxygen tension. In the absence of hypoxia, the carotid body is relatively insensitive to small changes in P_{CO_2} or [H+] but may respond considerably if the alterations are extreme (Fig. 6). In the steady state the response to CO_2 results entirely from changes in arterial [H+].[23] This is apparent in Figure 6*B*, where, for a given arterial [H+], there is a unique chemoreceptor response in spite of large differences in P_{CO_2} between the curves. In other words, in the steady state the carotid body appears to be H+-specific in its response to metabolic or respiratory acidosis. Increased CO_2 evokes a more prompt chemoreceptor response than an equivalent addition of fixed acid, probably because CO_2 diffuses more readily into the chemoreceptor cells to produce a faster alteration of the [H+]. As one might anticipate, the interaction between hypoxia and hypercapnia is in reality an interaction between hypoxia and [H+].[23]

THE CENTRAL CHEMOSENSITIVE AREA

Since CO_2 still increases breathing after denervation of the peripheral chemoreceptors, central chemosensitivity is of obvious importance in regulating ventilation. Such a response is possibly nonspecific, related to a stimulating effect of CO_2 on neurons in general, as, for example, in the reticular activating system. The fact that anesthetics depress selectively the response to CO_2 without impairing the reflex effect of hypoxia suggests the existence of areas of central chemosensitivity which are separate from the neurons of the respiratory center. Neither electrical recording from nor the microinjection of stimulating chemicals into the region of brainstem respiratory centers has supplied convincing evidence of chemoreceptor cells in this region.[26]

In 1954, Leusen[30] reported that ventilation in dogs could be changed by altering the P_{CO_2}-[H+] composition of fluid perfusing the ven-

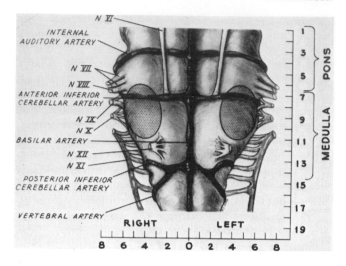

Fig. 7. Anterior surface of cat medulla showing area (shaded) where application of increased P_{CO_2} or [H+] stimulates ventilation. Topical application of 0.1 per cent procaine or cooling these areas causes apnea which persists at high P_{CO_2}. The areas are superficial, distant from the "respiratory center," and are bounded laterally by the IXth and Xth nerves. (From Severinghaus et al., *J. appl. Physiol.*, 1963, *18*:1155–1166.)

tricles and flowing out through the cisterna magna. This observation has led recently to the delineation of an area on the ventrolateral surface of the medulla (Fig. 7) which is exceedingly sensitive to changes in P_{CO_2}-[H+] of solutions bathing it.[34] This region lies close to the surface immediately medial to the entrance of the vagus and glossopharyngeal nerves into the brain stem. Increased P_{CO_2} or [H+] or solutions containing nicotine or acetylcholine stimulate breathing when topically applied to this area. Cold, 0.1 per cent procaine or stripping of the pial membrane depresses or obliterates ventilation. These facts, coupled with the rapidity of response to stimulation, suggest that the receptor cells are superficial and could respond to stimuli transmitted through cerebrospinal fluid. Although this area appears to play a major role in the response to P_{CO_2}-[H+], it should be emphasized that other central P_{CO_2}-[H+] sensitive sites affecting ventilation may also exist. Evidence on this point is inconclusive.

If the central chemosensitive area responds only to alterations in composition of cerebrospinal or brain extracellular fluid, its effect on ventilation is determined by the properties of the blood–brain barrier. This barrier is normally freely permeable to gases but much less permeable to ions. Therefore acid–base alterations in arterial blood may produce similar or diametrically opposite changes in cerebrospinal fluid depending on whether the blood [H+] changes are due to respiratory or metabolic abnormalities. For example, increase in arterial P_{CO_2} leads to a roughly comparable rise in cerebrospinal fluid P_{CO_2} with a resulting increase in [H+] of

both arterial blood and cerebrospinal fluid.* Conversely, administration of fixed acid raises arterial [H+] without a rise in P_{CO_2}. Increased arterial [H+] stimulates ventilation, lowering P_{CO_2} of the blood and cerebrospinal fluid, resulting in cerebrospinal fluid alkalosis and blood acidosis. Similarly, acute metabolic alkalosis of arterial blood produces acidosis of the cerebrospinal fluid. These "paradoxical" shifts have been documented by direct cerebrospinal fluid pH measurement.[14, 42, 47]

The differences, at least qualitatively, between peripheral and central chemosensitive areas are (i) only the former responds to hypoxia and (ii) the latter is somewhat isolated physiologically from arterial [H+] changes while being readily receptive to changes in P_{CO_2}.

VENTILATORY RESPONSES

In the following description, an attempt will be made to relate the effects of hypoxia, carbon dioxide, metabolic acid-base alterations and ex-

*Because of brain metabolism, brain tissue P_{CO_2} is normally higher than arterial P_{CO_2}. In the steady state the P_{CO_2} of blood draining the brain is nearly the same as that of the cerebrospinal fluid; mean brain tissue P_{CO_2} lies somewhere between that of arterial and cerebral venous blood. The normal cerebral arterial-venous difference for P_{CO_2} of 7 to 9 mm. Hg varies inversely with cerebral blood flow (the Fick equation), which is particularly affected by changes in arterial blood gases. For example, hypercapnia and hypoxia both increase cerebral blood flow, thereby decreasing the arterial-venous difference for P_{CO_2}.

ercise to a theory of respiratory control. Chemical, mechanical and nonspecific stimuli impinge upon the respiratory center (Fig. 8) to modify rate and depth of ventilation. In this discussion the respiratory center is regarded as possessing no receptor function of its own, serving only as an integrator and transmitter of input from various peripheral and central sources. Chemically mediated input is from the aortic and carotid bodies, which respond primarily to hypoxia, [H+] and changes in blood flow, and from a central chemosensitive area which responds to [H+]-P_{CO_2} only, and which may be isolated from arterial [H+] changes by the blood–cerebrospinal fluid barrier.

Shortly before 1946, Gray[15] presented his "multiple factor theory" in which the steady-state ventilatory response to P_{CO_2}, [H+] and P_{O_2} is described mathematically. According to his analysis, changes in alveolar ventilation are di-rectly proportional to arterial [H+] and arterial P_{CO_2}; changes in both yield a ventilatory response which is the sum of the expected contributions from each:

$$\dot{V}_AR = 0.22\,[H+]_a + 0.262\,P_{A_{CO_2}} - 18.0 \quad (1)$$

where $\dot{V}_AR$ is the ratio of observed to normal resting alveolar ventilation. (Gray also tried to include the effects of P_{O_2} into an additive relationship, but, as discussed below, the interaction of hypoxia with [H+] or P_{CO_2} is more than a simple summation.)

The above equation may be expressed more generally as:

$$\Delta\dot{V} = A\Delta[H+]_a + C\Delta P_{a_{CO_2}} \quad (2)$$

In the absence of hypoxia, the total change in ventilation ($\Delta\dot{V}$) may be accounted for addi-

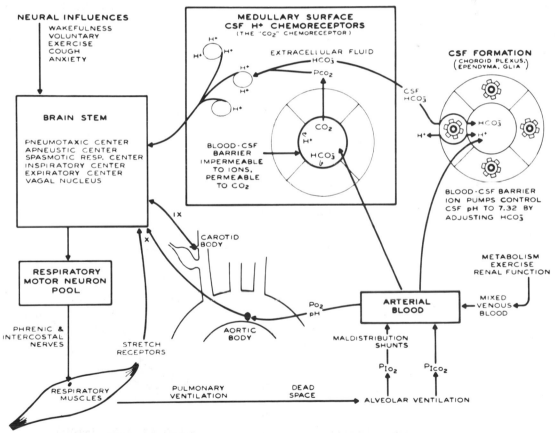

Fig. 8. Control of ventilation. Chemical input to the brain stem respiratory centers originates from peripheral chemoreceptors (the carotid and aortic bodies), and central chemosensitive areas, possibly responsive in part to cerebrospinal fluid [H+] alterations. (From Severinghaus and Larson, Chap. 49 in *Handbook of Physiology; Section 3: Respiration,* vol. 2. Washington, D.C., American Physiological Society, 1964.)

tively by changes in arterial [H+] and P_{CO_2}. Such a formulation is quantitatively descriptive of observed responses, but can shed no light on actual mechanisms of chemical control. P_{aCO_2} might act directly on a "CO_2-sensitive" arterial receptor (but not the carotid body which is [H+] specific in the steady state [Fig. 6]), or it might stimulate the central chemosensitive area, either directly or by altering local [H+]. The last possibility is the essence of Winterstein's "reaction theory," which postulates the following relationship:

$$\Delta \dot{V} = A\Delta[H^+]_a + B\Delta[H^+]_x \qquad (3)$$

where $A\Delta[H^+]_a$ represents the arterial hydrogen ion contribution to ventilation (which is not necessarily solely that of the aortic and carotid chemoreceptors), and $B\Delta[H^+]_x$ is the contribution to ventilation from [H+] at the central chemosensitive area. The $[H^+]_x$ affecting the central receptors may be reflected accurately in the immediately adjacent extracellular fluid, but it is not necessarily in equilibrium with [H+] measured elsewhere in the subarachnoid space.

Since $[H^+]_x$ cannot be measured by current techniques, Winterstein's theory can be tested only indirectly by comparing ventilatory responses to independent alterations in arterial and cerebrospinal fluid [H+]. In the following sections known ventilatory responses to the chemical stimuli of equation 3 will be presented and analyzed.

Acute Ventilatory Responses

Carbon Dioxide. The increase in breathing associated with a rise in inspired P_{CO_2} or in CO_2 production minimizes the increase in body P_{CO_2} which would otherwise result. Experimentally, the ventilatory response to CO_2 is determined by measuring the change in breathing induced by altering inspired CO_2. Such data are commonly presented as a "CO_2 response curve" (Fig. 9A), in which ventilation is plotted against alveolar (or arterial or jugular venous) P_{CO_2}. Figure 9B shows that considerable individual variation exists in response to altered P_{ACO_2}. The curve is more or less linear with a slope of 1 to 3 liters per minute per mm. Hg P_{CO_2}. This slope

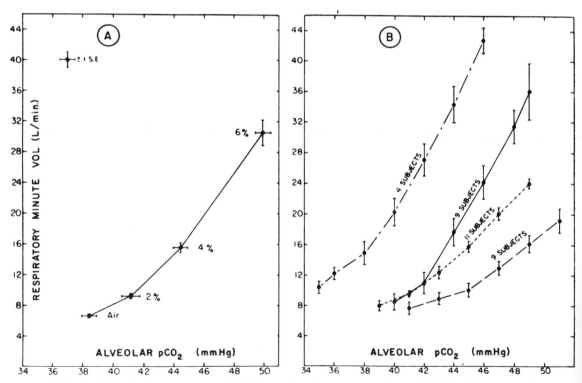

Fig. 9. Ventilatory response to inhalation of varying concentrations of CO_2 in 21 per cent O_2 in N_2. *A*, average response of 33 normal subjects. *B*, data grouped to show variability of response from high to low "sensitivity." (From Lambertsen, *Anesthesiology*, 1960, *21*:642–651.)

describes the "sensitivity" of ventilation to CO_2. Extrapolation of the curve to its intercept on the P_{CO_2} axis at zero ventilation determines the "apneic threshold." Though apnea can be induced in sleeping or anesthetized subjects by lowering $P_{A_{CO_2}}$, even severely reduced alveolar P_{CO_2}, as in hyperventilation, usually does not produce apnea in awake, unmedicated subjects, perhaps because of various nonspecific stimuli impinging on the respiratory center. Whether the decrease in slope of the CO_2 response curve at lower levels (the "hockey stick" configuration noted by some investigators) represents lessened responsiveness to CO_2 or a greater influence of counterbalancing stimuli at normal ventilations cannot be said. At inspired CO_2 levels exceeding about 10 per cent the slope also decreases; prolonged high levels of CO_2 may even lead to respiratory depression.[26] The high sensitivity of ventilation to increased CO_2 has led to the view that CO_2 is the major determinant of normal ventilation. However, the fact that arterial P_{CO_2} remains remarkably constant and varies little with small changes in inspired P_{CO_2} (Fig. 9) raises doubts whether it can be effective in regulating its own level.

CO_2 response curves provide a useful means of describing ventilatory performance under a variety of conditions.[1, 28] Sleep, depressant drugs and anesthetics, and chronic hypoventilation all shift the curve to the right and often decrease the slope.[40, 41, 45] Conversely, drugs— such as norepinephrine, progesterone and salicylates[28]—hypoxia, chronic hyperventilation and chronic metabolic acidosis displace the curve to the left, with or without changing the slope (see below).

Carbon dioxide appears to alter breathing principally by central action. Denervation of peripheral chemoreceptors has little effect on either normal resting breathing or the response to CO_2 (Fig. 2).[13] In the cat small increases of P_{CO_2} without hypoxia produce significant ventilatory responses with negligible increase in carotid chemoreceptor activity (Fig. 6). In the absence of other known peripheral chemoreceptors these observations imply a central action of CO_2 either through a specific effect of molecular CO_2 or through modification of $[H^+]$ at the central receptor. Equation 2 quantifies the response to CO_2, and equation 3 implies that the effect partly results from $[H^+]$ change at the central chemosensitive area.

Metabolic $[H^+]$ Changes. As described in equation 2, the ventilatory response to respiratory acidosis results from an increase in both $[H^+]_a$ and $P_{a_{CO_2}}$. In contrast, metabolic acidosis, whether occurring pathologically or experimentally, does not raise arterial P_{CO_2}. Rather the ventilatory response to arterial $[H^+]$ stimulation decreases P_{CO_2} such that the decrease in $C\Delta P_{a_{CO_2}}$ of equation 2 partially offsets the increase in $A\Delta[H^+]_a$. As described, for the same change in arterial $[H^+]$, the ventilatory response to metabolic acidosis is much less than that produced by inhalation of CO_2 (Fig. 1). Experimentally, if $P_{a_{CO_2}}$ is held constant (by adding CO_2 to the inspired gas) as fixed acid is added to the blood, the change in ventilation due to change in $A\Delta[H^+]_a$ of equation 2 alone is about 45 per cent of that resulting from the same $A\Delta[H^+]_a$ change produced by CO_2 inhalation. (This difference is apparent from the experimentally derived constants of equation 1, where $.22/(.22 + .262) = $ about 45 per cent).

Interpreting these data on the basis of the $[H^+]$ theory (equation 3) requires the assumption that, because the blood–brain or blood–cerebrospinal fluid barrier is poorly permeable to ions, arterial $[H^+]$ changes *per se* do not have ready access to the central chemosensitive areas. Increased arterial $[H^+]$ acts at arterial sites to increase ventilation. The resulting decrease in arterial P_{CO_2} is associated with a comparable fall in P_{CO_2} at the central chemosensitive area, yielding a decline in the ventilatory contribution of $B\Delta[H^+]_x$ from equation 3. This paradoxical central alkalosis with blood acidosis results from low permeability of the blood–cerebrospinal fluid barrier to ions combined with high permeability to the volatile acid, CO_2. Acute metabolic alkalosis yields reverse shifts with arterial alkalinity and cerebrospinal fluid acidity secondary to the rise in P_{CO_2} occurring with hypoventilation.[14, 42, 47]

Hypoxia. Oxygen lack stimulates ventilation solely by its effect on the carotid and aortic chemoreceptors. After removal or denervation of these structures, hypoxia not only fails to produce hyperpnea but, by acting centrally, may actually depress ventilation (Fig. 2). As shown by Haldane, a resting man at sea-level is relatively unresponsive to appreciable decreases in inspired P_{O_2} (Fig. 1); not until alveolar P_{O_2} has dropped below 50 to 60 mm. Hg[11] does ventilation begin to increase. This threshold does not

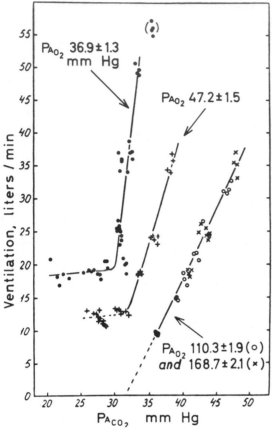

Fig. 10. Effect of acute hypoxia on the ventilatory response to CO_2 inhalation in an awake man. Inspired oxygen adjusted to keep $P_{A_{O_2}}$ constant at level indicated for each line. (From Nielsen and Smith, *Acta physiol. scand.*, 1952, 24:293–313.)

represent that of the chemoreceptors, since they are tonically active even at normal arterial oxygen tensions. For example, Figure 5 shows that in anesthetized cats some chemoreceptor discharge persists at oxygen tensions of 100 mm. Hg or greater. Moreover, chemoreceptor denervation in dogs reduces ventilation, as evidenced by a 3 to 4 mm. Hg rise in resting alveolar P_{CO_2} (Fig. 2). In man tonic chemoreceptor discharge is suggested by the "chemical denervation" experiments of Dejours.[9] In subjects breathing air at sea-level the inhalation of one or two breaths of pure oxygen causes a transient delayed decrease (about 11 per cent) in ventilation, suggesting that the elevated oxygen temporarily "turns off" the chemoreceptors. If the subject is breathing a mildly hypoxic mixture inadequate in itself to increase ventilation, a few breaths of pure oxygen produce an even more pronounced transient ventilatory depres-

sion. Conversely, sudden mild hypoxia (decrease in alveolar P_{O_2} of only 7 mm. Hg) causes a transient increase in ventilation.[21] Such observations indicate that chemoreceptor discharge is present at normal oxygen tensions and increases progressively with hypoxia insufficient to alter steady state ventilation. It should be emphasized that continued inhalation of pure oxygen or slightly hypoxic mixtures does not sustain this initial alteration of ventilation;* the responses are transient, either because of compensatory readjustments of CO_2 or because of adaptive behavior of the chemoreceptors to sudden changes in stimulus (see Chap. 14).[20] Though the biologic significance of normoxic chemoreceptor activity is difficult to assess, ventilatory responses to chronic hypoxia (see below) suggest that aortic and carotid bodies contribute significantly to ventilatory drive even at sea level.

The hypocapnia resulting secondarily from hypoxic hyperventilation partially counterbalances the hypoxic drive, both because decreased P_{CO_2} (or $[H^+]$) at the central chemosensitive area reduces its contribution and because lowered arterial P_{CO_2} reduces peripheral chemoreceptor sensitivity to hypoxia (Fig. 5). The role of hypoxia *per se* can be determined by adding CO_2 to the inspired gas to maintain a constant alveolar P_{CO_2}. When alveolar P_{CO_2} is thus held constant as alveolar P_{O_2} falls below 50 to 60 mm. Hg, the increase in ventilation is much greater than that occurring when P_{CO_2} is permitted to fall in response to hyperventilation.[4, 32] This enhancement of response to hypoxia at constant P_{CO_2} is much greater than expected from a simple additive relationship between the known ventilatory effects of CO_2 and of oxygen lack determined independently. The potentiating effects of these two stimuli on ventilation, first demonstrated by Nielsen and Smith in 1952 (Fig. 10),[38] can be explained by the more than additive effects of hypoxia and hypercapnia on peripheral chemoreceptor activity (Fig. 5). Further interaction may occur between a given peripheral

* Continuous inhalation of 100 per cent oxygen by resting man often produces a slightly greater ventilation than does inhalation of air. This increase may be due to elevated P_{CO_2} at the central chemosensitive area, for breathing pure oxygen is associated with a measurable increase in jugular venous P_{CO_2}. The rise in P_{CO_2} probably results from decreased cerebral blood flow and from diminution of the Haldane effect.

chemoreceptor input and elevated P_{CO_2} acting centrally.

CHRONIC VENTILATORY RESPONSES

Altitude Acclimatization. After acclimatization man can tolerate extremes of hypoxia that would be fatal in the unacclimatized state. The earliest of the adaptive responses to hypoxia is an increase in ventilation. The result is a minute volume which, after several days, is considerably greater than that resulting from acute exposure to the same degree of hypoxia. This increase in ventilation by lowering alveolar P_{CO_2} permits a roughly equivalent increase of alveolar P_{O_2}. In association with the increasing ventilation, the CO_2 response curve progressively shifts to the left (Fig. 11). Inhalation of oxygen at this time reduces ventilation by eliminating the hypoxic contribution to the resting minute volume, but breathing remains above its original sea level value, thus revealing a central readjustment.

Classically the increase in ventilation and the progressive fall of P_{CO_2} during acclimatization have been ascribed to renal excretion of $[HCO_3^-]$ in compensation for the hypoxically induced respiratory alkalosis. Because a fall in $[HCO_3^-]$ increases arterial $[H^+]$, renal compensation might explain the shift in the CO_2 response curve (see equation 2). However, most of the

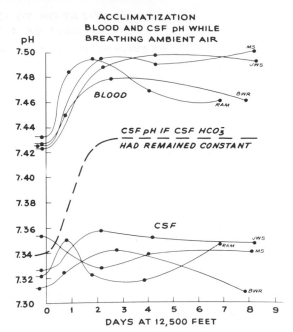

Fig. 12. Change in *p*H of arterial blood and cerebrospinal fluid of four subjects during 8 days' residence at 12,500 feet. The rise in arterial *p*H resulted from the fall in P_{aCO_2} and implies minimal renal compensation after 8 days. The dashed line shows the anticipated rise in cerebrospinal fluid *p*H had $[HCO_3]_{csf}$ not declined with the fall in P_{CO_2}. (Data from Severinghaus, personal communication.)

shift occurs within 24 to 48 hours, whereas arterial blood remains alkaline even after a week at high altitude (Fig. 12). Ventilatory readjustment despite arterial alkalosis is explained by the recent work of Severinghaus and co-workers[44] performed on subjects acclimatizing to 12,470 feet at the Barcroft Laboratory, White Mountain, California. In spite of a high blood *p*H, cerebrospinal fluid *p*H was scarcely elevated by the first sampling at 24 hours and was normal at all subsequent determinations (Fig. 12). Nevertheless, cerebrospinal fluid P_{CO_2} fell about as much as arterial P_{CO_2} (see footnote, p. 808). Therefore, to maintain a normal cerebrospinal fluid *p*H, the cerebrospinal fluid $[HCO_3^-]$ must have been reduced sufficiently to restore a normal $[HCO_3^-]/P_{CO_2}$ ratio. The constancy of cerebrospinal fluid *p*H suggests active transport of HCO_3^- out of cerebrospinal fluid. The rapidity of this readjustment is many times greater than that of renal compensation for arterial alkalosis.

According to equation 3, the rapid return to a normal cerebrospinal fluid $[H^+]$ restores the

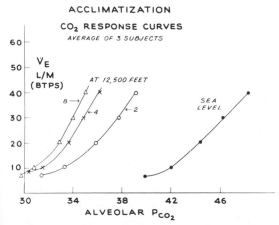

Fig. 11. Average ventilatory response of 3 subjects to inhalation of CO_2 at sea level and after 2, 4 and 8 days' residence at 12,500 feet. During determination of all curves $P_{I_{O_2}}$ was maintained at 190 mm. Hg to minimize contribution from the carotid and aortic bodies. (From Severinghaus *et al.*, *J. appl. Physiol.*, 1963, *18*:1155–1166.)

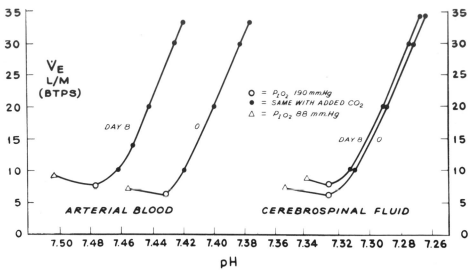

ACCLIMATIZATION TO 12,470 FEET ALTITUDE
AVERAGE OF 4 SUBJECTS
RESPONSE OF pH TO HIGH CO₂ AND LOW O₂

Fig. 13. Average ventilatory response of four subjects to fall in arterial and cerebrospinal fluid pH during inhalation of CO_2. Curves were obtained at sea level and after 8 days' acclimatization to 12,470 feet. The theoretical determination of these curves is described in the text. (After Severinghaus et al., *J. appl. Physiol.*, 1963, *18*:1155–1166.)

original central $B\Delta[H^+]_x$ contribution to ventilation. Adding this central contribution to the peripheral hypoxic drive increases ventilation significantly during the first days of exposure to high altitude. Oxygen administration at this time eliminates the hypoxic drive, but the resulting central acidosis due to acute rise in P_{CO_2} partially offsets the loss, leaving ventilation still above its original sea level value. The continued gradual decline of arterial P_{CO_2} during succeeding days may be associated with renal compensation for arterial alkalosis with slight resultant increase in the ventilatory contribution from peripheral chemoreceptors (Fig. 5).

From the CO_2 response curves of Figure 11, Severinghaus and co-workers plotted ventilation in relation to arterial and cerebrospinal fluid pH (Fig. 13). During CO_2 inhalation the rise in P_{CO_2} of lumbar cerebrospinal fluid lags considerably behind the ventilatory response. Therefore the ventilation–pH$_{csf}$ curves (Fig. 13) were calculated from an initial steady-state sample on the assumption that cerebrospinal fluid $[HCO_3^-]$ remained constant during the time required to determine CO_2 response. The close approximation of the ventilation–pH$_{csf}$ curves at high P_{O_2} before and after acclimatization implies that ventilation is uniquely determined by cerebrospinal fluid $[H^+]$ in the absence of a hypoxic contribution from the peripheral chemoreceptors. The ventilatory contribu-

tion from $A\Delta[H^+]_a$ of equation 3 would have to be virtually nonexistent under such conditions, a concept difficult to reconcile with most of the previously mentioned observations on the relative importance of arterial and central contributions to ventilation. Because calculated pH$_{csf}$ does not necessarily represent $[H^+]_x$ of equation 3, these curves may not be quantitatively significant.

Since the cerebrospinal fluid $[H^+]$ returns nearly to normal after 24 to 48 hours of acclimatization, equation 3 indicates that any increase in ventilation must result from change in the contribution of peripheral chemoreceptors responding principally to low arterial P_{O_2}. Similarly, at sea level tonic activity of the carotid and aortic chemoreceptors might determine the level at which ventilation (and hence arterial P_{CO_2}) is set in normal resting man.

Chronic Hypercapnia. Chronic hypercapnia with a compensatory rise in serum bicarbonate is most common in pulmonary or neurologic diseases causing hypoventilation. Metabolic alkalosis and prolonged exposure to high CO_2 environment are less common causes. Clinically obstructive lung disease in its more advanced stages may lead to CO_2 retention. The CO_2 response curve is shifted to the right, usually with a decrease in slope. Limited evidence suggests that once again cerebrospinal fluid [H+] is normal in spite of poorly compensated respiratory acidosis of the blood. Constancy of cerebrospinal fluid [H+] with elevated P_{CO_2} may explain the shift of CO_2 response curves (see equation 3). For various reasons—including hypoventilation, and alterations in distribution of pulmonary ventilation and blood flow—arterial P_{O_2} is commonly depressed in pulmonary diseases. The interaction of arterial hypoxia and acidosis on the peripheral chemoreceptors is sometimes the major drive sustaining ventilation in severe obstructive lung disease. Administration of oxygen, although relieving cyanosis, drastically reduces this arterial drive, causing additional CO_2 retention so that the patient may lapse into a coma. The result is a pink but prostrate patient who obviously requires ventilatory support as well as oxygenation. The Pickwickian syndrome is a hypoventilatory state which occurs in extremely obese persons. The hypoventilation may not be due simply to the abdominal and chest wall load of massive adiposity, but rather to depression of the central respiratory mechanism. The end result is similar to that in chronic lung disease, but in some instances it is apparently reversible by loss of weight.

Chronic Metabolic Acidosis. With chronic metabolic acidosis the CO_2 response curve is shifted to the left (Fig. 2) as in chronic hypoxia. Arterial and cerebrospinal fluid P_{CO_2} are both reduced; however cerebrospinal fluid [H+] is close to normal because of the same mechanism as that occurring during altitude acclimatization. The only distinction then between chronic metabolic acidosis and chronic hypoxia as they affect ventilation may be that, in the former instance, arterial [H+] is the extra driving force to ventilation while, in the latter, a lowered arterial P_{O_2} provides the drive.

Gaps in the Theory. The temptation is strong to attribute anatomic as well as physiologic significance to the arterial and central components of equation 3. For example, $A\Delta[H+]_a$ would represent the ventilatory contribution of the aortic and carotid bodies whereas $B\Delta[H+]_x$ would represent the contribution from a central area responding to local changes in extracellular fluid. Unfortunately, it is difficult to explain certain facts from anatomic separation of the factors in equation 3.

1. According to the above, the response to fixed acid administration would be eliminated by carotid and aortic body denervation. Indeed, mild metabolic acidosis does not appear to affect ventilation in awake, chronically denervated dogs[35] but more severe acidosis does (Fig. 2). Mitchell[36] ascribes the response to severe acidosis to leakage of H+ into cerebrospinal fluid. It is also possible that the stimulus to the central chemosensitive area may be a balance between arterial and cerebrospinal fluid [H+].

2. Lambertsen and co-workers[27] measured ventilation in man as alveolar P_{CO_2} was increased from 44 to 50 mm. Hg. If the associated fall in arterial pH was prevented by administration of $NaHCO_3$, ventilation was decreased by 45 per cent of the response to CO_2. This agrees well with the data on which Gray's equation was based. The experiment indicates that 45 per cent of the ventilatory response to CO_2 was related to arterial [H+] change, the remaining 55 per cent being due to CO_2 acting "elsewhere." It is difficult to believe that 45 per cent of the ventilatory response to CO_2 is mediated through the peripheral chemoreceptors, particularly since the response to CO_2 administration is so little affected by denervation of these structures (Fig. 2).[13]

3. Lambertsen's studies have been supplemented recently by observations on the ventilatory response of conscious goats to perfusion of the cerebral ventricular system with mock cerebrospinal fluid. Pappenheimer *et al.*[39] found that only 40 per cent of the ventilatory response during inhalation of CO_2 could be accounted for by change in cerebrospinal fluid [H+]. The remaining 60 per cent was presumably due to CO_2 acting "elsewhere," either directly or through associated changes in [H+].

Thus, the above experiments neither support nor refute the theory of [H+] specificity for the control of ventilation. They merely point out that neither arterial blood nor cerebrospinal fluid provides the whole explanation of the response to CO_2 inhalation. If a specific central H+ receptor exists, it may lie in an intermediate relationship between blood and cerebrospinal fluid wherein it is affected by a varying balance of stimuli from each source under varying conditions.

Exercise. Exercise produces the greatest ventilatory response of which man is capable under other than transient voluntary conditions (Fig. 1). The minute volume during maximum work by a trained athlete may closely approach

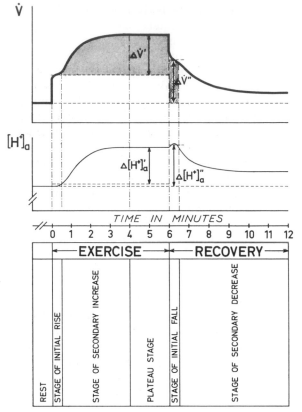

Fig. 14. Change of ventilation and arterial [H+] during onset of exercise and during recovery. The stages described refer solely to changes in ventilation. $\Delta\dot{V}'$ represents the increase of $\dot{V}$ from its mean value during the stage of initial rise to that in the plateau stage. Similarly $\Delta\dot{V}''$ represents the difference between the mean value of $\dot{V}$ during the stage of initial fall and the original resting level. In this study the $\Delta\dot{V}/\Delta\,[H+]_a$ ratio in the plateau stage was the same as in the stage of initial fall during recovery. (From Matell, *Acta physiol. scand.*, 1963, *58:* supplement 206.)

his maximum voluntary ventilation. During exercise, oxygen consumption is directly proportional to the intensity of work performed. In addition, ventilation bears a similar proportional relationship to oxygen consumption over a wide range of work loads (Fig. 1). Therefore, arterial P_{O_2} and P_{CO_2} change surprisingly little from normal resting values. Only at very high work levels do these relationships break down, resulting in relative hyperventilation for a given oxygen consumption. In spite of this overventilation, severe work in trained athletes produces arterial desaturation. The CO_2 response curve is displaced to the left during exercise but, interestingly, without a change in slope.[10] This suggests that chemical contribution to work

hyperpnea may be related additively to other stimuli.

At the onset of dynamic exercise, such as running or cycling, ventilation rises rapidly within a few seconds (Fig. 14). This is followed by a brief plateau, after which ventilation increases more slowly over several minutes to a constant steady state level. With cessation of work, ventilation immediately falls precipitously and then declines slowly toward normal during the ensuing minutes. These fast and slow components to both onset and cessation of exercise provide the basis for the neurohumoral theory of ventilatory control during exercise, as recently reviewed by Dejours.[10]

Over a wide range of work levels dynamic exercise is associated with relative constancy of arterial P_{CO_2} and P_{O_2}, slight rise in pH, a gradual increase in temperature, and an increase in sympathetic nervous system activity and in circulating catecholamines. Reflexes from moving joints or from muscle proprioceptors may contribute to respiratory drive. No single stimulus, nor even the additive combination of many, as determined out of context of true dynamic exercise, accounts for the magnitude of work hyperpnea.

Neural factors. The sudden increase in ventilation with onset of work is considered too rapid to result from chemical changes in exercising muscles. Furthermore, occluding the circulation with tourniquets prior to exercise does not alter the response. Therefore, the early response is regarded as neural in origin, via either cortical input to the respiratory center or reflex pathways from muscles or moving joints. There is no evidence concerning the quantitative contribution of these neural factors. Reflex pathways stimulated by motion do exist. For example, passive movement of extremities promptly increases ventilation proportionally with the frequency of motion.[10] Active movement, either unimpeded or against a load, is even more effective.

Kao[24] attempted to separate the neural from humoral contributions to work hyperpnea by cross circulation experiments in anesthetized dogs induced to exercise by electrical stimulation of limb nerves or muscles. The ventilatory response of the "humoral" animal receiving blood but no neural input from the exercising limbs was variable, depending upon the configuration of the circulatory anastomoses, but was insufficient to account for the entire ventilatory response to exercise. The "neural" animal demonstrated a much greater response to artificial exercise in spite of the decline in P_{CO_2} resulting from hyperventilation. Kao concluded that afferent impulses from exercising limbs are the prime determinants of work hyperpnea. These studies have been criticized because the ventilatory response to electrical stimulation might have resulted from significant activation of nonspecific input (e.g., pain) which is not present during voluntary exercise.

Humoral factors. Possible blood-borne stimuli affecting ventilation during exercise include P_{CO_2}, P_{O_2}, [H+], catecholamines and temperature. A 1° C. increase in body temperature may increase ventilation approximately 3.9 liters per minute per square meter, but temperature rise in exercise is too slow to explain the major portion of the steady-state response. The constancy of arterial P_{O_2} and P_{CO_2} would appear to rule out these factors as possible stimuli to work hyperpnea unless one postulates a sensitive negative feedback mechanism which counterbalances any change in stimulus. It is unlikely that arterial gas tensions can account for such delicate control. For example, Dejours' single-breath oxygen test suggests hypoxic drive to ventilation increases during exercise. As mentioned earlier, sympathetic nervous activity and circulating catecholamines increase during exercise. Cunningham *et al.*,[5] have shown that epinephrine and norepinephrine shift the CO_2 response curve to the left. Perhaps these factors act in part by decreasing peripheral chemoreceptor blood flow during exercise, causing a lower P_{O_2} and a higher P_{CO_2}-[H+] within chemoreceptor cells for a given set of arterial values. This could explain an increased hypoxic contribution to exercise ventilation despite normal arterial P_{O_2} and P_{CO_2}.[22]

The frustrating constancy of arterial blood gas tensions has caused some investigators to postulate a contribution from unknown metabolites of exercising muscle, but such suggestions are based more on uneasy ignorance than physiologic fact. Similarly, because mixed venous P_{CO_2} increases almost in direct proportion to the increase in ventilation during exercise, a pulmonary arterial chemoreceptor has been sought but not convincingly demonstrated. It seems more likely that the rise in mixed venous P_{CO_2} represents effect rather than cause. It is also possible that oscillations in $P_{a_{O_2}}$ and $P_{a_{CO_2}}$, greatly enhanced by exercise hyperpnea, might produce an increased peripheral chemoreceptor contribution to ventilation even though mean arterial values are identical to those occurring at rest.

Finally, [H+] may be important. Leusen[31] demonstrated increased lactic acid concentration and decreased [HCO_3^-] in cerebrospinal fluid during exercise. This acidosis might enhance the central contribution to exercise hyperpnea (equation 3). Particularly provoking is the recent work of Matell (Fig. 15).[33] Attributing the entire fast component of ventilatory response to neural factors, he analyzed the slow component in relation to arterial [H+]. As shown in Figure 15 the relationship agrees well with that resulting from similar changes in [H+] produced by CO_2 inhalation in resting man. Unfortunately, this still leaves something to be desired, since the work acidosis is metabolic at roughly normal P_{CO_2}, and therefore should yield only 45 per cent of the response produced by CO_2. What factors would interact to account for the remaining 55 per cent of the slow component are still unknown.

Function of Chemosensors. The preceding analysis of chemical ventilatory stimuli has attempted to hang a rather complex, diverse assortment of facts upon a simple framework of H+ control of breathing. Not all the facts fit perfectly. Nevertheless the concept has some usefulness, for it demands a questioning effort to relate the interactions of P_{CO_2}, P_{O_2} and [H+] with each other as well as with the various nonchemical stimuli. Arterial [H+]-P_{CO_2} relationships appear to be additive, hypoxic–hypercapnic ones more than additive. The nature of other interrelationships is yet to be determined, such as that between the fast and slow components of exercise, or that between the peripheral and central chemosensitive areas, or perhaps that between blood and cerebrospinal fluid at the central area. The mechanisms described appear to serve one basic purpose, the preservation of a constant internal [H+] and P_{O_2}. Mitchell (personal communication) has classified these mechanisms into peripheral and central, each possessing a fast and slow component of response. The fast component is ventilatory, both at the carotid and aortic chemoreceptors and at a central chemosensitive area. During exercise nonchemical stimuli also contribute to this fast response. The slow mechanism of internal environmental protection is ascribed to transport mechanisms capable of

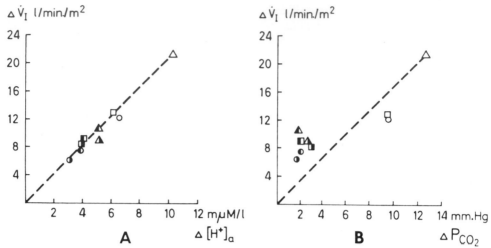

Fig. 15. Mean increments in ventilation plotted against (*A*) change in arterial [H+] and (*B*) change in P_{CO_2} during (i) CO_2 inhalation (open symbols), (ii) the stage of secondary increase in exercise, $\dot{V}'$ of Figure 14 (symbols filled on right side), and (iii) during early recovery, $\Delta\dot{V}''$ of Figure 14 (symbols filled on left side). The secondary change in ventilation during mild exercise ($\dot{V}_{O_2}$ of 1.5 liters per minute) and recovery appears to be altered by change in [H+]$_a$ to the same extent as during inhalation of CO_2. (From Matell, *Acta physiol. scand.*, 1963, *58*: supplement 206.)

altering [HCO_3^-] in response to changes in P_{CO_2}, thereby readjusting [H+]. The time constant of central [HCO_3^-] adjustment is many times faster than that of the kidney. The fast or ventilatory response buffers change in chemical environment in response to chemical stress, while the slow response permits fine readjustment of brain or body [H+] (and, less strikingly, P_{O_2}).

In maintenance of the internal milieu, control of brain–cerebrospinal fluid environment is separated from that of the rest of the body. At times the peripheral and central ventilatory mechanisms produce similar shifts in both places; at other times they tend to oppose each other, seeming to sacrifice P_{O_2} or peripheral [H+] change in order to minimize shift in brain–cerebrospinal fluid [H+]. This central protection results from several factors: (i) a blood–brain or blood–cerebrospinal fluid barrier which is poorly permeable to peripheral [H+]; (ii) a "central" chemoreceptor which alters ventilation to minimize [H+] changes resulting from acute change in P_{CO_2}; (iii) a change in cerebral blood flow in response to changes in arterial P_{CO_2} and P_{O_2}, minimizing the magnitude of these changes centrally; and (iv) a transport system for [HCO_3^-] to restore normal central [H+]. All these factors support the teleologic concept that brain environment is more closely regulated than that of the rest of the body.

REFERENCES

1. ALEXANDER, J. K., WEST, J. R., WOOD, J. A. and RICHARDS, D. W. *J. clin. Invest.*, 1955, *34*:511–532.
2. COMROE, J. H., JR., and SCHMIDT, C. F. *Amer. J. Physiol.*, 1938, *121*:75–97.
3. COMROE, J. H., JR. Chap. 23 in *Handbook of Physiology; Section 3: Respiration*, vol. 1. W. O. FENN and H. RAHN, eds. Washington, D.C., American Physiological Society, 1964.
4. CORMACK, R. S., CUNNINGHAM, D. J. C. and GEE, J. B. L. *Quart. J. exp. Physiol.*, 1957, *42*:303–319.
5. CUNNINGHAM, D. J. C., HEY, E. N., PATRICK, J. M. and LLOYD, B. B. *Ann. N. Y. Acad. Sci.*, 1963, *109*:756–769.
6. CUNNINGHAM, D. J. C. and LLOYD, B. B., eds. *The regulation of human respiration*. Oxford, Blackwell Scientific Publications, 1963.
7. DALY, M. DEB., LAMBERTSEN, C. J. and SCHWEITZER, A. *J. Physiol.*, 1954, *125*:67–82.
8. DE CASTRO, F. *Trab. Inst. Cajal Invest. biol.*, 1926, *24*:365–432.
9. DEJOURS, P., LABROUSSE, Y., RAYNAUD, J. and TEILLAC, A. *J. Physiol. (Paris)*, 1957, *49*:115–120.
10. DEJOURS, P. Chap. 25 in *Handbook of Physiology; Section 3: Respiration*, vol. 1 W. O. FENN and H. RAHN, eds. Washington, D.C., American Physiological Society, 1964.
11. DRIPPS, R. D. and COMROE, J. H., JR. *Amer. J. Physiol.*, 1947, *149*:277–291.
12. DUKE, H. N., GREEN, J. H. and NEIL, E. *J. Physiol.*, 1952, *118*:520–527.
13. GEMMILL, C. L. and REEVES, D. L. *Amer. J. Physiol.*, 1933, *105*:487–495.

14. GESELL, R. and HERTZMAN, A. B. *Amer. J. Physiol.*, 1926, *78:*610–629.
15. GRAY, J. S. *Pulmonary ventilation and its physiological regulation.* Springfield, Ill., Charles C Thomas, 1950.
16. HALDANE, J. and SMITH, J. L. *J. Path. Bact.,* 1892, *1:*168–186.
17. HEYMANS, J. F. and HEYMANS, C. *Arch. int. Pharmacodyn.,* 1927, *33:*272–370.
18. HEYMANS, C., BOUCKAERT, J. J. and DAUTREBANDE, L. *Arch. int. Pharmacodyn.,* 1930, *39:*400–450.
19. HEYMANS, C. and NEIL, E. *Reflexogenic areas of the cardiovascular system.* Boston, Little, Brown and Co., 1958.
20. HORNBEIN, T. F., GRIFFO, Z. J. and ROOS, A. *J. Neurophysiol.,* 1961, *24:*561–568.
21. HORNBEIN, T. F., ROOS, A. and GRIFFO, Z. J. *J. appl. Physiol.,* 1961, *16:*11–14.
22. HORNBEIN, T. F. and ROOS, A. *J. appl. Physiol.,* 1962, *12:*239–242.
23. HORNBEIN, T. F. and ROOS, A. *J. appl. Physiol.,* 1963, *18:*580–584.
24. KAO, F. F., In: *The regulation of human respiration.* Oxford, Blackwell Scientific Publications, 1963.
25. KAO, F. F., ed. *Symposium on cerebrospinal fluid and the regulation of ventilation.* In press.
26. KELLOGG, R. H. Chap. 20 in *Handbook of Physiology; Section 3: Respiration,* vol. 1. W. O. FENN and H. RAHN, eds. Washington, D.C., American Physiological Society, 1964.
27. LAMBERTSEN, C. J., SEMPLE, S. J. G., SMYTH, M. G. and GELFAND, R. *J. appl. Physiol.,* 1961, *16:*473–484.
28. LAMBERTSEN, C. J. Chap. 22 in *Handbook of Physiology; Section 3: Respiration,* vol. 1. W. O. FENN and H. RAHN, eds. Washington, D.C., American Physiological Society, 1964.
29. LANDGREN, S. and NEIL, E. *Acta physiol. scand.,* 1951, *23:*158–167.
30. LEUSEN, I. R. *Amer. J. Physiol.,* 1954, *176:*39–44; *idem,* 45–51.
31. LEUSEN, I. R., LACROIX, E. and DEMEESTER, G. *J. Physiol. (Paris),* 1960, *52:*151–152.

32. LOESCHCKE, H. H. and GERTZ, K. H. *Pflügers Arch ges. Physiol.,* 1958, *267:*460–477.
33. MATELL, G. *Acta physiol. scand.,* 1963, *58:*supplement 206.
34. MITCHELL, R. A., LOESCHCKE, H. H., MASSION, W. H. and SEVERINGHAUS, J. W. *J. appl. Physiol.,* 1963, *18:*523–533.
35. MITCHELL, R. A. and BAINTON, C. R. *Fed. Proc.,* 1964, *23:*259.
36. MITCHELL, R. A., BAINTON, C. R., SEVERINGHAUS, J. W. and EDELIST, G. *Physiologist,* 1964, *7:*208.
37. NAHAS, G. G., ed. *Ann. N. Y. Acad. Sci.,* 1963, *109:*411–948.
38. NIELSEN, M. and SMITH, H. *Acta physiol. scand.,* 1952, *24:*293–313.
39. PAPPENHEIMER, J. R., FENCL, V., HEISEY, S. R., HELD, D. *Amer. J. Physiol.,* 1965, *208:*436–450.
40. REED, D. J. and KELLOGG, R. H. *J. appl. Physiol.* 1958, *13:*325–330.
41. ROBIN, E. D., WHALEY, R. D., CRUMP, C. H. and TRAVIS, D. M. *J. clin. Invest.* 1958, *37:*981–989.
42. ROBIN, E. D., WHALEY, R. D., CRUMP, C. H., BICKELMANN, A. G. and TRAVIS, D. M. *J. appl. Physiol.,* 1958, *13:*385–392.
43. ROSS, L. L. *J. biophys. biochem. Cytol.,* 1959, *6:*253–262.
44. SEVERINGHAUS, J. W., MITCHELL, R. A., RICHARDSON, B. W. and SINGER, M. M. *J. appl. Physiol.,* 1963, *18:*1155–1166.
45. SEVERINGHAUS, J. W. and LARSON, C. P., JR. Chap. 49 in *Handbook of physiology; Section 3: Respiration,* vol. 2, Washington, D.C., American Physiological Society, In press.
46. WINTERSTEIN, H. *Pflügers Arch. ges. Physiol.,* 1911, *138:*167–184.
47. WINTERSTEIN, H., and GOKHAN, N. *Pflügers Arch. ges Physiol.,* 1952, *254:*85–86.
48. WINTERSTEIN, H. *New Engl. J. Med.,* 1956, *255:*216–223; *idem,* 272–278; *idem,* 331–337.
49. WITZLEB, E. *Pflügers Arch. ges. Physiol.,* 1952, *255:*181–188.

CHAPTER 43

Passive and Active Transport

By ARTHUR C. BROWN

INTRODUCTION[7, 9, 15]

A CHARACTERISTIC property of the living cell is its ability to maintain many substances at internal concentrations different from that in the surrounding medium. For particles able to pass through the cell wall, this finding is somewhat unexpected, since it appears to oppose the "natural" tendency of such particles to move down concentration gradients and eliminate concentration differences. When a cell dies, this ability is lost, and those substances which can pass through the cell wall equilibrate with the immediate surroundings.

The intracellular-extracellular concentration differences of many substances reflect the characteristics of the cell wall (rather than those of the cytoplasm). That region of the cell wall which sustains concentration and electrical gradients and manifests the transport mechanisms peculiar to living systems is called the cell membrane.

The forces responsible for transport through the cell membrane and an evaluation of their effect forms the subject matter of this chapter. The emphasis will be on the general physical basis of common characteristics and mechanisms, leaving details of membrane transport in specific organs to be covered in the appropriate chapters.

Role of Transport. One role of membrane transport in the economy of an individual cell is the maintenance of the proper intracellular composition. An appropriate intracellular environment is necessary for optimal function of the cell's biochemical apparatus. Also, transported particles may take part in other cellular functions; for example, the electrical and chemical energy created by the active separation of sodium from potassium is exploited by nerve and muscle cells for the rapid generation and propagation of action potentials.

To maintain a constant concentration of substances not produced or consumed within the cell, the average transport over an extended time must be zero; otherwise, the amount of substance in the cell would change progressively. If the substance is consumed or produced at a given rate, the net transport must proceed at an equal rate to assure stability of the cell's internal composition.

In some types of tissue, such as the capillary endothelium and the intestinal mucosa, membrane transport has an additional function related to the total economy of the body: i.e., the transfer of substances across a tissue layer, resulting in movement of material from one part of the body to another. While not incompatible with intracellular stability (net membrane transport into the cell may still be zero), this function does imply an asymmetry of particle movement through the cell wall (see Fig. 1).

Definitions.   *Flux.* Normally, transport is measured in terms of *flux* or transfer of material across a unit area in a given time. Typical units for flux are micrograms per square centimeter per hour, or picomoles per square centimeter per second.

Unidirectional flux. Frequently it is advantageous to consider the net flux across a membrane as the difference between two unidirectional fluxes. In Figure 2, unidirectional flux from side 1 to side 2 across the membrane,

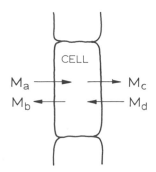

$$M_{cell} = M_a + M_d - (M_c + M_b)$$

$$M_{trans} = M_a - M_b = M_c - M_d$$

Fig. 1. The fluxes which must be considered in cellular exchange. M_{cell} is the net flux entering the cell, while M_{trans} is the net transport through the tissue layer (when the internal cell concentration is in a steady state). Note that the intracellular concentration can remain constant ($M_{cell} = 0$) even if a transcellular net flux is present ($M_{trans} \neq 0$).

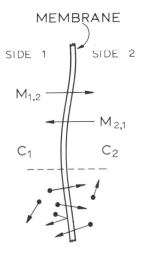

$$M_{net} = M_{1,2} - M_{2,1}$$

$$P = M_{1,2} / C_1 = M_{2,1} / C_2$$

Fig. 2. *Top,* unidirectional flux. *Bottom,* the statistical nature of diffusion. A net diffusion flux exists from side 1 to side 2 not because the individual particles on side 1 have a higher probability of penetrating the membrane than those on side 2, but simply because there are more of them on side 1.

noted as $M_{1,2}$ is defined as the rate at which particles from side 1 cross a unit area of the membrane and appear on side 2. Similarly, the unidirectional flux in the opposite direction, $M_{2,1}$, is the rate per unit area at which particles originating on side 2 reach side 1. Thus, the net transport from side 1 to side 2 is given by the difference between the two unidirectional fluxes, or

$$M_{net} = M_{1,2} - M_{2,1}$$

Steady state. The term "steady state," frequently used in discussing transport, means simply "not changing with time." Thus, a flux or concentration has reached a steady state when it is constant and no longer varies with time.

Equilibrium. A substance that is transported through a membrane is in equilibrium if it fulfills the following conditions: (i) its net flux across the membrane is zero (although the unidirectional fluxes may be appreciable); (ii) all movement through the membrane is due to "passive" forces, such as concentration gradient or electrical potential.

Passive. Movements or forces are defined as passive if they develop spontaneously and do not depend upon an energy supply linked to metabolism. Particle movements commonly treated in physical chemistry are passive, e.g., diffusion, migration of ions in an electric field, osmosis.

Active. Movements or forces are active in general if they are directly linked to and utilize the energy created by biologic metabolism at the site of transfer. A more specific definition and description of active transport through biologic membranes is given in later sections of this chapter. These forces are common in biologic systems, but not in inanimate systems.

Modes of Membrane Transport.[13, 28] The rate with which a substance passes through a membrane depends upon the balance between two factors: The first is the magnitude of forces responsible for the movement, such as concentration gradient or electrical potential gradient. The second factor is the ease with which the particle passes through the membrane; this is expressed as permeability or conductance or by some other appropriate term. The ease of particle movement within a membrane depends in turn upon the mode of transport. For most substances, the detailed mechanism of movement within membranes is un-

proved or unknown, but there are several plausible hypotheses. These include (i) direct passage through the lipoprotein membrane, (ii) movement through membrane pores, and (iii) pinocytosis.

Direct passage.[32] For substances which can penetrate the membrane structure, transmembrane movement is not especially difficult. How easily the membrane structure can be entered is determined by the "solubility" of the transported substance in the lipoprotein matrix of the membrane. This property is measured by the concentration ratio between the membrane substance and the extracellular (or intracellular) aqueous solution; this ratio is called the partition coefficient. Substances with a high partition coefficient can establish relatively high concentrations within the membrane; therefore, high intramembrane concentration gradients and high fluxes can be attained. Substances with low partition coefficients are greatly impeded by the membrane, since there are not sufficient particles within it to lead to an appreciable flux (see Fig. 3).

In general, the lipid molecules limit the direct transport through the membrane substance; thus, substances moving by this method must have a high lipid-to-water partition coefficient. The major substances transported by this mechanism are lipid-soluble organic materials and dissolved gases. However, a particle which normally cannot penetrate the membrane surface may do so if it combines with an appropriate intramembrane molecule, much as soap permits the mixing of normally immiscible grease and water. If this intramem-

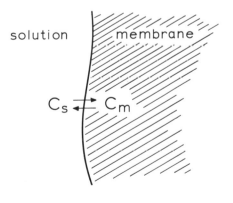

$$\text{Partition Coefficient} = C_m / C_s$$

Fig. 3. The partition coefficient.

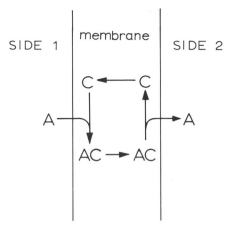

Fig. 4. Carrier-mediated transport of a particle, A, by an intramembrane molecule, C. If the reaction between A and C is passive, this mechanism is named *facilitated diffusion.* In contrast, if the carrier cannot return to side 1 without combining with another A (not shown) the mechanism is termed *exchange diffusion.* If the reaction between A and C involves metabolic free energy on one side of the membrane, then the carrier mechanism can form the basis for *active transport.*

brane molecule is free to move within the membrane, it can shepherd the transported particle through the membrane and release it on the other side, functioning as a *carrier* within the membrane (Fig. 4). Such a mechanism could explain the ability of particles with low partition coefficients in lipids to pass through the membrane at an appreciable rate. Diffusion through a membrane which is aided by combination with carriers is termed *facilitated diffusion.*

Transport within pores.[12, 16] The transport of non-lipid-soluble substances, including electrolytes, water and carbohydrates, might also be explained by the existence of small holes or pores through which they pass, rather than penetrating into the membrane structure itself. The rate of passage through a fenestrated membrane obviously depends partly on the particle size relative to the diameter of the pores. Thus, the relation between membrane permeability and particle size is a major experimental method for the study of movement through pores. In general, small particles are found to pass through membranes more rapidly than larger ones. For example, quiescent nerve axon membrane is more permeable to potassium and chloride ions than to the slightly larger sodium ions, while the even larger calcium, magnesium and sulfate ions pass much more slowly. The size important here is prob-

ably the hydrated diameter, since water molecules bound to the dissolved particle effectively increase its size.

Often, instead of allowing particles of all sizes to pass, the membrane exhibits a cut-off, so that few particles larger than the critical size can move through the membrane. If particles pass through pores with a fixed range of internal diameters, the mean pore size can be calculated from the mean "cut-off" diameter, while the distribution of pore sizes about the mean can be calculated from the sharpness of the cut-off.

Additional information on pore size may be deduced from the rate of water movement through the membrane. Water would be expected to be confined to pores, since it is not lipid-soluble. Within the pores, water will move either because of hydrostatic pressure gradients or because of diffusion. If hydraulic flow in the pore is laminar, the water flux under a hydrostatic pressure gradient, Q_h, is directly proportional to the number of pores per unit membrane area (n) and the fourth power of the pore radius, r^4, and will be inversely proportional to the pore's length, L. Thus $Q_h \sim (n/L)r^4$. Diffusion flux, Q_d, will be directly proportional to n and to the cross sectional area presented by the pore, πr^2, and will be inversely proportional to L: thus $Q_d \sim (n/L)\pi r^2$. By measuring Q_h and Q_d, and taking their ratio, (n/L) is eliminated, permitting the calculation of r, the mean pore radius.

Finally, with electron microscopy, membrane pores have been demonstrated directly in some tissues and their sizes estimated.

Thus, three lines of evidence—influence of size of dissolved particles on transmembrane movement, rate of water fluxes, and direct electron microscopic observation—indicate that for many biological membranes, the major mode of transport for small, lipid-insoluble particles is through membrane pores (see Fig. 5).

Pinocytosis.[19, 27] With electron microscopy, transported particles large enough to be seen

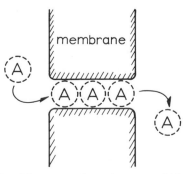

Fig. 5. Movement through pores within a membrane.

membrane

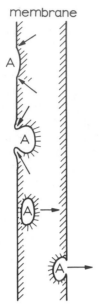

Fig. 6. Successive stages in pinocytotic transport through a membrane.

sometimes are not uniformly distributed within the membrane but instead appear to be contained inside small intramembrane droplets. These droplets or *vesicles* appear to be formed by a process similar to phagocytosis: membrane invagination enclosing particles at the membrane surface. Then the vesicles are thought to move through the membrane, emptying their contents on the opposite side (see Fig. 6). This process has been named *pinocytosis*.

Highly specific binding sites at the membrane surface where invagination occurs have been postulated. By this mechanism, attracted particles could be concentrated within the vesicle and thus would be selectively transported. Such sites could account for the ability of pinocytosis to discriminate between the various particles in the external medium.

Pinocytosis is particularly adapted to the transport of large particles which would otherwise have difficulty in penetrating the membrane structure. The extent to which it contributes to the movement of smaller particles, such as electrolytes and simple organic molecules, is unknown.

PASSIVE MECHANISMS

Diffusion. The particles of a fluid (whether liquid or gas) are in constant motion. This motion is erratic and rather irresponsible; the particles lurch to and fro at random, continually changing both the magnitude and direction of their velocities. If the velocity of a single particle is tabulated at intervals (say, once a second), all directions of movement appear with equal frequency and the average magnitude of the velocity is independent of direction. Although such meanderings, so erratic and unpredictable at any single moment and so symmetrical when averaged, may seem of little consequence, this is not the case.

Consider a membrane separating two solutions with a solute concentration C_1 on side 1 and concentration C_2 on side 2 (Fig. 2). Since the solute particles are moving, some occasionally enter the membrane and pass completely through it. The number of particles which move through a unit area of membrane in a given time is directly proportional to the rate at which particles strike the membrane, and this in turn is proportional to the number of solute particles near the membrane. Consequently, the unidirectional flux from a given side is directly proportional to the concentration on that side; the constant of proportionality is known as the permeability (P) of the membrane to that species of solute particles. Thus, $M_{1,2} = PC_1$. Similarly, the unidirectional flux in the opposite direction equals the concentration on the opposite side times the membrane permeability, or $M_{2,1} = PC_2$. The net transport rate is given by the difference between the two unidirectional fluxes, so

$$M_{net} = P(C_1 - C_2) \qquad (1)$$

This is the fundamental law describing passive diffusion through membranes.

The permeability of a membrane depends partly on its thickness: the farther the particle must traverse in its passage through the membrane, the lower its rate of transfer. In addition, permeability is determined by the energy necessary to pass through the membrane relative to the thermal energy of the diffusing particles: if considerable energy is necessary to pass through the membrane relatively few particles will have the required energy; if the membrane presents only a low energy barrier to transport, the probability that an individual particle will have the necessary energy is considerably greater. This factor, which depends upon the structure of the membrane relative to the energy distribution of the particles in the solution, is expressed by the *diffusion coefficient:* a high diffusion coefficient implies low energy requirements for membrane passage; a low value implies that the membrane severely impedes particle movement. Thus,

$$P = \overline{D}/x_o \qquad (2)$$

where $\overline{D}$ is the average diffusion coefficient within the membrane and x_o is the membrane thickness. Combining equations (1) and (2) and noting that the total rate of particle transport is the product of flux and area gives:

$$\text{Total transport} = MA = \overline{D}A\,(C_1 - C_2)/x_o \qquad (3)$$

Equation (3) implies that, to have rapid exchange without creating large concentration differences, a short diffusion distance and a large exposed area (as well as a high diffusion coefficient) are necessary. That nature is not ignorant of equation (3) is evident from the architecture of those organ systems whose functions include the rapid distribution of material by diffusion, e.g., the pulmonary alveoli, the intestinal mucosa, and the capillary beds of the circulatory system.

The differential form of the law of diffusion can be derived from the equations developed above. Consider the flux, not through the whole membrane, but rather through a thin lamina within the membrane. With the same reasoning as previously, the flux will be given by

$$M = -\overline{D}\,(\Delta C/\Delta x)$$

where ΔC is the concentration difference across the lamina and Δx is its thickness. The minus sign is necessary since the flux is from high concentration to low; in other words, if C is increasing with distance ($\Delta C/\Delta x$ positive), then the net flux is in the opposite (negative) direction.

If this lamina is taken progressively thinner, the ratio $\Delta C/\Delta x$ approaches the derivative $\partial C/\partial x$, since the derivative is defined as the limit of such a ratio. Also, $\overline{D}$ must approach D, the actual value of the diffusion coefficient at the place where the limit is taken. Thus,

$$M = -D\,(\partial C/\partial x) \qquad (4)$$

If the concentration varies in the y and z directions as well as the x direction, there will be components of the flux in all directions. Thus the directional derivative or gradient must be used in place of equation (4), so

$$M = -D \text{ grad } C \qquad (5)$$

It must be emphasized that diffusion is not a force within the ordinary meaning of the term. An individual molecule has no more tendency to move in the direction of lower concentration than in the direction of higher concentration; net transport is due only to a volume element of high concentration having more molecules and thus losing more than a comparable volume having a low concentration. That a large number of actions, each individually random, can have a systematic and predictable effect is familiar to anyone with even a rudimentary knowledge of statistics.

Concentration, Activity and Partial Pressure. It has been assumed that the net effect of a number of particles acting simultaneously is simply the sum or statistical average of the effects of particles acting independently. Thus, it was possible to show that diffusion flux should be directly proportional to concentration gradient or difference, since concentration is a measure of the number of particles in a given volume. However, when the particles become crowded together, as in a highly concentrated solution, the assumption of independent action may no longer be valid, and the diffusion equations must be modified.

At the concentrations encountered in the body, surrounding a dissolved particle with other particles of the same species or of different species (other than molecules of the solvent, water) in general reduces flux rate below that predicted by the equations of the previous section. To account for this effect what is usually done is to preserve the form of the preceding equations by substituting for concentration a new variable, derived from it, called the *activity.* Thus, the flux within the solution is proportional to the activity gradient; the flow across a cellular membrane depends upon the difference in activity on the two sides.[*] The activity may be thought of as the effective concentration, as opposed to the actual concentration or content.

Sometimes the laws of diffusion are written using the activity coefficient, defined by the equation

$$A = \gamma C \qquad (6)$$

where A is the activity, C the concentration and γ the activity coefficient. Thus γ may be

[*] Also, it can be shown that the rate of a chemical reaction depends upon the activities and not the concentrations of the participating species; that is, to be accurate the law of mass action should be written in terms of activity rather than concentration.

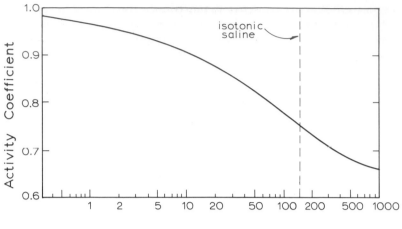

Fig. 7. The activity coefficient at increasing sodium chloride concentrations (logarithmic scale on the concentration axis).

viewed as the fraction of the concentration which is effective in determining diffusion, chemical reactions, etc. Either γC or A may be substituted for concentration in the equations of diffusion.

At low concentrations, activity and concentration values are almost identical (or the activity coefficient is approximately 1), since when the solution is dilute, dissolved particles per unit volume are relatively few, so the probability of two or more dissolved particles interacting is correspondingly low. For dilute solutions, the diffusion equations may be used as they are written in the preceding section. The question then arises: At what concentration does a solution cease to be dilute and become concentrated? Obviously, the transition is continuous so no single value of concentration can be given; however, some general statements may be made.

Concentrations in biological fluids usually are less than 0.01 molar. At these relatively low levels, little error is made by assuming that concentration and activity are approximately equal, except in one of three conditions.

First, when the particles in solution have a net charge (ions), the interaction between them is considerably greater than if they are electrically neutral. The charged particles tend to be surrounded by others of opposite charge because of electrostatic attraction, although thermal motion of the particles prevents the establishing of rigid bonds. When an ion moves, it must break away from the surrounding particles or else drag them along; in either case its movement, and therefore its rate of diffusion is decreased. Thus, as the solution becomes more concentrated and ionic interaction becomes increasingly prominent, the activity coefficient falls below 1. This effect in a sodium chloride solution is shown in Figure 7. For a NaCl solution isotonic with plasma, the activity is only about 75 per cent of the concentration. Adding additional ionic species, e.g., $KHCO_3$, to this solution

further reduces NaCl activity since K^+ and HCO_3^- ions contribute to the charged atmosphere surrounding Na^+ and Cl^-; for the same reason, $KHCO_3$ activity will be less than if NaCl were absent. In other words, the effects of various ions are cumulative, the reduction in activity coefficient of each individual species depending upon the total ionic strength of the solution. The ionic strength of blood plasma is about 244 mEq. per liter, resulting in an activity coefficient of approximately 0.7 for all univalent ions; activity of polyvalent ions is reduced even more since their higher charge produces even greater interaction.

Activity is also reduced by sites of attraction which immobilize certain solute molecules. These sites may be either fixed (e.g., along the capillary wall) or on another dissolved or suspended particle (e.g., plasma protein molecule). If the attraction is weak or the sites few, the movement of particles is little affected, but if attraction is strong and sites are plentiful, the effect on particle movement is great. (The stronger of these forces sometimes are called reversible bonds.) Because of the continuum of bond strengths, it cannot be said when a simple attraction becomes a chemical reaction. In any case, the number of particles which can participate in other activities is reduced. This sometimes is called the "free concentration" to distinguish it from the actual concentration or "total content."

Gases are usually treated in a special manner. Their activity in an aqueous solution depends upon the concentration of dissolved gas which is free to move. The "free" concentration frequently is difficult to measure directly since much of the dissolved gas may be immobilized by binding (e.g., O_2 to hemoglobin) or transformed into another chemical form (e.g., CO_2 to bicarbonate). However, the activity can be evaluated indirectly, since it is directly proportional to the partial pressure of that gas with which the solution is in equilibrium.* Thus, partial pressure gradient may be thought of as the driving force for the diffusion of gas.

In summary, the diffusion equations should be modified: (i) if the particles are charged, by multiplying the concentration by the activity coefficient to account for the electrical interaction between particles; (ii) if some of the solute molecules are bound, by substituting the "free concentration" for the total concentration or content; (iii) if the solute molecules are dissolved gas, by substituting partial pressure for concentration.

Electrical Forces. When an electrical potential is established across a biologic membrane, an additional influence is superimposed upon the random thermal motion of charged particles. On the positive side of the membrane, positively charged particles are repelled, thus increasing their rate of passage through the membrane; on the other hand, negative particles are attracted and, thus, tend to remain on this side. On the negative side of the membrane, the opposite occurs: positive particles tend to remain and negative particles tend to cross the membrane. Thus, an electrical potential difference destroys the symmetry of movement characteristic of thermal agitation of charged particles by establishing a preferred direction of transport.

Consider a membrane with the potential V_1 on side 1 and V_2 on side 2 and with equal concentration, C, of some particular solute on both sides of the membrane (only uniform concentrations will be considered here to avoid complications of simultaneous transport via diffusion) (Fig. 8). When the potential is applied, particles flow through the membrane from side 1 to side 2 with a magnitude of

$$M_{net} = zmC(V_1 - V_2) \qquad (7)$$

Here, m is the electrical permeability of the membrane (analogous to P, the diffusion permeability). The quantity z is the net number of electronic charges on a solute particle; the sign of z indicates whether the particle is positive or negative; for example, for sodium ion, $z = +1$; for chloride ion, $z = -1$; for calcium ion, $z = +2$. Thus, the electrical flux through the

* The use of partial pressure instead of fugacity, the analog of activity for gases, is valid only for ideal gases; however, in the normal physiologic range, little error is made by assuming that gases behave ideally.

membrane depends upon the driving force $(V_1 - V_2)$, the number of particles per unit volume, C, the ease with which the particles are electrically propelled through the membrane, m, and the charge on an individual ion, z.

Much as in the development of the diffusion equation (2), the electrical permeability of the membrane may be written as the ratio of a property inherent in the molecular structure of the membrane, η, divided by the membrane thickness, Δx.

$$m = \eta/\Delta x \qquad (8)$$

The value of the η depends upon the relationship between the energy imparted to charged particles by the electrical potential gradient and the energy barrier imposed by the membrane structure. Thus, the η is for electrical migration the same membrane property expressed by D for diffusion. The membrane would be expected to present a similar resistance to moving particles whether their source of energy was thermal agitation or electrical potential. At a constant temperature, the ratio between η and D is constant and is given by equation 8(a).

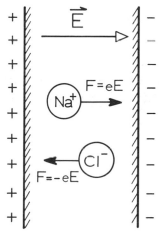

Fig. 8. Movement of charged particles due to a transmembrane electrical potential. The potential is associated with an electric field, *E*, within the membrane, leading to a force of *e* (the net charge) times *E*. The force is in the same direction as *E* for positively charged particles and in the opposite direction for negative particles; however, the movement of both types of particles leads to a net current flow from the positive side of the membrane to the negative side.

$$\eta/D = F/RT \qquad (8a)$$

Here, F is Faraday's constant, the net charge per mol of univalent ions (96,496 coulombs); T is the absolute temperature (measured in degrees Kelvin); and R is the gas constant, expressing the thermal energy per degree temperature (8.31 joules per mol per degree centigrade). Since the electrical energy gained by a charged particle in passing from one potential to another is directly proportional to its charge, the ratio F/RT indicates the ratio of the electrical energy (per volt) compared to the thermal energy as indicated by RT.

As in the derivation of equation (5), by substituting equation (8) into equation (7) and taking the limit as the region under consideration becomes progressively thinner, and by taking into account the direction of motion under an electrical potential difference, electrical flux can be written as

$$M = -\eta z C \, (\partial V/\partial x) \qquad (9)$$

Since the negative of the voltage gradient, $-(\partial V/\partial x)$, is equal to the electric field, E, equation (4) may be written as

$$M = \eta z C E \qquad (10)$$

Either equation (9) or (10) may be taken as the fundamental equation describing the movement of charged particles under the influence of an electric field.

A flux of charged particles represents an electric current. Specifically, the membrane current carried by any particular species of ions is given by

$$J = zFM \qquad (11)$$

where J is the current density (usually amperes per sq. cm.). Substituting into the above relation for M from equation (7) gives

$$J = z^2 FmC(V_1 - V_2) \qquad (12)$$

The product "z^2FmC" may be abbreviated by the single term "g," called the specific membrane conductance for the particular ionic species. Thus

$$J = g(V_1 - V_2) \qquad (13)$$

This is the equivalent of Ohm's law for a biologic membrane since it states that current density is equal to the product of conductance and potential difference. When a number of ionic species traverse the membrane independently, the total conductivity is simply the sum of the conductivities of the individual ionic species.

Water Movement and Osmosis.[2,14,24,26,31,35]

Water is not only the environment through which dissolved particles move while in solution, but is also itself capable of moving between various points within tissues and in particular of moving across membranes. Two types of forces are responsible for water movement.

The first type is ordinary mechanical force or pressure. If the pressures on each side of a membrane are not equal, water flows from the side of higher pressure to the side of lower pressure:

$$Q = P_h \, (Pr1 - Pr2) \qquad (14)$$

where Q is the net water flux from side 1 to side 2; P_h is the hydrostatic permeability of the membrane; and Pr1 and Pr2 are the respective pressures. If flow is through small holes or pores in the membrane, and if flow is laminar, P_h can be evaluated, by using Pousielle's law, from the length, radius and number of holes per unit area of membrane and the viscosity of water.

In addition, water has a second way of passing through membranes. Water molecules in the liquid state participate in the random thermal motion characteristic of all particles in the solution; thus, water can move by a mechanism similar to that responsible for solute diffusion. Suppose that a membrane, permeable to water, separates two aqueous solutions of different solute concentrations, C_1 on side 1 and C_2 on side 2, with $C_2 > C_1$. Because water has less tendency to move from a concentrated solution than from a dilute one, water will move from side 1 to side 2. The equation for water flux, like that for solute particle flux, may be written as

$$Q = P_{os}(a(H_2O)_1 - a(H_2O)_2) \qquad (15)$$

In this equation, $a(H_2O)_1$ and $a(H_2O)_2$ are the thermodynamic activities of water on the two sides of the membrane. Development of net water flux through a membrane because of a difference in water activity is usually called *osmosis*.

It must be pointed out that osmosis cannot be regarded as simple diffusion of water through a membrane. Measurements of water diffusion rate with isotopic tracers indicate that flux attributable to simple water diffusion alone is generally much less than that due to osmotic gradients. Why osmosis can produce such rapid water movement is not clear. Thus, although the source of energy responsible for diffusion and osmosis are similar—namely, the random thermal motion of particles in the solution—because of some mechanism not presently completely understood, a difference in water activity across a membrane usually leads to a greater water flow than can be explained by simple diffusion.

To evaluate osmotic flow from equation (15), the activity of water in the solution must be known. For dilute solutions, as discussed earlier, solute activity is adequately approximated by the concentration (or some modification, such as "free" concentration). However, in an aqueous solution, obviously water cannot be considered dilute. Thus, molar concentration is not an appropriate measure of water activity. There are several conventions for evaluating solvent activity; for dilute solutions, the most common is as follows:

The activity of any pure solvent is defined as unity (1). When solute particles are dissolved in the solvent, the activity of the solvent is reduced. For dilute solutions, the activity reduction is proportional to the number of dissolved particles, or

$$a(H_2O) = 1 - k\Sigma C \qquad (16)$$

C is the concentration of solute particles; k is a constant with an approximate value of 0.018 (its exact value is unimportant since it is usually incorporated into other constants in the flux equations); the summation sign, Σ, indicates that the concentrations of all species of particles are to be summed in evaluating the activity. Thus, water activity is not determined by water concentration, but rather by the total concentration of all particles dissolved in the water. The greater the concentration of dissolved particles, the more water activity is reduced.

Since the coefficient k does not vary appreciably within physiologic limits, the osmotic activity of any solution is determined mainly by the summed concentrations of the dissolved solutes, ΣC. The summed molar concentration is called the *osmolarity* of the solution. Each distinct species of particle is counted separately. Thus, for a substance whose constituents separate upon going into solution, the concentrations of the individual parts must be included in calculating osmolarity. For example, for a 1 mM. glucose solution, the osmolarity is 0.001 osmols or 1 milliosmol; for a 1 mM. solution of NaCl, the osmotic activity is approximately 2 milliosmols; for a 1 mM. solution of CaCl₂, the osmolarity is approximately 3 milliosmols. If the solutions become sufficiently concentrated that the dissolved particles interact, the osmotic effect is less than that predicted from equation (16), because such particles do not act independently and cannot be simply summed as independent species. For concentrated solutions, ΣC must be multiplied by a factor called the osmotic coefficient. For example, a 154 mM. NaCl solution (isotonic saline) has an osmotic activity of only 283 milliosmols, since its osmotic coefficient at this concentration is approximately 0.92; ($283 = 0.92 \times 2 \times 154$).

Equation (16) is based upon the fact that, for an ideal solution, the activity of any given substance is directly proportional to its mol fraction. The mol fraction of any substance is the number of mols of that substance per unit volume divided by the total number of mols of all substances per unit volume. For a solute, A, with water as the solvent, the mol fraction f_A, is

$$f_A = \frac{m_A}{m_A + m_{H_2O}} \qquad (17)$$

where m_A and m_{H_2O} are the number of mols per unit volume of A and of water respectively. For a dilute solution in which $m_A \ll m_{H_2O}$, equation (17) may be approximated by

$$f_A \approx \frac{m_A}{m_{H_2O}} \approx \frac{C_A}{55.5} \approx 0.018 \, C_A \qquad (17a)$$

The expressions on the right of (17a) follow from taking the unit volume equal to 1 liter, in which case m_A is simply the molar concentration, C_A, and m_{H_2O} is approximately 55.5 mols of H_2O per liter. Thus, in a dilute solution, solute concentration may be used as an index of solute activity, as was done in evaluating solute diffusion previously.

The mol fraction of the solvent, f_{H_2O}, is

$$f_{H_2O} = \frac{m_{H_2O}}{m_{H_2O} + m_A}$$

Again, using the approximation for a dilute solution in which $m_A \ll m_{H_2O}$

$$f_{H_2O} \approx 1 - \frac{m_A}{m_{H_2O}} \approx 1 - kC_A$$

Thus, for a pure solvent ($C_A = 0$), $f_{H_2O} = 1$, while the decrease in activity of the solvent when a substance is dissolved in it depends upon the solute concentration. If several species of dissolved particles are present, their effects are additive in reducing solvent activity, leading to equation (16).

Substituting the value of water activity derived from equation (16) into equation (15) gives

$$Q = P'(\Sigma C_2 - \Sigma C_1) \qquad (18)$$

Here, P' equals $k \times P_{os}$; this coefficient indicates the relation between osmolar difference and water flow. Note that equation (18) states that water moves from the side of low osmolarity to that of high osmolarity (since osmolarity and solvent activity of water are inversely related).

If a given solute can move freely across the membrane and come to equal concentrations on both sides, obviously it cannot contribute to sustained osmotic movement. Permanent osmotic effects are possible only from particles to which the membrane is impermeable or which cannot attain equal concentration for some other reason (such as electrical effects on charged particles or active transport). Thus, semipermeable membranes, which are permeable to water but not to some dissolved particles, can develop osmotic forces, but they are not the only types of membranes across which such forces can develop; any membrane able to prevent solute particles on either side from becoming equally concentrated can sustain permanent osmotic effects.

In evaluating osmotic water flow, only the concentrations of those substances which are out of concentration equality need be considered. Thus, only the concentrations of plasma proteins (and those charged particles which separate because of an electrical potential across the capillary wall) need be used to evaluate water movement across the capillary wall, since all other particles have the same concentration in plasma and interstitial fluid. However, in nerve or muscle cell membranes, the concentrations of sodium, potassium and chloride must be considered, even though the membrane is permeable to these ions, since they have greatly different concentrations intracellularly and extracellularly.

Osmotic differences do not always lead to water movement, since osmotic movement can be reduced by an opposing hydrostatic pressure. The hydrostatic pressure required to re-

duce net water flux to zero is a measure of the osmotic pressure across the membrane. Thus, *osmotic pressure* is the osmotic force across a membrane under conditions of no water flow; however, osmotic pressure is a fictional pressure in the sense that it cannot be measured directly with a manometer or any other pressure measuring device; its magnitude can be deduced only by measuring the hydrostatic pressure which neutralizes its effect.

From thermodynamic considerations, it can be shown that the relation between osmotic pressure and osmolarity is given by

$$\pi = RT\Sigma C \qquad (19)$$

where π is the osmotic pressure attributable to a solution with an osmolarity of ΣC, R is the gas constant, and T the absolute temperature. The net osmotic pressure developed across a membrane is the difference between the osmotic pressures on each side, or

$$\pi_{net} = \pi_2 - \pi_1 = RT(\Sigma C_2 - \Sigma C_1) \quad (19a)$$

As before, only solutes with differing concentrations on either side need be included in equation (19a).

Evaluating RT at 37° C. (310° K.) gives

$$RT = 25.4 \text{ atmospheres per osmol}$$
$$= 19,300 \text{ mm. Hg per osmol}$$
$$= 19.3 \text{ mm. Hg per milliosmol}$$

This value gives an idea of the large forces which can be developed by small differences in osmotic activity. That 180 grams of glucose (about 6 ounces) dissolved in a liter of water can support a column of distilled water over 300 meters high (about 1000 feet) seems preposterous but is true nonetheless.

The rate and direction of water movement through the membrane is determined by the combined effects of both hydrostatic and osmotic gradients. The net force causing water to leave side 1 is $(Pr1 - \pi_1)$. Thus water flows from the side with higher $(P - \pi)$ to the side with the lower. If the hydrostatic and osmotic forces just balance, so that

$$(Pr1 - \pi_1) = (Pr2 - \pi_2), \qquad (20)$$

there is no net water transport.

When cells with a given internal osmotic activity are exposed to a solution with a different osmotic activity, water flows through the cell membrane. Obviously, such water movement cannot continue indefinitely. If the external solution is hypotonic, the resultant water movement into the cell has three effects: (i) the intracellular solution becomes less concentrated, decreasing its osmotic activity; (ii) the extracellular solution may become more concentrated, increasing its osmotic activity; (iii) because of the water influx, the cell enlarges, increasing its wall tension. The increased tension may increase internal hydrostatic pressure, although the relation between internal pressure and cell volume depends on the elastic characteristics of the cell wall. Thus, the first two, and perhaps the third, of these effects progressively reduces water influx. If the cell can successfully withstand the mechanical stresses caused by its increased volume, equation (20) will eventually be satisfied, and net water movement will become zero. Similarly, if the cell is exposed to a hypertonic bathing solution, water leaves the cell, raising its internal osmotic activity, reducing the osmotic activity of the extracellular solution, and, perhaps, reducing the internal hydrostatic pressure. Again, the process continues until equation (20) is satisfied or until the integrity of the cell wall is lost.

In summary, water movement through a membrane depends upon both hydrostatic pressure and osmotic force. The osmotic force may be expressed in terms of (i) water activity, (ii) osmolarity or (iii) osmotic pressure; the relations between these quantities is given by equations (16) and (19). Osmotic pressure is particularly useful in evaluating the effect of combined osmotic and hydrostatic forces.

Another aspect of the lowered activity of water due to dissolved particles is a reduction of the ease with which water molecules leave the solution surface and escape into the atmosphere. In other words, the partial pressure of water vapor is reduced as the osmolarity increases. Advantage is taken of this dependence of P_{H_2O} on solute concentration in the design of osmometers, instruments used to measure osmotic activity. One major type of osmometer equilibrates a drop of the unknown solution with a liquid of known vapor pressure, and converts the results to millosmols. A second type is based on the fact that the temperature at which an aqueous solution and ice can exist in equilibrium (i.e., the freezing point) depends upon the solution vapor pressure; thus, freezing point depression can be used to measure osmolarity.

Effect of Water Flow on Particle Movement; Solvent Drag and Bulk Flow.[1, 33] When particles are transported through a membrane, osmotic forces may be developed which make water follow. The converse effect may also occur: the net flux of water through a membrane may move dissolved particles in the same direction.

When solute particles diffuse through a membrane, the fixed membrane structure slows particle motion, thus reducing the flux rate. However, when water is also moving through the membrane in the same direction, the water flux tends to carry the dissolved particles along. Similarly, water movement in the direction opposite to solute diffusion reduces the flux rate. Because this effect depends upon the difference between solute and solvent velocities, it is called *solvent drag*. The influence of solvent drag on particle motion depends on the relative magnitudes of dissolved particle interaction with the membrane and dissolved particle interaction with the water moving in the membrane.

If solute particles and water move through the membrane by separate pathways, their interaction is small and solvent drag effects do not occur. On the other hand, if the solute particles and water share a common transport pathway through the membrane, solvent drag effect upon solute transport may be large. In addition to solvent drag effects, solute movement is also influenced by the changes in concentration which occur along with a net movement of water through a membrane. When water leaves one side of a membrane, the concentration of solute particles on that side increases and that on the other side decreases. Thus, the movement of water establishes concentration gradients tending to move particles in the same direction as net water flux.

The sum of solvent drag and concentration effects may be so great that it dominates the movement of a given species of dissolved particles. In this case, the particles are swept through the membrane as if simply carried along in aqueous solution. Such particle movement is called *bulk flow* and is characterized by the relation

$$M = QC$$

where Q is net water flux, and C is the solute concentration on the side of the membrane from which the water movement originated.

Bulk flow is characteristic of extremely permeable membranes where the interaction forces between particles and membrane are small, e.g., in the systemic capillaries and the renal glomerulus.

ACTIVE TRANSPORT

Definition of Active Transport.[5] The mechanisms of membrane transport discussed in the preceding section have one property in common: they can cause a net flux of material only by decreasing or dissipating the total available (free) energy of the system. If no other mechanisms are present, the system will spontaneously decrease in free energy under the impetus of these forces until the minimum value is reached. At this point, the concentrations and free energy cease changing and the net fluxes of all particles are zero. In other words, the energy decreases until a thermodynamic equilibrium is reached. To call these influences on transport "passive" is not to deprecate their vigor or independence, but rather to indicate that they require no external energy. They occur in both living and nonliving material; the laws that describe them arise from purely physical properties of moving particles in the liquid state when interacting with a fixed structural matrix or membrane. Diffusion, electrostatic movement, osmosis and solvent drag are all passive mechanisms, although they do not exhaust the catalog of this type of transport.

The asymptotic approach to thermodynamic equilibrium is not characteristic of living organisms, and, indeed, is inconsistent with life as we know it. All living material can avoid, at least briefly, this energetically degraded condition. Since all matter has the mechanisms of passive transport, it is clear that living cells can maintain a steady state out of equilibrium only by supplying free energy at the same rate at which it is spontaneously degraded; the source of this energy is the biochemical metabolism of energetic substrates.

Two mechanisms are used by living cells to hold materials out of equilibrium across membranes. One is exemplified by the transport of O_2 and CO_2. Since O_2 is consumed within the cell, its partial pressure is lowered below that of the surrounding blood and interstitial fluid, thereby maintaining a flux of O_2 into the cell. In a similar manner, CO_2 is produced in the cell, causing a net efflux. The combination of O_2 with metabolic substrates makes free energy available at the expense of substrate energy; otherwise the reaction would not proceed spontaneously. Part of this energy is tapped to provide the gradients for O_2 and CO_2 diffusion. This mechanism is similar to that permitting the cell's internal metabolic mechanisms to function; that is, the tapping of substrate energy allows the biochemical reactions within the cell to be displaced from equilibrium, making it possible for a substance to proceed along (or around) biochemical pathways at a finite rate.

The second mechanism, and the one which concerns us, is the coupling of metabolic energy to transport within the membrane, i.e., *active membrane transport*. This term has been defined in various ways. To avoid confusion we shall classify a force influencing membrane transport of particles as active only if it meets the following criteria: (i) the force is located within the membrane; (ii) the force *directly* influences particle motion; (iii) the force tends to increase the free energy of the particle as it passes through the membrane; (iv) the force is established by and maintained through the consumption of free energy made available by metabolism. Thus, an *active* force may be viewed as a means of transferring energy released by biochemical reactions to particle movement through the membrane.

An example of active transport encountered previously is the movement of sodium through the axon membrane (Chap. 1). Since sodium moves out of the axoplasm against both a concentration gradient and an electric field, an additional force clearly must be invoked to explain its movement. This active force is provided by the coupled sodium–potassium "pump." However, the movements of chloride ion and water following sodium movement is not active since they are only *indirectly* linked to an active force. Thus, chloride moves only by the passive electrical forces established by the exchange of sodium for potassium and the subsequent potassium diffusion, while water moves passively only because of the osmotic gradients consequent to particle interchange. For the same reasons, sodium movement during the initial part of an action potential is not ascribed to active forces, because it is due to the passive or natural forces resulting from its concentration and electrical potential gradients. Thus, across any membrane, movement directly linked to active transport may exist simultaneously with passive movement linked only indirectly to active transport and with passive movement totally unconnected with active transport; also, the motion of the same particle may be dominated at one time by active forces, and, at another time, by passive forces.

In summary, a variety of forces influence the movement of particles across living membranes. Some are classified as passive, meaning that they reduce the system's free energy, require no outside energy supply, and occur in inanimate as well as living membranes. Other forces are classified as active, as defined above, and are characteristic of many biologic membranes. The detailed properties of active transport and the membrane mechanisms which may be responsible for energy coupling are the subjects of the remainder of this chapter.

General Characteristics of Active Transport. The molecular mechanisms of active particle transport through membranes may be simple modifications of similar passive mechanisms. However, the availability of and the dependence upon external energy gives active transport several characteristics not present in passive movement.

Dependence upon metabolic substrates.[20, 38] The energy which moves particles through the membrane comes from the free chemical energy of organic substrates, for example, glucose. Most sustained active transport is aerobic; thus, oxygen is consumed so that the withdrawal of either the substrate or oxygen eventually stops active transport (whereas passive transport would be relatively unchanged as long as the membrane remains intact).

The dependence of active transport upon energy sources is seen in the mammalian intestine. Normally, the transporting cells in the intestinal epithelium are supplied with oxygen through the mucosal capillaries. Active transport can be maintained even when intestinal segments are removed from the body and placed in a test tube, but only if oxygen-saturated solution is vigorously perfused by the mucosal surface. For optimal transport, the perfusing solution must contain glucose. Similar behavior is seen in the sodium–potassium pump in nerve axon. If nitrogen is flushed through the solution surrounding an excised axon to wash out the dissolved oxygen, the axon soon ceases to pump ions, and eventually the

internal solutions equilibrate with the external solutions and the membrane potential falls to zero.

Sensitivity to metabolic poisons. Because of their direct dependence upon cellular metabolism, active transport forces are particularly susceptible to metabolic poisons, i.e., agents which inhibit or divert metabolic reactions as in the action of DNP (dinitrophenol) on the rate of sodium extrusion from nerve (Chap. 1). DNP uncouples substrate utilization from oxidative phosphorylation so that less energy is available for active transport. (This observation also indicates that the products of oxidative phosphorylation must be intermediates in the transfer of free energy to active transport in this system.)

Ability to maintain concentration differences in the face of passive gradients. A passive gradient across membranes or cell layers not possessing active forces causes particle flux until a passive equilibrium is reached. An external free energy supply allows those membranes which can produce active forces to resist successfully the establishment of a passive equilibrium and maintain indefinitely concentration differences in the face of opposing passive forces.

Consider a membrane which separates two solutions of initially identical composition (Fig. 9). If the membrane begins to transport some species of particles actively, the concentration

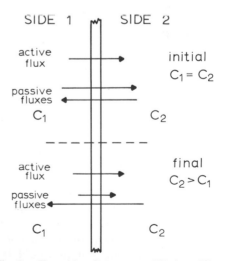

Fig. 9. Transition from an equilibrium ($C_1 = C_2$) to a steady state in which $C_2 > C_1$ because of active transport. The steady state is reached when the concentration difference leads to a net passive flux equal in magnitude and opposite in direction to the active flux.

on one side decreases and that on the other increases. This concentration difference has two effects. First, it leads to a passive diffusion flux in the direction opposite to the active transport; and, secondly, the minimum energy requirement for active transport goes up, since more free energy is required to transport particles from dilute to concentrated solutions than between solutions of equal concentration. As long as active transport flux is greater than opposing passive diffusion flux, concentration difference continues to rise. This greater concentration difference increases the passive flux and, because of increased energy requirements, may reduce active flux. Eventually, these fluxes become equal, after which the solution composition remains stable. The concentration ratio so established is called the maximum concentrating ability of the membrane or tissue; it is a measure of the relative magnitudes of active and passive forces. (For simplicity, diffusion is assumed above to be the only important mode of passive movement. The existence of other passive forces does not alter the general conclusion, although the analysis is more complex.)

Ability to maintain flux in the absence of passive gradients.[37] Just as an active transport force is able to maintain a steady state by balancing the effect of opposing passive forces, so can it, in the absence of passive opposition, establish a net flux across a membrane. For example, if plasma serum is introduced into the small intestine, it eventually becomes completely absorbed, although obviously no concentration gradient is present initially. (Note that this does not imply that every serum component is actively transported from the intestinal lumen, since transport of one or several particle species may create forces—e.g., electrical gradients, osmotic gradients—which cause the remaining particles to be absorbed passively.) Thus, active transport can lead to a net flux in the absence of or even when opposed by passive forces.

Saturation. For simple passive diffusion, the unidirectional flux increases linearly in direct proportion to the concentration. In contrast, an actively transporting system would be expected to be limited by the rate at which it can supply energy to the transported particles. At low particle concentrations, this maximum energy limitation may not be important. But at higher concentrations, its influence upon the membrane flux becomes increasingly significant. In other words, the flux rate would be concentration limited at low concentrations, but transport mechanism limited at high concentrations. Thus a plot of flux versus concentration levels off as the active transport mechanism becomes saturated. Such saturation is characteristic of many actively transporting systems.

Saturation is not unique to active transport systems. Although simple passive diffusion does not reach a saturation point, more complex passive processes may well exhibit flux maxima. For example, passive diffusion facilitated by intramembrane carriers, as discussed earlier, is limited by the number of carriers and the rate at which they can shuttle across the membrane.

Mechanism of Active Movement. To establish an actively transporting system, nature must solve two difficult problems: (i) coupling metabolically derived energy to moving particles and (ii) supplying this energy primarily to particles moving in one direction, since coupling energy to all particles traversing a membrane does not result in active transport. Thus, the particles traveling in the direction promoted by active transport must receive energy which is unavailable to or hinders particles moving in the opposite direction.

Because the molecular events within a membrane are difficult to investigate, direct experimental evidence establishing the detailed mechanism of active transport is not yet available. However, several plausible hypotheses have been postulated, each supported to some extent by indirect evidence. These are (i) carrier-mediated active movement, (ii) oriented binding sites within the membrane, and (iii) pinocytosis.

Carrier-mediated active transport.[18] The utility of a carrier molecule in shepherding particles through a membrane was noted earlier. The particle is bound to the carrier on one side of the membrane, moved through the membrane, and released from the carrier into the solution on the other side. The carrier then returns to its original site (see Fig. 4). Writing A for the transported particle and C for the carrier molecule, the reaction between them is

$$AC \rightleftharpoons A + C \qquad (21)$$

But how can a reaction, which on one side of the membrane goes spontaneously to the left, binding the particle, on the other side go spon-

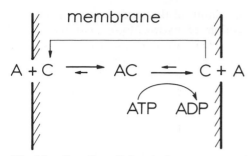

Fig. 10. Coupling of chemical energy to particle–carrier separation to produce active transport.

taneously to the right, releasing the particle? A localized catalyst alone cannot be responsible, because catalysis can alter only the rate, not the predominant direction or equilibrium constant of a reaction. Instead, a reaction will proceed spontaneously in the direction in which free energy is released. Thus, the direction of the reaction can be reversed only by altering the free energy evolved. How this could be accomplished is exemplified by the following:

Assume that the particle and carrier combine spontaneously, forming AC on one side of the membrane, and that AC then diffuses through the membrane. On the other side, conditions are such that AC dissociates when stochiometrically linked with a second reaction in which a high energy compound is degraded to a lower energy compound, say ATP ⟶ ADP; this energy released by the second reaction allows separation of the particle from the carrier. Thus, the reaction is spontaneous on one side of the membrane and utilizes a coupled, energy-evolving, auxiliary reaction to reverse on the other side of the membrane (see Fig. 10).

Thus, the particle is transferred from the solution on one side of the membrane to that on the other, possibly against passive forces, fueled by energy originally derived from metabolism—in other words, by active transport. Note that energy is used not in conjunction with movement within the membrane, but rather in conjunction with release from the carrier.

Directional sites.[3] Mobile carriers are not necessary for active transport; binding sites fixed in the membrane structure also could lead to active movement, if they could impart free energy to particles moving in a preferred direction.

For example, consider a sequence of binding sites lining a channel or pore through the membrane and having the following three properties (see Fig. 11): (i) The particle can become bound to the site from either the right or the left side. (ii) On one side, say the left, the binding is firm, but on the other, the right, it is weak. From equation (21), with C designating the binding site rather than the carrier, it can be said that if the particle is close to the site and on its right, the reaction tends to go to the right, whereas if the particle is on the left, the reaction tends to go to the left. (iii) The bond angle can fluctuate between the two positions.

Consider next a particle as it enters the channel from the left. When the particle nears a binding site, it is likely to be bound since strong bonds are formed on the left. When the bond configuration changes spontaneously, moving the particle to the right, the particle probably will be released, because of the weak binding on the right. Next the particle will be attracted to the adjacent site; in this manner the particle is "handed" from site to site and moves through the membrane from left to right.

But how can the molecular structure of the site change in this way, first binding and then releasing the transported particle? Such an alteration cannot be spontaneous, since it implies a change in the equilibrium constant or, in other words, a free energy change—hence, active transport.

Pinocytosis. The formation of vesicles and their movement within the membrane involve modifications of part of the membrane structure. Such modifications require energy. Thus,

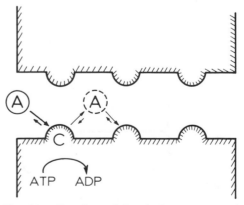

Fig. 11. Coupling of chemical energy to a fixed attraction site to produce active transport.

pinocytotic active transport is linked directly to energy supplying reactions in the production and movement of vesicles.

Control of Active Transport. The rate of active transport in a given tissue is not necessarily steady or constant, but usually varies to meet the changing needs of the body. Thus, following a burst of action potentials, active sodium extrusion from nerve axoplasm increases relative to the quiescent rate, to remove the accumulated sodium; the rate of absorption of ingested particles from the intestinal lumen into the capillaries varies with autonomic nerve activity; the renal excretion of several substances depends upon their plasma concentrations, through mechanisms depending in part upon active transport.

Knowledge of the processes involved in the control of active transport is still relatively sparse. However, several mechanisms may be postulated, each supported to some extent by experimental evidence. These mechanisms need not be mutually exclusive; frequently, the net transport rate may result from the balance of several influences.

Direct chemical and hormonal control.[4] Evidence from some tissues indicates that the velocity of active transport reactions may be controlled by chemicals either circulating in the blood or locally produced. For example, the effect of aldosterone on electrolyte balance is probably due directly to its stimulating action on the sodium–potassium pump, particularly in renal tubule cells. The action of various hormones

on the glands of the gastrointestinal tract, e.g., promotion of hydrochloric acid secretion by gastrin, likely are additional instances of such control. Exogenous chemicals may be effective also; for example, the drug Dilantin (diphenylhydantoin) appears able to mimic aldosterone, whereas the cardiac glycosides (such as digitalis) have been shown to have the opposite effect, inhibiting the sodium–potassium pump in cardiac muscle and other tissues.

Control through passive permeability.[6, 11, 25] When a particle moves through a tissue layer in which the active transport pump is confined to one surface, the flux rate can be effectively controlled by varying the passive permeability of the other surface. Figure 12 shows a possible configuration, with the particle A being actively extruded from one side of a representative cell while entering the cell passively on the other side. If the passive permeability is high, the active pump operates near its maximum rate. However, if the passive permeability is low, active pumping tends to exhaust the intracellular supply of A; thus, active pumping is limited by the rate of passive intracellular replenishment of A. In this way, changes in passive permeability can influence the rate of active transport.

Circulatory control. The cardiovascular system can influence the rate of active transport in two ways. First, for active movement to proceed, metabolic substrates must be furnished and metabolic end products must be carried away. Since most active transport energy depends eventually on aerobic reactions, a continuing supply of oxygen is also necessary. Substrate distribution and end product removal are the primary functions of the circulatory system. Thus, the rate of tissue perfusion can influence active transport by limiting the metabolic energy available to the transporting cells.

The second means of circulatory influence upon active transport is illustrated by the function of several types of glands, such as the salivary, sweat and mammary glands. The secretions of these glands consist primarily of substances simply extracted from surrounding interstitial fluid, frequently through active transport. The transport clearly cannot proceed more rapidly than permitted by the rate at which circulating blood restores the local interstitial supply of secreted particles. Sim-

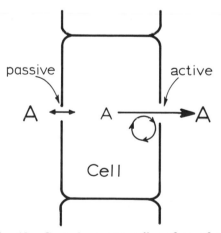

Fig. 12. Control on one cell surface of active transport rate due to changes in the intracellular concentration established through the passive exchange on the opposite surface.

ilarly, the circulation can sometimes promote active movement by reducing the local accumulation of transported material (for example, see the discussion of the role of the circulation upon intestinal absorption).

Thus the circulation affects active movement both through metabolic mechanisms and by reducing local concentration gradients of transported particles which might otherwise inhibit active movement.

Intracellular control. The mechanisms discussed above are particularly suitable for simultaneous control of many cells. However, in certain tissue, such as brain or spinal cord, adjacent cells may have different rates of activity, and thus widely varying requirements for active transport. For such tissue, a gross control mechanism which affects all cells similarly is clearly inappropriate. Instead, there must exist a method of adjusting the active transport of an individual cell to fit its own activity level.

At present, little is known about the details of such a mechanism. One hypothesis is that the active pumping rate of a given substance can be controlled by its intracellular concentration. For example, the sodium influx associated with action potentials tends to raise the intracellular sodium concentration of active cells. If increased sodium concentration stimulates active sodium extrusion, either directly or through the reduction in membrane potential associated with the ionic redistribution, active transport could be raised to accommodate the firing frequency. Such dependence upon concentration is a homeostatic or negative feedback mechanism, since any intercellular deviation from some ideal concentration would act upon the pumping rate in a manner to restore the ideal level.

QUANTITATIVE ASPECTS OF MEMBRANE TRANSPORT[30]

Simple Passive Movement. The complete description of exchange across membranes must include, besides a list of the forces influencing particle movement, the quantitative relations between these forces and the resulting fluxes. Ideally, this description would result in an equation accurately predicting particle flux as a function of concentration difference, membrane electrical potential, solvent drag force, active transport force, etc. Such an equation

would permit quantitative as well as qualitative insight into the mechanism of membrane transport.

However, the physical chemistry of membrane transport is not sufficiently developed to establish such an equation. Those influences of greatest interest to physiologists, such as active transport, are the least well understood. Thus, the major quantitative approach has been to derive flux relations from those forces whose theory is understood; these relations are then compared with those observed experimentally to determine what additional forces need be postulated.

The remainder of this section covers the theoretical development of two of these influences: (i) passive diffusion due to a concentration gradient and (ii) movement of ions due to an electrical potential gradient. The development will also be restricted to steady state fluxes, so that concentration distribution within the membrane does not change with time. Although phrased in terms of "membrane" transport, the subsequent equations and relations can be applied equally well to transport across complete tissue layers, such as capillary wall or intestinal epithelium.

The equations describing flux due to diffusion alone and movement in an electric field alone have been derived previously in differential form as equations (4) and (9), respectively. It is natural to assume that when both influences are present simultaneously, the net flux is simply the sum of the fluxes given by the two equations. If this assumption is valid, so that only the forces from electrical and concentration gradients are causing movement and these can be combined in a linear manner, transport is called "simple passive." Thus, the net flux for simple passive movement within a membrane is given by (employing equation 8a)*

$$M = -D\left(\frac{dC}{dx} + z\beta C\frac{dV}{dx}\right) \quad (22)$$

Here M is the net flux resulting from the combined effects of diffusion and electric migration, and β denotes the ratio F/RT. This may be condensed as equation (23).

* In equation (22) ordinary derivatives (d/dx) are substituted for the partial derivatives ($\partial/\partial x$) of equations (4) and (9), since we are confining ourselves to the one dimensional, steady state case. Thus C and V are functions only of x, the distance into the membrane.

$$M = -De^{-z\beta V} \frac{d}{dx} (Ce^{z\beta V}) \qquad (23)$$

The quantity in parentheses, $Ce^{z\beta V}$, is frequently called the electrochemical activity; it is, in a sense, the "effective" concentration under the influence of the potential, V. Its natural logarithm when multiplied by RT is the electrochemical potential, μ, which represents the work necessary to accumulate a concentration, C, at electrical potential, V, starting from some standard state. Thus,

$$\mu = RT \ln (Ce^{z\beta V}) + \mu_o$$
$$= RT \ln C + zFV + \mu_o \qquad (24)$$

where μ_o is the electrochemical potential in the standard state.

The further development from these equations depends upon the specific circumstances in which it is to be applied.

No net flux; Nernst equation. Suppose that an ionic species is in equilibrium so that its net flux across a membrane is zero. Thus, from equation (23)

$$0 = -De^{-z\beta V} \frac{d}{dx} (Ce^{z\beta V})$$

Since the product of the three terms, D, $e^{-z\beta V}$ and $d(Ce^{z\beta V})/dx$ in the above equation is zero, at least one of the individual terms must be zero also. The terms D and $e^{-z\beta V}$ are not zero since the membrane is assumed to be permeable and the potential finite, so it is the derivative $d(Ce^{z\beta V})/dx$ which must be zero. But the only function whose derivative is always zero is a constant. Thus the electrochemical activity, $Ce^{z\beta V}$, must be constant everywhere; and, thus it must be the same each side of the membrane:

$$C_1 e^{z\beta V_1} = C_2 e^{z\beta V_2} \qquad (25)$$

In this equation C_1, V_1 and C_2, V_2 represent the concentrations and the potential on side 1 and side 2 of the membrane.

Equation (25) can be rewritten in more familiar form by taking the logarithm of both sides and rearranging terms. Using the natural logarithm (ln) gives

$$V_2 - V_1 = \frac{1}{z\beta} \ln (C_1/C_2) \qquad (26a)$$

while taking the logarithm to the base 10 (log) gives

$$V_2 - V_1 = \frac{1}{z\beta \, \log e} \log (C_1/C_2) \qquad (26b)$$

Using the value of $1/\beta$ at 37° C. and noting that $1/\log e = 2.3$, these equations can be written as

$$V_2 - V_1 = \frac{27 \text{ mv}}{z} \ln (C_1/C_2)$$
$$T = 37° \text{ C. } (26c)$$

$$V_2 - V_1 = \frac{61 \text{ mv}}{z} \log (C_1/C_2)$$
$$T = 37° \text{ C. } (26d)$$

Equations (26a-d) are a particular form of the general relation usually named the *Nernst equation.*

The Nernst equation has three major applications in the study of membrane and tissue transport: (i) development of a criterion for passive equilibrium, (ii) prediction of the membrane potential, and (iii) derivation of the Gibbs–Donnan relation.

Criterion for passive equilibrium. If the electrical potential difference and the concentration of a dissolved species of particles (which have no net flux) are measured on each side of a membrane or tissue layer, and the experimental measurements are found to fit equation (25), it can be concluded that electrical and diffusion forces alone explain the observed concentration distribution. If the results do not fit the equation, an additional force acting on the particles as they move through the membrane (e.g., active transport) must be postulated to explain the deviation from the predicted results (assuming, of course, that the membrane is permeable to this species of particles). Specifically, if the left side of equation (25) is greater than the right a net diffusion–electrical force must cause particles to move from side 1 of the membrane to side 2; and, since net flux is zero, an opposing force must also exist. Similarly, if $C_2 e^{z\beta V_2} > C_1 e^{z\beta V_1}$, an additional force tending to move particles from side 1 to side 2 must be present (see Fig. 13).

In the terminology of Chapter 1, the Nernst equation and equation (25) will be satisfied only if the calculated ionic equilibrium potential is equal to the experimentally measured membrane potential. Thus, the Nernst equation can be used to determine the necessity for and the direction of membrane forces other than simple passive diffusion and electrical migration.

Prediction of the membrane potential. In general, the electrical potential across a membrane is determined by the complicated relations be-

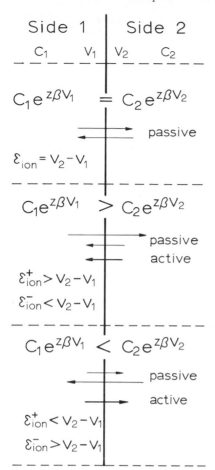

Side 1 | Side 2

C_1 V_1 | V_2 C_2

$$C_1 e^{z\beta V_1} = C_2 e^{z\beta V_2}$$

passive

$$\varepsilon_{ion} = V_2 - V_1$$

$$C_1 e^{z\beta V_1} > C_2 e^{z\beta V_2}$$

passive
active

$$\varepsilon^+_{ion} > V_2 - V_1$$
$$\varepsilon^-_{ion} < V_2 - V_1$$

$$C_1 e^{z\beta V_1} < C_2 e^{z\beta V_2}$$

passive
active

$$\varepsilon^+_{ion} < V_2 - V_1$$
$$\varepsilon^-_{ion} > V_2 - V_1$$

Fig. 13. Fluxes and electrochemical activities. If the electrochemical activity of a given ion is the same on both sides of a membrane (or the ionic equilibrium potential, ε_{ion}, is equal to the observed membrane or transtissue potential, $V_2 - V_1$), the passive unidirectional fluxes would be expected to be equal. If the electrochemical activity is not the same on the two sides but the net flux is zero, an additional influence, here noted as active, must be present to counteract the imbalance in passive electrochemical diffusion. This figure also indicates the relation between the ionic equilibrium potential for positive ions, ε^+_{ion}, and negative ions, ε^-_{ion}, and the potential difference in these circumstances.

tween the forces and fluxes for all the ionic species present. However, when the *passive flux of a single ionic species* dominates membrane exchange, the membrane potential approaches that predicted by the Nernst relation for that species (which is the same as the ionic equilibrium potential of Chapter 1). For this reason the axon membrane potential rises toward $(1/\beta)$ ln $([Na]_{out}/[Na]_{in})$ during the initial phase of the action potential when sodium movement

dominates, and declines toward $(1/\beta)\ln([K]_{out}/[K]_{in})$ during the falling phase of the action potential when membrane current is carried mainly by potassium ions.

Gibbs–Donnan equilibrium. An electrical potential can be maintained across a membrane by several mechanisms. Ions can be pumped through a membrane, thereby causing separation of electrical charges; such a pump is called "electrogenic" since it is the direct cause of the membrane potential. A pump also can cause two simultaneous active fluxes without net current flow ("nonelectrogenic"), with the membrane potential resulting from the passive redistribution of the pumped ions; this is exemplified by the coupled sodium–potassium pump described in Chapter 1. In both of these mechanisms, continuous active transport is required to sustain the membrane potential.

However, a membrane potential can be maintained by purely passive means, i.e., the simultaneous presence of both charged particles to which the membrane is impermeable and of other particles which can pass through the membrane. If the permeating particles are influenced only by simple passive forces, the resulting concentration distribution is called a *Gibbs–Donnan equilibrium*. In such an equilibrium, the direction of the potential change depends upon the charge of the nonpermeating ion. A positive potential will develop on the side with nonpermeating positive ions or a negative potential on that side with nonpermeating negative ions. The magnitude of the potential depends upon the ratio of concentrations of permeating and nonpermeating ions, as shown by the following example:

Suppose that two permeating ions, sodium and chloride, are passively distributed across a membrane, but that the solution on one side (here noted as side 2) also contains the nonpermeating anion, A^- (Fig. 14). Since only simple passive forces are present, the permeating ions must obey the Nernst relation:

$$[Na^+]_1 e^{\beta V_1} = [Na^+]_2 e^{\beta V_2} \tag{27a}$$

and

$$[Cl^-]_1 e^{-\beta V_1} = [Cl^-]_2 e^{-\beta V_2} \tag{27b}$$

Also, the requirement for electrical neutrality of the solutions on the two sides leads to two additional equations:

$$[Na^+]_1 = [Cl^-]_1 \tag{28a}$$

and

$$[Na^+]_2 = [Cl^-]_2 + [A^-]_2 \tag{28b}$$

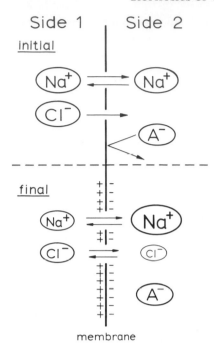

Fig. 14. Development of a membrane potential due to a nonpermeating ion. Initially, equal concentrations of NaCl and NaA are placed on each side of a membrane. If Na^+ and Cl^- can pass through the membrane but A^- cannot, the initial net flux of Cl^- will cause side 2 to become negative with respect to side 1. The membrane potential developed will in turn cause Na^+ to redistribute passively according to the Nernst relation and will progressively reduce net Cl^- flux. Final equilibration will take place when equation (31) is satisfied.

These four equations can be solved as follows to find the concentration distribution and electrical potential:

Multiply equations (27a) and (27b) to get the relation:

$$[Na^+]_1[Cl^-]_1 = [Na^+]_2[Cl^-]_2 \quad (29)$$

This equation often is formally called the *Donnan rule* (or the Gibbs–Donnan rule), although it is merely a simple consequence of the Nernst equation. Using equations (28a) and (28b) to eliminate the sodium concentrations from equation (29) and rearranging terms gives

$$\left(\frac{[Cl^-]_1}{[Cl^-]_2}\right)^2 = 1 + \frac{[A^-]_2}{[Cl^-]_2} \quad (30)$$

The chloride concentration ratio, as calculated from equation (30), is sufficient to determine the sodium concentration ratio and the membrane potential by using equations (27b) and (29), thereby giving the relation

$$e^{\beta(V_1 - V_2)} = \frac{[Na^+]_2}{[Na^+]_1} = \frac{[Cl^-]_1}{[Cl^-]_2}$$

$$= \left[1 + \frac{[A^-]_2}{[Cl^-]_2}\right]^{\frac{1}{2}} \quad (31)$$

Thus, nonpermeating anions, A^-, on side 2 cause sodium accumulation, a chloride depletion, and a reduced potential on side 2 relative to side 1; the magnitude of this effect is a function of the ratio of nonpermeating to permeating anions, $[A^-]_2/[Cl^-]_2$.

An important example of the Gibbs–Donnan relation is the equilibrium across the capillary walls as modified by the negatively charged plasma proteins. The charge carried by these proteins represents about 10 per cent of the total negative charge of the plasma anions. Thus, in those capillary beds impermeable to plasma proteins, plasma is slightly negative (about 1.3 mV) relative to the interstitial fluid; the interstitial concentrations of sodium and other univalent positive ions are less than their plasma values by a factor of about 0.95, while the concentrations of chloride and other univalent negative ions are more by a factor of about 1.05.

Net flux; Ussing equation.[36]   Using the Nernst equation to distinguish between passive transport and active transport is limited to circumstance for which the equation was derived, i.e., zero net flux. However, the existence of a net flux is normal in many organ systems, such as the gastrointestinal mucosa or the renal tubule. Thus, several more general criteria have been derived.

Equation (22) usually is taken as the starting point. By dividing both sides by $(-De^{-z\beta V})$ and noting that M is constant within the membrane in a steady state, this equation can be integrated to give

$$M\left[\int_{\text{side 1}}^{\text{side 2}}(-e^{z\beta V}/D)dx\right] = C_2 e^{z\beta V_2} - C_1 c^{z\beta V_1} \quad (32)$$

Unfortunately, the integral in brackets cannot be evaluated unless the diffusion coefficient, D, and the electrical potential, V, are known at all points within the membrane, and such data have never been obtained for biologic membranes. Sometimes, D is assumed to be constant and V to be a linear function of distance within the membrane; the resulting relation is known as the Goldman constant field equation. However, such assumptions cannot be directly verified.

Alternatively, by considering the unidirectional fluxes through the membrane, a relation can be developed in which the integral term does not appear. Such a relation was derived for biologic membranes by H. H. Ussing and, thus, is called the *Ussing criterion* for active transport.

Consider the application of equation (32) to the unidirectional flux $M_{2,1}$ (particles passing from side 2 to side 1). On side 1, the concentration of particles which contribute to this flux must be zero; thus for $M_{2,1}$, $C_1 = 0$, so that equation (32) becomes

$$M_{2,1}\left[\int_{\text{side 1}}^{\text{side 2}} (-e^{z\beta V}/D)dx\right] = C_2 e^{z\beta V_2} \quad (33a)$$

Similarly, for the particles which contribute to the flux in the opposite direction, $M_{1,2}$, the concentration, C_2, may be considered zero. Thus

$$M_{1,2}\left[\int_{\text{side 1}}^{\text{side 2}} (-e^{z\beta V}/D)dx\right] = -C_1 e^{z\beta V_1} \quad (33b)$$

Taking the ratio of equations (33a) and (33b) eliminates the integral term, giving the Ussing equation for the magnitude of the flux ratio:

$$\left|\frac{M_{2,1}}{M_{1,2}}\right| = \frac{C_2}{C_1} e^{z\beta(V_2 - V_1)} \quad (34)$$

Thus, even though the magnitude of neither of the unidirectional fluxes (or the net flux) can be predicted, the ratio of these fluxes is predictable and can be observed experimentally. The concentrations, C_1 and C_2, and the membrane potential, $V_2 - V_1$, can be assured directly, and the unidirectional fluxes can be evaluated by placing a radioactive isotope of the species whose flux is to be determined on one side of the membrane and then measuring its rate of appearance on the other.

If the results agree with equation (34), simple passive forces are sufficient to account for observed fluxes. Agreement with this equation does not rule out the possibility of other forces; however, it does imply that other forces are unnecessary to explain the data. If the equation is not satisfied, an additional force must be postulated; the direction of this force can be derived from considerations discussed in connection with the Nernst equation.

Movement against a passive gradient. If there is a difference in electrochemical activity, $Ce^{z\beta V}$, across a membrane, passive forces tend to cause a net flux from the side of higher activity to that of lower activity, since such a flux is a consequence of the spontaneous tendency to reduce the total chemical potential energy, μ. Thus a net flux from a region of high to one of low electrochemical activity (or potential) requires no external energy. However, if a net flux occurs in the opposite direction (i.e., from low to high electrochemical activity), the total energy inherent in the concentration and the electrical potential is increasing, as can be seen from equation (24); therefore additional energy must be supplied to sustain this flux. Thus, movement against an electrochemical activity gradient requires an active transport mechanism (assuming that other passive forces, such as solvent drag, have been taken into account).

Summary of mathematical criteria for active transport. If the net flux through a membrane occurs against an electrochemical gradient, active transport is indicated. If the net flux is in the direction of the electrochemical gradient and if in addition the unidirectional flux ratio fits Ussing's equation, no forces other than simple passive diffusion in an electric field need be postulated. If the net flux is in the direction of the electrochemical gradient but Ussing's equation does not hold, then active transport is not necessary to account for the energy change (although it may be present anyway), but the simple passive mechanisms which led to equation (34) are obviously insufficient to account for the observed fluxes; in this case more detailed investigation into the forces responsible is necessary.

ANNOTATED BIBLIOGRAPHY

A comprehensive coverage of membrane exchange and active transport can be found in Harris, *Transport and Accumulation in Biological Systems.*[13] Also, H. Davson, in his *Textbook of General Physiology,*[8] discusses a number of active transport systems. Much of this material as well as the pharmacology of membrane exchange is covered in two papers by A. M. Shanes, "Electrochemical aspects of physiological and pharmacological action in excitable cells," I and II.[34]

A discussion of the biochemical mechanisms of metabolic energy coupling to sodium ion movement is presented in the definitive review of J. D. Judah and K. Ahmed, "The biochemistry of sodium transport."[20] Particular aspects of membrane exchange have been discussed in two recent symposia: "Borderline problems around the field of active transport,"[10] and *The cellular functions of membrane transport.*[17]

The quantitative development of transport equations based on classical thermodynamics is exemplified in an important paper by Ussing, "The distinction by means of tracers between active transport and diffusion."[36] An attempt to employ the modern theory of irreversible thermodynamics in transport problems is developed by Kedem and Katchalsky in "A physical interpretation of the phenomenological coefficients of membrane permeability,"[21] and by Kimizuka and Koketsu in "Ion transport through cell membrane."[22] Alternative quantitative approaches which have been attempted include stochastic (probabilistic) models, e.g., Hodgkin and Keynes, "The potassium permeability of a giant nerve fiber"[16]; chemical kinetics models, e.g., Kirschner, "On the mechanism of active sodium transport across the frog skin"[23]; and the treatment of the molecular structure of the membrane as a sequence of energy barriers, e.g., Parlin and Eyring, "Membrane permeability and electrical potential."[29]

REFERENCES

1. ANDERSEN, B. and USSING, H. H. *Acta physiol. scand.,* 1957, *39:*228–239.
2. CHINARD, F. P. *Amer. J. Physiol.,* 1952, *171:*578–586.
3. CHRISTENSEN, H. N. In: *Membrane transport and metabolism,* A. Kleinzeller and A. Kotyk, eds. Prague, Czech. Acad. Sci., 1961.
4. CRABBÉ, J. *Endocrinology,* 1961, *69:*673–682.
5. CSAKY, T. Z. *Ann. Rev. Physiol.,* 1965, *27:*415–450.
6. CURRAN, P. F., HERRERA, F. C. and FLANIGAN, W. J. *J. gen. Physiol.,* 1963, *46:*1011–1027.
7. DANIELLI, J. F. *Circulation,* 1962, *26:*1163–1166.
8. DAVSON, H. *Textbook of general physiology,* 3d ed. Boston, Little, Brown and Co., 1964.
9. DAVSON, H. and DANIELLI, J. F. *The permeability of natural membranes.* Cambridge, Cambridge University Press, 1952.
10. *Fed. Proc.,* 1963, *22:*1–35.
11. FRAZIER, H. S., DEMPSEY, E. F. and LEAF, A. *J. gen. Physiol.,* 1962, *45:*529–543.
12. GOLDSTEIN, D. A. and SOLOMON, A. K. *J. gen. Physiol.,* 1960, *44:*1–17.
13. HARRIS, E. J. *Transport and accumulation in biological systems,* 2d ed. New York, Academic Press, 1960.
14. HAYS, R. M. and LEAF, A. *J. gen. Physiol.,* 1962, *45:*905–919.
15. HILLIER, J. and HOFFMAN, J. F. *J. cell. comp. Physiol.,* 1953, *42:*203–220.
16. HODGKIN, A. L. and KEYNES, R. A. *J. Physiol.,* 1955, *128:*61–81.
17. HOFFMAN, J., ed. *The cellular functions of membrane transport.* Englewood Cliffs, N. J., Prentice-Hall, 1964.
18. HOKIN, L. E. and HOKIN, M. R. *J. gen. Physiol.,* 1960, *44:*61–85.
19. HOLTER, H. In: *Enzymes and drug action.* Ciba Found. Symp. G. W. Wolstenholme, ed. Boston, Little, Brown and Co., 1962.
20. JUDAH, J. D. and AHMED, K. *Biol. Rev.,* 1964, *39:*160–193.
21. KEDEM, O. and KATCHALSKY, A. *J. gen. Physiol.,* 1961, *45:*143–179.
22. KIMIZUKA, H. and KOKETSU, K. *J. theor. Biol.,* 1964, *6:*290–305.
23. KIRSCHNER, L. B. *J. cell. comp. Physiol.,* 1955, *45:*61–87.
24. KOEFOED-JOHNSEN, V. and USSING, H. H. *Acta physiol. scand.,* 1953, *28:*60–76.
25. LEAF, A. and HAYS, R. M. *J. gen. Physiol.,* 1962, *45:*921–932.
26. MAURO, A. *Science,* 1957, *126:*252–253.
27. PALADE, G. E. *Anat. Rec.,* 1960, *136:*254.
28. PAPPENHEIMER, J. R. *Physiol. Rev.,* 1953, *33:*387–423.
29. PARLIN, R. B. and EYRING, H. In: *Ion transport across membranes.* New York, Academic Press, 1954.
30. PATLAK, C. S. *Biophys. J.,* 1961, *1:*419–427.
31. PONDER, E. Chap. 1 in: *The cell,* vol. II, Brachet and Mirsky, eds. New York, Academic Press, 1961.
32. RENKIN, E. M. *Amer. J. Physiol.,* 1952, *168:*538–545.
33. ROSENBERG, T. and WILBRANDT, W. *J. gen. Physiol.,* 1957, *41:*289–296.
34. SHANES, A. M. *Pharmacol. Rev.,* 1958, *10:*59–164.
35. TOSTESON, D. C. and HOFFMAN, J. F. *J. gen. Physiol.,* 1960, *44:*169–194.
36. USSING, H. H. *Acta physiol. scand.,* 1949, *19:*43–56.
37. USSING, H. H. and ZERAHN, K. *Acta physiol. scand.,* 1951, *23:*110–127.
38. ZERAHN, K. *Acta physiol. scand.,* 1956, *36:*300–310.

SECTION X

KIDNEY FUNCTION AND BODY FLUIDS

CHAPTER 44

The Kidney

By ALAN KOCH

REGULATION of the body fluids is accomplished primarily by the kidneys. These two organs, which together weigh only about 300 grams, directly control the volume and composition of the extracellular fluid, and exert indirect control over the intracellular fluid. This regulatory task is fulfilled so successfully that, over a wide range of water and solute intake, the volume and the composition of the fluids in the body are held remarkably constant. In order to effect this control, a great many different operations are required. The multiplicity of operations and the versatility of each lead to great diversity of renal function. This apparent complexity, however, can be explained by the electrochemistry of fluids, the permeability characteristics of renal structures, and metabolic pumps such as the ones already discussed in Chapters 1 and 43.

Properties of Solutions. A *solution* consists of a fluid medium, called the *solvent*, in which are distributed a number of particles, the *solute*. The concentration (C or [S]) of a substance in a solution is defined as the quantity present (Q) in mols, millimols, or micromols, divided by the volume (V) in liters or cubic centimeters through which it is distributed. The concept of concentration is frequently generalized to that of mol fraction. The *mol fraction* of a substance in a solution is defined as the number of molecules of that substance divided by the total number of molecules present in the solution.

As will be remembered from physical chemistry, the mol fraction of a solvent, and therefore of the total solute, can be measured by determination of the colligative properties of the solution. These properties include the lowering of the vapor pressure, elevation of the boiling point, lowering of the freezing point, and osmotic pressure. The changes are all measures of the same thing, the tendency of water molecules to escape from the solution. The physical chemistry of solutions is discussed lucidly by Moore.[24]

The relationship between the quantity present, the volume through which it is distributed, and the resulting concentration is given by:

$$C = \frac{Q}{V}$$

This relationship, which has been developed for a static system, can also be applied to a system, like the kidneys, in which fluids are moving. Only the steady state situation, i.e., the situation in which the concentration in the flowing fluid is not changing with time, will be considered. The *mass flow* is the quantity of solute (Q), in millimols or milligrams, which passes a cross section every minute and is symbolized by $\dot{Q}$.* The *volume flow* is the volume of the solvent which passes a cross section every minute and is symbolized by $\dot{V}$. In a given period, the quantity which passes a cross section is $\dot{Q}\Delta t$, and the volume through which it is distributed is the volume which passes, $\dot{V}\Delta t$. The concentration of material is still Q/V; hence, $C = \dot{Q}\Delta t / \dot{V}\Delta t$, and the equation is

$$C = \frac{\dot{Q}}{\dot{V}}$$

Terminology. Unfortunately, renal terminology arose independently, without reference to physical terminology. Concentrations were considered fundamental quantities, and mass or mass flows were derived from them. In addition, no explicit distinction is customarily made between mass and mass flow or between volume and volume flow. In standard renal notation, the plasma concentration is denoted by P, and

*Pronounced "Q dot"; the dot to express rate is a symbol going back to Sir Isaac Newton.

TABLE 1. *Correlation of Terms Describing Renal Function*

STANDARD RENAL NOMENCLATURE	MEANING	NOMENCLATURE USED HERE	UNITS
P_{Na}	Plasma concentration of Na^+	$[Na]_p$	$\mu M./cm.^3$ or $mM./liter$
U_G	Urinary concentration of glucose	$[G]_u$	$\mu M./cm.^3$, $mM./liter$, or $mg./cm.^3$
V	Rate of urine flow	$\dot{V}_u$	$cm.^3/minute$
$U_{Cl}V$	Rate of excretion Cl^-	$\dot{Q}Cl_u$	$\mu M./minute$
C_{PAH} or RPF	The rate of flow of plasma into the kidney, measured by the clearance of PAH	$\dot{V}_p$	$cm.^3/minute$
C_{in} or GFR	The rate of flow of glomerular filtrate into the nephrons, measured by the clearance of inulin	$\dot{V}_g$	$cm.^3/minute$
L_K or $C_{in} \times P_k$	The filtered load of K^+; i.e., the rate at which K^+ is filtered at the glomerulus	$\dot{Q}_{Kg}$	$\mu M./minute$
$\dfrac{C_{urea}}{C_{in}}$	The clearance ratio of urea; i.e., the fraction of the filtered urea which is excreted	$\dfrac{\dot{Q}_{urea_u}}{\dot{Q}_{urea_g}}$	no units

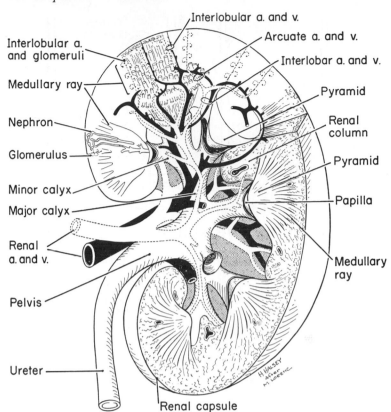

Fig. 1. Gross structure of the kidney, sagittal section. (After Smith, *Principles of renal physiology*. New York, Oxford University Press, 1956.)

a subscript is used to indicate the substance. The urinary concentrations are denoted by U, again with a subscript to indicate the substance. The rate of urine flow is denoted by V.

In this chapter, a different system of notation is used. The mass of a substance will be denoted by Q, the mass flow will be denoted by $\dot{Q}$, and $\dot{V}$ will indicate volume flow. Square brackets will be used to indicate concentration, and a subscript will tell where the concentration is measured. Table 1 gives the conversions between the two systems.

Functional Anatomy. GROSS STRUCTURE (Fig. 1). The medial side of the kidney contains a deep sinus through which the ureter and all the blood vessels enter or leave the renal parenchyma. Just outside the renal sinus, the ureter expands into the extrarenal pelvis, which continues inside the border of the sinus as the intrarenal pelvis. The intrarenal pelvis divides into two major calyces, each of which subdivides into two or three minor calyces. Each minor calyx terminates around the base of one or two papillae. Formed urine is delivered into the collecting duct system in the renal papillae, passes through the papillary duct system into a minor

calyx, and thence goes eventually to the bladder.

A medullary and a cortical type of tissue can be distinguished when the kidney is sectioned longitudinally. The triangularly shaped papillae give rise to medullary pyramids which, in turn, give rise to medullary rays; the over-all impression is one of a decrease in the density of medullary substance as the cortex is approached. Cortical substance lines the surface of the organ and, between medullary pyramids, dips in toward the medulla in the renal columns.

MICROSCOPIC STRUCTURE (Fig. 2).[23] The unit of structure and function in the kidney is the *nephron*. Renal parenchyma is composed of a great many nephrons, each with its associated blood supply. Urine is formed in the nephrons, and total renal function can be viewed as a summation of the function of about two million extremely similar but distinct units. A nephron is composed of two major sections, a *glomerulus* and a *tubule*. The glomerulus consists of Bowman's capsule, the spherical blind end of the tubule, and of coiled capillaries. These capillaries lie within an invagination of the capsule, which is formed of squamous epithelium.

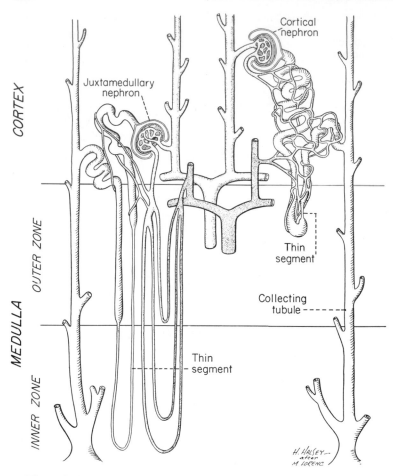

CORTEX

Cortical nephron

Juxtamedullary nephron

MEDULLA

OUTER ZONE

INNER ZONE

Thin segment

Collecting tubule

Thin segment

H. HALSEY—
after
M. LORENC

Fig. 2. Structural differences between cortical and juxtamedullary nephrons. (After Smith, *The kidney, its structure and function in health and disease.* New York, Oxford University Press, 1951.)

The tubular portion of the nephron begins at the glomerulus and undergoes several convolutions in this region, traveling generally outward toward the cortex. The tubule then straightens and descends in a straight line toward the medulla. The convoluted portion and the first part of the descending portion constitute the *proximal tubule*. Near the end of the descent the walls of the tubule become exceedingly thin. The thin-walled portion is termed the *thin segment* of the loop of Henle. After a sharp hairpin turn the tubule travels back toward its associated glomerulus in the cortex. Along this ascending limb the walls become thick again. The point of thickening marks the beginning of the *distal tubule*. In the region of the glomerulus, the tubule undergoes several more convolutions before emptying into the system of *collecting ducts*. These ducts travel in straight lines through the medulla; they accept fluid from several nephrons, coalesce, and then enter the renal papillae. Cortical substance is thus composed of glomeruli and the proximal and distal convoluted portions of the tubules; medullary substance is composed of the descending and ascending limbs of the tubules and the collecting duct system.

Short *afferent arterioles*, each feeding a glomerulus, arise from the intralobular arteries. Upon entering the corpuscle, the afferent arteriole arborizes into six to ten glomerular capillaries, which lie close to the invaginated surface of Bowman's capsule. The capillaries then recombine to form the *efferent arteriole*, which leaves the glomerulus and goes to the tubular portion of the nephron. Upon reaching the proximal portion of the tubule, the efferent arteriole arborizes into a second group of capillaries, the *peritubular capillaries*, which wind around the tubule. These capillaries traverse the entire length of the renal tubule, following both its descending course into the medulla and its ascending return. At this point, the capillaries coalesce to form the renal venules.

The kidney is abundantly supplied with nerves, which travel beside the major arteries and apparently innervate the arteriolar vasculature. There is no evidence that these nerves supply the nephron.

All tubules are not quite alike and all vascular supplies are not identical. Nephrons with glomeruli lying in the outer two-thirds of the cortex tend to have very short descending and ascending limbs and only vestigial loops of Henle. The efferent arterioles of these nephrons are very short, and the peritubular ramification occurs immediately and extensively. Nephrons whose glomeruli lie in the deeper third of the cortex have a rather different structure. These nephrons have long descending and ascending limbs, which penetrate deeply into the renal pyramids and possess well developed loops. The efferent arterioles of these nephrons tend to be long and, instead of ramifying extensively into peritubular capillaries, give rise to one or two long straight vessels, the *vasa recta*. These vessels follow the course of the nephron into and out of the medullary pyramids and do not appear to break up into true capillaries.

Précis of Renal Function. The quantity of blood entering the kidneys every minute represents one-fourth to one-fifth of the resting cardiac output. As the blood flows through the glomerular capillaries, about one-fifth of the plasma water passes through the membranes of the capillaries and glomerulus to enter the proximal portion of the renal tubule. The blood remaining in the vascular system enters the efferent arterioles and perfuses the tubules via the peritubular capillaries. The plasma water removed from the blood is termed the *glomerular filtrate;* the process of removal is *glomerular filtration.* Glomerular filtrate is an ultrafiltrate and normally contains no erythrocytes and little or no plasma protein. Other molecules which are sufficiently small to be in true solution pass freely through the glomerular membranes. All major ions, glucose, amino acids and urea appear in the glomerular filtrate at approximately the concentration at which they exist in the plasma.

In the tubule, both solute and water transport take place. Materials are transported across the tubular epithelium from the lumen of the tubule to the interstitial fluid surrounding the nephron and thence to the blood in the peritubular capillaries. This process is called *reabsorption* and results in the return of filtered material to the blood stream. Materials are also transported from the peritubular blood to the interstitial fluid, across the tubular epithelium, and into the lumen. This process is called *secretion* and results in an excretion which is more rapid than would be possible solely through

glomerular filtration. The terms reabsorption and secretion denote direction rather than a difference in mechanism. All the glucose that is filtered may return to the circulation and remain in the body as a result of complete reabsorption. Conversely, all the p-amino-hippuric acid (PAH) that enters the kidneys may leave in the urine, even though only one-fifth of the material is filtered. This complete excretion results from the efficient secretory system for PAH.

The proximal tubule reabsorbs physiologically important solute material and secretes organic substances that are destined for excretion. The filtered glucose and amino acids are reabsorbed, as are most filtered Na^+ and Cl^- and some filtered HCO_3^-. As solute particles are removed by active transport processes, the osmotic gradient produced causes reabsorption of water as well. The distal tubule and collecting duct are engaged primarily in the precise regulation of acid-base and K^+ balance. Since much of the filtered solute and water is reabsorbed proximally, both $\dot{V}$ and $\dot{Q}$ are relatively small in the distal tubule. Na^+ is reabsorbed distally as well as proximally, the distal mechanism being an ion exchange in which Na^+ reabsorption is balanced by H^+ or K^+ secretion. Final modification of urinary solute concentration to form a hypertonic urine probably occurs in the collecting ducts.

FLUID DYNAMICS

Two roles are played by the blood that enters the kidney. The first is to supply oxygen and metabolites to enable the kidney to function; this is the role filled by the blood in any organ. In the kidney, however, the blood must also supply the water and solute material which the kidney will process. Because of this latter role, fluid dynamics in the kidney differs from that in any other organ.

The volume of blood flowing into the kidney exceeds by far the amount needed to meet its requirements for oxygen and metabolites. Two corollaries of this high volume flow may be pointed out. First, the extraction of oxygen and metabolites is normally extremely low. Second, in an emergency such as hemorrhage, the reduction of renal blood flow which occurs causes an increase, or lessens a decrease, in the blood flow in other regions. Normally 1 to 1.5 liters of blood

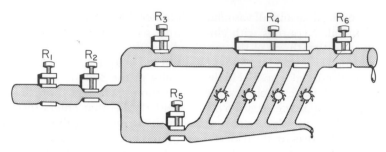

Fig. 3.   Analogue of fluid flow in the kidney. Resistances are designated as *R*, such as *R₁* in the distributing arteries, *R₂* in the afferent arteriole, *R₃* in the efferent arteriole, *R₄* in the peritubular capillary, *R₅* across the glomerular membrane, and *R₆* in the venous bed. The turbine wheels signify the active transport of solute.

enter the two kidneys each minute. After hemorrhage or severe injury, the flow may be reduced to as little as 250 ml. per minute.

Physiologic Analysis of Blood Flow.   The study of renal fluid dynamics involves an application of the principle that flow is equal to the pressure drop divided by vascular resistance (Ohm's law). This principle, as applied to renal fluid circulation, is illustrated in Figure 3, in which each screw clamp corresponds to a resistance to flow. The amount of resistance is shown by the degree of constriction of each clamp. Screw clamp R_1 indicates the resistance to flow from the renal artery to the afferent arterioles; R_2, through the afferent arterioles; R_3, through the efferent arterioles; R_4, through the peritubular capillaries; R_5, through the glomerular membrane; and R_6, through the entire venous bed. As fluid travels through the tubular portion of the nephron, it is removed and returned to the peritubular capillaries. This transfer is driven by the transport of solute and, in Figure 3, is indicated by the centrifugal pumps in the reabsorptive channels.

Two conclusions can be made from Figure 3. If the pressures at each point and all the resistances were known, the total flow and the flow in each limb could be calculated. Unfortunately, the resistances are not known but must be computed from the flows which have been estimated by other means. The main point is that *the total plasma flow is split at the glomerulus, some fluid being filtered to enter the tubular lumen and some continuing in the vascular system.* The relative size of the two flows is determined by the relative resistances in the two parallel branches. The ratio of the rate of glomerular filtration to the total rate of plasma flow is determined by the venous resistance and the resistances in the

two limbs. This ratio is referred to as the *filtration fraction.*

Filtration rate and renal plasma flow may be varied widely by both extrarenal and intrarenal factors. The glomerular filtration rate is determined by the resistance to flow across the glomerular capillary wall and the effective filtration pressure. Since protein does not pass the glomerular membrane freely, work must be done to separate the protein from the solution being filtered. The effective filtration pressure, therefore, is the pressure difference across the glomerular capillary wall less the osmotic pressure corresponding to concentration of nonpermeating solute in plasma:

filtration pressure = pressure in glomerular
capillaries, minus pressure
in capsular space, minus
osmotic pressure of plasma
protein.

The osmotic pressure term (π) is approximately equal to RT (R = universal gas constant; T = temperature) times the molar concentration of protein in the plasma. The protein concentration is about 1 m**M.** per liter, which corresponds to a value for π of a little less than 20 mm. Hg. At the normal mean arterial pressure of 100 mm. Hg, capillary pressure is probably about 70 mm. Hg, and intracapsular pressure is about 20 mm. Hg. Thus, the filtration pressure is about 30 mm. Hg (70 − 20 − 20).

Both capillary and intracapsular pressures vary with arterial pressure. Although the precise relations are unknown, it is unlikely that either are linear functions of the arterial pressure. Hence, filtration pressure would not be expected to bear a constant relation to arterial pressure. Indeed, it does not. Glomerular filtration starts at arterial pressures around 30 mm. Hg, rises rapidly in the region between 30 and 90 mm. Hg, and then rises more slowly or may even stay constant over the physiologic range of 90 to 180 mm. Hg (see Fig. 4). Presumably, no filtration occurs at very low pressures because the capsular back pressure and protein osmotic pressure have not been exceeded by the glomerular capillary pressure. The nonlinear pressure–flow relationship, seen after filtration has been instituted, probably reflects the manner in which glomerular capillary and intracapsular pressures change with arterial pressure.

The volume flow of plasma through the kidney depends directly on the driving pressure and inversely on the vascular resistance. Since renal venous pressure is normally zero, the driving pressure must be the arterial pressure. So long as resistances are constant, flow increases linearly with pressure. As arterial pressure is increased above 50 mm. Hg, vascular resistance increases so that the flow fails to increase as much as it would have (Fig. 4).

Control of Flow Rate; Autoregulation. The kidney is richly supplied with sympathetic nerves, all of which probably function to innervate vascular smooth muscle. The vasculature of the kidney is very labile, and in emergencies, such as hemorrhage or shock, much of the blood that normally perfuses the kidney is diverted to other regions. This would seem a reasonable mechanism for the body to possess since, in an emergency, the body can better afford to lose renal function for two or three hours than brain or cardiac function. Unfortunately, the response may outdo itself and, after severe blood loss or shock, the kidneys may become ischemic. A

protracted period of renal ischemia frequently initiates a degenerative process which culminates in renal failure with very low blood flow, little or no glomerular filtration, and tubular cell necrosis. Hence, after injuries in which the patient has undergone a period of shock, it is necessary to be on guard against renal failure.

In addition to this active, central control of the renal vasculature, the kidney also exhibits a form of self-control or *autoregulation*. This can be seen in the isolated, perfused kidney in which the pressure–flow relations described above, and illustrated in Figure 4, are still evident, although less pronounced. Thus, the continued existence of these nonlinear relations after the removal of nervous control would seem to indicate a regulating component characteristic of the kidney itself. The tendency for blood flow to level off with increasing pressure means that the renal vascular resistance increases somewhere as a function of pressure. The tendency of filtration rate to level off with increasing arterial pressure presumably is related, not to a change in filtration resistance, but to a change in the relationships between arterial pressure and the pressures involved in glomerular filtration. Thus, the two facets of autoregulation come about in different manners. Figure 3 shows that the change of a single resistance with pressure might account for the whole phenomenon. If either the preglomerular resistance, R_2, which corresponds to the resistance in the afferent arterioles, or the venous resistance, R_6, were to increase, total vascular resistance would increase and the filtration fraction would remain constant.

Two major theories have been advanced to explain autoregulation. Proponents of one theory have selected the afferent arterioles as the

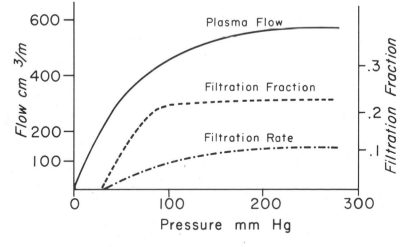

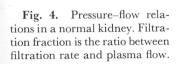

Fig. 4. Pressure–flow relations in a normal kidney. Filtration fraction is the ratio between filtration rate and plasma flow.

place where resistance changes as a function of pressure, and proponents of the other have chosen the venous bed. Those who favor the first theory advocate the presence of a myogenic reflex. A pressure sensor located within the kidney is postulated, and pressure variations in the region of this sensor result in contractions of vascular smooth muscle. Thus, a vessel's diameter is smaller at a higher pressure than at a lower pressure, and the resistance is increased.[48] The resistance is presumed to change in the afferent arterioles.

The second theory states that the resistance changes in the venous portion of the vascular bed. An increase in resistance results from an increase in extravascular pressure and a consequent decrease in the transmural pressure. Extravascular pressure increases because of an increase in vascular pressure at the level of the capillaries and a resulting increase in transcapillary filtration. The events required for and predicted by the tissue pressure hypothesis are known to take place. Thus, autoregulation by tissue pressure does occur.[17, 35] Whether there is an additional component derived from a myogenic reflex is not presently known.

Clearance Studies. This method, first used extensively by Smith, has quantified the study of normal and pathologic renal mechanisms. A clearance value expresses the degree to which a substance is removed from the blood by excretion into urine. This value is expressed not as a percentage but rather as the number of cubic centimeters which would be "cleared" were all of the substances removed. It is therefore the virtual rather than the actual amount of blood cleared. A good way of looking at clearance is that it is the number of cubic centimeters of blood which would have to be presented to the nephron to provide the amount of substance actually found in the urine, in a unit time.

$$\text{Clearance} = \frac{\dot{Q}_u}{C_p} \quad \text{or} \quad \frac{UV}{P} \quad \text{or}$$

$$\frac{\text{amount of substance in urine per minute}}{\text{concentration of substance in plasma}}$$

The units of clearance are those of volume flow, usually cubic centimeters per minute.

The clearances of two particular substances are especially important. The clearance of para-aminohippuric acid (PAH) is a measure of renal plasma flow; the clearance of inulin is a meas-

ure of the filtration rate. Knowledge of these volume flows allows calculation of some of the important relationships in renal fluid dynamics; it also enables us to know the mass flows of material entering the kidney or being filtered or being presented to the peritubular borders of tubular cells. The mass flow of a substance is the product of the volume flow of solute and the concentration of the material of interest.

CLEARANCE RATIOS. One can determine the clearance of glucose or sodium just as well as the clearance of inulin or of PAH. However, it is only in the latter two cases that any physical meaning can be attached to the term. The clearance of glucose is related in some manner to the excretion of glucose, but this information alone does not tell how the kidney handles glucose. A derived computation, the *clearance ratio*, does give important information about the way a substance is handled by the kidney. The clearance ratio is the ratio of the clearance of a substance to the clearance of inulin. The clearance of inulin gives the amount of glomerular filtration. If the latter amount is multiplied by the plasma concentration of the substance under investigation, the amount of the substance entering the tubule, the *filtered load,* is known. If the substance, in addition to being filtered, is also secreted by the tubule, the clearance of the substance will be higher than that of inulin. If the substance is reabsorbed, its clearance will obviously be lower.

These relationships may be developed as follows: The clearance of a substance is $\dot{Q}_u/C_p$ and the clearance of inulin is numerically equal to the filtration rate. Hence the clearance ratio is $\dot{Q}_u/C_p\dot{V}_g$. But $C_p\dot{V}_g$ is the filtered load of the material ($\dot{Q}_g$); therefore,

$$\text{Clearance Ratio} = \frac{\dot{Q}_u}{\dot{Q}_g} = \frac{UV}{P \times GFR}$$

$$= \frac{\text{concentration in urine} \times \text{urine volume}}{\text{concentration in plasma} \times \text{glomerular filtration}}$$

When the clearance ratio is less than 1, *net* reabsorption occurs, but it cannot be stated whether secretion also takes place. If filtration and reabsorption are the only processes operating, the clearance ratio gives a quantitative measure of the reabsorptive process; if secretion also occurs, a theoretical possibility, this ratio gives a minimum value for the reabsorptive process. When the clearance ratio is greater than 1, *net* secretion occurs. When filtration and secretion are the only processes operating, the clearance ratio gives a quantitative measure of the secretory process. The clearance ratio is 1 for inulin or for any substance which is handled like inulin.

Although the clearance experiment has been the technique most widely used in the study of renal function, other methods are also available. These include experiments in which a glomerulus or tubule is cannulated with a small capillary tube and fluid is collected from a single nephron. This procedure is difficult, as is the analysis of the minute quantity of fluid obtained, but it was by this *tour de force* that Richards and his group established the composition of glomerular fluids and the nature of glomerular function. These investigators showed that glomerular fluid is like plasma in all measurable ways and that it is derived from plasma simply by filtration. Later. Walker *et al.*[47] showed that the solute concentration remains constant in the proximal tubule, but that glucose and water are reabsorbed. The recent work of Wirz,[49, 50] of Ullrich,[43-46] and of Gottschalk,[15] which has included not only collection of tubular fluid but also analysis of whole renal slices, can be regarded an extension of Richards' pioneer investigations.

Clearance methods and the other methods discussed to this point are all steady state measurements. Techniques for studying transients have recently been developed. Chinard injects materials into the renal artery "instantaneously" and analyzes the patterns of their appearance in both renal venous blood and urine. He has shown that glucose is transported across renal cells without entering into cellular metabolism. In addition, he has reported many provocative findings pertaining to the handling of electrolytes by the kidney. More recently, another method has been developed by Malvin and Wilde and used by many workers. In so-called "stop-flow" experiments, the ureter is blocked for four to eight minutes. It is then opened and the accumulated tubular fluid is collected serially. The first samples are presumed to have come from the most distal portions of the nephron; later samples are presumed to have been "processed" by the more proximal portions. Considerable information on the localization of tubular function has been obtained in this manner. In the remainder of this chapter, information obtained by all these methods will be presented.

MEASUREMENT OF RENAL PLASMA FLOW. Blood flow could be measured by interrupting the renal artery or vein and inserting a flowmeter. Although this procedure has been followed experimentally, it is obviously not applicable to

man, and even in work on animals it is too difficult for routine determinations. Indirect methods are therefore used. The kidney is regarded as a Y tube of the type illustrated in Figure 5*b*. If renal tissue neither creates nor destroys a material, the rate at which the material enters the kidney through the renal artery must equal the rate at which it leaves by the two available routes, the renal vein and the urine. If the arterial and venous concentrations of such a substance and the rate at which it is excreted by the kidney are known, the rate at which plasma must enter the kidney can be calculated. This procedure is already familiar as the Fick principle (Chap. 33). Thus, if the renal arterial plasma concentration of a substance is 3 mg. per liter and the renal venous plasma concentration is 2 mg. per liter, 1 liter of plasma must pass through the kidney each minute in order to furnish sufficient material to account for an excretion rate of 1 mg. per minute. For substance S, the plasma flow ($\dot{V}_p$) is given by the formula:

$$\dot{V}_p = \frac{\dot{Q}_{su}}{[S]_a - [S]_v} \quad \text{or} \quad RPF = \frac{UV}{P_a - P_v}$$

$$\text{or} \quad \frac{\text{amount in urine per unit time}}{\text{loss per liter of plasma}}$$

All that is necessary is to collect urine in a given period of time and, sometime during this period, to obtain a sample of arterial plasma (systemic venous plasma will usually have about the same concentration) and a sample of renal venous plasma. The latter sample can be obtained by catheterization of the renal vein.

The method described is simple and appli-

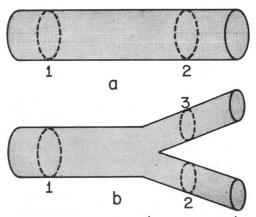

Fig. 5. *a*, Straight tube, $\dot{Q}_1$ must equal $\dot{Q}_2$. *b*, Branched tube, $\dot{Q}_1$ must equal $\dot{Q}_2 + \dot{Q}_3$.

cable to any substance that is neither destroyed nor created in the kidney. Renal venous catheterization is obviously the most difficult procedure, but this can be avoided by selecting a substance which, once it has entered the kidney, is entirely excreted in the urine. The two agents most commonly used are iodopyracet (Diodrast) and PAH. The renal venous plasma concentration of either of these agents is zero, and no renal venous plasma sample is needed. The rate at which the material enters the kidney is equal to the rate at which it is excreted, and the flow can be computed from the clearance of PAH:

$$\dot{V}_p = \frac{\dot{Q}_{PAHu}}{[PAH]_p} \quad \text{or} \quad RPF = \frac{U_{PAH}V}{P_{PAH}}$$

Any substance which is abstracted completely from renal plasma enters the nephron by two routes: (i) by filtration at the glomerulus; (ii) by transport across the tubular cells of the portion of the substance remaining in the plasma that passes along the peritubular capillaries. Further, the transcellular transport mechanism must be exceedingly active if the last trace of the material is to be removed from the plasma. A class of cyclic organic acids, including the two mentioned above, appears to be handled in the kidney in approximately this manner.

Even at low plasma concentrations of PAH (or other compounds of this group) about 10 per cent of the material is still present in renal venous plasma. Hence, the plasma flow computed from the PAH clearance is about 10 per cent lower than the actual flow. Indirect evidence suggests that the incomplete excretion of PAH results from shunting of blood through connective tissue or from the perfusion of damaged nephrons.[41] The plasma flow computed from PAH is sometimes called the "effective renal plasma flow" and that computed from the extraction, using the complete equation, the "total renal plasma flow."

MEASUREMENT OF GLOMERULAR FILTRATION RATE. Glomerular fluid cannot be sampled except in animal experiments, and even there the procedure is extremely difficult; hence clearance techniques are used. Consider a substance that is neither secreted nor reabsorbed by renal tubular cells (Fig. 5a). In the steady state, as much material leaves the nephron each minute as enters it; $\dot{Q}_g = \dot{Q}_u$. Since the concentration of this material in glomerular fluid is approximately the same as the concentration in plasma, knowledge of its rate of excretion and plasma concentration are sufficient to allow the computation of the rate of glomerular filtration.

If 210 mg. of the measuring material are excreted each minute, the same amount has entered the nephrons. If the plasma concentration is 2 mg. per ml., 105 ml. of fluid must enter the glomeruli each minute in order to account for the mass flow of the measuring material. We have already defined a clearance in such terms. The glomerular filtration rate can be calculated from the clearance of inulin.

$$V_g = \frac{\dot{Q}_{In_u}}{[In]_p} = GFR = C_{In} = \frac{U_{In}V}{P_{In}}$$

Several materials are suitable for the estimation of filtration rate. As stated, the substance must be neither created nor destroyed in the nephrons; further, its concentration in the glomerular filtrate should be proportional to the concentration in plasma. Other criteria which must be met are given by Smith.[39] The substance which fulfills these criteria best is *inulin,* a fructose polysaccharide derived from Jerusalem artichokes. In all species in which the inulin clearance has been examined, it appears to be an accurate measure of filtration. Other substances which may be used include ferrocyanide and sucrose in man and the dog and creatinine in the dog.

NORMAL VALUES OF FILTRATION RATE AND PLASMA FLOW. Renal mass and, consequently, the values for the filtration rate and plasma flow correlate fairly well with the body surface area. For this reason, values for the plasma flow and filtration rate in man are generally expressed in terms of surface area and then corrected to the value of a hypothetical man with a surface area of 1.73 sq. meters. In animals, this correction is frequently neglected. In men, plasma flow averages 655 ml. per minute, and the filtration rate 127 ml. per minute. In women, plasma flow averages 600 ml. per minute, and filtration rate 118 ml. per minute. Both volume flows decrease with increasing age and fall in an approximately linear fashion from the stated values at the age of about 30 years to approximately half those values by the age of 75. The measured values vary considerably in the absence of clinically detectable illness.

TUBULAR TRANSPORT

The main activity of the kidney is to transport solute materials and water across tubular cells. Such transport is termed *reabsorption* when its direction is from the tubular lumen to the interstitial fluid; it is termed *secretion* when its direction is from the interstitial fluid to the tubular lumen. The two terms denote the direction of the transport and have no implications as to the cellular basis of the transport. Transtubular transport is said to be *passive* when it can be accounted for on the basis of a *passive flux equation* (see below) and *active* when this equation does not account for the observed transport.

Principles of Transport. PASSIVE TRANS-PORT. The principles governing transport of solute across membranes, discussed fully in Chapters 1 and 43, will be briefly recapitulated here. The passive transport of a component of a solution across a membrane may result from one of two distinct types of motion. Movement of the whole solution through the membrane carries with it all specific components; this is termed *bulk flow*. Movement of the component through the solution lodged in the membrane and thus through the membrane itself is termed *diffusion*. Diffusion will occur regardless of whether the fluid in the membrane is moving or stationary. In general, both kinds of movement may exist, and the total movement of a component through the membrane is the sum of its bulk flow and its diffusion. Two factors are important in the diffusion term of the transport equation, the concentration gradient and the voltage gradient. To decide whether a specific substance is transported passively it is necessary to compare its transport quantitatively with that predicted by the equation derived below.

The bulk flow of a component in a solution is the product of the velocity of the solution with respect to the membrane and the concentration of the component in the solution. The *flux* in mols per sq. cm. per second due to bulk flow is given by the expression:

$$M_{bulk\ flow} = Cv$$

where v is the velocity. This equation is the same as $\dot{Q} = C\dot{V}$ given above since the integral of the flux over the total cross sectional area is the mass flow and the integral of the velocity over the total cross sectional area is the volume flow. The diffusion term generally includes the gradients of both concentration and voltage; these gradients will produce movement of the component through the solution as a whole. In one dimension, the gradient (grad) of a function may be defined as the rate of change of the function with distance. Movement through the solution is in the direction of the negative of the gradient (see Chap. 1).

Consider two different solutions of glucose separated by a membrane. Grad C is equal to $(C_1 - C_2)/\delta$, where δ is the thickness of the membrane. If the membrane is permeable to glucose, glucose will move from the side of higher concentration to the side of lower concentration, i.e., it will move down its gradient. The flux is given by the expression:

$$M = D\frac{C_2 - C_1}{\delta} = \frac{D}{\delta}(C_2 - C_1) = P(C_2 - C_1)$$

where D is the diffusion coefficient, and P the permeability. Permeability includes both the diffusivity within the membrane and the membrane thickness. In the same manner, if two identical solutions of NaCl are separated by a membrane which is permeable only to Na^+, and if a voltage gradient (grad ε) is impressed across the membrane by an external source, Na^+ will move down the voltage gradient. The flux of Na^+ will be from the side of higher electric potential to the side of lower electric potential. The magnitude of the flux will be proportional to the charge on the particle, to grad ε, and to the number of particles present which can move. The expression for net flux under these conditions is:

$$M = -D\frac{ZF}{RT}C\ grad\ \varepsilon$$

where Z is the charge of the particle, F is the Faraday, R is the universal gas constant and T is the absolute temperature. The diffusion term is the sum of the concentration and electrical terms:

$$M_{diffusion} = -D(grad\ C + \frac{ZF}{RT}C\ grad\ \varepsilon)$$

The total passive transport of a substance with respect to the membrane is the sum of the bulk flow and the diffusion terms.

$$M = -D(grad\ C + \frac{ZF}{RT}C\ grad\ \varepsilon) + Cv$$

In the steady state, when the volume flow is zero, this equation gives rise to the Ussing equation for passive transport. For a cation, this is:

$$\frac{M_{12}}{M_{21}} = \frac{C_1}{C_2}\exp\frac{ZF}{RT}(\varepsilon_1 - \varepsilon_2)$$

where M_{12} is the one-way flux from compartment 1 to compartment 2, and M_{21} is the reverse flux. At equilibrium, when the volume flow and net flux are both zero, the flux equation can be integrated to give the familiar Nernst equation, which for a cation is:

$$\varepsilon_1 - \varepsilon_2 = \frac{RT}{ZF}\log\frac{C_1}{C_2}$$

ACTIVE TRANSPORT. Transport is said to be active when, in addition to the passive terms, another term is required to describe it. Detectable active transport thus requires the combination of a pump that will move material across the membrane and relative impermeability that will prevent rapid diffusion of material back to the site from which it came. In the kidney, the transport of most physiologically important solutes is active. Specific examples include the reabsorption of Na^+ and glucose and the secretion of K^+ and PAH.

In some tissues (e.g., nerve, skeletal muscle and erythrocytes), the concentration gradient, the voltage gradient and the net flux can be measured; the experimental results can then be compared with a passive flux equation. However, in the kidney, this information is available for only a few solute species and only for a few conditions. When these data are available, the transtubular fluxes can be compared with the passive flux equation. When these data are unavailable, the decision that a substance is actively or passively transported must be based on indirect evidence. Fulfillment of four ancillary criteria provides strong presumptive evidence for active transport. These criteria are the demonstration of (i) a maximum rate of tubular transport, (ii) competition between similar molecular species, (iii) inhibition by metabolic inhibitors, and (iv) in certain cases, failure to vary in the expected manner with such variables as urine flow or pH.

The first two criteria imply a specific combination between the transported substance and the transport system at a limited number of sites. When all sites are occupied, a maximum rate of transport has been attained and further elevation of the plasma concentration of the material will not increase the rate of transport. If some sites are occupied with one molecular species, correspondingly fewer sites are available for transport of a similar compound handled by the same system. The third criterion implies that the transport requires energy derived from cellular metabolism. The fourth criterion is a portion of the definition given above of active transport. Glucose transport, for example, is not changed by wide variations in the rate of urine flow or the pH of urine. Reabsorption of urea, on the other hand, is closely related to the reabsorption of water, a finding that suggests that bulk flow may play a significant role.

Substances Passively Transported by the Kidney. Tubular transport of ammonia, of a group of organic acids and bases, of most or all of the filtered water, and of at least a portion of the filtered urea fit passive flux equations. In the case of weak acids or bases, the relative concentrations of the ionized and nonionized forms depend on the pH of the tubular fluid and on the dissociation constant of the substance. Each of the two forms must be treated separately, and the measured rate of excretion will be the sum of their individual rates of excretion. Chloride and bicarbonate are also transported passively; their tubular transport is determined by active sodium transport.

Substances Actively Transported by the Kidney. Substances transported actively are also influenced by passive effects, which in the kidney may be very large. Active transport systems in the kidney may be roughly divided into two classes, called for convenience types A and B. Whether the substance exhibits a transport maximum (Tm) is important in the dichotomy between types A and B.

CALCULATION OF TM. Tm is the maximum rate of tubular transport; it applies to reabsorption and secretion. By definition, a maximum can be determined only if the tubular cells can be presented with amounts greater than those they can transport. Tm is computed by comparing the amount excreted and the amount filtered during maximum transport, e.g., $\dot{Q}_g - \dot{Q}_u$. Tm is a positive quantity when there is net reabsorption and a negative quantity when there is net secretion. All of a reabsorbed substance, such as glucose, entering the tubule either must be transported or must appear in the urine. If the amount of glomerular filtration is determined from the inulin clearance, and if this amount is multiplied by the plasma concentration of glucose, the *quantity* of the substance entering the tubule per unit time (filtered load) is known. Subtracting from this the amount not transported—the amount appearing in the urine in the same unit time—tells how much passed through the tubular walls.

In conventional terms, the Tm of glucose is

$$Tm_G = C_{in}P_G - U_GV$$

or more simply

$$Tm_G = \dot{Q}_{g_G} - \dot{Q}_{u_G} = \dot{V}_g[G]_p - \dot{Q}_{u_G}$$

Then, $Tm_G = 350$ mg. per minute.

DEFINITION OF TYPE A AND TYPE B SYSTEMS. Tubular transport in a type A system exhibits a definite Tm and a sharp plateau; transport is relatively complete until the system is presented with more material than it can transport

(Tm is exceeded). Type B systems fail to transport material completely, even when the amounts presented to the cells are relatively small, and do not exhibit a sharp Tm within physiologically attainable ranges. Transport of glucose is a classic example of type A reabsorption, and transport of PAH of type A secretion. Na^+ transport is a classic example of type B reabsorption, and K^+ transport of type B secretion. In general, organic substances are processed in type A systems and ionic substances in type B systems. Transport of divalent ions is predominantly type A; transport of amino acids is intermediate.

The reasons for the differences in transport systems are not known. One way of visualizing the process is derived from enzyme kinetics and involves the following assumptions: (i) active transport requires a preliminary reaction between the transported material and some cellular element forming a precursor combination, (ii) a limited number of transport sites and hence a maximum rate of transport exists, (iii) the combination follows the law of mass action at low degrees of saturation of cellular elements, and (iv) the rate of transport is proportional to the amount of precursor formed.

The first and second assumptions imply a dissociation constant (K) for the combination of the cellular element and the transported material. The negative log of K would then be pK. When K is low (pK is high), the combination forms readily, and little material will escape transport until Tm is reached. Thus, when pK/Tm is high, transport will rise rapidly as a function of the amount of material presented to the cells until the filtered load ($\dot{Q}_g = \dot{V}_g \times C_p$) is about equal to Tm, and the plasma concentration will equilibrate in this region. In a system in which the ratio of pK/Tm is low (type B), transport will increase less rapidly as a function of load, and some material will always escape transport. Because of this latter factor, equilibration for a reabsorbed material will occur considerably below the maximum rate of transport in a type B system. Indeed, the maximum rate of transport may be so high as to be physiologically unattainable.

The relationship between the amount of material presented to the tubules per unit time and the amount transported in both type A and B systems is illustrated in Figure 6. Such graphs do not, however, indicate how urinary excretion varies as a function of plasma concentration for various systems. Two methods are commonly used to depict this relationship. The first is to superpose plots of the load presented to the cells, the amount of the material excreted, and the difference between the two, which represents the amount transported. All of these factors are presented as functions of the load. The second method is to plot the fraction of the filtered load excreted ($\dot{Q}_u/\dot{Q}_g$ = clearance ratio) as a function of the filtered load. Both of these plots are presented in Figures 7 and 8.

In a type A reabsorptive system, reabsorption is complete at low filtered loads, and there is no urinary excretion. The clearance ratio is therefore zero. As the load is increased above Tm, the increment in excretion is just equal to the increment in the load. At all plasma concentrations above that which produces a filtered load equal to Tm, the rate of excretion is given by the expression $\dot{Q}_u = \dot{Q}_g - Tm = C_p \times \dot{V}_g - Tm$. The clearance ratio also rises from zero and approaches 1 asymptotically.

Reabsorption in a type B system is never complete; some material is excreted even at the lowest filtered load. As the load is increased, reabsorption increases, but not at the same rate as the load. Thus excretion increases continuously. The clearance ratio starts at some value above zero and increases slowly and continuously toward 1. These relationships are illustrated in Figure 7.

Fig. 6. Distinction between type A and type B tubular transport.

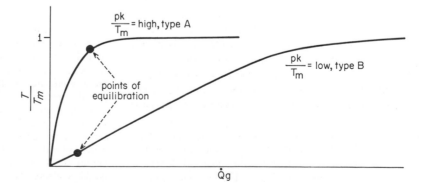

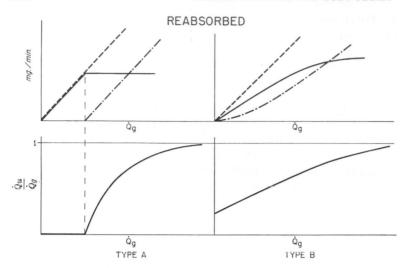

Fig. 7. Relationships between measures of tubular transport activity for a reabsorbed substance. *Upper graphs,* Dashed line, filtered load; solid line, tubular transport; dot-dashed line, excretion. *Lower graphs,* Clearance ratio as a function of filtered load.

In secretory systems, the material that appears in the urine is composed of two moieties, one which entered the lumen at the glomerulus and one which entered as a result of transtubular transport. The former, which is the filtered load, is always proportional to the plasma concentration (barring peculiarities in protein binding), whereas the latter depends on transport.

When the plasma concentration of a type A secreted material is low, all or a fixed fraction of the material which escapes glomerular filtration is transported. So long as the plasma concentration remains well below that resulting in Tm, the amount of solute contributed to the urine by both filtration and transport increases in proportion to the plasma concentration. In these circumstances, the clearance ratio remains constant and above 1. If the plasma concentration is such that the amount presented to the tubules is above Tm,* the amount secreted remains constant. Although the rate of excretion in urine still increases as the plasma concentration increases, the only cause for this greater excretion is the increase in the filtered load. Since the total excretion no longer increases at the same rate as the plasma concentration does, the clearance ratio falls. It declines asymptotically from its initial high value (which is characteristic for the substance) toward 1.

When a type B system is engaged in secretion, there is a continual decrease in the rate

*Remember that the amount presented to the tubules is equal to the amount which enters the kidney each minute, less the amount which is filtered at the glomerulus. The tubular load of PAH $= \dot{V}_p[PAH]_p - \dot{V}_g[PAH]_p = [PAH]_p(\dot{V}_p - \dot{V}_g)$.

at which excretion increases as tubular load increases. The clearance ratio thus falls throughout the whole range of plasma concentrations, approaching 1 as an asymptote. These relationships are illustrated in Figure 8.

Transport of Specific Substances. UREA.[36] Urea clearance ratios in mammals are always less than 1, indicating net reabsorption. The clearance ratio is a function of the rate of urine flow, being low (but not 0) for low values of flow and approaching 1 at very high values. This finding is largely responsible for the classic theory that urea is transported solely by passive diffusion. Reabsorption of luminal fluid elevates the intraluminal concentration and thus produces a concentration gradient between intraluminal and interstitial fluid. This concentration gradient is presumed to be the driving force for urea reabsorption. It is further presumed that renal epithelium is sparingly permeable to urea and that equilibration is never achieved. The disparity from equilibrium increases with increased urine flow, and thus the clearance ratio is increased as urine flow is elevated.

Urea is intimately involved in the production of concentrated urine. The maximum solute concentration that can be attained in urine increases with increasing urea concentration.[21] Although most solutes are concentrated in the interstitial fluid of the medulla (see the section on water), the ratio of the concentration in a medullary slice to the concentration in plasma is normally greater for urea than for any other solute. This ratio falls after protein deprivation and, concomitantly, the ability to produce a highly concentrated urine also decreases. In the presence of ADH, collecting duct membranes are freely permeable to urea and the concentration of urea in formed urine is the same as the concentration at the tip of the renal papillae. Although transfers of urea between medullary interstitial fluid and collecting ducts may be passive and may help to explain the high total solute concentration attainable in urine (because much of the solute is urea that could have entered the collecting duct passively as it passed through the medulla), the question remains, "how did the urea get so concentrated in the first place?"

Although diffusion undoubtedly plays a significant role in the tubular handling of urea, it is likely that active transport is also involved. The findings of Schmidt-Nielson[37] that the relationship between the rate of urine flow and the urea clearance ratio can be modified and that these modifications become manifest after protein deprivation; the demonstration of renal tubular secretion of urea in the bullfrog and other anurans;[8, 39] and the demonstration of active reabsorption in elasmobranchs;[39, 40] all indicate that a weak transport system might be involved.

GLUCOSE. Glucose transport was one of the first renal transport systems to be well delineated; the work was done by Shannon and Fisher.[38] Both stop-flow experiments and micropuncture studies[47, 50] indicate that glucose reabsorption occurs in the proximal tubule and normally proceeds there essentially to completion. Any glucose escaping reabsorption in this region is destined for excretion.

The maximum rate of transport is 375 mg. per minute ±80 mg. in men and slightly lower in women. Endocrine imbalances may alter Tm_G slightly, but, in the main, it is quite constant and depends only on the number of nephrons functioning. For this reason, measurement of Tm_G is sometimes used clinically to estimate the number of functioning nephrons.

This measurement is called "tubular reabsorptive capacity."

Several other monosaccharides, including fructose and galactose, are reabsorbed by systems which appear to share some element with glucose reabsorption. Xylose is reabsorbed wholly by the same system. The high xylose clearance ratio, the effective inhibition of xylose reabsorption by glucose, and the absence of a sharp Tm for xylose are all consistent with the assumption that the dissociation constant between xylose and the transport system is high (pK is low). The system appears to have a low value of pK/Tm for xylose and a high value for glucose. Hence, the system exhibits type A behavior for glucose and type B behavior for xylose.

If Tm_G is 375 mg. per minute and the filtration rate is 120 ml. per minute, one can compute the plasma concentration at which Tm_G is attained to be about 300 mg. glucose per 100 ml. of plasma. Since plasma glucose is normally under 100 mg. per 100 ml., one can predict that normal urine should be glucose-free and that the concentration of glucose in plasma is not normally controlled by the kidney.

Even though Tm_G is attained at plasma concentration of 300 mg. per 100 ml., some glucose appears in the urine when the plasma concentration is 200 mg. per 100 ml. This could be interpreted to suggest that glucose reabsorption exhibits characteristics intermediate between type A and type B systems. However, this apparently is not the case. Glucose reabsorption appears to be a very good type A system in each individual nephron. But there is statistical dispersion of both glomerular filtering capacity and tubular reabsorptive capacity. Thus, a nephron in which a "large" glomerulus is attached to a "small" proximal tubule reaches its individual Tm at a relatively low

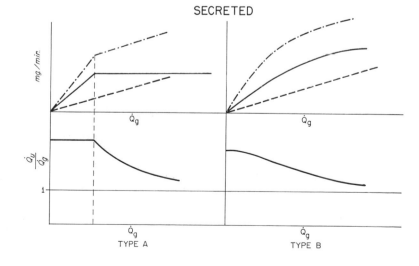

Fig. 8. Relationships between measures of tubular transport activity for a secreted substance. Symbols as in Figure 7.

plasma concentration. Conversely, if a "small" glomerulus is attached to a "large" proximal tubule, the nephron will not reach its Tm until relatively high plasma concentrations of glucose are reached. Recently, Oliver and associates have shown that the distribution of the ratio of glomerular activity to reabsorptive activity, which is calculated on the assumption that each individual nephron is a perfect type A system, agrees closely with distribution of sizes determined directly.[27]

PARA-AMINOHIPPURIC ACID. PAH is bound to plasma proteins; hence, its concentration is not the same in glomerular filtrate and in plasma. Instead, the concentration in the glomerular filtrate is the same as the concentration of unbound PAH in plasma water. In man, this value is taken to be 78 per cent of the total plasma concentration. So avid is the tubular transport system, or so rapid is the binding reaction, that tubular cells remove essentially all of the PAH—both bound and unbound— from the blood perfusing them, so long as the amount presented per minute is less than Tm. This secretory system, like the glucose reabsorptive system, is located in the very first portion of the nephron.[22, 32]

The Tm of PAH is 80 mg. per minute ±17 mg. in men and somewhat lower in women. The value is quite constant and is the basis for another clinical test of tubular functions that is similar to the use of Tm_G. Tm_{PAH} is considered an estimate of "tubular secretory capacity."

A large number of other compounds are transported by the same system. All are aromatic organic acids, the most important being penicillin. Before supplies of penicillin became plentiful, considerable effort was expended in attempting to inhibit this system. It was found that the transport involves two steps. The first is a specific combination with a "carrier" molecule; the second is transport of the resulting complex. Chemical reactions leading to the decomposition and release of the acid occur at the luminal border. Tubular secretion is competitively inhibited either by a compound which combines well with the carrier but which is transported only slowly, or, better, by a compound which combines well with the carrier but which cannot undergo the biochemical transformation necessary for decomposition. Probenecid (Benemid), which falls in the latter class, was developed as a result of these investigations. Penicillin is now cheaper than probenecid, and the original purpose of the drug is largely forgotten. However, it also inhibits the renal reabsorption of uric acid and is now widely used in the treatment of chronic gout.

SODIUM. Reabsorption of Na+ is involved with the transport of several other ions, being comprised of reabsorption in association with Cl- and HCO_3^- and reabsorption in exchange for H+ and K+. The preservation of charge neutrality requires the reabsorption of an anion or the secretion of a cation for each Na+ reabsorbed.* Hence, Na+ reabsorption is the sum of these ancillary ion transports. The transports of Cl-, HCO_3^-, H+ and K+ are discussed separately here.

Our knowledge of Na+ transport can be summarized in three statements: (i) Reabsorption of Na+ exhibits type B kinetics. (ii) Na+ are actively transported. (iii) The ancillary ion fluxes, anion reabsorption and cation secretion are capable of homeostatic modification.

Functional characteristics of Na+ reabsorption. Na+ reabsorption depends on the rate at which Na+ is filtered. Either an increase in the plasma Na+ concentration when the filtration rate is held constant, or an increase in the filtration rate when the plasma concentration is held constant, produces an increase in the rate of reabsorption. Neither of these functional relationships is well known. Probably, when all else is held constant, reabsorption is proportional to the filtration rate so that, as the filtration rate increases, reabsorption increases and the percentage of the filtered load which is reabsorbed remains constant. When the concentration of Na+ in plasma is increased, reabsorption increases less than proportionately and the percentage of the filtered load reabsorbed falls. However, concentrations of other ions in plasma may have an effect as well as other less well determined factors.

Active transport of Na+.[10] The conditions under which Na+ transport occurs indicate that it is active. Most of the filtered Na+ is reabsorbed in the proximal tubule. This region of the nephron is freely permeable to water. As Na+ and an associated anion are reabsorbed, water is reabsorbed in osmotically equivalent quantities. The mol fractions of both water and Na+ in proximal tubular fluid normally remain at the values found in plasma.[47] The inside of the

---

*The reabsorption of as little as one part in 1000 of the filtered Na+ without associated anion reabsorption or cation secretion would produce an increase in the potential across the tubular cell of at least 1 V. per minute. This is 30 to 50 times the steady state potential.

tubular cell is about 70 mV. negative to the interstitial fluid and about 50 mV. negative to the luminal fluid.[9] Hence, there is a transcellular potential difference of about 20 mV. across proximal tubular cells, with tubular fluid negative to peritubular blood. Since we know the concentrations of Na^+ in the fluids on either side of the tubular cell and the electric potential across the cell, we can compute the passive flux of cations. Normally the concentration gradient is zero and the voltage gradient is the only passive force present. The net passive flux, then, is in the direction of the negative of the gradient, i.e., from a region of high potential to a region of low potential. Were this the only force present, there would be net tubular secretion of cations. Inasmuch as Na^+ is reabsorbed, another force must act upon the ion. This force, which opposes the voltage gradient and produces Na^+ reabsorption, is active Na^+ transport.

The active transport step might be located at either of the two membranes of the tubular cell. From analysis of transcellular potential and concentration differences, no statement can be made about which membrane contains the active step. However, intracellular Na^+ concentration in several species has been estimated to range from 30 to 70 mM. per liter of cell water. Thus, as Na^+ passes from tubular lumen to cell fluid, it moves down a concentration gradient (from 150 mM. per liter to 70mM. per liter or lower) and down a voltage gradient (from -20 mV. to -70 mV. with respect to blood). Both the voltage and concentration gradients predict passive movement in the direction of the observed transport and no pump need be postulated at the luminal membrane. As Na^+ moves from cell fluid to blood, however, it moves up both a concentration gradient (from 70 mM. per liter or lower to 150 mM. per liter) and a voltage gradient (from -70 mV. to 0 mV.). Active transport is required for this step.

Sodium–potassium pump.[11] Considerable data have accumulated which indicate that plasma K^+ is involved in the transport of Na^+ across the renal cell. Digitalis compounds inhibit coupled $Na^+–K^+$ pumps. Apparently, they compete with K^+ for the transport system. Such compounds inhibit renal Na^+ transport and elevation of plasma K^+ antagonizes this inhibition. In fact, under certain conditions, elevation of plasma K^+ alone can enhance Na^+

reabsorption. These findings all suggest that the Na^+ pump in mammalian kidney is similar to that described previously for frog skin and that Na^+ transport takes place in a similar manner in these two tissues (see Chap. 43).

In the proximal tubule, the interstitial membrane is asumed to be freely permeable to K^+ and Cl^-, but not to Na^+. Na^+ is pumped across this membrane. The luminal border is permeable to Na^+ and Cl^-, but only poorly permeable to K^+. Reabsorption of Na^+ entails concurrent movement of Cl^-. The initial process is the active exchange wherein Na^+ is extruded from the cell and K^+ is taken up. As a consequence, the intracellular concentration of Na^+ is lowered and that of K^+ is raised. The concentration gradient of Na^+ between the luminal and the cell fluid increases, and Na^+ enters the cell from the lumen. As Na^+ crosses the luminal membrane, the resulting change in the voltage across the membrane drives Cl^- into the cell. The entering Na^+ replaces the Na^+ that has been pumped out, while the entering Cl^- elevates cellular Cl^-. Now the cellular concentrations of K^+ and Cl^- are both higher than they were. Both ions diffuse across the interstitial membrane. The over-all reaction is the reabsorption of one Na^+ and one Cl^-. No net transport of K^+ takes place, this ion simply plays the role of a catalyst. Since the active transport step is electrically neutral, the membrane voltages arise from differences in the passive permeabilities of the ions involved. Figure 9*A* illustrates this mechanism in the proximal tubule. HCO_3^- could be reabsorbed by this mechanism too, but is not known to be.

In the distal tubule, the permeability of the luminal membrane to Cl^- is assumed to be very low.

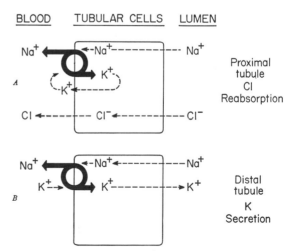

Fig. 9. *A*, Proposed mechanism by which a coupled $Na^+–K^+$ pump in proximal tubular cells causes Na^+ reabsorption with associated anion reabsorption. *B*, Proposed mechanism by which a similar pump in the distal tubular cells causes Na^+ reabsorption with associated K^+ secretion.

Chloride is probably pumped across this membrane (see below). Not all of the Na^+ that enters the cell from the lumen is accompanied by Cl^-, for the amount of Cl^- reabsorbed is presumably regulated by the magnitude of active Cl^- transport. The rest of distal Na^+ reabsorption is balanced by the secretion of cations, either K^+ or H^+. If we look only at K^+ secretion for a moment, the events ocurring in the distal tubular cell can be explained as follows: An exchange of Na^+ for K^+ takes place actively at the interstitial membrane and passively at the luminal membrane. H^+ secretion, either in the distal tubule or the collecting duct probably takes place in a similar manner. Figure 9B illustrates the action of this mechanism in the distal tubule.

Regulation of the ancillary fluxes is discussed under the individual ions involved.

CHLORIDE. Cl^- is reabsorbed in both the proximal and distal tubules, but primarily in the proximal tubule, where it is accounted for by passive forces. The transcellular potential across the proximal tubular cells is about 20 mV., the lumen negative to the plasma. So long as the concentration of Cl^- in tubular fluid is greater than 0.55 that of plasma, net reabsorption would be expected. More cogently, when single proximal tubules are held in the short circuit state, the current produced matches the Na^+ transport.[12] This strongly suggests that active transport of ions other than Na^+ is not appreciable.*

Conditions are different in the distal tubule. The transcellular potential averages about 60 mV., the lumen negative to the plasma. Thus, net reabsorption of Cl^- might be passive as long as the concentration of Cl^- in distal tubular fluid is greater than 0.1 that in plasma. However, Rector and Clapp[33] showed that, under the same conditions in which the transcellular potential averaged 60 mV., the average tubular fluid-to-plasma ratio of Cl^- concentrations was less than 0.05 and was occasionally as low as 0.001. Active transport of Cl^- must be present in the distal tubule.

Homer Smith[39] postulated two distinct processes for Na^+ and Cl^- reabsorption: (i) a

*Of course, other active transport is present. However, on a molar basis, the transport of organic acids, for example, is minute when compared to the transport of Na^+ and the current produced from such transport would not be noticed experimentally. Eighty per cent of the Na^+ is reabsorbed in association with Cl^-. If Cl^- were transported actively, one would expect the short circuit current to be considerably less than the isotopically determined Na^+ flux.

proximal process capable of transporting large amounts of solute, but incapable of producing any marked concentration gradients, and (ii) a distal process, of limited capacity, capable of producing and maintaining striking concentration gradients in either direction. The recent stop-flow experiments appear to support this view in that two regions of Na^+ and Cl^- transport have been found.[18, 32] A proximal region is sensitive to diuretic agents but does not lower luminal concentration. A distal region, on the other hand, lowers the concentration markedly but fails to respond to diuretic agents. The presence of an active transport system for Cl^- provides an explanation for these findings.

BICARBONATE.[13] Reabsorption of HCO_3^- begins in the early part of the proximal tubule and normally continues in the collecting duct. The reabsorption depends on the filtered load, as in type B systems. The amount of HCO_3^- reabsorbed also varies in proportion to the CO_2 tension of plasma. At a CO_2 tension of 1.25 mEq. per liter of plasma (37 mm . Hg), about 25 mEq. of HCO_3^- are reabsorbed per liter of glomerular filtrate. Prolonged respiratory acidosis enhances the effect of CO_2.[42]

About 20 per cent of the filtered Na^+ is reabsorbed with HCO_3^-. In the collecting duct, any HCO_3^- still present is reabsorbed as the result of H^+ secretion. Luminal HCO_3^- combines with the secreted H^+ to form H_2CO_3, which decomposes to form CO_2 and water. The CO_2 diffuses across the tubular cells to the peritubular blood; the water enters the tubular lumen.* The reaction results in the net reabsorption of Na^+ and HCO_3^-. It is not known how HCO_3^- is reabsorbed proximally. Two possibilities may be mentioned. H^+ secretion might extend throughout the proximal tubule, and proximal reabsorption might be secondary to H^+ secretion, just as distal reabsorption is. Alternatively, proximal HCO_3^- reabsorption might occur secondary to Na^+ reabsorption in the same manner as reabsorption of Cl^- does. Although the evidence is inadequate for differentiation of these possibilities, the former hypothesis is generally assumed to be correct.

The CO_2 tension is usually higher in urine than in plasma; but, when plasma HCO_3^- is low, urinary CO_2

*The amount of water secreted is minute. If all the filtered HCO_3^- is reabsorbed via H^+ secretion, about 0.04 ml. of water will be added to the luminal contents each minute.

tension may be lover than in plasma.[6] Low urinary CO_2 tension probably exists when HCO_3^- reabsorption is completed before the fluid leaves the proximal tubule—a reflection, but probably not a measure, of proximal reabsorption of HCO_3^-. Probably, urinary CO_2 tension is high when the distal H^+ secretory system is involved in HCO_3^- reabsorption. High urinary CO_2 tension reflects, and probably is a crude measure of, distal reabsorption of HCO_3^-.

HYDROGEN.[30] Pitts and Alexander's demonstration[31] in 1945 that H^+ is secreted into the renal tubule was a milestone for two reasons. First, it provided convincing evidence that physiologically important solutes are secreted by the renal tubule. Previously, secretion of only nonphysiologic organic dyes had been proved. The experiments of Pitts and Alexander indicated that tubular secretion is important in the control of normal body constituents. The second important facet of their experiments is that they indicated a fruitful approach to the analysis of electrolyte excretion (and of type B excretion in general). It is necessary to compare the quantities excreted and filtered rather than to compare clearances.

H^+ is secreted into the distal portion of the nephron in an exchange in which Na^+ is reabsorbed from the lumen and H^+ is secreted into it. Much of this exchange may take place in the collecting duct,[44] but it may also occur in the distal tubule. There is no sharply defined maximum rate, since the rate at which the ion exchange proceeds depends on the simultaneous availability of luminal Na^+ and cellular H^+. Thus, the rate of H^+ secretion tends to be increased both by an increase in the rate of Na^+ excretion (i.e., an increase in the rate at which Na^+ is presented to the distal tubular cells) and by an increase in the amount of cellular H^+ available to the transport mechanism.

Secretion of H^+ has three consequences: (i) it causes the reabsorption of filtered HCO_3^-; (ii) it acidifies the urine; and (iii) it is directly responsible for the secretion of NH_4^+. In the proximal tubule, H^+ secretion, if present, gives rise only to HCO_3^- reabsorption, as discussed earlier. Distally, when the reabsorption of HCO_3^- has been completed, additional secretion of H^+ leads to an acid urine. The transport systems appear to work with decreasing efficiency as the gradient of H^+ concentration is increased, and secretion comes to a halt when the ratio of H^+ across the cell membrane is about 400.

(The minimum urinary pH is about 4.4. If the pH of the tubular cell is about 7.0, the ratio of H^+ between the two solutions is $10^{2.6} = 400$.) The total amount of titratable acid that can be secreted therefore depends on the buffer capacity of urine. If the urine is highly buffered, large amounts of H^+ can be added to it without producing large changes in urinary pH. Conversely, when the buffer capacity is very low, only small amounts of H^+ can be added before urinary pH falls to such a low level that H^+ transport is reduced.

AMMONIA.[28] NH_3 is formed by the deamination of amino acids by the cells of the distal tubule or of the collecting duct. Ullrich *et al.*[45] have presented evidence that the site is the collecting duct. The luminal membrane is freely permeable to NH_3, and it diffuses into the tubular lumen. Here, the free base ionizes and produces its conjugate acid, NH_4^+. The tubular epithelium is only slightly permeable to NH_4^+, and most of this acid is therefore trapped in the lumen and destined for excretion. The relative concentrations of NH_3 and NH_4^+ in luminal fluid can be determined by solving the equilibrium equation $[NH_3] [H^+]/[NH_4^+] = K$, where K has the value of $10^{-9.3}$. Some of the NH_4^+ formed in the tubular lumen subsequently diffuses back into epithelial cells as a result of the concentration gradient of this ion, but the amount of this diffusion is probably small. The rate of ammonia excretion is the product of the urine flow and the concentration of NH_4^+ (the concentration of NH_3 is so low that it can be neglected). The major variables determining this concentration are the urinary pH and the rate at which NH_3 is produced by renal cells. The diffusion of NH_3 into the tubular lumen uses up H^+ and tends to keep the luminal pH from falling as rapidly as it would if NH_3 were not produced. Consequently, the secretion of NH_3 allows H^+ secretion to continue, and the continuance of H^+ secretion allows still more NH_4^+ to be excreted.

The secretion of each H^+ leaves a HCO_3^- within the tubular cell and also brings into the cell a Na^+. The Na^+ is transported out of the cell into the peritubular blood in association with the HCO_3^-. Thus, the secretion of each H^+, whether involved in reabsorption of HCO_3^-, urinary acidification or NH_4^+ excretion, results in the return of Na^+ and HCO_3^- to peritubular blood. When titratable acid and NH_4^+ are being excreted, renal venous blood

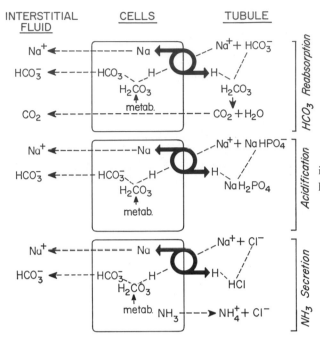

Fig. 10. Summary of effects of distal hydrogen ion exchange. Broken lines indicate passive transport; solid lines, active transport.

contains not only all the HCO_3^- that entered the kidney (for reabsorption of HCO_3^- is complete in this condition), but an additional amount of HCO_3^- equal to the amounts of titratable acid and NH_4^+ that have been excreted. These relationships are illustrated in Figure 10.

POTASSIUM.[4]   The clearance ratio of K^+ is normally less than 1, a fact demonstrating that K^+ is reabsorbed. In 1948, Berliner and Kennedy[1] and Mudge *et al.*[25] simultaneously reported that the clearance ratio of K^+ could exceed 1 and that tubular secretion, as well as tubular reabsorption, takes place. Reabsorption occurs in the proximal and secretion in the distal tubule. Almost all of the filtered K^+ is reabsorbed and almost all of the K^+ which appears in the urine enters the tubule via the secretory process.[3, 19] The secretory system has the important regulatory role. This system is an ion exchange in which luminal Na^+ is reabsorbed and interstitial K^+ is secreted.[2] The transport system is type B, the rate depending on the availability of both luminal Na^+ and cellular K^+. Although cellular K^+ is important in determining the rate of secretion, the K^+ must eventually come from the blood perfusing the cells. An equal amount of Na^+ is reabsorbed when K^+ is secreted, but this amounts only to about 1 per cent of the filtered Na^+. Thus, secretion of K^+ is important in the regulation of body

K^+, but is insignificant in the regulation of body Na^+.

Although the exact mechanisms are unknown, K^+ reabsorption takes place in the proximal tubule. Under suitable conditions, the phenomenon occurs even though the plasma K^+ concentration may be higher than the K^+ concentration in the proximal tubular fluid. Thus, since K^+ reabsorption can take place against both a concentration gradient and a voltage gradient (of 20 mV.; see section on Na^+),[5] an active process must be present. The distal tubular secretion probably also contains an active step since (i) it is inhibited by metabolic inhibitors,[26] (ii) it is independent of the rate of urine flow,[19] (iii) a maximum rate of transport has been observed in the chicken,[29] and (iv) it is homeostatic in nature. The process is an exchange of luminal Na^+ for cellular or interstitial K^+. Since the postulated mechanism for Na^+ involves such an ion exchange, since the agents which decrease Na^+ reabsorption also decrease K^+ secretion (as long as they do not produce a large change in the excretion of HCO_3^-), and since the conditions which favor Na^+ reabsorption while interdicting anion reabsorption also favor K^+ secretion, it seems likely that K^+ secretion in the distal tubule is accomplished by the mechanism which accomplishes the reabsorption of Na^+ in the proximal tubule.

WATER.[14] Most of the water filtered from the plasma in the glomeruli is reabsorbed in the tubules; only 1 to 2 per cent of the amount filtered is normally excreted in the urine. Both urine flow and the concentration of solute particles in the urine may vary widely; the rate of urine flow may be less than 1 per cent or more than 50 per cent of the rate of glomerular filtration, and the concentration of solute may vary from almost zero to three or four times the concentration in the glomerular filtrate.

The concentration of solute in the urine depends both on the concentration of antidiuretic hormone (ADH) in the plasma perfusing the kidney and on the rate of urine flow. ADH synthesis in the hypothalamus, its passage from the hypothalamus to the hypophysis, and its release into the blood stream are discussed in Chapter 57.

When plasma entering the kidney contains a high concentration of ADH, the solute concentration is higher in the urine than in plasma; urine is *hypertonic* to plasma. When little or no ADH enters the kidney, the concentration of solute is much lower in the urine than in plasma; urine is *hypotonic* to plasma. The rate at which ADH is released depends on the solute concentration in circulating plasma. If the concentration is high, the hypophysis releases ADH into the blood. When the hormone reaches the kidney, water reabsorption is promoted and the urine becomes hypertonic. The water returned to the body reduces the concentration of the solute in body fluids. Conversely, if the concentration of solute in plasma is low, ADH is not released. In these circumstances, hypotonic urine is excreted, and large amounts of water are lost from the body. This loss tends to concentrate body fluids.

Within the limits set by the concentration of ADH in the plasma entering the kidney, the concentration of solute in the formed urine depends on the rate of urine flow. At low rates of flow, solute concentration is relatively high; it decreases progressively as urine flow increases. Urinary concentration of solute as a function of both rate of urinary flow and release of ADH is depicted in Figure 11.

During the past 13 years, evidence has accumulated which largely explains the diluting and concentrating ability of the kidney. This explanation, termed the *renal medullary countercurrent theory*, postulates an active process that probably occurs in the ascending limb of the thin segment. Although the process is not well understood, it is clear that something is actively transported in this region. As a consequence, the recent findings on solute concentrations in different regions of the kidney (to be detailed below) and the older data on the concentration and dilution of urine all fit into a single unified theory.

The most important findings which gave rise to the countercurrent theory are as follows: (i) The mol fraction of solute is higher in slices of kidney taken from the medulla than in slices taken from the cortex. The deeper the site in the medulla from which the sample is derived, the higher the mol fraction of the solute.[46] When ADH is present in adequate amounts, the solute concentration of the formed urine approximates that at the tip of the renal papillae. During water diuresis, when ADH is absent, the solute concentrations of the papillary tips and formed urine are disparate.[49] These findings are shown in Figure 12.

(ii) Fluid can be collected from certain portions of the nephron by inserting small glass pipettes into individual tubules. Fluid collected from proximal tubules is always isotonic to systemic plasma. Fluid collected from the turn in the thin segment, at the tip of the papilla, is always hypertonic to systemic plasma, but of the same solute concentration as blood collected from blood vessels in that region and as papillary slices. Fluid collected from the proximal portion of the distal tubule is always hypotonic to systemic plasma. When ADH is present, the fluid in the distal portions of the distal tubule is isotonic to systemic plasma. In the collecting duct, the solute concentration of tubular fluid

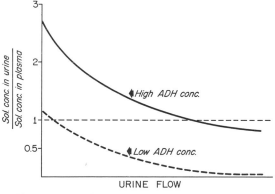

Fig. 11. Relationship between urine flow and the ratio of urinary to plasma solute concentration. *Solid line*, Dehydration; *dashed line,* hydration.

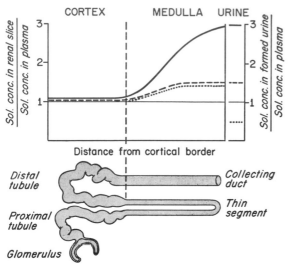

Fig. 12. Solute concentration in slices of kidney as a function of depth of juxtamedullary nephron is also shown to indicate structures present at each level. Concentrations are shown for three conditions: low urine flow with adequate ADH (*solid line*), high urine flow with adequate ADH (*dashed line*), and high urine flow with inadequate ADH (*dotted line*). It should be remembered that a renal slice contains both tubular contents and interstitial fluid. (Data from Ullrich and Jarausch, *Pflügers Arch. ges. Physiol.*, 1956, *262*:537–550, and Ullrich, Drenckhahn and Jarausch, *Pflügers Arch. ges. Physiol.*, 1955, *261*:62–77.)

continues to rise and the urine formed is hypertonic to systemic plasma. When ADH is not present, the solute concentration of the already dilute tubular fluid decreases as it passes through the distal tubule and the collecting duct. Thus, the urine formed is dilute. The solute concentration of luminal fluid as a function of distance along the distal tubule is depicted in Figure 13.

(iii) ADH increases the permeability of frog skin to water and to urea.[20, 34] The hormone has been shown to increase the permeability of mammalian collecting duct cells to urea.[18] From these and the functional data, ADH can safely be assumed to increase the permeability of distal tubular and collecting duct cells primarily to water and, to a limited extent, to solute materials.

The theory which fits these data together can be expressed as follows: In the proximal tubule, considerable solute reabsorption takes place. The membranes of the proximal tubular cells are freely permeable to water and, as this solute reabsorption occurs, an osmotically equivalent

amount of water is reabsorbed. Since the water permeability is high, no appreciable gradient of water concentration develops across proximal tubular cells. The fluid then enters the descending limb of the thin segment and progresses down through the renal medulla. As the fluid descends deeper into the medulla, the interstitial fluid opposite the tubular fluid has an increasingly high solute concentration. This portion of the nephron is also permeable, either to water or to solute materials, for, at the tip of the papillae, the solute concentration of tubular fluid is the same as that of the surrounding interstitial fluid but considerably higher than that of systemic plasma. As the fluid traverses the ascending portion of the thin limb, conditions change. Here, the membranes of the tubular cells are impermeable to water. In this region, an active transport process is present. Either solute is transported out of the tubular fluid into the medullary interstitium or, less likely, water is transported out of the interstitial fluid into the tubular fluid. Regardless of the exact process, the solute concentration of the tubular fluid is reduced and that of the medullary interstitial fluid is increased. Tubular fluid enters the early portion of the distal tubule hypotonic to systemic plasma. In the absence of ADH, neither the distal tubule nor the collecting duct is very permeable to water and most of the fluid that enters the distal tubule is destined for excretion. Indeed, under these conditions, which are those of a water diuresis, the solute concentration of the formed urine may be even lower than the solute concentration of the fluid entering the distal tubule. This is a reflection of the continuing reabsorption of solute in the latter portions of the nephron.[16] When

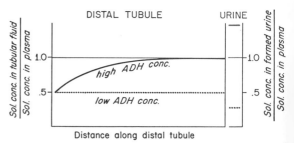

Fig. 13. Solute concentration of tubular fluid as a function of length along the distal tubule, when adequate amounts of ADH are present (*solid line*) and during water diuresis (*dotted line*). (Data from Wirz, *Helv. physiol. acta*, 1956, *14*:353–362, and Gottschalk and Mylle, *Amer. J. Physiol.*, 1959, *196*:927–936.)

ADH is present, the permeability of the latter portions of the nephron to water is great. On entering the distal tubule, water is immediately reabsorbed into the cortical interstitial fluid. Normally, in the first half of the distal tubule, sufficient water has been reabsorbed to bring the tubular fluid into osmotic equilibrium with cortical interstitial fluid, which has, of course, the same solute concentration as systemic plasma. This tubular fluid then enters the collecting duct and passes through the renal medulla once more. As when going through the descending limb of the thin segment, water passes out of the collecting duct into the concentrated interstitial fluid, producing a concentrated urine.

Collecting duct fluid equilibrates with the interstitial fluid at each level of the medulla and the final solute concentration of the formed urine is the same as that of the interstitial fluid at the tips of the papillae. Thus, water without an equivalent amount of solute is lost from both the descending limb of the thin segment and the collecting duct. This water enters the medullary interstitium. Solute without water is lost from the ascending limb of the thin segment. Both this solute and water must leave the medullary interstitial compartment via the blood vessels which perfuse this region. Considerable water without equivalent solute is also lost from the distal tubule. Here, however, the fluid enters the cortical interstitial compartment, is rapidly carried away by the rich cortical blood supply, and does not affect the balance of solute and water transport taking place in the medulla. Figure 14, showing the solute concentration of the tubular fluid and the interstitial fluid outside the tubule as a function of distance along the tubule for a straightened-out

nephron, depicts the transcellular water gradient. One can see that the solute-free water reabsorption that occurs in the early distal tubule in the descending limb of the thin segment, and in the collecting duct, would be expected on the basis of permeability of these membranes to water, but the production of a hypotonic tubular fluid in the ascending limb of the thin segment requires an active transport process.

Two questions remain to be answered: (i) What is the nature of the active process involved? Active transport of Na+ out of the ascending limb is probably involved, but there may be other active processes also. The findings that normal urea concentrations are required for normal concentrating ability and that urea normally is concentrated in the medulla, to a greater extent than any other solute, point to a unique role for this substance. High concentrations of a solute other than Na+ and Cl− must be present in the interstitial fluid to permit balancing of solute and water transport into and out of the medulla. (ii) Why does the blood flowing through the medulla not wash all the extra solute away (or supply sufficient water to bring the solute concentration down to isotonic levels)? The answer to this question comes out of the peculiar geometric arrangement of the blood vessels in this region. These vessels, termed the *vasa recta*, are long and straight and dive deeply into the medulla, take a sharp hairpin turn, and return. Indeed, all of the tubular structures tend to be packed tightly together so that ascending and descending tubes are in intimate contact. As the blood passes through the descending portions of the vasa recta, it loses water to the medullary interstitial fluid or gains solute material from it or both. As the blood later traverses the ascending portions of the vasa

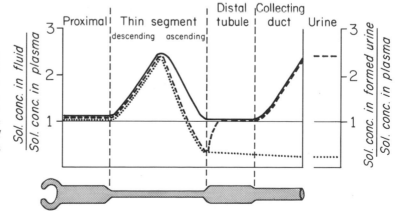

Fig. 14. Solute concentration in tubular fluid and in interstitial fluid opposite the tubule as a function of length along the nephron. Interstitial fluid outside the nephron (*solid line*); tubular fluid in the presence of adequate ADH (*dashed line*) and during water diuresis (*dotted line*).

recta, passing through regions where the solute concentration progressively decreases, it regains the fluid it lost on the way down. In addition, the solute and water that have entered the medulla from the nephron are also picked up. This is a true countercurrent exchange system; as such, it minimizes the amount of water and solute transfer that can take place for a given blood flow.

Finally, one can see how the theory described here accounts for the observed relationship between urine flow and solute concentration (Fig. 11). In the steady state, the amount of water that enters the medullary interstitial compartment must equal the amount removed per unit time. The rate of fluid leaving the medulla is determined by the active solute transport process but, for present purposes, can be considered as constant. The rate that water enters the medulla from the collecting duct is that which produces osmotic equilibrium at each level in the duct. If the volume flow through a section of the collecting duct is doubled while the interstitial concentration remains the same, twice as much fluid leaves that section to enter the interstitial compartment. Hence, if the volume flow entering the collecting duct is increased, more water enters the medullary interstitium for a time than leaves it. This lowers the solute concentration of the interstitial fluid and the solute concentration of urine produced is correspondingly lowered. The concentration–urine flow relation illustrated in Figure 11 is a reflection of the progressive dilution of the medullary interstitium with increasing volume flow entering the collecting duct.

INTEGRATION OF TUBULAR FUNCTIONS

As the glomerular filtrate enters the proximal tubule, transtubular transport of solute and water begins. Reabsorption of glucose and amino acids and the secretion of PAH occur only in this region of the tubule; the amounts of these substances leaving this region of the nephron are the amounts destined for excretion. As a result of the active transport of Na^+, both Cl^- and HCO_3^- are reabsorbed. About 90 per cent of the filtered Na^+ is reabsorbed by active transport in the proximal tubule. This process is responsible for most of the reabsorption of Cl^- and, usually, for about half the reabsorption of HCO_3^-. Most of the filtered K^+ is reabsorbed. The proximal tubule is freely permeable to water, and, as solute is reabsorbed, water is reabsorbed at an equivalent rate. The solute concentration in the luminal fluid leaving the proximal tubule is the same as that of systemic blood, but the volume flow has been reduced to about 10 per cent of the filtration rate.

The tubular fluid then enters the thin segment, which dips into the medulla. In the ascending limb of the loop of Henle, the tubular fluid is diluted and, concomitantly, medullary interstitial fluid is concentrated.

In the distal tubule and collecting duct, cation exchanges predominate. Luminal Na^+ is reabsorbed in exchange for both H^+ and K^+. Secretion of H^+ here normally accounts for about 9 per cent and secretion of K^+ for about 1 per cent of the total Na^+ reabsorption. Almost all of the K^+ appearing in the urine enters the lumen in the distal tubule via the secretory process. The distal secretion of H^+ brings about additional reabsorption of HCO_3^-. When the amount of HCO_3^- entering the distal tubule from the thin segment is large, the whole H^+ secretory system may be involved in reabsorption of HCO_3^-. When the amount of entering HCO_3^- is small, more H^+ is secreted per minute than is necessary to complete HCO_3^- reabsorption. The secretion of additional H^+ renders the tubular fluid acid. As the pH of luminal fluid falls, NH_3, which is produced in distal tubular cells, diffuses across the cell membrane into the tubular fluid. There, most of the NH_3 is converted into the conjugate acid, NH_4^+. K^+ secretion probably takes place in the distal tubule, whereas H^+ and NH_3 secretion probably occur in the collecting duct.

The distal tubule is permeable to water in the presence of ADH. When this hormone is present, the dilute tubular fluid entering the distal tubule rapidly loses water to the cortical interstitial compartment. Under these conditions, fluid leaving the distal tubule has a solute concentration the same as that of systemic blood. In the absence of ADH, water reabsorption does not occur, and the volume of fluid flowing out of the distal tubule is approximately the same as the volume flowing into it.

Upon leaving the distal tubule, the fluid enters the collecting ducts. These ducts traverse the medulla. When ADH is present, the epithelium of this region is permeable to water, which is abstracted from tubular fluid so that the urine is concentrated. The final concentration is approximately the same as that at the tip of the renal papillae. When ADH is not present, the collecting ducts act only as conduits, and the volume flow that enters is substantially identical to the urinary flow.

REGULATION OF PLASMA COMPOSITION

The kidney has so far been viewed as a machine with a set of transport properties built into it. The end result of these properties is that renal function maintains body composition rather constant. It is of some interest to look at the manner in which this control of body composition takes place. A dominant principle in the renal control of plasma composition is the *high turnover of plasma through the kidney*. In the normal man, with an extracellular space of about 15 liters and a filtration rate of 100 ml. per minute, half of the extracellular fluid in the body is filtered every 90 minutes. To see the effect of this high turnover rate, suppose the tubular reabsorption of sulfate was decreased by 10 per cent one morning. Sulfate would be excreted in the urine until the plasma sulfate concentration reached a new equilibrium level. This would be at 90 per cent of the original concentration. The concentration of sulfate would drop halfway toward its new level within two hours, and by eight hours, the end of a normal working day, the concentration would be essentially at its new equilibrium value. On the other hand, if the tubular reabsorption were to increase, urinary excretion would fall and plasma sulfate concentration would increase as sulfate and protein sulfhydryl were taken into the body. Little or no sulfate would be excreted until the plasma concentration had reached its new equilibrium value. Here, the time course would be determined, not by the characteristics of the kidney, but by the rate at which sulfate is taken into the body and produced from protein mercaptan.

Two other principles—*over-all body balance* and *glomerulotubular balance*—are involved in the control of body balance by the kidney. According to the first principle—that of over-all body balance—a person excretes material at the same rate at which it is taken in, over a long period. Although this is simply a statement of steady state conditions, it suggests the existence of both a method for sensing changes in net balance and a mechanism for modifying renal characteristics. These mechanisms are fairly well known for total solute concentration.

Changes in total solute concentration are detected by an osmoreceptor which in turn modifies the release of ADH. Changes in the level of circulating ADH then modify the renal characteristics in such a way that either a concentrated or a dilute urine may be excreted.

The control system for salt is less well worked out, but it has long been realized that some such mechanism for the maintenance of body volume must be present. Since osmolarity is controlled and since the dominant solute in the extracellular fluid is Na^+ with its associated anion, control of the total amount of Na^+ in the extracellular compartment along with control of osmolarity would act to control extracellular fluid volume. Conversely, control of extracellular volume, along with control of osmolarity would act to control the total amount of Na^+ in the extracellular fluid compartment. The present feeling is that the most significant control is probably around a correlate of volume, such as pressure in one or more specific sites. Although poorly understood at this time, the over-all balance exhibited by the body fluids assures us that a control system of some sort is present. However, over-all body balance does not require a controlled system in every case. There are many cases in which this balance is maintained by the kidney, even though its operating characteristics are fixed. In these cases, control is accounted for by the second major principle, that of glomerulotubular balance. According to this principle, the plasma concentration of a solute equilibrates in such a manner that the average rate of excretion equals the average rate of intake or production. The characteristics of this type of control are most easily seen in transport systems exhibiting type A kinetics. In systems showing type B kinetics, the processes are still present, although the control is not as precise.

Earlier in this section, we discussed what would happen if the intake of sulfate remained constant and the renal characteristics changed. Now, let us observe the same system in the more realistic situation in which the intake of sulfate varies, but the renal characteristics remain constant. As the intake rises, more sulfate is presented to the tubules. The Tm is eventually exceeded and the excess sulfate enters the urine, thereby reducing the plasma concentration toward its previous level. A reduction of sulfate intake reduces the plasma concentration and reduces excretion. Only after more sulfate has been taken into the body or produced and the plasma concentration is again brought to normal levels will urinary excretion take place. For a type A reabsorptive system, this relationship may be stated fairly precisely. Averaged over a period of time, the intake will equal the outgo:

$$\text{Plasma concentration} \times \text{filtration rate} =$$
$$\text{Tm} + \text{excretion} = \text{Tm} + \text{intake}$$

For type B reabsorptive systems, the amount transported is not Tm, but is related to the plasma concentration itself. For secretory systems, analogous relations exist. This sort of relation provides the basis for the clinical evaluation of kidney function from the blood urea nitrogen concentration. Even though there is not a sharp Tm in this case, blood urea becomes very high only when the filtration rate is markedly reduced.

The effect of glomerulotubular balance enters into the control of most solutes. For many of them, notably the important electrolytes and water, there are other control systems superimposed that modify the renal characteristics. Together, these two types of systems normally maintain plasma composition, and thus total body fluid composition, quite constant.

DIURESIS

The condition in which there is a high rate of urine flow is called "diuresis." Two general types exist: *water diuresis* and *osmotic diuresis*. A water diuresis occurs when the blood contains slight amounts of ADH. Solute transport is affected only minimally, but an abnormally high rate of water excretion is observed. The total solute concentration is very low and may be as low as one-tenth that of plasma. Ingestion of water causes a water diuresis by inhibiting the release of ADH, as does ingestion of alcohol. *Diabetes insipidus* is a state of permanent water diuresis caused by destruction of the posterior pituitary or of the supraventricular nucleus of the hypothalamus. Administration of exogenous ADH reduces a water diuresis.

Osmotic diuresis results from an increase in the rate of solute excretion. Since water excretion varies directly with solute excretion, an increase in the latter will cause an increase in the former. Generally, osmotic diuresis is induced either without change in water balance or in

association with mild dehydration. Adequate ADH is present to insure the formation of urine with a solute concentration the same as that at the tips of renal papillae. The sole cause for the increase in urine flow is an increase in solute excretion. Excessive excretion of any solute will produce an osmotic diuresis. Thus, in the diabetic patient, the concentration of glucose in the plasma is high, and the load of glucose filtered at the glomerulus is greater than Tm_G. Large amounts of glucose may be excreted in the urine. In addition, organic acids are incompletely metabolized, and these compounds must also be excreted. The consequent elevation of solute excretion brings about an elevation of urine flow. After large doses of urea have been administered, significant quantities may escape into the urine, producing osmotic diuresis. Inhibition of Na^+ reabsorption by diuretic agents produces an osmotic diuresis in which the high rate of excretion of Na^+ and its attendant anion are responsible for the increase in urine flow.

Regardless of the cause, if an osmotic diuresis is sufficiently severe, the rate of Na^+ excretion increases. An osmotic diuretic will lower the Na^+ concentration in the proximal tubules, thereby resulting in an appreciable diffusion of Na^+ back into the nephron from the peritubular blood. This passive back-diffusion reduces the net reabsorption.

Clinically useful diuretic agents decrease Na^+ reabsorption and thus lead to an increase in the rate of Na^+ excretion. This increase in the rate of Na^+ excretion is the primary and desired effect, and the increase in urine flow is an automatic consequence.

ENDOCRINE CONTROL OF RENAL FUNCTION

The kidneys are autonomous to a remarkable degree. Solute and water excretion vary widely with the composition of the plasma. This intrinsic regulation of renal function, however, can be modified by hormones. Regulation of renal function is a defense in depth; a mean value for the transport is established by the endocrine milieu, and moment-to-moment variations in transport around this mean result from local variations in the rate at which material is presented to tubular cells. We normally think only of these rapid changes; and, indeed, as long as the external environment is not varied too greatly, the slower hormonally induced changes in renal function may not appear. When severe stress is laid on the animal's regulatory systems, however, hormonal regulation is brought into play. Four different effects may be mentioned: those induced by ADH, by parathyroid hormone, by the renotrophic hormones, and by aldosterone. ADH has been discussed above; its effect, unlike that of other hormones, is rapid. The effect of ADH on tubular permeability of water is immediate, and changes in the ADH concentration in the blood lag only 10 to 15 minutes behind changes in the solute concentration.

Increases in the concentration of circulating parathyroid hormone increase the rate of phosphate excretion by reducing net tubular reabsorption. The release of parathyroid hormone is regulated by the plasma concentration of calcium; as the calcium concentration falls, the amount of circulating hormone rises. Plasma is nearly a saturated solution of calcium phosphate, and the product of the calcium and the phosphate concentrations is about constant. As more parathyroid hormone is released, more phosphate is excreted. The plasma phosphate concentration then falls, and the plasma calcium concentration rises. This last change reduces the release of the hormone. The kidney and the parathyroid gland work together to control calcium and phosphate balance.

Hormones of the third group modify cellular metabolism throughout the body, and renal cells are only one of their points of action. Somatotropin from the anterior pituitary, corticosterone and cortisol from the adrenal cortex, and thyroid hormone all exhibit a renotrophic action. That is, they increase the total amount of renal tissue, the plasma flow rate, the filtration rate and all renal function. This effect is not regulatory, but is exerted because renal cells, like all other cells, respond to these hormones.

Aldosterone, which is released from the adrenal cortex, has a striking effect on the renal transport of Na^+ and K^+. This effect develops over days or weeks and is of long duration. If excessive aldosterone is present, an excessive amount of Na^+ is retained in the body. K^+ secretion is also hyperactive, and an excessive amount of this ion is lost. Absence of the hormone leads to opposite changes. In adrenal insufficiency, the loss of Na^+ leads to a large loss of extracellular fluid. Circulatory collapse eventually ensues. Striking as the effects of aldosterone on renal ion transport are, this hormone probably is not primarily concerned with the regulation of renal function, for it seems to enhance the rate of active Na^+ extrusion from all cells in the body.[51]

Attention has been directed to the renal action of aldosterone for two reasons. First, the renal effect is the most obvious one in the body. As discussed in Chapter 1, a 5 per cent change in Na^+ pumping is barely detectable in muscle or brain tissue. In the kidney, however, a 5 per cent increase in Na^+ reabsorption results in striking retention of this ion. The situation is simply a reflection of the extremely high flux rates in the kidney and of the fact that Na^+ excretion is always very small in comparison with Na^+ reabsorption. Second, renal ion transport modifies the release of aldosterone itself.

There appear to be two important stimuli for aldosterone secretion: (i) the ratio of K^+ to Na^+ concentration in plasma, and (ii) the blood volume. At high values of the ion concentration ratio, aldosterone is released at a high rate. As a result of this increase in circulating aldosterone, Na^+ reabsorption and K^+ secretion increase so that the ratio is reduced. At low values of the ion concentration ratio, the opposite changes occur, and the ratio is brought back toward normal. Increase in blood volume decreases and depletion of blood volume increases the rate at which aldosterone is released. Since the blood volume varies with the size of the extracellular fluid compartment, Na^+ excretion will vary in such a manner as to tend to keep blood volume constant. At least some of the changes in aldosterone secretion are mediated through a system involving the kidney. Apparently, low arteriolar pressure is sensed by the juxtaglomerular cells in the kidney and, as a result, renin is released. Renin catalyzes the release of angiotensin II, which stimulates the release of aldosterone.[7] The kidney and the adrenal cortex therefore constitute a long-term controlling system which maintains the cation composition and volume of the plasma.

REFERENCES

1. BERLINER, R. W. and KENNEDY, T. J. *Proc. Soc. exp. Biol.* (*N. Y.*), 1948, *67*:542–545.
2. BERLINER, R. W., KENNEDY, T. J. and HILTON, J. G. *Amer. J. Physiol.*, 1950, *162*:348–367.

3. BERLINER, R. W., KENNEDY, T. J. and ORLOFF, J. *Amer. J. Med.*, 1951, *11*:274–282.

4. BERLINER, R. W. *Harvey Lect.*, 1961, *55*:141–172.

5. BLOOMER, H. A., RECTOR, F. C. and SELDIN, D. W. *J. clin. Invest.*, 1963, *42*:277–285.

6. BRODSKY, W. A., MILEY, J. F., KAIM, J. T. and NARESCHANDRA, P. S. *Amer. J. Physiol.*, 1958, *193*:108–122.

7. DAVIS, J. O. *Physiologist*, 1962, *5*:65–86.

8. FORSTER, R. P. *Amer. J. Physiol.*, 1954, *179*:372–377.

9. GIEBISCH, G. *J. cell. comp. Physiol.*, 1958, *51*:221–239.

10. GIEBISCH, G. *Circulation*, 1960, *21*:879–891.

11. GIEBISCH, G. *J. gen. Physiol.*, 1961, *44*:659–678.

12. GIEBISCH, G. and WINDHAGER, E. In: *Proceedings, International Union of Physiological Sciences*, vol. 1. New York, Excerpta Medica Foundation, 1962.

13. GILMAN, A. and BRAZEAU, P. *Amer. J. Med.*, 1953, *15*: 765–770.

14. GOTTSCHALK, C. W. *Physiologist*, 1961, *41*:35–55.

15. GOTTSCHALK, C. W. and MYLLE, M. *Amer. J. Physiol.*, 1959, *196*:927–936.

16. HILGER, H. H., KLUMPER, J. D. and ULLRICH, K. J. *Pflüg. Arch. ges. Physiol.*, 1958, *267*:218–237.

17. HINSHAW, L. B., DAY, S. B. and CARLSON, C. H. *Amer. J. Physiol.*, 1959, *197*:309–312.

18. JAENIKE, J. R. *J. clin. Invest.*, 1961, *40*:144–151.

19. KOCH, A., BRAZEAU, P. and GILMAN, A. *Amer. J. Physiol.*, 1956, *186*:350–356.

20. KOEFOED-JOHNSEN, V. and USSING, H. H. *Acta physiol. scand.*, 1958, *42*:298–308.

21. LEVINSKY, N. G. and BERLINER, R. W. *J. clin. Invest.*, 1959, *38*:741–748.

22. MALVIN, R. L., WILDE, W. S. and SULLIVAN, L. P. *Amer. J. Physiol.*, 1958, *194*:135–142.

23. MAXIMOW, A. and BLOOM, W. *Textbook of histology*, 7th ed. Philadelphia, W. B. Saunders, 1957.

24. MOORE, W. J. *Physical chemistry*, 2nd ed. New York, Prentice-Hall, Inc., 1955.

25. MUDGE, G. H., FOULKS, J. and GILMAN, A. *Proc. Soc. exp. Biol. (N. Y.)*, 1948, *67*:542–545.

26. MUDGE, G. H., FOULKS, J. and GILMAN, A. *Amer. J. Physiol.*, 1950, *161*:159–166.

27. OLIVER, J. and MacDOWELL, M. *J. clin. Invest.*, 1961, *40*:1093–1112.

28. ORLOFF, J. and BERLINER, R. W. *J. clin. Invest.*, 1956, *35*: 223–235.

29. ORLOFF, J. and DAVIDSON, D. G. *J. clin. Invest.*, 1959, *38*: 21–30.

30. PITTS, R. F. *Fed. Proc.*, 1948, *7*:418–426.

31. PITTS, R. F. and ALEXANDER, R. S. *Amer. J. Physiol.*, 1945, *144*:239–254.

32. PITTS, R. F., GURD, R. S., KESSLER, R. H. and HIERHOLZER, K. *Amer. J. Physiol.*, 1958, *194*:125–134.

33. RECTOR, F. C. and CLAPP, J. R. *J. clin. Invest.*, 1962, *41*: 101–107.

34. SAWYER, W. H. In: *The neurohypophysis, Symposium of the Colston Research Society*, H. HELLER, ed. New York, Academic Press, 1957.

35. SCHER, A. M. *Nature (Lond.)*, 1959, *184*:1322–1323.

36. SCHMIDT-NIELSEN, B. *Physiol. Rev.*, 1958, *38*:139–168.

37. SCHMIDT-NIELSEN, B. *Amer. J. Physiol.*, 1958, *194*:221–228.

38. SHANNON, J. A. and FISHER, S. *Amer. J. Physiol.*, 1938, *122*:765–774.

39. SMITH, H. W. *The kidney, its structure and function in health and disease*. New York, Oxford University Press, 1951.

40. SMITH, H. W. *Principles of renal physiology*. New York, Oxford University Press, 1956.

41. SMITH, H. W., FINKELSTEIN, N., ALIMINOSA, L., CRAWFORD, B. and GRABER, M. *J. clin. Invest.*, 1945, *24*:388–404.

42. SULLIVAN, W. J. and DORMAN, P. J. *J. clin. Invest.*, 1955, *34*:268–276.

43. ULLRICH, K. J., DRENCKHAHN, F. O. and JARAUSCH, K. H. *Pflüg. Arch. ges. Physiol.*, 1955, *261*:62–77.

44. ULLRICH, K. J. and EIGLER, F. W. *Pflüg. Arch. ges. Physiol.*, 1958, *267*:491–496.

45. ULLRICH, K. J., HILGER, H. H. and KLUMPER, J. D. *Pflüg. Arch. ges. Physiol.*, 1958, *267*:244–250.

46. ULLRICH, K. J. and JARAUSCH, K. H. *Pflüg. Arch. ges. Physiol.*, 1956, *262*:537–550.

47. WALKER, A. M., BOTT, P. A., OLIVER, J. and MacDOWELL, M. C. *Amer. J. Physiol.*, 1941, *134*:580–595.

48. WAUGH, W. H. and SHANKS, R. G. *Circulat. Res.*, 1960, *8*:871–888.

49. WIRZ, H. *Helv. physiol. acta*, 1956, *14*:353–362.

50. WIRZ, H. and BOTT, P. A. *Proc. Soc. exp. Biol. (N. Y.)*, 1954, *87*:405–407.

51. WOODBURY, D. M. and KOCH, A. *Proc. Soc. exp. Biol. (N. Y.)*, 1957, *94*:720–723.

CHAPTER 45

Physiology of Body Fluids

By DIXON M. WOODBURY

THE concepts of water and ion distribution at the cellular level, developed in Chapter 1, apply as well to the distribution of water and electrolytes between the various fluid compartments (see below) of tissues, organs and the whole body. The present chapter deals with the volume and the composition of the body fluids and with the factors which regulate and maintain them within narrow limits.

Because of their importance to many aspects of medicine, a sound knowledge and thorough understanding of the principles determining the dynamic state of body fluids and electrolytes are essential. Whether a physician is concerned with excessive electrolyte or water losses or both caused by diarrhea, cholera, suction drainage of gastrointestinal fluids during bowel surgery, or diabetes insipidus, or with retention of fluid and electrolytes which result from heart failure or liver disease, his therapeutic approach must always be based on fundamental principles of water and electrolyte distribution. Ignorance of such physiologic principles may cost lives and may jeopardize the results of the finest surgical skills.

Water is the solvent of the body fluids in which are dissolved numerous inorganic and organic solutes. The organic solutes are mainly foodstuffs and products of metabolism which are constantly moving in and out of cells, tissues or the body. Water and the inorganic substances constitute the stable *milieu interieur* of Claude Bernard and are the chief concern of this chapter. Water is distributed passively along with the electrolytes. The *milieu interieur* is maintained in a dynamic steady state, not at equilibrium, by the constant expenditure of energy derived from cellular metabolism. There are many extensive treatments of fluid and electrolyte physiology.[7, 13, 22, 39, 48, 58, 62, 69]

VOLUME AND COMPOSITION OF BODY FLUIDS

Water is the main volume-occupying substance (about 70 per cent of the body weight) in which the major cations (sodium, potassium, hydrogen, calcium and magnesium) and anions (chloride, bicarbonate and protein) of the body are dissolved. The distribution of water delineates the compartments in which the various biochemical reactions and ionic movements and exchanges between various water and solid compartments (e.g., bone) of the body take place.

Water Content and Distribution. In the organism as a whole, and in specific organs and tissues, the body fluids may be divided into two main compartments, the *extracellular* and the *intracellular*. The boundary between them is the cell membrane (Chap. 1). The *intracellular phase* is that portion of the total body water with its dissolved solutes which lies within cell membranes and is the site of all the metabolic processes of the body. The *extracellular phase* lies outside the cell membranes and is the compartment which provides a constant external environment for the cells.*

The extracellular fluid compartment is divided into a number of subcompartments. The *blood plasma* constitutes a major subcompartment of the extracellular fluid. Supporting tissues, collagen, connective tissue and bone con-

---

*This function was once served by the vast extracellular medium of the sea in ancient times when organisms were unicellular. The ionic composition of the extracellular fluid in present day animals reflects qualitatively the composition of the Cambrian ocean. In the Cambrian Period, when multicellular organisms are thought to have developed, the sea water was incorporated into the organism as extracellular fluid.

stitute another subcompartment. Although produced by cells, they are deposited as solid materials extracellularly, and thus are part of the extracellular space. Secretory cells produce solutions similar in composition to those of the extracellular fluid, e.g., cerebrospinal fluid. These solutions are secreted into portions of the body separated from the main extracellular space by a continuous layer of epithelial cells which modify the extracellular fluid passing through them. These modified extracellular fluids are called *transcellular fluids;* the volumes they occupy are the *transcellular subcompartment* of the extracellular space. They include the digestive secretions and the cerebrospinal, intraocular, pleural, pericardial, peritoneal and synovial fluids, the luminal fluid of the thyroid, the cochlear endolymph and the secretions of sweat glands and other glands. The final subcompartment of the extracellular space is the *interstitial fluid*. It is the fluid interposed between the rapidly circulating plasma and the cells. Interstitial fluid flows slowly through tissue interstices and bathes the cells, but is in rapid equilibrium with the blood plasma. Lymph is a small part of the interstitial space. Transcapillary fluid movements and formation of interstitial fluid and lymph are discussed in Chapter 32.

The intracellular fluid, like the extracellular, is nonhomogeneous even within single cell types, since many anatomic subdivisions exist in the cell. Striking differences in water content and ionic composition have been demonstrated between the cytoplasm, nucleus, mitochondria and microsomes of various cell types. Despite the nonhomogeneity of the intracellular fluids, the concept of a single intracellular compartment is useful in describing the fluid and electrolyte balance of the whole organism.

MEASUREMENT OF BODY FLUID COMPARTMENTS. Before the composition, volume, and fluid dynamics of the body compartments, organs and tissues can be discussed, it is necessary to understand how the various compartments are measured. The volume of water in each compartment cannot be measured directly. Indirect methods of measurement, called dilution techniques, are based on the relationship between the quantity of a substance present, the volume through which the substance is distributed, and the final concentration attained. The equation for this relationship is expressed as follows:

$$[C] = \frac{Q}{V}; \text{ hence } V = \frac{Q}{[C]},$$

where V is the volume (in milliliters or liters) through which the quantity Q (grams, kg. or mEq.) is distributed, yielding concentration [C] (grams per ml. or per liter; or mEq. per ml. or per liter). The dilution principle may be illustrated by an example. The volume of a beaker can be determined, without actually measuring its content in a graduated cylinder, by adding a known amount of material (Q)—for example, a dye—to the beaker, and then determining in a colorimeter its final concentration [C] after thorough mixing to insure uniform distribution. If 25 mg. of dye is added and the final concentration is 0.05 mg. per ml., then the volume of the beaker (V) from the above equation is:

$$V = \frac{25 \text{ mg.}}{0.05 \text{ mg. per ml.}} = 500 \text{ ml.}$$

Measurement of body fluid compartments by the dilution principle is only slightly more difficult. The method requires that the injected solute be evenly distributed but confined within the body fluid compartment to be measured. If the solute leaves the compartment by excretion in the urine, by transfer into another com-

partment where it exists in a different concentration, or if it is metabolized, then a correction for the loss must be made. The amount lost from the space to be measured is subtracted from the quantity administered:

$$\text{Volume of distribution} = \frac{\text{Quantity administered—Quantity removed}}{\text{Concentration}}.$$

Volume of distribution is defined as the volume of a solution having the same concentration as that in the plasma water, which would contain the quantity of test substance left in the body. Other requirements for the substances used are that they be nontoxic, be free of pharmacologic activity, and be readily determined analytically. The volume of distribution obtained from application of the method is usually calculated in liters and is generally expressed as a percentage of body weight in kilograms.

Two principal methods, with many variations,[70] are in use for measurements of body space by the dilution technique: (i) the *infusion–equilibration* method, and (ii) the *kinetic method, with or without extrapolation.*

The infusion–equilibration method. This is used for substances such as inulin which are rapidly excreted (Fig. 1*A*). A priming dose of the substance is given to saturate the system; then the material is infused slowly to maintain a constant plasma concentration. After a time sufficient to insure equilibration, a series of

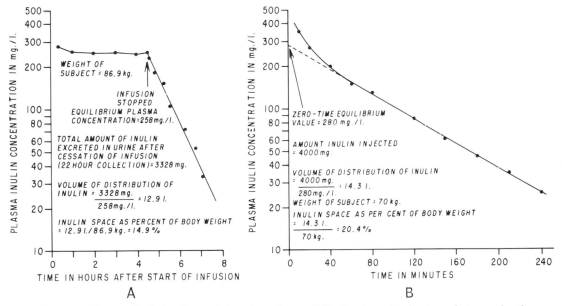

Fig. 1. Two methods for determining the volume of distribution of indicator substances by the dilution method.

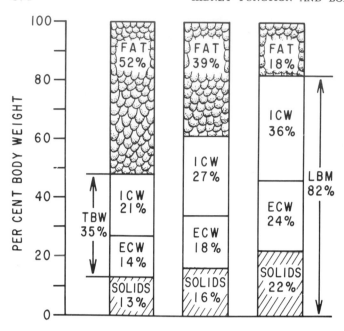

Fig. 2. The influence of fat content on the percentage body weight of the various fluid compartments. When fat content is high (left), the percentage of total body water, intracellular water, extracellular water and body solids is low; conversely, when fat content is low (right), the percentage values for water and solids are high. If the values for water and solids are compared on a fat-free basis (lean body mass) the percentages of water and solids are constant (73 per cent total body water, 27 per cent solids, in adults). *TBW* = total body water, *ICW* = intracellular water, *ECW* = extracellular water, *LBM* = lean body mass.

plasma samples are taken and the concentration of indicator is measured in each sample. When the plasma level becomes constant, the infusion is stopped and urine is collected until all the substance which was present in the body at the time the infusion ended has been excreted. This amount represents the quantity (Q) of material in the body at the end of the infusion. If this quantity is divided by the plasma concentration at the end of the perfusion, the volume of distribution of the indicator is obtained.

The kinetic method. A single dose of an indicator substance is injected and plasma concentrations of the substance are determined at various intervals after injection (Fig. 1B). Semilogarithmic plots (log concentration versus time) show an initial nonlinear decline of concentration but thereafter become a straight line. Extrapolation of the linear segment of the regression line to zero time gives the theoretical concentration if the injected substance were instantaneously distributed. The zero-time equilibrium concentration divided into the total quantity of substance given yields the volume of distribution of the indicator substance. Also, the volume of distribution at any point along the falling curve can be obtained by dividing the amount retained in the body at the time desired by the concentration in the plasma at the same time. The latter method can be used only if the material is lost in the urine and can be measured. If the substance is metabolized in the body, then the calculated volume of distribution is erroneous. The correct volume can be obtained by extrapolation to zero time as described above, if the rate of loss from the body is constant. Examples of the infusion–equilibration and kinetic methods with sample calculations are shown in Figures 1A and B.

TOTAL BODY WATER. Total body water con-

stitutes a very high and constant proportion of the body weight in the "average" lean man. Among individuals, the ratio of water to body weight varies inversely with the amount of fatty tissue, which contains practically no water. However, the relation between total body water and the weight of fat-free tissue only (*lean body mass*) is remarkably constant (Fig. 2) at 73.2 per cent.[44] In the newborn, the ratio is 82 per cent.

The value of 73.2 per cent water is so constant that it can be used to calculate the fat content of man as follows:[44]

Percentage of fat = 100 −

$$\frac{\text{Percentage of water in whole body}}{0.732}$$

Body fat, calculated from the specific gravity (G) of the body, agrees with the above calculation. One formula for fat content empirically derived from body specific gravity data is as follows:[33]

$$\text{Percentage of fat} = 100\left(\frac{5.548}{G} - 5.044\right)$$

Once fat content is obtained by the specific gravity method, then the percentage of body water can be obtained from the formula above. The results so obtained agree well with those obtained by desiccation and dilution techniques.[43] Calculation of fat content with these formulae, together with the data on total body water, supplemented by measurements of the metabolic balance, allow for an accurate study of changes in body composition (fat, water, and fat-free solids) under various physiologic and pathologic conditions.

The measurement of total body water by a dilution technique requires an indicator substance which diffuses rapidly through all body water, including the transcellular component. Deuterium oxide (D_2O), tritium oxide (HTO), antipyrine, and N-acetyl-4-amino antipyrine (NAAP) all yield values which correlate well with those obtained from desiccation or specific gravity measurements in man.[4, 18, 20, 43, 49, 53, 56, 71]

The hydrogen isotopes contained in these molecules exchange with hydrogen atoms in body water and with the exchangeable hydrogen atoms in organic molecules. Over the interval required for the equilibration of D_2O or HTO with body water these errors amount to a water equivalent of only 0.5 to 2.0 per cent of body weight in man[47] and, consequently, are insignificant. Antipyrine and NAAP are distributed throughout total body water and diffuse rapidly across cell membranes. However, antipyrine is metabolized by the body and also is excreted in the urine; hence, correction must be made for these losses by multiple sampling and use of the kinetic falling plasma method. NAAP is metabolized only negligibly by tissues and is excreted slowly in the urine.

A summary of current estimates of total body water obtained by the various methods is presented in Table 1.[19]

During the first year of life water content decreases principally because of contraction of the extracellular fluid volume. Thereafter, it decreases more slowly with age. After puberty, water content is higher for males than females because of differences in body fat content.

The body water is distributed unequally in the various tissues. Table 2 summarizes some of these differences. The exchange rate between tissue and plasma water (time for D_2O equilibration) is also indicated. Most of the water in the body is in muscle and skin, whereas the skeleton and adipose tissue contain the lowest percentages. The exchange rate of water is characteristic for each tissue; apparently each tissue regulates its own water exchange. The rates of exchange, for example, of visceral tissues are faster than those for bone and muscle. Factors which regulate movement of water in and out of cells and tissues are considered below.

EXTRACELLULAR FLUID. The varied results derived from anatomic, dilution, metabolic balance, and tissue studies of the extracellular space necessitate division of this space into various subcompartments. From anatomic and physiologic considerations the extracellular fluid is made up of the following subdivisions which were described above: plasma, interstitial and lymph fluid, connective tissue and cartilage, bone, and transcellular fluids. No single substance can be used to measure the whole fluid extracellular volume; therefore, measures of several substances are necessary.

Anatomic considerations. The histochemical characterization of the extracellular fluid and the electronmicroscopic appearance of the capillaries are described in Chapter 32.

The volume of the extracellular fluid has

TABLE 1. *Total Body Water in Normal Man as Measured by Different Methods*

GROUP	METHOD	TOTAL BODY WATER (PER CENT OF BODY WEIGHT)			
		0 to 1 Month	1 to 12 Months	1 to 10 Years	
Children	D_2O AP	75.7 (n=20)	64.5 (n=15)	61.7 (n=24)	
		10 to 16 Years	17 to 39 Years	40 to 59 Years	Over 60 Years
Adolescent and adult males	D_2O, HTO AP, G	58.9 (n=11)	60.6 (n=15)	54.7 (n=127)	51.5 (n=20)
Adolescent and adult females	D_2O, AP G	57.3 (n=7)	50.2 (n=61)	46.7 (n=38)	45.5 (n=14)

Values are means of all methods and the n values in parentheses are the number of subjects in each group. D_2O = deuterium oxide, AP = antipyrine and its derivatives, HTO = tritium oxide, and G = specific gravity. (Values taken from Edelman and Leibman, *Amer. J. Med.*, 1959, 27:256–277.)

TABLE 2. *Distribution of Water and Kinetics of Water Movement in Various Tissues*

TISSUE	PER CENT WATER	PER CENT BODY WEIGHT	LITERS WATER IN 70 KG. MAN	TIME FOR D₂O EQUILIBRATION (MINUTES)
Skin	72.0	18	9.07	120–180
Muscle	75.7	41.7	22.10	38
Skeleton	31.0	15.9	3.45	120–180
Brain	74.8	2.0	1.05	2
Liver	68.3	2.3	1.10	10–20
Heart	79.2	0.5	0.28	
Lungs	79.0	0.7	0.39	
Kidneys	82.7	0.4	0.23	
Spleen	75.8	0.2	0.11	
Blood	83	7.7	4.47	Erythrocytes 1/60
Intestine	74.5	1.8	0.94	Gastric juice, 20 to 30
Adipose	10	9.0	0.63	
Total body	62	100	43.4	180

(Water values from Skelton, *Arch. intern. Med.*, 1927, *40:*140–152; D₂O equilibration values from Edelman, *Amer. J. Physiol.*, 1952, *171:*279–296.)

been measured by various histologic techniques.[39] In sections of adult muscle the area not occupied by cells is 14.5 to 23 per cent of total muscle area; in young chick muscle it is about 50 per cent. In liver the histologically determined extracellular space is 24 per cent,[61] and in thyroid the stromal (nonfollicular) volume varies between 10 and 20 per cent.[31] These measurements agree well with the extracellular volumes determined by various indicator substances.

Blood and plasma volume.[37, 55] Plasma volume may be measured by either of two dilution techniques. In the first, substances used neither leave the vascular bed nor penetrate the erythrocytes; in the second, substances confined only to the erythrocytes are used. The two most useful indicators which are confined to the plasma are Evans blue (T 1824) and radioiodinated human serum albumin (RISA). Both are bound to plasma albumin;* Evans blue is bound *in vivo* after injection of the material; radioiodine is prebound *in vitro* to albumin before injection. The volume of distribution

*Since plasma albumin with its attached indicators leaks out of the circulation into the interstitial fluid, the plasma volume is slightly overestimated. Plasma volumes measured with radioiodinated gamma globulin and fibrinogen, proteins which do not generally leak out of the vascular system, are lower by 2 to 12 per cent than those determined by Evans blue and RISA.

measured is thus that of albumin. The kinetic-extrapolation method for analyzing the data is generally used. Total blood volume can then be obtained from the plasma volume and the hematocrit by the following formula:

$$\text{Blood volume} = \text{Plasma volume} \times \frac{100}{100 - \text{Hematocrit}}$$

The second method for measuring plasma volume is based on the fact that radioisotopes (P^{32} or Cr^{51}) penetrate red cells and become incorporated or firmly bound. The tagged cells are injected intravenously and their volume of distribution is measured. Plasma volume is then calculated from the measured red cell volume and hematocrit.

In man the average value for total blood volume is about 5.7 liters (range 4.09 to 7.76), which corresponds to an average of 7.7 per cent of body weight. Adult women probably have a lower average blood volume per unit body weight than do adult men, but the difference is not conclusive since sufficient data based on the best methodology are not available.

In adult males, the average values for plasma volume determined by four different methods tend to be slightly larger than those in females, but the overlap is considerable. The range of values for plasma volume is from 3.1 to 5.8 per cent of body weight for adult males, mean 4.2, and 2.7 to 5.2 per cent for adult females, mean 3.7.

Extracellular volumes. The remainder of the extracellular fluid consists of the following components: interstitial fluid and lymph, connective tissue, bone and transcellular fluids. The extracellular fluid in connective tissue appears to be similar to that found elsewhere. The volume of interstitial fluid and lymph cannot be obtained by dilution techniques, since no substance is known that distributes exclusively in this compartment. However, the volumes of distribution of many substances closely approximate the combined volume of the plasma and interstitial-lymph space. Therefore, the interstitial-lymph space may be computed by subtracting the plasma volume from these values. Such computed values may not be exact because some of the indicators penetrate into portions or all of the water of the connective tissue subdivision of extracellular fluid.[9, 36, 42, 68] Hence, a correction for the volume occupied by the substance in connective tissue water must be subtracted from the total volume of distribution of the indicator in order to obtain the true interstitial volume.

The substances which have been used for measuring the combined plasma-interstitial-lymph space plus a portion of the connective tissue space are of two types: (i) saccharides—inulin, raffinose, sucrose and mannitol, and (ii) ions—thiosulfate, sulfate, thiocyanate, chloride, bromide and sodium. Most of these substances are available labeled with radioactive isotopes; either the stable or radioactive forms may be used. The diffusion rates are in the order of inulin < raffinose and sucrose < mannitol and the inorganic ions; the molecular weights are in the reverse order.[59]

Two phases of inulin, sucrose or thiosulfate penetration into the extracellular space have been distinguished.[9, 42] A rapidly equilibrating phase with a half-time of 20 minutes or less has been identified with penetration into the plasma–interstitial fluid–lymph space. A slowly equilibrating phase, with a half-time of between 5 and 9 hours, is more difficult to identify. It has been suggested that this phase corresponds to the uptake of inulin in dense connective tissue, but more recent evidence suggests that it corresponds to the accumulation of localized clumps of inulin, probably within macrophages (Fig. 3). Thus, after the passage of time, inulin

loses one of the characteristics required of an indicator substance, namely, that of homogenous distribution. After 12 hours, inulin, and perhaps other saccharides such as sucrose, give erroneously high measures of extracellular space. Sulfate and mannitol spaces do not increase with increasing time in nephrectomized rats and appear to be suitable for long-term measures of extracellular space.

The "rapidly equilibrating space" measured thus consists of the plasma and interstitial-lymph spaces, plus that portion (60 to 80 per cent) of connective tissue water which is penetrated by inulin, sucrose and particularly the smaller molecules—thiosulfate, sulfate and mannitol—within less than 12 hours.[9, 16, 42, 68] The remaining portion of connective tissue water is probably intracellular, inasmuch as intracellular potassium concentration calculated on the basis of the difference between total connective tissue water and inulin space gives a value comparable to that found for other tissue cells. Consequently, interstitial water of connective tissue cannot be distinguished from the interstitial water of other tissues. For example, separation of the extracellular space of muscle into two subcompartments for water is not necessary. However, compartmentalization is necessary in the case of the ionic composition of connective tissue as discussed later.

Chloride was first used to estimate extracellular space by Fenn[23] and by Hastings and coworkers.[32, 33, 39] More recently Cotlove and Hogben[10] concluded that Cl⁻ space is a valid measure of total extracellular space including transcellular volumes. Although Cl⁻ does enter cells, these authors believe that Cl⁻ is actively transported out of most cells and that, except for erythrocytes, most cells contain negligible Cl⁻. However, their conclusion that Cl⁻ is actively extruded from all cells is based on the assumption that the slow component of inulin penetration represents entry into dense connective tissue, an assumption that is probably incorrect. Cl⁻ space is probably only a rough approximation of total extracellular volume.[5]

The *transcellular fluids* are formed by active transport mechanisms across epithelial cells. The cells modify the extracellular fluid to form the specialized secretion fluids. Total volume occupied by transcellular fluids is small: about 15.3 ml. per kg. body weight in man.[19] About half of this (7.4 ml. per kg.) is in the gastrointestinal lumen; cerebrospinal fluid constitutes

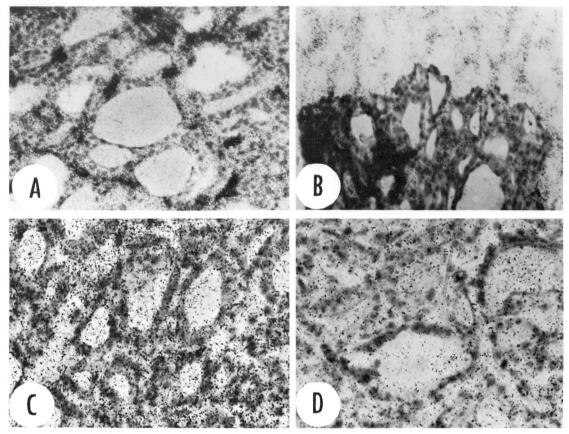

Fig. 3. H³-inulin, S³⁵O₄ and Cl³⁶ radioautographs of frozen section of rat thyroid. *A*, Radioautograph 24 hours after administration of H³-inulin. Note localized clumping of the inulin in the stroma (interstitium) outside the follicles. The follicular cells and lumen contain no radioactivity except that contributed by background fogging of the emulsion. *B*, Radioautograph 2 hours after administration of H³-inulin. Note the uniform distribution of the inulin in the interstitial space and its absence in the follicular cells and lumen. The upper portion of the picture shows the radioactive tracks in the emulsion without the superimposed thyroid section seen in the lower portion. *C*, Radioautograph 2 hours after administration of S³⁵O₄. The sulfate is distributed uniformly in the stromal and follicular luminal spaces; minute amounts are also present in the follicular cells. *D*, Radioautograph 2 hours after administration of Cl³⁶. The chloride is uniformly distributed in the stromal and follicular luminal spaces; smaller but still appreciable amounts are also present in the follicular cells. (Unpublished data of S. Y. Chow, W. S. Jee, G. N. Taylor and D. M. Woodbury).

2.8 ml. per kg. and biliary fluid, 2.1 ml. per kg. As previously mentioned, deuterium oxide, tritium oxide and antipyrine distribute rapidly and completely in the transcellular fluids; hence, transcellular fluid volume is included in the total body water measured by these substances. Small-molecule indicators of extracellular fluid volume enter the transcellular fluids (except cerebrospinal fluid) but large-molecule indicators do not measure these spaces well.

Physiologic considerations of extracellular fluids. The volume of the whole body extracellular space (Fig. 4) changes with age. For example,

the corrected bromide space in neonatal infants is about 360 ml. per kg. body weight for the first 48 hours and decreases progressively to a value of 267 ml. per kg. at one year to 250 ml. per kg. in late childhood, and finally to the adult value of 220 to 240 ml. per kg. Similar marked decreases in extracellular space with age occur in special tissues, particularly in muscle, heart and brain. In fetuses and premature infants extracellular volume constitutes the largest phase of total body water. With growth the extracellular fluid is replaced by intracellular fluid and cell solids.

The water content of bone, cartilage, tendon and connective tissue is summarized in Figure 4. In the whole body, total bone water constitutes only 49 ml. per kg. of body weight of which 28 ml. per kg. is extracellular and 21 ml. per kg. is bone matrix water.[16] In connective tissue, 70 per cent of the water is extracellular (41 ml. per kg.) and only 30 per cent (19 ml. per kg.) is inside the cell membrane. Much is bound to the bone crystals and hence slow (180 minutes) to equilibrate with tracers such as D_2O (Table 2). The amount of bone water is little altered by physiologic conditions, but decreases with age as deposition of bone mineral occurs.

INTRACELLULAR FLUID. Intracellular fluid volume cannot be measured directly by dilution, because there is no substance which distributes only in this compartment. It is obtained by subtracting the volume of the extracellular fluid from the total body or tissue water; any errors of extracellular volume measurement are magnified in determining intracellular volume "by difference." The volume of intracellular fluids is variable, but usually amounts to 30 to 40 per cent of body weight (see Fig. 4).

Ionic Composition of Body Fluids. The predominant cations of the body fluids are the

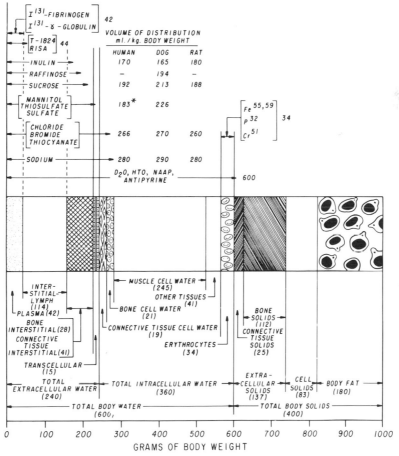

Fig. 4. Schematic drawing depicting the relation between the water and solid compartments of the body. The information below the anatomic diagram gives the names and volumes of the various anatomic compartments. The figures in parentheses are the volumes in grams per kg. body weight. The various substances which measure the physiologic spaces of the body water compartments are listed above the diagram. The figures after each substance are the volumes of distribution in ml. per kg. body weight. Both Na^+ and Cl^- penetrate cells as shown by their volumes of distribution. The amounts in cells as depicted on the chart represent penetration into all cells, including erythrocytes, and not just bone and connective tissue cells as illustrated. (From Elkinton and Danowski, *The body fluids.* Baltimore, Williams & Wilkins Co., 1955; and from Cotlove and Hogben, Chap. 27 in *Mineral metabolism*, Comar and Bronner, eds. New York, Academic Press, 1962.)

monovalent elements, Na^+ and K^+. The divalent cations Mg^{++} and Ca^{++} exist in body fluids only in relatively low concentrations. K^+ and Mg^{++} are the main intracellular cations, Na^+ and Ca^{++} the main extracellular cations. Na^+ and K^+ are widely spread throughout all subdivisions of the earth, the lithosphere, the hydrosphere, the atmosphere and the biosphere. The quantitative distinctiveness of the biopshere lies in the fact that its chemical composition is determined by the ability of organisms to concentrate elements and to synthesize new compounds.[57]

The chief anions of the body fluids are Cl^-, HCO_3^-, phosphate, organic ions and polyvalent proteins. The main intracellular anions are phosphate, protein and organic ions; and Cl^- and HCO_3^- are the predominant extracellular anions.* The sum of the concentrations of the cations equals the sum of the concentrations of the anions in each compartment, making the solutions electrically neutral. Inasmuch as all body compartments are in osmotic balance the total solute concentrations in the various compartments are the same. Total body water is, therefore, *determined by the total quantity of solutes in the body*. The distribution of water between the compartments is determined by the quantity of solute in each compartment. It is important, therefore, to study the total body stores of the major ions, distribution of the ions in various compartments of the body, and the factors which affect their distribution.

METHODS OF MEASUREMENT. Although the total body content of ions can be determined only by direct analysis of dead animals, the pools of ions readily available for maintenance of homeostasis, i.e., the total exchangeable ion content, can be determined by the *isotope dilution* method. This is simply another application of the relations between V, Q and [C]. Isotopes distribute to the same extent in the body fluids as do their normal counterparts.

SODIUM.[24] The total amount of Na^+ in the body depends upon the balance between intake and output. Since the average intake far exceeds minimum need, Na^+ balance must be rigidly controlled; this control is discussed below. The urine is the main route for excretion

*In some tissues the organic amino acid anions, glutamate and aspartate, are present in sufficient quantities to contribute significantly to the anionic content of cells. Similarly, lysine and arginine may contribute to the cation content of cells.

of Na^+ (90 to 95 per cent), but small amounts are lost in stool and in sweat.

The total body Na^+ content of the adult human male is 58 mEq. per kg. or about 4100 mEq. in a 70 kg. man. Its distribution is indicated in Table 3. Of this, about two-thirds is present in extracellular fluid, where it is the predominant cation. Between 5 and 10 per cent of the body Na^+ is within cells. The remaining 25 per cent is found in the crystal lattice of bone.

The amount of exchangeable Na^+ (in man) as determined by isotope dilution is much smaller than that determined by chemical analysis and averages about 41.0 mEq. per kg. of body weight. The nonexchangeable Na^+ fraction is located in bone, which makes up from 40 to 45 per cent of body weight. Between 20 and 35 per cent of bone Na^+ exchanges with radiosodium in 24 hours, after which the exchangeable Na^+ pool size increases about 1 per cent per day because of slow penetration of isotope into bone.[19]

The rapidly exchangeable (24-hour) Na^+ content of bone (6.4 mEq. per kg. of body weight) consists of all that in the bone extracellular space (3.8 mEq. per kg. of body weight) and some (2.6 mEq. per kg. of body weight) of that adsorbed to the outer surface of the hydroxyapatite crystal structure of bone. Na^+ and other ions are adsorbed in layers on the surface of the hydroxyapatite bone crystal in large amounts. The outer mineral layers of the bone crystal surface contain Na^+ which has been recently deposited and is completely exchangeable, whereas the inner mineral layers contain Na^+ which has been deposited for a long time and which is very slowly exchanged.

The exchangeable Na^+ of bone is of interest because it has been shown that in many situations involving loss of body Na^+, this cation is mobilized from the surface layers of bone. Also, a rise in extracellular Na^+ concentration is mitigated by entrance of some of the excess Na^+ into the bone stores of the body.

The total exchangeable Na^+ content of infants (76 mEq. per kg. of body weight) is considerably higher than that of adults and is equal to the total sodium content determined by chemical analysis.[26, 62] This means that all the bone Na^+ in infants is readily exchangeable with radiosodium. The higher value of total Na^+ in the young is due to the very large extracellular space of the infant; the amount decreases *pari passu* with decrease of extracellular volume.

TABLE 3. *Distribution of Sodium, Potassium, Magnesium, Chloride, and Bicarbonate in the Various Body Compartments of Man*

COMPARTMENT	SODIUM	POTASSIUM	MAGNESIUM	CHLORIDE	BICARBONATE
	(mEq. per kg. body weight)				
Plasma	6.5	0.2	0.08	4.5	1.1
Interstitial–lymph	16.8	0.5	0.12	12.3	2.9
Dense connective tissue and cartilage	6.8	0.2	1.0	5.2*	1.7
Exchangeable bone	6.4	4.1	1.0	4.3	0.8
Nonexchangeable bone	14.8	—	19.5	—	—
Transcellular	1.5	0.5	0.07	1.5	0.3
Total Extracellular	52.8	5.5	21.8	27.8	6.8
Total Intracellular	5.2	48.3	8.2	5.2	5.9
Total Body	58.0	53.8	30.0	33.0	12.7
Total Exchangeable	41.0	48.9	3.4, 4.9, 10†	33.0	12.7
Total body intracellular concentration (mEq. per liter i.c.w.)	14.4	134	22.8	14.4	16.4

Values for connective tissue and bone include only those portions that are considered extracellular and solids. (After Edelman and Leibman, *Amer. J. Med.*, 1959, *27*:256–277; Wacker and Vallee, *New Engl. J. Med.*, 1958, *259*:431–438; idem, 475–482; MacIntyre et al., *Clin. Sci.*, 1961, *20*:297–305; and Freeman and Fenn, *Amer. J. Physiol.*, 1953, *174*:422–430.)

* A fraction of skin chloride appears to be nonexchangeable as determined by radiochloride studies.

† Equilibrated for 24, 48 and 89 hours respectively. Total exchangeable magnesium is a function of time of equilibration.

Low values for total exchangeable Na+ have been observed in adrenal insufficiency and high values in edematous states and hypertension.

POTASSIUM.[72] The amount of K+ in the body depends on the balance between intake and output. The K+ content remains nearly constant in healthy adult life with only minor fluctuations from day to day. K+ is an integral part of protoplasm and in the developing organism the over-all K+ balance is positive. The turnover rate of K+ is higher in infants than in adults. Young rats do not grow normally on a K+-deficient diet. The normal intake of K+ is dietary and is derived from both animal and plant sources, both of which are rich in K+. The normal dietary intake of K+ ranges from 50 to 150 mEq. per day; this amount is also excreted daily. Most of the output is in the urine, but some is excreted in feces (9 mEq. per day); a very small amount is excreted in sweat.

Content and distribution. The total K+ content of the human adult male is 50 to 54 mEq. per kg. of body weight.[25] It is slightly lower in the female. The distribution of K+ in the various compartments of the body is summarized in Table 3. Only 10 per cent of the total K+ is in extracellular fluids; the bulk is located intracellularly. Almost 90 per cent of the intracellular K+ is found in muscle cells. The intracellular K+ concentration averaged over the whole body is 134 mEq. per liter of cell water. This value is close to the 150 mEq. per liter shown for muscle in Table 5.

The rate of K+ exchange between extracellular fluid and cells is rapid as compared to that of Na+, but varies with the type of tissue. For example, the time for equilibration between plasma K+ and tissue is 2 minutes for kidney; 8 to 10 minutes for intestine and lung; 90 to 100 minutes for liver, skin and spleen; 600 minutes for muscle mass; and greater than 62 hours for erythrocytes and brain. In all of these tissues, the K+ is completely exchangeable.[30, 72] Bone contains appreciable amounts of K+ (Table 3) which is completely exchangeable, although its rate of exchange is probably slow. Since 80 to 90 per cent of the total body

K^+ is in muscle, the quantity of exchangeable K^+ is a reasonably good measure of lean muscle mass. Although the cellular concentration of K^+ remains fairly constant with increasing age, total exchangeable K^+ is lower in infants and children than in adults. This is a reflection of the large extracellular space characteristic of children.[63, 64]

K^+ deficiency. Cellular stores of K^+ are depleted in a number of clinical conditions which result in excessive loss of the ion from the body. These losses occur either via the urine (as in adrenocortical hyperfunction, renal disease of various kinds, diuretic therapy and diabetic acidosis) or via the gastrointestinal tract (as in vomiting, diarrhea and continuous aspiration of intestinal fluids during surgery). The latter conditions result in rapid K^+ deficiency because the transcellular fluids which enter the gastrointestinal tract contain K^+ in concentrations 2 to 5 times higher than that of extracellular fluid. Reduction of K^+ stores causes characteristic clinical effects, mainly manifested in muscle tissue. In skeletal muscle, weakness develops and may progress to flaccid paralysis. Weakness in gastrointestinal smooth muscle leads to diarrhea, distension, and paralytic ileus; in vascular smooth muscle, weakness leads to hypotension. Loss of K^+ from cardiac muscle leads to tachycardia, arrhythmias and electrocardiographic changes characterized by a prolonged Q-T interval, T wave inversion and the appearance of U waves (cf. Chap. 36).

The reverse of these changes occurs in plasma and in total body K^+ during K^+ repletion. Increases in plasma K^+ levels occur in anuria, adrenocortical insufficiency, and excessive therapy with K^+ solutions. The rise in plasma K^+ is accompanied by an increase in cellular concentration, but the ratio of $[K^+]_i/[K^+]_o$ is decreased and transmembrane potential is reduced. If plasma K^+ continues to rise, progressive signs of K^+ intoxication appear. Hyperkalemia is even more dangerous than hypokalemia. Muscle weakness and central nervous system changes due to membrane depolarization are a striking feature of this condition. Cardiac effects include arrhythmias and progressive changes in the electrocardiogram (cf. Fig. 16, Chap. 36).

Regulation of potassium distribution. Observations in experimental animals and man have shown that the extracellular concentration of K^+ is increased by acidosis and decreased by alkalosis, regardless of how the pH change is produced. In the case of acidosis, K^+ is lost from the cells, particularly those of muscle, and this causes plasma K^+ concentration to rise, increasing K^+ excretion in the urine. Therefore, chronic acidosis results in a reduction of total body K^+. In alkalosis, K^+ moves into cells from the extracellular fluid, plasma K^+ decreases, but urinary K^+ excretion increases. This increase in urinary K^+ excretion is the result of local conditions in the kidney which strongly favor K^+ secretion. Thus, in both acidosis and alkalosis, there is a tendency for K^+ to flow from muscle cells, through the plasma, into the kidney, and out in the urine. Just as changes in acid–base status modify K^+ balance, changes in K^+ balance modify acid–base status. When excessive K^+ is administered, plasma K^+ concentration is elevated and active uptake of K^+ by cells is stimulated. Since active K^+ influx and Na^+ efflux are coupled (Chap. 1), cellular Na^+ concentration falls. H^+ efflux from cells is probably also coupled into the Na^+–K^+ pump, and its transport from cells to extracellular fluid is also increased. Thus the elevation of plasma K^+ concentration produces a decrease in cellular Na^+ concentration, an increase in cellular K^+ concentration, and an elevation in cellular pH (Table 4). A reflection of the transport of H^+ out of the cell is seen in the decrease in extracellular pH. The clinically more important condition of K^+ deficiency produces effects on extracellular and intracellular acid–base balance opposite from those produced by excessive K^+ administration. If body K^+ stores are depleted by reduced intake or excessive losses, an extracellular hypokalemic alkalosis develops. In the intracellular compartment, the concentration of Na^+ increases and of K^+ decreases and metabolic acidosis results (Fig. 5). Summaries of the evidence that cells are acidotic in K^+ deficiency and methods of measuring cell pH have been presented by a number of workers.[8, 17, 28, 35, 62, 66, 67]

The K^+ content of cells is maintained constant in practically all tissues at about 150 mEq. per liter by the Na^+–K^+ active transport system. As a result, the level of K^+ and Na^+ in cells is influenced by any condition or agent which alters the active transport system. The main regulator of cellular K^+ and Na^+ concentrations appears to be aldosterone, which

TABLE 4. *Effect of Elevated Plasma Potassium Concentration on Sucrose, Chloride and Sodium Spaces, and on Intracellular Electrolyte Concentrations of Rat Skeletal Muscle*

	INTERSTITIAL				INTRACELLULAR				SPACE					
	Volume (sucrose space)	$[Na^+]_e$	$[K^+]_e$	$[Cl^-]_e$	Volume	$[Na^+]_i$	$[K^+]_i$	$[Cl^-]_i$	Na^+	Cl^-	$\dfrac{[Cl^-]_o}{[Cl^-]_i}$	ε_{Cl}	$\dfrac{[K^+]_i}{[K^+]_o}$	ε_K
	per cent	mEq. per liter E.C.W.			per cent	mEq. per liter Cell H_2O			· per cent	per cent		mV.		mV.
Control	8.2	146.0	4.2	118.0	69.2	12.4	150	3.9	14.2	10.5	30.3	−88.9	35.7	−93.2
Nephrectomy	12.2	139.2	8.0	110.5	64.3	4.8	175	5.6	14.0	15.1	20.2	−78.0	21.9	−80.4

All chloride determinations made by the electrometric titration method of Cotlove *et al.*[17]

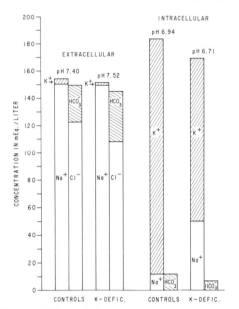

Fig. 5. Effect of chronic potassium deficiency on extracellular and intracellular pH and electrolyte values in rat skeletal muscle. Potassium lack produces an extracellular hypokalemic, hypochloremic, metabolic alkalosis, and an intracellular metabolic acidosis characterized by marked loss of K^+ and gain of Na^+. Note the decrease in the sum of Na^+ plus K^+ in the acidotic cells. As a result of the acidosis, total anionic charge on the protein in the cells is reduced; hence total cation concentration is decreased. (Adapted from Irvine *et al., Clin. Sci.,* 1961, *20*:1–18.)

probably acts by increasing active cation transport across cells.[73] The initial effect of the steroid is to increase K^+ and decrease Na^+ levels in all cells. The result of the aldosterone-induced increase in K^+ concentration of renal tubular cells is an increase in the urinary excretion of this cation. If the increased aldosterone output is maintained, then cellular K^+ deficiency results from chronic loss in the urine and the sequelae already discussed appear. Adrenocortical hypofunction causes opposite changes from hyperfunction. Initially, cellular K^+ is decreased and Na^+ increased, but as tubular cell K^+ decreases, K^+ excretion in the urine is reduced and plasma K^+ increases. The sequence of events is then the same as that discussed above for excessive K^+ administration and an extracellular hyperkalemic metabolic acidosis develops.

Loss of K^+ from cells may also result from massive breakdown or destruction of tissue. Each gram of nitrogen in protoplasm is associ-

ated with 2.4 mEq. of K^+ and this much is lost for every gram of nitrogen broken down. Repair of formation of new tissue is associated with K^+ uptake into cells.

The subcellular distribution of K^+ is characterized by heterogeneity. For example, mitochondria concentrate K^+ by a process which requires energy. *In vitro* incubation studies indicate, however, that the ratio of mitochondrial to suspending medium K^+ is low (about 2:1). In addition, some nuclei possess a low membrane potential (inside negative) and also concentrate K^+ slightly above the outside medium.[34] Depending on the pH of the medium, microsomes appear to "bind" K^+ in much the same manner as cationic exchange resins. Although many of the subcellular particles contain K^+ at concentrations higher than that of the surrounding cytoplasm, 65 to 85 per cent of cellular K^+ is in the cytoplasm proper. Brain mitochondria contain 30 per cent or more of the total tissue K^+.[34] Possibly the slowly exchanging fraction of K^+ which has been described for this tissue is due to slow penetration of K^+ into mitochondria.

MAGNESIUM.[65] Mg^{++} is predominantly an intracellular cation which is present in quantities second only to K^+. The element is important for living organisms and, in its absence, deficiency symptoms develop. In many respects, movements of Mg^{++} into and out of cells resemble those of K^+. Mg^{++} activates many enzymes, plays an essential role in neuromuscular function and is an important constituent of bone.

Mg^{++} is relatively abundant in foods; green plants contain large amounts inasmuch as the element is an integral part of the chlorophyll molecule. The daily intake of Mg^{++} in an average diet is about 25 mEq., of which about one-third is ordinarily absorbed. The daily requirement has not been established, but about 18 to 20 mEq. per day for adults, about 12.5 mEq. per day for infants and about 33 mEq. per day during pregnancy and lactation appear to be adequate to maintain Mg^{++} balance. In normal adults, the 5 to 12 mEq. which are absorbed daily is balanced by urinary excretion.

Content and distribution. The total content of Mg^{++} in the body averages 30 mEq. per kg. of body weight; its distribution is indicated in Table 3. Mg^{++} distribution is similar to that of K^+ except that a large amount is present in bone. It is present in the hydration shell and in the surface-bound ion layer but probably not in the crystal lattice interior. About two-thirds of the total body Mg++ is located in bone, 4 per cent in the extracellular fluid and connective tissue, and the remainder in cellular fluid. The highest amounts are found in skeletal muscle, brain and liver. On the assumption that Mg++ is not bound in cells, the calculated intracellular concentration in muscle is about 34 mEq. per liter of cell water.

The interstitial concentration of Mg++ is lower than its concentration in plasma because about 35 per cent of the plasma Mg++ is bound to protein. Thus, if the plasma concentration averages 2.0 mEq. per liter the interstitial concentration (after correction for the Donnan effect) averages 1.13 mEq. per liter. The ratio of Mg++ across the cell membrane is

$$\frac{34 \text{ mEq. per liter}}{1.13 \text{ mEq. per liter}} = 30.0$$

Since Mg++ is doubly charged, a membrane potential of 90 mV. predicts a passive ratio across the membrane of 1000, rather than the 32 that would be predicted for a monovalent ion. Since the ratio is less than one-thirtieth that predicted by passive distribution, Mg++ must be pumped out of muscle cells. Any cellular binding that may occur would make this argument even stronger.

When Mg++ is injected[28] and the turnover rates in the body pool are analyzed, four compartments can be distinguished.[1, 38, 54] A rapid compartment with a half-time of 1 hour contains less than 5 per cent of the body Mg++; this probably corresponds to the distribution throughout the extracellular fluid. An intermediate compartment with a half-time of 3 hours contains slightly more Mg++ and probably corresponds to its distribution through skin, connective tissue, liver, intestine and heart. A slower compartment with a half-time of one day contains about 20 per cent of the body Mg++; this represents exchange with muscle cells and erythrocytes. Finally, about two-thirds of the body Mg++ exchanges very slowly with a half-time of about 25 days. This is the so-called unexchangeable Mg++ situated on the inner surface layers of bone.

Magnesium deficiency and excess. The main symptoms of Mg++ deficiency are tetany, which is indistinguishable from hypocalcemic tetany, and occasionally, convulsions. Chronic deficiency in animals causes alopecia, skin lesions, hyperemia and fibrotic changes in the blood vessels. Both plasma and skeletal muscle Mg++ levels decrease markedly in humans,[38] but soft tissue Mg++ does not decrease in experimental animals.[2, 11] Total 24-hour exchangeable Mg++ is also decreased[28] because of the loss from the slowly exchangeable fraction in muscle[38] and bone.[2] Administration of Mg++ corrects the deficiency, but if excessive amounts are given, the following effects are noted: central nervous system depression and anesthesia, neuromuscular and ganglionic blockade, vasodilation and depression of the myocardium. Electrocardiographic changes similar to those produced by K+ excess are also noted.

Regulation of magnesium distribution. The factors regulating Mg++ levels in cells and plasma are not known. However, they appear to be correlated with aldosterone secretion, as is K+. As might be anticipated from the similarity of Mg++ to Ca++, parathormone mobilizes Mg++ from bone and increases its excretion in the urine. However, unlike Ca++, plasma Mg++ levels are decreased. The relation between acid–base changes and Mg++ metabolism has not been clearly elucidated, but the available data indicate that the movements of Mg++ in acid–base derangements are like those of K+.

CALCIUM. The physiology of Ca++ metabolism is discussed in Chapter 6.

CHLORIDE.[10] Cl−, like Na+, is confined mainly to the extracellular fluid and is the predominant anion of this fluid. It is present in cells, but unlike Na+, which is actively transported out of cells, the concentration of Cl− is usually determined by the membrane potential. In gastric and intestinal mucosa, however, Cl− is actively transported (see Chaps. 43 and 49).

Content and distribution. The total body Cl− content in man and experimental animals averages about 33 mEq. per kg. of body weight. The distribution of Cl− in the various fluid compartments is presented in Table 3. About 50 per cent of the Cl− is found in plasma and interstitial fluids. The content of Cl− in connective tissue is high and represents about 16 per cent of the total, as compared to 12 per cent of the total body Na+ found in connective tissue. Thus, some of the Cl− in connective tissue is either intracellular, bound to extracellular proteins, or more likely, both. Since not all of the Cl− present in connective tissue exchanges with radiochloride, some binding may occur.

Transcellular Cl− is a small, but important,

fraction of total body Cl⁻. The Cl⁻ concentration in such fluids varies from 20 mEq. per liter or less in sweat or colonic fluid to more than 150 mEq. per liter in actively secreted gastric acid. Approximately 40 per cent of transcellular fluid Cl⁻ is in the gastrointestinal tract and about 25 per cent is in cerebrospinal fluid.

Since Cl⁻ is passively distributed across cell membranes, most of the intracellular Cl⁻ is present in cells with low membrane potentials. These include smooth muscle, exocrine glands, liver, glia, connective tissue and erythrocytes. Erythrocytes contain approximately 40 per cent of this amount. Muscle cells contain an additional 20 per cent of the intracellular Cl⁻.

Values for exchangeable Cl⁻ reach about the same value as that obtained by chemical analysis if sufficient time is allowed for equilibration (24 to 48 hours). Most of the Cl⁻ is rapidly exchangeable and, in rats, only the Cl⁻ in skin, testes and brain is not completely exchanged with radiochloride within 30 minutes. After 24 hours, only the skin Cl⁻ is not equilibrated.

Regulation of chloride distribution. Except for acid–base derangements, changes in body Cl⁻ content are influenced by the same factors and in the same direction as are changes in body Na⁺ content. Changes in Cl⁻ levels secondary to acid–base distortions are covered in Chapter 46. Where Cl⁻ distribution is passive, its movement is governed by changes in the membrane voltage and thus, ultimately, by the activity of the sodium pump. In the case of tissues that actively transport Cl⁻, alterations of Cl⁻ distribution can be produced by inhibitors of the transport process.

BICARBONATE. The presence of HCO_3^- in the body is dependent on two factors: (i) the metabolic production of CO_2 by cells and (ii) the excess of cations, such as Na⁺, K⁺, Ca⁺⁺ and Mg⁺⁺, over nonlabile anions, such as Cl⁻, $SO_4^=$, $PO_4^{\equiv}$, and protein. HCO_3^- is a labile anion derived from the hydration of metabolically produced CO_2. The amount of HCO_3^- in body fluids is equal to the difference between the sum of the fixed cations and the sum of the fixed anions in any fluid. An excess of cations over anions causes the formation of HCO_3^- from the hydration of CO_2 and an excess of anions causes conversion of HCO_3^- to carbonic acid with liberation of CO_2. The role of HCO_3^-

in regulation of body acid–base balance is discussed in Chapter 46.

The total body HCO_3^- averages 13 mEq. per kg. of body weight. The total acid-releaseable CO_2 of the body, however, is much greater than this and amounts to approximately 76 mEq. per kg. of body weight.[27] The difference between these values is contributed by carbonate from the crystal lattice of bone.

The distribution of HCO_3^- in the various body fluids is indicated in Table 3. About half the HCO_3^- is in the extracellular compartment. The over-all average concentration in transcellular fluids is about the same as that in plasma, but the values in individual fluids vary considerably. The concentration is high in pancreatic fluid and aqueous humor but absent or extremely low in gastric acid. In transcellular fluids with high HCO_3^- concentrations, this anion is actively secreted; it appears that carbonic anhydrase is involved in the secretory process.

The other half of the total body HCO_3^- is present in cells. Muscle cells contain HCO_3^- at a concentration of about 12 mEq. per liter (Table 5) and most other cells contain it at higher concentrations. Thus, the concentration ratio of HCO_3^- across the muscle cell membrane $\left(\dfrac{[HCO_3^-]_o}{[HCO_3^-]_i} = \dfrac{26}{12} \right)$ is 2.2. This value is far from the value of 30 predicted by the membrane potential. Either HCO_3^- must be transported actively into cells or H⁺ must be transported actively out of them. The nature of and evidence for active transport of H⁺ or of HCO_3^- are discussed more fully in Chapters 1 and 46.

The average cell body concentration of HCO_3^-, 16 mEq. per liter, is not far from the values found in muscle, brain and heart. The over-all body *p*H is 7.23 as calculated from this value and from the assumptions that (i) P_{CO_2} is in equilibrium across all cell membranes and (ii) that the hydration reaction of $CO_2 \leftrightarrows H_2CO_3$ is in equilibrium everywhere. Values of over-all cellular *p*H of between 6.9 and 7.0 have been measured from the distribution of the weak acid 5,5-dimethyl-2,4-oxazolidinedione (DMO);[40, 50, 66] such observations have been made in muscle, brain and thyroid tissue. The interpretation appears to be that the reaction between CO_2 and H_2CO_3 is not always at equilibrium in cells. The cellular concentration of H_2CO_3 is higher and the cellular *p*H is lower than would be predicted on the assumption of equilibrium. In skeletal muscle, the cells do not contain carbonic anhydrase and this disequilibrium is

TABLE 5. *Intracellular Concentrations of Cations and Anions in Some Representative Tissues*

	ION	SKELETAL MUSCLE	CARDIAC MUSCLE	LIVER	THYROID GLAND	ERYTHROCYTES
		(mEq. per liter intracellular water)				
CATIONS	Na+	12	7	3	42	19
	K+	150	134	148	147	136
	Mg++	34	28	31	?	6
	Ca++	4	4	2	?	0
	Total	200	173	184		161
ANIONS	Cl−	4	4	16	19	78
	HCO$_3^-$	12	12	?	14	18
	PO$_4^{\equiv}$ + Organic	40				4
	Protein	54				36
	Total	110				136
Total mOsm. per liter		310				310
E.C.F. volume		8.2 per cent	19.5 per cent	15 per cent	30 per cent	—

greater than normally found in brain or thyroid tissue, where there are large amounts of this enzyme. After inhibition of this enzyme, the disequilibrium is enhanced in these latter tissues.

Present data indicate that all of the HCO$_3^-$ in the body is exchangeable. Factors affecting the distribution, excretion and transcellular movement of HCO$_3^-$ are discussed in Chapters 44 and 46. A summary of the quantitative aspects of HCO$_3^-$ and H+ turnover and distribution in man has been presented by Elkinton.[21]

Fluid Measurement and Composition in Isolated Tissues. Methods for measurement of whole body distribution of water and ions in the various fluid compartments of the body have already been described. These methods involve a knowledge of total body water and ionic content, the volume of the extracellular fluid, and the ionic composition of plasma. The same principles apply in isolated tissues. The extracellular volume, measured with one of the polysaccharides or with sulfate, the water and ionic composition of the plasma, and the total tissue water and electrolytes must be determined. From such raw data, the extracellular and intracellular values can be derived.

PLASMA. The values for water and electrolyte content are determined by standard techniques: the water content by desiccation, Na+ and K+ by flame photometry, and Cl− by any of several methods, the most accurate of which is that of Cotlove *et al.*[12] Since

ions are dissolved only in the aqueous phase of plasma, concentrations of electrolytes are expressed in terms of plasma water. The concentrations of the various ions in plasma and in plasma water are shown in Table 6. The solid content of plasma is made up mainly of negatively charged protein, which constitutes 6 to 8 per cent of plasma weight. Although the protein occupies a large volume, it makes up only a small portion of the anionic charge in plasma and contributes only a small fraction to the total plasma osmotic concentration. However, the protein is important in maintaining the differential concentration of ions between plasma and interstitial fluid via the Gibbs–Donnan distribution.

INTERSTITIAL FLUID. The concentration of any ion in the interstitial fluid is determined by its concentration in plasma and its Gibbs–Donnan distribution ratio. Capillary membranes are not freely permeable to protein, and hence interstitial fluid, unlike plasma, is nearly devoid of protein.[41] In any system in which two fluid compartments are separated by a membrane permeable to water and to all but one of the charged solutes (e.g., plasma protein), a potential difference develops across the membrane which affects the distribution of the ions present. The sequence of events leading to equilibration is similar to that described in Figure 3, Chapter 1. The concentration of Cl− in the plasma water must be less than in interstitial fluid because some of the negative charges are carried by proteins in plasma. The potential arises from the flow of Cl− ions down their concentration gradient from interstitial fluid to plasma, thereby charging the capillary membrane negatively on the plasma side. In

TABLE 6. *Concentrations of Cations and Anions in Plasma,*
Plasma Water and Interstitial Fluid

	ION	PLASMA* (mEq. per liter)	PLASMA WATER (mEq. per liter)	INTERSTITIAL FLUID† (mEq. per liter)
CATIONS	Na+	142	152.7	145.1
	K+	4.0	4.3	4.1
	Ca++	5.0	5.4	3.5
	Mg++	2.0	2.2	1.3
	Total	153.0	164.6	154.0
ANIONS	Cl−	102.0	109.9	115.7
	HCO_3^-	26.0	27.9	29.3
	$PO_4^=$	2.0	2.1	2.3
	Other	6.0	6.5	6.7
	Protein	17.0	18.2	0.0
	Total	153.0	164.6	154.0
Total mOsm. per liter		306.0	329.2	308.0

* A plasma water content of 93 per cent was used in the calculation.
† Gibbs–Donnan factors used are 0.95 for monovalent anions and 1.05 for monovalent cations.

turn, Na+ ions flow down the voltage gradient from interstitial fluid to plasma, i.e., they accompany Cl−. Hence there will be a net flow of Na+ and Cl− into plasma until the concentration of Na+ has increased enough to provide an equal counterflow. Thus, in the case of the capillary membrane, cations are less concentrated and anions are more concentrated in the interstitial fluid than in the vascular fluid. The total cation concentration balances the total anion concentration in each compartment. If equilibrium has been attained, one can use the Nernst equation to calculate the ratio of concentrations from the voltage or *vice versa* (see Chaps. 1 and 43). In addition, if water is to be in equilibrium, a hydrostatic pressure difference must be present across the membrane. In capillaries, the vascular side must be at a higher pressure than the interstitial side. The concentrations of permeant monovalent cations is about 5 per cent less and of permeant anions about 5 per cent more in interstitial fluid than in the capillaries from which this fluid derives, and the transcapillary voltage is about 1.3 mV. For divalent ions, there is about a 10 per cent difference in concentrations. The average concentrations of some of the ions in interstitial fluid as compared to their concentrations in plasma is presented in Table 6. It is of interest to note that the osmolar concentration of plasma protein must be about 1.5 mMol per liter to produce the observed osmotic pressure of 25 mm. Hg, while the equivalent concentration must be 17 mEq. per liter (Table 6) to produce the observed Gibbs–Donnan factor of 1.05; i.e., the average valence of plasma protein is about − 10.

INTRACELLULAR FLUID. In order to calculate the concentrations of ions in cell water, not only must tissue water and electrolyte content be known, but the volume of interstitial fluid present in the tissue must be determined. The volume of distribution of inulin is a measure of the latter. The calculation for muscle intracellular Na+ is as follows: Total muscle water = 0.774 kg. per kg. of fat-free wet muscle; total muscle inulin = 18.04 mg. per kg. of fat-free wet muscle; total muscle Na+ = 20.7 mEq. per kg. of fat-free muscle. The concentration of inulin in interstitial water is 220 mg. per kg. of water and the concentration of Na+ is 147 mEq. per kg. of water. The volume of interstitial fluid must be that volume required to account for the measured inulin or 18.04/220 = 0.082 kg. per kg. of fat-free wet muscle. This interstitial space of 8.2 per cent contains 0.082 × 147 = 12.1 mEq. per kg. of fat-free wet muscle of Na+. Hence 20.7 − 12.1 = 8.6 mEq. of Na+ that must be intracellular in every kg. of muscle. Since 0.082 kg. of water is interstitial, 0.774 − 0.082 = 0.692 kg. water which must be intracellular in every kg. of muscle. The concentration of Na+ within the cells is the quantity of intracellular Na+ divided by the volume of intracellular water: $[Na^+]_i$ = 8.6 mEq. per kg./0.692 kg. per kg. = 12.4 mEq. per kg. intracellular water. Values for the intracellular concentration of other solutes are calculated in the same manner.

Intracellular cation and anion of some representative tissues are summarized in Table 5. The intracellular values for each tissue appear to be characteristic of that tissue. It is evident, therefore, that each tissue has its own intrinsic mechanism for regulation of its internal composition. Note that HCO_3^- is higher than would be predicted by the transmembrane voltage. This discrepancy is due to the continuous metabolic production of CO_2 and its subsequent hydration within the cell which keeps HCO_3^- from ever attaining equilibrium. Rather, a steady state is reached in which intracellular HCO_3^- is higher than the equilibrium value. The dependence of the intracellular concentration of Cl^- on the membrane potential is dramatically illustrated by comparing the difference in concentrations between muscle and red blood cells. In muscle, where $\mathcal{E}_s$ is about 90 mV., intracellular Cl^- is only 4 mEq. per liter. In red blood cells, where the $\mathcal{E}_s$ is less than 10 mV., intracellular Cl^- is 78 mEq. per liter.

It is difficult to determine the total osmolar concentration in cellular fluid, because the total charge on the major anion, protein, is not known. However, if osmolar equilibrium with extracellular fluid is assumed (see below), one can estimate protein valence. The total molar concentration of protein is the difference between the total solute concentration in cells (equal to that in plasma) and the total solute concentration of the determined ions in those cells. The charge on that protein is the difference between the total concentration of determined cations and the total concentration of determined anions. The valence is calculated as the charge per mol of protein. Calculation from the muscle data in Table 6 yields a value of almost 3 for the valence of the protein.

EXCHANGES OF WATER AND ELECTROLYTES BETWEEN BODY COMPARTMENTS

The dynamics of fluid and electrolyte movements across the capillary endothelium and the cell membrane are an important aspect of body fluid physiology. Such movements are the basis for nourishment of cells and the maintenance of osmotic equilibrium between vascular, interstitial and intracellular spaces.

Plasma and Interstitial Fluids.[6, 45, 52] Water is continuously exchanged between the intravascular and interstitial fluids through the walls of capillaries. The fluid exchange depends upon the physical factors of diffusion and filtration and upon the colloid osmotic (oncotic) pressure of the plasma. Although there has been considerable discussion on the relative contributions of diffusion and bulk filtration in capillary exchange, the over-all result is that capillary exchange follows the general pattern first suggested by Starling. The dominant force

tending to move material from the vascular compartment into the interstitial compartment is the hydrostatic pressure of the blood. Since protein crosses the capillary membrane very slowly, its concentration in interstitial fluid is much lower than its concentration in plasma. The osmotic pressure corresponding to the difference in concentrations of protein constitutes the dominant force tending to bring material back from the interstitial compartment to the blood. At the arterial end of a capillary, the hydrostatic pressure is greater than the oncotic pressure and there is a net bulk movement of water, electrolytes and the small organic molecules from plasma into interstitial fluid. At the venous end of the capillary, the hydrostatic pressure has fallen and is below the oncotic pressure, and there is net bulk movement of water, electrolytes and small organic molecules back into blood. These transcapillary movements must balance in the steady state. Thus, an increase in vascular pressure or a decrease in plasma protein concentration (such as occurs in nephrosis or after severe burns) leads to a net transfer of fluid from vascular to interstitial fluid. The result is edema.

Although water and the dissolved electrolytes appear to cross capillaries only through a small portion of the capillary membrane, the respiratory gases appear to diffuse through the whole surface. This accounts for the rapidity of gas transport compared to that of water and electrolytes.

Interstitial and Intracellular Fluids. With a few exceptions, such as cells in the ascending limb of renal tubules and cells lining the ducts of sweat and salivary glands, all cells appear to be freely permeable to water. Hence, the total solute concentration of cell fluid is the same as that of interstitial fluid and water is exchanged quickly across cell membranes. The mechanisms of exchange of solutes between interstitial and intracellular fluids have already been discussed.

An interesting problem arises from the fact that cells contain considerable amounts of nonpermeating anion. Since interstitial fluid contains little or no protein, a Donnan equilibrium is set up across the cell membrane. The situation is similar to that across the capillary membrane with one important difference: cell membranes have remarkably low tensile strengths and are unable to support the pressure difference necessary to balance these forces. Active cation transport resolves the apparent difficulty. The low permeability and active transport of Na+ out of cells produces what is in effect a nonpermeating cation. This effect balances that of the nonpermeating anion within the cell. Consequently, conditions which increase the passive permeability of cells to Na+ or decrease the rate of active extrusion should unbalance this double Donnan system and lead to entry of water into cells. This has been found to be the case. The converse, that increased pumping should lead to a shift of water out of the cells, by increasing the effective impermeability to Na+ is also true and probably accounts for the finding that administration of deoxycorticosterone produces a shift of water out of cells.

If the active transport system of a cell is very efficient and essentially all of the interstitial Na+ can be considered impermeant, then the concentration of impermeant ion is higher outside than inside the cell. Since pressure differences cannot balance the osmotic forces, it would be expected that, under these conditions, cells would be slightly hypertonic. Robinson[51] found that there are circumstances in which cells do appear to be hypertonic. That the process which renders the cells hypertonic should be the active transport of solute material out of them is a fine physiologic paradox.

Alterations of Fluid and Electrolyte Balance. Examples of various clinical states characterized by changes in fluid volume or osmolal concentration induced by alterations in Na+ or water content are presented in Figure 6. Volume is indicated on the abscissa and osmolal concentration on the ordinate. The total quantity of solute material in a compartment is represented by the area.

Calculation of the shift in fluid compartments is based on the principle used throughout this chapter that $Q/V = [C]$. When only water has been added to or subtracted from a compartment or the body as a whole, the product of the concentration of a solute in a compartment and the compartmental volume is constant, and

$$C_{initial} \, V_{initial} = C_{final} \, V_{final}.$$

When solute material is added, the change in total quantity must first be calculated and then

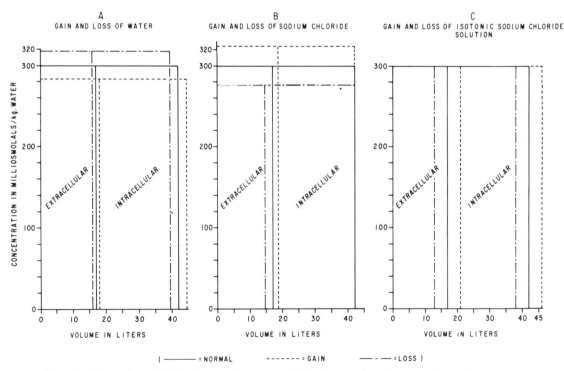

Fig. 6. Examples of clinical states characterized by changes in volume and osmolar concentration of extracellular and intracellular compartments. *Ordinate,* Concentration in mOsm. per kg. water. *Abscissa,* Volume of the compartment in liters. Solid lines represent the initial normal state, dashed lines the final state after *addition* of fluid or solute, and dot-dashed lines the final state after *loss* of water or solute. (After Darrow and Yannet, *J. clin. Invest.,* 1935, *14:*266–275.)

the relation between concentrations and volumes deduced.*

Changes in extracellular Na+ concentration accurately reflect changes in total osmolality; therefore, plasma Na+ level is used to predict volume and concentration changes in conditions of altered fluid and electrolyte balance.[74]

EXCESSIVE INTAKE OF WATER (HYDRATION). Hydration may result from excessive ingestion or decreased loss of water or from administration of antidiuretic hormone (ADH). The effect of oral ingestion of water on the volume and composition of the body compartments is shown in Figure 6A. After absorption from the intestinal tract, water distributes rapidly and uniformly throughout the body in proportion to the initial volumes of the extracellular and intracellular compartments.

Excessive water intake may produce the syndrome of water intoxication. The symptoms probably result from disturbed cellular metabolism secondary to decreased cellular electrolyte concentration. The disturbances are mainly related to the central nervous system: disorientation, convulsions and coma. Other disturbances are gastrointestinal dysfunction, muscular weakness and cardiac arrhythmias.

EXCESSIVE LOSS OF WATER (DEHYDRATION). Water loss by excessive evaporation through the lungs and skin or by lowered intake causes volume and composition changes opposite to those produced by hydration (Fig. 6A). The total osmolality of the body fluids is increased and the volumes of the intracellular and extracellular fluid compartments are decreased in proportion to their original volume.

EXCESSIVE INTAKE OF SOLUTE. Intravenous infusion of a strongly hypertonic solution of NaCl leads to the following sequence of events. The quantity of solute in the extracellular compartment increases and the volume also increases initially by the amount infused. Next water shifts from the intracellular to the hypertonic extracellular compartment. The final result is that solute concentrations are equalized and that the extracellular compartment

*Normally, intracellular solutes are regarded as remaining intracellular and extracellular solutes are regarded as remaining extracellular. Calculation of fluid balances in this manner is generally close enough to be adequate for clinical purposes. However, there may be secondary solute transfer across cell membranes, e.g., in severe dehydration.

has gained in volume in addition to the amount infused. The intracellular compartment has shrunk. The total solute in the extracellular compartment has increased by the amount of solute infused, but total cellular solute has remained unchanged. The solute concentration in both compartments has risen. Actually all these processes occur simultaneously.

Example: A 70 kg. man was given an infusion of 1 liter of a NaCl solution containing 1000 mOsm. (500 mEq. per liter).

Initial intracellular volume = 25 liters.

Initial extracellular volume = 17 liters.

Initial solute concentration in each compartment = 300 mOsm. per liter.

Quantity of solute in whole body initially = (25 liters + 17 liters) 300 mOsm. per liter = 12,600 mOsm.

Quantity of solute in whole body after infusion = 12,600 mOsm. + 1000 mOsm. = 13,600 mOsm.

Volume of water in whole body after infusion = (25 liters + 17 liters + 1 liter) = 43 liters.

Concentration in each compartment after

$$infusion = \frac{13,600 \text{ mOsm.}}{43 \text{ liters}} = 316 \text{ mOsm.}$$

per liter.

Quantity of solute initially and after infusion = 25 liters × 300 mOsm. per liter = 7500 mOsm.

Volume of intracellular compartment after

$$infusion = \frac{7500 \text{ mOsm.}}{316 \text{ mOsm. per liter}} = 23.7$$

liters.

Volume of extracellular compartment after infusion = 43 liters − 23.7 liters = 19.3 liters.

Thus, 19.3 liters − (17 liters + 1 liter) = 1.3 liters of water which have shifted from the intracellular to the extracellular compartment.

EXCESSIVE LOSSES OF SOLUTE. The changes which result from loss of NaCl without water from the extracellular fluid are opposite from those induced by excessive intake. Body NaCl may be depleted by reduced intake, adrenocortical insufficiency, peritoneal dialysis with 5 per cent dextrose solutions,[70] or by excessive parenteral therapy with NaCl-free solutions. Extracellular fluid becomes hypotonic and water transfers into cells. Cellular hydration and extracellular dehydration result (see Fig. 6B).

ISOTONIC EXPANSION OF VOLUME. If isotonic (0.9 per cent) NaCl is infused intravenously, the volume of the extracellular fluid is expanded without change in osmolality. Hence, there is no shift of water between extracellular and intracellular compartments and the intracellular compartment remains unchanged. Clinically, this condition is termed *edema*.

ISOTONIC CONTRACTION OF VOLUME. If both Na^+ and water are lost from the body such that plasma Na^+ concentration is not altered, the volume of the extracellular fluid is reduced with no change in the intracellular compartment. This state occurs in conditions such as hemorrhage, extensive burns, and mild loss of electrolytes from the gastrointestinal tract.

In the case of hemorrhage or severe burns, the water and electrolytes are frequently replaced without replacement of the plasma protein that has also been lost. This lowers the plasma protein concentration and upsets the fluid balance between the vascular and interstitial compartments. Severe edema may result.

EXCHANGES OF WATER AND ELECTROLYTES BETWEEN BODY AND EXTERNAL ENVIRONMENT

The body surface is a site of exchange of matter and energy between the organism and its environment. Heat is mainly exchanged across the body surface, and water and electrolytes are mainly exchanged across the lungs, alimentary tract and the kidney. The exchanges take place across specialized cell membranes between extracellular fluid and the environment.

Fluid Intake. The daily net turnover of water averages between 3 and 6 per cent of total body water, that is, between 1.5 and 3.0 liters.

The total volume of body fluid results from the balance between intake and output of water. Although solid foods provide a considerable quantity of water (both preformed and as water of oxidation), variation in water intake depends largely upon the volume of liquid ingested. Physiologic regulation of the volume imbibed depends on thirst, which is discussed in Chapters 11 and 17.

Fluid Absorption. The stomach absorbs practically no water; the intestinal mucosa absorbs ingested water and electrolytes as well as the digestive secretions. Since these secretions amount to more than 6 liters per day, interference with this reabsorptive process can rapidly lead to dehydration and Na^+ depletion. Because gastrointestinal secretions are higher in K^+ concentration than is plasma, continued loss of gastrointestinal secretions, as in diarrhea or vomiting, leads to K^+ deficiency. The main force for the movement of water is active Na^+ absorption throughout the whole length of the intestinal epithelium (see Chap. 50). The intestine also appears capable of actively absorbing Cl^-. Water movement is passive, secondary to solute movement. In the small intestine, the passive permeabilities to both water and ions are high. Appreciable concentration gradients are not maintained, but bulk absorption of large amounts of solute and water take place. In the colon, the passive permeabilities are lower and concentration gradients are produced and maintained. Thus colonic contents may have very low Na^+ concentrations. Because of the high permeability of the small intestine to water, chyme rapidly equilibrates with plasma. Thus, if hypertonic solutions are placed in the small intestine, water may first enter the intestinal lumen from the perfusing blood. Only later, as active solute transport continues, is the volume reduced.

Absorption of water and electrolytes is also influenced by adrenocortical hormones. Adrenocortical insufficiency results in a decreased rate of solute and water absorption. Deoxycorticosterone, ACTH and cortisone decrease the amount of Na^+ and Cl^- and increase the amount of K^+ left in the gastrointestinal tract.

Fluid Output. Most of the fluid loss from the body is "obligated" by renal osmotic forces and by cutaneous, pulmonary and oral evaporation. However, the variable or "facultative" loss of fluid depends upon excretion of water through the renal and glandular epithelia. Only the renal output is directed toward regulation of body fluids. The kidney helps to stabilize the osmolarity and volume of body fluids by eliminating or conserving water or Na^+. These functions are regulated by two independent neurohumoral systems, the "antidiuretic system" and the "antinaturetic system."

INSENSIBLE WATER LOSS. Water without

electrolyte is lost continuously through the skin and lungs by evaporation. Insensible water loss from both skin and lungs depends on the ambient temperature and the relative humidity; loss from the lungs is also modified by changes in respiratory rate.

SWEATING.[62]   Sweating is an active secretory process concerned mainly with temperature regulation. Thus, although sweating affects both salt and water, it is not directed toward fluid regulation. Most of the sweat glands are activated when demands for heat loss are increased, as in exercise or in elevated environmental temperature. Sweating rates as high as 70 ml. per minute over short periods or 1500 ml. per hour over several hours have been reported. Such high rates of sweating are not maintained; a decline occurs even though the water which is lost is replaced. Sweating is reduced when salt in excess of that lost is ingested or injected. Similarly, sweating may be reduced in severe dehydration, although moderate water depletion does not influence the rate of sweating.

The secretion of the sweat glands is an active process which takes place in two stages as illustrated in Figure 7. Sweat secretion represents one process by which transcellular fluids are formed, and the general principles discussed here for sweat also apply with only slight modifications to the secretory process in the other duct-possessing glands such as salivary, pancreatic, and lacrimal glands. The first stage is the formation of a primary secretion in the acini of the gland. The second stage is the modification of the primary fluid by reabsorption of salts and water in the ducts.

The primary secretion of sweat is thought to be formed by active transport of either Na^+ or Cl^-. As a result of the osmotic and voltage gradients created by the active solute transport, water and the unpumped ions move passively into the lumen. The primary secretion is approximately isotonic with plasma and the sum of the Na^+ and K^+ concentrations is equal to the sum of their concentrations in plasma. As the primary secretion flows down the sweat gland ducts, Na^+ but not K^+ is reabsorbed by an active process with a limited maximal capacity; Cl^- is reabsorbed passively secondary to the active Na^+ movement. Permeability of the duct wall epithelium to water is low; hence, reabsorption of water is limited but does occur secondary to active solute transport. As a result of these two processes—primary active solute and passive water secretion followed by active solute and passive,

limited water reabsorption—the concentrations of Na^+ and Cl^- in the sweat vary with the secretory rate but are always lower than their plasma concentrations. Therefore, the final secretory fluid is always hypotonic. The concentration of K^+ appears to be independent of the secretory rate, except that with low rates the concentration rises (Fig. 7). At high flow rates, the rate of passage of the primary secretion down the duct lumen exceeds the maximal sodium reabsorptive capacity; consequently, less Na^+ is reabsorbed. The faster the secretory rate of the primary secretion the higher the Na^+ (and Cl^-) concentration in the sweat (Fig. 7). The body adapts to excessive sweating, generally caused by heavy work in hot environments, by a reduction in secretory rate, a decrease in sweat sodium, and an increase in sweat potassium concentrations. This adaptation, however, occurs only when sodium is lost because of inadequate sodium replacement. The adaptation results in conservation of sodium and is undoubtedly due to aldosterone release secondary to sodium depletion. The effects of aldosterone and adaptation on sweat electrolyte concentrations are the same.

The magnitude of electrolyte and water losses from excessive sweating can be illustrated by the following example.[62] During maximal sweating, 11 to 15 liters of sweat may be pro-

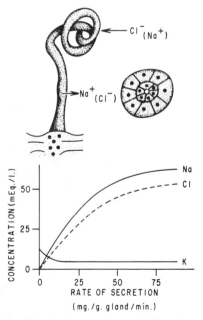

Fig. 7. Histologic structure and functional characteristics of sweat glands. Graph at the bottom shows that the concentration of Na^+ and Cl^- in sweat is determined by the rate of secretion. (After Ussing *et al.*, *The alkali metal ions in biology.* Berlin, Springer-Verlag, 1960.)

TABLE 7. *Average Daily Water Balance*

WATER INTAKE (APPROXIMATE)		WATER EXCRETION (APPROXIMATE)	
Drinking water	1200 ml.	Urine	1400 ml.
Water content of food	1000 ml.	Insensible water loss	900 ml.
Water of oxidation	300 ml.	Stool	200 ml.
	2500 ml.		2500 ml.

duced in 24 hours. This represents a water turnover of 25 per cent of total body water per day. If the average concentration of Na^+ in the sweat is 60 mEq. per liter, the 24-hour Na^+ turnover represents 20 to 30 per cent of total exchangeable Na^+. These turnover rates are so large that maintenance of normal homeostasis, even for short periods, rests almost entirely on a balanced replacement of water and NaCl losses.

OTHER MEANS OF FLUID EXCRETION.[62] Small amounts of water (approximately 100 to 200 ml. per day) and electrolytes are excreted with the feces and with glandular secretory products, such as salivary, lacrimal and genital secretions. During lactation, water and small amounts of electrolytes are lost through the mammary glands. The secretion of the transcellular fluids of these glands follows the same principles as described above for the sweat glands, that is, primary secretion followed by reabsorption. However, unlike sweat, the secretory fluid of many of these glands contains HCO_3^- in addition to Na^+, Cl^- and K^+.

Normal Fluid Balance. Despite wide variations in daily intake and output of water, total body fluid volume remains remarkably constant. In the adult, under normal conditions and over extended periods, the total intake must necessarily equal the total output. The several sources of water intake are (i) water ingested orally, (ii) water in food and (iii) water derived from oxidation of food. The water content of food contributes a considerable proportion of total intake, more than is often realized. For example, meat is 70 per cent water and certain vegetables and fruits are nearly 100 per cent water. Daily average values for the quantities of water taken into the body and excreted by various avenues are given in Table 7.

The requirement for water generally parallels energy metabolism, and it has been estimated to be approximately 1 ml. of water per calorie. The fluctuations in the total volume of

body fluid which occur during water loss and water replacement take place predominantly in the extracellular fluid. In infants, compared with adults, the total turnover of water represents a greater percentage of the volume of extracellular fluid; therefore, in infancy any excessive loss of fluid (diarrhea or vomiting) leads more rapidly to serious disturbances than in the adult. Daily changes in the total water content of the body are reflected by changes in body weight. This fact is utilized in the clinical estimation of water balance.

REGULATION OF VOLUME AND OSMOLARITY OF EXTRACELLULAR FLUID[14, 15, 29, 58]

That the total volume and osmolarity of the intracellular and extracellular compartments are rigidly controlled is evident from the small fluctuations which occur despite wide variation in dietary intake. Body weight may vary only 0.5 kg. per day if caloric balance exists and osmolarity is held constant to within 2 to 3 per cent. Intracellular volume and concentration are maintained constant by the factors already discussed. Regulation of these variables in the extracellular compartment is accomplished by control both of intake and output. The intake of water and salt is important for control of volume and osmolarity because deficits of Na^+ and water cannot be corrected solely by renal conservation mechanisms. *Excessive quantities in the body can be excreted, but deficits must be replaced by dietary intake.* The thirst mechanism plays an integral part in maintaining water homeostasis. Loss of water or gain of Na^+ induces thirst and the resulting increased intake of water, along with the renal compensating mechanisms restores the altered volume and concentration of the extracellular fluid to normal. Since, under ordinary conditions, the intake of both Na^+

and K^+ far exceeds the minimum need, regulation of salt intake normally plays very little part in maintaining the stability of extracellular fluid volume and composition.

The major control of these variables is accomplished by the kidney. Two aspects must be considered: the factors regulating volume and the factors regulating osmolarity (mainly Na^+ concentration). The *osmolarity* of the extracellular fluid is regulated by the control of free water excretion, whereas *volume* is regulated by the control of both Na^+ and free water excretion.

Osmolar Regulation. (See also Chaps. 11 and 57.) Osmolar changes in the extracellular fluid are sensed by osmoreceptors which regulate the release of antidiuretic hormone (ADH). Under normal conditions, the release of ADH is controlled almost entirely by changes in osmolarity. The osmoreceptor cells are probably located in the supraoptic and paraventricular nuclei of the hypothalamus. They are thought to act like osmometers, shrinking when the extracellular fluid is hypertonic and swelling when it is hypotonic. Shrinkage of the cells stimulates neural tracts leading from the osmoreceptors to the median eminence and the neurohypophysis via the supraoptic–neurohypophyseal tract; stimulation through this tract increases the release of ADH. ADH increases the permeability of the distal portions of the nephron to water and the urine is rendered hypertonic. The excretion of hypertonic urine tends to bring the plasma back to its normal osmolarity. This recovery is facilitated by increased intake of water. Conversely, swelling of the osmoreceptors inhibits the release of ADH. As the circulating ADH is destroyed, the distal portions of the nephrons become impermeable to water and osmotically free water is excreted into the urine. This tends to elevate plasma osmolarity and bring it back to normal.

Volume Regulation. Survival of the animal depends on the relative constancy of blood volume. Volume regulation involves a receptor–effector system which has the following components, each of which will be discussed in turn. (i) receptors which detect changes in volume of some portion of the extracellular fluid, (ii) an afferent limb, (iii) effectors which carry out the required adjustments to the volume change. Volume is regulated by two systems, one acting through aldosterone, the other through ADH. Normally the aldosterone system is the more important.

Aldosterone secretion is augmented by acute hemorrhage, acute suprarenal aortic constriction, low and high output cardiac failure, and vena caval constriction. In addition to these acutely induced volume changes, changes in volume resulting from alterations in Na^+ balance also influence aldosterone release.

Changes in aldosterone modify active Na^+ reabsorption in the kidney in the direction to bring extracellular volume back toward normal. Much evidence has accumulated that renin, a hormone derived from the juxtaglomerular apparatus of the kidney, controls the release of aldosterone.[14, 15, 60] In hypophysectomized rats, bilateral nephrectomy blocks the increased release of aldosterone which normally results from Na depletion; injection of renal extracts restores this response. The sequence of events appears to be as follows: The renal afferent arterioles are the volume receptors and are sensitive to changes in perfusion pressure. A decrease in stretch of these vessels, secondary to low perfusion pressure, causes a release of renin by the juxtaglomerular cells. The degree of granulation of juxtaglomerular cells is inversely related to the perfusion pressure of the arterioles. Since the amount of extractable renin present is directly proportional to the degree of granulation, more renin is available at low perfusion pressures than at high. Renin is a proteolytic enzyme which, after being released into the blood, acts on an α-2-globulin in the plasma to produce an inactive decapeptide (angiotensin I). Unknown plasma factors convert to the potent octapeptide angiotensin II, which then acts on the zona glomerulosa of the adrenal cortex to stimulate the release of aldosterone. Aldosterone, in turn, acts on the renal tubules to promote Na^+ reabsorption (see Fig. 8).

Volume regulation is also mediated through the ADH system. The observations of Gauer and Henry[29] suggest that moderate changes of blood volume have their prime effects on the low pressure side of the circulation. The large veins, right heart, pulmonary circulation and the left atrium contain 80 to 85 per cent of the total blood volume and are 100 to 200 times as distensible as the arterial side of the circulation. It appears, therefore, that receptors located in

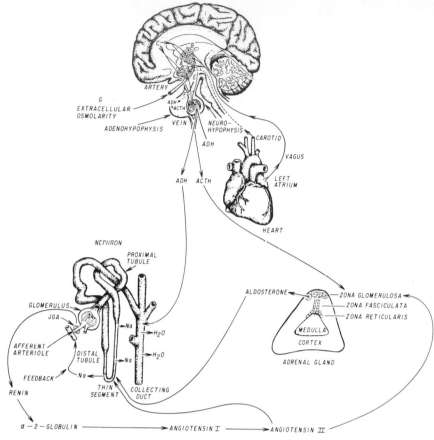

Fig. 8. Integrative mechanisms for regulation of volume and osmolarity of the extracellular fluid. *A,* Osmoreceptors in supraoptic nucleus of hypothalamus; *B,* osmoreceptors in paraventricular nucleus of hypothalamus; *C,* stimuli to supraoptic and paraventricular nuclei from higher brain centers; *JGA,* juxtaglomerular apparatus, which secretes renin.

the walls of this low pressure system could best measure the "fullness of the blood stream."[46] Receptors which sense changes in volume and relay information to the hypothalamo–neurohypophyseal–ADH system are mainly located in the left atrium and are sensitive to distension of the atrial wall. When blood volume increases, the atrial wall is stretched and receptors in the wall are activated. This results in inhibition of ADH release and water diuresis ensues. The elevated blood volume is thus restored to normal. The afferent path from the volume receptors is via the vagus nerve to the medulla and thence by unknown pathways to the supraoptic region.

Two reservations must be stated about volume regulation through the ADH system. First, it is an emergency system which is called into play only in severe derangements. When it is active, osmolar regulation is sacrificed and, after severe fluid loss, extracellular fluid may become increasingly hypotonic. Second, since the regulation uses changes in free water, most of the volume change takes place in the cells; next in the interstitial fluid, and the least in the blood volume. Indeed, if one considers the factors involved in the exchange of fluid across capillaries, it becomes evident that if water is to be lost and plasma protein to be concentrated, the requirement for *any* sustained loss of volume from the vascular system is that tissue interstitial pressure fall sufficiently to balance the increase in plasma oncotic pressure.

It appears that the renin–angiotensin system provides a reasonable basis for the physiologic regulation of aldosterone secretion. The alterations of aldosterone secretion which result from changes in daily Na+ intake are probably mediated through this negative feed-back system and provide one of the important means for regulation of the extracellular fluid volume and composition. The release of ADH is regulated by changes in osmolarity of plasma and, under exceptional circumstances, by changes in volume. This system provides a sensitive mechanism for the regulation of body solute concentration. The ADH system can also be strongly influenced by higher nervous activity.

REFERENCES

1. AIKAWA, J. K., GORDON, G. S. and RHOADES, E. L. *J. appl. Physiol.*, 1960, *15*:503–507.

2. BARNES, B. A. and MENDELSON, J. *Metabolism*, 1963, *12*: 184–193.

3. BEHNKE, A. R., JR., FEEN, B. G. and WELHAM, W. C. *J. Amer. med. Ass.*, 1942, *118*:495–498.

4. BRODIE, B. B., BERGER, E. Y., AXELROD, J., DUNNING, M. F., POROSOWSKA, Y. and STEELE, J. M. *Proc. Soc. exp. Biol. (N. Y.)*, 1951, *77*:794–798.

5. CHEEK, D. B. *J. Pediat.*, 1961, *58*:103–125.

6. CHINARD, F. P. *Bull. N. Y. Acad. Med.*, 1962, *38*:375–389.

7. COMAR, C. L. and BRONNER, F., eds. *Mineral metabolism*. New York, Academic Press, 1962.

8. COOKE, R. E., SEGAR, W. E., CHEEK, D. B., COVILLE, F. E. and DARROW, D. C. *J. clin. Invest.*, 1952, *31*:798–805.

9. COTLOVE, E. *Amer. J. Physiol.*, 1954, *176*:396–410.

10. COTLOVE, E. and HOGBEN, C. A. M. Chap. 27 in *Mineral metabolism*, vol. II, part B, B. L. COMAR and F. BRONNER, eds., New York, Academic Press, 1962.

11. COTLOVE, E., HOLLIDAY, M. A., SCHWARTZ, R. and WALLACE, W. M. *Amer. J. Physiol.*, 1951, *167*:665–675.

12. COTLOVE, E., TRANTHAM, H. V. and BOWMAN, R. L. *J. Lab. clin. Med.*, 1958, *51*:461–468.

13. DARROW, D. C. and HELLERSTEIN, S. *Physiol. Rev.*, 1958, *38*:114–137.

14.' DAVIS, R. O. *Progr. Cardiovasc. Dis.*, 1961, *4*:27–46.

15. DAVIS, R. O. *Physiologist*, 1962, *5*:65–86.

16. DOSEKUN, F. O. *J. Physiol.*, 1959, *147*:115–123.

17. ECKEL, R. E. and SPERELAKIS, N. *Amer. J. Physiol.*, 1963, *205*:307–312.

18. EDELMAN, I. S., HALEY, H. B., SCHLOERB, P. R., SHELDON, D. B., FRIIS-HANSEN, B. J., STOLL, G. and MOORE, F. D. *Surg. Gynec. Obst.*, 1952, *95*:1–12.

19. EDELMAN, I. S. and LEIBMAN, J. *Amer. J. Med.*, 1959, *27*:256–277.

20. EDELMAN, I. S., OLNEY, J. M., JAMES, A. H., BROOKS, L. and MOORE, F. D. *Science*, 1952, *115*:447–454.

21. ELKINTON, J. R. *Ann. intern. Med.*, 1962, *57*:660–684.

22. ELKINTON, J. R. and DANOWSKI, T. S. *The body fluids*. Baltimore, Williams and Wilkins Co., 1955.

23. FENN, W. O. *Physiol. Rev.*, 1936, *16*:450–487.

24. FORBES, G. B. Chap. 25 in *Mineral metabolism*, vol. II, part B, B. L. COMAR and F. BRONNER, eds., New York, Academic Press, 1962.

25. FORBES, G. B. and LEWIS, A. M. *J. clin. Invest.*, 1956, *35*:596–600.

26. FORBES, G. B. and PERLEY, A. *J. clin. Invest.*, 1951, *30*: 566–574.

27. FREEMAN, F. H. and FENN, W. O. *Amer. J. Physiol.*, 1953, *174*:422–430.

28. GARDNER, L. I., MACLACHLAN, E. A. and BERMAN, H. *J. gen. Physiol.*, 1952, *36*:153–159.

29. GAUER, O. H. and HENRY, J. P. *Physiol. Rev.*, 1963, *43*: 423–481.

30. GINSBURG, J. M. and WILDE, W. S. *Amer. J. Physiol.*, 1954, *179*:63–75.

31. HALMI, N. S., STUELKE, R. G. and SCHNELL, M. D. *Endocrinology*, 1956, *58*:634–650.

32. HASTINGS, A. B. *Harvey Lect.*, 1941, *36*:91–125.

33. HASTINGS, A. B. and EICHELBERGER, L. *J. biol. Chem.*, 1937, *117*:73–93.

34. HOLLAND, W. C. and AUDITORE, G. V. *Amer. J. Physiol.*, 1955, *183*:309–313.

35. IRVINE, R. O. H., SAUNDERS, S. J., MILNE, M. D. and CRAWFORD, M. A. *Clin. Sci.*, 1961, *20*:1–18.

36. KRUHØFFER, P. *Acta physiol. scand.*, 1946, *11*:16–36.

37. LAWSON, H. C. Chap. 3 in *Handbook of physiology, Section 2, Circulation*, vol. I. W. F. HAMILTON and P. DOW, eds. Washington, D.C., American Physiological Society, 1962.

38. MACINTYRE, I., HANNA, S., BOOTH, C. C. and READ, A. E. *Clin. Sci.*, 1961, *20*:297–305.

39. MANERY, J. F. *Physiol. Rev.*, 1954, *34*:334–417.

40. MANFREDI, F. *J. Lab. clin. Med.*, 1963, *61*:1005–1014.

41. MAURER, F. W. *Amer. J. Physiol.*, 1938, *124*:546–557.

42. NICHOLS, G., JR., NICHOLS, N., WEIL, W. B., JR., and WALLACE, W. M. *J. clin. Invest.*, 1953, *32*:1299–1308.

43. PACE, N., KLINE, L., SCHACHMAN, H. K. and HARFENIST, M. *J. biol. Chem.*, 1947, *168*:459–469.

44. PACE, N. and RATHBUN, E. N. *J. biol. Chem.*, 1945, *158*: 685–691.

45. PAPPENHEIMER, J. R. *Physiol. Rev.*, 1953, *33*:387–423.

46. PETERS, J. P. *Body water*. Springfield, Ill., Charles C Thomas, 1935.

47. PINSON, E. A. *Physiol. Rev.*, 1952, *32*:123–134.

48. PITTS, R. F. *Physiology of the kidney and body fluids*. Chicago, Year Book Medical Publishers, Inc., 1963.

49. PRENTICE, T. C., SIRI, W., BERLIN, N. I., HYDE, G. M., PARSONS, R. J., JOINER, E. E. and LAWRENCE, J. H. *J. clin. Invest.*, 1952, *31*:412–418.

50. ROBIN, E. D., WILSON, R. J. and BROMBER, P. A. *Ann. N. Y. Acad Sci.*, 1961, *92*:539–546.

51. ROBINSON, J. R. *Biol. Rev.*, 1953, *28*:158–194.

52. ROBINSON, J. R. Chap. 7 in *Mineral metabolism*, vol. I, part A, B. L. COMAR and F. BRONNER, eds. New York, Academic Press, 1960.

53. SCHLOERB, P. R., FRIIS-HANSEN, B. J., EDELMAN, I. S., SOLOMON, A. K. and MOORE, F. D. *J. clin. Invest.*, 1950, *29*:1296–1310.

54. SILVER, L., ROBERTSON, J. S. and DAHL, L. K. *J. clin. Invest.*, 1960, *39*:420–425.

55. SJOSTRAND, T. Chap. 4 in *Handbook of physiology, Section 2, Circulation*, vol. I. W. F. HAMILTON and P. DOW, eds. Washington, D.C., American Physiological Society, 1962.

56. SOBERMAN, R., BRODIE, B. B., LEVY, B. B., AXELROD, J., HOLLANDER, V. and STEELE, J. M. *J. biol. Chem.*, 1949, *179*:31–41.

57. STEINBACH, H. B. *Perspect. Biol. Med.*, 1962, *5*:338–355.

58. STEWART, C. P. and STRENGERS, T., eds. *Water and electrolyte metabolism*. Amsterdam, Elsevier Publishing Co., 1961.

59. SWAN, R. C., MADISSO, H. and PITTS, R. F. *J. clin. Invest.*, 1954, *33*:1447–1456.

60. TOBIAN, L. *Physiol. Rev.*, 1960, *40*:280–312.

61. TRUAX, F. L. *Amer. J. Physiol.*, 1939, *126*:402–408.

62. USSING, H. H., KRUHØFFER, P., THAYSEN, J. H. and THORN, N. A. *The alkali metal ions in biology*. Berlin, Springer-Verlag, 1960.

63. VERNADAKIS, A. and WOODBURY, D. M. *Amer. J. Physiol.* 1962, *203:*748–752.

64. VERNADAKIS, A. and WOODBURY, D. M. *Amer. J. Physiol.,* 1964, *206:*1365–1368.

65. WACKER, W. E. C. and VALLEE, B. L. *New Engl. J. Med.,* 1958, *259:*431–438; *idem,* 475–482.

66. WADDELL, W. J. and BUTLER, T. C. *J. clin. Invest.,* 1959, *38:*720–729.

67. WALLACE, W. M. and HASTINGS, A. B. *J. biol. Chem.,* 1942, *144:*637–649.

68. WEIL, W. B., JR. and WALLACE, W. M. *Pediatrics,* 1960, *26:*915–924.

69. WELT, L. G. *Clinical disorders of hydration and acid-base equilibrium.* Boston, Little, Brown & Co., 1955.

70. WHITE, H. L. and ROLF, D. *J. clin. Invest.,* 1958, *37:*8–19.

71. WIDDOWSON, E. M., McCANCE, R. A. and SPRAY, C. M. *Clin. Sci.,* 1951, *10:*113–125.

72. WILDE, W. S. Chap. 26 in *Mineral metabolism,* vol. II, part B, B. L. COMAR and F. BRONNER, eds. New York, Academic Press, 1962.

73. WOODBURY, D. M. and KOCH, A. *Proc. Soc. exp. Biol. (N. Y.),* 1957, *94:*720–723.

74. WYNN, V. *Lancet,* 1957, *273:*1212–1217.

CHAPTER 46

Regulation of pH

By J. WALTER WOODBURY

FOR continued survival, an animal requires a steady intake of food, oxygen and other nutrients and a steady output of waste products, carbon dioxide and water. The intake and output of these substances are closely regulated to the needs of the body, and their total body content remains constant over long periods. The lungs, kidneys, digestive tract and skin are the primary organs of intake and excretion; the activities of these organ systems are closely integrated, giving over-all regulation of body content of the many substances dissolved in the body fluids, e.g., sodium, potassium, chloride, hydrogen ion, bicarbonate, calcium, phosphate. Bodily function is extremely dependent on the hydrogen ion concentration ($[H^+]$) of the cells and extracellular fluids; this concentration is closely regulated by the combined activities of the lungs and kidneys. Although the $[H^+]$ in the body fluids is a million times smaller than the concentration of sodium ions, $[H^+]$ must be closely regulated because of the extreme reactivity of H^+, particularly with proteins. Even at the low $[H^+]$ found in the body, slight changes dramatically affect enzyme activity because the association or dissociation of a hydrogen ion with an enzyme changes the charge distribution throughout the molecule and thus affects its rate of combination with the substrate molecule. Hydrogen ions are much more reactive than sodium or potassium ions because the hydrated hydrogen ion (H_3O^+) is much smaller than the hydrated Na^+ and K^+ and hence is more strongly attracted to negatively charged regions of molecules; i.e., H^+ are generally much more tightly bound than Na^+ or K^+.

This chapter describes the mechanisms limiting the body's changes in $[H^+]$ in response to changes in total H^+ content and the regulatory mechanisms which reduce the changes in content and eventually restore the balanced condition. These buffering and compensatory changes are complex, but careful study of the components of the bodily response to acid–base changes can give a clear comprehension of the concepts involved and of the gaps in present knowledge of the subject. The fundamentals of acid–base regulation were elucidated by Van Slyke and his co-workers in the 1920's. Davenport's *The ABC of Acid–base Chemistry*[13] is a lucid and detailed account of the fundamentals of the subject. *The Acid–base Status of the Blood* by Siggaard-Andersen[39] is a more detailed account of the buffering properties of the blood and gives a different method of graphically analyzing acid–base data. Christensen[8, 9] has published programmed instruction books on acid–base balance which many students find useful. The presentation of acid–base data on the pH-$[HCO_3^-]$ diagram as espoused by Davenport and used by many earlier workers (see Van Slyke[49, 51]) simplifies interpretation of the data, compactly summarizes many regulatory processes and is used throughout this chapter.

Hydrogen Ion Balance. The body's total H^+ in normal conditions is such that the $[H^+]$ of the plasma is close to 40 nanomols per liter (40×10^{-9} mols per liter, $pH = 7.40$) and that of cells is about 100 nanomols per liter ($pH = 7.0$). An increased intake or production of acid in the body increases these concentrations, but much less than might be expected from the amount of acid added; i.e., most of the added H^+ combine with protein and other substances in the body and thus do not contribute to the body's $[H^+]$. Nevertheless, the restoration of normal conditions requires that exactly the amount of acid added be removed from the body. In those clinical situations in which the doctor must act to correct acid–base disturbances, he must be able to estimate how much excess acid or base the body has. Perhaps the most accurate way of obtaining such information is from a balance study, i.e., a careful accounting of the intake, production and excretion of acid; increase = income + production − outgo. However, such measurements are technically difficult, and some of them must be made *before* the patient becomes ill. However, the clinician usually must rely on measurements made after the patient becomes ill. The only measurements made routinely in the clinic on a patient's acid–base status are on the blood. This information together with other clinical information on the nature of the disease is used to diagnose the primary cause of the acid–base disturbance and the nature and amount of corrective therapy required, e.g., infusion or oral administration of base or acid. Estimates of body H^+ unbalance can be reasonably accurate if the principles involved are understood, e.g., the buffering properties of the body as a whole and the time course of the transient changes in H^+ content of the various body compartments. Although the fundamentals of acid–base chemistry of the blood were worked out 30 to 40 years ago, the conceptual framework presented in this chapter is largely new; well established facts are integrated with the newer knowledge of membrane ion transport and renal and respiratory functions to provide a cohesive view of acid–base balance in the body.

Carbonic and Noncarbonic Acids. There are two classes of acids of physiologic importance, carbonic acid and noncarbonic acids. These are distinguished on the basis of their mode of excretion: Carbonic acid is excreted via the lungs in the dehydrated form, CO_2. Noncarbonic acids are any other acids which do not dehydrate to form a volatile product and must, therefore, be excreted via the kidneys. Carbon dioxide and water are the most abundant end products of metabolism and CO_2 is excreted, on the average, as rapidly as formed. The metabolism of exogenous protein produces sulfuric and phosphoric acids which must be excreted by the kidneys as rapidly as formed. Other noncarbonic acids are the products of intermediary metabolism, e.g., lactic and aceto-acetic acids. These are normally metabolized as rapidly as produced but unbalances occur in exercise and other forms of tissue hypoxia and in diabetes.

Résumé of Compensatory Responses. The chapter can be outlined by briefly describing the sequence of changes which occur in the body in response to a sudden change in the body's H^+ balance. The response depends on whether the added acid is carbonic or non-carbonic, but the principles involved are better illustrated by considering what happens when the body has an excess of noncarbonic acid. In the clinic, such changes are commonly found to be associated with various types of pathologic conditions and illness.

The change in $[H^+]$ of the blood plasma after an intravenous infusion of a strong acid such as HCl follows an ever slowing time course: (i) The added acid largely disappears, first reacting with the hemoglobin, plasma proteins and bicarbonate of blood, but some of the added H^+ remains in the ionized form and raises $[H^+]$. This phase takes a few circulation times (a few minutes). As the blood circulates through the lungs, the excess CO_2 produced by the reaction of H^+ with HCO_3^- is excreted, reducing the $[H^+]$ slightly. (ii) The $[H^+]$ of the blood is further reduced in the tissues by diffusion of HCO_3^- (bicarbonate) ions into the blood from the interstitial spaces. The CO_2 thus produced by combination with H^+ is eliminated in the lungs. This interstitial buffering is complete in half an hour to two hours. (iii) The active H^+ transport system of the tissue cells (Chap. 1) is, in effect, inhibited and some of the excess H^+ enters the cells, reducing the excess in the extracellular space. The H^+ which enters cells largely disappears by combining with cellular proteins and bicarbonate. The time course of

this process is not known, except that it requires six to twenty-four hours. (iv) The raised $[H^+]$ of the blood increases respiratory minute volume, which further tends to eliminate CO_2 via the lungs. This removal of CO_2 reduces the $[H^+]$ of the blood and thus compensates, partially, for the excess noncarbonic acid in the blood. (v) If kidney function is normal, i.e., if the original disturbance is not due to a pathologic change in the kidney, the rate of acid secretion by the kidneys increases and the excess acid is excreted in about a week.

$[H^+]$ and pH. A current trend in the clinical literature is to express acidity in terms of $[H^+]$ rather than pH. By definition, pH $= -\log a_H$, where a_H is the hydrogen activity. The $[H^+]$ at body pH cannot be measured directly but is assumed equal to the hydrogen activity (see discussion of pH measurement). The pH terminology was originally introduced to permit convenient specification of the wide ranges of $[H^+]$ encountered in chemical experiments, e.g., from 1 to 10^{-14} mols per liter, pH's of 0 to 14. The range of blood $[H^+]$ compatible with life is about 20 to 160 nanomols per liter (pH 6.8 to 7.7), sufficiently small that $[H^+]$ can be used conveniently. Since concentration is a familiar concept, using $[H^+]$ routinely rather than pH would seem natural. However, as pointed out by Van Slyke[46] in 1922, pH must be used to give a clear, precise meaning to the general concept of buffering. This will be shown in the discussion of titration curves.

BUFFERS AND BUFFERING[5]

Electrolytes. Substances which ionize in water solution and hence can conduct a current are called electrolytes. The ionization process consists of the donation of all valence shell electrons by the cation to complete the valence shell of the anion. Electrolytes dissolve in water solutions because their charged ions are more strongly attracted to the dipolar water molecules than they are to each other. *Strong electrolytes* are completely ionized in solution, e.g., the reaction NaCl $\rightleftharpoons$ Na$^+$ + Cl$^-$ goes completely to the right at equilibrium; the affinity of the ions for water is much greater than their affinity for each other. Although strong electrolytes are completely dissociated, they act as if they were only about 80 per cent ionized because of the mutual electrostatic attractions of the anions and cations; i.e., activities are about 80 per cent of concentrations. Usually, in physiologic systems, it is sufficiently accurate to use the terms "concentration" and "activity" interchangeably. Most soluble salts and inorganic acids and bases are strong electrolytes. The ions found in plasma are formed from strong electrolytes, with a few exceptions, e.g., calcium and phosphate, protein.

Weak electrolytes ionize only partially; the anions and cations have about the same affinity for each other as they have for water. Thus, the concentrations of neutral molecules and ions in solution are comparable. The most important weak electrolytes are weak acids and bases, such as metabolic acids and ammonia.

Acids and Bases. Brønsted defined an acid as a substance which can supply H^+ (protons) and a base as a substance which can accept H^+. In aqueous solutions, H^+ are hydrated as are other ions, hence H_3O^+ is an acid. The hydrated form, H_3O^+, is implied by the symbol H^+.

The reaction $HCl \rightleftharpoons H^+ + Cl^-$ is characterized in the Brønsted formulation by calling HCl an acid since it can supply H^+; Cl^- is called the conjugate base since it can, at high $[H^+]$, accept H^+. A strong acid has a weak conjugate base. Similarly, a strong base has a weak conjugate acid. Table 1 gives several acids and their conjugate bases. Substances of particular interest are those which are more or less equally divided between the acidic and basic forms at body $[H^+]$. Thus, the imidazole side groups of hemoglobin undergo the following reaction: $HHb \rightleftharpoons H^+ + Hb^-$; the acid, HHb, dissociates to form H^+ and the conjugate base, Hb^-. HHb and Hb^- occur in about equal concentrations in the blood cells. This system acts like a base in respect to added acid and like an acid to added alkali.

TABLE 1. *Acids and Conjugate Bases*

ACID	=	H^+	+	CONJUGATE BASE
HCl	=	H^+	+	Cl^-
HCH_3COO	=	H^+	+	CH_3COO^-
H_2CO_3	=	H^+	+	HCO_3^-
HCO_3^-	=	H^+	+	$CO_3^=$
H_3O^+	=	H^+	+	H_2O
NH_4^+	=	H^+	+	NH_3
HOH	=	H^+	+	OH^-

Buffering. The concept of buffering arises from the properties of weak acids and bases, i.e., those that are incompletely dissociated at the $[H^+]$ under consideration. A half dissociated acid not only can supply H^+, but its basic form can also absorb H^+; hence, adding strong acid or alkali produces a smaller change in $[H^+]$ than would occur if the weak acid were not present. The potential number of H^+ is not changed but the number in the ionized form is reduced. This "masking" of H^+ is called *buffering*. Nearly all of the H^+ added in the form of strong acid combine with the ionized form of the weak acid. The amount of the buffer anion (or basic form of the weak acid) which is bound is nearly equal to that of the added acid, as long as the added amount is less than that of the buffer anion. *The near equality of added strong acid and amount of buffer anion disappearing is assumed in all the calculations given below.*

DISSOCIATION CONSTANT. The law of mass action describes the equilibrium condition of a chemical reaction. The condition of equilibrium for the reaction, $HA \rightleftharpoons H^+ + A^-$, where A^- is generally an organic anion in biologic systems, is given by the equation

$$K' = \frac{[H^+]\,[A^-]}{[HA]} \qquad (1)$$

where K' is the equilibrium or ionization constant characteristic of the particular reaction. By convention, concentrations are expressed in mols per liter. (A similar equation holds for weak bases, poorly ionizing substances in which the basic form has no charge, e.g., NH_4^+; their behavior will not be specifically discussed.) Because the constant, K', is defined in terms of concentration rather than activity its value varies somewhat with the ionic strength of the solution. The prime sign on the K is used to denote this. Since the ionic strength of body fluids is closely regulated, K' normally has one value for each reaction.

In the body, the principal weak acid buffering substances are proteins, particularly hemoglobin and organic and inorganic phosphates. Except when the partial pressure of CO_2 (P_{CO_2}) is held constant, bicarbonate is a poor buffer because, at body pH, carbonic acid is almost completely ionized. Since total amounts and concentrations of body buffers remain relatively constant in the steady state and since the body's total buffer concentration, [B], must consist of the sums of the concentrations of the acid and conjugate base forms, [B] = [HA] + [A⁻]. If [HA] = [A⁻], then, from Equation (1), [H⁺] = K′. Maximum buffer action occurs when [H⁺] is near the value of K′ so that weak acids and bases with dissociation constants of about 10^{-7} mols per liter are most effective at moderating [H⁺] changes due to added strong acid.

CALCULATION OF [H⁺] IN BUFFERED SOLUTIONS. Equation (1) can be used to calculate the changes in [H⁺] produced by adding a given amount of strong acid. Rearrangement gives

$$[H^+] = K' \frac{[HA]}{[A^-]} \qquad (2)$$

However, [HA] + [A⁻] = [B]. Eliminating [HA] in Equation (2) gives the relationship between [H⁺] and [A⁻]:

$$[H^+] = K' \frac{([B] - [A^-])}{[A^-]} \qquad (3)$$

The assumption stated above that all but a small fraction of added acid disappears by combining with A⁻ gives the relationship between [H⁺] and the amount of acid added.

Example: Since skeletal muscle contains considerable organic and inorganic phosphates, it is of interest to calculate the buffer properties of a Na_2HPO_4-NaH_2PO_4 solution containing 20 millimols per liter of phosphate. The K′ of the reaction is 1.5×10^{-7} mols per liter (150 nanomols per liter) at body ionic strength. Suppose that initially [HPO₄⁼] = [H₂PO₄⁻] = 10 millimols per liter so that [H⁺] = K′ = 150 nanomols per liter (Equation 2). Suppose that 5 mEq. of concentrated HCl of negligible volume are added to a liter of the solution, what is the final [H⁺] of the solution? What fraction of the added acid remains ionized?

Solution: The reaction is H⁺, Cl⁻ + 2 Na⁺, HPO₄⁼ ⇌ Na⁺, Cl⁻ + Na⁺, H₂PO₄⁻. If all of the added HCl combines with HPO₄⁼, then [HPO₄⁼] decreases from 10 to 5 millimols per liter and [H₂PO₄⁻] increases from 10 to 15 millimols per liter. Substituting these values in Equation (2) gives

$$[H^+] = K' \frac{[H_2PO_4^-]}{[HPO_4^=]} = 150 \, \frac{15}{5}$$
$$= 450 \text{ nanomols per liter.}$$

Thus the [H⁺] has increased 450 − 150 = 300 nanomols per liter. However, 5 millimols per liter = 5,000,000 nanomols of H⁺ per liter were added and only 300 of these (one in 17,000) remained in the ionic form after buffering. This calculation illustrates vividly the validity of the assumption that the change in buffer anion is equal to the added acid; the error is negligible. This can be seen by noting that the actual [H₂PO₄⁻] after adding acid is 15,000,000 − 300 = 14,999,700 nanomols per liter and [HPO₄⁼] is 5,000,300 nanomols per liter. The ratio of these two quantities is negligibly different from the ratio calculated above.

Dilution. Diluting a solution containing buffer has little effect on [H⁺]. For example, if the solution in the example were diluted with an equal volume of water, all concentrations would be halved but only momentarily since this is not an equilibrium condition. Consequently, nearly 75 nanomols of H₂PO₄⁻ dissociate to raise the [H⁺] from 75 to 150 nanomols per liter. This small change in [H₂PO₄⁻] has a negligible effect on [H₂PO₄⁻]/[HPO₄⁼] and hence on [H⁺].

TITRATION CURVES. The buffering properties of weak acids and bases are well illustrated by graphs showing the relationship between the amount of acid added and the resulting change in [H⁺] of the solution. Customarily, the independent variable, the amount of added acid, is plotted on the ordinate and the *p*H on the abscissa. Two ways of obtaining such a plot—called a titration curve—are shown in Figure 1 for the example considered above. Additional points are obtained in the same manner; for different amounts of added acid or base, the resulting [H⁺] is calculated from [H₂PO₄⁻]/[HPO₄⁼] (Equation 3). The pertinent values, including *p*H, are given in Table 2 and are plotted in Figures 1 and 2. In Figure 1*A*, the amount of acid or base added has been plotted, contrary to custom, on the abscissa against the resulting [H⁺] in the solution. Note that the units on the ordinate are a million times smaller (nanomols per liter) than those on the abscissa (millimols per liter). This curve serves to emphasize the small fraction of added H⁺ that remains in the ionized form after buffering. The relationship is not linear: Adding 2 millimols of strong acid per liter increases the [H⁺] from 150 to 225 nanomols per liter, ¾ times the original; adding 2 millimols of base per liter decreases [H⁺] to 100 nanomols per liter, a

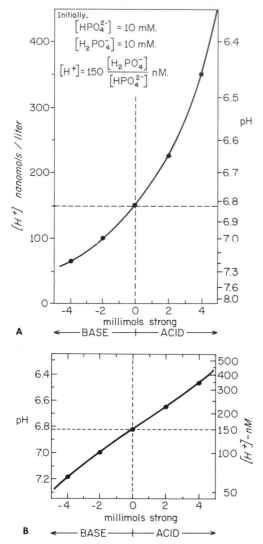

$$\text{Initially.}$$
$$\left[HPO_4^{2-}\right] = 10 \text{ mM.}$$
$$\left[H_2PO_4^-\right] = 10 \text{ mM.}$$
$$\left[H^+\right] = 150 \frac{\left[H_2PO_4^-\right]}{\left[HPO_4^{2-}\right]} \text{ nM.}$$

A

B

Fig. 1. Titration curves of 1 liter of a 20 millimol per liter solution of Na+, $H_2PO_4^-$–Na_2^+, $HPO_4^=$. Initially, $[H_2PO_4^-]$ = $[HPO_4^=]$ = 10 millimols per liter and $[H^+]$ = 150 nanoequivalents per liter. Points are from Table 2. Change in volume due to added acid is small enough to be neglected. *A*, $[H^+]$ plotted on linear ordinate scale (left) and corresponding *p*H (right). *B*, *p*H plotted linearly (left) with corresponding $[H^+]$ (right).

decrease to ⅔ the original. Thus, the fractional or percentage changes in $[H^+]$ are related since successive 2 millimol per liter increments increase $[H^+]$ by 50 per cent, i.e., from 100 to 150 and 150 to 225 nanomols per liter. This relationship holds only over the center range of acid or base additions (−4 to +4 millimols) but shows that using log $[H^+]$ or *p*H instead of

$[H^+]$ as one of the coordinates will give a linear titration curve over part of the range.

Figures 1*B* and 2 show titration curves of the same solution with *p*H as one coordinate. In Figure 1*B*, the scale on the abscissa is the same as in Figure 1*A*, but the ordinate is *p*H. The same range of $[H^+]$ values is covered in both parts of Figure 1. Over the same range of added acid, the titration curve is almost straight when *p*H is the ordinate. In Figure 2, *p*H is plotted on the abscissa and amount of acid on the ordinate, the same as in Figure 1*B* except for an interchange of coordinate axes and a wider range of values. Over this wider range, it can be seen that the titration curve is S-shaped, the *p*H changing rapidly for small additions of acid or base at the high and low ends as expected when the buffer is mostly converted to the acidic or basic forms.

Buffer value. A measure of the buffering effects of a solution is the slope of the titration curve at any point, i.e., the amount of acid or base that must be added to produce a *p*H change of 1 unit (a 10-fold change in $[H^+]$) if the titration curve were a straight line. *The buffer value of a solution is defined as the negative of the slope of the titration curve* (cf. Fig. 2). The steeper the curve, the greater the amount of acid which must be added to produce a given change in *p*H. This is the reason that *p*H is plotted on the abscissa; buffer value equals the

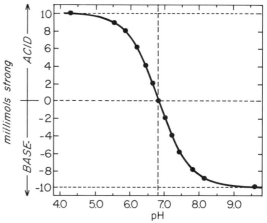

Fig. 2. Titration curve of 1 liter of a 20 millimol per liter Na+, $H_2PO_4^-$–Na_2^+, $HPO_4^=$ solution. Same as Figure 1*B* except that ordinate and abscissa have been interchanged and a broader range of *p*H's is covered. Slope of the curve at any point is the negative of the buffer value. Buffer value is maximum at 11.5 sl. at vertical dashed line. Points are from Table 2.

TABLE 2. *Titration of a 1 Liter Solution of NaH₂PO₄–Na₂HPO₄*
$H^+, Cl^- + 2\ Na^+, HPO_4^= \rightleftharpoons Na^+\ Cl^- + Na^+, H_2PO_4^-$
$Na^+, OH^- + Na^+, H_2PO_4^- \rightleftharpoons HOH + 2\ Na^+, HPO_4^=$
Initially $[H_2PO_4^-] = [HPO_4^=] = 10$ *millimols per liter*

	ADDED[1] MILLIMOLS PER LITER	$[H_2PO_4^=]$ MILLIMOLS PER LITER	$[HPO_4^=]$ MILLIMOLS PER LITER	$\dfrac{[H_2PO_4^-]}{[HPO_4^=]}$	$[H^+]$[2] NANOMOLS PER LITER	LOG $\dfrac{[H_2PO_4^-]}{[HPO_4^=]}$	pH[4]
	−10	0.0366	19.9634	0.00183	0.274[3]	−2.74	9.56
B	− 9	1.0	19.0	0.053	7.9	−1.28	8.10
A	− 8	2.0	18.0	0.11	16.6	−0.96	7.78
S	− 6	4.0	16.0	0.25	37.5	−0.60	7.42
E	− 4	6.0	14.0	0.43	65	−0.37	7.19
	− 2	8.0	12.0	0.66	100	−0.18	7.00
	0	10.0	10.0	1.0	150	0.00	6.82
	2	12.0	8.0	1.5	225	0.18	6.65
A	4	14.0	6.0	2.33	350	0.37	6.46
C	6	16.0	4.0	4.0	600	0.60	6.22
I	8	18.0	2.0	9.0	1350	0.95	5.87
D	9	19.0	1.0	19.0	2850	1.28	5.54
	10	19.9454	0.0546	365	54600[3]	2.56	4.26

1. Concentrated strong acid or base of negligible volume is added, i.e., 5 ml. of 2 M. acid contains 10 millimols. Except for additions of ±10 millimols, change in $[H_2PO_4^-]$ = amount acid added.

2. $[H^+]$ is given in units of nanomols per liter (10^{-9} mols per liter) $[H^+] = 150\ \dfrac{[H_2PO_4^-]}{[HPO_4^=]}$.

3. Equation (3) cannot be used to calculate these values.

4. Since $[H^+]$ is in nanomols per liter, pH $= 9 - \log [H^+] = 6.82 + \log \dfrac{[HPO_4^=]}{[H_2PO_4^-]}$.

magnitude of the slope instead of its reciprocal. Also, the linear midregion of the titration curve is a preemptory reason for using *p*H instead of [H⁺] in describing acid–base behavior in buffered systems such as the body.

The maximum buffer value of the 20 millimols per liter phosphate solution whose titration curve is shown in Figures 1*B* and 2 can be accurately calculated from Table 2. The addition of −2 millimols acid per liter (addition of base) increases the *p*H of the solution from 6.82 to 7.00; the addition of 2 millimols of acid per liter decreases the *p*H to 6.65. Hence, the buffer value defined as the negative of the slope of the titration curve is

$$\text{buffer value} = -\frac{(-2-2)\text{ millimols per liter}}{(7.00-6.65)\ p\text{H units}}$$
$$= \frac{4.0\text{ millimols}}{0.35\text{ liter} \times p\text{H units}}$$
$$= 11.4\text{ millimols per (liter} \times p\text{H)}$$

In words, 11.4 millimols of acid per liter must be added to the 20 millimols per liter phosphate solution to decrease the *p*H by 1 unit.

The units of buffer value are clumsy and lengthy and, since they are used frequently throughout this chapter, it is useful to define a new unit of buffer value. In view of D. D. Van Slyke's major pioneering contributions in this field, especially his analysis of buffering,[46] it is appropriate and fitting to call this new unit of buffer value a Van Slyke or more simply a *slyke*, abbreviated *sl.*, e.g., the maximum buffer value of a 20 millimols per liter phosphate solution is 11.5 slykes or 11.5 sl.

Another useful concept in describing the properties of buffered solutions is Van Slyke's *molar buffer value*,[46] defined as the buffer value of a 1 molar (1 mol per liter) solution, i.e., the number of mols (millimols) of acid required to reduce the *p*H of a 1 molar (1 millimolar) solution by 1 *p*H unit. In the example given above, the buffer value of a 20 millimols per liter phosphate solution was 11.5 sl., so that the molar buffer value is 11.5 millimols per liter × *p*H/20 millimols per liter = 11.5/20 per *p*H = 0.57 per *p*H unit. More accurately, the maximum buffer value of any weak acid or base is 0.575 per *p*H unit for each independently ionizing group on the molecule regardless of its structure.

Body Buffers. Considerable acid or base can be added to the body without producing lethal changes in pH because of the body buffer stores. Most of the body buffers are located intracellularly, the major exceptions being plasma protein and the small amount of phosphate in extracellular fluid. However, the hemoglobin of red cells, though intracellular, is more conveniently regarded as extracellular because it is confined to the blood and because it is readily available for buffering of extracellular acids. Intracellular buffers of tissue cells are phosphate, as already mentioned, and most of the various organic anions, including proteins, lumped into the category A^- in Chapter 1 and specified in more detail in Chapter 45. Since skeletal muscle is about half of the cellular mass, most intracellular buffering presumably occurs in muscle. Carbon dioxide readily penetrates cell membranes and thus is buffered by the whole body. On the other hand, noncarbonic acids penetrate cell membranes slowly so that excess extracellular acid is buffered initially in the blood and extracellular fluid. Hence, the buffering properties of hemoglobin must be known to calculate the amount of acid added to the extracellular fluid.

HEMOGLOBIN.[18, 31, 37, 53] Hemoglobin is specialized for carrying O_2 and CO_2 and also has a high buffer value over the normal range of body pH. As was seen in Chapter 40, these properties interact (Bohr effect) to reduce the pH changes produced by blood P_{CO_2} changes. Hemoglobin is a tetrahedral molecule consisting of four rather torturous globin chains each enfolding a heme group. There are two types of chains, alpha and beta, which are only slightly different from each other in structure. A hemoglobin molecule consists of a pair of alpha and a pair of beta chains, the members of each pair being placed oppositely across an axis of symmetry. Each chain is capable of taking up one molecule of O_2, which attaches to the iron in the center of the heme group. Complete oxygenation is associated with a displacement of the two beta chains toward each other.[31] The molecular weight of each chain is about 16,700,[18] one-fourth that of the whole molecule. It is customary in acid–base chemistry to take the oxygen combining weight, the weight of one chain as the molecular or com-

bining weight of hemoglobin. This custom will be followed here.

There are several kinds of dissociable groups in proteins which act as acids or bases of different strengths, e.g., free carboxyl, free amino, guanidino and imidazole groups. Of these, only the latter has a dissociation constant in the range of normal $[H^+]$ of blood; e.g., the dissociation constant of the carboxyl group of histidine is more than 10^{-2} mols per liter; that of the imidazole ring is about 10^{-6} mols per liter and that of the amino group is less than 10^{-9} mols per liter.[18] It must be kept in mind, however, that incorporating an amino acid into a protein can greatly modify the ionization constants of any remaining free groups in a manner which depends on the adjacent amino acid subunits.

Figure 3 shows idealized titration curves of 1 millimol per liter solutions of oxyhemoglobin and hemoglobin over the pH range 7 to 7.8.[22,53] The curves are nearly straight and parallel over this range and will be considered as such. The molar buffer value of hemoglobin is given by the magnitude of the slope of the curves in Figure 3 and is 3 per pH. This buffer value is almost entirely due to imidazole rings of histidine

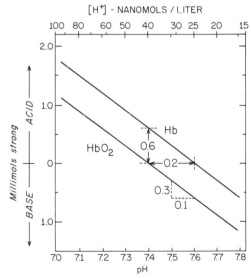

Fig. 3. Idealized titration curves of 1 millimol per liter solutions of oxyhemoglobin (HbO_2) and hemoglobin (Hb). The molar buffer value of hemoglobin in this range is 0.3/0.1 = 3 per pH. Oxygenation of Hb decreases pH by 0.2 unit or requires addition of 0.6 millimols of alkali to prevent change in pH. (After Wyman and German, *J. biol. Chem.*, 1937, *117*:533–550; and Wyman, *Adv. Protein Chem.*, 1948, *4*:407–513.)

subunits in the hemoglobin. Each of the four chains of hemoglobin has nine histidine subunits. The maximum molar buffer value of a single ionizable group is 0.575 per *p*H so that a molar buffer value of 3 per *p*H must arise from a minimum of $3/0.575 = 5.2$ dissociable groups. Hence, at least six and probably all nine of the histidines in a chain act as buffers in the 7 to 7.8 *p*H range since their dissociation constants are unlikely to be equal and the buffer value contributed by some of these groups will be less than maximal. The reaction of the imidazole ring of histidine with hydrogen ions[18] is

$$H^+ + \quad \begin{array}{c} N\!-\!\!-\!CH \\ \| \quad\quad \| \\ HC \quad\ C\!-\!CH_2\!- \\ \diagdown\ \diagup \\ N \\ H \end{array} \quad \rightleftharpoons$$

(basic form)

$$\begin{array}{c} HN^+\!\!-\!\!-\!CH \\ \| \quad\quad \| \\ HC \quad\ C\!-\!CH_2\!- \\ \diagdown\ \diagup \\ N \\ H \end{array}$$

(acidic form)

the neutral form being the hydrogen ion acceptor (base).

H+ liberating effect of hemoglobin oxygenation.[37,53] Oxygenation of hemoglobin changes the dissociation constant of one of the nine histidines in a hemoglobin chain, making it a stronger acid, i.e., at a given *p*H, the fraction of histidines in the uncharged, basic form increases by dissociating H+. The change is surprisingly large; the dissociation constant increases 18 times, from 0.118×10^{-7} to 2.09×10^{-7} mols per liter (11.8 to 209 nanomols per liter).[53] The result is that 0.6 millimol of strong base must be added for each millimol of hemoglobin to prevent a *p*H shift on oxygenation (Fig. 3). Conversely, if no base is added the *p*H shifts 0.2 units downward when hemoglobin is oxygenated. The size of these changes is reduced, however, by carbaminohemoglobin formation if CO_2 is present in the system[37] (see below).

THE CARBON DIOXIDE SYSTEM

There are two distinct aspects to the role of carbon dioxide in the body: (i) Carbon dioxide produced by metabolism acts as a strong acid at body [H+] because of the reactions $H_2O + CO_2 \rightleftharpoons H_2CO_3 \rightleftharpoons H^+ + HCO_3^-$. Carbon dioxide as such is not an acid since it contains no protons; H_2CO_3 is. On the average, the rate of CO_2 excretion must equal its rate of production. (ii) The partial pressure of CO_2 (P_{CO_2}) in the alveoli, blood and tissues is determined by the ventilatory rate of the lungs. The normal maintenance of a fixed alveolar P_{CO_2} ($P_{A_{CO_2}}$) means that the CO_2 system acts as an excellent buffer with respect to noncarbonic acids or bases which may be added to the blood by diet, metabolism or disease.

Carbon Dioxide System Equilibria and Kinetics. DISSOLVED CARBON DIOXIDE. All gases dissolve to some extent in water. At pressures less than 1 atmosphere the concentration of dissolved gas is proportional to the partial pressure of the gas in a vapor phase with which the water is equilibrated, e.g., by vigorous bubbling of the gas through the solution. Since arterial blood is usually equilibrated with alveolar air, the P_{CO_2} of arterial blood ($P_{a_{CO_2}}$) is simply that of a gas with which the blood is equilibrated. For plasma at body temperature, the proportionality constant relating the concentration of dissolved CO_2 in millimols per liter and P_{CO_2} in mm. Hg is 0.03:[50]

$$[CO_2] = 0.03\ P_{CO_2} \qquad (4)$$

The P_{CO_2} of alveolar air is about 40 mm. Hg, hence $[CO_2] = 0.03 \times 40 = 1.2$ millimols per liter.

HYDRATION OF CARBON DIOXIDE. Carbon dioxide reacts reversibly with water to form H_2CO_3. The equilibrium of the reaction $H_2O + CO_2 \rightleftharpoons H_2CO_3$ is far to the left and is attained slowly. At body temperature there are about 500 CO_2 molecules in solution for every H_2CO_3 molecule.[18] The equilibrium condition of the reaction is $K = [H_2CO_3]/[CO_2][H_2O]$. Hence $[H_2CO_3] = K'[CO_2]$ where $K' = K[H_2O]$ and $[H_2O]$ is constant. $[H_2CO_3]$ is proportional to $[CO_2]$, which is in turn proportional to P_{CO_2}. Since $[H_2CO_3]$ is some 500 times smaller than $[CO_2]$ it is customary to include $[H_2CO_3]$ in the term $[CO_2]$, both being proportional to P_{CO_2}. This inclusion has no practical effect on Equation (4). Hereafter, the term [CO_2] refers to the sum of the concentrations of H_2CO_3 and of dissolved CO_2.

The hydration of CO_2 is slow; at 38° C. about 5 seconds are required for half equilibration.[18] The reverse reaction, dehydration of H_2CO_3, is about 500 times faster since the equilibrium constant is the ratio of the backward and forward rate constants. The uptake of CO_2 in the tissues and its loss in the lungs is dependent on the rapidity of the hydration and dehydration reactions of CO_2 since blood spends only a few seconds in the tissue and lung capillaries. These kinetic considerations led to the discovery of an enzyme, carbonic anhydrase (CA), by Roughton which catalyzes the reaction

$$CO_2 + H_2O \overset{CA}{\rightleftharpoons} H_2CO_3$$

Carbonic anhydrase is found in high concentrations in red blood cells, ion secreting tissues and neuroglia. In blood, CA speeds up the reactions sufficiently to make diffusion the limiting factor in CO_2 exchange.

IONIZATION OF CARBONIC ACID. Carbonic acid dissociates rapidly to form hydrogen ions and bicarbonate ions: $H_2CO_3 = H^+ + HCO_3^-$. The equilibrium condition is

$$K_{H_2CO_3} = \frac{[H^+][HCO_3^-]}{[H_2CO_3]} \qquad (5)$$

The value of $K_{H_2CO_3}$ in dilute solutions is 1.6 $\times 10^{-4}$ mols per liter at 38° C.[18] Hence, carbonic acid is almost completely dissociated at body [H^+] (40 $\times 10^{-9}$ mols per liter). It is more convenient to write the equilibrium equation for the over-all reaction with [H_2CO_3] replaced by [CO_2] in Equation (5). The reaction and equilibrium condition are

$$CO_2 + H_2O = H_2CO_3 = H^+ + HCO_3^-$$

and $\qquad K' = \dfrac{[H^+][HCO_3^-]}{[CO_2]} \qquad (6)$

In plasma at 38° C., $K' = 8 \times 10^{-7}$ mols per liter.[26, 48, 49] For example, arterial [CO_2] was calculated above as $0.03 \times 40 = 1.2$ millimols per liter $= 1.2 \times 10^{-3}$ mols per liter. [H^+] of plasma is 40 nanomols per liter $= 4 \times 10^{-8}$ mols per liter. Thus [HCO_3^-] $= K'[CO_2]/[H^+]$ $= 8 \times 10^{-7} \times (1.2 \times 10^{-3}/4 \times 10^{-8}) = 2.4$

$\times 10^{-2}$ mols per liter $= 24$ millimols per liter, the normal value of bicarbonate concentration in plasma.

The equilibrium condition can be put into an even more usable form by substituting [CO_2] $= 0.03\ P_{CO_2}$ into the equation:

$$K' = \frac{[H^+][HCO_3^-]}{0.03\ P_{CO_2}} \qquad (7)$$

With this equation any one of the three important physiologic variables, [H^+], [HCO_3^-] and P_{CO_2} can be calculated if the other two are known. As shown below the acid–base status of the body can be estimated with reasonable accuracy from measurement of these quantities in the blood and from other clinical information.

MEASUREMENT OF pH, P_{aCO_2} [HCO_3^-]. [H^+] of blood can be calculated from Equation (7) if P_{CO_2} and [HCO_3^-] are known. Also [H^+] can be calculated from the pH as measured with a glass membrane electrode which is porous only to H^+ and thus develops a transmembrane potential proportional to the logarithm of the concentration (actually activity) ratio of H^+ across the membrane. The partial pressure of CO_2 in the blood can be estimated from alveolar P_{CO_2}, measured directly with a P_{CO_2} electrode or calculated from Equation (7) if pH and [HCO_3^-] are known. Bicarbonate concentration can be estimated from the total CO_2 content of a sample of blood plasma and either the pH or P_{CO_2} by using Equation (7). The total CO_2 concentration of a solution, [Total CO_2], is defined as the sum of [CO_2] and [HCO_3^-] where [CO_2] includes [H_2CO_3]. [Total CO_2] can be measured by adding an excess of strong acid to a sample of known volume, shaking vigorously and collecting and measuring the volume of CO_2 liberated. The strong acid drives the reaction, $H^+ + HCO_3^- \rightleftharpoons H_2CO_3 \rightleftharpoons H_2O + CO_2$ far to the right because of the high [H^+]. For example if [H^+] is increased to 0.1 mol per liter and P_{CO_2} is reduced to that of air (0.3 mm. Hg) then, from Equation (7), [HCO_3^-] $= 7.2 \times 10^{-5}$ millimols per liter, negligibly small compared with the normal plasma value of 24 millimols per liter.

[Total CO_2] estimation is simple and is done routinely in the clinic. Since [Total CO_2] $=$ [CO_2] $+$ [HCO_3^-], then [HCO_3^-] $=$ [Total CO_2] $-$ [CO_2] $=$ [Total CO_2] $- 0.03\ P_{CO_2}$. Substituting in Equation (7) gives

$$K' = \frac{[H^+]\,([\text{Total CO}_2] - 0.03\,P_{CO_2})}{0.03\,P_{CO_2}} \quad (8)$$

Usually, [Total CO$_2$] and pH are measured and P$_{CO_2}$ is calculated. For example, suppose that for a sample of plasma, [H$^+$] = 50 nanomols per liter and [Total CO$_2$] = 25.5 millimols per liter as determined by direct analysis. Solving Equation (8) for 0.03 P$_{CO_2}$ gives

$$0.03\,P_{CO_2} = \frac{[\text{Total CO}_2]}{K'/[H^+] + 1} = 25.5/(800/50$$
$$+ 1) = 25.5/11 = 1.5 \text{ millimols per liter.}$$

Hence, P$_{CO_2}$ = 1.5/0.03 = 50 mm. Hg and [HCO$_3^-$] = [Total CO$_2$] − 0.03 P$_{CO2}$ = 25.5 − 1.5 = 24 millimols per liter.

THE HENDERSON–HASSELBALCH EQUATION. The equilibrium condition for the CO$_2$ system is usually written in logarithmic form with [H$^+$] replaced by pH because the titration curve of hemoglobin and other blood buffers is a linear function when added acid is plotted as a function of the resultant pH. The equilibrium condition, K$'$ = [H$^+$][HCO$_3^-$]/0.03 P$_{CO_2}$, is transformed into the Henderson–Hasselbalch equation by taking the logarithm of both sides,

$$\log K' = \log[H^+] + \log\frac{[\text{HCO}_3^-]}{0.03\,P_{CO_2}}$$

Substituting pH = − log [H$^+$] and pK$'$ = − log K$'$ and rearranging terms gives

$$p\text{H} = \text{pK}' + \log\frac{[\text{HCO}_3^-]}{0.03\,P_{CO_2}} \quad (9)$$

K$'$ = 8 × 10^{-7}, so pK$'$ = − log 8 × 10^{-7} = − log 8 − log 10^{-7} = − 0.9 + 7 = 6.1. Thus the Henderson–Hasselbalch equation for plasma at 38° C. is

$$p\text{H} = 6.1 + \log\frac{[\text{HCO}_3^-]}{0.03\,P_{CO_2}} \quad (10)$$

For example, in normal plasma, [HCO$_3^-$] = 24 millimols per liter and [CO$_2$] = 0.03 P$_{CO_2}$ = 0.03 × 40 = 1.2 millimols per liter. Hence [HCO$_3^-$]/0.03 P$_{CO_2}$ = 24/1.2 = 20. The logarithm of 20 is the sum of the log of 2 and the log of 10; log 20 = log (2 × 10) = log 2 + log 10 = 0.3 + 1 = 1.3; pH = 6.1 + 1.3 = 7.4, the normal pH of plasma.

The Henderson–Hasselbalch equation shows clearly the effects of P$_{CO_2}$ on the acidity of a solution. An increase in P$_{CO_2}$ adds carbonic acid to the solution and titrates it in the acid direction (lower pH). Since [H$_2$CO$_3$] is proportional to P$_{CO_2}$ the actual amount of acid added and buffered cannot be calculated solely from the change in P$_{CO_2}$; if the solution is well buffered, considerable acid is added by any increase in P$_{CO_2}$; i.e., CO$_2$ continues to dissolve and hydrate to H$_2$CO$_3$ as the H$^+$ are taken up by the buffer. On the other hand, adding noncarbonic acid to a solution with constant P$_{CO_2}$ causes little pH change; most of the excess H$^+$ combines with HCO$_3^-$ and leaves the solution as CO$_2$.

Bicarbonate–Carbonic Acid as a Buffer at Fixed P$_{CO_2}$. **AMOUNT OF ADDED ACID.** The titration curves of a bicarbonate solution at various fixed P$_{CO_2}$ values are shown in Figure 4. These curves are determined in much the same ways as those of a phosphate buffer: Varying amounts of a strong, noncarbonic acid such as HCl are added to the solution which is equilibrated with a gas of fixed P$_{CO_2}$ by vigorous bubbling. After each addition of nonvolatile acid, a sample is taken and its pH is measured. Since the P$_{CO_2}$ is known, [HCO$_3^-$] can be calculated. These data can be plotted to give a titration curve (Fig. 4). However, the amount of noncarbonic acid added is equal to the decrease in [HCO$_3^-$] plus the negligible increase in [H$^+$]; the vast majority of added H$^+$ combine with bicarbonate to form carbonic acid and disappear into the gas phase as carbon dioxide. Therefore, the decrease in [HCO$_3^-$] closely approximates the amount of acid added; a plot of [HCO$_3^-$] against pH gives an upside down titration curve of the CO$_2$ system. It must be emphasized that *this is true only if the solution has no other buffer substances,* i.e., if other buffers were present, some of the added H$^+$ would combine with them and reduce the pH change and, more importantly, not all of the H$^+$ would combine with HCO$_3^-$; the amount of acid added would be greater than the decrease in bicarbonate. The estimation of the amount of added acid in solutions containing protein buffers and bicarbonate is described later.

TITRATION CURVES AT FIXED P$_{CO_2}$. At P$_{CO_2}$ = 40 mm. Hg and [HCO$_3^-$] = 24 millimols per liter, pH = 7.40 as calculated above. This is plotted as point A in Figure 4. Adding 5 millimols of strong acid per liter reduces [HCO$_3^-$] by

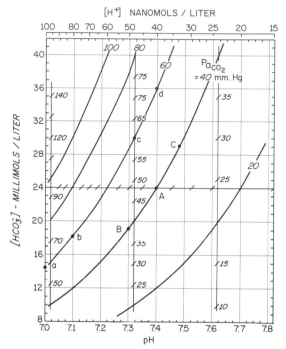

Fig. 4. The pH-[HCO_3^-] diagram for blood plasma. [H^+] is shown across the top. P_{aCO_2} isobars are calculated from the Henderson–Hasselbalch equation (Equation 10) with P_{aCO_2} held constant at the values attached to each curve. Any isobar can be superimposed on any other isobar by sliding the whole curve horizontally. At fixed pH, P_{aCO_2} is proportional to [HCO_3^-]. The vertical lines at pH's of 7.02, 7.32 and 7.62 have slanting scribe lines indicating the P_{aCO_2} at those points; the proportionality factors are 4, 2 and 1 respectively. Along any horizontal line, P_{aCO_2} is proportional to [H^+]; at [HCO_3^-] = 24 millimols per liter, P_{aCO_2} = [H^+] if P_{aCO_2} is given in mm. Hg and [H^+] in nanomols per liter. The slanting scribe marks along the [HCO_3^-] = 24 millimols per liter line indicate the P_{aCO_2} at the point as read off the [H^+] scale at the top. A P_{aCO_2} isobar is the titration curve of a HCO_3^-–H_2CO_3 solution with P_{aCO_2} held fixed. The slope of the curve represents the buffer value at that point and is 2.3 [HCO_3^-]. Point A is the normal value for human plasma, points B and C the changes caused by adding 5 millimols of strong acid and strong base respectively. See text for significance of small letters.

this amount to 19 millimols per liter. Hence pH = 6.1 + log 19/1.2 = 6.1 + log 15.8 = 6.1 + 1.2 = 7.30 (point B, Fig. 4). A negligible amount of the added strong acid remains in the ionic form since [H^+] = 10^{-pH} = $10^{-7.3}$ = $10^{-(8-0.7)}$ = $10^{-8} \times 10^{0.7}$ = 5×10^{-8} mols per liter = 50 nanomols per liter. In contrast, 5,000,000 nanomols (5 m**M.**) per liter were added. This value of [H^+] can also be obtained by reading from the scale at the top of Figure 4.

Similarly, adding 5 millimols of strong base per liter raises [HCO_3^-] to 29 millimols per liter and pH = 6.1 + log (29/1.2) = 7.48 (point C, Fig. 4). Other points for P_{CO_2} = 40 mm. Hg are calculated and plotted in the same way and a smooth curve is drawn through them to make the 40 mm. Hg isobar. The same procedure was used to construct the titration curves (isobars) for P_{CO_2} = 20, 60, 80 and 100 mm. Hg as shown in Figure 4.

ESTIMATION OF P_{CO_2} ON pH-[HCO_3^-] GRAPHS. As shown in Figure 4, P_{CO_2} isobars are concave upward. Solving the Henderson-Hasselbalch equation (10) for [HCO_3^-] gives

$$[HCO_3^-] = 0.03 \ P_{CO_2} \ 10^{pH - 6.1} \qquad (11)$$

showing that these curves are exponential for fixed P_{CO_2}. Study of this and Equation (10) reveals three properties of P_{CO_2} isobars which make it relatively easy to estimate the P_{CO_2} at points falling between the isobars shown on the graph:

(i) At constant pH, i.e., along any vertical line in Figure 4, P_{CO_2} is proportional to [HCO_3^-]. In particular if pH = 7.32, P_{CO_2} (in mm. Hg) = 2 · [HCO_3^-] (in millimols per liter) as shown by the vertical line at pH = 7.32 in Figure 4. The slanting marks show 5 mm. Hg intervals. Comparison with the left ordinate scale shows that P_{CO_2} is twice [HCO_3^-], e.g., at [HCO_3^-] = 20 millimols per liter, P_{CO_2} = 40 mm. Hg. Similarly, at pH = 7.02, P_{CO_2} = 4[HCO_3^-]; and at pH = 7.62, P_{CO_2} = [HCO_3^-].

(ii) At a fixed [HCO_3^-], P_{CO_2} is proportional to [H^+]. This is most easily seen from the equilibrium condition, $K' \cdot 0.03 \ P_{CO_2}$ = [H^+] · [HCO_3^-]. In particular, along the horizontal line at [HCO_3^-] = 24 millimols per liter, P_{CO_2} (in mm. Hg) = [H^+] (in nanomols per liter) as shown by the slanting marks along the [HCO_3^-] = 24 millimols per liter line.

(iii) Any P_{CO_2} isobar can be superimposed on any other isobar by sliding the whole curve horizontally, e.g., the 80 mm. Hg isobar is everywhere 0.3 pH to the left of the 40 mm. Hg isobar (Fig. 4).

CALCULATION OF pH. Remembering the relation log 2 = 0.3 allows the logarithms of most numbers to be rapidly estimated. For example, since log AB = log A + log B and log A/B = log A − log B and log 2 = 0.3, then log 4 = log 2 × 2 = log 2 + log 2 = 0.3 + 0.3 = 0.6, log 8 = 0.9, log 16 = 1.2, log 1.6 = log 16/10 = log 16 − log 10 = 1.2 − 1.0 = 0.2, log 5 = log 10/2 = log 10 − log 2 = 1.0 − 0.3 =

0.7, log 2.5 = log 10/4 = 0.4, log 1.25 = 0.1. With these values, a P_{CO_2} isobar can be calculated with sufficient accuracy for most purposes. For example, let P_{CO_2} = 60 mm. Hg; $[H_2CO_3]$ = 0.03 × 60 = 1.8 millimols per liter. Take 8, 10, 16 and 20 times 1.8, e.g., 8 × 1.8 = 14.4, 18, 28.8 and 36 millimols per liter. The logarithms of the ratio $[HCO_3^-]/0.03\ P_{CO_2}$ for each value are 0.9, 1.0, 1.2 and 1.3 and the corresponding *p*H's are simply 6.1 plus the log ratios, giving 7.0, 7.1, 7.3 and 7.4 respectively. These values are plotted as points a,b,c,d in Figure 4, sufficient to draw the P_{CO_2} = 60 mm. Hg isobar with considerable accuracy.

BUFFER VALUE OF BICARBONATE SOLUTION AT CONSTANT P_{CO_2}. Figure 4 shows that a solution containing HCO_3^- is an excellent buffer if P_{CO_2} is held constant. The buffer value at any point is, by definition, the slope of a P_{CO_2} isobar at that point. Since the curves are exponential the buffer value increases in direct proportion to $[HCO_3^-]$ and is independent of P_{CO_2} or *p*H. Calculation shows that buffer value = 2.3 $[HCO_3^-]$, e.g., buffer value = 55 sl. for $[HCO_3^-]$ = 24 millimols per liter. In other words, the molar buffer value is 2.3 per *p*H unit, a value 4 times that of an ordinary buffer (0.575 per *p*H unit). The fourfold improvement in buffer value is due to the fact that P_{CO_2} and thus $[H_2CO_3]$ are held constant. In an ordinary buffer, adding acid increases the concentration of HA and decreases that of A^- simultaneously; at constant P_{CO_2}, only the $[HCO_3^-]$ changes.

EFFECT OF DILUTION. As mentioned earlier, diluting a solution containing a buffer has practically no effect on the *p*H. However, this is not true of the bicarbonate–carbonic acid solution at fixed P_{CO_2}; $[H_2CO_3]$ is constant but $[HCO_3^-]$ is decreased and hence *p*H falls; e.g., if the volume of solution were doubled by adding water, $[HCO_3^-]$ would be halved and *p*H would thus fall by 0.3 (Fig. 4). Adding water is equivalent to adding acid and removing water is equivalent to adding base, the amounts per liter being equal to the change in $[HCO_3^-]$. Changes in the bodily water balance thus have acid–base effects.

TITRATION OF BLOOD

There are two ways of adding acid or base to a solution containing carbonic acid–bicarbonate and protein buffers; carbonic acid can be added by increasing the P_{CO_2} and a noncar-

bonic acid can be added directly. A change in P_{CO_2} titrates only the noncarbonic (protein) buffers present; the amount of added acid is equal to the increase in $[HCO_3^-]$ since a HCO_3^- appears with every H^+ when carbonic acid dissociates. Adding noncarbonic acid titrates both the carbonic acid–bicarbonate and protein buffers; the amount of added acid is proportional to the decrease in $[HCO_3^-]$ as explained below.

Titration of Blood with CO_2. Changing P_{CO_2} gives a direct indication of the buffer value of protein buffers alone. Since the amount of acid added per liter equals the increase in $[HCO_3^-]$, the titration curve is plotted on a *p*H-$[HCO_3^-]$ diagram such as that in Figure 4. Figure 5 illustrates the factors which determine

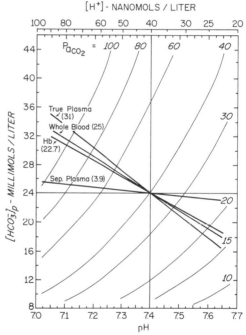

Fig. 5. CO_2 titration curves of blood and its components. Acid is added or removed by increasing or decreasing P_{aCO_2}. The amount of acid added is equal to the increase in $[HCO_3^-]$ because for every H^+ formed by the dissociation of H_2CO_3 a HCO_3^- also appears. The negative of the slope of the titration curve, the buffer value (in sl.) is shown in parentheses. Buffer value of homogenized whole blood is slightly higher (26.6 sl.) than that shown for nonhomogenized whole blood (25 sl.). True plasma buffer value (31 sl.) is higher than that of whole blood because of the Donnan equilibrium which forces most of the HCO_3^- formed in the cell into the plasma. True plasma is plasma equilibrated with red cells and then separated for analysis.

the buffer value of normal, oxygenated whole blood and plasma as determined by titration with CO_2.

BUFFER VALUE OF PLASMA PROTEINS. The buffer value of a solution containing more than one kind of buffer is simply the sum of the individual buffer values. The buffer value of blood is almost entirely due to hemoglobin and plasma proteins. The expected buffer value of plasma can be calculated from the amount of protein. Since plasma proteins are heterogeneous, buffer value is measured in millimols per gram times pH (gram-pH) rather than millimols per millimol times pH. According to Van Slyke and co-workers,[47] the buffer value of plasma proteins is 0.1 millimols of acid per gram-pH; that of hemoglobin is $3/16.7 = 0.18$ millimol per gram-pH. These values are about in the same ratio as the histidine contents of plasma proteins and hemoglobin.[18] A liter of plasma contains about 70 grams of protein, so buffer value $= 0.1 \times 70 = 7.0$ sl. Since a liter of blood contains 0.55 liter of plasma, the contribution of plasma to the buffer value of blood is $0.55 \times 7 = 3.9$ sl. (Fig. 5).

TITRATION OF HEMOGLOBIN WITH CO_2.[17, 49] A liter of red cells contains 334 grams or $334/16.7 = 20$ millimols of hemoglobin; a liter of blood contains 0.45 liter of red cells and $0.45 \times 20 = 9$ millimols of hemoglobin. The buffer value of hemoglobin in a liter of blood is thus $3 \times 9 = 27$ sl. However, the measured molar buffer value of hemoglobin is for a liter of water rather than a liter of solution; i.e., the volume of the hemoglobin is excluded in calculating buffer value.[22] A liter of blood contains 0.84 liter of water,[16] the rest being occupied mainly by hemoglobin and plasma proteins. Acid added to a liter of blood is, in effect, added to only 0.84 liter of water and is thus $1/0.84$ more concentrated than indicated by the change in blood $[HCO_3^-]$. Thus, the actual buffer value of hemoglobin in a liter of blood is $0.84 \times 27 = 22.7$ sl. (Fig. 5). It would be expected that the CO_2 titration curve of whole blood would be the sum of the curves for the contributions of plasma proteins and hemoglobin, $3.9 + 22.7 = 26.6$ sl. Although this is approximately correct, two further corrections are necessary to obtain the CO_2 titration curve of whole blood: (i) the solubility of CO_2 in red cell water is slightly different than that in plasma water.[50] This is a comparatively minor difference and will not be further considered. (ii) The red cell

membrane affects the distribution of HCO_3^- between cells and plasma.

TRANSMEMBRANE DISTRIBUTION OF BICARBONATE IN RED CELLS. The steady state in red cells as in other cells is maintained by a Na^+–K^+ exchange pump (Chap. 1). However, red cells differ from other cells in having a low transmembrane potential, about -10 mV., and in having membranes about 100 times more permeable to Cl^- and HCO_3^- than to K^+.[27] In excitable cells K^+ and Cl^- permeabilities are about equal. This high permeability to anions is necessary for rapid equilibration of CO_2 with blood; e.g., an increase in P_{aCO_2} rapidly increases $[H_2CO_3]$ in cells because of carbonic anhydrase; the H^+ formed are buffered by hemoglobin; $[HCO_3^-]$ of cells is increased and HCO_3^- exchanges for Cl^- in the plasma. The highly permeative HCO_3^- and Cl^- are equilibrated with the transmembrane potential so that their internal concentrations are only about 0.7 of their external concentrations. The solid content of cells and plasma decreases this factor to about 0.54. Because of this transmembrane equilibrium, most of the HCO_3^- is carried in the plasma even though it is formed in the red cells. Another factor affecting buffer value is that cell pH does not change as rapidly as plasma pH because of a change in the transmembrane potential with pH. With all these factors taken into account the buffer value of whole blood with respect to changes in cell pH is calculated as 37 sl.;[17] with respect to plasma pH, the abscissa in Figure 5, the buffer value is reduced to 25 sl. This value is slightly less than the 26.6 sl., calculated more directly above.

TITRATION CURVE OF TRUE PLASMA. When the $[HCO_3^-]$ of plasma $([HCO_3^-]_p)$ rather than whole blood is plotted on the ordinate, the slope of the titration curve is greater because at a fixed P_{aCO_2} the $[HCO_3^-]_p$ is higher. Plasma which is equilibrated with blood cells has a buffer value about 1.25 times that of whole blood: (buffer value of true plasma) $= 1.25$ (buffer value of whole blood) $= 1.25 \times 25 = 31$ sl. (Fig. 5). Plasma equilibrated with red cells and then separated for analysis of $[HCO_3^-]$ is called *true plasma* as compared with *separated plasma*, which is separated first and then titrated and analyzed.

The reduction of the buffer value of blood due to its solid content is almost exactly compensated for by the distribution ratio of HCO_3^- so that the buffer value of true plasma is the same as would be calculated for homogenized whole blood, i.e., 3.9 for plasma and $3 \times 9 = 27$ sl. for hemoglobin, the total being 30.9 sl., the same as that of true plasma. The buffer value of true plasma is used in estimating the change in pH caused by a change in P_{aCO_2}; the buffer value of whole blood is used in estimating the amount of noncarbonic acid added to the blood. Of course, buffer value depends on the concentrations of hemoglobin and plasma protein in blood.

CARBAMINOHEMOGLOBIN FORMATION.[18, 37, 53] Titrating protein solutions with carbon dioxide is complicated by the direct combination of CO_2 with free end amino groups of hemoglobin and plasma proteins to form a carbamino compound. The reaction is of the form $R-NH_2 + CO_2 \rightleftharpoons R-NHCOO^- + H^+$. Carbamic acids ($R-NHCOOH$) are fairly strong and completely dissociated at normal body pH. Carbaminohemoglobin forms only if the free amino group is in the uncharged form ($R-NH_2$ rather than $R-NH_3^+$) and the reaction is between the end amino group and dissolved CO_2, not bicarbonate or carbonic acid. An appreciable fraction of the [Total CO_2] of the blood is carbamino compounds of hemoglobin (about 1 millimol per liter of blood). The concentration of these compounds depends on the concentrations of dissolved CO_2 (hence on P_{aCO_2}) and of uncharged free amino groups in the solution (hence on the pH). An increase in P_{aCO_2} tends, on the one hand, to increase the concentration of carbamino compounds by increasing $[CO_2]$ and, on the other hand, to decrease their concentration by decreasing pH, which promotes formation of charged free amino groups according to the reaction, $R-NH_2 + H^+ \rightleftharpoons R-NH_3^+$, which is forced to the right. In living animals, the concentration of carbamino compounds is practically independent of P_{aCO_2}. Oxygenated hemoglobin contains about 0.1 millimol and reduced hemoglobin about 0.3 millimol of carbamino hemoglobin per millimol.[21] It is disputed whether this difference is due to special properties of hemoglobin, i.e., a free amino group whose dissociation constant is altered by oxygenation or simply due to the rise in pH when hemoglobin is reduced.[53] Recent evidence indicates that the former view is most likely correct.[37]

The change in amount of carboxyhemoglobin with the oxygenation of the solution means that some CO_2 (up to 30 per cent) is transported from the tissues to the lungs in this form. However, the role of carbamino compounds in the buffer value of the blood is practically negligible; the combination of CO_2 with hemoglobin releases H^+ which must be buffered just as those produced by dissociation of carbonic acid must be. The only difference with respect to acid–base behavior between the two is that bicarbonate ions penetrate the erythrocyte membrane easily whereas carbaminohemoglobin is confined to the cell because of the large size of the hemoglobin molecule.

Titration of Blood with Noncarbonic Acid. Adding noncarbonic acid to blood with P_{aCO_2} held constant titrates both the protein and carbonic acid–bicarbonate buffer systems in the acid direction. Since part of the added H^+ combines with hemoglobin and plasma proteins and part with HCO_3^- to form CO_2, the amount of added acid is greater than the decrease in bicarbonate concentration by the amount buffered by the proteins. This is different from a pure bicarbonate solution as described in connection with Figure 4. Since the state of dissociation of the various groups on protein molecules depends on pH but not on P_{aCO_2}, the amount of acid added can be determined by back-titrating to the original pH by reducing the P_{aCO_2}, thus removing carbonic acid and restoring the proteins to their original ionization state. At the original pH, the total change in $[HCO_3^-]$ of blood must equal the amount of acid added. In other words, since none of the added H^+ is now combined with the protein buffers, all of it must have combined with HCO_3^- and disappeared from the system in the form of CO_2. For this to happen, however, the P_{aCO_2} must be reduced, i.e., back-titrated in the alkaline direction.

TITRATION OF PLASMA WITH HCl. This method of estimating the excess noncarbonic acid concentration is illustrated in Figure 6. Consider first the simpler case in which separated plasma is titrated. Assume that 8 millimols of noncarbonic acid (HCl) are added per liter of plasma (with normal pH and $[HCO_3^-]$ and P_{CO_2} held constant at 40 mm. Hg). This titrates the plasma along the $P_{CO_2} = 40$ mm. Hg isobar toward lower pH and lower $[HCO_3^-]$ (from 0 to A in Fig. 6). Part of the added, completely dissociated acid reacts with the HCO_3^- to form carbonic acid, which is converted to CO_2 and eliminated. The rest of the acid reacts with the plasma proteins. The amount of added

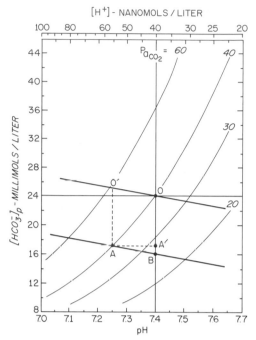

Fig. 6. Titration of plasma with noncarbonic acid; estimation of amount of noncarbonic acid added per liter of plasma. Adding 8 millimols of strong noncarbonic acid such as HCl titrates the plasma from O to A (P_{aCO_2} held fixed at 40 mm. Hg). Position of point A is determined by backtitrating along titration curve of plasma proteins to the original pH by lowering P_{aCO_2} and thus removing carbonic acid. Slope of the titration curve is independent of P_{aCO_2} and of pH. Thus a titration curve, AB, is constructed through A with a slope of -7 sl. (buffer value of plasma). The intersection of this line with original pH (point B) determines amount of noncarbonic acid added. Since the charge on the plasma protein is the same at B as at O (pH's are the same), all of the added acid must have combined with HCO_3^- and disappeared from the solution as CO_2. The distance OB is the amount of noncarbonic acid added: 8 millimols. The distance OA' is the amount of the original noncarbonic acid buffered by HCO_3^- at constant P_{aCO_2} and A'B the amount buffered by titration of the plasma proteins in the acid direction; i.e., A'B $= -7$ ($pH_A - pH_B$) $= 7 \times 0.15$ $= 1.05$ millimols per liter. Note that O'A $=$ OB.

H+ buffered by plasma protein is determined by back-titrating to the original pH by lowering the P_{CO_2}. The resulting reduction in $[H_2CO_3]$ also reduces the $[H^+]$ and $[HCO_3^-]$. The buffer value of plasma is not affected by adding excess noncarbonic acid so the titration curve is simply shifted to the left and down (AB, Fig. 6). At normal pH (point B), the amount of HCO_3^- removed must equal the amount of noncarbonic acid added since the

charge on the protein buffers depends only on the pH and it is normal. Thus point B is 8 millimols per liter directly below O. The vertical distance OA' represents the amount of acid originally buffered by HCO_3^-, and A'B is that buffered by plasma protein. Also the greater the buffer value of proteins, the less the change in $[HCO_3^-]$ of plasma produced by a given amount of acid.

TITRATION OF BLOOD WITH HCl. The buffer values of both whole blood and true plasma are directly dependent on the concentration of hemoglobin in blood but are affected by the transmembrane $[HCO_3^-]$ distribution ratio. As the hemoglobin concentration increases, so does the fraction of HCO_3^- outside cells and the difference between the buffer values of whole blood and separated plasma. Since hemoglobin content varies considerably between patients, direct measurements of hemoglobin content or buffer value of blood or true plasma are advisable in acid–base disorders. Siggaard-Andersen[39] has described a simple and reliable method of estimating buffer value graphically from measurements of pH at two known P_{CO_2} values. He also gives a graphic means of estimating the amount of extra noncarbonic base or acid (base excess) in the blood by using the buffer value and original pH. He points out that the amount of added noncarbonic acid in blood can be estimated as follows: Excess noncarbonic acid $= (1 - 0.00125\ [HbO_2]) \times$ change in $[HCO_3^-]$ of plasma at $pH = 7.4$ (distance OB', Fig. 7), where hemoglobin concentration, $[HbO_2]$, is in grams per liter. For $[HbO_2] = 150$ grams per liter (normal), the correction factor is 0.81.

The titration of whole blood with 8 millimols HCl per liter and the estimation of this quantity from the pH-$[HCO_3^-]_p$ diagram are illustrated in Figure 7. At $P_{CO_2} = 40$ mm. Hg, adding HCl titrates normal blood from O to A. The plasma $[HCO_3^-]$ at point A is such that drawing a titration curve with a slope of -31 sl. (true plasma) through A intersects the pH $= 7.4$ line at B', a point which is 9.9 millimols per liter below 0; i.e., excess noncarbonic acid in blood $= 0.81 \times$ the change in $[HCO_3^-]$ at pH of 7.4 $= 0.81 \times 9.9 = 8$ millimols per liter (distance OC, Fig. 7). This is a simple and accurate way to estimate excess noncarbonic acid and is preferred. Davenport[13] avoids the necessity for making this correction by assigning a buffer value of 21.6 sl. to true plasma, 0.7 of its

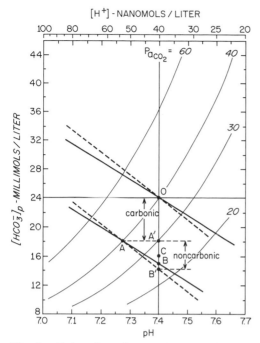

Three quantities are of importance in specifying an acid–base disturbance: pH, P_{CO_2} and the extra noncarbonic acid (proportional to the change in $[HCO_3^-]$ at normal pH). In specifying clinical acid–base disturbances, it is useful to have terms describing the direction of changes in these quantities. In addition, the *primary* disturbance or pathologic condition that *caused* the acid–base change must be distinguished from the further changes which may occur in the body to *compensate* for the original change.

Acidosis is defined as any condition in which the plasma pH is less than normal. The "normal" range of arterial blood pH is 7.35 to 7.45 (Fig. 8).[2, 13] Thus, any pH below 7.35 is clearly an acidosis. *Alkalosis* is defined as an arterial blood pH greater than 7.45. A condition in which arterial CO_2 pressure is greater than normal is usually accompanied by a fall in pH and for this reason is often called "respiratory acidosis." However, the noncommittal term *hypercapnia*, meaning raised P_{aCO_2}, is more accu-

Fig. 7. Estimation of noncarbonic acid excess in whole blood. See legend to Figure 6. Most correct estimate is OC = 0.81 OB′ = 8 millimols per liter. Line AB has a slope of −21.6 sl. (Davenport[13]). Distance OB is 8.7 millimols per liter, 9 per cent too high. (See text.) Note that a much larger fraction of the added noncarbonic acid was buffered by protein buffers of blood (A′B′) than was the case for separated plasma. Hence, the fall in pH was only 0.13 instead of 0.15 as in Figure 6. The portion of the added acid labeled carbonic (OA′) is that buffered by HCO_3^- and that labeled noncarbonic (A′B′) is the portion taken up by the protein buffers. Both are overestimated by 1/0.81.

normal value. In this case, excess noncarbonic acid is estimated by drawing a line, AB, of slope −21.6 sl. through A. The excess noncarbonic acid is estimated as 8.7 millimols per liter, 9 per cent too high. In view of the other errors involved, e.g., uncertainty of normal blood pH and plasma $[HCO_3^-]$ and errors of measurement, this estimate of excess noncarbonic acid suffices for most purposes. However, calculation of 0.8 × OB′ is scarcely less simple and is more accurate. Singer and Hastings[41] have given nomograms for calculating the amount of noncarbonic acid added to a liter of blood; these take account of the oxygenation of the hemoglobin. The method illustrated in Figure 7 is for use with fully oxygenated blood only. Other initial values must be used otherwise.

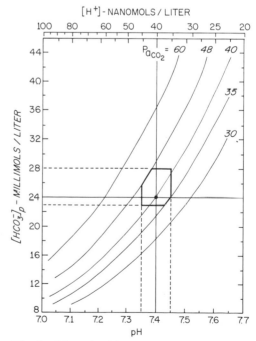

Fig. 8. Normal acid–base range in humans at sea level (any point within the hexagon). People living at higher altitudes have significantly different values. (After Davenport, *The ABC of acid–base chemistry*. Chicago, University of Chicago Press, 1958.)

rate. Since hypercapnia can occur simultaneously with alkalosis, "respiratory acidosis" is misleading. Similarly, *hypocapnia* refers to a condition of lower than normal P_{aCO_2}. The normal range of P_{aCO_2} in man is 35 to 48 mm. Hg (Fig. 8).

No satisfactory term for an excess or deficit of noncarbonic acids in the body has been generally accepted. The most common term is "metabolic acidosis" as distinguished from respiratory acidosis. However, "metabolic acidosis" is sometimes found when the pH is above normal, so the term acidosis is misleading. Noncommittal terms such as "nonvolatile" or "noncarbonic" seem to offer advantages. However, neither of these words lends itself to simple characterization of the condition resulting from an excess or deficit of nonvolatile or noncarbonic acids; "hypernoncarbonosis" or "hypernoncarbonicity" is clumsy. The terms "metabolic acidosis" and "alkalosis" are well established and will be used occasionally, but usually such changes will be termed excess (or deficit) of noncarbonic acids or noncarbonic acid excess or deficit.

Compensation. Most data indicate that pH or $[H^+]$ is the most important factor in determining the bodily response to acid–base unbalances. In addition to the buffers of the extracellular space, three other mechanisms either act to limit further the changes in pH, or, in the absence of permanent disability, to restore pH to normal. (i) H^+ are transferred across tissue cell membranes in a direction which changes blood pH toward normal. (ii) A deviation in pH changes respiratory minute volume and P_{aCO_2} so as to reduce the deviation. This is called *respiratory compensation* (of a primary noncarbonic acid excess or deficit) and is usually not complete, i.e., does not restore pH to normal. (iii) Renal excretion of noncarbonic acid or base increases to eliminate an excess of noncarbonic acid or to compensate for the pH changes due to an abnormal P_{aCO_2}. The latter is called renal compensation (of a primary hyper- or hypocapnia). Again it must be emphasized that the crux of clinical diagnosis is to distinguish between the cause of the disturbance, e.g., diabetes or emphysema, and the compensatory response, e.g., hyperventilation or renal excretion of noncarbonic acid (retention of alkali).

TITRATION OF THE WHOLE BODY WITH CARBON DIOXIDE

The whole body can be titrated with CO_2 by controlling the ventilation rate or the fraction of CO_2 in the inspired air; the buffer value of the body can be estimated from the resulting changes in $[HCO_3^-]_p$ and pH. Such data are commonly called a CO_2 uptake curve and $[HCO_3^-]$ or $[CO_2]$ is plotted against P_{CO_2} (see Fig. 3, Chap. 40). The resulting graph is curved and difficult to interpret; the pH-$[HCO_3^-]$ plot is linear and simple to interpret. Such data are obtained by having a volunteer hyperventilate for a few minutes, thus reducing the P_{ACO_2} and P_{aCO_2} and titrating the body in the alkaline direction, or by having the subject breathe 5 to 10 per cent CO_2 for a short time, thereby titrating his blood in the acid direction.[13] Arterial blood samples are taken at appropriate times. More recently, volunteers[3] have entered chambers where P_{CO_2} is held fixed and CO_2 titration curves are obtained for times up to an hour. Dogs have been subjected to the same procedure for days or weeks.[10, 34] The changes in $[HCO_3^-]$ and pH following a step change in P_{aCO_2} vary with exposure time, a factor insufficiently considered in the literature.

Titration of Extracellular Fluid with CO_2. If there were no appreciable interchange of hydrogen and bicarbonate ions between cells and the interstitial fluid (red blood cells excepted), changes in P_{ACO_2} would titrate cells and extracellular fluid independently of each other since the deviation of P_{CO_2} would be the same in both. Thus plotting $[HCO_3^-]_p$ against plasma pH would simply result in the titration curve of extracellular fluid (blood and interstitial fluids). Any difference between the measured CO_2 titration curve of the whole body and that of extracellular fluid must be attributed to movement of H^+ across cell membranes or to renal secretion or reabsorption of H^+.

The titration curve of the whole extracellular fluid can be calculated from the buffer value of 1 liter of blood and from the total volumes of blood and extracellular fluid. The buffer value of one liter of well mixed extracellular fluid is less than that of blood by the factor by which interstitial fluid dilutes protein buffers of blood. A typical value for the blood volumes of a 70 kg. man is 5.3 liters, 2.4 liters of red cells and 2.9 liters of plasma. Inulin space, the readily diffusible extracellular volume, is about 12 liters, and thus total extracellular volume, including red cells, is 12 + 2.4 = 14.4 liters (Chap. 45). The 5.3 liters of blood contain 5.3 × 9 = 47.7 millimols of hemoglobin, and 2.9 liters of plasma contain 70 × 2.9 = 203 grams of plasma protein. These amounts are contained in 14.4 liters of extracellular fluid so that a liter contains 47.7/14.4 = 3.3 millimols of hemoglobin and 203/14.4 = 14 grams of plasma protein. The molar buffer value of hemoglobin is 3.0 per *p*H, and so the buffer value due to hemoglobin in a liter of extracellular fluid is 3.0 × 3.3 = 10 sl. and that due to plasma protein is 0.1 × 14 = 1.4 sl. The pre-

dicted total buffer value of extracellular fluid is approximately 10 + 1.4 = 11.4 sl. The same buffer value for extracellular fluid can be obtained by multiplying the buffer value of homogenized blood, 31 sl., by the ratio of blood volume to extracellular volume: 31 × (5.3/14.4) = 11.4 sl. The error due to the transmembrane HCO_3^- distribution is nearly negligible because of the small fraction of the extracellular space occupied by red cell water.

Figure 9 shows the calculated CO_2 titration curve for extracellular fluid plotted on a *p*H-$[HCO_3^-]_p$ diagram and having a slope of 11.4 sl. (interstitial fluid $[HCO_3^-]$ is slightly higher because of the Donnan equilibrium across the capillary wall). For comparison, a total body CO_2 titration curve for humans is also shown. It is seen that the two slopes are equal within experimental limits. However, the slope of the whole body titration curve depends greatly on how long after a change in $P_{I_{CO_2}}$ the blood samples were taken for analysis because more than an hour must elapse before blood, interstitial fluid and tissue P_{CO_2} reach a new steady state. This period, called the mixing transient, is the time required for the blood, carrying CO_2 to the tissues, to raise tissue $[CO_2]$, $[H_2CO_3]$ and $[HCO_3^-]$ stores to their new values. Hence, the time course of the mixing transient in the CO_2 system of the body must also be studied to interpret whole body CO_2 titration curves properly, i.e., to determine whether transmembrane H^+ transfer occurs.

Mixing Transient in Body CO_2 Stores.[19, 44] The time course of CO_2 uptake by the lungs, blood, interstitial fluid and tissues, following a sudden increase in $P_{I_{CO_2}}$, is a complicated process, having several components. The approximate time courses of these changes in the whole body and in arterial and venous blood are shown in Figures 10 and 11. Figure 10*A* illustrates the process of CO_2 transport in the blood following a stepwise increase in $P_{A_{CO_2}}$. Following the increase in $P_{A_{CO_2}}$ and $P_{a_{CO_2}}$, the CO_2 content of blood in the pulmonary vein likewise increases suddenly. After a few tens of seconds, the time required for the high CO_2 blood to reach the tissue capillaries, the blood gives up most of its extra CO_2 (mainly HCO_3^-) to the interstitial fluid, or does not pick up its normal load of CO_2 in the tissues. The venous blood returning from the tissues has a P_{CO_2} about equal to that of the tissues and possibly

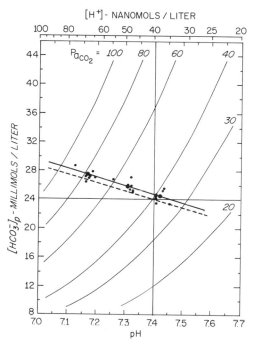

Fig. 9. CO_2 titration curve of extracellular fluid. Small points, individual measurements made on seven volunteer subjects; large points, average values for controls (breathing room air, right point) and for inspired CO_2 concentrations of 5 per cent (center) and 10 per cent (left). Arterial blood samples were drawn before and 10 to 60 minutes after an increase in $P_{I_{CO_2}}$. $P_{A_{CO_2}}$ depends on $P_{I_{CO_2}}$ and on alveolar ventilation. Solid line drawn through large points has a slope of −11.8 sl.; dashed line is the calculated titration curve of extracellular fluid and has a slope of −11.4 sl. (After Brackett, Cohen and Schwartz, *New Engl. J. Med.*, 1965, *272*:6–12.)

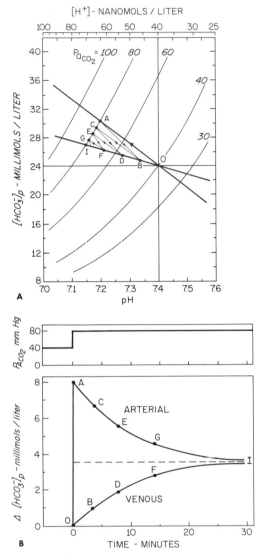

A

B

less than that of the arterial blood. The low CO_2 venous blood picks up another load of CO_2 in the lungs and carries it to the tissues, gradually filling up the tissues with CO_2. This process is illustrated in Figure 10A as movements on the pH-$[HCO_3^-]_p$ diagram and the time course is shown in Figure 10B.

The time necessary to reach a new steady state in a tissue thus depends on the ratio between tissue volume, V, and blood flow, $\dot{V}_b$, and on the buffer value of the tissue. If the same amount of CO_2 were delivered to the tissues every minute it would take about $V/\dot{V}_b$ minutes to fill up the tissue; e.g., for the whole body, V = 43.4 liters and $\dot{V}_b$, cardiac output, is about 5 liters per minute, so 43.5/5 = 8.7 minutes. However, the amount delivered to the tissues decreases in proportion as tissue $[HCO_3^-]$ builds up. Analysis shows that 63 per cent of the final amount is delivered in 8.7 minutes, 63 per cent of the remainder in the next 8.7 minutes and so on; i.e., this an exponential process with a time constant of 8.7 minutes. Unfortunately, this calculation is much too simple; the blood flow to various tissues and organs varies considerably, depending on bodily activity. The major determinant of equilibration time is blood flow in muscle, which constitutes nearly half the body mass. Blood flow to muscle is much lower than to most other tissues; at rest the time constant for filling the muscle with CO_2 is about 30 minutes. The time constant for most other tissues is about 2 minutes.[19] Blood flow to muscle may be halved during anesthesia and may increase severalfold in exercise. Hence the duration of the whole body transient state depends primarily on muscle blood flow. Normal body CO_2 production, about 0.23 liter per minute, does not affect these conclusions; however, increased CO_2 production due to exercise does produce a transient.

Figure 11 shows the approximate time course of changes in the total CO_2 content of the body in a person at rest. The initial rapid change is due to CO_2 uptake in blood; the successively slowing time course thereafter is due to extracellular and cellular uptake, the limiting factor

Fig. 10. The extracellular $[HCO_3^-]$ circulatory mixing transient following a change in $P_{A_{CO_2}}$ from 40 to 80 mm. Hg. *A,* Changes in plasma $[HCO_3^-]$ and pH of a segment of blood in successive passes through the lungs and tissues. At the time $P_{A_{CO_2}}$ was increased, the segment was in the lungs and was titrated from O to A along the true plasma titration curve. When the segment reached the tissues it gave up most of its excess $[H^+]$ and plasma $[HCO_3^-]$ to the extracellular space which is still at point O. This transfer moves the segment of blood to point B and titrates the extracellular fluid from O to B. On returning to the lungs, the blood segment is titrated from B to C, parallel to OA. This process continues, C to D, D to E, E to F, and so forth until the blood, extracellular fluid and intracellular fluid reach a new steady state at point I. *B, upper:* Time course of change in $P_{A_{CO_2}}$; *lower:* Time course of the changes, $\Delta[HCO_3^-]_p$, in $[HCO_3^-]$ of arterial and venous blood. The letters on the curves refer to corresponding points in Figure 10A. The arterial blood is presumed equilibrated with $P_{A_{CO_2}}$ and the venous blood with the extracellular fluid. All measurements must be made in fully oxygenated blood to be comparable. Curves are exponentials with time constant = 10 minutes; actual curves are more complicated.

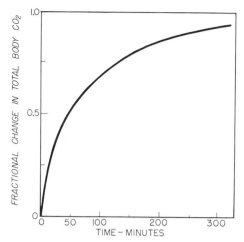

Fig. 11. Approximate time course of changes in total body CO_2 stores following an increase in P_{ACO_2}. *Ordinate:* Fraction of final change in total CO_2 stores of body. Over the time course shown, the change in CO_2 consists of dissolved CO_2, HCO_3^- and H_2CO_3. (After Fahri and Rahn, *Anesthesiology*, 1960, *21:*604–614; and Sullivan, Patterson and Papper, *Amer. J. Physiol.*, 1964, *206:*887–890.)

being the blood flow to the various tissues. It must be emphasized that changes in blood flow to muscle drastically alter this curve and the probable time course must be considered when estimating the acid–base status of a patient. Note that there are CO_2 transients when noncarbonic acid is given; some time is required for the CO_2 formed by combination of H+ with HCO_3^- to be carried from the tissues to the lungs.

Whole Body CO_2 Titration. Clearly, from the foregoing, nothing such as a unique whole body titration curve exists; the buffer value varies with time after the change in P_{ACO_2}, and the time of taking the sample must be stated. As pointed out by Fahri and Rahn,[19] taking account of the CO_2 transient explains the wide variations in measured buffer values obtained from whole body CO_2 titrations.[3, 10, 13]

From Figures 10 and 11 it can be predicted that CO_2 titration curves based on arterial blood sampling, as is commonly done, will have a buffer value near that of blood shortly after a change in P_{ACO_2} and that the buffer value will decrease steadily until it reaches the value for extracellular fluid (about 15 to 60 minutes). This expectation can be confirmed from experimental data. Davenport[13] took arterial blood samples from volunteers two to four minutes after the beginning of hyperventilation or

CO_2 inhalation. He obtained a buffer value of about 27 sl. (Fig. 12). Brackett and co-workers[3] took arterial blood samples from volunteers for periods up to an hour after they had entered a chamber containing air with an elevated P_{CO_2}. The major part of the CO_2 transient is over in about 10 minutes but there are slow changes throughout the hour. These data are plotted in Figure 9 for comparison with the calculated buffer value of extracellular fluid and also in Figure 12. The buffer value is 11.8

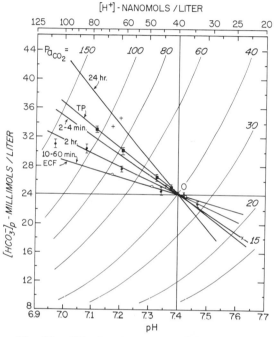

Fig. 12. CO_2 titration curves of the whole body at various times after a sudden increase in P_{ACO_2} (initial [HCO_3^-] and *p*H adjusted so lines go through 0). True plasma (TP, ■) and extracellular fluid (ECF) buffer curves are shown for reference. Measurements were made on true arterial plasma. At 2 to 4 minutes after P_{ACO_2} change, buffer value had fallen from 31 to 27 sl. (X); at 10 to 60 minutes to 11.6 sl. (0), the buffer value of extracellular fluid. Thereafter buffer value increases again due to transmembrane H+ transfer and renal compensation. In dogs, buffer value is 18.6 sl. after 0.5 to 2.0 hours (●), and approximately 48 after 24 hours (+). Reasons for early changes are shown in Figures 10 and 11. (2 to 4 minute curve after Davenport, *The ABC of acid-base chemistry*, Chicago, University of Chicago Press, 1958; true plasma and 10 to 60 minute curves after Brackett, Cohen and Schwartz, *New Engl. J. Med.*, 1965, *272:*6–12; 0.5 to 2 hour curve after Cohen, Brackett and Schwartz, *J. clin. Invest.*, 1964, *43:*777–786; 24 hour points after Polak, Haynie, Hays and Schwartz, *J. clin. Invest.*, 1961, *40:*1223–1237.)

sl., almost exactly that calculated above for extracellular fluid. Since these were normal, conscious volunteers, muscle blood flow was reasonably high and the CO_2 transient was probably over in about 45 minutes.

Titration curves obtained at later times should have the same slope as extracellular fluid unless there is transmembrane H^+ movement or renal compensation. Since renal compensation is slow—requiring many hours to many days to reach completion—any changes in buffer value in a matter of hours are due to transmembrane transfer or, more precisely, transfer out of the readily diffusible extracellular fluid. Cohen and co-workers[10] measured the CO_2 uptake of dogs after 0.5 to 2.0 hours in an atmosphere containing a fixed P_{CO_2}. The slope of the CO_2 titration curve is nearly -19 sl., considerably greater than that of the extracellular fluid of a dog (about the same as that of a human). Hence, some of the H^+'s appearing in the extracellular fluid because of the increased P_{CO_2} have penetrated the cell membrane. Presumably, even more will enter the cells during the following hours. After one day, $[HCO_3^-]$ has increased so that the buffer value is about 50 sl., but how much of this is due to increased renal acid excretion is not certain.[34] The available evidence indicates that approximately half of the acid added to extracellular fluid leaves it over a period of several hours. Further analysis of this phase of body buffering requires consideration of the mechanisms of transmembrane H^+ transfer and of the factors controlling these transfers.

INTRACELLULAR [H+] REGULATION[1, 6, 7, 20]

The extra HCO_3^- (loss of H^+) in the readily diffusible extracellular fluid a few hours after a decrease in its pH has two possible sources. (i) H^+ are exchanged between the slow extracellular fluid, the portion that equilibrates only slowly with inulin, e.g., connective tissue, tendon and bone, and the readily diffusible extracellular fluid. (ii) H^+ are transferred into tissue cells. It is unlikely that connective tissue, tendon or bone contributes substantially to the buffer value of the extracellular fluid in a time as short as a few hours. Bone probably plays an important role in buffering over days, weeks or months, but the turnover of bone HCO_3^- is too

slow to have an appreciable effect in an hour.[42] Similarly, the poor circulation to tendon and connective tissue and their consequent long turnover times indicate that these are also of little consequence over short times. Further, collagen has a low buffer value, about one-sixth that of hemoglobin. These considerations indicate that most of the body's buffer value not due to the blood comes from intracellular buffers. These intracellular buffers account for about half of the total after a few hours. This transmembrane H^+ transfer means that exact specification of the acid–base status of the body requires knowledge of the H^+ balance in the cells as well as in the extracellular fluid. Unfortunately, the factors governing transmembrane H^+ movements are poorly understood; however, certain general conclusions can be made which serve to integrate present knowledge. Muscle is the only tissue discussed here because it constitutes nearly half of the body mass and because transmembrane H^+ transfer has been most intensively studied in muscle. Other tissues, e.g., brain and liver, may play an important role also.

Intracellular pH. It was pointed out in Chapter 1 that H^+ are not equilibrated across muscle cell membranes; numerous indirect[6, 52] and a few direct measurements[7, 28] agree that intracellular pH of muscle is about 7.0 (6.8 to 7.2) whereas the pH would be 5.9 if H^+ were equilibrated with a transmembrane potential of -90 mV. Briefly, the inside negative potential difference across the membrane acts to drive the positively charged H^+ from outside to inside and HCO_3^- from inside to outside. If there were no counteracting outward transport of H^+, there would be a net inflow of H^+ and outflow of HCO_3^- until both were equilibrated. The external-to-internal ratios would be like that of Cl which is passively distributed: $[HCO_3^-]_o/[HCO_3^-]_i = [H^+]_i/[H^+]_o = 30$ (see Table 1, Chap. 1). The ratio would be somewhat larger because of CO_2 production in the cells. The actual ratio is $[H^+]_i/[H^+]_o = 10^{pH_o - pH_i} = 10^{7.4 - 7.0} = 2.5$ (range 1.6 to 4); i.e., internal $[H^+]$ is about 2.5 times external $[H^+]$ and external $[HCO_3^-]$ is 2.5 times internal $[HCO_3^-]$. *Despite the fact that $[H^+]$ in a muscle cell is greater than that outside, the tendency for them to diffuse out because of this concentration difference is far outweighed by the tendency for them to diffuse in because of the transmembrane voltage. Similarly, the net tendency for diffusion of HCO_3^- is outward.*

This point is made repeatedly in the first chapter about other ions and is re-emphasized here because it is generally ignored in the experimental literature on the body's acid–base status.

The disequilibrium of H^+ and HCO_3^- across the cell membrane indicates that either the membrane is impermeable to both these ions or that H^+ are actively transported out of the cell, or HCO_3^- into the cell or both. Although little direct evidence indicates that cell membranes —except those of red cells—are permeable to these ions, that they are completely impermeable seems unlikely. However, such ion impermeability would not hamper the diffusion of CO_2 from cells, since CO_2 penetrates all membranes easily but the ability of the cell to regulate its pH would be greatly limited. Most probably, H^+ and HCO_3^- are not equilibrated and are permeable and the disequilibrium is maintained by an active transport system which utilizes metabolic energy.

Estimation of Intracellular *p*H.[6, 52] The principal evidence for the existence of active transport is that internal pH is about 7.0. There are three ways of estimating intracellular pH: (i) Injecting pH-sensitive dyes into the cytoplasm, (ii) measuring the distribution of a weak acid or base between the tissue and interstitial fluid on the assumption that the membrane is relatively impermeable to the ionic form, (iii) direct measurements with an intracellular glass membrane H^+-sensitive electrode. The latter method is probably subject to the least number of uncertainties, but until recently such measurements were possible only in large fibers, e.g., squid giant axon or crab muscle fibers.[7] A new direct technique is based on ultramicroelectrodes (Chap. 1) made of pH-sensitive glass.[28] Both of these direct techniques indicate that intracellular pH is about 7.0.

The distribution pattern of a weak acid between plasma and tissues provides an estimate of the over-all pH of a tissue or of the whole body. This technique has recently received great emphasis because of the discovery by Waddell and Butler[52] that 5,5-dimethyl-2, 4-oxazolidinedione (DMO) is almost ideal for this type of measurement. The principle is that the dissociation of a weak acid depends on the $[H^+]$ of the medium. DMO has a pK' of 6.13, so that the ratio of ionized to nonionized DMO at plasma pH of 7.43 is 20 to 1, whereas this ratio in a cell at pH of 7.03 would be only 8 to 1. If the cell membrane is permeable to the acid (nonionized) form and relatively impermeable to the anionic form, intracellular pH can be calculated from measurements of tissue and plasma DMO concentrations, interstitial volume and plasma pH.

Carbonic acid can also be used to estimate pH$_i$. Measurements of tissue and plasma carbonic acid concentrations and the plasma pH permit the calculation of pH$_i$ from the Henderson–Hasselbalch equation. This method has been used extensively but is uncertain because CO_2 (carbamino or similar compounds) may combine directly with intracellular proteins and because cellular P_{CO_2} is an unknown amount higher than arterial P_{CO_2}. Generally speaking, pH$_i$ values calculated in this manner are somewhat higher than those obtained with DMO and intracellular pH electrodes.

The exact range of intracellular pH values is not known accurately, but the general agreement of many different methods in the hands of many different investigators strongly indicates that H^+ are not equilibrated in cells;[6, 20, 30, 52] the observed concentration is about 10 times lower than expected from the membrane potential and external concentration. Conway[11] contends that, in muscle, H^+ are equilibrated across the cell membrane on the basis that most of the muscle CO_2 is neither CO_2 nor HCO_3^-. The recent findings with DMO tend to discount this possibility.

Transmembrane Fluxes of H^+ and HCO_3^-. The net passive fluxes of H^+ and HCO_3^- through the membrane determine the rate of the active transport process. The desired quantity is the sum of the two fluxes; an influx of one H^+ is equivalent to an efflux of one HCO_3^- and of one H_2CO_3. The net flux of an ion depends directly on the membrane's permeability to it and the sum of the electrical and concentration forces acting on the ion. Since muscle transmembrane potential and concentrations of H^+, HCO_3^- and H_2CO_3 on both sides of the membrane are known, fluxes can be calculated if the permeability is known. Unfortunately, measuring the membrane's permeability to H^+ and HCO_3^- is difficult experimentally because these substances can combine and penetrate the membrane as carbonic acid and the turnover of H^+ with water and metabolites is rapid. However, hydrated hydrogen ions (H_3O^+) are much smaller than hydrated potassium ions and should, therefore, penetrate the membrane more easily. Some evidence[24] indicates that the permeability of the muscle fiber membrane to H^+, P_H, is about 100 P_K. Nevertheless, even if P_H is this high, the direct fluxes of H^+ are negligible because of their extremely low concentrations, about 10^{-4} millimols per liter (10^{-7} mols per liter); direct H^+ passive flux is about 0.003 of the passive K^+ flux (see Table 1, Chap. 1).

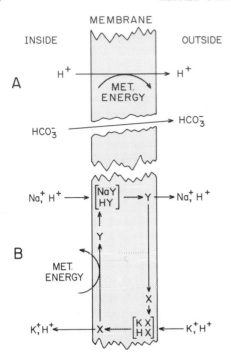

Fig. 13. Possible modes of transmembrane H+ transfer. *A,* Simple H+ pump with an accompanying leak of HCO$_3^-$. Because of low [H+], leakage of H+ is negligible unless membrane permeability to H+ is about 10^5 times greater than to K+. *B,* Two-way H+ transport via the coupled Na+-for-K+ pump (Chap. 1). Low internal [H+] is maintained because affinity of H+ for the Na+ carrier, Y, is about 2.5 times greater than the affinity of H+ for the K+ carrier, X.

Although it has long been thought that most cell membranes are impermeable to HCO$_3^-$,[6] the evidence considered above indicates that at least a substantial fraction of the total body cells are, in effect, permeable to HCO$_3^-$. Other data strongly support this conclusion.[1, 23, 30, 32, 33,45,52] The simplest interpretation of these data is that HCO$_3^-$ penetrates cell membranes with a time constant of a few hours. Several hours are required to reach a new steady state. In an 80 μ muscle cell this corresponds to a passive efflux of about 3 picamols per cm.²-sec. In mammalian muscles K+ fluxes are about 6 times greater.[12] P$_{HCO_3}$ would have to be only about 0.03 P$_K$, i.e., approximately equal to P$_{Na}$, to produce this HCO$_3^-$ flux because they are so far out of equilibrium (about 60 mV.). It is reasonable to suppose that P$_{HCO_3}$ is at least this large. Presumably this HCO$_3^-$ efflux is balanced by an equal active HCO$_3^-$ influx or more likely an active H+ efflux. Of course, such a transport system must not consume more

energy than produced by cellular metabolism (Chap. 1). Calculation shows that the transport work done on hydrogen or bicarbonate ions is considerably but not negligibly less than the work done in transporting Na+. Although some cells—e.g., glia, liver—may have transmembrane potentials low enough (20 mV. or less) that H+ and HCO$_3^-$ are equilibrated across the membrane as in red cells, it seems unlikely that average body cell P$_{HCO_3}$ could be much larger than the value calculated above; it seems too wasteful of energy to pump H+ out and then let it leak in at too great a rate. To a certain extent, such energy waste is the price that must be paid for relatively fast regulation of steady-state processes; slow leaks require little energy expenditure to maintain the steady state but a longer period is required to reach the steady state after a disturbance.

Nature of the H+ Pump. Although the necessity for a H+ pump seems well established, little is known of its kinetics or rate of operation. As mentioned in Chapter 1, evidence (ref. 15, Chap. 1) indicates that H+ are transported by the linked Na+-for-K+ pump which maintains the steady-state transmembrane potential and ion concentration differences. If it is supposed that H+ and Na+ compete for sites on the carrier molecule, Y (Fig. 5, Chap. 1), the ratio of affinities of the two for Y is proportional to the inverse ratio of their concentrations: [Na+]$_i$/[H+]$_i$ = 10^{-2} mols per liter/10^{-7} mols per liter = 10^5. On this basis then, H+ binds 100,000 times more readily to Y than Na+ does! Such a ratio of affinities is not unusual; the affinity of HCO$_3^-$ for H+ is greater than 10^5 times the affinity of HCO$_3^-$ for Na+ by several orders of magnitude, since at body concentrations, Na+, HCO$_3^-$ is completely ionized. The primary requirement of a carrier molecule for the Na+ pump is that it be highly selective for Na+ as compared with K+; the selectivity with respect to H+ can be low.

If Na+ and H+ compete for the Y carrier molecule it is equally likely that H+ also competes effectively with K+ for the K+ carrier molecule, X. If this is true, H+ is pumped out by combining with Y and pumped in by combining with X. The ratio of the affinities of H+ and K+ for X would be [K+]$_o$/[H+]$_o$ = 4 × 10^{-3}/4 × 10^{-8} = 10^5, the same ratio as was obtained for H+ and Na+ to Y. An exchange pump with high but different affinities for H+ on both legs would pump H+ both into and out of the cell and thereby maintain the observed steady state of Na+, K+ and H+. A system having such a two-way H+ pump with $P_{HCO_3} = 0$ is almost indistinguishable from one having a separate H+ pump and HCO_3^- leak. Two possible systems are diagrammed in Figure 13. Since neither alternative has direct experimental support, the second (Fig. 13*B*) will usually be used for these reasons: (i) It keeps attention focused on H+, which are the central topic of this chapter. (ii) The transmembrane shifts in Na+ and K+ which are found to occur in acid–base disturbances follow as natural consequences of this hypothesis. Davies and Keynes[15] have proposed a model of the Na+–K+ pump which is driven by an H+–OH− pump in which H+ combine with the X and Y molecules on their return trips through the membrane. (iii) Recent evidence[2a] indicates that administration of ouabain (a cardiac glycoside which is a potent inhibitor of active Na+–K+ transport) to rats causes roughly proportional increases in internal [H+] and [Na+] after one hour.

Buffer Value of Muscle. Regardless of the mechanism of transmembrane H+ transfer, its extent and rate are important determinants of the extent of extracellular and intracellular [H+] changes. As pointed out above (Fig. 12), the slope of the whole body CO_2 titration curve at 2 hours is about twice that of the extracellular fluid. The problem is to account for the buffer value of the whole body in terms of the buffer values of the various tissues and the consequent transmembrane H+ movement. Following an increase in P_{aCO_2}, there are two sources of extra H+ in the cell fluid: (i) the increased $[H_2CO_3]$ and (ii) inward transmembrane transfer of H+. The resultant change in internal [H+] depends on the buffer value of the internal medium, and the rates of transmembrane H+ transfer depend in turn on internal and external [H+].

The buffer value of intracellular fluid is not accurately known and certainly varies from one tissue to another but can be estimated in two ways: (i) from the amount of buffer material found in cells, e.g., the sum of buffer values of phosphate, protein and other materials determined by direct chemical analysis, (ii) titration of the tissue with CO_2 together with measurements of intracellular $[HCO_3^-]$ and *p*H.

Calculating tissue buffer value directly is hampered by lack of knowledge of the buffer values of tissue proteins; that the buffer value is as high as that of hemoglobin in terms of unit weight is unlikely. Since histidine is the main buffer protein at body *p*H, buffer value is roughly proportional to histidine content. From this it is estimated that the minimum buffer value of muscle protein is about 15 sl. Phosphate, inorganic and organic, is high in muscle, 40 to 70 millimols per liter.[11, 14] All of these phosphate compounds have pK's of about 6.5 except creatine phosphate with a pK of 4.5. Creatine phosphate thus has nearly zero buffer value at cell *p*H whereas the others have nearly maximal molar buffer values, 0.45 per *p*H. Noncreatine phosphate concentration is about 40 mEq. per liter, so buffer value is about $40 \times 0.45 = 18$ sl. Anserine and carnosine contribute about $15 \times 0.575 = 9$ sl. The total calculated buffer value is $15 + 18 + 9 = 42$ sl. This value agrees well with the measured buffer value of muscle homogenates.[17a]

Determining muscle buffer value directly is technically difficult; intracellular *p*H and $[HCO_3^-]$ must be estimated indirectly with large inherent errors and must be based on questionable assumptions. There are considerable data on the CO_2 titration curves of muscle but the results of different investigators differ.[20, 30, 52] The data on muscle from intact animals follow a general trend which can be reasonably well approximated by a straight line with a buffer value of 15 sl. The titration curve of excised muscle is apparently somewhat different.[1] Even taking account of the unknown amount of H+ transferred across the membrane, a great disparity exists between the measured and the calculated buffer values of muscle. If muscle were the only sink for excess H+ in the extracellular fluid, the increase of extracellular buffer value from 11 to 19 sl. over two hours as shown in Figure 12 would decrease the buffer value of muscle from the calculated value of 42 down to 30 sl. The reduction in buffer value of muscle is greater than the increase in the whole body buffer value because of the smaller slope of the P_{CO_2} isobars at the lower $[HCO_3^-]$ of muscle. The reason for the disparity between measured and calculated buffer values of muscle is not known.

There are two possible explanations for this discrepancy: (i) A large consistent error exists in the CO_2 titration curve of muscle or in the calculation of buffer value from muscle constituents. The most obvious possible source of such an error in the CO_2 titration curve is the assumption that tissue P_{CO_2} is equal to or differs by a constant amount from arterial plasma P_{CO_2}. In view of the slow transients in the CO_2 system, tissue P_{CO_2} is unlikely to have changed as much as P_{aCO_2}. Furthermore, the difference between tissue and venous P_{CO_2} decreases during CO_2 breathing because of CO_2-induced vasodilatation. Both factors would decrease the measured buffer value of muscle. (ii) Other tissues, e.g., brain and kidney, may extrude H^+ to maintain intracellular pH nearly constant despite the increased P_{CO_2}. Muscle would then take up not only H^+ added to the extracellular space by the increase in P_{CO_2} but also that added to the extracellular space by these tissues.

HYPERCAPNIA AND HYPOCAPNIA: COMPENSATORY RESPONSES

A maintained disturbance in alveolar ventilation produces a sequence of changes beginning with the CO_2 distribution transient and ending when renal H^+ secretion or reabsorption alters the body's noncarbonic acid content, compensating for the altered carbonic acid content and establishing a new steady state. Intermediate between these processes is a transfer of H^+ across cell membranes reducing the alteration in extracellular fluid pH. With respect to the extracellular fluid, this H^+ transfer is equivalent to renal compensation. Both the transmembrane H^+ transfer and renal regulation are active responses of the body to the altered acid–base status.

Transmembrane Ion Exchange. The ionic interchanges between cells and extracellular space in hyper- and hypocapnia have been studied by Pitts and co-workers.[23, 32, 33] They estimated extracellular and plasma volumes by the dilution method and measured plasma concentrations of the principal cations and anions in nephrectomized dogs before and during radical alterations of P_{aCO_2} induced by CO_2 breathing or hyperventilation. These data permit the calculation of total extracellular ion content. The nephrectomy was done to avoid complications due to renal compensation. The results of one of these experiments are plotted in Figure 14.

HYPERCAPNIA. The results of changing the composition of the inspired gas from room air to 20 per cent CO_2 and 80 per cent O_2 are shown by the curve OABC in Figure 14. Point

O is the control value, point A the hypothetical result of titrating extracellular fluid along a slope of approximately -8 to -10 sl. to P_{aCO_2} = 145 mm. Hg. Point A would have been reached about an hour after the start of CO_2 breathing if no transmembrane transfer of H^+ had occurred. Actually, the blood $[HCO_3^-]$ had increased more than expected in the hour and had reached point B. There was continuing transmembrane transfer of H^+ in the next hour and the plasma had moved approximately along the P_{aCO_2} = 145 mm. Hg isobar to point C. This is an extremely high P_{aCO_2}. Note that these changes move plasma pH toward normal and intracellular pH away from normal.

The expected increase in plasma $[HCO_3^-]$ is the product of the buffer value of the extracellular fluid and the pH change induced by the increase in P_{aCO_2}. This can be seen to be about 4 millimols per liter due to a pH decrease of about 0.5. The volume of the extracellular fluid was estimated at 6.55 liters so that $6.55 \times 4 =$ 26 millimols of HCO_3^- appeared in the extracellular fluid as a result of the buffering of added carbonic acid by plasma proteins and hemoglobin. Since most carbonic acid was buffered in the red cells and the HCO_3^- formed diffused mainly into the plasma and interstitial fluid, an equal amount of Cl^- must have entered the red cells (chloride shift). Although the results varied considerably in these experiments, approximately this amount of Cl^- disappeared from the extracellular fluid. Exact agreement cannot be expected because plasma $[K^+]$ was elevated, indicating a depolarization of muscle cells and a consequent uptake of Cl^-, possibly with H^+. In addition to the 26 millimols of HCO_3^- resulting from buffering, another 46 millimols appeared over 2 hours (C, Fig. 14). The Na^+ content of extracellular fluid increased by 40 millimols and K^+ content by 9 millimols, a total of 49 millimols, close to the change in HCO_3^-. There was, however, a consistent surplus of $Na^+ + K^+$ over HCO_3^-. This was found to be mostly attributable to an increase in extracellular phosphate concentration.

These results can be explained qualitatively at least by the two-way transport of H^+ via the Na^+–K^+ pump postulated above (Fig. 13B). The net outflux of HCO_3^- from cells is attributed to the net influx of H^+ because the $[H^+]$ in the extracellular fluid increases more than $[H^+]$ in the intracellular fluid along with a consequent greater increase in the amount of H+ carried inward on the K+ leg of the pump. The increased activity of the inward leg would also increase the activity of the outer leg and increase efflux of Na+. The result is a net exit of Na+ due to the increased pump activity and a net retention of K+ in the extracellular fluid due to the increased use of the inward leg by H+ and a net movement of H+ into cells. It is more difficult to explain this mixed outflux of Na+ and K+ in terms of a H+ pump–HCO_3^- leak model (Fig. 13*A*). Findings of this type are the experimental basis for postulating the H+, Na+–K+, H+ pump but are no more than suggestive.

HYPOCAPNIA. Pitts and co-workers[23, 32, 33] also studied the redistribution of ions in the extracellular fluid during extreme hyperventilation. The results of one experiment are illustrated in Figure 14 by the curve O'A'B'C' which has the same time significance as the curve OABC in CO_2 breathing. The most noteworthy feature of the experiment is the high rate at which the plasma [HCO_3^-] fell following the onset of hyperventilation. Balance studies showed that most of the fall in HCO_3^- was due to a large efflux of lactic acid from the cells and a decrease in phosphate. The large lactate production may have been due to fibrillation in muscle; high *p*H reduces [Ca++] and increases muscle excitability (Chaps. 2 and 5). In addition, there were modest losses of Na+ and much smaller losses of K+ from the extracellular fluid. The Cl− content increased about as expected from the titration of blood buffers in the alkaline direction. The exchange of cell H+ for plasma Na+ can be explained along the lines described above for hypercapnia: The fall in P_{aCO_2} titrates the extracellular fluid further in the alkaline direction than it does the cell fluid. Hence, the number of H+ entering on the inward leg of the pump decreases more than the number leaving on the outward leg. The decrease in [H+]$_o$ slows the pump so that there is a net inward leakage of Na+ and little change in net K+ flux because the decrease in the rate of the inward leg is due entirely to the fall in [H+]$_o$.

Control of Renal H+ Secretion. As mentioned previously (Chap. 44), the H+ and HCO_3^- concentrations in urine are determined by active cation exchange processes centered around a Na+-for-K+ exchange pump which presumably also pumps H+. The concern here

is not the mechanics of the process but the factors controlling the rates of H+ secretion and HCO_3^- reabsorption.

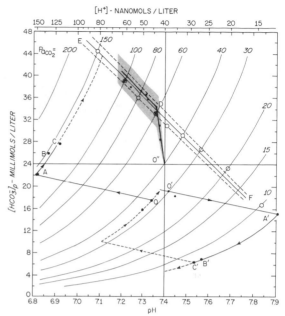

Fig. 14. Compensation of hypo- and hypercapnia by transmembrane H+ transfer and renal H+ secretion. Curves OABC and O'A'B'C' show extent of transmembrane H+ transfer in anesthetized, nephrectomized dogs. OA and O'A' are expected titration curves of extracellular fluid. B and C are actual values 1 and 2 hours respectively after increasing P_{ACO_2} to 145 mm. Hg by increasing P_{ICO_2}. H+ which left extracellular fluid were replaced by Na+ and K+. Primed points have same time significance with respect to start of hyperventilation which reduced P_{ACO_2} to 6 mm. Hg. Most of compensation is due to appearance of lactic acid in extracellular fluid; most of the remainder is due to uptake of Na+ and loss of H+ from cells. Actual sequence of experiment was O'A'B'C' OABC; O differs from O' because of insufficient recovery time from hyperventilation (dashed lines). Line FDE is limit of HCO_3^- reabsorption by kidneys, i.e., maximum attainable [HCO_3^-] in plasma, and thus represents maximum possible renal compensation of hypercapnia. Curve O''DE and surrounding band shows extent of renal compensation of hypercapnia in patients with chronic lung disease. This shows that, chronically, there is complete compensation, i.e., restoration of normal *p*H if P_{ACO_2} is 65 mm. Hg or less. For higher P_{ACO_2} values, compensation is limited by maximum reabsorptive ability of the kidney as shown by the coincidence of the curves, O''DE, and line FDE. (After Giebisch, Berger and Pitts, *J. clin. Invest.*, 1955, *34*:231–245; Pitts, *Harvey Lect.*, 1952–53, *48*:172–209; Pitts, *Physiology of the kidney and body fluids.* Chicago, Year Book Medical Publishers, 1963; Rector, Seldin, Roberts and Smith. *J. clin. Invest.*, 1960, *39*:1706–1721; and Refsum, *Clin. Sci.*, 1964, *27*:407–415.)

H+ SECRETION. Secretion of H+ can reduce the *p*H of the luminal fluid to about 4.4; the amount of H+ appearing in the urine depends on the amount of buffer in urine and on the rate of ammonia secretion. Phosphate is the only buffer of any consequence in urine, but the rate of filtration is relatively constant. The increased renal H+ secretion of hypercapnia and acidosis is due to increased ammonia production. Ammonia is formed in the kidney by metabolism and the neutral form distributes at equal concentrations in the cells and lumen. When the luminal fluid's *p*H is reduced by the secretion of H+, the ammonia takes up some of the H+ to become NH_4^+. The more acid the solution, the greater the concentration of NH_4^+ and the greater the rate of H+ excretion.

In either noncarbonic or chronic hypercapnic acidosis, several days to more than a week are needed to reach a new steady state despite a three- to tenfold increase in acid excretion after a few days. Thus a noncarbonic acid excess of 10 millimols per liter of extracellular fluid means that there are a total of 10 mEq. per liter $\times$ 14.3 liters = 143 millimols plus an unknown but roughly equal amount of excess acid in the body cells. A typical rate of acid secretion is about 1.5 mEq. per hour in normal man and 15 mEq. per hour in chronic noncarbonic acid excess. In a normal man about 2 $\times$ 143/1.5 = 192 hours = 8 days would be required to excrete the excess. However, acid production would increase during this period and a somewhat shorter time would be adequate. This is in addition to the normal metabolic production of noncarbonic acid.

HCO_3^- REABSORPTION IN CHRONIC HYPERCAPNIA. The kidneys respond differently to chronic hypercapnia and to noncarbonic acidosis. In the latter, renal compensation restores $[HCO_3^-]$ to normal, whereas in hypercapnic acidosis, renal compensation increases $[HCO_3^-]$ above normal. Consequently, the filtered load of HCO_3^- goes up and H+ secretion in the kidney is devoted increasingly to reabsorption of HCO_3^- rather than to acidifying the urine. Thus, the degree of renal compensation in chronic hypercapnia may be limited by the maximum HCO_3^- reabsorptive capacity of the kidneys, which in turn is determined by the maximal rate of H+ secretion in both the proximal and distal tubules. If this limiting bicarbonate concentration is reached, the filtered load of HCO_3^- equals the amount reabsorbed and the plasma level remains constant at its maximum possible value.

The renal reabsorption of HCO_3^- and secretion of H+ is a system of the B type; hence the system's kinetics are best presented in terms of the amount of HCO_3^- reabsorbed per liter of glomerular filtrate—i.e., concentration of HCO_3^- in the reabsorbate—rather than in terms of the amount reabsorbed per minute. When expressed in this way, HCO_3^- reabsorption shows a rather sharp threshold; the $[HCO_3^-]$ of reabsorbate is equal to the $[HCO_3^-]$ of filtrate; i.e., all is reabsorbed, until plasma $[HCO_3^-]$ (increased by HCO_3^- infusion) reaches about 26 millimols per liter.[33] At higher plasma $[HCO_3^-]$, reabsorbate $[HCO_3^-]$ is constant; i.e., under normal circumstances, the maximum HCO_3^- reabsorption is 26 millimols per liter of filtrate. However, this maximum value is directly dependent on P_{aCO_2}: the higher the P_{aCO_2}, the greater the reabsorbate $[HCO_3^-]$. The curve relating maximum reabsorbate $[HCO_3^-]$ to P_{CO_2}[33] closely resembles the CO_2 uptake curve of blood (Fig. 3, Chap. 40), which suggests that the curve is linear if plotted on the $[HCO_3^-]$-*p*H diagram and that reabsorbate $[HCO_3^-]$ is directly proportional to the $[HCO_3^-]$ in some special region, presumably the distal renal tubule cells, where the final HCO_3^- reabsorption takes place. Line EDF in Figure 14 shows that the maximum $[HCO_3^-]$ of reabsorbate varies directly with the *p*H, the apparent buffer value being 38 sl. The kind of mechanism giving rise to this type of reabsorptive behavior is not clear, but the maximum reabsorbate $[HCO_3^-]$ is clearly proportional to a $[HCO_3^-]$ in a special region which varies with P_{CO_2} in the same way as $[HCO_3^-]$ does in a buffer solution. In general terms, this might occur if the *p*H of renal tubular cells were closely regulated by the activity of H+ pumps in both membranes, both pumping toward the lumen at a rate controlled by the internal *p*H. Regardless of the mechanism, this dependence of reabsorbate $[HCO_3^-]$ on P_{CO_2} limits renal compensation for the acidosis of primary hypercapnia. If the plasma $[HCO_3^-]$ necessary to restore plasma *p*H to normal is less than the maximum reabsorbate $[HCO_3^-]$, then compensation is complete; i.e., *p*H returns to normal. This is illustrated by the band, O″DE in Figure 14, which represents the range of steady-state changes in $[HCO_3^-]_p$ found in a large number of patients with chronic hypercapnia due to a pathologic lung condition such as emphysema.[35] Despite considerable variation among patients, the average renal compensation falls almost exactly on the line of maximum reabsorbate [HCO_3^-] for P_{aCO_2} values greater than 65 mm. Hg (DE). Below 65 mm. Hg, compensation is practically complete (O″D). The correlation between these two sets of data (FDE and O″DE) is clearly the result of the same function, maximum renal HCO_3^- reabsorptive ability.

The extracellular fluid titration curve drawn through O″ parallel to OA in Figure 14, and the maximum renal compensation curve, O″DE, delimit the area in which the plasma [HCO_3^-] and *p*H of patients with primary hypercapnia will be found. Points not reasonably close to O″DE probably represent transient states if kidney function is normal. Points below the extracellular fluid titration curve and to the left of $P_{aCO_2} = 40$ mm. Hg represent a combination of primary hypercapnia and primary noncarbonic acid excess.

COMPENSATION OF CHRONIC HYPOCAPNIA. Chronic hypocapnia (hyperventilation) is infrequent but occurs in some forms of hysteria, drug medication (heavy salicylate therapy) and heart disease in which arterial oxygen concentration is sufficiently low to provide a significant hypoxic drive to ventilation. Clinically the extent of renal compensation in chronic hypocapnia is usually complete.[39]

NONCARBONIC ACID IMBALANCE

The whole body CO_2 titration curve gives a measure of the protein buffers present. The *p*H changes due to the addition of noncarbonic acid to the body are much smaller than those from adding an equal amount of carbonic acid because noncarbonic acids combine with both HCO_3^- and proteins, whereas carbonic acid combines with proteins only. The buffer value of the extracellular fluid at fixed P_{aCO_2} is the sum of the buffer values of HCO_3^- and proteins, $55 + 11 = 66$ sl. In cells [HCO_3^-] is about 10 millimols per liter and the contribution of cell protein and phosphate buffers—about twice that of HCO_3^-—is dominant.

Types of Noncarbonic Acid. Three categories of noncarbonic acid can be distinguished: (i) Sulfur- and phosphorus-containing substances in the diet which are metabolized to sulfuric and phosphoric acids. These are eventually excreted by the kidneys but must be buffered during their stay in the body. (ii) In some circumstances, organic acid products of intermediary metabolism accumulate in substantial quantities and must be buffered until excreted or until metabolized to CO_2 and water. For example, lactic acid is produced in great quantities in heavy muscular exercise when energy output temporarily exceeds oxygen supply. This produces a severe but temporary excess of metabolizable noncarbonic acid. Clinically more important is the acidosis of uncontrolled diabetes; accumulating metabolic intermediates may produce coma and death. In both cases, restoring normal conditions removes the excess acid quickly by converting it to CO_2, which is excreted rapidly. (iii) Hydration. Excess fluid intake temporarily dilutes all the solutes of the body water. The consequent reduction in [HCO_3^-] causes a corresponding increase in [H^+] if P_{aCO_2} is constant. However, there will be a compensatory hypocapnia. This type of acidosis is more rapidly corrected by excretion of the excess water than by renal secretion of the apparent excess H^+. Actually the acidosis of hydration is only seeming; the total body H^+ stores have not changed.

Ion Redistribution in Noncarbonic Disturbances. As with a change in P_{aCO_2}, handling of added noncarbonic acid involves at least three separate phases. (i) It takes approximately one-half hour for the extra CO_2 formed by the combination of H^+ with HCO_3^- to be excreted via the lungs.[29, 40] This is simply the time necessary for blood to carry the added acid to the interstitial fluid and to carry away the excess CO_2. Since the blood must mix only with the interstitial fluid, the time required is somewhat shorter than for CO_2. (ii) Several hours are required for transmembrane H^+ exchange and consequent cellular buffering. (iii) Several days are required to excrete the added acid in the urine. Exactly the same arguments apply for added alkali except that lactic acid production may be appreciable.

EXCESS OF NONCARBONIC ACID. Pitts and coworkers[32, 33, 45] have described transmembrane ion transfer during and after a large intravenous infusion of HCl into anesthetized and nephrectomized dogs. From the readily diffusible extracellular fluid volume and plasma electrolyte concentration, they estimated changes in extracellular electrolytes. In one experiment,

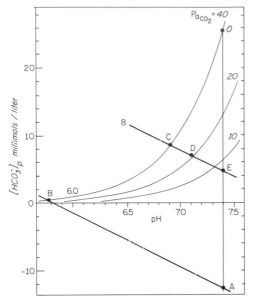

Fig. 15. Transmembrane H+ transfer and compensatory hypocapnia (hyperventilation) produced by infusion of HCl in anesthetized, nephrectomized dogs. OA, amount of HCl infused per liter of extracellular fluid including the water accompanying the HCl. Negative value of point A has no significance except that no amount of hyperventilation could actually back titrate extracellular fluid to initial pH. AB, titration curve of dog's extracellular fluid. C, pH after transmembrane H+ transfer but without respiratory compensation. D, after respiratory compensation which reduced P_{aCO_2} to nearly 20 mm. Hg and increased pH by 0.2. E, [HCO_3^-] after back titrating to initial pH by reducing P_{aCO_2} further to get OE, the amount of acid remaining in a liter of extracellular fluid. Pattern of cellular H+ uptake and Na+ and K+ loss is much the same as for hypercapnia (Fig. 14). ([HCO_3^-] corrected for effects of transcapillary Donnan ratio.) (After Swan and Pitts, *J. clin. Invest.*, 1955, *34*:205–212; and Pitts, *Physiology of the kidney and body fluids.* Chicago, Year Book Medical Publishers, 1963.)

illustrated in Figure 15, 161 millimols of HCl were infused over 1.5 hours into a dog with an extracellular volume of 4 liters before and 4.7 liters after the infusion. Total body water was about 9.7 liters. One hour after the infusion about half of the acid had disappeared from the readily diffusible extracellular fluid. Nevertheless, it is instructive to calculate the changes in pH that would have occurred if all the acid had remained in the extracellular fluid. In this case, 161/4.7 = 34.4 millimols of excess noncarbonic acid would have remained per liter of extracellular fluid. In addition, the water accompanying the HCl diluted the [HCO_3^-] from

25.6 to 25.6 × 4/4.7 = 21.8 millimols per liter. Thus, 38.2 millimols of acid were added per liter. The expected pH and [HCO_3^-] can be estimated by moving downward 38.2 millimols per liter from the original [HCO_3^-] along the pH = 7.4 line (O to A, Fig. 15) and drawing a CO_2 titration curve, AB, having the buffer value of extracellular fluid (8 sl.). The titration curve does not cross the original P_{aCO_2} isobar (about 40 mm. Hg) until pH has fallen to 5.78 and [HCO_3^-] to about 0.4 millimols per liter (point B). Such a large infusion of acid would have been fatal if it had all remained extracellular; e.g., red cells hemolyze at pH's somewhat higher than 6.5. Even if hyperventilation had reduced P_{aCO_2} to zero, the pH would have risen only to 5.82. Of the 38.2 millimols of HCl added per liter, 25.6 were buffered by HCO_3^- and 12.6 by blood protein buffers. Actually during the 1.5 hour infusion, somewhat less than half of the acid moved into cells because after 4 hours pH = 7.11 and [HCO_3^-] = 6.7 millimols per liter (point D). Drawing the titration curve through D gives [HCO_3^-] = 4.4 millimols per liter at pH = 7.4 (point E) and [HCO_3^-] = 8 millimols per liter and pH = 6.92 at P_{aCO_2} = 40 mm. Hg (point C). Hyperventilation reduced P_{aCO_2} to almost 20 mm. Hg, a value near that predicted by Gray's equation (Chap. 42). The total amount of acid remaining in the extracellular fluid is OE = 25.6 − 4.4 = 21.2 millimols per liter (about half of OA). This remaining acid was buffered in the following ways: (i) 3.8 millimols per liter were buffered by the reduction of [HCO_3^-] due to dilution as explained above. (ii) 15.1 millimols per liter combined directly with HCO_3^- to form CO_2. Of this, 1.3 millimols per liter were due to the reduction of P_{aCO_2} from 40 to 20 mm. Hg. In other words, 15.1 millimols per liter is the difference between the original [HCO_3^-] after dilution (21.8 millimols per liter) and the final value after respiratory compensation (6.7 millimols per liter). A direct estimate of the reduction in extracellular [HCO_3^-] was 14.5 millimols per liter, which agrees reasonably with the change of 15.1 millimols per liter estimated as shown in Figure 15. (iii) Another 2.4 mEq. of acid per liter were used in titrating hemoglobin and plasma proteins from pH 7.41 to 7.11 (E to D); 0.3 × 8 = 2.4 millimols per liter.

The difference between the added acid and the amount remaining in the extracellular fluid —17 to 17.5 millimols per liter—is the amount of noncarbonic acid which had penetrated cells. Direct measurements of [Na+] and [K+] in extracellular fluid show them to be increased 11.7 and 6.6 millimols per liter, respectively, for a total of 18.3 millimols per liter, which agrees reasonably with the 17 to 17.5 millimols of H+ per liter that disappeared from the extracellular fluid. It thus appears that exchanges of H+ for K+ and Na+ occur fairly readily between interstitial and tissue fluids. This exchange can be explained most simply by the scheme shown in Figure 13*B*. The increase in [H+] in the extracellular fluid increases the amount of H+ carried on the inward leg of the pump, K+ being left behind. The Na+–H+ exchange can be explained by supposing that increased [H+], like increased [K+] in the interstitial fluid, increases the pumping rate. It was pointed out in Chapter 1 that reducing external [K+] decreases the pumping rate. The increase in the rate of active Na+ extrusion is a natural consequence of increasing the inward pumping rate in a coupled pump; the increased efflux of Na+ is balanced by an increased influx of H+. Although other mechanisms can be proposed, Figure 13*B* provides a simple mnemonic for predicting direction of ion exchanges. However, it is not clear from this scheme that the Na+–H+ exchange should be about twice as great as the K+–H+ exchange, as is found in both hypercapnic and noncarbonic acidosis.

DEFICIT OF NONCARBONIC ACID. Pitts and co-workers[33] have also made ion balance studies of the response of dogs to large infusions of NaHCO3. The changes were generally opposite to those produced by infused HCl. There were, however, significant differences. (i) Considerably less transmembrane exchange occurred than in the noncarbonic acidosis; a third or less of the added alkali entered cells. This is probably because the initial change in extracellular *p*H is smaller for a given amount of alkali because of the upward curvature of the P$_{CO_2}$ isobars; e.g., at constant P$_{aCO_2}$ the addition of enough acid to reduce [HCO$_3^-$] from 24 to 12 millimols per liter reduces the *p*H by 0.3 from 7.4 to 7.1; adding an equal amount of alkali increases the [HCO$_3^-$] to about 36 millimols per liter and the *p*H by only 0.175. (ii) That portion of the alkali which left the extracellular fluid was almost entirely due to an uptake of Na+ and loss of H+ by cells, very little by K+-for-H+ exchange. Some of the alkali was neutralized by lactic acid produc-

tion. The cellular uptake of Na+ and loss of H+ must have resulted from inhibition of the Na+ pump or an increased Na+ entry. The former is more likely because the extracellular [K+] fell during the infusion. The fall in both [H+] and [K+] would inhibit the Na+ pump and cause net Na+ entry.

The acid–base changes associated with hyper- and hypokalemia are described in Chapter 45.

Respiratory Compensation. As pointed out in Chapter 42, alveolar ventilation is determined by the [H+] of blood, P$_{ACO_2}$ and P$_{AO_2}$. Thus, excess noncarbonic acid increases plasma [H+], which stimulates respiration, reduces P$_{ACO_2}$ and changes [H+] toward normal. This compensatory response will not restore [H+] to normal because the reduction in P$_{ACO_2}$ decreases the drive to the respiratory center; e.g., if compensation were complete, plasma [H+] would be normal and total drive to the respiratory center would be subnormal, as would alveolar ventilation. Gray's equation (Chap. 42), which describes the ventilatory response to changes in [H+] and P$_{ACO_2}$, can be used to predict the degree of respiratory compensation for noncarbonic acid unbalance. Since alveolar P$_{CO_2}$ is inversely proportional to alveolar ventilation,

$$\frac{P_{ACO_2} \text{ (Normal)}}{P_{ACO_2} \text{ (Exper.)}} = \text{ventilation ratio}$$
$$= 0.22 \, [\text{H+}] + 0.262 P_{ACO_2} - 18 \quad (12)$$

where [H+] is in nanomols per liter and P$_{ACO_2}$ in mm. Hg. This equation can be used to calculate P$_{ACO_2}$ as a function of plasma [H+] if alveolar and plasma P$_{CO_2}$'s are assumed equal. The resulting curve is plotted on the *p*H-[HCO$_3^-$] diagram in Figure 16 together with representative data from the clinical literature[4, 38] showing that the "Gray line" predicts the extent of compensation of chronic noncarbonic acid excess with reasonable accuracy. As a rule of thumb, compensation is about halfway between the P$_{ACO_2}$ = 40 mm. Hg isobar and the *p*H = 7.4 vertical line.

Respiratory compensation for a deficit of noncarbonic acid is usually rather less than predicted in the chronic state[36] but is clearly present in shorter-term disturbances produced by infusion or ingestion of NaHCO3 (Fig. 16).[4, 43] This short-term respiratory compensation (hypoventilation) is usually somewhat

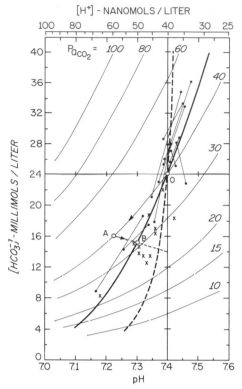

Fig. 16. Extent of respiratory compensation of noncarbonic acidosis. Solid line, the "Gray" line, extent of compensation predicted from Gray's equation relating alveolar ventilation to plasma [H+] and P_{aCO_2}. Dashed line, Predicted compensation on assumption that P_{aCO_2} term drops out after 24 hours because of compensatory changes in cerebrospinal fluid [HCO$_3^-$] (Chap. 42). Curve OAB illustrates how these points may be reached; excess noncarbonic acid titrates from O to A; hyperventilation due to stimulation of respiration by decreased pH titrates extracellular fluid along its buffer curve to B, a point on the Gray line. Solid dots connected by lines show the acid–base status of patients with normal renal function (upper group) and chronic renal insufficiency (lower group) before (lower) and after (upper) taking large doses of NaHCO$_3$ for three days. In general the changes tend to parallel the "Gray" line. Crosses show the acid–base status of another group of patients with chronic renal insufficiency. (After Bradley and Semple, *J. Physiol.*, 1962, *160*:381–391 (●). *Schwab, Klin. Wsch.*, 1962, *40:* 765–772 (X).)

less than predicted from Gray's equation. Evidence suggests that the constants in Gray's equation must be modified at low [H+]'s.[25] In addition, appreciable hypoventilation reduces P_{AO_2}, which may stimulate respiration. Hypoxic drive to respiration is probably the main reason for relatively small hypoventilatory compensation for chronic noncarbonic alkalosis.

ADAPTATION TO ALTERED P_{aCO_2}. It was pointed out in Chapter 42 that the effect of P_{aCO_2} on respiration is mediated through a [H+]-sensitive area in the fourth ventricle which is bathed by cerebrospinal fluid. However, the change in [H+] due to altered P_{aCO_2} is compensated for in about 24 hours by an appropriate change in cerebrospinal [HCO$_3^-$]. On this basis, the degree of respiratory compensation for noncarbonic acid excess should increase over 24 hours, at which time [H+] of plasma should be the main factor determining the respiratory minute volume (dashed line in Figure 16). However, this is supported by little clinical evidence.

SUMMARY AND CLINICAL IMPLICATIONS

The facts and principles developed in this chapter can best be summarized by reviewing the deductions that can be made about acid–base status of a patient from the position of a point on the pH-[HCO$_3^-$]$_p$ diagram. In addition to defining the direction of the acid–base unbalance—e.g., acidosis or alkalosis, hyper- or hypocapnia, excess or deficit of noncarbonic acid—the location of the point helps one to distinguish between the primary pathologic condition and the compensatory changes and to determine whether a steady state has been reached. More specifically, the answers to several questions are wanted: (i) Is the primary cause of the acid–base disturbance carbonic or noncarbonic? (ii) Have there been compensatory changes? If so, to what extent? (iii) Is the patient in a steady state of unbalance? If not, what is the phase of the transient state, i.e., mixing, transmembrane transfer or renal? What is the total unbalance in the extracellular fluid? (iv) Are corrective measures indicated, e.g., intravenous infusion of alkali or acid?

The manner and extent to which these answers are obtainable from the pH-[HCO$_3^-$]$_p$ diagram can best be illustrated by specific examples, but all clinical information should be used in reaching a decision. The following examples illustrate how the maximum information can be obtained from the position of a point on the pH-[HCO$_3^-$]$_p$ diagram (Fig. 17) and the limitations and uncertainties which hamper judgment.

Point A in Figure 17 (pH = 7.34, [HCO$_3^-$] = 31.5 millimols per liter) represents acidosis (slight), significant hypercapnia (P$_{aCO_2}$ = 60 mm. Hg) and a significant deficit of noncarbonic acid. (i) The primary pathologic condition is clearly hypercapnia. Cause of the hypercapnia must be determined by other means, e.g., lung function tests. (ii) Considering the variability of compensatory responses and the point's nearness to the renal compensation line, this is likely a complete renal compensation of the primary hypercapnia. (iii) The patient is likely in a steady state, having a chronic excess of carbonic acid and deficit of noncarbonic acid. (iv) There is a compensatory carbonic acid deficit of 7 millimols per liter of extracellular fluid (vertical distance between A and ECF, the extracellular fluid titration curve). (v) No acid–base corrective measures are indicated, since the patient is in a compensated steady state. Therapy would be directed toward improving lung function.

Point B (pH = 7.23, [HCO$_3^-$] = 32.5 millimols per liter) also represents a case of hypercapnia and acidosis. (i) The point is above the extracellular buffer line, so the primary disturbance is hypercapnia. (ii) This hypercapnia is partially compensated for by extra renal transmembrane H$^+$ transfer, renal acid excretion, or both. (iii) The point is well away from the region of maximal renal compensation, so the patient is in a renal transient state and probably a respiratory steady state. The phase of the transient state must be determined from the history of the disturbance. For example, point B may have been reached a few days after the onset of respiratory insufficiency, renal compensation not yet having had time to reach completion. On the other hand, point B may have been reached from point A in a few minutes following a sudden worsening of lung function, increase in P$_{ACO_2}$ and titration of the extracellular fluid in the acid direction. Since point B is on the extracellular titration curve through A, the deficit of noncarbonic acid at points A and B is 7 millimols per liter. These two possibilities can be distinguished from the history of the disturbance. If the second possibility were correct, the blood would move up the P$_{CO_2}$ isobar because of transmembrane transfer during the next few hours and to the maximum renal compensation curve over a period of days, provided that P$_{CO_2}$ remained

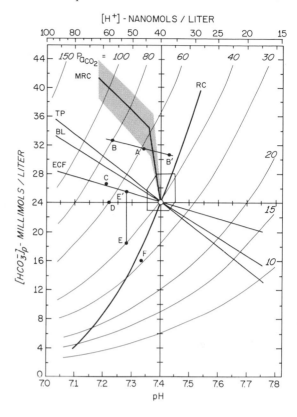

Fig. 17. Summary of acid–base principles. A point on this diagram permits a number of conclusions to be drawn concerning a patient's acid–base status and permits an estimate of his total extracellular fluid H$^+$ unbalance. Steady-state or chronic compensation lines for hypercapnia (maximum renal compensation line, MRC) and excess noncarbonic acid (respiratory compensation, Gray line, RC) are reproduced from previous figures. Points near these lines indicate that the patient is in a steady state. Points not close to these lines indicate a transient state. Areas below the titration line for extracellular fluid (ECF, slope = −11 sl.) indicate a transient in the CO$_2$ system due to recent addition of noncarbonic acid and that the point will likely approach the Gray line in a matter of hours; if kidney function is normal, point 0 will be reached in a few days. Points above the ECF line indicate a pathologic condition in the respiratory system and that the transient state of renal compensation will last many days. The hexagon in the middle indicates the normal range of variations; this range always must be taken into account in diagnoses. Amount of excess noncarbonic acid in the extracellular fluid can be estimated by multiplying the excess per liter (vertical distance between point and the ECF line) by the volume of extracellular fluid as estimated from body weight. Note that buffer value of ECF depends on blood hemoglobin concentration. TP and BL, titration curves respectively of normal true plasma (31 sl.) and normal blood (25 sl.).

constant. (iv) The noncarbonic acid deficit of 7 millimols per liter is secondary to the hypercapnia. (v) Therapy would center around improving respiratory function. The situation of sudden improvement in respiratory function (increase in minute volume) is depicted by point B' (pH = 7.43, $[HCO_3^-]_p$ = 30.7 millimols per liter). The decrease in $P_{A_{CO_2}}$ from 60 mm. Hg at A to 48 mm. Hg at B produced an alkalosis, with hypercapnia. If the history of respiratory disturbance is unknown, this might be diagnosed as a primary noncarbonic acid deficit with some compensatory hypercapnia. Corrective therapy such as infusion of noncarbonic acid might be advisable in the latter case but not in the former unless the improvement in lung function were permanent.

Point C (pH = 7.21, $[HCO_3^-]_p$ = 26.6 millimols per liter) falls near the extracellular fluid titration curve, so the disturbance is uncompensated primary hypercapnia. Therapy would be directed at improving respiratory function. This is a fairly improbable point since it would be found only up to an hour after onset of hypercapnia (movement along extracellular buffer line) or in acute increase of noncarbonic acid on top of a previously compensated hypercapnia (movement down P_{CO_2} = 70 mm. Hg isobar).

Point D (pH = 7.22, $[HCO_3^-]_p$ = 24 millimols per liter) is an acidosis with a combination of hypercapnia and noncarbonic acid excess: (i) The primary disturbances are hypercapnia and noncarbonic acid excess. (ii) No compensatory changes have occurred. (iii) This is almost certainly an acute, transient state. (iv) Noncarbonic acid excess amounts to 2 millimols per liter. (v) This state could be brought about, for example, by acute gastrointestinal upset in a patient with emphysema. Considerable gastric HCl may be lost from vomiting, which could more than neutralize the compensatory noncarbonic acid deficit. This condition is also frequently found following surgery.

Point E (pH = 7.28, $[HCO_3^-]_p$ = 18.3 millimols per liter) is acidosis with excess noncarbonic acid and normal P_{CO_2}. No compensatory changes have occurred and the patient is in a transient state or is a hyporeactor with respect to respiratory compensation. Another possibility is that the patient's blood normally has a rather high P_{CO_2}, say 48 mm. Hg, and that a $P_{a_{CO_2}}$ of 40 mm. Hg represents a substantial respiratory compensation for the primary noncarbonic acidosis. If kidney function is normal, this point represents a transient state of excess noncarbonic acid, which is excreted by the kidneys during the next several days provided there is no continuous extra source of the excess acid, such as in uncontrolled diabetes. In some instances, giving an intravenous infusion of $NaHCO_3$ might be desirable to neutralize some of the excess noncarbonic acid, the amount to be given depending on the total stores of noncarbonic acid excess in the body. However, on the basis of present knowledge, how much of the excess acid has gone into cells is nearly impossible to assess even if accurate data concerning the time course of the disease are available. Conservative therapy then is to approach but not to try to reach complete compensation. Mellemgaard and Astrup[29] recommend neutralizing only the excess noncarbonic acid in the extracellular fluid to avoid temporary overcompensation. The amount of $NaHCO_3$ to be administered is equal to the noncarbonic acid excess per liter of extracellular fluid times the number of liters of extracellular fluid. At point E, this would be 7 millimols per liter (distance EE', Fig. 17) × 14 liters extracellular fluid = 100 millimols of $NaHCO_3$ for a 70 kg. man. Mellemgaard and Astrup calculate the total extracellular unbalance by the formula 0.3 × body weight (in kg.) × excess noncarbonic acid per liter of blood. For a 70 kg. man this would be 0.3 × 70 × 8 = 170 millimols. The discrepancy between the estimates arises from the factor of 0.3 which relates extracellular volume to body weight. The extracellular volume of 14 liters used above is only 0.2 of body weight. If 0.3 × 70 = 21 liters is used instead of 14 liters for extracellular volume, the total excess noncarbonic acid is 7 × 21 = 150 millimols. Actually, of course, any such estimates have large errors and, since there is likely a roughly equal amount of excess noncarbonic acid in the cells, either method is an adequate approximation.

Point F (pH = 7.33, $[HCO_3^-]_p$ = 16 millimols per liter) represents about the same condition as E except that respiratory compensation is clearly substantial, about as expected from the Gray line. Except in kidney disease, this is a transient state with renal H+ excretion slowly restoring the blood to normal over several days. As excess noncarbonic acid is eliminated from the body, the blood will "move" along the Gray line toward normal, since the respiratory steady state is achieved in about an hour and hence will always be in the steady state during the renal transient. The same principles and considerations are used in interpreting points on the alkaline side of normal.

The large variations in the buffer value of blood following a sudden change in arterial P_{CO_2} (Fig. 10) indicate that caution is required in obtaining arterial blood samples from conscious patients; hyperventilation induced in a patient by the sight of a hypodermic needle and syringe approaching his arm will cause marked changes in the *p*H and $[HCO_3^-]$ of such samples. Venous blood samples are much more representative of the actual acid–base status of the tissue from which the blood comes, but the complication of correcting for the low oxygen tension and the difficulty in obtaining mixed venous blood samples (right atrium) make this procedure unattractive in the clinic.

The *p*H-$[HCO_3^-]_p$ diagram can be divided into several regions. A point to the left of *p*H = 7.4 is acidosis; to the right is alkalosis. Any P_{CO_2} greater than 40 is hypercapnia and less than 40 is hypocapnia. The body is in a steady state of acid–base balance at any point on the maximum renal compensation line and in a steady state of respiratory function anywhere along the Gray line but is in a transient state of renal acid secretion unless there is a pathologic renal condition. Points not near these lines represent different stages in the respiratory and renal system transients. Thus, a reasonably accurate picture of the acid–base status of a patient can be obtained by considering the factors which cause the blood to reach the state represented by a point on the *p*H-$[HCO_3^-]_p$ diagram.

REFERENCES

1. ADLER, S., ROY, A. and RELMAN, A. S. *J. clin. Invest.,* 1964, *44:*8–20.
2. ALTMAN, P. L. and DITTMER, D. S., eds. *Blood and other body fluids.* Washington, D.C., Federation of American Societies for Experimental Biology, 1961.
2a. BONDANI, A. and WITHROW, C. D. *Fed. Proc.,* 1965, *24:* 487.
3. BRACKETT, N. C., JR., COHEN, J. J. and SCHWARTZ, W. B. *New Engl. J. Med.,* 1965, *272:*6–12.
4. BRADLEY, R. D. and SEMPLE, S. J. G. *J. Physiol.,* 1962, *160:*381–391.
5. BUTLER, J. N. *Ionic equilibrium, a mathematical approach.* Reading, Mass., Addison-Wesley, 1964.
6. CALDWELL, P. C. *Int. Rev. Cytol.,* 1956, *5:*229–277.
7. CALDWELL, P. C. *J. Physiol.,* 1958, *142:*22–62.
8. CHRISTENSEN, H. N. p*H and dissociation.* Philadelphia, W. B. Saunders Co., 1963.
9. CHRISTENSEN, H. N. *Body fluids and the acid-base balance.* Philadelphia, W. B. Saunders Co., 1964.
10. COHEN, J. J., BRACKETT, N. C., JR. and SCHWARTZ, W. B. *J. clin. Invest.,* 1964, *43:*777–786.
11. CONWAY, E. J. *Physiol. Rev.,* 1957, *37:*84–132.
12. CREESE, R. *Proc. roy. Soc.,* 1954, *142B:*497–513.
13. DAVENPORT, H. W. *The ABC of acid-base chemistry.* Chicago, University of Chicago Press, 1958.
14. DAVEY, C. L. *Arch. Biochem.,* 1960, *89:*303–308.
15. DAVIES, R. E. and KEYNES, R. D. In: *Membrane transport and metabolism,* A. Kleinzeller and A. Kotyk, eds. London, Academic Press, 1961.
16. DILL, D. B., EDWARDS, H. T. and CONSOLAZIO, W. V. *J. biol. Chem.,* 1937, *118:*635–648.
17. DILL, D. B., TALBOTT, J. H. and CONSOLAZIO, W. V. *J. biol. Chem.,* 1937, *118:*649–666.
17a. ECKEL, R. E., BOTSCHNER, A. W. and WOOD, D. H. *Amer. J. Physiol.,* 1959, *196:*811–818.
18. EDSALL, J. T. and WYMAN, J. *Biophysical chemistry,* vol. 1. New York, Academic Press, 1958.
19. FAHRI, L. E. and RAHN, H. *Anesthesiology,* 1960, *21:*604–614.
20. FENN, W. O. *Ann. N.Y. Acad. Sci.,* 1961, *92:*547–558.
21. FERGUSON, J. K. W. *J. Physiol.,* 1937, *88:*40–55.
22. GERMAN, B. and WYMAN, J., JR. *J. biol. Chem.,* 1937, *117:* 533–550.
23. GIEBISCH, G., BERGER, L. and PITTS, R. F. *J. clin. Invest.,* 1955, *34:*231–245.
24. GILBERT, A. L. and LOWENBERG, W. E. *J. cell. comp. Physiol.,* 1964, *63:*359–364.
25. GRODINS, F. S. *Physiologist,* 1964, *7:*319–333.
26. HASTINGS, A. B., SENDROY, J., JR. and VAN SLYKE, D. D. *J. biol. Chem.,* 1928, *79:*183–192.
27. JOHNSON, S. L. and WOODBURY, J. W. *J. gen. Physiol.,* 1964, *47:*827–837.
28. LAVALLEE, M. *Circulat. Res.,* 1964, *15:*185–193.
29. MELLEMGAARD, K. and ASTRUP, P. *Scand. J. clin. Lab. Invest.,* 1960, *12:*187–199.
30. NICHOLS, G., JR. *J. clin. Invest.,* 1958, *37:*1111–1122.
31. PERUTZ, M. F. *Sci. Amer.,* 1964, *211:*64–76.
32. PITTS, R. F. *Harvey Lect.,* 1952–53, *48:*172–209.
33. PITTS, R. F. *Physiology of the kidney and body fluids.* Chicago, Year Book Medical Publishers, 1963.
34. POLAK, A., HAYNIE, G. D., HAYS, R. M. and SCHWARTZ, W. B. *J. clin. Invest.,* 1961, *40:*1223–1237.
35. REFSUM, H. E. *Clin. Sci.,* 1964, *27:*407–415.
36. ROBERTS, K. E., POPPELL, J. W., VANAMEE, P., BEALS, R. and RANDALL, H. T. *J. clin. Invest.,* 1956, *35:*261–266.
37. ROUGHTON, F. J. W. Chap. 31 in *Handbook of physiology, Section 3: Respiration,* vol. 1. W. O. Fenn and H. Rahn, eds. Washington, D.C., American Physiological Society, 1964.
38. SCHWAB, M. *Klin. Wschr.,* 1962, *40:*765–772.
39. SIGGAARD-ANDERSEN, O. *The acid-base status of the blood.* Baltimore, Williams and Wilkins Co., 1964.
40. SINGER, R. B., DEERING, R. C. and CLARK, J. K. *J. clin. Invest.,* 1956, *35:*245–253.
41. SINGER, R. B. and HASTINGS, A. B. *Medicine (Baltimore),* 1948, *27:*223–242.
42. SKIPPER, H. E., NOLAN, C. and SIMPSON, L. *J. biol. Chem.,* 1951, *189:*159–166.
43. STONE, D. J. *J. appl. Physiol.,* 1962, *17:*33–37.

44. SULLIVAN, S. F., PATTERSON, R. W. and PAPPER, E. M. *Amer. J. Physiol.,* 1964, *206:*887–890.

45. SWAN, R. C. and PITTS, R. F. *J. clin. Invest.,* 1955, *34:* 205–212.

46. VAN SLYKE, D. D. *J. biol. Chem.,* 1922, *52:*525–570.

47. VAN SLYKE, D. D., HASTINGS, A. B., HILLER, A. and SENDROY, J., JR. *J. biol. Chem.,* 1928, *79:*769–780.

48. VAN SLYKE, D. D. and SENDROY, J., JR. *J. biol. Chem.,* 1928, *79:*781–798.

49. VAN SLYKE, D. D. and SENDROY, J., JR. *J. biol. Chem.,* 1933, *102:*505–519.

50. VAN SLYKE, D. D., SENDROY, J., JR., HASTINGS, A. B. and NEILL, J. M. *J. biol. Chem.,* 1928, *78:*765–799.

51. VAN SLYKE, D. D., WU, H. and McLEAN, F. C. *J. biol. Chem.,* 1923, *56:*765–849.

52. WADDELL, W. J. and BUTLER, T. C. *J. clin. Invest.,* 1959, *38:*720–729.

53. WYMAN, J., JR. *Advanc. Protein Chem.,* 1948, *4:*407–531.

CHAPTER 47

Fluid Compartments of the Brain; Cerebral Circulation

By ROBERT B. LIVINGSTON, DIXON M. WOODBURY
and JOHN L. PATTERSON, JR.

Mechanics of Cerebrospinal Fluid

By ROBERT B. LIVINGSTON

CEREBROSPINAL fluid (CSF) is a clear, colorless solution found within the cerebral ventricles, the spinal canal, and the subarachnoid spaces. It forms a physically and chemically protective chamber for the brain. Cerebrospinal fluid is derived from the arteries entering the cranio-spinal compartment and drains into venous channels leaving this region; part escapes into lymphatic vessels by way of meningeal extensions along emergent cranial and spinal nerve roots. The pressure of CSF lies along the downward gradient between the arterial and venous pressures.

Each of the several parts of this hydraulic system communicates with the rest of the CSF pool, and there is evidence of more or less mixing or "circulation" of the liquid from its various sites of origin to the places where it is reabsorbed. The lateral ventricles and the third ventricle are connected by the two foramina of Monro; the aqueduct of Sylvius provides a narrow communication between the third and fourth ventricles (Fig. 1). In the roof of the fourth ventricle there are communications between the internal ventricular chambers and the external cranial and spinal subarachnoid spaces by way of the foramina of Magendie, Luschka and Elze. All four cerebral ventricles contain dense clusters of blood vessels which are supported by infolded extensions of the pia and ependyma. The capillaries are covered by a single layer of modified ependyma possessing

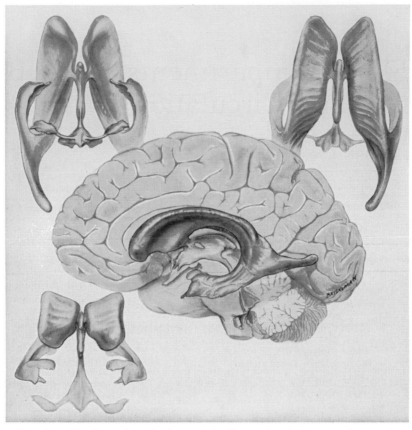

Fig. 1.   Drawing of brain and cerebral ventricles illustrating their approximate relationships. A left ventricular cast is superimposed upon a right cerebral hemisphere. An inferior, a superior and a frontal view of ventricular system, modified from Key and Retzius,[5] are added to this drawing. Large horn-shaped lateral ventricles are joined by foramina of Monro to midline third ventricle. This chamber narrows posteroinferiorly to form the long, narrow aqueduct of Sylvius, which connects with fourth ventricle. Cerebrospinal fluid finds access to cerebrospinal subarachnoid spaces through certain foramina in roof of fourth ventricle, and also from this ventricle directly into spinal canal.

many of the structural characteristics of glandular cells: many mitochondria, large Golgi bodies, large nuclei, one or more nucleoli and "secretory" granules and vacuoles. This epithelial layer possesses at its ventricular surface a brush border; many of the cells are ciliated. At the cells' basal end, the plasma membrane is infolded so that the cells interdigitate near the capillaries. (In this respect they resemble proximal renal tubule cells.) This relationship of epithelial cells is such that substances have to pass through rather than between cells to enter the CSF. These clusters of vessels, together with their covering epithelium, make up the chorioid plexuses which participate in the elaboration of CSF.

A consideration of the physiology of cerebrospinal fluid includes (i) it mechanical aspects,

(ii) the mechanisms of its formation, flow and reabsorption, and (iii) the fluid compartments of the brain and the "barriers" separating them.

SUPPORT OF BRAIN BY CEREBROSPINAL FLUID

Coverings of Brain.   Several anatomic and physical factors are important to an understanding of the normal stability of the brain *in situ.* The skull conforms only roughly to the outer surface of the brain. Nervous tissue has but feeble rigidity and offers very little resistance to changes in shape; it can easily be retracted by gentle pressure. Alone in the skull, unsupported by the leptomeninges and CSF, the brain would be subject to lethal damage under conditions of everyday life and could by no means withstand the punishment of even a minor head injury. Placed on a table, a fresh, unfixed brain proves so soft that it soon suffers distortion and even rupture because of the forces exerted by its own weight.

The dura mater, which is closely applied to the cranial vault and is in some places firmly adherent to the endosteum, somewhat more faithfully encloses the central nervous system. In addition, the dura mater affords two important partitions: the falx and the tentorium. The falx partially compartmentalizes the two cerebral hemispheres. The tentorium forms a fixed and relatively inelastic collar around the brain stem. Like the bony rim of the foramen magnum, this meningeal collar may become an instrument for the destruction of neighboring nervous tissue during compression of the skull at childbirth, during injury associated with violent acceleration of the head, and during elevation of intracranial pressure.

The arachnoid is applied closely to the dura mater and clings to it by virtue of the surface tension of a thin film of serous fluid. This prevents separation of the two surfaces unless forces sufficient to cause cavitation are applied, or unless air or blood is admitted into the plane of their separation—the potential subdural space. This film of fluid offers little resistance to movement of one surface upon the other, except in the region of the meningeal partitions already mentioned and at the points of entrance and exit of blood vessels, nerve roots, etc. Therefore, the brain is relatively free to slide within the cranial vault, a fact that has been demonstrated by substituting a translucent plastic cranium for the top of the skull.[7]

The arachnoid coat does not intimately follow the contours of individual sulci and fissures of the brain, whereas the pia mater is applied directly to the glia limitans itself (Fig. 2). As a consequence, the subarachnoid space is thin over the convolutions and deeper in the region of indentations of the brain, thus providing in certain regions enlarged spaces known as cisterns, in which a pooling of CSF occurs. Extensions of the subarachnoid space, known as the Virchow–Robin spaces, form perivascular sleeves covering the larger blood vessels during part of their penetration of the brain; the outer walls of these channels are formed by pial investments, and the inner walls are composed

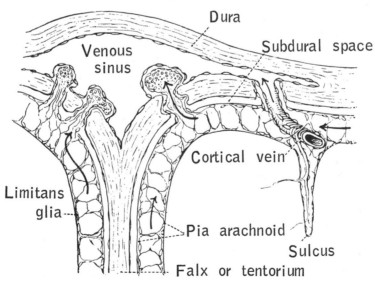

Fig. 2. Drawing of leptomeninges, illustrating subarachnoid space through which cerebrospinal fluid percolates. Fluid may escape by way of arachnoid villi, thin sacculations which penetrate venous sinus contained within dura, or by way of venules which ultimately drain into same sinus. Arachnoid and pia mater are joined by multitudinous filaments, the pia being closely applied to contours of brain, the arachnoid following the dura, separated from it by potential subdural space. In its course out of brain, the vein is separated from the pia by Virchow-Robin space. (Modified from Weed, *J. med. Res.,* 1914, *31*:57–92.)

of the mesenchymatous coverings of the vessels themselves.[6] These spaces can be seen to accompany both arteries and veins but evidently are obliterated through the loss of both pial and adventitial layers throughout the region of precapillaries, capillaries and venules. Cerebral capillaries thus are separated from nervous tissue only by a continuous basement membrane which they share with the adjacent neuronal and glial elements.

Between the arachnoid and pia, manifold fibrous tissue connections form a forest of delicate stanchions through which CSF percolates. These would appear to be too fine and insubstantial to be of importance in the support of such a heavy organ as the brain if it were not for the fact that the CSF imparts buoyancy to that structure.

Buoyancy of Neuraxis. Buoyancy of any body submerged in fluid is determined by the weight of the fluid displaced. The comparative densities of CSF and nervous tissue are such that a brain and spinal cord weighing about 1500 grams when removed from the craniospinal vault will have a net weight *in situ* of less than 50 grams.* When the virtual light weight of the brain in this situation is taken into account, it is understandable that the minute but manifold fibrous tissue connections between the arachnoid and pia can provide the nervous system with a protective suspension. The nervous system is supported by a combination of (i) the weight of CSF which it displaces; (ii) the profusion of filamentous connections in the pia-arachnoid; (iii) the surface tension between coapted arachnoid and dura mater; (iv) the dentate ligaments and other ligaments directly stabilizing the neuraxis; (v) compartmentalization by the dura mater, which is supported by the skeleton; and (vi), supplementarily, the blood vessels and nerve roots which enter and leave the central nervous system.

The importance of CSF in giving buoyancy to the brain and spinal cord becomes immediately obvious when an air or oxygen encephalogram is made. In this procedure, as much fluid as possible may be

* Weight of CNS *in situ* = weight of CNS in air

$$\left(1 - \frac{\text{s.g. CSF}}{\text{s.g. nervous tissue}}\right)$$

$$= 1500 \left(1 - \frac{\sim 1.007}{\sim 1.040}\right)$$

$$= \sim 48 \text{ grams}$$

withdrawn and replaced with gas in order to provide an x-ray contrast between nervous tissue and the ventricular and subarachnoid chambers. When this is done, the full weight of the nervous system rests upon delicate meningeal, nervous and vascular structures. Encephalography is usually decidedly painful because of traction upon nerve roots themselves or upon nerve fibers which course along the meninges or accompany blood vessels. If a large amount of fluid is withdrawn, deep sedation is required, and the procedure is followed by a headache which lasts for many hours. During this time the slightest jarring of the head will greatly intensify the pain.

By virtue of its buoyant effect, the CSF substantially reduces the momentum (inertia) of the brain in response to other acceleratory forces besides gravitation. *As a result of the support and protection of the central nervous system by its meningeal and watery envelopes, the feebly rigid brain can withstand stresses inflicted on the head in the course of everyday living.* Nevertheless, during severe head injury, the brain is subject to damage (i) by deformation or invasion of the skull, with direct damage thereby inflicted on the soft structures beneath, and (ii) by sudden angular acceleration which can cause shearing strains that tear or rupture nervous tissue and blood vessels. Holbourn has considered some of these factors relating to the mechanics of head injury and to the herniation of cerebral tissues through confined openings, e.g., the foramen magnum, the tentorial incisura or bony defects.[3, 4]

Hydrodynamics. The problem of CSF pressure and dynamics can be investigated by puncturing with a fine needle the lumbar subarachnoid space or the cisterna magna at the base of the occiput, or by inserting a needle through a trephine hole into one of the lateral cerebral ventricles. With this communication established, it is a simple matter to attach to the needle a graduated glass cylinder manometer or a mercury or strain gauge manometer which requires less displacement of fluid for pressure determinations. The procedure ordinarily is performed with the subject lying on his side, with the needle in the lumbar subarachnoid space. If he is relaxed and breathing quietly, the CSF pressure is normally found to be about 70 to 160 mm. H_2O.

The cranial vault and spinal column, together with the almost inelastic dura, form a semirigid chamber which is completely filled by the brain and spinal cord, the cerebrospinal vascular bed and the CSF. Because this chamber is semirigid and because its tissue and fluid contents are practically incompressible, it offers great resistance to swift movement or change in volume of any single constituent: there must be an almost exactly equal and opposite effect in one or another of the remaining components. These facts have become known as the Monro–Kellie doctrine. Ryder *et al.* have explored these mechanisms in detail.[9]

EFFECTS OF ACCELERATION. Because of the continuity of the venous column between the craniospinal and thoracic veins, and by virtue of the Monro–Kellie effect, the CSF helps preserve an effective arteriovenous siphon through the brain even during acceleration. Rapid positive angular acceleration (head toward the center of rotation) causes the pressure in arterial and venous channels and in the CSF to fall in direct proportion to the acceleration, so that essentially normal pressure differences are sustained. The relative incompressibility of the skull and its contents prevents collapse of the cerebral veins. There is an almost instantaneous decrease in cerebral vascular resistance, too. This decrease is considered to result from a passive distention of cerebral vessels in replacement of some intracranial CSF, which is displaced toward lower levels as a consequence of drainage of spinal venous plexuses into the veins of the abdomen and legs. It is evident that the maintained siphon effect, the patency of vessels and the lowered cerebral vascular

resistance all contribute to preserving an effective cerebral blood flow (Fig. 3).[2]

The osseous surroundings of the vertebral column tend to reduce the extent of headward flow of CSF when the body is tilted to the head-down position or during negative angular acceleration (feet toward the center of rotation). The rigidity of the intact skeleton surrounding the neuraxis thus tends to prevent undue displacement of the supportive CSF bath. Both vascular and CSF pressures may vary widely according to the forces involved, but they vary so nearly in parallel that very little strain is imposed on the venous walls. Even in extremely severe conditions, the protective bony and connective tissue coverings of the nervous system greatly reduce shifting of fluid parts and thereby largely prevent the deformation or displacement of nervous structures. When the skull is opened and its contents are exposed to atmospheric pressure, the cranial dura mater which would otherwise have been upheld by the bony vault falls in upon the brain, permitting a collapse of cerebral vessels and a marked displacement of CSF into the dependent regions. In such instances, cerebral blood flow is readily disturbed, and the cisternal and ventricular fluid pressures are above atmospheric.

During less rapidly imposed forces, relatively slow adjustments can occur through altered rates of formation and reabsorption of CSF. The brain itself is capable of some change in

Fig. 3. Mean arterial pressure at head level plotted against acceleration. Ordinates: pressure in mm. Hg and venous oxygen saturation in per cent. Abscissae: angular acceleration in units of gravity. Note that in spite of induced fall in mean arterial blood pressure cerebral venous oxygen saturation remains essentially constant during prolonged accelerations of 1 to 2 minutes. See text for explanation of role of intact skull and vertebral column, leptomeninges and cerebrospinal fluid in preserving cerebral blood flow during this stress. (Graph from Henry *et al.*, *J. clin. Invest.*, 1951, *30*:292–300.)

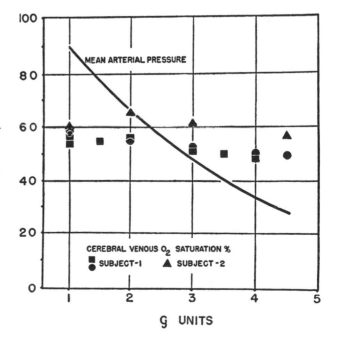

volume by the gain or loss of interstitial or intracellular fluid. Most of the leeway within the "hard bony box" enclosing the nervous system, however, is that provided by the inflow and escape of blood.

EFFECTS OF COMPRESSION OF VESSELS. Any interference with the flow of blood along vessels leading to and from the nervous system is accompanied by alterations in the pressure of the CSF and by whatever slight displacement of the fluid is permitted within the enclosed hydraulic system. The CSF pressure thus quickly reflects slight changes in the dimension of the local vascular bed. Since the thoracic and cerebrospinal veins are in direct continuity, respiratory movements, sneezing, coughing or straining are accompanied by changes in intracranial pressure. During inspiration, for example, the reduction of pressure in the superior vena cava and the increase of pressure in the inferior vena cava tend to shift CSF pressures so that there is a slight headward flow of CSF during inspiration and a reverse flow during expiration.

Prolonged hard straining of the thorax as in lifting, blowing or defecating, although causing a marked rise in arterial pressure, causes an equivalent rise in CSF pressure transmitted from the thoracic to the cerebral veins. Thus during straining there is a protection against rupture of cerebral vessels. However, such strains may be followed after their release by increased cardiac output (resulting from the entrance of dammed-up venous blood) on top of intense vasopressor responses (initiated reflexly during the continued thoracic strain)—the classic Valsalva phenomenon. The resulting high arterial pressure is now, after release of the strain, not balanced by an equivalent CSF pressure rise, and any likelihood of rupture of cerebral vessels associated with straining is increased at this moment.

Compression of the jugular veins or pressure applied to the abdomen will yield a prompt rise in CSF pressure. Compression of the jugular veins, however, will not be followed by a rise of fluid pressure in the lumbar subarachnoid space if there is a block anywhere in the spinal subarachnoid space, e.g., as in a spinal cord or meningeal swelling from tumor or inflammation. If there is only partial block, the pressure will rise slowly, and—after jugular compression is discontinued—return to the initial pressure will also be slow. The utilization of these facts is clinically important, and the jugular compression test, known as the Queckenstedt test,[8] has become an important part of CSF examination. However, if the suspected lesion is located at or above the foramen magnum, the Queckenstedt test will contribute no useful information and may be hazardous.

INTRACRANIAL PRESSURE AND VOLUME RELATIONS

Pressure Relations between Different Parts of CSF Compartment. Since all parts of the CSF pool communicate with each other, pressures determined at different sites are systematically related to each other according to the integrity of the skull and dura mater and to the posture or movement of the individual. When the subject is sitting up, the CSF pressure at the cisterna magna is approximately zero, that in the ventricle is below atmospheric pressure, and that in the lumbar region ranges up to 400 to 500 mm. H_2O. When the subject is horizontal, the pressures at these sites are approximately equal. Since the CSF is apparently in quite free communication with interstitial fluid, it is evident that a measurement of ventricular or subarachnoid pressure closely reflects the pressure acting upon neurons at the same horizontal level.

Pressure Relations between CSF and Vascular Bed. Considering the relationship between capillaries and interstitial fluid elsewhere in the body, one would predict that at equilibrium—that is, with equal rates of formation and reabsorption of fluid—the CSF pressure would be equal to the average capillary hydrostatic pressure less the capillary osmotic pressure. From Poiseuille's law the concept is derived that capillary pressure should be directly related to cerebral blood flow multiplied by the resistance to cerebral blood outflow plus the outlet venous pressure.[9]

Induced Changes in CSF Volume. If fluid is added to the CSF chambers, there must be a sharp transient rise in CSF pressure followed by immediate displacement of some of the blood volume contained in the distensible craniospinal vascular bed. A new unstable balance will follow with slightly elevated CSF pressure, tending to increase reabsorption of the fluid and return the system to equilibrium. (Depending upon the degree of distensibility and volume of the cerebral and systemic vascular pools, there may be considerable CSF volume change with relatively small pressure changes.)

The reverse tendency obtains when fluid is withdrawn, seepage occurring in the direction of restoring the initial CSF pressure and volume. When CSF is withdrawn, the vascular circuits temporarily expand until a new pressure relationship at a slightly lower level is achieved. Since the ability of the blood vessels to expand is limited by their structure, the vascular compensation for loss of relatively large amounts of CSF is inadequate, and low intracerebral pressures result. If sufficient spinal fluid is withdrawn, the resting pressure will reach an equilibrium with atmospheric pressure; free drainage will no longer be possible, and only a small additional amount can be withdrawn by application of moderate tension. Any further drainage can be accomplished only by waiting for further accumulation or by replacing the remaining fluid with some other substance. By injecting air or oxygen and withdrawing spinal fluid, and by changing the position of the subject in order to favor drainage of the ventricles, it is possible to obtain up to 200 ml. of the fluid. This amount probably represents the approximate total of fluid normally present.

It has been demonstrated that, although the capacity of the craniospinal chambers is limited, indefinite amounts of CSF can be added or withdrawn by small increments with a repetition of these pressure responses. The necessary conclusion is that the procedure of adding to or subtracting from the CSF volume induces alterations in pressure which result in net seepage in that direction which will restore the initial state.[9]

If the nervous tissue or the meninges are swollen, as by an expanding growth or an abscess, considerably less space is available within the semirigid bony enclosure for either CSF or the local blood volume. In these circumstances, the pressure falls to a greater extent and is less completely compensated after fluid is withdrawn. Conversely, if less of the total volume is occupied by the nervous system or meninges (atrophy or after surgical removal) and there is a relatively large pool of CSF, withdrawal of the same amount of fluid will be followed by only a slight reduction in its pressure. In 1923 Ayala, observing these facts, pointed out their usefulness in differentiating between expanding lesions and those featuring abnormally large accumulations of cerebrospinal fluid. Savitsky and Kessler computed an Ayala index as that number which is equal to the ratio of final to initial pressure multiplied by a factor of ten (equal to the number of milli-

liters of CSF withdrawn for this test). If the index is between 1 and 5, a diagnosis of space-occupying lesions is favored. Between 5 and 6, the index is considered equivocal, but above 6.5, the index is thought to indicate that an expanding lesion is probably not involved.[10]

Increased Intracranial Pressure.   Intracranial pressure may increase relatively abruptly or insidiously. Following a severe head injury associated with bleeding into the ventricles or into the substance of the brain itself, many of the pressure and blood–brain barrier relations (see below) are upset. Extravasations introduce a large quantity of plasma proteins into the normally nearly protein-free CSF, thereby tending by increased osmotic force to augment the CSF volume. Cellular elements tend to block some of the CSF reabsorptive mechanisms, thereby compounding the difficulty. In cases of inflammation or neoplasm, tissue expansion may also be rapid, so that in a period of a few hours or days blockade of the cerebral aqueduct or tentorial incisura or of the foramen magnum may occur. Cerebrospinal fluid volume and pressure rapidly elevated by any of these means will naturally interfere with cerebral blood flow. It is well known that in such circumstances the arterial blood pressure is reflexly adjusted to successively higher levels until the reflex mechanisms themselves fail (presumably because of anoxia of the brain stem) and death ensues. Surgical intervention to remove the cause of the high intracranial pressure or palliative decompression of the skull by craniotomy may be life-saving.

Increased intracranial pressure developing gradually over a period of months, as in the presence of slow growing neoplasms, may be associated with such gradual and adequate reflex adjustments of pressure relations that intact cerebral functions may exist with an intracranial pressure elevated three or four times normal. This may be the cause of an otherwise inexplicable and asymptomatic arterial hypertension.

Since the meningeal coverings of the cerebrum course outward along the optic nerve and the dura mater ends by attachment to the sclera, there is formed here a CSF *cul de sac*. Increased intracranial pressure may express itself by expanding this space against the limiting tension of the dura mater. In this way, increased intracranial pressure can embarrass venous and lymphatic return from the retina by obstructing the central vein traveling in the interior of the nerve and the associated lymph channels. Obstruction of the lymph channels is said to give rise to swelling of the nerve head, and obstruction of the vein to dilatation of retinal veins. Considerable circulatory interference may occur before vision is disturbed, but choked disc or papilledema and passive venous congestion can be identified by ophthalmoscopy.

Blood–Cerebrospinal Fluid–Brain Fluid Relations

By Dixon M. Woodbury

UNDERSTANDING the factors that govern the exchange of water and solutes between plasma and CSF, plasma and brain, and CSF and brain is basic to understanding CSF function and the so-called "blood–brain" and "blood–cerebrospinal fluid" barriers. It is essential to consider all these exchange processes because the central nervous system, including the CSF, is a multicompartment system of intimately related compartments. The membranes separating the compartments have different attributes which determine the nature and function of the contained fluids. The membranes separating CSF from plasma—the choroid plexus—is responsible for some aspects of the "blood–cerebrospinal fluid" barrier; that separating CSF from brain is the ependymal lining of the ventricles; that separating the plasma from the interstitial space of the brain constitutes the "blood–brain" barrier; the cellular membranes of the glial and neuronal cells make up two additional membranes to be considered.

Plasma–CSF Exchange[12, 13, 21]   Plasma solutes and fluid reach the CSF by two routes: directly across the choroid plexus and indirectly across the brain capillaries to the interstitial space of the brain and thence across the ependymal lining into the CSF. Because many substances traverse these two routes slowly as compared to the rate at which the substances penetrate other tissues, the concept of the blood–brain and blood–cerebrospinal fluid barriers has risen.

CEREBROSPINAL FLUID PRODUCTION. The cerebrospinal fluid is a transcellular fluid (see Chap. 45) actively secreted by the choroid plexuses of the lateral, third and fourth ventricles. This active secretion of the CSF appears to involve active transport of Na^+ via the $(Na^+ + K^+)$-activated ATP-ase system and Cl^- via the carbonic anhydrase system. That the secretory process is active and involves the choroid plexus is evidenced by the following observations:

(i) Hydrocephalus can be produced experimentally by obstructing the aqueduct of Sylvius.

(ii) Removing the choroid plexus in one lateral ventricle and blocking both foramina of Monro causes dilation of the lateral ventricle containing the choroid plexus and collapse of the one in which it is absent. Thus the CSF can be produced by the choroid plexus against a hydrostatic gradient.

(iii) A potential difference (positive on the CSF side) exists between CSF and extracellular fluid of the body, the magnitude of which is a reciprocal function of blood pH and varies from about -3 mV. at pH 7.6 to $+12$ mV. at pH 7.0.[14] In Table 1, the concentration ratios of various substances in CSF and plasma are compared to the ratios expected if each substance were distributed passively according to the observed potential difference. Na^+, Cl^- and Mg^{++} are the only substances listed that have a CSF/plasma ratio greater than or equal to the passive distribution ratio. Since Na^+ and Cl^- are predominant, their excessive amounts in the CSF suggest that either of these ions may be involved in the active production of CSF. None of the cations shown in Table 1 are distributed between blood and CSF passively according to the measured potential difference. Hence Na^+ must be actively transported into the CSF. In contrast, K^+ is actively transported outward from the CSF since the K^+ distribution ratio is below that calculated for passive distribution. Outward K^+ transport is probably coupled to inward Na^+ transport in this system, as it is in other systems throughout the body. Mg^{++} appears to be actively transported into the CSF and Ca^+, like K^+, out of the CSF. At normal pH, Cl^- appears to be distributed passively, but at higher blood pH (7.6) the ratio of CSF/plasma Cl^- concentration increases to 1.68.[21] This value is greatly out of equilibrium with the passive distribution ratio of 0.89, calculated from a potential difference of -3 mV. at a pH of 7.6 obtained from the data of Held *et al.*[14] Thus, Cl^- as well as Na^+ is probably actively transported into CSF. Table 1 also indicates that since the observed distribution ratios are much lower than those calculated for passive distribution, HCO_3^- and the other monovalent anions I^-, SCN^- and Br^- are actively transported out of the CSF a direction opposite to that of Cl^-. It has been suggested that active inward Cl^- transport is coupled to outward HCO_3^-, I^-, etc., transport.

(iv) Active secretion of CSF is further supported by the fact that its production is decreased by inhibitors which are known to block active transport of Na^+ and Cl^-. These include the carbonic anhydrase inhibitor, acctazolamide, which also reduces the CSF/plasma ratio of Cl^-, and, in cats, the digitalis alkaloids in doses sufficient to block active Na^+ transport and inhibit $(Na^+ + K^+)$-activated ATP-ase activity. This enzyme has been shown to be involved in the active transport of Na^+ and K^+. The metabolic inhibitor, 2,4-dinitrophenol, which also inhibits active Na^+ transport, decreases CSF production in the rabbit.

It is apparent, therefore, that production of CSF is a secretory process involving the expenditure of metabolic energy and occurring by the active transport of Na^+ and Cl^- across the epithelial cells of the choroid plexus and into the ventricle, water then following passively to maintain osmotic equilibrium. The mechanisms by which carbonic anhydrase, $(Na + K)$-activated ATP-ase, or other enzymes are involved in the secretory process are as yet unknown.

CEREBROSPINAL FLUID FLOW AND REABSORPTION. Once formed, the CSF flows through the ventricular system and subarachnoid spaces because of the pressure head produced by the secretory process. During this passage, the composition of CSF is altered to some extent by the passive diffusion of substances from the plasma via the cerebral capillaries, the interstitial spaces of the brain and across the ependymal lining, by the diffusion of substances out of it in the reverse direction (and of course by active outward transport across the choroid plexuses). These modifications can be studied by methods analogous to those used to demonstrate tubular reabsorption and secretion of substances in the kidney (Chap. 44). Pappenheimer *et al.*[19, 20] perfused an artificial CSF containing a substance like inulin throughout the ventricular system, introducing the fluid through a cannula in the lateral ventricle and collecting it from one in the cisterna magna. Inulin is used because it does not appreciably diffuse out of the ventricular system although it can leave via the subarachnoid space. Since it is diluted in the ventricular system during the perfusion process in proportion to the ratio of rate of CSF formation to inflow rate, the rate of formation of CSF can be obtained. For example, if the rate of

TABLE 1. *Distribution of Various Substances between Cerebrospinal Fluid and Plasma*

SUBSTANCE	RATIO CSF/PLASMA CONCENTRATION	RATIO FOR PASSIVE DISTRIBUTION AT $+5$ MV.*
Na^+	1.08	0.82
K^+	0.60	0.82
Cl^-	1.21	1.20
HCO_3^-	0.90	1.20
Mg^{++}	1.30	0.68
Ca^{++}	0.50	0.68
I^-	0.02	1.20
SCN^-	0.05	1.20
Br^-	0.72	1.20

*Based on a potential difference of $+5$ mV. (positive on CSF side) between extracellular fluid of body and CSF at normal body pH (Held *et al.*[14])

formation of fresh fluid in the ventricles is exactly equal to the perfusion inflow, then the inulin is diluted in half by the time it reaches the outflow cannula at the cistern. Thus:

$$V_f = \frac{V_i (C_i - C_o)}{C_o}$$

where V_f = rate of formation of CSF, V_i = perfusion inflow rate, C_i = concentration of inulin (or other substance being tested) in ventricular inflow, and C_o = concentration in cisternal outflow.

If the perfusion fluid contains a solute that leaves the fluid during its passage through the ventricular system, or if a solute is added to the perfusion fluid from the blood during the passage of the fluid, the rate of loss or addition of the solute can be determined by this procedure. Thus, precise changes in the composition of the CSF resulting from diffusion or active secretion of solutes into it from the blood or brain or out of it into the blood or brain can be detected. Furthermore, it has been demonstrated that the slope of the line relating inulin clearance to perfusion pressure is a measure of the coefficient of bulk absorption of CSF from the subarachnoid space into the blood via the arachnoid villi.[20] Therefore, the rate of CSF reabsorption by bulk flow is dependent on the hydrostatic pressure in the CSF system. However, Pappenheimer and his colleagues have shown CSF production to be relatively independent of hydrostatic pressure; this provides further evidence that CSF secretion is an active process.

By this elegant procedure, the rates of CSF production and reabsorption have been determined. The rate of bulk formation of CSF in cats, dogs and humans ranges from 0.2 ml. per minute to 0.5 ml. per minute. In man, this represents about 720 ml. per day and, since the total volume of CSF is around 120 ml., the daily turnover of the fluid is appreciable. The rate of bulk filtration of CSF through the arachnoid villi as measured by the perfusion technique is roughly equivalent to the filtration coefficient of the capillaries in 100 grams of mammalian skeletal muscle. The hydrodynamic permeability of the arachnoid villi is large compared to that of peripheral capillaries and bulk absorption appears to play a more prominent part in passage across arachnoid villi capillaries than across muscle capillaries.[19, 20] The fact that large protein molecules leave the CSF by passage through the arachnoid villi at nearly the same rate as smaller molecules such as inulin and sucrose demonstrates the importance of bulk flow in CSF reabsorption by this route.

The rate of exit of CSF via the arachnoid villi is pressure-dependent as described above. The arachnoid villi appear to be an aggregate of tubes opening directly into the lacunae laterales of the dural sinus if the pressure in the subarachnoid space is sufficiently high;[29] when the pressure is too low, the tubes collapse, preventing passage of blood into the subarachnoid space. Thus the arachnoid villi are structurally and functionally like a one-way valve. When CSF pressure is higher than venous sinus pressure, the leaflike valves open, and spinal fluid flows into the dural sinuses. When the venous sinus pressure exceeds that of spinal fluid the valves close, and blood cannot back up into the CSF. This, then, provides a mechanism whereby spinal fluid can be returned to the blood with considerable rapidity, and accounts for the exit of large molecules (protein, etc.) by bulk flow.

How the composition of CSF is changed as it flows through the ventricular-subarachnoid system is shown by studies on urea and creatinine movements as measured by the perfusion technique.[11] Urea enters the CSF by two routes. It diffuses into the CSF during the formation of the primary secretion by the choroid plexus, reaching a concentration about 60 per cent of that in plasma. However, its concentration in the subarachnoid fluid is 80 per cent of that in plasma, indicating that urea has diffused from the cerebral capillaries into the brain and thence into the CSF. This takes place because the concentration of urea in the brain water is nearly the same as in the plasma; hence the concentration gradient is from brain to CSF. This process could raise the urea concentration in CSF to that of the plasma. However, the failure to reach 100 per cent is explained by the fact that the entrance of urea into the brain across the cerebral capillaries is slower (so-called blood–brain barrier as discussed below) than the rate of reabsorption of urea into the blood from the CSF by bulk flow and diffusion. The 80 per cent level for urea concentration in CSF as compared to plasma, therefore, represents a steady-state value for the combined processes of filtration of urea into the CSF via the choroid plexus, slow diffusion into the CSF from the brain and reabsorption of urea into the blood at a relatively rapid rate. Thus, formation of CSF fluid is similar to the formation of urine in the renal tubules.

Creatinine behaves like urea, except that it cannot readily cross the choroid plexus; hence its concentration in the primary secretion is very low. However, the concentration of creatinine in the cisternal fluid is about 17 per cent of that in plasma. This appears to be derived almost entirely from creatinine entering the CSF by way of the plasma–brain route as described for urea. The passage of creatinine across the cerebral capillaries is slower even than that of urea, but the passage from brain to CSF is rapid, which appears to be true for most substances.[24] Thus, much of the creatinine that enters brain from plasma quickly drains into CSF and is carried away with the rapidly flowing fluid; hence the steady-state value is much lower than that of urea (17 versus 80 per cent). The steady-state value eventually reached in the CSF depends on: (i) the rate of passage of the substance from blood to brain as compared to its rate of reabsorption into the blood via the arachnoid villi, and (ii) its concentration in the fluid formed by the choroid plexus. The restricted diffusion of molecules across these two interfaces as compared to their rate of passage across other tissues (skeletal muscle, cardiac muscle, liver, etc.) has led to the phrases *blood–brain and blood–cerebrospinal fluid barriers*. These terms are useful only if they are defined in terms of rate constants for diffusion across the various interfaces of the brain and CSF (see below), or in terms of the volume a substance occupies in the brain.

Any process that decreases the flow of CSF, either by inhibiting production or by reducing reabsorption, increases the concentration of a solute entering the CSF from the brain and thereby tends to equalize its concentrations in the fluids of the two compartments. If CSF flow is completely stopped the concentrations of the substance in the CSF and brain interstitial water will be equal at equilibrium.

The passage of solutes from CSF through the brain to blood can also occur if the concentration in the CSF is higher than in brain. In this situation the limited passage of solutes from the brain into the cerebral capillaries causes accumulation in the brain, particularly if the rate of removal from the blood is more rapid than the rate of transfer out of brain. Bulk flow of CSF across the brain tissue and into blood, in addi-

tion to its bulk flow through the arachnoid villi, has been described.[24]

A final aspect of the exit of substances from the CSF must be considered. This is the reabsorption of solutes by active transport across the choroid plexus, probably of the fourth ventricle. Perfusion studies have shown that weak acids such as iodopyracet (Diodrast), p-amino hippurate and phenol red, and weak bases such as hexamethonium, decamethonium and N–methylnicotinamide are transported out of the CSF against an electrochemical gradient. This system is similar to the secretory system in the proximal renal tubule (Chap. 44) in that saturation phenomena and competition exist and a source of energy is required. Furthermore, as discussed above, iodide, thiocyanate, bromide and perchlorate are actively transported out of the CSF; saturation phenomena and competition also exist for transport of these monovalent anions, and the system resembles the comparable system present in the thyroid gland. In addition to playing a role in transporting these anions from CSF to blood against a concentration gradient, the epithelial cells of the choroid plexus concentrate them. How this cellular accumulation is related to their transcellular transport is unknown. Inhibition of the transport processes elevates both the CSF/plasma and brain/plasma ratios. Thus, these observations plus those cited above for substances that passively diffuse into the CSF from the brain via the cerebral capillaries illustrate the close relationship that exists between the CSF and the fluids of the brain. This relationship will be discussed further but the relations that exist between the fluids and electrolytes of plasma and brain and between various compartments of the brain must first be considered.

Plasma–Brain Fluid Exchange.[12, 13, 26] As mentioned earlier, the diffusion of most solutes across cerebral capillaries characteristically is slower than it is across capillaries in other tissues. The slower rates of penetration of various molecules into the brain as compared with skeletal muscle are shown in Figure 4 for urea, Cl^- and inulin; urea distributes in total brain water, Cl^- distributes primarily in interstitial fluid but also in cells, and inulin distributes in interstitial fluid only. It is evident that all three substances require a much longer time to equilibrate in brain than in muscle, indicative of a *blood–brain barrier*. Understanding the barrier phenomena requires knowledge of the

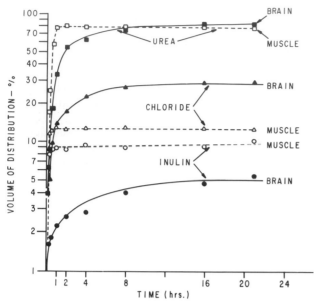

Fig. 4. Comparison of the uptake of radioactive isotopes of urea, chloride and inulin by cerebral cortex and skeletal muscle in rats as examples of the blood–brain barrier phenomenon. The ordinate is the volume of distribution of the substances measured (tissue/plasma ratio) in percentages. The abscissa is time in hours after administration of the isotopes. Note the very rapid attainment of equilibrium in muscle as compared to the much slower uptake by brain tissue.

anatomy and physiology of the various interfaces that substances must cross to enter the various compartments of the brain.

CEREBRAL CAPILLARIES. The existence of a barrier, as revealed classically by the failure of perfused trypan blue to stain the brain, has been attributed solely to restriction of diffusion by the various coverings that surround the brain capillaries. Which of these coverings, if any, is the morphologic correlate of the barrier is still open to question. The structure of the brain capillaries and the relationship of their coverings to the various compartments of the nervous tissue as elucidated by electron microscopy are shown in Figure 5. In this figure, the capillary endothelium appears to be continuous (without fenestrations); the cells overlap and are apparently sealed together by terminal bars. A dense continuous basement membrane is shared between these capillaries and the adjacent glia and nerve cells and their processes. This basement membrane is, in turn, nearly completely invested by a sheath of neuroglial processes that cover approximately 85 per cent of the total capillary surface; the

remaining 15 per cent is stated to be covered by other cellular elements, such as neurons. Thus, the blood–brain barrier, viewed electron microscopically, consists of the endothelial cells, the dense homogeneous basement membrane material, and the neuroglial processes. Figure 5 also shows the tight packing of cellular elements in the brain itself. The non-neuronal areas of brain are filled with glial cells. The spaces between the cells are 150 to 200 Å. wide. What appears to be interstitial space in light microscopy is the "watery" cytoplasm of the glia, particularly of the astrocytes. The narrow channels between the cells, however, represent the true interstitial space of the brain and have an estimated volume from electron micrographs of 4 per cent brain volume. However, physiologic estimates (see below) suggest that free diffusion of small solutes can take place in this space. It has been argued from the supposedly complete investment by cellular elements, mainly glia, that substances must pass from the plasma into the brain *across* rather than between cells, and this accounts for their restricted diffusion and the blood–brain barrier. Only solutes that readily penetrate cells would be able to enter the brain by this route. Thus, large water-soluble nonelectrolytes and strongly polar molecules could not penetrate. However, passage between the glial end-feet that surround the capillaries must also occur. The spaces between the glial end-feet and the other cellular elements are as large as 150 to 200 Å. and probably larger. A channel of this size allows free diffusion of most small molecules or ions such as Na^+, K^+, urea, etc., but may restrict slightly the passage of molecules larger than inulin, which has a radius of 15 Å. Inulin, which generally is confined to the extracellular space and hence does not cross cells, as described in Chapter 45, does, however, enter the brain and CSF on intravenous administration.[24] Entrance must be either by diffusion across the choroid plexus or from the cerebral capillaries through the channels between the glial end-feet and into the interstitial space of the brain. On intravenous injection, the concentration of inulin even in brain total water is higher than in the CSF determined at the same time;[24] and since inulin is confined to the interstitial space its concentration is considerably higher. Unless inulin is actively transported into the brain from the CSF, and there is no evidence for this, it must come from the cerebral capillaries and not the choroid plexus. It most probably enters directly into the interstitial space from the plasma via the channels between the cells and not across them. Evidence from other studies suggests that probably most water-soluble nonelectrolytes and strong electrolytes enter by this route. Lipid-soluble nonelectrolytes and weak electrolytes in their lipid-soluble nonionized form at body pH can also enter the brain from the cerebral capillaries by crossing the cellular elements which contain a lipoid-like plasma membrane which lipid-soluble molecules can penetrate.

Although the rate of entrance of inulin and other molecules into the brain is restricted in comparison with muscle and other tissues (Fig. 4), this barrier cannot be attributed to lack of passage across cells or entirely to restricted passage through narrow interstitial channels; other explanations must be invoked. The barrier is probably due to at least two other factors. (i) Pore size is restricted in the endothelium of the cerebral capillaries, so that molecular sieving occurs and slows passage of molecules, particularly large ones, into the interstitial fluid. This probably accounts for the

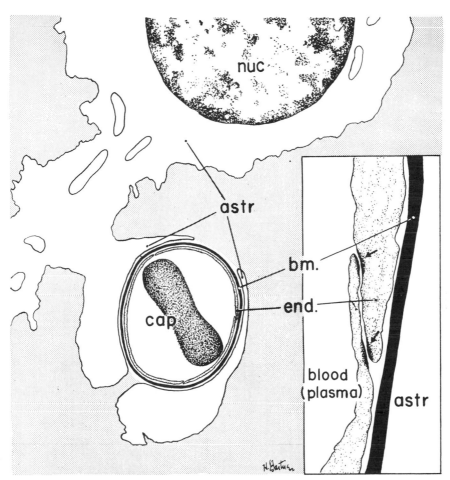

Fig. 5. Drawing based on electron photomicrograph at magnification × 6500; insert based on another electron photomicrograph at magnification × 90,000. The clear space represents a glial cell, including one of its major arms and a pair of perivascular feet almost completely surrounding a capillary. The stippled field represents the remainder of the parenchymal tissue, including nerve fibers, glial processes, etc. The capillary contains an erythrocyte. The capillary endothelium is seen to be surrounded by basement membrane. In the insert is shown the junction of two endothelial cells, the junction being sealed by terminal bar condensations indicated by arrows. The basement membrane is seen to be dense and continuous and is in effect shared by endothelium and the adjacent glial cell. (Drawing adapted from photomicrographs in: Maynard, E. A., Schultz, R. L. and Pease, D. C. *Amer. J. Anat.*, 1957, *100*:409–433.)

complete absence of protein in the brain interstitial fluid. (ii) Bulk flow of CSF through the interstitial channels of the brain and into the cerebral capillaries, as already described,[24] probably opposes solute entrance and slows solute passage into the brain.

Nicholls and Kuffler[18] have clearly shown that exchange of substances between blood and neurons in the leech central nervous system occurs by way of the small interstitial channels of 100 to 150 Å. that separate neurons from glia and that connect with the extracellular space of the connective tissue capsule, and not via exchange across the glia cells that almost surround the neurons. Thus, exchange from blood to neurons in this species occurs via the interstitial space; the same route appears to be used in the mammalian nervous system.

In neonatal animals the rates of penetration of inulin and Cl^- into the brain interstitial space are much faster than in adults.[28] Thus the blood–brain barrier is much less developed in the young than in adults; this is correlated with electron microscopic findings showing that the spaces between glia and neurons and between glial end-feet surrounding the capillaries are much wider than in adults; the extracellular space is correspondingly larger.[28]

INTERSTITIAL COMPARTMENT OF THE BRAIN. The volume of the brain's interstitial space determined by electron microscopy is only 4 per cent. Previous estimates of the brain interstitial space utilized the Cl^- space as a measure of its volume, based on the erroneous concept that this anion is not present in cells. Calculated values for Cl^- space gave volumes of 25 to 30 per cent, depending on the species used. It is now known that both neuronal and glial cells contain Cl^-, but at lower concentrations than in the extracellular fluid.[16] The Cl^- is distributed passively, however, according to the transmembrane potential. The true interstitial space, therefore, is less than the Cl^- space. The space of 4 per cent determined from the electron microscope, however, is probably too low. The cellular components of the brain swell extremely rapidly after death and this tends to shrink the interstitial space, so that the space determined from preparations fixed for electron microscopic studies is too small. Also studies on the electrical impedance of the brain indicate the space to be larger than 4 per cent,[23, 27] perhaps as large as that of Cl^-. Since some Cl^- is in glia, it has been suggested that a portion

of the current flow involved in impedance measurements is through glial cells and, consequently, that they are low resistance cells with an ionic concentration similar to that of interstitial fluid, i.e., low in K^+ and high in Na^+ and Cl^- (see below). The brain extracellular space must, therefore, be larger than 4 per cent and less than 25 to 35 per cent.

Studies with various indicators such as inulin, $SO_4^=$ and sucrose that are confined to the extracellular space have not proved useful for measurement of this space in the brain, because passage across the brain is slower than exit from the CSF by way of the arachnoid villi and because these substances cannot enter the CSF through the choroid plexus. This "sink" effect in the CSF reduces the steady-state concentration of the indicator substance in brain so that it is less than the concentration in the plasma but greater than the concentration in the CSF. Hence, the indicator underestimates the brain interstitial volume if calculated from the plasma concentration or overestimates it if calculated from the CSF concentration. Values calculated in this way from the brain and plasma concentrations have given spaces of 2 to 5 per cent for indicators such as inulin, $SO_4^=$ and sucrose. These results were originally interpreted to lend support to the volumes found from the anatomic studies. It is now clear that they underestimate the space. If inulin is perfused into a cerebral ventricle such as to maintain a constant CSF level and the plasma inulin concentration is maintained at a similar value, the "sink" effect in the CSF is prevented. In this case, the inulin concentration in all three compartments—plasma, interstitial and CSF—is the same and the true interstitial space can be measured. The values determined in this way are about 10 to 15 per cent.[13, 22, 31] Measurement of the extracellular volume of brain slices with various indicators *in vitro* yields values in the same range if correction is made for the swelling that occurs on incubation (see Davson[13] for summary). Volumes of this order have also been obtained from the second component of the radioactive Cl^- uptake curve in rat brain.[28] The uptake of radioactive Cl^- by the brain has three components. The fast one represents penetration into neurons, the second, passage of Cl^- from the plasma to brain interstitial fluid, and the third, penetration into glial cells.

In summary, it is apparent, contrary to the

views of some electron microscopists, that an interstitial space does exist in the brain and that its volume is about the same as that of skeletal muscle—10 to 15 per cent—a value larger than that determined from anatomic studies but less than the Cl⁻ space. That an interstitial space must exist is evident from an analysis of the electrolyte content of glial cells, as will now be discussed.

GLIAL COMPARTMENT OF THE BRAIN. The glial cells of the brain are estimated to occupy about one half of the total cellular volume. Since brain water is 79 per cent and interstitial fluid is 14 per cent of brain weight, the remainder of the volume of 65 per cent is cellular, consisting of about 30 per cent glial cells and 35 per cent neurons.[25]

The ionic concentrations in neuroglial cells have been obtained by several experimental approaches: (i) Neuronal degeneration in the lateral geniculate bodies of the cat and analyses of the remaining glial cells for electrolytes.[16] (ii) Analysis of the various components of brain radioactive uptake curves of Na, K and Cl by a graphical method; the various components of the uptake curves represent penetration of the ions into the three different brain compartments.[25, 28] (iii) Electrolyte analysis of glial tumors from human beings.[15, 30] A summary of volumes and ionic concentrations obtained by these methods, not only for glia, but also for neurons (calculated by difference from interstitial values and total brain water and electrolytes) and interstitial fluid is presented in Table 2. It is evident from this table that glial cells contain high concentrations of Na⁺ and Cl⁻, but in addition contain K⁺ in a concentration as high as that of neurons. Therefore, the glial cells have an active Na⁺–K⁺ pump, but rea-

sonably low transmembrane potentials ($<$ -50 mV.). Evidence from the impedance studies cited above and from tissue culture studies suggests that the glial cells have a low membrane resistance. However, studies with radioactive isotopes yield low permeabilities and hence suggest high resistance. In fact, one aspect of the blood–brain barrier can be attributed to the low rate of equilibration of isotopes that enter glial cells. This is supported by observations in young animals in which the glial cells are absent or greatly reduced in number as demonstrated by histologic examination. In such animals the glial component of the uptake curve is missing and equilibration of the isotopes in the brain is very rapid as compared with the rate of equilibration in the brain of adult animals.[28] Whether the glia are low-resistance or high-resistance cells requires further experimentation.

Passage of substances into glial and neuronal cells takes place from the interstitial space of the brain, and not by direct entrance into them from the plasma.

Although glial cells resemble the extracellular fluid in that they contain high concentrations of Na⁺ and Cl⁻, the fact that they contain a high concentration of K⁺ rules out their functioning as the interstitial space of the brain, as some anatomists who believe there is no interstitial space would like to think. Neither the observed membrane potential (-60 mV. or larger) of neuron cells nor the action potential would be possible in an environment of glial cells with no interstitial space that contain a K⁺ concentration equal to that of the neurons. This is most compelling evidence for an interstitial space in the brain.

The problem of cerebral edema is intimately

TABLE 2. *Calculated Volumes and Electrolyte Concentrations in Interstitial, Glial and Neuronal Compartments of the Brain*

COMPARTMENT	VOLUME %	Na⁺	K⁺	Cl⁻	SPECIES AND REFERENCE
		mEq./L. water			
Interstitial	14	142	2.4*	113	Rat, 25
Glial	30	47	160	35	Rat, 25
		98	126	75	Cat, 16
		77	83	55	Human glial tumors, 30
Neuronal	35	32	160	11	Rat, 25

* Assumed to be same as concentration in CSF.

involved with glial cell metabolism. In experimental cerebral edema induced by various procedures (hydration, hypoxia, triethyl tin), electron microscopic examination shows that the edema is confined mainly to the glial cells. Electrolyte analyses in such cases show marked increases in the Na^+ and Cl^- and decrease in the K^+ concentrations of the glial cells as determined by the radioactive uptake; in addition, the permeability of the glial cells to Na^+ and Cl^- is increased.[25] Thus, the edema is due to accumulation of Na and Cl, accompanied by water, in glial cells. This is the so-called "dry edema" described by pathologists before the advent of electron microscopy. If the edema is severe, the glial membranes rupture and the accumulated fluid also is found to be present in the interstitial space so-called "wet edema."

Other functions of the glial cells, such as nourishing the neurons and supporting the brain tissue as does the connective tissue in other organs have been postulated but not proved. It is also possible that glia serve as a sink for K^+ to prevent a rise in extracellular K^+ concentration in the narrow interstitial channels, during prolonged neuronal activity. During periods of quiescence the K^+ could be returned to the neurons and thereby excessive losses of K^+ from the nervous system during nervous activity would be prevented.

Cerebrospinal Fluid–Brain Fluid Exchange. The ependymal and pial linings are only slight barriers to the exchange of substances between the two fluids. The molecular weight partly determines the rate of exchange. Thus, the rate of penetration of various substances from CSF to brain is in the following order: iodide > sucrose > inulin > radio-iodinated serum albumin.[24] The rates in all cases, however, are faster than their movements across the cerebral capillaries or the choroid plexus. The concentration of ions in the CSF is probably the same as in the interstitial fluid with the exception of those that are actively transported out of the CSF and those that cannot pass through the choroid plexus (see above).

A postulated useful function of the CSF involves the intimate exchange between CSF and brain fluid. Any polar metabolite that enters the interstitial fluid of the brain would have difficulty leaving the brain through the capillaries because of the restricted passage by this pathway. It can readily diffuse in the other direction, however. Once it enters the CSF, it is rapidly removed either by bulk flow through the arachnoid villi or by an active transport mechanism.[21] Similarly, the concentration of potentially neurotoxic substances that could diffuse into the brain would be kept at a lower value and be more rapidly removed because of the sink effect of the CSF.

Circulation Through the Brain

By John L. Patterson, Jr.*

THE brain is one of the most actively metabolizing organs of the body. This metabolism depends for its ultimate energy supply primarily upon the aerobic combustion of glucose. Since there is little storage of glucose and oxygen, even brief interference with the cerebral circulation can bring about profound disturbances of neurologic and mental functions. Duration of consciousness, for example, is less than 10 seconds following complete cessation of circulation through the brain. These conditions

* Incorporating material written for the 17th edition by Dr. E. C. Hoff.

necessitate a large and continuously sustained cerebral circulation.

METHODS FOR MEASUREMENT OF BLOOD FLOW. The cerebral blood flow in man can now be measured with reasonable accuracy by techniques employing inert gases and based on the Fick principle. Of these, the nitrous oxide method of Kety and Schmidt[41] is the most important. Their technique is made possible by virtue of the almost complete separation of the intracranial and extracranial circulations in man. The subject breathes a low, subanesthetic concentration of nitrous oxide and the concentration of the gas is determined in serial samples of arterial and internal jugular venous blood. Since the initial concentration of this gas in the blood and brain is zero, its uptake per unit weight of brain can be learned from the amount of gas in a unit volume of jugular venous blood when the latter is in equilibrium with the concentration in the brain. Ten to 14 minutes of inhalation is required for the establishment of this equilibrium. The mean cerebral blood flow per unit weight of brain is obtained when the uptake value is divided by the mean difference between the arterial and internal jugular venous concentrations.

A method for examining the regional circulation of the brain in animals has been developed by Kety and his colleagues.[39] This technique involves the administration of a relatively inert radioactive gas. Its arterial concentration is monitored continuously, and the concentrations in specific regions are determined from radioautographs of sections of the brain after quick freezing. These data permit the estimation of blood flow in a given region—an important consideration, since large regional differences exist.

Total blood flow, as opposed to flow per unit weight of brain, can be determined by continuous or discontinuous injections of an indicator, such as Evans blue dye (T-1824), into one internal carotid artery. The concentration of the dye in the internal jugular venous blood is then determined (method of Gibbs). The technical problem of injection of the indicator has limited the usefulness of the method.

Useful information can be obtained by older methods of studying the cerebral circulation. The pial circulation has been directly visualized through a cranial window. Qualitative information regarding flow can be obtained by measuring with a thermocouple the rate at which the blood cools a warm wire inserted into the brain substance or into a vessel. Ingenious flowmeters have been interposed into the inflow or outflow systems. The arteriovenous oxygen difference of the brain can be used to measure continuously change in blood flow under conditions of constancy of the cerebral oxygen consumption, since, under these conditions, blood flow and the reciprocal of $(A-V)_{O_2}$ vary proportionally.[46]

In a recumbent person the normal blood flow averages about 54 ml. per 100 grams of brain tissue per minute, or about 750 ml. per minute for the whole brain. The corresponding oxygen consumption in conscious, alert individuals is 3.3 ml. per 100 grams of brain tissue, or about 45 ml. per minute for the entire brain. Thus the brain, representing only 2 per cent of the body weight, ordinarily receives about 16 per cent of the cardiac output and consumes nearly 20 per cent of the oxygen used by the entire body in the basal state. Nutritive requirements vary in different cerebral regions and within the same region under different states of activity. For example, in conscious cats the gray matter may have six times as much blood flow as white matter. In these animals stimulation of the retina by flashes of light increases the flow in the areas of the brain involved in visual function.[39]

A unique feature of the cerebral circulation is that it takes place within a relatively rigid container, the cranium. The spinal dural tube is somewhat less rigid, and, since its contents are continuous with those of the cranium, the volume of the system as a whole can actually be altered to a small extent. Since the brain is nearly incompressible, it follows that the combined volume of the brain tissue, cerebrospinal fluid and intracranial blood must be nearly constant, and that the volume of any one of these components can be increased only at the expense of one or both of the others. An early formulation of this concept, known as the "Monro–Kellie doctrine" or hypothesis, states, in essence, that the quantity of blood within the cranium must be approximately constant at all times, in health or disease. Obvious exceptions to this generalization are the cranium of a young child prior to union of the bony sutures and that of an adult with a cranial defect. It should be emphasized that the Monro–Kellie doctrine refers to quantity of blood, not to blood flow.

VASCULAR ARCHITECTURE AND INNERVATION.[48, 53, 54] The human brain is supplied with blood entirely by the internal carotid and vertebral arteries. At the base of the hemispheres these arteries are united by the circle of Willis and its six large branches, thus forming a manifold for distribution of blood. From these trunks, branches project into the cortical and subcortical tissues. In general, the internal carotid arteries supply blood to the anterior and middle portions of the brain on each side, whereas the basilar artery, formed by union of the two vertebral arteries, supplies the occipital

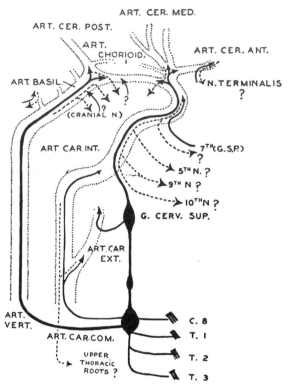

Fig. 6. Innervation of cerebral blood vessels—possible anatomic pathways. Efferent nerves are drawn in solid lines and afferent nerves in broken lines. (From McNaughton, *Res. Publ. Ass. nerv. ment. Dis.*, 1938, *18:* 190.)

lobes and the structures within the posterior fossa. Normally there is little exchange of blood between the right and left halves of the circle of Willis, probably because of an equality of blood pressure. Indeed, the communicating arteries of the circle of Willis form an inadequate anastomosis, so that blood flow to the brain following unilateral carotid ligation may be seriously disturbed, especially in elderly patients.

Two groups of cerebral veins, the external or superficial and the internal or deep, connected by anastomoses, open into the venous sinuses. These larger spaces are contained between folds of the dura mater or between the dura mater and the bone. The openings of the larger cerebral veins into these sinuses have no valves, but are kept patent and protected from closure by the structure of the dura mater around the orifices. Blood may leave the brain by the internal jugular veins (the most important outflow), by anastomoses with the orbital and pterygoid plexuses of veins, by way of emissary

vessels through the cranium, and by channels which join the vertebral plexus of veins. This last channel operates normally in some individuals and is capable of taking over venous drainage after occlusion of the jugular veins and even of the superior vena cava. Considerable mixing of venous blood from the two halves of the brain occurs. It has been estimated that approximately one-third of the blood in the internal jugular vein on one side normally derives from the opposite half of the brain.

The histologic appearance of the blood vessels of the brain is essentially that of vessels elsewhere in the body, although there are minor differences. It has been claimed by some that the arteries in the substance of the brain possess a thinner muscular layer than do arteries of comparable size elsewhere. The elastic fibers are possibly more numerous in cerebral arteries than in the vessels of other parts of the body and have a different arrangement. The veins have extremely thin walls composed largely of connective tissue. The tributaries of the veins are received at a much more obtuse angle than that at which the arterial branches are given off. Both arteries and veins are accompanied by myelinated and unmyelinated nerve fibers. The unmyelinated fibers are believed to carry vasomotor impulses; the myelinated fibers are thought to be sensory afferents. Sympathetic innervation to the internal carotid and vertebral arteries is derived from the stellate and superior cervical ganglia. Parasympathetic fibers to the pericarotid plexus pass from the facial nerve through the geniculate ganglion, and from there travel via the great superficial petrosal nerve. The degree of functional activity of these vasoconstrictor (sympathetic) and vasodilator (parasympathetic) fibers in man is uncertain. The meningeal vessels are supplied with fibers from the Vth, VIIth, IXth, Xth and XIIth cranial nerves (Fig. 6).

End-arteries of brain. On the theory that infarcts occur only where there is no anastomosis between arteries, Cohnheim in 1872 inferred that the vessels of the brain are terminal or end-arteries. Following from the observations by Pfeiffer, and more recently by Scharrer,[49] it has been agreed that the vast majority of arteries in the brains of opossums, cats, rats, rabbits and monkeys are end-arteries, but that no end-arteries are present in the human brain.

Precapillary anastomoses within the brains of rats, cats, rabbits, monkeys and man have been observed. However, such precapillary anastomosis is insufficient to maintain adequate circulation if an artery to a given area of the cerebrum is occluded. It is probable that minute vessels of the order of precapillaries anastomose with precapillaries, but that only rarely do cerebral arteries *per se* anastomose with each other. Everywhere, gray matter has a far richer, denser vascular supply than does the white matter, a finding consistent with the higher rate of metabolism of the gray matter. Within the gray matter itself the vascularity varies in different cellular layers of the cortex and in different subcortical ganglia. This relative vascularity of various parts of the brain and the peculiarities of capillary structure and arrangement[56] may be factors in the localization of disease in various parts of the nervous system.

Regulation of the Cerebral Circulation. The general principle that regional blood flow is regulated to serve the metabolic needs of the tissues holds true for the brain. The over-all metabolism of the brain, as indicated by its oxygen consumption, is remarkably uniform, although the metabolic needs of local areas undoubtedly do vary. Contrary to expectation, recent studies have shown that the cerebral oxygen consumption is the same during such extremes of the conscious state as severe intellectual activity and sleep.[45, 56] This situation necessitates a system of regulation which will insure a nearly constant level of blood flow through the brain rather than a system adaptable to widely fluctuating metabolic and, therefore, circulatory needs. Symptoms of serious cerebral ischemia develop when the blood flow is reduced to about 60 per cent of its value in the resting recumbent state,[33] emphasizing the relatively narrow range of permissible variation in the blood flow through the brain.

The rate of blood flow through the brain is determined by (i) the effective perfusion pressure, which is the difference between the arterial and venous pressures at brain level and (ii) the cerebral vascular resistance, which is the hindrance imposed on the flow of blood through the cerebral vessels. Perfusion pressure is largely determined by the mean arterial blood pressure, but changes in cerebral blood flow do not, as was once believed, passively follow changes in this pressure. When the numerous mechanisms which control peripheral vascular tone and the rate and force of contraction of the heart fail to maintain normal arterial blood pressure, intrinsic mechanisms are brought into play to alter cerebral vascular resistance. This resistance actually represents the resultant of all factors which impede blood flow through the cerebral vessels and includes (i) those factors which affect the caliber of the lumen of the blood vessels—the muscular tone and elastic state of the vascular wall, the external pressure on the vessels (i.e., intracranial pressure), and structural changes secondary to disease; and (ii) blood viscosity. These major determinants of cerebral blood flow are schematically represented in Figure 7.

EFFECTIVE PERFUSION PRESSURE. The major component of the net or effective cerebral perfusion pressure is the arterial pressure at brain level. The pressure in the internal jugular veins in a subject in the recumbent position is less than 10 mm. Hg in health and, since mean arterial pressure is 90 to 95 mm. Hg, the venous pressure hinders only slightly the outflow of blood from the brain. Change in venous pressure with change in body position, to be discussed later, assumes some importance in the maintenance of cerebral blood flow when the subject stands. The multiple nervous, humoral and mechanical mechanisms which insure a normal systemic arterial blood pressure are considered in detail in Chapters 33 and 34. That moderate variation in arterial pressure occurs in health during the stresses of normal daily activity—and that still greater variation occurs in disease states—necessitates active mechanisms for effecting adjustments in the vascular bed of the brain. Examples of such pressure variations are the fall in arterial pressure at brain level when the upright posture is assumed, the rise in pressure associated with anxiety, and the fall in pressure which occurs when an area of heart muscle is suddenly deprived of its blood supply.

CEREBRAL VASCULAR RESISTANCE. Active changes in the caliber of the cerebral vessels reduce the fluctuations in blood flow which are secondary to changes in arterial pressure, so that the variations in flow are smaller than the variations in pressure. The effects of abnormal arterial oxygen and carbon dioxide tensions on the functions of the brain are also offset in some degree by active adjustments in cerebral vascular resistance. The common method of ob-

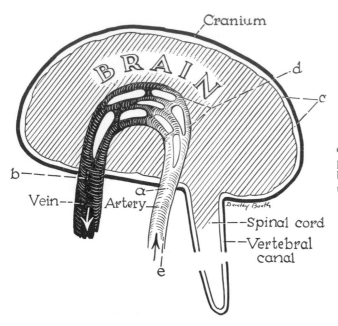

Fig. 7. Schematic representation of major determinants of cerebral blood flow: *a*, arterial pressure at brain level; *b*, venous pressure at brain level; *c*, intracranial pressure; *d*, state of the vascular bed; *e*, viscosity of the blood.

taining a figure for the cerebral vascular resistance has been to divide the mean arterial pressure (or, more accurately, the effective perfusion pressure) at brain level by the cerebral blood flow.

Intracranial pressure is one of the influences which regulate the cerebral circulation, although its role is a secondary one. This term is applied to the pressure in the space between the skull and the brain, and, therefore, the pressure on the subarachnoidal fluid and presumably also in the ventricles of the brain, since the two spaces are in communication. Intracranial pressure is approximately the same as or very slightly higher than the pressure in the venous sinuses. The intracranial pressure is affected by both the arterial and the intracranial venous pressure, but particularly the venous pressure, which it tends to parallel. Changes in intracranial pressure with shifts in body position approximately balance the changes in intracranial venous pressure (presumably also in capillary pressure) and in this way exert a stabilizing effect on the vascular bed of the brain.

As long as the intracranial pressure remains well below that of the arteries supplying the brain, the circulation in this region is not critically affected, and there may be little change in systemic blood pressure, pulse rate or respiration. In man the intracranial pressure must be 450 mm. of water (33 mm. Hg) or higher before mean cerebral blood flow is significantly reduced.[43] The patients in this study showed an excellent correlation between the level of the intracranial pressure and both the calculated cerebral vascular resistance and the mean arterial blood pressure. Such correlation with arterial pressure was observed in acute experiments on animals in Cushing's classic studies. Under conditions of high intracranial pressure, the reduction in blood flow through the medulla stimulates the cardioinhibitory center, causing a slower heart beat; at the same time it also stimulates the vasomotor center, producing a general vasoconstriction in the rest of the body. The effects of this vasoconstriction are a rise in the arterial pressure and an increase in cranial circulation. It is obvious that, if intracranial pressure were raised to the level of systolic arterial pressure and maintained there, cerebral blood flow would cease.

CHEMICAL CONTROL. The major mechanism of intrinsic control of the cerebral circulation resides in the responses of the blood vessels to changes in blood gas tension. The effects of alteration in the tension of oxygen and carbon dioxide in the arterial blood have been extensively studied in recent years. Under conditions of stable oxygen consumption and carbon dioxide production, any change in blood flow will result in changes in the oxygen and carbon dioxide tensions in the capillaries, venules and veins. The most important adjustment which the cerebral vessels are called upon to make is the dilator response to a fall in arterial pressure and the resulting fall in blood flow. With diminished blood flow and constant metabolism, each unit of flowing blood will have a greater amount of oxygen extracted from it and a greater amount of carbon dioxide added. Oxygen tension will therefore fall in the intracerebral blood and also in brain tissue, and the carbon dioxide tension will rise. Both of these changes in gas tension are stimuli to vasodilatation. Conversely, a rise in arterial pressure with an increase in blood flow will produce an increase in oxygen tension and a decrease in carbon dioxide tension, both of these changes being vasoconstrictor stimuli. The effect of the increased oxygen tension is, however, probably so small as to be of no significance. The relation to cerebral vascular control of the changes in blood pH associated with these changes in gas tension is unclear at present.

The results of a number of investigations[42, 52, 57] on the effects of alteration in arterial carbon dioxide tension are presented in composite form in Figure 8. The right side of the curve shows the increase in cerebral blood flow which occurs in response to an elevation in arterial carbon dioxide tension above the normal mean of 40 to 41 mm. Hg. There is little or no change in flow until the carbon dioxide tension has increased by about 4 mm. Hg, but beyond this point there is a rapid and progressive increase in blood flow with additional increases in carbon dioxide tension. An increase of 16 mm. Hg in carbon dioxide tension will, on the average, double the cerebral blood flow and an increase of 38 mm. Hg will triple the flow. The intense dyspnea experienced by the subject makes study beyond this point difficult. Most of the increase in blood flow can be attributed to active cerebral vasodilatation, with a rise in arterial blood pressure making a small contribution. For example, an increase of 14 mm. Hg in carbon dioxide tension was associated with a 14 mm. Hg rise in mean arterial blood pressure. The left side of the curve in Figure 8 shows the strikingly different response of the cerebral circulation to a reduction in the arterial carbon dioxide tension. Although the threshold of the mean response cannot be identified with complete precision, it is probable that a very small (about 2 mm. Hg) reduction in the arterial carbon dioxide tension initiates vasoconstriction. The reduction in blood flow per unit change in carbon dioxide tension is far smaller than the increase in flow when the tension is raised. Most of the change in flow is at-

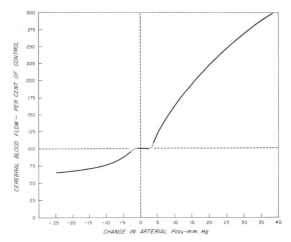

Fig. 8. The full range of response of the cerebral blood flow to elevation and to reduction in arterial CO_2 tension. (Composite curve from data of Kety and colleagues and Patterson and colleagues.)

tributable to vasoconstriction, since an appreciable fall in arterial blood pressure occurs only when the carbon dioxide tension is markedly reduced. A decrease in carbon dioxide tension of 25 mm. Hg is associated with a decrease in blood flow of about 35 per cent, and extrapolation of the curve suggests that the maximum reduction in flow obtainable will not exceed 40 per cent. This is fortunate, since serious cerebral hypoxia would result if the vasoconstriction were more intense.

Blood pH falls as the blood carbon dioxide tension increase and rises as the tension decreases, when the changes in carbon dioxide are primary. It has been thought that alterations in blood pH produce effects which parallel those of changes in carbon dioxide tension, but recent observations on induced acidosis and alkalosis in man have cast doubt on this view.[52] It is probable that an increase in pH produces moderate cerebral vasodilatation, but the effect of a reduction in pH is unclear. Present evidence favors the conclusion that alterations in blood pH play a minor role in the control of the circulation in the brain.

The oxygen tension in the blood vessels of the brain is the second major factor in chemical control of the cerebral circulation. The full range of the response has been investigated in less detail than has the response to carbon dioxide. The reduction in arterial oxygen tension resulting from inhalation of a 10 per cent oxygen mixture produces a relatively marked vasodilatation, with an increase in blood flow amounting to 35 per cent.[42] It is probable that the reduced arterial oxygen tension would have produced a greater increase in blood flow if the associated increase in pulmonary ventilation had not caused a simultaneous 4 mm. Hg fall in arterial carbon dioxide tension. When 85 to 100 per cent oxygen is inhaled, the cerebral blood flow is reduced 13 per cent, but inhalation of 50 per cent oxygen causes minimal vasoconstriction.[42] The vasoconstrictor effect of a high arterial oxygen tension raises questions regarding possible contraindications to the use of oxygen. It is probable that even 100 per cent oxygen produces insufficient slowing of the cerebral circulation to constitute a strong contraindication except in patients with far advanced cerebral vascular disease. The effect of 100 per cent oxygen in depressing pulmonary ventilation in states of arterial hypoxia is another matter, however.

It is reasonable to ask how these data on the effects of altered arterial blood gas tensions relate to normal control of the cerebral circulation. It is probable that these changes in blood gas tension, and perhaps also the associated changes in tissue gas tension, act directly upon the smooth muscle of the vascular wall, although local perivascular nervous pathways conceivably could be involved. As previously discussed, changes in gas tension in the blood in the capillaries, venules and veins occur secondarily to changes in blood flow. It is not known whether these secondary changes in carbon dioxide and oxygen tension produce quantitatively the same responses as those produced by primary alterations in the arterial gas tensions, but the directional effects are the same and it is likely that the responses are of similar magnitude. Apparently the gas tension changes in capillary and venous blood cause vasomotor reactions in the arterioles "upstream," but the mechanism for this retrograde effect is not known. It can be calculated that a 25 to 30 per cent fall in cerebral blood flow is required to raise end-capillary and venous carbon dioxide tension to the approximate vasodilator threshold, but this calculation does not take into account the simultaneous effect of the fall in oxygen tension, which almost certainly advances the vasodilator response. It is not known whether the effects of alterations in the carbon dioxide and oxygen tensions are additive or synergistic.

When the changes in arterial gas tension are primary, as for example in hyperventilation with resulting reduction in arterial carbon dioxide tension, competitive effects can be introduced. The vasoconstriction resulting from the lowering of carbon dioxide tension in turn results in a decrease in blood flow. Since hyperventilation adds very little oxygen to normal arterial blood, the effect of the reduction in cerebral blood flow will be a fall in capillary and venous oxygen tension. These changes in oxygen tension are vasodilator stimuli which will oppose the constrictor effect of the fall in arterial carbon dioxide tension. Furthermore, it can be seen that the fall in capillary and venous carbon dioxide tension will be smaller than the fall in arterial carbon dioxide tension since more carbon dioxide from the brain will be added to each unit of flowing blood. One effect of this mechanism is the prevention of extreme reduction in tissue carbon dioxide tension. The rise in arterial pH associated with hyperventilation may also help limit the magnitude of the vasoconstriction produced by a fall in arterial carbon dioxide tension. In contrast, the forces opposing vasodilatation when arterial carbon dioxide tension is raised are relatively weak.

A number of disease states are associated with changes in the tensions of the arterial blood gases, and these in turn affect the cerebral circulation. In patients whose abnormalities are of long standing, the changes in the circulation in the brain may be quantitatively smaller than those changes which would occur in health in response to brief changes in gas tension. Blood vessels which have undergone structural changes, e.g., atherosclerosis, may be less responsive than normal vessels to either acute or chronic abnormality of the blood gases.

VASCULAR REACTIONS TO PRESSURE.   There is some evidence[34, 35, 38] that arteries and arterioles actually "feel" the distending pressure in the lumen and react by constricting in response to pressure elevation and by dilating in response to pressure reduction. This response of vascular smooth muscle apparently is not mediated through nervous pathways. Such an active mechanism would protect the brain during extreme fluctuations in systemic arterial pressure. It is to be distinguished from the passive changes in the caliber of capillaries and veins that occur with changes in transmural pressure.

NEUROGENIC CONTROL.   The innervation of

the blood vessels of the brain was described earlier. The participation of this innervation in the control of the cerebral circulation has not been fully clarified, despite many investigations of the problem. The studies have, of necessity, been carried out mainly on animals, since both direct stimulation and the cutting of nerves are often required.

In man, according to Forbes,[36] no positive evidence of vasomotor nerves in the brain has been obtained, although both myelinated and unmyelinated nerves may be histologically demonstrated on intracranial blood vessels. Reduction in sympathetic inflow by local anesthetic block of the stellate ganglion does not alter the cerebral blood flow in man.[50]

The function of sympathetic fibers has been demonstrated by Forbes in animals.[37] A slight but definite constriction of the pial arteries followed electrical stimulation of the cervical sympathetic nerve. Stimulation of the stellate ganglion was without effect.

The evidence on neurogenic control, drawn from numerous sources, may be briefly summarized as follows: A degree of neurogenic control of the cerebral vascular bed probably exists, but this control is weak. It may participate in fine adjustments but does not effect major changes in cerebral vascular resistance. Perivascular nerves may have a role in local vascular control within the brain, but the nature of this role is speculative at present.

Cerebral Circulation in Certain Physiologic States. AGING. Conflicting findings have been reported on the effect of the aging process, perhaps because it is difficult to include only "normal" subjects in the older age groups. A slight decrease in blood flow and oxygen uptake per unit weight of brain in older persons without overt evidence of vascular disease has been reported.[40] No significant change in either variable was found in a more recent study in which a group with a mean age of 72 years was carefully selected to exclude persons with even slight evidence of vascular disease.[32] Significantly, in this same study a group of elderly persons with asymptomatic arteriosclerosis had a slight reduction in cerebral blood flow and oxygen consumption. It thus appears that chronologic age *per se* is not responsible for any reduction in blood flow and metabolism.

STANDING. When a person stands up, the cerebral blood flow decreases 21 per cent, but cerebral oxygen consumption does not change.[50] The decrease in blood flow results from a fall in mean arterial pressure at brain level, averaging 29 mm. Hg in one study[51] and 19 mm. Hg in another.[47] An important factor in the postural adjustment is a 7 mm. Hg average fall in jugular venous pressure which offsets about one-third of the decline in arterial pressure.[47] At the same time, the cerebrospinal fluid pressure at brain level falls to the same degree as the venous pressure, thus assisting in the maintenance of the normal caliber of the cerebral veins and probably of the capillaries. Changes in gas tensions in the cerebral capillaries and veins, secondary to a decrease in blood flow as previously described, may make a small contribution to the circulatory adjustment. In some individuals an increase in pulmonary ventilation in the upright position is sufficient to reduce the arterial carbon dioxide tension by several millimeters of mercury and therefore to offset the intrinsic adjustment.

REFERENCES

MECHANICS OF CEREBROSPINAL FLUID

1. AYALA, G. *Z. Neurol. Psychiat.*, 1923, *84:*42–95.
2. HENRY, J. P., GAUER, O. H., KETY, S. S. and KRAMER, K. *J. clin. Invest.*, 1951, *30:*292–300.
3. HOLBOURN, A. H. S. *Lancet*, 1943, *245:*438–441.
4. HOLBOURN, A. H. S. *J. Neurosurg.*, 1944, *1:*190–200.
5. KEY, E. A. H. and RETZIUS, G. *Studien in der Anatomie des Nervenssystems und des Bindegewebes.* Stockholm, Samson och Wallin, 1875–1876.
6. PATEK, P. R. *Anat. Rec.*, 1944, *88:*1–24.
7. PUDENZ, R. H. and SHELDON, C. H. *J. Neurosurg.*, 1946, *3:*487–505.
8. QUECKENSTEDT, H. *Dtsch. Z. Nervenheilk.*, 1916, *55:*325–333.
9. RYDER, H. W., ESPEY, F. F., KIMBELL, F. D., PENKA, E. J., ROSENAUER, A., POLOLSKY, B. and EVANS, J. P. *J. Lab. clin. Med.*, 1953, *41:*428–435.
10. SAVITSKY, N. and KESSLER, N. M. *Arch. Neurol. Psychiat. (Chic.)*, 1938, *39:*988–1002.

BLOOD–CEREBROSPINAL FLUID–BRAIN FLUID RELATIONS

11. BRADBURY, M. W. B. and DAVSON, H. *J. Physiol.*, 1964, *170:*195–211.
12. DAVSON, H. Chap. 72 in *Handbook of physiology; Section 1: Neurophysiology, vol. 3,* J. Field, ed. Washington, D. C., American Physiological Society, 1960.
13. DAVSON, H. *Ergebn. Physiol.* 1963, *52:*20–73.
14. HELD, D., FENCL, V. and PAPPENHEIMER, J. R. *Fed. Proc.*, 1963, *22:*332.
15. KATZMAN, R. *Neurology*, 1961, *11:*27–36.
16. KOCH, A., RANCK, J. B., JR. and NEWMAN, B. L. *Exp. Neurol.*, 1962, *6:*186–200.

17. MAYNARD, E. A., SCHULTZ, R. L. and PEASE, D. L. *Amer. J. Anat.*, 1957, *100*:409–433.

18. NICHOLLS, J. G. and KUFFLER, S. W. *J. Neurophysiol.*, 1964, *27*:645–671.

19. PAPPENHEIMER, J. R. and HEISEY, S. R. In: *Drugs and membranes*, C. A. M. Hogben, ed. New York, Pergamon Press, 1963.

20. PAPPENHEIMER, J. R., HEISEY, S. R. and JORDAN, E. F. *Am. J. Physiol.*, 1961, *200*:1–10.

21. RALL, D. P. In: *The cellular functions of membrane transport.* J. F. Hoffman, ed. Englewood Cliffs, N. J., Prentice-Hall, 1964.

22. RALL, D. P., OPPELT, W. W. and PATLAK, C. S. *Life Sciences*, 1962, *2*:43–48.

23. RANCK, J. B., JR. *Exp. Neurol.*, 1963, *7*:153–174.

24. REED, D. J. and WOODBURY, D. M. *J. Physiol.*, 1963, *169*:816–850.

25. REED, D. J., WOODBURY, D. M. and HOLTZER, R. L. *Arch. Neurol.*, 1964, *10*:604–616.

26. TSCHIRGI, R. D. Chap. 78 in *Handbook of physiology; Section 1: Neurophysiology, vol. 3,* J. Field, ed. Washington, D. C., American Physiological Society, 1960.

27. VAN HARREVELD, A., MURPHY, T. and NOBEL, K. W. *Amer. J. Physiol.*, 1963, *205*:203–207.

28. VERNADAKIS, A. and WOODBURY, D. M. *Arch. Neurol.*, 1965, *12*:284–293.

29. WELCH, K. and FRIEDMAN, V. *Brain*, 1960, *83*:454–469.

30. WOODBURY, D. M. and JARCHO, L. (Unpublished observations.)

31. WOODWARD, D. and REED, D. J. (Personal communication.)

CIRCULATION THROUGH THE BRAIN

32. DASTUR, D. K., LANE, M. H., HANSEN, D. B., KETY, S. S., BUTLER, R. N., PERLIN, S. and SOKOLOFF, L. *Effects of aging on cerebral circulation and metabolism in man.* National Institutes of Health Monograph. In press.

33. FINNERTY, F. A., WITKIN, L. and FAZEKAS, J. F. *J. clin. Invest.*, 1954, *33*:1227–1232.

34. FOG, M. *J. Neurol, Psychiat.*, 1938, *1*:187–197.

35. FOLKOW, B. *Acta physiol. scand.*, 1953, *27*:99–117.

36. FORBES, H. S. *Arch. Neurol. Psychiat. (Chic.)*, 1940, *43*:804–814.

37. FORBES, H. S. and COBB, S. S. *Brain*, 1938, *61*:221–233.

38. FORBES, H. S., NASON, G. I. and WORTMAN, R. C. *Arch. Neurol. Psychiat. (Chic.)*, 1937, *37*:334–350.

39. FREYGANG, W. H., JR. and SOKOLOFF, L. *Advanc. biol. med. Phys.*, 1958, *6*:263–279.

40. HEYMAN, A., PATTERSON, J. L., JR., DUKE, T. W. and BATTEY, L. L. *New Engl. J. Med.*, 1953, *249*:223–229.

41. KETY, S. S. and SCHMIDT, C. F. *J. clin. Invest.*, 1948, *27*:476–483.

42. KETY, S. S. and SCHMIDT, C. F. *J. clin. Invest.*, 1948, *27*:484–492.

43. KETY, S. S., SHENKIN, H. A. and SCHMIDT, C. F. *J. clin. Invest.*, 1948, *27*:493–499.

44. LASSEN, N. A. *Physiol. Rev.*, 1959, *39*:183–238.

45. MANGOLD, R., SOKOLOFF, L., CONNER, E., KLEINERMAN, J., THERMAN, P. G. and KETY, S. S. *J. clin. Invest.*, 1955, *34*:1092–1100.

46. PATTERSON, J. L., JR., HEYMAN, A. and BATTEY, L. L. *J. clin. Invest.*, 1955, *34*:1857–1864.

47. PATTERSON, J. L., JR. and WARREN, J. V. *J. clin. Invest.*, 1952, *31*:653.

48. Research Publications, Association for Research in Nervous and Mental Diseases, 1938, *18*:1–979.

49. SCHARRER, E. *Quart. Rev. Biol.*, 1944, *19*:308–318.

50. SCHEINBERG, P. and JAYNE, H. W. *Circulation*, 1952, *5*:225–236.

51. SCHEINBERG, P. and STEAD, E. A. *J. clin. Invest.*, 1949, *28*:1163–1171.

52. SCHIEVE, J. F. and WILSON, W. P. *J. clin. Invest.*, 1953, *32*:33–38.

53. SCHMIDT, C. F. *The cerebral circulation in health and disease.* Springfield, Ill., Charles C Thomas, 1950.

54. SHENKIN, H. A., HARMEL, M. H. and KETY, S. S. *Arch. Neurol. Psychiat. (Chic.)*, 1948, *60*:240–252.

55. SOKOLOFF, L. *Pharmacol. Rev.*, 1959, *11*:1–85.

56. SOKOLOFF, L., MANGOLD, R., WECHSLER, R. L., KENNEDY, C. and KETY, S. S. *J. clin. Invest.*, 1955, *34*:1101–1108.

57. WASSERMAN, A. J. and PATTERSON, J. L., JR. *J. clin. Invest.*, 1961, *40*:1297–1303.

SECTION XI

DIGESTION AND EXCRETION

CHAPTER 48

Motility of the Gastrointestinal Tract

By THEODORE C. RUCH

THE integrity of living organisms can be maintained only if adequate materials are available to supply the energy-yielding oxidative reactions and to furnish the building blocks for repair, growth and reproduction. Structurally simple organisms such as protozoa may acquire nutrients by diffusion or phagocytosis, with digestion occurring intracellularly. In the vertebrates, a highly specialized digestive system reduces ingested foods to chemical entities which are readily transported by the circulatory system. These digestive systems are composed of a great variety of structural elements and are capable of executing a multitude of diverse functions. Structurally and functionally vertebrate digestive systems are highly adapted for the efficient execution of the processes of digestion and absorption. The duplication of function which is encountered frequently is at least partially responsible for the fact that digestion and absorption may be impaired in disease but are seldom totally abolished. The margin of safety thus provided (a form of error control) appears to be a fundamental characteristic of biologic systems.

STRUCTURE AND FUNCTION

In essence, the digestive tract is a tube designed for the task of receiving, digesting and absorbing the chemical substances which constitute the ingested food. In general, the digestive tube consists of an inner lining, *the mucous membrane,* composed of epithelium and connective tissue (*lamina propria*); the mucous

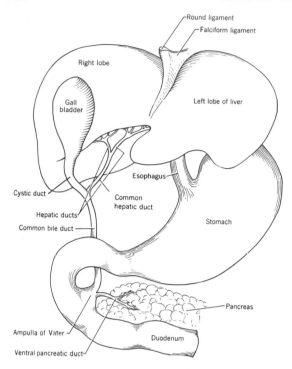

Fig. 1. Stomach, duodenum, liver and gallbladder of man. (From Montagna, *Comparative anatomy.* New York, John Wiley & Sons, 1959.)

membrane is in turn surrounded by a series of muscular coats. In most parts of the digestive tract the mucous membrane is demarcated by a thin muscular layer, the *muscularis mucosae.* The loose connective tissue which lies beneath the muscularis mucosae (when the latter is present) is called the *submucosa.* This is in turn surrounded by two or three layers of smooth muscle. The entire tube is surrounded by a sheath of connective tissue, the *serosa.* In the small intestine the mucous membrane is highly folded to form the *intestinal villi,* whose chief function appears to be the presentation of a large absorptive area through which digested food materials can be transferred to the circulatory system. It has been estimated that the ratio of mucosal to serosal surface in the dog's small intestine is 8.5:1. Histologically, the stratified squamous epithelium of the oral cavity, pharynx and esophagus gives way to a simple columnar epithelium at the cardia, the entry of the esophagus into the stomach. The latter type of epithelium, which is perhaps best suited for the rapid passage of water and solutes from the lumen into the circulatory system or from the blood stream into the lumen, is found throughout the stomach and the small and large intestines. Stratified squamous epithelium appears again only in the anal region.

Musculature. In man the upper portion of the esophagus contains striated muscle, the middle portion contains a mixture of striated and smooth muscle, and the lower part contains only smooth muscle. The latter is not arranged in the pattern of circular and longitudinal layers typical of the other parts of the alimentary tract, although two distinct layers are recognizable. The outer, longitudinal coat is present throughout the stomach and the small and large intestines, but is rather incomplete in the latter. The circular layer tends to become more pronounced caudad in the alimentary canal. A third muscular coat is apparent, the oblique layer.

The stomach deviates considerably in shape from the other tubular portions of the digestive system (Fig. 1). Although digestion does take place in the stomach, this organ serves the very useful purpose of a reservoir which influences considerably the physical consistency and osmotic pressure of its contents and the rate at which these contents are supplied to the delicate structure of the small intestine.

Sphincters. Much of the earlier interpretation of the movements of chyme from one portion of the alimentary tract to another was based upon the supposed function of the several sphincters: the inferior esophageal, the pyloric, the ileocecal, and the internal and external anal sphincters. In man the inferior esophageal is frequently indistinct—more of a functional than an anatomic sphincter. On the other hand, the pylorus is formed by a distinct thickening of the circular fibers of the muscularis externa and by the infiltration of connective tissue into the muscular layer, but surgical removal of the pyloric sphincter does not appear to affect the rate of emptying of the stomach or alter in any way the sequence of mechanical events in stomach and intestine. In short, we are confronted with a definite lack of agreement between anatomic predictions and physiologic thinking, which are usually in close agreement.

Innervation and Plexuses. The extrinsic innervation of the gastrointestinal tract from the sympathetic and parasympathetic divisions of the autonomic nervous system has been described in Chapter 10. Most of the basic movements of the gastrointestinal tract are maintained after sectioning of the extrinsic nerve supply, but at least in the upper end of the tract they are not as strong, as well coordinated, nor as well adjusted to unusual loads placed upon them. Emotional influences on the gastrointestinal tract, of key importance in psychosomatic medicine, are obviously served by influences exerted by hormones in the blood stream or nerve impulses in the extrinsic nerves. Nevertheless, the basic functioning of the gastrointestinal system is dependent upon the plexuses, which have not yet been clearly described in detail.

The plexuses of the gastrointestinal tract are those lying outside the serosal coat of the gastrointestinal walls and the intramural plexuses. The former include the celiac, the two mesenteric and the hypogastric plexuses. Pregangli-

onic sympathetic fibers which have not synapsed in the prevertebral chain enter these plexuses and then divide into branches and synapse with the cell bodies of postganglionic fibers. These postganglionic fibers, upon entering the walls of a viscus, traverse the mural plexuses to reach their effector organs (blood vessels, longitudinal or circular muscular layers, muscularis mucosae and the glands of the intestines). However, they do not form synaptic connections with either motor or afferent neural elements within the mural plexus. Thus, their reflex activity is either as the efferent limb of a spinal reflex or a hypothecated axon reflex with a sensory and an effector branch of the postganglionic fiber. These have not been proved anatomically or physiologically.

Fig. 2. Diagrammatic representation of relations of the elements of gut plexuses as seen in longitudinal section of gut wall. *Muc.,* mucosa; *m.m.,* muscularis mucosae; *s.m.,* submucosa; *Pl.s.m.,* submucous plexus; *c.m.,* circular muscle; *Pl.sym.,* sympathetic plexus; *Pl.m.,* myenteric plexus; *l.m.,* longitudinal muscle; *s.s.,* subserosa; *s.s.pl.,* subserous plexus; *Gn.coel.,* celial ganglion; *Sym.f.,* sympathetic fibers; *Vag.f.,* vagal fibers; *V.,* vessel. (From Hill, *Philos. Trans.,* 1927, *B215:375.*)

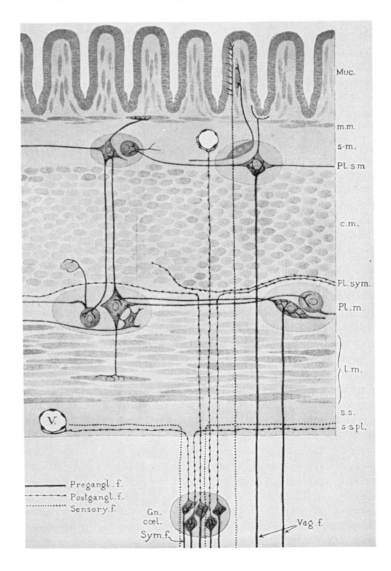

The intramural plexuses are of two types, those that contain cells and those that are made up of fibers from these cells or from those in the extraserosal ganglia dichotomizing and passing to the structures innervated.

The *myenteric plexus of Auerbach* lies between the circular and longitudinal coats of the intestine and consists of a meshwork of myelinated and unmyelinated fibers with collections of cell bodies at the nodal points. The internal *submucosal plexus of Meisner,* situated between the muscularis mucosae and the circular muscles, contains a few cell bodies of postganglionic parasympathetic fibers which distribute their axons through the internal plexus to the glands and muscle cells of the mucosa and to the mucosa muscularis. Here also are the cell bodies of afferent neurons which sense the state of the mucosa and send axons to the cell bodies of both the submucosal and the myenteric plexus. Neurons which sense muscular stretch are probably found in the myenteric plexus. Together these sensory cells are the afferent limb of the *enteric reflex* arcs which function after complete decentralization of a segment of the gastrointestinal tract. (Other afferent fibers course through the plexuses to traverse the splanchnic, vagus or other visceral nerves and have cell bodies in the appropriate sensory ganglion.)

Motility. Functionally, movements of the gastrointestinal tract are of three kinds: (i) fragmentation, (ii) mixing, and (iii) propulsive. The distinction is not absolute. Mastication both fragments and mixes. Peristalsis, a progressive wave of constriction, if vigorous and extended (so-called peristaltic rushes) is clearly propulsive. Slight peristaltic movements that barely indent the wall of the viscus or a stronger wave that dies out quickly may be more significant in mixing than in propulsion. On the whole, earlier physiologists were concerned with getting the digesta through the long and tortuous digestive tube; recently the emphasis has been on leisurely progression making for a thorough digestion and extraction of materials and water.

Soon after the discovery of x-rays by Roentgen, Walter B. Cannon[6] applied them to the study of gastric motility. They permit direct visualization and the making of still or motion pictures[28, 30] of the gastrointestinal movements without anesthesia. X-rays give a *normal* view of gastrointestinal activity save in one respect; the liquid barium meal is handled differently than an ordinary meal because it is heavier. The method is objective and can be made quantitative. It is probable that the full value of the many innovations in roentgenologic technique has not yet been realized.

Despite attempts to maintain normal or nearly normal conditions, direct visualization of the intestinal tract after opening the abdomen or of isolated segments in an organ is fraught with danger and is highly subjective.

For several decades the favored laboratory procedure for studying motility was the balloon at the end of a tube connected to a manometer or a tambour, a shallow vessel covered by a thin rubber diaphragm, the movements of which were magnified by a light lever, writing upon a moving paper covered by a film of soot. The balloon recording has some virtues, but it has many vices, such as inertia and nonlinearity, but more importantly, distension of a balloon is a really potent stimulus of gastrointestinal activity. Except in the body of the stomach and in the lower reaches of the colon, the presence of a firm, sizeable object like an inflated balloon is definitely unphysiologic.

A great stride forward was made when Quigley and his co-workers[5, 24-27] introduced inertialess methods for measurements of intraluminal pressure in animals and Code et al.[8] applied them to man. A tiny pressure-sensitive transducer is introduced into the gut and the wires from it lead to an amplifying and recording system. Alternatively, a tube with small membrane-covered openings is connected with an external recording apparatus. Nowadays, the tube or wire is not necessary, since small transducers and telemetering devices can be enclosed in a capsule and swallowed; no reach of the bowel is sacred. These devices faithfully record pressures; two or more spaced along the gut record pressure gradients which, in fact, determine the translocation of liquids and semiliquids in a tube. Such recorders being pressure sensors by definition can only indirectly measure movement of the wall of the viscus. Suppose a ringlike progressive constriction (peristalsis) reduced the area of the intestinal lumen by one half. If the luminal contents were in one case water and one case molasses, the resistance to forward and backward movement would result in very different intraluminal pressures. Or if points A and B, a few centimeters apart, are contracting in a

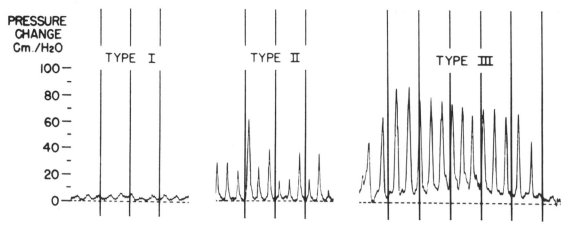

Fig. 3. Types of gastrointestinal movements based on pressure recording from the pyloric antrum. Time: vertical lines equal 1 minute. (From Code *et al.*, *Amer. J. Med.*, 1952, *13*:328–351.)

ring-like fashion (segmentation) and are constricting and relaxing in the exact reciprocal to each other, quite strong movements would (and do) result in little pressure increase. Or, to take another example, intestinal pressure in the colon is less in a diarrheic than in a constipated patient, because the resistance to forward movement of liquid feces is small.[10] It is clear that, valuable as pressure measurements are, they only indirectly reflect the *movement* of a viscus. Methods that record movements quantitatively are needed.

The movements throughout the gastrointestinal tract are sufficiently similar that they

have been described under three categories, Types I, II and III, though each type will vary somewhat from region to region or one type may be absent. This nomenclature, developed by Templeton and Lawson,[32] is without prejudice in respect to function. In Figure 3 it is seen that the major difference between the types is in the pressure generated. The frequency in the particular example does not vary greatly. Fun-

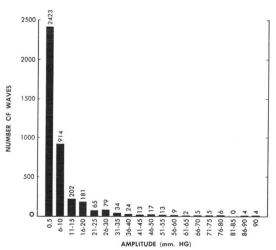

Fig. 4. Histogram showing the number of waves falling in successive amplitude ranges. Gastric intraluminal pressure was recorded by transducers 12 hours postabsorptive. (From Smith and Texter, *Amer. J. digest. Dis.*, 1957 n.s. *2*:318–326.)

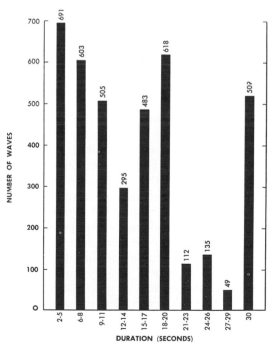

Fig. 5. Histogram showing number of waves falling into successive duration ranges. Conditions as in Figure 4. (From Smith and Texter, *Amer. J. digest. Dis.*, 1957, n.s. *2*:318–326.)

damentally, it is the amplitudes which differentiate Type I from Type II and the fact that in Type III waves either Type I or Type II are superimposed on a rhythmically elevated base line. It is these slow contractions (see Fig. 14) that constitute the differential activity.

Figures 4 and 5 show clearly that, for example, gastric contractions, 12 hours postabsorptive, do not fall into two or three amplitude groups, nor do those of the duodenum.[32] Duration of gastric and duodenal contractions suggests a class corresponding roughly to Type III waves, i.e., with 2 per second frequency.

Classified according to what can be observed with the naked eye in an animal with open abdomen, movements are described as (i) segmentation, (ii) pendular and (iii) peristaltic, as defined and described below. Peristaltic movement occurs in all segments between the esophagus and the colon, but it differs in appearance and neural control in the various segments of the gastrointestinal tract.

MASTICATION

Mastication is a voluntary act which accomplishes two functions: mixing the ingested food with the saliva and reducing the food particles to a size convenient for swallowing. Carnivores, on the whole, swallow relatively large food particles, whereas man usually reduces food to somewhat smaller size before permitting it to reach his stomach. Mastication is intimately related to the proper stimulation of the salivary glands. The secretion of saliva in turn brings about the lubrication of the bolus in preparation for deglutition and initiates (in man and some other animals) the digestion of starch. The articulation of the mandible with the skull permits a great variety of movements.

Some faddists have assumed that prolonged chewing of food has great value because they believe it promotes more complete digestion of the food mass. Two considerations may be cited against this view. First, salivary digestion continues in the stomach for about a half hour after the first bolus enters the stomach. Second, fluids leave the stomach more quickly than does semifluid and relatively solid material. Too prolonged chewing means that only highly fluid material reaches the stomach; since it leaves the viscus sooner, it is possible that there

would be some failure of desired gastric digestion.[16]

Some measurements have been made of the force exerted during crushing and chewing. Howell and Manly[19] have determined the biting force in human subjects to be from 11 to 25 kg. for incisors, and from 29 to 90 kg. for molars.

DEGLUTITION[7, 10, 14, 15, 29, 31]

Swallowing may be initiated voluntarily but is completed reflexly. Broadly speaking, deglutitional movements, although involving a complex musculature, reduce to (i) inhibition of contraction, which opens the passage ahead of the bolus, and (ii) those which close the passage behind the bolus and sweep out any remnants of food. The sequential inhibition and contraction of muscles in swallowing is shown in Figure 6. The application of cinefluoro-

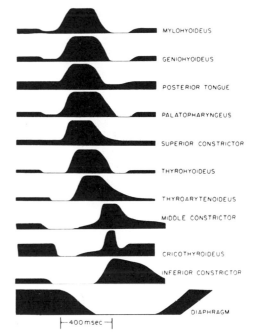

Fig. 6. Schematic summary of electromyographic activity in deglutition from dog "medulla preparation." Height of line for each muscle indicates intensity of action observed, ranging from complete silence to maximum occurring in deglutition. In certain muscles, firing more intense than represented here was observed in other synergies. Action of diaphragm is that seen in eupnea. Contours of rise and fall of activity are not considered accurate. (From Doty and Bosma, *J. Neurophysiol.*, 1956, *19*:44–60.)

graphic[29, 31] and pressure recording techniques[15] has proved more illuminating than fluoroscopic studies of swallowing.

The first stage is the shaping and fashioning of the bolus at the back of the tongue. The bolus is propelled through the pharyngeal gate by an elevation of the tongue against the hard palate, the gate having been opened slightly in advance by an elevation of the soft palate and a relaxation of the faucial pillars. The gate is closed behind the bolus by a backward pressure of the tongue. Contraction of the superior and middle constrictors of the pharynx forces the bolus along.

The next stage, in which the bolus passes through the laryngeal pharynx, is an active one involving constriction by the pharyngeal walls, backward bending of the epiglottis, and an upward and forward movement of the larynx and trachea observable from the outside as the bobbing of the Adam's apple. Closure of the larynx to prevent entrance of food into the trachea is accomplished not only by the lidlike action of the epiglottis but also by closure of the glottis. (The tip of the epiglottis can be removed without interference with swallowing.) Swallowing ends with contraction of the inferior constrictor (cricopharyngeus) behind the bolus, completing a stripping action by the wave of contraction passing through the pharyngeal musculature. This event may be continued by a peristaltic wave stripping the esophagus; this usually does not occur when swallowing is repeated rapidly. Those interested in the pharyngeal mechanics of the competitive and convivial ingestion of large quantities of malted liquids should study the cinefluorographic analysis by Ramsey *et al.*[28]

Esophagus. The esophagus is a muscular tube closed at the upper end by the superior esophageal sphincter (inferior pharyngeal constrictor) at the pharyngo-esophageal junction and by the inferior esophageal or cardiac sphincter at the lower end. The striated muscle at the pharyngo-esophageal junction tonically exerts a pressure of 15 to 23 mm. Hg above atmospheric pressure, whereas that in the remainder of the resting esophagus is identical with intrathoracic pressure, 5 mm. Hg below atmospheric at end of expiration and 10 mm. Hg below at the end of quiet inspiration. Thus, unless large chunks of food are swallowed, there is no pressure to be overcome in the esophagus by the swallowing mechanism until the junction of the esophagus and the cardia of the stomach is reached.

The esophagus appears to have two modes of reaction: One is peristaltic and propulsive; the other is a nonperistaltic, nonpropulsive contraction involving a wide extent of the esophagus, of unknown function but possibly of "psychosomatic" significance.[11, 23, 29] Figure 7 illustrates, on the left, the appearance of a peristaltic wave recorded from a tube composed of three independent catheters with their openings spaced 5 cm. apart. In the record on the left, the peaks of contraction are spaced out on the time axis, denoting progression; in the right-hand record, the peaks coincide in time. Although nonpropulsive spasms occur in normal persons, they appear to be considerably more frequent during emotional strain such as may be created by a psychiatric interview.

Esophageal Phase of Swallowing. Two sphincters and three forces are involved in transferring food from the posterior pharynx to the stomach, and the relative importance of these varies with posture, the physical state of the food, etc.: (i) momentum imparted by the pharyngeal phase of swallowing, (ii) force on the bolus exerted by esophageal peristalsis and (iii) gravity. In the brief period in which the pharyngo- or superior esophageal sphincter is open and the pharyngeal muscle contracted, a high pressure (80 mm. Hg) is generated which expels liquid food with some momentum into the esophagus. This explains why liquid can be drunk with the head below stomach level. Note in Figure 8, however, that the entrance of the bolus into the relaxed esophagus produces only a small pressure rise, in contrast to the large pressure rise which begins a second later and mounts slowly while the pharyngeal sphincter closes quickly and strongly, effectively preventing regurgitation. For water or liquid foods the impetus of pharyngeal swallowing and gravity is sufficient to bring the food to the esophageal-cardiac junction within a second.

Esophageal Peristalsis. This is of three kinds. As noted above, the first, or primary peristalsis originates subsequent to the pharyngeal phase of swallowing. Secondary peristalsis occurs if an object or piece of food sticks in the esophagus. Then the pharyngo-esophageal sphincter closes and peristaltic waves continue to be generated until the object is dislodged and forced along to the stomach. Except for their

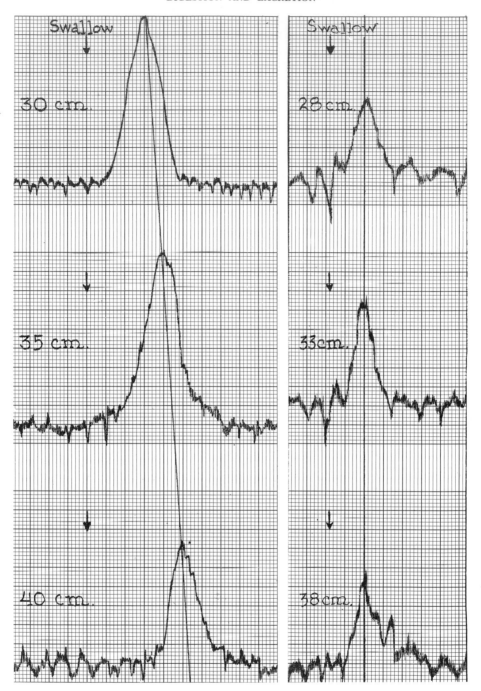

Fig. 7. Pressure records of peristaltic (left) and nonperistaltic (right) esophageal contractions following swallowing recorded from three catheters with tips at the distance from the incisors given by the figures at the left of each record. (From Nagler and Spiro, *J. clin. Invest.,* 1961, *40*:954–970.)

afferent origin, secondary waves appear identical to the primary waves following swallowing. In fact, when a normal bolus is swallowed, secondary peristalsis initiated by its presence in the esophagus may reinforce primary peri-

stalsis. Tertiary peristalsis occurs in the lower smooth muscle segment of the esophagus, is not dependent upon extrinsic innervation, and is stimulated by the presence of food. It may accomplish in quadrupedal animals what gravity can accomplish in man—a sweeping out of the lower end of the esophagus.[21]

The peristaltic wave generates a peak pressure of 100 cm. H_2O,[10] and moves down the esophagus at 2 to 4 cm. per second. Thus, a bolus of food propelled by a peristaltic wave would reach the inferior esophageal sphincter in about nine seconds.

The esophageal peristaltic wave, unlike that in the small intestines, is not propagated by an intrinsic plexus since it "jumps" a complete transection of the muscular coats of the esophagus if the extrinsic innervation is preserved. Just after the wave reaches the cut end of the esophagus it appears in the segment immediately below. The esophageal peristaltic wave is produced by a temporospatial discharge from the swallowing center in the medulla oblongata of the brain through the extrinsic nerves of the esophagus so that its successive segments are sequentially activated. (The simplest analogy would be the traversing fire of a machine gun.)

The peristaltic wave, though propulsive, is only weakly so in man (estimated at 5 to 10 grams force exerted on a bolus[12]). This reflects the fact that most modern men are deliberate eaters (masticators rather than bolters), and all have the third factor, gravity, assisting peristalsis in the sitting or upright position. Whether in man a zone of relaxation immediately precedes the zone of peristaltic contraction of the esophagus is doubtful, and it would be of doubtful utility in normal deliberate eating since the esophagus is normally relaxed. On the other hand, inhibitory relaxation of the inferior esophageal sphincter is critical, but it begins with the initiation of the peristaltic wave, well ahead of the arrival of the peristaltic

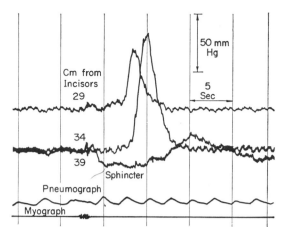

Fig. 9. Behavior of inferior esophageal sphincter, which opens (fall of pressure) about one second after swallowing (myograph, lower line), in contrast with the peristaltic pressure wave, which reaches the lower esophagus several seconds later. Note that the pressure in the sphincter (and lower esophagus 39 cm. from incisors) remains elevated after the large decline in esophageal contraction. (From Davenport, *Physiology of the digestive tract.* Chicago, Year Book Medical Publishers, Inc., 1961; based on Code and Schlegal, *Gastroenterologia,* 1956, *86:*135–150.)

wave at the junction (Fig. 9). Thus, water falling down the esophagus in approximately one second is only momentarily arrested by the relaxing sphincter. The fluid swallowed may pass into the stomach before the peristaltic wave arrives. A large, firm bolus will proceed at the rate of the peristaltic wave, arriving at the inferior esophageal sphincter in nine seconds. Food of intermediate consistency will require intermediate transit times.

The inferior esophageal sphincter remains open until the peristaltic wave reaches it and then closes as a continuation of the peristaltic wave. For 5 to 10 seconds the sphincter maintains a pressure three to four times its normal resting pressure of 5 mm. Hg. During this time, any small increase in pressure in the stomach resulting from the sudden entry of food would have subsided.

While valvelike action of the sphincter has been postulated from the angle at which the esophagus enters the cardia of the stomach, the weak contraction of the sphincter is the only known means by which regurgitation is prevented. From pressure recordings it is known that in the lower end of the esophagus there is a segment of contraction where resting pressure exceeds that in the stomach. According to Nagler and Spiro, in normal subjects this zone

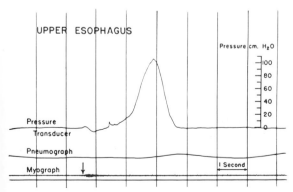

Fig. 8. Pressure changes in esophagus after swallowing. (From Fyke and Code, *Gastroenterology,* 1955, *29:*24–34.)

extends 1 to 3 cm. below the diaphragmatic hiatus and 1 to 2 cm. above, the effective hiatus being the region at which the pressures reverse from thoracic (-5 to -10 mm. Hg) to abdominal pressure ($+0$ to -5 mm. Hg) at inspiration. In some, the abdominal segment is lacking.[23] The intra-abdominal segment of the sphincter may be of importance in preventing gastroesophageal reflux. Being within the abdomen, the intra-abdominal segment is exposed to any increase in intra-abdominal pressure, so that a weak sphincter contraction prevents reflux even when intra-abdominal pressure is greatly elevated. Any condition, such as pregnancy, which causes the intra-abdominal segment to disappear by pushing it upward would favor reflux.[22] Regurgitation of stomach contents damages the esophageal mucosa.

Involuntary eructation or belching is physiologically beneficial but socially harmful. Stomach gas, formed mainly from swallowed air, rests harmlessly as a bubble in the fundus of the stomach. If the bubble is large enough to extend below the cardiac sphincter, the opening of the sphincter consequent to swallowing during a meal (or excessive beer drinking) allows gas to escape, but, unfortunately, not all of it. Belching is likely to occur with monotonous regularity as the fundus refills and is partially emptied of gas.

Achalasia.   Once incorrectly termed cardiospasm, *achalasia* is failure of the cardiac or inferior esophageal sphincter to open in the esophageal sequence of swallowing. Food accumulates in the widely distended esophagus and decomposes. The inferior esophageal sphincter is not, as once thought, in a state of spastic contraction due to a supposed overactive sympathetic innervation. The true cause of achalasia is the inability of the extrinsic nerves to open the sphincter consequent to swallowing, which failure is due to a degeneration of Auerbach's plexus and, hence, of the postganglionic fibers of the vagus nerve. The plexus is lacking not only at the sphincter but throughout the lower reaches of the esophagus so that lack of the peristaltic propulsive wave is added to the failure of the sphincter to open in retarding or preventing food from entering the stomach. As would be predicted from Cannon's law of denervation (Chap. 10), such degeneration of the postganglionic parasympathetic fibers renders the smooth muscle of the esophagus highly sensitive to parasympathomimetic agents.

The effects of extrinsic nerve stimulation and section on the inferior esophageal sphincter are confusing to the point that the sympathetic division was believed to close the sphincter, so that sympathectomy was once practiced for the relief of achalasia. It is clear that the vagus nerve contains fibers ending on postganglionic excitatory neurons producing peristaltic waves and others ending on postganglionic fibers inhibitory to the sphincter. These extrinsic fibers are activated by the swallowing center in the medulla oblongata to give the effective sequence of peristaltic wave and sphincter opening and closing. The failure of the vagal-induced opening of the inferior esophageal sphincter (inhibition) is the causative factor in achalasia.

GASTRIC MOTILITY

Morphologically, histologically and functionally the stomach is divisible into two parts. The corpus and fundus together form a somewhat bulbous thin-walled storage and secretory chamber, and the pars pylorus, or antrum, is a narrower, more muscular, non-acid-secreting area where food is fragmented, mixed with digestive juices and partially digested. There is no structural discontinuity between these regions, which are only structural and functional modifications of a basic pattern.

Gastric Filling and Prefilling Period.   The empty human stomach is something of a laboratory artificiality, since in an affluent society one meal or snack is usually taken before the stomach has disposed of the previous one. The empty stomach is no longer empty when a balloon at the end of a stomach tube is passed into it and distended for recording movements. Artifacts have resulted from this procedure. With modern methods of transducer recording the pressures and movements of the empty stomach can be recorded.

When empty, the stomach is resting, or nearly so. The pressure is about 5 mm. Hg and equal to intra-abdominal pressure. Two kinds of pressure waves can be recorded with open-tip catheters: small (1 mm. Hg), long (5 to 20 seconds), frequent ones; and larger (5 mm. Hg) and somewhat longer waves (3 per second). These waves may be regular or irregular. If irregular, they occur at intervals which are multiples of 20 seconds.

It was pointed out in discussing visceral sensation that bouts of stronger gastric activity occur, which, though less than the gross contractions recorded from ingested balloons, may have a role in producing "hunger pangs." Since they may not, they will be only briefly described here. These waves occur at the basic gastric rhythm for man—3 per second—and appear to be a periodic augmentation of the second rhythm described above. After a period of quiescence, the 3 per second waves become stronger and at some point become sharply rising waves lasting more than 20 seconds so that the next wave builds on the contraction residual of the preceding one. The resulting increase in the baseline lasts for a minute or two and resembles the tetanic contraction of skeletal muscle.

Apart from their possible role in hunger, no function has been ascribed to these gastric waves.

Filling pressure. It is a fact that the stomach of man and animals can be filled by small or even large increments with little increase in intraluminal pressure apart from the transient increase following each increment. This is illustrated in Figure 10 for slow filling of the rabbit's stomach, the intragastric pressure rising only 30 millimeters of H_2O. This behavior of the stomach has conventionally been termed *"receptive relaxation,"* by which is meant some active process by which the tone of the gastric muscle is inhibited and the muscle relaxed so that the increment of volume produces little increase in intraluminal pressure. Such an active process is postulated even though so-called receptive relaxation occurs after section of extrinsic nerve innervation and no mural reflex mechanism for an active receptive relaxation is known.

Much the same behavior in response to filling is exhibited by the urinary bladder and much the same interpretation was once made (see Chap. 51). It is quite probable that in the stomach, as in the bladder, no inhibitory neural mechanism exists nor needs to exist to permit a viscus to fill without large rises in intraluminal pressure. Belief to the contrary is based on a confusion between intraluminal pressure (P) and intramural tension (T) and failure to apply the law of Laplace to the stomach. This law, which is as valid for biologic tissue as for inanimate material, states that transmural pressure (P) is directly proportional to the *ratio* of tension (T) to radius of curvature (R):

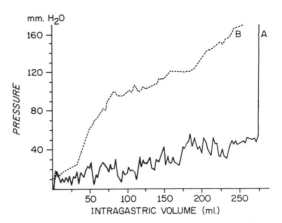

Fig. 10. Pressure-volume curves of the rabbit's stomach when 2.5 ml. of fluid (abscissa) was introduced into the closed stomach every 2.5 minutes. *A*, Stomach *in situ* but the rabbit is anesthetized. At the end of the sharp rise on curve A the stomach ruptured. *B*, Stomach excised and in a bath of isotonic NaCl at body temperature. Similar rising curves have been obtained from the innervated urinary bladder when exposed. (From Grey, *Amer. J. Physiol.,* 1917, *45:*272–285.)

$$P = k(T/R)$$

where k depends upon the geometric shape. Thus, the intraluminal pressure will rise little if the tension, which depends upon circumference, increases at the same rate as the radius, since, in this case, their ratio remains constant. The intramural tension, however, rises, and a thin-walled viscus can rupture at low intraluminal pressure. The situation is analogous to pushing at right angles against a string fixed at both ends—a small pressure suffices to break it. For further details and analogies, see Chapter 51 on the urinary bladder.

Although the specific experiments have not been performed on the stomach, it is safe to conclude that "receptive relaxation" as an active neural or muscle mechanism is a redundant hypothesis, and that the phenomenon so described is a *physical* property of the stomach wall.

GASTRIC MOVEMENTS AND EMPTYING

Grützner's[17] old and widely quoted experiment in which he fed colored foods *seriatim* to rats showed that the food arranges itself in the body of the stomach in distinct layers. The earliest bolus is pushed to the periphery—i.e., toward the greater curvature—and succeeding morsels are layered in concentric crescents, the most recently swallowed bolus nearest the cardia. A somewhat similar layering in man has been demonstrated by alternating barium-treated with untreated food. Layering remains little disturbed for more than an hour. Thus, only the outermost layer of food comes in intimate contact with the enzymes and HCl of the gastric juice and is subjected to its digestive and solvent action. Salivary digestion can continue for some time at the higher pH persisting in the innermost portion of the food mass. Gentle peristaltic waves begin within a few minutes after food enters the stomach. They recur at 3 per second intervals and are initiated by the stretch of the musculature resulting from the presence of food. Small peristaltic waves which travel only a short distance do not reach the pylorus but nudge off liquid and food particles from the main mass and mix them with HCl and gastric juice.

The antrum of the stomach is the site of vigorous churning of the stomach chyme. As digestion proceeds, peristaltic waves at the fundamental gastric rhythm (3 per second) make deep indentations in the antral wall, pushing the liquid food mass against and through the pyloric sphincter, which is open. Since the peristaltic ring of contraction is not closed and the pylorus is longer than the sphincter, gastric chyme squirts backward through it at high velocity, the whole procedure being calculated to break up particulate matter and mix it with the HCl and digestive enzymes received from the body of the stomach. Occasional peristaltic waves are sufficient to obliterate the lumen, and sometimes the antrum appears to contract as a unit, so-called "antral systole."

The pyloric sphincter is a true anatomic sphincter. The circular muscle is greatly thickened and shot through with bundles of connective tissue. It seems not, however, to play an important role in controlling gastric emptying, which proceeds more or less normally after surgical removal of it.

In view of the vigorous and occasionally obliterative peristaltic contractions passing over the antrum toward the pylorus, it might be expected that the stomach would be quickly emptied and, consequently, that undissolved chunks of food would be passed into the duodenum. Reasoning from anatomy supported by some physiologic evidence, physiologists long considered the pylorus to be the gate prohibiting the exit of food from the stomach until some optimal state of the chyme is supposedly achieved. Once acidity was thought to be the key that unlocked the gate. Studies of Thomas and of Quigley, who introduced the use of transducers, and their co-workers have radically altered this picture, as summarized by Thomas[34] and shown in Figure 11.

1. The pylorus is open or its mucosa in weak apposition during most of the gastric emptying cycle, both when the antrum is inactive and between antral peristaltic waves. Gastric contents escape only during a peristaltic wave and then only in small amounts. During a peristaltic wave the pylorus remains contracted longer than the antrum and duodenal bulb, preventing regurgitation of duodenal contents. Vagal discharges do not organize this sequence of events, although vagotomy does reduce the amplitude of the peristaltic contractions, thus reducing the emptying rate of the stomach.

2. The driving force of the emptying process is the pressure differential between the gastric and the duodenal sides of the pylorus. Pressure is built up by steady contractions and peristaltic waves. These in turn probably are initiated in response to the stretch of the smooth muscle coats of the gastric wall by the presence of food in the stomach. The rate of emptying is a *linear* function of gastric volume until the stomach is nearly empty.

3. The steady contraction and peristalsis of the stomach—the driving forces of the emptying process—are profoundly influenced by the state of the duodenum. Distension of the duodenum, mechanical irritation of it and the presence of hypertonic or hypotonic solutions and foodstuffs or their breakdown products in it reduce the motility of the gastric musculature. Thomas lists the latter in the order of their potency (in the concentrations usually encountered) as: fats, fatty acids, proteases, peptones, amino acids, sugars and other products of starch digestion, and hydrogen ions (pH 3.5 to 6.0). The inhibitory efficacy of protein breakdown products is questionable.

4. The "feed-back" mechanisms by which the duodenum controls gastric tone and peristalsis, and hence gastric emptying, are twofold: (i) a quick-acting *enterogastric reflex* employing the vagus nerves and (ii) a slow-acting (3 to 4 seconds) humoral mechanism—*enterogastrone*, i.e., a secretion of the duodenum in response to a variety of stimuli which is carried

to the stomach by the blood stream and is inhibitory to gastric motility. This hormone is also a potent inhibitor of acid secretion of the stomach. The details of its release, etc., will be discussed in the next chapter. It suffices now to say that acid, nonspecific irritants, and the products of protein digestion seem to work through the vagal reflex mechanism, whereas fats and carbohydrates work mainly through the humoral mechanism, although a reflex component has also been clearly demonstrated.[28] The control is exerted on the amplitude but not the frequency of gastric peristalsis.

5. Reflex influences of the stomach and ileum upon each other have been described. Shortly after food enters the stomach, the motility of the ileum is increased. Conversely, if the ileum is full, the emptying of chyme from the stomach is delayed. Distension of the colon also inhibits gastric motility. The splanchnics presumably are the efferent fibers involved.

6. Stimulation of the vagus centrally by circulating insulin plays a role in the regulation of gastric emptying. The administration of insulin augments gastric motility if the vagal nerve supply to the stomach is intact. Vagotomy, on the other hand, increases the time required for the stomach to empty.

Vomiting. The act of vomiting causes an ejection of gastric contents through the esophagus and mouth. The material which is removed from the alimentary tract by this process may consist only of gastric contents, but in severe and prolonged vomiting it may also contain appreciable amounts of intestinal material. Vomiting is usually a reflex act; its stimulus may arise in many parts of the body. Most frequently, vomiting is initiated by irritation of the oropharynx or the gastrointestinal mucosa. Other loci are the semicircular canals (motion sickness) and the genitourinary tract. In some persons any disagreeable emotion or noxious stimulus may set the whole process in operation. As described in Chapter 17, central emetic agents act not upon the vomiting center but upon a chemoreceptive trigger zone nearby, in the floor of the fourth ventricle.

No matter what the cause, the familiar pattern of events which follows is the same. Nausea and excessive salivation herald the deep inspirations which are part of the retching movements. Usually the glottis is closed and the nasal passages are protected against the influx of vomitus. The fundus of the stomach, the cardia and the esophagus are relaxed, while the pylorus and the pyloric region of the stomach appear to contract. Forceful descent of the diaphragm and contraction of the abdominal

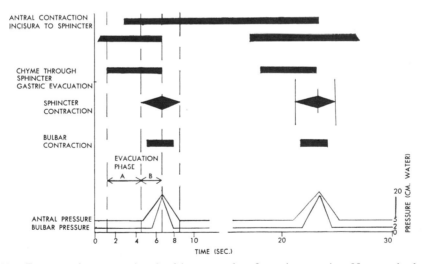

Fig. 11. Events and pressures involved in two cycles of gastric emptying. Note at the bottom of the figure that gastric (antral) pressure exceeds duodenal (bulbar) pressure by 3 cm. of water and emptying occurs during 4½ seconds in phase A. Emptying continues in the next 3 seconds (phase B) as the antrum develops 20 cm. of water pressure against the closing sphincter and the bulbar contraction. The short-lived sphincter contraction marks the greatest pressure differential between the stomach and duodenum so that chyme moves until the sphincter is completely closed. The sphincter stays closed only long enough to prevent regurgitation. (From Quigley and Louckes, *Amer. J. digest. Dis.*, 1962, 7:672–676.)

muscles exert enough pressure upon the contents of the stomach to force such material through the relaxed cardia and esophagus. Whether the stomach musculature takes any propulsive part in the act of vomiting is problematic. If the stomach is removed, administration of a suitable emetic will still elicit typical retching movements. Conversely, paralysis of the abdominal musculature prevents vomiting. In addition to nausea and salivation, vomiting is accompanied by weakness, perspiration, pallor, lacrimation and, often, a fall in blood pressure.

MOVEMENTS OF THE SMALL INTESTINE

Several important events occur in the small intestine which will be listed now and discussed in detail in the next two chapters. Into the duodenum are poured the main agents for digestion and absorption—the powerful enzymatic and alkaline juices secreted by the pancreas and the bile from liver and gallbladder. Along the small intestine digestive secretions of lesser importance are added from glands in the walls of the small intestine. As will be brought out in the next chapters, digestion in the stomach is only preparatory (and dispensable since complete gastrectomy [removal of the stomach] is compatible with life), and digestion is substantially completed when the intestinal chyme passes into the colon. The contribution of the small intestine to the digestive process is, then, a thorough mixing of the digestive juices with the chyme received from the stomach and a usually leisurely, but sometimes brisk, propulsion along the two or three yards of intestine which separate the stomach from the colon. While it is important for one meal to make way for the next, more important is the retention, mixing, digesting and absorption of food in the intestine. Mixing, or trituration, which means the same thing, is accomplished by *segmentation and pendular movements*. Propulsion is accomplished by short peristaltic sweeps and by *peristaltic rushes,* which go for long distances—sometimes the whole length of the small intestine—and are clearly propulsive.

Segmentation Movements. In viewing the opened abdomen of a dog or cat, the small intestine at any one moment looks like a string of fat, egg-shaped sausages. Suddenly each sau-

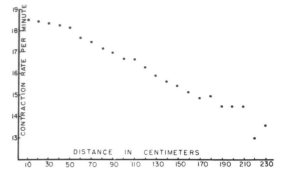

Fig. 12. The rate of rhythmic segmentation contractions at various distances along the small intestine indicating an oral-aboral gradient. (From Hasselbrack and Thomas, *Amer. J. Physiol.*, 1961, *20*:955–960.)

sage is divided in half, the halves of the proximal and distal sausage quickly joining to make a new sausage. Soon thereafter another sudden segmentation movement divides it and each half-segment rejoins the divorced half-segments. Such segmentation occurs at regular intervals for a short time; it then ceases but appears in another portion of the intestine. These contractions occur more frequently in the duodenum than in the jejunum or ileum. The necessity for mixing the intestinal contents with digestive secretions is, of course, greatest in the upper region of the duodenum where the acid gastric chyme must be mixed with the alkaline pancreatic juice and its powerful enzymes requiring an alkaline environment. In the lower parts of the small intestine where digestion is virtually complete, little activity is needed.

The rates of segmentation movements for various sections of the intestine are shown in Figure 12. There is a definite gradient, with the highest rate at the duodenum near the entrance of the bile duct, which, cooling experiments indicate, is a pacemaker influencing more distal segments.[18] The basic rate seems to be determined by the plexuses of the intestinal wall, but a variety of influences affect their amplitude, namely: feeding (+) and fasting (−), vagal stimulation and parasympathomimetic drugs (+) and anticholinesterase (+), while sympathetic stimulation and/or release of epinephrine by artificial or natural means (fear) decreases them.

Pendular Movements. In the opened abdomen of a rabbit or other laboratory animal, a loop of intestine is seen to undergo a rhythmic back and forward or *pendular movement.* Such a movement would mix, though not propel the intestinal chyme forward. Just how such movements are effected is not known. Permitted to guess, one would think of longitudinal fibers contracting and relaxing. To what degree such movements occur in the normal, closed abdomen of animals and man is not known. It is difficult to see how pendular movements, unless very vigorous, could be great because of the resistance presented by adjacent segments of intestine. However, a rapid back and forth oscillation of a column of intestinal contents has occasionally been observed in man during fluoroscopic observation.

Peristalsis.   The classic work of Bayliss and Starling[2] on peristalsis led these workers to formulate the "law of the intestine." They had found that, when the intestinal wall is stimulated, a local contraction of the muscular coats occurs. This contraction passes as a wave down the intestine, as they thought, preceded by a wave of inhibition. These pressure changes have been recorded by many workers with the aid of inflated balloons introduced into the lumen of the intestine. The contraction wave clearly serves to force the contents of the alimentary tract to move caudad; the state of relaxation which precedes the wave has been viewed as lowering the resistance to forward movement of the intestinal contents. Alvarez[1] vigorously challenged the functional significance of Starling's "law of the intestine" because it had been demonstrated with balloons placed in the denervated bowel of animals which had received castor oil, both irritative procedures, and in a herbivorous laboratory animal which generally has a full jejunum in contrast with the nearly empty jejunum of other animals and man. With the aid of somewhat different techniques, Alvarez found that electrical stimulation of the serosal surface of the rabbit's intestine resulted in contraction both above and below the point of stimulation. Alvarez concluded that the wave of contraction runs caudad without being preceded by relaxation.

Apart from a potential role in pendular movements, the function of the longitudinal muscular layer of the small intestine is not clear. Most descriptions of peristalsis speak only of circular contractions. Perhaps the simplest view is that the two muscular coats act synergistically. When the circular coat contracts, the longitudinal muscle also contracts, pulling the intestinal wall orad over the caudad segment of chyme. The segment of chyme has moved forward *vis à vis* the wall of the intestine. The ground gained is not lost when the longitudinal coat relaxes because the circular contraction moves on.

Movements of the Muscularis Mucosae. The function of this structure is something of a mystery. It acts independently of the circular and longitudinal coats and it contracts rather than relaxes in response to sympathetic nerve stimulation and adrenergic agents. It responds to mechanical contacts which would be supplied by an undigested fragment of food, a piece of bone, or any small foreign object. Anyone who has watched a piece of wood in the ocean has noticed how inefficient waves are in moving an object until there is substantial water movement at the tide line. The role of the most inner muscular layer may, therefore, be protective, serving to transport undigestible objects that come in contact with the intestinal wall.

Contraction of the muscularis mucosae throws the intestinal mucosa into ridges, longitudinal and circular, which conceivably are on a small scale a mechanism for promoting absorption comparable to the haustral ridges in the colon. Intestinal villi are caused to sway back and forth by contraction of the muscularis mucosae. This movement, while it causes the finger-like villi to move, cannot be the only function of the inner muscular layer because it, but not villi, are found in the colon. Furthermore, the villi of the small intestine can contract independently of the muscularis mucosae.

Muscle Tone and Tonus Rhythm.   Hollow organs make long, slow changes in the tension of their walls. Small unpropagated contractions, often rhythmic, occur "spontaneously" and are augmented by stretch. As will be shown in the next section, tonus and rhythmic contractions are myogenic activities.

Integration and Control of Motility. Smooth muscles of the gastrointestinal tract possess the ability to initiate spontaneous contractions, often rhythmic and augmented by stretch. That such contractions are myogenic can be demonstrated by the use of plexus-free circular muscle, obtained by stripping away the longitudinal coat and Auerbach's plexus, a technique employed by Gasser and others. Properly prepared, such strips of muscle are proved free of nerve cell bodies by microscopic examination. Although they may contain some nerve fibers, these can be anesthetized by local anesthesia. These preparations show spontaneous rhythmic contractions and respond to acetylcholine with increased tone and at times with an increase in the magnitude of the contractions. Both atropine and epinephrine may inhibit contractions. Although the basic mechanism of tone and rhythmic contractility are inherent in the muscle, it is probable that the myenteric plexus releases enough acetylcholine in the vicinity of the muscle fiber to provide a background of stimulation. It seems possible that pendular movements and tonus rhythm of the alimentary tract may be ascribed directly to these spontaneous contractions of intestinal smooth muscle.

On the other hand, the propagated peristaltic waves require the mediation of the enteric plexus—most likely of Auerbach's myenteric plexus located between the circular and longitudinal muscle coats. This plexus, it will be remembered, is largely of parasympathetic origin, but may transmit some sympathetic fibers. The peristaltic wave has its origin in the *myenteric reflex*.[4] If the intestinal mucosa is lightly stroked, or if the intestine is stretched longitudinally, a powerful sustained contraction occurs orad to the stimulation. Alternatively, the rhythmic activity is heightened. In either case the myenteric reflex would propel the contents of the intestine toward the rectum. This reflex is integrated by the myenteric plexus.

Thus, smooth muscle may itself initiate contractions in response to suitable stimuli but depends for propagation of these contractions upon the integrity of the intrinsic nerve supply. In addition, motor activity may be influenced by certain humoral agents: for example, the inhibition of gastric motility by enterogastrone and by reflexes. Integration of activity in widely separated regions of the alimentary tract requires the mediation of the extrinsic nerve supply.

In the maintenance of a slow enough progression of chyme to insure digestion and absorption but fast enough to prevent a traffic jam, one part of the gut may influence the other through short and long reflexes. The gastroileac reflex is an example of the latter. Distension of the stomach by eating will increase the activity of the lower ileum and with each peristaltic wave the ileocecal sphincter opens. This gastroileac reflex is balanced by a reciprocal ileogastric reflex set off by distension of the ileum and slowing or inhibition of gastric motility, thus allowing the events in the lower intestine to keep pace with events in its upper end.

MOVEMENTS OF THE COLON

In man the functions of the large intestine are relatively few but important. This organ conserves water, acts as a temporary storage place for the waste products of digestion, and to a limited extent it can absorb food materials which may find their way into it. In addition, the colon acts as an incubator for numerous bacteria which, through their ability to synthesize certain nutritional factors, contribute to the over-all nutritional status of the individual.

The temporary storage function of the colon is documented by its size, distensibility, and periodic and relatively sluggish motility. During its prolonged stay in the colon, water is progressively absorbed, so that the liquid chyme is transformed into semisolid feces; a substantial amount of water is thus conserved. The relative quiescence of the proximal colon may be correlated with the comparatively slight development of the myenteric plexus and its scanty extrinsic innervation, derived from the vagus nerve. In the more distal portions, the excitatory innervation is derived from the pelvic nerve and the myenteric plexus is more abundant.

The movements of the colon may be divided into the autogenic and the exogenic. In the first category are the familiar segmentation movements which divide the colon into sausage-like segments, *haustrations*. Apparently these haustral contractions are stationary or progress only a short distance, rolling the fecal contents, mixing them and exposing them to the mucosal surface under considerable pressure. They may correspond to Type II waves[9] which generate 60 to 80 cm. H_2O (Fig. 13).* Exposure of all the contents to the mucosa is, of course, a greater problem here than in the small intestine, owing to the colon's larger diameter. Peristaltic movements and weak antiperistalsis sometimes occur. The occurrence of antiperistalsis supports the belief that the main function of colonic movement is not propulsion but retention and mixing to promote absorption.

Despite the use of open-end catheters to

* Colonic contraction types are shown in this and in Figures 13 to 15.

avoid the stimulation from balloons and the use of combined pressure and radiographic observation, descriptions of colonic activity differ. As in the stomach, when open-tipped catheters are used for recording (children and adults), there is no grouping of colonic pressure waves into Types I, II and III either by amplitude or duration.[12a] However, there are regional differences in amplitude; the longer waves are considerably more frequent in the lower rectum than in the sigmoid and rectosigmoid. Waves in the Type I range were most frequent; other observers record more Type II activity.[12b] Quiescent periods and independent pressure waves in two recording sites (nonpropulsive movements) are characteristic of the colon.[12b] The strong Type IV waves (Fig. 15), once considered to be abnormal, are probably the normal propulsive waves of the lower colon[12b] simply seen frequently when the lower bowel is made more active by disease or cathartics;[12a] they have been recorded antecedent to a bowel movement. The wave may be progressive or may involve an expanse of the distal colon, but in both cases, it would be propulsive.

Improved methods of recording indicate that we should think of Types I to IV as ranges on a smooth continuum, that Types I to III are mixing and squeezing and that Type IV is propulsive, being very numerous in diarrheal children or after administration of a cathartic.

Propulsive movements which sweep over the colon, effectively translocating the colonic contents, occur several times a day. These are called *peristaltic rushes*. The strongest propulsive movement is caused by a *mass contraction* of one section of the colon, completely emptying its contents into the next section (see Fig. 16). This

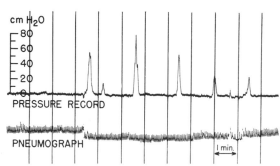

Fig. 13. Type II waves recorded by a pressure transducer in the pelvic colon of man. They are the most frequently recorded pressure waves, and are identified with mixing rather than propulsion because tandem systems of balloons do not show marked progression. They do move short distances as described for haustral contractions. (From Code *et al., Ann. N. Y. Acad. Sci.*, 1954, *58*:317–335.)

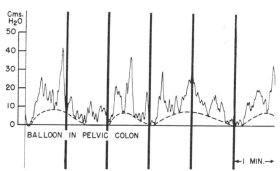

Fig. 14. Type III waves (dashed line) on which are superimposed Type I and II waves (continuous line) recorded from the pelvic colon of a normal person after ingestion of food. Code and his co-workers suggest that these low (10 cm. H_2O), slow (1 or 2 minutes in duration) waves aid absorption by increasing luminal pressure. Time between heavy lines equals 1 minute. (From Spriggs *et al., Gastroenterology*, 1951, *19*: 480–491.)

Fig. 15. Type IV waves recorded from tandem balloons in the transverse colon. Note that these strong waves (to 100 cm. H_2O) in the records from the two balloons coincide in time, indicating that they are propulsive but not progressive and can be equated with mass contractions. (From Code *et al., Amer. J. Med.*, 1952, *13*:328–351.)

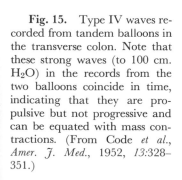

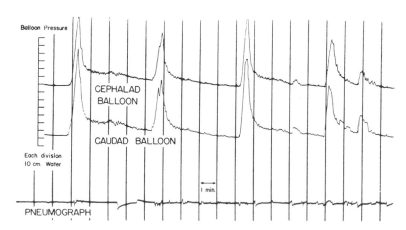

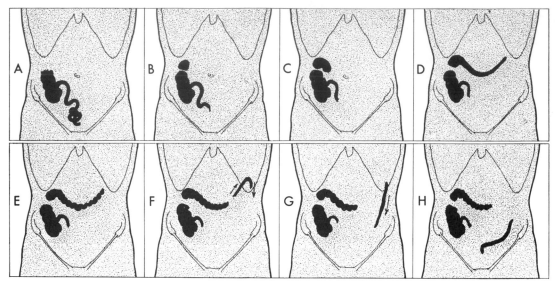

Fig. 16. Drawings of a mass movement of a barium meal taken 5 hours previous to *A,* where the barium from the ileum is collecting in the cecum. During *B* a normal meal was eaten; the cecum and ascending colon became fuller. In *D* the separated portion of the accumulated digesta suddenly passed across the transverse colon (first constricted and then segmented); and after about five minutes the shadow grew longer and suddenly passed around the splenic flexure, down the descending (*G*) and sigmoid colon (*H*). (From Davenport, *Physiology of the digestive tract.* Chicago, Year Book Medical Publishers, Inc., 1961.)

is often initiated by the gastrocolic reflex, which occurs along with the gastroileac reflex. The reflex stimulus combines with the stimulus originating locally from stretching of the colonic walls, the resulting translocation of contents ending the stimulus. The effect of the gastrocolic and local reflexes are such that soon after a meal, mass contractions have transported colonic contents into the rectum, distending it. The resulting sensations are the basis for the common experience of feeling the need to defecate following a meal. "Reflex" is perhaps a misnomer because, in fact, the pathway by which the stomach exerts its effect upon the colon is not known. It is said to survive section of extrinsic nerves and interruption of the mural plexuses.

In reviewing the passage of food through the gut, the pattern seems to be qualitatively similar throughout. Food in varying degrees of digestion falls or is propelled by an active, progressive contraction, which closes sphincters behind it. The presence of food and chyme stimulates the propulsive activity by local action and at the same time relaxes sphincters ahead if they are contracted, and farther along clears the way by promoting intestinal and defecatory action.

Megacolon. Auerbach's myenteric plexus, along a narrow band centered on the rectocolonic junction, is subject to degeneration, blocking both peristaltic and mass contractions. This can result in enormous accumulation of fecal matter in the normal bowel above the disordered segment, resulting in *megacolon* comparable to the megaesophagus resulting from achalasia as described earlier. This condition is not, as once thought, caused by (inhibitory) sympathetic overactivity, nor is it relieved by sympathectomy.

Laxation. Food can affect laxation in two ways, (i) by its bulk, upon which the colonic wall may contract, and (ii) by the presence of substances which have a druglike action on the intestine. Food that contains a significantly larger amount of indigestible material or roughage passes through the intestinal tract quickly. In their studies with wheat bran, Cowgill and Sullivan[10a] obtained data suggesting that in healthy men an intake of not less than 90 to 100 mg. of crude fiber per kilogram of body weight per day should be associated with satisfactory laxation as determined by amount of material eliminated and the subjective impressions of the individual. Observations of patients suffering from chronic constipation

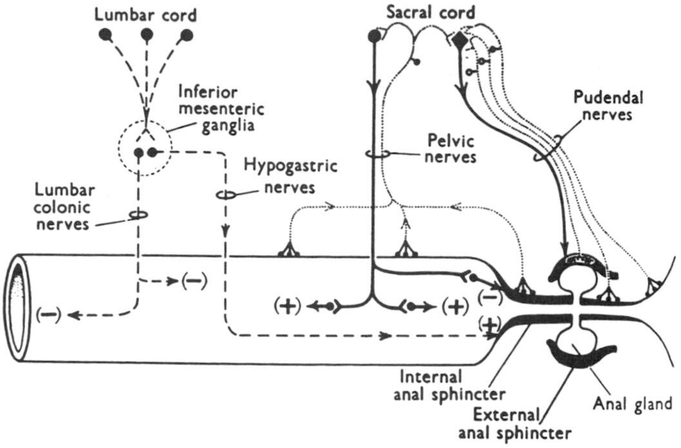

Fig. 17.   Diagram of innervation of anal sphincters and distal colon of cat. (From Bishop *et al.*, *J. Physiol.*, 1956, *134:* 229–240.)

showed that they, as compared with normal subjects, had greater capacity to break down in the alimentary tract (possibly by bacterial action) the crude fiber present in certain fruits and vegetables, with resultant failure to secure satisfactory laxation. It has since been shown that what has been called crude fiber consists chiefly of lignin, cellulose and hemicellulose, these carbohydrates being present in varying amounts. They undergo bacterial decomposition in the large intestine, lignin being the most resistant and hemicellulose the least.

Defecation.   The desire to defecate is felt only when the feces, propelled by mass peristaltic movement, have actually entered the rectum and produced some distension. The internal and external anal sphincters prevent the escape of the accumulated fecal mass. The internal anal sphincter consists of a thickening of the circular layer of smooth muscle. The tonic contraction of the external sphincter is maintained by the pudendal, a somatic nerve.[3] Distension of the colon reflexly opens the sphincter by inhibiting this tone. While there are distinct species differences, in man the lumbar sympathetics are probably excitatory to the internal sphincter; the parasympathetic innervation via the pelvic nerve is inhibitory, as shown in Figure 17. The sympathetic innervation plays no role in defecation;[13] in fact, the act can be executed by patients whose upper sacral segments have been destroyed. These reflex-like contractions are ascribed to a peripheral nerve plexus. However, the integrity of the sacral cord segments and the parasympathetic fibers brings about a stronger and more effective defecatory reflex.

The act of defecation as it occurs normally is partly a voluntary and partly an involuntary

act. When distention of the rectum becomes sufficient to constitute an adequate stimulus, contraction of the colon and relaxation of the anal sphincters leads to evacuation of the fecal mass. The reflexes concerned here involve only the sacral portions of the spinal cord. The voluntary part of the act of defecation involves relaxation of the external sphincter, but may include contractions of the diaphragm and the abdominal muscles.

REFERENCES

1. ALVAREZ, W. C. *An introduction to gastroenterology.* New York, Paul B. Hoeber, Inc., 1940.
2. BAYLISS, W. M. and STARLING, E. H. *J. Physiol.*, 1899, *24:*99–143.
3. BISHOP, B., GARRY, R. C., ROBERTS, T. D. M. and TODD, J. K. *J. Physiol.*, 1956, *134:*229–240.
4. BOZLER, E. *Amer. J. Physiol.*, 1949, *157:*329–337.
5. BRODY, D. A., WERLE, J. M., MESCHAN, I. and QUIGLEY, J. P. *Amer. J. Physiol.*, 1940, *130:*791–801.
6. CANNON, W. B. *Amer. J. Physiol.*, 1898, *1:*359–382.
7. CODE, C. F., CREAMER, B., SCHLEGEL, J. F., OLSEN, A. M., DONOGHUE, F. E. and ANDERSEN, H. A. *An atlas of esophageal motility in health and disease.* Springfield, Ill., Charles C Thomas, 1958.
8. CODE, C. F., HIGHTOWER, N. C. and MORLOCK, C. G. *Amer. J. Med.*, 1952. *13:*328–351.
9. CODE, C. F., WILKINSON, G. R., JR. and SAUER, W. G. *Ann. N. Y. Acad. Sci.*, 1954, *58:*317–335.
10. CONNELL, A. M. *Gut*, 1962, *3:*342–348.
10a. COWGILL, G. R. and SULLIVAN, A. J. *J. Amer. med. Ass.*, 1933, *100:*795–802.
11. CREAMER, B., DONOGHUE, F. E. and CODE, C. F. *Gastroenterology*, 1958, *34:*782–796.
12. DAVENPORT, H. W. *Physiology of the digestive tract.* Chicago, Year Book Medical Publishers, Inc., 1961.
12a. DAVIDSON, M., SLEISENGER, M. H., ALMY, T. P. and LEVINE, S. Z. *Pediatrics*, 1956, *17:*807–819; 820–833.
12b. DELLER, D. J. and WANGEL, A. G. *Gastroenterology*, 1965, *48:*45–57.
13. DENNY-BROWN, D. and ROBERTSON, E. G. *Brain.*, 1935, *58:*256–310.

14. Doty, R. W. and Bosma, J. F. *J. Neurophysiol.*, 1956, *19*:44–60.

15. Fyke, F. E., Jr. and Code, C. F. *Gastroenterology*, 1955, *29*:24–34.

16. Gianturco, C. *Amer. J. Roentgenol.*, 1934, *31*:735–744.

17. Grützner, P. *Pflüg. Arch. ges. Physiol.*, 1905, *106*:463–522.

18. Hasselbrack, R. and Thomas, J. E. *Amer. J. Physiol.*, 1961, *201*:955–960.

19. Howell, A. H. and Manly, R. S. *J. dent. Res.*, 1948, *27*:705–712.

20. Inglefinger, F. J. *Physiol. Rev.*, 1958, *38*:533–584.

21. Magee, D. F. *Gastro-intestinal physiology*. Springfield, Ill., Charles C Thomas, 1962.

22. Nagler, R. and Spiro, H. M. *Gastroenterology*, 1961, *40*:405–407.

23. Nagler, R. and Spiro, H. M. *J. clin. Invest.*, 1961, *40*:954–970.

24. Quigley, J. P. and Brody, D. A. *Amer. J. Med.*, 1952, *13*:73–81.

25. Quigley, J. P., Werle, J. M. and Brody, D. *Amer. J. digest. Dis.*, 1940, *7*:434–435.

26. Quigley, J. P., Werle, J. M., Ligon, E. W., Jr., Read, M. R., Radzow, K. H. and Meschan, I. *Amer. J. Physiol.*, 1941, *134*:132–140.

27. Quigley, J. P., Zetelman, H. J. and Ivy, A. C. *Amer. J. Physiol.*, 1934, *108*:643–651.

28. Ramsay, G. H., Watson, J. S., Gromiak, R. and Weinberg, S. A. *Radiology*, 1955, *64*:498–518.

29. Rubin, J., Nagler, R., Spiro, H. M. and Pilot, M. L. *Psychom. Med.*, 1962, *24*:170–176.

30. Rushmer, R. F. and Hendron, J. A. *J. appl. Physiol.*, 1951, *3*:622–630.

31. Smith, H. W. and Texter, E. C. *Amer. J. digest. Dis.*, 1957, N. S. *2*:318–326.

32. Templeton, R. D. and Lawson, H. *Amer. J. Physiol.*, 1931, *96*:667–676.

33. Texter, E. C. *J. Amer. med. Ass.*, 1963, *184*:640–647.

34. Thomas, J. E. *Physiol. Rev.*, 1957, *37*:453–474.

CHAPTER 49

Secretions of the Digestive Tract

By DONAL F. MAGEE

SECRETION, a component of the gastrointestinal triad (movement, secretion and absorption), involves both passive and active transport of materials in the gastrointestinal tract. The basic mechanisms of secretion have been quantitatively described in Chapter 43. This chapter will primarily be concerned with the amount, composition and activities of specific secretions and with control of the secretory process in relation to the ingesta.

The oral cavity, with its associated glandular structures, teeth and tongue, is the site of considerable alteration in the chemical and physical structure of the ingested food. Man's conscious awareness of food is dependent upon sensory stimuli carried to the central nervous system by several pathways, chiefly those for vision, olfaction and taste. Sensory impulses are also conveyed from the alimentary tract by the afferent fibers of the autonomic nervous system. It is a familiar fact that the sight, smell and taste of food (even the thought of food) can profoundly influence various parts of the digestive system. This is the first link in a complicated and highly coordinated chain of events which results in the almost complete digestion and absorption of the ingested food.

SALIVARY GLANDS

All mammals have three pairs of salivary glands. In man these are known as the parotid, the submandibular and the sublingual glands. In most animals the submaxillary glands correspond to the submandibular glands of humans. In addition to the major salivary glands there are small mucin-secreting glands throughout the mouth and pharynx.

Saliva. Man produces about one liter of saliva daily, of which about two-thirds is secreted by the submandibular glands, one-fourth by the parotids and the remainder by the sublingual and small buccal glands. Neither the glands nor their secretions (saliva) are identical. Histologically, the sublingual gland is composed of mucin-secreting cells only, the submandibular gland of both mucin-secreting and serous cells, and the parotid gland only of serous cells. Mucinous secretion is clear, viscous and slimy to the touch, similar to the secretion from the glands of the nose seen especially during a "cold." Serous secretion, however, is thin and watery, consisting simply of a solution of electrolytes in water. The parotid gland also secretes an enzyme, amylase, which splits starch and glycogen into maltose. It acts optimally at pH values close to neutrality (normal for saliva) and in the presence of inorganic anions, usually Cl^-. Chewing mixes saliva fairly thoroughly with food, permitting amylase activity to be very extensive. Amylase continues to act in the stomach until inactivated by acid-containing gastric juice, which may require several hours to penetrate the food mass.

Salivary secretion is vitally important to the ingestion of food, since without saliva we could neither swallow nor taste dry foods. However, saliva also performs an important function in the maintenance of oral hygiene. In addition to rinsing the buccal cavity continuously, saliva also seems to contain an antimicrobial substance. This substance may be the thiocyanate ion which is known to be present in the saliva. In any event, oral infections are rare after surgery even though maintenance of an aseptic field is not possible. If salivary secretion stops, the breath becomes fetid in an hour or so, and after a week or more dental caries occur.

Regulation of Secretion. Salivary secretion copiously increases when appetizing food is seen or imagined or taken into the mouth. Sour substances, as well as nausea, are potent stimulants. Chewing movements also stimulate the flow of saliva even though the substance chewed is tasteless (paraffin wax). The glands are not subject to stimulation and are therefore in a truly basal state only during sleep, at which time only the buccal and the sublingual glands are active.

The regulation of salivary gland secretion, unlike that of glands lower in the digestive tract, is entirely dependent on their innervation. Each of the major glands has both sympathetic and parasympathetic innervation. The parasympathetic fibers to the parotid and submandibular glands travel with the auriculotemporal nerve and chorda tympani, respectively. Stimulation of either of these nerves produces a copious flow of dilute juice from the corresponding gland and greatly increases its blood flow. Atropine depresses the parasympathetic secretory effect but leaves the blood flow effect unchanged. The chorda tympani's vasodilator effect on the submandibular gland, first noted by Claude Bernard in 1852,[3] is one of the best examples of neurally mediated vasodilatation. This vasodilatory effect is apparently not cholinergically mediated. It seems to result instead from the interaction of plasma with an enzyme released by the chorda tympani, producing an atropine-resistant vasodilator called bradykinin.[20]

The role of sympathetic innervation in salivary gland function is disputed.[7] Salivation is depressed not only when parasympathetic discharge is blocked with atropine, but also during sympathetic discharge such as results from fright, apprehension or epinephrine injection. Furthermore, sympathetic stimulation produces vasoconstriction, which also may inhibit secretion. Under normal circumstances, then, parasympathetic fibers would seem to be secretory and sympathetic inhibitory.

However, several experimental studies seem to contradict this interpretation. They indicate that the sympathetic and parasympathetic divisions innervate the *same* cells and that both are excitatory. In fact, these studies often show that sympathetic stimulation increases rather than inhibits salivary secretion (dog and cat submaxillary, rabbit parotid). Furthermore, stimulation of the cervical sympathetics after stimulation of the chorda tympani consistently increases secretion.

If pharmacologic blocking agents are used to block sympathetic vasoconstriction, sympathetic stimulation produces a greater but transitory secretory effect. In experimental circumstances, sympathetic stimulation evidently

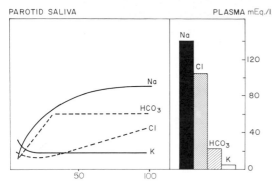

PAROTID SALIVA   PLASMA mEq./l

Fig. 1. Electrolyte composition of parotid saliva at various flow rates. *Abscissa,* Secretory rate in mg. of saliva per gram of gland per minute. *Ordinate,* Concentration in mEq. per liter. (From Bro-Rasmussen *et al., Acta physiol. scand.,* 1956, *37*:97–113.)

produces a brief stimulation of salivary secretion from the submandibular and parotid glands. It is not proved, however, that these nerves stimulate secretion in normal conscious animals.

If the parasympathetic nerve supply to the parotid or submandibular glands of anesthetized animals is cut, a profuse *"paralytic" secretion* develops after a few days and lasts for a few weeks. This so-called paralytic secretion can probably be explained by the denervation hypersensitivity phenomenon. After parasympathetic denervation, the glands become hypersensitive to circulating epinephrine. It occurs only in animals anesthetized with drugs that liberate epinephrine from the adrenal medulla, e.g., morphine. The phenomenon fails to occur after bilateral removal of the adrenal glands. Classically, this phenomenon has been described as hypersensitivity to the postganglionic mediator of the nerve that has been cut (Cannon's law). In the salivary glands, however, a paradoxical reaction is seen since sympathetic denervation and parasympathetic denervation both produce hypersensitivity to acetylcholine and epinephrine or norepinephrine.

Parasympathetic denervation of the glands destroys their ability to respond to functional requirements and, after the denervation secretion ceases, the glands atrophy. As pointed out above, unlike the gastric glands and pancreas, the salivary glands have no hormonal control.

Electrolyte Secretion.[6, 7] The main electrolytes in saliva are Na^+, K^+, HCO_3^- and Cl^-. With the exception of K^+, ion concentrations in saliva are generally lower than in plasma. The level of HCO_3^- is higher than that of Cl^-,

and the K^+ level is always at least twice as high as it is in plasma. At higher rates of secretion HCO_3^- is also much higher than in plasma (Fig. 1*A*).

At lower rates of secretion parotid and submaxillary secretions are hypotonic, the concentrations of all ions except K^+ being much lower than in plasma. As the rate of secretion increases, the osmolarity of the saliva increases to a plateau, primarily because most electrolytes are reabsorbed from the nearly isotonic fluid as it passes down the collecting ducts from the secretory cells. As secretion increases in rate, this reabsorptive mechanism becomes progressively outdistanced. The maximal reabsorptive capacity of the gland is reached at about 50 per cent of the maximal secretory rate, as seen in Figure 2*A*.[6] Beyond this point, a nearly isotonic fluid is secreted. At maximal

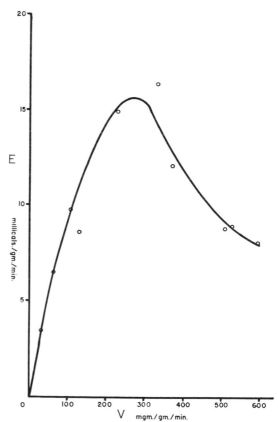

Fig. 2. Minimum work per gram of secretion per minute (E) versus rate of saliva secretion in mg. of saliva per gram of gland per minute (V). Work falls off at rates in excess of 50 per cent of the maximal secretory rate because of the production of an isotonic fluid beyond this point. (From Burgen, *J. cell. comp. physiol.,* 1955, *45*:465–477.)

secretion rates, therefore, the osmolarity will be close to that of plasma. Recent studies on infant rats indicate that the ducts can secrete as well as absorb electrolytes and water, and at all flow rates they secrete potassium. Potassium apparently has an important but undetermined role in regulating the flow rate of saliva since flow is greatly reduced in animals fed a diet deficient in potassium, although the Na+ and K+ concentrations in the juice remain normal.[33]

The composition of saliva is somewhat related to the nature of the food eaten. This is true only because electrolyte concentration varies with the volume of saliva secreted, and a copious secretion results from appetizing and acid foods but not from unappetizing and tasteless foods.

GASTRIC SECRETION

The stomach is both a storage and digestive organ. It is a digestive organ by virtue of its secretions and by virtue of its mechanical activity, which mixes food and secretions. This mixing reduces solid food to a fluid gruel or chyme prior to entry into the duodenum. Following an ordinary meal the contents of the fundus of the stomach remain solid for hours. Only in the distal, muscular, pyloric part of the stomach are the contents fluid.

The digestive secretion of the stomach contains (i) hydrochloric acid, the proteolytic enzyme pepsin and unimportant amounts of lipase; (ii) mucin, which has a protective and lubricant function; (iii) water and ions—sodium bicarbonate, chloride and small amounts of potassium; and (iv) intrinsic factor, which is necessary for the absorption of anti–pernicious anemia factor.

The makeup of the secretions varies in different parts of the stomach. The pyloric part of the stomach produces no acid and only small amounts of pepsin, and contains none of the cells identified histologically with acid and pepsin production (Fig. 3). The remainder of the stomach, apart from a collar about a centimeter wide around the esophageal opening, contains parietal (oxyntic) cells which secrete acid, and chief (peptic) cells which secrete pepsin. The cells in the cardiac gland area (the collar around the esophageal opening) are identical in appearance with those of the pyloric gland area.

On gross inspection the gastric mucosa is seen to be thrown into folds and ridges, especially in the fundus. On microscopic examination the flattened mucosa is seen to be covered with small dimples (gastric pits or *foveolae*), lined by the same columnar mucus-secreting epithelium as the intervening gastric mucosal surface (Fig. 3). Secretory granules with the same staining properties as mucin can be seen in the free borders of these epithelial cells. The cells at the bottoms of the gastric pits are often seen in mitosis. These are the germinative centers from which, by migrating up to the sur-

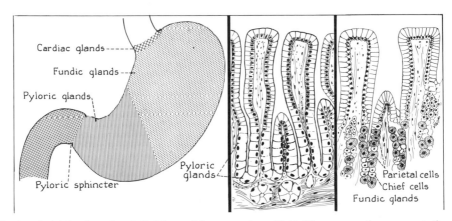

Fig. 3. *Left,* The functional divisions of the stomach.   *Right,* Diagrammatic representation of the fundic, acid-secreting part of the stomach. Note the concentration of stippled parietal cells in the neck region of the glands. The stippling does not represent secretory granules; only the chief cells contain these.   *Center,* Diagrammatic representation of the pyloric area (antrum) of the stomach showing pyloric glands. Here there are no parietal or chief cells. This figure is representative also of the non-acid-secreting cardiac area.

face, damaged or dead surface epithelial cells are replaced. Into the bottom of each gastric pit four or five narrow straight gastric glands open. In the fundic region these glands secrete acid and pepsin. Except for a small area at the neck of the gland the gastric glands are lined by chief cells. Lying close to the gland lumen but usually separated from it by the chief cells are the parietal cells which communicate with the lumen by way of canaliculi. At the neck of the gland the parietal cells are especially numerous, often in direct contact with the gland lumen.

In the pyloric and cardiac gland areas the gastric glands are lined by cells that appear to be mucin-secreting and contain granules that give some staining reactions for mucin. The glands in these areas are characterized by the absence of parietal or chief cells.

COMPONENTS OF GASTRIC SECRETION

Acid. The stomach is unique in that it secretes large volumes of a strong acid. This acid often damages the mucosa of the duodenum, producing duodenal ulcer. Interest is greater, therefore, in gastric acid secretion than in other phases of gastrointestinal physiology.

When the mechanics of gastric secretion are considered, the components of gastric juice other than acid are usually lumped together as nonparietal secretion. This gastric component consists of pepsin, mucin and the sodium salts of chloride (125 mEq. per liter) and bicarbonate (45 mEq. per liter). It is alkaline in reaction and isotonic with blood, and comes from the whole stomach including the pyloric and cardiac areas. The nonparietal element of the actively secreting human stomach amounts to approximately 2.5 ml. per minute, most of which comes from the fundic, acid-secreting part of the stomach. The pyloric and cardiac areas are the largest blocks of nonparietal secreting mucosa in the stomach, but, strangely, their secretion is small (2 to 3 ml. per hour from the pylorus) and is not influenced by food or drugs which increase gastric secretion. Nonparietal secretion in these areas can be increased, but only slightly, by direct mechanical or chemical irritation.

The acidity of the total gastric juice varies; the higher the secretory rate the greater the acidity and, of course, the lower the pH. The explanation for this might be that with increasing stimulation the parietal cells produce

a secretion of increasingly high H+ concentration or an increased volume of secretion with a fixed acid concentration: thus, when the rate of acid secretion is low, its dilution by nonparietal secretion is great and the pH is consequently high. That the latter explanation is true has been indicated by Hollander[23] and by Gray *et al.*[14] Hollander plotted concentration of acid against nonacid (neutral) chloride, which is nonparietal, and found that as the acid concentration rose neutral chloride fell. At very high rates of secretion it almost disappeared. On extrapolation the straight line obtained cut the abscissa at an acidity of 167 mEq. per liter (Figs. 4, 5). This is the theoretical value for

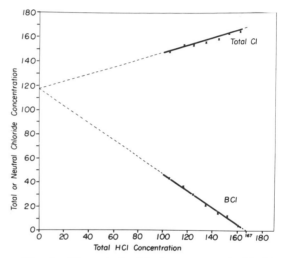

Fig. 4. The relationship between total chloride and acid concentrations in gastric juice in millimols. As the acid concentration rises the total chloride also rises slightly but the nonacid component (BCl) falls, almost to disappear at 160 millimols. (From Hollander, *J. Biol. Chem.,* 1932, *97*:585–604, Figs. 3 and 7.)

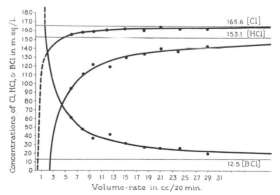

Fig. 5. The relationship between gastric secretory rate, acidity, total chloride and nonacid chloride (BCl). The fine horizontal lines are the numerical limits toward which the variables tend. (From Gray, Bucher and Harmon, *Amer. J. Physiol.,* 1941, *132*:504–516.)

pure acid undiluted by nonparietal secretion. The straight line relationship indicates that the concentration of HCl elaborated by the parietal cell is constant and that only the volume varies. The concentration of acid Cl⁻ must be less than 167 mEq. per liter, since the K concentration of gastric juice is constant at about 7 mEq. per liter, whatever the acidity. Hollander's data lead us to conclude that the parietal cell of the dog secretes acid chloride with a concentration of 160 mEq. per liter and 7 mEq. per liter of neutral chloride associated with the K which must be present in the parietal as well as the nonparietal secretion. Consequently, the dog's parietal cell produces a juice which is isotonic with the animal's blood plasma.

Production of hydrochloric acid. From the physiologist's point of view, the ability of parietal cells to elaborate a secretion whose pH is less than 2 is one of the more intriguing, still unsolved problems in ion transport. From the clinical point of view, as noted above, gastric acid production is also important. Excessive production of acid is involved in ulcer formation, whereas deficient production of acid may give rise to malabsorption phenomena.

Ion transport across the stomach mucosa involves two components, (i) a basal, continuous component and (ii) a stimulated component, which occurs in the presence of histamine, cholinergic agents or gastrin or during anxiety states and the cephalic phase of secretion.

The basal transport is a secretion of Cl⁻ into the lumen of the stomach. Using a modification of Ussing's frog skin technique (see Chap. 43), Hogben demonstrated that this Cl⁻ transport is active.

When a piece of isolated bullfrog gastric mucosa is mounted between two chambers containing identical solutions, an electric potential develops with the mucosal side about 35 mV. negative to the serosal side. When this mucosa is held in the short circuit condition, the current that is delivered by the mucosa can be accounted for by the transport of Cl⁻. In addition, Hogben noted a large component of exchange of Cl⁻ across the mucosa without net transport, a phenomenon termed exchange diffusion. Heinz and Durbin[19a] observed that both the one-way fluxes of isotopic Cl⁻ (flux from serosal to mucosal side of the mucosa, and that in the opposite direction) fell when the Cl⁻ concentration was lowered on the mucosal side only. Thus, the picture that emerges from these experiments is that Cl⁻ is actively transported into the lumen of the stomach. This transport is accomplished by a carrier mechanism which not only transports Cl⁻ from serosal to mucosal sides of the stomach but also transports it in the opposite direction. Indeed, most of the action of this carrier is exchange and only a small portion of its activity produces *net Cl⁻ transport.* Further, almost all of the transport of Cl⁻ in either direction is carrier-mediated. This Cl⁻ pump generates the voltage normally found across the gastric mucosa.

After being stimulated with histamine, the stomach secretes acid into the lumen. Hydrogen ion is secreted and active Cl⁻ transport is increased by an equivalent amount. Thus, the secretion of acid is not an electrogenic process. Basal Cl⁻ transport can be inhibited without affecting acid secretion and acid secretion can be inhibited without affecting basal Cl⁻ transport.[12a] Acid secretion might take place by the independent transport of H⁺ and additional Cl⁻ or the two might be transported as a unit. In either case, the ions must be considered independently in an analysis of the transport, for they exist independently on both sides of the gastric mucosa. Although the transmucosal potential is in the direction to favor the entry of cations, its magnitude is by no means sufficient to account for H⁺ entry passively. Blood bathes the nutrient side of the mucosa and the H⁺ concentration there is 4×10^{-8} mEq. per liter (a pH of 7.4). The concentration of H⁺ in the secretate during acid secretion is about 150 mEq. per liter. Thus the ratio of concentration of H⁺ across the mucosa is almost 4 million to one. For there to be net passive secretion of H⁺, the potential across the mucosa would have to be at least 400 mV., a value which is six to ten times that ever observed. Thus, H⁺ is also pumped across the gastric mucosa.

The H⁺ that is to be pumped is formed *de novo* within the cells of the gastric mucosa. It could be formed by the dissociation of water, in which case oxygen utilization could be coupled to H⁺ secretion only as an energy source. As many as 14 mols of H⁺ might be transported per mol of oxygen utilized in this situation. Alternatively, some of the H⁺ taken from organic substrates during carbohydrate metabolism might be trapped and used by the transport system. Thus, some of the energy made available by substrate oxidation would not be used to generate high energy phosphate bonds but would be coupled directly into driving the H⁺ transport system. The reaction would proceed as illustrated below and no more than 4 mols of H⁺ could be produced per mol of oxygen utilized.

$$4H + O_2 + 2H_2O \rightarrow 4OH^- + 4H^+$$

on respiratory enzyme   in cell   on transport system

This mechanism has been called a "redox" pump.[10] In experiments in which the change in H^+ transport per unit change in O_2 utilization has been measured, this ratio has been found to be less than 4 when the stomach is stimulated with histamine or cholinergic drugs.[37a] However, inhibition of H^+ secretion, either by addition of sodium thiocyanate or by passing a strong electric current through the mucosa, indicates values of the ratio of H^+ transport to O_2 utilization as high as 13.[13a] Hence a "redox" pump cannot account for H^+ transport under all conditions.

Regardless of the detailed mechanism of H^+ transport, the secretion of each mol of H^+ leaves a mol of OH^- within the gastric cell. Carbon dioxide, derived both from the metabolism of the cell and from the perfusing blood, is used to neutralize this OH^-. The reaction is:

$$OH^- + CO_2 \rightleftharpoons HCO_3^-$$

The HCO_3^- so formed is then extruded into blood so that, for every mol of H^+ secreted into the stomach, one mol of HCO_3^- is put into gastric venous blood. After an appetizing meal, sufficient H^+ may be secreted into the stomach to produce a measurable elevation in systemic plasma HCO_3^- concentration. This elevation has been called the *alkaline tide*. The elevation of plasma HCO_3^- concentration may be great enough to cause a transient excretion of HCO_3^- by the kidneys. The reaction depicted above is a consequence rather than a cause of H^+ secretion, and H^+ secretion can continue even if this reaction does not take place. However, if this OH^- were not neutralized, its intracellular accumulation would damage the cell. The high concentrations of carbonic anhydrase found in gastric mucosa are apparently there to catalyze this hydroxylation of CO_2.

Pepsin. Less is known about pepsin than about HCl secretion, probably because it is more complicated. Pepsin is a protein with a molecular weight of 34,500. Like other proteolytic enzymes, it is stored in its cell of origin (chief cell) as an inactive precursor or zymogen (pepsinogen). Activation of pepsin, which occurs only in an acid medium (activation is optimal at pH 2), is accomplished by the removal of peptides from the pepsinogen molecule; i.e., gastric acid activates pepsinogen. The molecular weight of pepsinogen (42,000) is therefore greater than that of pepsin. One of these peptide fragments is a pepsin inhibitor at pH values above 3.5. Pepsin acts well only

on denatured proteins, and gastric acid effects denaturation. Acid is necessary also because the optimal pH for pepsin digestive activity is between 1.5 and 2. Thus HCl facilitates protein digestion in three ways.

Pepsin attacks many proteins but produces only slight hydrolysis since it acts only at a few discrete points on the molecule (see Fig. 9). The protein breakdown thus is unlikely to proceed beyond the polypeptide stage. The extent of peptic digestion of protein in the stomach is an index of the mixing of gastric juice with food. Salivary amylase acts only above pH 4.5 and pepsin only at a much lower pH. In man, two hours after a solid meal amylase is still active and peptic activity only slight. This means that the mass of food in the fundus of the stomach is only slowly penetrated by gastric juice or, for that matter, by fluid ingested after eating. The only part of the stomach in which thorough mixing takes place is the muscular pyloric antrum.

Mucin. That of gastric origin is very like that of nasal origin during a "cold." It is slimy and may be perfectly clear where secretion is profuse, but generally it contains opaque lumps of surface epithelial cells and dried-up mucin.

REGULATION OF GASTRIC SECRETION[15, 16, 26]

Cephalic Phase (Fig. 6). In most dogs and some humans protected from the sight or smell of food the juice secreted by the empty stomach is neutral or slightly alkaline. In experimental animals the sight or smell of appetizing food elicits secretion of acid, pepsin and mucin. The expectation of food produces variable responses in man, but appetizing food placed in the mouth even if unswallowed elicits secretion.

These responses are abolished by bilateral section of the vagus nerves. Stimulation of the peripheral ends of the cut vagi will elicit secretion of acid, pepsin and mucin after a curiously long latent period (six to ten minutes). The juice secreted during the other phases of gastric secretion, described below, is low in pepsin; however, after eating, pepsin secretion is high for several hours. This gives rise to the belief that the cephalic (vagal) phase of secretion continues long after the meal has been swallowed.

This phase of secretion, so completely dependent on the integrity of the vagi, has assumed great importance since bilateral vagal

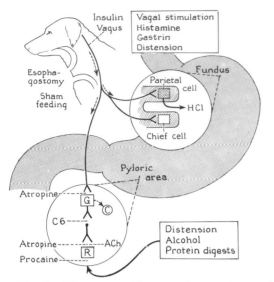

Fig. 6. Diagram to illustrate the regulation of gastric acid secretion. The vagus nerve is represented as innervating the parietal and chief cells in the fundic mucosa and a hypothetical gastrin cell (G). Both insulin and sham feeding via the esophagostomy will cause vagal stimulation of these three cells. The factors in the upper box all act directly on the cells of the fundic mucosa. Histamine and gastrin are disputed pepsin stimulants. The factors in the lower box act on a procaine-sensitive structure (R) standing for a hypothetical receptor. Pharmacologic evidence indicates the existence of a cholinergic reflex with at least one synapse between (R) and the gastrin cell (G). Liberated gastrin enters the general circulation through capillaries (C). (C6 is hexamethonium, a ganglionic blocking agent.)

section has become a popular treatment for duodenal ulcer. Low blood glucose levels (less than 50 mg. per 100 ml.) are known to stimulate directly or indirectly the vagal nucleus in the medulla. If the vagi have been completely sectioned, however, gastric secretion will not be stimulated by low blood glucose.

Gastric Phase. When food is introduced into the stomach through a fistula or if it is swallowed, gastric secretion begins even though the vagi have been cut. That this *gastric phase* of secretion depends on the pyloric (non–acid-secreting) part of the stomach can easily be proved. If the pyloric part of the stomach is separated from the main stomach and transplanted as a pouch elsewhere (Fig. 6), the stomach secretes acid when the pouch is distended or when alcohol or protein breakdown products are introduced into it. A transplanted pyloric pouch when distended causes a similarly transplanted and therefore denervated pouch of fundic mucosa to secrete. The mediation of this response must be hormonal. The name *gastrin* has been given to this hormone. This hormonally produced juice, unlike cephalic phase juice, is high in acid and low in pepsin and mucin. It is never pepsin-free and, in fact, the pepsin rises *pari passu* with the acidity but it is always low.

Four things prevent stimulation of gastric acid secretion by the pyloric gastrin mechanism: (i) local anesthetization of the mucosa (procaine), (ii) administration of ganglionic blocking agents, (iii) atropine administration, and (iv) a low intrapyloric *p*H.

These facts have been synthesized into the following system: (i) Release of gastrin from a pyloric cell, not yet identified, is effected by stimulation of a receptor in the pyloric mucosa sensitive to stretch and chemical substances and blocked by procaine. (ii) Between this receptor and the gastrin cell must exist a synapse. (iii) Because atropine blocks gastrin release, the presynaptic fiber must be cholinergic. That mediation is cholinergic is consistent with the fact that acetylcholine itself when introduced into the pyloric pouch causes acid secretion from the main stomach. This is not blocked by local anesthetics.

The inhibition of the pyloric "gastrin" mechanism produced by a low *p*H in the pyloric part of the stomach is an inhibitory or negative feedback system which regulates the production of acid by the body of the stomach and prevents excessive acidity in the pylorus. At acidity values in the pyloric pouch higher than *p*H 2, stimulation of gastrin release from it by any means is virtually impossible. This feedback inhibitory mechanism comes into play at *p*H 3, becoming increasingly effective as the *p*H falls. The probable mechanism for this is direct inhibition of gastrin production.[34] This is disputed by some who postulate an inhibitory hormone which acts to antagonize the action of stimuli on the parietal cell. The evidence for an inhibitory hormone is not as satisfactory as that for inhibition of gastrin release.

Relationship between the vagus nerves and gastrin. It would be wrong to suppose that the gastrin mechanism and the vagal mechanisms regulating gastric secretion are quite unrelated. They can function independently as outlined above, but they are interrelated. For example, gastrin is released more easily from a pyloric pouch if the vagal innervation is intact than if the pouch is denervated. Furthermore, if an animal with an innervated pyloric pouch and a denervated fundic pouch is sham fed, secretion from the fundic pouch is stimulated to a small extent. This does not happen if the pyloric pouch is denervated. Clearly then, impulses passing down the vagi can release gastrin from the pyloric part of the stomach. (A sham fed animal is one in which food does not enter the stomach but drops to the floor through the divided cervical esophagus [Fig. 6].)

In addition to this interaction, the innervated fundic part of the stomach is much more sensitive to gastrin and indeed to any stimulation of acid secretion than is a denervated part. Afferent as well as efferent fibers may be involved in this sensitization, since it has recently been found that direct mechanical stimulation of innervated fundic mucosa will result in acid and pepsin production and that in an animal with one vagus cut stimulation of the central end of the cut vagus will increase acid and pepsin secretion. Also there is evidence for the existence of mechanoreceptors in the mucosa of the stomach.

Gastrin or histamine. The final proof of a hormone's existence is its isolation from the tissue from which the suspected hormone is believed to be secreted and from no other tissue. A substance stimulating acid secretion has been isolated from the pyloric part of the stomach but not from the fundus or intestine below the duodenum. Tissue extracts often contain histamine, which is a potent stimulant of gastric acid secretion; whether gastrin is or is not histaminic has long been debated. In fact, histamine gastric juice is identical with that secreted during the gastric phase of secretion, i.e., it is low in pepsin. It is unlikely, however, that histamine is gastrin because (i) a histamine-free gastrin is effective, (ii) new purified gastrin is more potent than histamine, weight for weight, and (iii) histamine in doses required to stimulate gastric secretion affects blood pressure whereas gastrin does not.

Good evidence exists for the view that histamine is nevertheless the final common mediator between any stimulus, gastrin or vagal impulses, and the parietal cell. Histamine is always found in gastric juice, and its amount varies directly with the output of acid.[9] The gastric mucosa produces a great amount of histamine but has no enzymes for its destruction.

Intestinal Phase. The intestinal phase of gastric secretion starts when gastric chyme enters the duodenum or if the duodenum is distended. This phase involves a hormonal link, since appropriate stimulation of the duodenum causes a denervated fundic pouch to secrete. Insofar as it has been studied, the mechanism for release of the hormone from the duodenum and the hormone itself seem to closely resemble the gastrin mechanism. The introduction of foodstuffs into the duodenum does not cause secretion of gastric acid in atropinized animals nor if the duodenal mucosa is anesthetized. Some investigators have isolated an intestinal gastrin low in potency compared with that from the pyloric part of the stomach.

Intestinal Inhibition of the Stomach.[35] In the duodenum, as in the stomach, a feedback mechanism exists which effects a decrease in gastric motility and secretion however stimulated. This inhibitory mechanism is elicited by excessive acidity, distension and hypertonic solutions of various sorts (electrolytes, sugar, peptone, etc.). The duodenum therefore acts as a regulator of gastric emptying as well as of secretion. Many patients who have undergone surgical gastroenterostomy, in which this feedback mechanism is by-passed, suffer symptoms when food is discharged *en masse* into the small intestine (dumping syndrome). This inhibitory mechanism is continuously or "tonically" active, since removal of the duodenum or its translocation to a spot lower down the intestine results in an increase in gastric acid production.

Emulsified fat certainly, and hypertonic solutions, sugars and peptones probably, inhibit the stomach by causing release of an inhibitory hormone (*enterogastrone*) from the duodenal mucosa. Extracts of duodenum with enterogastrone activity have been prepared which inhibit both gastric motility and secretion of acid and pepsin. They are not as effective as fat in the duodenum.

The mechanism by which the inhibitory action of acid is produced is uncertain. Acid in the duodenum, which is a more effective inhibitor of the innervated than the denervated stomach, produces no effect if the duodenal mucosa is anesthetized.

A feedback mechanism to prevent the duodenum from becoming too acid would seem physiologically useful, since the optimal *p*H for pancreatic digestion is close to neutrality and since high acid concentrations produce ulceration of the duodenum. However, secretion of acid can be effectively inhibited only at very low duodenal pH levels (less than 2.5), which would be a coarse feedback system.

Ulcer. Since the stomach secretes a strong acid and a proteolytic enzyme, why does not the stomach digest itself? The answer is that it sometimes does, but it is still remarkable that it does not do so more often. The mucosa of the stomach has a high intrinsic resistance to gastric digestion. Gastric juice erodes skin, muscle and intestinal mucosa, but gastric mucosa only under exceptional circumstances. The stomach mucosa secretes a protective coat of mucin which increases in viscosity as the pH falls. It mixes poorly with gastric contents, tending to coat the bolus as well as the mucosa. Of itself, mucin does not inhibit pepsin and it is a very poor buffer, but it holds bicarbonate, which, of course, does act as a buffer. Mucin, therefore, in effect interposes a viscous, fairly concentrated bicarbonate solution between the gastric contents and the gastric mucosa.[19]

The duodenum also produces mucin and bicarbonate, but its mucosa is much more susceptible to gastric digestion than is that of the stomach; correspondingly, duodenal ulcer is much more common than gastric ulcer. The average duodenal ulcer patient produces much more acid than do normal people, both from the empty stomach and after stimulation with histamine. The gastric ulcer patient, on the other hand, on the average produces less acid than normal. The duodenal ulcer patient generally has more parietal cells than normal and the gastric ulcer patient less than normal. The conclusion, drawn from these observations, is that the defect in the gastric ulcer lies in the gastric mucosal defenses and that in the duodenal ulcer gastric hypersecretion is the fault. The cause of hypersecretion is disputed. Some say vagal hyperactivity is the cause. Certainly vagal section is a useful treatment, but this is not proof that overactivity of the vagus is the cause. Other evidence implicates the anterior pituitary and adrenal cortex. Daily administration of ACTH or corticoids increases basal and stimulated acid secretion after a week or so and may produce ulceration. Some say that the parietal cell count increases.[31] Patients with atrophy of the adrenal cortexes (Addison's disease) generally have achlorhydria. This puzzle remains.

It is anticlimactic to conclude, after several decades of research, that gastric secretion is essential only for the production of ulcers and for the absorption of vitamin B_{12} (the anti–pernicious anemia factor). If the stomach is removed the most obvious defects result from loss of its storage capacity. Only small meals can be eaten and intestinal distension and rapid transit cause symptoms and impaired digestion. Vitamin B_{12} must be given parenterally, since without intrinsic factor produced by the fundus of the stomach it cannot be absorbed.

PANCREATIC SECRETION

The pancreas is made up of endocrine and exocrine parts. The exocrine pancreas, which has a digestive function, consists of the acini and collecting ducts. The acinar cells, which in fact form the acini, contain zymogen granules. Within the acini there are smaller centroacinar cells which are a continuation of the cells of the small ducts which lead from them (Fig. 7). The acinar cells manufacture enzymes and the centroacinar cells produce sodium bicarbonate and water.

The evidence for this is indirect, but the presence of granules in the acinar cells, their disappearance following the administration of drugs which stimulate enzyme secretion and the determination that isolated granules possess the expected enzyme activities indicate that the cells with granules do produce enzymes. After ligation of the pancreatic duct the acinar cells degenerate earlier than the ductules and centroacinar cells, and *pari passu* the ability to secrete enzymes disappears before that to secrete bicarbonate and water. It is probable therefore that the duct and centroacinar cells secrete the water and bicarbonate.

COMPONENTS

Electrolytes. The pancreatic juice of all animals studied contains sodium chloride and bicarbonate, as well as a small, constant concentration of potassium (9 mEq. per liter) and the enzyme proteins in solution. The protein content of the juice is variable but often reaches 3 per cent. The juice is normally of low viscosity and crystal clear. The inorganic solids also are variable in amount. The sum of the concentrations of chloride and bicarbonate salts is constant. At low rates of secretion $[Cl^-]$ is greater than $[HCO_3^-]$, but as the secretory rate increases the bicarbonate concentration rises to a plateau of 120 to 130 mEq. per liter

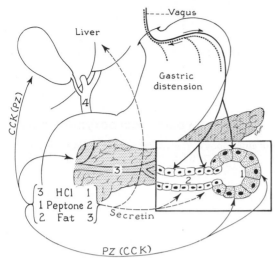

Fig. 7. Diagram illustrating the release and actions of the pancreatic hormones. HCl, peptone and fat, lower left, act on the intestinal mucosa. The numbers on the left represent the potency order in releasing pancreozymin and to the right in releasing secretin. The pancreozymin lines, PZ, are also labeled CCK (cholecystokinin) since these might be one hormone. PZ acts on the pancreatic acinar cells (1). CCK acts to contract the gallbladder and relax the sphincter of Oddi, which is situated at the lower end of the bile duct (4) just before it joins the main pancreatic duct (3). In man secretin likely acts on the ductule (2) cells. It also acts on the liver to increase bile flow.

Both enzyme production and water production are increased by gastric distension. The afferents (interrupted) and efferents (continuous) which mediate this reflex are indicated.

maltotriose units. The optimum pH for amylase activity is 6.9, and below 4.5 activity ceases. In the presence of inorganic anions, amylase splits 1–4 glycosidic linkages in the middle of the long side chains of starch and glycogen. As the fragments become shorter, amylase acts less readily. At points of branching the glycosidic linkage is 1–6; amylase does not split these. Of all the pancreatic enzymes, amylase is the most robust. Unlike lipase and the proteases themselves, it resists proteolytic destruction. This resistance depends on the fact that amylase contains calcium.

Lipase.[1, 21] This enzyme splits most natural fats and several synthetic esters. Fats containing long-chain saturated fatty acids are especially susceptible to lipase. Lipase is secreted in active form but its activity is enhanced by amino acids, calcium ions and bile salts. Heightening of activity by bile salts is due in part to their detergent action. Since lipase can act only at the oil-water interface, the finer the emulsion the greater the activity. Secondly, bile salts reduce the pH optimum for lipase from 8.1 to 6. The duodenal pH is never as high as 8.1, but is generally in the neighborhood of 6 after eating.

Lipase probably hydrolyzes completely no more than about 5 per cent of the fat which enters the duodenum. By its action it produces a mixture of tri-, mono- and diglycerides and free fatty acids, which in the presence of bile

and the [Cl⁻] falls correspondingly. The sodium and potassium concentrations remain unchanged (Fig. 8). At all rates of secretion the juice is isotonic with plasma. It was seen in the discussion of gastric secretion that highly acid gastric contents enter the duodenum; yet even after meals the duodenal pH rarely falls below 5. Only the pancreas produces enough alkaline juice to bring about such a prompt increase in pH.

Ninety-five per cent of the protein in the juices investigated is enzyme protein. Pancreatic enzymes are capable of breaking down all the major food stuffs to simple constituents. Carbohydrates, fats and proteins are digested by amylase, lipase and a variety of proteases respectively.

Amylase. Pancreatic amylase and parotid amylase are identical. Amylase splits starch and glycogen to their constituent maltose or

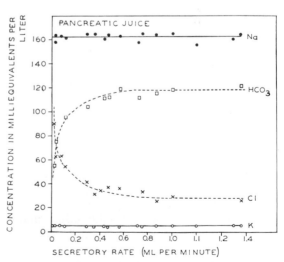

Fig. 8. The relationship between the electrolyte concentrations in pancreatic juice and the secretory rate. (From Bro-Rasmussen *et al., Acta physiol. scand.*, 1956, *37*:97–113.)

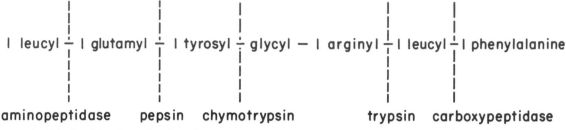

Fig. 9. The sites of action of various proteolytic enzymes on a hypothetical peptide. (From Magee, *Gastro-intestinal physiology,* Springfield, Ill., Charles C Thomas, 1962.)

salts form stable micellar aggregates.[21] These are then absorbed. It is known that fatty acids in the first and third positions are easily removed from the triglyceride but the middle acid in the second position is removed only with difficulty.

Lipase can form fats as well as split them. If triolein and palmitic acid are fed, mixed tri- and diglycerides containing both oleic and palmitic acids can be recovered from the duodenum. Complete synthesis does not occur since free glycerol is rapidly absorbed. Conditions in the gut favor hydrolysis since the products of hydrolysis are absorbed. Pancreatic lipase plays no part in the reassembly of hydrolyzed fat in the mucosa prior to entry into the lymphatics. Only triglyceride fat is found in the intestinal lymphatics.

Proteases. Pancreatic proteases, like pepsin, are secreted as inactive zymogens. Active protease within the gland would destroy it; indeed, this occasionally happens in the disease called acute pancreatitis. Once the pancreatic juice enters the intestine a proteolytic enzyme secreted by the intestinal mucosa, *enterokinase,* activates one of the zymogens, *trypsinogen,* by splitting a peptide containing five amino acids from it. The major fragment, now called *trypsin,* activates the other proteases by a similar process and even activates more trypsinogen. The activation of trypsinogen seems to be the sole function of enterokinase. If trypsin is present in pancreatic juice, it can be assumed that all of the proteases are no longer present as zymogens but as active enzymes.

Apart from trypsinogen, the other major zymogens are *chymotrypsinogen* and *procarboxypeptidase.* Trypsin splits a fragment from each of these with resultant activation. In respect to site of action, the proteases are extraordinarily precise; trypsin, chymotrypsin and carboxypeptidase act at entirely different points on the peptide chain (Fig. 9). Pancreatic proteases do not reduce proteins entirely to their constituent amino acids. Some amino acids are formed but peptides are the main product and these require intestinal peptidases for complete digestion.

In addition to the major enzymes already discussed, the pancreas produces two enzymes which act on nucleoproteins (ribonuclease and deoxyribonuclease) and a cholesterol esterase. The physiologic role of cholesterol esterase is controversial, but it probably splits rather than forms cholesterol esters prior to absorption.

Trypsin Inhibitor. Pancreatic juice also contains a polypeptide which is a potent trypsin inhibitor. This may be looked upon as a protective device since the conversion of trypsinogen to trypsin is crucial to the production of active proteases. Even small amounts of active trypsin in the juice within the ducts could have disasterous consequences to the gland. Unless massive activation of trypsinogen takes place pancreatic trypsin inhibitor by combining with trypsin completely inactivates it both as a protease and enzyme activator.

REGULATION OF PANCREATIC SECRETION (see Fig. 7)

When the duodenum is empty of gastric contents pancreatic secretion is very slow, amounting to only 1 to 2 ml. per hour. However, when gastric acid or chyme enters the duodenum 3 to 4 ml. per minute of juice rich in enzymes may be secreted. This stimulation is mainly hormonal. Consistent with the origin of pancreatic secretion from two cell types, one producing enzymes and the other producing water and bicarbonate, there are two hormones —pancreozymin, which stimulates enzyme secretion, and secretin, which stimulates water and bicarbonate secretion. These two hormones are released from and are found most abundantly in the duodenal mucosa. They are also released in decreasing amounts along the aboral reaches of the small intestine. The lower half of the small intestine secretes none.

That these are hormones has been adequately proved with transplanted loops of intestine and transplanted pancreatic tissue.[29] The intravenous injection of gastric chyme will not stimulate pancreatic secretion; it must act on the intestinal mucosa. Finally, a highly purified secretin and a less pure pancreozymin have been isolated from the duodenum.

Pancreozymin.[15] Low duodenal pH is a rather weak stimulant of pancreatic enzyme secretion (pancreozymin release); stronger stimulants include peptones, amino acids, fats, fatty acids and soaps. When pancreozymin is administered intravenously the secretion of all enzymes increases, but secretin-free pancreozymin does not increase the volume of juice secreted. Pancreozymin has not yet been separated from cholecystokinin, the gallbladder-contracting hormone; it remains possible that pancreozymin and cholecystokinin are identical.

Secretin.[27] "Secretin" was the name originally applied to an extract of intestinal mucosa which had many or all of the effects described above and below in this section. With further refinement of extraction and assay processes, the name "secretin" was applied to the hormone of the secretin group having the pedestrian job of stimulating the flow of water and bicarbonate. Secretin, a polypeptide (molecular weight 5,000), probably stimulates the production of bicarbonate, the water following passively. Pure secretin increases only the secretion of water and bicarbonate. (It also stimulates bile secretion; see below.) It therefore increases the volume of pancreatic juice but not the output of enzymes. Pancreatic juice is never enzyme-free, but in ideal experiments with animals secretin greatly reduces the enzyme concentration without affecting the total enzyme output. Secretin release is most effectively stimulated by low intraluminal pH, peptones and hypotonic solutions acting on the duodenal mucosa. Fatty acids and soaps are less effective in releasing secretin. Therefore since acid is not the only stimulant of secretin release adequate volumes of pancreatic juice are secreted even in persons with achlorhydria.

The means by which acid and the other stimulating agents act on duodenal mucosa is not clear. There is evidence that if local anesthetics are applied to the duodenal mucosa, the stimulation of juice volume by intraduodenal acid and other substances is no longer seen, and after cholinergic (atropine) blocking agents an increase in enzyme output can no longer be elicited from the duodenum.

Innervation of the Pancreas.[15, 29] The innervation of the pancreas plays a part in the regulation of its secretion, but it is a relatively minor one. There is a regulatory reflex between stomach and pancreas with an afferent limb in the vagus from the stomach and a vagal efferent limb to the pancreas.[39] Distension of the stomach increases the volume and enzyme concentration of the pancreatic juice in the absence of gastric contents in the duodenum.* Since continued secretion is stimulated by digestion products, this reflex probably ensures the presence of pancreatic juice in the duodenum in anticipation of the arrival of chyme from the stomach.

Stimulation of the vagi or administration of cholinergic drugs increases the enzyme concentration in pancreatic juice but not necessarily its volume. In some species (pig, cat, sheep), but not in others (dog), vagal stimulation and cholinergic drugs increase the volume of juice. It seems, however, that whether or not vagal stimulation increases volume, the pancreas in the vagotomized animal is much less sensitive to intravenous secretin. In dogs on normal diets, the daily volume of juice recovered through chronic pancreatic fistula is reduced by half after bilateral division of the vagal nerves.[18]

In dogs the sympathetic innervation of the pancreas is inhibitory since bilateral splanchnic nerve section increases the daily volume of juice from chronic pancreatic fistulas by 40 per cent.[18]

A cephalic phase of pancreatic secretion dependent on vagal innervation has been described.[11] It is said to begin within a minute of the start of sham feeding in animals in which gastric acid is diverted from the duodenum to avoid pancreatic secretion caused by the entry

---

*It is now clear that there is also a hormonally mediated gastric phase of pancreatic secretion. Meat extract placed in a pyloric pouch will increase the enzyme output by the pancreas, and every gastrin preparation tested has pancreozymin activity.

of acid into the duodenum as a result of the cephalic phase of gastric secretion.

The vagal activity may release secretin and pancreozymin, but the evidence is at present equivocal.

DIGESTIVE EFFECTS OF PANCREATECTOMY

In the absence of the exocrine secretions of the pancreas the most obvious defect is impaired fat absorption, resulting in bulky, soft, foul smelling feces containing substantial amounts of fat. This impaired absorption is due both to the loss of lipase and to the absence of the bicarbonate of the pancreatic juice from the intestine. However, even without pancreatic lipase, 70 per cent of the dietary fat is absorbed as opposed to the 95 per cent normally absorbed.

That protein digestion and absorption are impaired is often overlooked because the steatorrhea resulting from pancreatectomy is such an obvious and unpleasant symptom. After pancreatectomy, ligation of the pancreatic duct or degeneration of the acinar tissue of the pancreas, animals invariably lose weight and in 5 to 15 weeks develop fatty infiltration of the liver. This results from deficiency in absorbed methionine and choline, a consequence of the absence of pancreatic proteases and lipase in the duodenum. Normal levels of liver fat can be restored by feeding methionine, choline, pancreatic juice or crystalline trypsin.[8]

BILE AND THE GALLBLADDER

Bile Salts. Bile is both a digestive juice and an excretory medium. As noted earlier, bile salts facilitate the digestion and the absorption of fat; but even the bile salts themselves are an excretory product. They are the principal end product and excretory form of cholesterol and have almost identical ring structures (Fig. 10). Bile salts are made up of a number of bile acids which vary in importance from species to species. In man, cholic, chenodeoxycholic and deoxycholic acids are most important; in dogs, only cholic and deoxycholic acids are found. The bile acids exist in bile as the sodium salts of either glycine or taurine conjugates. The nature of the conjugate varies with the animal species. In man, taurine and glycine conjugates are present in almost equal amounts; in dogs, only taurine conjugates are found.

Cholic and chenodeoxycholic acids are both primary bile acids, synthesized *de novo* by the liver; deoxycholic, a secondary acid, is simply cholic acid which has undergone bacterial alteration in the intestine. The salts of both primary and secondary bile acids are reabsorbed into the portal blood and re-excreted by the liver. This excretion–reabsorption cycle is called the enterohepatic circulation and because of it only a fraction of the bile salts (one-tenth to one-fifth) are newly synthesized. The rest is bile salt that has been through the enterohepatic circulation up to ten times. Normally

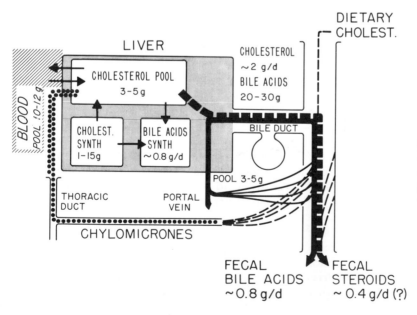

Fig. 10. Summary of cholesterol turnover in man (g/d means grams per day). (From Borgström, CIBA Foundation Symposium, *Biosynthesis of terpenes and sterols.* Boston, Little, Brown & Co., 1959.)

the effect of bile acid synthesis is to keep the pool size constant by adding an amount equal to that lost. In man, 5 to 10 per cent is lost with each circuit because of bacterial action which goes farther than that which produces deoxycholic acid. These products of extensive bacterial action are not absorbed and appear in the feces (Fig. 10). The size of the bile acid pool in man is estimated as 3 to 5 grams and the daily production of bile as 0.8 gram. This corresponds to a loss of 0.6 gram of cholesterol per day plus other steroids. If for any reason bile salt is not reabsorbed from the intestine (e.g., if it is lost through an external bile fistula), the level of the blood bile acid declines, the *de novo* production of primary bile acids by the liver increases, the plasma cholesterol (the source of bile acids) falls, and the turnover of cholesterol increases. If the level of bile acids in the blood rises, as happens when the bile duct is blocked or occluded, the synthesis of primary bile acids falls, because the blood level rises, the turnover of cholesterol falls and the plasma cholesterol rises. Some sort of control system is operating.

All bile acids are formed in the liver, primarily from cholesterol. If cholesterol labeled in the ring system is injected, over 90 per cent of it is eventually recovered from bile acids. Some procedures seem to accelerate this process, e.g., the administration of corn or olive oil or high protein diets.

Bile salts are all surface active. They facilitate not only the action of pancreatic lipase, as previously mentioned, but also the absorption of free fatty acids which result from the action of lipase.

Bilirubin.[32]   Bile derives its color—golden brown—from bilirubin. (Bile that is refluxed into the stomach from the duodenum is green because in an acid medium it is oxidized to biliverdin, a green substance.) Bilirubin is the excretory end product of hemoglobin breakdown and is not manufactured solely by the liver but in all the tissues which destroy red cells. However, it is all excreted by the liver and appears in the feces. The characteristic color of normal feces is due to bilirubin. Insignificant amounts of bilirubin are absorbed from the gut. Man produces between 0.5 and 2 grams of bilirubin daily.

Bilirubin appears in the bile as a diglucuronide. If the liver is unable to conjugate bilirubin with glucuronic acid, bilirubin does not appear in the bile but builds up in the blood, resulting in jaundice. On the other hand, if the bile duct is obstructed, conjugated bilirubin still produced by the liver gains entry to the blood stream and jaundice occurs, but in this form bilirubin also appears in the urine.

Volume and Electrolyte Concentration. Bile as it leaves the liver contains 2.3 per cent solids, about half of which are bile salts, and has a *p*H of 7.6. Bile leaving the gallbladder is concentrated about ten times, if calculated in terms of bile salts and bilirubin. Sodium chloride and bicarbonate are actively absorbed by the mucosa of the gallbladder. Water is absorbed passively.[12] In man and the animals having gallbladders, the liver secretes bile continuously. In the fasting state, however, bile does not enter the duodenum; the sphincter at the lower end of the common bile duct is closed and the bile accumulates and is concentrated in the gallbladder.

Cholecystokinin. The gallbladder contracts and its sphincter relaxes in response to the hormone *cholecystokinin*. This substance enters the blood stream when fats, along with acid and protein breakdown products, enter the intestine. That the response is hormonally mediated is clear. A transplanted gallbladder contracts when food is placed in a transplanted loop of duodenum. In cross-circulation experiments, food in the duodenum of one animal causes the gallbladder of the other to contract. If local anesthetics are applied to the duodenal mucosa, food is then unable to cause release of cholecystokinin and gallbladder contraction.[24] This is reminiscent of the release of gastrin from the pyloric mucosa. The autonomic nerves have only a very weak effect on the gallbladder musculature. Extracts of duodenum with cholecystokinin activity have been prepared but injected intestinal contents themselves do not possess such activity. So far the active duodenal extract cannot be separated from pancreozymin.

The human liver during fasting probably produces between 500 and 700 ml. of bile daily. This can easily be accommodated in the gallbladder. When food is eaten the sphincter relaxes and the gallbladder contracts and expels concentrated bile into the gut.[24] Then hepatic bile pours into the intestine, by-passing the gallbladder; the flow increases much above fasting secretory rates by virtue of the absorption and re-excretion of bile salts and of the stimulatory action of circulating secretin which is liberated by food in the intestine.

Formation. The volume of bile produced per unit time is related directly to the rate of bile salt secretion. Thus, in the fasting state little bile is secreted because no bile salt is absorbed from the gut. It has all been absorbed. If bile salt is added to the blood either by absorption from the gut or by intravenous injection, it is excreted by the liver and the output of bile salt and the bile volume rise accordingly. This is not the cause of every physiologic increase in bile volume, however. The hormone secretin increases bile volume but not the output of bile salts or bilirubin. Secretin is, in other words, a hydrocholeretic. After a meal, secretin and the enterohepatic circulation together increase bile flow. During fasting, the enterohepatic circulation stops, secretin production ceases, and that part of the bile acid pool which forms the enterohepatic circulation is sequestered in the gallbladder.

Some animals lack gallbladders. They are all either continuous eaters (rats) or continuous digesters like ruminants.

Both hepatic bile and gallbladder bile are isotonic with plasma. However, the Na$^+$ concentration of gallbladder bile, often in excess of 300 mEq. per liter, is higher than would be expected of an isotonic solution. This occurs because in concentrated solutions the bile salts form aggregates.

The water appears in hepatic bile as two moieties, (i) that associated with bile acids and (ii) that associated with electrolytes. Secretin stimulates the formation of the latter only. As the volume of the nonbile acid or secretin-stimulated component rises, HCO$_3^-$ rises and Cl$^-$ concentration falls just as in pancreatic juice (Fig. 8). Filtration is not important in bile formation since the well oxygenated isolated perfused liver secretes against a pressure higher than the blood pressure.

A few substances are actively secreted into bile, including bile salts, bilirubin, penicillin and some dyes, of which sulfobromophthalein (Bromsulphalein) is important. Such dyes are used as tests of liver function. The transport mechanism seems to be common to all since they compete with each other.[37]

For many years attempts have been made to determine whether nerves or neurohumoral agents influence the flow rate or composition of hepatic bile. It has been claimed recently, for example, that insulin hypoglycemia increases bile flow if the vagi are intact. None of these studies, however, is altogether convincing.

SECRETION BY THE SMALL INTESTINE AND THE COLON

Histologically the mucosa of the small intestine, except for the first part of the duodenum immediately adjacent to the pylorus, presents a uniform appearance, being constituted of villi and the crypts of Lieberkuehn between the bases of the villi. The villi are covered with a layer of simple cuboidal and columnar cells interspersed with mucus-secreting goblet cells. The cells on the surface of the villi are mature; the immature cells of the Lieberkuehn crypts move up to replace the older epithelial cells at the surface of the villi as they are shed. Many of the cells in the crypts and in the tubular glands leading into the crypts seem to be secretory since they contain granules which are discharged following administration of pilocarpine.

Brunner's Glands.[17] The duodenum histologically resembles the rest of the gut except that in the first part unique glandular structures lie between the circular muscle and the muscularis mucosae. These are the Brunner's glands (Fig. 11). They communicate with the lumen of the intestine through ducts which open into the crypts of Lieberkuehn. These glands closely resemble the pyloric glands of the stomach, but their position is outside the muscularis mucosae whereas the pyloric glands are inside. Brunner's glands behave differently from either the pyloric glands or the secretory cells of the rest of the intestine in that their secretion increases in response to feeding.

If the first part of the duodenum is brought to the surface as a pouch it will secrete in response to feeding whether it is innervated or not. In the innervated preparation in a fasted animal, vagal stimulation or section of the splanchnic nerves greatly increases secretion.[41] Therefore, both hormonal and nervous regulation of the secretion occur. Indeed, crude preparations of secretin when given by intravenous injection increase both the secretion[36] and motility of the Brunner's gland area. Vagal and hormonal stimulation may not act directly on the Brunner's gland cells because both forms of stimulation increase motility, and movement itself stimulates the glands.

Direct chemical (0.1 N HCl) or mechanical irritation appears to increase Brunner's gland secretion, though this is not certain since the mucosa of the duodenal pouch containing Brunner's glands may be responsible for the secretion.

The secretion from the first part of the duodenum, which is mostly from Brunner's glands, is more viscous and contains more bicarbonate than that from the rest of the small intestine. It is clear and mucinous and has a pH in dogs and pigs of 7.2 to 7.5. Rabbits have unusually abundant duodenal secretion with a pH which often reaches 8. Juice collected from the whole duodenum in dogs, to which the Brunner's glands make only a small contribution, has been found to amount to over 300 ml. daily with a pH of 6.9.[28] Whether Brunner's glands produce enzymes is not known, because the associated duodenal mucosa does produce enzymes.[13]

One would suspect that this ring of glands, so close to the stomach, from which acid contents pour, might play a role in neutralizing gastric contents. This is unlikely, since the volume of juice and its bicarbonate, its only buffer, is tiny in comparison with the volume and acidity of gastric contents entering from the stomach.[13] Brunner's secretion probably protects the duodenal mucosa by adhering to it and retaining HCO_3^- in the same fashion as gastric mucin (see above).

Intestinal Secretion.[13] Loops of intestine with nerves intact spontaneously produce a small secretion called *succus entericus;* the rate of secretion has been estimated to be only 50 ml. per hour for the whole small intestine below the duodenum. By contrast, the duodenum, as mentioned above, secretes profusely (150 to 920 ml. daily) in conscious dogs, whether fed or fasted.[28] Stimulation of the vagi, which has no effect on this secretion, probably has no significant effect on secretion from any part of the small intestine below the Brunner's gland zone.

Denervated loops of small intestine secrete profusely for two to three weeks after denervation. This does not mean, however, that the secretory cells are under nervous control, because the hypersecretion following denervation could well be secondary to the hypermotility and mucosal engorgement which invariably follow denervation of the intestine. Local intraluminal irritation by hydrochloric or acetic acid, other chemicals or mechanical means increases secretion.

Succus entericus is isotonic with blood. In addition to the usual electrolytes, Na^+, K^+, Cl^- and HCO_3^-, it contains mucin, amylase and enterokinase. Even though a Thiry-Vella loop (Fig. 11) of intestine does not increase its secretion in response to a meal, the existence of a secretory hormone, *enterocrinin,* has been postulated but not yet proved.

Enzymes other than amylase and enterokinase have been reported (e.g., peptidase, invertase, lactase, maltase and lipase), but these vary with the amount of cellular debris in the juice and are not found in centrifuged juice.[41] The existence within the epithelial cells of enzymes which split disaccharides and amino peptidase has now been established.

The pH of uncontaminated jejunal juice is about 7.2 and of ileal juice 7.6. After a meal the pH of the intestinal content is low in the duodenum, 4.5 to 6.5, and rises progressively to 7.3 in the ileum. The electrolyte concentration of intestinal juice is variable, but its continued loss generally produces acidosis because the HCO_3^- concentration is usually higher and the Cl^- lower than in plasma. The K^+ concentration of upper intestinal secretion is approximately equal to that of blood, but from the ileum it may reach three times that of the plasma.

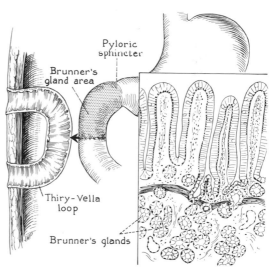

Fig. 11. Diagram showing the Brunner's gland area, Thiry-Vella loop preparation and the histologic appearance of the duodenal mucosa and the Brunner's glands. The narrow band of the muscularis mucosae can be seen separating the glands from the mucosa. A few glands can be seen perforating the muscularis *en route* to opening into the crypts.

Secretions by the Colon. The secretion of the colon, even scantier than that of the small intestine, is thick and mucinous and is increased by mechanical irritation of the mucosa. Most notably, the composition of the stimulated secretion has a high concentration of K^+, often in excess of 20 mEq. per liter. Chloride and bicarbonate are present in about equal concentrations. The colon contains no enzymes other than those derived from bacteria or cellular debris which has come from the small bowel. In cats, Wright and Florey[40] were able to increase secretion from the distal colon by stimulating the pelvic motor nerves to the distal colon and rectum. No other nervous or hormonal regulation is known or postulated. The colonic secretion appears to lubricate rather than digest.

REFERENCES

1. ANNEGERS, J. H. *Arch. intern. Med.,* 1954, *93:*9–22.
2. BERGSTROM, S. In: *Biosynthesis of terpenes and sterols,* G. E. W. Wolstenholme and M. O'Connor, eds. Boston, Little, Brown and Co., 1959.
3. BERNARD, C. *C. R. Acad. Sci. (Paris),* 1852, *55:*341.
4. BORGSTRÖM, B. Chap. 4 in *Lipide metabolism,* Bloch, K. E., ed. New York, John Wiley & Sons, 1960.
5. BRO-RASMUSSEN, F., KILLMAN, S. and THAYSEN, J. H. *Acta physiol. scand.,* 1956, *37:*97–113.
6. BURGEN, A. S. V. *J. cell. comp. Physiol.,* 1955, *45:*465–477.
7. BURGEN, A. S. V. and EMMELIN, N. G. *Physiology of the salivary glands.* Baltimore, Williams & Wilkins, 1961.
8. CHAIKOFF, I. L. and ENTENMAN, C. *Advanc. Enzymol.,* 1948, *8:*171–202.
9. CODE, C. F. In: *Histamine,* CIBA Foundation Symposium. Boston, Little, Brown and Co., 1956.
10. CONWAY, E. J. *The biochemistry of gastric acid secretion.* Springfield, Ill., Charles C Thomas, 1953.
11. CRITTENDEN, P. J. and IVY, A. C. *Amer. J. Physiol.,* 1937, *119:*724–733.
12. DIAMOND, J. M. *J. Physiol.,* 1962, *161:*442–473.
12a. DURBIN, R. P. and HEINZ, E. *J. gen. Physiol.,* 1958, *41:* 1035–1047.
13. FLOREY, H. M. and HARDING, H. E. *Proc. roy. Soc.,* 1935, *117B:*68.
13a. FORTE, J. G. and DAVIES, R. E. *Amer. J. Physiol.,* 1964, *206:*218–222.
14. GRAY, J. S., BUCHER, G. R. and HARMAN, H. H. *Amer. J. Physiol.,* 1941, *132:*504–516.
15. GREGORY, R. A. *Secretory mechanisms of the gastrointestinal tract.* London, Edward Arnold, 1962.
16. GROSSMAN, M. I. *Physiologist,* 1963, *6:*349–357.
17. GROSSMAN, M. I. *Physiol. Rev.,* 1958, *38:*675–690.
18. HAYAMA, T., MAGEE, D. F. and WHITE, T. T. *Ann. Surg.,* 1963, *158:*290–294.
19. HEATLEY, N. G. *Gastroenterology,* 1959, *37:*313–317.
19a. HEINZ, E. and DURBIN, R. P. *J. gen. Physiol.,* 1957, *41:* 101–117.
20. HILTON, S. M. and LEWIS, G. P. *J. Physiol.,* 1955, *128:* 235–248.
21. HOFMANN, A. F. and BORGSTRÖM B. *Fed. Proc.,* 1962, *21:* 43–50.
22. HOGBEN, C. A. M. *Amer. J. digest. Dis.,* 1959, *4:*184–193.
23. HOLLANDER, F. *J. biol. Chem.,* 1932, *97:*585–604.
24. HONG, S. S., MAGEE, D. F. and CREWDSON, F. *Gastroenterology,* 1956, *30:*625–630.
25. HUNT, J. N. and PATHAK, J. D. *J. Physiol.,* 1960, *154:*254–269.
26. JAMES, A. H. *The physiology of gastric digestion.* London, Edward Arnold, 1957.
27. JORPES, J. E., and MUTT, V. *Gastroenterology,* 1959, *36:* 377–385.
28. LANDOR, J. H., BRASHER, P. H. and DRAGSTEDT, L. R. *Arch. Surg.,* 1955, *71:*727–736.
29. MAGEE, D. F. *Gastrointestinal physiology.* Springfield, Ill., Charles C Thomas, 1962.
30. REHM, W. *Amer. J. digest. Dis.,* 1959, *4:*194–207.
31. REID, N. C. R. W., HACKETT, R. M. and WELBOURN, R. B. *Gut,* 1961, *2:*119–122.
32. SCHACHTER, D. *Med. Clin. N. Amer.,* 1963, *47:*621–628.
33. SCHNEYER, C. A. and SCHNEYER, L. H. *Proc. Soc. exp. Biol. (N. Y.),* 1961, *108:*584–586.
34. SHAPIRA, D. and STATE, D. *Gastroenterology,* 1961, *41:*16–23.
35. SIRCUS, W. *Quart. J. exp. Physiol.,* 1958, *43:*114–133.
36. SONNENSCHEIN, R. R., GROSSMAN, M. I. and IVY, A. C. *Acta med. scand.,* 1947, *128* (Suppl. 196):296–307.
37. SPERBER, I. *Pharmacol. Rev.,* 1959, *11:*109.
37a. VILLEGAS, L. and DURBIN, R. P. *Biochim. biophys. Acta,* 1960, *44:*612–613.
38. WHEELER, H. O. *Med. Clin. N. Amer.,* 1963, *47:*607–620.
39. WHITE, T. T., LUNDH, G. and MAGEE, D. F. *Amer. J. Physiol.,* 1960, *198:*725–728.
40. WRIGHT, R. D. and FLOREY, H. W. *Quart. J. exp. Physiol.,* 1938, *28:*207–229.
41. WRIGHT, R. D., JENNINGS, M. A., FLOREY, H. W. and LIUM, R. *Quart. J. exp. Physiol.,* 1940, *30:*73–120.

CHAPTER 50

Absorption from the Gastrointestinal Tract

By ARTHUR C. BROWN and EDWARD J. MASORO

THE fundamental function of the gastrointestinal tract is the transport of ingested particles from the gastrointestinal lumen into the systemic circulation, a process known as absorption. It is accomplished mainly by the epithelial mucosal cells which line the luminal surface of the small intestine. This transport and its underlying mechanisms are described in this chapter.

GENERAL FACTORS INFLUENCING ABSORPTION[25, 34, 62]

Area. From the relation, total transport rate = area × flux, it is clear that, whatever the mechanism by which particles are moved into the intestinal mucosa, a large exposed area makes for a more rapid transport rate. The structure of the small intestinal mucosa is consistent with its physiologic function: the surface available for transport is increased in several ways until it is very large indeed—some 100 times greater than the total external surface of the body.

The intestine is a long tube coiled within the abdominal cavity. The area of the luminal surface is increased over that of a simple cylindrical tube by various projections into the lumen (Fig. 1). The first are the infoldings of mucosal tissue (folds of Kerkring). Second are the slender villi which project from the mucosal tissue, greatly increasing the number of epithelial cells exposed to the lumen and whose constant motion aids local mixing of the luminal contents. Third are the subcellular microvilli, which greatly increase the area of an individual epithelial cell available for intestinal absorption.

Circulation. The movement of absorbed particles into the circulatory system is accomplished by the intestinal capillaries and lymphatics. The intestinal capillary bed follows the villous projections and forms a diffuse network just below the outer cells. The lymphatic system also extends into the villi through the closed end central lacteal vessels. This arrangement is advantageous, since it minimizes the distance that an absorbed particle must traverse by diffusion within the mucosa.

To prevent the accumulation of absorbed particles within the intestinal mucosa and the consequent reduction of absorption due to back diffusion gradients, it is necessary that the

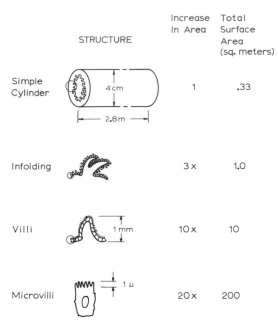

STRUCTURE	Increase In Area	Total Surface Area (sq. meters)
Simple Cylinder 4 cm 2.8m	1	.33
Infolding	3 x	1.0
Villi 1 mm	10 x	10
Microvilli 1 μ	20 x	200

Fig. 1. Various ways of increasing the surface area of the intestinal mucosa over that of a simple cylinder. Circles indicate region shown on the subsequent drawings. (After Wilson, *Intestinal absorption.* Philadelphia, W. B. Saunders Co., 1962.)

transported particles be rapidly carried away. Thus, an efficient absorptive process demands a high rate of intestinal blood flow. In a man at rest, the intestinal perfusion rate represents approximately 20 to 30 per cent of the cardiac output (1 to 2 liters per minute).[10]

The lymphatics contribute a much slower rate of fluid flow to the intestinal drainage, approximately 1 to 2 ml. per minute in man.[65] The osmotic and hydrostatic forces of the interstitial fluid lead to the continuous formation of lymph in the central lacteal vessels; the lacteals drain into the larger lymph-collecting vessels, a process aided by the pumping action of villal movement.

Thus, an absorbed particle may be removed from the intestinal mucosa by one of two routes: the capillaries or the lymphatics. Because the capillary blood flow is about one thousand times greater than the rate of lymph formation, it is clear that those substances which pass equally well through the capillary or lymphatic walls will be carried away mainly in the blood. These include water, inorganic ions, monosaccharides, amino acids, etc. However, some absorbed substances which are greatly impeded by the capillary wall pass

readily through the more permeable lymphatics —for example, triglycerides, proteins, cholesterol; for these substances, the lymphatic system provides the major route of intestinal drainage.[42]

Electrical Potential. Since charged particles are absorbed at varying rates, a charge separation and consequent electrical potential difference across the intestinal epithelium is to be expected. Although the potential between the lumen and the intestinal capillaries has not been directly measured, the potential between the lumen and serosal surface or between the lumen and the systemic venous blood is believed to be a good approximation. These latter potentials, easily measured, indicate that the lumen is slightly negative—3 to 10 mV.—with respect to either blood or the serosal surface. The exact magnitude of the potential (and even its sign) depends upon the ionic composition of the solution within the lumen and the exact location along the intestine at which the measurement is made.[15] The potential seems too small to be a major factor in the absorption of monovalent ions; however, for more highly charged particles, it could exert an appreciable influence. The most probable source of the potential is the vigorous active absorption of sodium ions, a process which leaves the lumen electrically negative.

Acidity. The pH of the stomach contents (normally 2 to 5) is rapidly raised to about 6 as the chyme enters the duodenum. The pH increases progressively as the chyme proceeds along the small intestine, reaching a value of about 8 in the ileum.[7]

Epithelial Permeability. The permeability of the intestinal epithelium to particles varies over an enormous range: for example, in man the maximal rate of water absorption is almost 1 mol per minute,[7, 62] whereas vitamin B_{12} is absorbed at a rate of about 0.001 μM. per day[29] —a ratio of over one trillion to one. The major determinant of the ease with which a particle passes through the epithelium and into the circulation is its size: Only small particles are absorbed at an appreciable rate, and the smaller the particle the faster the rate. The marked dependence upon size suggests that absorption through the epithelial membrane occurs by passage through membrane pores. In recent experiments, a mean pore diameter of 8 Ångstroms was calculated for the intestinal mucosa.[44] Since there must be a spread in pore

TABLE 1. *Permeability of Intestinal Epithelium*

	PARTICLE DIAMETER (Å)*
Very highly permeable	
Water	3.0
Highly permeable	
Monovalent inorganic ions	6.5 (sodium)
Monosaccharides	7.2 (glucose)
Amino acids	
Monoglycerides	
Slightly permeable	
Divalent inorganic ions	8.3 (calcium)
Disaccharides	8.8 (sucrose)
Peptides	
Impermeable	
Polysaccharides	30.4 (inulin)
Highly charged inorganic ions	
Proteins	

*The molecular diameters for typical particles are calculated from the diffusion rate in free solution by using the modified Stokes' Law (Robinson and Stokes, *Electrolyte solutions.* London, Butterworths Scientific Publications, 1959.)

size, particles larger than this size may be able to pass through some of the pores. However, as particle size increases, there will be fewer pores through which transport can occur, leading to progressively lower transport rates.

The general classification of permeability as related to particle size is shown in Table 1. In the use of this table two features must be noted. First, although size determines into which major classification a particle falls, rank order of permeability within each classification depends upon the specific mechanism by which the particle is transported. For example, glucose, which is actively transported, is absorbed more rapidly than the passively absorbed pentoses, even though the latter are slightly smaller. Second, lipid soluble substances are absorbed at a faster rate than predictable from their size alone, presumably because they dissolve in the membrane substance and can diffuse directly through the membrane as well as through the pores. Even for the lipid-soluble substances, however, smaller particles are in general absorbed more rapidly than larger ones.

ELECTROLYTES AND WATER[17]

Water. Approximately 8 liters of water are absorbed from the small intestine every day. Some of the water is contained in the dietary intake as ingested liquid and as liquid water incorporated into solid foods. However, most of the water is in the secretions of the gastrointestinal tract itself, where it acts as a lubricating agent and as a carrier for digestive enzymes (see Table 2).

The determinants of water movement be-

TABLE 2. *Average Fluid Exchange along the GI Tract**

	RATE OF WATER EXCHANGE (LITERS PER DAY)	TIME IN TRANSIT
Mouth		1 minute
Diet	+1.5	
Saliva	+1.5	
Net entering stomach	3.0	
Stomach		1 to 3 hours
Gastric juice	+3.0	
Net entering intestine	6.0	
Intestine		3 to 5 hours
Liver bile	+0.5	
Pancreatic secretion	+2.0	
Absorption	−8.0	
Net entering colon	0.5	
Colon		12 to 15 hours
Absorption	−0.4	
Net excreted in feces	0.1	

*The rate of water exchange is the daily average for an adult. A plus sign indicates water added to the GI tract by ingestion or secretion; a minus sign indicates water removed from the tract by absorption. The time in transit is the period spent by food (or chyme, or feces) in each of the divisions of the tract.

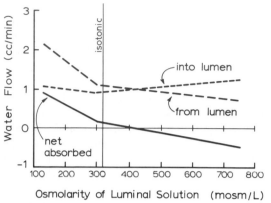

Fig. 2. The rate of water movement across the intestinal wall as a function of the osmolarity of sodium chloride in the lumen (dog ileum, *in vivo*). The upper dashed curves indicate the unidirectional flows—lumen to blood and blood to lumen. The lower solid curve shows the net flow, which is equal to the difference between the unidirectional flows; positive values indicate net absorption and negative values net secretion. As the osmolarity of the luminal solution increases, the unidirectional flux from the lumen decreases sharply, while the luminal fluid influx remains approximately constant. As a result, water is rapidly absorbed from dilute luminal solutions, but actually is lost into the lumen if the solution within the ileum is sufficiently concentrated. The crossover point is about 400 milliosmols, indicating that water can still be absorbed from an isotonic solution. Since osmosis alone could not lead to absorption from an isotonic solution, these data may indicate that direct coupling of water to solute influx is partially responsible for water movement. (After Visscher *et al., Amer. J. Physiol.,* 1944, *142*:550–575.)

tween the intestinal lumen and the blood are usually assumed to be passive. Specifically, these are (i) osmotic forces produced by solute concentration gradients, (ii) hydrostatic pressure differences between the intestinal lumen and the capillaries and (iii) the tendency of solute particles which are being absorbed to pull along associated water molecules. Of these three, the osmotic force is probably the most important and the hydrostatic pressure the least important; for most purposes, hydrostatic pressure can probably be neglected. For example, the hydrostatic filtration pressure of the systemic capillaries can be balanced by an osmotic difference of only 1 or 2 milliosmols. The experimental evidence on the role of hydrostatic pressure is equivocal,[4, 27, 57] but it appears unlikely that hydrostatic pressure within the intestinal lumen has a major influence on normal function.

By moving water, osmosis tends to maintain osmotic equilibrium between the intestinal contents and the epithelial interstitial fluid and plasma. Since osmosis is a passive influence, it cannot cause absorption against a water activity gradient. Rather, net water absorption by osmosis depends upon sufficient particle absorption to deplete the luminal solute concentration, lowering its osmolarity and thus establishing an osmotic difference across the intestinal epithelium. Because the mucosa is very permeable to water, only a relatively small osmotic depletion is necessary for the water absorption rate to keep pace with particle movement.[60]

Absorption of water also is influenced directly by the absorption and distribution of dissolved particles (as contrasted with osmosis, which depends on the effect of dissolved particles on water activity). In some circumstances, while solute particles are being absorbed, water moves in the absence of an osmotic difference or even against an opposing osmotic gradient, if the osmotic gradient is not too large. The mechanism of this water movement is unknown; it may be the inverse of solvent drag, with solute particles dragging along some of their associated hydration water, or it may be due to local osmotic and hydrostatic gradients within the mucosal tissue produced by particle absorption.[23] In any case, the mechanism is assumed to be passive (see Fig. 2). The dependence of both this direct mechanism and osmosis upon solute movement is probably responsible for the observation that water is absorbed maximally from *in vitro* preparations only when metabolism is adequate to provide energy for the active transport of dissolved particles.[23, 27, 57]

It should be pointed out that a semipermeable membrane is not necessary to produce osmotic forces. The essentials for osmotic movement are (i) a membrane through which water can pass, and (ii) a difference in water activity on the two sides of this membrane (usually measured in terms of the concentration of dissolved particles). A semipermeable membrane such as the capillary endothelium meets these requirements, since the impedance to plasma protein movement into the interstitial space leads to a difference in water activity (although the small—about 1.4 milliosmolar—concentration of plasma proteins keeps the resulting osmotic forces to moderate values). However, the active transport of solute particles across a membrane obviously also affects water activity and thus can lead to osmosis.

Although gastrointestinal absorption has been extensively investigated, there are few definitive experiments. No experiment conclusively eliminates an active transport component in the absorption of water. Indeed, the hypothesis of active water absorption is periodically revived.[27, 59] The general consensus that water movement is entirely passive is based on the lack of experiments which can be interpreted only in terms of active water transport, together with an implicit assumption about natural thrift: Nature, having once labored mightily to bring forth a particular physiologic mechanism does not lightly produce issue again. In other words, the active transport of solute particles is well documented in many tissues, as is the ability of water to move passively; therefore, in the absence of definite experimental proof to the contrary, it is reasonable to assume that the same mechanism operates here as in other tissues rather than to postulate a specific and unique system to move water actively across the intestinal mucosa.

The sequence of events following the entry of gastric chyme into the intestine is as follows: If upon entering the intestine, the solution is far from isotonic, the initial water movement is in a direction to bring the luminal contents toward isosmolarity with blood and interstitial fluid (as modified by direct effect of particle movement). This initial tendency toward equilibration takes place in the duodenum. Subsequent water absorption is dependent upon particle absorption; water moves to the extent necessary to maintain the established osmotic balance (for example, 3.2 ml. of water per milliosmol of solute absorbed from an isotonic solution). This water may be thought of as being osmotically "obligated" to solute particles.

Clinical difficulties with water absorption most frequently are not due to any intestinal impediment to water movement, but rather are caused by incomplete particle absorption. For example, the diarrhea associated with intestinal hypermotility is due to the insufficient time allowed for absorption of dissolved particles (particularly in the large intestine) and the consequent excretion of these particles along with their osmotically obligated water. Similarly, the effectiveness of the cathartic Epsom salt ($MgSO_4 \cdot 7H_2O$) is due to the relative impermeability of the small intestinal epithelium to the ions Mg^{++} and $SO_4^{=}$.

Sodium and Chloride. The intestine is very permeable to *sodium* ion; thus, there are large passive fluxes of sodium in both directions through the intestinal epithelium. Superimposed upon the passive exchange is an active flux of sodium from lumen to interstitial fluid (Fig. 3). This active flux is responsible for net absorption of sodium and contributes, as well, to the absorption of other substances.

Several lines of evidence indicate that sodium is actively absorbed. Sodium can move against an electrochemical gradient. If a metabolic poison is administered, the active portion of the flux is eliminated. Or if a length of intestine is removed from the animal and is externally perfused, active sodium transport from mucosal to serosal surface occurs only when glucose and oxygen are present in the perfusing solution. In summary, the ability of sodium to move against an electrochemical gradient and the dependence of this ability upon metabolic integrity and the supply of metabolic substrates is convincing evidence that the intestine can actively transport sodium.[23, 24, 55]

The quantitative relation between the active and passive fluxes, as measured in the rat jejunum *in situ*, is illustrated in Figure 4. In this figure, the flux is plotted as a function of the luminal concentration of sodium ion. The passive flux from blood to lumen is relatively constant, as might be expected, since the interstitial fluid sodium ion concentration is controlled mainly by its equilibration with plasma sodium. Both active and passive influxes (lumen to blood) are, of course, zero when no sodium is present

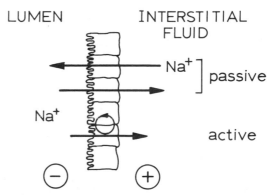

Fig. 3. The exchange of sodium across the small intestinal epithelium is made up of a passive influx and efflux and an active efflux. The passive fluxes are determined by the concentration and electrical gradients (and perhaps also solvent drag forces). The active flux depends on the cell's ability to couple some metabolic energy cycle to sodium movement. (Positive and negative signs indicate the normal electrical polarity assumed to exist across the epithelial cells.)

in the lumen; as the luminal sodium concentration is raised, both influxes increase. Thus, at low luminal concentrations, there is a net flux into the lumen, whereas at high concentrations there is a net absorption. The point of transition, where the total unidirectional flux from lumen to blood exactly equals that in the opposite direction (from blood to lumen), will be called the luminal balance concentration. For *in situ* rat jejunum, the balance concentration is about 65 mM. per liter for sodium. Clearly, if no other dissolved particle movements were to occur, the luminal sodium concentration would approach asymptotically the balance concentration whether the initial solution introduced into the lumen were high or low in sodium. The difference between the balance concentration and the plasma concentration of sodium is determined by the relative magnitudes of the active and passive forces.

The details of the mechanism by which sodium is actively transported through the intestine is unknown; most frequently a carrier molecule is assumed.

The absorption of *chloride* ion appears to share most of the characteristics of the absorption of sodium ion. Chloride is exchanged between the intestinal lumen and the blood by passive unidirectional fluxes of a lesser magnitude, apparently, than those for sodium, prob-

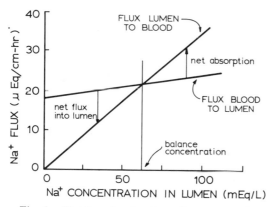

Fig. 4. Unidirectional sodium fluxes across the rat jejunum *in vivo* as a function of the Na+ concentration in the intestinal lumen. The difference between these curves is the net flux, and their point of crossing (zero net flux) is labeled "balance concentration." If there were no active transport, the balance concentration would be near the plasma sodium concentration; the actual balance concentration of about 65 mM. per liter indicates that active absorption plays a major role in sodium movement. (After Curran and Solomon, *J. gen. Physiol.,* 1957, 41:143–168.)

ably because of the lower membrane chloride permeability. In addition, chloride appears to be actively absorbed,[23, 24, 37] leading to a balance concentration of perhaps 50 mM. per liter.

Several recent papers have challenged the existence of an active transport mechanism for chloride ion, at least in the isolated intestine.[15, 16, 55] Instead, it is claimed that chloride is absorbed passively following the active transport of sodium. On the other hand, evidence for active chloride absorption *in vivo* appears valid. Whether this is simply a difference between the *in vivo* and *in vitro* state, or whether a more complex explanation is necessary to resolve these apparently contradictory conclusions is not clear at present.

Finally, it should be noted that, for any substance, the characteristics of exchange between the lumen and the capillaries are not necessarily uniform throughout the small intestine; the various regions may have different, if presumably complementary, roles in intestinal absorption. In particular, sodium and chloride appear to be treated differently in the duodenum than in the remainder of the intestine, since the duodenum acts as an equilibration chamber, bringing these substances toward concentration levels similar to that of plasma; active absorption appears to occur only in the more distal regions.[32]

Other Monovalent Ions. The exchange of *potassium* across the intestinal epithelium is mainly passive. There is some evidence indicating a small active transport flux of potassium also, but into rather than out of the lumen. One must not assume that because a solute is not actively absorbed it is not absorbed at all; in fact, most of the potassium which enters the intestine is transported into the blood. This is accomplished by passive potassium movement down an electrochemical gradient produced by the active absorption of other ions (mainly sodium) and the concentrating effect of the absorption of water (see section on Interaction).

Studies on the absorption of *bicarbonate ion* are complicated since it combines with H+ to form carbon dioxide by way of carbonic acid, and since the epithelial cells can also produce carbon dioxide or bicarbonate or both. Thus, a change in luminal concentration of bicarbonate ion may be due not only to bicarbonate absorption, but also to a change in luminal pH (which shifts the balance between bicarbonate and carbon dioxide as determined by the Henderson–Haselbalch equation), or it may be due to bicarbonate produced metabolically within the intestinal cells and secreted into the lumen. These interactions lead to simultaneous alterations in bicarbonate, P_{CO_2}, and pH, making it difficult to separate cause from effect.[51] In any case, whether by active or passive means, and whether in the form of HCO_3^- or dissolved CO_2, ingested and secreted bicarbonate is rapidly absorbed from the intestinal lumen into the blood.

Iodide and fluoride ions are readily absorbed by the intestine. Iodide appears to be actively secreted into the lumen, but not in amounts sufficient to prevent its almost complete absorption by passive mechanisms. In this characteristic, iodide resembles potassium ion.

Divalent Ions. The quantity of divalent ions which must be absorbed to keep the body in chemical balance is relatively low, approximately one gram of calcium per day (for an adult), a similar amount of phosphorus, and smaller amounts of iron, magnesium, zinc, manganese and copper. However, the permeability of the intestine to divalent ions is so low that even these small absorption requirements frequently are met only with difficulty. The precarious balance between supply and demand for several of these ions is maintained through special absorptive mechanisms.

Calcium. The intestinal epithelium appears more permeable to calcium ion than to any other common divalent cation. Even so, there may be considerable difficulty in absorbing sufficient calcium to meet the needs of the body, particularly in younger persons, in whom these needs are high. (In adults, the opposite may be true: More calcium may be absorbed than can be conveniently excreted.[58])

Because of the limited solubility of many common calcium salts, much of the ingested calcium may not be in a form suitable for absorption. Thus, calcium precipitated as calcium phosphate or citrate cannot contribute to the influx of ionic calcium. Since these are salts of weak acids, a low intestinal pH tends to keep calcium in solution and thus favors its absorption, whereas an alkaline intestinal environment has the opposite effect.

The fraction of calcium absorbed from the intestinal lumen depends upon the body needs; patients on low calcium diets show an increased capacity for absorption. This regulation of absorptive capacity seems to result from the synergistic action of vitamin D and perhaps parathyroid hormone.[21]

Whether the calcium transport mechanism is active or whether calcium moves only passively down an electrochemical gradient remains to be determined.[61]

Iron. The daily requirement for iron in an adult male is only about 1 mg. (It is about 2 mg. for an adult female because of the loss of iron in menstrual blood.) This is about 10 per cent of the iron ingested daily. However, the capability for iron absorption is so low that difficulty in extracting even this small amount is not unusual.

Both inorganic iron salts and the digestion products of ingested iron-containing organic substances contribute to the ionic iron in the intestine. The iron exists in two ionic forms, ferric (Fe^{+++}) and ferrous (Fe^{++}). There is some interchange between these forms through local oxidation–reduction reactions. The acid environment of the stomach promotes reduction, thereby favoring the conversion of ingested iron to the ferrous form. This is propitious, since, although the intestinal permeability to ferrous ion is low, it is much greater than that to ferric ion, as would be expected from the relative sizes of the hydrated divalent and trivalent forms. The absorption may involve active transport and a carrier molecule or receptor; ferritin has been suggested for this role. Iron can also exist as a non-ionized constituent of insoluble salts; in this form it is unavailable for absorption. Several substances including phosphate can precipitate iron from the luminal solution.

The efficiency with which iron is absorbed appears to depend in part upon bodily requirements. When iron stores become depleted, such as in pregnancy, the fraction of iron extracted increases. A high internal concentration of iron may depress absorption but, evidently, does not reduce it to zero. This is unfortunate, since the body possesses no mechanism for getting rid of excess iron, and the ingestion of a large amount may have serious, even fatal, consequences.

Other Divalent Ions. Phosphorous is absorbed mainly as phosphate ion ($HPO_4^=$ and $H_2PO_4^-$). The absorption of phosphate ion appears to be passive; but evidence for an active component recently has been presented.[9, 31, 46]

Sulfate is only slightly absorbed, as is magnesium (Mg^{++}). Strontium (Sr^{++}) may share a common absorptive mechanism with calcium.

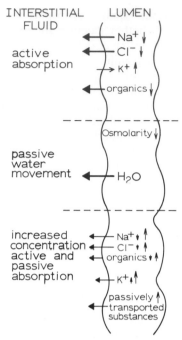

Fig. 5. Interaction of water and solute particle absorption. These steps are illustrated as occurring in sequence, but of course they may occur simultaneously. The initial driving force is the active absorption of electrolytes (for example, sodium and chloride) and small organic molecules. This reduces the luminal solution concentration of these substances, causing a reduction in osmolarity and water efflux. The loss of water from the lumen prevents a further fall in concentration of the actively absorbed particles and concentrates the remaining substances, thus aiding the absorption of both actively and passively transported solutes. Even potassium, which may be actively extruded into the lumen, is sufficiently concentrated by the water movement that it is almost completely absorbed.

Interaction of Absorption of Electrolytes and Water. As the gastric chyme progresses into the duodenum, purely passive influences tend to equilibrate the intestinal contents with plasma. Superimposed upon the passive forces is the active absorption of several of the inorganic ions. Small organic molecules produced from the digestion of more complex organic foodstuffs are also actively transported into the blood. As a result, the intestinal solution eventually has a lowered total solute concentration (tonicity), leading to a passive efflux of water from the intestine.

This movement of water has two important consequences: (i) The intestinal solutes are prevented from becoming so dilute that active absorption is no longer possible (c.f. discussion of sodium absorption). (ii) Those solutes not actively absorbed are concentrated above their level in plasma, setting up a concentration gradient leading to purely passive absorption.

Consequently, substances which pass through the intestinal mucosa easily (water, monovalent ions, small organic molecules, etc.) are almost completely absorbed whether or not they are actively transported. For example, if a solution similar in composition to plasma enters the duodenum, it leaves the small intestine at a lower sodium concentration (sodium actively absorbed) and a higher potassium concentration (potassium passively absorbed, perhaps in the face of an opposing active secretion). Despite the increased concentration, most of the potassium as well as sodium is absorbed because of the large fluid efflux (see Table 3 and Fig. 5.).

Regulation of Absorption. Those substances, such as calcium and iron, which require special mechanisms for transport are regulated by the rate at which these special mechanisms operate. The substances which easily permeate the intestinal mucosa are absorbed in an essentially unregulated manner. Thus, for most ingested material, absorption is

TABLE 3.

	CONCENTRATION	FLUID VOLUME	AMOUNT
Entering duodenum			
Sodium	140 mEq. per liter		840 mEq.
Potassium	4 mEq.	6 Liters	24 mEq.
Leaving ileum			
Sodium	125 mEq.		63 mEq.
Potassium	6 mEq.	0.5 Liters	3 mEq.
Fraction absorbed			
Sodium			93%
Potassium			88%

a rather nonspecific process: Almost everything absorbable is absorbed, independent of the body's needs or even of possible harm. For these substances, regulation is accomplished by rate of ingestion, excretion and utilization (metabolism), but not by absorption.

ORGANIC MATERIALS

Carbohydrate. Carbohydrates are absorbed primarily in the small intestine since the stomach has little ability to do so and the large intestine has neither the ability nor the opportunity. Most of the dietary carbohydrate is absorbed in the first half of the small intestine. This portion has also been shown to have a greater absorptive capacity for hexoses than the lower half.[7] Polysaccharides and disaccharides are absorbed at a slow, physiologically insignificant rate. However, during the digestive processes in the mouth, stomach and intestine, these compounds are converted to the more rapidly absorbed monosaccharides.

In the lumen of the gut, the major dietary polysaccharides, starch and glycogen, are hydrolyzed with the aid of salivary and pancreatic amylase. The product of this hydrolysis is a disaccharide, maltose, which is then bound to or taken up by cells of the intestinal mucosa and further hydrolyzed to the monosaccharide, glucose.[47] Also hydrolyzed on or in the intestinal mucosal cell are the disaccharides, sucrose (table sugar) and lactose (milk sugar), which break down respectively to the monosaccharides, fructose and glucose and to galactose and glucose. Glucose is by far the most abundant monosaccharide resulting from digestive hydrolysis and is absorbed by the small intestine at very high rates.

Considerable evidence indicates that glucose is absorbed by an active transport process: (i) Its absorption is greatly curtailed if the gut is made anaerobic. (ii) Glucose absorption is inhibited by various inhibitors of energy metabolism, e.g., iodoacetate (which blocks the Embden–Meyerhof pathway of carbohydrate metabolism), malonate and fluoroacetate (the tricarboxylic acid cycle), cyanide (electron transport), and 2,4 dinitrophenol (an uncoupler of oxidative phosphorylation). (iii) Glucose absorption is also inhibited by phlorhizin,[11] whose action is especially pertinent to the question of active transport. Recent investigation has shown that it interferes with the passage of glucose between the lumen and the epithelial cell. (iv) Further proof of active transport is seen in the fact that glucose is absorbed against a concentration gradient.[3]

Although the chemistry of active glucose absorption has been extensively investigated, none of the reactions that might be expected seem to be involved in the transport process. Phosphorylation of the glucose molecule (presumably catalyzed by the enzyme, hexokinase) was considered essential for many years but has now been thoroughly disproved. Nevertheless, the glucose molecule must have certain chemical structural properties for active transport to occur. For example, a hexose must have a D-pyranose ring and the hydroxyl group on carbon 2 must be in the configuration shown in Figure 6. Sodium and potassium ions are also involved in the active transport of hexoses,[52] but the biochemical nature of this interaction has not been established.

The galactose molecule also meets the known chemical structural requirements for active glucose absorption. In fact, it might be predicted that galactose is absorbed by the same active transport system as glucose. This prediction is supported by considerable evidence. For example, the same metabolic inhibitors that block glucose absorption also inhibit galactose absorption. Galactose competitively inhibits glucose absorption and glucose has a similar effect on galactose absorption.[19, 28] In most species galactose is absorbed faster than glucose when intestinal concentrations are held equal.[20] However, the usual dietary intake of glucose is far greater than that of galactose; thus glucose is absorbed at a faster rate.

Fructose is a hexose which is structurally very different from glucose and galactose. Although it is not actively transported by the intestine, fructose is not absorbed by diffusion alone. As summarized in Figure 7, the absorp-

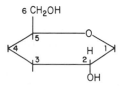

Fig. 6. A hexose molecule which satisfies the structural requirements for active transport. Note the D-pyranose ring and the position of the hydroxyl group on carbon 2.

Fructose Absorption

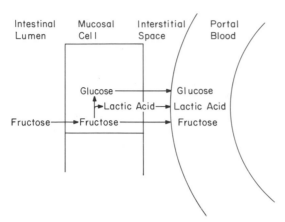

Fig. 7. Pathways of fructose absorption. Fructose is not actively absorbed but diffuses into the mucosal cell. From the mucosal cell, it may diffuse directly into the interstitial space and portal blood or may be converted to other substances which are then transported into the portal blood.

tion of fructose is greatly accelerated by its conversion to other substances in the mucosal cell.[40] Some fructose diffuses across the mucosal cell and into the portal blood, and some is converted by the mucosal cell to lactic acid (the amount varying markedly from species to species), which then enters the portal blood. Finally, some fructose is converted to glucose, which is actively transported through the mucosal membrane. The maximum rate of fructose absorption by these combined mechanisms is about half that of glucose and galactose.

The ability to absorb carbohydrate varies greatly with changing physiologic conditions. During exposure to cold the intestinal absorption of carbohydrate is speeded up. Undoubtedly this response has great survival value, since only a great increase in food intake could sustain the marked increase in metabolic rate necessary for exposure to cold over months or even years. The rate of glucose absorption is increased in hyperthyroidism and decreased in hypothyroidism, changes that seem to reflect the metabolic rate and food intake.

In diabetes mellitus the rate of glucose absorption in the intestine is increased even though the metabolic rate is not elevated. However, the diabetic is hyperphagic and the change in the glucose absorption capacity

probably is an adaptive response to the increased glucose made available to the intestine.

Food restriction leads to a complicated change in the capacity of the intestine to absorb glucose. This capacity is increased by undernutrition but decreased by total fasting (i.e., ingestion of water only).

On leaving the cells of intestinal mucosa, the hexoses can enter with equal ease either the blood or lymph vessels of the intestine. Since blood flows so much more rapidly than lymph, more of it is available to pick up and remove substances which permeate the capillary endothelium. Thus, most of the absorbed carbohydrate is carried from the intestine by the portal blood.

The primarily portal transport of hexose from the intestine is important in the consideration of intermediary metabolism. Because the liver is interposed between most of the absorbed carbohydrate and the systemic circulation, it is in a favorable position to alter the carbohydrate metabolically.

Fat. Although dietary lipids vary widely in chemical structure, triglycerides are overwhelmingly the most abundant. Their absorption varies with the specific chemical nature of each triglyceride, but those usually found in the diet are absorbed quite well. The upper jejunum appears to be the most active site of absorption.

Efficient absorption of triglyceride requires pancreatic lipase and bile salts. Bile salts— good emulsifying agents—apparently aid in making a triglyceride emulsion in the lumen of the intestine, thus enabling pancreatic lipase to catalyze the lipolysis of triglyceride. In this hydrolysis approximately 75 per cent of the fatty acid ester of the triglyceride is converted to free fatty acid (FFA). Also produced are monoglycerides and small amounts of glycerol and diglycerides; a little triglyceride is not changed.

For many years it was believed that the emulsified lipids were absorbed intact through the intestinal mucosa by a process akin to pinocytosis. However, the amount absorbed in this manner is probably insignificant.

As summarized in Figure 8, FFA and monoglyceride apparently combine with bile salts and sodium ion to form a micellar solution in the lumen. The lipid micelles—30 to 100 Ångstroms in diameter[33]—enter the intermicrovillar spaces and then penetrate the mucosal cell. This penetration is not an energy-requiring process, resulting instead from the solubility of the fatty acids and monoglycerides in the cell's lipid membrane.[38]

Once in the intestinal mucosal cell, the long chain FFA and monoglycerides are converted back to triglyceride. Since within the mucosal cell monoglycerides can be hydrolyzed with the aid of an esterase to FFA and glycerol, the following classic sequence[39] of reactions might be expected to bring about the resynthesis of triglyceride:

$$\text{ATP} \longrightarrow \text{AMP}$$

a. FFA + CoA $\longrightarrow$ Fatty acyl-CoA

b. 2 Fatty acyl CoA + Lα-glyccrophosphate $\longrightarrow$ phosphatidic acid + 2 CoA

c. Phosphatidic acid $\longrightarrow$ α, β-diglyceride + P_i

d. α, β-diglyceride + Fatty acyl CoA $\longrightarrow$ Triglyceride + CoA

Another pathway, however, which may be of even greater importance in the resynthesis of triglyceride involves esterification of the absorbed monoglyceride by FFA to yield triglyceride. While the biochemical details of these reactions are not fully known, the FFA presumably is converted to fatty acyl-CoA, which then esterifies the monoglyceride.[13]

The triglycerides leave the small intestine as large particles, 0.5 to 1.0 μ in diameter, called chylomicrons. These particles consist of about 86 per cent triglyceride, 3 per cent cholesterol, 9 per cent phospholipid and 2 per cent protein.[43] Since the chylomicrons are presumably much too large to pass through capillary endothelium, they are carried away primarily by the lymph system.[5] Precisely how and where the chylomicrons are formed in the intestinal wall and how they are released to the lymph are as yet unknown. They may be extruded into the lymph by the endoplasmic reticulum of the mucosal cell.

Glycerides containing short chain fatty acids (less than 12 carbon atoms) usually make up only a small fraction of the total dietary fat. On entering the mucosal cell, these acids are not esterified, passing instead directly into the portal blood.[36]

Cholesterol is also absorbed by the small intestine, probably in much the same way as monoglyceride and FFA. Bile salts are necessary,[56] and cholesterol esters in the intestinal lumen are hydrolyzed to cholesterol and FFA before absorption occurs.[54]

Cholesterol crosses the intestinal cell very slowly.[8] It is ultimately carried away from the intestine in the chylomicron package, where much of it is in esterified form.[7] It is presumably esterified within the mucosal cell, just prior to leaving the cell.[49]

Phospholipids are enzymatically hydrolyzed during digestion to FFA. This FFA is un-

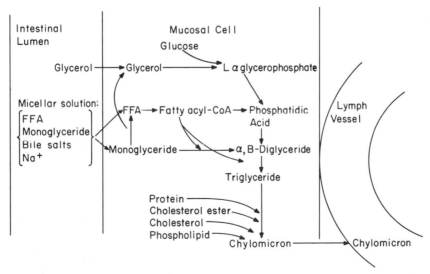

Fig. 8. Processes believed to be involved in fat absorption. The micellar solution of FFA, monoglycerides, bile salts and sodium ion enters the mucosal cell. Triglycerides are resynthesized in the cell and enter the lymph vessels via the chylomicron package.

doubtedly treated the same as that arising from triglyceride hydrolysis.[2] A little phospholipid is apparently absorbed without prior hydrolysis.[6] The role of phospholipid in the emulsification of other lipids or in the formation of micellar solutions is not clear.

Protein and Amino Acids. Unlike the human newborn, the newborn of many mammalian species can absorb intact protein from the gastrointestinal tract.[14] However, as they mature they lose this ability and, consequently, adult mammals, including man, can absorb no more than traces of intact protein or peptide.[12, 26] Before dietary protein can be absorbed, it must be hydrolyzed to amino acids. This hydrolysis begins in the lumen of the stomach and small intestine, where protein is broken down to peptides with the aid of proteolytic enzymes. These peptides are then bound to or are taken up by the brush border of the intestinal mucosal cell, where, with enzymes called peptidases, they are further hydrolyzed to amino acids.[35]

Amino acids are absorbed by the mucosal cell and transported—most of them by an active system—to the portal blood.[64] Three transport systems for amino acids have thus far been identified. (i) In one system, which serves neutral amino acids, L-stereoisomers are transported preferentially; the D-isomers are also transported, but more slowly. Other structural requirements of this system include a free carboxyl group with both an amino group and a hydrogen on the α-carbon.[45] Although the side chain of the amino acid does not seem to be specifically involved, a charged group will prevent transport. Both pyridoxal phosphate[1] and sodium ion[35] are involved in the transport. (ii) Another system transports L-cystine and the basic amino acids, lysine, arginine and ornithine.[30] (iii) A third system transports proline and hydroxyproline.

If a transport system exists for the dicarboxylic amino acids, aspartic and glutamic acids, it has yet to be delineated. They undergo extensive transamination within the mucosal cell, which tends to obscure possible transport mechanisms.

The absorption of traces of intact protein has no importance nutritionally, but it does have antigenic significance. Therefore, it must be kept in mind when considering allergy and related problems.

Nucleic Acids and Related Compounds. It is known that dietary nucleic acids are usually completely absorbed from the small intestine, but doubt exists regarding the chemical form absorbed. The intestine can absorb nucleotides and nucleosides as well as free purine and pyrimidine bases. However, it appears that the digestion of nucleic acids produces only nucleosides or free bases.[63] Nucleosides are absorbed by diffusion, but pyrimidine bases reportedly are actively transported.[53]

Vitamins. Fat-soluble vitamins (A, D, E and K) in the intestinal lumen apparently are absorbed by diffusion.[62] Their absorption is closely related to fat absorption, and bile salts are necessary.

Water-soluble vitamins (B group and C), with the exception of vitamin B_{12}, are also absorbed by diffusion. Vitamin B_{12} has a specific transport system,[18] a detailed discussion of which would involve the trail of research leading to an understanding of pernicious anemia and its treatment.

REFERENCES

1. AKEDO, H., SUGAWA, T., YOSHIKAWA, S. and SUDA, M. *J. Biochem. (Tokyo)*, 1960, *47*:124–130.
2. ARTOM, C. and SWANSON, M. A. *J. biol. Chem.*, 1948, *175*: 871–881.
3. BÁRÁNY, E. H. and SPERBER, E. *Arkiv. Zool.*, 1942, *34*: 1–31.
4. BLICKENSTAFF, D. D., BACHMAN, D. M., STEINBERG, M. E. and YOUMANS, W. B. *Amer. J. Physiol.*, 1952, *168*: 303–310.
5. BLOOM, B., CHAIKOFF, I. L., REINHARDT, W. O., ENTENMAN, C. and DAUBEN, W. G. *J. biol. Chem.*, 1950, *184*: 1–8.
6. BLOOM, B., KIYASU, J. Y., REINHARDT, W. O. and CHAIKOFF, I. L. *Amer. J. Physiol.*, 1954, *177*:84–86.
7. BORGSTRÖM, B., DAHLQUIST, A., LUNDH, G. and SJÖVALL, J. *J. clin. Invest.*, 1957, *36*:1521–1536.
8. BORGSTRÖM, B., LINDHE, B-Å. and WLODAWER, P. *Proc. Soc. exp. Biol. (N.Y.)*, 1958, *99*:365 368.
9. BORLE, A. B., KEUTMANN, H. T. and NEUMAN, W. F. *Amer. J. Physiol.*, 1963, *204*:705–709.
10. BRANDT, J. L., CASTLEMAN, L., RUSKIN, H. D., GREENWALD, J. and KELLY, J. J. *J. clin. Invest.*, 1955, *34*: 1017–1025.
11. BRÜCKER, J. *Helv. physiol. pharmacol. Acta*, 1951, *9*:259–268.
12. CHRISTENSEN, H. N. *Biochem. J.*, 1949, *44*:333–335.
13. CLARK, B. and HUBSCHER, G. *Biochim. biophys. Acta (Amst.)*, 1961, *46*:479–494.
14. CLARK, S. L., Jr. *J. biophys. biochem. Cytol.*, 1959, *4*:41–50.
15. CLARKSON, T. W., CROSS, A. C. and TOOLE, S. R. *Amer. J. Physiol.*, 1961, *200*:1233–1235.
16. CLARKSON, T. W., ROTHSTEIN, A. and CROSS, A. *Amer. J. Physiol.*, 1961, *200*:781–788.

17. COMAR, C. L. and BRONNER, F., eds. *Mineral metabolism*, vols. 1 and 2, parts A and B. New York, Academic Press, 1964.

18. COOPER, B. A. and CASTLE, W. B. *J. clin. Invest.*, 1960, *39:* 199–214.

19. CORI, C. F. *Proc. Soc. exp. Biol. (N.Y.)*, 1926, *23:*290–291.

20. CORI, C. F. *Physiol. Rev.*, 1931, *11:*143–275.

21. CRAMER, C. F. In: *The transfer of calcium and strontium across biological membranes*, R. H. Wasserman, ed. New York, Academic Press, 1963.

22. CSAKY, T. Z., HARTZOG, H. G., and FERNALD, G. W. *Amer. J. Physiol.*, 1961, *200:*459–460.

23. CURRAN, P. F. *J. gen. Physiol.*, 1960, *43:*1137–1148.

24. CURRAN, P. F. and SOLOMON, A. K. *J. gen. Physiol.*, 1957, *41:*143–168.

25. DAVENPORT, H. W. *Physiology of the digestive tract*. Chicago, Year Book Medical Publishers, 1961.

26. DENT, C. E. and SCHILLING, J. A. *Biochem. J.* 1949, *44:*318–333.

27. FISHER, R. B. *J. Physiol.*, 1955, *130:*655–664.

28. FISHER, R. B. and PARSONS, D. S. *J. Physiol.*, 1953, *119:* 224–232.

29. GLASS, G. B. J., BOYD, L. J. and STEPHANSON, L. *Proc. Soc. exp. Biol. (N.Y.)*, 1954, *86:*522–526.

30. HAGIHIRA, H., LIN, E. C. C., SAMIY, A. H. and WILSON, T. H. *Biochem. biophys. Res. Commun.*, 1961, *4:*478–481.

31. HARRISON, H. E. and HARRISON, H. C. *Amer. J. Physiol.*, 1963, *205:*107–111.

32. HINDLE, W. and CODE, C. F. *Amer. J. Physiol.*, 1962, *203:* 215–220.

33. HOFMANN, A. F. and BORGSTROM, B. *Fed. Proc.*, 1962, *21:* 43–50.

34. HOGBEN, C. A. M. *Ann. Rev. Physiol.*, 1960, *22:*381–406.

35. HOLT, J. H. and MILLER, J. D. *J. Lab. clin. Med.*, 1961, *58:* 827.

36. HUGHES, R. H. and WIMMER, E. J. *J. biol. Chem.*, 1935, *108:*141–144.

37. INGRAHAM, R. C. and VISSCHER, M. B. *Amer. J. Physiol.*, 1936, *114:*681 687.

38. JOHNSTON, J. M. In: *Advances in lipid research*, D. Kritchevsky and R. Paoletti, eds. New York, Academic Press, 1963.

39. KENNEDY, E. P. *Ann. Rev. Biochem.*, 1957, *26:*119–148.

40. KIYASU, J. Y. and CHAIKOFF, I. L. *J. biol. Chem.*, 1957, *224:*935–939.

41. LANDAU, B. R., BERNSTEIN, L. and WILSON, T. H. *Amer. J. Physiol.*, 1962, *203:*237–240.

42. LANDIS, E. M. Quoted in T. H. Wilson, *Intestinal absorption*, Philadelphia, W. B. Saunders Co., 1962.

43. LAURELL, C. B. *Acta physiol. scand.*, 1954, *30:*289–294.

44. LINDEMANN, B. and SOLOMON, A. K. *J. gen. Physiol.*, 1962, *45:*801–810.

45. LIN, E. C. C., HAGIHIRA, H. and WILSON, T. H. *Amer. J. Physiol.*, 1962, *202:*919–925.

46. MCKENNY, J. R. Ph.D. thesis, University of Washington, 1964.

47. MILLER, D. and CRANE, R. K. *Biochim. biophys. Acta (Amst.)*, 1961, *52:*281–293; idem, 293–298.

48. MUELLER, J. H. *J. biol. Chem.*, 1916, *27:*463–480.

49. MURTHY, S. K., DAVID, J. S. K. and GANGULY, J. *Biochim. biophys. Acta (Amst.)*, 1963, *70:*490–492.

50. NEWEY, H., PARSONS, B. J. and SMYTH, D. H. *J. Physiol.*, 1959, *148:*83–92.

51. PARSONS, D. S. *Quart. J. exp. Physiol.*, 1956, *41:*410–420.

52. RIKLIS, E. and QUASTED, J. H. *Canad. J. Biochem.*, 1958, *36:*347–362.

53. SCHANKER, L. S. and TOCCO, D. J. *J. Pharmacol. exp. Ther.*, 1960, *128:*115–121.

54. SCHONHEIMER, R. and HUMMEL, R. *Hoppe-Seylers Z. physiol. Chem.*, 1930, *192:*114–116.

55. SCHULTZ, S. G. and ZALUSKY, R. *J. gen. Physiol.*, 1964, *47:* 567–584, idem, 1043–1059.

56. SIPERSTEIN, M. D., CHAIKOFF, I. L. and REINHARDT, W. O. *J. biol. Chem.*, 1952, *198:*111–114.

57. SMYTH, D. H. and TAYLOR, C. B. *J. Physiol.*, 1957, *136:* 632–648.

58. THOMAS, W. C., JR. and HOWARD, J. E. Chap. 21 in *Mineral metabolism*, Vol. 2, part A, Comar, C. L. and Bronner, F., eds. New York, Academic Press, 1964.

59. VISSCHER, M. B. Chap. 4 in *Metabolic aspects of transport across cell membranes*, Murphy, Q. R., ed. Madison, Wisc., University of Wisconsin Press, 1957.

60. VISSCHER, M. B., ROEPKE, R. R. and LIFSON, N. *Amer. J. Physiol.*, 1945, *144:*457–463.

61. WASSERMAN, R. H., ed. *The transfer of calcium and strontium across biological membranes*. New York, Academic Press, 1963.

62. WILSON, T. H. *Intestinal absorption*. Philadelphia, W. B. Saunders Co., 1962.

63. WILSON, T. H. and WILSON, D. W. *J. biol. Chem.*, 1958, *233:*1544–1547.

64. WISEMAN, G. *J. Physiol.*, 1953, *120:*63–72.

65. YOFFEY, J. M. and COURTICE, F. G. *Lymphatics, lymph, and lymphoid tissue*. Cambridge, Mass., Harvard University Press, 1956.

The Urinary Bladder

By THEODORE C. RUCH

THE function of the bladder is of great concern to urologists and neurologists and of some concern to neurophysiologists. Conflicting concepts, unphysiologic terminology, ignorance of fundamental anatomy and physiology of such structures as the "internal sphincter," and the intermixture of mechanical, pathologic and neural factors—all contribute to making bladder function a complex subject.

Innervation of Bladder. The motor nerve supply to the bladder and its sphincters is derived from both divisions of the autonomic nervous system and from the somatic nervous system (Fig. 1). Afferent and efferent fibers are conducted in the same nerves.

Parasympathetic. The preganglionic fibers supplying the bladder issue from the spinal cord mainly at S_3, although there is a small contribution from S_2, S_4, or both. Heimburger et al.[13] established this outflow in man by root blocks. The sacral outflow accounts for the vulnerability of bladder control in lesions of the conus medullaris or the cauda equina. The preganglionic fibers traverse the *pelvic* nerves (nervi erigentes) and the inferior hypogastric plexus, intermingling with sympathetic fibers, to synapse with postganglionic neurons in the ganglion clumps lodged in the bladder wall. These fibers constitute the efferents for the detrusor muscle and the internal sphincter.

Sympathetic. The preganglionic outflow is from the upper lumbar and lower thoracic segments of the spinal cord. Fibers from the lumbar prevertebral ganglia and the preaortic nerve plexus descend along the abdominal aorta to form, at its bifurcation, the "presacral nerve"—more properly the superior hypogastric plexus—which, in turn, divides into two strands, the hypogastric nerves. The hypogastric nerves, coursing along the anterior surface of the sacrum, join the inferior hypogastric plexus and are distributed to the bladder. The sympathetic fibers appear to play little or no part in micturition; those to the internal sphincter (motor) probably prevent reflux into the bladder during ejaculation.

Somatic. Somatic efferent fibers are confined to the external sphincter and prostatic urethra, which they reach by way of the third and fourth anterior roots and the pudendal nerve.

Afferent. The afferent fibers for the micturition reflex (and for the sense of bladder fullness) traverse the pelvic nerve. Painful impulses from the bladder dome are conducted by the hypogastric nerves; those from the trigone by the pelvic nerve. Sensory impulses from the urethra traverse the pudendal nerve.

Clinical and Laboratory Study of Bladder. The methods commonly used for clinical and laboratory study of the bladder are (i) retrograde cystometry (catheter passed through the urethra and connected with a manometer), (ii) the new method of direct cystometry[25] (needle penetrating the bladder wall) yields information about the sphincters (Fig. 2), (iii) telemetering capsules like needles introduced through the bladder wall reflect resistance in the urethra as well as detrusor power; (iv) cystography with x-ray opaque substances; (v) cystoscopy, a viewing of the bladder wall which yields a surprising amount of functional information; and (vi) the recording of times and volumes of micturition.

CYSTOMETRY. The cystometer is used to determine a pressure–volume curve of the bladder by means of a fluid (or air) source, a manometer (fluid or isometric), and a catheter connected by a three-way stopcock. The intravesical pressure should be measured while the bladder is connected with the manometer and disconnected from the filling reservoir, and after the fluid has ceased to flow. Fluid is introduced into the bladder either steadily (at a slow rate) or in volume increments spaced a few minutes apart. Pressure is plotted against volume to yield a cystometrogram. Rhythmic tonus waves, the threshold, vigor and duration of the micturition reflex, and subjective sensations are all important and are noted on the record.

As shown in Figure 3, the cystometrogram or pressure–volume curve typically consists of two parts with the first segment divided again into two parts:* (i) an initial rise when the first increment is added (segment Ia), which is probably due to pressure of the fluid above the bladder neck and of intra-abdominal pressure.[34,36,37] (ii) segment Ib, a prolonged, nearly flat segment (0 to 10 or 15 cm. H_2O), the steepness of

*When it is necessary to distinguish between the two components of segment I, segments Ia and Ib can be used. This terminology replaces that introduced by the author.[31, 36]

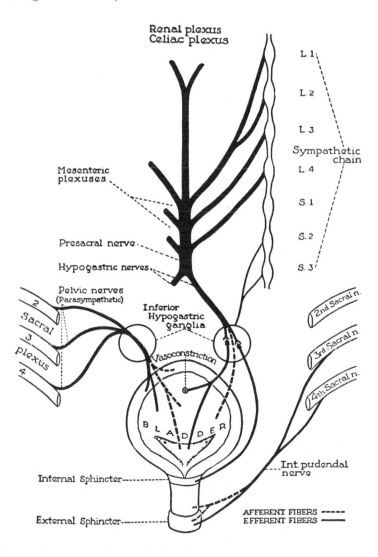

Fig. 1. Diagram showing efferent and afferent pathways to bladder and sphincters. Postganglionic parasympathetic neurons are omitted. (From McLellan, *The neurogenic bladder.* Springfield, Ill., Charles C Thomas, 1939.)

Renal plexus
Celiac plexus
Mesenteric plexuses
Presacral nerve
Hypogastric nerves
Pelvic nerves (Parasympathetic)
Sacral plexus 2 3 4
Inferior Hypogastric ganglia
Vasoconstriction
B L A D D E R
Internal Sphincter
External Sphincter

L. 1
L. 2
L. 3
Sympathetic chain
L. 4
S. 1
S. 2
S. 3
2nd Sacral n.
3rd Sacral n.
4th Sacral n.
Int. pudendal nerve

AFFERENT FIBERS -----
EFFERENT FIBERS ———

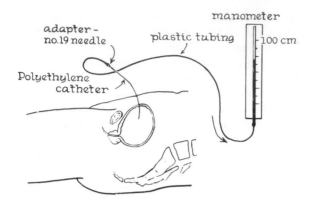

Maximal voiding pressures

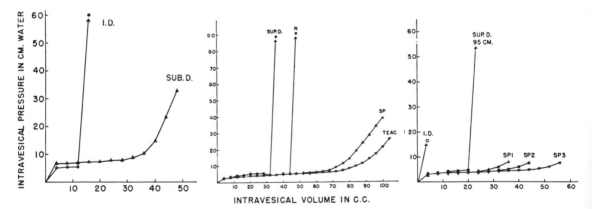

which is held to reflect detrusor "tonus;"* (iii) in a normally innervated bladder a sharp rise of pressure ensues, indicating a micturition reflex contraction of some strength (150 cm.). The threshold for micturition is, then, the volume of filling (stretch) just previous to the reflex. When reflex micturition is wanting, the micturition pressure rise is replaced by a rapid rise. Segment II probably represents the passive stretch of elastic connective tissue of the vesical wall. The cystometrogram therefore reflects two bladder phenomena: (i) the amount of bladder tonus and (ii) the threshold and strength of the micturition contraction of the detrusor. The third problem of micturition is, of course, the control of the sphincters.

Bladder Hypotonus. A normal bladder holds its contents under very low pressure, usually less than 10 cm. H_2O. Moreover, it holds increasing volumes of fluid with little increase in intravesical pressure. (Hydroureter is thus prevented.) In clinical parlance, a steeper than normal curve is termed "hypertonic," and a flatter than normal curve, "hypotonic." The significance of the slope of the curve, i.e., of bladder tonus, has long been confusing. Many writers,[9, 10, 23, 24] directly or by implication, consider bladder tonus a reflex phenomenon. They liken it to the stretch reflex ("tonus") of skeletal muscle or ascribe it to a "peripheral re-

*The term "tonus," recognized by physiologists as a cloak for ignorance, is used here operationally to mean "that which is reflected in the pressure–volume curve of the bladder."

Fig. 2. *Upper,* The method of direct cystometry. *Lower,* The range of voiding pressures occurring in patients having obstruction of the urinary passage. (From Murphy and Schoenberg, *J. Urol.,* 1960, *84*:106–110.)

Fig. 3. Cystometrograms obtained in cats after various neural lesions of brain stem or spinal cord and after autonomic blocking agents (*TEAC*). Long arrows represent micturition and point to dot or square giving pressure generated. Threshold is next volume to right of point where arrows originate. Note the three phases of cystometrograms seen when micturition is absent, e.g., *SUB.D.* and *SP.* The abbreviations *I.D., SUB.D.* and *SUP.D.* mean inter-, sub- and supracollicular decerebration; *SP1, SP2* and *SP3,* successive determinations after spinal transection. (After Tang and Ruch, *Amer. J. Physiol.,* 1955, *181*:249–257.)

flex" served by an intramural plexus of the bladder wall. However, a myotatic reflex yields a steadily increasing reflex contraction to increasing stretch (see Fig. 7, Chap. 7), whereas the bladder accommodates a new volume *with little persisting increase in pressure*. This superficially resembles a lengthening reaction, but no such inhibitory reflex has been demonstrated. The flatness of the initial limb of the normal cystometrogram is sometimes accounted for by assuming that the stretch reflex arcs are activated at low volumes but are "inhibited" from the brain. These are all "neurogenic" theories of bladder tonus. A second view, the myogenic theory, is that the reaction to stretch and supposed accommodation are largely properties of the smooth muscle and connective tissue of the bladder wall, and are entirely nonreflex and non-neural in origin. These two hypotheses lead to quite different interpretations of the neurogenic disturbances of bladder function. The first emphasizes the overactivity or release of tonic bladder reflexes, spinal or peripheral. The second emphasizes the physical state of the bladder wall as a result of infection and of changes secondary to interferences with the micturition reflex, e.g., stretching or shrinking.

Nesbit and Lapides,[26] Tang and Ruch,[36] and Carpenter and Root[8] studied the effects of anesthesia, spinal or root section and autonomic blocking agents on segment Ib of the cystometrogram in human patients and experimental animals. Whereas all abolish micturition, none reduces bladder tonus, which indicates that it is not reflex in nature (Fig. 3). Furthermore, brainstem transections, which greatly augment (release) limb reflex tonus and the excitability of the micturition reflex, also fail to influence bladder tonus.[36] This also is true of patients with greatly overactive micturition reflexes due to cortical lesions.[1] Even death or deep anesthesia is ineffective. The one factor which will alter the initial limb of the cystometrogram is the stretch produced by the accumulation of urine or that involved in a cystometric determination when the bladder is unprotected by the micturition reflex, as after spinal or pelvic nerve section. Successive decreases in bladder tonus occur after each of a series of cystometric determinations (Fig. 3, right). Changes which might be ascribed to a drug or a sacral nerve section are actually due simply to the stretch involved in the control cystometric determination.

PHYSICAL ANALYSIS OF BLADDER TONE. A physical analysis of bladder tone confirms the above physiologic analysis and reveals a common interpretative error in cystometry.[6, 33, 40] If the response of the bladder to increasing volume is thought of in terms of mural tension rather than intravesical pressure, any need to postulate a reflex or other "vital" explanation for the flatness of segment Ib of the cystometrogram disappears. Analysis shows that the tension in the bladder walls is steadily mounting as volume increases. This is easily visualized if you consider two points on the bladder as connected by a string. Even when the pull (tension) on a long string is very high, little pressure is exerted upon your finger when you attempt to bend the string. The difference between pressure and mural tension derives from the law of Laplace.

Consider the bladder as a perfect sphere composed of two hemispheres as in Figure 4A. The pressure in the bladder as recorded in the cystometrogram is acting to force the two hemispheres apart. This total force must be P (force per unit area) times the area of the imaginary circular plane separating the two hemispheres, or $P \cdot \pi R^2$. This total force must be just balanced by the forces in the vesical wall at the junction of the two hemispheres. If these forces are of magnitude T per unit length of wall, then T times the circumferences ($T \cdot 2\pi R$) is the total force in the vesical wall holding the hemispheres together. This permits writing the equation of Laplace for a sphere:

$$T \cdot 2\pi R = P\pi R^2 \text{ or } P = 2(T/R)$$

The variables in this equation are plotted along with the cystometrogram in Figure 4B. The radius, R, is derived from the volume, V, assuming a spherically shaped bladder, from the geometric relation

$$V = (\tfrac{4}{3}) \pi R^3 \text{ or } R = \sqrt[3]{(\tfrac{3}{4}\pi)} V.$$

The pressure, P, is that which is directly measured when obtaining the cystometrogram. The tension, T, is calculated from the values of P and R using the law of Laplace as derived above. Tension can be expressed also as a function of pressure and volume by combining the two preceding relations:

$$T = (P/2) \cdot \sqrt[3]{(\tfrac{3}{4}\pi)} V = 0.31 \cdot P \cdot \sqrt[3]{V}.$$

In the initial segment of these curves (below about 35 cc. volume), equivalent to segment Ib of Figure 3 the tension and the radius both increase but at an approximately proportional rate, so that the pressure remains relatively constant. This increase in tension with stretch would be expected in any elastic material, whether living or inanimate, which obeys Hooke's law; thus, it is unnecessary to postulate an active "receptive relaxation" to explain a nearly flat cystometrogram. At higher volumes (above 35 cc. volume, equiv-

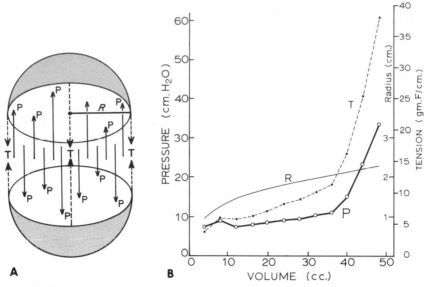

Fig. 4. *A,* Schematic diagram which aids in the derivation of the law of Laplace. *B,* Plot of radius (R) and intravesical pressure (P) showing that mural tension (T) rises even when the pressure curve is relatively flat. (Data from Tang, *J. Neurophysiol.,* 1955, *18:*583–595.)

alent to segment II), the tension increases much more rapidly than the radius, leading to a steep rise in pressure. This increase in tension may simply be a consequence of exceeding the elastic range, since apparently the mural tissue passively becomes "stiffer" at large extensions. This interpretation is consistent with the hysteresis effect described above in neurally inactive bladders.

From this, it is clear that more information could be obtained about the mechanical state of the bladder tissue by plotting tension as a function of extension (or radius inferred from volume) rather than using the conventional cystometrogram plotting pressure versus volume.

The graphs in Figure 4*A* are derived from measurements of cat bladder; however, results from the human bladder are essentially similar, as confirmed by Hinman and Miller.[14]

It is apparent that the flatness of segment Ib of the cystometrogram requires no explanation in terms of reflex inhibitory relaxation. At the higher volumes of segment II, the sharply rising tension and stress mean that elastic elements are no longer approximating Hooke's law or, more probably, that some inelastic connective tissue element such as collagen has come into play.

Bladder Hypertonus. In extreme form hypertonus is manifested by an infected and fibrotic decentralized bladder (Fig. 5) or in the so-called uninhibited bladder, which differs by

exhibiting strong micturition contractions; both show a so-called "climbing type" of cystometrogram. Convincing evidence that so-called "hypertonus" is also a physical rather than a reflex or neural phenomenon was given by Veenema *et al.*[39] In dogs, they prevented urine from entering the bladder by leading the ureters to the exterior of the body. Several days later, cystometrograms were obtained under general and spinal anesthesia to abolish the micturition reflex. The result seen in Figure 6 suggests that the "climbing" type of curve, like that seen in patients, is a rapidly developing physical change due to shrinkage of the bladder rather than to any type of neurogenic hypertonus. This experiment imitates the shrinkage of the bladder caused by small, frequent micturitions. Thus, the two series of studies suggest that abnormalities in segment Ib of the cystometrogram are the result of physical changes in the bladder wall, the "flat" type of curve being caused by stretch and the "climbing" type by shrinkage. Neither is a reflex phenomenon.

Rhythmicity.[29, 30] Observed with an isometric cystometer, the cat's bladder, containing 12 to 20 ml. of fluid, commences to contract rhythmically. The rate is slow, one contraction every two or three minutes; the duration is 5 to 15 seconds and the amplitude 1 to 2 cm.

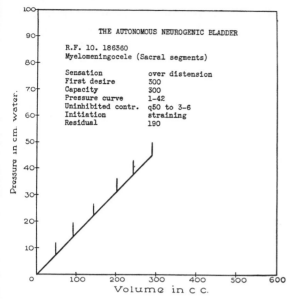

Fig. 5. The type of climbing tonus curve due to decentralization and resultant infection of the bladder. The vertical lines represent small micturitions. (From McLellan, *The neurogenic bladder.* Springfield, Ill., Charles C Thomas, 1939.)

H_2O. With increased filling the rate and amplitude (to 4 to 5 cm.) increase and the contractions may fuse to cause leakage about the catheter. Like bladder tonus, decerebration, spinal transection, lumbosacral rhizotomy, or mural ganglionectomy did not abolish this rhythmicity, nor did ganglionic blocking agents (TEAC or atropine). Plum and Colfelt[30] concluded therefore that the rhythmic contractions were myogenic and suggest that they are involved in micturition by increasing afferent discharge to the spinal cord. However, rhythmic contractions can be augmented or inhibited by cortical stimulation.[12]

In man, rhythmicity is influenced by the higher levels of the nervous system and exhibits the same behavior in response to drugs and functional denervation and the same accelerated tempo and increased amplitude prior to micturition as in the cat.

Micturition.[9, 16, 21, 22] Micturition involves the contraction of the detrusor muscle of the bladder and the opening and closing of the sphincters. The detrusor contraction is a spinal stretch reflex subject to inhibition and facilitation from higher centers.

Rhythmic contractions of myogenic origin (see above) can build up into weak and brief emptying contractions. While voluntary micturition begins with a relaxation of perineal musculature the smooth muscle of the bladder is under direct voluntary control and micturition can occur without contraction of striated muscle.[9, 22]

The external sphincter (m. compressor urethrae), almost nonexistent in the female, can in the male be powerfully contracted voluntarily and stop the flow of urine during detrusor contraction. However, the external sphincter cannot be opened voluntarily; it opens by a reflex inhibition of tonic pudendal nerve discharge from afferent fibers originating in the bladder and urethra.

The external urethral sphincter, examined electromyographically,[11] behaves much like the external anal sphincter (Chap. 48). It exhibits a tonic activity which increases in frequency as the bladder is filled and ceases several seconds before micturition starts. This inhibition of tone is a reflex originating in the bladder wall and carried out by the sacral segments; it is very sensitive to spinal shock. Attempting to force fluid through the distal urethra by increasing pressure causes a progressively stronger contraction of the sphincter muscle. The stimulus for this activity is mainly the stretching of the distal urethral wall. The sphincter can withstand a perfusion pressure of 50 cm. H_2O, much higher than the pressure at which flow starts in micturition; the stretch reflex of the sphincter, like that of the detrusor, may be hyperactive. Thus, spasticity of the external sphincter and the pelvic floor and de-

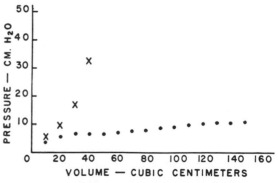

Fig. 6. Cystometrogram of dog with micturition prevented by general anesthesia and local anesthesia of sacral roots (*dots*). Crosses show pressure-volume relation 39 days after both ureters were transplanted to exterior of body. (From Veenema *et al., J. Urol.,* 1952, 68:237–241.)

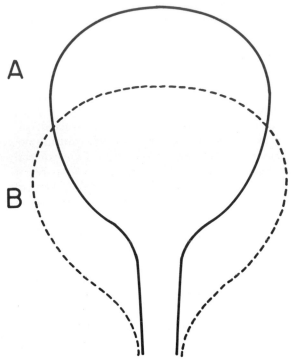

Fig. 7. Outline of the bladder wall before (A) and just after (B) a micturitional contraction of the detrusor, showing that the critical proximal centimeters of the urethra have increased in diameter (because longitudinal muscle has contracted, making the distance between two points less and obliterating the angle between body and urethra). (After Lapides, *J. Urol.,* 1958, *80:*341–353.)

pression of the reflex arc between bladder and sphincter are factors in neurogenic bladder dysfunction in man;[4] the pudendal nerve is sometimes sectioned to decrease the resistance of the external sphincter.

That the internal sphincter is a gate opened by the pelvic nerve or the sympathetic nerve fibers or by impulses traversing a neural plexus has been directly disproved. Lapides,[21] from experiments based on hydrodynamic principles, supports the view that the internal sphincter opens purely mechanically as a result of contractions of the detrusor muscle and its extensions in the sphincter. The internal sphincter is not truly a sphincter in the literal sense, since the fibers which enclose its opening have no annular organization, arising instead from the detrusor muscle and running longitudinally.

The wall tension opposing distension is exerted by the mechanical properties (tonicity) of the smooth muscle and elastic fibers. That the sphincter resists bladder pressure successfully follows from the law of Laplace, $P = T/R$ (see above and also Chap. 27), since the radius of the urethra is much smaller than that of the bladder and hence the urethral wall exerts a much greater pressure. Stretching (dilation), which reduces wall tension of the sphincter, causes incontinence. Shortening the urethra diminishes and stretching it longitudinally increases resistance to flow through it. Lapides[21] has shown that a tubular "neourethra" fashioned from the fundus wall if 4 cm. long restrains urine when the bladder is at rest and opens during micturition. There can be no question of inhibitory relaxation of such artificial sphincters. This is strong evidence that the urethra opens and closes by an active contraction of the longitudinal muscle. As shown in Figure 7, Lapides visualizes the bladder, which ordinarily resembles a chemical flask (Florence), as becoming pear-shaped during micturition because contraction of the longitudinal muscles makes the sphincter wider and shorter and allows intravesicular pressure to overcome the pressure exerted by the sphincter walls.

From the passive nature of the internal sphincter action, Bradley *et al.*[5] reasoned that an effective stimulus of the bladder musculature could empty it and developed an apparatus for doing this by burying a radio frequency receiver beneath the skin. The receiver is activated with an external radio frequency source of power.

CLINICAL CORRELATIONS. *Tabetic bladder dysfunction.* The most severe neurogenic disturbance of bladder function is that occurring clinically with tabes dorsalis or experimentally after section of the sacral posterior roots. Progressive enlargement and overflow incontinence commence immediately and persist; the micturition reflex is in complete and enduring abeyance. Voluntary micturition is possible only with great effort. The micturition reflex suffers the same fate as the stretch reflex in deafferented skeletal muscle. The segment Ib of the pressure–volume curve is lower and flatter than normal, and the segment II shifts to the higher volumes. Without good reason, this is commonly ascribed to loss of a tonic stretch reflex. Actually, the hypotonus simply represents changes in the property of the smooth muscle secondary to prolonged dilatation. The primary difficulty, therefore, is the absence of the micturition reflex which normally protects the bladder muscle from stretching. Exactly the same situation exists during the initial stages of spinal shock following transection (Fig. 4).

Decentralized or autonomous bladder. Lesions of the conus medullaris, cauda equina or pelvic nerve destroy entirely the efferent as well as the afferent connections of the bladder. The bladder is thus decentralized except for the unimportant sympathetic efferent and afferent connections. The behavior of the bladder is conditioned by the smooth muscle and by whatever neural control is effected through the mural plexus.[9, 20, 23, 24] Initially no active micturition contractions are elicited by effort or in cystometric examination. There is overflow incontinence. Later, a remarkable change occurs; small, brief waves of contraction occur spontaneously or in reaction to stretch or increased intra-abdominal pressures. The larger waves are accompanied by opening of the sphincters, but are inadequate in tension and duration for effective micturition. This results in escape of only small amounts of fluid, leaving residual urine. Such contractions, and particularly the partially coordinated action of the sphincter and detrusor, are often held to mean that the mural plexus serves a "peripheral" reflex. Several facts are difficult to square with the assumption of an independently active peripheral plexus; e.g., no such activities follow interruption of the spinal reflex arcs for micturition by posterior root section. The bladder wall undergoes great hypertrophy after decentralization, which may alter the initial limb of the cystometrogram.

Automatic bladder of spinal transection. As noted, the initial stage of acute spinal shock following transection of the spinal cord above the sacral region is like that following decentralization. No micturition reflex is elicitable; after a period of retention, overflow incontinence supervenes. The retention apparently represents failure of the sequential detrusor-sphincter action. In favorable cases an automatic or "reflex" bladder is established, sometimes with a large residual urine resulting from the weakness and brevity of the micturition reflex; at other times the micturition reflex seems hyperirritable. The lack of voluntary control and knowledge of the time of micturition can be

partly circumvented by using sensory stimulations or bladder pressure to precipitate micturition. Some victims of spinal injury develop what is termed *hypertonic cord bladder*[24] or a *reflex neurogenic bladder*[23] or commonly the "uninhibited cord bladder." The Ib segment of the cystometrogram rises sharply, quite strong micturition contractions occur with small degrees of filling (100 ml.), and residual urine is small. Smaller, spontaneous, regularly occurring detrusor contractions are also present. These phenomena do not appear to occur in spinal animals, and no clear physiologic interpretation is possible. The possibility of an irritative basis as in cystitis must be taken into account. This prediction is borne out by Plum and Colfelt's[30] observation that a chemically induced cystitis can increase bladder tone, enhance rhythmicity and lower the micturition threshold. The first two occur in the preganglionic denervated bladder and the latter may well result when extrinsic nerves are intact. In short, the phenomena ascribed to "disinhibition"—small, frequent emptying—may often be a result of infection rather than disinhibition of the micturition reflex. It is not unlikely that the afferent nerves producing such small, frequent micturitions are nociceptive and different from the stretch afferents involved in normal micturition.

Encephalic Control of Micturition. Micturition, a stretch reflex of the bladder, like the stretch reflex of the skeletal muscle,[32] is subject to control, facilitatory and inhibitory, from several levels of the nervous system. These are summarized in Figure 8, right. For both skeletal and vesical reflexes the basic arc is spinal and, since they both fail for a period after spinal transection, they both must depend on the brain for facilitation. One origin of the facilitatory impulses for the bladder, as stated by

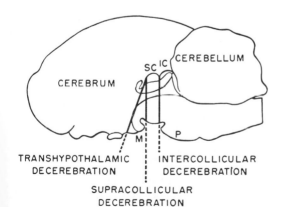

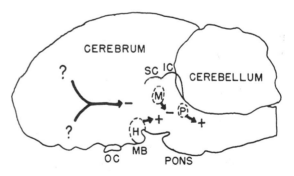

Fig. 8. Schematic sagittal section of cat's brain showing on left transections employed in studying brain stem control of micturition. Diagram at right shows locus of areas (*H,M,P*), as determined by transections and Horsley–Clarke lesions, which facilitate and inhibit micturition: + means facilitation and − means inhibition of micturition reflex; *SC* and *IC*, superior and inferior colliculi; *M* and *MB*, midbrain and mammillary bodies; *OC*, optic chiasm. (From Tang, *J. Neurophysiol.*, 1955, *18*:583–595, and Tang and Ruch, *J. comp. Neurol.*, 1956, *106*:213–245.)

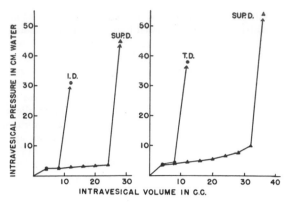

Fig. 9. Cystometrograms after transections of the brain stem establishing a posterior hypothalamic (right) and a midbrain (left) brainstem micturition center. For planes of transection and abbreviations see Figure 8, and for explanation see text. (From Tang and Ruch, *Amer. J. Physiol.*, 1955, *181*:249–257.)

Barrington[2] and others,[16, 35] lies in the anterior pontine region in the location indicated in Figure 8. Section above this level, as in the classic intercollicular decerebration, results in extremely hyperactive micturition reflexes.[35] Cooling[10] or focal lesions at this level or section just below it results in a "spinal" cystometrogram, i.e., complete failure of micturition because a facilitatory area has been destroyed (Fig. 3). The micturition reflex is thus comparable to decerebrate rigidity, although one is phasic and the other postural. This pontine area is a center rather than a way station from higher centers since it facilitates after levels above it are removed.

Because the stretch reflex of the skeletal muscles and the vasoconstrictor neurons of the sympathetic nervous system are tonically facilitated from medullary levels, a similar tonic facilitation of vesical reflexes would be predicted, but is not revealed by transection experiments. Stimulation experiments by Kuru and co-workers[17-19, 38] indicate that the lateral reticular area of the medulla is facilitative to micturition (as it is to skeletal stretch reflex) and sends fibers mainly in the posterolateral column to the sacral region. The medial (and posterior) bulbar area is "vesico-inhibitory" by way of the ventral reticular tract. These areas, if tonic, are exactly balanced or have no ascending afferent input because a section below the anterior pontine micturition facilitatory area is equivalent to a spinal transection. A possibility is that pontine and higher centers exert their influence in part through bulbar facilitatory and inhibitory areas[19] of Kuru which would then be "way stations" rather than "centers."

The extremely low threshold of the micturi-

tion reflex in the intercollicular decerebrate preparation (I.D. in Fig. 3) indicates that areas above this level have a net inhibitory effect, and this is borne out experimentally. A transhypothalamic section preventing the cerebral cortex, basal ganglia and anterior hypothalamus from acting on the sacral micturition reflex arc lowers the threshold (TD in Fig. 9), proving that the structures above have a strong net tonic inhibitory effect. A section through the anterior midbrain (SUP. D.) causes a rise in threshold, proving the existence of a posterior hypothalamic facilitatory center. If the experiment begins with the same supracollicular decerebration (SUP. D. in left of Fig. 9) the same high threshold is obtained, and after an intercollicular decerebration a few millimeters caudally a low threshold is obtained (see Fig. 3), proving the existence of a midbrain inhibitory center (M in Fig. 8).

There exists, therefore, a tonic influence from at least four levels of the nervous system, and successive levels are alternately inhibitory and facilitatory (see Fig. 10).

Stimulation experiments add the information that the cerebellum exerts both excitatory and inhibitory effects on the bladder through one of the brainstem regions described above since the effects occur after decortication.[7] The inhibitory cortical areas have recently been demonstrated.

Considerable clinical information[1] has placed a sensory "center" for the control of micturition (and defecation) in the superior frontal gyrus at the midline and on the adjoining medial surface as shown in Figure 11.

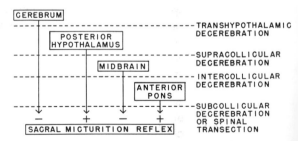

Fig. 10. A summarizing diagram indicating the net facilitatory or inhibitory action of various levels of the nervous system deduced from surgical procedures shown at the right. For simplicity, the diagram does not take into account the possibility that the descending pathways from the higher structures terminate on lower ones, including the bulbar reticular inhibitory and facilitatory areas of Kuru and co-workers.[17, 18, 38] (From Tang, *J. Neurophysiol.*, 1955, *18*:583–595.)

Pathologic and surgical damage to this area may end the desire to micturate and reduce the awareness that micturition is imminent. The ability to restrain micturition or to stop it, once begun, is also impaired. Cystometric curves resemble very closely those seen after decerebration in cats and suggest that the bladder reflex is freed from inhibition. The micturition reflex threshold is as low as 100 ml. and incontinence occurs not as an overflow phenomenon but through overactivity of the unopposed subcortical facilitating centers. As pointed out above, after a transection leaving the posterior hypothalamus intact, the micturition reflex is overactive, which is consistent with these clinical observations.

That many areas are probably involved in micturition is shown by stimulation experiments (Fig. 12). These areas are sensorimotor areas I and II, anterior cingulate, orbital and piriform regions.[12]

In view of the multiple cortical areas and brainstem levels involved in bladder function, it is not surprising that the spinal pathways are in doubt. One is posterolateral and superficial.[16]

The higher control of the micturition reflex obviously is far more complex than the disinhibition of a spinal reflex described in the clinical literature.[23, 25] At the same time it is more understandable in familiar neurophysiologic terms. In fact, no better illustration of the similarity between the higher control of somatic and autonomic reflexes can be found than that obtained by comparing the micturition reflex

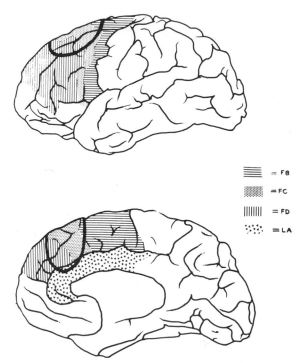

Fig. 11. The area of the human cerebral cortex concerned with initiation and inhibition of micturition (superimposed on cytoarchitectural areas of Von Economo). (From Andrew and Nathan, *Brain,* 1964, *87*:233–262.)

with the myotatic reflex of the hind limb following lesions at different levels of the nervous system. However, certain differences must be kept in mind; e.g., neither the spinal cord nor the brain controls bladder tone, which is a peripheral non-neural phenomenon, whereas the tone of somatic muscles originates entirely

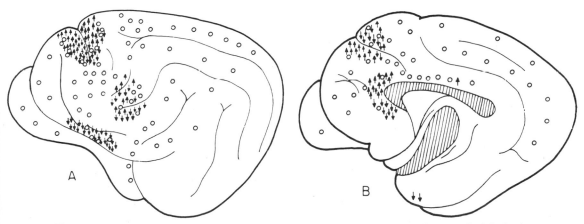

Fig. 12. The cat's brain in lateral (*A*) and medial (*B*) views, showing four cortical loci where electrical stimulation causes bladder contraction, ↑, or relaxation, ↓, or no response, ◯. Note that some of the areas are divided into an inhibitory and an excitatory zone; the area on the orbital surface is purely inhibitory. (From Gjone and Setekleiv, *Acta physiol. scand.,* 1963, *59*:337–348.)

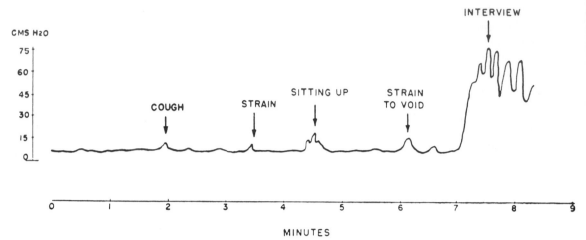

Fig. 13.   Intravesical pressures obtained from a patient during maneuvers which increase intra-abdominal pressures contrasted with those obtained during a stressful psychiatric interview. (From Straub, Ripley and Wolf, *Res. Publ. Ass. nerv. ment. dis.*, 1950, *29*, 1019–1029.)

in spinal reflexes and suprasegmental mechanisms. The neural mechanism for efficient storage and expulsion of urine consists of the sacral spinal reflex arcs, the anterior pons, the midbrain, the posterior hypothalamus and the cerebral cortex. The neural mechanism which determines when and where this mechanism will operate, a matter of considerable importance to the individual, is the contribution of the cerebral cortex.

Psychosomatic Aspects.   Because the "resting" experimental animal shows no change in bladder tonus when its neural axis is sectioned at various levels does not mean that the bladder is not subject to phasic influences from higher centers. Students commonly observe that impending examinations may cause urinary frequency. Experimentally, psychological stimuli such as those involved in a psychiatric interview have been shown to cause the bladder to contract more strongly than do some physiologic stimuli (Fig. 13). While cortical and subcortical centers do not tonically influence bladder tone, electrical stimulation of these centers causes the bladder to contract. Psychological stimuli may be likened therefore to direct brain stimulation.

REFERENCES

1. ANDREW, J. and NATHAN, P. W. *Brain*, 1964, *87*:233–262.
2. BARRINGTON, F. J. F. *Brain*, 1921, *44*:23–53.
3. BORS, E. *Urol. Surv.*, 1957, *7*:177–250.
4. BOYARSKY, S. *Symposium on the neurogenic bladder.* Durham, North Carolina. In press.
5. BRADLEY, W. E., WITTMERS, L. E. and CHOU, S. N. *J. Urol. (Baltimore)*, 1963, *90*:575–582.
6. BRODY, D. A. and QUIGLEY, J. P. *Bull. math. Biophys.*, 1948, *10*:25–30.
7. BRUHN, J. M., FOLEY, J. O., EMERSON, G. M. and EMERSON, J. D. *Amer. J. Physiol.*, 194, *201*:700–702.
8. CARPENTER, F. G. and ROOT, W. S. *Amer. J. Physiol.*, 1951, *166*:686–691.
9. DENNY-BROWN, D. and ROBERTSON, E. G. *Brain*, 1933, *56*:149–190; 397–463.
10. EAST, N. R. *Supraspinal control of bladder reflexes.* M. A. Thesis, University of Washington, Seattle, 1948.
11. GARRY, R. C., ROBERTS, T. D. M. and TODD, J. K. *J. Physiol.*, 1959, *149*:653–665.
12. GJONE, R. and SETEKLEIV, J. *Acta physiol. scand.*, 1963, *59*: 337–348.
13. HEIMBURGER, R. F., FREEMAN, L. W. and WILDE, N. J. *J. Neurosurg.*, 1948, *5*:154–164.
14. HINMAN, F., JR. and MILLER, E. R. *Trans. Amer. Ass. Genitourin. Surg.*, 1963, *55*:13–20.
15. JUUL-JENSEN, P. *Acta neurol. scand.*, 1962, *38*(Suppl. 3): 113–130.
16. KERR, F. W. L. and ALEXANDER, S. *Arch. Neurol. (Chic.)*, 1964, *10*:249–261.
17. KURU, M., KOYAMA, Y. and KURATI, T. *J. comp. Neurol.*, 1960, *115*:15–25.
18. KURU, M., KURATI, T. and KOYAMA, Y. *J. comp. Neurol.*, 1959, *113*:365–388.
19. KURU, M., MAKUYA and KOYAMA, Y. *J. comp. Neurol.*, 1961, *117*:161–178.
20. LANGWORTHY, O. R., KOLB, L. C. and LEWIS, L. G. *Physiology of micturition.* Baltimore, Williams & Wilkins, 1940.
21. LAPIDES, J. *J. Urol.*, 1958, *80*:341–353.
22. LAPIDES, J., SWEET, R. B. and LEWIS, L. W. *J. Urol.*, 1957, *77*:247–250.
23. MCLELLAN, F. C. *The neurogenic bladder.* Springfield, Ill., Charles C Thomas, 1939.
24. MUNRO, D. *New Engl. J. Med.*, 1936, *215*:766–777.

25. Murphy, J. J. and Schoenberg, H. W. *J. Urol.*, 1960, *84:*106–110.
26. Nesbit, R. M. and Baum, W. C. *Neurology*, 1954, *4:*190–199.
27. Nesbit, R. M. and Lapides, J. *Arch. Surg.*, 1948, *56:*138–144.
28. Nesbit, R. M., Lapides, J., Valk, W. W., Sutler, M., Berry, R. L., Lyons, R. H., Campbell, K. N. and Moe, G. K. *J. Urol.*, 1947, *57:*242–250.
29. Plum, R. *Arch. Neurol. (Chic.)*, 1960, *2:*497–503.
30. Plum, F. and Colfelt, R. H., *Arch. Neurol. (Chic.)*, 1960, *2:*487–496.
31. Ruch, T. C., Chap. 48 in *Handbook of Physiology, Section 1: Neurophysiology,* vol. II, J. Field, ed. Washington, D.C., American Physiological Society, 1960.
32. Sherrington, C. S. *Brain,* 1915, *38:*191–234.
33. Smith, R. F., Watson, M. R. and Ruch, T. C. Unpublished observations.
34. Tang, P. C. *Brain stem control of micturition and respiration.* Ph.D. Thesis, University of Washington, Seattle, 1953.
35. Tang, P. C. *J. Neurophysiol.,* 1955, *18:*583–595.
36. Tang, P. C. and Ruch, T. C. *Amer. J. Physiol.,* 1955, *181:* 249–257.
37. Tang, P. C. and Ruch, T. C. *J. comp. Neurol.,* 1956, *106:* 213–246.
38. Tokunaga, S. and Kuru, M. *Jap. J. Physiol.,* 1959, *9:* 365–374.
39. Veenema, R. J., Carpenter, F. G. and Root, W. S. *J. Urol.,* 1952, *68:*237–241.
40. Winton, F. R. and Bayliss, L. E. *Human physiology.* Boston, Little, Brown & Co., 1955.

SECTION XII

METABOLISM

CHAPTER 52

Regulation of Energy Exchange

By JOHN R. BROBECK

THE common observation that men and women reach a plateau of body weight when they become young adults suggests some kind of natural balancing of energy gain and energy output which tends to stabilize the size of energy reserves. This stabilization occurs because the body has mechanisms for control of food intake, activity, heat production and heat loss. Such control is spoken of as a regulation, because it tends to preserve a given variable at a constant level under a given set of conditions, and because it alters the variable when changes occur in the environment or within the body.

Perhaps the clearest example of regulation is body temperature, and it is also the best understood. One can easily identify the mechanisms by which heat production is either increased or decreased and those by which heat loss is enhanced or diminished. All of these mechanisms are controlled by the central nervous system. Through the functioning of specialized cells sensitive to heat, the brain is given information about the temperature of the inside and the surface of the body. This information (and related information about other physiologic variables) is integrated by the brain into a control pattern typical of the situation, and

heat loss and production are adjusted to achieve a certain mean body temperature. In many circumstances these adjustments are amazingly well suited to the conditions, so that the central body temperature deviates very little.

The mechanisms regulating body temperature are used as a model for study and description of other regulations. The model can also be applied to control of food intake and activity, but these two variables are not as constant as body temperature and less is known about the control systems. Nevertheless, food intake is considered first here because it is the only energy source; temperature, activity and energy storage then follow as variables in energy disposition.

CONTROL OF FOOD INTAKE

Sensations of hunger and satiety cannot be studied in laboratory animals because both terms imply a subjective experience or "feeling" which can be verified only in humans. In the laboratory, however, an animal's food intake can be measured directly, experimental conditions can be controlled and altered individually, and by measuring the amount of food ingested per unit time, one may draw conclusions regarding the function of mechanisms which normally impel the animal to eat more or less as circumstances may require. From this type of study, the following relationships have been established: (i) Within certain limits, the common laboratory animals can compensate for periods of food deprivation by increasing their intake when food is again made available. (ii) Animals forced to run eat more than do inactive controls. (iii) Normal, immature animals increase their food intake as growth occurs. (iv) Hypophysectomy depresses food intake and growth. (v) Injection of anterior lobe extracts, which cause nitrogen retention, increases food intake in intact as well as hypophysectomized animals. (vi) Insulin increases food intake when administered before feeding time. (vii) Depancreatized animals with the hyperglycemia and glycosuria of "pancreatic" diabetes eat large amounts of food. (viii) Administration of thyroid preparations increases food intake; (ix) thyroidectomy depresses feeding by about 20 per cent at the usual room temperatures. (x) Food intake is lower during estrus than during diestrus, and (xi) increases during lactation. (xii) In cold environments food consumption rises; (xiii) in hot environments it falls below normal levels. (xiv) During fever the food intake is spontaneously depressed (in human subjects as well as in experimental animals). (xv) Animals and patients whose stomachs have been denervated or even completely removed eat the same amount of food as normal controls, although their feeding habits may be changed in such a way that they eat smaller amounts but eat more often.

Most of these observations apply to human subjects as truly as to experimental animals, but data obtained in the laboratory are more impressive than clinical results because human "appetite" is influenced by a multitude of factors, including mental or psychic attitudes, which either do not exist or can be fairly well controlled in the lower animals.

With the exception of fever and, possibly, insulin hypoglycemia, all of the experimental conditions enumerated above are alike in that each of them represents a change in the rate of energy expenditure to which the animal responds with an alteration of food intake. During recovery from fasting, during growth or

nitrogen retention, lactation, cold exposure, exercise, pancreatic diabetes, experimental hyperthyroidism and, possibly hyperinsulinism, the energy requirement of the animal is increased; *hyperphagia* or increased food intake therefore appears to be a compensatory process. And the decreased food intake of exposure to warm environments or following hypophysectomy or thyroidectomy similarly reflects the diminished energy requirements of the animal in question. The significance of these adjustments in maintaining energy balance does not need further comment. Only during fever is the food intake *decreased* while the total energy expenditure is *increased* above normal levels.

There is another condition characterized by increased food intake: hypothalamic obesity, induced by clinical or experimental lesions in the hypothalamus as discussed in Chapters 11 and 55. In most experimental animals, the appropriate lesions are made surgically, but in mice they can be made by injection of gold thioglucose.[6, 10] These animals eat large quantities of food—as much as two or three times the normal daily intake. Since their rate of energy expenditure is at first not much affected, their hyperphagia upsets the normal equilibrium between intake and output, and the animals are faced with the problem of getting rid of a huge food surplus. They dispose of this by burning some of it and by storing the remainder (the larger portion) as fat, with the result that they eventually become remarkably obese. This condition (Chap. 11, Fig. 4) is said to be caused by "hypothalamic hyperphagia." It has been observed in rats, cats, dogs and monkeys, and there is no reason to question its identity with the obesity of human subjects who suffer from tumors, infections or other pathologic processes involving the base of the brain, including the hypothalamus.

Hypothalamic hyperphagia must be distinguished from all of the other types of hyperphagia enumerated above. In growth, hyperthyroidism and cold exposure, the increased food intake is a compensatory response to a condition of altered energy expenditure. Energy equilibrium is not disturbed by the extra food but rather is maintained, and the animal's ability to increase its food intake proves that the mechanisms which regulate the energy supply are functioning normally. However, in the animal with hypothalamic lesions, the increased food consumption appears to be the re-

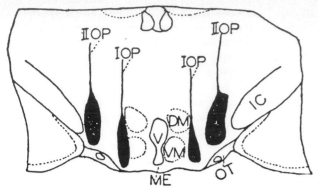

Fig. 1. Transverse section through tuberal region of hypothalamus. Medial lesions (*IOP*) induced hyperphagia and obesity; lateral lesions (*IIOP*) abolished feeding. *ME,* Median eminence; *OT,* optic tract; *IC,* internal capsule; *DM,* dorsomedial nucleus; *VM,* ventromedial nucleus; *V,* third ventricle. (From Anand and Brobeck, *Yale J. Biol. Med.,* 1951, *24:*123–140.)

sult of a basic disturbance in the regulatory mechanisms themselves.

Another kind of feeding disturbance can be induced by injury to the hypothalamus, when the lesions are bilaterally symmetrical and restricted to the lateral hypothalamic area at the level of the median eminence (Fig. 1). Follow-

ing such injury animals exhibit a complete and prolonged failure of spontaneous feeding, although they have no other obvious abnormalities.[1] They will starve to death with food present in their cages, showing not the slightest interest in the food; yet they may be kept alive and in good condition by intragastric feeding. Electrical stimulation of these regions is followed by a considerable increase in food intake in otherwise normal animals.[5] The lateral hypothalamus evidently contains a mechanism essential for feeding behavior, and it is probably the unopposed activity of this mechanism that causes hyperphagia in animals with lesions in the medial part of the hypothalamus. The medial and lateral mechanisms evidently interact in the normal regulation of feeding.

Feeding behavior is probably based upon certain reflexes initiated by the sight, sound or odor of food, or by contact with it. Those reflexes which do not involve the special senses are completed through the lower brain stem, since Miller and Sherrington[12] observed reflex chewing and swallowing in decerebrate cats. The reflexes causing an animal to move toward a source of food and to grasp it with hands or mouth are more complex, possibly requiring

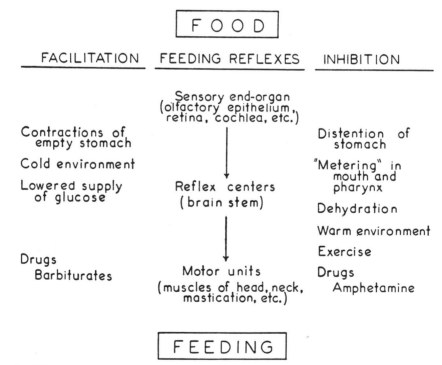

Fig. 2. Diagram of basic reflex pathways concerned with feeding, showing factors believed to facilitate and to inhibit these reflexes.

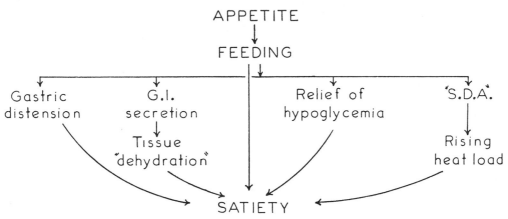

Fig. 3. Outline of factors known to play a part in converting *appetite* into *satiety*. The process of eating, itself, is one such factor; others include the reactions and mechanisms listed on the diagram.

activity of higher levels of the nervous system. The hypothalamus may act to facilitate or to inhibit these reflexes (Fig. 2). If the facilitation is removed by lateral lesions, the reflexes are not completed and feeding is abolished, whereas if the inhibition is removed by more medial lesions, the animals overeat and become obese. Regulation of feeding, however, is not achieved autonomously, but is integrated with other regulations concerned with energy exchange. The hyperactivity preceding the feeding period and that of animals deprived of food (above) seem to be examples of the interaction of these regulations. Other examples will possibly be discovered through further study.

Another topic of some interest is the nature of the changes within the body which are capable of signaling to the brain that feeding has taken place or is necessary. Perhaps one kind of signal increases appetite and diminishes satiety, thereby increasing food intake. (This same signal may also bring about the increase in generalized or locomotor activity which normally anticipates a feeding period.) Another kind of signal, or the first signal in reverse direction, may indicate that feeding has taken place, that nourishment is on its way to the tissues, and that feeding should cease.

There is no lack of possible reactions in the body that might serve as these signals. Several of the prominent ones are shown in Figure 3. First of all there is the act of eating. Experiments by Janowitz and Grossman[8] have revealed that in chewing and swallowing food a certain degree of satiation is produced, even if the food does not reach the stomach. Filling the

stomach is another important reaction that has been studied by several investigators, including Carlson.[3] Mayer's experiments have implied some relationship to blood sugar levels or, better, to the availability of glucose to the nervous system.[11] Other studies have emphasized the correlation between thirst and hunger and also the relationship between feeding and the conditions of temperature regulation. Perhaps the list should be extended to include the products of digestion. The function of the nervous system is to integrate all of these changes—and any others yet unknown—into a common denominator, the activity of neurons responsible for finding food and eating it.

CONTROL OF MOTOR OUTPUT

Measurement of Locomotor Activity. The measurement of motor output requires the use of apparatus specifically adapted to the type of activity in question. Experimental animals ordinarily do not accomplish "work" as man does, but they do use food energy for muscular contractions, especially those contractions by means of which they move from one place to another. With appropriate apparatus this locomotor activity can be measured and may be taken, in the words of Slonaker,[16] "as an indicator of all of the activities of an individual. Numerous observations of the activities of the rat readily convince one of the fact that though running is only one phase of activity, it goes hand in hand with and is proportional to the other activities."

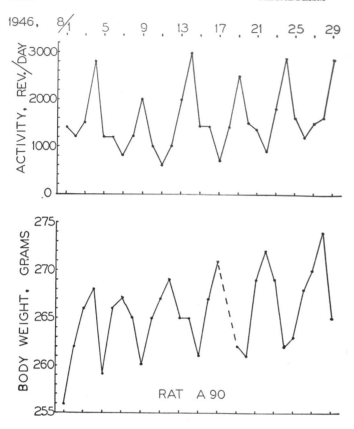

Fig. 4. Rhythms of activity and body weight. Weight gain occurs during diestrus, weight loss during estrus. (From Brobeck *et al.*, *Endocrinology*, 1947, *40*:65–72.)

Normal activity rhythms. A convenient and widely used device for measuring locomotion is called the "activity cage"; it consists either of a table or a wide wheel which rotates freely on a bearing-suspended shaft. A counter records each revolution as the animal turns the cage on its axis. Beside the "activity" cage there is usually a small "living" cage in which food and water are provided. With this type of apparatus some of the factors which influence motor output have been discovered. Wang[18] and Slonaker[17] have shown that the sex cycle of the female definitely affects spontaneous activity, since, on the day of estrus, rats run eight or ten times as much as on the intervening days of their cycle (Fig. 4). Ovariectomy abolishes this estral hyperactivity, and the implantation of ovaries subsequently restores the response. Male rats fail to show a similar rhythm, although castrated males with implanted ovaries are said to undergo cyclic changes in activity which suggest the female type of behavior. Richter[14] discovered that both male and female rats accomplish most of their running just before they begin to eat and that the ingestion of food is followed by a period of quiescence.

Browman[2] found that still another rhythm of activity is associated with the diurnal cycle of light and dark. Rats are more active in the dark, and by artificial control of the lighting conditions, the rats can be made to run more during the dark daytime periods than during the lighted nighttime hours. Browman found also that temperature variations tend to influence the activity when the effect of light and dark has been abolished by blinding the animals. His blinded rats ran more in cooler than in warmer environments.

The results of all these experiments can be summarized with the statement that the activity of rats is increased by the dark, in cold environments, during starvation (Fig. 5), just before feeding time and, in the female, during estrus; activity is depressed in the light, in warm environments, after feeding, and during diestrus, pregnancy, pseudopregnancy and lactation. The cause of activity rhythms is not known, and at the present time one cannot say whether each rhythm is unique in its origin or whether all depend upon some common basic mechanism. From a metabolic point of view, their control has one distinctive feature, in that at least three of the conditions in which hyperactivity occurs are characterized by either an actual or an incipient energy deficit. In cold exposure and during estrus, and in the short interval just before a feeding period, the rat is undergoing a progressive depletion of energy reserves because of either an increased energy output or a limitation of supply. But in the face of this real or threatened deficit, the animal further increases the rate of energy utilization by indulging in the luxury of hyperactivity (Fig. 4). A related phenomenon appears when the food intake is arbitrarily restricted in quantity; on an amount of food which allows a regular gain of body weight by inactive rats, animals free to run in activity cages will exercise enough to bring about a continual weight loss (Fig. 6). Whatever the nature of the mechanisms regulating motor output, it is clear that their function is not directed solely toward the goal of energy balance.

Deficits of Control. In a certain few clinical conditions, one of which is an infectious disease called *encephalitis lethargica,* muscular ac-

tivity may be reduced even to the point of complete flaccidity of all the voluntary muscles. At autopsy, neurons of the posterior hypothalamus have been found to be damaged or destroyed as the result of the infection, and this observation had led to the opinion that normal activity is maintained in some way by this part of the brain stem. This opinion is supported by studies on monkeys, cats and rats.[7, 13] Animals with experimentally produced discrete lesions of the central and posterior hypothalamus become lethargic and tend to be somnolent; in activity cages the rats may run little or not at all. Ranson suggested that the hypothalamus is a "waking center," and, from his experiments and those of other investigators, one may conclude that this part of the diencephalon participates in some way in the normal regulation of motor output.

Contrasting with the lethargy and inactivity of animals with certain hypothalamic lesions is a state of almost continuous locomotion that has been produced in rats, cats and some monkeys by the bilateral ablation of portions of the

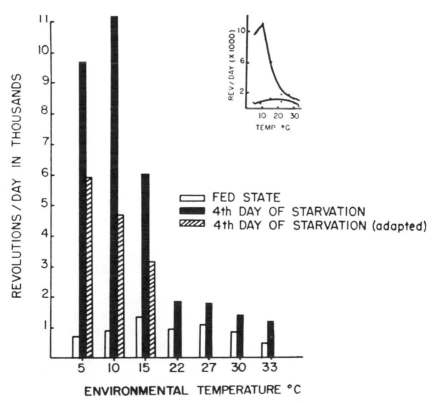

Fig. 5. Effect of starvation and a cold environment upon spontaneous activity of rats. (From Stevenson, J. A. F. in *Cold Injury, Third Conference,* pp. 165–168. New York, Josiah Macy, Jr. Foundation, 1954.)

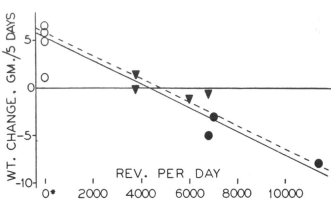

Fig. 6. Negative correlation between locomotor activity and weight gain in female rats maintained on constant food intake in constant temperature room. *Cages closed to prevent running. (From Brobeck, *Amer. J. Physiol.*, 1945, *143*:1–5.)

frontal lobe (see also Chap. 23). Animals subjected to this operation move almost constantly about the cage. As Ruch and Shenkin pointed out,[15] the disturbance is not one of generalized irritability and hyperexcitability, because the animals are in other respects docile and quiescent. The operation specifically changes the amount of the animal's locomotion. Ruch and Shenkin produced hyperactivity in monkeys by bilateral lesions in a small area on the orbital surface of the frontal lobes, whereas Davis[4] found hyperactivity only in animals having injury to the tip of the caudate nuclei, which underlie the areas removed by Ruch and Shenkin. These authors further observed that regulation of food intake was normal in their monkeys; in spite of the high level of energy expenditure occasioned by their hyperactivity, the animals lost only a small amount of weight because they ate more food than they had eaten before the operation.

Experimental study suggests, therefore, that at least two levels of the central nervous system participate in the normal control of motor output: the hypothalamus and the frontal cortex, especially a specific area on the orbital surface of the frontal lobe. At the present time it is impossible to say whether these two levels function together to bring about the normal rhythms of locomotor activity. It is fairly clear, however, that the energy utilization of normal animals may undergo large quantitative changes because their motor output varies from time to time, and that in certain circumstances these variations may tend to upset rather than preserve energy equilibrium.

In normal man the motor output may vary all the way from the relaxation of deep sleep to the heroic efforts associated with athletic records or deeds of valor. The energy requirements of various types of activity are fairly well known, as are the adjustments in the several functions comprising what is known as the physiology of muscular exercise. Less attention has been given to the control of this activity, that is, to what might be called the "willingness" to work. Why are some persons more energetic than others? Why does a team play well one day and poorly another? Under what conditions is the work output the greatest, and what determines the efficiency of the work? All of these questions are of interest, and possibly important, in industry as well as in sports, but few data are available to answer them. A method for conducting research in this field is suggested by the report of Kraut and Muller,[9] who studied the work output of men during the war in Germany when food supplies were limited. Providing extra food increased the work done by the men; but even greater rises in work were induced by offering cigarettes as a reward in place of food. In these men, as in laboratory animals, the control of work output was not necessarily directed toward the goal of energy balance.

REGULATION OF BODY TEMPERATURE

In the preceding sections of this chapter two of three aspects of energy exchange have been discussed: food intake and voluntary work output. These are largely behavioral in nature. The third aspect, the regulation of body temperature, is mainly physical and to understand it requires a knowledge of the way heat is generated and moved through, into or out of the body. This is the subject matter of the next two chapters. In the final chapter of this section, certain biochemical aspects of energy metabolism are discussed.

REFERENCES

1. ANAND, B. K. and BROBECK, J. R. *Yale J. Biol. Med.,* 1951, *24:*123–140.
2. BROWMAN, L. G. *J. exp. Zool.,* 1943, *94:*477–489.
3. CARLSON, A. J. *Control of hunger in health and disease.* Chicago, University of Chicago Press, second imp., 1916.
4. DAVIS, G. D. *Locomotor hyperactivity induced by cerebral lesions in the monkey.* Ph.D. thesis, Yale University, 1951.
5. DELGADO, J. M. R. and ANAND, B. K. *Amer. J. Physiol.,* 1953, *172:*162–168.
6. DRACHMAN, R. H. and TEPPERMAN, J. *Yale J. Biol. Med.,* 1954, *26:*394–409.
7. HETHERINGTON, A. W. and RANSON, S. W. *Amer. J. Physiol.,* 1942, *136:*609–617.
8. JANOWITZ, H. D. and GROSSMAN, M. I. *Amer. J. Physiol.,* 1949, *159:*143–148.
9. KRAUT, H. A. and MULLER, E. A. *Science,* 1946, *104:*495–497.
10. MARSHALL, N. B., BARRNETT, R. J. and MAYER, J. *Proc. Soc. exp. Biol. (N. Y.),* 1955, *90:*240–244.
11. MAYER, J. *Ann. N. Y. Acad. Sci.,* 1955, *63:*15–43.
12. MILLER, F. R. and SHERRINGTON, C. S. *Quart. J. exp. Physiol.,* 1916, *9:*147–186.
13. RANSON, S. W. *Harvey Lect.,* 1936–37, *32:*92–121.
14. RICHTER, C. P. *Quart. Rev. Biol.,* 1927, *2:*307–343.
15. RUCH, T. C. and SHENKIN, H. A. *J. Neurophysiol.,* 1943, *6:*349–360.
16. SLONAKER, J. R. *J. Anim. Behav.,* 1912, *2:*20–42.
17. SLONAKER, J. R. *Amer. J. Physiol.,* 1925, *73:*485–503.
18. WANG, G. H. *Amer. Nat.,* 1924, *58:*36–42.

CHAPTER 53

Energy Metabolism

By ARTHUR C. BROWN and GEORGE BRENGELMANN

INTERNAL ENERGY

Role of Food.[1, 23] That a man must eat in order to remain alive is both generally accepted and true; but why this is so is far from obvious. An initial guess might be that food is essential to produce energy within the body, but this is negated by the law of conservation of energy: i.e., energy can be neither created nor destroyed (with some rather spectacular and worrisome exceptions which, although important in world politics, are not directly involved in energy metabolism). Thus, the body cannot consume or produce energy; at most it can convert energy between its various forms. This can be elaborated into a second guess, more plausible but still specious: the body loses energy continuously to the environment, mainly in the form of heat; therefore, the continuous consumption of food whose energy can be converted into heat is necessary to maintain thermal balance. If this were true, then a man encased in a perfectly insulating material could exist indefinitely without eating. The reader would be ill advised to attempt such an experiment, since the subject would die from hyperthermia within a few hours and thus would be freed from the necessity of further food consumption only in a rather perverse sense.

To understand the role of food in the maintenance of life, it is necessary to probe more deeply into the body's need for energy.

Those bodily phenomena associated with life are characterized by the natural or spontaneous tendency to run down by dissipating their available energy. For example, because of its viscosity, the blood loses mechanical energy continuously as it passes through the peripheral circulation, the rate of pressure drop being a measure of this energy loss. To propagate an action potential down an axon, part of the energy stored across the axon membrane must be used up. Similarly, other vital processes draw upon their particular form of stored or potential energy.

To sustain life, this energy must be restored.

Ideally, the biological energy could be taken from a variety of sources, since, given proper circumstances, any form of energy may be completely converted into any other form. But conditions within the body are not suitable for such universal interconversion:

First, in the body, thermal or heat energy cannot be changed into any of the other energy forms. Efficient utilization of thermal energy requires large temperature differences;* however, bodily processes are essentially isothermal (constant temperature). Mechanical energy, electrical energy and chemical free energy are converted readily to heat, but within the body, the reverse is impossible. Thus, the heat which results from the dissipation of other energy forms is essentially a waste product and must be lost from the body.

Second, other forms of external energy, such as light, electricity and mechanical energy, cannot fuel the body simply because the body does not possess the appropriate energy-coupling mechanisms. Man accrues no useful energy from lying in the hot sun, from standing on a vibrating machine or from sticking his finger into an electric light socket. These energy sources are not, like heat, prevented by thermodynamic laws from fueling the body; rather, the basic design of humans and other animals simply contains no provision for the use of such external energy sources.

The single form of energy which animals can utilize is that inherent in specific molecular configurations of certain ingested substances: the chemical free energy of food. This ability is due to the development of the biochemical, structural and physiologic apparatus which permits the transformation of chemical free energy into the other energy forms essential for life.

This may be stated another way: Life as we know it is characterized by a definite structure of cells, tissues, etc., a relatively high concentration of energetic biochemical compounds, and the maintenance of other forms of potential energy such as electrical potential and pressure. This implies an ordered and organized arrangement of atoms which is always out of equilibrium. The spontaneous or natural tendency is to dissipate this order and excess energy and thus approach equilibrium. By utilizing food, structure and internal energy are maintained. Thus we do not really consume energy; all the

* The initiated will recognize the Second Law of Thermodynamics.

energy of food is eventually lost from the body, although usually in another form. Instead we use the highly structured arrangement of chemical bonds in food, the chemical free energy, to purchase internal order and displacement from equilibrium. When, for an individual, this is no longer possible, the spontaneous influences dominate and he approaches a state of physical and chemical equilibrium with his surroundings—i.e., death.

The source of the chemical free energy used by man is provided either directly or indirectly by plants: directly when plants are eaten or indirectly when other animals are eaten whose food chain begins with plants. Plants, of course, do not manufacture energy *de novo*, but instead utilize the high energy photons emitted as solar radiation. The sun obtains its energy from nuclear reactions inherent in the primordial energy source of the universe. The discussion of the origin of this primordial energy involves either advanced physics or metaphysics, depending upon one's inclinations, but in either case need not be pursued further here.

Thus, man is an ultimate parasite upon the energy stores of the universe, consuming energy as a highly organized chemical structure and emitting it mainly as heat, in which form it is of no use whatsoever.

Energy Units. Among the various units commonly used in measuring energy are foot-pounds, ergs, joules, kilowatt-hours, watt-seconds, electron volts, British thermal units and calories. The unit usually employed in human metabolism is the kilocalorie (Kcal.), also called the kilogram calorie or the large Calorie. In terms of heat, one Kcal. is approximately the quantity of energy necessary to raise one kilogram of water (or one liter of water) by one degree centigrade. A kilocalorie is equal to 1000 "common" or "small" calories. The "calories" referred to in standard human nutrition tables which list energy content of various foods are actually Kcals.

The rate of energy conversion per unit time, sometimes termed *power*, is usually expressed in human metabolism as Kcals. per hour. This can be converted to the common physical unit of joules per second or watts by the relation

$$1 \text{ Kcal. per hour} = 1.16 \text{ watts.}$$

The physiologically "average" man, having a mass of 70 kilograms (154 pounds) and a surface area of 1.73 square meters, sitting quietly reading this chapter will be converting energy at the approximate rate of 85 Kcal. per hour, or about the same as a 100 watt light bulb. One hundred men similarly employed in the same room would generate 10 kilowatts of heat, an amount sufficient to cause appreciable discomfort in the absence of adequate ventilation.

Internal Energy Utilization. From the viewpoint of energy metabolism, man is a thermodynamic machine who consumes energy from food, converting or degrading this energy, and then passing it on to the environment. Thus, energy metabolism requires consideration of (i) the amount of energy intake, (ii) the rate of energy conversion or energy output, both of which are discussed in succeeding sections, and (iii) the general utilization of energy within the body.

Entropy and free energy. Part of the energy obtained from food is thermodynamically obligated for conversion to heat since the entropy of metabolic end products is greater than that of the initial substrates. In other words, the heat energy content and free energy content of food are not necessarily identical, the latter being generally somewhat less. Thus, even if the maximum amount of useful or free energy is extracted from food, when it is metabolized, some heat must be produced. The fraction of the energy thus obligated to heat is not large; for example, in the metabolism of glucose, entropy increase accounts for about 5 per cent of the total energy.

The preceding is an application of the thermodynamic relation

$$\Delta G = \Delta H - T\Delta S$$

where ΔG is the free energy change, ΔH is the enthalpy change, ΔS is the entropy change, and T is the absolute temperature. It can be shown that ΔG is the maximum amount of useful energy which can be extracted from a constant temperature and pressure process, while ΔH represents the total heat plus useful energy change, again at constant temperature and pressure. In most human metabolic processes, T is constant, at about 37° C. or 310° K. Also, the entropy generally increases; for example, in the oxidation of glucose, the entropy total of the initial products $C_6H_{12}O_6 + 6O_2$ is 0.345 (Kcal. per mol per degree C.) while the entropy of the final products $6CO_2 + 6H_2O$ is 0.407 (Kcal. per mol per degree C.). Thus, $T\Delta S$ is positive, so the change in total energy, ΔH, is greater than the maximum change in free energy, ΔG; the difference

between these two represents energy which must be converted to heat.

High energy intermediates. Thus, perhaps 95 per cent of the ingested energy is potentially available as free energy. But, before such energy can be utilized, it must be present in the appropriate chemical form. An example of such a chemical substance capable of fueling a wide variety of vital activity is adenosine triphosphate, ATP. In this sense, ATP can be viewed as an energy shuttle, using the free energy of the food to synthesize its high energy phosphate bonds, and then releasing the energy in these bonds to such processes as muscle contraction and active sodium transport.

However, the conversion of food energy into a high energy biochemical compound is far from perfectly efficient. For example, the complete oxidative metabolism of 1 mol of glucose —free energy: 686 Kcal. per mol—produces only 38 mols of ATP, in which the free energy of hydrolysis is about 9 Kcal. per mol. Thus, more than one half of the potentially available free energy is wasted because of biochemical inefficiency; this wasted energy appears instead as heat, in which form it is lost from the body to the environment.

Biochemical and structural steady state. Once reduced to a useful form, the free energy is employed in a variety of bodily functions. One of these is the maintenance of the biochemical and structural integrity of the body.

In its normal function, the body must maintain relatively high concentrations of high energy compounds. These concentrations are high in the sense that they are greater than the equilibrium concentrations: i.e., concentrations which would occur under the sole influence of passive forces. Thus, high energy compounds are continually breaking down spontaneously, generally releasing heat. Since these compounds are essential for proper operation of the body's chemical machinery, they must be resynthesized to maintain steady state levels; this resynthesis requires free energy. The net result is the evolution of heat and the consumption of free energy.

In a similar way, the cellular and subcellular structural elements, composed of highly organized compounds in higher than equilibrium concentrations, also tend to break down spontaneously. To maintain life, these must be resynthesized, again at the expense of free energy.

Thus, the structural integrity of the body as well as its biochemical integrity depend upon an adequate supply of free energy.

Internal work. Another category of internal energy utilization is internal work. The circulation of the blood and the movement of air into and out of the lungs dissipate mechanical energy into heat, which energy must be restored through muscular contraction fueled by chemical free energy. The propagation of action potentials dissipates electrical energy into heat; the electrical energy must be restored by active transport of ions fueled by chemical free energy. Thus, the net result for these and other organ systems which perform physical work within the body is the conversion of mechanical or electrical potential into thermal energy and the concurrent restoration of this potential by drawing upon the chemical free energy.

External work. All of the processes discussed above—obligatory entropy increase, inefficiency of free energy conversion, maintenance of biochemical and structural integrity, internal physical work—although they differ greatly in most respects, share a common energy end product: heat. However, skeletal muscle contraction makes possible an additional end product for energy, external work performed on the environment.

When skeletal muscle is activated, its rate of chemical energy conversion increases. Some of this energy simply is transformed into the various heats associated with the contraction cycle —heat of activation, heat of shortening, and so forth. But since skeletal muscle can cause external movement, some of the chemical energy may be utilized to perform external physical work in the form of force applied through a distance, e.g., lifting a weight against gravity or sliding an object against the retarding influence of friction. The fraction of the total energy converted into mechanical work depends upon the pattern of contraction as determined by the loading of the muscle—i.e., isometric (constant length), isotonic (constant force), inertial load (force depends upon acceleration), viscous load (force depends upon velocity), elastic load (force depends upon length), or some combination of these. Under the most favorable conditions in an isolated muscle, approximately 40 per cent of the total energy may be converted to mechanical work. In contrast, when muscle contraction is isometric, no external work is possible since, although a force

is developed, the distance moved is zero; thus, all the chemical energy utilized appears as heat. In normal contraction, external work generally is intermediate between these two extremes.

Some confusion exists on the meaning of the term "work" when applied to muscle contraction, to exercise, etc. For example, if a subject holds a 10 Kg. (22 pound) weight horizontally at arm's length, the physicist would correctly claim that the subject is doing no physical work, since the weight is stationary. (However, no evidence can be found that a physicist has ever attempted this experiment.) But the physiologist would claim, also correctly, that physiologic work has increased significantly, since this task has increased the subject's oxygen consumption, heat production, metabolic rate, etc. Thus, in discussions of "work," the external, physical, force-times-distance work must be carefully distinguished from the internal rate of free energy expenditure.

A second point worth noting is that although a muscle can convert chemical free energy into mechanical energy, the reverse cannot occur. For example, consider the cycle of lifting a weight vertically from a table and then gently replacing it. As the weight is being lifted, the arm muscles do physical work on the weight, increasing its gravitational potential. As the weight is being replaced, it does an equal amount of physical work on the muscles, but this work is not converted into chemical potential; rather it is simply lost as heat due to muscle viscosity. The inability of muscle to utilize external mechanical energy, or, in a larger sense, the inability of the body to utilize any energy source other than food free energy, is an unfortunate oversight in the physiologic design of our bodies which is particularly annoying in these times of low cost electrical energy and high food prices.

Efficiency of exercise. The efficiency of the body considered as a mechanical machine fueled by chemical energy can be calculated from the ratio of external work to internal energy conversion rate. *Gross efficiency* is defined as (external work)/(total internal energy conversion rate) and *net efficiency* is defined as (external work)/(internal energy conversion rate increase necessary to accomplish the work). Thus a person who begins to exercise by doing external work at the rate of 20 Kcal. per hour might show a steady state metabolic rate increase from 80 Kcal. per hour just before exercise to 180 Kcal. per hour during exercise; this would give a gross efficiency of $20/180 = 11$ per cent and a net efficiency of $20/(180 - 80) = 20$ per cent.

Under optimal conditions, the net efficiency of the body as a machine is about 25 per cent. This is greater than the efficiency of a steam

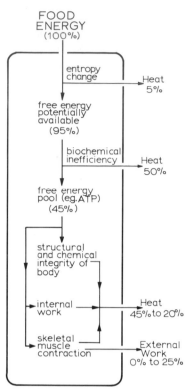

FOOD ENERGY (100%)

entropy change

Heat 5%

free energy potentially available (95%)

biochemical inefficiency

Heat 50%

free energy pool (eg. ATP) (45%)

structural and chemical integrity of body

internal work

Heat 45% to 20%

skeletal muscle contraction

External Work 0% to 25%

Fig. 1. Summary of the distribution of ingested food energy within the body and its transfer to the environment.

engine, about equal to the efficiency of an internal combustion engine, and greatly inferior to the efficiency of a well designed electric motor. The body's efficiency in exercise is less than that of isolated muscle, since in exercise energy expenditure is increased for circulation, respiration and other internal supportive activities not present in isolated muscle preparations.

In typical circumstances, the mechanical efficiency of the body is considerably less than 25 per cent. For example, the reader of this book undoubtedly has an efficiency at this moment of close to 0 per cent, since he is doing almost no external work at all (unless he has very unusual study habits).

In summary, chemical free energy is utilized in a variety of body processes (see Fig. 1). The end product of all of these processes is heat, or, for skeletal muscle contraction, both heat and external work. The distribution between heat and work is variable; at maximum efficiency the distribution is 25 per cent work, 75 per cent heat; more typically, work accounts for only a few per cent of the final energy and heat accounts for all the rest.

ENERGY INTAKE

Energy Equivalents. The evaluation of human energy intake is greatly simplified by the thermodynamic relation that the energy available from any chemical reaction is entirely determined by the initial substrates and end products. Thus, the available energy is completely independent of the particular chemical pathway by which the reaction proceeds; which intermediates are formed, which enzymes are utilized, or even whether the reaction occurs in the body or in the test tube are all extraneous in determining the energy change. For example, the oxidation of glucose is given by the stochiometric relation shown in Figure 2. From this it may be calculated that ingesting and absorbing 1 gram of glucose increases the body's free energy content by 3.81 Kcal. (686 Kcal./ 180 grams = 3.81). Although the energy is actually released only as metabolism occurs, glucose normally does not leave the body in any form except as its oxidation end products; thus, the absorption of glucose may be considered identical to increasing the internal free energy content of the body.

From Figure 2 it is possible also to calculate the oxygen consumption necessary to burn 1 mol of glucose, the volume of carbon dioxide produced, etc., since all of these quantities are determined by balancing this simple chemical reaction and not by the biochemical mechanisms employed. The biochemical pathways are, of course, far from unimportant, since they control both the particular uses to which the energy is put and the fraction of the available free energy which is usefully utilized instead of simply being degraded into heat. However, from the viewpoint of general energy intake, the initial and final products alone determine the energy content of food.

Measurement of Food Energy. Advantage is taken of the independence of available energy from chemical pathway by measuring the energy inherent in various foods under the most convenient conditions, i.e., *in vitro* outside the body. The instrument generally used for this measurement is the *bomb calorimeter,* a sealed container filled with pure oxygen to ensure complete combustion, in which a known amount of the food to be tested is ignited electrically (see Fig. 3). By measuring the heat released upon oxidation and dividing by the amount of food, the caloric value in kilocalories per gram can be calculated.

GLUCOSE (carbohydrate)

$$C_6H_{12}O_6 \quad + \quad 6\,O_2 \quad = 6\,CO_2 + 6\,H_2O + 686\,Kcal.$$

180 gm.   134.4 L.   134.4 L.   108 ml.

TRIBUTYRIN (lipid)

$$C_3H_5O_3(OC_4H_7)_3 + 18\tfrac{1}{2}\,O_2 = 15\,CO_2 + 13\,H_2O + 1941\,Kcal.$$

302 gm.   414.4 L.   336.0 L.   234 ml.

LEUCINE (amino acid)

$$C_6H_{13}O_2N \quad + \quad 7\tfrac{1}{2}\,O_2 \quad = 5\tfrac{1}{2}\,CO_2 + 5\tfrac{1}{2}\,H_2O + \tfrac{1}{2}\,CO(NH_2)_2 + 780\,Kcal.$$

131 gm.   168.0 L.   123.2 L.   99 ml.   1/2 mol

UREA

$$CO(NH_2)_2 \quad + \quad 1\tfrac{1}{2}\,O_2 \quad = \quad CO_2 \quad + 2\,H_2O + N_2 \quad + \quad 151\,Kcal.$$

60 gm.   33.6 L.   22.4 L.   36 ml.   22.4 L.

ETHANOL

$$C_2H_5OH \quad + \quad 3\,O_2 \quad = 2\,CO_2 + 3\,H_2O + 327\,Kcal.$$

46 gm.   67.2 L.   44.8 L.   54 ml.

Fig. 2. Chemical oxidation of typical substrates.

Two cautions must be noted in applying bomb calorimetric values to human metabolism. First, the bomb calorimeter burns all foods to their final oxidation products, but this is not necessarily true for the body, particularly in the metabolism of proteins. Thus, the nitrogenous end products of human protein metabolism are urea, uric acid, ammonia, etc., and not the nitrogen gas or oxides of nitrogen characteristic of the bomb calorimeter. Human metabolism does not break down proteins to their lowest energy state; in other words, the oxidation of urea releases further energy. Thus, the energy released by the bomb calorimeter is greater than that released by an equal amount of protein burned in the body.

Fortunately, the bomb calorimeter values can be corrected without the necessity of *in vivo* measurements, by burning in the calorimeter the appropriate amount of the human metabolic end product, e.g., urea, and simply subtracting the heat so obtained from heat of the total oxidation of protein. This computation is possible because, as has been continually emphasized, the energy available from any reaction depends only upon the states of the initial and final constituents, and not upon the details of the transition. Thus, the energy of the reaction protein → urea must be the difference between the energy of the reaction protein → nitrogen and urea → nitrogen (see Fig. 4).

A similar correction is not necessary for

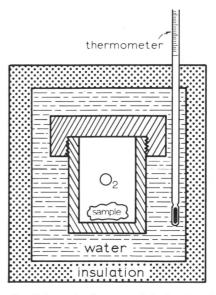

Fig. 3. Schematic diagram of the bomb calorimeter. The electric leads used to initiate the oxidation are not shown. The outer insulation is used to confine the evolved heat. The sealed inner chamber in which the reaction takes place is surrounded by water; the water increases the thermal capacity and distributes the heat evenly.

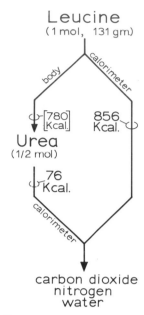

Leucine
(1 mol, 131 gm)

[780]
Kcal.

856
Kcal.

Urea
(1/2 mol)

76
Kcal.

carbon dioxide
nitrogen
water

Fig. 4. Two pathways for oxidation of leucine. Both branches, the direct oxidation and the oxidation via urea, must have identical total energy release, 856 Kcal. per mol. Thus, the energy of the biologic metabolism must be the difference between the energy released from oxidation of leucine and oxidation of urea in the bomb calorimeter.

carbohydrates and lipids, since they are generally reduced to the identical end products of carbon dioxide and water in both the body and the calorimeter.

The second source of possible difficulty in applying calorimetric measurements to human energy intake concerns food absorption. Substances which are ingested but not absorbed cannot, of course, contribute to body energy. When burnt in the calorimeter, cellulose shows an energy content similar to that of other carbohydrates; but in the human body, cellulose has no energy value simply because it cannot be digested by human gastrointestinal enzymes and thus cannot pass through the intestinal epithelium.

The normal diet, particularly in the more affluent countries, consists almost entirely of easily digested foods, so that almost all of the ingested energy is actually absorbed, if gastrointestinal function is normal. However, in some circumstances, such as an unusually high intake of indigestible fibrous materials or other roughage, or in a condition of pathologic malabsorption, such as diarrhea, the fraction of ingested energy which the body can absorb may be considerably reduced below the normal level.

Energy Content.[9, 24]   *Carbohydrates.*   All carbohydrates do not have identical energy values in terms of Kcal. per gram. However, the energy values are sufficiently similar to permit a single figure to be used for all foods in this category. Taking the common carbohydrates in the proportion in which they normally occur in the diet gives a mean value of about 4.1 Kcal. per gram of carbohydrate oxidized. Since these carbohydrates are almost completely absorbed, the "physiologic" caloric value—the Kcal. per gram *ingested*—is only slightly lower: about 4 Kcal. per gram (see Table 1).

In theory, it would be possible to evaluate the exact carbohydrate energy intake by quantitative chemical analysis of the ingested food into its constituent carbohydrates, multiplying the amount of each constituent by its energy value and the fraction presumed absorbed, and then summing the individual values. However, in practice the inherent variability in absorption introduces sufficient uncertainty that it is doubtful if accuracy is increased by using this complicated procedure rather than simply using 4 Kcal. per gram of ingested carbohydrate.

Proteins.   In the bomb calorimeter, the energy of the commonly consumed proteins averages 5.4 Kcal. per gram (although energy values vary widely among the various types of proteins). The energy remaining in the nitrogenous end products excreted from the body lowers the potential energy release to 4.2 Kcal. per gram absorbed. Lack of complete absorption further reduces the available energy; the commonly accepted value for the calorie content of protein is 4 Kcal. per gram ingested.

Not all of the absorbed proteins—or, more accurately, the amino acids into which the proteins are degraded by the digestive enzymes—are oxidized, since some are incorporated into cellular constituents, hormones, etc. However, this retained protein is included in the energy intake, since it is either replacing an equivalent amount of internal protein which is being catabolized and thus releasing chemical energy, or it is contributing to growth and thus increasing the body energy stores (cf. Energy Balance).

Lipids.   Lipids are the most "energy dense" of common foods, animal fats averaging 9.4 Kcal. per gram and vegetable fats and oils averaging 9.1 Kcal. per gram; the net dietary mean for all fats is 9.3 Kcal. per gram. Inability to absorb fat completely reduces the effective physiologic energy equivalent to 9 Kcal. per gram ingested.

Alcohol. Although ethanol is generally consumed for other than nutritional reasons, its energy content is quite substantial; when oxidized in a bomb calorimeter, ethanol releases 7.13 Kcal. per gram. Ingested alcohol is rapidly and essentially completely absorbed into the blood, whence it is distributed throughout the body and metabolized over several hours. Because ethanol is volatile (in other words, exhibits a relatively high vapor pressure at body temperature), some passes from the blood into the pulmonary alveoli and is lost from the body via respiration. Also some is excreted in the urine. However, the total amount lost through the respiratory and renal systems is small, generally no more than a few per cent. Thus, most of the ethanol consumed is eventually oxidized, leading to a physiologic value of 7 Kcal. per gram, which is only slightly below the bomb calorimeter figure.

The high caloric content of alcoholic beverages is assumed to be a prominent factor in the pathology of chronic alcoholism. Many alcoholics compensate for the energy gained from alcohol by reducing their energy intake of more normal foods. Although, in terms of energy, a calorie derived from the chemical potential of alcohol is as good as a calorie obtained from any other source, in terms of nutrition such a dietary imbalance is unfortunate, since it frequently results in a lack of necessary vitamins, essential amino acids, etc. The chronic degenerative tissue changes seen in long-term excessive alcohol consumption may well be due as much to nutritional deficiency disease as to alcohol *per se.*

Since a fraction of ingested alcohol, albeit small, is lost through respiration, the content of alcohol in expired gas can be used as an index of blood concentration. This is the basis of the commercial "drunkometers" frequently used by law enforcement agencies to assess degree of intoxication. Such tests must be conducted under standardized conditions, since the concentration of alcohol vapor in expired gas, like the concentration of every other respiratory gas, depends upon such factors as tidal volume and respiratory dead space, as well as upon blood levels.

Miscellaneous. The remainder of ingested substances, although they may be important in particular aspects of body metabolism, contribute little to energy intake. Inorganic materials, such as water, sodium, potassium and chloride ions, undergo no chemical transformations within the body and cannot contribute to the available energy. Other organic materials, for example the vitamins, are simply too small in amount to add a significant amount to the

TABLE 1

FOOD	ENERGY (KCAL. PER GRAM)			RESPIRATORY EQUIVALENT			VOLUME	
	Bomb Calorimeter	Human Oxidation	Physiologic Value	Oxygen (Kcal. per Liter)	CO_2 (Kcal. per Liter)	RQ $\left(\dfrac{V_{CO_2}}{V_{O_2}}\right)$	Oxygen (Liters per Gm.)	CO_2 (Liters per Gm.)
Carbohydrate	4.1	4.1	4	5.05	5.05	1.00	0.81	0.81
Protein	5.4	4.2	4	4.46	5.57	0.80	0.94	0.75
Lipid	9.3	9.3	9	4.74	6.67	0.71	1.96	1.39
Ethanol	7.1	7.1	7	4.86	7.25	0.67	1.46	0.98
Standard average				4.83	5.89	0.82		

total available energy. Thus, carbohydrates, proteins, lipids and, in some cases, alcohol constitute the only energy sources which need be considered in energy intake.

METABOLIC ENERGY OUTPUT

Measurement of Metabolic Rate. *Direct measurement.*[2, 18] The direct method for measuring metabolic rate is similar in principle to the calorimetric technique used for evaluating the energy content of foods. It is based on a device called the *human calorimeter* or *whole body calorimeter*. One form consists of a sealed insulated chamber in which the subject is placed. Heat is removed from the chamber by water circulated through coils; the rate of heat transfer is computed from the temperature rise and rate of flow of the water. Air for respiration is circulated through the chamber and its water vapor content is analyzed. For the performance of external work, an ergometer can be included inside the chamber (see Fig. 5).

Energy is lost from the calorimeter by three modes: heat transfer to the water (and perhaps to the circulating air), latent heat of vaporization inherent in the water vapor added to the air by the subject and removed from the chamber by the air circulation system, and any work performed on external objects. When the subject and the chamber reach steady state

temperatures so that no heat is being stored (cf. Heat Storage, Chap. 54), the total energy loss from the chamber must be equal to the subject's rate of energy utilization.

The direct measurement of energy output has the advantage of being based only on conservation of energy and not upon any assumptions about the physiology of energy metabolism—energy pathways, oxygen utilization, which food is being oxidized to provide the energy, etc. Thus, its accuracy is limited only by technical skill in construction of the calorimeter and the heat measuring instruments. It has the disadvantage of requiring a large, expensive and elaborate device, the human calorimeter; also it is limited to measurements of activities which can be carried out within a sealed chamber. As a result, the human calorimeter is infrequently employed except in specialized research.

Indirect measurement.[13] In the steady state, the release of energy from food is associated with the consumption of oxygen and the production of carbon dioxide. The relation between energy release and gas volumes is stochiometric for any particular reaction. Unfortunately, the gas exchanged is not the same for all foodstuffs, so, unless the precise composition of the substance being metabolized at any moment is known, an exact computation of energy release based on the oxygen consumption or carbon dioxide production is not possible.

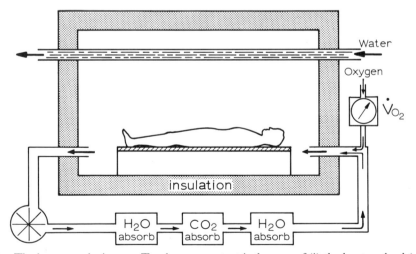

Fig. 5. The human calorimeter. Total energy output is the sum of (i) the heat evolved (measured from the temperature rise of the water flowing in coils through the chamber), (ii) the latent heat of vaporization (measured from the amount of water vapor extracted from the circulating air by the first H_2O absorber), and (iii) work performed on objects outside the chamber. CO_2 must be absorbed to prevent its accumulation within the chamber; this process evolves water, so a second H_2O absorber is needed. Oxygen consumption can be measured by noting the rate at which O_2 must be added to keep the chamber in a steady state.

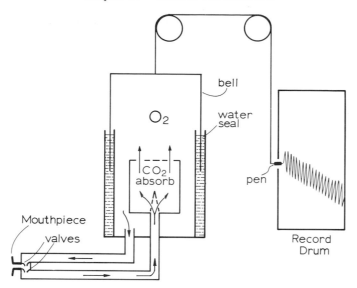

Fig. 6. A spirometer arranged for oxygen uptake measurement. The mouthpiece is placed between the subject's lips and teeth; extraneous gas exchange is prevented by use of a noseclip (and, in case of ruptured tympanic membrane, ear plugs). To avoid greatly increasing the effective dead space, separate tubes with valves to prevent mixing are used for inspired and expired gas. The CO_2 absorber prevents accumulation of expired carbon dioxide in the closed system. The volume of oxygen remaining in the spirometer is recorded by a pen writing on paper attached to a rotating drum.

However, energy output can be estimated from the following considerations. It has been found that a subject at rest, in a steady state, post-absorptive, oxidizing an "average" diet generates about 4.83 Kcal. for every liter of oxygen he consumes. The energy–oxygen ratios for any of the various categories of foods listed in Table 1 are not greatly different from the standard average of 4.83 Kcal. per liter of O_2; carbohydrates are within 5 per cent, proteins within 8 per cent, lipids within 2 per cent, and ethanol within 1 per cent of this figure. In other words, the Kcal. per liter of O_2 is not strongly dependent upon which type of food is being burnt. For example, in the worst case when protein only is serving as the substrate for energy metabolism (a very unlikely circumstance), the energy output calculated from standard average will deviate less than 8 per cent from the true value. More typically, the deviation between true and calculated values would be expected to be no more than a few per cent. Thus, calculating metabolic rate from the rate of oxygen consumption using the formula

$$\text{Metabolic rate} = 4.83 \, \dot{V}_{O_2} \qquad (1)$$

can, if properly employed yield reasonably accurate results.

In theory, the rate of carbon dioxide production

could be used in the same manner as equation (1) for calculating metabolic rate. However, several considerations limit the utility of such a measurement. First, the ratio of metabolic energy output to $\dot{V}_{CO_2}$ is relatively sensitive to the type of foodstuff metabolized, much more so than is true for oxygen. This introduces the possibility of significant deviation between the assumed standard average of 5.89 Kcal. per liter CO_2 and the actual respiratory caloric equivalent of the food undergoing oxidation. Second, the body possesses large carbon dioxide stores, such as dissolved CO_2, bicarbonate ion and carbamino-CO_2. The amount of these stores depends upon acidity, the partial pressure of carbon dioxide in the body, which is in turn influenced by respiratory ventilation, etc. A decrease in plasma pH or a period of hyperventilation tends to reduce the body carbon dioxide content by increasing the CO_2 in expired air. Upon collecting the expired gas, this volume of CO_2 can in no way be distinguished from that due to metabolism. Thus, because of its greater variability with respect to substrate utilized and because of the greater ease with which it can be removed from (or added to) body stores, carbon dioxide is inferior to oxygen as an indirect measure of metabolic rate.

Indirect techniques.[6, 7, 11] The method most frequently used clinically for determining oxygen consumption rate is the *closed circuit* technique. It utilizes a spirometer of the same type used in measuring lung volumes (Fig. 6). The spirometer is filled with oxygen, a carbon dioxide absorber is placed in the expired air line, and the subject is connected by means of a mouthpiece or a face mask to form a closed system. Upon inspiration, oxygen from the spirometer flows into the lungs, where some is absorbed and partially replaced with carbon dioxide; upon expiration, the carbon dioxide is removed by the CO_2 absorber and the remainder of the expired gas returns to the spirometer. At the completion of a number of respiratory cycles, the volume contained in the spirometer will have decreased by just that amount of oxygen which was consumed. Thus, the rate of change of spirometer volume is a direct measure of oxygen consumption rate.

The *open circuit* method of measuring oxygen consumption is based upon the Fick principle: the decrease in oxygen concentration between inspired and expired gas (oxygen extraction) at a given gas volume flow is an index of the oxygen consumption rate. In a typical application of this method, the subject inspires ambient air; the expired air is directed by valves into a large bag (Douglas bag) or into a large spirometer (Tissot spirometer). A CO_2 absorber is unnecessary, since gas is not rebreathed. At the end of the collection period, the volume expired and the composition of both inspired and expired gas are determined; from these data the oxygen consumption is calculated.

Applying the Fick principle to pulmonary gas exchange is not quite as simple as the corresponding application to, for example, the circulatory system. The basic equation for oxygen uptake is

$$V_{O_2} = F_{IO_2}V_I - F_{EO_2}V_E \qquad (2)$$

which simply states that the oxygen consumed is the difference between the amount inspired and that expired. However, the inspired and expired volumes are not in general the same because of the difference between the amount of O_2 extracted and the amount of CO_2 added. Since the volume V_I is not directly measured and since it cannot be assumed to be equal to V_E, the application of equation (2) requires further elaboration.

The volume expired is equal to the volume inspired less the oxygen extracted plus the carbon dioxide added, or

$$V_E = V_I - V_{O_2} + V_{CO_2} \qquad (3)$$

(This equation applies to the volumes and concentrations measured after passing the gas through a drying agent or corrected to the dry state; otherwise the relation must be modified to include the water vapor added by the lungs.) If the inspired gas is free of CO_2, the total amount of carbon dioxide expired is given by

$$V_{CO_2} = F_{ECO_2}V_E \qquad (4)$$

By substituting equation (4) into equation (3) to eliminate V_{CO_2}, solving for V_I, and substituting this into equation (2), one obtains the relation

$$V_{O_2} = V_E(F_{IO_2} - F_{EO_2})\left[\frac{F_{IO_2} - F_{EO_2} - F_{IO_2}F_{ECO_2}}{(1 - F_{IO_2})(F_{IO_2} - F_{EO_2})}\right] \qquad (5)$$

This gives the oxygen consumption in terms of the volume expired and the oxygen and carbon dioxide fractions in the inspired and expired gas. The first product on the right, $V_E(F_{IO_2} - F_{EO_2})$ is simply the volume expired times the oxygen extraction, which is the approximate oxygen consumption ignoring the difference between V_E and V_I. The term enclosed in square brackets is the correction factor due to RQ effects. If RQ = 1.0, so that $(F_{IO_2} - F_{EO_2}) = F_{ECO_2}$, the correction factor becomes exactly 1, since for this RQ, $V_I = V_E$. Taking more typical values, for example, inspiring room air with 20.9 per cent oxygen ($F_{IO_2} = 0.209$) and expired air containing 16.2 per cent oxygen and 4.0 per cent carbon dioxide ($F_{EO_2} = 0.162$, $F_{ECO_2} = 0.040$), leads to a correction factor of 1.043; in other words, the results of the simple computation $V_E(F_{IO_2} - F_{EO_2})$ must be increased by 4.3 per cent to get the true value of oxygen consumption.

Gas volume corrections. Because a gas changes in volume depending upon its temperature, pressure and water vapor saturation, measurement and comparison of gas volumes is meaningful only when corrected to some standard or uniform state. The appropriate standard state depends upon the topic under consideration. For example, in determining pulmonary capacities, gas volumes measured by the spirometer should be corrected to body temperature and pressure saturated (BTPS), since this is the state of the gas within the lungs.

In metabolic investigations, the quantity of fundamental interest is mols of gas rather than gas volume *per se*; a chemical reaction is a relation between mols (and not volumes) of the various substances and end products. Since, in the physiologic range, gases behave approximately as ideal gases, the mols and volume are directly proportional, but the constant of proportionality depends upon the state of the gas. By convention, for metabolic work the standard state is taken as 0° C. temperature, 760 mm. Hg pressure, and dry (STPD), in which state one mol of gas occupies a volume of 22.4 liters. All the metabolic tables in this chapter refer to gas volume at STPD.

Gas volumes can be converted from one state (state 1) to another (state 2) by rote application of the formula

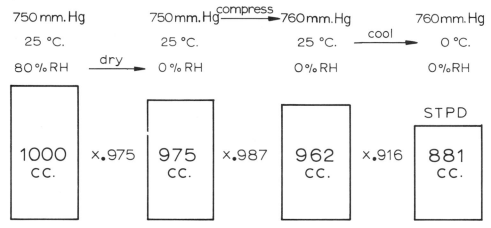

Fig. 7. Correction to STPD by successive steps. Drying a gas originally at 750 mm. Hg, 25° C., and 80 per cent relative humidity (P_{H_2O} = .8 × 24 = 19 mm. Hg) reduces its volume by (750 − 19)/750 = .975. Compressing the dry gas to 760 mm. Hg reduces the volume by 750/760 = .987. Finally, cooling to 0° C. (or 273.1° absolute) reduces the volume by (273.1)/(273.1 + 25) = .916.

$$V_2 = V_1 \left(\frac{P_1 - P_{1H_2O}}{P_2 - P_{2H_2O}} \right) \left(\frac{T_2 + 273.1}{T_1 + 273.1} \right) \quad (6)$$

where V_1, T_1, P_1 and P_{1H_2O} are respectively the volume, temperature (in degrees C.), total pressure and partial pressure of water vapor (both in mm. Hg) for state 1; V_2, T_2, P_2 and P_{2H_2O} are the similar quantities for state 2. In the particular case in which the state 2 is STPD, equation (6) reduces to

$$V_2 = 0.36 \, V_1 \left(\frac{P_1 - P_{1H_2O}}{T_1 + 273.1} \right) \quad (7)$$

The correction factor can be evaluated also by considering sequentially the alterations in volume in the individual processes (see Fig. 7). For example, in converting ambient gas to STPD, we may consider the first step as removing the water vapor, which reduces the volume to $\dfrac{P_A - P_{H_2O}}{P_A}$ of its original value (where P_A is the ambient pressure). Next, compressing the gas to 760 mm. Hg changes its volume by a factor of $\dfrac{P_A}{760}$. Finally, cooling to 0° C. (273.1 absolute temperature) from the original temperature of T_A (or 273.1 + T_A absolute temperature) reduces the volume by $\dfrac{273.1}{273.1 + T_A}$. The product of these three factors gives the total correction of equation (7).

The vapor pressure of water, P_{H_2O}, is sometimes expressed in terms of gas temperature and relative humidity (RH). To evaluate P_{H_2O} from these data, the maximum vapor pressure ($P_{H_2O \, max}$) at that temperature is found from a table or graph (Fig. 8) and multiplied by the relative humidity:

$$P_{H_2O} = RH \times P_{H_2O \, max} \quad (8)$$

Determination of energy source.[18] In studies of whole body metabolic function, it is frequently essential to determine the type of substrate furnishing the energy in any particular circumstance. When dietary intake is limited to the normal constituents of carbohydrates, proteins and lipids, such a determination is possible from the measurement of oxygen consumption, carbon dioxide production and urinary nitrogen.

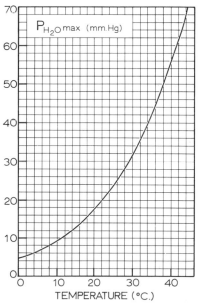

Fig. 8. The maximum partial pressure of water vapor in air (100 per cent RH) as a function of temperature.

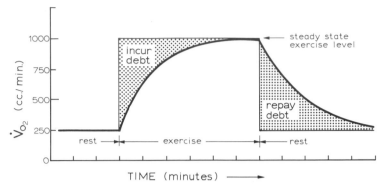

Fig. 9. The time course of oxygen uptake when metabolic rate suddenly changes by a factor of 4. The initial lag at the beginning of exercise creates the oxygen debt; the excess O_2 consumption at the end of exercise repays the debt. The volume of debt incurred and repaid can be evaluated by measuring the area of the shaded regions.

The average nitrogen content of protein is 16 per cent by weight. When protein is metabolized, this nitrogen is incorporated into simpler compounds which are excreted in the urine. Since the total quantity of nitrogen from other ingested compounds (e.g., choline, purines, pyrimidines) is normally quite small, all the urinary nitrogen may be assumed to have originated from protein. Thus, the protein metabolized may be computed from the formula

$$N = 0.16\,P \qquad (9)$$

where N is the quantity of nitrogen obtained from a chemical analysis of urine and P is the quantity of protein, both measured in grams.

The other two measurements needed are the volumes of oxygen consumed and of carbon dioxide produced. From the volume equivalents of Table 1, we may write

$$V_{O_2} = 0.81\,C + 0.94\,P + 1.96\,L \qquad (10)$$

and

$$V_{CO_2} = 0.81\,C + 0.75\,P + 1.39\,L \qquad (11)$$

where C, P and L are amounts of metabolized carbohydrate, protein and lipids in grams.

Equations (9), (10) and (11) constitute a set of three simultaneous equations. If quantities on the left, N, V_{O_2} and V_{CO_2} are measured, the three unknowns C, P and L can be calculated.

Oxygen debt.[10, 14, 15, 20] The proportional relation between energy output and oxygen consumption holds only for steady states. When energy output is rapidly changing, the response of oxygen consumption tends to lag behind. A particular aspect of this lag is the pheomenon termed *oxygen debt.*

If a subject, previously at rest, suddenly begins to exercise vigorously at a constant rate, although his oxygen consumption begins to rise almost immediately, several minutes will elapse before his rate of O_2 uptake attains a value appropriate for his level of energy expenditure (see Figs. 9 and 10). Because in this interval his oxygen consumption was insufficient to meet his metabolic requirements, he has incurred an oxygen debt or oxygen deficit. The amount of debt incurred is defined as the difference between the volume necessary for the steady-state maintenance of the activity and that volume actually consumed.

If, after reaching a steady state in exercise, the subject suddenly resumes resting, the oxygen uptake response again lags, remaining for some time above the metabolic requirements of the resting state. This is the period of repayment of the oxygen debt. The amount repaid is defined as the excess volume consumed above the steady-state requirements.*

Since, at the beginning of exercise the inspired oxygen is insufficient to supply the total energy expended, clearly, internal energy stores which can be rapidly mobilized must be tapped during this period. Three energy sources appear to be involved:

(i) The initial source of internal energy is probably the high energy intermediates at the site of activity such as adenosine triphosphate (ATP) and, particularly, phosphocreatine.

*Some authors limit the use of the term "oxygen debt" to the excess oxygen consumption following activity and use the term "oxygen deficit" to identify the initial lag in O_2 uptake. In this chapter, the more descriptive terminology of "repay" and "incur" oxygen debt is employed.

(ii) Cellular glycogen and blood glucose are tapped as an energy source, since they can re-synthesize high energy phosphate compounds without requiring extra oxygen intake via anaerobic glycolysis. A direct consequence is the accumulation of the end product of glycolysis, lactic acid. Some diffuses into the circulation raising blood levels of lactate for the duration of exercise. For example, the normal blood lactate of about 0.1 mg. per ml. is approximately doubled during mild exercise such as walking and can increase by about ten times in maximal work.

(iii) The third source is the oxygen stored in the blood and in muscle myoglobin.

At the termination of exercise, the incurred oxygen debt must be repaid to bring the body back to its initial state; i.e., the concentration of high energy phosphate compounds must be restored, the lactate oxidized or glycogen re-synthesized, and the oxygen saturation of myoglobin and venous hemoglobin returned to resting levels. All these require oxygen in excess of the resting steady state energy requirements. In addition, the increased oxygen delivery to restore the incurred debt after exercise requires increased internal work, in the form of higher heart rate, increased cardiac output, etc., which in itself requires extra oxygen consumption.

Thus, incurring an oxygen debt is associated with depletion of anaerobic energy stores and stored oxygen, while repayment is associated with restoration of the stores plus the extra internal work (Fig. 11).

The amount of oxygen debt is roughly proportional to the severity of the exercise. For severe work, a debt on the order of 5 liters of O_2 equivalent can be incurred. The amount repaid is similar to that incurred but the two

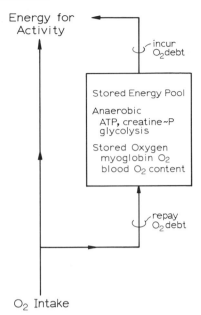

Fig. 11. Internal pathways for incurring and repaying oxygen debt.

are not necessarily identical since the reactions involved in repayment are not the stochiometric reverse of those by which the debt is incurred.

Even in light, sustained exercise, debt incurred at the beginning of exercise is not repaid until exercise is completed, though the oxygen consumption throughout the exercise is considerably below the maximum $\dot{V}_{O_2}$. Thus, O_2 debt, at least in moderate exercise, is *not* due to the inability of the cardiopulmonary systems to deliver inspired oxygen to the tissue. Rather, it must be concluded that O_2 debt is associated with (but not necessarily identical to) the stimulus for greater oxygen uptake. In other words, oxygen consumption increases only as debt is incurred; consumption remains high until the debt is repaid.

Factors Determining Energy Expenditure. *Size.*[5, 12] That a large person in general has a higher metabolic rate than a small one is not surprising, but not so obvious is exactly what is meant by "large" and "small." For example, weight (or, more accurately, mass) is not a good index, since individuals of identical weight but different body proportions (somatotypes) may have quite different metabolic rates.

The normal measure of body size used in human metabolism is body surface area, usually expressed in units of square meters (m^2). To facilitate comparison between subjects differing in size, metabolic rates are expressed in terms of energy output per unit time per unit area

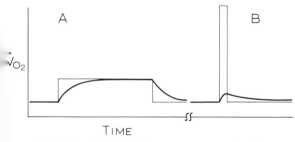

Fig. 10. Patterns of oxygen consumption in exercise. In the moderate, sustained exercise shown in A, a steady state is reached long before the end of exercise. In brief, intense exercise shown in B, such as the 100 meter dash, almost all the energy is furnished from internal stores, which are reformed after the end of the exercise.

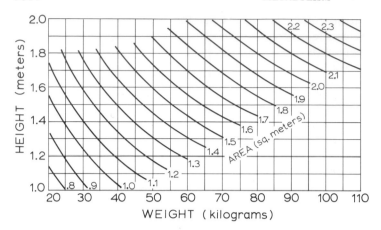

Fig. 12. Surface area as a function of height and weight. (After DuBois and DuBois, *Arch. intern. Med.,* 1916, *17*:863–871.)

(usually Kcal. per m²-hr.). The utility of surface area as a measure of size derives from the experimental observation that subjects of various weights, heights, somatotypes, etc., may have greatly different total metabolic rates, but (under standardized conditions) their metabolic rates *per unit area* are quite similar.

Surface area can be measured directly by, for example, completely wrapping the subject with tape something like an Egyptian mummy, peeling off this covering in sections, flattening the sections, and measuring the total planar area. Fortunately, such Spartan procedures are seldom necessary, since it has been found that surface area can be accurately predicted from height and weight. Such data are available in tabular form, as a graph (Fig. 12), or can be computed from the equation

$$\text{Area (m}^2) = 0.202 \times W^{0.425} \times H^{0.725}$$

where W is the weight in kilograms and H is height in meters.

It has been claimed that the relation between metabolic rate and body surface area is fortuitous, without physiologic basis, and several alternative measures have been proposed. One such measure is based on the contention that fat tissue has relatively low metabolism, and so adds little to total body energy output. Thus, it is claimed that metabolic rate should be expressed per kilogram of *lean body mass,* i.e., the total body mass less that due to fat.[8, 16, 19, 21]

Two methods are used for evaluating the lean body mass. One technique involves injecting a known amount of some substance which distributes evenly throughout lean tissue but does not penetrate adipose tissue. By measuring the blood equilibrium concentration of this substance, the lean "space" can be calculated and from this, the lean body mass. The second method is based on the fact that fat has a slightly lower density than other body tissues; thus net body density is an index of the fraction of fatty tissue. Density is calculated from specific gravity, which is determined by comparing the subject's weight when he is completely immersed in water with his weight in air.

Another proposed alternative to surface area results from the purely empirical observation that if the metabolic rates of a large number of animals ranging in size from birds to cattle are plotted against body weight on a logarithmic graph, a straight line results (Fig. 13).[17] Since the slope of this line is about 0.75, and since a straight line on a logarithmic graph implies a power relation, it is claimed that metabolic rate should be expressed in terms of (Kg.)^{0.75}.

Of the relative merits of these methods of measuring body "size"—surface area, lean body mass, (Kg.)^{0.75}—the authors' opinion is the following: Lean body mass has much to recommend it in theory, but, difficulty in measurement precludes its use in anything but specialized research. The measure (Kg.)^{0.75} has some utility in animal experiments, particularly when surface area tables may not be available. However, for human work surface area is the measure of choice since (i) it is easily calculated, (ii) it appears to be as suitable as any of the proposed substitutes, (iii) it is

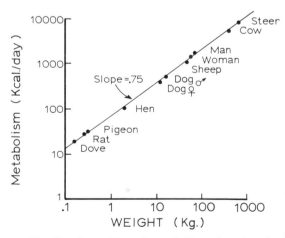

Fig. 13. Logarithm of metabolism plotted against logarithm of weight. (After Kleiber, *Hilgardia,* 1932, *6:* 315–353.)

TABLE 2. *Energy Expenditure for Various Activities*

	Kcal. per m²-hr.
REST	
Sleeping	35
Lying awake	40
Sitting upright	50
LIGHT ACTIVITY	
Writing, clerical work	60
Standing	85
MODERATE ACTIVITY	
Washing, dressing	100
Walking (3 mph)	140
Housework	140
HEAVY ACTIVITY	
Bicycling	250
Swimming	350
Lumbering	350
Skiing	500
Running	600
SHIVERING	to 250

buttressed by long use in physiologic research, much of the results of which would have to be recalculated if surface area were replaced by some other measure.

Activity.[10, 22] The level of activity or rate of exercise markedly affects the rate of energy output, leading to large changes in metabolic rate.

The lowest metabolic rate normally experienced is during sleep. A normal 20-year-old male will exhibit a rate of about 35 Kcal. per m²-hr. when sleeping. If he wakes up but remains lying quietly, his metabolic rate rises to about 40 Kcal. per m²-hr. Sitting upright further increases his rate to approximately 50 Kcal. per m²-hr. Exercise of any sort causes a further rise depending upon the severity of the work (see Table 2). The maximum steady-state energy output for a person in good physical condition is in the order of 350 Kcal. per m²-hr., a factor of 10 greater than the minimum rate during sleep. Metabolic rates two or three times the steady state maximum are possible for short periods. Thus, at least transiently, a man can work at a metabolic rate appreciably greater than 1 horsepower (746 watts, 641 Kcal. per hr.), although at most 25 per cent of this energy is available for external work.

The large effect of physical activity upon energy metabolism is not shared by mental activity. The increase in metabolic rate due to vigorous mental exercise, such as solving mathematical problems or reading this text, is so small as to be almost unmeasureable. As Benedict states, "The cloistered scholar at his books may

be surprised to learn that the extra calories needed for one hour of intense mental effort would be completely met by the eating of one oyster cracker or one-half of a salted peanut."

Age and sex. The metabolic rate under standard conditions (resting quietly), rises rapidly in the first few weeks after birth, reaches a peak in early youth, and then declines slowly and more or less continuously throughout the remainder of life (see Table 3).

Females generally have about a 10 per cent lower metabolic rate under standard conditions than males of the same age and size. The lower rate has been attributed to the greater proportion of body mass in subcutaneous fat for the female.

Temperature. Body temperature influences

TABLE 3

AGE (years)	METABOLIC RATE (Kcal. per m²-hr.)	
	Males	Females
Birth	30	30
1	55	52
2	57	53
3	55	52
5	53.0	51.6
6	52.7	50.7
7	52.0	49.3
8	51.2	48.1
9	50.4	46.9
10	49.5	45.8
11	48.6	44.6
12	47.8	43.4
13	47.1	42.0
14	46.2	41.0
15	45.3	39.6
16	44.7	38.5
17	43.7	37.4
18	42.9	37.3
19	42.1	37.2
20–24	41.0	36.9
25–29	40.3	36.6
30–34	39.8	36.2
35–39	39.2	35.8
40–44	38.3	35.3
45–49	37.8	35.0
50–54	37.2	34.5
55–59	36.6	34.1
60–64	36.0	33.8
65–69	35.3	33.4
70–74	34.8	32.8
75–79	34.2	32.3

metabolic rate in two ways. First is the direct effect of temperature on all body functions. A decrease in temperature causes slower heart rate, lower cardiac output, reduced rate constants for the chemical reactions involved in energy utilization, etc., all leading to a lower metabolic rate. A rise in body temperature has the opposite effect.

For over-all metabolism, a temperature alteration of 1° C. causes metabolic rate to change by a factor of about 1.1 (or 10 per cent increase). This relation is cumulative; i.e., a rise of 2° C. increases metabolism by a factor of $(1.1)^2$, and a 1° C. drop decreases metabolism by $(1.1)^{-1}$, or, in general, a change of temperature, ΔT causes a $(1.1)^{\Delta T}$ change in metabolic rate. Thus, a patient with a 40° C. fever would be expected to exhibit a resting metabolic rate about 33 per cent higher than at 37° C. This effect is passive and depends only on the inherent temperature sensitivity of the metabolic reactions which underlie vital activity.

The second influence of temperature upon metabolic rate is limited to homeotherms. To maintain body temperature in a cold environment, homeotherms are able to convert chemical energy into heat by the random contraction of muscle motor units, i.e., by shivering. The energy expended in shivering depends upon the severity of the cold stress; in extreme stress, shivering can reach 250 Kcal. per m^2-hr., a rate of metabolism equivalent to heavy exercise (see also the discussion of nonshivering thermogenesis, Chap. 55). The requirements of homeotherms also increase metabolism slightly during heat stress because energy is needed for increased cutaneous blood flow and for secretion of sweat, although the magnitude of this effect is not large.

Thus, energy expenditure is lowest at normal body temperature and in a neutral thermal environment, for which the central and environmental temperatures are sufficiently high to suppress shivering but not so high that passive (and homeostatic) effects lead to increased metabolic rate.

Specific dynamic action. If a subject who has previously been fasting eats some protein-rich food, his metabolic rate will show a transient increase, beginning about an hour after the meal and lasting for several hours. The total excess energy expenditure over that characteristic of the fasting level is proportional to the amount ingested, and represents about 30 per cent of the caloric value of the protein. For example, if 25 grams of protein are ingested, with a total energy equivalent of 25 × 4.0 = 100 Kcal., the net metabolic increase totaled over the next several hours would be 30 Kcal. Thus, an increase in energy intake in the form of protein causes a rise in general energy metabolism; this effect is known as the specific dynamic action (SDA) of protein.

The mechanism of SDA is not completely understood. It is not associated with digestion or absorption of proteins, since intravenous injection of the equivalent amino acids leads to the same rise in metabolism. It is not due to the oxidation of those particular amino acid molecules which have been absorbed. The most likely explanation is an influence of amino acid concentration upon intermediary metabolism, but the details of this effect are not presently clear.

Carbohydrates and lipids are reported also to induce a metabolic rate increase due to specific dynamic action, but the magnitude of the effect is small, amounting to at most 5 per cent of their caloric energy value.

Endocrine. Many hormones influence energy metabolism (see Chap. 60). Of particular importance are epinephrine, which mobilizes and increases utilization of carbohydrates, and thyroxin, which affects the basic metabolism of most body tissues.

Race and climate. Natives of the tropics have a resting metabolic rate about 10 per cent below the standard values for North Americans or Europeans. Whether this is due to inherent racial variation or to climate is not clear, since some, but not all, individuals from temperate climates who move to the tropics show a drop in metabolic rate of about the same magnitude. Attempts to show higher metabolism for Eskimos have been inconclusive.

Pregnancy. In about the sixth month of pregnancy, the mother's rate of metabolism begins to increase and continues to rise until delivery, at which time it is about 20 per cent above the normal level. After birth, the mother's metabolism drops by approximately the metabolic rate of the newborn infant. Thus, at least near full term, the prepartum increase is due almost entirely to the additional metabolism of the fetus and not to any particular influence of pregnancy on the mother's energy expenditure.

Basal Metabolic Rate.[13] *Basal state.* Because of the many variables which influence energy output, measurement of "inherent" metabolic rate is possible only under precisely standardized conditions. When the following standard conditions are met, the rate of metabolism so measured is called the basal metabolic rate (BMR):

(i) The effects of variations in body size are eliminated by dividing the metabolic rate by the surface area, expressing the rate in terms of Kcal. per m²-hr.

(ii) Activity is standardized by taking the measurement when the subject is in a steady state, lying quietly awake.

(iii) Differences in age and sex are compensated for by expressing the results as a percentage of the deviation from the metabolic rate of normal subjects of the same age and sex (see Table 3). Thus, if a 21-year-old male subject has an energy output of 50.0 Kcal. per m²-hr. under basal conditions, his BMR is +22 per cent (sometimes simply written +22), since the normal value for a 21-year-old male is 41.0 Kcal. per m²-hr. If his energy output were 36.0 Kcal. per m²-hr., his BMR would be −12 per cent. The effects of other variables such as race can be standardized in the same way, i.e., by comparing the metabolic rate with that shown by similar normals.

(iv) Temperature is eliminated as a variable by conducting the test in a comfortable, thermally neutral environment and by making the measurement only when the subject's internal temperature is normal.

(v) The effect of specific dynamic action is excluded by having the subject fast for several hours before the test. Usually the measurement is taken in the morning, the subject having been instructed not to eat after consuming dinner the previous night. This fast also tends to standardize the source of internal metabolic energy, thus increasing the accuracy of the conversion between energy output and oxygen uptake.

(vi) The subject is instructed to relax to eliminate the effects of excitement and to reduce sympathetic activity and epinephrine release.

When the above conditions are met, the subject is said to be in the basal state. The basal metabolic rate is nothing more nor less than the rate of metabolism in the basal state. It is not the lowest rate, since metabolism would decrease if the subject were allowed to fall asleep. Phrases such as "basal metabolic rate of exercise" or "BMR during sleep" are self-contradictory.

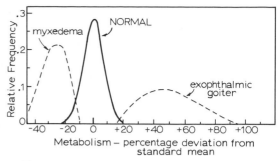

Fig. 14. Probability distribution of basal metabolic rate. Myxedema is associated with hypothyroidism, exopthalmic goiter with hyperthyroidism. (From Boothly, Berkson and Plummer, *Ann. intern. Med.*, 1937, *11*:1014–1023.)

Range of normal BMR.[3,13] The precision of a single BMR measurement is better than 5 per cent. In other words, the deviation between successive measurements on a given subject at one session would be expected to be less than 5 per cent.

The probability distribution of basal metabolic rates obtained from a sample of normal subjects is illustrated in Figure 14. The distribution is centered around the standard value of Table 3, with an approximate range of ±15 per cent. Distributions for two types of thyroid disease are noted also.

BMR abnormalities.[4] The remaining variables such as endocrine abnormalities or biochemical aberrations cannot, of course, be eliminated by adjusting the conditions of the test or the mode of expressing the results. Therefore, the BMR measurement is diagnostic for these abnormalities.

The most common cause of an abnormal BMR is associated with thyroid disease. An excess secretion of thyroid hormones (hyperthyroid) leads to high metabolic rates while thyroid deficiency (hypothyroid) causes decreased basal energy output. For many years, measurement of BMR was an important technique in the diagnosis of thyroid disease. However, recently, BMR has been partially replaced by more specific tests based on thyroid metabolism of radioactive iodine.

ENERGY BALANCE

Energy intake is determined by food eaten and absorbed; energy output is determined by the factors enumerated in the previous section. Normally, the mechanisms of hunger, satiety,

Table 4

DAILY ENERGY INTAKE	
300 Gm. carbohydrate (4 Kcal./gm.)	1200 Kcal.
100 Gm. fat (9 Kcal./gm.)	900 Kcal.
100 Gm. protein (4 Kcal./gm.)	<u>400</u> Kcal.
Total intake	2500 Kcal.
DAILY ENERGY EXPENDITURE	
8 Hrs. sleeping (35 Kcal./m²-hr.)	280 Kcal./m²
10 Hrs. writing, reading (60 Kcal./m²-hr.)	600 Kcal./m²
3 Hrs. dressing, eating (100 Kcal./m²hr.)	300 Kcal./m²
3 Hrs. walking, light exercise (140 Kcal./m²-hr.)	<u>420</u> Kcal./m²
	1600 Kcal./m²
× Surface area of 1.73 m²	2768 Kcal.
+SDA effect (30% of 400 Kcal.)	<u>120</u> Kcal.
Total expenditure	2888 Kcal.
Daily energy deficit	388 Kcal.

voluntary work rate, etc., act to maintain input and output in proper balance over any extended period. When, for physiologic or psychologic reasons, such a balance is not maintained, the energy difference must be made up by internal storage.

In a well nourished adult with a normal diet, an excess of energy output over intake leads to metabolism, and thus loss, of stored body fat.* Similarly, when intake exceeds output, the difference is stored as an increase in body fat, since the body possesses no mechanism for "excreting" excess energy as it does, for example, excess salt or water.

This relation between energy balance and stored fat is the basis of dietary control of body weight. Suppose a person has an energy output of 2888 Kcal. per day, as illustrated in Table 4. If he is limited to an intake of 2500 Kcal. per day, the 388 Kcal. deficit will be furnished by the daily metabolism of $388/9.3 = 42$ grams (about $1/10$ pound) of body fat. (Note that here the appropriate metabolic value for fat is 9.3 Kcal. per gram, since we are referring to fat in the body actually being metabolized, not ingested fat.)

On this diet, body weight would be expected to decrease linearly at the rate of 42 grams per day. Over a short interval retention of body water may obscure weight changes due to fat metabolism. However, if the energy deficit is maintained for a sufficient period, body water

* This is not true in extreme starvation, in which any available body constituent, particularly protein, may be burned for its energy.

will eventually return to its normal value and weight loss will follow the predicted slope (see Fig. 15).

In contrast to the adult, the child requires an excess of energy intake over expenditure to furnish substrates for natural increase in body mass. However, the intake associated with normal growth represents only a small fraction of the total energy consumption. For example, an average boy of 15 years (the age of maximum increase in mass) increases his weight at the rate of 10 Kg. per year (22 pounds per year) or 27 grams per day. Of this amount, about

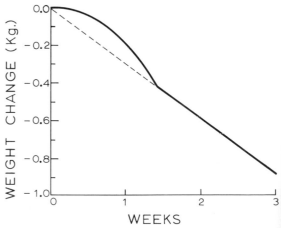

Fig. 15. Typical time course of weight loss during a period of constant difference between metabolic expenditure and caloric intake. The dotted line indicates the cumulative caloric deficit converted to equivalent weight of fat; the heavy line indicates the actual weight change.

70 per cent represents an increase in body water and inorganic minerals; the remaining 30 per cent, or 8.2 grams per day represents increasing body organic material, mainly protein. However, a 15-year-old boy will have a daily energy intake of about 3500 Kcal., furnished, on an average diet, by the absorption of 500 grams of carbohydrate, protein and fat. Thus, of the total organic intake of 508 grams, less than 2 per cent is obligated to normal growth, and the remaining 98 per cent is metabolized for energy expenditure.

If the child's energy intake exceeds his energy output plus growth requirements, the excess, as in the adult, will be deposited as body fat.

REFERENCES

1. ATWATER, W. O. and BENEDICT, F. G. *Bulletin No. 69,* Washington, D.C., U. S. Dept of Agriculture, 1899.
2. BENEDICT, F. G. *Science,* 1915, *42:*75–84.
3. BOOTHBY, W. M., BERKSON, J. and DUNN, H. L. *Amer. J. Physiol.,* 1936, *116:*468–484.
4. BOOTHBY, W. M., BERKSON, J. and PLUMMER, W. A. *Ann. intern. Med.,* 1937, *11:*1014–1023.
5. BROBECK, J. R. Chap. 48 in *Medical physiology and biophysics,* 18th ed. T. C. Ruch and J. F. Fulton, eds. Philadelphia, W. B. Saunders Co., 1960.
6. CARLSON, L. D. In: *Methods in medical research.* Chicago, Year Book Medical Publishers, Inc., 1954.
7. CARPENTER, T. M. *Publ. No. 216.* Carnegie Institution of Washington, 1915.
8. CONSOLAZIO, C. F., JOHNSON, R. E. and MAREK, E. *Metabolic methods.* London, H. Kimpton, 1951.
9. DAVIDSON, S., MEIKLEJOHN, A. and PASSMORE, R. *Human nutrition and dietetics.* Baltimore, Williams & Wilkins, 1959.
10. DILL, D. B. *Physiol. Rev.,* 1936, *16:*263–291.
11. DOUGLAS, C. G. *J. Physiol.,* 1911, *42:*xvii–xviii.
12. DUBOIS, D. and DUBOIS, E. F. *Arch. intern. Med.,* 1916, *17:*863–871.
13. DUBOIS, E. F. *Basal metabolism in health and disease,* 3rd ed. Philadelphia, Lea and Febiger, 1936.
14. HILL, A. V., LONG, C. N. and LUPTON, H. *Proc. roy. Soc.,* 1924, *97:*84–138.
15. HUCKABEE, W. A. *J. clin. Invest.,* 1958, *37:*255–263.
16. KEYS, A. and BROZEK, J. *Physiol. Rev.,* 1958, *33:*245–325.
17. KLEIBER, M. *Physiol. Rev.,* 1947, *27:*511–541.
18. LUSK, G. *The elements of the science of nutrition,* 4th ed. Philadelphia, W. B. Saunders Co., 1928.
19. McCANCE, R. A. and WIDDOWSON, E. M. *Proc. roy. Soc.,* 1951, *138:*115–130.
20. MARGARIA, R., EDWARDS, H. T. and DILL, D. B. *Amer. J. Physiol.,* 1933, *106:*689–715.
21. MILLER, A. T., JR. *Methods in medical research,* vol. 6. Chicago, Year Book Publishers Inc., 1954.
22. PASSMORE, R. and DURNIN, J. *Physiol. Rev.,* 1955, *35:*801–840.
23. SCHRÖDINGER, E. *What is life? The physical aspect of the living cell.* London, Cambridge University Press, 1955.
24. WIDDOWSON, E. M. *Proc. Nutr. Soc.,* 1955, *14:*142–154.

CHAPTER 54

Temperature Regulation

By GEORGE BRENGELMANN and ARTHUR C. BROWN

EVERY living organism produces heat; this heat is either lost to the environment or stored in the body. If the heat content of the body increases, the body temperature rises and, consequently, heat transfer to the environment is increased. Any animal, therefore, tends to reach a steady-state of thermal exchange with the environment.

In most animals and in all plants, neither the rate of heat production nor the ease with which it is lost to the environment are associated primarily with temperature regulation. In these organisms, internal temperature fluctuates passively with environmental temperature, merely remaining sufficiently above environmental temperature to allow metabolic heat to be eliminated. Such animals are termed *poikilothermic* or "cold-blooded." This latter term is a misnomer, since in a hot environment, "cold-blooded" animals have high internal temperatures. Furthermore, poikilotherms are not nec-

essarily indifferent to fluctuations in internal temperature; for example, reptiles seek out warm sunny spots on cold mornings. However, these responses are behavioral, an attempt to alter the local environment; they are not internal or physiologic.

For a relatively few animal species—including most birds and mammals—heat is not simply a waste metabolic byproduct; rather, its production and loss are regulated to maintain internal body temperature within narrow levels over a wide range of environmental conditions. Such animals are called *homeothermic* or "warm-blooded," of which a conspicuous example is man.

Normal Body Temperature. Although the mechanisms involved in homeothermy tend to stabilize internal body temperature, they cannot completely prevent temperature variation in response to internal and environmental thermal stresses. Thus, "normal" body temperature

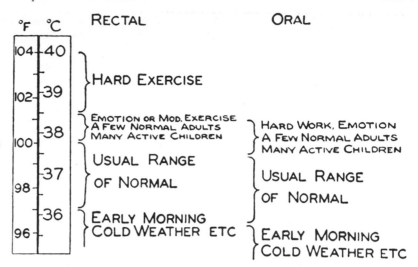

Fig. 1. Normal temperature ranges. (From DuBois, *Fever and the regulation of body temperature.* Springfield, Ill., Charles C Thomas, 1948.)

implies specific conditions under which the measurement is made. It is quite normal for an athlete to have a rectal temperature of 40° C. just after an arduous race. Figure 1 shows the temperature range that may be expected in normal subjects under various circumstances.

"Normal temperature," in the usual clinical sense, refers to that temperature expected in a healthy individual not currently or recently subjected to thermal stress. Normal rectal temperature is commonly taken as 37.0° C. (98.6° F.); oral, 36.7° C. (98.1° F.). These temperatures agree well with mean values obtained from large numbers of individuals.

In 46 male medical students, who had avoided heavy exercise, food, drink, and tobacco for two hours, mean rectal and oral temperatures, after thirty minutes of rest, were 37.11° C. (98.80° F.) and 36.72° C. (98.09° F.), respectively. The standard deviation for both measurements was 0.21° C. No measurement differed from the mean by more than 0.5° C.[31] In another experiment, temperatures were measured in 276 medical students seated in class, with no restrictions as to previous activity; the mean oral temperature was 36.7° C. (98.1° F.).[25] Under these less well-controlled conditions, both a larger standard deviation and range of measurements were observed, as shown in Figure 2.

Fig. 2. *A,* Oral temperatures of 276 medical students with no restrictions as to previous activity. (After Ivy, *Quart. Bull. Northw. Univ. med. Sch.,* 1944, *18:*22–32.) *B* and *C,* oral and rectal temperatures respectively in 46 medical students who had avoided exercise, food, drink and tobacco. (After Tanner, *J. Physiol.,* 1951, *115:* 371–390.)

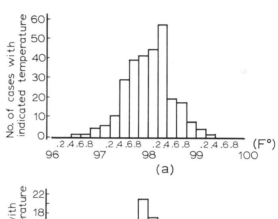

(a)

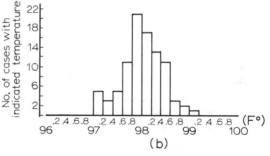

(b)

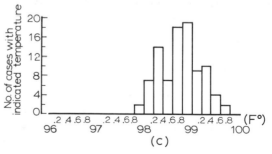

(c)

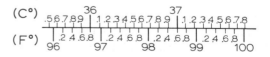

Thus, deviations of 0.5° C. from mean temperatures can be expected in healthy individuals, even under carefully controlled conditions. In more typical circumstances, much larger deviations are found. Furthermore, an individual's temperature may differ with time even though other conditions are constant. Both a diurnal variation and longer-term fluctuations, such as that associated with ovulation may be 1.0° C. or more.[12, 30]

Therefore, when a patient has a temperature deviating 1.0° C. above that indicated by the arrow at 37.0° C. on the clinical thermometer, it may actually be his "normal" temperature at that particular time. On the other hand, a rectal temperature of 38° C. may indeed be evidence of fever. But, it would only be one indication; additional information, especially the time course of temperature, would be required. The proper approach to evaluating an elevated temperature requires an appreciation of the range of normal temperatures and an understanding of the factors determining body temperature.

These factors are (i) the exchange of heat between the body and the environment, (ii) the production and distribution of heat within the body, and (iii) the neural mechanisms involved in homeothermy.

HEAT EXCHANGE WITH THE ENVIRONMENT

Convection. If body surface temperature is warmer than environmental air temperature, heat flows from the body to the surrounding air. As this air is heated, it rises and is replaced by the more dense, cooler air. Thus, cool air moves continuously up to the body surface, is warmed by body heat, and then flows away, resulting in a net heat loss from the surface. This transfer of heat to a moving fluid is termed *convection* (see Fig. 3).

If air movement is due only to local heating by the body, the convection is called *natural*. If external influences—winds, electric fans, etc.—contribute to the air movement, the convection is termed *forced*.

Heat loss by convection depends upon the existence of a temperature gradient between the body surface and ambient air. If the surface and air are at the same temperature, there can be no convective heat transfer; if the gradi-

ent is reversed with the air warmer than the surface, the body actually gains heat by convection. Thus, the first factor which determines heat transfer by convection is $(T_s - T_a)$, the difference between the surface temperature of the object and that of the ambient air.

The rate of convective heat exchange depends also upon the exposed surface area of the body (A_c). This exposed area is always less than the body's total surface area, since some regions, such as the axilla or the inner aspect of the thigh, tend to impede air circulation and thus do not contribute appreciably to convective exchange. Also, the exposed area is not constant but depends upon posture: curling up tends to reduce area and thus conserve body heat, while extending the limbs maximizes the exposed area. In a typical stance with the legs together and the arms close to the sides, about 80 per cent of the body's total surface area is involved in efficient convective heat exchange.

Another influence is the rate at which convective currents bring air to the body surface to participate in heat exchange. This is termed the convection coefficient, K_c; this coefficient is determined by several factors, including free air velocity, density, and viscosity, and the shape of the surface. Figure 4 shows the value of K_c as a function of wind velocity, averaged over the whole body in a normal environment.

If these influences are combined, the net heat lost via convection (H_c) may be calculated from the equation

$$H_c = K_c A_c (T_s - T_a) \qquad (1)$$

A positive value for H_c indicates convective heat loss; a negative value (due to $T_a > T_s$) means that the body is gaining heat from convection.

For example, consider a resting nude individual exposed to air at 29° C. with a wind velocity of 9 cm. per second $(K_c = 6)$—a reasonably neutral environment. In these circumstances skin temperature averages approximately 33° C. (If the individual were clothed, the outside surface temperature of the clothing rather than skin temperature should be used for T_s.) If the total area is 1.7 meters A_c typically is about 1.5 meters².

Substituting these values in equation (1) gives a heat loss rate of 36 Kcal. per meter²-hour. A quietly resting individual of this size has a total metabolic rate of approximately 85

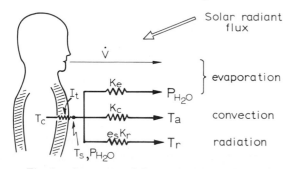

Fig. 3. Summary of the modes of heat loss. Heat is lost via the respiratory tract at a rate proportional to the ventilation, $\dot{V}$. The rest of the heat produced within the body is brought to the body surface through the equivalent tissue insulation, represented by the resistor, I_t. Heat that reaches the surface is transferred to the environment through the three parallel pathways of radiation, convection and evaporation, represented by resistors with conductances of $e_s K_r$, K_c and K_e. The heat flow per unit exposed area through each path depends upon the driving temperature difference (or P_{H_2O} difference) times the respective conductivity term. The total heat transferred from the surface is simply the sum of these three pathways, times the exposed surface area, less any incident heat flux from solar or similar radiation.

Kcal per meter²-hour. Thus, if this individual is in thermal equilibrium (i.e., losing as much heat as he is producing), 42.5 per cent of his heat loss is via convection. As is evident from equation (1), this fraction can vary widely depending upon external conditions.

Radiation. The surface of the body emits electromagnetic energy in discrete packets called photons. These photons travel with the speed of light until they are absorbed, generally at some solid (or liquid) surface in the environment. Both the average energy of the photons and their rate of emission increase as the temperature of the surface is raised. Similarly, dense objects in the environment also emit energetic photons, some of which are absorbed at the surface of the body. This process, known as radiation, results in the exchange of energy between body and its radiant environment (see Fig. 3).

The equation describing the rate of thermal exchange by radiation is

$$H_r = K_r A_r e_s (T_s - T_r) \qquad (2)$$

Here H_r is the rate of radiant energy exchange. A_r is the body surface area effective in radiation; as with convection, this effective area is less than the total surface area since body sur-

faces radiate partly to each other and only partly to the environment. The radiation coefficient, K_r, depends upon the basic physical constants associated with radiation and the absolute temperature. Within the usual range of temperatures, K_r is relatively constant, averaging approximately 7.0 Kcal. per hour per meter² per degree C. T_r is the environmental radiant temperature, namely, the temperature of those environmental objects with which radiant exchange is occurring. T_r may not be identical with the ambient air temperature.

The emissivity of the body surface, e_s, is the fraction of the incident energy which is absorbed and the fraction of the maximum possible radiant energy which is actually emitted. Absorption and emission are two aspects of the same physical property; i.e., an efficient emitter is also an efficient absorber, so a single number describes both qualities. An object with an emissivity of 1, the ideal "black body," absorbs all the energy incident upon it and emits the maximum amount consistent with its temperature. A surface with an emissivity of 0 absorbs no energy (i.e., it is perfectly reflecting) and emits no energy. All real surfaces fall somewhere between these two extremes.

From the obvious variations of cutaneous pigmentation, it would seem that emissivity and thus radiant exchange should be quite variable from one person to another. However, such is not the case, since the emissivity of the skin is not constant but is different for photons of dif-

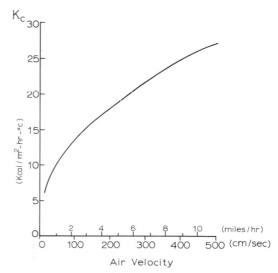

Fig. 4. Dependence of convection coefficient on wind velocity.

ferent energies. The photons whose energies lie in the visible spectrum are, indeed, differentially reflected depending upon skin pigmentation; however, the photons most important for thermal exchange lie in the far infrared region. At these lower energies, most surfaces are almost perfect absorbers (all have emissivities close to 1).

In a typical environment, radiation accounts for much of the energy exchange. In the previous example (with $T_s = 33°$ C., $T_r = 29°$ C., and $A_r = 1.5$ meters^2), radiant heat loss is 42 Kcal. per hour or 49 per cent of the equilibrium heat exchange.

When an intense point source of radiation is present, an additional heat flux must be added to that calculated from equation (2). A good example is solar radiation. The energetic photons emitted by the sun produce an energy flux at the earth's surface of about 1150 Kcal. per hour per meter^2. Since much of this energy is in the visible region, skin pigmentation is of some significance here: very dark skin absorbs about 82 per cent of the incident solar radiation while very fair skin absorbs about 65 per cent. Light colored clothing can reflect up to 60 per cent at these wave lengths, and thus can partially protect against the large incident solar flux.

The reader who remembers his physics may be confused by the form of equation (2), since, according to the Stefan-Boltzmann law, radiant exchange is proportional to the difference between the fourth powers of surface temperature and environmental radiant temperature ($T_s^4 - T_r^4$), where both temperatures are absolute or in degrees Kelvin (K). However, the Stefan-Boltzmann expression can be factored into the two terms ($T_s^3 + T_s^2 T_r + T_s T_r^2 + T_r^3$) ($T_s - T_r$). The first factor does not vary greatly within the physiologic range because it is evaluated in terms of absolute temperature, which changes less than 20 per cent with a temperature change of 0° C. to 50° C. (273° K to 323° K); thus it can be incorporated into the coefficient K_c along with the Boltzmann constant. The second term, $T_s - T_r$, which does appear in equation (2) can be expressed in degrees Centigrade as well as Kelvin because it is a difference; the size of the degree gradation is the same in both systems, only the zero level is different.

It may also be wondered why the emissivity of the environment does not contribute to equation (2) in a manner similar to the emissivity of the body surface. The reason is that the area of absorbing surfaces in the environment is large compared to the radiating area of the body surface. Once a photon leaves the body surface, the probability of returning to the body is small. Though it may be reflected on its first interaction, it will probably be absorbed on a subsequent

interaction before it chances to return to the body surface. Thus, the environment is an almost perfect absorber independent of the reflecting characteristics of each environmental surface.

Evaporation. When water passes from a liquid to a gaseous state, energy must be supplied. The thermal energy required, when the process occurs at constant temperature, is termed the *latent heat* of vaporization. In the physiologic range of temperatures, the latent heat of water is approximately 580 Kcal. per liter (0.58 Kcal. per gram) of liquid vaporized. The large amount of heat absorbed in the evaporation of water makes this mechanism a potent influence upon thermal balance (see Fig. 3).

Some of the water lost to the environment simply diffuses passively through the skin to the body surface. Since the epidermis is only slightly permeable to water, the rate of water exudation through this mechanism is relatively small; in typical circumstances it may amount to 10 ml. per hour.

Expired air is almost completely saturated with water, even at high ventilation rates. This water is evaporated from the moist lining of the respiratory tract, removing latent heat at the rate of about 9 Kcal. per hour at a normal ventilation rate and proportionately more at higher ventilation rates. This heat is supplied by the blood; the perfusion in the respiratory tract is so rich that very little change in temperature is associated with the heat loss, and most of the respiratory tract is therefore held close to arterial blood temperature.

In man, respiratory heat loss is simply an accidental feature of pulmonary gas exchange. However, in furred mammals, whose ability to lose heat through the external surface is limited by the thermal insulation of the body fur, respiratory heat loss is an important effector mechanism for temperature regulation. These animals increase heat loss by panting, i.e., very rapid but shallow breathing (small tidal volume) which increases total ventilation without proportionately increasing alveolar ventilation, since much of the additional air movement ventilates only the anatomic dead space. Thus, heat loss from the respiratory tract is increased without unbalancing blood gas concentrations.

For an individual resting in a neutral or cool thermal environment, the total evaporative heat loss from both transcutaneous diffusion and respiratory ventilation is relatively minor

—about 15 per cent of the total heat loss. We are usually unaware of this loss; hence it is termed "insensible perspiration." However, in a warm environment, evaporation becomes the dominant factor in heat exchange because the active secretion of sweat increases greatly the amount of water available for evaporation at the surface of the body.

In contrast with passive cutaneous diffusion, sweating involves the extrusion of water from specialized glands (eccrine glands*) within the skin as an active thermoregulatory effector mechanism. These sweat glands are innervated only by the sympathetic nervous system, but differ from other sympathetic end organs in that they are cholinergic. They secrete sweat only when stimulated, the quantity depending directly upon the stimulus rate. Relatively large amounts of fluid can be lost by sweating. In a hot environment or during severe exercise, an average individual can secrete well over 1 liter of sweat per hour (Fig. 5).

The quantity of heat lost from the surface by evaporation depends upon the rate of fluid secretion and the capacity of the environment to remove water vapor. If the ambient air is dry and moving rapidly, the evaporative heat loss is limited only by the rate of sweat secretion. Under these conditions,

$$H_e = 580 (R_{H_2O}) \qquad (3)$$

Here, H_e is the rate of evaporative heat loss (in Kcal. per hour), R_{H_2O} is the rate of water secretion (in liters per hour), and the constant, 580 Kcal. per liter, is the latent heat of vaporization of water at normal surface temperature.

If, on the other hand, the air is moist and stagnant, the evaporative heat loss is limited by the ability of the ambient air to remove water

* There are two types of sweat glands—the *eccrine* glands and the *apocrine* glands. Only the eccrine glands are associated with temperature regulation. These glands are widely distributed on the body surface. Those on the palms of the hands and the soles of the feet are exceptional and respond to anxiety, mental stress and similar states rather than a rise in temperature.

The *apocrine* glands are found mainly in the axillary and pubic regions. These glands secrete a creamy substance rich in organic matter. This substance is attacked by the skin flora; the decomposition products are responsible for the characteristic body odors. The apocrine glands are adrenergic, not cholinergic. Apocrine secretion can be increased by emotional stress, a response partly mediated by the adrenal medulla.

from the skin. In this circumstance, the heat loss is:

$$H_e = K_e A_w (P_{sH_2O} - P_{aH_2O}) \qquad (4)$$

P_{sH_2O} and P_{aH_2O} are respectively the partial pressures of water at the surface of the body and in the ambient air. (The ratio of the actual partial pressure to the maximum partial pressure of saturated air at the same temperature is called the *relative humidity*.) The difference between these two pressures is the driving force for water vapor movement and is analogous to the temperature difference controlling convective and radiant heat loss. A_w is the moist area of the skin participating in evaporative exchange; K_e is the evaporative coefficient determined from the latent heat of water vaporization and the rate of ambient air movement at the skin; it varies with wind velocity in a manner similar to K_c.

The actual evaporative heat loss is equal to the result of equation (3) or that of equation (4), whichever is smaller. If H_e from equation (3) is greater than that calculated from equation (4), the evaporative heat loss is limited by

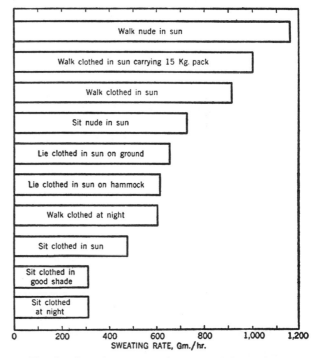

Fig. 5. Sweating rates under 10 conditions of exposure to desert at air temperature of 100° F. dry bulb. (From Gosselin, p. 64, in Adolph *et al.: Physiology of man in the desert.* New York, Interscience Publishers, Inc., 1947.)

the sweat rate. If H_e from equation (4) is greater, the body is secreting more water than can be evaporated. This excess fluid drips off the body and is of no advantage since water must evaporate for body heat to be absorbed.

Other modes. Heat may be exchanged with the environment by direct conduction to objects with which the body is in physical contact, such as when an individual is seated. Also, net heat transfer results when ingested materials warm or cool to body temperature. However, these are negligible except in unusual circumstances, such as sitting nude in a metal chair or eating a large quantity of ice cream.

HEAT TRANSFER WITHIN THE BODY

Heat lost to the environment is transferred from the site of production to the body surface (or the epithelial lining of the airways) by combined *conduction* and *circulatory convection* (see Fig. 3).

In any material, heat tends to flow down a temperature gradient by transfer of thermal energy between adjacent atoms. This process, conduction, results in heat transfer *through* a material, in contrast to convection, which involves bulk movement of material. The ratio of the temperature gradient to the heat flux is known as the volume conductivity. The tissues of the body are not particularly good heat conductors; conductivity of unperfused body tissues is comparable to that of cork, as shown in Table 1. Values reported for various tissues (or even measurements on the same tissue by different investigators) may differ by as much as a factor of five; nonetheless, all body tissues fall in the category of poor conductors.

Thus, if the heat exchange within the body

TABLE 1. *Rate of Heat Flow through a Slab of Material, 1 Cm. Thick, 1 Meter² in Area, per Degree (Centigrade) Temperature Difference between Faces*

	KCAL. PER HOUR
Eiderdown, felt	0.36
Cork	16
Beef muscle, fat[23] (unperfused)	18
Silver	36,000

were solely conductive, large internal temperature gradients would be necessary to conduct metabolic heat away. Compensating for changing internal and external thermal stress would be difficult, since the thermal conductance of any particular tissue is constant.

Effect of Circulation. Convective heat transfer occurs within the body with the bulk movement of body fluids. Of primary importance is forced convection via the circulatory system. The circulation affects heat distribution within the body in three ways:

(i) *Minimizing temperature differences within the body.* In well-perfused tissues, the distances over which heat must be transferred by conduction alone (between the cells and the blood stream) are very small because of the profuse distribution of capillaries, and temperature differences necessary to transfer heat to the blood stream amount to only hundredths of a degree. In tissues with high rates of metabolism and perfusion, metabolic heat is removed with only a slight increase in temperature of the blood flowing through the tissues.* In tissues cooler than the incoming blood, heat is supplied by the blood to the tissue. Thus, the circulation cools some tissues and warms others, maintaining much of the body mass at an almost uniform temperature.

(ii) *Controlling effective body insulation.* The systemic capillaries perfusing cutaneous tissue do not extend into the superficial epidermis. Heat is transferred through this outermost layer solely by conduction. If cutaneous capillaries are fully dilated, blood flows close to the surface, and adequate rates of heat transfer are established with only a few tenths of a degree difference between blood and surface temperature. However, when cutaneous vessels are constricted, heat must be transferred to the body surface by pure conduction over much larger distances, requiring correspondingly larger temperature differences. Intermediate vasomotor states result in combined conduction and convection in the partially perfused subepidermal layers. Thus, the ease of heat transfer to the body surface is altered by cutaneous vasomotor changes which, in effect, alter the thickness of an insulating "shell" separating the deeper "core" tissues from the environment.

---

* The heat removed from or added to a body through which a fluid passes is directly proportional to the flow rate and the difference between the inflow and outflow temperatures.

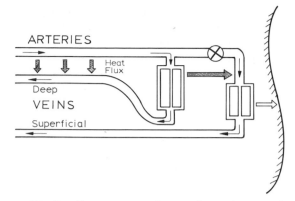

Fig. 6. Countercurrent heat exchange in extremities. When "valve" is open (i.e., cutaneous vasodilation), blood flow is routed through superficial capillary bed, allowing efficient transfer of heat to body surface. Blood returning through superficial veins does not exchange significant amounts of heat with deep arterial blood. When "valve" is closed (i.e., cutaneous vasoconstriction) superficial blood flow is reduced, and most blood returns via deep veins.

Thus, heat loss is reduced both by the increased effective insulation of superficial tissues and by the precooling of blood reaching the capillary bed by heat exchange between deep arteries and veins.

(iii) *Countercurrent heat exchange between major blood vessels.* The blood perfusing the extremities passes outward from the heart along the arterial system, loses heat in the surface capillaries, and returns to cool the body by mixing with venous blood from the warm internal organs. The heat lost in this manner can be reduced if the arterial and venous blood supplying the limb exchange heat through the vessel walls. Thus, the blood reaching the superficial regions is precooled, the capillary-surface gradient is reduced, and less heat is lost from the blood, while the venous blood returning to the heart is partially rewarmed. The net effect is to conserve heat.

The extent of countercurrent exchange is controlled by the relative distribution of venous return from the extremities to the deep and superficial vessels. If the blood returns to the heart via the superficial veins, conductive transfer to the deep arteries is minimal. If the deeper veins are utilized for the venous return, internal heat conservation is facilitated (Fig. 6).

Internal Temperature Distribution. The detailed pattern of temperature distribution throughout the body is complex; the factors influencing local tissue temperatures—local heat production, local circulation, and local temperature gradients—differ throughout the body and change in time.* However, certain general characteristics are apparent. Most of the body metabolic heat is produced in the deep organs—heart, viscera, brain, etc.—except during vigorous exercise. For this heat to be lost, these organs must be warmer than the perfusing blood or the surrounding tissue. Similarly, deeper tissue in general would be expected to be warmer than more superficial tissue (Fig. 7).

Visualizing the body as a central core at uniform temperature surrounded by an insulating shell is a useful (though oversimplified) concept. Those perfused tissues with temperatures within a few tenths of a degree of, say, rectal temperature are considered to be the body core. Thus, the core comprises almost the entire body when cutaneous vasodilation is maximal, and the shell is reduced to the thickness of the epidermis.

* For a detailed mathematical exposition of these influences, see Brown.[6]

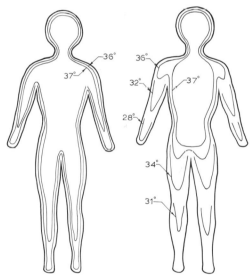

Fig. 7. Isotherms (surfaces connecting points of equal temperature) in the body. *Left,* isotherms in a warm environment; *right,* in a cold environment. The innermost isotherm may be considered as the boundary of the body "core"; the core includes most of the body in hot environments. When heat must be conserved, the core contracts to the proportions indicated in the left. In severe cold exposure, the combined effect of vasoconstriction and countercurrent heat exchange results in the pattern of isotherms shown in the limbs—the distal portions of which become part of the body "shell" and fall nearly to environmental temperatures. (After Aschoff and Wever, *Naturwissenschaften,* 1958, *45:*477–485.)

When heat must be conserved, vasoconstriction reduces circulation to the periphery, the central core contracts, and the thickness of the shell increases. The vasoconstriction directly reduces the ease of heat transport to the surface, and indirectly reduces heat loss to the environment by lowering the surface temperature. Thus, in extreme cold, the temperature of the central organs is maintained at the expense (i.e., cooling) of the more peripheral tissue, particularly the extremities.

The fingers have more surface per unit volume than the arms, the arms more surface area relative to their volume than the trunk.* This large surface area is advantageous in losing heat to a warm environment but is disadvantageous when heat must be conserved. Despite complete cutaneous vasoconstriction, the net insulation of the tissues surrounding the central larger vessels of the limbs is not sufficient to prevent cooling of the blood; but countercurrent heat exchange permits the development of large longitudinal temperature gradients along the vessels and the limbs, and the entire distal portion of the extremity becomes part of the shell. Thus, heat is conserved, but fingers, toes, and similarly situated tissue may be severely cooled in the process (Fig. 7).

Body Surface Temperature. Normally, body surface temperature lies somewhere between that of the body core and that of the surroundings. When the ease of heat transfer from the body core to the surface is increased, surface temperature rises toward that of the body core. When tissue conductance is reduced, surface temperature falls toward that of the environment. Thus, the victim of Raynaud's disease who complains of cold extremities even though room temperature is normal has a rational basis for his complaint because his extremities actually are cold; vasospasm has caused the temperature of the cutaneous thermoreceptors to fall toward environmental temperature. Conversely, the warm, comfortable feeling induced by alcoholic beverages is not only the result of a general euphoria but is also due to the vasodilating effect of alcohol.

When surface evaporation carries away much of the heat, skin temperature may no longer lie between the environmental and core temperatures, but may be lower than both. Thus, heat can move from the core to the sur-

*The surface to volume ratio of a cylindrical object is inversely proportional to its diameter.

face down a temperature gradient, even when the environmental temperature exceeds 37° C.

Thus, skin temperature at any point is the resultant of the factors determining heat transfer from the interior and the ease of heat transfer to the environment. These factors vary over the body surface, and so, therefore, does skin temperature. Figure 8 shows the distribution of skin temperature of a nude male subject at various environmental temperatures.

Net Tissue Insulation and Effect of Clothing. The net tissue insulation, I_t, is defined as the heat flow per unit surface area divided into the temperature difference necessary to produce this heat flow in a steady state, or

$$I_t = \frac{T_c - T_s}{H/A} \qquad (5)$$

where H is the total heat flow through the surface (all heat except that lost via respiration), A is the body surface area, T_c is the core or central temperature, and T_s is the mean surface temperature. The mean surface temperature is evaluated by multiplying the temperature of each body surface region by the fraction of body area it represents, and summing. The following equation is commonly employed:[20]

$$T_s = 0.07\,T_{Feet} + 0.32\,T_{Legs} + 0.18\,T_{Chest} +$$
$$0.17\,T_{Back} + 0.14\,T_{Arms} + 0.05\,T_{Hands}$$
$$+ 0.07\,T_{Head}.$$

Body insulation in a comfortable environment typically is about 0.08° C. per Kcal. per hour per meter². Heat-induced vasodilation may reduce this to 0.02° C. per Kcal. per hour per meter². The vasoconstriction caused by cold exposure can increase tissue insulation to 0.2° C. per Kcal. per hour per meter² in a normal person, while an obese individual with a large amount of subcutaneous fat may have an even larger tissue insulation.[10] Rewriting equation (5) as follows

$$T_c = T_s + (H/A)\,I_t \qquad (6)$$

reveals that an animal, by increasing its heat production or its tissue insulation, or both, can maintain core temperature in conditions which cause surface temperature to drop. However, man has an additional resource, namely, wearing clothing to increase his total insulation.

The environmental physiologist views cloth-

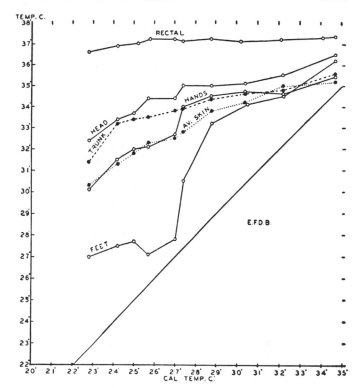

Fig. 8. Skin and rectal temperatures of a nude male resting quietly in still air. (Cal. temp. refers to air temperature.) (From DuBois, *Bull. N.Y. Acad. Med.,* 1939, *15*:143–173.)

ing simply as additional insulation (I_{cl}) in series with that of the tissues. Thus equation (6) becomes

$$T_c = T_s + (H/A)(I_t + I_{cl}). \quad (7)$$

Here T_s represents the mean temperature of the surface of the clothing, since this is now the surface where heat exchanges with the environment. A normally dressed laboratory worker in the U.S. will have an I_{cl} of about 0.1° C. per Kcal. per hour per meter². (Insulation values for various types of clothing may be found in reference 28.)

Body Heat Content. When the rate of heat loss to the environment is not balanced exactly by the rate of heat production, the difference is added to or removed from the body heat stores. A change in heat content (ΔQ) is accompanied by a temperature change, as given by the formula

$$\Delta Q = cM(\Delta T_b)$$

where c is the specific heat capacity, M is the body mass, and ΔT_b is the change in the mean body temperature. The specific heat of body tissue is approximately 0.83 (Kcal. per °C. per

kg.). This relatively high value is due to the high water content of body tissue. If the mean body temperature of a 70 kg. man dropped 1° C., the heat loss would be

$$\Delta Q = 0.83 \times 70 \times 1 = 58 \text{ Kcal.}$$

When the body is subjected to thermal stress, the change in internal temperature is not uniform, making the computation of mean body temperature a complex problem. However, mean body temperature can be estimated roughly from a weighted average of skin and core (rectal) temperatures. Under normal conditions, the weighting factors are about 0.3 and 0.7, so

$$T_b = 0.3 T_s + 0.7 T_r.$$

In a cold environment when the "shell" becomes thicker and the core smaller, the weighting factor for T_s increases to about 0.4 and T_r decreases to about 0.6. In warm environments the core expands, leading to weighting factors of about 0.2 and 0.8 for T_s and T_r respectively.[7, 21]

The rate of change of heat content, dQ/dt, is determined by the difference between the rates of body heat production and heat loss:

$$H_{produced} - H_{lost} = \frac{dQ}{dt} = cM\frac{dT_b}{dt}.$$

When the environmental thermal stress changes, heat production and heat loss are transiently imbalanced. As the body approaches a new state of thermal equilibrium, the rate of change of temperature decreases until $(dT_b/dt) = 0$ and heat production and heat loss are again equal. Because of the high heat capacity of an adult, heat production and loss may be unbalanced for perhaps several hours with only slight alteration in body temperature.

This has two advantages. First, levels of motor responses need not be instantaneously in proportion to the severity of the existing thermal stress, i.e., the thermal lag damps out transient changes in the environment. Second, the long latency provides time to escape from highly stressful environments in which adequate physiologic compensation is impossible.

NEURAL STRUCTURES INVOLVED IN TEMPERATURE REGULATION

Thermoreceptors. It is obvious from subjective experience that temperature receptors are distributed over the entire body surface. In addition, there is a mechanism deep within the brain capable of responding directly to local changes in temperature. There may also be re-

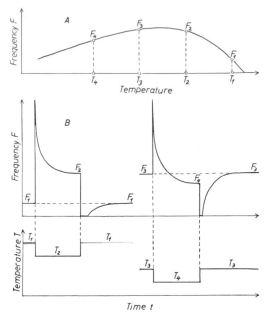

Fig. 10. Impulse frequency of a single cold fiber. *A*, With constant temperatures, and *B*, with rectangular temperature jumps. (From Hensel, *Acta physiol. scand.*, 1953, *29*:109–116.)

ceptors located elsewhere within the core of the body.

Peripheral reception. The properties of cutaneous nerve endings responding to temperature have been discussed in Chapter 14, particularly with regard to the sensation of temperature. It is generally assumed that the same receptors and associated spinothalamic pathways are involved in the control of body temperature.

The cutaneous thermoreceptors fall into two distinct categories—cold receptors and warm receptors (Fig. 9). Both groups of cutaneous thermoreceptors exhibit rapid adaptation; i.e., they are particularly sensitive to rate of change of temperature. As shown in Figure 10, the phasic discharge rate while temperature is changing in the appropriate direction is much higher than the tonic rate that persists as the new temperature is held constant. This pattern is reflected in the subjective thresholds for thermal sensation. A small change in temperature, subthreshold in the sense that it evokes no noticeable sensation if the change is gradual, can evoke a distinct but temporary sensation of warming or cooling if the same change is effected rapidly.

Central reception. Thermoreception in the brain is shown by the fact that experimentally

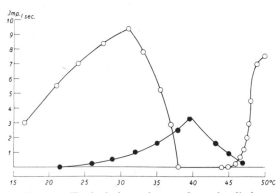

Fig. 9. Typical dependence of steady discharge rate of cold fibers (open circles) and warm fibers (filled circles) in cat lingual nerve upon tongue temperature. The behavior of the cold receptor above 45° C. is presumably associated with the sensation of "paradoxical" cold. (From Dodt and Zotterman, *Acta physiol. scand.*, 1952, *26*:345–357.)

induced changes in brain temperature cause thermoregulatory responses. An increase in brain temperature causes increased evaporative heat loss and vasodilation; a sufficient decrease causes vasoconstriction and shivering. These effects can be produced while other body temperatures are independently held constant; therefore, they must be initiated directly by the change in brain temperature. The existence of specialized thermosensitive endings or other structures specific for this function is not necessarily implied, because any temperature-dependent neural function (such as synaptic transmission) could constitute the mechanism for capability to respond to local temperature.

The hypothalamus is the major site of thermosensitivity. Accurate stereotaxic probing for thermally sensitive areas in the brain has been made possible through the recent development of needle-shaped probes, called thermodes, which produce highly localized changes in brain temperature.[2, 14] Long-term implantation of thermodes has been done in experimental animals, enabling study of responses to thermal stimulation of the brain in intact, unanesthetized preparations. These studies have shown that thermoregulatory responses to both cooling and heating can be elicited in the anterior hypothalamus.[1, 15]

This thermosensitive property has been further confirmed by direct recording of temperature-dependent firing rates of individual anterior hypothalamic neurons (Chap. 11, Fig. 3). Of course, the firing frequency of spontaneously active neurons in many parts of the body may change when their local temperature is changed. However, the specific hypothalamic neurons assumed to be associated with temperature reception are particularly sensitive, showing a several fold steeper dependence of firing rate upon local temperature than other hypothalamic neurons.

The existence of other thermoreceptors is not so well supported. However, this possibility has not been ruled out. In the last few years, a group of German investigators have worked with anesthetized dogs prepared so that the temperatures of the brain and skin can be independently controlled. They found that, with skin and brain temperatures held constant, thermal stimulation of central regions of the trunk initiated thermoregulatory responses, particularly upon cooling in the vicinity of the spinal column.[29] On the other hand, Downey and co-workers[11] cooled regions within the trunk of unanesthetized rabbits by circulating cold water through heat exchangers surrounding

various major blood vessels. Only slight elevation in metabolism was found and this could well have been caused by incidental cooling of skin areas supplied by the vessel or by slight cooling of the brain from cooled blood mixed with the general circulation. Thus, whether other receptors besides those of the skin and the hypothalamic region contribute to temperature regulation is not clear at present.

Structures Involved in Central Integration. That body temperature is regulated implies the existence of central neural integrative mechanisms which process afferent inputs from thermosensitive receptors and produce appropriately graded efferent signals. The many levels of integration converging on the final sudomotor, vasomotor, and somatic motor effectors affecting the body thermal balance have been indicated earlier in this text. The temperature regulation system is obviously interdependent with the cardiovascular and respiratory systems, and can be influenced by voluntary behavior, e.g., voluntary inhibition of shivering. A small amount of sudomotor and vasomotor activity can be elicited in the spinal animal below the level of transection, showing the existence of a spinal level of integration.

However, a high decerebrate animal displays essentially normal body temperature regulation if the transection does not encroach upon the hypothalamic region, whereas decerebrations which remove hypothalamic tissue interfere markedly with temperature regulation. The decerebrate preparation with all hypothalamic tissue removed is poikilothermic. Therefore, the hypothalamus appears to be the major and essential level for the control of body temperature.

The structures involved in this integrative function appear to be confined to the anterior and posterior hypothalamus. These regions are connected by bilateral tracts coursing through the lateral hypothalamus. The roles of the anterior and posterior regions are functionally separate to some degree. Lesions in the posterior hypothalamus may produce deficits in the body defenses against cooling with relatively little effect on the defenses against overheating, and the reverse pattern is associated with anterior lesions.

In fact, until recently it was widely held that the major central integrative mechanisms involved in body temperature regulation are found in two anatomically and functionally separate regions within the hypothalamus. According to this "dual center" theory, a heat dissipation center in the anterior hypothalamus and a heat conservation center in the posterior hypothalamus govern the body defenses against overheating and cooling, respectively, and activity in one center inhibits activity in the other via the interconnecting tracts. The effects of discrete brain lesions in the anterior, posterior, and lateral hypothalamus appeared to confirm this theory (though these lesions generally involved extrahypothalamic as well as hypothalamic tissue).

As pointed out in Chapter 11, numerous recent reports indicate that this dual center theory is oversimplified, particularly with regard to the strict separation of the functions associated with the anterior and posterior regions. Furthermore, there is evidence that other regions in the vicinity, including an area just anterior to the hypothalamus proper, may contain important integrating mechanisms involved in defense against both cooling and heating, and must be included with the regions essential for normal thermoregulation. Thus the hypothalamus (perhaps including nearby regions) is the center for temperature regulation, but the detailed functional relations between the various structures is not so clear as was formerly believed.

How the old theory should be modified is controversial, because of conflicting data obtained by various investigators and, unfortunately, because of different criteria for testing thermoregulatory behavior. Keller[26] points out that some lesions which appear to abolish a thermoregulatory response in fact only alter the sensitivity or threshold and these retained functions are not observed unless more extreme thermal stresses than usual are applied.

Keller further points out that thermal behavior in chronic preparations changes during the postoperative period. These changes are not necessarily complete even after a month or more. He found the thermoregulatory responses of one dog to be substantially different when tested four weeks after surgery and one year later. Clearly, conflicting interpretations can result when different criteria are used to determine the time at which the effects of a lesion can be observed without interference from surgical trauma or other factors including possible long-term and continuous development of normally subsidiary neural mechanisms.

A further complication is that the anterior hypothalamic mechanism which detects changes in local temperature is conceptually distinct from what is usually thought of as an integrative mechanism. If both functions are present in the anterior hypothalamus,

they are abolished together by ablation in this region. Both would be elicited by stimulation, but perhaps with very different thresholds. It is difficult to see how the component due to disturbance of the integrative function *per se* can be separated out from the other effects.

BEHAVIOR OF THE TEMPERATURE REGULATION SYSTEM[8, 9, 13, 18, 19, 24, 28]

Zones of Regulation. The behavior of the thermoregulatory effectors may be described in terms of three characteristic zones: the zone of vasomotor regulation, the zone of metabolic regulation, and the zone of sudomotor regulation.

Zone of vasomotor regulation. Under conditions of mild thermal stress and mild exercise, changes in tissue insulation resulting from altered vasomotor state suffice to regulate the balance between heat loss and heat production and prevent alterations of deep body temperature. In these circumstances, evaporative heat loss is small, almost entirely from insensible water loss, and metabolic rate is not elevated except in association with voluntary movement.

In man, average skin temperature in this zone ranges approximately from 31° to 34° C., depending on the vasomotor state. The associated subjective sensation is one of thermal neutrality.

Whenever possible, man selects clothing appropriate to the environmental temperature ranges to remain in the zone of vasomotor regulation. The environmental temperature range which characterizes this zone depends on many factors (wind velocity, clothing insulation, etc.). For a nude subject resting quietly in relatively still air, the range is about 28° to 31° C.[23] For a normally clothed subject, the center of the range is about 21° C., which corresponds to a normal comfortable environmental temperature.

Zone of metabolic regulation. When increased tissue insulation alone is not sufficient to prevent excessive heat loss, body temperature can be maintained only if metabolic heat production increases. Normally, this is accomplished by increasing muscle activity, either by voluntary motion or by involuntary shivering. Other heat-producing mechanisms (nonshivering thermogenesis, see Chap. 55) may also contribute, but have not been conclusively demonstrated in man. The metabolic rate of a man exposed acutely to cold does not elevate appreciably until shivering begins.[23] However, in animals exposed chronically to cold, metabolic rate can increase without increased muscular activity. This type of response is part of the phenomenon of long-term acclimation to cold and is presumably mediated by synergistic action of the endocrine system and the autonomic nervous system.

Using muscular contraction to increase heat production has attendant disadvantages. In the first place, vigorous shivering is exhausting. Secondly, the increased blood flow to the peripheral musculature decreases effective tissue insulation. Also, disturbing surface air by muscular movement increases convective heat loss. Thus, shivering itself increases the loss of heat to the environment; perhaps one third of the heat produced by shivering is wasted.

Zone of sudomotor regulation. During vigorous exercise, and when environmental temperature rises above the neutral zone, tissue insulation cannot decrease sufficiently to permit dissipation of the body heat; also the metabolic rate cannot decrease below that associated with the level of body activity. Thus, to maintain thermal balance, heat must be lost by evaporation of sweat.

In this zone, sweat rate increases as environmental temperature rises. Peripheral vasodilation continues to increase, permitting ready transfer of body heat from the interior to the surface where it can be lost via evaporation; but this also obligates much of the cardiac output solely to temperature regulation. Inappropriately, heat production increases slightly; sweating and increasing blood flow require metabolic energy and, in addition, increasing body temperature elevates tissue metabolism (see Chap. 53).

Control of the Thermoregulatory Effectors. *Negative feedback from central temperature.* The hypothesis that central temperature directly affects the state of the effectors was proposed long before hypothalamic thermosensitivity was demonstrated experimentally.* In other words, it was assumed that it is not merely a fortuitous response to changing environmental stress which keeps the deep body temperature constant; rather the motor mechanisms are controlled by deviations of the central temperature from the normal value (sometimes called the *set point* or *reference temperature*) in such a manner as to return the central temperature itself to the normal level (Fig. 11).

From this simplified point of view, the temperature regulation system is a negative feedback control system. It possesses the three types of elements essential in such a system: (i) receptors which sense the existing central (con-

---

*It was natural to make this hypothesis because the simplest way to account for the constancy of central temperature is to assume that it is directly sensed and that this information is utilized in negative feedback control.

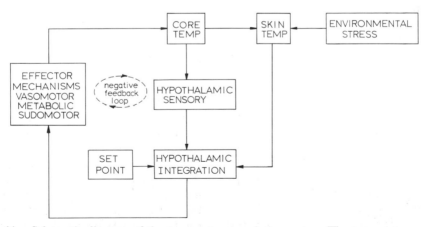

Fig. 11. Schematic diagram of the temperature regulation system. The temperature sensed by the hypothalamus (which is presumably related to central temperature) and the cutaneous temperature are compared to the set point, and effector mechanisms are activated in proportion to the deviations. The left side is the negative feedback loop which stabilizes central temperature. The input from cutaneous temperature is not part of the negative feedback loop, but may contribute to temperature stability by anticipating central temperature change and speeding up system response.

trolled) temperature; (ii) effector mechanisms —vasomotor, sudomotor, and metabolic— which are capable of altering the central temperature; and (iii) integrative structures which presumably compare sensed temperature to "normal" temperature (the *set point* or *reference temperature*), determine whether existing temperature is too high or too low, and activate the appropriate motor response. It is a *feedback* system since incidental changes in central temperature set in motion a sequence of events which eventually affect (or feed back upon) central temperature. It is a *negative* feedback system because a spontaneous deviation of central temperature in one direction sets into play mechanisms which tend to displace that temperature in the opposite (negative) direction; a rise in central temperature activates heat loss mechanisms, while a fall in central temperature activates heat conservation and heat production mechanisms. Clearly, homeothermy is the result of this negative feedback.

The reference temperature or set point *does not necessarily represent a temperature which actually exists somewhere in the hypothalamus or anywhere else in the body.* Rather, it represents that hypothalamic temperature at which the transition is made between the activation of those mechanisms which tend to raise body temperature and the activation of those mechanisms which tend to lower it.

The temperature regulation system frequently is compared to the temperature control of a modern centrally heated house: the house thermostat is analogized to the hypothalamic "thermostat," the house furnace to the metabolic "furnace," and so forth. This analogy has some validity, but it is inaccurate in several important respects. First, the temperature regulation system has several effector mechanisms at its disposal rather than the single one of turning on the furnace. Second, the typical home thermostat has only two responses: either to turn the furnace (or stoker) on full blast or to turn it completely off; the physiologic integrating center is able to grade motor response in proportion to the severity of the environmental stress. (For a description of off-on control, proportional control, integral control, and other types of temperature control systems, see Hardy.[19, 22]) Finally, the home heating system is controlled by only one temperature, that at the thermostat, whereas the "output" of the thermoregulatory effectors is influenced by skin temperature as well as hypothalamic temperature and perhaps by other central temperatures.

Feedback from cutaneous temperature. Apparently, skin temperature is directly involved in control of the thermoregulatory effectors. For example, in man shivering may occur immediately upon exposure to cold. Not only does this happen before there is time for the effect of the cooling to decrease central temperature, but the central temperature may actually show a transient rise.

Animal experiments on the effects of locally heating the hypothalamus also indicate that hypothalamic temperature alone cannot account for the total response. In the experiments of Fusco *et al.,*[14] unanesthetized dogs fitted with chronically implanted thermodes were placed in a calorimeter which permitted direct measurement of heat loss. Hypothalamic heating which altered tissue conductance at environmental (calorimeter) temperatures above 26° C. and mean skin temperatures about 35° C. produced little effect when the air temperature was 14° C. and the skin temperatures below 32° C. (Fig. 12). Other experimenters[27] have shown that whole body temperature changes (including the hypothalamus) are more effective than equal hypothalamic temperature changes alone in eliciting thermoregulatory response.

The response to environmental or deep body temperature which is independent of hypothalamic temperature may not be due solely to feedback from the cutaneous temperature receptors. The possibility that other temperatures, particularly extracerebral central temperatures, are sensed and contribute to feedback regulation has not been ruled out. However, in the absence of a clear demonstration of the contribution of these receptors, it is a logical experimental goal to attempt to characterize the temperature regulation system in terms of skin and brain temperatures only.

Combined role of central and cutaneous temperatures. The evaluation of the relative contribution of, and the interaction between, hypothalamic and skin temperatures in the control of the motor mechanisms has been attempted by a number of investigators. The general technique is to measure and/or control skin temperature and (so far as possible) hypothalamic temperature, and at the same time to measure the vasomotor, the sudomotor, and the metabolic response.

Along these lines, Benzinger and his co-workers have developed an effective approach which can be used with human subjects.[3] In their experiments, skin temperatures were held at desired levels by varying air temperatures or by immersing the subject in water, a situation in which the convective heat exchange is so efficient that skin temperature differs insignificantly from water temperature. Central temperatures were placed at desired levels by pre-cooling or preheating the subject, or by having him exercise or ingest large quantities of ice.

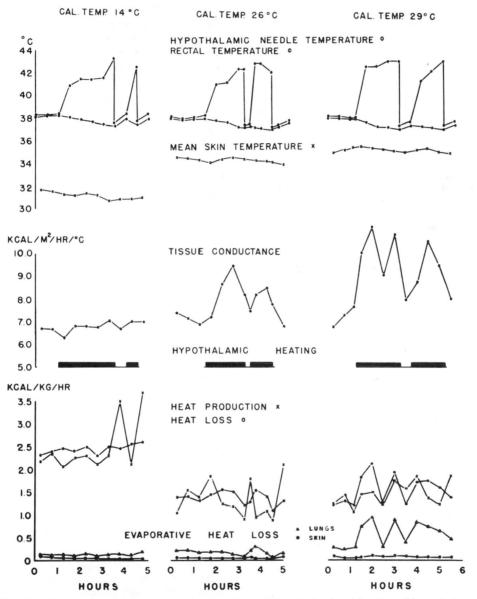

Fig. 12. Graphs showing responses of unanesthetized dog during local heating of hypothalamus using implanted electrodes. Experiments were conducted at three different environmental temperatures, 14°, 26° and 29° C. From above downward, curves show hypothalamic temperature, rectal temperature and mean skin temperature; tissue conductance and time of hypothalamic heating; heat production and heat loss; evaporative heat loss through lungs and skin. The data demonstrate the sensitivity of the hypothalamic mechanism to local heating and show that the nature of the dog's responses depends upon environmental temperature. For example, at 29° C. the local heating led to an increase in tissue conductance and evaporative heat loss that were not seen at 14° C. (Note: tissue conductance is the reciprocal of tissue insulation.) (Fusco, M. M., Ph.D. dissertation, University of Pennsylvania, 1959.)

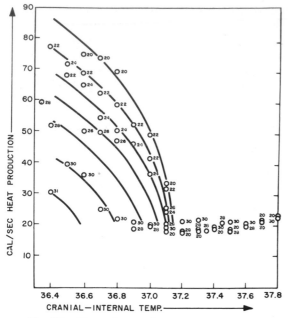

Fig. 13. Dependence of metabolic rate on central temperature (measured at tympanic membrane) in subject A. The relationship depends upon the skin temperature, as shown by the curves connecting points of constant skin temperature. Above 37.1° C. internal temperature, no elevation of metabolic rate occurs even with skin temperatures as low as 20° C. (1 cal. per second = 3.6 Kcal. per hour.) The effect of skin temperature is not merely to change the set point, i.e., shift the curve of metabolic rate vs. central temperature to the left or right, because the individual curves are of different shape as well as displaced along the central temperature axis. (From Benzinger and Kitzinger, Chap. 56 in *Temperature—Its measurement and control in science and industry.* Vol. 3, part 3. J. D. Hardy, ed. New York, Reinhold Publishing Corp., 1963.)

Tympanic membrane temperature was used as an index of brain temperature. This site was selected on the basis of experiments comparing the tympanic membrane temperature with sphenoid sinus temperature and intranasal temperatures.[4] These correlated well with one another and also with observed thermoregulatory responses, in contrast to rectal temperature, which did not precisely follow the cranial temperatures, particularly in periods of changing thermal state. Thus, they assumed that the tympanum temperature is an adequate index of hypothalamic temperature.

The results of these experiments are summarized in Figures 13 and 14. In Figure 13, the metabolic rate for different combinations of skin and central temperatures is shown. At a tympanic membrane temperature below 37.1°

C., the metabolic rate depends partly upon skin temperature. At 36.8° C., for example, the metabolic rate found with the skin temperature at 22° C. is three times higher than that found at a skin temperature of 30° C. However, if the skin temperature were held at 22° C. and the central temperature elevated 0.3 C.,—36.8° to 37.1° C.—the metabolic rate would be reduced by a factor of three. In other words, in these examples a drop of 0.3° C. in central temperature is associated with the same effect on metabolic rate as a drop of 8° C. in skin temperature. The data of Figure 13 also imply that at central temperatures above 37.1° C. metabolic rate remains at the basal level independent of skin temperature.

Figure 14 indicates that sweating did not result unless central (tympanic) temperature exceeded a minimum of 36.9° C. Above this threshold, sweating increased rapidly with

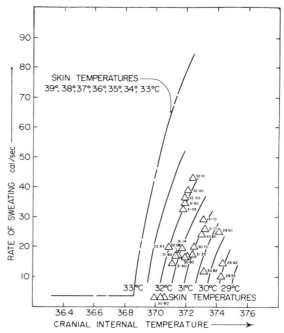

Fig. 14. Dependence of sweat rate on central temperature (measured at tympanic membrane) in subject B. Here, also, the relationship depends upon the skin temperature, though no inhibition of sweating resulted unless skin temperature was below 33° C. A central threshold for sweating is indicated; i.e., sweating did not result unless central temperature exceeded 36.8° C. (1 cal. per second = 3.6 Kcal. per hour, corresponding to evaporation of approximately 6 ml. of sweat per hour.) (From Benzinger and Kitzinger, Chap. 56 in *Temperature—Its measurement and control in science and industry, vol. 3, part 3,* J. D. Hardy, ed. New York, Reinhold Publishing Corp., 1963.)

slight increases in central temperature. This relationship was found to be independent of skin temperature unless skin temperature fell below 33° C., in which case the curves to the right illustrate the mutual dependence of sweating on skin and central temperatures.

Figure 13 comprises the results of many different experiments over a long period of time on one subject. So does Figure 14, though a different subject was used. Presumably, other individuals would display similar characteristics but with individual variations in the specific values of the critical temperatures.

The results summarized in Figures 13 and 14 exhibit several generally agreed upon characteristics, at least in their qualitative aspects. It is generally agreed that sweating is predominantly controlled by central temperature and that shivering is inhibited when the central temperature is high. Also, it is generally agreed that a much larger change is necessary in skin than in central temperature to produce a given thermoregulatory response, a fact which should not be surprising, since it is central temperature and not skin temperature which is maintained within narrow limits by the temperature regulation system. The existence of temperature thresholds is also generally accepted. Figure 13 shows that no appreciable elevation in metabolic rate occurred with skin temperatures above 31° C., and a similar threshold for shivering has been quoted by other workers.[24]

The asymmetry between the responses defending against cooling and the responses defending against overheating, evident upon comparison of Figures 13 and 14, has long been recognized. The body much more vigorously defends against overheating than against cooling; the significance of this is apparent when the limits of survival of thermal extremes are compared. Thermal death results with body temperatures exceeding 45° C. but a hypothermia with central temperatures below 24° C. can be tolerated, provided intensive medical care is available (the temperature regulation system is completely inoperative at such low temperatures and rewarming will not occur unless heat is supplied from an external source).

Unfortunately, the results of animal experiments involving direct measurement of hypothalamic temperature raise perplexing questions which cannot be resolved simply by invoking the matter of differences between species. A fundamental implication of Benzinger's work is that, for each combination of skin and central temperatures, there is a uniquely determined thermoregulatory response. Recently, Hammel *et al.*[16] have summarized results of animal experiments which suggest that other factors besides absolute levels of skin and central temperatures are involved in the determination of the thermoregulatory "output," factors perhaps not apparent in the results obtained by Benzinger *et al.* because of uniform experimental conditions such as time of day, position of the subject, and even such factors as emotional state of the subject.

For example, Hammel *et al.* have shown by direct measurement that hypothalamic temperature fluctuates spontaneously; yet these fluctuations appear to be unaccompanied by changes in the state of the thermoregulatory effectors. Hypothalamic temperature, like any other in the body, depends upon local rates of metabolism and perfusion. Factors other than thermal stress can affect both of these variables. When an animal suddenly lowers its head, the hypothalamic temperature changes, probably because of a change in perfusion due to purely physical causes. A drop of as much as 0.5° C. may result when a dog lowers his head, and with no accompanying thermoregulatory response, though data such as that of Figures 13 and 14 imply that substantial responses must occur for changes of the order of hundredths of a degree in other circumstances. Other variables not related to thermal stress, including emotional state, sleep, feeding, etc., have also been observed to be associated with fluctuations of hypothalamic temperature which produce no thermoregulatory response. Therefore, Hammel *et al.* have concluded that the control mechanism must include some means of compensation for these factors which, they propose, is the spontaneous or compensatory variation of the set points.

A number of important properties of the feedback control from hypothalamic and skin temperatures still remain virtually unexplored. For example, the dynamic properties have not been closely examined, though indirect evidence indicates that rate of change of skin temperature and perhaps of central temperature also, are important inputs of the system. For example, a decreasing cutaneous temperature is easily as effective in causing a metabolic rate increase as a low cutaneous temperature *per se;* similarly, a rising (but still cool) skin temperature depresses the rate of heat production.[5]

Another unanswered question is whether equal areas of skin are equally represented in the central integrative mechanism. The receptors are not uniformly distributed and it has been suggested that certain skin areas, particularly the face and arm, are disproportionately significant in the peripheral contribution to thermoregulatory behavior.

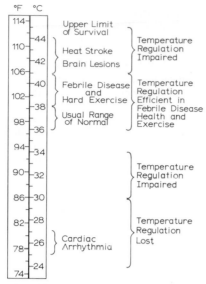

Fig. 15. Extremes of body temperature. (After DuBois, *Fever and the regulation of body temperature,* Springfield, Ill., Charles C Thomas, 1948.)

PATHOPHYSIOLOGY OF TEMPERATURE REGULATION

Limits of Survival. Deviations of about 2° C. in central body temperature from the normal level of about 37.5° C., in general do not seriously impair body function (Fig. 15). As the temperature rises above this range (hyperthermia), central nervous system function deteriorates and, at about 41° to 42° C., severe convulsions occur. A further increase to 44° to 45° C. leads to irreversible protein denaturation and rapid death. Thus, normal body temperature is only several degrees below the upper limit of survival; severe hyperthermia presents a true medical emergency.

If body temperature drops below the normal limits ("hypothermia"), all nervous function is depressed. At about 33° C., consciousness is lost. Temperature regulation itself is progressively impaired; below about 30° C. central temperature regulation is almost completely lost and the subject becomes poikilothermic. At about 28° C., discoordination of cardiac muscle frequently leads to cardiac fibrillation and death. In the operating room, such fibrillation often either can be avoided or can be corrected by a massive electrical shock to resynchronize the muscle fibers ("defibrillation"). Tissues can survive low temperatures, and tissue metabolic requirements are reduced as the tissue temperature decreases. Thus, during surgical hypothermia, prolonged operations are possible with blood circulation severely reduced.

Fever. In the most common type of fever, the rise in body temperature is not due to a breakdown of the temperature regulation system. The system behaves normally except that the "set point" or "reference" temperature of the integrative center appears to be increased. At the beginning of a fever, body temperature as sensed by the thermoreceptors is compared to the new reference level and found to be low. Thus the individual responds physiologically *as if he were cold.* Heat loss is reduced by vasoconstriction and heat production may be increased by shivering. The sensation of cold or chill frequently occurs at the beginning of fever; the individual may respond by pulling on more covers or turning up the room heat. As a result, body temperature rises until the new reference level is reached, and will then be regulated at this higher level.

When the cause of the fever is removed, the reference level returns to the normal value. Since the sensed body temperature is now above the reference temperature, the individual responds *as if he were too warm.* Cutaneous vasodilatation and sweating increase heat loss, shivering is inhibited, and covers are thrown off. Body temperature returns to its normal level and the febrile episode is over (see Fig. 16).

Fever may be caused by a primary neurologic disorder, but the most common cause is the presence in the blood of certain chemical compounds called "pyrogens." The mechanism by which pyrogens affect the reference level is unknown.

Since bacterial infection is frequently accompanied by fever, various investigators have tried to show a positive value for increased body temperature in repelling bacterial invasion. However, such demonstrations have not yet been convincing. Clinically, fever is regarded as disadvantageous to the patient, and attempts are made to reduce its severity. In extreme fever, physical cooling is employed, e.g., an ice water enema. In more moderate cases, treatment with antipyretic drugs generally is adequate.

The most frequently used antipyretic drug is aspirin (acetylsalicylic acid). Its action is unusual in that the magnitude of its effect depends upon the severity of the original distur-

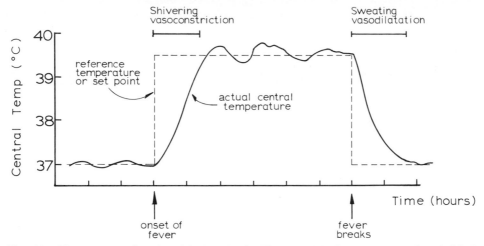

Fig. 16. Time course of typical febrile episode. The actual body temperature lags behind the rapid shifts in set point. Note that regulation is maintained during the fever but is less precise, so that temperature fluctuations are generally greater than normal.

bance. Thus, the higher the fever, the greater the drop in body temperature produced by aspirin; if an individual with normal body temperature takes aspirin, his temperature remains essentially unchanged. Thus, aspirin appears to block the effect of pyrogens, allowing the reference level to return to its normal value.

REFERENCES

1. ADAMS, T. *J. appl. Physiol.,* 1963, *18:*772–777.

2. ADAMS, T. *J. appl. Physiol.,* 1964, *19:*338–340.

3. BENZINGER, T. H. and KITZINGER, C. Chap. 56 in *Temperature—Its measurement and control in science and industry,* vol. 3, part 3, J. D. HARDY, ed. New York, Reinhold Publishing Corp., 1963.

4. BENZINGER, T. H. and TAYLOR, G. W. Chap. 10 in *Temperature—Its measurement and control in science and industry,* vol. 3, part 3, J. D. HARDY, ed. New York, Reinhold Publishing Corp., 1963.

5. BRENGELMANN, G. L. and BROWN, A. C. *Physiologist,* 1963, *6:*146.

6. BROWN, A. C. *Bull. math. Biophysics,* 1965, *27:*67–78.

7. BURTON, A. C. and BAZETT, H. C. *Amer. J. Physiol.,* 1936, *117:*36–54.

8. BURTON, A. C. and EDHOLM, M. B. In: *Man in a cold environment,* L. E. BAYLISS, W. FELDBERG and A. L. HODGKIN, eds. London, Edward Arnold Ltd., 1955.

9. CARLSON, L. D. *Man in cold environment.* Fairbanks, Alaska, Arctic Aeromedical Laboratory, Ladd Air Force Base, 1954.

10. CARLSON, L. D., HSIEH, A. C. L., FULLINGTON, F. and ELSNER, R. W. *J. Aviat. Med.,* 1958, *29:*145–152.

11. DOWNEY, J. A., MOTTRAM, R. F. and PICKERING, G. W. *J. Physiol.,* 1964, *170:*415–441.

12. DUBOIS, E. F. *Fever and the regulation of body temperature.* Springfield, Ill., Charles C Thomas, 1948.

13. VON EULER, C. *Pharmacol. Rev.,* 1961, *13:*361–398.

14. FUSCO, M. M., HARDY, J. D. and HAMMEL, H. T. *Amer. J. Physiol.,* 1961, *200:*572–580.

15. HAMMEL, H. T., HARDY, J. D. and FUSCO, M. M. *Amer. J. Physiol.,* 1960, *198:*481–486.

16. HAMMEL, H. T., JACKSON, D. C., STOLWIJK, J. A. J., HARDY, J. D. and STROMME, S. B. *J. appl. Physiol.,* 1963, *18:*1146–1154.

17. HANNON, J. P. and VIERECK, E. (eds.) *Neural aspects of temperature regulation.* Fort Wainwright, Alaska, Arctic Aeromedical Laboratory, 1961.

18. HARDY, J. D. (ed.) *Biology and medicine,* vol. 3, part 3 of *Temperature—Its measurement and control in science and industry,* J. M. HERZFELD, ed. New York, Reinhold Publishing Corp., 1963.

19. HARDY, J. D. *Physiol. Rev.,* 1961, *41:*521–606.

20. HARDY, J. D. and DuBois, E. F. *J. Nutr.,* 1937, *15:*461–475.

21. HARDY, J. D. and DuBois, E. F. *J. Nutr.,* 1937, *15:*477–497.

22. HARDY, J. D. and HAMMEL, H. T. Chap. 54 in *Temperature—Its measurement and control in science and industry,* vol. 3, part 3, J. D. HARDY, ed. New York, Reinhold Publishing Corp., 1963.

23. HARDY, J. D. and SODERSTROM, G. F. *J. Nutr.,* 1938, *16:*493–509.

24. HEMINGWAY, A. *Physiol. Rev.,* 1963, *43:*397–422.

25. IVY, A. C. *Quart. Bull. Northw. Univ. med. Sch.,* 1944, *18:*22–32.

26. KELLER, A. D. Chap. 49 in *Temperature—Its measurement and control in science and industry,* vol. 3, part 3, J. D. HARDY, ed. New York, Reinhold Publishing Corp., 1963.

27. LIM, T. P. K. In: *Neural aspects of temperature regulation,* J. P. HANNON and E. VIERECK, eds. Fort Wainwright, Alaska, Arctic Aeromedical Laboratory, 1961.

28. NEWBURGH, L. H. (ed.) *Physiology of heat regulation and the science of clothing.* Philadelphia, W. B. Saunders Co., 1949.

29. RAUTENBERG, W., SIMON, E. and THAUER, R. *Pflügers Arch. ges. Physiol.,* 1963, *278:*337–349.

30. SELLE, W. A. *Body temperature.* Springfield, Ill., Charles C Thomas, 1952.

31. TANNER, J. M. *J. Physiol.,* 1951, *115:*371–390.

CHAPTER 55

Factors Influencing Intermediary Metabolism

By EDWARD J. MASORO

In mammals as in other forms of living organisms, metabolism involves a variety of intermediary pathways, each composed of many enzymatically controlled chemical reactions. The rates of these various reactions are not constant but vary with the changing physiologic requirements. The detailed picture of the enzymatic machinery is described in any present day course in biochemistry; the responses of this metabolic machinery to physiologic changes will be the subject of this chapter.

The way in which metabolism changes during eating and during subsequent postabsorptive periods will be considered first, after which the effect of dietary composition and of time course of eating will be taken up. It will become evident that the physiology and intermediary metabolism of adipose tissue deserve attention. Next, the way in which the intermediary metabolic machinery of the mammal responds to three specific physiologic challenges —undernutrition, exposure to cold and muscular exercise—will be discussed. It should be recognized that intermediary metabolic responses occur in response to most physiologic challenges. The three examples mentioned above were chosen because they illustrate metabolic adaptations generally. Lastly, the metabolic problem peculiar to an affluent society will be considered, i.e., overnutrition resulting in obesity.

Certain terms used in this chapter require definitions. The storage of chemical energy will be called "positive energy balance," and its depletion will be termed "negative energy balance." The maintenance of energy stores at a relatively constant level will be called "energy balance." It should be made clear that the term "energy balance" refers to a relatively constant level of energy stores over a prolonged period (weeks or at least days) and is not concerned with fluctuations from meal to meal.

It is important to have a reference diet for comparison, because the nature of the diet greatly influences metabolic behavior. A diet composed largely of carbohydrate with moderate amounts of fat and protein will serve as the standard to which other diets will be compared and will be denoted "the standard mixed diet," e.g., carbohydrate $>$ 50 per cent, fat about 10 per cent, protein 20 to 25 per cent.

To understand this chapter the reader should be familiar with the chemical details of intermediary metabolism. Figure 1 provides a general scheme of the more important pathways and their interactions.

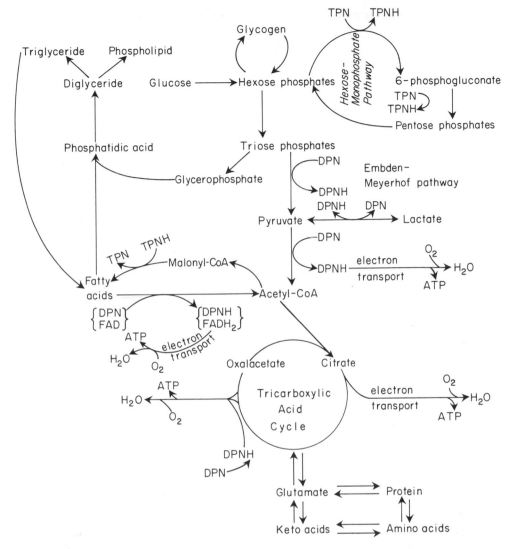

Fig. 1.   General scheme of intermediary metabolism.

INTERMEDIARY METABOLIC CHANGES DURING THE ABSORPTIVE–POSTABSORPTIVE CYCLE

Man, like many other mammals, does not ingest food continuously but eats periodically; i.e., he is a meal-eater. Even animals in energy balance ingest during the eating phase an amount of chemical energy greatly in excess of their immediate energy needs, and part of it is stored for use during the noneating phase. The way the periodic input of the chemical energy from the standard mixed diet is translated into a continuous output of energy for physiologic needs is briefly outlined in Figure 2.

The first temporary storage depot encountered is the stomach, which releases the partially digested food to the intestine, from which absorption occurs. This absorptive phase is generally followed by a period during which no absorption occurs from the intestine, i.e., the postabsorptive phase, the length of which is determined by the eating pattern of the species or individual. Thus, during the absorptive phase of the cycle the animal stores energy, and during the postabsorptive phase of the cycle, it partially depletes the energy reserves. As might be expected, such a sequence of events involves profound changes in intermediary metabolism.

During the absorptive phase, glucose[22] provides the major energy source, being burned in

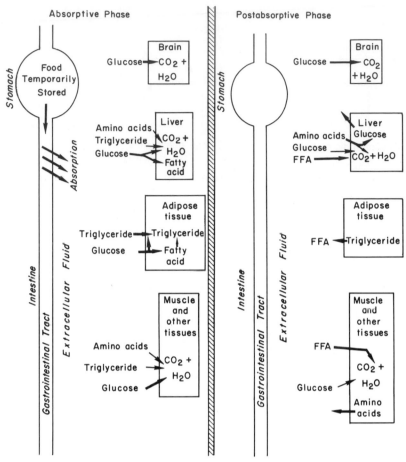

Fig. 2. Metabolic changes during absorptive–postabsorptive cycle. Heavy arrows denote processes occurring at rapid rates; light arrows denote processes occurring at slow rates.

the tissue to CO_2 and H_2O. Some protein is oxidized to CO_2 and H_2O, but it makes up only a small fraction of the foodstuffs catabolized. Similarly, a small amount of fat is oxidized to CO_2 and H_2O, but most is stored in the adipose tissue as triglyceride.[22] The tendency of fat to be stored rather than oxidized is related to what is called the sparing action of carbohydrate metabolism on fat oxidation. The sparing action[12] has been proved by measuring rates of fatty acid oxidation by tissues from animals fed varying amounts of carbohydrate. A high rate of carbohydrate metabolism such as follows intake of the standard mixed diet inhibits fatty acid oxidations and promotes the uptake and storage of fat in adipose tissue, by a mechanism to be described under Physiology of Adipose Tissue. If the meal is large, excess carbohydrate may also be stored, some as glycogen but most as fat created by the conversion of glucose to fatty acid and the sub-

sequent formation of triglyceride.[23] For mobile forms of life, the significance of storing the energy of glucose as fat instead of glycogen is that fat takes up less volume and weighs less per calorie of stored chemical energy than glycogen.

As the postabsorptive period progresses, the carbohydrate catabolism gradually gives way to fatty acid oxidation. During the postabsorptive phase,[11] the fatty acids in the extracellular fluid are largely derived from adipose tissue. This fat mobilization is of major significance because it provides a continuous energy supply at a time when foodstuffs are no longer being absorbed. The increased oxidation of fatty acids may be correlated with the absence of the sparing action of carbohydrate on fat catabolism and the mobilization of fatty acids from the adipose tissue.[12]

During both the absorptive and the postabsorptive phases, the brain and nervous system continue to oxidize glucose at a steady rate.[20] Indeed, these tissues would soon deplete the extracellular fluid of glucose if the liver did not increase its rate of conversion of protein and amino acids to sugar (gluconeogenesis) and release this newly formed glucose into the extracellular fluid during the postabsorptive phase. The brain, unlike most other tissues, is not dependent on insulin secretion of the pancreas in regard to its ability to utilize glucose.[4] During the postabsorptive period, insulin levels probably decline, and insulin-responsive tissues (muscle, adipose tissue, etc.) oxidize little glucose, thereby permitting brain and other insulin-nonresponsive tissues to utilize available glucose. The major reason for low rate of glucose oxidation by most of the tissues probably is the inhibitory action of an increased level of free fatty acid (FFA) on the capacity of tissue to oxidize glucose.[33]

Under postabsorptive conditions similar to those utilized for the BMR determinations, the mixture of materials being catabolized is estimated to be about 20 per cent carbohydrate, 70 per cent fat, 10 per cent protein. Because much of the carbohydrate oxidation occurs in the brain, most of the tissues must be oxidizing fat almost exclusively.

METABOLIC RESPONSE TO THE CHEMICAL NATURE OF THE DIET

The chemical nature of foodstuffs has a marked effect on intermediary metabolism. To study these effects, certain extreme diets have been employed experimentally, and three such diets will be considered, one high in fat, one high in protein and one high in carbohydrate but fat-free. Although these diets will be considered from an experimental viewpoint, it should be realized that such extreme diets are sometimes ingested by man for various other reasons, e.g., survival situations, medical problems, personal idiosyncrasies, etc.

High-Fat Diet. As adaptation to a high-fat diet takes place, the capacity of the tissues to oxidize fat greatly increases[30] but the ability to oxidize glucose is curtailed.[13] In fact, animals adapted to a high-fat diet respond to a test load of glucose with a blood sugar change somewhat like that of a diabetic. The probable reason is that the rate of glucose utilization is decreased by direct inhibition (e.g., by FFA)

and the insulin secretion rate in response to a glucose load is not increased as much as usual.

The brain continues to function normally in animals adapted to a high-fat diet even though the blood sugar falls to levels that would cause convulsions[30] in animals fed the standard mixed diet. One can only conjecture that the brain has gained the capacity to utilize glucose even at very low extracellular concentrations, or more likely, that the brain has become able to oxidize substrates other than glucose.

A high-fat diet markedly inhibits fatty acid synthesis.[23] The biologic importance of the restricted utilization of acetyl CoA for fatty acid synthesis becomes clear when the metabolic problems of this dietary situation are considered. The abbreviated metabolic scheme in Figure 3 will assist in this consideration. With the ingestion of a high-fat diet, little glucose is available to the tissues. Therefore, little acetyl CoA is formed from glucose by way of reaction sequence I. However, acetyl CoA is generated at a high rate by way of fatty acid oxidation. Therefore, if reaction sequence III were not greatly inhibited during the high-fat dietary regimen, a great amount of the fatty acid undergoing β-oxidation would be recycled, energetically an apparently inefficient process. The mechanism by which a high-fat diet inhibits sequence III is not completely understood, but it is not related to the concentration of fat in tissues.[23] However, some evidence indicates that the intracellular FFA concentration may be the primary determinant for the inhibition of fatty acid synthesis.[23] FFA added to adipose tissue *in vitro* inhibits fatty acid synthesis; also fatty acid synthesis by liver homogenates is depressed by FFA.

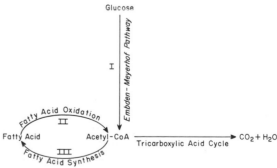

Fig. 3. Abbreviated scheme of the interaction between carbohydrate oxidation and fatty acid oxidation and synthesis.

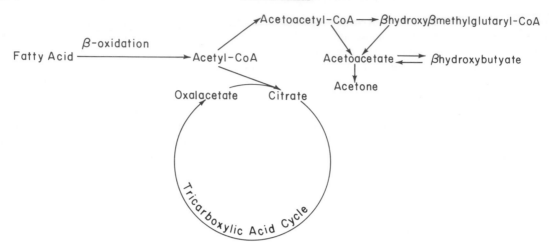

Fig. 4. Intermediary pathways involved in the formation of ketone bodies by the liver.

It has long been known that a high-fat diet induces ketosis, a condition characterized by excess acetoacetic and β-hydroxybutyric acids in the body fluids. These so-called ketone bodies are generated in the liver from acetyl CoA by pathways summarized in Figure 4. It has generally been thought that the ketosis following a high-fat diet relates primarily to the lack of dietary carbohydrates. However, it has recently been shown that upon adaptation to a high-fat diet, ketosis tends to disappear provided the caloric intake is sufficient to meet caloric output.[30] The ketosis decreases at a time when the blood sugar falls to very low levels. It would seem, therefore, that ketosis is related not to carbohydrate lack but rather to insufficient caloric intake and increased fat mobilization from adipose tissue. Such a conclusion may appear rather puzzling, since in caloric insufficiency, as in ingestion of a high-fat diet, fat is the major metabolic fuel. The answer to this paradox may lie in the fact that during caloric insufficiency, the fuel is transported in the blood mainly as FFA, whereas during ingestion of fat, a large amount of transport occurs as triglyceride. It is known that the organism oxidizes FFA at rates proportional to blood FFA concentration.[1] Probably during caloric restriction, high levels of plasma FFA force the liver to oxidize more FFA to acetyl CoA than can be utilized in the tricarboxylic acid cycle. If so, the liver would condense the excess acetyl CoA, thus generating ketone bodies. Implicit in this theory is the assumption that triglycerides could not in a similar way overwhelm the hepatic cell with excess acetyl CoA.

High-Protein Diet. High-protein diets also lead to alterations in intermediary metabolism. Many amino acids are good precursors of carbohydrates, i.e., the so-called glucogenic amino acids. Therefore, when the diet is high in protein, a high rate of gluconeogenesis, i.e., conversion of amino acids to glucose, would be expected. The capacity of animals on such a diet to utilize carbohydrate as tested by glucose tolerance tests and RQ measurements is somewhat less than that of animals fed the standard mixed diet.[5] One must conclude, therefore, that there is an increased rate of direct oxidation of deaminated intermediates of amino acids to CO_2 and H_2O.

It has been established that mammals can convert protein to fat.[34] It would be expected that high-protein meal-eaters in energy balance might temporarily store energy by converting protein to fat. However, it has been shown experimentally that fatty acid synthesis is markedly decelerated during the ingestion of high-protein diets but not to as low a level as occurs during the ingestion of a high-fat diet.[25] Thus, the chemical nature of the temporary energy stored in the protein-fed animal remains undecided; possibly energy is stored temporarily as protein in animals in energy balance. However, if an animal were ingesting enough protein to produce a marked positive caloric balance, all the evidence suggests that much of it would be converted to fat for storage in the adipose tissue.

High-Carbohydrate–Fat-Free Diet. A diet that is almost free of fat but high in carbohydrate content also causes an altered intermediary metabolism. Tissues of animals thus fed readily utilize carbohydrates along various pathways, e.g., direct oxidation to CO_2 and H_2O,[5] glycogenesis[5] and lipogenesis.[25] It should be emphasized that fatty acid synthesis rates are higher in animals in energy balance maintained on this diet than in animals fed the standard mixed diet. Since meal-eating animals fed a high-carbohydrate, fat-free diet are flooded with an excess of calories in the form of carbohydrate, it is not surprising that glucose conversion to fatty acids becomes a quantitatively major pathway.

INFLUENCE OF EATING PATTERNS

Not only the character of the diet but also the temporal pattern of feeding alters metabolism. Such change can be detected in rats trained to ingest meals at regular intervals rather than being allowed to follow their normal eating pattern of nibbling *ad libitum.*

Body weights of meal-eaters and nibblers ingesting an identical quantity and type of food are approximately the same, but the body composition differs. The meal-eater has a higher percentage of fat content and a lower percentage protein content than the nibbler.[6] Since fat is much richer in calories than protein, clearly the meal-eater retains more calories than the nibbler. Thus meal-eating must decrease caloric expenditure. Although some reduction in thyroid activity occurs in meal-eating rats,[6] it has recently been shown that resting metabolism is increased in meal-eaters and that the decreased caloric expenditure of meal-eaters relates either to a decreased level of physical activity or to an increased efficiency of physical activity.[10]

Still other studies indicate that meal-eating affects certain specific intermediary metabolic pathways. Far more of a glucose test load is converted to fat by meal-eaters than by nibblers. Also, enzymatic and isotopic studies show that the hexose monophosphate pathway of carbohydrate metabolism is hyperactive in liver and adipose tissue of meal-eaters.[6] Whether these metabolic changes are the cause or the result of the increased caloric retention is not certain at present. The extent to which the temporal pattern of food intake influences metabolism of other species, and in particular man, has still to be extensively explored. In chickens and

monkeys, experimentally induced atherosclerosis is exacerbated by causing these animals to become meal-eaters.[6, 8] This finding raises the broad question of the role of eating pattern as opposed to nature of the diet in the etiology of disease. There is suggestive evidence that in man nibbling decreases dietary protein requirements and that nibbling may decrease susceptibility of man to metabolic diseases such as atherosclerosis and diabetes mellitus.[7]

PHYSIOLOGY OF ADIPOSE TISSUE

It is evident that adipose tissue, which is the organism's major reservoir of chemical energy, plays a key role in the physiologic responses of intermediary metabolism. Figure 5 is a schematic representation of the salient metabolic events which occur in adipose tissue.

When a sizeable amount (500 kilocalories [kcal.] or so) of standard mixed diet is ingested and absorbed, both triglyceride (in the form of chylomicrons) and glucose become abundant in the blood. As discussed above, much of this triglyceride is deposited in the adipose tissue, a process which will now be traced in detail. Triglyceride enters the adipose tissue cell by process I in Figure 5, which probably involves lipolysis to FFA and glycerol. It has not been established whether lipolysis occurs immediately prior to or during entry.[37] The glycerol yielded during lipolysis is not metabolized to an appreciable extent by adipose tissue[39] and is carried away by the blood to the liver and

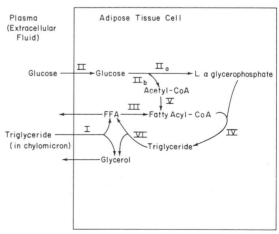

Fig. 5. Scheme of the major metabolic activities occurring in adipose tissue.

other tissues capable of utilizing it. The fate of the FFA depends on the amount of carbohydrate available to the metabolic machinery of the adipose tissue cell. For example, following a meal of the standard mixed diet, glucose enters the adipose tissue cell by pathway II, under the influence of insulin; glucose entry occurs at high rates only when insulin levels are normal.[37] Some of the glucose is converted to (L)α glycerophosphate by reaction series IIa; the (L)α glycerophosphate reacts with fatty acyl-CoA (formed from the FFA by reaction III) to yield triglyceride by way of reaction series IV. Moreover, whenever the intake of carbohydrate is well in excess of the immediate energy requirements of the organism, the adipose tissue also converts a considerable amount of the glucose to fatty acids and consequently to triglycerides by reactions II_b, V, IV. The combined reactions make up the phenomenon of fat deposition. (L)α glycerophosphate is essential for the esterification of fatty acids in the form of triglycerides. Since the adipose tissue can generate (L)α glycerophosphate in quantity only when a supply of dietary carbohydrate is available, fat deposition readily occurs in the fed state, but not appreciably in the unfed state. This is a simple but effective mechanism regulating deposition and mobilization of energy reserves.

Adipose tissue contains active lipases[37] that continuously hydrolyze triglyceride to FFA and glycerol (VI). Whether the FFA is then released to the extracellular fluid or is re-esterified to triglyceride depends largely on the availability of (L)α glycerophosphate. During the absorptive phase, when blood sugar and insulin levels are high, glucose is converted at an appreciable rate to (L)α glycerophosphate in adipose tissue. Thus, most of the FFA formed in adipose tissue by lipase activity may be recycled to triglyceride. However, when blood sugar and insulin levels are low, as for example during the postabsorptive period, (L)α glycerophosphate is not readily available. Therefore, FFA leaves the adipose tissue cell and upon leaving is bound to albumin for transport in the blood to other tissues. Lipolysis, followed by release of FFA to the blood, is the process of fat mobilization which makes available to other tissues of the body the chemical energy stored in adipose tissues. The control system is basically simple; i.e., lack of food is accompanied by low rate of generation of (L)α glycerophosphate,

which in itself promotes fat mobilization by preventing re-esterification of FFA released by adipose tissue lipases.

However, the total control system is more complicated and many influences are brought to bear on the basic biochemical control system described above. For example, it has been suggested, in certain cases of caloric restriction, insufficient ATP is available to the adipose tissue for fatty acid activation to fatty acyl CoA (III) thus causing FFA to be released rather than re-esterified. Also, the rates of many of the reactions are under endocrine, neural or other physiologic controls. For example, the level of glucose in the blood is one determinant of whether net fatty acid mobilization or net storage of triglyceride takes place. Insulin, by influencing the rate of entry of glucose into adipose tissue cells and by depressing the lipase catalyzing reaction VI, plays an important regulatory role in fat mobilization.[37] As would be expected, insulin administration to a normal animal causes fat deposition, whereas in a condition of uncontrolled diabetes mellitus the fat stores are largely depleted.

Unilateral sympathectomy causes accumulation of triglyceride in the adipose tissue of the denervated side, but stimulation of the sympathetic nerves results in fat mobilization.[38] In man emotional stresses trigger release of FFA from adipose tissue. It seems clear that neural activity plays an important role in the regulation of adipose tissue metabolism.

Epinephrine and norepinephrine cause the liberation of FFA from adipose tissue, presumably by activating a lipase[37] catalyzing reaction VI (Fig. 5). A number of materials, chemically quite different, also cause release of FFA from adipose tissue,[2] e.g., ACTH, growth hormone, thyroid-stimulating hormone, fat-mobilizing peptide isolated from human urine, posterior pituitary lipid-mobilizing material, glucagon, etc. Little is known concerning the physiologic significance of these substances.

The thyroid and adrenal cortex play a permissive role in the mobilization of fat from the adipose tissue.[36] For instance, epinephrine does not readily cause the release of free fatty acid from adipose tissue of thyroidectomized or adrenalectomized animals. Administration of thyroxine or glucocorticoids, respectively, restores the ability of adipose tissue to respond to the fat-mobilizing effect of epinephrine.

INTERMEDIARY METABOLIC RESPONSES TO PHYSIOLOGIC CHALLENGES

During the course of life, the mammal faces a variety of challenges which are met by altered behavioral responses, cardiovascular adjustments, etc. One of the most fundamental kinds of response to such challenges is the response of intermediary metabolism. Three important physiologic challenges and the intermediary metabolic responses to them will now be discussed.

Undernutrition. When sufficient food is not available, man suffers from undernutrition, an insufficient caloric intake, which is usually but not always accompanied by malnutrition, i.e., the lack of specific substances such as vitamins, essential amino acids, minerals, etc. Total fasting, the limiting condition of undernutrition, is a serious challenge. Yet, provided water is available, most mammals can meet this problem quite successfully for some time. In a normal environment most humans can survive 30 days' starvation and some can probably sustain a 60-day fast. Of course, survival capacity depends on many other factors, e.g., general health, environmental temperature, work performed, etc.

The most prominent feature of starvation is a loss of body weight. For example, a 63-kg. man reached a body weight of 52 kg. after a 30-day fast, and a 26.3-kg. dog was found to reach a body weight of 9.8-kg. after a 117-day period of fasting. Weight loss advances rapidly at first but tapers off as fasting progresses. The BMR declines throughout the fasting period. Starved prisoners in German concentration camps often had BMR of −40. Adjustment of BMR has obvious survival value since a low metabolic rate betokens decreased rate of depletion of chemical energy reserves.

During the first few days of fasting, the blood sugar remains at the usual postabsorptive level.[21] However, after a month of fasting the blood sugar falls to about 75 per cent of this value.[21] The response to glucose tolerance tests indicates that during starvation most tissues have decreased capacity to utilize carbohydrates.[5] Evidence has recently been presented indicating that the higher rate of release of fatty acids and ketone bodies for oxidation by muscle and other tissues is responsible for this depression in carbohydrate utilization.[33] This phenomenon is called "hunger diabetes." Hepatic glycogen is greatly depleted after one or two days of fasting, but is partially restored as starvation continues. The concentration of muscle glycogen also declines, but the percentage decrease is much less than that in liver and the glycogen content of the heart may actually increase during fasting.

Fatty acid synthesis stops almost completely during even short periods of fasting.[23] In negative energy balance, acetyl CoA is primarily oxidized and not used appreciably in synthetic reactions.

Gluconeogenesis increases during fasting and is essentially the sole source of glucose for the brain, which continues to oxidize large amounts of it. Decreased carbohydrate utilization by other tissues is important in ensuring the brain a continuous sugar supply, an absolute necessity for survival.

Measurements of urinary nitrogen excretion suggest that protein catabolism decreases progressively as fasting continues.[21] Since this reduction in total protein catabolism occurs while hepatic gluconeogenesis from protein is augmented, direct oxidation of deaminated amino acid intermediates must be reduced to low levels. Just prior to death from starvation, urinary nitrogen excretion[21] usually rises abruptly—a last-gasp catabolism of body protein.

Mobilization and oxidation of triglyceride energy stores from adipose tissue are major features of energy metabolism in the fasting organism.[14] Because adipose tissue contains large reserves of triglyceride, fat catabolism can support life for prolonged periods of starvation. In contrast, stored energy in the form of glucose and glycogen in man amounts to only about 300 kcal., enough energy for a very few hours under ordinary circumstances.

The intermediary steps and controlling factors in fat mobilization during starvation were outlined above. The plasma FFA level increases during fasting, and sometimes the hepatic fat content[30] also increases. There is an increase in the capacity of tissue to oxidize fatty acids.[21] Fairly often ketosis occurs,[30] probably resulting from the high plasma FFA, which causes increased hepatic oxidation of fatty acids to acetyl CoA. When the rate of conversion of acetyl CoA to acetoacetate and β-hydroxybutyrate increases, the concentration of blood ketones in the body increases, a con-

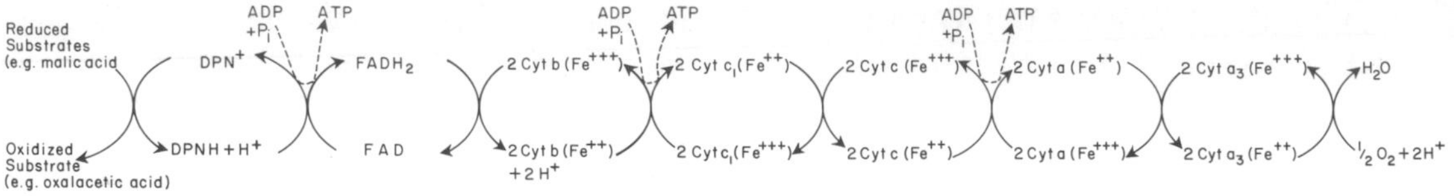

Fig. 6. Electron transport and coupled phosphorylation. Broken lines refer to multistep, incompletely known reactions.

dition described as ketonemia. Ketone bodies can be used as an energy source by extrahepatic tissues, but as the rate of production increases, ketone bodies are also excreted as their salts in the urine. When ketonemia or ketonuria or both exist, the organism is said to be in a state of ketosis.

In summary, the responses of the intermediary metabolic processes to fasting enable the animal to (i) supply the brain with glucose and (ii) draw on its energy reserves in adipose tissue. So successful are these metabolic adjustments that the mammal can survive for long periods without any exogenous source of energy.

Exposure to Cold. Exposure to cold environment is a challenge which the mammal meets partly by increasing heat production.[9] During the initial exposure, heat production is increased by shivering, i.e., shivering thermogenesis. The biochemical basis of shivering thermogenesis presents no difficulty; the muscular contraction (shivering) generates heat by splitting ATP to ADP without net mechanical work, increasing muscle ADP concentration. Increased ADP concentrations stimulate the electron transport system and oxygen consumption; thus, substrate is utilized at an increased rate as the ADP is reconverted to ATP. For a long time, fat was thought to be the substrate preferentially used for this increase in oxidative metabolism, but recent evidence suggests that fat, carbohydrate and protein are all involved.[9]

Rats and probably other species as well stop shivering as exposure to cold continues. Yet the high rate of heat production is maintained, suggesting that some other mechanism supplants shivering as a thermogenic source. Norepinephrine may be involved, for it has a powerful calorigenic action when administered to animals subject to prolonged exposure to cold.[18] Although hormonal or neural agents are undoubtedly involved in triggering metabolic events, the basic alteration in pathways of intermediary metabolism is unknown.

In general terms, nonshivering thermogenesis must involve one or both of the following mechanisms: (i) an increased ATP utilization by processes not giving rise to a net work yield or (ii) an increased electron transport related to decreased phosphorylative efficiency. Specific biochemical mechanisms have been suggested and experimentally investigated.

1. The uncoupling of oxidative phosphorylation is one mechanism suggested. Figure 6 describes a tightly coupled system in which ADP is required as a phosphate acceptor for the phosphorylation reactions of the electron transport system. Indeed, the rate of electron transport of a tightly coupled system is probably controlled by the availability of ADP and P_i.[40] However, with an uncoupled system, electron transport could occur without the requirement of ADP as a phosphate acceptor. Since ADP availability is believed to limit electron transport in a coupled system, clearly an uncoupled system is capable of much higher rates of electron transport and heat production. *In vitro* experiments on mitochondria indicate that uncoupling of oxidative phosphorylation occurs on prolonged exposure to cold.[31] However, a final answer must await the development of experimental techniques permitting investigation of the uncoupling phenomenon *in vivo*.

2. The existence of one or more electron transport pathways of low phosphorylative efficiency (calorigenic shunts) has been suggested as a possible biochemical basis for nonshivering thermogenesis.[32] Figure 7 is an abbreviated scheme of a pathway of this type. In this scheme, the TPNH-linked electron transport, an inefficient one in phosphorylation, provides a heat-producing pathway. Since availability of ADP would not limit the rate of electron transport along this pathway, availability of substrate for the various dehydrogenases (e.g., isocitric dehydrogenase) probably regulates electron transport. Evidence for this theory is preliminary and the activation of

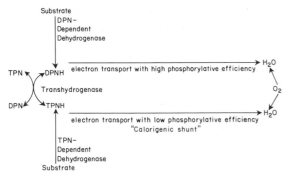

Fig. 7. Low efficiency electron transport systems as "calorigenic shunts" in nonshivering thermogenesis.

calorigenic shunts in the electron transport of animals exposed to cold for prolonged periods is not unequivocally established.

3. The increased turnover of dietary carbohydrate via fatty acid synthesis provides a heat-producing cycle[24] (Fig. 8) and might be important in nonshivering thermogenesis. Since the fatty acid synthesis phase requires a total TPNH and ATP input exceeding the potential ATP that can be realized during the fat catabolism phase, the fatty acid synthesis–catabolism cycle is an example of an ATP-utilizing heat-generating cycle. Evidence for this is equivocal.

4. The lipolysis–fatty acid esterification cycle of adipose tissue (Fig. 9) is always operating at high rates and is obviously an ATP-utilizing heat-generating cycle important to homeotherms.[2] It has been suggested that this

cycle increases in nonshivering thermogenesis, but since it has not been carefully investigated, the concept remains only an intriguing possibility.

Muscular Exercise. Vigorous muscular exercise is a severe metabolic challenge because it increases energy expenditure suddenly to very high levels. For many years carbohydrates were considered the main, if not the sole, fuel for muscular activity. Muscular work does not involve an appreciable increase in protein metabolism.[19] However, recent work proves that carbohydrate is not always the prime fuel for exercise. In strenuous but short periods of exercise (e.g., a 100-yard dash), carbohydrate is the main source of fuel, probably because during strenuous activity, muscle metabolism is partially anaerobic. Because carbohydrate via glycolysis is a quantitatively important anaerobic energy source, substantial glycolysis in the muscle cell must occur.

During prolonged exercise (e.g., a marathon run), primarily aerobic conditions prevail. If the subject is in a fed state during this prolonged exercise carbohydrate serves as the main fuel.[16] However, prolonged exercise often takes place when the organism is postabsorptive and is then supported by fatty acid catabolism. FFA is made available by increased fat mobilization from adipose tissue, probably activated by neural mechanisms. The exercising muscle removes and oxidizes the FFA brought to it by the blood and also oxidizes fatty acid already present in the muscle cell in the form of triglyceride and phospholipid. Therefore, it is evident that fat as well as carbohydrate can effectively support the high energy requirements of contracting muscle.

The term "oxygen debt" refers to the excess of O_2 consumed after exercise, i.e., the amount

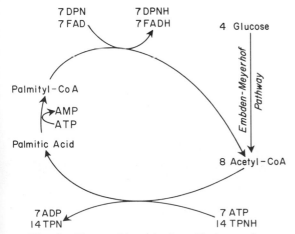

Fig. 8. Fatty acid synthesis–oxidation cycle as a heat-generating system.

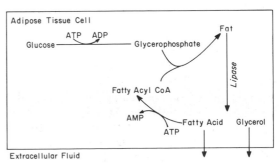

Fig. 9. The lipolysis–fatty acid esterification cycle of adipose tissue as a heat-generating cycle.

consumed in excess of resting O_2 utilization. The O_2 debt is primarily related to anaerobic metabolism brought about by the inability of the circulatory system to supply sufficient O_2 to the muscles during exercise. During the first few minutes of moderate exercise, O_2 consumption does not increase sufficiently to meet energy requirements; therefore, anaerobic sources are drawn upon. After the first few minutes, O_2 consumption becomes just sufficient to meet the energy requirements but not sufficient to repay the O_2 debt contracted during the first few minutes. The absolute magnitude of O_2 debt has a limiting ceiling, but the rate at which the debt is contracted is variable. For example, during a 100-yard dash a considerable O_2 debt accumulates in 10 seconds, but in a mile run the O_2 debt may be gradually contracted over 4 to 5 minutes. The biochemical basis of this phenomenon lies in the use of anaerobic energy yielding reactions involving ATP and creatine phosphate as well as the breakdown of glycogen by glycolysis. Lactate accumulation is significant because the generation of ATP from ADP by anaerobic glycolysis involves the conversion of diphosphoglyceraldehyde to diphosphoglyceric acid catalyzed by a DPN-linked dehydrogenase. Since O_2 is not available, another hydrogen acceptor is required to regenerate DPN from DPNH; the reduction of pyruvate to lactate serves this purpose.

Following exercise, the increase in O_2 consumption above resting values (which defines the O_2 debt) relates to the rapid resynthesis of phosphocreatine and the slow resynthesis of glycogen, which, by utilizing ATP, maintain ADP at levels permitting an increased rate of electron transport. The accumulated lactate is oxidized by a DPN-dependent dehydrogenase to pyruvate, which is in turn utilized at increased rates.

OVERNUTRITION AND THE PROBLEM OF OBESITY

In a society of abundance, man faces the problem of overnutrition, i.e., persisting positive caloric balance which leads to obesity. Obesity is a condition of increased body weight with a body composition disproportionately high in fat. In metabolic terms, excess reserve energy is stored as triglyceride in the adipose tissue, which is seemingly capable of almost unlimited expansion of size and mass.

In our culture obesity is considered unattractive, and for this reason alone it constitutes a problem frequently encountered by physicians. More importantly, there is overwhelming evidence that obesity leads to premature death,[26] the death rate for adults between 20 and 40 years of age being much greater for the obese than for the general population. In particular, obese subjects are especially susceptible to cardiovascular disease.

Many physicians lightly dismiss obesity with the glib statement that the obese person eats too much. This is obviously true because energy intake must exceed energy output for obesity to occur. However, as an expert has pointed out, such a pronouncement is no more useful in understanding causes and treatment than the equally superficial statement that the alcoholic drinks too much.

Real understanding of human obesity in terms more penetrating than the "eat too much" principle has been extremely elusive. Recently experimentally induced obesity in animals has provided much information which hopefully can provide some understanding of human obesity. Experimental obesity can be produced by surgical lesions in the ventromedial nuclei of the hypothalamus;[17] alternatively these nuclei can be destroyed by orally administered gold thioglucose.[29] The primary consequence of such lesions is hyperphagia, i.e., a great increase in food intake.[3] Metabolic alterations result secondarily as adaptive responses to high food intake. For example, in hyperphagic animals the rate of fatty acid synthesis increases greatly, but this increased lipogenesis is the result rather than the cause of high food intake.[36]

Some members of a genetic strain of mice (the obese hyperglycemic strain) become very obese when allowed to eat *ad libitum*[27] (Fig. 10). Even when food is restricted to the amount eaten by normal mice and body weight is held at normal levels, these animals accumulate a higher body fat content than do normal mice.[27] Obesity of the *ad libitum* fed, obese-hyperglycemic mice is thus only partly due to excess food intake. The fairly low energy expenditure of these mice accounts at least in part for their obesity.[27]

Obese-hyperglycemic mice exhibit many abnormal metabolic characteristics. Unlike the metabolic changes associated with obesity resulting from hypothalamic lesions, many of the metabolic alterations in obese-hyperglycemic mice are not easily ascribed to secondary adaptations to excessive food intake. Hyperglycemia of these mice[27] is probably due to their very high resistance to the action of insulin. More significantly with respect to obesity, they have a high rate of lipogenesis, which remains elevated even when the food intake is restricted to a degree at which fatty acid synthesis normally becomes a minor metabolic activity.[27] Moreover, their adipose tissue does not readily release FFA to the blood under conditions which normally promote fat mobilization, e.g., during fasting or following epinephrine administration.[36] Failure to mobilize fat may account for the lowered capacity of the hyperglycemic-obese animals to maintain body temperature in the cold.[27]

Although it is clear that the metabolic peculiarities of hyperglycemic-obese mice are not secondary to overeating, the true cause is unknown. Some abnormalities may be genetically determined. Perhaps the metabolic defects cause improper signals to be sent to the hypothalamic centers regulating food intake, resulting in an improper regulation of food intake in relation to energy expenditure.

A strain of mice with pituitary tumors secreting excessive amounts of ACTH show a high incidence of obesity.[15] In these animals excess ACTH secretions stimulate the adrenal cortex to secrete excess glucocorticoid, which causes

hyperglycemia and, in turn, hyperinsulinism. The high insulin levels promote glucose translocation from the extracellular fluid into the adipose tissue cell, increased fatty acid synthesis and triglyceride formation from FFA within the adipose tissue cell (see section on Physiology of Adipose Tissue). The high insulin levels also cause the animals to eat more food by inducing a transient hypoglycemia. Thus, obesity results from combined abnormalities of metabolism and food intake.

It would be well to consider further the problem of human obesity on the basis of recent gains in knowledge of experimental obesity in animals.

1. The kinds of genetic obesity in experimental animals discussed so far have been metabolic; i.e., so-called inborn errors of metabolism were present. However, other types of genetically determined abnormality, e.g., in the neural mechanism controlling food consumption, can also be involved. Unfortunately, the question of the genetic basis of human obesity has been badly neglected, partly because the common therapy aims at getting the patient to eat less; such therapy would be adversely affected if the patient thought his obesity was inherited and therefore beyond his control. It is established, however, that some cases of human obesity do have a genetic basis.[36]

2. Environmental and social factors are also undoubtedly important in the etiology of obesity. A rat's environment can be experimentally altered so that the animal's physical activity is

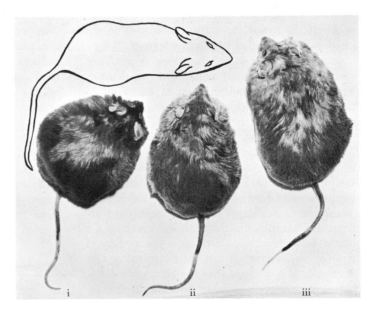

Fig. 10. Three types of obesity in mice: (i) the hereditary obese-hyperglycemic syndrome; (ii) obesity due to hypothalamic lesions effected by the stereotaxic methods and (iii) by injection of goldthioglucose. The insert shows a normally thin mouse. (Photograph furnished by J. Mayer.)

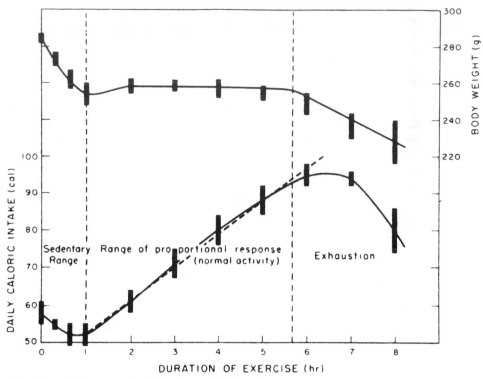

Fig. 11. Voluntary caloric intake and body weight as functions of exercise in normal rats. (From Mayer, In: *Fat metabolism,* V. A. Najjar, ed. Baltimore, The Johns Hopkins Press, 1954.)

greatly changed. Food intake varies directly with physical activity over a wide range and energy balance is maintained. However, at very low levels of physical activity, food intake does not decline proportionately as expected but may actually increase,[26] thus inducing a positive caloric balance (Fig. 11). Not surprisingly, in many cases human obesity is related to a low level of physical activity.[28]

3. Faulty neural mechanisms controlling food intake may result from injury or disease. The experimental counterpart of this kind of human obesity is induced by surgical or chemical damage to the hypothalamus.

4. The importance of the endocrine system in the development of obesity has been belittled. The obesity of animals with ACTH-secreting pituitary tumors is a clear example of primary endocrine obesity. Indeed, the obesity in men with Cushing's disease probably results from mechanisms similar to those described for tumor-bearing animals although a complicated change in adipose tissue distribution is also involved. It is obvious that the relationship between the endocrine system and obesity should

not be relegated to the category of past misconceptions but should be seriously considered in any exploration of the causes of human obesity.

5. Finally, psychologic factors must not be forgotten, nor is it likely that they will be. Indeed, so much emphasis has been laid on psychologic factors that they are often almost the only ones considered regarding the development of obesity. Clearly, cerebral activity can influence the hypothalamic centers regulating food intake. Also, cerebral activity can markedly affect intermediary metabolism by influencing autonomic neural and endocrine activity. Therefore, psychologic factors can be and probably are of great importance in the development of human obesity. However, the thoughtful physician will maintain a sufficiently open mind to include a consideration of neurophysiologic, endocrinologic and metabolic factors.

REFERENCES

1. Armstrong, D. T., Steele, R., Altszuler, N., Dunn, A., Bishop, J. S. and De Bodo, R. C. *Amer. J. Physiol.,* 1961, *201*:9–15.

2. BALL, E. G. and JUNGAS, R. L. *Proc. nat. Acad. Sci. (Wash.)*, 1961, *47:*932–941.
3. BROBECK, J. R., TEPPERMAN, J. and LONG, C. N. H. *Yale J. Biol. Med.*, 1943, *15:*831–853.
4. CANTAROW, A. and SCHEPARTZ, B. *Biochemistry.* 3rd ed. Philadelphia, W. B. Saunders Co., 1962.
5. CHAMBERS, W. H. *Physiol. Rev.*, 1938, *18:*248–296.
6. COHN, C. and JOSEPH, D. *Amer. J. clin. Nutr.*, 1960, *8:* 682–690.
7. COHN, C., JOSEPH, D. and ALLWEIS, M. D. *Amer. J. clin. Nutr.*, 1962, *11:*356–361.
8. COX, G. E., TAYLOR, C. B., COX, L. G. and COUNTS, M. A. *Arch. Path.*, 1958, *66:*32–52.
9. DEPOCAS, F. *Brit. med. Bull.*, 1961, *17:*25–31.
10. FÁBRY, P., PETRÁSEK, R., HORÁKOVÁ, E., KONOPÁSEK, E. and BRAUN, T. *Brit. J. Nutr.*, 1963, *17:*295–301.
11. FREDRICKSON, D. S. and GORDON, R. S., JR., *Physiol. Rev.*, 1958, *38:*585–630.
12. FRITZ, I. B. *Physiol. Rev.*, 1961, *41:*52–129.
13. GARNER, R. J. and ROBERTS, R. *Biochem. J.*, 1955, *59:* 224–228.
14. GOODMAN, H. M. and KNOBIL, E. *Endocrinology*, 1959, *65:*451–458.
15. HAUSBERGER, F. X. and RAMSAY, A. J. *Endocrinology*, 1959, *65:*165–171.
16. HAVEL, R. J., NAIMARK, A. and BORCHGREVINK, C. F. *J. clin. Invest.*, 1963, *42:*1054–1063.
17. HETHERINGTON, A. W. and RANSON, S. W. *Anat. Rec.*, 1940, *78:*149–172.
18. HSIEH, A. C. L. and CARLSON, L. D. *Amer. J. Physiol.*, 1957, *190:*243–246.
19. KARPOVITCH, P. V. *Physiology of muscular activity.* Philadelphia, W. B. Saunders Co., 1959.
20. KETY, S. S. In: *Metabolism of the nervous system*, D. RICHTER, ed. New York, Pergamon Press, 1957.
21. KEYS, A., BROZEK, J., HENSCHEL, A., MICKELSEN, O. and TAYLOR, H. *The biology of human starvation.* Minneapolis, University of Minnesota Press, 1950.
22. LEWIS, K. F., ALLEN, A. and WEINHOUSE, S. *Arch. Biochem.*, 1959, *85:*499–511.
23. MASORO, E. J. *J. Lipid Res.*, 1962, *3:*149–164.
24. MASORO, E. J. *Fed. Proc.*, 1963, *22:*868–873.
25. MASORO, E. J., CHAIKOFF, I. L., CHERNICK, S. S. and FELTS, J. M. *J. biol. Chem.*, 1950, *185:*845–856.
26. MAYER, J. In: *Fat metabolism*, V. A. NAJJAR, ed. Baltimore, The Johns Hopkins Press, 1954.
27. MAYER, J. *Amer. J. clin. Nutr.*, 1960, *8:*712–718.
28. MAYER, J. *Ann. Rev. Med.*, 1963, *14:*111–132.
29. MAYER, J. and MARSHALL, N. B. *Nature (Lond.)*, 1956, *178:*1399–1400.
30. MAYES, P. A. *Metabolism*, 1962, *11:*781–799.
31. PANAGOS, S., BEYER, R. E. and MASORO, E. J. *Biochim. biophys. Acta*, 1958, *29:*204–205.
32. POTTER, V. R. *Fed. Proc.*, 1958, *17:*1060–1063.
33. RANDLE, P. J., GARLAND, P. B., HALES, C. N. and NEWSHOLME, E. A. *Lancet*, 1963, *1:*785–789.
34. RAPPORT, D. *Physiol. Rev.*, 1930, *10:*349–472.
35. SELLERS, E. A., SCOTT, J. W. and THOMAS, N. *Amer. J. Physiol.*, 1954, *177:*372–376.
36. TEPPERMAN, J. *Metabolic and endocrine physiology.* Chicago, Year Book Medical Publishers, Inc., 1962.
37. VAUGHAN, M. *J. Lipid Res.*, 1961, *2:*293–314.
38. WERTHEIMER, E. and SHAPIRO, B. *Physiol. Rev.*, 1948, *28:*451–464.
39. WIELAND, O. and SUYTER, M. *Biochem. Z.*, 1957, *329:* 320–331.
40. WILLIAMS, G. R. *Rev. canad. Biol.*, 1959, *18:*217–226.

SECTION XIII

ENDOCRINE SYSTEM

CHAPTER 56

The Hormones

By JANE A. RUSSELL

HISTORICAL SURVEY
FUNCTIONS OF HORMONES

METHODS OF STUDY
Bio-assay methods

THE several endocrine glands and their secretions, the hormones, constitute a system for regulating the rates of growth, development and function of certain tissues and the rates of many of the metabolic processes within the body.[1, 3, 4, 5] The endocrine glands are considered as a system and not solely as separate organs, for the hormones seldom act independently of one another or of metabolic events within the body. Moreover, the endocrine system is closely linked, both developmentally and functionally, to the nervous system. In a general sense, the hormones have been considered by some to be a primitive type of integrative device which in higher forms has been superseded in part by the nervous system. Acting more or less independently of nervous regulation in some respects, in others the endocrine system is so related to the nervous system that in effect it serves functionally as an extension of it. This intimate connection between the nervous and endocrine systems allows psychic influences to modify hormonal activities. Numerous clinical and experimental observations attest this relationship.

The hormones may be defined as specific substances secreted by particular organs into the general circulation, which carries these substances to their sites of action elsewhere in the body. Here they *regulate the rates* of specific processes, without contributing significant amounts of energy or matter to the tissues.* Because of the regulatory nature of their roles, either a deficiency or an excess in the circulating levels of the hormones may lead to disorders in the normal development and function of the body.

Hormones of various sorts appear to occur throughout the animal kingdom. Those which are best known, and which will be considered here, are those peculiar to the vertebrates. With respect to most parts of the endocrine system, homologous glandular structures and often identical secretions are found in all vertebrate classes. The relatively little known invertebrate hormones appear to be different substances only rather distantly analogous in their actions to those of the higher animals.

HISTORICAL SURVEY

Despite centuries of observations of the effects of castration in man and animals and of clinical disorders now known to relate to the endocrine

* Substances which have many of the properties of hormones according to this definition, but which differ in that they are produced by all or many tissues rather than by a specific organ, have been called parahormones. An example of this class is carbon dioxide, which acts through nervous mechanisms to regulate the respiratory rate.

system, a clear concept of the general nature of the physiologic role of the endocrine glands did not develop until the end of the nineteenth century. Knowledge of the specific functions of these organs began to accumulate only in the early part of this century and has continued at an accelerating rate since that time. The idea of endocrine function is often attributed to Claude Bernard, who in 1855 first described "internal secretion" by an organ of the body; but, as he used the term, it referred to the liberation of metabolites from the liver (this in itself was a revolutionary view at the time) and did not include the concept of the hormone as it is known today. Shortly before, in 1849, Berthold had shown that atrophy of a capon's comb could be prevented by grafting testicular tissue elsewhere in the body of the bird, but this observation remained unnoticed until much later. Apparently without knowledge of Berthold's work, Brown-Séquard and others some 25 years later attempted similar experiments with testicular extracts and grafts in other species, with results which were controversial rather than enlightening.

The eventual stimulus to sound experimental study of the ductless glands came from clinical observation. Association of diseased states of the thyroid and of the adrenal glands with certain clinical syndromes had been made earlier: Toxic or exophthalmic goiter was described by Graves in 1835 and by Basedow in 1840, and a peculiar syndrome accompanied by destruction of the adrenal glands was described by Addison in 1855. To this list was later added myxedema, described first by Gull in 1873 and observed after thyroidectomy in 1883 by the Reverdins and Kocher. These clinical findings suggested to Semon that cretinism, adult myxedema and the post-thyroidectomy syndrome must all be due to failure of thyroid function, and this was confirmed experimentally by Horsley in 1888. Soon thereafter, thyroidectomized animals and myxedematous patients were treated successfully by substitution of fresh or dried thyroid tissue given by mouth.

Up to this date, the nature of endocrine function was unknown. From the time of Addison it had been considered probable that the normal function of the adrenal and other ductless glands must be to remove hypothetical noxious substances from the blood. The "detoxification" theory was applied also to the thyroid gland,

and then to the pancreas after Minkowski first produced experimental diabetes mellitus in 1890, and to the parathyroid glands a few years later. It was only after the demonstration of substitution therapy in hypothyroid states, mentioned above, that the modern concept of endocrine function began to emerge. This view —that some organs may regularly liberate into the blood stream substances which are necessary for the normal development and function of other parts of the body—appears to have been first clearly stated by Brown-Séquard and D'Arsonval in 1891. The older idea of detoxification was only slowly relinquished, however, and indeed it still recurs from time to time.

The concept that excess of an endocrine secretion could also produce disease, although it now appears to be a natural corollary of the earlier observations on deficiency of hormones, was only rather gradually developed. Several observations of hyperthyroidism induced by the taking of excessive amounts of thyroid substance, the demonstration of hyperplasia of the thyroid in Graves' disease, and the adenomatous changes seen in the pituitary body in acromegaly and gigantism led finally to the general acceptance of this view in the early years of this century.

The final stage in the development of the modern view of endocrine function was its linkage to Claude Bernard's concept, discussed in previous chapters, that the internal environment is maintained relatively constant. The secretion of a hormone in response to a specific stimulus, and thus the intermediation of a hormone in a physiologic response, was first observed by Bayliss and Starling in 1902 in their work on the intestinal hormone, secretin. That hormonal mechanisms might regularly take part in the reactive systems which help to maintain the constancy of the internal environment was apparently first suggested by Starling in 1923, when he called them examples of the "wisdom of the body." Cannon,[1] amplifying this view, included the secretions of certain endocrine organs as integral parts of homeostatic regulation by the autonomic nervous system. Since that time, most of the hormones have come to be considered parts of a larger and more general system, which—like the nervous system—has as its function the integration of the activities of the various parts of the body into those of a coordinated unit.

The name "hormone," from the Greek word meaning arousing or setting in motion, was proposed by Starling in 1905, and although it is hardly applicable in the strict sense to all the endocrine secretions now known, it has been universally adopted as the general term for such secretions.

FUNCTIONS OF HORMONES

The actions of the hormones may usually be included in one of the following categories: (i) morphogenesis, e.g., control of the development and maturation of the gonads and secondary sex organs, of metamorphosis in lower forms, and of the growth of the bones; (ii) integration of autonomic function and of "instinctual" behavior patterns, such as extension of sympathetic system responses and control of sex and maternal behavior; and (iii) maintenance of the internal environment: regulation of the disposition of foodstuffs, electrolytes and water in the body.

The mode of action of the hormones is always regulatory. That is, the hormones do not initiate processes completely *de novo,* but must always have present the normal tissues and enzyme systems upon which to work. A trophic hormone cannot, of course, induce growth of the target organ unless the gland is present in a potentially functional state. Conversely, many processes which are affected by the hormones may display also a considerable degree of autonomy. For example, metabolic reactions which are greatly accelerated *in vivo* by certain hormones may be observed to proceed at measurable rates even in the complete absence of the hormones, either *in vivo* or *in vitro.* The mechanisms by which the hormones bring about their effects are unknown. Although several of these agents produce characteristic effects in surviving tissue slices or minces, convincing evidence that these effects can occur in the absence of intact cells has been obtained only in one or two instances, and in no case has it yet been possible to explain the physiologic activity of the hormone completely on the basis of its actions in a cell-free system. In all probability, the hormones do act by influencing the effectiveness of some specific enzyme systems, but this may be done not in the usual catalytic sense but rather by alteration in the physical or chemical organization of enzyme systems within the cells or in the transport of substrates for enzyme action through cell membranes or into certain parts of the cell.

The endocrine glands obviously may be affected by physiologic mechanisms common to the rest of the organism. The metabolic or nutritional state of the body may influence not only glandular function but also the responsiveness of the organs or tissues affected by the hormones. Moreover, secretion by the endocrine organs can also be affected by the presence of other hormones, by nervous stimuli in many instances, and by other specific environmental factors such as the blood sugar level. Each hormone, then, is not only a regulator itself; its output and effective function may in turn be modified by other factors. Probably no changes occur in, or are forced upon, one part of the endocrine system without inducing some degree of alteration in the function of other parts. In consequence, interpretation of experimental and clinical observation of the effects of deficiency or of excess of a particular hormone has often been difficult. Only with greater knowledge concerning the integration of the endocrine system have some general principles of its operation become clear.

From present evidence, it seems probable that each endocrine organ has normally, when the organism is in a resting state, a fairly constant characteristic rate of secretion of its hormone or hormones, and that this rate is then played upon by changing concentrations of humoral factors or by nervous mechanisms which act as stimuli peculiar to that organ. In general, the response of the endocrine organ to the stimulus is one which tends by various devices to restore the organism to its original state, as it was before the introduction of the change which was the stimulus. Examples of this regulatory role are numerous. Elevation of the blood sugar level is a stimulus to the secretion of insulin, which hastens the removal of sugar from the blood; hypoglycemia is a specific stimulus to the secretion of epinephrine, which in turn enhances the release of sugar from the liver. The regulation of the rate of secretion of the trophic hormones of the pituitary body by the circulating level of the secretions of their target organs also is an example of homeostasis. Deficiency of the gonadal, thyroid or adrenocortical hormones brings about an increase in the rate of secretion of the pituitary hormones controlling these organs, thereby tending to increase the rate of release of the former and to restore the normal hormonal balance. Similarly, the administration of an excess of gonadal, thyroid or adrenocortical hormones appears to depress the secretion of the respective trophic hormones. This principle—that the endocrine system acts generally in a homeostatic fashion—has provided a framework for many otherwise uncorrelated observations, and, although it may not hold true for every aspect of hormonal activity, it has become a most useful concept.

METHODS OF STUDY

The existence of a great many different hormonal factors has been postulated at one time or another, but in many instances the observations on which these theories were based were not critical. For convincing evidence of the presence of a new hormone, or for new functions of known hormones, at least two types of observations are required: the production of a specific syndrome in the absence of the hormone in question and specific physiologic responses to the exogenous administration of the hormone by grafting or implantation of glandular tissue or by infusion of an extract of the tissue. The latter demonstration should include both successful replacement therapy in subjects lacking the hormone and further exaggeration of characteristic effects of the hormone in intact individuals. Confirmatory evidence of hormonal function may sometimes be obtained from the demonstration of histologic or chemical changes in the secreting organ in various physiologic and pathologic states in which the activity of the gland is known to be altered.

Further investigations then concern chemical characterization of the hormone, its mode of action, and factors regulating its secretion. The isolation and identification of the active principle is often exceedingly difficult, requiring the combined efforts of physiologists, biochemists and pharmacologists. The chemical nature of the known hormones is various; most of them are unstable, and many of them are proteins or peptides difficult to separate from other cellular materials. The hormones are found in the secreting organs only in minute amounts. In most cases the only guide to their presence is their physiologic activity. In each case, suitable methods of bio-assay must, therefore, be de-veloped for use both in preparing the hormone and in estimating the concentrations of the hormone in body tissues and fluids in physiologic and clinical studies.

Bio-assay methods. These procedures have become essential tools in modern research in endocrine physiology, but the principles used have not been as widely appreciated as they should be. In such methods, a characteristic physiologic effect of the hormone is made the basis of a quantitative assessment of the amount of the active principle present in a given preparation. The effects of a hormone are often qualitative rather than quantitative, or, if they can be measured, are related to the amount of active substance used in the test over only a narrow range of responses. The degree of response—or, if the observations are qualitative, the proportion of positive reactions—is very rarely directly proportional to the amount of active principle given. Instead, the response is related to dosage in one of a variety of complex ways, such as to a function of the logarithm of the dose. Finally, both biologic variation in response (which may be large) and errors inherent in the method of observation may enter into the measurements. It is thus apparent that bio-assay methods at best can never be as precise as chemical measurements. In order to make the tests in any way quantitative, certain principles must be followed strictly.[2]

The first principle in modern bio-assay methods is that the effects of an unknown preparation must be compared with those of a standard preparation containing the same active principle and no others that may interfere with the test. This procedure allows the expression of the activity of the unknown relative to a fixed standard rather than to a variable test object. To render this comparison as accurate as possible, a number of experimental designs have been evolved. If the effects of the standard can be shown to be sufficiently reproducible, comparison of the response of the unknown with a standard dose–response curve is feasible; but usually it is better to test simultaneously two or more doses of both the unknown and the standard. In any case, an essential feature of all comparisons is arrangement of the dosages so that the responses to standard and to unknown are of approximately the same magnitude. Thereby, errors deriving from the complex dose–response relationship are minimized and the major factor relating the unknown and standard potencies is the ratio of the amounts used in the test, which can be measured accurately.

To allow for biologic variation in response to the hormone, a number of observations must be made at each dose level. Obviously, if more than one test animal is used, the subjects must be as uniform as possible in past history and present condition. The numbers of observations required for any particular degree of precision will, of course, vary with the particular test and the conditions in which it is used, and can be determined only by experiment. If the assay has been properly designed, the degree of confidence which can be placed in the figures obtained may be evaluated by statistical methods. It has been found that even in the best bio-assay methods, when all possible precautions are taken, the error is still rather large, the 95 per cent confidence limits (the range of values within which 95 per cent of the observations may be expected to fall) being in these instances of the order of $\pm$ 15 to 20 per cent of the true values. For the majority of the methods now in use, the possible error is much greater still. Consequently, it is to be expected that only relatively large changes in the hormone content of the body tissues and fluids in experimental or pathologic conditions may be detected by biologic methods.

In experimental work on the hormones, a large variety of animal species have been used. Although there is general similarity in the endocrine physiology even of quite different species, appreciable quantitative variations have been noted, and sometimes—with respect to finer details of hormone activity—there are qualitative differences as well. Many discrepancies between the results and occasionally between the views of different investigators have been due to differences between the species and strains of experimental animals used. These differences are not altogether disadvantageous, for variety in experimental approach may be facilitated by species differences, and often also the comparative physiology is informative. Nevertheless, generalizations from observations made only in one species may be at times misleading, and for the complete understanding of the physiology and pathology of the endocrine glands in man, careful clinical observation and experiment remain essential.

REFERENCES

1. CANNON, W. B. *The wisdom of the body.* 2nd ed. New York, W. W. Norton & Co., Inc., 1939.
2. EMMENS, C. W., ed. *Hormone assay.* New York, Academic Press, Inc. 1950.
3. GORBMAN, A. and BERN, H. A. *A textbook of comparative endocrinology.* New York, John Wiley & Sons, 1962.
4. PINCUS, G. and THIMANN, K. V., eds. *The hormones; physiology, chemistry, and applications.* New York, Academic Press, Inc., Vol. 1, 1948; Vol. 2, 1950; Vol. 3, 1955.
5. TURNER, C. D. *General endocrinology.* 3rd ed. Philadelphia, W. B. Saunders Co., 1960.

CHAPTER 57

The Hypophysis

By JANE A. RUSSELL

THE hypophysis is perhaps the most important single endocrine organ, for its several hormones dominate the activities of the gonads, adrenal cortex and thyroid gland and in addition exert important independent effects. This gland, earlier called the pituitary in reference to a supposed association with the secretion of phlegm, is now also named the hypophysis cerebri, or hypophysis, in reference to its location beneath the brain. Two types of tissue enter into the formation of the hypophysis in embryo. The anterior or glandular portion arises from Rathke's pouch, an evagination of epithelial tissue from what will become the roof of the mouth, and the posterior or neural portion originates as a process of neural ectoderm from the tissue which will form the floor of the third ventricle. The glandular lobe becomes sealed off from the oral epithelium and is eventually separated from it completely by the sphenoid bone, but the neural lobe remains intimately connected with the hypothalamic areas through numerous nerve fibers and some glandular elements which constitute the pituitary stalk. In most species the hypophysis rests in a depression in the sphenoid called the sella turcica. It may be separated from the brain by the diaphragma sella, a membrane of dural origin which is penetrated by the stalk.

Several subdivisions of the hypophysis may be distinguished anatomically. (i) The *adenohypophysis* includes (a) the large *pars distalis* (or anterior lobe proper); (b) the *pars tuberalis,* a much smaller segment which extends some distance up along the stalk; and (c) the *pars intermedia,* a section which varies widely in size in different species and which is often but not invariably separated by a cleft from the rest of the glandular lobe. (ii) The *neurohypophysis* consists of (a) the neural lobe proper, or infundibular process, and (b) the infundibulum, which includes the stalk and the median eminence of the tuber cinereum. The glandular and neural portions of the hypophysis are commonly but not always accurately referred to as the anterior and posterior lobes, respectively. A diagrammatic section of the hypophysis is shown in Figure 1.

The glandular portion (adenohypophysis) consists of large polyhedral cells arranged in irregular cords or nests separated by sinusoids. Three principal types of cells can be identified: chromophobe (with poorly staining cytoplasm), eosinophil (acidophil) or α cells, and basophil or β cells. The latter two types contain numerous granules which stain characteristically. Several forms of both the α and β types of chromophil cell have been distinguished in the

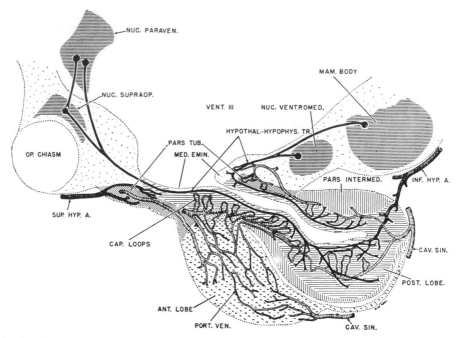

Fig. 1. Principal neural and vascular connections of hypophysis of the cat, in schematic longitudinal section. (Drawn by H. W. Ades.)

rat pituitary in varying physiologic conditions. The chromophobe cells are believed to be inactive forms (immature or exhausted) of the secretory α and β cells. The blood supplied to these portions of the pituitary arises from branches of the internal carotid artery, traverses the pituitary portal system into the gland (see below), and drains into the surrounding dural sinuses. Relatively very few nerve endings can be demonstrated in the adenohypophysis.

The posterior lobe, on the other hand, is distinguished by its rich nerve supply, a large part of the tissue consisting of branching unmyelinated nerve fibers. Formerly it was thought that these fibers innervated some peculiar cells, called pituicytes, which then secreted the hormones of this gland. However, the pituicytes may in fact be glial cells. According to Bodian,[11] the nerve endings may be seen as fine rodlike structures arranged in palisades which abut on capillaries lying in the septa between lobules of the gland. The nerve cell bodies and fibers supplying the posterior lobe contain granules which appear to be secretory in nature, and material staining in the same fashion is seen in the neural lobe, varying in amount with the secretory level of the gland.[72] It has been suggested, therefore, that the nerve cells themselves are the source of the hormone.

In any event, since the nerve fibers all arise in certain hypothalamic nuclei, these areas together with the neurohypophysis constitute a continuous functional unit. The blood supply to the neural lobe proper enters posteriorly and is largely distinct from that to the glandular lobe.

Physiologically, it has been possible for the most part to distinguish only the two main divisions of the hypophysis, the glandular and neural lobes behaving in effect like two independent organs without connection or common control. The glandular lobe is not autonomous in function, however, for many physiologic and clinical observations indicate that nervous mechanisms can affect the actions of this part of gland as well as those of the neurohypophysis. For instance, the occurrence of ovulation after coitus in certain species and the effects of light on gonadal function in birds can be explained only in this way. Until relatively recently it has not been understood how the central nervous system might exert such control over the glandular lobe, for convincing anatomic evidence of direct neural or vascular connections between the higher centers and the anterior pituitary is lacking. Wislocki[87] in 1937 and later Green and Harris[30] described in several species what is now called the *pituitary portal system* (Fig. 1). This is a rich capillary plexus formed from branches of the internal carotid artery and lying between the pars tuberalis and the median eminence. From this plexus arise sinusoidal capillary loops which enter the infundibulum, where they appear to be invested by nerve fibers from the hypothalamus, and which then return to the plexus. The blood from these capillaries then drains via the portal venules into the sinuses of the glandular lobe, supplying much or all of the circulation to this part of the hypophysis. In view of these anatomic relationships, a neurohumoral junction between some of the hypothalamic nuclei and the adenohypophysis at this point was postulated by Harris,[35, 36] and this view has been amply supported by more recent investigations. Nervous impulses reaching certain hypothalamic nuclei, from which nerve tracts descend into the infundibular region, appear to initiate the secretion by the nerve endings of chemical mediators. These humoral agents then are carried through the portal capillaries just described into the adenohypophysis, where they serve to control the secretion of its hormones. Several such neurohumoral agents have now been described.[33, 61] Most of them stimulate the secretion of specific hormones and have been termed "releasing factors"—corticotrophin releasing factor or CRF, luteinizing hormone releasing factor or LRF, and so forth. In at least one case, for control of prolactin secretion, the neurohumoral factor appears to be inhibiting. Evidence for the existence of these factors has come mainly from observations on the effects of lesions in the hypothalamus on pituitary function and on the actions of extracts of hypothalamic tissue on release of the respective hormones by adenohypophysial tissue *in vitro*. These neurohumors generally have yet to be obtained in sufficient quantity for complete biologic and chemical characterization, nor have all the hypothalamic nuclei concerned with control of the adenohypophysis been identified with certainty. Some aspects of this work will be discussed in connection with the control of secretion of certain individual trophic hormones.

THE ADENOHYPOPHYSIS

Effects of Hypophysectomy. Early attempts at determining the effects of hypophysectomy resulted ambiguously, for the animals usually died from attendant injury to the brain or from infection, or, if they survived, some of the effects observed often were due to damage in the hypothalamic area. Removal of the pituitary body by a trans-sphenoidal route, which in part avoids these difficulties, was first performed in the dog by Aschner in 1910–1912.[4] A similar operation was devised for the rat by P. E. Smith in 1926, and the relative ease with which this procedure may be performed in this species has greatly facilitated experimental work upon the physiology of the hypophysis.[76] Animals of many other species have since been operated upon in this manner.

The effects of excising either the whole hypophysis or the adenohypophysis alone include: (i) Atrophy of the gonads and accessory sex organs in the adult, or, in the young, failure of these organs to mature, with resulting complete sterility. (ii) Atrophy of the adrenal cortex, with consequent metabolic derangements. (There is not, however, complete lack of adrenal cortical function.) (iii) Atrophy of the thyroid, low metabolic rate, and other sequelae of thyroid deficiency. (iv) Failure of lactation (hypophysectomy performed late in pregnancy or postpartum). (v) Cessation of growth in the young, some loss of body tissue in the adult, reversion of the hair coat, etc., to the juvenile form. (vi) Alterations in the metabolism of carbohydrate, fat and protein, including hypersensitivity to insulin, a tendency toward hypoglycemia and rapid loss of glycogen stores in fasting, diminished fat catabolism, amelioration of diabetes mellitus or phlorhizin diabetes, and loss of nitrogen from the body. (vii) In amphibia and fish, blanching of the pigment cells of the skin (chromatophores) and failure of the usual adaptive changes in these cells.

Complete operative removal of the pituitary usually is not fatal in itself, in spite of the numerous derangements which it engenders. Secretion of aldosterone by the glomerular zone of the adrenal cortex continues at rates sufficient to prevent any great loss of salt, so that the hypophysectomized subject does not exhibit critical adrenal insufficiency. Hypophysectomized animals tend to have a subnormal life-span, however, for they are very sensitive to such deleterious agencies as infections and cold. Also, hypoglycemia may develop if the appetite fails for any reason or if food is withheld for any length of time, and in some species this is a common cause of early death.

The clinical counterpart of hypophysectomy in the adult—usually the result of infarction or tumor of the pituitary—is known as Simmonds' disease. The most prominent symptoms of this disorder are atrophy of the gonads and accessory sex organs, low metabolic rate, a very pale waxy skin, a tendency toward hypoglycemia, insulin sensitivity, liability to shock in surgical procedures or other stressful conditions and sometimes signs of adrenal insufficiency. Emaciation, cachexia and premature senility have been considered also to be symptomatic; but in fact marked loss of body substance is not an invariable consequence of hypophysial insufficiency, and when it occurs it may be in large part the result of inanition.[14, 74] Insufficiency of the adenohypophysis in young individuals causes dwarfism; this may be accompanied by other signs of pituitary dysfunction, depending on the degree and type of abnormality in the hypophysis.

Removal of only the neural lobe of the pituitary has much less serious consequences than complete hypophysectomy or removal of the anterior lobe alone. In some species, as in the dog, it is difficult to remove all the secreting posterior lobe tissue, for some is found extending into the tuber cinereum; in these species, simple postlobectomy may then have few sequelae. Even with complete removal of the neurohypophysis, the only marked physiologic effect in mammals is the development of permanent polyuria or diabetes insipidus. After complete hypophysectomy, on the other hand, polyuria of any severity is seen only temporarily. The disappearance of the diabetes insipidus otherwise seen in the absence of the posterior lobe may be due in part to atrophy of the adrenal and thyroid glands; for adrenalectomy and particularly thyroidectomy have an ameliorating effect on diabetes insipidus, possibly by diminishing the solute load on the renal tubules. Also, some degree of reorganization may occur eventually in the severed ends of the hypothalamic-hypophysial nerve tracts, with partial resumption of secretory function at this site.

Hormones of Adenohypophysis. The anterior lobe of the pituitary is the source of at least six distinct hormones: four trophic hormones—the two *gonadotrophins, adrenotrophin* and *thyrotrophin*—which have the unique property of controlling in more or less complete degree the functional integrity of other major endocrine glands; the *lactogenic* hormone or prolactin, which may be similarly classed in some respects; and the *growth* or *somatotrophic* hormone. In addition to these six hormones, yet another distinct substance with endocrine activity is found in the pituitaries of animals from all vertebrate classes. This is the *melanocyte-stimulating* hormone, which in amphibia and some other lower orders produces changes in the color of the skin when the animal is placed in the dark. From evidence obtained in amphibia, this substance seems to have its origin in the intermediate lobe of the hypophysis; but in mammalian species it is found in all parts of the gland and in practice is obtained from the posterior lobe.

Some attributes of crude pituitary extracts, particularly those connected with metabolic effects, have not yet been assigned finally to any one of these known hormones. Present evidence indicates that these probably can be ascribed mainly to the growth and adrenocorticotrophic hormones.

The six hormones mentioned above, plus the melanocyte-stimulating hormone, have all been obtained in highly purified or concentrated forms from the pituitaries of several species, so that there is no doubt about their separability into distinct entities. All are protein or polypeptide in nature. Although homologous hormones obtained from different species are quite similar in biologic effects, several have been found to differ somewhat in their chemical constitutions and properties, and in certain instances a notable degree of species specificity in activity is evident as well.

Which of the three types of cell found in the adenohypophysis secrete the different hormones is not entirely clear. From pathologic evidence it seems probable that the growth hormone is secreted by the α cells. The degranulation and vacuolation of the β cells which occur after gonadectomy or thyroidectomy indicate that the gonadotrophins and thyrotrophin have their origin in these cells, and different types of β cell, distinguishable morphologically, may give rise to these two respective hormones. Evidence concerning the source of lactogenic hormone is controversial, and little is known about the site of formation of adrenocorticotrophin.

TROPHIC HORMONES. The results of excess or deficiency of the trophic hormones are of course mediated through their effects on the respective target glands. In all cases the trophic hormones not only are essential for the complete morphologic development and normal function of the organs affected, but also promote actively the formation and secretion of hormones by these glands. When present in excess, they induce first functional and later morphologic hypertrophy. The trophic pituitary hormones appear to be secreted not at constant rates but in amounts varying with the physiologic state of the animal. Thus they act as sensitive regulators of the endocrine functions of the target organs.

Factors which in turn regulate the production of the trophic hormones by the adenohypophysis include at least two devices. The circulating level of the target organ hormone in most cases controls inversely the secretion of the respective trophic hormone. That is, when the "end-hormone" is high in concentration, the output of the hypophysial hormone is low; or, when the former is low or absent, the output of the trophic hormone is much increased. Several examples of this relationship will be discussed later. These responses are somewhat slow, however, so that it is unlikely that this type of control is responsible for the minute-to-minute regulation of secretion of the trophic hormones.

A second, probably more important,[32,33,60,61] device, neurosecretory regulation via hypothalamic pathways and the pituitary portal system, has been described above (p. 1090). When appropriate lesions are placed in the hypothalamus, varying degrees of gonadal atrophy ensue, and the adrenals and thyroid, although they do not necessarily become completely atrophic, fail to respond to stimuli which are ordinarily effective. In some cases, notably in connection with adrenotrophin, a very rapid increase in secretion of the trophic hormone has been demonstrated after purely neurogenic stimuli when the hypothalamus is intact, but not when the hypothalamus has been damaged or when certain centers have been depressed by drugs such as morphine. In addition to these two general mechanisms, it is possible also that either certain hypothalamic centers or the hypophysis itself can respond specifically to changes in other metabolic or humoral agents, such as the level of blood glucose, local temperature or the like; but the evidence for these types of control is as yet only suggestive.

Gonadotrophins. In the early work of Asch-ner[4] on the effects of hypophysectomy in dogs, atrophy of the genital organs was seen. Enlargement of the ovaries and formation of numerous corpora lutea in normal rats treated with pituitary extract were demonstrated by Evans and his collaborators in 1922, and later these investigators indicated the chemical distinction of the gonadotrophic from the growth-promoting factor in the extracts.[24] In the course of further efforts by several groups of investigators to purify the gonadotrophic fraction, it was found that this material also could be separated into two parts. When given separately in small amounts, these factors had relatively little effect on the ovaries of hypophysectomized rats, but when recombined the factors produced marked enlargement of these organs. The two pituitary gonadotrophins have since been obtained in highly purified and concentrated forms, but they have not been entirely characterized chemically. One, called the follicle-stimulating hormone (FSH), has as its chief function in the female the development of the ovarian follicles up to the point of ovulation; in the male its function is the development of the seminiferous tubules and maintenance of spermatogenesis. The other pituitary gonadotrophin is called either the luteinizing hormone (LH) or the interstitial cell-stimulating hormone (ICSH). The two descriptive names arose because factors effective in the female and male, respectively, but now known to be identical, were at one time thought to be distinct. In the female, the luteinizing hormone cooperates with the follicle-stimulating factor in the final stages of follicular development and ovulation, and probably in the secretion of estrogen; it then alone induces development of lutein tissue. In the male, this hormone induces development of the interstitial tissues of the testis (Leydig tissue) and the secretion of androgen. The follicle-stimulating hormone is usually detected biologically by the development of numerous follicles and enlargement of the ovaries in the immature or hypophysectomized rat. The test is more sensitive when the action of FSH is augmented by a constant amount of LH or of human chorionic gonadotrophin. The luteinizing hormone is assayed by the degree of enlargement it produces in the accessory sex organs, such as the seminal vesicles, in the immature or hypophysectomized male rat, or by decrease in ascorbic acid content of the ovaries in the pseudopregnant rat.

Gonadotrophins are secreted also by the placenta. These substances, often called chorionic gonadotrophins or anterior pituitary-like hormones (APL), are found in large amounts in the urine and blood of pregnant women, the blood of pregnant mares, and the tissues and urine of patients with certain genital tumors (chorionepithelioma and hydatidiform mole). They have been shown to be produced in cultures of placental tissue *in vitro,* and to be excreted after ovariectomy by pregnant women and mares. In biologic effects, human chorionic gonadotrophin (HCG) resembles LH (ICSH), whereas the hormone obtained from the pregnant mare behaves like a mixture of the two pituitary gonadotrophins. The chorionic hormones differ distinctly from the hypophysial hormones in chemical properties but are also protein in nature.

Lactogenic hormone (prolactin, luteotrophin). The existence of a pituitary hormone affecting lactation was first shown by Stricker and Greuter in 1928. Later, Riddle and others found that a similar factor controls proliferation of the crop gland and secretion of crop milk in pigeons, and a convenient method of testing for the hormone based on this effect led to the early isolation of the lactogenic substance in highly purified form. In mammals, the hormone appears to be responsible for the initiation and maintenance of lactation in the prepared mammary gland (previously brought to a responsive stage by the action of ovarian hormones). More recent work indicates that in certain species the lactogenic hormone also directly affects the ovary, aiding in the maintenance of the corpora lutea once they are formed and allowing the continued secretion of progesterone. This "luteotrophic" effect can be detected by the inducement of deciduoma formation in response to a foreign body (a characteristic effect of progesterone) in the uterus of the hypophysectomized rat.

Thyrotrophin. Depression of the metabolic rate and involution of the thyroid epithelium in hypophysectomized dogs were first noted by Aschner; and shortly thereafter Smith and Allen independently observed that the pituitary body was necessary for thyroid development in the tadpole and that it could be replaced by implantation of anterior pituitary tissue. Hyperplasia of the thyroid gland in normal animals following the administration of pituitary extracts was first observed in the guinea pig by

Loeb and Bassett in 1928. The thyrotrophic hormone has now been separated from other known pituitary hormones and obtained in highly active form, but it has not yet been purified. It has been assayed by its effects on the size or iodine content of the thyroid gland of young chicks or guinea pigs, on the height of the thyroid epithelium in a variety of species, or on the uptake into or the discharge of radioiodide from the thyroid.

Adrenotrophin. Atrophy of the adrenal cortex after removal of the pituitary body and its repair following the implantation of fresh pituitary tissue were first observed in the rat by P. E. Smith in 1926.[76] At about the same time, pituitary extracts which were growth-promoting were noted by Evans and collaborators to induce also hypertrophy of the adrenal cortices of normal animals. In 1943, the adrenocorticotrophic hormone (ACTH) was obtained from sheep and from swine pituitaries as an apparently pure protein. In 1951–1952, however, several groups of investigators showed that ACTH could be prepared as a much smaller molecule, a polypeptide which was many times more active on a weight basis than the protein ACTH. Such substances have now been obtained in highly purified form from sheep and hog pituitaries, and their structures have been determined.[51] The hormones from both species contain 39 amino acids in a single chain, with molecular weights of about 4500; they are 100 to 200 times as active as the standard protein hormone. The sequence of amino acids (starting from the N-terminal end) in the peptide ACTH from sheep is as follows:

Ser-Tyr-Ser-Met-Glu-His-Phe-Arg-Try-Gly-
 1   2   3   4   5   6   7   8   9   10

Lys-Pro-Val-Gly-Lys-Lys-Arg-Arg-Pro-Val-
11 12 13 14 15 16 17 18 19 20

Lys-Val-Tyr-Pro-Ala-Gly-Glu-Asp-Asp-Glu-
21 22 23 24 25 26 27 28 29 30

Ala-Ser-Glu-Ala-Phe-Pro-Leu-Glu-Phe.
31 32 33 34 35 36 37 38 39

The sequence in the hormone from pig pituitaries differs slightly from this in a few positions only. In both species, still smaller molecules having ACTH activity can be prepared by limited digestion with pepsin or with acid; the last 11 amino acid residues (29 to 39 inclusive)

are not necessary for complete activity. The peptide hormone is rapidly absorbed and destroyed when it is injected into animals, so that for maximal effect it must be given either very frequently or in a "depot" form, from which it is slowly released. It is supposed that in the pituitary the peptide hormone must be either adsorbed on or combined with cellular proteins, but it is not known how or in what form the material is actually secreted.

Highly purified peptide ACTH preparations have been shown not only to control the activity and development of the adrenal cortex, but also, independently of their effects on cortical secretion, to have some degree of melanocyte-stimulating activity and to have certain metabolic effects similar to those exhibited by growth hormone. The physiologic significance of these activities is not known.

The hormone has usually been detected by its ability to effect repair or maintenance of cortical tissue in hypophysectomized animals when the material is given over a period of several days. Another specific and extremely sensitive method developed by Sayers *et al.*[71] makes use of the disappearance of ascorbic acid from the adrenal glands within an hour after the hormone is given to hypophysectomized rats.

MELANOCYTE-STIMULATING HORMONE. The secretion by the hypophysis of amphibia of a hormone which controls pigmentation in the skin and the responses of this pigmentation to light were shown many years ago by Smith, Allen and others. The principal effect of the hormone is to cause immediate dispersion of the pigment granules in the chromatophores (melanocytes) of the skin and so to cause an apparent "expansion" of these cells and an increase in light absorption and in intensity of color in the skin. The same effects are produced on the skin of amphibia by extracts from the pituitaries of animals of all classes, including man. The active principle has been given many names, among them the chromatophore-exciting or -expanding hormone, the melanocyte-stimulating hormone (MSH), melanotrophin and intermedin. The latter term has been suggested because, in amphibia at least, the substance appears to arise in the pars intermedia of the hypophysis. The hormone can be assayed by its effects on the skin color in intact frogs or toads, or better, by the increase in light absorption induced in the isolated skin of the frog.

The hormone became of particular interest to mammalian physiologists rather recently when it appeared that MSH was related to or might even be identical with ACTH. This suggestion was based on the observations that crude peptide ACTH preparations displayed appreciable MSH activity and that certain changes in the pigmentation of the skin and nevi in man seemed to be related to changes in the secretion of ACTH. It has now been found that the two substances are in fact quite distinct. MSH has been obtained in two different pure forms from the pituitaries (posterior lobes) of swine and cattle, and the structures of these have been determined.[37, 52] The form first characterized (called β-MSH) contains 18 amino acids, and as obtained from the pig has the following sequence:

Asp-Glu-Gly-Pro-Tyr-Lys-Met-Glu-His-Phe-
 1   2   3   4   5   6   7   8   9   10

Arg-Try-Gly-Ser-Pro-Pro-Lys-Asp.
 11   12   13   14   15   16   17   18

A similar form of β-MSH obtained from bovine pituitaries differs from this only in containing serine instead of glutamic acid at the 2 position. α-MSH from the pig is a shorter chain in which the central sequence (2–12) is closely similar to that in β-MSH (5–15):

(Acetyl-N) Ser-Tyr-Ser-Met-Glu-His-Phe-
            1   2   3   4   5   6   7

Arg-Try-Gly-Lys-Pro-Val (NH₂)
 8   9   10   11   12   13

The potency of these substances as MSH is about 100 times that of pure ACTH, but they have no ACTH activity or other known biologic effects. Highly purified ACTH preparations, on the other hand, do exhibit significant MSH activity. This is undoubtedly a consequence of the fact that the two hormones have extensive sequences of amino acid in common. The entire sequence in α-MSH, except for its terminal modifications, is identical with the first 13 amino acids in ACTH, and in β-MSH the amino acids at positions 5, 7–13 and 15 are identical with the sequence 2, 4–10 and 12 in ACTH and in α-MSH. Thus, ACTH and MSH "overlap" to a large degree in structure as well as to some extent in biologic activity.

Preparations of MSH bring about changes in the color of the skin and nevi in man; the excretion of MSH-like material is increased in pregnancy and in adrenocortical deficiency, both conditions in which pigmentation is often increased; and cortical hormones suppress the excretion of the MSH-like substance.[49] However, it is not yet certain whether MSH itself is regularly secreted in higher animals, or whether the active factor in these species is in fact ACTH.

GROWTH HORMONE. A relationship between the pituitary gland and growth of the body was first indicated by the pathologic changes seen in the pituitary gland in acromegaly. This rather rare disorder, first described by P. Marie in 1886, is characterized by progressive enlargement of the ends of the long bones, thickening of the skull, lengthening of the jaw, overgrowth of the skin, and enlargement of the viscera. Gigantism was later seen to be a juvenile form of the same disease. After Aschner first showed that hypophysectomy in young animals resulted in dwarfism, it was recognized that the pituitary gland must be the source of an endocrine secretion which increases body growth. The first successful attempt to influence growth by hormone treatment was that of Long and Evans, who in 1921 produced giant rats by the long-continued daily injection of an extract of ox pituitaries. Similar results have since been obtained in several species.

The growth-promoting hormone, or somatotrophin, from the anterior pituitary has since been obtained from ox pituitaries in virtually pure form,[51, 53, 77, 86] and its chemical and biologic properties have been extensively investigated.[77] It is a globulin with molecular weight about 45,000 and isoelectric point about pH 6.8. Some progress has been made in the elucidation of the structure of the hormone, and it has been reported that the hormone remains active after limited proteolytic digestion, but the form responsible for its biologic activity has not yet been defined. Crude alkaline or saline extracts of ox pituitaries are usually rich in growth hormone, and many of the original observations on the biologic properties of the substance, such as those described below, were made with these extracts or with only partially purified materials. Most of these effects have since been obtained also with the highly purified substance.[69, 77]

Since crude preparations of growth hormone from other species, such as the sheep or pig, have been effective in the rat, dog and cat, it

has been supposed until recently that somatotrophins from various mammalian species would be closely similar if not identical substances. However, the hormone has now been prepared in relatively purified forms from a variety of species (pig, sheep, horse, monkey, man, whale and certain fishes), and these have been found to differ considerably in some of their chemical properties (molecular weight, amino acid composition, isoelectric point, etc.) and in biologic specificity. All of these hormones, except those from the fish, are active in the rat. On the other hand, extensive trials in human subjects and in monkeys with bovine and porcine hormones have yielded only equivocal or, more often, entirely negative results. It has now been found that somatotrophin obtained from the monkey is extremely effective in promoting nitrogen retention and bone growth in the monkey, and that hormones from both simian and human sources induce nitrogen retention in both the monkey and man.[46, 47, 62] Apparently, then, the biologic specificity of the growth hormones is such that they are able to act "downward" in the evolutionary line but not "upward." These observations make it seem unlikely that growth hormone preparations can be obtained in sufficient quantities for wide clinical use in man; but it is still possible either that the purified hormone from some other species may be found to resemble human growth hormone sufficiently to be effective when given in large doses, or that an active "core" will be found common to the several forms of hormone and thus will allow the preparation of material active in man from the hormone of some subprimate species.

Hormonal Regulation of Growth. In order to study the actions of a factor controlling growth, such as the pituitary growth hormone, it is necessary to define what is meant by the term "growth" and to consider the criteria to be used in measuring it. Gain in weight is the most usual measure, but without other data gain in weight alone is not sufficiently specific; obviously retention of water would not constitute growth, nor would deposition of fat alone. For true growth, there must be accretion of tissue which has a constitution fairly similar to that of the original body. When the gain in weight is sufficiently great, there may be no doubt that gross increments in the amounts of tissue and size of the supporting structures have occurred. More precise and sensitive indica-

Fig. 2. Effect of chronic treatment with anterior pituitary extract in young dog. *Lower,* Male dachshund given daily intraperitoneal injections of pituitary extract containing growth hormone, from 6th to 32nd week of life. *Upper,* Littermate male, untreated. (From Evans *et al., Growth and gonad-stimulating hormone of the anterior hypophysis.* Berkeley, University of California Press, 1933.)

tions of growth in animals are changes in the amount of protein in the body, or in the amount of nitrogen retained, and in the size or structure of the bones. By these criteria, the pituitary growth hormone does effect true growth, both in young and in adult animals.

EFFECTS ON BONE GROWTH. In animals whose long bone epiphyses have not yet closed, continued treatment with anterior pituitary extracts will accelerate the growth of both bones and tissues, inducing nearly symmetrical enlargement of all features. The rat, in which the major epiphyses remain open until very late in life, may be made to double its normal size. In adults whose epiphyses are closed, growth-promoting extracts produce a picture identical with that seen clinically in acromegaly; wherever endochondral bone exists, or some remnants of cartilage persist, both chondrogenesis and osteogenesis are initiated, producing the large and characteristically misshapen bones. If an excess of growth hormone is present during both the juvenile and adult stages, features of both gigantism and acromegaly may be induced. Figure 2 shows the effects of continued treatment with pituitary extract in the dachshund. Overgrowth of the skeletal system and skin is obvious, and visceral enlargement is also present. It will be noted that the achondroplasia normal in this breed of dog has not been affected by the treatment.

When the young animal is hypophysectomized, growth ceases. Both chondrogenesis and osteogenesis come to a standstill, leaving the epiphyses not completely closed but remaining as thin cartilaginous plates. These quiescent zones may be reactivated by growth hormone administered at any later time, even into senescence, to give the appearance of young, growing bone.[7, 75, 77] Chondrogenesis seems primarily affected, followed by ossification. The effects of the growth hormone upon bone, then, appear to be to induce the persistence of the normal juvenile growth pattern. A sensitive method of assaying growth hormone is based upon the widening of the proximal tibial epiphysial cartilage in young hypophysectomized rats, as seen in Figure 3.

EFFECTS ON SOFT TISSUES. With regular administration of growth hormone, enlargement of the whole body occurs. All or nearly all organs and tissues seem to take part in the response, but they do not all necessarily show the same degree of effect.[31] The functional efficiency of organs enlarged under the influence of the hormone may vary. In the muscles of adult rats treated with growth hormone, the maximal tension developed on stimulation was not increased above normal, so that the tension per unit cross-sectional area was low. On the other hand, the kidney is responsive to growth hormone not only in size but also in certain functional respects. The renal plasma flow, glomerular filtration rate, and functions dependent on these factors are particularly affected.[77] Organs whose growth and development is controlled primarily by other hormones, such as the adrenal cortex or the secondary sex organs,

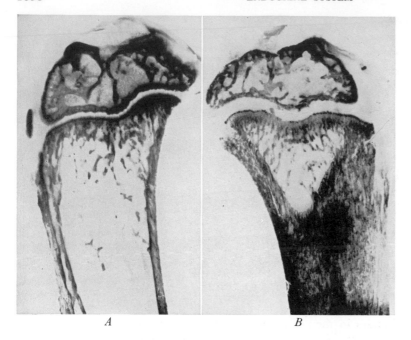

A   *B*

Fig. 3. Effect of growth hormone on proximal tibial epiphysis of rat (tibia split longitudinally and stained with silver nitrate). *A*, Tibia from untreated hypophysectomized rat. *B*, Tibia from hypophysectomized rat treated with growth hormone for 4 days. (Both animals 34 days of age, 16 days postoperative.) Note increase in width of cartilage (unstained band). (From Evans *et al., Endocrinology,* 1943, *32:*14.)

may respond to growth hormone also, although usually the effect is not more than in proportion to changes in body weight. It has been observed recently, however, that the presence of somatotrophin may in some cases greatly augment the effectiveness of the respective trophic hormone. Such "synergism" between growth hormone and other hormones has been shown clearly in respect to the action of ACTH on the adrenal cortex and to that of androgens on the preputial glands, and may well be found to occur elsewhere as well.

BODY COMPOSITION AND NITROGEN METABOLISM. That the gain in body weight induced by growth hormone is due to an increment of tissue and not to the accumulation of fat or water alone is shown by analysis of the whole bodies of the treated animals. Some data of this type obtained by Young[89] are shown in Table 1. Three series of analyses were performed, one of treated rats given food *ad libitum,* one of treated animals restricted in their food intake to the same amount given to control rats, and one of untreated animals. Both groups of rats

TABLE 1. *Composition of Material Added to the Bodies of Rats as the Result of Pituitary Treatments**

GROUP	TOTAL BODY WEIGHT G.	AMOUNTS ADDED OF					BODY LENGTH MM.
		Protein g.	Fat g.	Ash g.	Water g.	Energy Cal.	
1. Constant diet (52 Cal./day)	+ 80.3	+19.2	− 12.3	+4.6	+ 69.8	−39	+ 9.4
2. Unlimited diet (74 Cal./day)	+132.8	+25.6	− 2.0	+1.9	+105.7	+78	+16.2

*Alkaline extract of ox pituitaries equivalent to 125 mg. fresh anterior lobe tissue was given to each rat daily for 9 weeks. Untreated control rats fed 52 Cal. per day gained an average of only 1 gram during this time and did not increase in body length. The figures are averages of data from 10 rats in each group.

(From Young, *Biochem. J.,* 1945, *39:*515–536.)

TABLE 2. *Composition of the Bodies of Hypophysectomized and Normal Rats Pair-Fed During 33 Days Following Operation**

GROUP[†]	COMPOSITION IN GM. PER 100 GM. INITIAL BODY WEIGHT			
	Total Wt.	Protein	Fat	Water
Initial	100.0	17.8	13.1	64.0
Final				
Controls	81.2	18.2	5.3	54.0
Hypophysectomized	74.0	14.3	9.3	45.7

*The food intake was that amount eaten voluntarily by the hypophysectomized animals.

†16 rats in each group.

(From Lee and Ayres, *Endocrinology,* 1936, *20:*489.)

given growth hormone (crude anterior pituitary extract) gained weight, while the untreated animals did not. The animals which were unrestricted in their food intake showed a marked increase in appetite and gained the most, but even when the food intake was restricted, a considerable gain in weight occurred, amounting to 34 per cent of the initial weight in two months' time. This gain was confined wholly to protein, water and salts, and was accompanied by a loss of fat. Results similar to these have been obtained also with highly purified growth hormone preparations given to either normal or hypophysectomized animals.

An increase in the amount of body tissue over that of the controls with the same food intake may seem to require a reduction in the proportion of this food used for supplying energy. But neither a diminution in metabolic rate or in activity, nor any remarkable gain in efficiency of utilization of the food ingested, has ever been observed in animals given pituitary extracts. The data in Table 1 show that in this experiment body fat had been metabolized in place of the food calories which were stored as tissue protein. Since the added tissue containing these calories weighed more than the fat from which the energy came, a net gain in dry weight was possible.

The effects of growth hormone on the deposition of body protein can be observed not only when the hormone is given regularly, as in the experiments just described, but also when the nitrogen balance is measured over periods of a few days.[77] Although some of this nitrogen will be lost when the hormone is discontinued, a permanent net gain in body protein usually results. Further, some effects of the hormone on nitrogen metabolism are demonstrable under

appropriate conditions within a few hours. The concentration of free amino acids in the blood and tissues falls, and at the same time the rate of urea production is diminished sharply. The latter effect is best seen when a standard amount of protein hydrolysate is given intravenously.[68, 69, 77] The increase in the effectiveness of the hormone when increased amounts of nitrogen are made available suggests that the hormone affects primarily the synthesis of protein, rather than any phase of its catabolism.

After the removal of the hypophysis, mature rats at first tend to lose weight—perhaps as much as 10 to 15 per cent of the body weight—in the weeks following the operation, and then they may remain stable or lose ground only very slowly for a considerable time. Part of this loss of weight is due to diminished appetite, but if the hypophysectomized rats are compared with normal animals given the same amount of food, they still lose more weight than the controls.[48] Analysis of the bodies of such animals, as seen in Table 2, shows that the hypophysectomized animals lose more protein (in this case the controls lost none) and water, and much less fat than the normal rats. Even more dramatic evidence of the effect of the loss of growth hormone is seen when the nitrogen excretion is measured in the first few days after hypophysectomy (Fig. 4). In these experiments, in which the diet would just allow some growth in the unoperated group, the hypophysectomized rats excreted twice as much nitrogen as the control animals. When growth hormone was given during the postoperative period, this nitrogen loss was abolished. It is evident that somatotrophin is required for normal retention of body protein, not only in young animals but in adult or nongrowing animals as well.

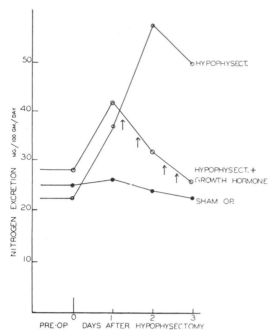

Fig. 4. Nitrogen excretion immediately after hypophysectomy in rats. Growth hormone, 0.25 mg. per 100 grams, was given on the second and third days after operation. The diet, containing 6 per cent casein, was fed for four days before and three days after operation. The average food intake was similar for all groups. (Six to eight observations per group, standard error 1 to 3 mg. per 100 grams.)

The stabilization of body weight and nitrogen balance of hypophysectomized animals some time later after operation probably is due to the atrophy of the thyroid and adrenal glands which occurs by that time, for the rate of catabolism of endogenous protein is known to be diminished in animals lacking the secretion of either of these organs.

Relationship of growth hormone to other hormones. Growth of animals may be influenced by many factors —genetic, nutritional, hormonal and metabolic. It is not to be expected, therefore, that maximal effects of the growth hormone can be obtained if any other requisite of normal growth is deficient. For example, Gordan et al.[29] showed that the amount of growth and nitrogen retention induced in normal adult rats by treatment with growth hormone is strictly dependent on the amount and quality of protein fed. Similarly, adrenalectomized animals do not grow or respond to growth hormone unless the hemodynamic state is fully maintained by adequate substitution therapy.

The relationship of the thyroid hormone to the growth hormone is more complicated. Thyroidectomized animals grow very little; they can be made to grow by administration of either thyroid or pituitary extracts. Hypophysectomized animals, however, will not grow in response to thyroxin. If hypophysectomized-thyroidectomized rats are given growth hormone, they will grow fairly well, but greater growth is obtained when a normal complement of thyroxin is given in addition. Apparently thyroid hormone is required not only for maximal activity of either endogenous or exogenous growth hormone, but also for the normal secretion of this hormone by the pituitary gland.[22, 75] It should be noted that although the presence of some hormone from the thyroid and the adrenal glands is necessary for maximal response to the growth hormone, such effects are not dependent on *increased* secretion by these glands. The thyrotrophic and adrenotrophic hormones are not essential to growth hormone activity.

Available evidence indicates that insulin may be required for the usual effects of growth hormone on nitrogen metabolism. Depancreatized dogs treated with pituitary extract do not retain nitrogen unless insulin is also given. It has been suggested that not only the normal amount of insulin is required for this effect, but that extra insulin also may have to be secreted to allow the growth hormone to act.[58]

The converse question is whether any other hormonal factors can induce protein synthesis and body growth in the absence of the hypophysis. As noted above, the thyroid hormone does not do so. The androgens have been reported to bring about some degree of nitrogen retention after hypophysectomy; but much of the nitrogen increase was found in the accessory sex organs and was not distributed among other organs as it is when growth hormone is given.[73] It is doubtful, therefore, whether the androgen induced much true growth in this case.

Salter and Best[70] reported that when large amounts of insulin were given together with the large amounts of food required to prevent hypoglycemia, hypophysectomized rats increased in weight and retained appreciable amounts of nitrogen as well as a great deal of fat. They suggested, therefore, that insulin could be considered to be a growth hormone. However, it had been shown earlier that, when hypophysectomized rats were force-fed ample amounts of food during the first few weeks after operation, they lost very little nitrogen as compared to animals fed *ad libitum*. More recently, Wagner and Scow,[83] force-feeding rats over longer periods after hypophysectomy, observed an increase in body weight due mainly to fat deposition but partly to protein retention similar to that seen by Salter and Best; but there was no difference between force-fed animals given insulin and those not given the hormone. Similarly, hypophysectomized rats in which gross hyperphagia was induced by the placement of lesions in the hypothalamus also retained some nitrogen and much fat, regardless of whether insulin was given.[44] It is likely, therefore, that overfeeding by itself can induce some deposition of protein in the absence of the hypophysis, as it does in its presence, but that excess insulin is not required for this effect.

Metabolic Functions of the Anterior Pituitary Gland.

Both removal of anterior pituitary gland and the administration of whole extracts made from the gland have been shown to affect profoundly several phases of the metabolism of carbohydrate and fat, as well as protein metabolism.[5, 8, 16, 18, 40, 41, 67] The many effects of the pituitary extracts have given rise to various names for the responsible factor or factors—among them the diabetogenic, glycotropic, glycostatic and ketogenic "hormones"—according to the effect observed. None of these factors has been demonstrated to be a distinct entity different from all other known pituitary hormones; and although it may be that such exist, current evidence suggests that all of the many phenomena seen may be attributed to growth hormone, or to adrenotrophin acting through the secretion of the adrenal steroids, or to the combined actions of the two factors. The major observations concerning the role of the pituitary gland in the metabolism of carbohydrate and fat are as follows.

(i) *Blood glucose and tissue glycogen stores.* A tendency to develop hypoglycemia spontaneously has been widely noted in hypophysectomized animals. If such animals are well fed, there are usually no noteworthy changes in the levels of glucose and glycogen in the body, but if they are deprived of food for even short periods, the glycogen stores first tend to diminish more rapidly than normally, and then the blood sugar begins to fall. The rate at which these changes appear during fasting varies considerably with species, being much more evident in smaller animals such as the rat than in large animals like the dog. In fasted adrenalectomized animals, similar changes in blood sugar and liver glycogen may be seen, but muscle glycogen is much less rapidly depleted than it is after hypophysectomy. This rapid loss of carbohydrate in fasted hypophysectomized animals may be prevented by adrenocortical hormones, presumably through their property of stimulating gluconeogenesis. However, pituitary extracts will maintain normal muscle glycogen levels during fasting even in the absence of the adrenal glands, and purified growth hormone free of adrenotrophin has also been found active in this respect. Thus the adrenal cortex appears to be in part responsible for the maintenance of normal blood sugar and liver glycogen in fasting, whereas the pituitary gland more directly affects muscle glycogen maintenance.

The concentration of glycogen in the heart, unlike that in other muscles, normally rises during fasting. This paradoxical effect was first noted many years ago in the dog and has since been seen in several species. It has now been found in the rat that the hypophysis is necessary for the increase to occur, and that growth hormone not only permits the cardiac glycogen to increase during fasting in the hypophysectomized animal but also hastens and augments the increase which occurs in the normal.[2] Cortical hormones do not reproduce the effect of growth hormone in this respect, but the presence of a small amount of cortical hormone seems to be required for maximal activity of growth hormone.

(ii) *Utilization of carbohydrate.* Fed carbohydrate tends to disappear more rapidly from the body in hypophysectomized animals than in normal animals. The R.Q. is high both in fasting and in fed animals, probably indicating increased utilization of carbohydrate. This conclusion is supported by the observation that the removal of glucose from the blood is much more rapid in hypophysectomized eviscerated rats and rabbits than in control eviscerate preparations. These changes are not observed in adrenalectomized animals. In acute experiments in rats either pituitary extract or purified growth hormone lowers the R.Q. and increases the deposition of fed carbohydrate, particularly in muscle.[42, 59] The cooperation of both pituitary and adrenal hormones may be required for this effect.

(iii) *Metabolism of fat.* That pituitary extracts are ketogenic and also cause accumulation of fat in the liver, this fat coming from the body depots, has been known for many years. Both the ketogenic and "adipokinetic" effects have been reproduced with purified growth hormone, and in addition the concentration of unesterified fatty acids in the blood increases strikingly after administration of growth hormone.[28, 85] These effects taken together indicate that growth hormone induces release of fatty acids from adipose tissue and consequent increase in utilization of fat in peripheral tissues as well as in the liver. Increased fat metabolism would be an expected concomitant of the decrease in carbohydrate utilization noted above, but whether the effect on fat or on carbohydrate metabolism is primary or whether the effects are independent is not known. None of these effects on fat metabolism are reproduced consistently by adrenocortical steroids given to intact animals. However, cortical factors have seemed to be synergistic or permissive for the actions of the pituitary factor, especially in relation to accumulation of liver fat, and also cortical steroids are ketogenic and may be lipolytic in adipose tissue in animals lacking insulin (see Chap. 58). Since in the intact animal growth hormone does not raise the blood glucose immediately, any tendency to induce lipolysis in adipose tissue would not be inhibited by glucose plus insulin as it would be after administration of cortical steroid. Thus it may be that both pituitary and adrenal factors tend to promote fat mobilization and utilization but that the action of growth hormone is much more easily demonstrable in usual conditions. Unfortunately, neither growth hormone nor cortical steroids have promoted release of fatty acids nor otherwise affected fat metabolism consistently when applied to isolated adipose tissue *in vitro*, so the mechanism of these effects remains unknown.

Preparations from the pituitary other than growth hormone, including ACTH, and also materials from other sources, such as urine and blood, also have been shown to be ketogenic in animals, even in the absence of the adrenal glands,[23] and also ACTH has been shown to promote release of fatty acids from adipose tissue *in vitro*.[39, 84] However, since many factors may influence ketogenesis and since also a great many other substances can effect lipolysis in adipose tissue *in vivo* and *in vitro,* the physiologic significance of these effects remains in doubt.

(iv) *Sensitivity to insulin.* Hypophysectomized animals are extremely sensitive to the hypoglycemic effects of insulin, an observation first made in 1924 by Houssay and since confirmed in a variety of animal species and in clinical cases of hypopituitarism. A considerable part of the increased sensitivity may be the result of adrenal cortical atrophy, for adrenalectomized animals are also very sensitive though less so than are hypophysectomized subjects. Crude pituitary extracts, adrenotrophin or adrenal steroids given a few hours before the insulin will prevent or diminish its usual hypoglycemic effects in both normal and hypophys-

ectomized animals. On the other hand, pituitary extract has also been reported to be effective in this respect in adrenalectomized rabbits, and growth hormone free of adrenocorticotrophin has been seen to oppose the action of insulin.[17, 59] It appears, then, that both independent pituitary factors and the adrenal cortical hormones are able to diminish the usual effects of insulin. The contra-insulin factor or factors are often called glycotropic substances, because it was once thought that they acted by increasing the lability of the liver glycogen.

(v) *Pancreatectomy.* If animals which have been made diabetic by removal of the pancreas (see Chap. 58) are then hypophysectomized, a considerable amelioration of the symptoms of diabetes mellitus is observed. Such doubly operated upon animals are known as Houssay preparations, after the discoverer of the phenomenon.[40, 41] They survive for long periods without insulin, may have blood sugar levels often in the normal range or below, and show little glycosuria or ketonuria, normal fasting nitrogen excretion rates, improved glucose tolerance, and increased or normal R.Q.'s after carbohydrate. The Houssay animal is, however, an unstable creature, easily thrown into extremes of either diabetes mellitus or hypoglycemia by alterations in its state of nutrition, by infections, or by other extraneous influences. The suggestion is strong that the pancreatic hormone, insulin, and one or more pituitary factors are opposed with respect to their normal effects on carbohydrate metabolism. In the absence of both hormones a relatively normal state ensues, but without their protecting regulation the animal is at the mercy of its environment.

As shown by Long and Lukens, adrenalectomy has a very similar effect on pancreatic diabetes, so that part of the Houssay phenomenon may be the result of adrenal atrophy (see Chap. 59). However, the diabetic state may easily be restored in the Houssay animal by treatment with pituitary growth hormone, whereas cortical steroids, which are ketogenic in such a preparation, do not reproduce the full diabetic state. Since this effect is obtained in the absence of the pancreas, the antagonism between insulin and the pituitary factors affecting carbohydrate metabolism cannot be the result of direct chemical interaction between the hormones, but must be physiologic.

(vi) *Pituitary diabetes.* When crude anterior

pituitary extract is given to adult dogs or cats over a period of several days, a state generally similar to pancreatic diabetes may be temporarily induced.[40, 41, 55, 88] Characteristic observations in this state include elevation of the blood sugar, glycosuria, ketonuria and polyuria. The nitrogen balance is positive during this phase, however, rather than negative as in pancreatic diabetes. In species other than the dog and cat, diabetes is rarely induced when the pancreas of the animal is intact, but if the animal has been partially depancreatized to a point just short of producing diabetes, the pituitary extract will induce a diabetic state comparable to that seen in intact dogs and cats. On the cessation of treatment, the pituitary diabetes disappears within a few days.

In animals which are resistant to the diabetogenic effects of pituitary preparations, hypoglycemia rather than hyperglycemia may be seen, and, on continued treatment, an increase in size and number of the islet cells may occur.[59, 64] A specific pancreatrophic factor in the pituitary gland has been suggested as responsible for these effects, but, since hypophysectomized animals show no signs whatever of deficient pancreatic function, this seems unlikely. It is probable that increased islet activity is indirectly called forth to oppose other metabolic effects of the extracts. If the response is adequate, the animal appears resistant to the diabetogenic factor; if it is not, diabetes ensues.

The nature of the hypophysial diabetogenic factor is not known certainly. Typical pituitary diabetes can be produced in dogs and cats by small amounts of purified growth hormone,[13, 15] and no chemical separation of the growth-promoting and diabetogenic activities has yet been achieved.[64] On the other hand, this diabetes is demonstrable only with difficulty in the absence of the adrenal glands; and, moreover, glycosuria can be induced in intact animals of many species with either ACTH or cortical steroids. Hence, both hypophysial and adrenal factors may be implicated. Current evidence suggests that growth hormone is probably the primary diabetogenic agent found in pituitary extracts, but that ACTH, acting through the adrenal steroids, may play a supporting or synergistic role in eliciting this response.

(vii) *Permanent pituitary diabetes (metahypophys-ial diabetes)*. If diabetes is first induced as described above and then maintained for several weeks by the continued administration of pituitary preparations (with increasing dosage if required), then when treatment is stopped the diabetes mellitus may persist indefinitely.[19, 20, 56] This diabetic state is practically indistinguishable from that induced by pancreatectomy, except that survival without insulin is usually much longer. Examination of the pancreas indicates severe damage to the islet cells which normally secrete insulin, so that to all intents pancreatic diabetes mellitus has been induced by the prolonged treatment.[9, 65] If treatment with insulin is instituted during the early stages of the pituitary diabetes, the development of permanent diabetes may be prevented. It has therefore been suggested that continued exposure to the pituitary factor calls forth such an increase in the production of insulin that the islet cells become exhausted and so undergo the degenerative changes which are later evident in the permanent diabetic phase. Purified growth hormone preparations are capable of inducing permanent diabetes,[12] but neither ACTH nor adrenal hormones have been demonstrated to reproduce this effect.

SUMMARY OF METABOLIC EFFECTS OF ANTERIOR PITUITARY GLAND. It is not yet possible to state the exact role of the hypophysis in the intermediate metabolism of carbohydrate and fat. The tenor of the data is that the pituitary gland, acting both directly and through the adrenal cortex, exerts effects which are opposed to those of insulin. Normal metabolism requires the presence of all three of these factors; in the absence of one of the opposing hormones, exaggeration of the effects of the antagonist is seen, whereas in the absence of both, a relatively normal but very unstable state ensues. The relationship of the hormones of the pituitary to those of the adrenal cortex in these respects is less clear. Part of the action of the hypophysial hormones, notably that on gluconeogenesis, is undoubtedly mediated via the adrenal cortex, but that part affecting the utilization of body carbohydrate and fat seems to be directed by factors acting independently of the adrenal glands. The apparent parallelism between some of the effects of the pituitary factor (growth hormone?) and the cortical steroids, as on the utilization of fed carbohydrate (p. 1133), may be similar end-results produced by different mechanisms, or an expression of synergism between the two types of hormones.

Growth Hormone in Plasma. The concentration of growth hormone in the blood of normal animals is so minute as to escape detection by any of the usual bioassay methods, and virtually none is present in the urine, so that no direct measure of changes in its rate of secretion has been possible. Recently, however, Berson and his collaborators have applied their method of immuno-radiochemical assay, previously employed for insulin, to the measurement of growth hormone in human plasma.[27,66] The concentrations normally present in the adult subject are of the order of a few micrograms per liter of plasma. Remarkably, the concentration of growth hormone has been found to increase greatly during fasting, even for short periods of time, and to increase very quickly in response to hypoglycemia. This confirms previous suggestions from indirect evidence that growth hormone was normally secreted in the adult and that its secretion rate might vary with nutritional state.[69] Because of the actions of growth hormone to diminish the utilization of glucose and to increase that of fat, described above, these observations suggest that growth hormone secretion may function regularly in the well known adaptations of metabolism in animals to the availability of nutrients.

THE NEUROHYPOPHYSIS

Hormonal Activities. Although pharmacologic effects of posterior pituitary extracts had been known for many years, the hormonal nature of neurohypophysial function was not shown conclusively until much later. Three types of activity have been attributed to extracts of the posterior lobe in mammals. In 1895, Oliver and Schaffer noted that pituitary extracts would raise the blood pressure of animals. This pressor effect was later indicated to be due to peripheral arteriolar or capillary constriction. Similar extracts also induce strong contractions of the isolated uterus, an effect first noted by Dale in 1906. Other smooth muscle also constricts, but the uterine musculature is most affected. Hence, the principle responsible for the effect is called oxytocic, from the Greek words meaning rapid birth. Extracts of the posterior pituitary have since been used clinically as pressor agents and also particularly to induce uterine contractions during and after parturition. Later, posterior lobe extracts were found also to suppress water excretion and to control diuresis in cases of diabetes insipidus. When given to normal, fully hydrated subjects, such extracts cause increased reabsorption of water by the kidneys and possibly also increased excretion of salt. The loop of Henle is believed to be the site of this action.[79] The mechanisms by which the antidiuretic factor affects renal function and body water are discussed further in Chapters 44 and 45.

Chemical fractionation of posterior lobe extracts was first achieved by Kamm *et al.* in 1928, when they succeeded in separating two fractions containing principally the oxytocic and vasopressor factors, respectively. The antidiuretic factor accompanied the vasopressor substance in this fractionation. Both substances appeared to be polypeptides. In 1950–1953, Du Vigneaud and co-workers obtained two distinct substances in pure form, one of them with oxytocic activity and the other a vasopressor and antidiuretic agent. In a brilliant series of investigations, these workers then succeeded not only in determining the structures of these substances but also in synthesizing them from their constituent amino acids.[21] Both are basic peptides containing 8 amino acids in a cyclic disulfide form. Vasopressin from ox pituitaries has the following constitution:

$$\text{CyS—Tyr—Phe—Glu(NH}_2)\text{—Asp(NH}_2)\text{—CyS—Pro—Arg—Gly—NH}_2$$

Vasopressin from the pig differs from this material in the substitution of lysine for arginine. Although the structures of the hormones from other mammalian species have not all been established in detail, there is reason to believe that most of them are identical with that from the ox, given above. Oxytocin from ox pituitaries (and presumably also that from other species) has a very similar structure, differing only in two amino acids:

$$\text{CyS—Tyr—Ileu—Glu(NH}_2)\text{—Asp(NH}_2)\text{—CyS—Pro—Leu—Gly—NH}_2$$

The two hormones overlap to some degree in biologic activity as well.[80] Whereas pure oxytocin has very slight if any pressor or antidiuretic activity, the pure vasopressin-antidiuretic hormone possesses also about one-tenth the oxytocic potency shown by the primary oxytocic substance.

Some additional types of biologic activity have now been attributed to the purified oxytocic hormone.[80] This substance is the milk-ejection or milk "let-down" factor which is secreted during nursing or milking and which induces contraction of the myo-epithelial cells surrounding the alveoli of the mammary gland. The oxytocic factor also may induce a fall in the blood pressure; this effect is marked in avian species and is often used as the basis of assay for this hormone. Vasopressin displays both of these activities about in proportion to its oxytocic activity in other respects. Both vasopressin and oxytocin have been found to reproduce the effects of pituitary extracts in inducing spawning behavior in fish.

In addition to the polypeptides, another substance has also been obtained from posterior lobe tissue, a protein which appears pure by all the usual criteria and which exhibits all three types of posterior lobe activity.[43, 81] The molecular weight of this substance is about 30,000, its isoelectric point 4.8—clearly very different from the properties of the smaller active substances described above. The activities per unit weight are very much less than those of the smaller fractions, but the three types of activity are found in a constant proportion identical with that observed in the native gland and shown by the preparations obtained serially during the purification of the protein. It is not yet known whether this protein is merely a factitious adsorbent of the smaller molecules, or whether it is in fact a normal form of the hormone. If the latter were the case, the complex might be secreted as such, or it could function as a storage aggregate which was cleaved intracellularly before the secretion of one or both of the separable factors.

Control of Secretion by the Neurohypophysis. Experimental work on the hormonal role of the neurohypophysis has been concerned mainly with the antidiuretic factor. The only considerable effect of removal of the posterior pituitary without damage to the hypothalamus is the induction of polyuria. A very large volume of dilute urine is secreted constantly. As a consequence, there is also great thirst and a high intake of water (polydipsia). The clinical counterpart of this condition, diabetes insipidus, has long been recognized, its distinction from diabetes mellitus (in which polyuria and glycosuria coexist) being attributed to Willis in the 17th century. The only other disorders which have been supposed to be due to posterior lobe deficiency in mammals are some difficulty in parturition and in lactation, but these have not been constant findings.

Neurohypophysial function—at least with respect to the secretion of the antidiuretic factor—appears to be completely under nervous control. It will be recalled that certain hypothalamic nuclei are intimately connected with the pars nervosa through the pituitary stalk (Fig. 1). The classic work of Ranson and his colleagues[25] demonstrated that if the pituitary stalk is sectioned or if the supraoptic nuclei are destroyed, the effect on water excretion is as if the neurohypophysis itself had been removed. In these conditions the pars nervosa shows atrophic changes and is apparently completely nonfunctional. Conversely, if the neural lobe is removed, degenerative changes may be seen in the hypothalamic nuclei (supraoptic and paraventricular nuclei) from which come the nerves which end in the posterior pituitary. Evidently the antidiuretic function of the posterior pituitary is controlled through the hypothalamico-hypophysial nerve tracts. A material which stains selectively by Gomori's procedure, and also with reagents which react with disulfides (such as occur in the posterior lobe hormones) is found not only in the posterior hypophysis proper but also throughout the hypothalamico-neurohypophysial tracts and in the attached hypothalamic centers.[1, 6, 50, 72] This material disappears from the neurohypophysis when the animal is subject to dehydration, and it is restored on repletion with water, suggesting that the "neurosecretory" granules are either identical with or intimately related to the antidiuretic hormone. When the hypothalamico-hypophysial tracts are cut or the neurohypophysis is removed, this material then tends to accumulate in the proximal ends of the cut neurons. Further, considerable amounts of ADH-active substance can be extracted from the hypothalamus.[54, 57, 80] These and related observations indicate that the neurohypophysial hormones probably are formed in the neurons of these tracts, rather than in the gland itself. The hormones seem to be stored in the posterior lobe, however, and presumably they are secreted from there.

Further evidence of the endocrine nature of neural lobe function has been obtained through study of factors affecting the secretion of water by the kidney.[45, 78, 79] When normal animals are deprived of water, they secrete only a small volume of concentrated urine. Hypophysectomized animals or those from which the neural lobe only has been removed (or rendered inactive by stalk section or lesions in the hypothalamus) continue to secrete urine at the previous rate, even though great dehydration results. If sodium chloride is administered to normally hydrated animals, water secretion is delayed, but, again, hypophysectomized animals do not respond. Apparently either dehydration or the taking of salt, which results in a relative deprivation of water, brings about an increase in the release of the antidiuretic hormone by the pituitary and, by this means, the conservation of water. A substance having antidiuretic properties has been found in the urine of normal rats but not of hypophysectomized rats under these conditions.[3, 26]

Verney has shown that the urine volume is controlled by changes in the osmotic concentration of the blood.[82] If during water diuresis of normal animals a hypertonic solution of salt, dextrose, or sucrose is injected into the carotid artery, a prompt diminution in the rate of water excretion is seen. In mammals in which the neural lobe is absent or nonfunctional, such a change does not occur. An increase of as little as 2 per cent in the effective osmotic concentration of the plasma suffices to induce a prompt increase in the output of ADH and concomitant reduction in urine flow. When the osmotic concentration is diminished, as by the ingestion of a rather large volume of water, the secretion of ADH is suppressed; but it is difficult to demonstrate the effects of small changes in concentration here because the circulating hormone must have time to die away before evidence of reduction in ADH activity can become evident. Verney has suggested the presence in the hypothalamic nuclei of "osmoreceptors," organs sensitive to differences in osmotic concentration of the intracellular and extracellular fluids, which then transmit stimuli to the neural lobe via the supraoptic-hypophysial tracts.

The secretion of ADH seems to be responsive not only to change in osmotic concentration of the plasma but also to a number of other stimuli which presumably either act directly on the hypothalamic centers or reach these centers through neural pathways. After placing fine electrodes in the neural lobe of the rabbit, Harris was able to stimulate this organ electrically by remote control in the unanesthetized intact animal.[34] In such circumstances weak stimuli caused the inhibition of water diuresis, an increase in chloride excretion, and marked activity of the uterine musculature in the rabbit prepared by estrogen treatment. No change in blood pressure was observed. This was the first convincing evidence for the physiologic secretion of the oxytocic factor by the neural lobe.

The careful studies of Verney have shown that pain or even relatively mild emotional disturbances will cause diminution in urine flow, presumably by stimulating the secretion of ADH.[82] In patients who have fainted from any cause, increased amounts of ADH-active material are found in the urine. Many drugs have similar effects, among them acetylcholine, nicotine, morphine and ether. On the other hand, ethyl alcohol strongly inhibits the secretion of the hormone. This effect no doubt accounts for the well known diuretic action of alcohol.

Indirect evidence suggests rather strongly that the ADH-producing system can respond also to change in the effective blood volume, even when the latter is unaccompanied by change in osmotic concentration. This work has been well summarized by Strauss.[78] Any large or sudden expansion of the extracellular fluid or plasma volume, as by injection of isotonic fluids, is followed by an increase in urine flow which may be due to inhibition of ADH secretion. Conversely, reduction of the blood volume (as by venesection, application of tourniquets about the limbs, or even the assumption of a passive erect posture) tends to decrease the urine flow. The breathing of air at negative pressure has been observed to have the same effect as expansion of the blood volume, and so has distension of the left atrium.[38] It is supposed, therefore, that the stimulus in these cases is not change in the blood volume itself but alteration in pressure or stretch somewhere in the thoracic vascular system, probably in the heart or pulmonary veins.[38] Impulses from this region would then affect the activity of the hypothalamic-hypophysial system and inhibit the secretion of ADH.

The well known diuretic response to sudden chilling of the skin may be explicable in the same way, since the peripheral vasoconstriction in response to cold would result in a relative increase in the blood volume in the central vessels.

Whether the neurohypophysis plays any significant physiologic role in the regulation of blood pressure is not known. Since the antidiuretic and vasopressor activities appear to be properties of the same molecule, and since much smaller amounts of the substance are required to affect water excretion than to increase the blood pressure, the vasopressor action may represent a pharmacologic effect of excessive amounts of the antidiuretic factor.

REFERENCES

1. ADAMS, C. W. M. and SLOPER, J. C. *J. Endocr.*, 1956, *13:* 221–228.
2. ADROUNY, G. A. and RUSSELL, J. A. *Endocrinology*, 1956, *59:*241–251.
3. AMES, R. G., MOORE, D. H. and VAN DYKE, H. B. *Endocrinology*, 1950, *46:*215–227.
4. ASCHNER, B. *Pflüg. Arch. ges. Physiol.*, 1912, *146:*1–146.
5. ASTWOOD, E. B. *The hormones*, 1955, *3:*235–308.
6. BARRNETT, R. J. *Endocrinology*, 1954, *55:*484–501.
7. BECK, H., ASLING, C. W., SIMPSON, M. E., EVANS, H. M. and LI, C. H. *Amer. J. Anat.*, 1948, *82:*203–217.
8. BENNETT, L. L. and EVANS, H. M. *The hormones*, 1955, *3:*235–308.
9. BEST, C. H., CAMPBELL, J., HAIST, R. E. and HAM, A. W. *J. Physiol.*, 1942, *101:*17–26.
10. BILLENSTEIN, D. C. and LEVEQUE, T. F. *Endocrinology*, 1955, *56:*704–717.
11. BODIAN, D. *Johns Hopk. Hosp. Bull.*, 1951, *89:*354–376.
12. CAMPBELL, J., CHAIKOFF, L. and DAVIDSON, I. W. F. *Endocrinology*, 1954, *54:*48–58.
13. CAMPBELL, J., DAVIDSON, I. W. F., SNAIR, W. D. and LEI, H. P. *Endocrinology*, 1950, *46:*273–281.
14. COOKE, R. T. and SHEEHAN, H. L. *Brit. med. J.*, 1950, *(1):*928–931.
15. COTES, P. M., REID, E. and YOUNG, F. G. *Nature (Lond.)*, 1949, *164:*209–211.
16. DEBODO, R. A. and ALTSZULER, N. *Vitam. and Horm.*, 1957, *15:*205–258.
17. DEBODO, R. C., KURTZ, M., ANCOWITZ, A. and KIANG, S. P. *Amer. J. Physiol.*, 1950, *163:*310–318.
18. DEBODO, R. C., STEELE, R., ALTSZULER, N., DUNN, A. and BISHOP, J. S. *Recent Progr. Hormone Res.*, 1963, *19:*445–482.
19. DOHAN, F. C., CHAMBERS, A. H. and FISH, C. A. *Endocrinology*, 1941, *28:*566–579.
20. DOHAN, F. C., FISH, C. A. and LUKENS, F. D. W. *Endocrinology*, 1941, *28:*341–357.
21. DU VIGNEAUD, V. *Harvey Lect.*, 1954–5, *50:*1–26.
22. EARTLY, H. and LEBLONDE, C. P. *Endocrinology*, 1954, *54:* 249–271.
23. ENGEL, F. L. and ENGEL, M. G. *Endocrinology*, 1958, *62:* 150–158.
24. EVANS, H. M., MEYER, K. and SIMPSON, M. E. *Growth and gonad-stimulating hormone of the anterior hypophysis.* Berkeley, University of California Press, 1933.
25. FISHER, C., INGRAM, W. P. and RANSON, S. W. *Arch. Neurol. Psychiat. (Chic.)*, 1935, *34:*124–163.
26. GILMAN, A. and GOODMAN, L. *J. Physiol.*, 1937, *90:*113–124.
27. GLICK, S. M., ROTH, J., YALOW, R. S. and BERSON, S. A. *Recent Progr. Hormone Res.*, 1965, *21:* (in press).
28. GOODMAN, H. M. and KNOBIL, E. *Endocrinology*, 1961, *69:* 187–189.
29. GORDAN, G. S., BENNETT, L. L., LI, C. H. and EVANS, H. M. *Endocrinology*, 1948, *42:*153–160.
30. GREEN, J. D. and HARRIS, G. W. *J. Endocr.*, 1947, *5:*136–146.
31. GREENBAUM, A. L. and YOUNG, F. G. *J. Endocr.*, 1953, *9:* 127–135.
32. GREER, M. A. *Recent Progr. Hormone Res.*, 1957, *13:*67–104.
33. GUILLEMIN, R. *Recent Progr. Hormone Res.*, 1964, *20:*89–122.
34. HARRIS, G. W. *Phil. Trans.*, 1947, *B232:*385–441.
35. HARRIS, G. W. *Physiol. Rev.*, 1948, *28:*139–179.
36. HARRIS, G. W. *Neural control of the pituitary gland.* Baltimore, Williams & Wilkins Co., 1955.
37. HARRIS, J. I. and ROOS, P. *Biochem. J.*, 1959, *71:*434–451; HARRIS, J. I. *Ibid.*, 451–459.
38. HENRY, J. P. and PEARCE, J. W. *J. Physiol.*, 1956, *131:* 572–585.
39. HOLLENBERG, C. H., RABEN, M. S. and ASTWOOD, E. B. *Endocrinology*, 1961, *68:*589–598.
40. HOUSSAY, B. A. *New Engl. J. Med.*, 1936, *214:*961–986.
41. HOUSSAY, B. A. *Endocrinology*, 1942, *30:*884–897.
42. ILLINGWORTH, B. A. and RUSSELL, J. A. *Endocrinology*, 1951, *48:*423–434.
43. IRVING, G. W., JR. and DU VIGNEAUD, V. *Ann. N. Y. Acad. Sci.*, 1943, *43:*273–308.
44. KENNEDEY, G. C. and PARROTT, B. M. V. *J. Endocr.*, 1958, *17:*161–166.
45. KERRIGAN, G. A., TALBOT, N. B. and CRAWFORD, J. D. *J. clin. Endocr.*, 1955, *15:*265–275.
46. KNOBIL, E. *Recent Progr. Hormone Res.*, 1959, *15:*1–58.
47. KNOBIL, E., MORSE, A., WOLF, R. C. and GREEP, R. O. *Endocrinology*, 1958, *62:*348–354.
48. LEE, M. O. and AYRES, G. B. *Endocrinology*, 1936, *20:*489–495.
49. LERNER, A. B., SHIZUMI, K. and BUNDING, I. *J. clin. Endocr.*, 1954, *14:*1463–1490.
50. LEVEQUE, T. F. and SCHARRER, E. *Endocrinology*, 1953, *52:* 436–447.
51. LI, C. H. *Advanc. Protein Chem.*, 1956, *11:*101–190.
52. LI, C. H. *Advanc. Protein Chem.*, 1957, *12:*270–317.
53. LI, C. H., EVANS, H. M. and SIMPSON, M. E. *J. biol. Chem.*, 1945, *159:*353–366.
54. LLOYD, C. W. and PIEROG, S. *Endocrinology*, 1955, *56:*718–726.
55. LUKENS, F. D. W. *Amer. J. med. Sci.*, 1946, *212:*229–240.
56. MARKS, H. P. and YOUNG, F. G. *J. Endocr.*, 1939, *1:*470–510.
57. MELVILLE, E. V. and HARE, K. *Endocrinology*, 1945, *36:* 332–339.
58. MILMAN, A. E., DEMOOR, P. and LUKENS, F. D. W. *Amer. J. Physiol.*, 1951, *166:*354–363.
59. MILMAN, A. E. and RUSSELL, J. A. *Endocrinology*, 1950, *47:* 114–128.

60. MUNSON, P. L. and BRIGGS, F. N. *Recent Progr. Hormone Res.,* 1955, *11*:83–118.
61. NALBANDOV, A. V., ed. *Advances in neuroendocrinology,* Urbana, Ill., University of Illinois Press, 1963.
62. RABEN, M. S. *Recent Progr. Hormone Res.,* 1959, *15*:71–105.
63. REID, E. *J. Endocr.,* 1952, *8*:50–55; 1953, *9*:210–223.
64. RICHARDSON, K. C. and YOUNG, F. G. *J. Physiol.,* 1937, *91*:352–364.
65. RICHARDSON, K. C. and YOUNG, F. G. *Lancet,* 1938, *234:* 1098–1101.
66. ROTH, J., GLICK, S. M., YALOW, R. S. and BERSON, S. A. *Diabetes,* 1964, *13*:355–361.
67. RUSSELL, J. A. *Physiol. Rev.,* 1938, *18*:1–27.
68. RUSSELL, J. A. *Fed. Proc.,* 1955, *14*:696–705.
69. RUSSELL, J. A. *Amer. J. clin. Nutr.,* 1957, *5*:404–416.
70. SALTER, J. M. and BEST, C. H. *Brit. med. J.,* 1953, (*2*): 353–356; *Canad. J. Biochem. Physiol.,* 1957, *35*:913–922.
71. SAYERS, M. A., SAYERS, G. and WOODBURY, L. A. *Endocrinology,* 1948, *42*:379–393.
72. SCHARRER, E. and SCHARRER, B. *Recent Progr. Hormone Res.,* 1954, *10*:183–239.
73. SCOW, R. O. *Endocrinology,* 1952, *51*:42–51.
74. SHEEHAN, H. L. and SUMMERS, V. K. *Quart. J. Med.,* 1949, N.S. *18*:319–378.
75. SIMPSON, M. E., ASLING, C. W. and EVANS, H. M. *Yale J. Biol. Med.,* 1950, *23*:1–27.
76. SMITH, P. E. *Amer. J. Anat.,* 1930, *45*:205–273.
77. SMITH, R. W., GAEBLER, O. H. and LONG, C. N. H., eds. *The hypophyseal growth hormone, nature and actions,* New York, Blakiston Division, McGraw-Hill Book Co., 1955.
78. STRAUSS, M. C. *Body water in man,* Boston, Little, Brown and Co., 1957.
79. VAN DYKE, H. B. *Physiology and pharmacology of the pituitary body.* Chicago, University of Chicago Press, 1936, vol. 1; 1939, vol. 2.
80. VAN DYKE, H. B., ADAMSONS, R., JR. and ENGEL, S. L. *Recent Progr. Hormone Res.,* 1955, *11*:1–42.
81. VAN DYKE, H. B., CHOW, B. F., GREEP, R. O. and ROTHEN, A. *J. Pharmacol.,* 1942, *74*:190–209.
82. VERNEY, E. B. *Proc. roy. Soc.,* 1947, *B135*:25–106.
83. WAGNER, E. M. and SCOW, R. O. *Endocrinology,* 1958, *61*: 419–425.
84. WHITE, J. E. and ENGEL, F. L. *J. Clin. Invest.,* 1958, *37*: 1556–1563.
85. WILGRAM, G. F., CAMPBELL, J., LEWIS, L. and PATTERSON, J. *Diabetes,* 1959, *8*:205–210.
86. WILHELMI, A. E., FISHMAN, J. B. and RUSSELL, J. A. *J. biol. Chem.,* 1948, *176*:735–745.
87. WISLOCKI, G. B. *Anat. Rec.,* 1937, *69*:361–387.
88. YOUNG, F. G. *Biochem. J.,* 1938, *32*:513–523.
89. YOUNG, F. G. *Biochem. J.,* 1945, *39*:515–536.

CHAPTER 58

Pancreas

By CHARLES J. GOODNER and JANE A. RUSSELL

OF all the hormones, insulin, from the pancreas, has been the most extensively studied, both experimentally and clinically. Its exact role in intermediate metabolism is, however, still incompletely known. That the pancreas had other than digestive functions was first indicated by von Mering and Minkowski in 1889, when they discovered that pancreatectomy in the dog was followed by the excretion of sugar in the urine and other metabolic abnormalities resembling those seen in the clinical state, diabetes mellitus. The latter disease—a rather common disorder in man—is characterized in its most severe form by polyuria, glycosuria, ketonuria, marked wasting of the body and early death in a comatose state. Minkowski further showed that ligation of the pancreatic duct alone did not induce diabetes. This fact, together with the later observation that the onset of diabetes in depancreatized animals could be delayed by subcutaneous grafts of pancreatic tissue, first suggested that the pancreas had an internal as well as an external secretion.

The presence in the pancreas of small islets or nests of cells which differed histologically from the acinar tissue had been noted by Langerhans in 1869. These islets were shown not to be connected to the duct system into which the external secretion of the pancreas flows. When it was found that the islets of Langerhans remained normal in appearance after ligation of the pancreatic ducts, whereas the acinar tissue became atrophic, it was considered that the islets must be the source of the internal secretion, and the still hypothetical hormone was given the name insulin.

The pancreatic islets, although small, are numerous; their total volume amounts to approximately 1 to 3 per cent of that of the whole pancreas. The islets are composed of at least two kinds of cells which differ in the staining properties of their granules. One type, the larger but less numerous, are called α cells; the other type, the β cells, are now considered to be the ones which secrete insulin. This was suggested by observations made after subtotal pancreatectomy, when degenerative changes in the remaining β cells and diabetes mellitus were seen to develop coincidentally. This view has been amply confirmed by the development of diabetes following the selective destruction of the β cells by alloxan and by anterior pituitary extracts (Chap. 57). More recent studies with the isolated islet cell organ of the teleosts have directly demonstrated insulin production by this tissue.[22]

Electron microscopic studies during stimulation of insulin secretion by glucose have provided a picture of the secretory process in the β cell.[30] The distinctive β cell granules, which on light microscopy stain purple with aldehyde fuchsin, appear as small electron dense granules with the electron microscope. During insulin secretion these granules move to the cell membrane and disappear into the intercellular spaces. After a few hours granules reform along the endoplasmic reticulum. The β cell granules have been isolated for study by differential centrifugation and have been found to contain aggregates of insulin. Its presence in the β cell has also been confirmed through specific staining reactions with fluorescein-labeled antibodies to insulin.[31]

INSULIN

Following the indication of the existence of an internal secretion of the pancreas, many attempts were made in the early years of this century to prepare from pancreatic tissue a substance which could be used to treat diabetic patients. All such efforts were unsuccessful, the products being either inactive or toxic, until the work of Banting and Best in 1921.[5] Believing the presence of pancreatic digestive enzymes in the extracts to be the cause of their inactivation, these workers extracted the pancreatic tissue of dogs after atrophy of the acinar tissue had been induced by preliminary duct ligation. The extracts so made were found to lower the blood sugar and to prolong the lives of diabetic dogs. Later, Collip, working with Banting and Best, prepared active extracts from cattle pancreas and developed the method by which insulin is now prepared on a large scale for clinical use.

Chemistry. The hormone is a protein and has been obtained in highly purified forms, both as crystals containing small amounts of zinc and in the amorphous state. The order of arrangement of all the amino acids in the insulin molecule was determined by Sanger in 1955, thus making insulin the first protein to have its constitution so established.[53] The smallest active unit consists of two peptide chains, one (A) of 21 amino acids and the other (B) of 30 amino acids joined by two disulfide bridges of cystine. The form for human insulin may be sketched as follows:

Insulins from a variety of mammalian species have identical structures except for differing amino acids in positions 8, 9 and 10 within the secondary disulfide ring in the A chain and in the C-terminal amino acid (position 30) of the B chain. The hormone is inactivated when the disulfide bridges are broken.

Katsoyannis[25] achieved the remarkable feat of synthesizing the A and B chains of insulin, starting from simple amino acids. Using the method of Dixson and Wardlaw, he recombined the artificial A and B chains and recovered biologically active insulin. These studies confirmed the structure of insulin proposed by Sanger and provided the techniques necessary for definitive studies of structural functional relationships in the insulin molecule.

Metabolism. Intravenously injected crystalline insulin promptly lowers the blood sugar but the effect dissipates within one or two hours. Studies with I^{131}-labeled insulin have established that the insulin molecule is rapidly removed from the circulation.[64] The half-time for disappearance of plasma insulin is less than 30 minutes in man. Mirsky[44] has characterized an enzyme system, termed insulinase, which is present in liver, kidney and muscle and is capable of rapidly destroying insulin. Similar activity has been identified in other tissues.[17] Tomizawa[59] purified the enzyme from liver and showed that it cleaves the two insulin chains by transferring hydrogen from reduced glutathione to the disulfide bridges. After reductive cleavage the peptide chains undergo further proteolysis to amino acids. In the intact animal, insulin is secreted into the portal circulation and traverses the liver before entering the general circulation. Studies with labeled insulin[45] and endogenously secreted insulin indicate that about 50 per cent of the newly secreted insulin is trapped and degraded by the liver during a single passage. Certain physiologic states affect its rate of degradation. In pregnancy the rate is accelerated and the placenta actively traps and degrades insulin.[19] In rats treated with thyrox-

```
        |―――――――――――――――――――|
Gly―――――CyS―CyS―Thr Ser Ileu―CyS―――――CyS―Asp (NH2)      (A)
 1       6    7|   (8,  9,  10)   11        20|  21
              |                               |
Phe――――――――CyS――――――――――――――――――――――CyS―――――――Thr          (B)
 1            7                              19      (30)
```

ine or epinephrine insulin degradation is accelerated. Attempts to demonstrate any abnormality of insulin destruction in human diabetes have been unsuccessful to date.[44]

Because of insulin's short duration of action various modified insulin preparations have been developed to slow absorption for better clinical effectiveness. These modifications include formation of relatively insoluble complexes of insulin with protamine or globin (large basic proteins) and preparation of buffered large zinc crystal aggregates of insulin in the lente series of insulins. With such modified insulins many diabetic patients may be treated adequately by means of a single daily injection.

Assay of Insulin.   Since the discovery of insulin, the assay of insulin in pancreatic tissue or extracts has been based on its ability to lower the blood glucose either in diabetic or, more often, in normal animals. By comparison of the hypoglycemic activity of the unknown extract with that of a standard insulin preparation in a sufficient number of animals, the assay can be made quite precise, but it is not sufficiently sensitive to detect insulin in body fluids. More recently, attempts have been made to assay insulin in blood plasma by means of its effects on glucose uptake or glycogen synthesis in rat diaphragms *in vitro*.[20, 49, 61] These techniques permit detection of insulin in plasma but lack precision. In 1958 the rat epididymal fat pad was employed for insulin assay by Martin and Renold.[41] This tissue proved to be extremely sensitive to insulin, and insulin-like activity in plasma was easily measured. The apparent concentration of insulin in plasma with the fat pad assay is several times higher than that determined with the diaphragm techniques[61] or the immunoassay method. Yalow and Berson,[70] making use of the antigenic properties of insulin, developed a radioimmunoassay for insulin. This technique (now expanded to assays of growth hormone, glucagon, parathormone, thyrotropin and other peptide hormones) is based upon the competitive binding of labeled and unlabeled insulin by a specific antibody to insulin. Immunoassay techniques are very sensitive and reproducible. As illustrated in Figure 1, both the fasting level and the rise in plasma insulin after glucose loading are easily measured. The finding that insulin levels become supranormal in humans with "adult" type of diabetes after glucose loading (also shown in Fig. 1) has prompted a resurgence of interest in the role of contrainsulin factors in the pathogenesis of human diabetes.

Experimental Diabetes.   Several methods have been developed for producing diabetes experimentally. Early studies of experimentally produced diabetes were done on pancreatectomized dogs. Subsequent observations on other species have shown considerable variation in the expression of insulin deficiency after pancreatectomy. Studies of pancreatic diabetes are always complicated by the simultaneous loss of exocrine pancreatic function.

Diabetes may also be produced by the drug alloxan.[37] This agent exerts selective destructive action upon the β cells of the islets of Langerhans. After the administration of a single dose of alloxan (about 50 mg. per kg. intravenously) pathologic changes are seen in the β cells within a few minutes, and after several days these cells may have disappeared completely. The degree of damage produced by a given dose of alloxan varies considerably but the diabetes is generally incomplete unless repeated doses are administered or partial pancreatectomy is performed as well. In alloxan diabetes the acinar portion of the pancreas is not damaged and therefore exocrine function of the pancreas is preserved.

A third form of experimental diabetes can be induced by infusion of insulin antiserum.[69] Insulin antibodies produced in one species, when infused into a second species, induce an acute but reversible diabetic state (Fig. 2). The thiazide drugs, particularly diazoxide, produce reversible diabetes in animals or man. The mechanism of this effect is not presently established. In addition, certain rodents (the Chinese hamster[42] and the Egyptian sand rat[46]) exhibit spontaneous diabetes and are being used as models for investigation of genetically determined diabetes.

The classic studies of Houssay demonstrated that an intact endocrine system is necessary for full expression of the diabetic state after pancreatectomy. Removing the pituitary gland from pancreatectomized animals resulted in a marked amelioration of the diabetic state. These studies led to the concept that normal metabolic regulation results from a balance between insulin action and various other endocrine principles opposing insulin effects. These studies plus clinical observations of the appearance of secondary diabetes in acromegaly, Cushing's syndrome (adrenal hyperfunction),

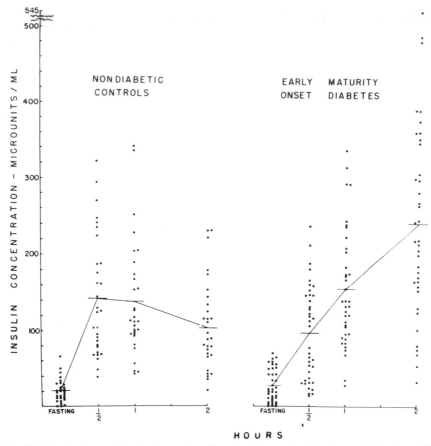

Fig. 1.   Fasting levels and rise in plasma insulin after glucose loading in nondiabetic and diabetic subjects. Note supranormal insulin level in adult type diabetes.

thyrotoxicosis and pheochromocytoma (excessive catecholamine production) led to the experimental induction of diabetes with hormones. Prolonged treatment with ACTH, glucocorticoids,[38] glucagon[54] and growth hormone[14] have all produced forms of experimental diabetes (see Chap. 57 for discussion of metahypophyseal diabetes).

Effects of Insulin Deficiency.   The derangements of metabolism which occur in the absence of insulin in otherwise intact animals are evidenced in the following ways:

Hyperglycemia.   An abnormally high blood sugar level is typical of insulin deficiency. Under normal circumstances the blood sugar is maintained within a narrow concentration range. In diabetes this normal regulation is disturbed. In mild diabetes, upon glucose loading, the blood sugar rises to higher than normal levels and returns slowly to the normal fasting range. In states of more pronounced insulin deficiency the normal fasting blood sugar concentration is not achieved between meals or

during an overnight fast. In severe diabetes the blood sugar remains at high levels continuously.

In the normal animal two simultaneous events serve to reduce the blood glucose to normal after glucose ingestion. First, as the blood sugar rises the liver stops releasing glucose (its normal metabolic function in fasting) and instead begins to take up glucose.[58a] This shift in hepatic glucose metabolism takes place when the blood sugar is between 100 and 150 mg. per 100 ml. Secondly, the rate of utilization of blood glucose by the peripheral tissues is greatly accelerated under the influence of insulin. In diabetes both of these regulatory functions fail. The liver continues to produce glucose from amino acids and glycerol (gluconeogenesis) in spite of the presence of hyperglycemia, and the rate of utilization of glucose by the peripheral tissues remains low. Studies of gluconeogenesis in experimental diabetes have demonstrated large increases in the formation of glucose from labeled precursors both *in vitro* and *in vivo*.[62a]

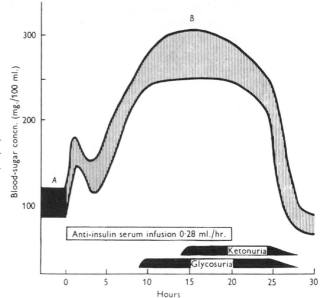

Fig. 2. Hyperglycemia, glycosuria, and ketonuria produced a few hours after initiation of intravenous infusion of anti-insulin serum into rats. (From Armin *et al., J. Physiol.,* 1960, *153:*146.)

The activities of key enzymes in the pathway of gluconeogenesis have been found elevated in livers from diabetic rats.[4] Studies in human diabetic subjects with labeled precursors also demonstrate increased gluconeogenesis in the presence of hyperglycemia.[12a] Studies of net glucose output in diabetic animals and man have consistently demonstrated the failure of hepatic glucose production to decrease in the presence of an elevated blood sugar level. Thus hyperglycemia in diabetes is the result of markedly reduced peripheral utilization of glucose and the continued production of glucose by the liver despite the presence of hyperglycemia.

TABLE 1. *Excretion of Glucose, Nitrogen and Minerals in Diabetes Mellitus**

	URINE VOL. (ml.)	GLUCOSE (gm.)	KETONES (gm.)	NITROGEN (TOTAL) (gm.)	MINERALS Na (mEq.)	K (mEq.)	Cl (mEq.)
Case *1*							
Controlled with insulin (12 days)	1209	0	0.1	11.8	89	58	83
Without insulin (severe acidosis) (4 days)	2621	150	17.7	18.7	174	152	131
Recovery with insulin (5 days)	1020	0	0.3	11.4	66	8	89
Case *2*							
Controlled with insulin (16 days)	1536	0	0.0	14.4	85	67	88
Without insulin (little acidosis) (11 days)	2004	125	0.5	18.3	121	81	108
Recovery with insulin (4 days)	1010	0	0.2	13.5	35	46	32

* Average daily urinary excretion rates in two patients in successive periods with and without insulin. Constant amounts of food and water were given daily during the entire period of study: Case 1—125 grams carbohydrate, 140 grams fat, 75 grams protein; Case 2—165 grams carbohydrate, 155 grams fat, 87 grams protein.

(From Atchley *et al., J. clin. Invest.,* 1933, *12:*297.)

Diuresis. When the blood sugar rises above 150 to 200 mg. per 100 ml. the filtered load of glucose exceeds the reabsorptive capacity of the renal tubules and glycosuria results (see Chap. 44). Glucose, as an osmotically active molecule in the urine, obligates the excretion of water. As hyperglycemia progresses in diabetes, polyuria ensues. During this osmotic diuresis, large amounts of salts are also excreted. The loss of water provokes thirst and polydipsia. The data in Table 1, reported by Atchley *et al.,*[3] indicate how much glucose, water and salt are lost in diabetic humans given constant amounts of fluid and food. Even when no acidosis was present (Case No. 2), sodium and chloride were lost in amounts equivalent to 200 to 300 ml. of extracellular fluid per day. Continued salt and water losses of this magnitude must eventually deplete the extracellular fluid volume to a critical degree. In human diabetes water loss occasionally becomes so pronounced that profound hyperosmolality alone leads to coma.[50]

Polyphagia. In spite of the hyperglycemia, the combination of the large losses of glucose in the urine and the inadequate utilization of glucose by tissues in the absence of insulin is perceived by the organism as starvation. Hunger is induced, giving rise to a pathologic increase in food consumption termed polyphagia, the third cardinal manifestation of diabetes (polydipsia, polyuria, polyphagia).

Ketosis. Because of the lack of insulin effect on adipose tissue, the lipolysis and fatty acid liberation characteristic of starvation proceed unchecked (see Chap. 55). This uncontrolled catabolic state leads to excessive ketone production in the liver, elevation of plasma ketones, overloading of the organism's buffering capacity and subsequent metabolic acidosis. With the onset of systemic acidosis, additional sodium and potassium are lost in the urine in association with the ketone bodies. In Table 1, comparing the data obtained in two diabetic patients indicates the great additional loss of base which occurred when the ketosis was severe (Case No. 1). The acidosis, together with the depletion of salts and water resulting from diuresis, may cause a shocklike state, coma and death. For the maintenance of life in the diabetic animal, the degree of ketosis induced is the most critical factor.

Nitrogen loss. In addition to changes in carbohydrate and lipid metabolism in diabetes, protein metabolism is disordered in the absence of insulin. Negative nitrogen balance occurs as diabetes progresses and leads to depletion of tissue protein,[11] weight loss and death, even if acidosis is avoided. The large nitrogen losses associated with diabetes are also illustrated by the data in Table 1. Thus, it can be seen that the effects of insulin deficiency are manifested in all three areas of metabolism involving carbohydrates, lipids and protein.

Effects of Insulin. Giving insulin to the diabetic animal reverses all of the metabolic alterations observed. The precise site or sites at which insulin acts have not been fully identified. Its general functions in metabolic regulation can best be summarized by separately considering its role in the fed and fasted states.

During ingestion of food in animals, insulin plays a key role in promoting the entry of small molecules into the cells (glucose, amino acids, potassium) and their subsequent synthesis into larger molecules either as storage forms for subsequent recall (glycogen and triglycerides) or as cytostructural tissue components (proteins, nucleic acids). In this regard then, insulin is the major hormone promoting the storage of fuels and is also important for tissue renewal. Insulin may be regarded as a growth hormone since both insulin and pituitary growth hormone are required for normal growth.

In the fasting state insulin plays an equally important role. By virtue of insulin's ability to regulate the rate of lipolysis in adipose tissue, free fatty acids can become the major cellular fuel, without the risk of ketoacidosis. At the same time insulin regulates hepatic and peripheral glucose metabolism in fasting to allow the establishment of a stable blood glucose concentration just sufficient for meeting the needs of the central nervous system without excessive gluconeogenesis.

Glucose metabolism. In the absence of insulin, glucose utilization by the whole animal is markedly slowed as shown by the delayed removal of administered glucose from the blood and the excretion of much of a glucose load in the urine. Giving insulin after glucose loading corrects this defect and is followed by a prompt and rapid decline in the blood glucose concentration.

Stimulation of glucose uptake by insulin is also demonstrable in eviscerated animals,[66] in isolated perfused extremities, during transit of blood through the forearm (after local infusion of insulin into the brachial artery)[2] and upon incubation of various tissues *in vitro*. Stemming from the observations of Levine *et al.* that injection of insulin increases abruptly the volume in which galactose* is distributed in eviscerated dogs, considerable evidence supports the view that one major action of insulin is to facilitate transport of glucose and related molecules into the cell.[33] Under the influence of insulin, glucose metabolism via all pathways is accelerated. The products produced in various tissues reflect the predominant pathways of the particular tissue. Thus glycogen, lactic acid and CO_2 constitute the major products of glucose metabolism in muscle, and fatty acids, glyceride, glycerol and triglyceride, as well as CO_2 are formed in adipose tissue. Whether insulin alters the intracellular disposition of glucose in addition to facilitating its inital transport into the cell or whether all of the effects of insulin upon glucose metabolism can be ascribed to the transport effect alone has been extensively debated but remains unresolved. Abnormalities in the enzymatic steps within the diabetic cell have been demonstrated. In glucose metabolism, the initial step beyond transport—phosphorylation of glucose by glucokinase—has been found depressed in tissues from diabetic animals. However, correction of this activity after insulin injection requires several hours and therefore may not be due directly to insulin. Synthesis of glycogen from glucose is also depressed in diabetic liver, muscle and adipose tissue. Insulin has been shown to activate the enzyme UDP-glucose-alpha-glucan transglucosylase (glycogen synthetase) *in vitro* in muscle preparations,[62] and this finding constitutes the most direct evidence for intracellular activities of insulin upon glucose metabolism beyond the transport step. In certain tissues glycogen accumulates in the absence of insulin. The glycogen of heart muscle, the β cell itself, kidney and skin is increased in severely diabetic animals, while the glycogen content of skeletal muscle and adipose tissue is subnormal in total insulin deficiency.

Insulin increases glucose metabolism in a variety of other tissues besides muscle and adipose tissue, including mammary gland,[16] anterior pituitary,[18] peripheral nerve,[15] spinal cord,[47] white blood cells,[28] the lens of the eye,[28] and the aorta.[65]

*Galactose was selected for this experiment because it was not appreciably metabolized and therefore an increase in distribution volume primarily reflected translocation.

The role of insulin in regulating hepatic metabolism has been the subject of much debate.[35] In isolated liver slices, insulin does not consistently increase glucose uptake, lipogenesis or synthesis of glycogen, nor can any effect of insulin on the distribution of nonmetabolizable sugars be demonstrated in this organ. Studies of glucose distribution space in liver slices have shown that, unlike muscle and other insulin-sensitive tissues, the liver cell is freely permeable to glucose in the absence of insulin.[9] However, the marked changes in metabolism in liver slices from diabetic animals—i.e., increased gluconeogenesis, virtual absence of lipogenesis, reduced glycogenesis and increased ketone production—suggest an important role for insulin in hepatic metabolism.[12] However, reversal of these changes in animals treated with insulin requires 4 to 24 hours of pretreatment with the hormone. Such delayed response and the lack of consistent *in vitro* effects suggest that insulin's action on liver metabolism might be mainly secondary to its action elsewhere in the animal body.

On the other hand, recent lines of evidence indicate a more direct role of insulin in hepatic metabolism. Older studies on diabetic men had shown that insulin would reduce the output of glucose from the splanchnic area,[8] but these observations were not critical because the apparent reduction in glucose output by the liver could have been due to increased uptake of glucose by the intestines and other nonhepatic tissue in the area drained by the portal vein. Three different techniques have now been used to study the action of insulin on the liver alone: direct observation of hepatic glucose output *in vivo*, observations on the rate of dilution of injected or infused isotopic glucose by nonisotopic glucose coming from the liver, also *in vivo*, and measurement of glucose and other metabolites in the medium perfusing the isolated surviving liver. In dogs studied *in vivo* by either of the first two procedures, insulin given alone usually either has not changed hepatic glucose output or has produced only a transient decrease, soon superseded by an enhanced glucose output in response to the hypoglycemia induced by insulin acting elsewhere in the body.[63] However, when marked hypoglycemia has been avoided by slow infusion of small amounts of insulin, inhibition of glucose output by the liver now has been demonstrated clearly Madison *et al.*,[39] using dogs with portocaval anastomosis to separate hepatic from splanchnic metabolism and measuring glucose concentrations in arterial and hepatic venous blood, were the first to show such an effect (Fig. 3). Since the livers of such animals are abnormal in many ways, it was not clear that the results would apply to normal subjects. However, other studies have provided support for these

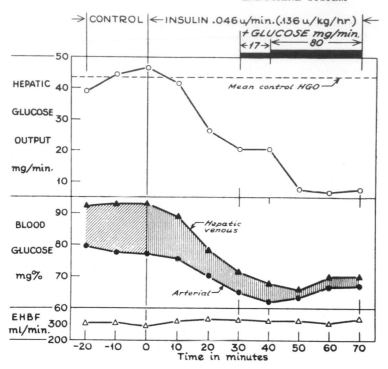

Fig. 3. Mean changes in hepatic venous and arterial glucose concentrations, hepatic blood flow, and the hepatic glucose output during the slow infusion of glucagon-free insulin plus glucose. (From: Madison *et al., J. clin. Invest.,* 1960, *39*:507–522.)

observations. Recently, Steele *et al.,*[58b] infusing modest amounts of insulin together with C^{14}-glucose in amounts to prevent hypoglycemia, observed marked reductions in hepatic glucose output in normal intact dogs.

Haft and Miller[21] reported some time ago that net glucose uptake was increased when insulin was added to the medium perfusing isolated livers from diabetic rats. Using an improved perfusion system to minimize damage to the liver, Mortimer[44] has further demonstrated that insulin decreases glucose output by the normal rat liver. Both in the latter experiments and in those of Steele *et al.* referred to above, the reduction in hepatic glucose output was paralleled by a reduction in net glycogen loss from the livers. Taken together, these observations indicate that insulin can diminish the release of glucose from the liver. The precise site of action of insulin in controlling the release of glucose from the liver remains to be established.

Because insulin is secreted into the portal circulation, much of the hormone reaches the liver before becoming available for peripheral tissues. This anatomic relation lends credence to a special role of insulin in hepatic metabolism. Indeed, when insulin has been perfused into the portal circulation in small amounts, its effects are qualitatively different than when it is infused intravenously.[40a]

Lipid metabolism. Insulin plays an important role in lipid metabolism[23, 67] (Chap. 55). In addition to its major effect of stimulating for-

mation of lipids from glucose in adipose tissue, insulin may also affect lipolysis directly. Jungas and Ball[24] have observed that in a glucose-free medium insulin decreases the rate of glycerol and fatty acid release by epinephrine-stimulated adipose tissue. When insulin is given to fasting or diabetic animals, one of its earliest effects is a precipitous fall in the plasma level of free fatty acids[7] (Fig. 4). This effect of insulin probably represents the sum of several activities. First, by increasing the glucose metabolism of adipose tissue, esterification of fatty acids with alpha-glycerophosphate is accelerated. Second, at the same time, insulin probably directly inhibits hydrolysis of triglycerides and release of free fatty acids and, with step one, shifts the net metabolism of the adipose tissue from release of fatty acids to their storage as triglyceride. Third, the uptake of fatty acids by the liver in diabetic animals may be enhanced after injection of insulin.[56] These effects of insulin in regulating the flux of free fatty acids from adipose tissue lead directly to a consideration of insulin's role in preventing ketosis.

The liver is the major source of the blood ketone bodies (acetoacetic acid, betahydroxybutyric acid and acetone). These substances are synthesized from the condensation of two molecules of acetyl CoA. As the amount of free fatty acids reaching the liver increases during lipolysis, whether in fasting or in diabetes, the liver is unable to dispose of the increased acetyl CoA produced by oxidation of fatty acids and, when fatty acid liberation from adipose tissue reaches high levels, ketonemia ensues. Ketone bodies are not abnormal substances; they are present in the blood and urine of healthy individuals in the fasted state. The ketone bodies serve as fuel for most peripheral tissues.

In diabetes, however, the production of ketones exceeds the capacity of the peripheral tissues to oxidize them to CO_2 and H_2O, leading to their accumulation in the plasma. In addition, Beatty *et al.*[6] have reported that muscle fibers from diabetic rats utilize ketones poorly *in vitro* and that this defect is corrected upon addition of insulin. Intact diabetic animals display reduced peripheral utilization of infused ketones as well, which is also corrected by insulin.[55] Thus, ketosis in diabetic animals results from increased production of ketones secondary to increased fat mobilization and perhaps from diminished peripheral utilization secondary to lack of insulin at the peripheral tissues.

Protein metabolism. Insulin has a fundamental effect upon protein metabolism.[36] Administered to diabetic animals, insulin reverses the negative nitrogen balance characteristic of uncontrolled diabetes; at the same time the plasma concentration of free amino acids diminishes during insulin administration.[52] Sinex *et al.*[57] and Krahl[27] demonstrated that insulin enhanced incorporation of C_{14}-labeled amino acids into muscle protein in vitro. Demonstration of this over-all stimulation of protein synthesis by insulin has prompted extensive investigation, attempting to define the specific steps affected by insulin. Transport of amino acids from the exterior to the interior of the cell has been examined by using the nonutilized amino acid, alpha-aminoisobutyric acid (AIB). Insulin enhances accumulation of this model amino acid into rat diaphragm even without glucose in the medium.[26] Thus, insulin seems to enhance the first step necessary for protein synthesis—the transport of amino acids into the cell.

Within the interior of the cell insulin also stimulates specific steps in protein synthesis. Insulin appears to enhance protein synthesis in isolated subcellular fractions (mitochondria), in peptide bonding by microsomes *in vitro* and in synthesis of RNA in the intact cell.[36, 68] That insulin acts independently upon protein synthesis and upon membrane transport has been reinforced by experimentation with specific blocking agents. Eboué-Bonis *et al.*[13] studied insulin effect upon the synthesis of RNA from labeled adenine and the simultaneous transport of glucose into rat diaphragm in the presence of inhibitors of protein synthesis. The transport of glucose into diaphragm was not inhibited by these blocking agents, but the effect of insulin upon protein synthesis was completely abolished. These data clearly demonstrate that the effects of insulin upon glucose transport do not depend upon stimulation of protein or RNA synthesis.

In summary, insulin acts on several metabolic steps with the result that the use and storage of carbohydrates, lipids and amino acids are facilitated. Glucose utilization is promoted by increased transport of glucose across cell walls, particularly in muscle and adipose tissue, with subsequent storage of the transported glucose as glycogen in muscle and as triglyceride in adipose tissue. Insulin may specifically stimulate glycogen synthesis in muscle and liver and specifically inhibit lipolysis of triglyceride in adipose tissue. Insulin probably acts directly on the liver to reduce glucose output, perhaps by accelerating glyco-

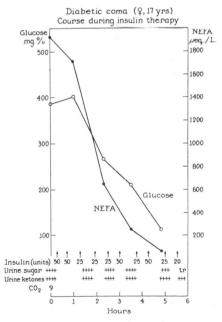

Fig. 4. Prompt reduction in nonesterified fatty acids (free fatty acids) caused by injection of insulin into patients with ketosis. (From Bierman *et al., Diabetes,* 1957, 6:475–479.)

gen synthesis. Amino acid transport into the tissues is stimulated by insulin, and subsequent synthesis of amino acids into proteins is enhanced by stimulation of steps in the metabolism of RNA. Since insulin seems to act at cell membrane as well as intracellular sites, a unified concept of insulin action is difficult to formulate. One possibility is that the intracellular actions of insulin are mediated through translocations at the membranes of the intracellular organelles.

Control of Insulin Secretion. Before assay of plasma insulin was possible, insulin secretion could be studied only by such relatively insensitive techniques as following changes in blood glucose concentration, beta cell degranulation and pancreatic insulin content. Early studies suggested that stimulation of the right vagus nerve causes insulin secretion. Later studies—demonstrating that the surgically transplanted (denervated) pancreas still regulated the blood glucose—cast doubt on neurogenic regulation and suggested a humoral mechanism.[1] That this humoral factor controlling the release of insulin was the level of blood glucose was suggested by many observations.[15a] With sensitive assays, it became possible to demonstrate the development of release of insulin directly from the pancreas after infusion of glucose into the pancreatic artery. When glucose is administered to normal humans, plasma insulin rises promptly and in parallel with the plasma glucose concentration (Fig. 1). Metz[43] studied the relationship between insulin secretion and plasma glucose concentration in phloridzinized dogs and found that the insulin concentration correlated directly with arterial glucose over a wide range from 40 to 600 mg. per 100 ml. In the isolated perfused pancreas, insulin release is directly related to changes in the glucose concentration of the perfusing medium. Studies to define the biochemical pathways within the beta cell are being done with histochemical techniques and on microdissected beta cells.[32]

The secretion of insulin is reflected histologically by degranulation of the beta cell. When insulin secretion is stimulated chronically by prolonged glucose infusion or by sulfonylurea drugs, the secretory granules become depleted yet insulin production continues. Studies of isolated secretory granules suggest that they represent a relatively insoluble, storage form of insulin. It is probable that the granules provide insulin for immediate release after meals but

are not a necessary precursor of plasma insulin under circumstances requiring prolonged secretion of the hormone.

In addition to the islets being directly stimulated by glucose, insulin secretion increases after infusion of other substances. The sulfonylurea drugs used in therapy of diabetes directly stimulate insulin release. The amino acid leucine causes insulin release spontaneously in some children with hypoglycemic attacks, in patients with islet cell tumors and in normal humans after sulfonylurea priming. The role of the vagus is being re-examined with newer assay techniques; these studies indicate that the vagus may function in regulating blood glucose under certain physiologic conditions. Central nervous system control over pancreatic function is suggested by the carotid perfusion studies of Sakata et al.[53a] In these studies, raising the carotid arterial glucose concentration in the head of a rabbit caused a fall in the glucose concentration in the rest of the body. Kuzuya[29] has demonstrated secretion of insulin into pancreatic venous blood in dogs after vagal stimulation.

The problem of how insulin secretion is regulated in fasting—a circumstance in which sustained minimal insulin secretion is necessary to prevent excessive ketosis—led Madison et al.[40] to examine the effect of ketones themselves upon insulin secretion. Infusing ketones into the pancreatic artery caused release of insulin, thereby suggesting that there is a potential self-regulating cycle for adjustment to fasting.

Hypoglycemia. Just as raising plasma glucose above the fasting level stimulates insulin secretion to restore the previous balance, so lowering it calls forth regulatory factors to raise glucose back to normal. Cannon first demonstrated the role of the sympathetic nervous system in elevating blood glucose during emotional stress. When plasma glucose falls below 50 mg. per 100 ml. (or falls very rapidly even at higher concentrations), centers in the cervical spinal cord[10] and higher (hypothalamus, brain stem, paleocerebellum) respond by stimulating discharge of the sympathetic nervous system, giving rise in part to the characteristic symptoms of hypoglycemia (sweating, tachycardia and pallor). Hypoglycemia also stimulates release of glucagon from the α cells of the pancreas (*vide infra*). Glucagon and epinephrine both activate phosphorylase in the liver, thereby tending to restore the blood glucose through glycogenolysis. A falling blood glucose is also accompanied by a rising plasma growth hormone concentration[51] and, if pronounced, by secretion of adrenocorticotrophin as well. Together these hormonal changes oppose insulin action, mobilize glycogen and, if repeatedly induced, accelerate gluconeogenesis. Somogyi[58] clearly demonstrated these effects by provoking repeated hypoglycemia in normal subjects. Greatly reduced glucose tolerance appeared in healthy subjects after as few as two or three hypoglycemic challenges. In diabetic patients, exacerbation of diabetes with hyperglycemia and ketosis commonly follows a severe insulin hypoglycemic reaction.

Hypoglycemic symptoms are referable primarily to the nervous system; in addition to the sympathetic discharge, dizziness, confusion, incoordination, slurred speech, stupor and finally coma and convulsions appear as hypoglycemia is prolonged. These effects, which reflect the dependence of nervous tissue upon glucose for energy metabolism, are rapidly reversed by administration of glucose. If hypoglycemia remains uncorrected for longer than one or two hours, however, irreversible lesions in the brain may lead to death. Some irreversible damage probably accompanies even brief hypoglycemia and if repeated episodes occur, progressive neurological damage may result.

GLUCAGON

Early insulin preparations often produced immediate elevations of blood glucose before the characteristic hypoglycemic response. The cause of this activity—glucagon or the pancreatic glycogenolytic factor—was subsequently isolated and proved to be a distinct peptide containing 29 amino acids without disulfide rings. Glucagon stimulates glycogenolysis in liver but not in muscle by activating phosphorylase in the same manner as epinephrine (Chap. 59).[48] Repeated injections of glucagon stimulate gluconeogenesis and glycogenolysis, producing sustained but reversible hyperglycemia. Glucagon also stimulates lipolysis in adipose tissue and release of free fatty acids. Glucagon has been identified in the α cell of the islet of Langerhans with immunofluorescent techniques.[5a] The glucagon content of the pancreas is diminished by the α cytotoxic effect

of cobalt chloride. Unger *et al.*[60] have successfully adapted the immunoassay technique to assay of plasma glucagon. With this technique the suspected hormonal function of glucagon in regulating blood glucose has been amply documented. Glucagon was found to rise in plasma during fasting as the blood glucose fell. If hypoglycemia was induced with phloridzin or insulin, glucagon appeared promptly in pancreatic vein blood and if the hypoglycemia was terminated by glucose infusion, glucagon secretion ceased as plasma glucose and insulin rose. Thus glucagon and insulin appear to constitute a reciprocal system of hormones for blood glucose regulation by the islets of Langerhans.

REFERENCES

1. ANDERSON, E. and LONG, J. A. *Endocrinology*, 1947, *40:* 92–97.
2. ANDRES, R. and ZIERLER, K. L. *Amer. J. Physiol.*, 1956, *187:*583.
3. ATCHLEY, D. W., LOEB, R. L., RICHARDS, D. W., JR., BENEDICT, E. M. and DRISCOLL, M. E. *J. clin. Invest.*, 1933, *12:*297–326.
4. ASHMORE, J., HASTINGS, A. B., NESBETT, F. B. and RENOLD, A. E. *J. biol. Chem.*, 1956, *218:*77–88.
5. BANTING, F. G. and BEST, C. H. *J. Lab. clin. Med.*, 1922, *7:*251–266; 464–472.
5a. BAUM, J., SIMONS, B. E., UNGER, R. H. and MADISON, L. L. *Diabetes*, 1962, *11:*371–374.
6. BEATTY, C. H., MARCÓ, A., PETERSON, R. D., BOCEK, R. M. and WEST, E. S. *J. biol. Chem.*, 1960, *235:*2774–2777.
7. BIERMAN, E. L., SCHWARTZ, I. L. and DOLE, V. P. *Amer. J. Physiol.*, 1957, *191:*359–362.
8. BONDY, P. K., BLOOM, W. L., WHITNER, V. S. and FARRAR, B. W. *J. clin. Invest.*, 1949, *28:*1126–1133.
9. CAHILL, G. F., JR., ASHMORE, J., RENOLD, A. E. and HASTINGS, A. B. *Amer. J. Med.*, 1959, *26:*264–282.
10. CANTU, R. C., WISE, B. L., GOLDFIEN, A., GULLIXSON, K. S., FISCHER, N. and GANONG, W. F. *Proc. Soc. exp. Biol.* (*N.Y.*), 1963, *114:*10–13.
11. CHAIKOFF, I. L. and FORKER, L. L. *Endocrinology*, 1950, *46:*319–326.
12. CHERNICK, S. S. and CHAIKOFF, I. L. *J. biol. Chem.*, 1951, *188:*389–396.
12a. DeMEUTTER, R. C. and SHREEVE, W. W. *J. clin. Invest.*, 1963, *42:*525–533.
13. EBOUÉ-BONIS, D., CHAMBAUT, A. M., VOLFIN, P. and CLAUSER, H. *Nature*, 1963, *199:*1183–1184.
14. EVANS, H. M., MEYER, K., SIMPSON, M. E. and REICHERT, F. L. *Proc. Soc. exp. Biol.* (*N.Y.*), 1932, *29:*857–858.
15. FIELD, R. A. and ADAMS, L. C. *Medicine*, 1964, *43:*275–279.
15a. FOÁ, P. P., WEINSTEIN, H. R., and SMITH, J. A. *Amer. J. Physiol.*, 1949, *157:*197–204.
16. FOLLEY, S. J. In: *Hormonal factors in carbohydrate metabolism; Ciba Foundation colloquia on endocrinology*, G. E. W. Wolstenholme, ed. Boston, Little, Brown and Co., 1953.

17. FREINKEL, N. and GOODNER, C. J. *J. clin. Invest.,* 1960, *39:*116–131.

18. GOODNER, C. J. and FREINKEL, N. *J. clin. Invest.,* 1961, *40:*261–272.

19. GOODNER, C. J. and FREINKEL, N. *Endocrinology,* 1960, *67:*862–872.

20. GROEN, J., KAMMINGA, C. E., WILLEBRANDS, A. F. and BLICKMAN, J. R. *J. clin. Invest.,* 1952, *31:*97–106.

21. HAFT, D. E. and MILLER, L. L. *Amer. J. Physiol.,* 1958, *192:*33–42, *193:*469–475.

22. HUMBEL, R. E. *Biochim. biophys. Acta (Amst.),* 1963, *74:* 96–104.

23. JEANRENAUD, B. *Metabolism,* 1961, *10:*535–581.

24. JUNGAS, R. L. and BALL, E. G. *Biochemistry,* 1963, *2:*383–388.

25. KATSOYANNIS, P. G. *Diabetes,* 1964, *13:*339–348.

26. KIPNIS, D. M. and NOALL, M. W. *Biochim. biophys. Acta. (Amst.),* 1958, *28:*226–227.

27. KRAHL, M. E. *Science,* 1952, *116:*524.

28. KRAHL, M. E. *The action of insulin on cells.* New York, Academic Press, 1961.

29. KUZUYA, N. *Diabetes mellitus.* Third International Congress of Diabetes Federation, Dusseldorf, July 1958, pp. 759–761.

30. LACY, P. E. *Diabetes,* 1962, *11:*509–513.

31. LACY, P. E. and DAVIES, J. *Diabetes,* 1957, *6:*354–357.

32. LACY, P. E. and WILLIAMSON, J. R. *Diabetes,* 1962, *11:* 101–104.

33. LEVINE, R. *Diabetes,* 1961, *10:*421–431.

34. LEVINE, R., GOLDSTEIN, M., HUDDLESTUN, B. and KLEIN, S. A. *Amer. J. Physiol.,* 1950, *163:*70–76.

35. LITWACK, G. and KRITCHEVSKY, D. *Actions of hormones on molecular processes.* New York, John Wiley & Sons, Inc., 1964.

36. LUKENS, F. D. W. *Diabetes,* 1964, *13:*451–461.

37. LUKENS, F. D. W. *Physiol. Rev.,* 1948, *28:*304–330.

38. LUKENS, F. D. W., COHEN, S. N. and GOTO, Y. *Diabetes,* 1961, *10:*182–189.

39. MADISON, L. L., COMBES, B., ADAMS, R. and STRICKLAND, W. *J. clin. Invest.,* 1960, *39:*507–522.

40. MADISON, L. L., MEBANE, D., UNGER, R. H. and LOCHNER, A. *J. clin. Invest.,* 1964, *43:*408–415.

40a. MADISON, L. L. and UNGER, R. H. *J. clin. Invest.,* 1958, *37:*631–639.

41. MARTIN, D. B., RENOLD, A. E. and DAGENAIS, Y. M. *Lancet,* 1958, *2:*76–77.

42. MEIER, H. and YERGANIAN, G. A. *Proc. Soc. exp. Biol. (N.Y.),* 1959, *100:*810–815.

43. METZ, R. *Diabetes,* 1960, *9:*89–93.

44. MIRSKY, I. A. *Diabetes,* 1964, *13:*225–229.

44a. MORTIMER, G. E. *Amer. J. Physiol.,* 1963, *204:*699–704.

45. MORTIMORE, G. E., TIETZE, F. and STETTEN, D. W., JR. *Diabetes,* 1959, *8:*307–314.

46. SCHMIDT-NIELSEN, K., HAINES, H. B. and HACKEL, D. B. *Science,* 1964, *143:*689–690.

47. RAFAELSEN, O. J. *Lancet,* 1958, *2:*941–943.

48. RALL, T. W., SUTHERLAND, E. W. and BERTHET, J. *J. biol. Chem.,* 1957, *224:*463–475.

49. RANDLE, P. J. *Brit. med. J.,* 1954, *1:*1237–1240.

50. ROSSIER, P. H., REUTTER, F. and FRICK, P. *Dtsch. med. Wschr.,* 1961. *86:*2145–2148.

51. ROTH, J., GLICK, S. M., YALOW, R. S. and BERSON, S. A. *Diabetes,* 1964, *13:*355–361.

52. RUSSELL, J. A. and CAPPIELLO, M. *Endocrinology,* 1949, *44:*127–133.

53. RYLE, A. P., SANGER, F., SMITH, L. F. and KITAI, R. *Biochem. J.,* 1955, *60:*541–546.

53a. SAKATA, K., HAYANO, S. and SLOVITER, H. A. *Amer. J. Physiol.,* 1963, *204:*1127–1132.

54. SALTER, J. M., DAVIDSON, I. W. F. and BEST, C. H. *Diabetes,* 1957, *6:*248–252.

55. SCOW, R. O. and CHERNICK, S. S. *Recent progr. Hormone Res.,* 1960, *16:*497–545.

56. SHOEMAKER, W. C., ASHMORE, J., CARRUTHERS, P. J. and SCHULMAN, M. *Proc. Soc. exp. Biol. (N.Y.),* 1960, *103:* 585–588.

57. SINEX, F. M., MACMULLEN, J. and HASTINGS, A. B. *J. biol. Chem.,* 1952, *198:*615–619.

58. SOMOGYI, M. *Amer. J. Med.,* 1959, *26:*169–191.

58a. SOSKIN, S., ESSEX, H. E., HERRICK, J. F. and MANN, F. C. *Amer. J. Physiol.,* 1938, *124:*558–567.

58b. STEELE, R., BISHOP, J. S., DUNN, A., ALTSZULER, N., RATHGEB, I., and DEBODO, R. C. *Amer. J. Physiol.,* 1965, *208:*301–306.

59. TOMIZAWA, H. H. and HALSEY, Y. D. *J. biol. Chem.,* 1959, *234:*307–310.

60. UNGER, R. H. and EISENTRAUT, A. M. *Diabetes,* 1964, *13:*563–568.

61. VALLANCE-OWEN, J. and HURLOCK, B. *Lancet,* 1954, *1:*68–70.

62. VILLAR-PALASI, C. and LARNER, J. *Biochim. biophys. Acta. (Amst.),* 1960, *39:*171–173.

62a. WAGLE, S. R. and ASHMORE, J. *J. biol. Chem.,* 1963, *238:*17–20.

63. WALL, J. S., STEELE, R., DEBODO, R. C. and ALTSZULER, N. *Amer. J. Physiol.,* 1957, *189:*43–50.

64. WELSH, G. W. III, HENLEY, E. D., WILLIAMS, R. H. and COX, R. W. *Amer. J. Med.,* 1956, *21:*324–338.

65. WERTHEIMER, H. E. and BENTOR, V. *Diabetes,* 1962, *11:* 422–425.

66. WICK, A. N., DRURY, D. R., BANCROFT, R. W. and MACKAY, E. M. *J. biol. Chem.,* 1951, *188:*241–249.

67. WINEGRAD, A. I. and RENOLD, A. E. *J. biol. Chem.,* 1958, *233:*267–272.

68. WOOL, I. G. and MUNRO, A. J. *Proc. Nat. Acad. Sci.,* 1963, *50:*918–923.

69. WRIGHT, P. H. *Amer. J. Med.,* 1961, *31:*892–900.

70. YALOW, R. S. and BERSON, S. A. *J. clin. Invest.,* 1960, *39:*1157–1175.

The Adrenals

By JANE A. RUSSELL

THE paired adrenal (or suprarenal) glands, like the hypophysis, are double organs composed of two distinct types of tissue of different origin and function. In mammals and birds the larger, glandular portion, called the cortex, surrounds tissue of neural origin, the medulla. The two portions are quite separate in the elasmobranch fishes, and in other lower forms various transitional stages exist. The adrenal cortex, or corresponding glandular tissue, arises from the mesoderm in the urogenital zone. Small nests of adrenal glandular cells (called accessory cortical tissue, or "cortical rests") may also be found outside the adrenal capsule in the region of the kidneys or gonads. The medullary tissue, on the other hand, develops from the primitive cells of the sympathetic ganglia, originally from the neural crest, and remains intimately connected with the splanchnic sympathetic nerve supply. Tissue similar to that of the adrenal medulla, called chromaffin tissue, is found also in small bodies adjoining the chain of sympathetic ganglia. In some lower vertebrates these bodies alone represent adrenal medullary tissue, the cortical portion being replaced by a single interrenal body. Although it seems unlikely that the close anatomic approximation of the two portions of the adrenal in the higher animals has been purely fortuitous, no physiologic necessity for the relationship is known.

THE ADRENAL CORTEX

Adrenal cortical tissue consists of large granular cells arranged in what appear to be loose cords or nets separated by sinusoids. Recent studies have shown, however, that the rat adrenal cortex is in fact a tunneled continuum, so that the "cords" are more properly considered as cross sections of sheets of cells.[53] Three strata can be distinguished by the structural arrangement of the cells and blood vessels: a thin glomerular layer next to the fibrous capsule, a broad fascicular zone in which the capillaries run radially, and, next to the medulla, the reticular zone in which the blood vessels are dilated and tortuous. The cells are very rich in lipoids, particularly cholesterol and steroids, and also in ascorbic acid. Changes in the amounts of these substances, measured chemically or histologically, afford some measure of the activity of the gland in varying physiologic conditions.

Cortical tissue exhibits remarkable powers of regeneration and hypertrophy: After removal of one gland, the other will enlarge to twice its normal size; after removal of both, cortical rests may enlarge until their volume approaches that of the original glands; or after enucleation (removal of the contents of the capsule, leaving only shreds of the glomeruli attached), the cor-

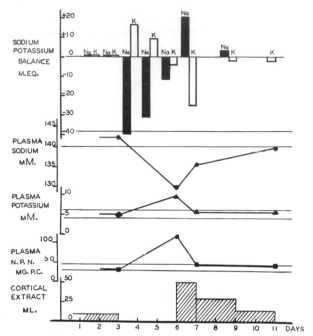

Fig. 1. Effects of withdrawal and replacement of adrenal cortical extract in an adrenalectomized dog. Constant amounts of food and water were given during period of observation. Fine lines indicate approximate range of values seen in normal animals. Note large loss of sodium and retention of potassium on withdrawal of hormone, and reversal of changes on readministration of extract. (After Harrop *et al., J. exp. Med.,* 1936, *64:* 233.)

tical tissue can be completely regenerated. It has been believed that in the adrenal cortex new cells regularly form in the periphery and move gradually toward the reticular zone, but recently this idea has been disputed. Nevertheless, during regeneration glomerular cells give rise to all zones of the cortex.

That the adrenal cortex is an endocrine organ essential for life, or practically so, was demonstrated by several investigators during the years 1920–1930. Earlier disagreement as to its importance was shown to be due on the one hand to the great susceptibility of adrenalectomized animals to shock and sepsis, which were often immediately fatal, and, on the other, to the frequent hypertrophy of cortical rests which would maintain the animal indefinitely once the critical postoperative period was passed. The removal of the adrenal medullae alone was shown not to endanger life.

Adrenocortical Insufficiency. After removal of the adrenal glands, a variety of metabolic defects become evident.[52, 75] At first, if

operative shock has been avoided, the animal appears relatively normal, but later a decline sets in, rather abruptly in some cases, and death occurs in most species within a week or two. The symptoms before death include loss of appetite, vomiting, diarrhea, asthenia, a variable degree of hypoglycemia, hypotension, hemoconcentration, fall in blood pressure and renal failure. In young animals, growth ceases; in older ones, there is usually loss of weight. The adrenalectomized animal is also extremely susceptible to stresses of all types, such as trauma, cold, heat, toxins and infections. The cause of death varies. Vascular collapse, with hemoconcentration and renal failure, is probably the most common cause, but in some species, such as the rat, hypoglycemia may be fatal before the full course of the other defects is run. Death from intercurrent infection or other stress is common in all species.

In man, chronic adrenal insufficiency, known as Addison's disease, has similar consequences. Usually there is gradual development of weakness, digestive disturbances and hypotension, punctuated by more acute crises resembling the terminal stages after adrenalectomy. Eventually, death occurs in such a crisis. There is also in man a peculiar pigmentation of the skin and mucous membranes which is not seen in animals.

The biochemical changes associated with adrenal cortical insufficiency—as yet incompletely understood—concern the concentrations of electrolytes and water, and the metabolism of carbohydrates and proteins. Low concentrations of sodium and chloride in the plasma and prolongation of life by the administration of salt were first observed by Baumann[44] in 1927. Some years later Loeb and co-workers observed similar changes in patients with Addison's disease, and also found that restricting the amount of salt in the diet would precipitate the crisis of adrenal insufficiency. Since that time it has been well established that in the absence of the adrenals there is excessive excretion of sodium and chloride by the kidney and diminished clearance of potassium (Fig. 1).[33, 34, 52, 75] In consequence, the plasma sodium falls and the plasma potassium rises. These changes are accompanied by movement of water and potassium into the cells (Table 1) and usually by loss of total body water, with consequent diminution in the extracellular fluid volume.[23, 32] The blood pressure then begins to fall, the blood becomes more concentrated, and as a result the renal glomerular filtration rate is progressively diminished. The elevation of the blood nonprotein nitrogen which is often seen is probably a consequence of this renal insufficiency.[43]

The excretion of extra water is also much delayed, and an excess of water may be toxic. This is believed to result in part from accumulation of water intracellularly and in part from increased resorption of water by the kidney.[24] Measurement of the ability to excrete water and to retain salt is often helpful in the diagnosis of adrenal insufficiency (Addison's disease or hypopituitarism) in man. A rather large amount of water is given by mouth (20 ml. per kg.) and the excretion of water and of sodium or chloride is determined hourly for the next several hours. In the absence of adrenal cortical function, the volume of urine is very low, but sodium chloride continues to be excreted.

If sufficient amounts of sodium chloride with water are given to adrenalectomized animals, the downward course may be slowed or prevented entirely.[33, 75] The salt which continues to be lost in the urine is replaced by this treatment, and in addition the resulting diuresis helps to wash out the potassium which otherwise tends to accumulate. Normal blood pressure, circulation and kidney function (other than with respect to salt excretion) are all maintained (Table 2), and the appetite and digestion are improved. Young rats given 1 per cent salt in their drinking water will grow at almost normal rates. The balance of dietary sodium and potassium—as well as the amount of sodium—is important, for a high intake of potassium is deleterious, and in some species reduction in potassium intake as well as increase in sodium is required for complete maintenance. Since adrenalectomized animals may be kept alive for indefinite periods by controlling the amounts of salts ingested, the adrenal cortex to this extent cannot be said to be absolutely essential for life. However, the salt-treated adrenalectomized animal is by no means restored entirely to normal, and some of the remaining defects often endanger life.

The partial success of salt treatment in adrenal insufficiency allows a distinction to be drawn between what may be called the direct and the indirect effects of lack of the adrenal cortex. By "direct" effect is meant one which can be prevented or repaired only by treatment with cortical extract or derived substances, whereas by "indirect" is meant an effect which can be prevented by means other than hormonal substitution. For example, since rats with adrenal insufficiency absorb carbohydrate from the gastrointestinal tract at a slower rate than normal, it has been supposed by some that the adrenal hormones must be concerned

TABLE 1. *Plasma and Tissue Electrolytes in Adrenalectomized Rats**

	SERUM				MUSCLE (PER KG. OF FAT-FREE TISSUE)	
	Na mM.	K mM.	Cl. mM.	N.P.N. mg./100 ml.	Na mEq.	K mEq.
Normal	144	5.2	105	35	23.6	109
Adrenalectomized, untreated	136†	7.4	97	96	18.8	117
Adrenalectomized, given sodium salts	143	5.7	102	28	23.6	109
Adrenalectomized, given cortical extract for 48 hrs.	143	5.5	101	22	21.0	106

*All the adrenalectomized rats were allowed to become insufficient before treatment was started with sodium salts (chloride and bicarbonate) or extract. The figures are averages from groups of 8 to 20 rats.

†The drop in serum sodium in species other than the rat is often even more extreme. Harrison and Darrow[32] report an average value of 126 mM. in an untreated adrenalectomized dog.

(From data of Harrison and Darrow, *J. clin. Invest.*, 1938, *17*:77.)

TABLE 2. *Kidney Function in the Adrenalectomized Dog**

| | URINE:PLASMA RATIO OF K | PLASMA N.P.N. mg./100 ml. | CLEARANCES OF | |
			Urea ml./min.	Creatinine ml./min.
Normal	28	16	33	58
Adrenalectomized, untreated	10	72	8	21
Adrenalectomized, given sodium salts	6	32	25	37
Adrenalectomized, given cortical extract with salts	29	15	30	45

* All estimations were made on the same animal; each figure is the average of five determinations.
(From data of Harrison and Darrow, *Amer. J. Physiol.*, 1939, *125*:631.)

generally with the phosphorylation and absorption of glucose. But it has been shown that in normal rats a degree of inanition such as is usual in untreated adrenalectomized rats may alone result in low gastrointestinal absorption rates. Moreover, adrenalectomized rats whose appetite and food intake have been well maintained by adequate salt treatment can absorb glucose at perfectly normal rates. Evidently the cortical hormones need have no direct effect on glucose absorption; the absence of the adrenals influences this process only indirectly through decreasing the food intake. Other indirect effects of adrenal insufficiency include hemoconcentration, renal failure and loss of body weight and depot fat.

The direct effects of adrenal insufficiency—which are incompletely reparable, if at all, by the administration of salt or other such measures—include the following:[52, 75]

(i) Renal function with respect to sodium and potassium remains defective, only the consequences of these derangements being prevented by salt therapy. The susceptibility to water intoxication also is not alleviated.

(ii) Sensitivity to stress, e.g., to cold or trauma, and liability to shock persist. The vascular system of an animal lacking adrenocortical function appears to be unable to maintain responsiveness to constrictor agents, or to continue for very long the adjustments which are necessary to maintain the blood pressure and the normal distribution of body fluids when the system is taxed in any manner.[22, 54]

(iii) The work capacity of muscles of adrenalectomized animals, as judged by their abil-ity to respond to prolonged repeated stimulation, is greatly diminished.[37, 38] This effect appears not to be due to any great extent to hypoglycemia or to intrinsic defects within the muscle; but, since it is associated with hemodynamic collapse, it may result mainly from the inability of the animal to maintain its cardiovascular responses to the demands imposed by continued work.

(iv) The thymus and lymph nodes tend to be enlarged and the blood lymphocyte counts to be high. The involutional changes which ordinarily take place in these tissues when an animal is subjected to fasting, trauma or other stresses do not occur in the absence of cortical function.[14]

(v) Alterations in the metabolism of carbohydrate and of protein are demonstrable in appropriate circumstances.[17] As long as salt-maintained animals are well fed and kept in good condition, there may be no important changes in the carbohydrate levels of the body; but when these animals fast or fail to eat well for any reason, hypoglycemia becomes prominent and the liver is rapidly depleted of glycogen. The amount of nitrogen lost from the body during fasting is often less than normal. Hence, it has been suggested that the adrenalectomized animal is unable to draw upon body protein to the normal extent to maintain its blood sugar and liver glycogen during fasting.

The idea that the adrenalectomized animal suffers mainly from a defect in the rate of withdrawal of body protein for catabolism is supported by a variety of observations. No important changes in the catabolism of carbohydrate or of exogenous protein have ever been shown. In the eviscerated preparation, however, the rate of release of amino acids from the tissues is significantly reduced in the absence of cortical steroids and is restored in their presence.[5] In fasting diabetic or phlorhizinized animals, the amounts of glucose and nitrogen excreted are diminished proportionately after adrenalectomy and also are restored by appropriate therapy with cortical extracts.[45, 48] Finally, adrenalectomy abolishes the usual "nitrogen catabolic response" to "stress" (i.e., the increase in the rate of loss of nitrogen from the body [often but not always accompanied by an increase in liver glycogen] which occurs when an animal is subjected to trauma, such as surgery, to anoxia or to many drugs).[39, 52] Although it is often said that gluconeogenesis is defective in the absence of cortical hormones, in most instances the defect must reside mainly in the accessibility of protein for use in gluconeogenesis, rather than in the latter process itself.

Although most of the alterations in carbohydrate and protein metabolism in adrenal-deficient animals may be explained by the defect in protein withdrawal, this may not be the only metabolic abnormality. Deposition of liver glycogen from glucose is slow, and ketogenesis in fasting is subnormal. These defects may be due in part at least to the poor hemodynamic state, rather than to intrinsic changes in these processes; for the adrenalectomized subject, even when maintained with salt, is not normal in this respect, and the circulation of blood and lymph through the viscera is undoubtedly subnormal. On the other hand, a number of other observations suggest that loss of cortical steroids may lead, at least in some circumstances, to a relative increase in the utilization of carbohydrate and a decrease in mobilization and use of fat. These changes are similar to those observed after hypophysectomy, but of lesser extent. They are best seen in the depancreatized animal which is then adrenalectomized and maintained with salt or small amounts of cortical hormones.[45, 48] As after hypophysectomy, the diabetes is considerably ameliorated by this procedure. Survival is much prolonged, the blood glucose may be within the normal range, ketonemia is diminished, and the glucose tolerance is improved, although usually still subnormal. The diabetes may be reinstated by the administration of large amounts of cortical hormone, or by anterior pituitary hormones in the presence of smaller amounts of cortical steroids. It is possible that the apparent resumption of carbohydrate utilization and reduction in fat catabolism in these conditions is the result of deficient activity of those anterior pituitary factors which require cortical hormones for their full expression (see Chap. 57).

The varied manifestations of adrenal cortical deficiency do not yet permit the statement of a single unique primary defect. If such a defect does exist, as it well may, the end-results which are seen evidently differ according to the functions of the individual organs or systems affected.

Adrenocortical Hormones.   Attempts to maintain life in adrenalectomized animals with extracts of adrenal cortical tissue were disappointing until in the early 1930's the fat-soluble nature of the active principle became apparent. Then in the years 1934 to 1938 not one but several such substances were obtained in pure form and their constitutions determined. All proved to be steroids. By 1942, no less than 28 different steroid compounds had been isolated from the adrenal. Only six of these, however, displayed any type of activity expected of an adrenocortical hormone.[56] The remaining steroids include progesterone (which has since been reported to show a slight degree of cortical hormonal activity) and some of its derivatives, several weakly androgenic substances, and a variety of inactive compounds now known to be either intermediates in the formation of the active steroids or else degradation products.

In addition to these steroids, an amorphous fraction also was obtained which was quite active in the maintenance of life in the adrenalectomized animal but which differed in its chemical properties from any of the pure active substances then known. The active principle of this fraction was isolated in 1952 and 1953 by Simpson and Tait and their collaborators,[29, 67] and was shown to be extremely potent in promoting the renal retention of salt. When the structure of this material was elucidated shortly thereafter, it proved to be unique among the steroids in bearing an aldehyde group on carbon 18 and was then given the name *aldosterone*. The discovery and properties of this substance have been reviewed by Gaunt *et al.*[25]

The structures of the seven naturally occurring active cortical steroids, including aldo-

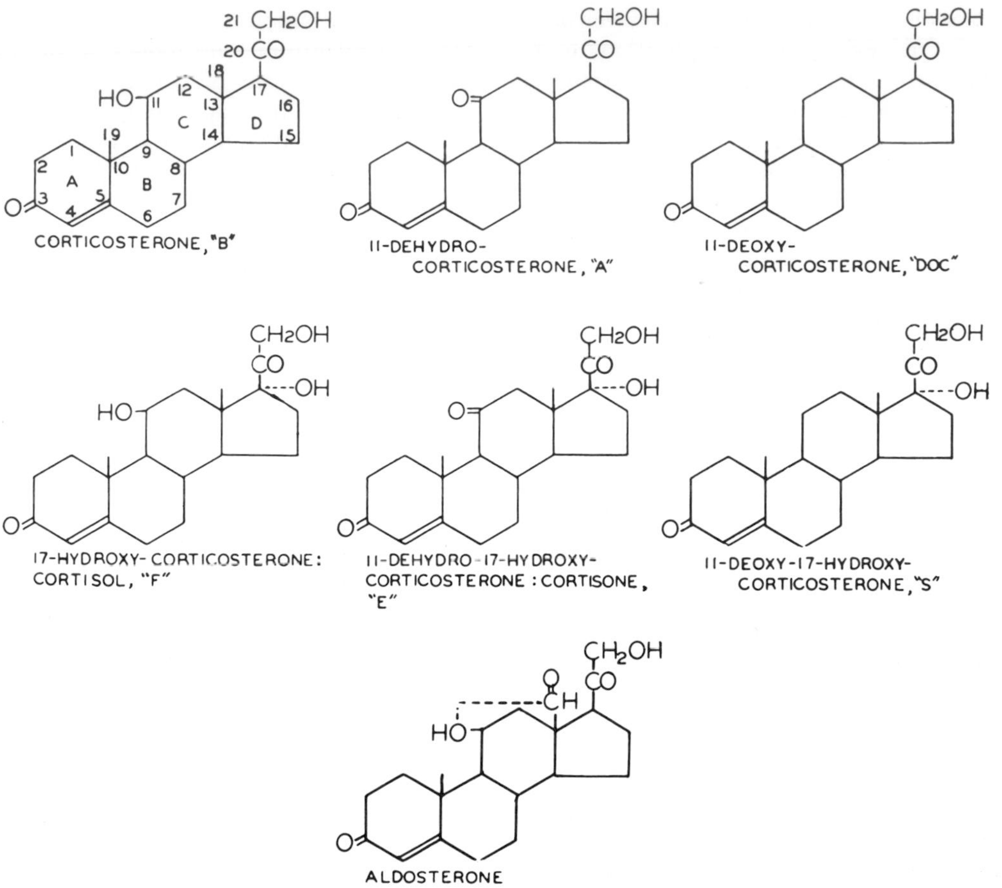

Fig. 2. Structural formulae of the active adrenocortical steroids. In that for corticosterone, the numbers and letters are those used conventionally in designating configuration of steroid compounds. Structures essential for any type of adrenal hormonal activity are the 3-keto, Δ-4 unsaturated grouping in ring A and the two-carbon α-ketol side chain at C-17. An oxygen at C-11 is characteristic of adrenal steroids and is essential for most kinds of activity.

sterone, are given in Figure 2. These are all closely similar, differing only in the presence or absence of hydroxyl or ketone groupings at carbon 11 and/or the α-hydroxyl at carbon 17. As indicated below, however, these apparently minor differences, together with the aldehyde of aldosterone, are responsible for large differences in the type and degree of hormonal activity displayed by the compounds.

Since the pure cortical steroids are obtained from natural sources only in very small amounts, extensive physiologic investigation and clinical use of these materials awaited practical methods of synthesis. The first to be so prepared, and for many years the only pure steroid which was widely available, was 11-deoxycorticosterone (DOC), synthesized from plant sterols by Reichstein in 1937. The bio-

logic properties of this steroid were soon found to differ profoundly from those of the 11-oxycorticoids, which are the main components of adrenocortical extracts. For this reason, extracts rather than pure steroids were employed in the majority of the original investigations on the physiologic activities of cortical hormones, such as those described below. The discovery in 1949 of the remarkable pharmacologic and therapeutic influences of the 11-oxycorticoids in certain disease states then stimulated intensive efforts toward the practical synthesis of these compounds. This was finally achieved in 1952 through 1954 by the combined work of many chemists. The first 11-oxysteroid to be prepared was 17-hydroxy, 11-dehydrocorticosterone (Kendall's compound E), which was then given the name *cortisone*.

The next was 17-hydroxycorticosterone (Kendall's compound F); this is usually called *hydrocortisone,* since it differs from cortisone only in the hydroxyl replacing the ketone of carbon 11, but it is more properly designated *cortisol.* Further, a number of analogues of the cortical steroids have now been prepared, most of them differing from the parent compounds (usually cortisone or cortisol) in further unsaturation of the A or B rings, in the addition of halogen at carbon 9, or of a methyl group at position 2, 6 or 16, or in combinations of these changes. Many of these substances are much more active than the naturally occurring steroids. This greater activity is due partly to the fact that the synthetic compounds may be more slowly destroyed in the body than the corresponding natural substances, but certain of these structural modifications can confer disproportionate activity in certain respects. These synthetic compounds are now being used increasingly for therapeutic purposes.

Secretory products of the adrenal cortex. The nature of the adrenal hormone as secreted by the gland has been elucidated only recently. As indicated above, only small amounts of any of the numerous adrenal steroids can be obtained from glandular tissue. However, as shown a number of years ago, adrenal venous blood from the normal or stimulated gland is extremely active biologically. This indicates that the adrenal steroids are not stored in the gland in any quantity, but are formed and secreted on demand, as it were. Analysis of adrenal venous effluents has become practicable only with the recent development of suitable chromatographic techniques for the separation and identification of the several steroids. In a survey of a variety of species, Bush[6] has found that in all cases the principal steroids quantitatively are corticosterone and cortisol. The ratio of these two steroids varies widely, however. In man and in the dog, the 17-hydroxy form (cortisol) predominates, whereas the principal compound in the rat and some other species is corticosterone. Smaller amounts of other steroids are secreted also. In Table 3 are shown values obtained for the dog by Farrell and associates.[20, 55] These probably represent maximal rates of secretion, since the blood was obtained during acute laparotomy and cannulation of the adrenal vein. Available evidence indicates a similar relative distribution of forms in man. An idea of the rate of secretion of cortical steroids in man may be obtained from the fact that an addisonian patient can be well maintained by the daily administration of about 10 mg. of cortisol together with small amounts of deoxycorticosterone or fluorocortisol for salt retention.

Excretion products from adrenal cortex. A very large number of different steroids, some of them of adrenal origin and some from the gonads, have been isolated from human urine. Most of these are excreted either as glucuronides or as sulfates and require hydrolysis before either chemical or biologic estimation. Of the steroids apparently related to the cortical hormones, most are inactive compounds in which one or more of the requisite structural details have been lost or altered in some way. The major metabolites of this type are now thought to be the "tetrahydro" derivatives, i.e., those in which the only change from the original form has been the addition of hydrogen in the A ring to form the saturated hydroxylated derivative in place of the unsaturated ketone. Further reduction may also occur at the C-20 ketone in the side chain.

The active adrenal steroids are secreted unchanged only in minute amounts. As assayed by the glycogen deposition test, the output of the

TABLE 3. *Cortical Steroids in Adrenal Venous Blood in the Dog**

STEROID	NORMAL DOG μg./kg. hr.	HYPOPHYSECTOMIZED DOG μg./kg. hr.
Cortisol	32 (23–46)	2–3
Corticosterone	13	1–2
Deoxycortisol ("S")	4	0.3
Deoxycorticosterone	0.3	0.04
Aldosterone	0.3	0.14

* Averages of eight or more observations. (Farrell *et al., Amer. J. Physiol.,* 1955, *182:*269–272.)

so-called "glucocorticoids" in man amounts to the equivalent of less than 0.1 mg. per day of cortisone normally and does not exceed a few milligrams per day even in extreme hypercorticalism. A number of chemical methods measuring different groups yield higher values. For example, the "reducing steroids," which contain the α-ketol side chain at C-17 and which therefore will reduce alkaline copper solutions, include all the active adrenal steroids and also many inactive compounds; they are found in normal human urine in larger amounts than the glucocorticoids and may be excreted in considerable quantities (up to 20 mg.) in cases of adrenal hyperfunction. Another chemical method is based on the triose structure of the side chain of adrenal steroids containing the 17-hydroxyl group. This grouping allows the formation of an osazone with phenylhydrazine which can be measured spectrophotometrically (Porter-Silber reaction). This procedure is fairly specific for cortical steroids; but it includes inactive substances such as 17-hydroxy DOC (Reichstein's compound S) as well as derivatives of cortisone and cortisol, and it does not measure corticosterone or its metabolites or steroids reduced at the C-20 oxygen. It is obvious, therefore, that, since no one biologic or chemical method can measure all the compounds of adrenal origin but no others, attempts at providing a specific index of cortical function through measurement of a single type of excretion product can be expected to meet with only limited success.[60]

Another class of compounds found in the urine also is related in part to the adrenal cortex.[50] These are the neutral (i.e., nonphenolic) 17-ketosteroids, substances which bear a single oxygen atom at C-17 rather than a side chain and which are identified by certain color reactions of this group. Included in this class are several of the androgens as well as a number of inactive compounds (but not estrone, which is a phenol as well as a 17-ketosteroid). These substances are excreted by adult men and women in varying amounts, the average for normal men somewhat exceeding that for women or castrate men. In patients with Addison's disease, only very small quantities of the ketosteroids are excreted, whereas in subjects with adrenal hyperplasia or tumors the amounts may be exceedingly large. Thus, the 17-ketosteroids arise in part from the testes but mainly from adrenal tissue. However, these substances are not major metabolic products of normal adrenal steroids, for only small amounts of 17-ketosteroids are excreted after the administration of even quite large doses of cortical hormones. As indicated below, the 17-ketosteroids seem rather to be by-products of cortical activity, or in some cases they may be considered abnormal products.

Biogenesis of the adrenal steroids. The mechanism of formation of the cortical steroids carries important implications for the understanding of the normal physiology of the adrenal gland and of pathologic aberrations in its function. This mechanism has been studied mainly by two methods: first, the characterization and assay of excretion products in conditions of adrenal hyperactivity or following the administration of presumed intermediates in the formation of the hormones, or, second, by study of the reactions carried out by isolated adrenal tissue.[35] By comparing the products obtained in a wide variety of such experiments, it is now possible to prepare an outline of the pathways by which the cortical steroids are synthesized *in vivo,* as summarized briefly on page 1129.

As has long been known, cholesterol occurs normally in the adrenal cortex in very high concentrations and is depleted when the gland is stimulated actively. This suggests that cholesterol may be the principal precursor of the steroid hormones, and this has been confirmed by studies with labeled sterol. However, both cholesterol and the hormones can be formed *de novo* from small molecules such as acetate, and so it is not certain that cholesterol is the only precursor. Present evidence suggests that a minimal rate of steroidogenesis can occur without the formation of cholesterol as an intermediate; however, for rapid formation of hormone (as after stimulation), preformed cholesterol is probably the major source.

Available evidence indicates that the steps between cholesterol and the finished hormones occur in the order shown in the diagram (page 1129). The early removal of the long side chain and oxidation of the A ring (step 1) result in the formation of progesterone, which now appears as a key intermediate. The next step (2), hydroxylation at C-17, is not obligatory; but if it occurs it precedes further reactions. This results in the formation of two series of compounds, those with and those without the 17-hydroxyl. As noted above, the relative preponderance of these two series of steroids varies

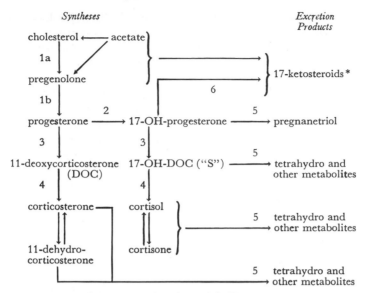

Syntheses

Excretion Products

Reactions: 1. a. Removal of side chain of cholesterol. b. Formation of Δ-4,3-keto grouping.
2. 17-hydroxylation.
3. 21-hydroxylation.
4. 11-hydroxylation.
5. Inactivation by reduction of A ring, also 20-keto group.
6. Removal of C-20,21, side chain.

*Includes androgens. Many of these are oxygenated at C-11, as in step 4

with species. In men, as well as many other species, the 17-hydroxyl series is the more important quantitatively. The next step (3), which occurs with either progesterone or 17-OH-progesterone, is hydroxylation at C-21; finally, at step 4, oxygen is introduced at C-11 to form corticosterone or cortisol. Oxidation of the hydroxyl at C-11, with formation of dehydrocorticosterone (compound A) or cortisone, may occur; but, if so, it is readily reversible. Present evidence suggests that aldosterone is derived from corticosterone. The further metabolism of the steroid hormones, such as the formation of the inactive tetrahydro derivatives, takes place mainly after the hormones have been secreted from the adrenal, in the liver and possibly elsewhere in the body.

The formation of 17-ketosteroids has not been clarified in detail. It is known that the side chains of 17-hydroxy steroids are rather readily cleaved to yield 17-ketosteroids, and 17-hydroxyprogesterone has been shown to give rise to certain of these substances (step 6) as well as to reduction products similar to the tetrahydrocortical steroids (pregnanetriol; step 5). In certain diseases of the adrenal these changes occur together: formation of androgens and the excretion of 17-ketosteroids and of

pregnanetriol appear to be increased approximately in parallel. It is therefore supposed that the 17-ketosteroids may arise in part as by-products at this stage of steroidogenesis. Other evidence of a chemical nature suggests, however, that some or all of the ketosteroids may be formed at an earlier stage.

In certain individuals, one or another of the steps of the synthesis may be defective. This leads to relative or absolute deficiency of the normal adrenal steroids, increased secretion of ACTH in response to this deficiency (p. 1135), and consequent enlargement of the adrenal gland and overproduction of intermediate products and related substances. In most of the cases which have been studied in detail, hydroxylation at C-21 (step 3) seems to be limited, but in others oxygenation at C-11 (step 4) is deficient. Characteristic excretion products include pregnanetriol and related compounds and abnormal quantities of 17-ketosteroids. The condition, which is termed congenital adrenal hyperplasia, has as its principal symptoms virilization or precocious maturity. These are no doubt consequences of the overproduction of androgenic 17-ketosteroids accompanying the compensatory hypertrophy of the adrenals which results from the basic insufficiency.

Hormonal Actions of Adrenal Steroids. Physiologic evaluation of the adrenocortical hormones has faced peculiar difficulties in the variety of effects attributable to cortical activity and in the number of different steroids which have been obtained. Quantitative assays of extracts or of isolated compounds have been attempted by many methods.[11, 12] The most common procedures have been based on effects in adrenalectomized animals on (i) maintenance of life and normal composition of the body fluids in dogs; (ii) growth and survival in young rats; (iii) protection against some stress, such as cold; (iv) work capacity of muscles during continued stimulation; (v) deposition of glycogen in the liver in fasting rats or mice; (vi) involution of lymphoid tissue such as the thymus; (vii) depletion of circulating lymphocytes or, more often, of blood eosinophils; or (viii) inhibition of certain types of inflammatory reactions. Also, measurements have been made in normal animals of (ix) retention of sodium or radiosodium or of (x) reduction in the ratio of excretion of radiosodium and radiopotassium. A selection of data showing comparative activities of the adrenal steroids by some of these methods is given in Table 4. The physiologic bases of these tests are discussed further below.

On the basis of comparisons like that shown in Table 4, two principal types of cortical steroids have been distinguished: those which are most active in the retention of salt and in the maintenance of life, typified by deoxycorticosterone and often termed "mineralocorticoids"; and those such as cortisone and cortisol which are relatively inactive in these respects but which are most potent in a variety of other activities characteristic of cortical steroids, as in protection against "stress" or in affecting carbohydrate and protein metabolism. The latter group of steroids have usually been termed "11-oxycorticoids," since they have appeared to be distinguishable from the "mineralocorticoids" on this basis; or, often, they are called "glucocorticoids," in reference to their efforts on glycogenesis in the liver. However, recent observations on aldosterone and some synthetic analogues of cortical steroids show that this distinction is not complete. Aldosterone, the most active natural steroid in respect to renal retention of salt, is itself an 11-oxycorticoid and appears to have about the same order of activity as a glucocorticoid as its parent compound, cortico-sterone. Further, the halogenated oxycorticoids, such as fluorocortisol, are also very active in salt-retention but at the same time are several-fold more potent as glucocorticoids than the naturally-occurring parent substances. Although steroids which are highly active in mineral metabolism can be distinguished from those which are not, the "glucocorticoid" properties of these substances are not necessarily related inversely to their "mineralocorticoid" activities.

Maintenance of life and sodium retention. All of the naturally-occurring cortical steroids listed in Table 4, like the extracts of adrenal tissue from which they were originally obtained, can maintain life and a semblance of health in adrenalectomized animals. As indicated in the Table, however, the degree of activity of the individual steroids differs considerably. Since their potencies in this respect closely parallel their respective activities in the retention of sodium, it appears that the latter effect is the most critical factor for the maintenance of life. This is in agreement with the fact, mentioned earlier, that the provision of extra sodium salts alone may suffice to support an adrenal-deficient subject. However, the correction by cortical steroids of the critical disturbances in distribution of electrolytes and water results, not simply from amelioration of symptoms, as is the case with salt treatment, but is due instead to specific effects upon the renal tubules.[3, 33, 57] In either normal or adrenalectomized animals, small amounts of the steroids increase the reabsorption of sodium ion in the distal tubule and also usually increase the clearance of potassium ion. The concentrations of electrolytes in the body fluids of the deficient subject are thus restored and normal blood volume and pressure are maintained. As with salt treatment, the indirect effects of cortical insufficiency also are abolished, and renal function, appetite, digestion and growth all may be fully corrected by these steroids.

Although the mechanism of action of the "mineralocorticoids" is different from that of salt therapy, their effects resemble those of salt in that they tend to be limited virtually to the restoration of the hemodynamic state and its attendant phenomena. Deoxycorticosterone has no other actions to speak of and cannot substitute fully for the normal cortical secretion. Aldosterone, the natural hormone for salt retention, does have other properties in addition to its effect on the renal tubule,[25, 67] but this steroid is so enormously potent in salt retention and needs to be secreted or given in such small amounts that in fact its practical effects also are limited to mineral metabolism. The same is true to a lesser extent of the halogenated corticoids, an amount optimal for sodium retention being insufficient to replace the normal adrenal secretion in other respects. Thus, although the mineralocorticoids are able to maintain life through their important physiologic effects on renal function, these substances do not provide complete replacement of cortical function.

Before the discovery of aldosterone, the identity of the substance or substances responsible for the salt-retaining activity of the adrenal secretion was unknown. Deoxycorticosterone itself was not known to be secreted in sufficient amounts; but, since all of the active steroids exhibit some degree of activity, it was supposed that some mixture of the known hormones might possibly suffice. Now, however, the very great potency of aldosterone makes it obvious that this steroid is the principal active hormone in this respect. From the figures for secretion of steroids by the dog shown in Table 3, combined with the data for their relative potencies in Table 4, it may be calculated that aldosterone accounts for about 70 per cent of the salt-retaining activity of adrenal venous blood in the normal animal, the other 11-oxycorticoids about 20 per cent, and deoxycorticosterone the remainder. Available data indicate a similar order in these respects in other species, except

TABLE 4. *Relative Potencies of Adrenocortical Steroids*

	COMPARED WITH DEOXYCORTICOSTERONE = 100			COMPARED WITH CORTISOL = 100			
	Maintenance of Adrex. Dogs[a]	Salt Retention[b]	Excretion Ratio Na^{24}/K^{42}[c]	Liver Glycogen Deposition[d]	Muscle Work (Ingle)[d]	Thymus Involution[e]	Inhibition of Inflammation[b]
Natural steroids							
Cortisol (17-OH corticosterone, hydrocortisone [F])	3–5	±	7	100	100	100	100
Cortisone (17-OH, 11-Dehydrocorticosterone [E])	3–5	±	6	65	62	65	30–75
Corticosterone (B)	15	+	14	35	30	28	30
11-Dehydrocorticosterone (A)	12	+	7	30	20	23	30
17-OH, 11-Deoxycorticosterone (S)	?	3	8	<1	<1	0	0
11-Deoxycorticosterone (DOC)	100	100	100	<1	<1	0	0
Aldosterone	2000–4000	3000–4000	12000	20–30	+	+§	?
Synthetic steroids							
Prednisolone (Δ 1 cortisol)	1	±		300–400		400	300
9 α Fluorocortisol	900	500		1200		900	700–1300

± Variable positive or negative effect. + Positive effect, not quantitated.
§ Significant effect on thymus with impure preparations; eosinopenic activity, 25.
a Swingle *et al.*[73]
b Singer and Borman;[69] Lyster *et al.*;[49] Chen and Wickel;[7] Stafford *et al.*[70]
c Simpson and Tait;[66] Grundy *et al.*[29]
d Dorfman.[11]
e Stephenson.[71]

TABLE 5.   *Effects of Adrenal Cortical Extract on Carbohydrate Stores
and Nitrogen Excretion in Normal Fasting Rats*[*][†]

	LIVER GLYCOGEN	MUSCLE GLYCOGEN	BLOOD AND TISSUE FLUID GLUCOSE	TOTAL GLUCOSE	NITROGEN EXCRETED (12 HOURS)
Untreated rats	7	253	37	297	54
Cortical extract given hourly	79	260	54	383	81
Increase	72	(not significant)	17	89‡	27‡

[*] Fasted 24 hours, with treatment during last 12 hours.
[†] All values are mg. per 100 gm. body weight.
[‡] Note that the ratio of extra glucose to extra nitrogen is 3.3, indicating that the new carbohydrate
    could all have come from the body protein metabolized during the period.
(From data of Long *et al., Endocrinology,* 1940, 26:309.)

that corticosterone may be somewhat more or less important according to the quantity secreted.

"Oxycorticoid" effects. The adrenal steroids which are oxygenated at C-11, unlike the corresponding deoxy compounds, are able to reverse all of the abnormalities seen in adrenalectomized animals. As shown in Table 4, although the several steroids vary in relative potency, they display closely parallel activities on liver glycogen deposition, on muscle work performance, in involutional action on the thymus and in inhibition of inflammation. From the data available at present, approximately the same relative activities also appear to obtain in respect to nitrogen catabolic effects, to depletion of blood lymphocytes and eosinophils, to the distribution of water in the body and its excretion, and also to the protection of adrenal-deficient subjects against such stresses as surgical trauma, hemorrhage, cold or the administration of certain drugs. It seems likely, therefore, that all of the steroids of this class have much the same actions and functions, differing only in quantitative potency. The two steroids which are now known to comprise the bulk of the normal secretion of the adrenal, cortisol and corticosterone, are entirely typical of this class.

The effects of these steroids are most easily demonstrated in adrenalectomized animals. However, if sufficiently large doses are given, exaggerated or "supranormal" effects can be obtained in intact subjects in most instances. Difficulty in obtaining an exaggerated response may be explained in part by suppression of the animal's own adrenal secretion in the presence

of excess hormone (see below); or in some cases other factors than the amount of cortical hormone limit the response. With sufficient dosage of any of the oxycorticoids, the following effects may be induced in normal or adrenal-deficient subjects:

(i) In fasting rats or mice, a marked increase in the liver glycogen is induced within a few hours (Table 5). The blood glucose is increased to a small degree, and the muscle glycogen does not change appreciably. Therefore, the glycogen in the liver must have been newly formed from noncarbohydrate precursors. Since this increase in body carbohydrate is accompanied by a considerable increase in the excretion of nitrogen, it appears that the new carbohydrate is derived from protein broken down under the influence of the hormone.[47] The same conclusions may be drawn from the parallel increases in glucose and nitrogen excretion seen when phlorhizinized adrenalectomized animals are given the steroids. Excess cortical steroids have little effect on glycogen formation from exogenous amino acids. Therefore, the action of the cortical steroids here does not appear to be upon the process of gluconeogenesis *per se,* but rather upon the provision of amino acids from the body proteins.

(ii) The oxygenated adrenal steroids have been observed in general to have a catabolic effect on protein metabolism. In fasting animals the nitrogen excretion is usually increased, and in fed subjects a negative nitrogen balance is usual; or, with heavy overdosage with the hormones, a profound loss of body substance may be induced. Most of the organs of the body are affected in this circumstance. The lymphoid tissue exhibits the greatest effect, but skin, muscle and many visceral organs also undergo severe depletion of substance.[65] An increase in plasma amino nitrogen has been seen in eviscerated animals given cortical steroids.[5] The liver, on the other hand, usually shows little effect, or may even increase in size. This is understandable, because the amino acids coming from the peripheral tissues must all be funneled through the liver as they are catabolized. Although the enhancement of protein catabolism by cortical hormone is ordinarily one of its most prominent effects, this is not an entirely obligatory action, for it may be modified or even abolished by administration of excess carbohydrate or potassium salts and by other factors. Small amounts of cortical hormones given alone have relatively little effect on nitrogen loss, but when they are given in conditions which normally tend to induce nitrogen loss (as during fasting, trauma, anoxia or the like), the cortical hormone may hasten or augment the catabolic response.[17, 41] In the adrenalectomized subject, in which this response does not otherwise occur, the cortical hormones thus appear to play a "permissive" role in the nitrogen catabolic effect.[16, 38, 39]

(iii) When rather large amounts of the oxygenated adrenal steroids are given to rats, the severity of a pre-existent diabetes may be increased, or, in intact animals force-fed a diet high in carbohydrate, glycosuria may be induced *de novo*.[40, 42] Because under these conditions the nitrogen excretion is not as greatly increased as the glycosuria, it has been considered that the hormones must inhibit the utilization of carbohydrate as well as act to increase its production. In recent work with radioglucose, little evidence of disturbed oxidation of carbohydrate was seen, but massive dilution of the glucose with nonisotopic carbohydrate—that is, a very high rate of gluconeogenesis—was observed in animals given an overdose of cortisone.[78] Apparently, then, increased gluconeogenesis from some source is one major factor contributing to the "diabetogenic" effect of cortical hormone. Another factor may be a fat-mobilizing action of cortical steroids. Although in intact animals these hormones have little, if any, ketogenic effect or tendency to increase liver fat, such actions have been demonstrated clearly in animals lacking insulin (depancreatized-hypophysectomized rats).[64] Presumably the increase in blood glucose brought on concomitantly by cortical steroids, with consequent increase in insulin secretion, normally limits the expression of this tendency to increase fat mobilization. Such an effect on lipolysis in adipose tissue, with increase in plasma fatty acids, would tend to diminish carbohydrate utilization and might explain the appearance of glycosuria without corresponding protein loss that occurs when large doses of cortical steroids are administered to intact animals.

(iv) The distribution of water and salts within the body and the excretion of water can be affected by the active cortical steroids independently of any action they may have on renal excretion of electrolytes. If adrenalectomized animals are allowed to develop renal insufficiency and then without further food, water or salts, are treated with adequate amounts of cortical hormone, the extracellular fluid volume and blood pressure are restored toward normal, hemoconcentration is reduced, and the animal again becomes active and vigorous even though the concentrations of electrolytes in the plasma may remain abnormal.[72, 74] The withdrawal of water from intracellular sites and the apparent increase in circulating electrolytes[23] seem to result from changes in the "permeability" of cells, or, possibly more correctly, from changes in the responsiveness of the capillaries which in turn would affect permeability functions.

Probably related to this phenomenon is the frequent observation of water diuresis following the administration of excess cortical hormones to either normal or adrenal-deficient subjects.[24] This is especially prominent in the presence of a water load. The 17-hydroxycorticoids, such as cortisol, are the most active substances in this respect, as they are in all other aspects of cortical function except salt retention. In consequence, although these steroids can in fact increase renal tubular reabsorption of sodium to some degree, their usual effect is to induce not salt retention but instead a loss of salts with the water excreted.

(v) The adrenal steroids oxygenated at C-11 exhibit striking effects on certain tissues of mesenchymal origin. The number of circulating lymphocytes and eosinophils is markedly diminished within an hour or two after the administration of these compounds,[14, 77] and later the thymus and lymph nodes may undergo drastic involution.[2, 15] Similar effects are seen in conditions of moderately severe "stress" in the intact animal, but not in the absence of the adrenals. It was this observation by Selye which first led to the concept of a generalized "alarm reaction" which included the response of the adrenal cortex to nonspecific stimulation. However, as in the nitrogen catabolic effect, small amounts of cortical steroids which have little effect by themselves may greatly potentiate the actions of other damaging agents. The mechanism of the "thymolytic" effect is not at all understood. It seems to be closely related in its occurrence to the general catabolic action of the steroids, and it may represent another aspect of the same effect exhibited by an especially sensitive type of tissue.

(vi) When the active steroids are given in excess over periods of hours or days, they affect profoundly the inflammatory responses of the tissues in a variety of circumstances: local inflammatory reactions to contact with irritating substances are greatly diminished or delayed, hypersensitivity reactions tend to be suppressed, the healing of wounds and development of fibrous tissue is delayed, and the normal capacity of the tissues to localize certain infectious agents may be considerably diminished.[13, 26, 52, 77] The symptomatic relief of rheumatoid arthritis seen during treatment with cortisone or ACTH, reported by Hench and his co-workers,[36] probably results from suppression of an inflammatory reaction, and the dramatic results of these hormones in serum sickness and other acute hypersensitivity states are certainly due to this effect.[77] Although this alteration in the usual reactions of the tissues is beneficial in many instances, such as those just mentioned, it may in other circumstances be distinctly deleterious, for the inflammatory response is part of the normal mechanism by which infection is combated and healing promoted in the tissues. These actions of the cortical steroids may well be related to the general nitrogen catabolic effects and/or to the lympholytic actions of the hormones; but, again, the fundamental mechanism is unknown.

(vii) The cortical steroids, when given in sufficient amount, are able to restore completely, or nearly so, the resistance of adrenal-deficient subjects to various stresses such as cold, toxic substances and the like.[52] Continued forced exercise, as in the Ingle muscle work test (see p. 1124), probably may be considered as a rather severe generalized type of stress, and the restoration of the ability of the adrenal-ectomized animals to do prolonged muscle work may be another example of such "resistance." The cortical steroids also restore to normal the constrictor responses of the capillaries to pressor agents.[22, 54] In most of these effects the oxycorticoids are the most effective steroids, but those of the "mineralocorticoid" type also can contribute to the protective effect in some circumstances. There is no convincing evidence that cortical hormones can increase appreciably the resistance of normal individuals to nonspecific stresses. It is probable that at least part of the protective action of cortical steroids against stresses of varied nature is due to redistribution of water and salts, maintenance of pressor responses and like activities, thus allowing proper hemodynamic adaptation to the demands of changing internal and external environments.

As is the case with adrenal deficiency, the manifold actions of the oxysteroids do not yet suggest any single point of activity which can explain all of their effects. If there is a common locus of function, it seems to lie in the functional integrity of the membranes of many types of cells. The actual point of activity might then be either on mechanisms within the cells which support membrane phenomena, or on the permeability of the membranes themselves—or even, as some observations suggest, on properties of the "ground substance" which is the medium of transport into and out of cells.

Hyperfunction of the adrenal cortex occurs rather rarely in man. In its classic form, known as Cushing's syndrome, it is characterized by a distinctive facies with rounding of the face and localized deposition of fat in the shoulders and trunk, by loss of body protein, osteoporosis, fragile skin and poor wound healing, and weakness, by resistance to insulin, and frequently by hypertension.[1] Adrenocortical tumors often secrete an excess of androgenic substances, producing virilism in women and precocious maturity in young individuals.

Relationship of Hypophysis to Adrenal Cortex. The function of the adrenal cortex is controlled almost completely by the adrenotrophic hormone from the adenohypophysis (ACTH). Hypophysectomized animals do not usually die of adrenocortical deficiency, although, except for the critical disturbances in electrolyte metabolism, they show all the other abnormalities of adrenalectomy previously described. From this it has appeared that either the normal cortical steroids continue to be secreted in very small amounts, or, as was proposed by Deane and Greep[9, 10] on the basis of morphologic studies of the adrenal cortex, formation of glucocorticoids ceases but salt-active corticoids continue to be secreted by one part of the cortex (the glomerular zone). It has now been found that the latter is more nearly the case. Analysis of adrenal venous blood in dogs (Table 3) and in rats has shown that, whereas the output (maximal) of most of the corticosteroids falls to low levels within a few hours after hypophysectomy, the output of aldosterone continues at something like half the normal rate.[20, 55, 68] Also, when portions of the adrenal glands of rats are incubated *in vitro,* aldosterone is produced only by the section adjacent to the capsule,[27] as predicted by the studies of Deane and Greep.

After hypophysectomy, the secretion rates of all of the steroids—inactive forms as well as major hormones—except aldosterone are reduced about in the same proportion (Table 3). This fact, together with more extensive evidence on the effects of ACTH on the biogenesis of steroids in the adrenal,[35] indicates that the action of the trophic hormone is not on any of the later steps in the synthesis of the active forms (outlined on p. 1129). Instead, the effect must be on the rate of provision of some primary precursor, such as pregnenolone (step 1a or 1b). The formation of aldosterone from corticosterone would then resemble the other transformations in its independence of ACTH. Aldosterone normally constitutes only a minute part of the total steroid secretion (about 1 per cent). Since after hypophysectomy the secretion of steroids is not abolished but reduced only to about 10 per cent of normal, aldosterone still constitutes only a small fraction of the total steroid output, even in the absence of ACTH. Hence, although the rate of formation of the presumed common precursor of all the steroids must be low after hypophysectomy, the output of aldosterone can continue at nearly normal rates regardless of whether the trophic hormone is present. Other factors controlling the secretion of aldosterone are discussed below.

The administration of ACTH to normal or hypophysectomized animals is followed by all the consequences expected from increased secretion of glucocorticoids—nitrogen loss, gluconeogenesis, lympholysis, inhibition of inflam-

mation and the like—and the hypophysectomized animal shows also improved resistance to stress. Some degree of salt retention also is common, probably indicating some increase in the secretion of aldosterone. An increase in the output of 17-ketosteroids usually accompanies the increase in secretion of cortical hormones. As shown by analysis of the adrenal venous effluent, the increase in hormone secretion occurs within minutes after the injection of ACTH. If the application of ACTH is continued for many hours or days, histologic changes indicating increased activity in the cortex are seen; and, after some days, considerable enlargement of the gland occurs. An early and striking effect of ACTH on the adrenal is reduction in its content of ascorbic acid. This action is the basis of a highly specific and sensitive test for ACTH activity in pituitary preparations and in body fluids when these are given to hypophysectomized animals; in intact animals, it can be used as an indicator of endogenous ACTH secretion.[61, 63]

When an animal is maintained in stressful conditions—as in the cold—for any length of time, the adrenal cortex becomes enlarged; or, if part of the adrenal tissue is removed or damaged, the remainder will hypertrophy. These changes do not occur in the absence of the pituitary. The secretion of ACTH, and hence cortical activity, must then vary with physiologic demand. More detailed studies of adreno-hypophysial relationships have been made possible by observations on changes in excretory products from adrenal hormones, on effects of endogenous cortical steroids on blood lymphocytes and eosinophils, or particularly in experimental animals, on changes in the adrenal ascorbic acid as an indicator of ACTH secretion. By the use of these and related methods in a variety of situations, it has been found that ACTH secretion and consequent cortical activity are increased by almost any change in the internal or external environment.[60] All types of stress—trauma of any kind, cold, heat, pain or fright, infections or inflammation—induce prompt activation of the adrenal cortex. Similarly, ACTH secretion is enhanced by hypoglycemia or by a large number of drugs, including morphine, ether, nicotine and histamine, but not the barbiturates, and it seems also to be increased by moderate exercise. None of these effects is seen in the absence of the hypophysis. Thus, not only does the adrenal cortex secrete its hormones continuously for normal metabolism, but also it must be able to increase its secretion in response to almost any noxious stimulus; and this response is completely controlled by the hypophysial adrenotrophin. These facts, together with the evident necessity for cortical hormones for normal resistance to stress, suggest that responses of the pituitary–adrenal system must play a large part in the regulatory systems which help to protect the animal from environmental hazards.[38, 60]

Control of ACTH Secretion. The mechanisms which bring about the response of the pituitary–adrenal system in exigent circumstances are currently under active investigation. One factor which is known to affect ACTH production is the level of cortical steroids in the body. Chronic cortical insufficiency leads to an increase in the amount of ACTH in the blood and to the hypertrophy of any remaining cortical tissue. Conversely, excess of hormone not only will induce regression of the adrenal cortex by suppressing ACTH secretion, but also, to judge from its effects on the adrenal ascorbic acid, it can prevent the release of ACTH during acute stress. Thus the anterior pituitary and adrenal cortex are in a reciprocal relationship, and any temporary excess or deficiency of either hormone will tend automatically to bring about a restoration of the normal hormonal balance.

These relationships have suggested that nonspecific stress could stimulate the secretion of ACTH by lowering the blood level of the steroids, presumably by somehow inducing increased "utilization" of these materials.[60] However, it is now known that the level of cortical hormone in the blood or tissues is not in fact diminished by stressful stimuli. Moreover, the response of the pituitary to such measures is so very rapid (within minutes or seconds) that it does not seem likely that sufficient destruction of the circulating steroids could possibly occur in time to stimulate the pituitary solely by this means. Finally, Sayers has shown by assay of the ACTH content of the blood of adrenalectomized rats that nonspecific stimuli can bring about increased secretion by the pituitary in the absence of any cortical hormone.[58, 76] Primary control of ACTH secretion must reside in the hypothalamic–pituitary relation (see below). The "reflex" suppression of ACTH secretion by increased cortical hormone levels may be important in limiting the duration of pituitary activity once it has started its response to a stress stimulus.

Stimulation of the hypophysis seems to occur by nervous mechanisms via the hypothalamus and the pituitary–portal circulation (Chap. 57). A considerable number of investigators have now shown that if lesions are placed in appropriate areas of the hypothalamus, usually in or near the median eminence, the common responses of the pituitary system to nonspecific stress are lacking.[28, 62] This has been shown after trauma, several drugs or hypoglycemia, by use of changes in adrenal ascorbic acid, in blood lymphocytes or eosinophils, or in adrenal vein corticoids. The adrenal gland in these cases does not undergo atrophy, indicating that a "basal" level of ACTH secretion continues, but the system is unable to respond to further stimulation. Similarly, pharmacologic blockade of the hypothalamic connections can be induced with certain drugs, a combination of morphine and a barbiturate inhibiting the response of the adrenal to all types of stimuli.[51] It has now been found possible to induce pituitary–adrenal activation in the absence of the hypothalamic link (presence of hypothalamic lesions or blockade) by the administration of suitable extracts of the hypothalamus (median eminence area) or of the posterior pituitary.[59,62] Also, similar extracts have been shown to induce the release of ACTH by pituitary tissue incubated or cultured *in vitro,* and a substance inducing adrenal activation has been demonstrated in plasma from the pituitary portal vein of the dog. This material, called the "corticotrophin releasing factor," abbreviated as CRF, has not yet been identified completely. In its chemical properties it is quite similar to the posterior pituitary peptides, and indeed vasopressin seems to have some degree of CRF activity; but chemical separation of the two substances and comparison of their biologic activities show clearly that they are not identical.[30,31] Thus, there is every indication that the regulation of ACTH secretion in response to nonspecific stimuli is mediated via hypothalamic nervous connections and a specific neurohumoral factor acting on the anterior hypophysis.

Another suggested trigger mechanism for the pituitary response is that epinephrine, the secretion of the adrenal medulla, may be a specific stimulant to ACTH secretion.[46] The adrenal medulla is known to be activated via the sympathetic system in all types of stress; the earliest responses of the adrenal cortex to certain stimuli may be reduced or eliminated by surgical interference with the sympathetic–adrenomedullary system; and very small amounts of epinephrine will activate the pituitary–adrenal mechanism even when the pituitary has been transplanted elsewhere in the body. However, since adrenodemedullated or even sympathectomized animals do not appear to suffer from cortical deficiency when faced with stressful stimuli, this cannot be an important mechanism controlling ACTH production.

Control of Aldosterone Secretion. Although the secretion of aldosterone is controlled only to a relatively slight extent by pituitary ACTH, many observations show that aldosterone secretion also is not constant but appears to be regulated by physiologic demand.[4, 18] One principal controlling factor seems to be the intake of sodium salts or some function of the sodium supply, for the secretion of aldosterone is much increased during sodium deprivation in man, dog and rat. A number of other regulating mechanisms also have been suggested, the most important of these having to do with effects of changes in body fluid volume or some function of the extracellular fluid volume. A marked increase in aldosterone secretion may occur during blood loss or contraction of body water, even when there is no change in the sodium concentration of the plasma, and similar effects are seen during occlusion of the vena cava. Conversely, distension of the right atrium results in a significant reduction of aldosterone secretion. These observations suggest that aldosterone secretion is responsive to "volume receptors" in the thoracic area in the same way that antidiuretic hormone is responsive to volume functions elsewhere. Farrell[19] has presented evidence that these and other factors regulate aldosterone secretion through neurohumoral factors having their source in the midbrain area. Still other observations suggest that the secretion of aldosterone may be controlled by factors arising in the kidney. Davis[8] and others have reported that angiotensin II, derived from the action of renin on substrates in plasma, stimulates the secretion of aldosterone by the adrenal cortex isolated *in situ*. The juxtaglomerular apparatus of the kidney is believed to be responsive to the sodium concentration of the plasma and possibly to other stimuli and so

to mediate the control of aldosterone secretion via the actions of renin and angiotensin.[4]

THE ADRENAL MEDULLA

The early discoveries of powerful pharmacologic activity in extracts of adrenal tissue and of secretion of a pressor agent by the adrenal medulla led to the belief, held for many years, that the medulla rather than the cortex was the more important organ. It is now known, of course, that it is the cortex which is essential for life and that removal or denervation of the adrenal medullae without significant damage to the cortices has no obvious ill effects on the health, vigor and reproductive ability of experimental animals.[6, 26, 29] In explanation of this paradox, the emergency theory of epinephrine action (see p. 1144) suggests that removal of the adrenal medullae has appeared to be without effect because its consequences have been observed only in animals leading a sheltered life in the laboratory, and that more demanding environs would reveal greater importance of medullary activity for normal life. In fact, the adrenodemedullated animal does not seem to be particularly sensitive to exigent circumstances, responding in nearly normal fashion to cold, trauma or the like. The only consequences which can be observed regularly are those concerned with carbohydrate metabolism: if hypoglycemia is induced by insulin, recovery of the blood glucose level is rather slower than in the normal subject; and glycogenolysis in muscle (as evidenced by loss of glycogen in the tissue and increase of lactate in the blood) does not occur as it normally does during hypoglycemia or after operative trauma or similar stimuli. These deficiencies do not seem to be of any great functional importance. It is probable that the actions of the sympathetic nervous system, which closely resemble those of the medullary secretion, may suffice for the animal economy in most situations.

The secreting cells of the adrenal medullae are modified ganglion cells, called pheochromocytes because of their distinctive color reactions. They are in intimate connection with preganglionic fibers of the sympathetic nervous system and their secretory activity appears to be controlled completely by stimulation through these nervous pathways. Stimulation through the splanchnics calls forth a marked increase in the amounts of hormone released, whereas section of the splanchnic nerve prevents any secretion.[7] Ganglionic blocking agents also inhibit the secretory activity of the adrenal medulla. The centers which relay stimuli to the gland are located in the posterior hypothalamus.

In addition to the adrenal medullae proper, many small masses of tissue closely resembling the medullae in origin, structure and staining characteristics occur elsewhere. These bodies are found adjacent to the chain of sympathetic ganglia (where they are known as paraganglia), near the bifurcation of the common carotids (here they are called the carotid glands), and in the liver and heart, as well as elsewhere. They contain substances which react chemically like those in the adrenal medullae, and tumors arising from this tissue sometimes produce symptoms identical with those due to excessive medullary secretion. Whether this extramedullary tissue is normally secretory is not known for certain, but there seems to be no reason why it should not be so.

Chemical Nature and Mode of Action of Epinephrine. Oliver and Shäfer in 1895 first observed that extracts of adrenal tissue had a powerful vasopressor action.[39] An active principle was isolated by Aldrich and by Takamine independently in 1901 and was later shown to be a derivative of tyrosine and to have the following constitution:

$$(l) \; HO \overset{\displaystyle H \atop \displaystyle O}{\bigcirc} CH\,(OH) \cdot CH_2NH \cdot CH_3$$

It is variously called epinephrine, adrenaline or adrenine. (Adrenalin is a proprietary name.) This compound was long considered to be the only hormone of the adrenal medulla. However, it was demonstrated in 1949–1950 that the adrenals contain and secrete yet another active substance.[4, 16, 22] This material, called norepinephrine, noradrenaline or arterenol, differs from epinephrine only in lacking the terminal methyl group. The two compounds are nearly identical in chemical properties, but, although they are generally similar in biologic behavior, they display some differences in nature and degree of activity (see Table 6). Extracts of the adrenal usually contain some two to five times as much epinephrine as norepinephrine, depending on species and age; on sympathetic stimulation, the gland apparently liberates the two substances about in proportion to content. Available evidence indicates that norepinephrine is formed first in all pheochromocytes, and also probably in most sympathetic nerves, and that in the adrenal medullae it is then methylated to form epinephrine.

The epinephrines are quite reactive substances and are readily oxidized to inactive forms, either *in vitro* or *in vivo*. As catechol derivatives, they give distinctive color reactions with ferric and with chromium salts and are responsible for the so-called chromaffin reactions by which adrenomedullary and similar tissues are identified histologically. Oxidation under carefully controlled conditions leads to the formations of adrenochromes, which are derivatives of indole. These substances condense with ethylenediamine to form stable fluorescent compounds, or they may be converted in alkali to the adrenolutines, which are also fluorescent; these procedures form the bases of sensitive and relatively specific chemical procedures for the estimation of the epinephrines in the body fluids. By this means, it has been estimated that the blood of resting normal men contains about 1 μg. per liter of total catechol amines. The hormones are rapidly inactivated in the body, and only minute amounts of the unchanged epinephrines are normally excreted. The major metabolic products seem to be inactive O-methylated derivatives (called the metanephrines) which may be excreted largely as glucuronides. Also, the hormones may be inactivated by amine oxidases, or both types of reactions may occur.[48] Because these hormones are so quickly destroyed, their action in the body is of very brief duration. When administered intravascularly, their effects are evident almost immediately, but are evanescent. If they are given subcutaneously, however, attendant vasoconstriction in this area slows their absorption, so that maximal effects are seen within 15 to 30 minutes. For prolonged activity, they are also sometimes given in oil intramuscularly.

A large number of synthetic substances chemically related to the epinephrines have been found to have pharmacologic actions similar in one or another respect to the hormones.[31] These substances, together with the epinephrines, are known as sympathomimetic agents.

Because of the similarity between the effects of sympathetic stimulation and of epinephrine, it was long ago suggested that epinephrine might regularly be liberated at the nerve endings and there serve to mediate the impulse from nerve to muscle. As Cannon and Rosenblueth[7] first showed, some sympathomimetic material is indeed liberated from many tissues when the sympathetic innervation is stimulated. The biologic activity of this substance or group of substances was found to be not quite identical with that of epinephrine, and so it was provisionally called sympathin (q.v.). Evidence provided by von Euler[15, 16] and others now indicates that the sympathomimetic substance found in sympathetic nerves and liberated on stimulation is mainly norepinephrine. No purely excitatory or purely inhibitory compounds, corresponding to the hypothetical sympathin E and sympathin I, have been discovered. It is not known whether the sympathins liberated at neuromyal junctions normally diffuse into the blood stream in sufficient amounts to have significant effects elsewhere in the body. If so, their actions would resemble more nearly those of norepinephrine than those of epinephrine.

When the epinephrines act upon smooth muscle and related structures their effects are very similar to those obtained by stimulating the muscle through its sympathetic nerve supply. An intact nerve is not required, however; indeed, most organs are sensitized to these substances by prior denervation. The epinephrines must act therefore not on the nerves or nerve endings but on the effector cells. Since the action of these substances is excitatory in some tissues but inhibitory in others, it seems likely that that site of action is some specialized receptor in the muscle cell which is distinct from the contractile fibers.

Effects of Medullary Hormones. The epinephrines have as their most striking property the ability to affect profoundly the contractility of cardiac and smooth muscle. In addition, epinephrine in particular affects the rate of certain processes in carbohydrate metabolism in striated muscle and liver; both hormones may affect also the secretory activity of the anterior pituitary, the salivary glands and some other organs, and both hormones are lipolytic in adipose tissue.

Actions on smooth muscle. Perhaps because of the well known pressor action of medullary hormones, these substances have usually been considered to be primarily stimulatory in effect. In fact, both epinephrines may act either as ex-

citatory or as inhibitory agents, depending on the organ affected and in some instances on the physiologic state of that organ.[5, 20, 21] Table 6 gives a summary of some of the actions of these substances, together with approximate figures for their relative activities where these are known. As may be seen, with few exceptions the effects of the two substances are in the same direction. Both tend in general to be stimulatory in the vascular system but to be inhibitory in the viscera. When they are excitatory, the activity of the two compounds is of the same order, with epinephrine usually somewhat the more potent. In inhibitory effects, epinephrine is frequently, but not always, much more active than norepinephrine.

In the vascular system the epinephrines have in general a constrictor effect which is particularly noticeable in the skin and mucosa, the splanchnic bed, the kidneys and the cerebral area. Applied locally to the capillary bed of the mesentery, the hormones constrict the metarterioles and precapillary sphincters and so divert much of the blood from the smaller capillaries through only a few main channels of circulation.[8] The pallor of the skin and mucosa typical of medullary hormone action is probably induced in the same way. The two epinephrines seem to have about the same order of activity on the blood vessels in most areas, with the important exception of those in skeletal muscle. In the latter tissue epinephrine has a transient dilatory effect rather than a constrictor action, and the blood flow through a limb may be increased.[1, 22] Norepinephrine, on the other hand, has always been reported to diminish the blood flow through skeletal muscle. Such a difference in activity is in accord with observations in man that peripheral vasoresistance is much increased by norepinephrine but is unchanged or may be diminished by epinephrine.[13, 23]

In the heart both the epinephrines are powerful and specific stimulants of the myocardium and conductile tissue, increasing the force, amplitude and frequency of contraction. As a result of their combined actions on the heart and on the blood vessels, these hormones then raise the blood pressure, the pulse rate and, usually, the cardiac output. The two substances differ somewhat in their effects, however; with epinephrine, only the systolic pressure is increased, presumably because its vasodilator activity in the skeletal muscle bed leads to little change in

TABLE 6. *Comparative Physiologic Activities of Epinephrine and Norepinephrine*[*]

TEST ORGAN OR SYSTEM	EFFECT[†]	RELATIVE ACTIVITY, E/N[†]	REMARKS[†]
Blood pressure Man, cat, dog	Increase	0.2–0.5	E: systolic mainly N: both systolic and diastolic

Blood vessels
  Rabbit's ear
  Denervated limb
	Constriction
	E: Dilation
	N: Constriction
		1–3	

Vasoresistance
    (man)
  Coronary circulation
	E: Decrease
	N: Increase
	Dilation
		
		1 approx.	

Heart
  Frog, perfused
  Dog, amplitude of
    contraction
	Excitation
	Increase
		20
		0.3–1	

Eye Iris dilators	Excitation	15 approx.	Denervated organs sensitized more to N than to E, so activities become approximately equal
Nictitating membrane	Excitation	>10	

Viscera
  Bronchi, histamine
    contr. in guinea pig
	Inhibition	15–20	

Uterus, nonpregnant (rat, cat)	Inhibition	50–150	Both E and N excitors in rabbit, activity ratio 2–5

Intestine
    rat colon
    ileum, rabbit or
      guinea pig
	Inhibition
	Inhibition
		0.2–1
		1–3	

* Data on relative activities mainly from Burn and Hutcheon,[5] Gaddum *et al.*,[21] Lands,[31] and Luduena *et al.*[33]

† E = epinephrine; N = norepinephrine.

total vasoresistance, whereas with norepinephrine both the systolic and the diastolic pressures are elevated.[1, 13, 23] Hence, norepinephrine usually exhibits a greater total pressor activity than does epinephrine. In intact subjects, the increase in diastolic pressure after norepinephrine commonly results in reflex slowing of the heart, whereas after epinephrine tachycardia is typical. Both substances are inhibitors, i.e., dilators, in the coronary circulation.

In other organs, the effects of the medullary hormones vary. They are constrictor in the iris dilator and in the nictitating membrane, and these effects have been much used as internal indicators of medullary secretion. Here, epinephrine is much more active than norepinephrine, and it was the difference in this respect between administered epinephrine and the effects of splanchnic stimulation which first suggested that another pressor substance in addition to epinephrine might be secreted by the gland.[4] Other sites of excitation by these substances include the sphincters of the gastrointestinal tract and bladder, the splenic capsule and the pilomotor muscles. In the gut, on the other hand, the action is usually to inhibit motility, and the bronchial musculature is relaxed. The uterus of the nonpregnant animal is commonly inhibited also, especially by epinephrine, but the pregnant uterus may be excited by these hormones.

Because of these marked effects on the smooth musculature and on the heart, epinephrine finds important pharmacologic uses as a local vasoconstrictor in surgery, as a broncho-dilator in asthma and similar allergic states, and as a heart stimulant in acute emergencies.

Action on skeletal muscle. As was first shown in the pioneer work of Oliver and Shäfer[39] and later in more extended observations by Gruber,[25] epinephrine prolongs the contractile response of muscle during tetanic stimulation and increases the response of the muscle after partial fatigue. This effect was thought for many years to be related to some aspect of neuromuscular transmission; but it has now been shown to occur in isolated tissue whether stimulated directly or indirectly.[3] Cori and Illingworth[12] have suggested that this action possibly may be a consequence of the effect of epinephrine on the enzyme phosphorylase. During the early stages of active contraction of muscle, glycogenolysis occurs rapidly, presumably supplying energy for resynthesis of ATP and hence for continued contraction; but the phosphorylase, which catalyzes the first stage of glycogen breakdown and which seems to be limiting in glycogenolysis, is partially inactivated during exercise (see below). As shown by Cori and Illingworth, epinephrine enhances the rate of resynthesis of the active form of phosphorylase in fatigued muscle. This should allow glyco-genolysis to proceed further and could be responsible for the action of the hormone on the ability of muscle to continue responding to stimulation.

Action on carbohydrate metabolism. As has long been known, epinephrine is a hyperglycemic agent. Less well appreciated is the fact that it has equally marked effects on muscle glycogen and on the lactic acid content of muscle and blood. The hexose phosphate content of muscle also is much increased.[11] These observations indicate that epinephrine acts at an early stage of glycogenolysis, prior to the formation of glucose-6-phosphate, in both muscle and liver. In liver, glucose is then freed by a phosphatase, but in muscle, which lacks the phosphatase, the glycolytic cycle may go to completion with the formation of lactic acid.[10] The lactic acid formed in muscle may be in part later resynthesized to glycogen *in situ,* but much of it diffuses into the blood stream, from which it is largely removed by the liver and returned into glycogen or glucose. Thus both liver and muscle glycogen—the former directly and the latter indirectly—contribute to the increase in blood sugar brought about by epinephrine.[9] These relationships, known as the Cori cycle, may be schematized in the following manner:

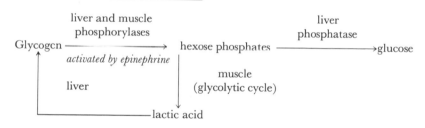

The changes in blood glucose and lactate and in glycogen stores are indicated in Figure 3. It may be noted that the liver glycogen tends to be higher after epinephrine, rather than lower, because of synthesis of glycogen from lactate which has been released from muscle.

The biochemical site of action of epinephrine has been elucidated by Cori, Sutherland and their co-workers.[40, 43, 44] As they showed some years ago, the limiting reaction in glycogenolysis is phosphorolysis, the formation of glucose-1-phosphate from glycogen, which is catalyzed by the enzyme phosphorylase. When liver slices or isolated muscle was incubated with epinephrine the activity of phosphorylase was increased, thus accelerating glycogenolysis.

Subsequently, the phosphorylases of these tissues and also of heart muscle were found to exist in two forms, one active in itself, the other inactive, and subject to interconversion by specific enzyme systems. Inactivation is accompanied by loss of phosphate from the enzyme, reactivation by addition of phosphate from ATP. The activating enzyme therefore is called dephospho-phosphorylase kinase. The effect of the epinephrines (and also of glucagon in liver) is to enhance the activity of the kinase system and so to increase or maintain the amount of phosphorylase in the active form.

More recently, further details of this action of the epinephrines and of glucagon have been uncovered.[45] Activation of the kinase first was

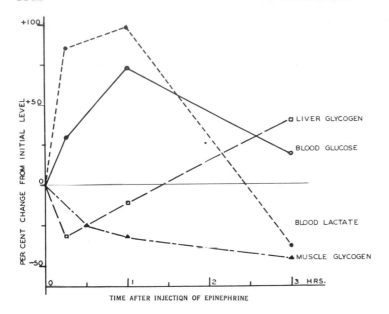

Fig. 3. Effects of epinephrine (0.2 mg. per kg. subcutaneously) on tissue glycogen levels, and concentrations of glucose and lactate in blood of normal fed rats. Initial levels (in mg. per 100 g) were: for muscle glycogen, 570; for liver glycogen, 2400; for blood glucose, 129; for blood lactate, 16. (After Cori et al., *J. biol. Chem.*, 1930, *86:*375 and *Amer. J. Physiol.*, 1930, *94:*557, and unpublished data [Russell].)

found to depend on the formation under the influence of epinephrines of a heat-stable factor which then was effective in the absence of the hormones and in cell-free systems. This factor later was identified as adenosine-3',5'-phosphate, or cyclic adenylic acid (AMP), in which one phosphate group is esterified at two places in the ribose moiety to form a cyclic structure. This substance is formed from ATP by an enzyme system known as the cyclizing enzyme or "cyclase," and both the compound and the enzyme have been found very widely distributed in animal tissues. Cyclic 3',5'-AMP activates the dephospho-phosphorylase kinase in muscle and liver by unknown mechanisms, and possibly may serve to activate a variety of other enzyme systems in other tissues. In skeletal muscle, heart and liver, the epinephrines appear to augment the activity of the cyclizing enzyme and thus increase the concentration of the cyclic AMP, which in turn activates the kinase responsible for converting inactive phosphorylase in these tissues to its active form.

In resting skeletal muscle the phosphorylase normally exists mainly in the inactive or *b* form. It is partly converted to the active or *a* form when the muscle is stimulated to contract and then is inactivated as the muscle fatigues. A conspicuous degree of reactivation of phosphorylase by epinephrine is demonstrable in muscle in which the enzyme has been inactivated during exercise,[12, 32] and as noted above, this action may be responsible for the increase in contractile response of muscle during tetanic

stimulation or in fatigue. In the heart, phosphorylase similarly is found mainly in the inactive *b* form and is activated by the epinephrines. However, this action has not been related clearly to the inotropic effects of the hormones in this organ.[37]

Part of the hyperglycemia induced by epinephrine appears to be due to diminution in the rate of glucose utilization by the peripheral tissues. The glucose tolerance is much reduced in eviscerated or normal subjects, and the arteriovenous glucose difference continues to be small even when the arterial blood glucose level is quite high.[9, 19, 30, 41, 42] This may be due to inhibition of hexokinase by accumulated hexose phosphate in muscle, or it may be in part the result of increased utilization of fatty acids released into plasma by the lipolytic action of the hormones in adipose tissue (see below).

The increase in blood sugar is brought about by quite small amounts of epinephrine—in some species by less than is required to raise the blood pressure. Norepinephrine, on the other hand, has relatively little effect in this respect. In hyperglycemic activity, norepinephrine has been reported to be from one-fifth to one-twentieth as active as epinephrine.[14] Neither lactacidemia nor glycogenolysis in muscle has been observed with moderate doses of norepinephrine. After very large doses, the blood lactate may rise, but only much later than after epinephrine; this suggests that the tissue anoxia produced by vasoconstriction is the mechanism here rather than a direct effect on glycogenolysis.[2, 34] Norepinephrine also has relatively little effect on phosphorylase activity in muscle and liver, although in heart it appears to be as effective as epinephrine.[44]

The different effects of epinephrine and norepinephrine on glycogenolysis may explain some of the differences in their physiologic activities. As has long been known, reduction in *p*H inhibits motility of smooth muscle *in vitro* and produces vasodilation *in vivo*. Lundholm has presented evidence showing that the vasodilator activity of epinephrine in skeletal muscle is related to the production of lactic acid, and that the inhibitory effects of both epinephrines in several kinds of smooth muscle may be correlated with the degree of glycogenolysis induced.[35, 36, 38] It seems likely that the general vasoconstrictor action of epinephrine is modified in skeletal muscle by the concomitant effects of the hormone on the metabolism of the muscle. The difference in metabolic activities of epinephrine and norepinephrine also probably accounts for yet another phenomenon. After adrenomedullation, neither hypoglycemia nor severe operative trauma has any effect on the muscle glycogen or blood lactate, although in intact animals strong glycogenolysis regularly occurs in such conditions.[2] Norepinephrine may be secreted at nerve endings and elsewhere, but it is evident that even after massive sympathetic stimulation the only source of significant quantities of circulating epinephrine is the adrenal medulla.

Glycogenolytic activity by epinephrine following sympathetic stimulation is a rather common occurrence in normal individuals. In states of emotional excitement, hyperglycemia and even glycosuria are often noted. Similarly, after injuries of all kinds and after many drugs, hyperglycemia and lactacidemia are common. Hypoglycemia of moderate degree also leads to glycogenolysis in muscle and to a rebound of the blood glucose. The susceptibility of glycogen to epinephrine makes it necessary to avoid adrenal-stimulating drugs, such as morphine or ether, and operative trauma or anoxia as well, in any studies of the metabolism of glycogen.

The hyperglycemic effect of epinephrine is in physiologic counterpoise to the action of insulin. When the blood sugar is low (either because of insulin action or from other causes) the secretion of epinephrine is stimulated, and so the return of the blood sugar to normal is hastened. One of the few abnormalities of the adrenodemedullated animal is its slow spontaneous recovery from hypoglycemia. Since increasing the blood sugar calls forth secretion of insulin, it is apparent that these hormones together contribute greatly to the homeostatic regulation of the blood sugar. However, it should be noted that, although epinephrine and insulin are opposed with respect to their effects on the blood sugar, the antagonism does not extend to most other aspects of the physiology of either hormone. Epinephrine cannot be classed as a diabetogenic substance.

Lipolytic action. Despite scattered reports of ketonuria and of increase in liver fat after epinephrine injection and other suggestions of effects of the medullary hormones on fat metabolism, little has been known with certainty about such actions until quite recently. Now, however, studies of plasma fatty acids (nonesterified fatty acids, FFA) and their release from adipose tissue have shown clearly that both epinephrine and norepinephrine promote lipolysis in adipose tissue (for review, see Vaughan[47]). This action appears to be due to activation of a tissue lipase and to be distinct from the actions of the hormones on carbohydrate metabolism. Recent evidence suggests that the mechanism of this activation may be similar to that by which these substances activate phosphorylases in other tissues, i.e., via the formation of cyclic 3',5'-AMP by activation of the cyclizing enzyme system.

In vivo, plasma fatty acids are increased by both hormones but much more so by norepinephrine than by epinephrine. Probably this difference is related to the much greater hyperglycemia after epinephrine, which together with insulin would tend to inhibit the release of the fatty acids from the adipose tissue. The increases in plasma fatty acids are produced by concentrations of the hormones within the higher range of normal, and similar effects have been reported to be produced by emotional disturbances, presumably mediated by adrenomedullary secretion. Hence, these actions may be significant in the physiologic control of fat metabolism.

Other activities. Epinephrine has been shown to increase secretion by the anterior pituitary of adrenotrophin, thyrotrophin and gonadotrophins. Insofar as available data indicate, norepinephrine is relatively feeble in this regard. The physiologic significance of these effects is not known, but some of the actions previously attributed to epinephrine now seem to be more directly those of other hormones. For example, involution of lymphoid tissue—long known to follow the administration of epinephrine—is now known to be brought about by the adrenal cortical steroids secreted in response to adreno-corticotrophin.

The secretory activity of the salivary glands is decreased by epinephrine, but sweating is increased. Both of these effects are readily apparent in man in states of anxiety or fear.

An immediate but short-lived increase in the oxygen consumption follows the administration of epinephrine. The mechanism of this action is not known, but it is thought to be related to the metabolism of the lactic acid released from muscle.

Control of Adrenomedullary Secretion. Factors affecting the secretion of epinephrine were first studied by Cannon and his co-workers,[6] who used the biologic actions of the hormones, such as those on heart rate or on contraction of the nictitating membrane, as internal indicators of medullary activity. By these means, it was soon found that the rate of secretion by this organ varied widely under different circumstances. In basal conditions, as in deep sleep or narcosis, little secretion seemed to be produced; in normal waking conditions, there was just detectable activity; but on stimulation by such procedures as pain, cold or anoxia, by emotional excitement, or by hypoglycemia, secretion of the hormone was greatly increased. These observations have been confirmed more recently by pharmacologic or chemical assays applied to the adrenal gland or adrenal venous blood in animals, or to urinary excretory products in man.[16, 20] Among other stimuli shown to elicit increased medullary activity are exercise (even walking at a moderate pace), anxiety as well as fear or anger, hemorrhage or hypotension, and many drugs, including morphine and ether. The lability of the sympathetic–adrenomedullary system must be recalled in the interpretation or planning of any experimental procedure in man or animals.

All of these stimuli to adrenomedullary secretion are transmitted via hypothalamic nervous centers and the sympathetic innervation of the gland. Direct stimulation of certain centers in the posterior paraventricular area of the hypothalamus may induce a tenfold increase in the rate of medullary secretion. The secretion

of epinephrine and of norepinephrine may be controlled differentially. According to Folkow and von Euler,[18] stimulation of certain areas in the hypothalamus enhances the secretion of epinephrine more than that of norepinephrine, whereas stimulation of other areas nearby has the converse effect. Further, different external stimuli may elicit adrenal secretion in which the proportions of the two hormones differ characteristically. Afferent nerve stimulation or pain seems to increase mainly epinephrine output, whereas asphyxia has little differential effect and carotid occlusion increases norepinephrine secretion to a greater extent. Several workers agree that hypoglycemia stimulates the secretion of epinephrine almost exclusively.[17, 24, 27, 28] Studies in man and other primates seem to indicate that anxiety and related emotional states stimulate mainly norepinephrine secretion. Thus, two semidistinct systems may exist for the control of adrenomedullary activity.

The function of the adrenomedullary activity has been thought by Cannon and others to be one of adaptation—an emergency mechanism helpful in preparing an animal for "flight or fight" or other activity.[6] The secretion of epinephrine is undoubtedly augmented by noxious stimuli, and many of its effects (such as the increase in heart action and in blood flow through the muscles, or as the "warming up" of the glycogenolytic system) may be considered useful responses to these stimuli. However, it is not clear that the secretion of epinephrines is a necessary or even completely desirable occurrence in higher animals when they are endeavoring to adapt to environmental changes. Some early data purported to show that adrenodemedullated animals could not withstand trauma, cold and the like as well as normal animals; but these observations were made before the importance of the adrenal cortical function was realized, and in many cases damage to the cortices incidental to the removal of the adrenal medullae was responsible for the changes seen. Reinvestigation of some of these points is now required.

As almost anyone knows from personal experience, medullary secretion in response to purely emotional stimuli is not always helpful and may sometimes be almost paralyzing. It is debatable whether this represents a useless physiologic "fault" or whether it is the price one pays for the possession of an autonomic system which is helpful in real, if not fancied, emergencies.

REFERENCES

The Adrenal Cortex

1. Albright, F. *Harvey Lect.,* 1942–43, *38:*123–186.
2. Baker, B. L., Ingle, D. J. and Li, C. H. *Amer. J. Anat.,* 1951, *88:*313–349.
3. Barger, A. C., Berlin, R. D. and Tulenko, J. F. *Endocrinology,* 1958, *62:*804–815.
4. Blair-West, J. R., Coghlan, J. P., Denton, D. A., Goding, J. R., Wintour, M. and Wright, R. O. *Recent Progr. Hormone Res.,* 1963, *19:*311–362.
5. Bondy, P. K., Ingle, D. J. and Meeks, R. C. *Endocrinology,* 1954, *55:*355–360.
6. Bush, I. E. *J. Endocr.,* 1953, *9:*95–100.
7. Chen, G. and Wickel, A. *Endocrinology,* 1952, *51:*21–25.
8. Davis, J. O. *Recent Progr. Hormone Res.,* 1961, *17:*293–352.
9. Deane, H. W. and Greep, R. O. *Endocrinology,* 1949, *45:* 42–55.
10. Deane, H. W., Shaw, J. H. and Greep, R. O. *Endocrinology,* 1948, *43:*133–153.
11. Dorfman, R. I. Pp. 325–362 in *Hormone assay,* Emmens, C. W., ed. New York, Academic Press, 1950.
12. Dorfman, R. I. *Physiol. Rev.,* 1954, *34:*138–166.
13. Dougherty, T. F. *Recent Progr. Hormone Res.,* 1952, *7:*307–330.
14. Dougherty, T. F. and White, A. *Endocrinology,* 1944, *35:* 1–14.
15. Dougherty, T. F. and White, A. *Amer. J. Anat.,* 1945, *77:*81–116.
16. Engel, F. L. Pp. 62–78 in *Pituitary-adrenal function,* Amer. Assoc. for Advancement of Science, Washington, 1950.
17. Engel, F. L. *Endocrinology,* 1952, *50:*462–477.
18. Farrell, G. *Physiol. Rev.,* 1958, *38:*709–728.
19. Farrell, G. *Recent Progr. Hormone Res.,* 1959, *15:*275–298.
20. Farrell, G. L., Rauschkolb, E. W. and Royce, P. C. *Amer. J. Physiol.,* 1955, *182:*269–272.
21. Fried, J. and Borman, A. *Vitam. and Horm.,* 1958, *16:*304–374.
22. Fritz, I. and Levine, R. *Amer. J. Physiol.,* 1951, *165:*457–465.
23. Gaudino, M. and Levitt, M. F. *J. clin. Invest.,* 1949, *28:* 1487–1497.
24. Gaunt, R., Birnie, J. H. and Eversole, W. J. *Physiol. Rev.,* 1949, *29:*281–310.
25. Gaunt, R., Renzi, A. A. and Chart, J. J. *J. clin. Endocr.,* 1955, *15:*621–646.
26. Germuth, F. G. *Pharmacol. Rev.,* 1956, *8:*1–24.
27. Giroud, C. J. P., Stachenko, J. and Venning, E. H. *Proc. Soc. exp. Biol. (N. Y.),* 1956, *92:*154–158.
28. Greer, M. A. *Recent Progr. Hormone Res.,* 1957, *13:*67–104.
29. Grundy, H. M., Simpson, S. A., Tait, J. F. and Woodford, M. *Acta endocr. (Kbh.),* 1952, *11:*199–220.
30. Guillemin, R. *Recent Progr. Hormone Res.,* 1964, *20:*89–122.
31. Guillemin, R. and Schally, A. V. Pp. 314–327 in *Advances in neuroendocrinology.* A. V., Nalbandov, ed. Urbana, University of Illinois Press, 1963.
32. Harrison, H. E. and Darrow, D. C. *J. clin. Invest.,* 1938, *17:*77–86.

33. Harrison, H. E. and Darrow, D. C. *Amer. J. Physiol.,* 1939, *125:*631–643.
34. Harrop, G. A., Nicholson, W. M. and Strauss, M. J. *exp. Med.,* 1936, *64:*233–251.
35. Hechter, O. and Pincus, G. *Physiol. Rev.,* 1954, *34:*459–496.
36. Hench, P. S., Kendall, E. C., Slocumb, C. H. and Polley, H. F. *Arch. intern. Med.,* 1950, *86:*545–666.
37. Ingle, D. J. *Endocrinology,* 1944, *34:*191–202.
38. Ingle, D. J. *J. Endocr.,* 1952, *8:*xxiii–xxxvii.
39. Ingle, D. J. *Acta endocr. (Kbh.),* 1954, *17:*172–186.
40. Ingle, D. J. *Diabetes,* 1956, *5:*187–193.
41. Ingle, D. J., Meeks, R. C. and Thomas, K. E. *Endocrinology,* 1951, *49:*703–708.
42. Ingle, D. J., Sheppard, R., Evans, J. S. and Kuizenga, M. H. *Endocrinology,* 1945, *37:*341–356.
43. Locket, M. F. *J. Physiol.,* 1949, *109:*250–257.
44. Loeb, R. F. *Harvey Lect.,* 1941–42, *37:*100–128.
45. Long, C. N. H. *Harvey Lect.,* 1936–37, *32:*194–228; also, *Medicine,* 1937, *16:*215–247.
46. Long, C. N. H. *Fed. Proc.,* 1947, *6:*461–471.
47. Long, C. N. H., Katzin, G. and Fry, E. G. *Endocrinology,* 1940, *26:*309–344.
48. Long, C. N. H. and Lukens, F. D. W. *J. exp. Med.,* 1936, *63:*465–490.
49. Lyster, S. C., Barnes, L. E., Lund, G. H., Meinzinger, M. M. and Byrnes, W. W. *Proc. Soc. exp. Biol. (N. Y.),* 1957, *94:*159–162.
50. Mason, H. L. and Engstrom, W. W. *Physiol. Rev.,* 1950, *30:*321–374.
51. Munson, P. L. and Briggs, F. N. *Recent Progr. Hormone Res.,* 1955, *11:*83–107.
52. Noble, R. L. In: *The hormones,* vol. 2. Pincus, G. and Thimann, K. V., eds. New York, Academic Press, 1950; ibid., vol. 3, 1955.
53. Pauly, J. E. *Endocrinology,* 1957, *60:*247–264.
54. Ramey, E. R., Goldstein, M. S. and Levine, R. *Amer. J. Physiol.,* 1951, *165:*450–455.
55. Rauschkolb, E. W., Farrell, G. L. and Kaletsky, S. *Amer. J. Physiol.,* 1956, *184:*55–58.
56. Reichstein, T. and Shoppee, C. W. *Vitam. and Horm.,* 1943, *1:*346–413.
57. Roberts, K. E. and Pitts, R. F. *Endocrinology,* 1952, *50:* 51–60.
58. Royce, P. C. and Sayers, G. *Endocrinology,* 1958, *63:*794–800.
59. Saffran, M. *Canad. J. Biochem. Physiol.,* 1959, *37:*319–330.
60. Sayers, G. *Physiol. Rev.,* 1950, *30:*241–320.
61. Sayers, G. and Sayers, M. A. *Endocrinology,* 1947, *40:* 265–273.
62. Sayers, G., Redgate, E. S. and Royce, P. C. *Ann. Rev. Physiol.,* 1958, *20:*243–274.
63. Sayers, G., Sayers, M. A., Liang, T. Y. and Long, C. N. H. *Endocrinology,* 1946, *38:*1–9.
64. Scow, R. O., Chernick, S. S. and Guarco, B. A. *Diabetes,* 1959, *8:*132–142.
65. Silber, R. H. and Porter, C. C. *Endocrinology,* 1953, *52:* 518–525.
66. Simpson, S. A. and Tait, J. F. *Endocrinology,* 1952, *50:*150–161.
67. Simpson, S. A. and Tait, J. F. *Recent Progr. Hormone Res.,* 1955, *11:*183–209.
68. Singer, B. and Stack-Dunne, M. P. *J. Endocr.,* 1955, *12:* 130–145.
69. Singer, F. M. and Borman, A. *Proc. Soc. exp. Biol. (N. Y.),* 1957, *92:*23–26.
70. Stafford, R. O., Barnes, L. E., Borman, B. J. and Meinzinger, M. M. *Proc. Soc. exp. Biol. (N. Y.),* 1955, *89:*371–374.

71. STEPHENSON, N. R. *Canad. J. Biochem. Physiol.*, 1956, *34:* 253–258.

72. SWINGLE, W. W., BRANNICK, L. J., OSBORN, M. and GLENISTER, D. *Proc. Soc. exp. Biol. (N. Y.),* 1957, *96:* 446–452.

73. SWINGLE, W. W., BRANNICK, L. J., PARLOW, A. F. P., BAKER, C. and LeBRIE, S. *Endocrinology,* 1956, *59:*226–232.

74. SWINGLE, W. W., PARKINS, W. M., TAYLOR, A. R. and HAYS, H. W. *Amer. J. Physiol.,* 1936, *116:*438–445.

75. SWINGLE, W. W. and REMINGTON, J. W. *Physiol. Rev.,* 1944, *24:*89–127.

76. SYDNOR, K. L. and SAYERS, G. *Endocrinology,* 1954, *55:* 621–636.

77. THORN, G. W., FORSHAM, P. H., FRAWLEY, T. F., HILL, S. R., ROCHE, M., STACHELIN, D. and WILSON, D. L. *New Engl. J. Med.,* 1950, *242:*783–793, 824–834, 865–872.

78. WELT, I. D., STETTIN, D. W., INGLE, D. J. and MORLEY, E. H. *J. biol. Chem.,* 1952, *197:*57–66.

THE ADRENAL MEDULLA

1. BARCROFT, H. and KONZETT, H. *J. Physiol.,* 1949, *110:* 194–206.

2. BLOOM, W. R. and RUSSELL, J. A. *Amer. J. Physiol.,* 1955, *183:*356–364.

3. BROWN, G. L., BÜLBRING, E. and BURNS, B. D. *J. Physiol.,* 1948, *107:*115–128.

4. BÜLBRING, E. and BURN, J. H. *Brit. J. Pharmacol.,* 1949, *4:* 202–208.

5. BURN, J. H. and HUTCHEON, D. E. *Brit. J. Pharmacol.,* 1949, *4:*373–380.

6. CANNON, W. B. *Bodily changes in pain, hunger, fear, and rage.* 2nd ed. New York, D. Appleton & Co., 1929.

7. CANNON, W. B. and ROSENBLUETH, A. *Autonomic neuroeffector systems.* New York, Macmillan Co., 1937.

8. CHAMBERS, R. and ZWEIFACH, B. W. *Amer. J. Anat.,* 1944, *75:*173–205.

9. CORI, C. F. *Physiol. Rev.,* 1931, *11:*143–275.

10. CORI, C. F. *Endocrinology,* 1940, *26:*285–296.

11. CORI, C. F. and CORI, G. T. *J. biol. Chem.,* 1931, *94:*581–591.

12. CORI, G. T. and ILLINGWORTH, B. *Biochim. biophys. acta,* 1956, *21:*105–110.

13. DiSALVO, R. S., BLOOM, W. L., BRUST, A. A., FERGUSON, R. W. and FERRIS, E. B. *J. clin. Invest.,* 1956, *35:*568–577.

14. ELLIS, S. *Pharmacol. Rev.,* 1956, *8:*485–562.

15. VON EULER, U. S. *Pharmacol. Rev.,* 1951, *3:*247–277.

16. VON EULER, U. S. *Noradrenaline.* Springfield, Ill., C. C Thomas, 1956.

17. VON EULER, U. S. and LUFT, R. *Metabolism,* 1952, *1:*528–532.

18. FOLKOW, B. and VON EULER, U. S. *Circulation Res.,* 1954, *2:*191–195.

19. FRITZ, I. B., SHATTON, J., MORTON, J. V. and LEVINE, R. *Amer. J. Physiol.,* 1957, *189:*57–62.

20. GADDUM, J. H. and HOLTZBAUER, M. *Vitam. and Horm.,* 1957, *15:*151–203.

21. GADDUM, J. H., PEART, W. S. and VOGT, M. *J. Physiol.,* 1949, *108:*467–481.

22. GOLDENBERG, M., FABER, M., ALSTON, E. J. and CHARGAFF, E. C. *Science,* 1949, *109:*534–535.

23. GOLDENBERG, M., PINES, K. L., BALDWIN, E. DeF., GREENE, D. G. and ROH, C. E. *Amer. J. Med.,* 1948, *5:*792–806.

24. GOLDFIEN, A., ZILELI, M. S., DESPOINTS, R. H. and BETHUNE, J. E. *Endocrinology,* 1958, *62:*749–757.

25. GRUBER, C. M. *Amer. J. Physiol.,* 1914, *33:*335–355.

26. HARRIS, R. E. and INGLE, D. J. *Amer. J. Physiol.,* 1940, *130:*151–154.

27. HÖKFELT, B. *Endocrinology,* 1953, *53:*536–540.

28. HOLTZBAUER, M. and VOGT, M. *Brit. J. Pharmacol.,* 1954, *9:*249–252.

29. INGLE, D. J., HALES, W. M. and HASELRUD, G. M. *Amer. J. Physiol.,* 1936, *114:*653–656.

30. INGLE, D. J. and NEZAMIS, J. E. *Endocrinology,* 1950, *46:* 14–20.

31. LANDS, A. M. *Pharmacol. Rev.,* 1949, *1:*279–309.

32. LEONARD, S. L. *Endocrinology,* 1957, *60:*619–624.

33. LUDUENA, F. P., ANANENKO, E., SIEGMUND, O. H. and MILLER, L. C. *J. Pharmacol.,* 1949, *95:*155–170.

34. LUNDHOLM, L. *Acta physiol. scand.,* 1950, *21:*195–204.

35. LUNDHOLM, L. *Acta physiol. scand.,* 1956, *39*(Suppl. 133): 1–52.

36. LUNDHOLM, L. and MOHME-LUNDHOLM, E. *Acta physiol. scand.,* 1957, *38:*237–254.

37. MAYER, S. E., COTTON, M. DeV. and MORAN, N. C. *J. Pharmacol. exp. Therap.,* 1963, *139:*275–282.

38. MOHME-LUNDHOLM, E. *Acta physiol. scand.,* 1953, *29* (Suppl. 108):1–63.

39. OLIVER, G. and SHÄFER, E. A. *J. Physiol.,* 1895, *18:*230–276.

40. RALL, T. W., SUTHERLAND, E. W. and BERTHET, J. *J. biol. Chem.,* 1957, *224:*463–475.

41. SOMOGYI, M. *J. biol. Chem.,* 1950, *186:*513–526.

42. SOMOGYI, M. *Endocrinology,* 1951, *49:*774–781.

43. SUTHERLAND, E. W. *Ann. N. Y. Acad. Sci.,* 1951, *54:*693–706.

44. SUTHERLAND, E. W. and CORI, C. F. *J. biol. Chem.,* 1951, *188:*531–543.

45. SUTHERLAND, E. W. and RALL, T. W. *Pharmacol. Rev.,* 1960, *12:*265–299.

46. TULLAR, B. F. *Science,* 1949, *109:*536–537.

47. VAUGHAN, M. *J. Lipid Res.,* 1962, *2:*293–316.

48. WEINER, N. In: *The hormones,* vol. 4, Pincus, G., Thimann, K. V. and Astwood, E. B. eds. New York, Academic Press, 1964.

CHAPTER 60

The Thyroid Gland

By SEYMOUR J. KLEBANOFF

THE function of the thyroid gland in vertebrates, including man, is to synthesize and secrete biologically active iodinated organic compounds in response to the animal's needs.

In certain protochordates (forms intermediate between invertebrates and vertebrates), an organ—the endostyle—in the floor of the pharynx iodinates proteins and excretes them into the gastrointestinal tract.[13] They are digested and the products of digestion are absorbed. The ammocoete, the larva of the lamprey, a cyclostome, is a primitive vertebrate in which the endostyle loses its connection to the pharynx during metamorphosis and becomes an organ of internal secretion.[13] The evolution of specialized thyroid tissue may have been required to maintain the high iodide concentration needed for iodoprotein synthesis when the organism moved from sea to land, where iodine is scarce.[19]

In man, the thyroid gland develops from the floor of the pharynx as an invagination of the gastrointestinal tract at the junction of the first and second branchial arches and migrates down the midline to the neck.[8] The site of origin is marked by a dimple on the base of the tongue—the foramen cecum. The thyroglossal duct, which marks the path of migration, usually atrophies completely before birth. Its persistence may lead to cystic enlargement, forming a thyroglossal cyst. By about the fifteenth week of embryonic life the gland begins to synthesize thyroid hormones.

STRUCTURE[59]

In mammals the thyroid consists of two lobes fixed by fibrous tissue to either side of the trachea and joined by a thin isthmus of thyroid or connective tissue over the anterior surface of the trachea below the cricoid cartilage. The pyramidal lobe, a vestige of the thyroglossal duct, often arises from the isthmus. Aberrant thyroid tissue may lie along the thyroid migration path or elsewhere in the neck or upper thoracic region. The gland is variable in size, with an average weight in the normal man of 12 to 22 grams. The lateral lobes measure approximately 4 cm. from the upper or superior pole to the less prominent lower or inferior pole.

The parathyroid glands usually lie adjacent to the posterior surface of the lateral lobes and may be embedded in thyroid tissue. The recurrent laryngeal nerves lie between the lateral lobes and the trachea and may be damaged during surgery.

Thyroid tissue consists of small follicles which are the primary anatomic and functional units of the gland. They are roughly spherical, lined with a single layer of epithelial cells and filled with a homogeneous gelatinous material called colloid (Fig. 5). The inner or apical cell surface is covered with tiny villi which greatly increase the area of contact between colloid and cell. The basal or outer cell surface is adjacent to a capillary. Minute pores in the capillary endothelial lining allow plasma to come into direct contact with the basement membrane of the cell. The thyroid cell contains a nucleus, usually near its base; numerous rod shaped mitochondria; a Golgi apparatus, consisting of numerous vesicles or sacs near the nucleus; and endoplasmic reticulum consisting of vesicles or channels (ergastoplasmic vesicles) on the outer surface of which are many particles rich in ribonucleic acid (ribosomes). Many of the thyroid vesicles contain material indistinguishable from colloid and are called colloid droplets or "secretory" droplets. A second type of parenchymal cell called the parafollicular or light cell is present in small numbers in the follicular lining. These cells do not come into direct contact with the colloid and their function is unknown. Between the follicles is a small amount of loose connective tissue richly invested with capillaries and lymph vessels.

The thyroid gland has an abundant blood supply, which has been estimated at 3 to 7 ml. per gram of tissue per minute,[44] or about 1 per cent of the cardiac output. It is innervated by sympathetic and parasympathetic fibers, which enter the thyroid with the blood vessels and form extensive plexuses in the walls of the small arteries. This innervation does not have a direct secretory effect on the thyroid cells but affects thyroid function indirectly by controlling the rate of blood flow. Sympathetic stimulation decreases and parasympathetic stimulation increases blood flow and iodide uptake.[44] Nervous stimuli do not directly affect the secretion rate of thyroid hormone but may affect the gland's response to thyroid-stimulating hormone (TSH).[44]

THYROID HORMONES

The successful treatment of hypothyroidism by thyroid extracts in the early 1890's stimulated extensive investigation of the chemistry of

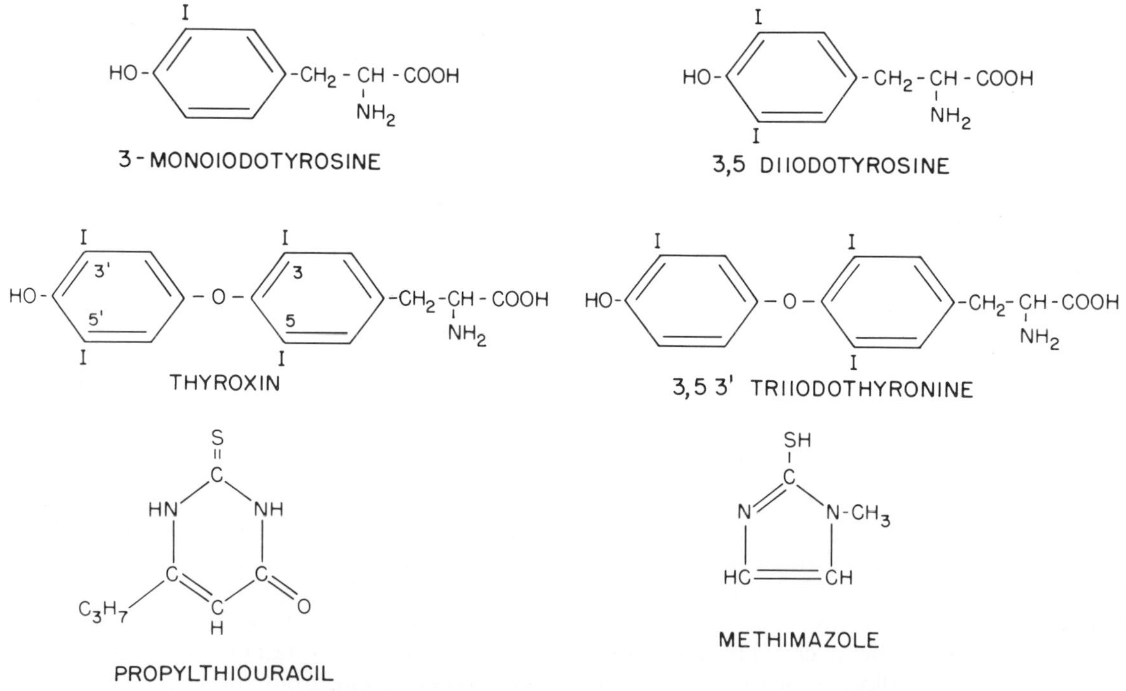

Fig. 1. Structural formulas of compounds related to the thyroid gland.

thyroid tissue. Baumann in 1895 reported that the thyroid gland contained an extremely high concentration of iodine. Kendall in 1914 isolated from the hydrolysate of thyroid tissue a small amount of a crystalline material which contained 65 per cent iodine and which was physiologically active.[31] He called this substance *thyroxin.* In 1926–27, Harington established the structure of thyroxin, which he confirmed by synthesis,[23] as the tetraiodo derivative of the p-hydroxyphenyl ether of tyrosine (Fig. 1). A second physiologically active hormone, 3, 5, 3′ triiodothyronine, a compound similar in structure to thyroxin, except that it lacks one iodine in the phenolic ring (Fig. 1), also is present in the thyroid.[21]

Recently, a substance—thyrocalcitonin— which lowers serum calcium and inorganic phosphate levels, has been partially purified from the thyroid glands of a number of species[26] (see Chap. 61). It is distinct from thyroxin and triiodothyronine and may be a polypeptide. Its physiologic role is unknown.

ABSORPTION AND DISTRIBUTION OF IODIDE

The use of radioactive iodide (I*) as a biologic "tracer" has greatly increased our knowledge of iodide metabolism. The isotope most commonly employed is I^{131}, which has a half-life of 8.1 days. Other isotopes of iodine, e.g., I^{125} (half-life, 60.2 days) and I^{132} (half-life, 2.3 hours) also are used. A tracer dose of I* is one which does not increase appreciably the total amount of iodide in the body and, therefore, has no pharmacologic effect but which mixes with an inorganic iodide "compartment" (or "pool") of the body and labels it. The distribution and chemical transformations of the isotopic label can be determined by isolation and measurement with suitable detectors. Endogenous iodide metabolism can be followed in this way since it is assumed that endogenous iodide and I* are metabolized in the same way. An outline of iodide metabolism is shown in Figure 2.

Iodine is a rare element irregularly distributed over the earth's surface. Its concentration in sea water is about ten times that in fresh water, and it is found in relatively high concentration in sea food and in vegetation growing close to the sea (Table 1). Since a deficiency of iodine in the diet may exist in certain areas and may lead to goiter (see below), iodized salt containing 0.005 to 0.01 per cent iodide is generally employed as table salt.

In the average North American diet, 100 to 200 μg. of iodine are ingested per day as in-

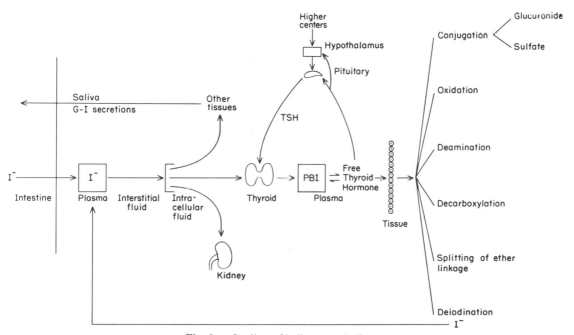

Fig. 2. Outline of iodine metabolism.

TABLE 1. *Average Iodine Content of Certain Foods*

	Iodine content (μg/kg)				Iodine content (μg/kg)	
	Fresh basis	Dry basis			Fresh basis	Dry basis
MILK & MILK PRODUCTS				**SHELL FISH**		
Milk (cow's)	35			Crab and crabmeat	308	1292
Cheese	51			Oysters	577	4712
Butter	56			Clams	783	3595
Mean	47			Lobster	1020	4744
				Shrimps	1300	4987
EGGS				Mean	798	3866
Hen's eggs Mean	93			**CEREAL GRAINS & PRODUCTS**		
MEAT & MEAT PRODUCTS				Rice	22	39
Mutton	27			Maize	27	43
Beef	28			Wheat	37	44
Veal	28			Flour	42	
Pork	45			Bread	58	
Bacon	77			Barley	58	92
Lard	97			Oats	60	91
Mean	50			Rye	72	84
FISH				Mean	47	65
(i) Marine Fish				**VEGETABLES**		
Sole	163	1072		Mangolds	11	192
Sea bass	250	471		Gourds, pumpkins, marrow	12	600
Sardines	284	745		Cauliflower	12	221
Mackerel	371	1031		Beetroot	21	233
Halibut	520	2225		Onions	22	204
Herring	520	1358		Cucumber	25	400
Sea perch	742	3105		Lettuce	26	668
Cod	1463	7493		Carrots	38	202
Haddock	3180	15941		Turnips	40	343
Mean	832	3715		Asparagus	42	1102
(ii) Anadromous Fish				Potatoes	45	197
Sea trout	320	1028		Cabbage	52	260
Salmon	341	1030		Spinach*	201	1636
Mean	330	1029		Watercress*	180	1600
(iii) Freshwater Fish				Mean*	29	385
Carp	17	68		**LEGUMES**		
River bass	30	115		Peas	23	223
Lake trout	31	88		Beans	36	245
River perch	40	194		Mean	30	234
Mean	30	116		**FRUITS**		
FISH OILS				Pears	10	62
Salmon oil	2450			Tomatoes	17	196
Cod-liver oil	8387			Apples	16	277
All others taken together	3052			Cranberries	29	100
Mean	4630			Mean	18	159

*Excluded from calculation of mean. (From Wayne, E. J., Koutras, D. A. and Alexander, W. D. *Clinical aspects of iodine metabolism.* Oxford, Blackwell Scientific Publications, Ltd., 1964. Reproduced by permission of the publisher.)

organic iodide, iodine or organically bound iodine. Most of the ingested iodine and organically bound iodine is reduced to inorganic iodide in the gastrointestinal tract prior to absorption. Exceptions are the thyroid hormones and certain drugs, such as dyes used in x-ray visualization of the gallbladder, which may be absorbed intact. Absorption can occur at all levels of the gastrointestinal tract but is greatest in the small intestine. It is extremely rapid, particularly in a fasting state, when 5 per cent of an oral dose of I* is absorbed per minute.[30]

Iodide enters the blood stream, where its plasma concentration averages 0.3 to 0.5 μg. per 100 ml. The RBC: plasma iodide ratio is 1:1.8, which is equivalent to the relative water distribution between RBC and plasma. Iodide readily passes out of the blood stream into the interstitial spaces and from there into certain cells of the body. Ultimately, its area of distribution is 35 per cent of the body weight, almost twice the volume of the extracellular fluid. Iodide is concentrated by certain cells against an electrochemical gradient—the phenomenon of the iodide "trap." Organs concentrating iodide in this way include salivary gland, mammary gland, stomach, thyroid, skin (rat), choroid plexus and placenta.[10] The iodide concentration in the cell or in the cellular secretions may be 20 to 40 times that of serum.

Some of the iodide which leaves plasma is secreted in sweat, saliva and gastrointestinal secretions. The latter portion is largely reabsorbed along with dietary iodide, but some may be lost from the body. Small amounts of iodine also may be lost in sweat and expired air. Secretion of iodide in the milk of lactating females can result in considerable iodine loss. Under normal conditions, most of the iodide leaving plasma is either taken up by the thyroid (about one-third) or excreted by the kidney (about two-thirds). The amount of iodide taken up by the thyroid in humans varies from 0.5 to 6.0 μg. per hour; the mean is 2.2 μg. per hour.[57] The mean urinary iodine excretion (which is almost entirely iodide) is 150 μg. in 24 hours.[42] It is lower in goitrous regions of the world, where the dietary intake of iodine is low. Iodide is excreted by the glomerulus and reabsorption by the renal tubules is passive and incomplete. There is no tubular secretion of iodide.

SYNTHESIS OF THYROID HORMONES

The γ rays of I[131] can be measured by a sensitive detector positioned over the thyroid gland; the "thyroid uptake test" (which measures the percentage of a dose of I* present in the gland at a standard time after administration) is now a routine diagnostic procedure. The uptake of I[131] is high in hyperthyroidism and low in hypothyroidism (Fig. 3). The accumulation of I* by the gland, i.e., the trapping of iodide and the synthesis of thyroid hormones, is measured during the early stages of the thyroid uptake test. As the labeled hormones are secreted, the I* concentration of the gland reaches a maximum and falls. The secreted hormones are metabolized in the peripheral tissues and the released iodide re-enters the blood stream. The I* concentration of the thyroid gland continues to fall at a slower rate as some of the newly released I* re-enters the thyroid gland and some is lost from the body. This dynamic picture is best seen in the hyperthyroid state (Fig. 3), in which the metabolism of iodine is accelerated.

The iodinated components of the gland are many and are constantly being synthesized and removed, i.e., are in constant "turnover." They include 3, 5 diiodotyrosine (40 to 45 per cent), 3 monoiodotyrosine (15 to 20 per cent),

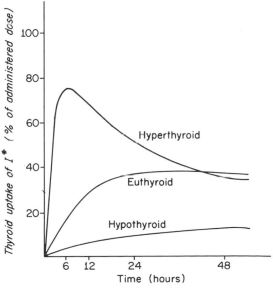

Fig. 3. Typical iodine uptake curve in euthyroid, hypothyroid and hyperthyroid subjects.

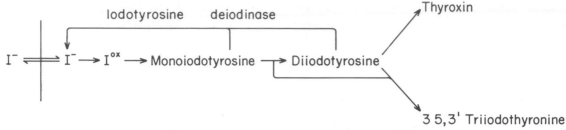

Fig. 4.   Pathway of thyroid hormone synthesis.

thyroxine (10 to 15 per cent) and 3, 5, 3′ triiodothyronine (2 to 3 per cent of the total iodine). Neither mono- nor diiodotyrosine has hormonal activity. Trace amounts of 3, 3′ diiodothyronine, 3, 3′, 5′ triiodothyronine, and iodohistidine also have been reported to be present in the thyroid gland. The pathway of thyroid hormone synthesis is shown in Figure 4.

Thyroidal Iodide Transport.[22, 61]   Iodide is transported across the cell membrane against an electrochemical gradient. The thyroid: serum (T/S) ratio is normally about 25:1. It is decreased by hypophysectomy, excess iodide and thyroid hormone administration and is increased by thyrotrophin. Antithyroid agents, such as propylthiouracil, which inhibit the conversion of iodide to organic form but do not affect the transport mechanism (see below) can increase the T/S ratio to 500:1. Iodide appears to be concentrated at the basal membrane against an electrical potential of 50 mV. (i.e., the intracellular potential is about 50 mV. negative with respect to the interstitial fluid) and to move down an electrical gradient into the lumen, which has the same potential as the interstitial fluid.[63]

Mechanism of iodide concentration.[22, 61]   Iodide transport against an electrochemical gradient indicates that iodide does not cross the membrane by simple diffusion but by an active transport mechanism which requires an intact cell and the participation of metabolic processes. Concentration of iodide *in vitro* is decreased by inhibitors of respiration such as cyanide, by anaerobiasis, and by agents which uncouple oxidative phosphorylation such as dinitrophenol or Dicumarol. The latter finding suggests that the synthesis of the high-energy phosphate bonds of adenosine triphosphate (ATP) is required for iodide transport. Thyroid gland contains adenosine triphosphatase (ATP-ase) activity, i.e., the ability to cleave the terminal phosphate group of ATP. This activity requires Na+ and K+, is stimulated by thyrotrophin both *in vivo* and *in vitro,* and appears to be present in the cell membranes.

Ouabain and other cardiac glycosides inhibit Na+ and K+ transport and, as a result, the Na+ and K+ dependent ATP-ase activity of the cell. The transport of iodide into the thyroid gland also is inhibited by cardiac glycosides. Therefore, the energy released during the cleavage of the ATP molecule by the Na+ and K+ dependent ATP-ase systems may be the source of energy for the transport of iodide across the cell membrane. A final group of inhibitors of iodide transport, certain anions such as thiocyanate and perchlorate, are considered later. Iodide may combine temporarily with some component of the cell membrane which serves as an iodide carrier. The nature of the carrier is unknown.

The iodine introduced into the cell as inorganic iodide is in reversible equilibrium with plasma iodide and can be discharged from the gland by thiocyanate[54] or perchlorate ions.[64] Normally, little discharge of intrathyroidal iodide by these agents is observed, which indicates that iodide is rapidly converted to organic form.

Iodination of Tyrosine.[40, 52]   Most of the thyroidal iodotyrosines are in peptide linkage because of the direct iodination of the tyrosine residues of thyroglobulin. Thyroglobulin is a large glycoprotein (molecular weight approximately 650,000) present mainly in the colloid of the follicular lumen. It contains 4 per cent carbohydrate, 3 per cent tyrosine and iodine in amounts varying from 0.1 to 0.9 per cent of the total molecular weight.[15] Iodinated proteins other than thyroglobulin also are present in the thyroid gland,[15] as are small amounts of free iodinated organic compounds. The site of iodination of thyroglobulin is controversial. Autoradiographic studies suggest that iodination occurs within the lumen of the thyroid follicle at the periphery of the colloid near or on the surface of the microvilli.[4, 46] On the other hand, iodination of tyrosine by isolated thyroid cells apparently free of extracellular colloid suggests intracellular iodination.[53] It is possible that the enzymes of the iodination process are formed in the cells and are observed there under *in vitro* conditions but are normally secreted into the lumen to exert their effect.

Mechanism of synthesis of thyroid proteins and secretion into follicular lumen. Amino acids activated and transferred to soluble RNA are laid down in correct sequence on ribosomes coated with template or messenger RNA, specific for thyroglobulin. The proteins formed on the ribosomes migrate through the walls of the endoplasmic reticulum into the lumen of the ergastoplasmic vesicles.[37] The protein moves to vesicles located near the apical membrane, probably via intermediate passage through the sacs of the Golgi apparatus. The apical vesicle membrane fuses with the apical cell membrane and then ruptures, releasing its contents into the follicular lumen.

The iodination of tyrosine residues of thyroglobulin is initiated by iodide oxidation. Recent evidence suggests that this reaction requires H_2O_2 and is catalyzed by a peroxidase.[2] A second enzyme, tyrosine iodinase, may be required to catalyze the reaction between the oxidized form of iodide and tyrosine,[16] but the nature of this enzyme is unknown.

A peroxidase is defined classically as an enzyme which catalyzes the oxidation of a number of substances by H_2O_2. The evidence for peroxidase involvement in iodotyrosine synthesis is as follows: (i) Peroxidase(s) is present in the thyroid gland; (ii) highly purified peroxidases from nonthyroid tissue catalyze the iodination of tyrosine when given the same cofactors necessary for the iodination of tyrosine by thyroid preparations; and (iii) the iodination of tyrosine by cell-free thyroid preparations requires a H_2O_2 generating system.

Low molecular weight inhibitors of tyrosine iodination, e.g., ascorbic acid and reduced glutathione, are present in thyroid homogenates.[32, 43] The concentration of these labile cellular components and the ratio between their oxidized and reduced states may serve as a metabolic control of iodination *in situ*. Endogenous factors which influence H_2O_2 formation in the cell may also regulate the iodination process. The effect of antithyroid agents on the iodination process is considered below.

Coupling Reaction.[52] In the coupling reaction, the iodinated hydroxyphenyl group of one diiodotyrosine molecule is joined to the phenolic hydroxyl group of a second diiodotyrosine molecule, with the formation of thyroxin. The pyruvic acid analogue of diiodotyrosine, p-hydroxy diiodophenylpyruvic acid, may be an intermediate. Since a thyroid deiodinase

capable of the conversion of thyroxin to triiodothyronine has not been found, triiodothyronine is probably synthesized by a coupling reaction between mono- and diiodotyrosine or their derivatives. The thyroid hormones formed are in peptide linkage in thyroglobulin.

The evidence for the coupling reaction is as follows: (i) *In vivo* experiments employing I* suggest that diiodotyrosine is a precursor of thyroxin. I* is very rapidly incorporated into mono- and diiodotyrosine, and as the I* content of the latter falls, the level of radioactive thyroxin increases; (ii) synthesis of thyroxin by iodination of triiodothyronine has not been observed; (iii) coupling can be produced *in vitro*. Incubation of diiodotyrosine at an alkaline *p*H in the presence of oxygen results in the formation of a small amount of thyroxin,[56] and this reaction is stimulated by oxidizing agents such as hydrogen peroxide or iodine. It may be catalyzed at neutral *p*H by a peroxidase.[67]

Thyroid hormones, stored in the follicular colloid as part of the thyroglobulin molecule, are released by proteolytic enzymes and approximately 100 μg. are secreted per day. The total amount of iodine in the average human thyroid is about 8 mg., or about 0.05 per cent of the glandular wet weight. Since only about 1 per cent of the total glandular iodine is secreted per day, adequate blood hormone levels can be maintained for several months after cessation of new synthesis.

Free iodotyrosines released during the proteolytic process are rapidly deiodinated in the gland by an enzyme, iodotyrosine deiodinase, and the iodide released is utilized for further synthesis of thyroid hormone. Iodide is thus conserved. Iodotyrosine deiodinase does not deiodinate iodotyrosines in peptide linkage or iodothyronines.

Nonthyroidal Thyroxin Synthesis. Although most, if not all, of the thyroid hormones are normally synthesized in the thyroid gland, nonthyroidal thyroxin synthesis also may occur. Some invertebrates which do not have a thyroid gland synthesize thyroxin, suggesting that thyroxin precedes the evolution of the thyroid gland in nature.[19] Thyroidectomized animals placed on a high iodide diet continue to grow, and small amounts of labeled thyroxin can be detected in the plasma following I* administration.[52] Thyroxin can be formed *in vitro* by the nonenzymatic iodination of certain proteins containing tyrosine (e.g., casein) by elemental iodine[33] and may be formed *in vivo* by a similar mechanism following iodide oxidation at a nonthyroidal site.

TRANSPORT OF THYROID HORMONES IN BLOOD[47, 51]

Thyroglobulin is not a normal constituent of plasma but is present only when the thyroid gland has been extensively damaged by disease, radiation or surgery. The circulating thyroid hormones are the amino acids L-thyroxin and 3, 5, 3′ triiodo-L-thyronine, which are largely bound to the plasma proteins. At physiologic concentrations, thyroxin is bound (i) to a glycoprotein—the thyroxin-binding globulin (TBG)—running between the α_1 and α_2 globulins on electrophoresis, (ii) to a protein — the thyroxin-binding prealbumin (TBPA)—which runs anodal to albumin on electrophoresis, and (iii) to serum albumin. When a small amount of labeled thyroxin (3 μg. or less) was added to normal human serum in one study, 57 per cent was bound to TBG, 32 per cent to TBPA, and 11 per cent to albumin.[38] TBG is the chief thyroxin-binding protein despite its low concentration in plasma (about 1 mg. per 100 ml.).

Triiodothyronine is present in plasma in minute amounts (less than 5 per cent of the thyroxin concentration). It is bound by TBG about one-third as well as thyroxin and is not bound by TBPA; as a result, it passes out of the blood stream much more readily than thyroxin, has a more rapid action, and may account for one-quarter or one-third of the total metabolic effect of the secreted thyroid hormones.

The half-life of thyroxin in blood is about 6 days and that of triiodothyronine about 2.5 days. If a single large dose of thyroxin is given, the first detectable change in metabolic rate is seen in 2 or 3 days and the maximum effect in about 10 days (see Fig. 8); with small daily doses the maximum cumulative effect is reached in several weeks. With triiodothyronine the first changes in metabolic rate are evident in 12 to 24 hours and the maximum effect in 2 to 3 days after a single dose. The maximum effect of a given dose of triiodothyronine is considerably greater than that of thyroxin, but since the metabolic rate also falls more rapidly after triiodothyronine, the total effects of single doses of the two substances, as summated over many days, may not be greatly different.

The thyroid hormones in plasma are precipitated with the plasma proteins by protein precipitants such as trichloroacetic acid, but are separated from the plasma proteins by extraction with certain organic solvents such as ethanol or normal butanol. This forms the basis for the determination of protein-bound iodine (PBI) and butanol-extractable iodine (BEI) as a measure of thyroid hormone levels in blood. The concentration of thyroid hormone in normal human plasma is very small. The PBI ranges from 4 to 8 μg. of iodine per 100 ml. and the BEI is slightly lower.

Plasma protein-bound thyroxin is in reversible equilibrium with a small amount of free thyroxin (about 1/1000 or 0.1 per cent of the total). It is the free thyroxin which leaves the blood stream to exert its metabolic effect on the peripheral tissues and its regulatory effect on thyroid function via anterior pituitary and hypothalamic centers.

In most instances, changes in PBI are accompanied by similar changes in the free plasma thyroid hormone level and in the amount of hormone supplied to the tissues.

TABLE 2. *Certain Extrathyroidal Thyroxin Parameters in Hypothyroid, Euthyroid and Hyperthyroid Patients*

	HYPOTHYROID	EUTHYROID	HYPERTHYROID
Total extrathyroidal organic iodine (μg.)	244	488	1137
Turnover rate of thyroxin (percentage per day)	7.3	10.5	16.9
Half-life of thyroxin in serum (days)	2.7	6.2	9.4
Daily degradation or removal of thyroxin (μg.)	18	51	197
Concentration of free thyroxin in serum (M)	0.29×10^{-10}	1.3×10^{-10}	5.3×10^{-10}

(After Sterling, K. *Mayo Clin. Proc.,* 1964, *39*:586–608.)

TABLE 3. *Effects of Genetic Variations in the Level of Thyroxin-Binding Globulin (TBG)*

	NORMAL	EXCESS TBG	NO TBG
Serum PBI (μg. per 100 ml.)	4-8	12-16	2
Serum BEI (μg. per 100 ml.)	3.3-6.3	12-13	—
Basal metabolic rate (BMR)	Normal	Normal	Normal
Serum cholesterol concentration	Normal	Normal	Normal
Thyroidal uptake of I*	Normal	Normal	Normal
Half-life of thyroxin in serum (days)	6.6	12.2	3.0
Turnover rate of thyroxin (percentage per day)	10.5	5.7	23.1
Total extrathyroidal organic iodine (μg.)	548	1099	264
Daily degradation or removal of thyroxin (μg.)	57	63	61

(After Sterling, K. *Mayo Clin. Proc.*, 1964, *39*:586–608. "Excess TBG" data were taken from Beierwaltes, W. H. and Robbins, J. *J. clin. Invest.*, 1959, *38*:1683–1688. "No TBG" data were taken from Ingbar, S. H. *J. clin. Invest.*, 1961, *40*:2053–2063.)

Thus, in hypothyroid states with PBI values of 0 to 2 μg. per 100 ml. and in hyperthyroidism, in which the PBI may be 15 to 20 μg. per 100 ml., there is a corresponding variation in free thyroid hormone levels and in the rate of disappearance of thyroxin from plasma (Table 2). Under these circumstances the PBI is an important measure of thyroid function, i.e., of the ability of the individual to synthesize and secrete thyroid hormone adequate to his needs. Because of the difference in protein binding of thyroxin and triiodothyronine, thyroxin administration to a hypothyroid subject will increase the PBI to a greater degree than equivalent triiodothyronine administration.

The PBI may be outside the normal range with otherwise normal thyroid function if a variation in the thyroxin-binding capacity of serum occurs without a corresponding variation in the supply of thyroid hormone to the tissues. The thyroxin-binding capacity of serum depends on the level of the thyroxin-binding proteins in the serum and on the affinity of the thyroid hormones for these proteins. The level of thyroxin-binding proteins is increased in pregnancy[14] and by estrogen administration,[14] and is decreased by androgens[17] with a corresponding alteration in the PBI. Hereditary variations in the TBG levels also occur (Table 3). The size of the extrathyroidal organic iodine pool (largely thyroxin) varies directly and the turnover rate of thyroxin varies inversely with the thyroxin-binding protein levels so that the total amount of thyroxin removed or degraded per unit time (the product of the turnover rate and the thyroxin pool size) is normal (Table 3).

Certain drugs, e.g., salicylates, dinitrophenol and diphenylhydantoin, can displace thyroxin from its plasma protein-binding sites[62] and shift the protein-bound thyroxin $\leftrightarrows$ free thyroxin equilibrium to the right. The result is a decrease in PBI without a corresponding decrease in the free thyroxin level in plasma. Indeed, there may be evidence of excess free thyroid hormone, i.e., decreased TSH secretion and thyroid activity.

In summary, the thyroxin-binding proteins transport the hormones from their site of production to the peripheral tissues. The concentration of thyroxin-binding proteins in plasma and their affinity for the thyroid hormones regulate the level of free thyroid hormone in plasma and, therefore, the rate of entry of the hormone into the cell.

TISSUE METABOLISM OF THYROID HORMONES[51]

Free plasma thyroid hormone is presumably in equilibrium with free hormone in the cell and the latter is, in turn, in equilibrium with intracellular protein-bound hormone. Thyroid hormone is found in almost every tissue of the body. Skeletal muscle, which makes up almost half the body mass, takes up most of the thyroid hormone. Liver, however, has the greatest ability to concentrate and metabolize thyroxin per unit mass. Within the cell, thyroxin is found in all the major subcellular fractions, the largest proportion being in the soluble cytoplasmic fraction.

The thyroid hormones are metabolized in a number of ways. These include deiodination, conjugation, deamination (or transamination), decarboxylation, splitting the ether linkage, and oxidation of the phenolic group.

Deiodination occurs in the liver and skeletal muscle. The iodide formed is either excreted in the urine or taken up by the thyroid gland. 3, 5, 3'-Triiodothyronine does not appear to be a major product of the peripheral deiodination of thyroxin.

Both thyroxin and triiodothyronine are conjugated in the liver and their phenolic glucuronides or sulfate esters have been detected in the bile. Glucuronide conjugation occurs more readily with thyroxin and sulfate conjugation more readily with triiodothyronine. The sulfate ester of triiodothyronine has been detected in blood. The conjugates undergo hydrolysis in the gastrointestinal tract and the free hormone is either reabsorbed or lost in the feces. The total fecal excretion of iodine (organic plus inorganic) in humans is 10 to 60 μg. per day, of which the largest proportion is organic.[55]

Deamination (or transamination) of the thyroid hormones occurs in the liver and kidney. The products of this reaction, the pyruvic acid analogues of thyroxin or triiodothyronine, are extremely unstable and undergo reduction to form the lactic acid derivatives, or decarboxylation to form the acetic acid derivatives. These derivatives may, in turn, be deiodinated or conjugated. The degradation of thyroxin by rat liver microsomes has been found to involve the cleavage of the diphenyl ether linkage.[65]

REGULATION OF THYROID FUNCTION BY THYROTROPHIN[24, 41]

Thyroxin synthesis and secretion depend almost completely on the presence of the pituitary gland. When the pituitary is absent the thyroid decreases in size, the follicular cells become thin and flat, and the follicular lumen fills with colloid (Fig. 5). Although the thyroid of an hypophysectomized animal has an intrinsic level of thyroxin synthesis and secretion, it is extremely low; most of the usual sequelae of thyroidectomy are seen after hypophysectomy. All phases of thyroid iodine metabolism are depressed.[52] The rate of release of preformed thyroxin is decreased, as is the gland's iodide concentrating ability. The conversion of inorganic iodide to mono- and diiodotyrosine and of diiodotyrosine to thyroxin also is depressed. The latter may be more sensitive to the pituitary's absence than the iodination of tyrosine.[52]

The atrophic thyroid gland of the hypophysectomized animal can be made to hypertrophy by injecting an anterior pituitary extract. The active principle is called thyrotrophin or the thyroid-stimulating hormone (TSH). When TSH is administered, thyroid epithelial cells increase in size, become cuboidal or columnar in shape, and mitotic figures appear. The epithelial lining projects into the follicular lumen and much of the colloid disappears (Fig. 5). With continuous stimulation by TSH, the thyroid gland undergoes hypertrophy and hyper-

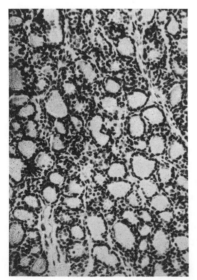

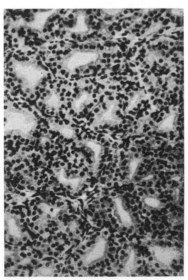

A   B

Fig. 5. Sections from thyroids of hypophysectomized rats: *A*, untreated; *B*, given thyrotrophic hormone. Note increased height of epithelial cells, loss of colloid, and increase in size of many of the vesicles under influence of the hormone. (From Evans, in: *Science in progress, fifth series,* New Haven, Yale University Press, 1947, p. 315.)

plasia and becomes more vascular. These alterations normally are associated with augmented secretion of thyroxin, as evidenced by increased PBI and by elevation of the basal metabolic rate.

Primary Site of Action of TSH. All phases of thyroidal iodine metabolism, depressed following hypophysectomy, are stimulated by TSH. The proteolytic degradation of thyroglobulin and the release of thyroid hormone are accelerated. The trapping of iodide by the thyroid gland is increased, as are the iodination of tyrosine residues of thyroglobulin and the synthesis of thyroxin. The deiodination of free iodotyrosines is accelerated. In addition to its effect on iodine metabolism, TSH stimulates many other aspects of thyroidal metabolism,[18] including glucose oxidation, carbon dioxide release, free fatty acid release, inorganic phosphate incorporation—particularly into phospholipids—and nucleic acid synthesis. Whether one primary effect of TSH could account for all these findings is not clear. It has been suggested that an increase in DPN+ kinase activity by TSH, thereby increasing conversion of DPN+ to TPN+, accelerates carbohydrate metabolism and causes the shift in favor of the hexose monophosphate shunt which is observed a few minutes after TSH administration.[39] Such a mechanism might profoundly affect all aspects of thyroid metabolism, including hormonogenesis.

TSH, a glycoprotein with a molecular weight estimated at 25,000, is found in a specific type of basophil cell (thyrotroph) from the anterior lobe of the pituitary. Its secretion is controlled by the blood concentration of free thyroid hormone which, when increased, inhibits TSH secretion. In thyroidectomized rats, thyrotrophs secrete maximally in the absence of inhibition by thyroid hormone and show degranulation, enlargement and hyalinization (thyroidectomy cells). The level of TSH in plasma is very low and difficult to detect. It may be increased to 100 times normal in the absence of the thyroid gland.

The thyroid hormones inhibit anterior pituitary secretion of TSH both directly and indirectly via the hypothalamus.

The evidence for hypothalamic control is as follows: (i) Injecting thyroxin directly into the hypothalamus inhibits thyroxin secretion by the thyroid after a latent period of 6 to 9 hours[66] (inhibition is immediate following direct anterior pituitary injection of thyroxin); (ii) a lesion of the hypothalamus in the midline between the paraventricular nucleus and the median eminence (or pituitary stalk section) results in a suppression of thyroid activity; (iii) electrical stimulation of specific hypothalamic areas results in pituitary thyrotroph stimulation, decreased pituitary and increased plasma TSH concentrations and thyroid stimulation.[11]

The hypothalamic control of TSH secretion appears to be transmitted to the anterior pituitary by the hypothalamo-pituitary portal system (a vascular system in the pituitary stalk which transports venous blood from a primary capillary plexus in the hypothalamus to a secondary capillary plexus in the anterior pituitary). A humoral agent of hypothalamic origin (thyrotrophin-releasing factor, TRF) may be involved, or the hypothalamus may control TSH secretion by altering the concentration of thyroid hormone which reaches the pituitary.

The interrelationship between hypothalamic, pituitary and thyroid factors forms the basis for the negative feedback mechanism of thyroid control. When the plasma level of free thyroid hormone is decreased, the pituitary is stimulated both directly and via the hypothalamus to produce more TSH. Increased blood TSH levels in turn stimulate thyroid hormone production. The opposite occurs if the free thyroid hormone level of plasma is increased.

ANTITHYROID AGENTS (GOITROGENS)[20, 35]

Many substances which inhibit thyroxin synthesis can produce an enlargement of the thyroid gland (goiter). Some of these agents are now extensively used in studies of thyroid physiology and in diagnosis and treatment of certain thyroid diseases. Goiter formation involves the following sequence of reactions: (i) The antithyroid agent or goitrogen inhibits thyroxin synthesis; (ii) the continued secretion of hormone without replacement results in the depletion of thyroxin stores; (iii) the concentration of thyroid hormone in blood falls; (iv) this stimulates the pituitary, both directly and via the hypothalamus, to secrete more TSH; (v) TSH stimulation of the thyroid over a suitable period causes the gland to enlarge. The enlarged thyroid appears histologically to be hyperplastic, as if TSH had been given (Fig. 5). Enlargement of the gland requires an intact anterior pituitary and can be prevented by administration of thyroxin or triiodothyronine, which inhibit pituitary secretion of TSH. Antithyroid agents fall into the following groups:

1. **Thiocyanate, Perchlorate and Related Anions.** Several monovalent anions inhibit the concentration of iodide by the thyroid gland and cause the free iodide within the gland to be discharged into the blood stream. Thus, the gland becomes iodine-deficient and thyroxin synthesis is decreased. Perchlorate is one of a group of anions which competitively inhibit iodide concentration on the basis of a similarity in ionic charge and volume. It is concentrated to some extent by the thyroid gland and does not undergo metabolic transformation. It has no effect on the organic binding of iodide by the gland. Thiocyanate, on the other hand, is concentrated only slightly, if at all, by thyroid tissue, which oxidizes it to sulfate. Thiocyanate also inhibits the iodination of tyrosine. The antithyroid effect of thiocyanate therefore may be due to a mechanism different from that of perchlorate. In addition to thiocyanate and perchlorate, monovalent anions with antithyroid properties include chlorate, hypochlorite, periodate, iodate, biiodate, nitrate, monofluorosulfonate, difluorophosphate and fluoroborate.[3, 64] The inhibition of thyroid function and consequent goiter formation may be overcome completely by administration of iodide.

2. **Thiocarbamides.** Compounds which have the thionamide group $\left(s{=}c{<}_{}^{n{=}}\right)$ exert a striking goitrogenic effect. The most active of these compounds contains a thiourylene group $\left(s{=}c{<}_{n{=}}^{n{=}}\right)$, although one nitrogen may be replaced by sulfur or oxygen. Among the most widely used compounds of this group are substituted thiouracils, such as methyl- or propylthiouracil, and mercaptoimidazoles, such as 1 methyl-2-mercaptoimidazole (methimazole) (Fig. 1). Rats fed 0.1 mg. of propylthiouracil per 100 grams per day develop goiters. Methimazole is about 100 times as effective as propylthiouracil in man. Compounds of this type are considerably more goitrogenic when the dietary iodine is low.

Thiocarbamides do not inhibit the concentrating of iodide by the thyroid gland but rather inhibit the binding of iodide to thyroglobulin. The conversion of diiodotyrosine to thyroxine, of monoiodotyrosine to diiodotyrosine, and of tyrosine to monoiodotyrosine is inhibited by increasing concentrations of propylthiouracil.[29] As a result, the organic iodine content and the percentage of I* converted to organic form in the thyroid are greatly decreased in the propylthiouracil-treated animal (Table 4). Thiocarbamides also inhibit the peripheral deiodination of thyroxin and increase the fecal excretion of thyroxin.

3. **Iodide.** Paradoxically, iodide ion, an essential component of the thyroxin molecule, inhibits thyroxin synthesis and release when given in large amounts. Iodide had been used for many years in the clinical treatment of hyperthyroidism. The dosage of iodine required for suppression of the thyroid (in man about 10 to 100 mg. per day) is far in excess of that used prophylactically for simple goiter (about 0.1 mg. per day).

Excess iodide suppresses the secretion of thyroid hormone and, as a result, the thyroid follicles accumulate colloid and swell, the process of involution. Involution is associated with a decreased vascularity of the gland. A thyrotoxic patient treated first with a thiocarbamide drug until euthyroid and then with iodide to decrease vascularity is in an optimum condition for surgical thyroidectomy. Excess iodide also

TABLE 4.   *Effect of Propylthiouracil on the Thyroid Gland**

	WT. OF THYROID (mg.)	IODINE IN THYROID (mg. per 100 gm.)		I* (PERCENTAGE OF AMOUNT GIVEN, AFTER 6 HOURS)		
		Organic	Inorganic	Total	Organic	Inorganic
Normal group	20	48.0	1.2	26	25.0	1.0
Propylthiouracil-treated group	58	0.6	0.5	6	0.5	5.5

Rats were given propylthiouracil for 16 days (0.15 per cent in the diet) and then tracer amount of I.

(From Taurog, A., Chaikoff, I. L. and Feller, D.D. *J. biol. Chem.*, 1947, *171*:189.)

inhibits the conversion of iodide to organic form. Both the iodination of tyrosine and the coupling to form thyroxin are inhibited. The inhibitory effect of excess iodide is usually transient, disappearing after a few days even though high iodide levels are maintained. Hence, goiter is seldom seen after administration of excess iodide alone. It has been suggested that the adaptation to high iodide levels is due to a reduction of the thyroid's capacity to concentrate iodide. Under these circumstances the intracellular level of iodide is not sufficient to maintain the inhibitory effect despite high extracellular levels.[9]

4. **Natural Goitrogens.** It has long been known that certain plant foods, notably cabbage, turnips and rutabagas, can induce goiters in animals fed large quantities for some time. The active antithyroid agent called goitrin has been identified as 5-vinyl 2-thiooxazolidone,[5] a compound related in structure to the thiocarbamide group. This agent is present in the seeds of most crucifers, and in the edible portion of some, as an inactive thioglycoside precursor—progoitrin—from which it is released through hydrolysis by an enzyme, myrosinase, present in the seeds or in gastrointestinal bacteria. Like the thiocarbamides, goitrin inhibits the conversion of iodide to organic form. Other antithyroid agents, e.g., thiocyanate, also occur in food. In some instances excessive ingestion of foods containing naturally occurring goitrogens may contribute to the development of goiter in man.

5. **Other Compounds.**[20] Other compounds which have weak antithyroid properties include various sulfonamides, as well as certain sulfonamide derivatives such as the sulfonylurea antidiabetic agent carbutamide. Para-amino salicylic acid, used in the treatment of tuberculosis, and p-amino benzoic acid also may be goitrogenic in high doses. Amphenone, an adrenal enzyme inhibitor used clinically, has weak antithyroid properties, as does aminotriazole, resorcinol, acetazoleamide (Diamox) and various other substances. These agents appear to inhibit the binding of iodide to thyroglobulin.

GOITER IN MAN

Visible enlargement of the thyroid gland occurs frequently in man. The most common type, unaccompanied by any other obvious sign of abnormal thyroid function and not associated with a pre-existing pathologic condition of the thyroid such as infection or malignancy, is called a simple nontoxic goiter. Enlargement of the thyroid in simple goiter results from an increased output of TSH, which, in turn, results from at least marginally low levels of circulating thyroid hormone. This compensatory response is adequate in simple nontoxic goiter since sufficient thyroid hormone is produced by the enlarged gland to maintain adequate thyroid function. However, if thyroxin synthesis remains subnormal, hypothyroidism becomes evident despite the great increase in thyroid tissue. A goiter also may be associated with hyperfunction of the thyroid gland (toxic goiter).

Table 5 lists some of the causes of goiter in man. Simple nontoxic goiters have been endemic for centuries in many areas of the world. These have been called "endemic goiters" in contrast to "sporadic goiters" which are simple nontoxic goiters in persons not living in endemic areas. Although the cause of endemic goiter is not known in all cases, it appears certain that an important contributing factor is a relative or absolute deficiency of iodine in the diet or drinking water. A relationship between the geographic distribution of iodine deficiency in the soil and in foodstuffs and the prevalence of goiter has been established. Marine and Kimball in 1920 demonstrated conclusively that the ingestion of a small amount of extra iodide by people in an iodine-deficient area for a year or two greatly decreased the incidence of goiter.[36] The thyroid regularly enlarges up to several times its normal size in animals maintained on diets very low in iodine; this enlargement is prevented completely by the addition of a small amount of iodide to the diet. For prevention of goiter, the dietary intake recommended for normal subjects is about 0.1 mg. per day, with additional allowances during pregnancy. Since foods grown in soils deficient in iodine may not contain this amount, iodized table salt is widely used.

That simple goiter is not due solely to an iodine-deficient diet is indicated by the fact that not all persons on a comparable diet in an endemic area develop goiter. Furthermore, simple goiter may develop in inhabitants of nonendemic areas. A contributing factor may be the ingestion of goitrogens (see above), and iodine deficiency or goitrogen ingestion or both may be superimposed on a minimal hereditary defect in thyroxin synthesis.

TABLE 5. *Causes of Goiter*

A. Iodine deficiency
B. Excessive intake of goitrogen
    1. Natural goitrogens
    2. Iatrogenic goitrogens
    3. Industrial goitrogens
C. Hereditary defect in thyroid hormone synthesis
    1. Iodide-trapping defect
    2. Iodide-organification defect
    3. Iodotyrosyl-coupling defect
    4. Thyroid hormone release defect
    5. Iodotyrosine dehalogenase defect
    6. Defect associated with abnormal serum iodoprotein
D. Increased need for thyroid hormone
    1. Puberty
    2. Pregnancy
    3. Menstruation
    4. Lactation
E. Pituitary or hypothalamic dysfunction
F. Primary thyroid disease

If a severe hereditary defect in thyroxin synthesis is present, compensation is inadequate, and goiter associated with hypothyroidism results.[45] Congenital goitrous cretinism may result from inherent defects in the trapping mechanism, in the ability to iodinate tyrosine, in the conversion of diiodotyrosine to thyroxin, in the secretion of thyroid hormones, and in the deiodination of iodotyrosines; it also may be associated with abnormal iodoproteins in the blood.

Simple goiter often is first evident during stress, e.g., puberty or childbirth, when the requirement for thyroid hormone is increased. Thyroid enlargement may result from increased or abnormal stimulation caused by a pituitary, central nervous system, or other dysfunction. For example, the serum of certain patients with Graves' disease contains an abnormal thyroid stimulator which differs from TSH in that its thyroid effect in assay animals is delayed and prolonged.[1, 34] This substance—the long-acting thyroid stimulator (LATS)—is produced independently of the normal thyroid–pituitary negative feedback control system. Finally, thyroid gland enlargement or goiter may result from primary thyroid disease such as infection or malignancy.

FUNCTION OF THYROID HORMONE

The normal growth, development and wellbeing of man or animals depends on the maintenance of normal thyroid function. Such individuals are "euthyroid." Although partial or complete loss of thyroid function or an increase in thyroid activity in man or animals does not rapidly result in death, severe and widespread disturbances occur.

Hypothyroidism in Man. Individuals who produce thyroid hormone inadequate to their needs are said to be hypothyroid. In infants hypothyroidism is termed cretinism. It is caused by inadequate production of thyroid hormone. If maternal thyroid function is normal, transplacental passage of thyroid hormone maintains the fetus in a euthyroid state and clinical evidence of hypothyroidism is not observed until some time after birth.

Cretinism in the past was observed rather frequently in areas of endemic goiter and was most commonly caused by maternal iodine deficiency. Congenital absence of the thyroid (athyreotic cretinism), maldevelopment with misplacement of the thyroid, a genetic defect in hormone synthesis, and the excessive intake of antithyroid agents by the mother also may lead to cretinism. This disorder is characterized by dwarfism, mental deficiency which may approach idiocy, and a peculiar infantile facies due to poor development of the naso-orbital bones (Fig. 6). The tongue is enlarged and often protrudes. The skin is thick, the pulse is slow, and muscular weakness and gastrointestinal disturbances (poor eating pattern, con-

stipation, enlarged abdominal viscera with abdominal protuberance) are common. Growth
and skeletal development are delayed. The
"bone age" of the individual (i.e., the age as
estimated by comparing the number of centers
of ossification observed on x-ray with that expected) is below the actual age and can be
used as an aid in diagnosis and therapy (Fig.
6). It is important that cretinism be treated
with thyroid hormone at a very early stage if
extensive changes in the nervous system and
severe mental deficiency are to be avoided.

Hypothyroidism which develops later in life
was first carefully described by Sir William
Gull in 1874 and was called myxedema by
Ord in 1878. This term is still widely used
although it describes only one of the abnormalities usually seen in adult thyroid deficiency. Myxedematous infiltration results in a
peculiar thickening and puffiness of the skin
and subcutaneous tissues, particularly of the
face and extremities. The skin is dry, coarse,
cool, pale, waxy, and often has a yellowish tint.
The hair is dry, brittle and sparse. There is a
characteristic expressionless or masklike facies
(Fig. 7). Infiltration of the vocal cords and enlargement of the tongue results in a husky,
slow, slurred speech. Muscle weakness, prolonged tendon reflexes, intolerance to cold and
mental deterioration, ranging from lethargy
and forgetfulness to psychoses, are usually
present.

The term myxedema resulted from the belief that
mucus accumulated in the tissues. Considerable water,
nitrogenous material and salts are held in the interstitial spaces of the skin and some edema of internal
organs may exist, particularly in the heart, which is
often enlarged. The accumulated material contains
mucoproteins (proteins combined with mucopolysaccharides such as hyaluronic acid and chondroitin
sulfuric acid) in excessive amounts. Mucoproteins are
highly ionized and characteristically hygroscopic.
Presumably the increase in mucoproteins is responsible for the retention of water and salt interstitially.

Adult hypothyroidism can be primary or
secondary. In primary hypothroidism the decreased production of thyroid hormone is due to
an abnormality primarily of thyroid origin.
The thyroid gland may be absent or malfunctioning. In the former case, the thyroid is usually destroyed insidiously with no apparent
cause. However, the cause may be obvious pre-
existing disease, surgery or I* therapy. Primary
hypothyroidism due to a malfunctioning thyroid is usually associated with a compensatory

enlargement of the gland. In secondary hypothyroidism, the primary lesion, which is not in
the thyroid but is in the pituitary or hypothalamic region, causes a decrease or absence of
TSH secretion.

When no pre-existing cause of destruction of the
thyroid is apparent, serum often has high levels of
antibodies to protein components of the thyroid gland.
A current view is that primary hypothyroidism may
be the end stage of an autoimmune disease in which
thyroid gland destruction is the end result of a reaction between thyroid antigens and antibodies to those
antigens produced in the same individual. This pre-
supposes abnormal release of the antigens, probably
during a previously unnoticed disease of the gland.

Hyperthyroidism in Man. Individuals who
produce thyroid hormone in excess of their
needs are said to be hyperthyroid. Hyperthyroidism (or thyrotoxicosis) may be caused by
excessive ingestion of thyroid hormone (thyrotoxicosis factitia), or by excessive production of
the hormone by the thyroid gland. In the
latter instance, the thyroid gland is usually

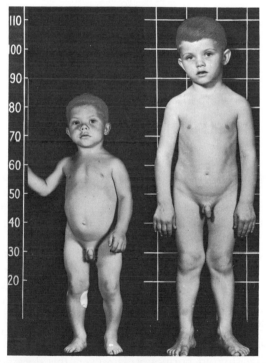

Fig. 6. *Left,* Untreated cretin, age 6 years and 2
months. Bone age, 6 months. Note infantile naso-orbital
configuration and protuberant abdomen. No goiter
was observed. *Right,* Same patient, at age 7½, after
treatment with thyroid for 16 months. Grew 7½ inches,
attaining the height of an average 5¼-year-old. Bone
age, 5 years. (From Asper and Wiswell, *Amer. J. Med.,*
1956, *20:*732. Patient of Dr. Lawson Wilkins.)

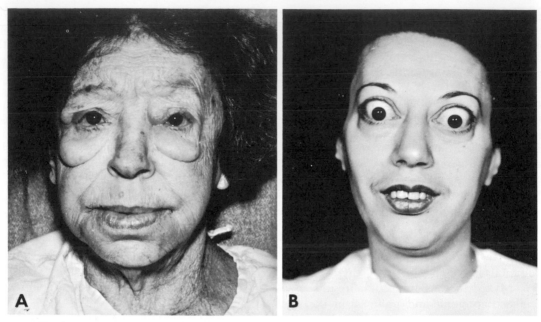

Fig. 7. *A,* Spontaneous idiopathic hypothyroidism (myxedema). Note periorbital edema, coarse skin, dry hair and dull expression. *B,* Hyperthyroidism with diffuse goiter (Graves' disease). Note widening of the palpebral fissures, wide stare and protrusion of the eyeballs. Patient has slight diffuse enlargement of the thyroid with fullness of the neck. (*B* from *Textbook of endocrinology,* 3rd ed., R. H. Williams, ed. Philadelphia, W. B. Saunders Co., 1962.)

enlarged. The enlargement may be nodular (toxic nodular goiter, Plummer's disease) or, more commonly, diffuse (toxic diffuse goiter, Graves' disease). The latter is classically associated with (i) signs and symptoms of hyperthyroidism, (ii) eye changes, the most striking of which is exophthalmos, and (iii) goiter (Fig. 7).

In hyperthyroidism, the metabolic rate is elevated and an intolerance to heat develops. There is often a loss of weight and weakness. Sweating, flushing, rapid respiration, palpitations, increased gastrointestinal activity, increased thirst or appetite, and fine tremors of the muscles are seen. The heart seems particularly affected and may exhibit a marked tachycardia and an increased cardiac output. Emotional disturbances and nervousness are usual in man.

Most of the signs and symptoms of hyperthyroidism are due to the excessive secretion of the thyroid hormones. However, this does not cause the exophthalmos and goiter of Graves' disease. Exophthalmos has been produced in animals by injecting anterior pituitary extracts. The exophthalmos-producing substance (EPS) of the pituitary is distinct from TSH.[12] A cause of the goiter in Graves' disease may be the long-acting stimulator (LATS) considered above. Some of the parameters of the extrathyroidal thyroxin pool in hypothyroidism, euthyroidism and hyperthroidism are shown in Table 2.

Calorigenic Effect.[6, 50] Thyroxin's most striking effect in intact homeothermic animals (animals whose body temperature is maintained over a narrow range despite changes in environmental temperature) is the stimulation of oxygen consumption and heat production. By increasing heat production to match heat loss thyroid hormones assist in the maintenance of body temperature when environmental temperature is low. This "calorigenic" effect of thyroxin is not observed in adult animals whose body temperature varies with the surrounding temperature (poikilotherms).[7]

The calorigenic effect, originally demonstrated by Magnus-Levy in 1895, forms the basis for measuring the basal metabolic rate (BMR) in man as a test of thyroid function. The BMR, which measures the rate of heat production (or oxygen consumption) of a subject at rest, is considered in detail in Chapter 53. If the metabolic rate is, say, 10 per cent less than the average, the BMR is said to be −10 per cent; if it is 20 per cent above the average, it is said to be +20 per cent. The normal range of the BMR is from −15 to +15 per cent. After thyroidectomy the BMR falls gradually at a diminishing rate until it reaches a minimum of about −25 to −35 per cent, in 40 to 60 days in man or two to three weeks in the rat.

This slow fall in BMR is due in part to the slow disappearance of thyroxin from the body; the half-life of thyroxin in plasma, normally about six days, may be increased to nine days or longer in hypothyroidism (Table 2). The gradual fall in BMR following thyroidectomy also may be due to a slow decrease in concentration of a critical thyroxin-dependent enzyme or cofactor.

Effect on Growth and Maturation.[6, 50] In addition to its calorigenic effect, thyroxin is essential for proper growth and maturation, as indicated in man by the cretin's abnormal development. Normal growth requires the combined action of both pituitary and thyroid hormone as well as other factors. Young thyroidectomized animals grow slowly for a time and then remain dwarfed. Treating such animals with small amounts of thyroid hormone allows growth to proceed normally only in the presence of an intact pituitary. Conversely, thyroid hormone is required for an optimum growth response to pituitary growth hormone in the hypophysectomized animal. Thyroxin's effect on tadpole metamorphosis is a striking example of its role in maturation.[13] Tadpole metamorphosis is greatly accelerated by adding thyroxin to the aquarium water and can be completely blocked by antithyroid agents.

General Metabolic Effect.[6, 50] Thyroxin has widespread effects on all aspects of metabolism. Nitrogen retention and protein synthesis are increased by physiologic amounts of thyroxin. This is especially evident when normal growth has been prevented by prior thyroidectomy. An excess of thyroxin may lead to weight loss and negative nitrogen balance, particularly if caloric intake does not rise proportionately with the increase in thyroxin level.

In thyroxin deficiency, the plasma cholesterol level is usually elevated; in thyroxin excess it may be decreased.[32a]

The mechanism of this cholesterol-lowering effect is unknown but does not appear to be a simple response to the calorigenic effect of thyroxin. Dinitrophenol, which also increases oxygen consumption, does not lower cholesterol levels. The fall in cholesterol levels may precede the hypermetabolic effect of thyroxin. Because of this probable dissociation of hypermetabolic and cholesterol-lowering effects, much effort has been expended in searching for analogues of natural thyroid hormones which would have a disproportionately large cholesterol-lowering effect, as compared to the hypermetabolic effect, in the hope that such compounds would be effective cholesterol-lowering agents in man. This has met with some success.

Thyroxin enhances the absorption of glucose from the gastrointestinal tract. Increased breakdown of glycogen to glucose (glycogenolysis) may deplete the glycogen store of the liver, heart and striated muscle. Gluconeogenesis (the conversion of amino acids to glucose) also is increased, partly because of an increase in output of adrenocortical hormones. The blood sugar level also tends to increase, thereby stimulating the β cells of the pancreas to secrete insulin, which, in turn, increases utilization of glucose by the peripheral tissues. Consequently, the glucose tolerance curve is flat in hypothyroidism and is high and prolonged in hyperthyroidism. If the pancreatic reserve is diminished, as by partial pancreatectomy, prolonged administration of thyroid hormone may lead to exhaustive degeneration of the β cells and thus to diabetes (metathyroid diabetes).[28]

Thyroxin is required for the liver to convert carotene to vitamin A. Elevated blood carotene levels in hypothyroidism may give the skin a yellowish tint. In hyperthyroidism, accelerated metabolism increases the requirement for certain vitamins, and relative deficiencies (e.g., thiamine deficiency) may occur.

Mechanism of Action.[27, 32b, 50, 60] The mechanism of action of the thyroid hormones is unknown. The problems in its elucidation are many. Unlike many hormones, there is not a specific end organ for thyroxin in mammals. Since many tissues respond to it, one cannot look for uniqueness in the biochemical makeup of a particular thyroxin-sensitive tissue. Whether thyroxin has a single mechanism of action or whether its different effects are initiated by different mechanisms is also unclear. Unlike the calorigenic effect of epinephrine or dinitrophenol, the effect of the thyroid hormones on the intact animal is evident only following a lag period measured in days (Fig. 8). The duration of the lag period depends on the species, the particular thyroid hormone or analogue employed, the dose and route of administration and the size and metabolic rate of the animal.

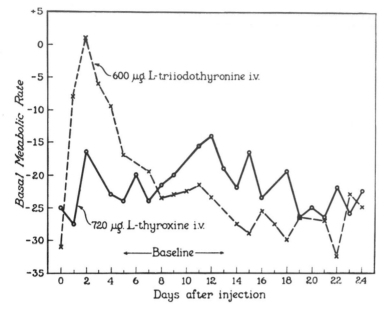

Fig. 8. Basal metabolic rates after injection of equimolar amounts of triiodothyronine and thyroxin. In this series of 8 myxedematous patients the average peak calorigenic effect was 2.2 days after intravenous injection of triiodothyronine and 9.4 days for thyroxin. (From Blackburn *et al.*, *J. clin. Invest.*, 1954, *33*:819–824.)

The cause of the lag period is unknown. Several possibilities exist. (i) The lag period may be the time required for the conversion of thyroxin to an active form. In view of the finding that the lag period following triiodothyronine administration is shorter than after thyroxin administration (Fig. 8), it has been proposed that thyroxin is converted to triiodothyronine in the peripheral tissues and that the latter substance is the active form of the hormone. The process of deiodination would, according to this concept, account in part for the lag period. However, although thyroxin can be deiodinated to triiodothyronine *in vivo* in certain tissues, the conversion does not appear to be obligatory for thyroxin action. Tetraiodo- and triiodothyroacetic acids ("tetrac" and "triac"), in which an acetate side chain replaces an alanine side chain, are highly active analogues of the thyroid hormones and have a relatively short lag period. These compounds can be formed from the thyroid hormones in the liver and kidney. However, it is generally considered that the acetic acid analogues are products of thyroid hormone breakdown and their formation is not required for hormone action. (ii) The passage of thyroid hormone into the cells and to its site of action may be delayed by protein binding. Triiodothyronine and the acetic acid analogues act more rapidly than thyroxin partly because they are less firmly bound to the plasma proteins and hence are more readily available to the tissues. Although protein binding accounts for much of the lag period following thyroxin administration, it does not appear to account for all of it. (iii) The lag period may be necessary, in part, for a build-up of cellular constituents which precedes the hypermetabolic effect. This is supported by the finding that inhibition of protein synthesis by puromycin or of messenger RNA synthesis by actinomycin D largely abolishes the calorigenic effect of thyroid hormones in the intact animal.[49, 58] Several enzyme and coenzyme levels are increased by thyroid hormone

administration; however, it is not clear which of these changes, if any, account for the hypermetabolic effect.

The calorigenic effect is observed not only in the intact animal but also in animal tissues. Various tissues removed from animals made hyperthyroid by injection of thyroid hormone have an increased rate of oxygen consumption *in vitro*, whereas some tissues removed from thyroidectomized animals have a decreased rate of oxygen consumption (Table 6). Many effects of thyroxin also have been found on cell-free tissue preparations and on isolated enzyme systems; however, in no instance can the calorigenic effect *in vivo* be unequivocally attributed to the effect on the cell-free system.

Thyroxin has several properties which may contribute to its action on cell-free systems. (i) It is a relatively efficient chelating agent and certain enzyme reactions dependent upon or inhibited by trace metals are affected by thyroxin *in vitro*. In most instances the trace metal is an essential component of an enzyme system and chelation by thyroxin results in inhibition. Occasionally the metal acts as a trace inhibitor and thyroxin stimulates the enzyme reaction by its removal. (ii) The phenolic hydroxyl group of thyroxin can be alternately oxidized and reduced *in vitro*, and thyroxin may act as an oxidation–reduction catalyst in certain cell-free systems. (iii) Thyroxin is readily deiodinated and the deiodination may be necessary for hormone action. It is not clear whether one or more of the above properties of thyroxin can account for its physiologic action *in vivo*.

TABLE 6. *Summary of Oxygen Consumption Changes Produced in Rat Tissues by Thyroidectomy or Thyroxin Injection**

TISSUE	PERCENTAGE CHANGE PRODUCED BY	
	Thyroidectomy	Thyroxin
Liver	−20	+ 62
Diaphragm	−31	+ 73
Kidney	−15	+ 48
Salivary gland	−22	+ 34
Pancreas	−20	+ 51
Heart	−38	+132
Epidermis	−71	
Lung	+ 2	
Brain	− 2	+ 7
Spleen	− 5	+ 3
Testis	+ 2	+ 13
Seminal vesicle	− 3	0
Prostate	− 1	+ 4
Ovary	− 1	− 2
Uterus	0	− 3
Thymus	− 9	+ 8
Lymph node	− 2	+ 4
Gastric smooth muscle	+ 4	+ 3
Dermis	0	
Adenohypophysis	+49	− 36

*Animals were at least one month post-thyroidectomy. Thyroxin injected at 1 to 2 mg. per kg. per day into thyroidectomized rats for 4 to 6 days and tissues removed one day after the last injection.

(From Barker, S. B. Chapter 10 in *The thyroid gland,* vol. 1, Pitt-Rivers, R., and Trotter, W. R., eds. London, Butterworth & Co., 1964.)

The most studied of the *in vitro* effects of thyroxin on cell-free systems is its effect on intact mitochondria. Mitochondria are intracellular organelles which carry out many reactions essential to the cell's survival. Among these reactions is oxidative phosphorylation. In this process, the energy liberated during the oxidation of metabolites and the transfer of electrons along the respiratory chain to molecular oxygen is captured in a chemical form (i.e., the high-energy phosphate bonds of adenosine triphosphate, ATP) which can subsequently be utilized for muscular and chemical work. Adding thyroxin to intact mitochondria causes an uncoupling of oxidative phosphorylation; i.e., the mitochondria continue to take up oxygen, but do not continue to synthesize the high-energy phosphate bond of ATP. Under these circumstances oxidation may be more rapid, but it is less efficient; i.e., more of the energy is dissipated as heat. Thyroxin also causes mitochondrial swelling, and it is probable that the effect of thyroxin on oxidative phosphorylation is secondary to structural changes in the mitochondria. Several agents other than thyroxin (e.g., inorganic phosphate, calcium ions, phloridzin) cause both swelling of mitochondria and uncoupling of oxidative phosphorylation *in vitro* but do not have an effect comparable to that of thyroxin *in vivo*.

Thyroxin also stimulates protein synthesis both *in vitro* and *in vivo*, and it has been suggested that the calorigenic effect is secondary to the stimulation of protein synthesis.[40a, 49, 58]

There appears to be a synergistic relationship between the thyroid hormones and the catecholamines, epinephrine and norepinephrine.[25] Thyroid hormones augment many of the responses of the organism to catecholamines, and catecholamines in turn accentuate the effects of the thyroid hormones. The nature of this relationship is not known.

REFERENCES

1. Adams, D. D. *J. clin. Endocrinol.,* 1958, *18*:699–712.
2. Alexander, N. M. *J. biol. Chem.,* 1959, *234*:1530–1533.
3. Anbar, M., Guttman, S. and Lewitus, Z. *Nature,* 1959, *183*:1517–1518.
4. Andros, G. and Wollman, S. H. *Proc. Soc. exp. Biol.* (*N.Y.*), 1964, *115*:775–777.
5. Astwood, E. B., Greer, M. A. and Ettlinger, M. G. *J. biol. Chem.,* 1949, *181*:121–130.

6. BARKER, S. B. Chap. 10 in *The thyroid gland*, vol. 1, Pitt-Rivers, R. and Trotter, W. R., eds. London, Butterworth & Co., 1964.

7. BERN, H. A. and NANDI, J. Chap. 4 in *The hormones*, vol. IV, PINCUS, G., THIMANN, K. V. and ASTWOOD, E. B., eds. New York, Academic Press, 1964.

8. BOYD, J. D. Chap. 2 in *The thyroid gland*, vol. 1, PITT-RIVERS, R. and TROTTER, W. R., eds. London, Butterworth and Co., 1964.

9. BRAVERMAN, L. E. and INGBAR, S. H. *J. clin. Invest.*, 1963, *42:*1216–1231.

10. BROWN-GRANT, K. *Physiol. Rev.*, 1961, *41:*189–213.

11. D'ANGELO, S. A., SNYDER, J. and GRODIN, J. M. *Endocrinology*, 1964, *75:*417–427.

12. DOBYNS, B. M. and STEELMAN, S. L. *Endocrinology*, 1953, *52:*705–711.

13. DODD, J. M. and MATTY, A. J. Chap. 13 in *The thyroid gland*, vol. 1, PITT-RIVERS, R. and TROTTER, W. R., eds. London, Butterworth and Co., 1964.

14. DOWLING, J. T., FREINKEL, N. and INGBAR, S. H. *J. clin. Endocrinol.* 1956, *16:*1491–1506.

15. EDELHOCH, H. and RALL, J. E. Chap. 6 in *The thyroid gland*, vol. 1, PITT-RIVERS, R. and TROTTER, W. R., eds. London, Butterworth and Co., 1964.

16. FAWCETT, D. M. and KIRKWOOD, S. *J. biol. Chem.*, 1954, *209:*249–256.

17. FEDERMAN, D. D., ROBBINS, J. and RALL, J. E. *J. clin. Invest.*, 1958, *37:*1024–1030.

18. FREINKEL, N. Chap. 7 in *The thyroid gland*, vol. 1, PITT-RIVERS, R. and TROTTER, W. R., eds. London, Butterworth and Co., 1964.

19. GORBMAN, A. *Physiol. Rev.*, 1955, *35:*336–346.

20. GREER, M. A., KENDALL, J. W. and SMITH, M. Chap. 14 in *The thyroid gland*, vol. 1, PITT-RIVERS, R. and TROTTER, W. R., eds. London, Butterworth and Co., 1964.

21. GROSS, J. and PITT-RIVERS, R. *Biochem. J.*, 1953, *53:*645–652; 652–657.

22. HALMI, N. S. Chap. 4 in *The thyroid gland*, vol. 1, PITT-RIVERS, R. and TROTTER, W. R., eds. London, Butterworth and Co., 1964.

23. HARINGTON, C. R. and BARGER, G. *Biochem. J.*, 1927, *21:*169–181.

24. HARRIS, G. W. In: *Comparative endocrinology*, GORBMAN, A., ed. New York, John Wiley and Sons, 1959.

25. HARRISON, T. S. *Physiol. Rev.*, 1964, *44:*161–185.

26. HIRSCH, P. F., VOELKEL, E. F. and MUNSON, P. L. *Science*, 1964, *146:*412–413.

27. HOCH, F. L. *Physiol. Rev.*, 1962, *42:*605–673.

28. HOUSSAY, B. A. *Vitamins and Hormones*, 1946, *4:*187–206.

29. IINO, S., YAMADA, T. and GREER, M. A. *Endocrinology*, 1961, *68:*582–588.

30. KEATING, F. R., JR. and ALBERT, A. *Recent Progr. Hormone Res.*, 1949, *4.*429–481.

31. KENDALL, E. C. *Trans. Ass. Amer. Physicians*, 1915, *30:*420–449; *ibid.*, *31:*134–145.

32. KLEBANOFF, S. J., YIP, C. and KESSLER, D. *Biochim. biophys. Acta (Amst.)*, 1962, *58:*563–574.

32a. KRITCHEVSKY, D. Chap. 5 in *Actions of hormones on molecular processes*, LITWACK, G. and KRITCHEVSKY, D., eds. New York, John Wiley and Sons, 1964.

32b. LITWACK, G. Chap. 3 in *Actions of hormones on molecular processes*, LITWACK, G. and KRITCHEVSKY, D., eds. New York, John Wiley and Sons, 1964.

33. LUDWIG, W. and VON MUTZENBECHER, P. *Hoppe-Seylers Z. physiol. Chem.*, 1939, *258:*195–211.

34. MCKENZIE, J. M. *J. clin. Endocrinol.*, 1960, *20:*380–388.

35. MALOOF, F. and SOODAK, M. *Pharmacol. Rev.*, 1963, *15:*43–95.

36. MARINE, D. and KIMBALL, O. P. *Arch. intern. Med.*, 1920, *25:*661–672.

37. NADLER, N. J., YOUNG, B. A., LEBLOND, C. P. and MITMAKER, B. *Endocrinology*, 1964, *74:*333–354.

38. OPPENHEIMER, J. H., SQUEF, R., SURKS, M. I. and HAUER, H. *J. clin. Invest.*, 1963, *42:*1769–1782.

39. PASTAN, I., HERRING, B. and FIELD, J. B. *J. biol. Chem.*, 1961, *236:*PC 25.

40. PITT-RIVERS, R. and CAVALIERI, R. R. Chap. 5 in *The thyroid gland*, vol. 1, PITT-RIVERS, R. and TROTTER, W. R., eds. London, Butterworth and Co., 1964.

40a. PRICE, S. Chap. 4 in *Actions of hormones on molecular processes*, LITWACK, G. and KRITCHEVSKY, D., eds. New York, John Wiley and Sons, 1964.

41. PURVES, H. D. Chap. 1 in *The thyroid gland*, vol. 2, PITT-RIVERS, R. and TROTTER, W. R., eds. London, Butterworth and Co., 1964.

42. RIGGS, D. S. *Pharmacol. Rev.*, 1952, *4:*284–370.

43. SCHUSSLER, G. C. and INGBAR, S. H. *J. clin. Invest.*, 1961, *40:*1394–1412.

44. SÖDERBERG, U. *Physiol. Rev.*, 1959, *39:*777–810.

45. STANBURY, J. B. *Recent Progr. Hormone Res.*, 1963, *19:*547–572.

46. STEIN, O. and GROSS, J. *Endocrinology*, 1964, *75:*787–798.

47. STERLING, K. *Proc. Mayo Clin.*, 1964, *39:*586–608.

48. TAPLEY, D. F. *Proc. Mayo Clin.*, 1964, *39:*626–636.

49. TATA, J. R. *Nature*, 1963, *197:*1167–1168.

50. TATA, J. R. Chap. 2 in *Actions of hormones on molecular processes*, Litwack, G. and Kritchevsky, D., eds. New York, John Wiley & Sons, 1964.

51. TATA, J. R. Chap. 8 in *The thyroid gland*, vol. 1, Pitt-Rivers, R. and Trotter, W. R., eds. London, Butterworth and Co., 1964.

52. TAUROG, A. *Proc. Mayo Clin.*, 1964, *39:*569–585.

53. TONG, W., KERKOF, P. and CHAIKOFF, I. L. *Biochim. Biophys. Acta (Amst.)*, 1962, *60:*1–19.

54. VANDERLAAN, J. E. and VANDERLAAN, W. P. *Endocrinology*, 1947, *40:*403–416.

55. VAN MIDDLESWORTH, L. *Recent Progr. Hormone Res.*, 1960, *16:*405–438.

56. VON MUTZENBECHER, P. *Hoppe-Seylers Z. Physiol. Chem.* 1939, *261:*253–256.

57. WAYNE, E. J., KOUTRAS, D. A. and ALEXANDER, W. D. *Clinical aspects of iodine metabolism*. Oxford, Blackwell Scientific Publications, Ltd., 1964.

58. WEISS, W. P. and SOKOLOFF, L. *Science*, 1963, *140:*1324–1326.

59. WISSIG, S. L. Chap. 3 in *The thyroid gland*, vol. 1, Pitt-Rivers, R. and Trotter, W. R., eds. London, Butterworth and Co., 1964.

60. WOLFF, E. C. and WOLFF, J. Chap. 11 in *The thyroid gland*, vol. 1, Pitt-Rivers, R. and Trotter, W. R., eds. London, Butterworth and Co., 1964.

61. WOLFF, J. *Physiol. Rev.*, 1964, *44:*45–90.

62. WOLFE, J., STANDAERT, M. E. and RALL, J. E. *J. clin. Invest.*, 1961, *40:*1373–1379.

63. WOODBURY, D. M. and WOODBURY, J. W. *J. Physiol.*, 1963, *169:*553–567.

64. WYNGAARDEN, J. B., WRIGHT, B. M. and WAYS, P. *Endocrinology*, 1952, *50:*537–549.

65. WYNN, J. and GIBBS, R. *J. biol. Chem.*, 1964, *239:*527–529.

66. YAMADA, T. and GREER, M. A. *Endocrinology*, 1959, *64:*559–566.

67. YIP, C. and KLEBANOFF, S. J. *Biochim. Biophys. Acta (Amst.)*, 1963, *74:*747–755.

CHAPTER 61

The Parathyroid Glands*

By D. HAROLD COPP

THE parathyroid glands are the smallest of the endocrine organs. Their total weight in an adult man is approximately 100 mg.; in a rat they weigh less than 0.5 mg. However, they play a vital role in calcium homeostasis in higher vertebrates, and their removal, particularly in young animals, frequently leads to hypocalcemic tetany and death. The glands are small paired bodies which arise from the endoderm of the third (parathyroid III) and fourth (parathyroid IV) branchial clefts and, as their name implies, are usually found in close association with the thyroid gland.[51] Their location varies in different animals. Accessory parathyroid tissue is common in man and may be widely scattered in the neck and upper mediastinum, a tendency which complicates the problems of the surgeon looking for a parathyroid tumor. In man, these glands are external to the thyroid, with parathyroid IV near the superior pole and parathyroid III variable in position but usually near the third tracheal ring. In cattle and sheep, parathyroid III is located in the upper pole of the thymus at some distance from the thyroid, and is ten times larger than parathyroid IV, which, indeed, is often vestigial. In the pig the latter disappears. In rats only parathyroid III, which lies on the surface of the thyroid, shows significant growth.

The parenchymal cell of the parathyroid is the chief cell, a cuboidal cell 6 to 12 μ in diameter with no granules in the cytoplasm. The

cytoplasm stains with variable intensity, thereby serving to distinguish the very pale clear cells ("Wasserhelle") from the dark chief cells.[51] Rucart[50] observed in rabbits that conditions tending to raise the calcium level cause hyperplasia of the dark cells, whereas conditions associated with lowered calcium levels result in hyperplasia of the clear cells. He believed this might indicate secretion of two distinct hormones. Under the electron microscope, chief cells stimulated by conditions promoting parathormone production show typical droplet formation and evidence of secretion.[49] In the human, clumps of granular oxyphilic cells appear a few years before puberty. The function of these cells is not known.

HISTORY

Because of their small size, the parathyroids were overlooked by early anatomists and physiologists. They were first observed in 1855 by the embryologist Remak in the the course of dissecting a newborn cat. He described at the upper pole of the thymus a tiny gland that was undoubtedly the superior parathyroid. Seven years later, the English zoologist Owen noted a small yellow gland close to the thyroid in an African rhinoceros which he was dissecting. However, the honor of naming the parathyroid glands fell to the Swedish scientist Sandström,[53] who thoroughly described them but failed to comprehend their physiologic significance. Gley[24] first recognized the biologic importance

*This chapter in the 18th edition was by Jane A. Russell.

of the gland. He observed that the effects of total thyroidectomy in the dog were much more severe than in the rabbit, but could be duplicated in the latter if the tiny parathyroid glands were also removed. The difference between thyroidectomy and parathyroidectomy was clearly demonstrated by Vassale and Generali,[64] who observed that thyroidectomy leads to the slow development of cretinism, whereas total removal of parathyroid tissue in young animals is usually followed rapidly by tetany, convulsions and death. It was believed that this syndrome, which occurred frequently after surgical thyroidectomy in the human, might be associated with an antitoxic action of the glands. However, their true function in calcium metabolism was finally recognized in 1909, when MacCallum and Voegtlin[37] clearly demonstrated that removal of the parathyroids resulted in tetany and a profound fall in blood calcium that could be relieved almost immediately by intravenous injection of calcium salts. They postulated an endocrine function of the glands in regulating blood calcium, but it was another 16 years before Collip[11] finally succeeded in preparing a physiologically active extract which raised the plasma calcium level in both parathyroidectomized and normal dogs. Since that time, this hormone, commonly called *parathormone*, has been further purified by Aurbach[3] and Rasmussen and Craig.[46] These advances, along with improved methods for calcium determination and an increased interest in bone physiology, have greatly stimulated work in the parathyroid field.[26, 36, 39, 45]

PARATHORMONE

Chemistry and Assay Methods. The original Collip[11] method for preparation of parathyroid extract was considered rather drastic at the time. It consisted of heating the minced glands in 5 per cent HCl in a water bath at 100° C. for one hour and subsequent purification by repeated isoelectric precipitation. However, this basically is still the method used for preparing commercial parathyroid extract (Para-thor-mone, E. Lilly & Co.).

Following total parathyroidectomy, the serum calcium normally falls and the serum phosphate rises. Administration of the Collip extract reverses this, elevating the serum calcium and lowering the serum phosphate in both parathyroidectomized and normal dogs. The standard U.S.P. unit of parathormone activity is defined as 1/100th of the amount necessary to raise the calcium content of 100 ml. of the blood serum of normal dogs (mature males weighing 10 to 12 kg.) 1 mg. per 100 ml. within 16 to 18 hours after administration. On this basis, 125 units of parathormone activity can be extracted from 1 gram of fresh beef parathyroid tissue. However, this assay method is cumbersome and not particularly precise. Munson[36] has described an improved method using rats weighing 200 grams which have been maintained four days on a low-calcium diet. The animals are parathyroidectomized and the dose of test material is injected subcutaneously. The level of serum calcium six hours later is related to the standard curve based on preparations of known parathormone activity. This method is relatively precise for a biologic assay and has provided the basis for further purification of parathormone. A second assay, based on the phosphaturic action of parathormone in the rat, has also been useful.

In 1959, Aurbach[3] and Rasmussen and Craig[46] announced almost simultaneously the isolation of a practically pure polypeptide with an activity of 2500 to 3000 U.S.P. units of parathormone per mg. The method was based on phenolic extraction and subsequent purification by countercurrent distribution, using the Munson assay[36] to follow biologic activity. One kg. of fresh beef parathyroid tissue yields 50 mg. of parathormone (125,000 U.S.P. units).

A chromatographic method of isolation on Sephadex G-50 was later devised which was simpler and gave separation almost as good as the countercurrent distribution technique.[47] The purified polypeptide (parathormone C) has a minimum molecular weight of 8447, and contains 73 amino acid residues and a single terminal amino acid, alanine. It is believed that this represents the true native hormone. Using different methods, Rasmussen and Craig[48] isolated a number of smaller parathyroid peptides having considerably reduced biologic activity. These, they believe, might represent partially hydrolyzed forms of the native hormone, which still retain the active core. As with ACTH, mild oxidation resulted in partially reversible inactivation.[48] Oxidation of the sulfur on one of the methionines ($R-S-CH_3$) to the sulfoxide ($R-SO-CH_3$) resulted in reversible inactivation; further oxidation to the sulfone ($R-SO_2-CH_3$) was irreversible.[48] The purified hormone has a much more evanescent action than crude extract when injected subcutaneously unless it is administered with gelatin, plasma protein or oil.[4, 43] Since the purified hormone has both hypercalcemic and phosphaturic action, it is no longer necessary to postulate two hormones for these effects.[45]

The availability of highly purified parathormone has greatly stimulated studies of its mode of action. It has also made possible the use of very sensitive methods for immunoassay[9, 59] similar to those used for measuring growth hormone and glucagon. The smallest amount detected so far with the complement fixation technique[59] is 0.084 U.S.P. units per ml. Another method[9] based on competitive inhibition of binding of I^{131}-labeled parathormone is said to detect levels as low as 0.0015 to 0.006 U.S.P. units per ml. The latter method has enabled the detection of parathormone activity in the plasma of patients with hyperparathyroidism and some normal subjects, but not in hypoparathyroidism.

Action of Parathormone. Removal of all parathyroid tissue is normally followed by a fall in plasma calcium and a rise in plasma phosphate. When Albright and Ellsworth[1] administered parathyroid extract to a patient with hypoparathyroidism they observed a prompt increase in urine phosphate and a fall in serum phosphate accompanied by a slow rise in serum calcium (Fig. 1). The *phosphaturic theory* of parathormone action is based on these observations. They suggested that the primary action of parathormone was to promote phosphate excretion by the kidney and that the rise in serum calcium was secondary to the fall in serum phosphate, which reduced the Ca × P product.

The opposing *osteolytic theory* postulated a primary effect on bone.[61] While it is now established that the hormone acts on both kidney and bone, the effect on blood calcium can be produced in nephrectomized animals in which the serum phosphate levels are maintained by peritoneal lavage[27] so that the basic assumption of the phosphaturic theory—that calcium mobilization is solely an indirect effect—is no longer tenable. There is considerable evidence for a direct osteolytic action on bone. Barnicot[5] observed local bone resorption when parathyroid tissue was placed in close proximity to bone *in vivo*. A similar effect was observed when parathyroid extract or purified parathormone was added to the medium of tissue cultures of bone.[23, 35] There was a rise in the calcium and citrate in the medium and an increase in the number and activity of osteoclasts—the multinucleate giant cells associated with bone destruction. This was also observed by Toft and Talmage[62] *in vivo* in the rat, in which the number of osteoclasts in bone diminished after parathyroidectomy but was increased when

parathyroid extract was administered. However, the rise in plasma calcium precedes the increase in osteoclasts, and Bélanger *et al.*[8] believe that they are not essential to the osteolytic process. When they stimulated endogenous parathormone production by hypocalcemia or administered parathyroid extract to rats, dogs and chicks, they observed a loss of bone mineral around large osteocytes buried in trabecular and cortical bone. This was associated with metachromatic staining changes, suggesting alteration in the properties of the bone matrix locally. In the process of osteolysis, both matrix and mineral must be affected. Bates *et al.*[7] have demonstrated an increase in hydroxyproline levels in plasma and urine following administration of parathyroid extract, presumably released by breakdown of bone collagen. Parathormone also increases the citrate output by bone, and an attractive theory was formulated which attributed the calcium mobilization to the solubilizing effect of chelation of calcium with citrate. However, citrate output was insufficient to account for all the calcium mobilized, and the current view of Neuman's group[34] is that parathormone increases production of both lactic acid and citric acid by bone cells, and that the resulting fall in pH locally is responsible for the solubilizing of bone mineral.

As Talmage and Elliott[57] have shown with Ca^{45}, the calcium mobilized by parathormone action appears to come from the deep bone stores rather than from recently deposited calcium. This is consistent with the view that, rather than acting superficially, the hormone promotes resorption of stable bone. Its effect is somewhat similar to that of vitamin D, and the two appear to act synergistically.

Parathormone has important effects on phosphate metabolism, particularly prominent in the hypoparathyroid state. This was first clearly demonstrated by Albright and Ellsworth[1] in the classic experiment illustrated in Figure 1. When parathyroid extract was administered acutely to a hypoparathyroid patient, there was an abrupt and marked increase in the rate of phosphate excretion by the kidney which was observed within an hour of the administration of the hormone. Associated with this phosphaturia, there was a progressive fall in serum phosphate. The blood calcium rose somewhat more slowly, reaching a maximum value at 12 to 18 hours. Based on these observations, Albright postulated, as pointed out above, that

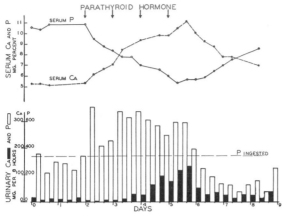

Fig. 1. Effects of parathyroid hormone (50 units per day) in patient with idiopathic hypoparathyroidism. Food constant in amount and composition was given during each 8 hour period. Note immediate increase in excretion of phosphate (negative balance) accompanied by reversals of the high serum phosphate and low serum calcium levels, and much later increase in urinary calcium (as serum calcium rose above 8 mg. per cent). (After Albright and Ellsworth, *J. clin. Invest.*, 1929, 7:183–202.)

the primary effect of parathormone was to cause phosphaturia, which, by lowering the serum phosphate and the Ca × P product, would secondarily promote the resorption of bone mineral and elevate the serum calcium.

Although a direct action on the kidney tubule, increasing phosphate excretion, has been thoroughly demonstrated, Albright's belief that there is no direct effect of parathormone on bone is, as shown above, clearly untenable. The second aspect of his theory, that the mineral depot of calcium and phosphate is manipulated through increased phosphate excretion and lowered blood levels of phosphate is a discarded hypothesis. It is only in certain circumstances and in a certain percentage of hypoparathyroid cases (about 50 per cent) that increased kidney output of phosphate in response to parathormone exceeds the increased output of phosphate from bone.

What significance can then be attached to the action of parathormone on the renal tubule? Certainly the renal action will facilitate disposal of phosphate liberated with calcium by increased resorption of bone. The associated fall in serum phosphate will also reduce the rate of mineral deposition in bone (by analogy with low phosphate rickets), and this action would summate with osteolysis in increasing the level of serum calcium. Whether parathormone has

a broader role in controlling blood phosphate levels (which are rather poorly stabilized) is a matter of speculation.

The parathyroids are also involved in magnesium metabolism.[38] Experimental magnesium deficiency in the rate produces hypercalcemia, hypophosphatemia and increased phosphate clearance by the kidney, suggesting stimulated parathormone production. Parathyroidectomy results in a fall in plasma magnesium, although not as great as the fall in calcium. However, hypomagnesemia may become a problem in chronic hypoparathyroidism.[28] Continuous intravenous infusion of pure parathormone into rats causes a profound fall in urinary calcium and magnesium with retention of both cations, and it has been suggested that this may be one of the mechanisms involved in magnesium homeostasis.[38]

Parathormone has a number of other important effects. Foulks and Perry[21] have suggested that parathormone may be involved in the transfer of phosphate from extracellular to intracellular space. In contrast to the effect on phosphate, parathormone appears to promote calcium retention by the kidney by increasing its reabsorption by the renal tubules.[32, 56] This effect, usually masked by the accompanying hypercalcemia, may be a factor in raising the blood calcium level. There is also some evidence that the hormone increases intestinal uptake of calcium. Parathyroidectomy reduced and parathormone administration increased the absorption of calcium from isolated sacs of rat small intestine[44] and from intestinal loops in dogs.[19]

To demonstrate the normal physiologic response to parathormone or parathyroid extract, it is preferable to administer the substance by continuous intravenous infusion since this is the way the hormone would normally be secreted by the gland. Figure 2 shows the typical response of a parathyroidectomized dog which has been continuously infused with 1 U.S.P. unit per kg. per hour.[12] After an initial latent period of 30 to 60 minutes the plasma calcium begins to rise, reaching normal levels in 12 to 15 hours. Thereafter, the calcium level is maintained by only 0.1 U.S.P. unit per kg. per hour. This may represent the normal hormone output of the dog. Continuous infusion of 4 to 8 mg. of calcium per kg. per hour is required to provide similar maintenance of normal plasma calcium levels in a parathyroidectomized dog, which may be an indication of the rate of calcium mobilization from the skeleton produced by the relatively small maintenance dose of parathormone.

Regulation of Parathyroid Function. Hyperplasia of the parathyroid glands occurs in a number of conditions which tend to lower plasma calcium levels, including low-calcium diets, vitamin D deficiency, pregnancy and lactation. It would seem logical that the level of calcium in blood should affect the function of the parathyroids, much as the level of blood glucose affects the function of the islets of the pancreas. By varying dietary intakes of calcium and phosphate, Stoerk and Carnes[54] found the degree of parathyroid hyperplasia to be related to the degree of hypocalcemia. Changes in serum phosphate were effective only if they altered the calcium level. Hyperplasia of parathyroid tissue has also recently been demonstrated in tissue cultures in which the level of calcium in the medium was reduced.[42, 49] Direct proof of parathormone production stimulated by hypocalcemia was provided by the experiments of Patt and Luckhardt.[41] They perfused low calcium blood through the thyroid–parathyroid gland complex which had been removed from a dog and collected the perfusate. When the serum so obtained was injected into normal or parathyroidectomized dogs, it caused a rise in serum

calcium similar to that obtained with parathyroid extract. These experiments provided the basis of McLean's[39] *negative feedback hypothesis,* which proposed that a fall in plasma calcium would stimulate parathormone production, which in turn would increase calcium mobilization from bone and restore the blood level to normal. Hypercalcemia would tend to suppress parathormone production and therefore would have the opposite effect.

To study this system, Copp and Davidson[16] perfused the glands with high- or low-calcium blood while retaining them in the circulation. Hypocalcemic stimulation increased plasma calcium to a level approaching that obtained in the same animal by continuous intravenous infusion of 20 U.S.P. units of parathyroid extract per kg. per hour. The rate of biosynthesis must be remarkable, for less than 20 mg. of dog parathyroid tissue produced in two hours the equivalent of 0.2 mg. parathormone. This is the amount of hormone which can be extracted from 4 grams of fresh beef parathyroids. The experiment was later repeated in a preparation in which the glands were actually removed from the body, although the connections to the circulation were maintained.[15] Calcium or EDTA, a calcium chelator, was added in appropriate proportions to blood drawn from the carotid to raise or lower the calcium level, and this blood was then pumped through

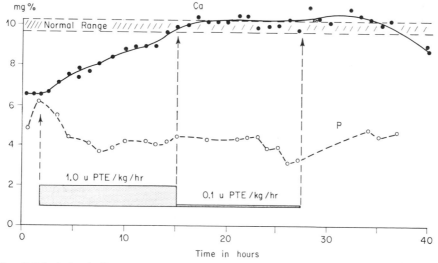

Fig. 2. Solid circles indicate restoration of the normal plasma calcium level in a thyroparathyroidectomized dog by continuous intravenous infusion of 1 U.S.P. unit parathyroid extract (Parathor-mone, E. Lilly & Co.) per kg. per hour, and maintenance by infusion of 0.1 U.S.P. unit per kg. per hour. Open circles show changes in phosphorus levels. (From Copp, D. H., In: *Bone as a tissue.* New York, McGraw-Hill Book Co., 1960.)

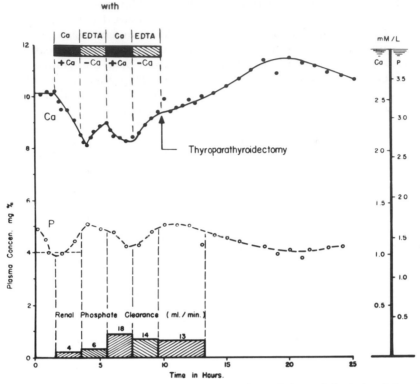

Fig. 3. Changes in plasma calcium during excessive perfusions of the isolated thyroid-parathyroid glands in a fasted dog with blood alternately high and low in calcium. The glands were removed as indicated at the end of the last EDTA perfusion. (From Copp *et al.*, *Endocrinology*, 1962, *70*:638–649.)

the superior thyroid artery to both thyroid and parathyroid glands. Blood flowing out of the cut veins draining the glands was collected and returned to the body continuously through the jugular vein. Typical responses to high and low calcium perfusion of the glands are shown in Figure 3. Since there were no nervous connections, nor were other endocrine glands involved, these experiments indicate a direct humoral control of parathyroid function by the level of calcium in the blood flowing through it. It appears to provide a very efficient system of negative feedback.

CALCITONIN AND THYROCALCITONIN

From studies of isolated thyroid–parathyroid gland complex perfused with high-calcium blood, Copp[15] found that the fall in systemic

plasma calcium was much more rapid than that following surgical parathyroidectomy, so that it could not be explained on the basis of suppressed parathormone production.[15] This was particularly significant in dogs in which the output of endogenous parathormone had first been stimulated by a low-calcium perfusion (see Fig. 2). Subsequent high-calcium perfusion caused a prompt fall in systemic plasma calcium, whereas thyroparathyroidectomy was followed by a prolonged rise typical of the response to parathormone injection in the dog.[16] On the basis of these experiments, Copp *et al.*[15] concluded that high-calcium perfusion of the glands had released a fast-acting hypocalcemic factor to which they gave the name *calcitonin* since it was evidently involved in regulating the calcium level or "tone" in body fluids. Since both thyroid and parathyroids were perfused, the hormone might have been derived from either gland. However, the same prompt hypocalcemic response was obtained when the superior parathyroid was perfused with high-calcium blood in sheep, in which the gland is quite separate from the thyroid.[17] On the basis of these experiments it was concluded that the parathyroid was the source of this new hormone. In experiments paralleling those of Patt and Luckhardt,[41] high-calcium blood was collected after perfusing the thyroid–parathyroid complex, and was subsequently injected into other dogs.[15] A single injection resulted in a prompt transient fall in plasma calcium, reaching its lowest point in 20 to 30 minutes and returning to normal within 60 minutes. Repeated injections at 20-minute intervals continued to depress the plasma level, but the effect did not persist more than 30 minutes after the last injection (see Fig. 4). Extracts of beef parathyroid tissue with similar hypocalcemic activity have been obtained and are effective in sheep and dogs at dosages of 0.1 to 0.5 mg. per kg.

Because of the rather prolonged action of parathormone in the dog and in man, Rasmussen[45] predicted that this would lead to oscillation and "overshoot" in the feedback system.

The fast, short action of calcitonin would tend to check the effect of excessive parathormone and prevent such overshoots. Several experiments indicate that the parathyroids do in fact control hypercalcemia. Eger and Titze[20] observed that the hypercalcemia and bone changes associated with hypervitaminosis D were much more severe in parathyroidectomized animals. This was also observed when parathyroidectomy was performed in dogs[14] and in rats[10, 55, 63] following administration of large doses of parathyroid extract.

Recently, a hypocalcemic factor has been extracted from the thyroid and has been termed *thyrocalcitonin.*[29] Thyrocalcitonin has been extracted from the thyroid glands of a number of different species and appears to be a polypeptide.[30] A highly purified substance,[60] recently obtained, appears to be a single polypeptide chain with a molecular weight of 8700—very similar to that of parathormone. It differs in a number of respects from the parathyroid factor, calcitonin, which has a very short action and is ineffective in rats. In contrast, thyrocalcitonin has a much more prolonged action (several

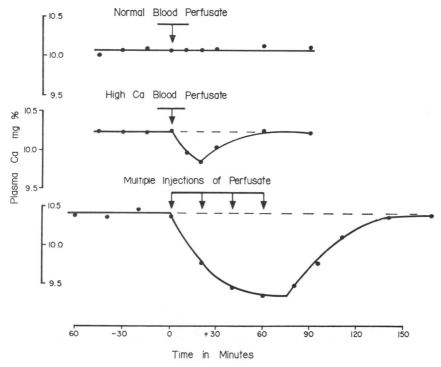

Fig. 4. Effective injection of plasma from perfusates of the isolated thyroid-parathyroid glands. In the upper two curves, points represent averages for each group (6 dogs); bottom curves show averages for a single dog and effect of repeated injections of 50 ml. aliquots of plasma from a high calcium thyro-parathyroid perfusate. (From Copp *et al., Endocrinology,* 1962, *70:*638–649.)

hours) and is very effective in rats. It lowers serum calcium and serum phosphate, perhaps by promoting bone uptake of these elements.[58] Recent experiments have shown that perfusion of the thyroid alone with solutions of high calcium concentration may have a hypocalcemic effect, so that thyrocalcitonin may have been involved in the original experiments of Copp et al.[15] Possibly, calcitonin and thyrocalcitonin are identical, although the evidence now available suggests that they are distinct entities. The problem is complicated by the close association of the two glands and species difference in response. An analogy may be drawn to the regulation of blood sugar, in which two relatively long-acting antagonistic hormones, insulin and somatotrophin, are involved along with the short-acting hormone, glucagon.

CALCIUM HOMEOSTASIS

The primary function of the parathyroids is the regulation of the level of calcium ion in body fluids, which has been referred to by McLean and Hastings as "one of nature's physiological constants."[40] Indeed, calcium is one of the most precisely controlled constituents of plasma; the normal diurnal fluctuations are within the range of $\pm$ 5 to 10 per cent.[18] This is no doubt related to the important functions of calcium with respect to the activity of many enzyme systems, membrane permeability and neuromuscular excitability. The normal level in plasma is 10 mg. per 100 ml. (5 mEq. per liter), of which approximately half is bound to protein. When the ionized calcium drops below half of the normal value, signs of increased neuromuscular excitability, tetany and convulsions may develop. Although gain and loss of calcium depends on the balance between the absorption from the intestinal tract and loss by excretion in the feces, urine and sweat, the acute regulation of the plasma calcium level depends primarily on the vast reservoir of calcium present in the skeleton (1 kg. in an adult man), and the thyroid and parathyroid glands. The latter appear to act like thermostats or "calciostats" to adjust the level of calcium in blood.[18] A small part of the skeletal calcium (3 to 5 grams), probably on the crystal surfaces of bone adjacent to the circulation, forms a labile calcium pool from which calcium may be withdrawn or to which it may be added without the mediation of the parathyroids. This labile pool acts as a buffer to reduce fluc-

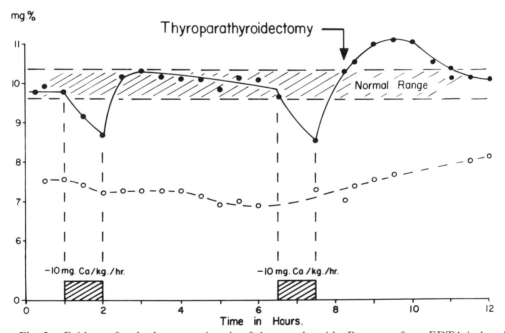

Fig. 5. Evidence for the homeostatic role of the parathyroids. Recovery from EDTA-induced hypocalcemia seen in the same animal with intact parathyroids and after total thyroparathyroidectomy was performed. (From Copp, *Yearbook of endocrinology, 1961–1962 series,* Chicago, Year Book Medical Publishers, 1962.)

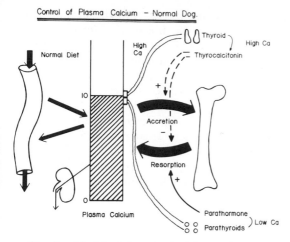

Control of Plasma Calcium – Normal Dog.

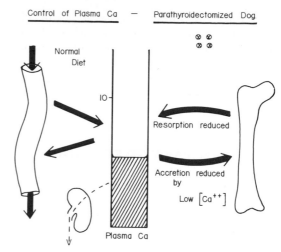

Control of Plasma Ca — Parathyroidectomized Dog.

Fig. 6. Model of the principal factors involved in control of the plasma calcium level.

Fig. 7. Control of plasma calcium after parathyroidectomy.

tuations in the blood calcium level. The availability of this pool depends on bone blood flow, estimated to be 5 to 8 per cent of the resting cardiac output. However, as is true for acid–base buffers, this mechanism will not bring the blood calcium back to the initial level. Precise homeostatic control requires the presence of functioning parathyroid tissue. In dogs with intact parathyroids, Sanderson *et al.*[52] showed that the plasma calcium returned to the initial level within a few hours after it had been artificially raised by injection of calcium or lowered by injection of the calcium-complexing agent, EDTA. This fast recovery did not occur in thyroparathyroidectomized dogs.

The control system involved is remarkably sensitive. The experiments on perfusion of the isolated glands[15] demonstrated that a reduction of 2 mg. per 100 ml. (1 mEq. per liter) provided an adequate stimulus for endogenous parathormone production, while a similar rise in the calcium in the perfusing blood caused a release of thyrocalcitonin. Indirect perfusion experiments indicate that a fall of as little as 3 per cent in the plasma calcium level stimulated endogenous parathormone production, while a rise of 5 per cent appeared to be an adequate stimulus for thyrocalcitonin.[13] A typical example of homeostatic control is shown in Figure 5. A one-hour infusion of the calcium-chelating agent, EDTA, lowered the level in blood and stimulated endogenous parathormone production, which caused a rapid mobilization of calcium from bone. When the infusion was stopped, the blood calcium rose rapidly but

was suddenly checked just above the initial level, presumably by release. The experiment was repeated and parathyroidectomy was performed after the EDTA infusion, so that the source of thyrocalcitonin was eliminated. The calcium level now overshot the normal range as predicted by Rasmussen.

The principal factors involved in calcium homeostasis are shown diagrammatically in Figures 6 and 7. In the adult, the absorption of calcium from the diet and the loss in excreta are normally balanced, as is the release of calcium by bone resorption and the deposition of calcium in new bone. A fall in plasma calcium will stimulate parathormone production and increase the resorption process, thus restoring the normal level. The precise action of thyrocalcitonin is unknown, but it presumably acts to shift calcium into bone since it does not affect excretion of calcium in the urine. When the parathyroids are removed, the resorptive process slows while accretion continues, so that there is a net shift of calcium into bone and a fall in the blood level. There is evidence that the rate of bone mineralization is dependent on both the phosphate and the calcium level in blood. As the plasma calcium level decreases, bone uptake of calcium also diminishes, until it comes into balance with the reduced rate of calcium release. An uneasy equilibrium is established—usually at 5 to 7 mg. per 100 ml. A high-calcium diet, particularly when given with high doses of vitamin D, will increase calcium absorption from the gut and compensate for the reduced rate of bone resorption. Indeed, under these circumstances it is even possible for hypercalcemia to occur in spite of the hypoparathyroid state. The most reliable evidence of functioning parathyroid tissue is a normal stable plasma calcium level and the capacity for rapid homeostatic recovery after injection with calcium or EDTA.

HYPOPARATHYROIDISM

The severity of the symptoms which follow complete removal of parathyroid tissue varies greatly depending on age, species and diet. The symptoms are much more severe on a low-calcium diet and in young animals in which there are heavy demands on calcium for new bone formation. The cardinal biochemical changes are low serum calcium and high serum phosphate levels, and diminished excretion of both of these elements in urine.[2] Symptoms are related primarily to the hypocalcemia and include hyperirritability of the nervous system, with latent or frank tetany. Carpopedal spasm is an early indication of this state as is twitching of the face in response to tapping of the facial nerve (Chvostek's sign). Generalized convulsions may develop, leading to respiratory paralysis and death unless the hypocalcemia is relieved by intravenous infusion of calcium salts. Complications of chronic hypoparathyroidism include aplasia or hypoplasia of the teeth in children and lenticular cataracts. Fortunately, the condition is extremely rare—a tribute to the remarkable efficiency of these tiny glands. Evident or latent hypoparathyroidism does develop frequently following surgical extirpation of the thyroid[22] and may often be detected by signs of latent tetany and a low plasma calcium level obtained on routine examination. The most definitive test is the EDTA tolerance test proposed by Jones and Fourman,[31] in which plasma calcium is lowered by the infusion of EDTA, and the pattern of recovery is determined for the next 24 hours. As observed in the dog by Sanderson et al.,[52] recovery is rapid if normal parathyroid tissue is present, but is greatly delayed if the parathyroids are nonfunctional or absent. Since the acute symptoms of tetany are due to hypocalcemia, immediate relief can be obtained by intravenous injection of calcium salts. Long-term treatment of hypoparathyroidism with parathyroid extract or parathormone is impractical because of cost and the development of immunity to the hormone. However, good results may often be obtained by giving a high-calcium diet and reducing phosphate intake. Patients who fail to respond adequately to this regimen may be treated successfully with large doses of vitamin D (calciferol) or dihydrotachysterol (A.T. 10), far in excess of those required to prevent or treat rickets, i.e., 200,000 to 400,000 units of vitamin D or 5 to 10 mg. of A.T. 10. Because of a danger of producing hypercalcemia on this regimen, it is important to test routinely the plasma and urine calcium of patients under treatment.

HYPERPARATHYROIDISM

This relatively rare condition is usually caused by a tumor in one of the parathyroids or in accessory parathyroid tissue.[2] The condition is much more common in women, possibly because of the repeated hypocalcemic stresses of pregnancy and lactation. The signs and symptoms result from excessive parathormone production. It is often referred to as a disease of "moans, stones and bones" for pain, kidney stones and bone lesions are frequent features. There is frequently, although not invariably, radiologic evidence of increased bone destruction. In severe cases, there may be many areas of demineralization of cystic appearance associated with increased osteoclast activity. This extreme form of bone involvement is referred to as *osteitis fibrosa cystica* or *von Recklinghausen's disease* and frequently results in multiple pathologic fractures. The most important single biochemical finding is an elevated plasma calcium, although this may not be very great (+ 1 mg. per 100 ml.) possibly because of the moderating effect of calcitonin from normal parathyroid tissue. The hypercalcemia is associated with hypercalciuria, which accounts for the other common complication of hyperparathyroidism —kidney stones. These may occur even in the absence of evident bone involvement, and in all cases of recurrent kidney stones hyperparathyroidism should be suspected. In extreme cases, the plasma calcium may rise to 15 mg. per 100 ml. or higher. The effects of such severe hypercalcemia are muscle weakness, depression of the nervous system and abdominal pain. There is also prolongation of cardiac systole due to hypercalcemia. Prolonged hypercalcemia may lead to calcifications in the soft tissues[2] in addition to renal stones.

Although a number of diagnostic tests have been suggested,[25] the most dependable criterion of hyperparathyroidism is still the demonstration by a reliable assay of a persistent elevation of the plasma calcium level. The severity of the hypercalcemia may often be increased by restricting the intake of phosphate (phosphate deprivation test). Other possible causes of hypercalcemia, including multiple myeloma, malignancy (particularly with bone involvement), vitamin D overdosage, hyperthyroidism, sarcoidosis and the milk–alkali syndrome, should be ruled out. In cases of primary hyperparathyroidism, the plasma phosphate is usually low, and the blood alkaline phosphatase is elevated, particularly if bone involvement is extensive. The tubular reabsorption of phosphate (TRP) is reduced but since this is also affected by the dietary intake of phosphate, it is important to compare the results with those for normal subjects on a similar diet. Once the condition has been diagnosed, the only treatment available is surgical removal of the parathyroid tumor responsible for the excessive hormone production. Following the operation, mild hypoparathyroidism with low plasma calcium and magnesium levels may occur.

Secondary hyperparathyroidism, with hyperplasia of the glands and excessive parathormone production, may occur as a complication of a number of conditions which tend to lower plasma calcium. These include renal failure with phosphate retention (renal rickets), low calcium diets, pregnancy and lactation, and low vitamin D rickets. Bone involvement may be severe in these cases. However, when the originating cause is removed, the parathyroids usually return to normal function within a few months, and surgical intervention is not indicated.

REFERENCES

1. ALBRIGHT, F. and ELLSWORTH, R. *J. clin. Invest.*, 1929, *7:* 183–201.
2. ALBRIGHT, F. and REIFENSTEIN, E. C., JR. *The parathyroid glands and metabolic bone disease.* Baltimore, Williams & Wilkins Co., 1948.
3. AURBACH, G. D. *J. biol. Chem.*, 1959, *234:*3179–3181.
4. AURBACH, G. D. *Endocrinology*, 1959, *64:*296–298.
5. BARNICOT, N. A. *J. Anat. (Lond.)*, 1948, *82:*233–248.
6. BARTTER, F. C. *J. clin. Endocrinol.*, 1954, *14:*826–827.
7. BATES, W. K., McGOWEN, J. and TALMAGE, R. V. *Endocrinology*, 1962, *71:*189–195.
8. BÉLANGER, L. F., ROBICHON, J., MIGICOVSKY, B. B., COPP, D. H. and VINCENT, J. In: *Mechanisms of hard tissue destruction.* Washington, D.C., American Association for the Advancement of Science, 1963.
9. BERSON, S. A., YALOW, R. S., AURBACH, G. D. and POTTS, J. T., JR. *Proc. nat. Acad. Sci. (Wash.)*, 1963, *49:*613–617.
10. CAMERON, E. C. and COPP, D. H. *Proc. Soc. exp. Biol. Med. (N.Y.)*, 1963, *114:*278–280.
11. COLLIP, J. B. *J. biol. Chem.*, 1925, *63:*395–438.
12. COPP, D. H. Chap. 13 in *Bone as a tissue,* K. Rodahl, J. T. Nicholson and E. M. Brown, eds. New York, McGraw-Hill Book Co., 1960.
13. COPP, D. H. In: *Yearbook of endocrinology,* 1961–1962 series, G. S. Gordan, ed. Chicago, Year Book Medical Publishers, 1962.
14. COPP, D. H. *Oral Surg.*, 1963, *16:*872–877.
15. COPP, D. H., CAMERON, E. C., CHENEY, B. A., DAVIDSON, A. G. F. and HENZE, K. G. *Endocrinology*, 1962, *70:* 638–649.
16. COPP, D. H. and DAVIDSON, A. G. F. *Proc. Soc. exp. Biol. Med. (N.Y.)*, 1961, *107:*342–344.
17. COPP, D. H. and HENZE, K. G. *Endocrinology*, 1964, *75:* 49–55.
18. COPP, D. H., MENSEN, E. D. and McPHERSON, G. D. *Clin. Orthop.*, 1960, *17:*288–296.
19. CRAMER, C. F. *Endocrinology*, 1963, *72:*192–196.
20. EGER, W. and TITZE, G. *Klin. Wschr.*, 1942, *21:*859–862.
21. FOULKS, J. G. and PERRY, F. A. *Amer. J. Physiol.*, 1959, *196:*561–566.
22. FOURMAN, P., DAVIS, R. H., JONES, K. H. MORGAN, D. B. and SMITH, J. W. G. *Brit. J. Surg.*, 1963, *50:*608–619.
23. GAILLARD, P. J. *Develop. Biol.*, 1959, *1:*152–181.
24. GLEY, E. *C.R. Soc. Biol. (Paris)*, 1897, *4:*18–20.
25. GORDAN, G. S., EISENBORG, E., LOKEN, H. F., GARDNER, B. and HAYASHIDA, T. *Recent Progr. Hormone Res.*, 1962, *18:*297–326.
26. GREEP, R. O. and TALMAGE, R. V., eds. *The parathyroids.* Springfield, Ill., Charles C Thomas, 1961.
27. GROLLMAN, A. *Endocrinology*, 1954, *55:*166–172.
28. HANNA, S., NORTH, K. A. K., MacINTYRE, I. and FRASER, R. *Brit. Med. J.*, 1961, *2:*1253–1256.
29. HIRSCH, P. F., GAUTHIER, G. F. and MUNSON, P. L. *Endocrinology*, 1963, *73:*244–252.
30. HIRSCH, P. F., VOELKEL, E. F., SAVERY, A. and MUNSON, P. L. *Fed. Proc.*, 1964, *23:*204.
31. JONES, K. H. and FOURMAN, P. *Lancet*, 1963, *2:*119–121.
32. KLEEMAN, C. R., BERNSTEIN, D., ROCKNEY, R., DOWLING, J. T. and MAXWELL, M. H., *Yale J. Biol. Med.*, 1961, *34:*1–30.
33. KUMAR, M. A., FOSTER, G. V. and MacINTYRE, I. *Lancet*, 1963, *2:*480–482.
34. MARTIN, G. R. FIRSCHEIN, H. E., MULRYAN, B. J. and NEUMAN, W. F. *J. Amer. chem. Soc.*, 1958, *80:*6201–6204.
35. MECCA, C. E., MARTIN, G. R. and GOLDHABER, P. *Proc. Soc. Exp. Biol. Med. (N.Y.)*, 1963, *113:*538–540.
36. MUNSON, P. L. *Ann. N. Y. Acad. Sci.*, 1955, *60:*776–795.
37. MacCALLUM, W. G. and VOEGTLIN, C. *J. exp. Med.*, 1909, *11:*118–151.
38. MacINTYRE, I., BOSS, S. and TROUGHTON, V. A. *Nature (Lond.)*, 1963, *198:*1058–1060.
39. McLEAN, F. C. *Clin. Orthop.*, 1957, *9:*46–60.

40. McLean, F. C. and Hastings, A. B. *Amer. J. med. Sci.,* 1935, *189:*601–613.

41. Patt, H. M. and Luckhardt, A. B. *Endocrinology,* 1942, *31:*384–392.

42. Raisz, L. G. *Nature (Lond.),* 1963, *197:*1115–1116.

43. Rasmussen, H. *Endocrinology,* 1959, *64:*367–372.

44. Rasmussen, H. *Endocrinology,* 1959, *65:*517–519.

45. Rasmussen, H. *Amer. J. Med.,* 1961, *30:*112–128.

46. Rasmussen, H. and Craig, L. C. *J. Amer. chem. Soc.,* 1959, *81:*5003.

47. Rasmussen, H. and Craig, L. C. *Biochim. biophys. Acta (Amst.),* 1962, *56:*332–338.

48. Rasmussen, H. and Craig, L. C. *Recent Progr. Hormone Res.,* 1962, *18:*269–289.

49. Roth, S. I. and Raisz, L. G. *Clin. Invest.,* 1964, *13:*331–345.

50. Rucart, G. *C. R. Soc. Biol. (Paris),* 1951, *145:*342–344.

51. Rucart, G. *Les parathyroides: physiologie et morphologie.* Paris, Editions le François, 1952.

52. Sanderson, P. H., Marshall, F. and Wilson, R. E. *J. Clin. Invest.,* 1960, *39:*662–670.

53. Sandström, I. *Upsala Läk.-Fören. Förh.,* 1880, *15:*441–471.

54. Stoerk, H. C. and Carnes, W. H. *J. Nutr.,* 1945, *29:*43–50.

55. Stoerk, H. C. and Celozzi, E. *Proc. Soc. exp. Biol. Med. (N.Y.),* 1963, *114:*714–718.

56. Talmage, R. V. *Ann. N. Y. Acad. Sci.,* 1956, *64:*326–335.

57. Talmage, R. V. and Elliott, J. R. *Endocrinology,* 1958, *62:*717–722.

58. Talmage, R. V., Neuenschwander, J. and Kraintz, L. *Endocrinology,* 1965, *76:*103–107.

59. Tashjian, A. H., Jr., Levine, L. and Munson, P. L.: *Endocrinology,* 1964, *74:*244–254.

60. Tenenhouse, A., Arnaud, C. and Rasmussen, H. *Proc. nat. Acad. Sci.,* 1965, *53:*818–822.

61. Thompson, D. L. and Pugsley, L. I. *Amer. J. Physiol.,* 1932, *102:*350–354.

62. Toft, R. J. and Talmage, R. V. *Proc. Soc. exp. Biol. Med. (N.Y.),* 1960, *103:*611–613.

63. Tweedy, W. R. and Chandler, S. B. *Amer. J. Physiol.,* 1929, *88:*754–760.

64. Vassale, G. and Generali, F. *Arch. ital. biol.,* 1896, *25:*459–464.

SECTION XIV

REPRODUCTION

CHAPTER 62

Physiology of Reproduction in the Female

By THOMAS R. FORBES

INTRODUCTION

An indispensable attribute of all living things is their ability to reproduce themselves or their kind. Although most vital functions are performed within one living body and without the aid of another, in higher forms specialization has led to a division of the mechanisms of reproduction between two sexes, and the contributions of both are therefore essential if the reproductive process is to be completed. The demands of engendering, producing and nurturing a new organism are great enough so that the responsibility is withheld from the very young and the old, being reserved for that intermediate period when the organism has reached full development but has not yet lost strength and vigor.

The early studies on reproduction were concerned mainly with the elucidation of the morphologic differences and homologies of the male and female. Sperm were seen by microscopists in the seventeenth century but, curiously enough, the first mammalian ova were not described as such until 1827. Later investigations were concerned with the cytologic aspect of the marriage of the sperm and the ovum to produce a single cell capable of multiplication and differentiation and finally of becoming another individual of the species. At the same time the somatic differentiation of the developing organism was studied. Embryologists learned to associate a sequence of morphologic alterations with the production of new generations of gametes and with the protection and nourishment of the fertilized ovum, embryo, fetus and newborn animal or infant.

In 1672, a young Dutch physician, Regnier de Graaf, first described the ovarian follicle (graafian follicle). He, however, mistook the follicles for eggs, undoubtedly influenced by observations on the ovaries of birds. He considered that "all men and animals take their origin from an egg—existing before coitus in the female testicles."* The ova were not discovered until 1827, when Karl Ernst von Baer first observed the barely macroscopic globules in the ovarian follicles of a dog. Although sperm are much smaller than ova, their discovery followed that of the large graafian follicles by only a few years, probably because the independent existence of sperm in a fluid medium facilitated their microscopic observation. Antony von Leeuwenhoek first illustrated mammalian sperm in 1678.

The nervous system was first studied in great detail as a system facilitating internal coordination of body function. Early observations indicated, however, that some other mechanisms regulate at least certain aspects of reproductive phenomena. The relation of the gonads to certain sexual manifestations was known from ancient times. Experiments involving gonadal ablation and transplantation confirmed these assumptions. Subsequently extracts of the gonads, and finally chemical substances isolated from the gonads, were found to be active in substituting for some gonadal functions. Almost simultaneously, the pituitary gland was shown to regulate the functions of the gonads, and, more recently, the function of the mammary glands. Many specific hormones, several of which have been isolated as chemical entities, enter into the physiologic aspects of reproduction. Even so, the mechanisms regulating some aspects of the phenomena are not yet known, and the probable interrelations of the known hormones are understood incompletely.

*For an excellent account of de Graaf's studies, with full bibliographic description of his works and translations of the more important passages, see Catchpole, H. R. *Bull. Hist. Med.,* 1940, *8:*1261–1300.

THE OVARY AND ITS HORMONES

During the period of active sexual life, the ovaries undergo rhythmic structural and functional changes which are associated with modifications in the structure and function of other tissues, glands or organs, and even in the behavior of the mammalian organism. The maturation of the ova in mammals is not a continuous process but an interrupted one: one follicle or group of follicles in the adult ovary grows, matures and ovulates at one time, and others do so at more or less regular, successive intervals. The intervals determined by the cyclic ovarian changes are designated *estrous cycles* in the nonprimate mammalian species and *menstrual cycles* in man and other primates. These two cycles are similar in that they both reflect the activity of the ovaries, but they are quite different in detail.

The term *estrus* (*oestrus* is preferred by the British) was first used by Walter Heape in 1901 to denote the periods of sexual excitement or "heat" occurring in many animals. (The adjectival form is *estrous.*) Animals of many species have periods of sexual activity restricted to but a few weeks or months during one or two seasons of the year, and are known as seasonal breeders. In some of these species the females are continually receptive to the male ("in estrus") for a period of weeks or months provided copulation does not occur. Other species show a series of estrous cycles, and in the absence of copulation eventually become anestrous at the beginning of the nonbreeding season.

Evidence of ovarian endocrine function was first obtained by observing animals after ovariectomy. The genital tissues retained their infantile characteristics if the animals were young when ovariectomized; the uteri, mammary glands and vaginal mucosa atrophied if sexually mature animals were ovariectomized. Successful transplants or grafts of ovaries made at various sites largely restored the atrophic genital tissues.†

†Successful transplantations of gonads in mammals have been made from the normal to an abnormal site in one individual (autotransplantation), or from one individual to a closely related individual within the same species (homotransplantation). Grafts of ovaries of one species into another (heterotransplantation) or even between unrelated animals of the same species are seldom if ever successful. Grafts of gonads can be most successfully made in gonadectomized hosts.

The early experiments did not clearly reveal whether the follicles or the corpora lutea that formed after ovulation were the source of the endocrine secretion. Histologic examination of the ovarian tissues indicated that the corpora lutea were more obviously glandular than the granulosa cells and surrounding theca of the follicles. In rabbits the corpora lutea were first noted to be essential for the growth of the endometria to a condition permitting implantation of fertilized ova. Pregnancy terminated in rabbits and in animals of several other species when the corpora lutea were removed.[15]

The ovary is surrounded, except at the hilus, by a layer of cuboidal epithelial cells which constitute the germinal epithelium (Fig. 1). In some species new ova may arise from this layer and migrate into the ovary even during adult life, but it is doubtful if new ova arise after birth in man. The ovaries at birth contain several hundred thousand ova—a number which progressively diminishes throughout life. The ova develop within follicles which have an inner layer or layers of granulosa cells and outer layers of cells contributed by the ovarian stroma, the theca. A mature follicle contains a cavity filled with liquor folliculi, surrounded by a syncytial mass of granulosa cells. In one clump of these cells, the cumulus oophorus, the ovum is embedded. Surrounding the basement membrane upon which the outermost granulosa cells rest are two layers of ovarian stroma forming a vascular theca interna, which may contain cells with cytoplasmic secretory granules, and a more fibrous theca externa. At ovulation the mature ovum (in man about 120 μ in diameter) escapes. The granulosa cells transform into the

luteal cells of a corpus luteum. The vascular ovarian stroma consists of fibroblast-like cells in animals of most species. The stromal cells, however, change in appearance under some conditions.

Most of the ova do not attain maturity. During an average human life span only 400 to 450 may be released. The remainder and by far the greater number of the ova and their follicles regress at different stages in their development.

The endocrine function of the testis was first made clear in 1849 by Arnold Berthold. He was so impressed by the secondary sexual characters of cockerels that he used them in his experiments. Castrated cockerels (capons) acquired a normal cock's appearance and attitude when testes were transplanted into their abdominal cavities. Berthold deduced that, since the nerves to the testes had been severed, these glands must exert their influence on the body by releasing a substance into the blood stream. This simple but brilliant experiment and conclusion established the science of endocrinology. Although Leydig described the glandular interstitial cells in the intertubular areas of the testis in 1857, they have only recently been shown to be the source of male hormones. The endocrine activity of the ovaries was first shown convincingly when Emil Knauer (1896) noted that autotransplantation of ovaries prevented the atrophy of the uterus subsequent to ovariectomy and that neural connections between the uteri and ovaries, if they did exist, were not essential.

In 1917, Stockard and Papanicolaou discovered that the types of cells obtained in smears of the vaginal epithelia of guinea pigs could be correlated with the development of follicles in the ovary. When large follicles formed and ovulated, the epithelial cells were cornified.

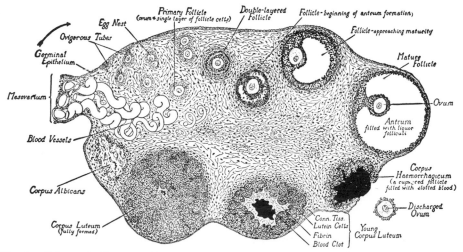

Fig. 1. Schematic diagram of mammalian ovary showing sequence in origin, growth and rupture of ovarian follicle and formation and retrogression of a corpus luteum. (From Patten, *Embryology of the pig,* 2nd ed. New York, McGraw-Hill Book Co., Inc., 1944; with permission.)

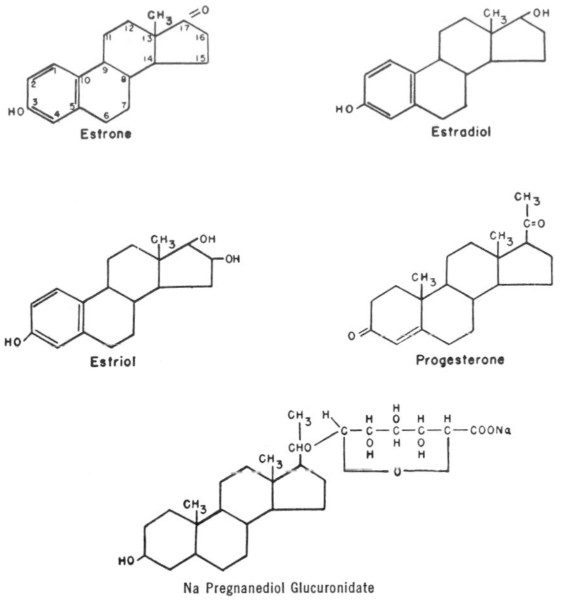

Fig. 2. Structural formulae of three normally occurring estrogens, of progesterone and of sodium pregnanediol glucuronidate.

Similarly, in rats and mice the vaginal mucosa cast off cornified epithelial cells which were detectable in smears at those times during the cycle when large or ovulating follicles were present. The morphologic changes in the vaginal smear indicative of estrus appeared in some animals in which ovulation and the formation of corpora lutea did not occur, indicating that the follicles alone could elicit cyclic activity. Liquor folliculi from large follicles or lipoid-soluble extracts of this liquor contained a substance which would induce vaginal cornification in castrated mice, i.e., which would replace the endocrine function of the ovaries with their large follicles. Allen and Doisy,[4] who in 1923 first demonstrated the active substance in cell-free preparations, called it the ovarian follicular hormone or the primary ovarian hormone. Although the granulosa cells were first thought to secrete follicular hormone, later histologic and histochemical studies indicate that the theca interna is probably its source.[22]

The "primary ovarian hormone" was detected also in corpora lutea, blood, other body tissues and urine; in fact, the urine of pregnant women contains large amounts of the estrogenic substance. Two active chemical compounds were identified in pregnancy urines, one called *estrone* and one called *estriol*. Later a third and very active chemical was extracted from pigs'

ovaries and was identified as a partially reduced derivative of estrone called *estradiol-17β*. Estrone and estradiol-17β, but probably not estriol, are present in human follicular fluid (Zander, Brendle, *et al.,* 1959). All these compounds produce vaginal cornification and other changes in the genital tissues. Collectively they are called *estrogens* (adjective, *estrogenic*). Estrogens are produced also by the testes of stallions, by adrenal glands and by placentae.

A number of synthetic chemicals which do not possess a cyclopentenophenanthrene nucleus also possess estrogenic activity. The most active of these compounds, 4,4'-dihydroxy-α,β-diethylstilbene, or, as it is commonly called, *stilbestrol,* is almost five times as active as estrone. Many combinations of alkyl groups have been substituted for the ethyl groups. During absorption by the gastrointestinal tract, stilbestrol is less readily destroyed than the normally occurring estrogens, and hence is more suitable for oral administration.

Estrogen is assayed biologically in castrated rats or mice by determining the minimal amount required to produce vaginal cornification from 48 to 56 hours after the first of a series of injections. The International Unit (I.U.) is 0.1 μg. of estrone, or approximately 1 Mouse Unit (M.U.). In other biologic tests now available for detecting much smaller amounts of hormone, the response to local application of the hormone in the rat's vagina or the immature rat's uterus is determined. Physicochemical methods are available for the gravimetric measurement of individual estrogens.

The corpora lutea which develop from the ruptured follicles are associated temporally and physiologically with uterine changes which facilitate implantation of the ovum, with mammary development, and with the maintenance of pregnancy. In 1929 Corner and Allen prepared extracts of sow corpora lutea which would maintain pregnancy in ovariectomized rabbits and would induce an endometrium suitable for implantation of a blastocyst. The hormone isolated from these extracts was called *progesterone.* It has also been found in human adrenal cortex, placenta, fluid from ripe ovarian follicles, fat, and blood and in corresponding animal tissues. Several apparent metabolites of progesterone are known. Two which are biologically active are 20α-hydroxy-Δ⁴-pregnen-3-one and 20β-hydroxy-Δ⁴-pregnen-3-one; these differ from progesterone only in that a hydroxy group replaces the ketone group at the C-20 position. Another metabolite active by animal test is 16α-hydroxy-progesterone. Compounds having activity similar to that of progesterone are called *progestins*. Inactive, closely related compounds isolated from the urine of pregnant women include pregnanolone, pregnanediol (excreted as sodium pregnanediol glucuronidate; see Fig. 2), pregnanetriol, etc.

Progestins may be determined biologically by their capacity to induce formation of a progestational endometrium in young adult rabbits. One mg. of progesterone, for example, equals 1 International Unit (I.U.), the amount of hormone which, when injected during a period of five days, will elicit a well developed progestational reaction by the sixth day (a Corner-Allen unit). Much smaller amounts are effective when applied directly to the endometrium. Solutions containing as little as 0.25 μg. progesterone per 1 ml. will induce a positive response if 0.00075 ml. is injected directly into a ligated segment of the uterus of an ovariectomized mouse of the CHI strain.[42] Biologic tests assay the collective, progesterone-like activity of all substances in a test preparation. Physicochemical techniques measure individual steroids separately and gravimetrically.

REGULATION OF OVARIAN FUNCTION

The rhythmic estrous or menstrual cycles are the result of humoral interreactions between the ovaries and the pituitary. The relation between the ovaries and the pituitary gland was first realized when disturbances in genital development and function were noted in patients with hypophysial tumors of certain types. When techniques were devised whereby pituitaries could be removed from experimental animals, the interpretations made from the earlier observations became established facts. The pituitary became known as the director of ovarian function.[66, 67] The ovarian-stimulating activity of the pituitary—it also stimulates the testes—is referred to as gonadotrophic activity. The gonad-stimulating substances are called gonadotrophins. The rhythmic nature of ovarian activity could not be explained on the basis of hypophysial dominance alone; the pituitary in turn is influenced by the ovaries. This reciprocal relationship between the pituitary and the ovaries provides a basis upon which the female sexual cycles may be explained.

Almost simultaneously Aschheim and Zondek[5] and Smith and Engle[67] observed that urine of pregnant women and pituitary glands from animals of several species contain substances which will incite precocious sexual maturity by direct stimulation of the gonads of immature animals. Furthermore, the ovaries of animals from which the pituitary glands were removed during immaturity remained small, and the follicles failed to grow to a large size. The gonadal deficiencies following pituitary ablation and their restoration by replacement therapy definitely established the pituitary as a gland concerned in reproduction.

Among at least some species of animals the pituitary glands of adult males and females are known to differ, and this difference is determined by the gonads. Ovaries transplanted into intact or castrated adult male rats fail to show cyclic changes of the usual type. The ovarian follicles grow but fail to ovulate and corpora lutea do not form. It is known that male rats' hypophyses contain more gonadotrophin than those of the females but will not establish a rhythmic relationship with the transplanted ovaries, whereas ovaries transplanted into ovariectomized adult female rats show the usual cyclic changes.

If, within one day after birth of the donors, testes are transplanted into litter-mate female rats, the pituitary glands of the hosts will be physiologically similar to those of males.[55] Even if the graft is removed after sexual maturity the former host remains in constant estrus and fails to show estrous cycles. The testes transplanted into the immature animal induce an irreversible change in the female host's pituitary. More recently it has been shown that the ovarian cycles may be similarly modified in rats treated with certain androgens during their early postnatal life. The sex difference in the hypophysis is apparently determined by the gonad.

Extracts or implants of pituitary glands induce precocious growth of the ovarian follicles in immature experimental animals.[32] In rats and mice these stimulated follicles may ovulate and form corpora lutea. The injection of some relatively purified pituitary extracts produced growth mainly of the ovarian follicles; others induced ovulation and the formation of corpora lutea as well. These observations led to the impression that at least two pituitary gonadotrophic hormones exist, an assumption that has since been demonstrated to be a fact. One hormone, called follicle-stimulating hormone (FSH), induces ovarian follicular growth in immature or in hypophysectomized female rats. A second pituitary hormone when given by itself has little or no effect on the size of the ovaries, but when administered with a small dose of FSH induces follicular maturation, ovulation and the formation of corpora lutea. It is called luteinizing hormone (LH) or interstitial cell-stimulating hormone (ICSH) because it also acts on the interstitial cells of both ovaries and testes.[46] A small amount of LH greatly augments the response to a small dose of FSH (synergistic effect). Before extensive follicular growth and maturation will occur in hypophysectomized rodents, both gonadotrophic hormones must be injected. A third pituitary hormone, the lactogenic hormone, may be essential for the functional development of the corpora lutea (Fig. 3). FSH and LH are mucoproteins. In the rat they are produced by two specific cell types located in the peripheral (FSH) and central (LH) regions of the pars distalis. Lactogenic hormone is an unconjugated protein of large molecular size.[14]

The manner in which the ovarian and gonadotrophic hormones reciprocally and jointly act to establish the estrous or menstrual cycles is not definitely known. The estrous cycles in rats have been explained as follows: The pituitary hormone, FSH, especially when a little LH is present (synergistic effect), stimulates follicular growth and the production of estrogen. The estrogen acts upon the pituitary to stimulate the formation of increased amounts of LH (this has been demonstrated) and to cause a decrease in the amount of FSH. Under such conditions, ovulation and the formation of corpora lutea occur. When the corpora lutea begin to regress, the amounts of ovarian hormones are reduced, with the result that the pituitary again produces FSH to repeat the cycle, a very probable sequence since the amount of FSH increases after castration or ovarian insufficiency. Cyclic changes in the amount of LH have been demonstrated in the pituitaries of rats, the greatest amount being found at estrus.

Similar reciprocal gonadal-hypophysial relationships probably exist during the menstrual cycle in man, but they have not been so thoroughly demonstrated. It is believed that FSH is secreted in quantity during the week and a half after menstruation, stimulating the follicle to complete its development. Estrogen is also secreted during this time. Then ovulation occurs, and release of LH supervenes as that of FSH diminishes. There follow cyclic variations in the levels of excretion of urinary gonadotrophin, the greatest amount appearing during the midcycle, usually just before or about the time of the peak of estrogen excretion. Very small amounts of hormone are present in the early part of the cycle (see Fig. 4).

The corpora lutea formed during the normal four- to five-day estrous cycles of rats and mice were considered for many years to be nonfunctional. Now bio-assay has demonstrated progestin in the plasma of mice during proestrus, estrus and metestrus, and the mouse is added to the list of species, including man, which liberate progestin before ovulation as well as during the life of the corpus luteum.

If mating occurs, even sterile mating in some species, the corpora lutea attain larger size, and more pronounced evidence of their activity is demonstrated. Estrus is prevented for a longer period, progesterone-like material is found in the blood for a longer period, and more advanced endometrial changes occur. Following sterile mating the estrous cycle is inhibited for approximately 12 days in rats and mice, and *pseudopregnancy* is said to occur (normal pregnancy lasts 19 to 21 days). Animals of many species have prolonged periods of anestrus after ovulation associated with sterile

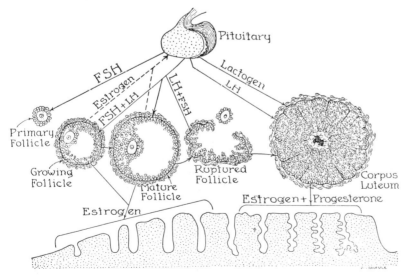

Fig. 3. Ovarian and pituitary interrelationships in mammalian cycle. FSH (follicle-stimulating hormone) is responsible for follicular growth. FSH and a small amount of LH (luteinizing hormone) stimulate further follicular growth and estrogen production, which in turn increases amount of LH produced. Large amounts of LH and probably small amounts of FSH induce ovulation. Corpora lutea develop under the influence of LH and become functionally active in presence of lactogen.

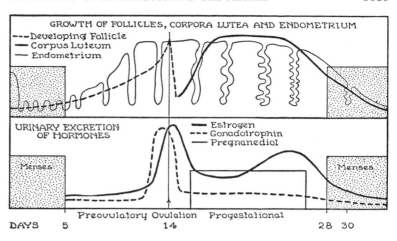

Fig. 4. Diagrammatic presentation of increased thickness of endometrium and changes in shape of endometrial glands in relation to size of ovarian follicles and corpora lutea and urinary excretion of sex hormones and gonadotrophins during a menstrual cycle.

mating or other suitable stimulation, electrical or physical, as with a glass rod. During these periods large corpora lutea are found in the ovaries, progestational changes occur, and deciduomata form in properly stimulated uteri. The injection of gonadotrophin also produces pseudopregnancy in normal rats. Hypophysectomized rats do not form functional corpora lutea when FSH and LH are injected; uterine deciduomata do not develop in the adequately traumatized uteri. If lactogenic hormone is administered, however, the corpora lutea produce progesterone, which will facilitate the formation of deciduomata. These experiments demonstrate that at least in this species the final development and functional activity of the corpora lutea depend upon a distinct hormone, the lactogenic hormone, which is also called *lactogen, mammotrophin, prolactin* or *galactin*. Evidence for the luteotrophic action of this hormone in other species is unconvincing.

It was thought that the gonadotrophin excreted in the urine of women during pregnancy produced primarily LH effects in laboratory animals and had an inhibiting effect upon human ovaries. Observations indicate that the progestational stage of the human menstrual cycle is prolonged when large amounts of this gonadotrophin are injected daily; the corpora lutea are maintained in a functional state for longer periods, and pregnanediol is excreted in the urine during this time. The daily injection of 5000 to 10,000 I.U. has a luteotrophic effect. Ovulation has not been induced consistently in women under experimental conditions. Apparently a delicate balance between the amount of FSH and LH must be maintained for follicular growth, and this balance must be readjusted at a proper time to induce ovulation. Follicles may be stimulated to a point beyond which they can be induced to ovulate and

thus may become cystic. After much research on the most desirable balances between FSH and LH and on the duration and total doses of the gonadotrophic treatment, it has become possible to induce ovulation rather consistently in monkeys.[37]

THE MENSTRUAL CYCLE

A menstrual cycle is the interval which in the normal nonpregnant primate extends from the onset of one period of uterine bleeding to the onset of the following period. The most frequent length of the cycle in women is 28 days, although it may range from 20 days to about 35 days in apparently normal individuals and even in the same individual.[34] It has been well stated that the one regularity of the menstrual cycle is its irregularity. This variability is not unexpected since so many factors influence the cycle.

The menstrual cycle is divided into several phases, determined largely by the histology of the endometrium (Fig. 4). The first part of the cycle, the period of *menstruation*, or the *menses*, most frequently lasts five days, although again the length of the period may vary. During menstruation hemorrhage occurs in the endometrial stroma, which degenerates and, together with the unclotted interstitial blood, is sloughed into the uterine lumen to attain exit through the vagina as the menstrual discharge. The second period of the cycle is called the *preovulatory stage* (proliferative stage) and lasts for approximately seven to ten days.[27] Epithelium grows out from the remnants of glands in the lamina basalis to repair the uterine mucosa, and the entire endometrium increases in thickness. The straight uterine glands which develop at this time are lined by columnar epithelium. The third period of the cycle is called the *progestational stage* (secretory stage). This period extends over approximately the last 12 to 24 days of the cycle. The endometrium during this period is modified progressively until the stroma becomes loose and edematous and the actively secreting glands become extremely folded and tortuous. Such an endometrium is ready for the implantation of a fertilized ovum. If a fertile ovum is not available, however, the uterine mucosa again degenerates and menstruation begins. The changes in the developing endometrial structure are not rapid; they blend into one another. Actually, different areas of the uterine lining of the same individual may be at different stages at any one time.

The first menstrual period at puberty is called the *menarche*. The absence of menses subsequent to menarche is designated as *amenorrhea*. Certain premonitory symptoms, such as pains in the back or head or a general feeling of discomfort, frequently precede the onset of menstruation. When these symptoms are unusually painful and protracted, the condition is called *dysmenorrhea*. Approximately 35 ml. of blood are usually lost during menses, although the amount may range from 10 to 200 ml. The discharged blood characteristically does not clot during normal menses.

Some authors include two other stages: a stage of repair following menstruation and an "interval" stage during the middle of the cycle. These stages are not included in the preceding classification because the period of repair occurs during menstruation as well as subsequent to it. The "interval" implies a period of rest or absence of change which does not necessarily exist. It should be remembered that, although the existence of definite stages is implied, the endometrial changes are progressive rather than steplike. A progestational or secretory stage does not appear in those cycles in which ovulation does not take place. In such cycles the term "premenstrual" phase would be more satisfactory. The morphologic condition of the endometrium at different stages of ovarian development was first associated and described by Hitschmann and Adler.[41]

Relation Between the Ovaries and the Menstrual Cycle. Just before the onset of menstruation the corpus luteum begins to regress. The secretion of progesterone by the corpus luteum, diminishing for several days

past, almost stops. The endometrium which developed under the influence of this hormone cannot be maintained. The resulting rapid endometrial degeneration is accompanied by sloughing and hemorrhage. During and after menstruation one or more follicles of moderate size begin to grow more rapidly than other similar follicles. As the rapidly growing follicles attain large sizes, the endometrium increases in thickness. By approximately the midpoint of the menstrual cycle one follicle attains maturity and ovulates. The other larger follicles usually regress—become *atretic*. After ovulation the follicle collapses; the granulosa cells are transformed into luteal cells and become well vascularized to form a corpus luteum. During this period the progestational endometrium develops under the influence of the hormones produced by the corpus luteum.[41] Actually, progestins are also present in the fluid of the ripe follicle.

The preovulatory type of endometrium is attained during the period of follicular growth and the progestational type during the period of luteal development. The rhythmicity of the uterus is maintained by the rhythmic changes in the ovaries. During some cycles ovulation may not occur and corpora lutea may fail to form. Such a cycle would be sterile and might be considered abnormal. An *anovulatory* cycle is superficially indistinguishable from an *ovulatory* cycle. If a corpus luteum does not form, a progestational endometrium does not develop. The large follicle or follicles persist about two weeks beyond the usual time of ovulation and, as they undergo atresia, uterine hemorrhage and slough take place. In such circumstances menstruation occurs from a preovulatory type of endometrium.

Endocrine Factors in the Menstrual Cycle. When ovariectomized at any time during the latter two or three weeks of the menstrual cycle, women usually show uterine bleeding within two to six days after the operation. Also, menstruation usually follows section or damage to the spinal cord when these lesions occur during the latter part of the cycle. The entire cycle may be shortened to 12 days or more in such cases. Monkeys menstruate subsequent to ovariectomy even if the operation is performed as early as the seventh day of the cycle.[3] Also, (i) experimental section of the ventral roots of the lower thoracic or upper lumbar spinal nerves, (ii) hemisection of the cord, or (iii) section of the splanchnics is followed by precocious uterine bleeding. Subsequent cycles in these animals occur at intervals similar to those observed preoperatively, an indication that the neural lesions probably produce only transitory trophic deficiencies in the ovaries, deficiencies which are reflected by uterine regression and bleeding.

Estrogens administered to ovariectomized primates in adequate amounts for 10 days or more induce endometrial hypertrophy; if the stimulus is sufficient, a preovulatory or proliferative type of endometrium develops.[27] Uterine bleeding occurs within 6 to 10 days after the discontinuance of the injections, the so-called *estrogen-withdrawal bleeding* or menstruation from a proliferative endometrium (Fig. 5). If estrogens are given daily in large amounts, menstruation may be prevented for very long periods; if the dosage is small, periodic bleeding may occur in spite of continuous treatment, the uterus periodically seeming to become refractory to the levels of hormone administered.

When estrogens are given to intact monkeys or women, menstruation is inhibited if the administration is started during the first part of the cycle but not if it is started during the latter part of the cycle. Approximately two days after the removal of a functional corpus luteum, menstruation occurs and cannot be prevented even if estrogens are injected. The simultaneous administration of estrogen and progesterone induces a progestational (secretory, or pre-

menstrual) endometrium, which bleeds within two to three days if injections of both hormones are discontinued or if progesterone alone is withheld, demonstrating again that estrogens will not prevent bleeding from a progestational endometrium that develops in the normal cycle or is induced experimentally (see Fig. 5).

Menstruation cannot be considered to be an actively induced process.[16] It occurs upon cessation of stimulation of the endometrium, and from either a preovulatory or a progestational endometrium; it accompanies uterine involution or regression. Although the uteri of all mammals regress cyclically, marked hemorrhage or menstruation is limited to the noncornuate uteri of primates.

The factors associated with menstruation have been studied in great detail in monkeys by direct observation of the uterine mucosa subsequent to transplantation into the anterior chamber of the eye.[48] The endometrial transplants undergo cyclic changes similar to those of the intact uteri. One to five days before the onset of bleeding, the endometrial circulation is impaired, apparently by an unusual resistance to flow through the coiled arteries in the deeper layers of the endometrium. During this period, the endometrium regresses and becomes thinner. Four to 24 hours before menstruation the coiled arteries constrict for periods of several hours, further reducing the blood supply to the peripheral tissues. At intervals, first one and then another artery dilates,

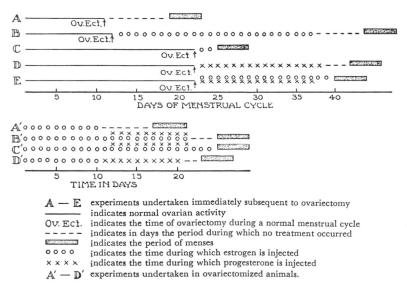

Fig. 5. Diagram of experimental procedures undertaken on women or female monkeys to elucidate the problem of menstruation.

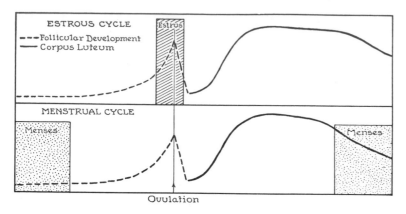

Fig. 6. Diagrammatic presentation of homology of ovarian changes in estrous and menstrual cycles. Cycles are dated from their most obvious events, estrus and menstruation.

and hemorrhage occurs from the distal arterioles or capillaries into the superficial parts of the endometrium, forming small hematomas. After a short period (30 seconds to a few minutes) of hemorrhage, the arteries again contract and bleeding ceases. Other coiled endometrial arteries likewise dilate, bleed and constrict, although not simultaneously. Each artery bleeds only once during each cycle; successive series of arteries bleed at different intervals throughout the menstrual period, so one small area of endometrium may hemorrhage, slough and be repaired before another area has sloughed.

Induction of menstrual bleeding by drugs or means which will effect ischemia or hyperemia or alter vascular permeation by fluids has often been attempted, but the results have not contributed significantly to the explanation of periodic hemorrhage.

Physicochemical assays of plasma from peripheral blood obtained during the usual human menstrual cycle show only slight amounts of progesterone during the first two weeks. At about midcycle there is a rapid and conspicuous rise to perhaps 2 μg. per 100 ml. plasma, the rise coinciding with an elevation in waking body temperature (see below). The level remains high for a few days, then declines. Following the decline but while the hormone is still detectable in the plasma, menstruation begins.[71] Bioassay of comparable samples reveals curves for concentrations of progestin in the plasma which qualitatively are strikingly similar to those developed by physicochemical assay. Quantitatively, however, the bioassays indicate activity equal to at least 100 times that amount of progesterone shown gravimetrically to be present.[28] It seems likely that the discrepancy is due partly to the additive effect of

progestins other than progesterone which may be present but chiefly to synergistic action among several compounds in the blood. Physicochemical assays have demonstrated progesterone, the α and β isomers of 20-hydroxy-Δ^4-pregnen-3-one, 16α-hydroxyprogesterone, and 17α-hydroxyprogesterone in extracts of human corpora lutea.[75, 76]

In most but not all women the body temperature on awakening in the morning is 0.6 to 0.8° F. higher during the luteal phase of the menstrual cycle than during the follicular phase. This rise follows closely on, and is apparently directly related to, the elevation in plasma progesterone.[28, 71] A similar elevation may be induced in postmenopausal women by the injection of this hormone. A definite rise in waking temperature in the normal cycle also signals the probable occurrence of ovulation.

Because the amounts of the various estrogens in peripheral blood are extremely small, their detection and accurate measurement have presented many problems. Available data suggest that during the human menstrual cycle there may be concentrations of up to 1.5 μg. estrone, 0.8 μg. estradiol-17β, and 0.8 μg. estriol per 100 ml. peripheral plasma.[31, 53] Fluctuations in level have not yet been correlated with phases of the cycle.

Hormones may possibly be consumed in eliciting response in the end-organs upon which they act, may be transformed to inactive compounds at sites removed from the end-organ, or may be excreted in the urine. The amounts of estrogen, progesterone or gonadotrophin produced may be estimated very roughly by determining the amounts of exogenous hormone necessary to restore the function of genital tissues after ovariectomy. The rates at which some of these hormones are excreted may indicate the time and possibly the rate of their production. Estrogen is excreted in the urine in detectable amounts throughout the menstrual cycle, but in the greatest quantity at the middle of the cycle. Some women may show a second period of increased elimination of estrogens during the latter third of the cycle, but the rate of excretion is always greater during the progestational stage than during the preovulatory phase (Fig. 4).

In ovariectomized women, approximately 0.40 mg. is the minimal amount of estrone which must be injected daily to produce an endometrium which will undergo menstrual hemorrhage subsequent to discontinuance of the injections.[69] About 10 mg. of estrone is required per cycle. Because only an amount equivalent in activity to that of about 1 mg. of estrone is excreted per cycle, it might be concluded that only about one-tenth of the total amount that is produced is eliminated. Such a percentage is comparable to that excreted after injection of known doses. The pregnanediol (as sodium pregnanediol glucuronidate) content of the urine during six to 12 days of the latter part of the cycle can be determined gravimetrically. This excretory product of progesterone usually first appears in the urine in detectable amounts about two days after ovulation and is not excreted in appreciable amounts during the two days before menstruation. Pregnanediol is excreted during the periods when active corpora lutea are present in the ovaries and therefore is not found during anovulatory cycles. About 200 mg. of progesterone must be injected over a ten-day period into a castrate woman in order to achieve excretion of pregnanediol equal to that occurring in the normal menstrual cycle (20 to 60 mg. of pregnanediol glucuronidate).[52, 68]

Blood levels of progestin and urinary excretion of the estrogenic hormones and pregnanediol correlate rather closely with the sequence of ovarian changes on the one hand, and with the functional changes in the endometrium on the other. Estrogens apparently are produced also by the corpora lutea; estrogenic activity in extracts of these glands has been demonstrated. The increased elimination of estrogens during the latter part of the cycle adds further evidence for the duality of the endocrine activity of the corpora lutea.

Comparison of Menstrual and Estrous Cycles. Among the majority of subprimate species the most obvious manifestation of sexual activity in the females occurs during the period of receptivity to the males (estrus). Their cycles are dated from the onset of one period of estrus to the onset of the next, and are called estrous cycles (Fig. 6). Some species, such as the rat and mouse, have cycles of four to five days; the guinea pig's cycle lasts about 16 days. Many modifications of the estrous cycle occur in animals of different species. In rabbits, prolonged periods of estrus terminate only with copulation which results in pregnancy, or, if the matings are sterile, in pseudopregnancy. In the absence of mating, a prolonged anestrus follows the protracted estrus.

Ovulation occurs during estrus so that the ovum may be available for fertilization by the sperm. During the menstrual cycle ovulation occurs at the intermenstruum. If ovulation were taken as the point of reference to start both kinds of cycles, they would be comparable insofar as the sequence of ovarian changes is concerned.

Estrous behavior or sexual receptivity of laboratory animals may be induced subsequent to ovariectomy by the injection of large amounts of estrogens. The administration of small amounts of estrogens when followed by small doses of progesterone will also induce estrous behavior in ovariectomized rats and guinea pigs. Probably the injected hormones reproduce the conditions eliciting estrus during the normal cycle. Sexual receptivity in subhuman primates is greatest during the intermenstrual period. In man the periods of greatest sexual receptivity have been less definitely determined.

OVULATION

In man ovulation normally occurs spontaneously, that is, without the imposition of extrinsic stimuli. A rapid growth of the follicles must occur during the few hours preceding rupture, or at least such is true for all experimental animals. The actual rupture of the follicle in animals has been said to result (i) from increased intrafollicular pressure accompanying an augmented secretion of liquor folliculi, (ii) from ischemia and loss of tissue viability secondary to the increased follicular pressure, and (iii) from enzymes which digest the follicular wall. If any of these theories is correct for ovulation in woman (none will account for the formation of cystic follicles), the increased follicular pressures or enzymes or other factors antedating ovulation nevertheless must result from gonadotrophic stimulation.

Ovulation normally occurs subsequent to copulation in rabbits, ferrets, cats and in some other species. The inciting stimulus in these animals is in part neural. The neural stimulation attending mating does not involve the ovaries directly, because transplanted ovaries deprived of their normal innervation or ovaries of sympathectomized animals will ovulate; also, direct stimulation of the ovarian innervation will not provoke ovulation. Intravenous injection of gonadotrophins does, however, induce ovulation. The stimulus of copulation acts upon the hypophysis to release an ovulation-stimulating hormone. If a rabbit's pituitary is removed more than one hour subsequent to mating, ovulation will nevertheless occur in another nine hours or so, whereas, if hypophysectomy is performed immediately after copulation, follicular maturation and rupture do not result. The release of gonadotrophin following copulation has been shown also by changes in the cellular structure and by decrease of hormone content of the pituitary gland.

The pathways of transmission of the ovulatory stimuli have been investigated extensively.[32] Section of the sacral cord and abdominal sympathectomy, or removal of the superior cervical ganglia and thoracolumbar sympathectomy, did not prevent postcoital ovulation in rabbits. The sympathetic system has little to do in the regulation of gonadotrophic hormones. Faradic stimulation of the brain, pituitary or tuber cinereum resulted in ovulation. Rabbits with sectioned hypophysial stalks did not ovulate after mating. On the other hand, rats in which the pituitary has been removed and retransplanted into the sella turcica may show complete cycles, and section of the stalk does not prevent ovulation, demonstrating a species difference. It is quite possible that the restoration of normal pituitary secretion of gonadotrophins after stalk section is dependent upon the re-establishment of an adequate hypothalamico-hypophysial vascular connection. Evidence is accumulating from animal experiments that the hypothalamus controls the adenohypophysis through a humoral agent which may be transported to the hypophysis via its portal vessels,[35, 51] although the hypothalamus does not appear to regulate the secretion of prolactin. It should be recalled that in rats, as in primates, follicular rupture occurs spontaneously, i.e., without the added stimulus of copulation. In these species another mechanism intrinsic to the animal must be active in periodically inciting the excretion of gonadotrophin.[35] The application of acetylcholine to the pituitary gland of rats has resulted in pseudopregnancy, and the injection of epinephrine into the pituitary gland of the estrous rabbit has induced ovulation. Furthermore, the injection of drugs that inhibit adrenergic activity inhibited ovulation in rabbits subsequent to mating.

Neural lesions may modify sexual behavior as well as other reproductive functions. Hypothalamic lesions in guinea pigs may prevent either estrous behavior or ovarian development; in fact, it has been indicated that the hypothalamus may regulate gonadotrophic function in this species. More work must be done before much can be said about the neural factors in the physiology of reproduction in other than a few species of animals. Lesions of the central nervous system undoubtedly disturb reproduction in man. Hypothalamic lesions may lead to menstrual irregularities or hypofunction. On the other hand, hypothalamic injury may cause precocious sexual maturity. The genital abnormalities in these cases are usually associated with other evidences of pituitary dysfunction.

Time of Ovulation. Many attempts have been made to estimate the time of ovulation in man. Direct methods such as recovery of ova from the uterine tubes, identification of recent corpora lutea, recovery of young embryos, and observations on pregnancies subsequent to restricted intercourse have been used. Attempts to associate ovulation with basal body temperatures, types of cells in the vaginal smears, endometrial structure, excretion of preganediol and of gonadotrophin, intermenstrual hemorrhage and pain, and fluctuation in electric potentials have been used as indirect methods of estimating the time of ovulation. In rhesus monkeys, Hartman has been able to determine the time of ovulation by digital palpation of the ovaries through the rectal walls and has checked his observations further by controlled matings. In a large series of animals ovulations occurred between the eighth and 23rd days of the 28-day cycles, the greater number occurring between the 10th and the 13th days. In man, ovulation apparently takes place usually at comparable times of the cycle, essentially in the middle of the cycle. In abnormally long or short cycles the preovulatory portions show the greater variation and the postovulatory periods tend to be the most nearly uniform, usually 14 to 16 days. It is difficult to ignore some reports that ovulation and fertilization may occur at unusual times of the cycle, even during menstruation.

LIFE CYCLE OF THE OVARY

At birth the ovary consists largely of groups of ova and primary follicles in a vascular stroma. Germinal epithelium invests the ovarian surface except at the hilus. Interstitial cells which appear to be secretory have been observed in the ovaries of newborn animals of some species, but the cells disappear shortly after birth. In girls, extensive follicular growth does not occur until the onset of puberty at 10 to 14 years of age.

Puberty. At this time the *secondary sexual characters* begin to develop; pubic and axillary hair starts to grow, and an adult type of body contour appears. The *accessory reproductive organs*—the uterus, vagina and mammary glands—start to mature. Hypogonadal females or persons ovariectomized before puberty do not experience the usual development of secondary sex characters or accessory reproductive organs.

Puberty terminates at menarche. The age at which the first indication of puberty appears and the rate of the development of the accessory reproductive organs preceding menarche differ from individual to individual. The menstrual periods usually begin in girls between 13 and 15 years of age, although the age at menarche may range from 10 to 18 years. The early cycles are irregular; several months of amenorrhea may intervene between menses. Follicles may fail to rupture, so that many early cycles may be anovulatory. After a succession of irregular cycles, more or less regular ovulatory menstrual cycles supervene.

During the prepubertal stage, very little gonadotrophic hormone can be detected in the urine, and it is probable that no more than small amounts are produced. At puberty the quantity of urinary gonadotrophin increases,

to approach that excreted by the adult. That puberty must be initiated by the pituitary is indicated by the fact that the ovaries of immature animals can be stimulated with gonadotrophic hormones. What regulates the initiation of gonad stimulation by the pituitary is unknown. It is interesting that at the time of puberty one of the most usual concomitant phenomena is an accentuation of the rate of body growth. If accentuated growth occurs at an early age the menstrual cycles start at a correspondingly early date, and a delayed accentuation of somatic growth is usually associated with a late menarche. The year of the greatest increment of growth is usually the year of menarche. This relation between the growth-stimulating and gonadotrophic functions of the pituitary affords material for conjecture.

Albright *et al.*[2] have described the occurrence of hypo-ovarian states in patients of less than normal stature. Such individuals produce gonadotrophic hormone but little sex hormone and presumably are also deficient in growth hormones. On the other hand, precocious sexual maturity due to gonadal tumors, to adrenal cortical tumors of some types, or to some intracranial neoplasia with resulting hypergonadism may be associated with small stature; growth of these individuals is usually augmented during the early stages of the disease but stops precociously after the brief, abnormally early, accentuated phase. As a result such individuals are usually dwarfed as well as sexually precocious.

Menopause. After 30 to 40 years of menstrual cycles the number of follicles in the ovaries is depleted. The menses may become profuse (*menorrhagia*) and painful (*dysmenorrhea*), or the cycles may become short and irregular, eventually ceasing entirely. The cyclic production of ovarian hormones ceases, the mammary glands atrophy, and the uterus and vagina show variable amounts of regression. This period of gradual subsidence of ovarian function is called the *climacteric* and culminates in the complete cessation of cyclic ovarian activity, the *menopause*. Urinary excretion of estrogen declines and that of pregnanediol ceases, but the excretion of gonadotrophic hormone is augmented. The gonadotrophic hormone in the urine of postmenopausal women contains relatively large amounts of a substance that stimulates ovarian follicles and small amounts of the agent that incites the formation of corpora lutea; in this respect the urinary hormone resembles the follicle-stimulating hormone

(FSH) of the pituitary gland. Augmented excretion of gonadotrophic hormone also occurs in artificial menopause induced by surgical removal of the ovaries or x-ray sterilization during the period of sexual maturity. The hormone in the urines of menopausal women is apparently of hypophysial origin and may decrease when estrogens are injected.[62] The conclusion must be that the menopause results from senile changes in the ovary. In the absence of the inhibiting or regulatory effect of ovarian hormones upon the hypophysis, the latter produces an excessive amount of gonadotrophic hormone. Pubertal changes in the pituitary which result in the initiation of gonadotrophic activity are not reversed at the menopause; the pituitary, once it starts to stimulate ovarian function, attempts to continue even after the ovary no longer responds.

In addition to the morphologic regression of the accessory genital organs, vasomotor and personality changes frequently accompany the menopause. Vasomotor changes (hot flashes) result from a vascular dilation in the skin of the head, neck and upper trunk, with flushing, increased sweating and a sensation of suffocation. The hot flashes may be stopped by injecting estrogens, even in amounts inadequate to decrease the amount of urinary gonadotrophin. The treatment of menopausal *symptoms* is one of the most common clinical uses of estrogens. The ovarian deficiency after the menopause may not be sufficient to permit complete atrophy of the vaginal mucosa or to result in the disappearance of ovarian hormones from the blood or urine; subthreshold cycles may even occur.

MECHANISM OF SPERM TRANSPORT

The sperm are deposited in the vagina at copulation and must move or be transported through the uterine cervix, fundus and tubes to approach and fertilize an ovum. Sperm in some species appear in the uterus immediately after copulation, but the means of their rapid movement through the cervix is not understood. The quality of the mucus secreted by the cervical glands changes during the menstrual cycle, the mucus being much thinner close to the time of ovulation. The less viscous cervical secretions probably make sperm transport through the cervical canal less difficult. Transport through the uterus is facilitated by uterine contractions. Transport through the tubes perhaps is provided by paths of upward beating cilia (the greater number of cilia beat toward the uterus to assist in the downward transport of the inert ovum, however), by antiperistaltic tubal contractions, or by a tendency of sperm to swim against a current created by the downward beating cilia, and hence to orient themselves up the tubes and be largely or entirely self-propelled. When sperm from two species or sperm and some nonmotile substance are placed simultaneously in the vagina, uterine cervix or uterus of experimental animals, the sperm do not attain the same levels of the genital tract at the same time, indicating that both the intrinsic motility of the sperm and uterine factors are involved in sperm transport. In addition to permitting the passage of sperm, the cervical mucus must prevent the passage of the vaginal bacterial flora into the usually aseptic uterus.

PREGNANCY

An ovum must be fertilized within a few hours after it leaves the follicle at ovulation; at least, such conclusions have been drawn from extensive observations upon laboratory animals.[8] If guinea pigs are inseminated artificially from 12 to 18 hours after ovulation, there is a high incidence of pregnancies terminating in abortion and of failure of pregnancy to occur. Artificial insemination during estrus, and therefore within three or four hours either before or after ovulation, institutes normal pregnancies. The period of fertilizability of the ovum must be brief. The ovum is fertilized while migrating through the uterine tube. During the completion of its journey to the uterus, the fertilized ovum divides to form a mass of cells (*morula*), still surrounded by the zona pellucida. Unfertilized ova usually reach the uterus before dissolution.

As the number of cells increases, the cell mass acquires a central cavity. The mass is now called a *blastocyst*. It develops in the uterus within a few days after ovulation and at a time when the endometrium is showing early progestational proliferation. The blastocyst remains free in the uterus for a few days before implantation, during which time the zona pellucida is dissolved. In some mammalian species the blastocysts may remain in this stage for weeks or months before implanting and continuing their growth. The earliest intrauterine human and monkey blastocysts that have been observed have been about seven days old, and may still have been free in the uterus; at least one human morula has been seen. The process of attachment (implantation) is instigated by the blastocyst. From it the extraembryonic trophoblast grows and invades the endometrium. Cells from the developing blastocyst and from the uterine decidua contribute to the placenta. In some animals the mechanical stimulus of a foreign body other than an ovum, or irritation of the lining of the uterus, may elicit a response of the progestational endometrium with the result that deciduomata (the maternal components of the placenta) form. Similar observations have not been made in women; here the maternal part of the placenta has formed only in contact with the developing trophoblast.

The implanted embryo has a definite effect upon the maternal organism. The corpus luteum extends its period of endocrine activity to about one month. Follicular growth and ovulation are inhibited. The uterine lining fails to undergo the usual menstrual regression. Estrogen is produced in larger amounts subsequent to implantation, and gonadotrophin is released in such large amounts that, by the time the expected menstrual period is missed, enough gonadotrophin is excreted to give a positive test for pregnancy.[26, 33]

Aschheim and Zondek[5] discovered large amounts of gonadotrophic hormone in the urines of pregnant women (anterior pituitary-like hormone, APL; pregnancy urine hormone, PU; or prolan) and suggested that its detection constitutes a test for pregnancy. In this test 2 ml. of urine or an alcoholic precipitate of urine are injected into immature mice (or rats). The animals are killed four days (100 hours) after the first of six injections, which are given during the first two days, and their ovaries are examined. An increase in the weight of the ovaries with the formation of large follicles and corpora lutea, some of which may show hemorrhagic spots (blood points), constitutes a positive response. Friedman discovered that a single intravenous injection of pregnancy urine induces ovulation in young or isolated female rabbits.[30] Ruptured follicles can be detected within 24 hours after the injection. It is necessary that the rabbits be isolated, as they ovulate upon copulation or even upon simulated copulatory movements by other females. Ovulation occurs within about ten hours after copulation or after the injection of gonadotrophin or PU in this species. The Aschheim-

Zondek and Friedman tests have become routine diagnostic procedures. False positive responses are given with urine of patients with certain genital tumors, among them chorioepitheliomas, which contain tissue similar to that which produces gonadotrophin in the normal placenta. False negative reactions rarely or never occur. Another type of pregnancy test is based on the ability of the gonadotrophin in the urine of a pregnant subject, when injected into male frogs or toads, to induce the release of sperm, which can then be detected in urine taken from the cloaca of the test animal. If pregnancy urine is injected intravenously into the adult female rat, the ovaries will show a distinct hyperemia in two hours.

New techniques based on immunologic reactions give much promise as pregnancy tests.

After the first month of pregnancy the ovaries may be removed and the pregnancy continues to a successful termination in man and in monkeys.[36, 49] The placenta apparently takes over most if not all of the endocrine function of the ovaries. The pituitary glands have been removed from animals of some species during the latter part of the first half of gestation and pregnancy has continued in a normal manner.

Large amounts of estrogen, pregnanediol and gonadotrophin are excreted during pregnancy (Fig. 7). The peak of gonadotrophin excretion occurs at about the 45th to 50th day or about one month after the first missed menses; over 100,000 Rat Units may be excreted daily. The rate of gonadotrophin excretion varies among different individuals. Pregnanediol and estrogens are excreted in progressively larger amounts as pregnancy progresses, tending to be maximal a few days before parturition. Circulatory plasma levels of estrogen and progestin, on the other hand, show relatively little change after the first weeks of pregnancy in women and monkeys. Plasma progestin levels, whether measured in terms of amount by physicochemical assay or in terms of activity by bioassay, are comparatively low.[29, 72, 75] The average progesterone concentration in plasma from peripheral blood obtained during the second half of pregnancy has been found to be 14 to 15 μg. per 100 ml.[64, 73] Average estrogen levels in one study of plasmas from late human pregnancy were 2.6 to 10.3 μg. per 100 ml. for estrone, 1.2 to 2.9 μg. per 100 ml. for estradiol-17β, and 4.3 to 17.5 μg. per 100 ml. for estriol.[58] Average values from later studies fall within these ranges.

Since pregnanediol is a metabolite of proges-

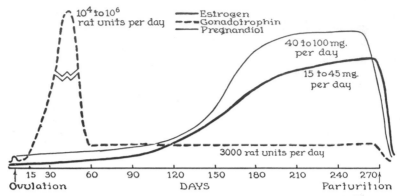

Fig. 7. Diagrammatic presentation of urinary excretion of estrogen, pregnanediol, and gonado-trophins during pregnancy. At peak of gonadotrophin excretion over 100,000 Rat Units are elimi-nated daily; 60 to 100 mg. of pregnanediol and 15 to 45 mg. of estrogens are also excreted daily at period of maximal output. The greatest part of the estrogen is estriol, which is much less active biolog-ically than estrone or estradiol, so that bioassay technique will not reveal such large amounts. Of total, as much as 1 to 3 mg. may be estrone.

terone and since the excretion of pregnanediol increases steadily during pregnancy, it seems likely that the secretion of progesterone also increases during this time but that most of the hormone is promptly metabolized into inactive compounds. However, very few measurements have ever been made of the rate of secretion of steroid sex hormones. The large amounts of gonadotrophin apparently have a stimulating effect upon the ovary; some evidence exists that the gonadotrophin may assist in maintaining function of the corpora lutea during early pregnancy.

Uterus. The adult, nonpregnant uterus contracts rhythmically. The contractions help to pump the blood through the organ. Direct measurement of muscle pressures at the corpus, isthmus and cervix have shown that during the preovulatory stage of the menstrual cycle the uterus undergoes small rhythmic contractions at an increasingly rapid rate. The contractions reach their greatest frequency at about the time of ovulation. In the progestational stage they are more irregular, of greater amplitude, and become progressively slower. The contractions are least frequent during menstruation. Throughout an anovulatory cycle they are of the preovulatory type, as would be expected in the absence of a functional corpus luteum (Fig. 8).[40] Curiously enough, contractions continue for years after the menopause.

Distension of the nonpregnant uterus increases the power of the contractions.[57, 60] At all stages of the cycle Pituitrin usually increases uterine tone and the amplitude of the contrac-

tions, although the changes may be slight. This hormone has its greatest effect on the human uterus in the late premenstrual stage. Dysmen-orrhea may be caused by uterine ischemia associated with strong myometrial contractions. Emotional stress may increase myometrial activity during the premenstrual phase.

Contractions of the nonpregnant human uterus have been recorded by inserting a small thin-walled balloon through the cervix into the lumen of the fundus and then filling the balloon and a tube connected to it with water at a pressure of 10 to 40 mm. Hg. The volume of the uterine lumen varies with the stage of the cycle, tending to be greatest during the progestational stage. The uterine contractions of experimental animals may be studied by a similar technique, by direct observation of the uterus at laparotomy, through a "window" in the abdominal wall or *in vitro*.

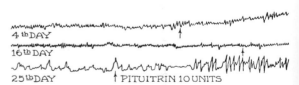

Fig. 8. Recordings of uterine contractions obtained from a 25-year-old woman by use of an intra-uterine balloon. At points designated by arrows 10 units of Pituitrin was injected. Pregnanediol did not appear in urine of patient until about 18th day of cycle, so first two recordings were taken during pre-ovulatory stages. Biopsies taken on 28th day of cycle showed a progestational endometrium. (After Henry and Browne, *Amer. J. Obstet. Gynec.*, 1943, *45*:927–949.)

Studies of strips of uterine muscle from castrated rabbits revealed that if a rabbit had been pretreated with estrogen, the muscle under isometric conditions developed increasing tension as a result of electrical stimulation at intervals of one minute. The contraction record exhibited the "staircase" phenomenon already familiar from studies of cardiac muscle. On the other hand, if a castrate doe had been pretreated with progesterone, the contractions showed the opposite effect, a "negative staircase."[20] This important experiment confirmed and extended earlier observations that in animals estrogens have a stimulating effect, and progesterone a quieting effect, on the uterus. Progesterone has the same action on human uterine muscle *in vitro*.

Direct stimulation in nonpregnant women of the presacral (hypogastric) nerves which carry the sympathetic innervation of the uterus resulted in contraction followed by a period of inhibition. Stimulation during the follicular phase of the menstrual cycle caused relatively slight contraction followed by conspicuous decrease in tone. Similar stimulation during the secretory phase was followed by much stronger contraction and little loss in tone.[12]

The human uterus contracts throughout pregnancy. Until about the thirtieth week, activity is relatively slight, contractions occurring approximately once a minute in restricted areas of the uterus.[11] The pregnant woman is not aware of them. They facilitate the return of venous blood. Stronger, definitely noticeable contractions involving the entire uterus also occur, but are infrequent until the end of pregnancy, when they become common (Braxton Hicks contractions). Uterine contractions are initiated by two "pacemakers," one near each utero-tubal junction. Intrauterine pressures, as determined by direct measurement in monkeys of pressures in the amniotic cavity and in the intervillous spaces of the placenta, fluctuate directly and proportionately with contractions of the uterine muscle.[17]

During pregnancy the uterus undergoes much growth so that it can continue to enclose the embryo and fetus and can become powerful enough to dilate the cervix at term.[59, 60] The human uterus exclusive of its contents may increase twenty times in weight during gestation. The factors regulating uterine growth and enlargement are not fully understood. From study of human *ectopic* (extrauterine) pregnancies and of experiments in animals with bicornuate uteri in which pregnancy has occurred in one horn and has been prevented in the other, it is clear that the empty uterus or uterine horn grows but does not attain the size it would reach in a normal pregnancy. In women, growth of the uterus occurs most rapidly during the third, fourth and fifth months of gestation. It is due in considerable measure to endocrine stimulation, occurring in experimental animals even when the nerves to the uterus are divided. The swelling of the amniotic sac stretches and further enlarges the uterus in the second half of pregnancy.

Circulation.   The uterine circulation plays several roles. It is influenced by phases of the menstrual cycle and pregnancy. In turn, the uterine vessels help to transport the hormones indispensable to these activities. Finally, the climactic process of parturition profoundly affects the circulation.

The vasomotor innervation of the uterine and vaginal vessels appears to be entirely sympathetic. Abolition of this innervation by transection of the spinal cord is followed by dilation and congestion of the uterine blood vessels but, as previously noted, such denervation does not interfere with pregnancy and parturition.

Endocrine control of the uterine vessels is probably much more significant than their neural regulation.[60] It is well established that injected estrogens, and to a lesser extent progesterone, have a vasodilating effect in both endometrium and myometrium. The increasing vasodilation during the follicular phase and diminishing vasodilation during the secretory phase of the menstrual cycle follow the corresponding waxing and waning of blood levels of the female sex hormones.* The experimental administration of estrogen results in uterine hyperemia before uterine metabolism increases, further evidence that the endocrine effect is directly on the blood vessels. Another result of such an experiment is that the uterine venous blood is arterial in color, proof that the volume of circulation has increased to the point where the oxygen requirements of the tissues are exceeded. A third effect is that fluid is lost from the capillaries and tissue edema results.

In normal early human pregnancy, both the total blood flow to the uterus and its total oxy-

---

*"Hot flashes," vasomotor disturbances of the menopause, are relieved by the administration of estrogens, but the mechanism here is not clear.

gen consumption increase absolutely and progressively from the 9th to the 28th week, but both actually remain constant during this period in relation to the increasing weight of the pregnant uterus. The same is true for umbilical blood flow and fetal oxygen consumption.[6] In early pregnancy the uterine blood flow is great enough so that the amount of oxygen delivered to the tissues exceeds requirements; as a result, the uterine veins have a high oxygen content. In the ensuing months the minute volume of blood to the uterus appears to increase, a peak being reached near the end of the second trimester of pregnancy. Thereafter, the blood flow remains relatively constant, although the metabolic requirements of the uterine contents continue to increase, so that the uterine venous blood contains less and less oxygen. The blood flow appears to be correlated with the size of the placenta and not with the oxygen requirements of the tissues supplied. In the final month of pregnancy the human uterus receives maternal blood at the rate of 750 ml. a minute; four-fifths of this amount pass through the placenta.[9]

Placenta. The placenta serves two primary functions. First, it is an organ of exchange between the mother and embryo or fetus; second, it is an endocrine gland producing internal secretions to maintain a compatible environment for the two closely related organisms. At the time of fertilization the mammalian ovum contains a small amount of nutriment in its cytoplasm, an amount which will support only a very limited growth. The uterine secretions may maintain embryonic growth for a brief period—certainly this must occur in the opossum, in which the ova never become implanted—but the greater amount of nutriment is received in man by the direct contact of the fetal portion of the placenta with the maternal blood. The exchange of gases through the placenta is not considered here.

As an endocrine gland the placenta produces estrogens, progestins and gonadotrophin. These hormones have all been obtained by extraction of placental tissue; they are more abundant in the fetal part, the chorionic trophoblast, than in the decidua. Probably the syncytial (peripheral) layers of the trophoblast are concerned with production of the steroid hormones and the cytotrophoblast (deepest layers) produces the gonadotrophins.[70] Histochemical studies suggest the presence of steroids in the protoplasm of the syncytium (syntrophoblast).

Human placental tissues grown in cultures will produce gonadotrophin that can be bioassayed in immature mice; the cultures contain largely the Langhans cells of the cytotrophoblast.[43] Also the amount of gonadotrophin produced by the intact placenta tends to parallel the amount of cytotrophoblast, which is maximal early in pregnancy and decreases later in pregnancy.

In one study of full-term human placentas average estrogen concentrations were: estrone, 51.3 μg. per kg. of tissue; estradiol-17β, 170.2 μg. per kg.; estriol, 314.6 μg. per kg.[23] Comparison of relative estrogen levels in umbilical venous blood and maternal peripheral blood make it clear that estrogen is being secreted by the placenta and not simply being transported into that organ from a maternal source.[44, 63]

Concentrations of progesterone and of the α and β isomers of 20-hydroxy-Δ^4-pregnen-3-one in human placentas increase steadily as pregnancy progresses.[73] In the last month before term, according to one study, levels usually exceeded 2 μg. progesterone per gram of wet tissue and reached an average of 0.26 μg. 20-hydroxy-Δ^4-pregnen-3-one per gram of wet tissue.[75] When concentrations of progestins in human umbilical arterial and venous bloods were determined by physicochemical assay and compared, levels of progesterone were significantly higher in the vein, while amounts of 20α- and 20β-hydroxy-Δ^4-pregnen-3-one and of 17α-hydroxy-progesterone were definitely greater in the artery. This evidence argues for placental production of progesterone and for fetal secretion of the other three progestins.[74]

Various investigators have suggested that this organ may secrete other protein and steroid hormones, but the proof of this is not yet conclusive.[63]

The placenta seems to have a definite life span. If monkey or mouse fetuses are destroyed *in utero* without detaching the placentas, the latter will persist, to be delivered at the time of normal parturition. Under such conditions the placentas continue to produce hormones in much the same manner as during normal pregnancy, insofar as revealed by the weight of the host, the development of the mammary glands and the structure of the vaginal epithelium.

Influence of Maternal Hormones upon Embryo and Fetus. The large amounts of circulating gonadotrophic and steroid hormones are not without effect on the intrauterine young of some species. The ovaries may be somewhat stimulated; in man the uterus, vagina, prostate and sometimes the mammary glands of the newborn are hypertrophied or stimulated, presumably by the high levels of estrogen. Rapid involution follows birth. Menstruation is sometimes observed within a few days after birth and is attributed to cessation of exposure to maternal hormones. Large amounts of estrogen, when injected into pregnant rodents, have produced anomalous development of the accessory genital organs of the fetuses, although androgens have provoked more striking genital changes when similarly administered, not only to pregnant rodents, but to monkeys. It is possible that high levels of estrogens during pregnancy may influence male embryos so that male pseudohermaphrodites, which are not rare in the human population, result.

PARTURITION

Each species has a characteristic period of gestation, ranging from 12 or 13 days in the opossum to 20 or 21 months in the elephant. In man, pregnancy lasts about nine calendar months or ten lunar months. Slight variations in duration are not uncommon. It has been suggested that the period of gestation is a multiple of the estrous or menstrual cycle; for example, in man it is equal to ten average menstrual cycles.

Uterus. Following the 30th week of human pregnancy, uterine contractions very slowly increase in frequency and intensity.[11] During the last month the fetal head moves down into the pelvis. The contractions become coordinated, lose their local character, and involve more and more of the uterus. At the beginning of true labor they occur every 10 or 15 minutes and may continue to be painless. Their frequency gradually increases until they come every three to five minutes, and by now they may be extremely painful. During this *first stage* of labor the fibrous uterine cervix, which throughout pregnancy has had a lumen of a very few millimeters, is gradually forced to dilate. The dilation is achieved by the hydraulic and mechanical pressures produced by the muscular fundus or body of the uterus. The contractions continue to increase in frequency, lasting perhaps a minute each. They are strong-

est in the upper part of the fundus and weakest near the cervix. They start near the uterine tubes and progress downward.[60] Ultimately the cervix is fully dilated, being stretched until its internal diameter is perhaps 10 centimeters, and offers no further obstruction to the passage of the fetus. This completes the first stage of labor. During the *second stage*, the baby is born. While the uterine contractions have been strong enough to complete stage one, in stage two the mother must help by "bearing down," that is, by inflating her lungs, holding her breath, and strongly contracting her abdominal muscles. With this assistance, the baby is expelled through the cervix and vagina and emerges into the outside world. In the *third stage*, usually lasting only a few minutes, the placenta is delivered. Uterine contractions continue after stage three and may be stimulated by the administration of an *oxytocic* drug or hormone, as prompt reduction of uterine size and maintenance of muscular tonus helps to control postpartum hemorrhage. Progesterone, when administered to patients with painful postpartum uterine contractions, alleviates the pain, although without inhibiting the contractions.

Much information about uterine activity has been obtained by direct measurement of amniotic fluid pressures conveyed through a fine catheter introduced through the anterior abdominal wall and into the amniotic sac. Amniotic fluid pressures of course reflect total pressures exerted by and on the uterus. Myometrial pressures at various locations have been obtained by recordings from several very small, water-filled microballoons on the tips of catheters implanted at various sites in the uterine wall. Contractions were found to have an intensity equal to the pressure of 30 mm. Hg at the beginning of labor and 50 mm. Hg at its end. Tonus of the uterine muscle between contractions also increases. After labor, the contractions rapidly diminish in strength and frequency but persist for some time, occurring about every 10 minutes at 12 and 24 hours after delivery.[11]

Circulation. During parturition, systolic and diastolic blood pressures usually rise by 10 to 20 mm. Hg.[25] The circulation through the uterus and the placenta is modified by the high intrauterine pressure which develops during labor pains; the arterial pressure rises and the pulse pressure increases (Figs. 9 and

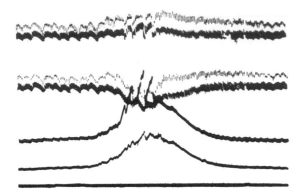

Fig. 9. Pressure relations during labor. From above downward: arterial pressure, arterial pressure minus uterine pressure, uterine pressure, uterine pressure minus gastric pressure.

10). A uterine contraction forces 250 to 300 ml. of venous blood from the placenta,[39] thereby increasing the venous return. In spite of this rise in blood pressure, there is a fall in the head of pressure irrigating the placenta because the intrauterine pressure rises more than the blood pressure.

An increase in intrauterine pressure brought about by contraction of both the uterus and the abdominal wall does not, on the other hand, impair the uterine circulation, since abdominal pressure is transmitted directly to the thoracic and abdominal blood vessels. Thus the increased intrauterine blood pressure is balanced by intra-abdominal pressure, and there is no net change in the pressure which irrigates the uterus unless straining is prolonged for 10 or 15 seconds and interferes with the venous return to the heart. Reflex bearing down efforts last such a short time that this activity plays no role. Voluntary bearing down is often prolonged at the urging of the obstetrician, and then the circulation may fail for want of venous blood. After delivery of the placenta, there is a rapid drop in uterine blood flow. There is a further reduction of blood flow as the uterus involutes.

Careful measurements indicate that during the course of normal labor the blood flow through the placenta is insured by the natural relationship between intrauterine and arterial pressure. Unfortunately this is not true when drugs such as ergot or Pituitrin are administered to hasten the course of labor. In such a case, there results an abnormally high intrauterine pressure which is maintained for a relatively long period. This elevated intrauterine pressure prevents blood from reaching the placenta for a length of time sufficient to produce signs of serious fetal asphyxia (cardiac slowing, weak fetal heart sounds, or even cessation of heartbeat).

Initiation and Control of Parturition. The independence of uterine muscular activity from extrinsic innervation has been shown by studies on parturition in animals whose spinal cords have been bisected or whose sympathetic chains have been completely removed.[59] Spinal anesthesia in women does not interfere with normal contractions of the uterus.[11] Stimuli may act upon the uterus in man via extrinsic innervation, however, since emotional disturbances may provoke premature parturition.

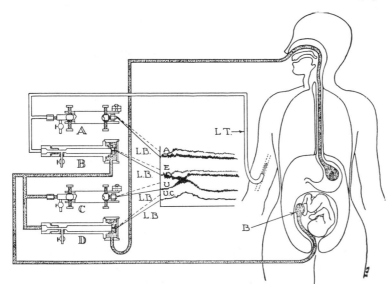

Fig. 10. Diagram showing simultaneous recording of arterial pressure (A), of head of pressure irrigating placenta (E), of intrauterine pressure (U), and of force which uterine wall contributes to intrauterine pressure. E is obtained by leading arterial pressure to optical manometer, membrane of which is enclosed in chamber to which intrauterine pressure is led. Contribution of uterine wall to intrauterine pressure is measured by a similar differential manometer which subtracts intragastric pressure from uterine pressure.

The cause of the termination of a normal human pregnancy is uncertain, although numerous experiments have been undertaken in search of the mechanism. Enormous doses of estrogen have been administered without altering the course of pregnancy in monkeys and man. Estrogen and progesterone levels were compared in the plasma of seven women who underwent cesarean section and eight who had normal labor. There was considerable variation in the (uncorrected) values for estrone, estradiol-17β, estriol and progesterone, but for no hormone was there a statistically significant difference between the two groups. Thus it does not appear that labor is initiated by a change in the peripheral plasma levels of any of these hormones.[1, 31] In many species the removal of the corpora lutea terminates pregnancy; however, this is not true in man, very likely because the placenta alone can produce an adequate supply of progestin. The administration of progesterone, or the experimental production of a new group of functional corpora lutea by the injection of gonadotrophins during the latter part of gestation, may prevent or delay parturition in laboratory animals.[38] Under such conditions the young continue to grow and may attain sufficient size to rupture the uterus or may die *in utero* several days after the expected parturition. The onset of parturition in some laboratory animals may result from a decline in the circulating level of progesterone, but this is apparently not the case in man, where the progestins are reported to be absent from peripheral blood or to be present in very low concentrations during pregnancy.[10, 29, 75]

Present evidence suggests that the powerful and frequent contractions characteristic of labor do not normally occur until the end of pregnancy either because they are "blocked" by effective concentrations in the uterine muscle of progestin supplied by the placenta or because *oxytocin,* a hormone of the posterior lobe of the pituitary, is released in quantities sufficient to stimulate these contractions. Some understanding of the mechanisms of labor have come from *in vitro* studies with uterine muscle and from observations on normal and experimental animals, but it is clear that caution must be exercised regarding assumptions that identical factors control normal human labor.[13, 19, 21, 45, 56]

Serum calcium and lipid levels increase in birds when eggs are being formed. Similar changes occur in birds when estrogens are injected; very high levels of serum calcium and lipids may result. In addition, osseous trabeculae grow into the marrow, increasing the amount of bone. Extreme endosteal ossification occurs in the bones of estrogen-treated mice and the breaking strength of their femurs is increased. The negative calcium balances in some women with postmenopausal osteoporosis become positive when estrogens are administered, and the symptoms are alleviated.

Estrogens cause a dissolution of the pubes at the symphyses in animals of some species, in this way increasing the size of the birth canal. In guinea pigs a relaxation of the pubes precedes parturition and can be reproduced in nonparous animals by estrogen and a distinct hormone, *relaxin.* The loosening of the sacroiliac joints and pubic symphyses during pregnancy in some women probably results from the action of ovarian hormones.

DEVELOPMENT AND FUNCTION OF MAMMARY GLANDS

Milk is necessary for the postpartum nutrition of the young of most species during the period of adaptation to extrauterine life.[18] The mechanisms regulating and synchronizing mammary development and function with sexual and reproductive functions are distinctly mammalian and might be considered a comparatively recent phylogenetic acquisition, although some fish possess intrauterine mechanisms for feeding their young. It is not unexpected, therefore, that the physiologic regulatory mechanisms of mammary growth and function differ from those of the other female accessory organs.

Normal Development. The breasts are modified skin glands which are first formed during embryonic life and which frequently undergo considerable development during the late fetal stage, presumably under the influence of circulating hormones produced in the placenta. The intrauterine influences persisting until birth may be responsible for cystic distension of the breast with a serous fluid called witch's milk. Soon after birth the breasts, if hypertrophied, again become small and remain so until the onset of puberty. With the rather sudden appearance at puberty of ovarian activity, the breasts hypertrophy, and both the stroma and the parenchyma increase in amount. After menarche further mammary growth occurs, probably in cycles paralleling the menstrual cycles. Cyclic mammary growth occurs during the estrous cycles of young mammals of some species.[47]

The prepubertal glands consist of rudimentary ducts extending but a short distance beneath the flattened nipple areas. During puberty and adolescence the ducts grow by apical proliferation and the number of branching ducts increases until a complex compound tubular gland is formed. It is probable that some alveoli also develop during the menstrual cycles. The greater number of mammary alveoli, however, develop during pregnancy, probably during the first part of pregnancy, transforming the breast to a compound tubulo-alveolar gland. Although the gland may be morphologically complete during the latter part of gestation, lactation usually does not begin until after parturition. If the breasts are suckled and the accumulated colostrum and milk are removed, the gland may function for many months—in some instances for periods of several years. Eventually the glands regress and the alveoli are largely reabsorbed, leaving again essentially a compound tubular mammary structure. After the menopause only the larger ducts may persist in an abundant fibrofatty stroma.

Lactation except following pregnancy is rare in man. Acidophilic cell tumors of the pituitary are associated with acromegaly; during the early stages of this disease spontaneous lactation frequently occurs.

Experimental Studies. Comparatively few observations have been made on the influence of hormones on the human breast. Hypogonadal or postmenopausal women have some breast hypertrophy following topical or systemic applications of estrogens. A feeling of fullness and tenderness of the breasts may occur at the same time. It is assumed that a growth of the parenchymal tissues occurs under such conditions.

Administration of estrogen is followed by varying degrees of mammary development in different species. In immature castrate monkeys and guinea pigs, for example, estrogen induces complete development of the mammary glands at a rate approaching that seen in pregnancy. In the dog, on the other hand, estrogen alone induces little or no mammary growth. Progesterone alone induces either duct or alveolar growth in several species; usually, more rapid and extensive growth occurs after administration of both hormones than after administration of either one singly. Mammary development normally goes to completion only during pregnancy and pseudopregnancy, periods when both estrogen and progesterone are being secreted.

Hypophysectomy appears largely to inhibit or prevent the mammary growth response to estrogen and progesterone (except in mice). Lactogenic hormone and other protein preparations of the pituitary provide at least partial replacement therapy. Administration of preparations of cattle anterior pituitary is followed by mammary growth in castrated and intact male mice, even though no other hormone is given. Some pituitary factor seems to be necessary for mammary growth; in this respect the breasts differ from other accessory genital tissues such as the vagina and uterus, which respond to the ovarian steroids in the absence of the hypophysis. The mechanism of mammary development is further complicated when an explanation is sought for the unilateral proliferation of the subjacent breast tissue that follows cutaneous application of estrogens in amounts too small to elicit systemic effects. If estrogens act indirectly through the pituitary upon the mammary glands, such reactions would not be expected; all the glands should be stimulated. Estrogen can act directly upon the subjacent mammary tissue in intact but not in hypophysectomized animals, however. Further work must be done on more species before the endocrine stimulation of mammary growth is understood. A specific hypophysial hormone may be required or, possibly, the general debility of hypophysectomized animals may be responsible for the restriction of mammary growth.

Lactation. Although the breasts grow when estrogens are administered to intact animals, a pituitary hormone is necessary to stimulate mammary secretion. The lactogenic hormone induces lactation when injected into animals with completely developed mammary glands. The cuboidal or low columnar cells of the alveoli and the smallest ducts increase in height and elaborate and excrete milk which distends the glands. Normal lactation ceases immediately when the hypophysis is removed, but is maintained if lactogen and adrenotrophic hormone or lactogen and adrenal cortical extracts are given. The maintenance of approximately normal adrenal function or an adequate supply of exogenous adrenal cortical hormone is necessary before lactation can be maintained in hypophysectomized animals. In most species studied, both the onset and the maintenance of lactation require lactogen. The amount of milk secreted during the peak of lactation cannot be increased by lactogen, but, during the declining phase of milk secretion, milk production may be increased in goats and cows. Lactogen has been used clinically in attempts to increase the milk yield in nursing women, but the results have not been convincing. It is probable that deficiencies in milk production are usually caused by factors other than inadequate lactogen.

The lactogenic activity of pituitary extracts was first shown by Stricker and Grüter in 1928 and was confirmed by many other investigators. Riddle[61] noted that the pituitary hormone which induced growth of the pigeon's crop gland (for the production of "pigeon's milk") was the same as the one stimulating lactation. The stimulation of the growth of the pigeon's crop gland is the basis for a bioassay for lactogen. The bioassay facilitated the chemical isolation of lactogen by White *et al.*, who prepared the first pituitary hormone to be obtained in a pure state. One International Unit equals 0.1 mg. of the International Standard Lactogenic Hormone. Prolactin is present in the blood during the first and last parts of the menstrual cycle.[65]

Normally lactation begins about the time of parturition or shortly thereafter. The synchronization of the onset of lactation with parturition has been explained by assuming that estrogen or progesterone produced during pregnancy inhibits the liberation of lactogen by the pituitary and that withdrawal of these hormones after parturition permits lactogen production and the onset of lactation. Clinically, for reasons that are not clear, estrogen may either inhibit or stimulate lactation. Estrogen does not prevent the action of lactogen when these hormones are given together, a finding indicating that the steroid hormone acts upon the pituitary and not upon the mammary glands directly. Monkeys given estrogens for long periods begin to lactate. Similarly, young virgin goats or heifers subjected to prolonged treatment with the synthetic estrogen stilbestrol begin to lactate and

may produce large quantities of milk. Estrogen increases the lactogen content of the pituitary glands of nonparous or male rats; this action is prevented by simultaneous administration of progesterone. In cows the amount of milk produced is increased up to 30 per cent (and the amount of solids in the milk may be increased) by administering thyroxin or thyroglobulin. During lactation the amount of thyrotrophic hormone produced is increased. Lactation may occur in thyroidectomized animals, but the amount of milk is below normal.

Evidence regarding endocrine factors in the initiation and maintenance of lactation is contradictory. Species differences are important. Although hypotheses have been developed in an attempt to reconcile all the findings, further work is required.[18, 47]

Extracts of the posterior hypophysis (oxytocin) incite the removal of milk from the breast by causing a contraction of the muscle or contractile elements of the alveoli and ducts.[7, 50] Glands from which as much milk has been removed as can be obtained by usual means yield additional quantities when oxytocin is given. The increased intramammary pressure subsequent to administration of oxytocin can be readily demonstrated by cannulating the primary ducts.

Suckling in lactating rats stimulates the production of milk in nonsuckled glands for a longer period than when suckling is not permitted, indicating some neural mechanism in the regulation of lactation. Denervated glands lactate if suckling is permitted on some innervated nipples, but lactation fails when only the denervated nipples are suckled. The stimuli provoked by suckling in rats apparently pass along the dorsal roots of the spinal cord and ipsilaterally toward the brain via the ventral portion of the lateral funiculus.[24] How much of a role the stimulus of nursing plays in lactation in animals of other species is less certain.

PHYSIOLOGY OF THE VAGINA

The profound and rapid transformation of the vaginal epithelium in rats and mice was mentioned with reference to the bioassay of estrogens. In these species the rapid proliferation of the deeper cells may result in a complete replacement of the entire vaginal epithelium within three days. Administration of estrogen may transform a vaginal epithelium, only two or three cell layers thick in a castrated mouse or rat, into a thick, stratified squamous structure, the outer layers of which consist of cornified cells. At the same time the large numbers of polymorphonuclear leukocytes characteristic of the diestrous vaginal wall and contents disappear.

In man, marked changes also occur in the vaginal structure. At birth the vaginal epithelium is thick, a response to the high estrogen content of the intrauterine environment. Within a few days the vaginal epithelium is again thin and remains so until puberty. Periodic changes in the epithelium occur during the menstrual cycles and may be detected by the examination of smears of the vaginal contents. The changes are not so easily discerned or in many cases so definite as in rodents. During the midintermenstruum the smears contain few leukocytes and many isolated cornified or partially cornified cells with very small pyknotic nuclei; the vaginal pH is low, and the glycogen content of the cells is high. During the progestational stage the partially cornified cells appear in clumps, noncornified epithelial cells increase in number, and leukocytes and bacteria are abundant. Some investigators consider the human vaginal smears sufficiently definitive to permit an estimation of adequate therapy. Estrogen administered to the postmenopausal patient will induce a type of vaginal mucosa characteristic of the midintermenstrual period. The addition of progesterone will transform the cornified epithelium into one similar to that seen during the normal premenstrual stage.[54]

The presence of glycogen in the vaginal epithelial cells is apparently attributable to the action of both estrogen and progesterone. The function of the intracellular glycogen is unknown, although the suggestion has been made that it is responsible for the high acidity of the vaginal secretions. The glycogen content is highest in the premenstrual period, and the pH is lowest during the midcycle; the alkaline cervical secretions may reduce the acidity during the latter part of the cycle.

SOME ADDITIONAL ACTION OF FEMALE SEX HORMONES

Animals of several species, when given estrogens such as estradiol or stilbestrol for long periods, will acquire uterine or mammary cancers or tumors of the pituitary glands, testicular interstitial cells or lymphoid tissues. Prolonged and continuous exposure to the estrogens is usually required before tumors appear. Mammary cancers also depend in part upon co-existing genetic susceptibility and in some species upon the presence of a specific virus. The viruses are sometimes transmitted vertically from generation to generation through the mother's milk or even through the placenta.

The transformation of normal organs or tissues to cancerous growths is often a stepwise process, and the hormones associated with tumorigenesis are probably associated only with some of the stages involved in this process. Hypophysectomy prevents mammary tumor formation in otherwise susceptible mice. This operation does not prevent the growth of mammary cancers after they have become truly cancerous, but some adenomas of the mammary tissue will regress. Furthermore, most of the hormones associated with tumorigenesis have been demonstrated to be effective only in vivo and under circumstances that involve either endocrine imbalances or marked disturbances of function directly regulated by other endocrine glands. The best evidence for a direct tumorigenic effect of estrogens is provided by the early appearance of epidermoid carcinomas of the uterine cervix and upper vagina of mice when the hormones are applied directly to the tissues. All other tumors that appear as a result of endocrine modification are less adequately understood.

Pituitary tumors occur in mice given estrogen for prolonged periods, but this effect is probably secondary to modification of the pituitary–hypothalamic relationship by the hormones. Pituitary glands transplanted subcutaneously or intrasplenically, that is, to sites remote from the usual hypothalamic connections also become tumorous in female mice; estrogen does not accelerate the tumorous transformation.

Indirect evidence indicates that the gonadotrophic hormones of the pituitary gland are also tumorigenic when they act uninterruptedly. If the ovaries of rats or mice are transplanted into their spleens so that their hormones are carried into the liver, there to be largely transformed, or if rats and mice have restricted ovarian function, they acquire ovarian granulosa cell tumors. In such circumstances the abnormal ovarian–hypophysial relationships are presumably responsible for the neoplastic change. Androgenic hormone such as testosterone does not prevent ovarian tumors in mice with transplanted ovaries, indicating that this steroid does not have the same effect upon the pituitary–hypothalamic mechanism as do estrogens.

Some cancers are dependent for their growth upon the presence of hormones. The control, at least for a while, of some prostatic cancers in man by castration is an example of hormonal regulation of cancer growth. In general, with time, cancers are increasingly independent of hormones and become autonomous. Usually only temporary control of cancerous growth has occurred by endocrine modification, even in selected patients.

INACTIVATION OF SEX HORMONES

When estrogens are injected into man only a small portion of the original hormone may be recovered in the urine. The greater part of the hormones is destroyed or inactivated within the body. The liver is an active site of destruction of hormones. In experimental animals estrogens are usually more effective when injected subcutaneously than when placed in the peritoneal cavity or spleen; hormones in the abdominal sites are absorbed and carried by the portal venous system to the liver. The incubation *in vitro* of estrogens with minced or finely sliced liver of some animals results in the rapid destruction of the hormone. Men or women with severe liver disease may show hyperestrogenic responses, apparently elicited by the endogenous hormones which are not destroyed rapidly enough to prevent their accumulation above threshold levels. It has been assumed that an "estrinase" may be present in hepatic and other estrogen-destroying tissues. Tyrosinase will also inactivate estrogens *in vitro*—as will unidentified enzymes in the blood of some species. The end-products of these reactions are not known. Estrogens may be metabolized to less active or inactive compounds. The activity of estradiol and estrone is reduced under some conditions by transformation into estriol, which is excreted as a water-soluble conjugated estrogen. The current idea of hormonal interconversion is: estradiol $\rightleftharpoons$ estrone $\rightarrow$ estriol. Inactivation may involve conjugation. Incubation of estrogens with kidney slices and perfusion of kidneys *in vitro* with estrogens also result in inactivation of some of the hormone, suggesting a role for the kidney *in vivo*.

The progestin content of blood in the renal veins of rabbits and monkeys, as determined by bioassay, is less than that of their renal arterial blood. Progesterone is changed in part into the inactive pregnanediol, excreted in the urine as sodium pregnanediol glucuronidate. Other metabolites include 20α-hydroxy-Δ^4-pregnen-3-one, 20β-hydroxy-Δ^4-pregnen-3-one, 16α-hydroxyprogesterone, 17α-hydroxyprogesterone, etc. The equivalent of somewhat less than one-half of the progesterone injected is usually recovered as metabolites under the best conditions. The liver may inactivate progesterone by linking it in some manner to protein.

Whether hormones are utilized in the reactions they incite or whether they act as catalysts has been considered. Conclusive evidence is lacking. The estrogens might well be considered as stimulators of growth of the genital tissues *in vivo* at all stages from at least late fetal life until death. They have not been effective in stimulating the growth of tissues *in vitro*. Progesterone, although it will also stimulate the growth of some genital tissues when given in large amounts, is more intimately concerned with the differentiation of tissues, their stimulation to secretory activity, particularly in the case of progestational endometrium and mammary gland tissue, and the accumulation of glycogen in the vaginal mucosa.

REFERENCES

1. AITKEN, E. H., PREEDY, J. R. K., ETON, B. and SHORT, R. V. *Lancet*, 1958, *2*:1096–1099.
2. ALBRIGHT, F., SMITH, P. H. and FRASER, R. *Amer. J. med. Sci.*, 1942, *204*:625–648.
3. ALLEN, E. *Contr. Embryol. Carneg. Instn.*, 1927, *19*:1–44.
4. ALLEN, E. and DOISY, E. A. *J. Amer. med. Ass.*, 1923, *81*:819–821.
5. ASCHHEIM, S. and ZONDEK, B. *Klin. Wschr.*, 1928, *7*:1404–1411.
6. ASSALI, N. S., RAURAMO, L. and PELTONEN, T. *Amer. J. Obst. Gynec.*, 1960, *79*:86–98.
7. BARGMANN, W. *Endeavour*, 1960, *19*:125–133.
8. BLANDAU, R. J. and YOUNG, W. C. *Amer. J. Anat.*, 1939, *64*:303–329.
9. BROWNE, J. C. M. *Cold Spr. Harb. Symp. quant. Biol.*, 1954, *19*:60–70.
10. BUTT, W. R., MORRIS, P., MORRIS, C. J. O. R. and WILLIAMS, D. C. *Biochem. J.*, 1951, *49*:434–438.
11. CALDEYRO-BARCIA, R. *2e Cong. Internat. Gyn. et Obst. Montréal*, 1958, *1*:65–102.

12. CALDEYRO-BARCIA, R. and ALVAREZ, H. *J. appl. Physiol.,* 1954, *6:*556–558.

13. CALDEYRO-BARCIA, R. and SERENO, J. A. In: *Oxytocin,* R. Caldeyro-Barcia and H. Heller, eds. New York, Pergamon Press, 1961.

14. COHEN, H. Chap. 4 in *The endocrinology of reproduction,* J. T. Velardo, ed. New York, Oxford University Press, 1958.

15. CORNER, G. W. *Amer. J. Physiol.,* 1928, *86:*74–81.

16. CORNER, G. W. *Harvey Lect.,* 1932–1933, 67–89.

17. CORNER, G. W., JR., RAMSEY, E. M. and STRAN, H. *Amer. J. Obst. Gynec.,* 1963, *85:*179–185.

18. COWIE, A. T. and FOLLEY, S. J. Chap. 10 in *Sex and internal secretions,* W. C. Young, cd. Baltimore, Williams & Wilkins, 1961.

19. CSAPO, A. I. *Ann. N. Y. Acad. Sci.,* 1959, *75:*790–808.

20. CSAPO, A. I. and CORNER, G. W. *Endocrinology,* 1952, *51:* 378–385.

21. CSAPO, A. I. and LLOYD-JACOB, M. A. *Amer. J. Obst. Gynec.,* 1963, *85:*806–812.

22. DEMPSEY, E. W. and BASSETT, D. L. *Endocrinology,* 1943, *33:*384–401.

23. DICZFALUSY, E. and LINDKVIST, P. *Acta endocrin.,* 1956, *22:* 203–223.

24. EAYRS, J. T. and BADDELEY, R. M. *J. Anat. (Lond.),* 1956, *90:*161–171.

25. EDWARDS, E. M. *J. Obst. Gynaec. Brit. Emp.,* 1958, *65:* 367–370.

26. EVANS, H. M., KOHLS, C. L. and WONDER, D. H. *J. Amer. med. Ass.,* 1937, *108:*287–289.

27. EVERETT, J. W. Chap. 8 in *Sex and internal secretions,* W. C. Young, ed., Baltimore, Williams & Wilkins, 1961.

28. FORBES, T. R. *Amer. J. Obst. Gynec.,* 1950, *60:*180–186.

29. FORBES, T. R. *Endocrinology,* 1951, *49:*218–224.

30. FRIEDMAN, M. H. *Amer. J. Physiol.,* 1929, *90:*617–622.

31. GREENE, J. W., JR. and TOUCHSTONE, J. C. *Amer. J. med. Sci.,* 1959, *238:*772–784.

32. GREEP, R. O. Chap. 4 in *Sex and internal secretions,* W. C. Young, ed. Baltimore, Williams & Wilkins, 1961.

33. HAIN, A. M. *J. Endocrinol.,* 1940, *2:*104–110.

34. HAMAN, J. O. *Amer. J. Obst. Gynec.,* 1942, *43:*870–873.

35. HARRIS, G. W. *Neural control of the pituitary gland.* London, Edward Arnold, 1955.

36. HARTMAN, C. G. *Proc. Soc. exp. Biol. (N.Y.),* 1941, *48:*221–223.

37. HARTMAN, C. G. *Contr. Embryol. Carneg. Instn.,* 1942, *30:* 111–126.

38. HECKEL, G. P. and ALLEN, W. M. *Amer. J. Obst. Gynec.,* 1938, *35:*131–137.

39. HENDRICKS, C. H. *Amer. J. Obst. Gynec.,* 1958, *76:*969–982.

40. HENRY, J. S. and BROWNE, J. S. L. *Amer. J. Obst. Gynec.,* 1943, *45:*927–949.

41. HITSCHMANN, F. and ADLER, L. *Mschr. Geburtsh. Gynäk.,* 1908, *27:*1–82.

42. HOOKER, C. W. and FORBES, T. R. *Endocrinology,* 1947, *41:*158–169.

43. JONES, G. E. S., GEY, G. O. and GEY, M. K. *Johns Hopkins Hosp. Bull.,* 1943, *72:*26–38.

44. KAUFMANN, C. and ZANDER, J. *Ciba Symp.,* 1959, *7:*146–162.

45. KUMAR, D., GOODNO, J. A. and BARNES, A. C. *Amer. J. Obst. Gynec., 84:*1111–1115.

46. LI, C. H. and EVANS, H. M. In: *The hormones,* vol. 1, G. Pincus and K. V. Thimann, eds. New York, Academic Press, 1948.

47. LINZELL, J. L. *Physiol. Rev.,* 1959, *39:*534–576.

48. MARKEE, J. E. *Contr. Embryol. Carneg. Instn.,* 1940, *28:*219–308.

49. MELINKOFF, E. *Amer. J. Obst. Gynec.,* 1950, *60:*437–439.

50. NICKERSON, K., BONSNES, R. W., DOUGLAS, R. G., CONDLIFFE, P. and DU VIGNEAUD, V. *Amer. J. Obst. Gynec.,* 1954, *67:*1028–1034.

51. NIKITOVITCH-WINER, M. and EVERETT, J. W. *Endocrinology,* 1958, *63:*916–930.

52. OBER, K. G. and WEBER, M. *Klin. Wschr.,* 1951, *29:*53–55.

53. OERTEL, G. W. *Klin. Wschr.,* 1961, *39:*492–493.

54. PAPANICOLAOU, G. and SHORR, E. *Amer. J. Obst. Gynec.,* 1936, *31:*806–831.

55. PFEIFFER, C. A. *Amer. J. Anat.,* 1936, *58:*195–225.

56. POSE, S. V. and FIELITZ, C. In: *Oxytocin,* R. Caldeyro-Barcia and H. Heller, eds. New York, Pergamon Press, 1961.

57. POSSE, N. *Acta obstet. gynec. scand.,* 1958, *37:*Suppl. 2.

58. PREEDY, J. R. K. and AITKEN, E. H. *Lancet,* 1957, *272:* 191–192.

59. REYNOLDS, S. R. M. *Physiology of the uterus,* 2d ed. New York, Paul B. Hoeber, 1949.

60. REYNOLDS, S. R. M. *Physiological bases of gynecology and obstetrics.* Springfield, Ill., Charles C Thomas, 1952.

61. RIDDLE, O. and BATES, R. W. In: *Sex and internal secretions; a survey of recent research,* 2d ed., E. Allen, ed. Baltimore, Williams & Wilkins, 1939.

62. ROWLANDS, I. W. and SHARPEY-SCHAFER, E. P. *Brit. med. J.,* 1940, *1:*205–207.

63. RYAN, K. J. *Amer. J. Obst. Gynec.,* 1962, *84:*1695–1713.

64. SHORT, R. V. *J. Endocrinol.,* 1960, *20:*xv-xvi.

65. SIMKIN, B. and ARCE, R. *Proc. Soc. exp. Biol. (N.Y.),* 1963, *113:*485–488.

66. SMITH, P. E. *Amer. J. Anat.,* 1930, *45:*205–273.

67. SMITH, P. E., and ENGLE, E. T. *Amer. J. Anat.,* 1927, *40:* 159–217.

68. VENNING, E. H. and BROWNE, J. S. L. *Endocrinology,* 1940, *27:*707–720.

69. WERNER, A. A. and COLLIER, W. D. *J. Amer. med. Ass.,* 1933, *101:*1466–1472.

70. WISLOCKI, G. B. and BENNETT, H. S. *Amer. J. Anat.,* 1943, *73:*335–449.

71. WOOLEVER, C. A. *Amer. J. Obst. Gynec.,* 1963, *85:*981–988.

72. ZANDER, J. *Klin. Wschr.,* 1955, *33:*697–701.

73. ZANDER, J. In: *Recent progress in the endocrinology of reproduction,* C. W. Lloyd, ed. New York, Academic Press, 1959.

74. ZANDER, J. In: *Progesterone and the defence mechanism of pregnancy,* G. E. W. Wolstenholme and M. P. Cameron, eds. London, J. & A. Churchill, 1961.

75. ZANDER, J., FORBES, T. R., VON MÜNSTERMANN, A. M. and NEHER, R. *J. clin. Endocrinol.,* 1958, *18:*337–353.

76. ZANDER, J., THIJSSEN, J., and VON MÜNSTERMANN, A. M. *J. clin. Endocrinol.,* 1962, *22:*861–862.

CHAPTER 63

Reproduction in the Male

By CHARLES W. HOOKER

THE part played by the male in reproduction is the production of spermatozoa and their delivery in suitable condition for fertilization of the ovum produced and housed in the female. The elaboration of spermatozoa occurs in the testes; the remainder of the genital system (Fig. 1) consists of excurrent ducts that store and convey the spermatozoa to the exterior and of a series of glands whose secretions are added to the fluid containing the outgoing spermatozoa. In addition to producing spermatozoa, the testes are responsible for the functional maintenance of the rest of the genital system and for the development and maintenance of many of the somatic traits that are considered masculine. The latter functions of the testes are

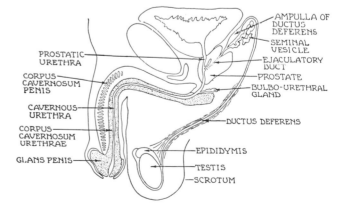

Fig. 1. Diagram of male genital system.

mediated by their internal secretions, and the testes, in turn, are governed primarily by the hypophysis and its gonadotrophic hormones.

SPERMATOGENESIS AND SPERMATOZOA[4, 10]

The mature spermatozoon is a unique and highly differentiated cell which, to accomplish its mission, must be motile, must be capable of entering the ovum, must be capable of initiating the development of the ovum, and must furnish the genetic contribution of the male to the potential offspring. Spermatozoa are produced in prodigious numbers; for example, the ram produces upward of four billions daily. The numbers involved in fertilization, however, are by no means as great. Although the number in one ejaculation may be several millions, the number reaching the site of fertilization may be as few as 100 in the rat,[7] and only one fertilizes the ovum.

Morphologic development of spermatozoa occurs in the tortuously coiled seminiferous tubules (Fig. 2), which make up the bulk of the testis and which contain two categories of cells: spermatozoa and their antecedent cells, and the cells of Sertoli. As a rule, spermatozoa taken from the testis are not functionally mature, full motility and fertilizing capacity usually being attained only after a period in the male and

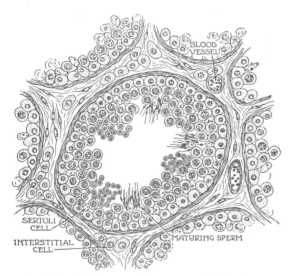

Fig. 2. Small area of human testis, showing one tubule and portions of several others in cross section, and intertubular tissue.

female genital tracts. Although a low level of movement may be exhibited by sperm recovered directly from the testis, they experience during their residence in the epididymis changes that have not been fully identified but that confer upon them a capacity for vigorous movement. Despite the capacity for motility, spermatozoa appear to be quiescent during their storage in the genital ducts of the male. The attainment of capacity to fertilize the ovum appears to necessitate incubation for a time in the tubal fluid of the female,[48] where partial loss of the cap and acrosome occurs, at least in some species, as well as certain enzymatic changes.

Motility is an obvious attribute of viability of spermatozoa, but movement may be exhibited by spermatozoa that are incapable of fertilizing ova. This circumstance is well illustrated by the observation in the guinea pig that motility may be shown by epididymal spermatozoa for approximately 60 days after separation of the epididymis from the testis, whereas fertilizing capacity persists only 20 to 30 days.[63] Moreover, it is said that the fertilizing capacity of spermatozoa in successive ejaculates declines, and that lowered fertility may result from prolonged sexual rest. In the former instance physiologically immature spermatozoa may be present, and in the latter circumstance the spermatozoa may be senile. In any case, these possibilities are taken into account in the practice of artificial insemination in domestic animals. In most mammals the duration of viability of spermatozoa is much briefer in the genital tract of the female than in that of the male. In the female guinea pig, for example, motility was observed for 41 hours after mating or artificial insemination and fertilizing capacity apparently persisted no more than 22 hours[57]—in contrast to many days' persistence of viability in the genital tract of the male guinea pig.

More than one mechanism may be involved in the transportation of spermatozoa. Travel through the seminiferous tubules and the vasa efferentia into the epididymis may be the consequence of their being carried in the flow of fluid in this direction, perhaps propelled by undulating contractions of these tubules. Transport through the epididymis and the more distal ducts of the male is generally attributed to contractions sweeping along the walls of these ducts. The velocity of independent movement of ejaculated spermatozoa (of the order of 1 to 3 mm. per minute) is not sufficient to account for the rate of transportation to the site of fertilization in the females of many species: 30 minutes in the rat, 15 minutes in the mouse, 2 to 4 minutes in the cow, and 30 minutes to 3 hours in the human being. Contractions of the uterus and tubes are assumed to be chiefly responsible, and oxytocin appears to be involved in rapid migration in some species.[27] In many animals spermatozoa reach the site of fertilization before the ova are released by the ovary. As an example, the rat ovulates approximately ten hours after the onset of sexual receptivity at estrus, and sperm transport to the site of fertilization in the tube requires 30 minutes.[6] Accordingly, it is possible for spermatozoa to have to wait more than nine hours for the arrival of the ova.

The unique structure of spermatozoa and their great activity pose for them problems in nutrition and metabolism. The mature sperm cell is essentially a bare nucleus with a flagellum-like tail, and it has no cytoplasm for storing nutritive material. Within the testis it is possible that nutrients are transferred to sperm cells from the cells of Sertoli with which the spermatozoa are connected during their development.[18] Sertoli cells have also been said to resorb regressed spermatozoa.[53] After leaving the testis, spermatozoa probably receive their nutrients from the components of the seminal fluid.

The inactivity of spermatozoa during their storage in the male has been variously explained, but the inactivity probably contributes much to their longevity, as suggested by their brief survival after motility expresses itself. In any case, spermatozoa of many mammals, including man, have been used successfully in artificial insemination after long periods of storage at low temperatures, especially when the semen has been equilibrated with glycerol before freezing.

The fate of dead spermatozoa is not known with certainty, but one possibility is that such spermatozoa or their disintegration products are absorbed through the epithelial lining of the genital tract in both the male and the female. This possibility may not be unimportant in view of the thoroughly documented fact that spermatozoa possess antigenic properties.

GENITAL TRACT

The testes arise in the abdominal region of the embryo and typically descend into the scrotum late in fetal life. The cause and mechanism of the descent are not understood, but not infrequently one and occasionally both testes fail to descend, the condition being known as cryptorchidism. Spermatogenesis is disturbed in the undescended testis, sometimes to the point of complete arrest. The adverse effect of cryptorchidism appears to be largely the result of the higher temperatures to which the testes are subjected. The temperature of the scrotum is slightly lower than that of the abdominal cavity. Experimental procedures and many febrile diseases that raise the temperature of scrotal testes also suppress spermatogenesis, sometimes to the extent of causing sterility. Another serious aspect of failure of descent is the greater liability of the undescended testis to becoming cancerous.[9] After leaving the testis, spermatozoa pass successively through the ductuli efferentes, the ductus epididymis, the ductus deferens, the ejaculatory duct and the urethra. The epididymis and the ampulla of the ductus deferens also serve as depots for the storage of spermatozoa.

The principal glands associated with the genital tract are the seminal vesicles, the prostate and the bulbo-urethral glands, and the greater part of the volume of the seminal fluid is furnished by these glands. Generally speaking, the fluid secreted by each gland has its own characteristic components,[43] and certain of these compounds are believed to be important factors in supporting the highly active movements of ejaculated spermatozoa. Compounds that are secreted by one of these glands in one species may be secreted by another of these glands in a different species. This circumstance is not inconsistent with the fact that in some species one gland may be either lacking or small relative to another of the accessory glands of reproduction.

In man the characteristic constituent of the fluid of the seminal vesicles is fructose. The concentration of this unusual sugar in semen exceeds that of glucose in the blood, but fluctuates with the level of blood glucose. Mann has proposed that in the gland glucose is converted into fructose, with glycogen and phosphohexoses serving as intermediary compounds.

Fructose serves as a chief source of energy for ejaculated spermatozoa. Another constituent of fresh semen is phosphorylcholine. This substance liberates choline; the presence of choline is the basis for one of the older tests for semen in legal medicine. The observation that the greater part of the phosphorus content of semen is furnished by the seminal vesicles has led to the suggestion that phosphorylcholine is derived from the seminal vesicles. The physiologic significance of the compound seems to be unknown. It is now recognized that the seminal vesicle does not store spermatozoa, either living or dead. Similarly, the old notion that the intensity of the sex drive may be related to the degree of distention of the seminal vesicles may not be correct.[3]

The constituents of semen, derived primarily or solely from the prostate,[31] are acid phosphatase, citric acid, calcium and a fibrinolysin. The phosphatase is present in semen in very large quantities, and seems to be contributed solely by the prostate. The physiologic significance of this enzyme is not known, and, despite its high concentration in prostatic tissue, it does not enter the blood stream except when malignant growth occurs in the prostate. This fact has been of clinical significance. The functions of prostatic citric acid are not known, but it has been suggested that it may benefit spermatozoan motility; that it may exert a protective action against anti-invasin, thereby facilitating the action of hyaluronidase; that it may be related to coagulation and liquefaction of semen; and that it may be involved in the calcium binding of semen. The fibrinolysin of prostatic fluid is primarily responsible for the liquefaction of coagulated semen.

In many rodents ejaculated semen coagulates in the vagina and cervix, forming the so-called copulation or vaginal plug. The plug consists of fluid of the seminal vesicles coagulated by an enzyme secreted in one of the pairs of lobes of the prostatic complex. The function of the copulation plug is not known, but it has often been suggested that it prevents escape of semen from the genital tract of the female. Semen in certain primates coagulates, and in the monkey a specific area of the prostate contains the coagulating enzyme.[59] Whether a similar functional localization obtains in the human prostate has not been determined. The function served by coagulation of the ejaculum in primates is not known. It is interesting, however,

that coagulation of semen is in some respects like the coagulation of blood; upon standing the coagulum liquefies.

It seems clear that the secretions of the prostate and seminal vesicles are not essential in the fertilization of the ovum, as shown by successful artificial inseminations with spermatozoa taken from the epididymis. It seems equally clear that in more usual circumstances these secretions contribute to fertilization for the reasons suggested above. In the rat removal of either prostate or seminal vesicles does not abolish conception. Ligation of both glands, however, does prevent conception.[5] The specific defection has not been fully identified.

A group of modified sebaceous glands, the preputial glands, are situated in the prepuce in the region of the corona and discharge their secretion onto the glans penis. Smegma is largely the accumulated secretion of these glands.

ERECTION

Erection is primarily a vascular phenomenon and is dependent upon the morphologic pattern of the penis. This organ consists of three cylindrical masses of erectile tissue, two corpora cavernosa penis which lie side by side and above a third cord of erectile tissue, the corpus cavernosum urethrae, which transmits the urethra. The expanded distal end of the corpus cavernosum urethrae forms the glans. Each corpus cavernosum is surrounded by a dense fibrous coat, the tunica albuginea, and all three are enclosed by a layer of fairly dense fascia. At the root of the penis the corpora cavernosa penis diverge laterally as the crura to attach to the pubic arch, and each is covered by a sheet of skeletal muscle, the ischiocavernosus muscle. The expanded corpus cavernosum urethrae extends in the midline to the point of entry of the prostatic urethra and is also covered by a sheet of skeletal muscle, the bulbocavernosus.

The erectile tissue receives arterial blood by way of terminal branches of the internal pudendal arteries. These are (Fig. 3) a pair of dorsal arteries that lie on the dorsal surface of the tunica albuginea, a cavernous artery running longitudinally in each corpus cavernosum penis, and a pair of bulbourethral arteries that enter the corpus cavernosum urethrae at the bulb and course longitudinally forward. Branches of these arteries open into the cavernous spaces. Venous blood leaves the penis by way of two veins, the superficial dorsal vein, which drains the glans and the corpus cavernosum urethrae, and the deep dorsal vein, which lies between the dorsal arteries and receives tributaries from the corpora cavernosa penis.

The erectile tissue of the corpora cavernosa is a spongelike system of irregular vascular spaces that are interspersed between the arteries and veins. In the flaccid state these spaces are more or less collapsed and contain little blood; during erection they are quite large cavities distended with blood. This is the immediate mechanism of erection.

The intima of the arteries of the penis has longitudinal ridges that serve to occlude the arteries partially and to restrict the quantity of blood entering the cavernous sinuses.[37] Upon dilatation of these arteries the flow of blood into the penis is tremendously increased and the sinuses are filled. The larger veins of the penis are said to possess funnel-like valves that impede the return of blood from the penis.[37] Moreover, distension of the vascular spaces is thought to press the veins of the cavernous bodies against the tunica albuginea and to restrict escape of blood from the spaces through these veins. Thus, the principal event appears to be arterial dilatation; restriction of venous return appears to be largely passive. The pressure in the cavernous spaces during erection approximates that in the carotid artery.[28] It has frequently been suggested that contractions of the ischiocavernosus muscles assist in erection by constricting the veins. Such action is now considered to be minor.[28, 37] Return of the penis to the flaccid state is initiated by constriction of the arteries. A gradual escape of blood from the cavernous spaces would lower the pressure in the vascular spaces and presumably would result in a reduction of the passive constriction of the veins, and hence a progressively more rapid return of flaccidity.

Dilatation of the penile arteries and erection are induced by stimulation of the pelvic splanchnic nerves, whence their name *nervi erigentes* (Fig. 4). Stimulation of the sympathetic nerve supply results in constriction of the arteries of the penis and subsidence of erection. A center for reflex erection apparently exists in the sacral spinal cord, as shown by stimulation of the glans eliciting erection only when the pudendal nerve is intact. Psychic stimulation will produce erection after destruction of the sacral cord but not after destruction of the lumbar cord.

EJACULATION

As used commonly, this term covers two distinct actions.[55] The first, emission, is the sudden contraction of the smooth muscle of the internal genital organs that delivers semen into the urethra. The second, or ejaculation in the restricted sense, is the expulsion of seminal fluid from the urethra by contraction of the bulbocavernosus muscle (a skeletal muscle). The process is basically a reflex phenomenon (Fig. 4). The afferent impulses arise chiefly in the sense organs of the glans and are transmitted by the internal pudendal nerves to the spinal cord. Efferent impulses leave the upper lumbar segments of the spinal cord, travel over the lumbar rami communicantes and hypogastric nerves through the hypogastric plexus and evoke emission. The impulses that provoke ejaculation are parasympathetic and travel over the internal pudendal nerves. It is generally thought that an ejaculatory center

Fig. 3. Cross-section of shaft of penis. (After Callander, *Surgical anatomy.* 2nd ed., Philadelphia, W. B. Saunders Co., 1940.)

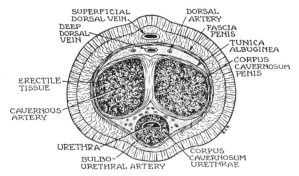

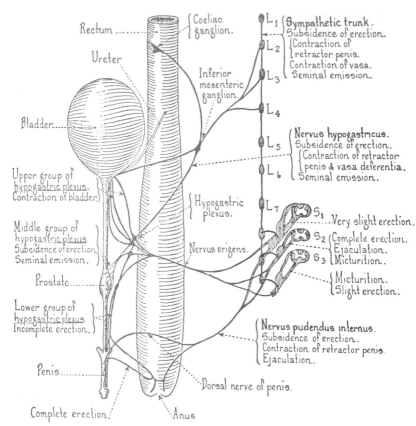

Fig. 4. Diagram summarizing functional innervation of genital organs of male cat. (From Semans and Langworthy, *J. Urol.*, 1938, *40*:836–846.)

in the lumbosacral spinal cord integrates the reflexes. The neural control of emission and ejaculation as described here was worked out in the cat by Semans and Langworthy,[55] but the same pattern of control appears to obtain in man.[62]

For many years it was suspected that the several glands discharge their secretions in an orderly sequence during emission. By chemical study of "split ejaculates" Huggins and McDonald[32] have shown that the prostate discharges its secretion before discharge of the seminal vesicles.

The several sensations associated with ejaculation constitute the orgasm. The origin, with respect to both mechanism and location, of these sensations is not fully known. Afferent impulses presumably reach the cerebral cortex, much like impulses giving rise to other visceral sensations. Inasmuch as sexual sensations are of a primitive nature, it is usually assumed that many of the afferent impulses do not ascend higher than the thalamus. The impulses apparently spread through much of the auto-

nomic nervous system and elicit reactions in other viscera.

STERILITY AND FERTILITY

In recent years the problem of sterility has received much attention, and one of the significant consequences of this study is the recognition that in barren marriages the husband is the sterile individual at least as often as is the wife. It will be evident that the circumstances of human reproduction make the factors in fertility quite difficult to assess. An ovum is available but once a month, if that often, and its viability is apparently so brief that conception might be considered fortuitous under the most favorable circumstances.

The *sine qua non* for male fertility is adequate numbers of viable spermatozoa in the ejaculum, and much attention has been devoted to defining adequate numbers and adequate viability.[41] The average number of spermatozoa in each milliliter of ejaculated semen of fertile men is probably approximately 100 millions, but the variation is great. It is often said that fewer than 60 million sperm in a milliliter of semen is an indication of probable sterility. Sperm counts as low as 20 million per ml. have, however, been found in men of proved fertility. The total number of spermatozoa in an ejaculation depends upon the volume of the ejaculum, the average in fertile men being approximately 3 ml. The volume of the ejaculum has been examined with reference to fertility and sterility, but a satisfactory correlation seems not to have been made. Quite low volumes may be seen in sterile men with no spermatozoa, but this condition may be associated with hypogonadism.

Abnormal spermatozoa, with two heads or two tails for example, are fairly common, and several authors have suggested that when they amount to 20 per cent of the total count sterility is probably present. A low general level of spermatozoan motility has been associated with sterility, and it has been emphasized that mere movement cannot be considered adequate motility.

The chief constituents of semen have been discussed earlier. It will be apparent that defects in the secretion of certain of these compounds might be expected to impair fertility. The possibility here seems not to have been sufficiently studied to permit generalizations.

Why millions of spermatozoa must be introduced into the female genital tract to insure fertilization of one ovum by a single spermatozoon is still an unanswered question. For a time the finding that semen and sperm suspensions contain high titers of the mucolytic enzyme hyaluronidase seemed to offer an answer. This enzyme was found capable of liquefying *in vitro* the gel that surrounds newly ovulated ova of rats and rabbits. The possibility that millions of spermatozoa are necessary to furnish enough hyaluronidase to denude the ovum and thus to permit its penetration by one successful spermatozoon suggested the use of the enzyme in management of sterility. Most of the clinical trials were unsuccessful, and the small numbers of spermatozoa arriving at the ovum would rule against an appreciable quantity of hyaluronidase reaching the ovum. Most workers agree, however, that hyaluronidase may facilitate penetration of the ovum and its adnexa by the sperm. Another action of hyaluronidase may lie in its enabling spermatozoa to burrow through the plug of mucus in the cervical canal.[39]

EFFECTS OF CASTRATION—TRANSPLANTATION OF TESTES

Excision of the testes produces permanent sterility by removing the site of production of spermatozoa. This operation in adults of all higher animals and man also results in atrophy of the genital tract and in regression of many masculine characters. If the castration is done prior to the attainment of sexual maturity, the genital organs remain infantile, and many masculine traits fail to manifest themselves. The effects of castration are dramatic in many animals, as is obvious in comparing the physique and temperament of the bull and the ox or of the stallion and the gelding. In the fowl, castration results in a regression of the florid head furnishings (comb, wattles, ear lobes) of the cockerel to the pallid, modest structures of the capon (Fig. 5). The striking

Fig. 5. Head of White Leghorn cockerel (left) and of capon (right), showing effects of castration upon comb, wattles and ear lobes.

growth of the antlers in some male deer or of the horns in certain rams is prevented by castration. Other structures normally developed only in the male, such as the spurs of the cockerel, are not influenced by castration.

The effects of castration are less conspicuous in man than in the animals mentioned, but they are no less profound.[25, 60] If a child is castrated, the pubertal changes do not occur. The high pitch of the voice is retained; the beard and body hair develop poorly; the body proportions do not become masculine; the genital organs, both internal and external, remain infantile in size and structure; masculine aggressiveness is deficient or absent. If the operation is performed after puberty, the effects are similar but often less striking, and some of them may require a long period to become apparent.

As with other endocrine glands, the first attempts at replacement therapy after castration consisted of the transplantation of testes. Testicular transplants have been made with various degrees of success in many species of animals. If the graft takes, it is usually capable of substituting for the somatic actions of the host's testes. In the 1920's testicular transplants ("goat glands" or "monkey glands") to man received wide popular attention, and many therapeutic claims were made for them. Of course, in the establishment of a testicular graft many of the factors operate that influence any other transplantation. Of these, one of the most significant is the taxonomic or chemical kinship of host and donor species or individuals. Suffice it to say, the practice with respect to human hosts has apparently been largely abandoned.

ANDROGENS—CHEMISTRY AND METABOLISM

Although Brown-Séquard's report in 1898 of rejuvenation after injections of aqueous extracts of testicular tissue into himself created much interest, it is generally agreed that the first active testicular extract was prepared in 1927 by McGee, who employed fat solvents. Similar extracts were soon found capable of correcting the recognized changes produced in a variety of animals by castration. Masculinizing activity was also found in extracts of urine, blood, cerebrospinal fluid and bile; the epididymis is apparently the only organ besides the testes, however, whose extracts contain significant levels.

Several pure male hormone compounds (androgens) have been obtained from natural sources or synthesized.[38] Androsterone was prepared from human urine in 1931 by Butenandt and synthesized in 1934 by Ruzicka. Testosterone was obtained from testicular tissue of bulls in 1935 by David, and synthesized in the same year by Ruzicka and by Butenandt. These are the most active of the androgens, one International Unit of biologic activity being present in 100 μg. of androsterone and in 13 to 16 μg. of testosterone. Several compounds related to androsterone and known collectively as 17-ketosteroids have been isolated from human urine. Some of these substances are active biologically as androgens; others are not.

Testosterone is generally presumed to be the male sex hormone secreted by the testis, although it appears to have been fully identified in testicular tissue from bulls and horses only. Much progress has been made toward elucidation of the biosynthesis of this complex substance,[14] and the chemical pathways seem to be much the same as those followed in the biosynthesis of the steroid hormones of the ovary and adrenal. Indeed, so many interconversions between steroid compounds have been reported that the specificity of the glands of origin, of the secreted hormones, and of patterns of secretion, once a standard tenet in endocrinology, seems increasingly an artificial concept. The compound 17-hydroxyprogesterone appears to be the immediate precursor of both androgens and estrogens, going to androstenedione, which undergoes reduction to form testosterone. Androstenedione and testosterone have been converted to estradiol by human ovary in vitro. The 17-hydroxyprogesterone is apparently derived from progesterone, classically the hormone of the corpus luteum, which, in turn, is apparently derived from cholesterol with pregnenolone as an intermediate stage. Progesterone may be converted by adrenal cortex to various of the cortical steroids. The interrelations of the biosynthesis of the steroid hormones and their interconversions suggest an attractive explanation of certain of the abnormal functions of steroid-producing glands, including the testis. They also offer challenges to the analysis of the regulation of these glands.

Testosterone has been identified in systemic

blood,[14] the level being somewhat less than 1 μg. per 100 ml. of plasma from normal men. Human plasma also contains 17-ketosteroids in amounts paralleling urinary titers in different individuals.[19]

The excretion of increased amounts of androsterone and certain other 17-ketosteroids in the urine following administration of large amounts of testosterone to men[13] is evidence that these substances are metabolites of testosterone (Fig. 6). The level of urinary 17-ketosteroids is, however, subject to wide variation that depends upon many considerations, and much of the 17-ketosteroid in the urine is derived from adrenal rather than testicular precursors.

As is the situation with other steroid hormones, testosterone disappears rapidly from the animal given this substance. West[61] reported that at least 90 per cent of testosterone disappeared from the blood within ten minutes after intravenous administration. The largest quantity entered fat depots, but disappeared from this site within three hours. Testosterone labeled with radioactive carbon was also rapidly lost in mice and rats, the major portion of the radioactivity being found in urine and feces.[2]

Thus far, the liver and the kidney are the identified sites of inactivation of testosterone. The liver of the rat has been studied most in this respect, and the ability to inactivate testosterone *in vivo* persists even after the liver is subjected to poisoning and to dietary stress.[20] Liver from rats fed a diet deficient in niacin and tryptophane, however, had a diminished capacity to inactivate testosterone *in vitro*.[8] Inactivation of testosterone by rats' liver *in vitro* is an oxidative process, and certain of the enzyme systems involved have been studied. Bile from human subjects given large amounts of testosterone has been found to show no increase in 17-ketosteroids or androgens, although urinary 17-ketosteroids were much increased.[54]

Estrogenic as well as androgenic substances have been extracted from testicular tissue. The urine of normal men contains estrogenic material, and the urine of the stallion is the richest known natural source of estrogens. After castration in both man and the stallion, the urinary excretion of estrogens is greatly decreased. The function of testicular estrogen has not been determined.

Assay of androgens. The original extraction and later purification and synthesis of androgenic com-

pounds depended upon having at hand means of recognizing the active substance. Since the chemical nature of these substances was unknown, biologic responses to them were necessarily employed. These biologic tests are still valuable in the assay of the androgen, rather than the 17-ketosteroid, content of various tissues and fluids. The basis of the tests is the prevention or correction of changes produced by castration in certain animals. Probably the most widely employed reaction is growth of the comb of the capon (see Fig. 5), and it is upon this reaction that the International Unit (I.U.) of androgenic activity is based. The International Unit is activity equal to that of 100 μg. of pure androsterone. The standard test involves the daily intramuscular or subcutaneous injection of the unknown material into a group of Leghorn capons over a period of five days. At the end of this period the change in the size of the comb in response to 1 I.U. of androgen daily is an increase of 5 mm. in the length plus the height. Another widely used test involves maintenance or restoration of the weight and microscopic structure of the seminal vesicles (Fig. 7) and prostate glands of castrated rats.

The usual procedures in bioassaying androgens employ systemic, i.e., subcutaneous or intramuscular, administration. When application is directly to the target organ, a response is elicited by much smaller amounts of androgen. For example, distinct growth of the comb of the capon has been provoked by a total of 1.2 μg. of androsterone applied directly to the comb, whereas the required daily dose of this substance is of the order of 100 μg. when given systemically. It may be significant that testosterone and androsterone exhibit almost identical biologic activity when applied directly to

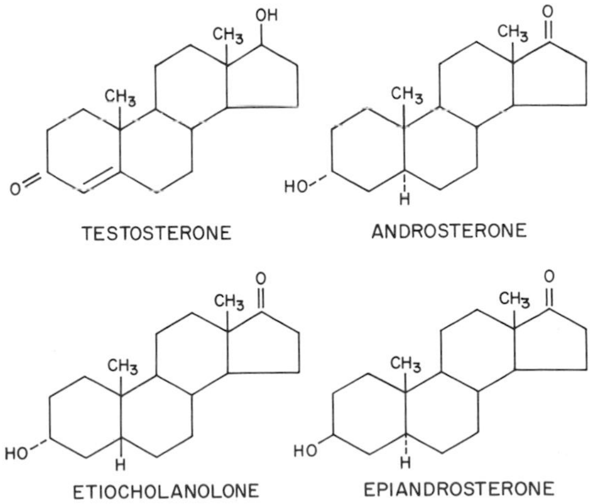

Fig. 6. Testosterone and three urinary 17-ketosteroids that are considered to be its metabolites.

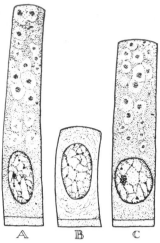

Fig. 7. Cells from epithelium of seminal vesicle of rat to show effect of castration and restitution by injected androgen: *A,* from normal animal; *B,* 20 days after castration; *C,* from a 20-day castrate treated with androgen. (Redrawn from Moore *et al., Amer. J. Anat.,* 1930, *45*:109–136.)

the target organ, despite the fact that testosterone is roughly seven times as active as androsterone when they are administered systemically.

ACTIONS AND FUNCTIONS OF ANDROGENS

The actions of the androgenic hormones involve many parts of the body and many physiologic functions not obviously related to reproduction.[25, 60] The list of functions or actions of androgenic hormones is impressive, but probably is still incomplete. Their identification has been based upon study of the effects of castration or of testicular insufficiency, the repair of these changes by administration of androgens, the effects of excessive amounts of administered androgens, and the correlation of levels of excreted 17-ketosteroids with different bodily states.

Genital System. Each of the several portions of the genital tract (see Fig. 1) is under the controlling influence of the testicular hormone. In the absence of adequate androgen, in the boy or in the eunuch for example, the scrotum is small and its proximal end tends to be wider than the distal end. After puberty the scrotum is much larger, with the distal portion expanded and the proximal portion relatively

narrower.[23] To some extent, the size and conformation of the scrotum depend upon the weight and degree of distension exerted by the testes; but in the absence of testes the scrotum may approach normal size and configuration when adequate androgen is supplied artificially. The full development of the penis likewise is contingent upon stimulation by androgen; it remains infantile when insufficient androgen is available and grows when androgen is administered.[25, 60] The several excurrent ducts are also dependent upon androgen for the establishment and maintenance of mature size and structure. The attainment and maintenance of adult size and secretory function in the accessory glands of reproduction—seminal vesicles, prostate, bulbo-urethral glands—also require adequate stimulation by androgen.[50] The effects of androgen are shown most conspicuously by the epithelium of these glands (Fig. 7); indeed, the height of the epithelium is often, within limits, proportional to the level of stimulating androgen. As would be anticipated, the level of secretory activity of these epithelia is controlled by androgen and is reflected in the amount of each of several compounds in the accumulated secretions of the several glands.

The control of the structure and function of the normal prostate gland by androgen suggests that benign hypertrophy of the prostate may perhaps be related to some aberration in the action or production of androgens. This prostatic change is common in men in the later decades of life, and consists of enlargement of one or more portions of the prostate and concomitant difficulty in voiding urine. On the basis of prostatic control at earlier ages, hypertrophy would appear to demand a greatly increased level of stimulation by androgen; yet it occurs at ages when the production of androgen has presumably declined. Some authors have reported the condition developing many years after castration; others have observed regression of the enlarged prostate and a relief of the urinary distress upon castration. Still other investigators have reported relief of the urinary difficulties after administration of androgen without any effect upon the prostate itself; the symptomatic relief is attributed to a strengthening of the bladder musculature sufficiently to overcome the urethral obstruction. Finally, the level of excretion of 17-ketosteroids by patients with prostatic hypertrophy is reported to be not significantly different from that by men of the same age without prostatic disease. The observations are too inconsistent and conflicting to permit a decision as to whether androgens are an important factor in this disease. Estrogens have also received consideration as possible etiologic agents, largely because they modify the prostate glands in mice and rats—the most striking effect being a squamous metaplasia—and cause urinary retention. No convincing evidence for the involvement of estrogens in the disease has been advanced, and the possibility is apparently losing favor.

In contrast, carcinoma of the prostate may be strikingly affected by androgen,[34] and castration has become a widely employed therapeutic measure. The operation apparently does not always influence the primary tumor nor does it prolong the life of the patient, but it may cause a dramatic regression of the metastatic growths and an almost immediate diminution in the pain that characteristically accompanies this tumor. The administration of estrogens has the same general effects, presumably by producing a physiologic castration through inhibition of the hypophysis.

Hair. Hair is a conspicuous secondary sex characteristic, the type, pattern and degree of growth differing in the two sexes and influenced by androgen. The extent of the influence of the androgen evidently depends upon the genetic constitution of the individual, and every generalization apparently has its exceptions in virile men. Growth of hair over the trunk and the extremities is heavier in the presence of androgens. Hair in the axillary and pubic regions depends upon androgen for its full development; it does not appear until puberty, and is sparse in castrates and in eunuchoid men.[25, 60] After castration pubic hair is less luxuriant, and the upward extension of the superior border often disappears. The pattern of head hair is different in the two sexes and is apparently determined by androgen.[23] In immature boys and in girls and women the hairline on the forehead is in the form of a continu-

ous bow-like curve (Fig. 8). In mature men the hairline is usually marked by a recession (calvity) over the lateral frontal region on each side. Calvities are poorly developed or absent in some unquestionably virile men, but apparently they are always absent in hypogonadal or prepubertally castrated men, and can usually be induced in the latter by administration of androgen. This sexual difference in growth of head hair is probably related to common baldness, which is traditionally found only in the male, begins only after puberty, is absent in prepubertally castrated men, and frequently appears after masculinization of women. Moreover, the condition may be induced in many castrated men by administration of therapeutic levels of androgen. Baldness appears to be an hereditary trait that requires a physiologic level of androgen for its development; that is, no amount of androgen can induce baldness in an individual not carrying the hereditary factors for the condition.[26]

Sebaceous glands. The sebaceous glands of the skin are also influenced by androgens. Acne vulgaris, an inflammation of the sebaceous glands, does not appear until puberty, but during adolescence is present in the majority of both males and females. Inasmuch as the disorder does not develop in castrates, but may be induced by administered androgens, androgen appears to be a prerequisite and incitant of acne, although a variety of other factors may also be involved.[24] The high incidence of acne in females does not argue against the primacy of androgen in causing the disorder, inasmuch as androgens are normally present in fairly high levels in the female. A basis for the acnegenic action of the androgens may lie in their enhancing secretory activity of the sebaceous glands as revealed by oiliness of the skin in normal subjects beginning at puberty and in hypogonadal patients upon treatment with androgen.

Color of skin. The color of the skin is also influenced by androgens. In castrates and eunuchoids the skin is furrowed or finely wrinkled, soft and sallow. After administration of androgens and in normal men the skin is firmer and ruddier and has a darker color.[25, 60] Castrates have little or no ability to tan, but the skin may tan many months after exposure to sunlight upon administration of androgen.[25] In a spectrophotometric study[17] it was found that, as compared with normal men, castrates have a lower quantity of hemoglobin in the skin and that a higher proportion

Fig. 8. Patterns of distribution of head hair. Hairlines of child and adult woman are alike, while that of adult man usually shows an indentation in lateral frontal region. (From Greulich *et al., Monogr. Soc. Res. Child Dev.,* 1942, 7:1–85.)

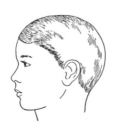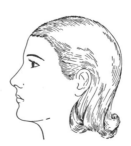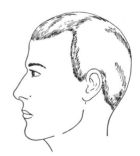

is reduced hemoglobin; carotene is present in greater amounts in the skin; melanin levels are slightly subnormal. Administration of androgen brought the levels of all of these substances within the normal range.

Subcutaneous fat. In many instances the pattern of distribution of subcutaneous fat appears to be influenced by androgens.[25, 60] In normal adults abdominal fat usually accumulates above the umbilicus in the male and below the umbilicus in the female. In castrates, fat frequently accumulates in the mammary region, over the trochanters, and in the mons pubis, although these fatty depots may be absent in other castrates of long standing. The ability of administered androgens to modify fat distribution has not been forcibly demonstrated.

Voice. One of the most readily recognized actions of androgens is upon the depth of the voice.[25, 60] The eunuchoid and prepubertal castrate retain the voice of the immature boy. Administration of androgens results in a lowering of the voice, which may, however, take the form merely of hoarseness. These vocal changes may not be accompanied by any special enlargement of the laryngeal cartilages. Androgens affect the voice of women in much the same way, causing hoarseness and deepening. Castration after puberty frequently has no effect upon the depth of the voice.

Skeleton. There are many indications that the androgens affect skeletal growth, but the relationship appears beset with inconsistencies. The pubertal spurt in somatic growth suggests that androgen may be the stimulus. On the other hand, the prepubertal castrate and the eunuchoid are frequently tall and characterized by a disproportionately great length of the bones of the extremities. The administration of androgens is reported to accelerate the closure of the epiphyses and to lead to the termination of growth in tall eunuchoid boys.[35] Contrariwise, the same dose levels of androgens are reported to provoke growth in stunted, eunuchoid boys.[51] The effects on animals are equally confusing. Administration of large amounts of androgens retards growth in rats; but when large amounts of androgens are given along with large amounts of estrogen, somatic growth is less inhibited than when estrogens are given alone.

Muscle. The usually greater muscularity of the male appears to be at least partially attributable to androgen. Muscular growth and increased strength are pubertal traits, and a relative muscular weakness usually characterizes castrated and eunuchoid men.[60] A striking generalized muscular hypertrophy may be induced in guinea pigs by administration of androgens.[49] Increased muscular strength and endurance have also been induced in castrated and hypogonadal men by administration of androgens.[56] To what extent these effects are the result of increased well-being and metabolic improvement has not been fully determined.

Vascular system. A testicular deficiency arising before puberty is characteristically accompanied by pale-

ness. Occasionally postpubertal deficiency precipitates hot flashes and flushing of the skin similar to those of the menopausal female.[25, 60] In analyzing the apparent relationship of the cardiovascular system and androgens it has been found that the cutaneous vascular bed of castrates is smaller than in normal men and has less blood flowing through it, and that cutaneous areas with large venous beds contain more reduced hemoglobin, suggesting a venous dilatation in these areas. These changes were reversed by administration of testosterone propionate, and in more "arterial" regions of the skin the volume of blood was increased and it contained more oxyhemoglobin.[17] The small blood vessels of the skin are characterized by fluctuations in excitability in castrated men, and their excitability is reduced by administration of testosterone.[52] The effects of androgens upon blood vessels have led to their use as therapeutic agents in vascular disease.

Metabolism. Androgens cause retention of nitrogen, sodium, potassium, inorganic phosphorus and chlorides, with the effect being less in intact than in castrated or eunuchoid men.[36] Creatine is excreted in quite small amounts in normal men, although prepubertal boys, castrates and eunuchoids ordinarily exhibit a creatinuria. This difference in creatine metabolism and excretion is partially to be attributed to androgens inasmuch as these substances usually reduce creatinuria and increase creatine tolerance. The basal metabolism may increase 5 to 15 per cent during treatment with androgen without any change in respiratory quotient, this despite a gain in body weight that may, however, be partially the result of retention of electrolytes and water. As might be expected in the light of their effects upon metabolism, treatment with androgens is also reported to produce significant increases in red cell count, hemoglobin, and hematocrit values.[45] These changes in the blood are considered comparable to those occurring during normal adolescence.

In addition to the numerous actions of androgens in the male, these substances have important effects in the female that have prompted their clinical employment in a variety of gynecologic disorders.

ANDROGENS IN DIFFERENT PERIODS OF LIFE

A plausible interpretation of *embryonic sexual differentiation* is the genetic determination of the differentiation of the morphologically indifferent gonad into a testis or ovary. The newly differentiated testis could conceivably secrete an androgen which would provoke growth and differentiation in the male components of the morphologically bipotential genital tract, and either provoke or allow regression of the female components. The results of experiments involving administration of sex hormones to embryos of many species have apparently lent support to the concept of a directional influence of these hormones. In general, androgens have stimulated the male homologues and estrogens the female homologues.[21] Although these effects have not been entirely uniform, the evidence, including the consequences of castration of the embryo, increasingly indicates that the embryonic gonad, especially the testis, has a directional influence in embryonic sex differentiation. Once embryonic sexual differentiation is completed, the sex hormones may cause abnormal development of the genital system in the fetus and be important factors in such malformations as pseudohermaphroditism.[21]

Puberty. During childhood there is normally little evidence of the activity or presence of the testicular hormone.[23] Small amounts of 17-ketosteroids are present in the urine, but these substances may be adrenal in origin. At puberty, however, a dramatic change occurs. In the short span of a few years the child is transformed into a man. The genital system undergoes rapid growth and maturation, and secondary sex characters, such as the beard, body hair and deeper voice, appear.[23] These changes are clearly dependent upon androgens, as shown by their absence in the castrate and by their evocation by administered androgens. This fact, plus the observation that the changes are preceded and accompanied by accelerated growth of the testes, supports the almost universal belief that pubertal changes result from an abrupt and conspicuous increase in the production of androgen by the testes. This entirely plausible explanation, however, is not supported by the few studies the problem has received. Most investigators have reported a steady increase in the excretion of androgen or 17-ketosteroids with increased age during puberty and adolescence, with no conspicuous increase to coincide with the onset of puberty.[23] It has been pointed out, however, that variation among individuals of the same age is great with respect to degree of sexual maturation and that comparisons should be made not with age but with development. In the bull, the rise in testicular androgen with increased age was found to be uniform in the young animal, and no conspicuous alteration in level accompanied pubertal changes.[20] The little evidence avail-

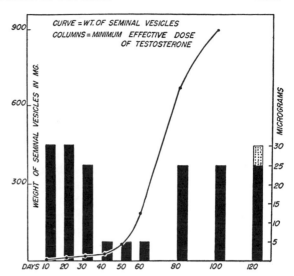

Fig. 9. Chart showing dose level of testosterone required at different ages to elicit response in seminal vesicles of rats castrated at birth. Curve shows growth of seminal vesicles of normal rats. (From Hooker, *Endocrinology*, 1942, *30*:77–84.)

able accordingly suggests that pubertal changes are not the result of a greatly increased production of androgen. Work with laboratory animals[29] indicates that a major factor responsible for pubertal changes is a tremendous increase at this age in the responsiveness of the tissues to androgen (Fig. 9).

Sexual Maturity. During sexual maturity androgens are responsible for the maintenance of most sex characteristics, as shown by the effects of castration. The absence of evident fluctuations in masculinity possibly indicates a steady state of production and action of androgen. Some tendency toward cyclic patterns has been suggested, but has not been established.

Old Age. It is popularly supposed that the decline in vigor in advanced age is the result of decline in testicular activity. The level of urinary androgen and 17-ketosteroids in man is somewhat lower, and in the bull the level of testicular androgen is diminished,[30] but whether these levels are sufficiently decreased to account for senile changes is not established. Many clinical endocrinologists recognize a male climacteric occurring at about the same age as the menopause in women. It is characterized by decline in vigor and by vascular instability and other phenomena not unlike those of the menopause, and can frequently be alleviated by the administration of androgens.[25, 60]

SITE OF PRODUCTION OF TESTICULAR ANDROGEN

The tubules of the testis are situated in a meshwork of intertubular connective tissue, which contains, among other cellular entities, numbers of epithelioid cells resembling gland cells—the interstitial cells of Leydig (Fig. 2). Androgen secreted by the testis obviously must be elaborated in either or both the tubules and the intertubular tissue. That the tubules are not the primary source of the androgen is shown by the usual absence of castration phenomena after atrophy or damage of the tubules, provided the intertubular tissue remains essentially normal. Moreover, tubular growth is not accompanied by an increase in the androgen content of the testes.[30] If the tubules are not the source of the androgen, obviously the intertubular tissue must perform this function. Stimulation of the testis by gonadotrophins results in evident production of androgen only if the Leydig cells are visibly affected.[22] Large quantities of androgen are apparently secreted by experimental tumors of the Leydig cells in mice and by spontaneous interstitial cell tumors in boys. Finally, changes in level of testicular androgen in the bull are paralleled by appropriate cytologic changes in the Leydig cells.[30] The life history of the Leydig cells in several species, including man,[1] is similar to that in the bull. It is almost certain that the Leydig cells are the site of production of testicular androgen.

The site of production of testicular estrogen is not known with certainty. Testicular tumors composed of Sertoli cells secrete much estrogen,[33] but the Leydig cells may also produce estrogen in the normal testis.

REGULATION OF TESTIS BY HYPOPHYSIS

The testis is under the control of the hypophysis, as shown by atrophy of the testes and the appearance of castration changes after hypophysectomy and by the restoration of full testicular function upon the administration of suitable gonadotrophic substances. Of the two hypophysial gonadotrophins, follicle-stimulating hormone (FSH) and luteinizing hormone (LH) or interstitial-cell-stimulating hormone (ICSH), FSH apparently has no influence upon the production of androgen when given alone. Purified

ICSH, however, is capable of provoking the production of sufficient androgen to restore the reproductive system to an essentially normal condition. When the two purified gonadotrophins are given simultaneously the effect upon production of androgen is greater than when ICSH is given alone.[22] Although the rat has been the favorite species for such studies, it has also been observed that administration of human chorionic gonadotrophin to normal men is followed by hyperplasia of the Leydig cells and increased production of androgen (and estrogen) as shown by increase in urinary 17-ketosteroids (and estrogens).[42] A direct effect of gonadotrophins upon the testis is indicated by increased levels of androgen when the testis is perfused with gonadotrophin[44] and when gonadotrophin is included in the culture medium of testicular tissue cultured *in vitro*.[40]

The testes, in turn, affect the production of gonadotrophins by the hypophysis. Castration is followed by cytologic changes in the hypophysis and by an increase in the gonadotrophin content of the hypophysis, blood and urine. The administration of androgen to the castrate restores the normal cellular composition of the hypophysis and returns the several gonadotrophin levels to normal. In the intact individual the administration of androgen depresses the gonadotrophin level. Thus, there exists a mutual regulation of gonadotrophin and androgen production. The "feedback" influence of androgen upon secretion of hypophysial gonadotrophin in the male dog appears to be indirect and to operate through the hypothalamus.[11]

The seminiferous tubules are also at least partially controlled by the hypophysis, but the details may seem a bit confusing. Hypofunction of the hypophysis results in defective spermatogenesis, and hypophysectomy is followed by atrophy of the tubules and cessation of spermatogenesis. In adult animals FSH will maintain or restore spermatogenesis after hypophysectomy. In immature rodents administration of FSH is followed by growth of the testes and enhancement of spermatogenic activity. Spermatogenesis is maintained in rats by administration of LH beginning at hypophysectomy, but this substance has little restorative effect upon spermatogenesis if its administration is delayed until testicular atrophy has occurred. Neither FSH nor LH has hastened the appearance of spermatozoa in the immature animal. Thus, the hypophysial gonadotrophin that appears to affect spermatogenesis directly is FSH, although the action may be limited to the early stages in spermatogenesis; LH appears to have no direct effect upon spermatogenesis. It will be appreciated that circumstances in man do not readily lend themselves to rigorous analysis. In any case, failure of spermatogenesis in man is not consistently corrected by administration of gonadotrophins. Indeed, damage to the seminiferous tubules has followed administration of chorionic gonadotrophin.[42]

Although the fact seems paradoxical, injections of testosterone sustain spermatogenesis in hypophysectomized animals;[47] even more striking is the fact that testosterone will restore spermatogenesis after atrophy of the tubules has become pronounced as a result of hypophysectomy. These observations have been made in a number of laboratory animals, including the monkey. The means by which testosterone exerts its gametogenic action is not known. The observation that intratesticular pellets of testosterone maintain spermatogenesis in neighboring tubules better than in tubules further from the pellet suggests that the action in this circumstance is direct.[15] As though making provision for action of androgen upon the spermatogenesis, the capillary system in the rat's testis is described[46] as so arranged that blood reaches the capillaries coursing along the tubules only after passing capillaries in intertubular wedges of connective tissue containing the Leydig cells. That the gametogenic action of testosterone is not primarily a consequence of its androgenicity is suggested by the fact that certain other steroid compounds have a similar action.[47] Notable among these substances is pregnenolone which as such has no other obvious biologic action.[16]

EXTRATESTICULAR ANDROGEN

In addition to being produced by the testes, androgenic substances are also elaborated in other sites, notably the adrenal glands and the ovaries, and especially by tumors of these organs. Certain tumors of the adrenal cortex in boys may induce precocious puberty, and in women these tumors may be masculinizing to the extent of provoking growth of a beard, a generalized hypertrichosis, lowering of the voice, and even baldness. After removal of the tumor the masculine traits regress, showing the tumor to be the source of the androgen. An increase in urinary 17-ketosteroids usually accompanies these tumors.[58] Indeed, such a rise may be pathognomonic for certain adrenal tumors.

A number of experiments in animals have shown that androgen may be produced by the normal adrenal gland. In the prepubertal rat the presence of androgen is indicated by the cytology of the prostate upon which castration has no effect at this age, although adrenalectomy promptly results in typical castration atrophy of this organ. The administration of adrenotrophic preparations has been reported to evoke the production of androgen in castrated but not in adrenalectomized rats.

Certain ovarian tumors in women are also virilizing, inducing masculinization comparable to that in the presence of virilizing tumors of the adrenals. In several species of laboratory animals the ovaries may exert masculinizing actions under various experimental conditions, many of which involve an alteration of gonadotrophic stimulation of the ovaries. In some animals the androgen is apparently secreted by the interstitial cells of the ovary, whereas in other species the cells of the theca interna are thought to have this function.

REFERENCES

1. ALBERT, A., UNDERDAHL, L. O., GREENE, L. F. and LORENZ, N. *Proc. Mayo Clin.,* 1955, *30:*31–43.
2. BARRY, M. C., EIDINOFF, M. L., DOBRINER, K. and GALLAGHER, T. F. *Endocrinology,* 1952, *50:*587–599.
3. BEACH, F. A. *Hormones and behavior.* New York, Paul B. Hoeber, Inc., 1948.
4. BISHOP, D. W. Chap. 13 in *Sex and internal secretions,* 3rd ed., W. C. Young, ed. Baltimore, Williams & Wilkins, 1961.
5. BLANDAU, R. J. *Amer. J. Anat.,* 1945, *77:*253–272.
6. BLANDAU, R. J. and MONEY, W. L. *Anat. Rec.,* 1944, *90:* 255–260.
7. BLANDAU, R. J. and ODOR, D. L. *Anat. Rec.,* 1949, *103:* 93–110.
8. BRYSON, M. J., SAMUELS, L. T. and GOLDTHORPE, H. C. *Endocrinology,* 1950, *47:*89–96.
9. CAMPBELL, H. E. *Arch. Surg.,* 1942, *44:*353–369.
10. CHANG, M. C. and PINCUS, G. *Physiol. Rev.,* 1951, *31:*1–26.
11. DAVIDSON, J. M. and SAWYER, C. H. *Proc. Soc. exp. Biol. (N.Y.),* 1961, *107:*4–7.
12. DAVIS, C. D., PULLEN, R. L., MADDEN, J. H. M. and HAMBLEN, E. C. *J. clin. Endocrinol.,* 1943, *3:*268–273.
13. DORFMAN, R. I., COOK, J. W. and HAMILTON, J. B. *J. biol. Chem.,* 1939, *130:*285–295.
14. DORFMAN, R. I., FORCHIELLI, E. and GUT, M. *Recent Progr. Hormone Res.,* 1963, *19:*251–267.

15. Dvoskin, S. *Amer. J. Anat.*, 1944, *75*:289–327.
16. Dvoskin, S. *Endocrinology*, 1949, *45*:370–374.
17. Edwards, E. A., Hamilton, J. B., Duntley, S. Q. and Hubert, G. *Endocrinology*, 1941, *28*:119–128.
18. Elftman, H. *Anat. Rec.*, 1950, *106*:381–393.
19. Gardner, L. I. *J. clin. Endocrinol.*, 1953, *13*:941–947.
20. Grayhack, J. T. and Scott, W. W. *Endocrinology*, 1951, *48*:453–461.
21. Green, R. R. *J. clin. Endocrinol.*, 1944, *4*:335–348.
22. Greep, R. O., Van Dyke, H. B. and Chow, B. F. *Endocrinology*, 1942, *30*:635–649.
23. Greulich, W. W., Dorfman, R. I., Catchpole, H. R., Solomon, C. I. and Culotta, C. S. *Monogr. Soc. Res. Child Dev.* 1942, *7*:1–85.
24. Hamilton, J. B. *J. clin. Endocrinol.*, 1941, *1*:570–592.
25. Hamilton, J. B. Chap. 17 in *Glandular physiology and therapy*, 2d ed., prepared under the auspices of the Council on Pharmacy and Chemistry of the American Medical Association. Philadelphia, J. B. Lippincott Co., 1942.
26. Hamilton, J. B. *Amer. J. Anat.*, 1942, *71*:451–480.
27. Hays, R. L. and Vandemark, N. L. *Amer. J. Physiol.*, 1953, *172*:557–560.
28. Henderson, V. E. and Roepke, M. H. *Amer. J. Physiol.*, 1933, *106*:441–448.
29. Hooker, C. W. *Endocrinology*, 1942, *30*:77–84.
30. Hooker, C. W. *Amer. J. Anat.*, 1944, *74*:1–37.
31. Huggins, C. *Physiol. Rev.*, 1945, *25*:281–295.
32. Huggins, C. and McDonald, D. F. *J. clin. Endocrinol.*, 1945, *5*:226–231.
33. Huggins, C. and Moulder, P. V. *Cancer Res.*, 1945, *5*:510–514.
34. Huggins, C., Stevens, R. E., Jr. and Hodges, C. V. *Arch. Surg.*, 1941, *43*:209–223.
35. Hurxthal, L. M. *J. clin. Endocrinol.*, 1943, *3*:12–19.
36. Kenyon, A. T., Knowlton, K., Sandiford, I., Koch, F. C. and Lotwin, G. *Endocrinology*, 1940, *26*:26–45.
37. Kiss, F. *Z. Anat. Entwickl.-Gesch.*, 1921, *61*:455–521.
38. Koch, F. C. *Physiol. Rev.*, 1937, *17*:153–238.
39. Kurzrok, R. and Miller, E. G., Jr. *Amer. J. Obst. Gynec.*, 1928, *15*:56–72.
40. Lostroh, A. J. *Proc. Soc. exp. Biol. (N.Y.)*, 1960, *103*:25–27.

41. MacLeod, J. In: *Studies on testis and ovary; eggs and sperm*, E. T. Engle, ed. Springfield, Ill., Charles C Thomas, 1952.
42. Maddock, W. O. and Nelson, W. O. *J. clin. Endocrinol.*, 1952, *12*:985–1014.
43. Mann, T. and Lutwak-Mann, C. *Physiol. Rev.*, 1951, *31*:27–55.
44. Mason, N. R. and Samuels, L. T. *Endocrinology*, 1961, *68*:899–907.
45. McCullagh, E. P. and Jones, R. *J. clin. Endocrinol.*, 1942, *2*:243–251.
46. Müller, I. *Z. Zellforsch.*, 1957, *45*:522–537.
47. Nelson, W. O. *Cold Spr. Harb. Symp. quant. Biol.*, 1937, *5*:123–135.
48. Noyes, R. W. *Obst. gynec. Surv.*, 1959, *14*:785–797.
49. Papanicolaou, G. N. and Falk, E. A. *Science*, 1938, *87*:238–239.
50. Price, D. and Williams-Ashman, H. G. Chap. 6 in *Sex and internal secretions*, 3rd ed., W. C. Young, ed. Baltimore, Williams & Wilkins, 1961.
51. Rapfogel, I. *Endocrinology*, 1940, *27*:179–184.
52. Reynolds, S. R. M., Hamilton, J. B., DiPalma, J. R., Hubert, G. R. and Foster, F. I. *J. clin. Endocrinol.*, 1942, *2*:228–236.
53. Rolshoven, E. *Anat. Anz.*, 1947, *96*:220–226.
54. Rubin, B. L., Dorfman, R. I. and Miller, M. *Endocrinology*, 1952, *51*:463–468.
55. Semans, J. H. and Langworthy, O. R. *J. Urol.*, 1938, *40*:836–846.
56. Simonson, E., Kearns, W. M. and Enzer, N. *Endocrinology*, 1941, *28*:506–512.
57. Soderwall, A. L. and Young, W. C. *Anat. Rec.*, 1940, *78*:19–29.
58. Talbot, N. B., Butler, A. M. and Berman, R. A. *J. clin. Invest.*, 1942, *21*:559–570.
59. Van Wagenen, G. *Anat. Rec.*, 1936, *66*:411–421.
60. Vest, S. A. and Barelare, B., Jr. *Clinics*, 1943, *1*:1216–1265.
61. West, C. D. *Endocrinology*, 1951, *49*:467–473.
62. Whitelaw, G. P. and Smithwick, R. H. *New Engl. J. Med.*, 1951, *245*:121–130.
63. Young, W. C. *J. Morph.*, 1929, *48*:475–491.

INDEX

Page numbers in *italic* type refer to illustrations.